The Good Pub Guide 2003

Edited by Alisdair Aird

Deputy Editor: Fiona Stapley

Managing Editor: Karen Fick
Research Officer: Elizabeth Adlington
Associate Editor: Robert Unsworth
Editorial Assistance: Fiona Wright

EBURY PRESS
LONDON

Please send reports on pubs to

The Good Pub Guide
FREEPOST TN1569
WADHURST
East Sussex
TN5 7BR

or contact our website:
www.goodguides.com

Good Guide publications are available at special discounts for bulk purchases or for sales promotions or premiums. Special editions, including personalized covers, excerpts of existing Guides and corporate imprints, can be created in large quantities for special needs. Enquiries should be sent to the Sales Development Department, Random House, 20 Vauxhall Bridge Road, London SW1V 2SA (020 7840 8400).

This edition first published in 2002 by Ebury Press,
Random House, 20 Vauxhall Bridge Road,
London SW1V 2SA

The Random House Group Limited Reg. No. 954009

www.randomhouse.co.uk

1 3 5 7 9 10 8 6 4 2

Cover design by 2H Design
Cover photograph © PhotoAlto

A CIP catalogue record for this book is available from the British Library.

ISBN 0 09 188625 2

Typeset from author's disks by Clive Dorman & Co.
Edited by Pat Taylor Chalmers
Printed and bound in Great Britain by Cox and Wyman Ltd, Reading, Berkshire

Contents

Introduction

Top pubs for wine, whisky and beer

Each year our most rewarding task is identifying those select few pubs which are the current stars in the pub firmament – those pubs whose excellence puts them right at the top, in their particular field.

Over 40 of the main entries brew their own beer. Pubs where these own-brews are an outstanding draw are the Burton Bridge Inn in Burton upon Trent (Staffordshire), the Brewery Tap in Peterborough (Cambridgeshire), the Brunswick in Derby, the Flower Pots at Cheriton (Hampshire), the Church Inn at Uppermill (Lancashire – such a bargain), the Marble Arch in Manchester (same chapter – remarkable for its organic beers), the Grainstore in Oakham (Leicestershire & Rutland), the Gribble at Oving (Sussex), and the New Inn at Cropton and Fat Cat in Sheffield (Yorkshire). For its splendid Grainstore beers, Tony Davis's Grainstore in Oakham is **Own Brew Pub of the Year 2003.**

The very best of Britain's beer pubs naturally keep their ales in perfect condition, and on top of that keep a changing flow of interesting beers from far and wide. This labour of love demands enthusiasm, hard work, and real know-how. The current champions are the Hobgoblin in Reading (Berkshire), the Bhurtpore at Aston (Cheshire), the Watermill at Ings (Cumbria), the Sun in Feering (Essex), the Wine Vaults in Southsea (Hampshire), the Fat Cat in Norwich (Norfolk), the Crown at Churchill and Halfway House at Pitney (Somerset), and the New Barrack in Sheffield and Marton Arms in Thornton in Lonsdale (Yorkshire). With its remarkable choice of two dozen or more interesting changing real ales in good condition, Colin Keatley's Fat Cat in Norwich is **Beer Pub of the Year 2003.**

Without brewers, there would be no pubs; and it's almost as true to say that without good brewers there would be no good pubs. This year, several brewers have stood out because the quality of their beers is taking them into more and more pubs, often distant from their home territory – and with some this is coupled with a praiseworthy low-price policy. The brewers who are currently tripping off readers' tongues are Sharps (Cornwall), Shepherd Neame (Kent), Holts (Lancashire), Batemans (Lincolnshire), Hook Norton (Oxfordshire), Adnams and St Peters (Suffolk – we have stretched definitions a little to include St Peters Brewery as a pub entry in this edition, at South Elmham), Hop Back (Wiltshire), Black Sheep, Sam Smiths and Timothy Taylors (Yorkshire), Fullers (London) and Tomos Watkins (Wales). **Brewer of the Year 2003** is Fullers of London. Their beautifully crafted beers are sold in London at prices which are very fair for that expensive city, and are increasingly available very much more widely. Also, Fullers' well run tied pubs are generally attractive in their own right.

A pub with two dozen different real ales is something very special. But with whisky, Britain's other main national drink, the variety can be altogether richer. Quite a lot of pubs now keep up to 30 or so different single malts. A few enthusiastic landlords take the trouble to track down many more than this. Each of these pubs gives you a choice approaching 100 or more: the Crown & Horns at East Ilsley (Berkshire), the Bhurtpore at Aston (Cheshire), the Hardwick Inn near Hardwick Hall (Derbyshire), the Nobody Inn at Doddiscombsleigh (Devon), the Britons Protection in Manchester (Lancashire chapter), the Bulls Head at Clipston (Northamptonshire), the Cross Guns near Bradford-on-Avon (Wiltshire), the Marton Arms at Thornton in Lonsdale (Yorkshire), and in Scotland the Bow Bar and Kays Bar in Edinburgh, Burts Hotel in Melrose, and the Eilean Iarmain at Isle Ornsay (not so many, but an exceptional choice of the interesting vatted – or blended – malts). Colin Elsdon's Marton Arms at Thornton in Lonsdale, with over 200 whiskies including plenty of interesting rarities, and a splendid atmosphere to try them in (not to mention comfortable beds for sleeping it off) is **Whisky Pub of the Year 2003.**

Any good pub worth its salt now has decent wine. These days, many have better wines than you'd find in a typical wine bar. In the very best pubs for wine, the choice is superb. Indeed, our shortlist of these top places is far from short: the Crooked Billet at Newton Longville and Five Arrows in Waddesdon (Buckinghamshire), the Pheasant at Keyston (Cambridgeshire), the Trengilly Wartha near Constantine (Cornwall), the Nobody Inn at Doddiscombsleigh (Devon), the Rose at Peldon (Essex), the Bell at Sapperton (Gloucestershire), the Wykeham Arms in Winchester (Hampshire), the Red Lion at Freshwater (Isle of Wight), the Olive Branch at Clipsham (Leicestershire), the George of Stamford (Lincolnshire), the Blue Ball at Triscombe (Somerset), the Cornwallis at Brome and Crown in Southwold (Suffolk), the Pear Tree at Whitley (Wiltshire), and the White Swan in Pickering (Yorkshire). With a broad-ranging and interesting choice of 250 wines, any of which they will open and sell by the glass, John Gilchrist and Emma Sexton of the Crooked Billet at Newton Longville take the title of **Wine Pub of the Year 2003**.

The best pub food

Nearly all the best dining pubs now offer imaginative fresh fish dishes. Many places with more modest aspirations are following their example, so that you can now enjoy fresh fish in almost all good pubs. A few pubs really specialise in fish. The top ones are the Drewe Arms at Broadhembury, the Anchor at Cockwood and the Start Bay at Torcross (Devon), the West Bay in West Bay (Dorset), the Inn For All Seasons at Little Barrington (Gloucestershire), the New Inn at Shalfleet (Isle of Wight), the Applecross Inn, the Crown in Portpatrick, the Seafood Restaurant & Bar in St Monance, the Tayvallich Inn, and the Morefield Motel in Ullapool (Scotland), and the Penhelig Arms in Aberdovey (Wales). Judith Fish's Applecross Inn at Applecross, stunningly set over the sea from Skye, is **Fish Pub of the Year 2003**.

Over 130 main entries have qualified for our Bargain Award this year, giving good food value at rock-bottom prices. Some of these manage to conjure up really interesting dishes on a shoe-string. Prime among these are the Sweeney & Todd in Reading (Berkshire), the Cambridge Blue in Cambridge, the Old Ale House in Truro (Cornwall), the Black Dog at Dalton-in-Furness (Cumbria), the Jolly Sailor in Orford (Suffolk), the Red Lion at Kilmington (Wiltshire), the Fat Cat in Sheffield (Yorkshire), and the Pendre at Cilgerran (Wales). Debra and Jeff Warren's Pendre at Cilgerran – last year's winner – again romps away with the title of **Bargain Food Pub of the Year 2003**, for its excellent imaginative cooking at unbeatably low prices.

The shortlist for Dining Pub of the Year is now a very distinguished gathering. These pubs have gifted chefs using carefully sought out local produce to excellent effect. And what is very exciting is that dozens of other pubs are snapping closely on the heels of these culinary top dogs. This year's front runners are the Old Coastguard in Mousehole (Cornwall), the Drunken Duck near Hawkshead (Cumbria), the Dartmoor Inn at Lydford (Devon), the Bell at Horndon-on-the-Hill (Essex), the White Horse at Frampton Mansell (Gloucestershire), the Lough Pool at Sellack (Herefordshire), the Olive Branch at Clipsham (Leicestershire), the Ratcatchers at Cawston (Norfolk), the Falcon at Fotheringhay (Northamptonshire), the Lamb in Burford (Oxfordshire), the Ring o' Roses at Holcombe (Somerset), the Jolly Sportsman at East Chiltington (Sussex), the Howard Arms at Ilmington (Warwickshire), the Pear Tree at Whitley (Wiltshire), the Star at Harome and the Three Acres in Shelley (Yorkshire – an outstanding area for first-class dining pubs), the Eagle in Central London, and the Bear in Crickhowell (Wales). Andrew and Jacquie Pern's Star at Harome, a charming pub with very go-ahead young licensees, is **Dining Pub of the Year 2003**.

Landlords, landladies and pubs – the very best

For some reason, the great majority of really good pubs are outside the major towns and cities. But nevertheless there are plenty of outstanding town pubs to be found. Current front-runners are the Albion in Chester, the Britons Protection in Manchester (Lancashire chapter), the Adam & Eve in Norwich (Norfolk), the Turf Tavern in Oxford, the Basketmakers Arms in Brighton (Sussex), the Garrick in Stratford-upon-Avon (Warwickshire), the Dandy Lion in Bradford-on-Avon (Wiltshire), the Golden Lion in Settle (Yorkshire), the Jerusalem Tavern and the Cittie of Yorke (Central London), and the Abbotsford and the Bow Bar in

Edinburgh (Scotland). Peter Barnett's very well run Britons Protection in Manchester is **Town Pub of the Year 2003.**

There are hundreds of unspoilt pubs in the *Guide*. These (including some new finds this year) are special favourites: the Cock at Broom (Bedfordshire), the Bell at Aldworth (Berkshire), the Queens Head at Newton (Cambridgeshire), the Drewe Arms at Drewsteignton, the London at Molland, the Bridge in Topsham, the Rugglestone near Widecombe and the Northmore Arms at Wonson (Devon), the Bear at Alderwasley and Dead Poets in Holbrook (Derbyshire), the Red Lion at Ampney St Peter and the Boat at Ashleworth Quay (Gloucestershire), the Harrow at Steep (Hampshire), the Red Lion at Snargate (Kent), the Victoria in Durham (Northumbria chapter), the Star in Bath, Waggon & Horses at Crowcombe, Tuckers Grave at Faulkland and Rose & Crown at Huish Episcopi (Somerset), the Murrell Arms at Barnham and Royal Oak at Wineham (Sussex), the Case is Altered at Five Ways and Beacon in Sedgley (Warwickshire chapter), the Birch Hall at Beck Hole and Whitelocks in Leeds (Yorkshire), and the Cresselly Arms at Cresswell Quay and Plough & Harrow at Monknash (Wales). Colin Jackson's Birch Hall at Beck Hole, part pub and part sweetie shop, is a glorious anachronism, and is the **Unspoilt Pub of the Year 2003.**

Over 500 of the main entries have bedrooms. Rather over half of these have our Stay Award, showing that readers have found them enjoyable places to stay in overnight. Quite a few of these inns are really special: the Drunken Duck near Hawkshead (Cumbria), the Manor Hotel at West Bexington (Dorset), the New Inn at Coln St Aldwyns (Gloucestershire), the Inn at Whitewell (Lancashire), the Nevill Arms at Medbourne (Leicestershire), the White Horse at Brancaster Staithe and Victoria at Holkham (Norfolk), the Morritt Arms at Greta Bridge (Northumbria), the Lamb in Burford (Oxfordshire), the Angel in Lavenham and the Crown at Snape (Suffolk), and the Crab & Lobster at Asenby, the Star at Harome, the White Horse in Pickering, the Yorke Arms at Ramsgill and the Boars Head in Ripley (Yorkshire). Richard Bowman's civilised, comfortable and distinctive Inn at Whitewell is **Inn of the Year 2003.**

This new edition of the *Guide* carries over 2,000 new entries in the Lucky Dip sections. No doubt future editions will see many of these introductions promoted to the main entries. There is certainly a good deal of new blood among the main entries of this edition: it has 139 newcomers. A dozen stood out as particularly memorable, during our anonymous inspections: the Old Coastguards in Mousehole (Cornwall), the Bear at Alderwasley (Derbyshire), the Dartmoor Inn at Lydford and London at Molland (Devon), the Horse & Groom at Upper Oddington (Gloucestershire), the Chestnut Horse at Easton (Hampshire), the Verzons at Trumpet (Herefordshire), the Red Lion at Stodmarsh (Kent), the Lion at Hampton Loade (Shropshire), the Carew Arms at Crowcombe (Somerset), the Toll Gate at Holt (Wiltshire), the Bell & Cross at Holy Cross (Worcestershire), and the Shibden Mill in Halifax (Yorkshire). With something to suit everyone, and bags of character, John Holland's Chestnut Horse at Easton is **Newcomer of the Year 2003.**

This year, the top ten pubs are the Queens Head at Tirril (Cumbria), the Bell at Horndon-on-the-Hill (Essex), the Bell at East Langton (Leicestershire), the Welby Arms at Allington (Lincolnshire), the Queens Head at Bramfield (Suffolk), the Horseshoe at Ebbesbourne Wake (Wiltshire), the Star at Harome and Three Acres in Shelley (Yorkshire), the Plockton Hotel at Plockton (Scotland) and the Bear in Crickhowell (Wales). Chris Tomlinson's Queens Head at Tirril, brewing its own beer, with good food and wine, and great atmosphere particularly in its ancient front tap room, is **Pub of the Year 2003.**

Some pubs are winners because of the super people running them. This year, the top landlords and landladies are Aubrey Ball of the Millstone at Barnack (Cambridgeshire), Neil Girling of the Sloop at Bantham, and Robin Bean and Charles Hume Smith and their families of the Five Bells at Clyst Hydon (Devon), Jane and Simon Hudson of the Weighbridge just outside Nailsworth, and Peter and Assumpta Golding of the Horse & Groom at Upper Oddington (Gloucestershire), Sian and Mark Vallely of the Butchers Arms at Woolhope (Herefordshire), Trevor and Ann Cooper of the Five Bells at Broadwell (Oxfordshire), Alan East of the remarkable Yew Tree at Cauldon (Staffordshire), Anthony and Patricia Bath of the

Horseshoe at Ebbesbourne Wake (Wiltshire), Andy and Sue Cole of the Wombwell Arms at Wass (Yorkshire), and Debra and Jeff Warren of the Pendre at Cilgerran (Wales). For their excellent service and really heart-felt warmth and friendliness, Peter and Assumpta Golding of the Horse & Groom at Upper Oddington take the title of **Licensees of the Year 2003.**

Beer prices

Our annual national price survey shows that the price of a pint of beer is nudging at the £2 level, now averaging £1.99. Beers from the big international brewing combines (whose best-known brands of real ale are Tetleys, John Smiths, Theakstons, Flowers, Boddingtons, Courage, Worthington and Bass) average between £1.92 and £1.98 a pint (that is, just a shade below this national norm). Often, the best way of getting value for money on the beer front is to choose a beer from one of the smaller brewers. The Table which follows shows how smaller brewers compare with the £1.99 national average price. We have included only those brewers whose beers we found offered as the cheapest by at least two pubs, and we have excluded Channel Islands brewers, which work under a more lenient tax regime. The number in brackets after each name shows the number of pubs we found offering their beer as its cheapest – obviously, the more pubs, the more reliable our price.

£/pint	
£1.46	Sam Smiths (7)
£1.54	Castle Rock (5)
£1.59	Barnsley (3)
£1.60	Burton Bridge (2)
£1.63	Hydes (2)
£1.65	Hanby (2)
£1.70	Lees (2)
£1.77	Robinsons (6), Greenalls (2)
£1.78	Thwaites (5)
£1.79	Daleside (2)
£1.80	Hobsons (9), Teignworthy (3)
£1.83	Batemans (8), Malvern Hills (2)
£1.84	Donnington (4)
£1.85	Mansfield (4), Burtonwood (3), Hardys & Hansons (2), Wychwood (2)
£1.86	Jennings (15), Wye Valley (4)
£1.87	Yates (3), Branscombe Vale (2)
£1.88	Branoc (2), Jollyboat (2)
£1.90	Grainstore (3), Nethergate (2)
£1.92	Uley (3)
£1.93	Brains (8), Goffs (2)
£1.94	Sharps (14)
£1.95	Banks's (16), Otter (16), Cotleigh (10), Goachers (4), Princetown (3), Ridleys (3), Moorhouses (2)
£1.96	St Austell (9), Bath (2)
£1.97	fff (3)
£1.98	Hook Norton (56), Black Sheep (32), Butcombe (15), Archers (6), Oakham (5), Moles (2), Skinners (2), St Peters (2)
£1.99	Marstons (5), Hop Back (4)
£2.00	Smiles (2)
£2.01	Wadworths (28)
£2.01	Shepherd Neame (16)
£2.03	Gales (6), Summerskills (2)
£2.04	Fullers (21), Exmoor (10), Belhaven (9)
£2.05	Ringwood (23), Palmers (10), Morrells (4), Broughton (3), Becketts (2), Tolly (2), Wickwar (2)
£2.06	West Berkshire (6)
£2.07	Dartmoor Best (7), Everards (4), Ushers (3)
£2.08	Goddards (2)
£2.09	Greene King (120)

£2.10	Badger (25), Cheriton (6), King (2)
£2.11	Adnams (75)
£2.13	Youngs (20), Woodfordes (8)
£2.14	Brakspears (33)
£2.15	Caledonian (10), Charles Wells (9)
£2.18	Harveys (21), Larkins (6), Timothy Taylors (3)
£2.25	Milton (2)
£2.28	Orkney (2)

Other beers we found at extremely low prices, but just in single pubs, were Holts, Wyre Piddle, Bathams, Itchen Valley, Clarks, Camerons, Bullmastiff, Black Dog and York. All these were £1.70 a pint or less (very much less in the case of Holts and Wyre Piddle).

The 2002 Budget halved the rate of beer duty for the smallest brewers (those brewing less than a set limit which works out at about five million pints a year). This should cut the price of their beers by 14p a pint. As a very rough guide, if you have heard of a brewer that is not local to you, then that brewer is probably too big to benefit from the full duty cut (there is to be some tapered duty relief for brewers exceeding the limit). That's to say, familiar names such as Adnams, Batemans, Brakspears, Fullers, Harveys, Ringwood, Sam Smiths, Timothy Taylors and Youngs won't get the cut. But if you have not heard of the brewer, then it's quite likely that it will be eligible for the duty cut. Also, pubs brewing their own beers are well within the limit. So this new duty concession will reinforce the golden beer price rule – that small is beautiful.

The cheapest area for drinks is unquestionably Lancashire. In our survey of prices in 1,288 pubs nationwide, we found beer there was typically 23p a pint cheaper than the national average. The Table below shows how much extra people in other areas now have to pay for their beer:

How much extra you pay per pint

5p	Cheshire
6p	Nottinghamshire
8p	Cumbria, Herefordshire, Yorkshire
10p	Staffordshire
12p	Northumbria
13p	Shropshire
14p	Derbyshire, Worcestershire, Wales
17p	Cornwall
19p	Gloucestershire, Leicestershire
20p	Devon, Warwickshire
22p	Somerset
25p	Bedfordshire, Dorset, Essex, Lincolnshire, Northamptonshire
27p	Wiltshire
29p	Hertfordshire, Isle of Wight
31p	Hampshire, Norfolk, Suffolk
33p	Cambridgeshire
34p	Kent, Oxfordshire, Sussex, Scotland
40p	Berkshire
42p	Buckinghamshire
48p	Surrey, London

All those areas where beer costs 25p a pint plus more than in Lancashire – that's to say, all those listed above, from Bedfordshire on – have now breached the £2 a pint barrier.

This year's trends

'I'm not staying off suite', said one well travelled 10-year-old we know, and customer pressure of that sort is leading to very substantial improvements in the standard of pub bedroom accommodation. The move to better pub bedrooms (and what might be called ensuitification) is one of the most striking current trends.

Trend number two is the growing availability of really good coffee in pubs, and often of a choice of teas and infusions too.

Trend number three is in fact a return to a very old-fashioned pub virtue: more and more pubs now have daily newspapers out for their customers.

Trend number four is the explosion of interest among pub chefs in natural ingredients, often fresh local produce. This is having a splendid effect on pub food quality.

Trend number five is towards menu flexibility. More pubs now offer cut-price small helpings (for children, or for anyone with a smaller appetite – a real boon for older customers). And (slightly different this, though it brings similar benefits) more pubs are doing split pricing on some dishes, the full price for a main-course helping, and the lower price for a starter or 'light bite' helping.

All these are good changes. Some trends are less welcome.

This year notices have cropped up in quite a few pubs, asserting that smoking is allowed throughout the premises. These notices have been produced and promoted by an outfit which gets funding from the Tobacco Manufacturers Association. This flies directly in the face of the main purpose of legislation to prohibit cigarette advertising, which is of course to stop the promotion of smoking itself.

Noise pollution, to many readers just as annoying as smoke if a good deal less harmful, is on the remorseless increase. In last year's edition of the *Guide*, 52% of pubs had piped music; this year, the proportion has climbed to 57%.

Traditional pub games, though, are in grave decline. Last year, 400 of our main entries had darts boards; this year, the number has fallen to 364 – a drop of 7% in the proportion of pubs with darts. And bar billiards is becoming a seriously endangered species, offered now by only one in 45 pubs, compared with one in 37 last year – a 12% drop. Indeed, pubs with boules now clearly outnumber pubs with bar billiards.

We have mentioned air pollution and noise pollution. A new threat is menu pollution. It's bad enough when good cooks follow the estate agents' example in over-describing their food. This is how one pub hypes its actually very enjoyable salmon fish fingers: 'Scottish salmon digits heavenly dusted in cracked black peppercorns and pan flashed before being nappied with a cream glace built up with a dash of brandy, a touch of mustard and a scattering of green peppercorns'.

Eager to follow the gifted chefs who are setting high new standards in the quality of pub cooking, many pub chefs are doing the right thing – simply doing their best work possible, on ingredients which they have chosen with care. But others are putting all their imagination and flights of fancy into the menu, instead of the food itself. Peppering their menus with trendy chef-speak – tian, coulis, jus, compote, vierge, galette and so forth – they paint mouth-watering pictures of dishes that turn out to be very ordinary and lack-lustre.

With flowery descriptions of ordinary pub food raising expectations so high, it's no wonder that we get so many letters of disappointment from readers: 'A big let-down, food doesn't deliver what it promises'; 'Too expansive and over-elaborate menu'; 'Food only average in spite of the menu's great promise'; 'Menu is over-ambitious and the kitchen can't live up to it'; 'Promises much but delivers little'; 'Extensive menu which does not meet expectations'; 'Fancy menus for simple/plain dishes with watery sauces'; and so on.

The lesson is clear: a fanciful menu should put you on your guard. It may sometimes be that a proud chef is honestly trying to describe his masterpiece as fully as possible. But the best pub chefs are usually content to let their food speak for itself, to your taste buds, and don't need menu spin to hype it up.

Finally, one entirely innocuous and rather endearing retro pub food trend. This year that trio that was so popular in the 1960s and early 1970s is firmly back on stage: whitebait, chicken chasseur, and crème brûlée.

Tailpiece

This year we asked all 1,318 pubs in the main section of the *Guide* whether they allowed customers to bring in dogs. This is the first national survey of just how many pubs allow dogs. The total was much higher than we expected: 60% of pubs allow dogs inside. Most of these allow them in the bar, but not in other parts of the pub. However, one in three of the pubs that do welcome dogs allow them in any part of their premises, including eating areas. We give details for each pub in the text.

What is a Good Pub?

What is a Good Pub?

The main entries in this book have been through a two-stage sifting process. First of all, some 2,000 regular correspondents keep in touch with us about the pubs they visit, and nearly double that number report occasionally. We are now also getting quite a flow of reports through our www.goodguides.com web site. This keeps us up-to-date about pubs included in previous editions – it's their alarm signals that warn us when a pub's standards have dropped (after a change of management, say), and it's their continuing approval that reassures us about keeping a pub as a main entry for another year. Very important, though, are the reports they send us on pubs we don't know at all. It's from these new discoveries that we make up a shortlist, to be considered for possible inclusion as new main entries. The more people that report favourably on a new pub, the more likely it is to win a place on this shortlist – especially if some of the reporters belong to our hard core of about 500 trusted correspondents whose judgement we have learned to rely on. These are people who have each given us detailed comments on dozens of pubs, and shown that (when we ourselves know some of those pubs too) their judgement is closely in line with our own.

This brings us to the acid test. Each pub, before inclusion as a main entry, is inspected anonymously by the Editor, the Deputy Editor, or both. They have to find some special quality that would make strangers enjoy visiting it. What often marks the pub out for special attention is good value food (and that might mean anything from a well made sandwich, with good fresh ingredients at a low price, to imaginative cooking outclassing most restaurants in the area). Maybe the drinks are out of the ordinary (pubs with several hundred whiskies, with remarkable wine lists, with home-made country wines or good beer or cider made on the premises, with a wide range of well kept real ales or bottled beers from all over the world). Perhaps there's a special appeal about it as a place to stay, with good bedrooms and obliging service. Maybe it's the building itself (from centuries-old parts of monasteries to extravagant Victorian gin-palaces), or its surroundings (lovely countryside, attractive waterside, extensive well kept garden), or what's in it (charming furnishings, extraordinary collections of bric-a-brac).

Above all, though, what makes the good pub is its atmosphere – you should be able to feel at home there, and feel not just that *you're* glad you've come but that *they're* glad you've come.

It follows from this that a great many ordinary locals, perfectly good in their own right, don't earn a place in the book. What makes them attractive to their regular customers (an almost clubby chumminess) may even make strangers feel rather out-of-place.

Another important point is that there's not necessarily any link between charm and luxury – though we like our creature comforts as much as anyone. A basic unspoilt village tavern, with hard seats and a flagstone floor, may be worth travelling miles to find, while a deluxe pub-restaurant may not be worth crossing the street for. Landlords can't buy the Good Pub accolade by spending thousands on thickly padded banquettes, soft music and menus boasting about signature dishes nesting on beds of trendy vegetables drizzled by a jus of this and that – they can only win it, by having a genuinely personal concern for both their customers and their pub.

Using the *Guide*

THE COUNTIES
England has been split alphabetically into counties, mainly to make it easier for people scanning through the book to find pubs near them. Each chapter starts by picking out the pubs that are currently doing best in the area, or are specially attractive for one reason or another.

The county boundaries we use are those for the administrative counties (not the old traditional counties, which were changed back in 1976). We have left the new unitary authorities within the counties that they formed part of until their creation in the most recent local government reorganisation. Metropolitan areas have been included in the counties around them – for example, Merseyside in Lancashire. And occasionally we have grouped counties together – for example, Rutland with Leicestershire, and Durham with Northumberland to make Northumbria. If in doubt, check the Contents.

Scotland and Wales have each been covered in single chapters, and London appears immediately before them at the end of England. Except in London (which is split into Central, East, North, South and West), pubs are listed alphabetically under the name of the town or village where they are. If the village is so small that you probably wouldn't find it on a road map, we've listed it under the name of the nearest sizeable village or town instead. The maps use the same town and village names, and additionally include a few big cities that don't have any listed pubs – for orientation.

We always list pubs in their true locations – so if a village is actually in Buckinghamshire that's where we list it, even if its postal address is via some town in Oxfordshire. Just once or twice, when the village itself is in one county but the pub is just over the border in the next-door county, we have used the village county, not the pub one.

STARS ★
Really outstanding pubs are picked out with a star after their name. In a few cases, pubs have two stars: these are the aristocrats among pubs, really worth going out of your way to find. The stars do NOT signify extra luxury or specially good food – in fact some of the pubs which appeal most distinctively and strongly of all are decidedly basic in terms of food and surroundings. The detailed description of each pub shows what its particular appeal is, and this is what the stars refer to.

FOOD AND STAY AWARDS
The knife-and-fork rosette shows those pubs where food is quite outstanding. The bed symbol shows pubs which we know to be good as places to stay in – bearing in mind the price of the rooms (obviously you can't expect the same level of luxury at £40 a head as you'd get for £100 a head). Pubs with bedrooms are marked on the maps as a square.

This wine glass symbol marks out those pubs where wines are a cut above the usual run, and/or offer a good choice of wines by the glass.

The beer tankard symbol shows pubs where the quality of the beer is quite exceptional, or pubs which keep a particularly interesting range of beers in good condition.

£
This symbol picks out pubs where we have found decent snacks at £2.20 or less, or worthwhile main dishes at £5.50 or less.

RECOMMENDERS

At the end of each main entry we include the names of readers who have recently recommended that pub (unless they've asked us not to).

Important note: the description of the pub and the comments on it are our own and not the recommenders'; they are based on our own personal inspections and on later verification of facts with each pub. As some recommenders' names appear quite often, you can get an extra idea of what a pub is like by seeing which other pubs those recommenders have approved.

LUCKY DIPS

The Lucky Dip section at the end of each county chapter includes brief descriptions of pubs that have been recommended by readers, with the readers' names in brackets. As the flood of reports from readers has given so much solid information about so many pubs, we have been able to include only those which seem really worth trying. Where only one single reader's name is shown, in most cases that pub has been given a favourable review by other readers in previous years, so its inclusion does not depend on a single individual's judgement. In all cases, we have now not included a pub in the list unless readers' descriptions make the nature of the pub quite clear, and give us good grounds for trusting that other readers would be glad to know of the pub. So the descriptions normally reflect the balanced judgement of a number of different readers, increasingly backed up by similar reports on the same pubs from other readers in previous years. Many have been inspected by us. In these cases, LYM means the pub was in a previous edition of the *Guide*. The usual reason that it's no longer a main entry is that, although we've heard nothing really condemnatory about it, we've not had enough favourable reports to be sure that it's still ahead of the local competition. BB means that, although the pub has never been a main entry, we have inspected it, and found nothing against it. In both these cases, the description is our own; in others, it's based on the readers' reports. This year, we have deleted many previously highly rated pubs from the book simply because we have no very recent reports on them. This may well mean that we have left out some favourites – please tell us if we have!

Lucky Dip pubs marked with a ☆ are ones where the information we have (either from our own inspections or from trusted reader/reporters) suggests a firm recommendation. Roughly speaking, we'd say that these pubs are as much worth considering, at least for the virtues described for them, as many of the main entries themselves. Note that in the Dips we always commend food if we have information supporting a positive recommendation. So a bare mention that food is served shouldn't be taken to imply a recommendation of the food. The same is true of accommodation and so forth.

The Lucky Dips (particularly, of course, the starred ones) are under consideration for inspection for a future edition – so please let us have any comments you can make on them. You can use the report forms at the end of the book, the report card which should be included in it, or just write direct (no stamp needed if posted in the UK). Our address is The Good Pub Guide, FREEPOST TN1569, WADHURST, East Sussex TN5 7BR. Alternatively, you can get reports to us immediately, through our web site www.goodguides.com.

MAP REFERENCES

All pubs outside the big cities are given four-figure map references. On the main entries, it looks like this: SX5678 Map 1. Map 1 means that it's on the first map at the end of the book. SX means it's in the square labelled SX on that map. The first figure, 5, tells you to look along the grid at the top and bottom of the SX square for the figure 5. The third figure, 7, tells you to look down the grid at the side of the square to find the figure 7. Imaginary lines drawn down and across the square from these figures should intersect near the pub itself.

The second and fourth figures, the 6 and the 8, are for more precise pin-pointing, and are really for use with larger-scale maps such as road atlases or the Ordnance Survey 1:50,000 maps, which use exactly the same map reference system. On the relevant Ordnance Survey map, instead of finding the 5 marker on the top grid you'd find the 56 one; instead of the 7 on the side grid you'd look for the 78 marker. This makes it very easy to locate even the smallest village.

Where a pub is exceptionally difficult to find, we include a six-figure reference in the directions, such as OS Sheet 102 map reference 654783. This refers to Sheet 102 of the Ordnance Survey 1:50,000 maps, which explain how to use the six-figure references to pin-point a pub to the nearest 100 metres.

MOTORWAY PUBS

If a pub is within four or five miles of a motorway junction, and reaching it doesn't involve much slow traffic, we give special directions for finding it from the motorway. And the Special Interest Lists at the end of the book include a list of these pubs, motorway by motorway.

PRICES AND OTHER FACTUAL DETAILS

The *Guide* went to press during the summer of 2002. As late as possible, each pub was sent a checking sheet to get up-to-date food, drink and bedroom prices and other factual information. By the summer of 2003 prices are bound to have increased a little – to be prudent, you should probably allow around 5% extra by then. But if you find a significantly different price please let us know.

Breweries or independent chains to which pubs are 'tied' are named at the beginning of the italic-print rubric after each main entry. That generally means the pub has to get most if not all of its drinks from that brewery or chain. If the brewery is not an independent one but just part of a combine, we name the combine in brackets. When the pub is tied, we have spelled out whether the landlord is a tenant, has the pub on a lease, or is a manager. Tenants and leaseholders of breweries generally have considerably greater freedom to do things their own way, and in particular are allowed to buy drinks including a beer from sources other than their tied brewery.

Free houses are pubs not tied to a brewery, so in theory they can shop around to get the drinks their customers want, at the best prices they can find. But in practice many free houses have loans from the big brewers, on terms that bind them to sell those breweries' beers. So don't be too surprised to find that so-called free houses may be stocking a range of beers restricted to those from a single brewery.

Real ale is used by us to mean beer that has been maturing naturally in its cask. We do not count as real ale beer which has been pasteurised or filtered to remove its natural yeasts. If it is kept under a blanket of carbon dioxide to preserve it, we still generally mention it – as long as the pressure is too light for you to notice any extra fizz, it's hard to tell the difference. (For brevity, we use the expression 'under light blanket pressure' to cover such pubs; we do not include among them pubs where the blanket pressure is high enough to force the beer up from the cellar, as this does make it unnaturally fizzy.) If we say a pub has, for example, 'Whitbreads-related real ales', these may include not just beers brewed by the national company and its subsidiaries but also beers produced by independent breweries which the national company buys in bulk and distributes alongside its own.

Other drinks: we've also looked out particularly for pubs doing enterprising non-alcoholic drinks (including good tea or coffee), interesting spirits (especially malt whiskies), country wines (elderflower and the like), freshly squeezed juices, and good farm ciders. So many pubs now stock one of the main brands of draught cider that we normally mention cider only if the pub keeps quite a range, or one of the less common farm-made ciders.

Bar food refers to what is sold in the bar, not in any separate restaurant. It means a place serves anything from sandwiches and ploughman's to full meals, rather than pork scratchings or packets of crisps. We always mention sandwiches in the text if we know that a pub does them – if you don't see them mentioned, assume you can't get them.

The *food listed* in the description of each pub is an example of the sort of thing you'd find served in the bar on a normal day, and generally includes the dishes which are currently finding most favour with readers. We try to indicate any difference we know of between lunchtime and evening, and between summer and winter (on the whole stressing summer food more). In winter, many pubs tend to have a more restricted range, particularly of salads, and tend then to do more in the way of filled baked potatoes, casseroles and hot pies. We always mention barbecues if we know a pub does them. Food quality and variety may be affected by holidays – particularly in a small pub, where the licensees do the cooking themselves (May and early June seems to be a popular time for licensees to take their holidays).

Any separate *restaurant* is mentioned. But in general all comments on the type of food served, and in particular all the other details about bar food at the end of each entry, relate to the pub food and not to the restaurant food.

Children's Certificates exist, but in practice *children* are allowed into at least some part of almost all the pubs included in this *Guide* (there is no legal restriction on the movement of children over 14 in any pub, though only people over 18 may get alcohol). As we went to press, we asked the main-entry pubs a series of detailed questions about their rules. *Children welcome* means the pub has told us that it simply lets them come in, with no special restrictions. In other cases we report exactly what arrangements pubs say they make for children. However, we have to note that in readers' experience some pubs make restrictions that they haven't told us about (children only if eating, for example). Also, very occasionally pubs which have previously allowed children change their policy altogether, virtually excluding them. If you come across this, please let us know, so that we can clarify the information for the pub concerned in the next edition. Beware that if children are confined to the restaurant, they may occasionally be expected to have a full restaurant meal. Also, please note that a welcome for children does not necessarily mean a welcome for breast-feeding in public. If we don't mention children at all, assume that they are not welcome. All but one or two pubs (we mention these in the text) allow children in their garden or on their terrace, if they have one. In the Lucky Dip entries we mention children only if readers have found either that they are allowed or that they are not allowed – the absence of any reference to children in a Dip entry means we don't know either way.

This year for the first time we asked all main entries what their policy was about *dogs*, and if they allow them we say so. Generally, if you take a dog into a pub you should have it on a lead. We also mention in the text any pub dogs or cats (or indeed other animals) that we've come across ourselves, or heard about from readers.

Parking is not mentioned if you should normally be able to park outside the pub, or in a private car park, without difficulty. But if we know that parking space is limited or metered, we say so.

We now say if a pub does not accept *credit cards*; some which do may put a surcharge on credit card bills, as the card companies take quite a big cut. We also say if we know that a pub tries to retain customers' credit cards while they are eating. This is a reprehensible practice, and if a pub tries it on you, please tell them that all banks and card companies frown on it – and please let us know the pub's name, so that we can warn readers in future editions.

Telephone numbers are given for all pubs that are not ex-directory.

Opening hours are for summer; we say if we know of differences in winter, or on particular days of the week. In the country, many pubs may open rather later and close earlier than their details show unless there are plenty of customers around (if you come across this, please let us know – with details). Pubs are allowed to stay open all day Mondays to Saturdays from 11am (earlier, if the area's licensing magistrates have permitted) till 11pm. However, outside cities most English and Welsh pubs close during the afternoon. Scottish pubs are allowed to stay open until later at night, and the Government has announced plans to allow later opening in England and Wales too, and it's just possible that the law will be changed during the currency of this edition. We'd be very grateful to hear of any differences from the hours we quote. You are allowed 20 minutes' drinking-up time after the quoted hours – half an hour if you've been having a meal in the pub.

Bedroom prices normally include full English breakfasts (if these are available, which they usually are), VAT and any automatic service charge that we know about. If we give just one price, it is the total price for two people sharing a double or twin-bedded room for one night. Otherwise, prices before the / are for single occupancy, prices after it for double. A capital B against the price means that it includes a private bathroom, a capital S a private shower. As all this coding packs in quite a lot of information, some examples may help to explain it:

£65	on its own means that's the total bill for two people sharing a twin or double room without private bath; the pub has no rooms with private bath, and a single person might have to pay that full price.
£65B	means exactly the same – but all the rooms have private bath
£50(£65B)	means rooms with private baths cost £5 extra
£35/£50(£65B)	means the same as the last example, but also shows that there are single rooms for £35, none of which have private bathrooms

If there's a choice of rooms at different prices, we normally give the cheapest. If there are seasonal price variations, we give the summer price (the highest). During the winter, many inns, particularly in the country, will have special cheaper rates. And at other times, especially in holiday areas, you will often find prices cheaper if you stay for several nights. On weekends, inns that aren't in obvious weekending areas often have bargain rates for two- or three-night stays.

MEAL TIMES

Bar food is commonly served from 12-2 and 7-9, at least from Monday to Saturday (food service often stops a bit earlier on Sundays). If we don't give a time against the *Bar food* note at the bottom of a main entry, that means that you should be able to get bar food at those times. However, we do spell out the times if we know that bar food service starts after 12.15 or after 7.15; if it stops before 2 or before 8.45; or if food is served for significantly longer than usual (say, till 2.30 or 9.45). Though we note days when pubs have told us they don't do food, experience suggests that you should play safe on Sundays, and check first with any pub before planning an expedition that depends on getting a meal there. Also, out-of-the-way pubs often cut down on cooking during the week, especially the early part of the week, if they're quiet – as they tend to be, except at holiday times. Please let us know if you find anything different from what we say!

NO SMOKING

We say in the text of each entry what, if any, provision a pub makes for non-smokers. Pubs setting aside at least some sort of no smoking area are also listed county by county in the Special Interest Lists at the back of the book.

DISABLED ACCESS

Deliberately, we do not ask pubs questions about this, as their answers would not give a reliable picture of how easy access is. Instead, we depend on readers' direct experience. If you are able to give us help about this, we would be particularly grateful for your reports.

PLANNING ROUTES WITH THE GOOD PUB GUIDE

Computer users may like to know of a route-finding programme, Microsoft® AutoRoute™ Great Britain 2003 Edition, which shows the location of *Good Pub Guide* pubs on detailed maps, works out the quickest routes for journeys, adds diversions to nearby pubs – and shows our text entries for those pubs on screen.

OUR WEB SITE (**www.goodguides.com**)

Our Internet web site combines material from *The Good Pub Guide* and its sister publication *The Good Britain Guide* in a way that gives people who do not yet know the books at least a taste of them. The site is being continually improved and expanded, and we hope to use it to give readers of the books extra information. You can use the site to send us reports – this way they get virtually immediate attention.

CHANGES DURING THE YEAR – PLEASE TELL US

Changes are inevitable, during the course of the year. Landlords change, and so do their policies. And, as we've said, not all returned our fact-checking sheets. We very much hope that you will find everything just as we say. But if you find anything different, please let us know, using the tear-out card in the middle of the book (which doesn't need an envelope), the report forms here, or just a letter. You don't need a stamp: the address is The Good Pub Guide, FREEPOST TN1569, WADHURST, East Sussex TN5 7BR. As we have said, you can also send us reports by using our web site: **www.goodguides.com**.

Author's Acknowledgements

The *Guide* could not exist without the unstinting help we have from the many thousands of readers who report to us on the pubs they visit. For the tremendous amount of help they've given us this year, I am deeply grateful to Richard Lewis, Ian Phillips, George Atkinson, Kevin Thorpe, Michael Doswell, Michael and Jenny Back, CMW, JJW, Dennis Jenkin, Dr and Mrs M E Wilson, LM, Susan and John Douglas, Roger and Jenny Huggins, Dave Irving, Ewan McCall, Tom McLean, Tracey and Stephen Groves, the Didler, Rona Murdoch, Peter and Audrey Dowsett, John Beeken, Joan and Michel Hooper-Immins, Steve Whalley, Tom Evans, Phyl and Jack Street, Ann and Colin Hunt, Martin and Karen Wake, W W Burke, Pete Baker, Tony and Wendy Hobden, E G Parish, Paul and Ursula Randall, Pat and Tony Martin, Howard Dell, MDN, Val and Alan Green, MLR, E D Fraser, Jenny and Brian Seller, Alan and Paula McCully, Charles and Pauline Stride, Pamela and Merlyn Horswell, Lynn Sharpless, Stephen, Julie and Hayley Brown, John Evans, Andrew Crawford, Graham Coates, Simon Collett-Jones, Ted George, Guy Vowles, John Saville, Andy and Jill Kassube, Tina and David Woods-Taylor, Peter Meister, Derek and Sylvia Stephenson, Nick Holding, Michael Butler, JHBS, Dr and Mrs A K Clarke, John Foord, Bob and Maggie Atherton, Joyce and Maurice Cottrell, Mike and Mary Carter, Paul Humphreys, Duncan Cloud, B, M and P Kendall, Michael Porter, Neil and Anita Christopher, Peter F Marshall, Peter Scillitoe, R T and J C Moggridge, Lorraine and Fred Gill, Comus and Sarah Elliott, Mayur Shah, Marjorie and David Lamb, Dick and Madeleine Brown, Alan M Pring, Kevin Blake, B and K Hypher, John Wooll, Ian and Nita Cooper, J F M and M West, Jim Bush, KC, Gerry and Rosemary Dobson, Margaret Ross, David Crook, Mike Ridgway, Sarah Miles, Pete and Rosie Flower, Dave Braisted, Bernie Adams, Mike Rowan, Margaret Dickinson, Malcolm Taylor, Pete Yearsley, Richard Fendick, M Borthwick, Richard Stancomb, Michael Dandy, Roger Everett, Bruce Bird, M G Hart, Michael and Marion Buchanan, Brian and Anna Marsden, Martin Jennings, Colin and Dot Savill, Mike and Heather Watson, P Abbott, John Kane, Basil Minson, Tim and Ann Newell, Richard and Margaret Peers, Eric Locker, Darly Graton, Graeme Gulibert and Phil and Sally Gorton.

Warm thanks too to John Holliday of Trade Wind Technology, who built and looks after our state-of-the-art database; and above all to the thousands of devoted publicans, who give us all so much pleasure.

Alisdair Aird

Bedfordshire

A very pretty pub joins the main entries this year: the Cross Keys at Totternhoe. Two other pubs to pick out here, both on particularly good form this year, are the Knife & Cleaver at Houghton Conquest (by far the best pub in the area for a special meal out, and our clear choice as Bedfordshire Dining Pub of the Year), and the delightfully unspoilt Cock at Broom. On a summer's day the Globe by the canal at Linslade is a pleasant refuge, as is the big informal riverside garden behind the Bell at Odell. In the Lucky Dip section at the end of the chapter, current favourites include the Cornfields at Colmworth, Black Horse at Ireland (a reliable dining pub), Rose & Crown at Ridgmont and Bedford Arms at Souldrop. Drinks prices in the county are not far off the national average, with a Greene King beer often the cheapest stocked; the main local brewer is Charles Wells of Bedford. To benefit from the cheaper pints possible with the new lower duty rate for small brewers, look out for beers from Potton, or B&T of Shefford.

BIDDENHAM TL0249 Map 5

Three Tuns £

57 Main Road; village signposted from A428 just W of Bedford

The very reasonably priced, enjoyable food is one of the main draws at this thatched village pub, especially at lunchtime. It might include soup (£2), sandwiches (from £2; soup and sandwich £3.50), ploughman's (£3.50), ham and egg (£4), home-made dishes such as curry (£6), steak and kidney pie and meat or vegetarian lasagne (£6.50), steaks (from £8.50), puddings (£2.30), and children's menu (£2.50); the dining room is no smoking. As well as a friendly bustling atmosphere, the lounge has low beams and country paintings, and well kept Greene King IPA and Abbot and a guest such as Bass on handpump. A simpler public bar (where dogs are welcome) has darts, table skittles, dominoes and a fruit machine. There are seats in the attractively sheltered spacious garden, and a big terrace has lots of picnic-sets. The very good children's play area has swings for all ages. *(Recommended by BKA, Ian Phillips, Terry Mizen, Colin and Janet Roe, Michael Tack, Maysie Thompson)*

Greene King ~ Tenant Alan Wilkins ~ Real ale ~ Bar food (not Sun evening) ~ No credit cards ~ (01234) 354847 ~ Children in eating area of bar ~ Dogs allowed in bar ~ Open 11.30-2.30, 6-11; 12-3, 7-10.30 Sun

BROOM TL1743 Map 5

Cock ★

23 High Street; from A1 opposite northernmost Biggleswade turnoff follow Old Warden 3, Aerodrome 2 signpost, and take first left signposted Broom

There's no bar counter at this friendly welcoming and unspoilt 17th-c pub, and the very well kept Greene King IPA, Abbot and Ruddles County are tapped straight from the cask, by the cellar steps off a central corridor running down the middle of the building. The four cosy rooms have remained almost untouched over the years, with simple latch doors, winter log fires, low ochre ceilings, stripped panelling and farmhouse-style tables and chairs on antique tiles; piped music, darts, table skittles, cribbage and dominoes. Readers enjoy the good straightforward bar food which includes sandwiches (from £2.85), home-made soup (£2.95), ploughman's (from

£4.55), vegetarian lasagne (£5.95), scampi or filled yorkshire puddings (£5.95), breaded plaice filled with prawns and mushrooms or large cod (£6.95), cajun chicken (£7.25), 8oz sirloin steak (£8.95), and Sunday roast (£6.95). There are picnic-sets on the terrace by the back lawn, and a fenced-off play area; caravanning and camping facilities are available. *(Recommended by JP, PP, Des and Jen Clarke, J D M Rushworth, S F Parrinder, P Smith, the Didler, Stephen, Julie and Hayley Brown, JWAC, Ian Phillips, David R Crafts, Pete Baker, B, M and P Kendall)*

Greene King ~ Tenants Gerry and Jean Lant ~ Real ale ~ Bar food (not Sun evening) ~ Restaurant ~ (01767) 314411 ~ Children in restaurant and family room ~ Dogs allowed in bar ~ Open 12-3(4 Sat), 6-11; 12-4, 7-10.30 Sun

HOUGHTON CONQUEST TL0441 Map 5

Knife & Cleaver

Between B530 (old A418) and A6, S of Bedford

Bedfordshire Dining Pub of the Year

There's no denying that this attractive 17th-c dining pub, with its smart new inn-sign, is very restauranty, but given the scarcity of good dining pubs in this part of the country we'd be doing readers a disservice if we decided that its thorough-going emphasis on food disqualified it as a pub. It has a good bar menu, including sandwiches (from £3), soup of the day such as wild garlic and herbs with goats cheese croûtons (£3), ploughman's (£4), grilled provençale bread with flaked smoked mackerel in horseradish mayonnaise on marinated tomatoes (£4.95), steak, blue stilton and mushroom sauce baguette (£6.25), dish of the day such as beef and stilton crêpe with sweet tomato sauce or smoked haddock and scallop pie with mashed potato topping or thai-style seafood noodles (£6.50), and moules marinière (£7.25). Puddings (£3.25) might include pear and almond tart, sticky toffee pudding and compote of rhubarb and strawberries with crumble ice cream, and there's a proper cheeseboard (£4). Dishes are stylishly presented, imaginative and fully flavoured, taking the same care over ingredients and cooking as the separate restaurant menu (and the good daily fresh fish menu can be served in either bar or restaurant). Service is really welcoming and efficient. The relaxed and comfortable bar has maps, drawings and old documents on the walls, panelling which is reputed to have come from nearby ruined Houghton House, and a blazing fire in winter; the airy no smoking conservatory restaurant has rugs on the tiled floor, swagged curtains, cane furniture and lots of hanging plants, and there's also a no smoking family room. Well kept Bass and Batemans XB on handpump, Stowford Press farm cider, over two dozen good wines by the glass, and a fine choice of up to 20 well aged malt whiskies; unobtrusive piped music. Beware that it does get very busy, and on Saturday evening if the restaurant is fully booked they may not serve bar meals. There are tables on the terrace in a neatly kept garden, and the church opposite is worth a look. *(Recommended by Bob and Maggie Atherton, David and Ruth Shillitoe, Maysie Thompson, Mandy and Simon King)*

Free house ~ Licensees David and Pauline Loom ~ Real ale ~ Bar food (12-2.30 (2 Sat), 7-9.30; not Sun evening) ~ Restaurant ~ (01234) 740387 ~ Children welcome ~ Open 12-2.30(2 Sat), 7-11; 12-3(cl evening) Sun; closed 27-30 Dec ~ Bedrooms: £49B/£64B

KEYSOE TL0762 Map 5

Chequers

Pertenhall Road, Brook End (B660)

Comfortable seats in one of the two neat and simple beamed rooms (which are divided by an unusual stone-pillared fireplace) lend an air of the 1960s to this pleasant village local, and the friendly licensees go out of their way to make customers feel at home. Bar food is very popular, with sandwiches, plain or toasted (from £2.50), home-made soup (£2.75), garlic mushrooms on toast (£3.75), ploughman's (£4), chilli con carne (£6), home-made steak and ale pie or scampi (£6.50), chicken breast stuffed with stilton in a chive sauce (£8.25), steaks (from

£9.75), blackboard specials, and children's dishes (£3.25). The handpumps on the stone bar counter serve well kept Fullers London Pride and Hook Norton Best, and they have some malt whiskies, and mulled wine in winter; darts, shove-ha'penny, bar billiards, dominoes and piped local radio or music. Tables and chairs on the back terrace look over the garden, which has a play tree, swings and a sand-pit.
(Recommended by Michael and Jenny Back, Maysie Thompson)

Free house ~ Licensee Jeffrey Kearns ~ Real ale ~ Bar food (not Tues) ~ (01234) 708678 ~ Children in family room and restaurant ~ Open 11.30-2.30, 6.30-11; 12-2.30, 7-10.30 Sun; closed Tues

LINSLADE SP9225 Map 4

Globe

Globe Lane, off Stoke Road (A4146) nr bridge; outside Linslade proper, just before you get to the town sign

This whitewashed 19th-c pub is nicely set below the embankment of the Grand Union Canal – a perfect spot to while away a sunny afternoon watching life on the water. Understandably busy in summer when there's a jolly bustling atmosphere, it has enough tables outside to cope, most of them along the towpath, with others in a very well equipped fenced-off play area with climbing forts and equipment, and also some in the garden under the trees alongside the car park. Inside, cosy and attractive beamed and flagstoned rooms have intriguing quotations on the walls, and log and coal fires. Well kept beers are Greene King IPA, Abbot and Ruddles and a guest such as Everards Tiger; piped music. Bar food includes baked potatoes and ploughman's (£4.95), battered haddock (£6.50) and rump steak (£7.95); efficient service; no smoking restaurant. To get there you come down a little private road that seems to take you further into the countryside than you really are (there's plenty of parking past the pub), and the Cross Bucks Way leads off from just along the canal.
(Recommended by Ian Phillips, John Saville, Susan and John Douglas)

Greene King ~ Manager Nick Hughes ~ Real ale ~ Bar food (not Sun evening in winter) ~ Restaurant ~ (01525) 373338 ~ Children in eating area of bar and restaurant ~ Dogs allowed in bar ~ Open 11-11; 12-10.30 Sun

ODELL SP9658 Map 4

Bell

High Street/Horsefair Lane; off A6 S of Rushden, via Sharnbrook

There's plenty of room for diners in the five little low-ceilinged rooms which loop around a central servery at this pretty stone and thatched village pub. It's furnished with handsome old oak settles, bentwood chairs and neat modern furniture on slightly worn red carpets, and countryside prints. Some areas have shiny black beams, and there's a log fire in one big stone fireplace, and two coal fires elsewhere. Reasonably priced bar food includes sandwiches (from £2.50), omelettes (£4.50), ploughman's (from £4.75), ham, egg and chips (£6), liver and bacon (£6.50), and daily specials from the board such as vegetable lasagne (£5.60), mushroom and asparagus pasta and salad (£6.25), smoked bacon steak with cumberland sauce (£7.25), lamb or chicken curry (£7.95), braised lamb shank (£8.95); usual children's dishes (from £2.30) and puddings such as crunchy Dime Bar gateau and cheesecake (from £3.15); well kept Greene King IPA, Abbot and Ruddles County and a guest such as Wadworths 6X on handpump, and piped music. It's pleasing outside, with picnic-sets on the flower-filled terrace overlooking a wooded garden, giving an attractive walk down through a wild area to a bridge over the Great Ouse. Children will enjoy watching the garden roamings of Lucy the eleven-year-old goose, and the golden pheasants, cockatiels and canaries in their aviary. Further along the road is a very pretty church, and the pub is handy for the local country park. *(Recommended by Ian Phillips, Anthony Barnes, CMW, JJW, Maysie Thompson)*

Greene King ~ Tenants Derek and Doreen Scott ~ Real ale ~ Bar food (12-2, 7-9.30; not Sun evening) ~ (01234) 720254 ~ Children welcome ~ Open 11-2.30, 6-11; 12-2.30, 7-10.30 Sun

RISELEY TL0362 Map 5

Fox & Hounds

High Street; village signposted off A6 and B660 N of Bedford

Head here if you're a steak fan: you can choose the piece of meat you want and how you want it cooked, and you're then charged by the weight – say, £11.60 for 8oz rump, £12.60 for 8oz of sirloin and £14.20 for fillet (not Saturday lunchtime). Blackboards show other dishes, using local supplies, such as roasted tomato soup (£3.25), pâté (£3.50), home-made steakburgers (£5.50), steak, stilton and pork pie or fillet of local trout (£9.50), salmon escalope with smoked salmon and wine sauce (£10.50), and puddings such as spotted dick or steamed ginger (£3.25). Even if you don't see anything you fancy, it's worth asking: they're very obliging here, and will try and cope with particular food requests. It's a cheerfully bustling place, and does get busy. As they don't take bookings on Saturday night be prepared for a long wait for your table, and your food. A relaxing lounge area, with leather chesterfields, lower tables and wing chairs, contrasts with the more traditional pub furniture spread among timber uprights under the heavy low beams – this year, you'll find the dining tables are bigger; unobtrusive classical or big band piped music. Charles Wells Eagle and Bombardier with perhaps a changing guest such as Marstons Pedigree are kept well on handpump, alongside a decent collection of other drinks including bin-end wines and a range of malts and cognacs. An attractively decked terrace with wooden tables and chairs has outside heating, and the pleasant garden has shrubs and a pergola. *(Recommended by Colin and Janet Roe, Michael Sargent, Ian Phillips, Bob and Maggie Atherton)*

Charles Wells ~ Managers Jan and Lynne Zielinski ~ Real ale ~ Bar food (11.30-1.45, 6.30-9.30; 12-2, 7-9 Sun) ~ Restaurant ~ (01234) 708240 ~ Children welcome ~ Dogs welcome ~ Open 11.30-2.30, 6.30-11; 12-3, 7-10.30 Sun

STANBRIDGE SP9623 Map 4

Five Bells

Station Road; pub signposted off A5 N of Dunstable

This attractive old pub is stylishly decorated, keeping the feel of a smartly relaxed country pub, but adding a fresh, contemporary zip. There are rugs, armchairs and sofas, candles on the neatly polished tables, exposed beams and wooden floors, and careful spotlighting that creates quite different moods around the various areas (of which perhaps the cosiest is the small corner by the fireplace). The big, brighter restaurant leads into a large garden with plenty of good wooden tables and chairs, and perfectly mown lawns; more outside tables nestle under a big tree at the front. There's quite an emphasis on the imaginative food, which might include big well presented sandwiches (£4.95), tatin of marinated tomatoes with mozzarella and honey-roast figs (£10.95), fried bass on buttered linguini with raspberry and ginger sauce (£11.95), and roast poussin on a cassoulet of spring vegetables (£13); the menu highlights which wines will best suit most dishes; no smoking restaurant. They have occasional themed evenings – on St George's Day for example, or during Wimbledon; the chefs trained at hotels such as the Lanesborough in London, and use the gourmet nights to show off what they can do. Well kept Bass and Wadworths 6X and perhaps a guest such as Hook Norton on handpump; piped music. *(Recommended by MP, Stephen Archer, Ian Phillips, Bob and Maggie Atherton)*

Traditional Freehouses ~ Licensee Andrew MacKenzie ~ Real ale ~ Bar food ~ Restaurant ~ (01525) 210224 ~ Children in eating area of bar and restaurant ~ Open 12-11; 11-11 Sat; 12-10.30 Sun

Stars after the name of a pub show exceptional character and appeal. They don't mean extra comfort. And they are nothing to do with food quality, for which there's a separate knife-and-fork symbol. Even quite a basic pub can win stars, if it's individual enough.

TOTTERNHOE SP9821 Map 4

Cross Keys

Castle Hill Road, off A505 W of A5; if coming from Dunstable via the B489, keep on through village towards Lower End and Eaton Bray

This black and white half-timbered pub is a lovely sight, with its colourful hanging baskets and window boxes, spick-and-span shutters, and little bedroom windows peeping out under the thatch. Its small public bar and slightly larger but still compact lounge are charming too, with heavy beams, some ancient timbering and brickwork, even what looks like medieval stonework lower down on the walls and in the inglenook fireplace closest to the road. It's also very popular, but the friendly and accommodating hard-working licensees keep things running smoothly, with a real welcome for families. Enjoyable carefully prepared home-made food includes sandwiches (from £1.85), ploughman's (from £4.35), spinach and ricotta cannelloni (£5.20), lasagne (£5.65), chicken curries (from £6.15), smoked cod poached with chives (£6.35), rabbit or game pie (£6.85), steak and kidney pudding (£7.25), a handful of daily specials such as spaghetti bolognese (£5.95), and puddings (£2.65); no smoking restaurant, may be piped music. Well kept Adnams Broadside, Greene King IPA and Old Speckled Hen and a guest such as Wadworths 6X. There are tables out in front under cocktail parasols, and good views from the large attractive garden running down from the car park, with an extensive play area in the orchard below (and the grassy remains of a Norman motte and bailey fort at the end of the Chilterns Ridge above). It's not far from Whipsnade, and green lane or Icknield Way walks. *(Recommended by MP, Len Banister, David and Anthea Eeles)*

Inn Business ~ Tenants Mike Rutter and Jason Gault ~ Real ale ~ Bar food (12-2.30, 6.30-8.30; not Sun evening) ~ Restaurant ~ (01525) 220434 ~ Children in eating area of bar and restaurant ~ Occasional singer ~ Open 11.30-3, 6-11; 11.30-11 Sat; 12-10.30 Sun

TURVEY SP9452 Map 4

Three Cranes

Just off A428 W of Bedford

The airy two-level carpeted bar at this friendly stone-built 17th-c coaching inn has a solid-fuel stove, a quiet décor including old local photographs and Victorian-style prints, and an array of stuffed owls and other birds in the no smoking main dining area; there are plenty of sensible tables with upright seats; piped music. Half a dozen well kept real ales include Adnams, Fullers London Pride, Greene King Abbot and IPA, Hook Norton Best and a guest such as Smiles on handpump. At lunchtime bar food includes sandwiches (from £2.75), ploughman's (£4.95), battered haddock (£6.50), curry (£6.95), lasagne (£7.25) and a daily special such as lamb and cranberry casserole (£6.95). The evening menu is slightly different, with dishes such as baked bass topped with walnuts and lemon butter (£10.50) and 8oz sirloin (£11.50); there are picnic-sets in a neatly kept sheltered garden with a climbing frame, and in summer, the pub front is filled with colourful hanging baskets and window boxes. *(Recommended by I C Millar, Maysie Thompson, Blaise Vyner, Anthony Barnes, Mike Ridgway, Sarah Miles, Michael Dandy, Steve and Sue Griffiths)*

Greene King ~ Managers Paul and Sheila Linehan ~ Real ale ~ Bar food (12-2, 6.30-9.30) ~ Restaurant ~ (01234) 881305 ~ Children in eating area of bar and restaurant ~ Open 11-2.30, 6-11; 12-3, 6-10.30 Sun ~ Bedrooms: £40.50S/£55S

Three Fyshes

A428 NW of Bedford; Bridge Street, W end of village

Although Greene King have this friendly traditional pub on the market, it's well worth a visit, as it's nicely placed next to the River Ouse, with good views of a mill and the river from the garden at the back (which has picnic-sets and room for children to run around). It's attractive inside too, with a charming squint-walled stone corridor that links the cosy flagstoned public bar (which has a big inglenook) with the main room: heavy beams, a carpet and flagstone floor, dark wood close-set tables and chairs, a large box window seat and another stone inglenook fireplace flanked by comfortable sofas (lovely roaring fires in winter). The good choice of mostly traditional bar food might include soup (from £2.50), stilton mushrooms (£4.75), goat cheese croustade (£4.25), sausages and mash (£7.75), half shoulder of lamb (£8.95), duck breast with pink peppercorn sauce (£9.25) and steaks (from £7.50), as well as specials such as baked bream in an indonesian-style marinade or chicken breast stuffed with cream cheese and apricots (£7.95). Pleasant efficient service; three well kept real ales on handpump include Greene King IPA, Ruddles County and a guest. Hanging baskets in summer; piped music. The car park is 50 metres away. *(Recommended by Michael Tack, Mike Ridgway, Sarah Miles, Blaise Vyner, George Atkinson)*

Greene King ~ Manager Tim Fradgley ~ Real ale ~ Bar food (12-2.30, 6.30-9.30; 12-3, 7-9 Sun) ~ Restaurant ~ (01234) 881264 ~ Children welcome ~ Dogs welcome ~ Open 11-3, 6-11; 11-11 Sat; 12-10.30 Sun

Lucky Dip

Besides the fully inspected pubs, you might like to try these Lucky Dips recommended to us and described by readers (if you do, please send us reports: www.goodguides.com).

Bedford [TL0748]
Foxy Fish [Barns Hotel, Cardington Rd]: Smartly refurbished hotel bar in converted 17th-c manor house just outside town; lots of tables on polished flagstones, decent food; keg beers, piped music; charming relaxing terrace by calm stretch of River Ouse, attractive bedrooms *(BB)*

Biggleswade [TL1944]
Brown Bear [Hitchin St; from A6001 follow sign for Hitchin Street shops]: A main entry in 2002 for its welcoming licensees' great choice of changing real ales from small breweries, its many foreign beers and its buoyant atmosphere; the pub, still friendly, has since been sold to a chain, with less uncommon ales such as Flowers IPA, Greene King Old Speckled Hen, Marstons Pedigree, Shepherd Neame Spitfire, Timothy Taylors Landlord and Theakstons XB, Black Bull and Old Peculier *(Richard Lewis, Ian Phillips, LYM, Pete Baker)*
Wheatsheaf [Lawrence Rd]: Unpretentious local, as they used to be a few decades ago; one small very friendly room, well kept Greene King ales inc Mild, darts, dominoes and cards, TV for horseracing, no food or music *(Pete Baker)*

Colmworth [TL1058]
☆ *Cornfields* [Wilden Rd]: Early 17th-c, more restaurant than pub, with interesting stylish food, helpful young waitresses, well kept Adnams and Bass, good house wines; big log fire and low armchairs in small low-beamed bar; front picnic-sets, small garden, large comfortable well equipped bedrooms in new extension *(Michael Sargent, Anthony Barnes)*

Great Barford [TL1252]
Golden Cross [Bedford Rd]: Thriving atmosphere in main-road pub with pretty back restaurant serving good chinese food (worth booking); pristine tables, white linen cloths and napkins, very attentive service *(Sarah Markham)*

Harrold [SP9456]
Oakley Arms [between A6 and A428, E of Northampton; High St]: Several rooms round central bar with beams, pictures and brass, Charles Wells real ales, good value food (separate lunchtime and evening menus), cheerful welcome; piano, may be piped music *(V Green)*

Ireland [TL1341]
☆ *Black Horse* [off A600 Shefford—Bedford]: Busy and attractive dining pub consistently reliable for wide choice of good value plentiful piping hot food from lunchtime ciabattas up, good fresh ingredients, very good puddings, sizeable smart lounge and charming family dining area, well kept Bass and Charles Wells Bombardier, good range of wines and good coffee, attentive service from very helpful friendly staff; plenty of tables in neat front garden with play area, cottage bedrooms – peaceful rural setting *(Mike and Marian Bister, Michael Sargent, V Green, BB, Dr DJ Darby, Brian Root, Bob and Maggie Atherton, Maysie Thompson)*

Kensworth [TL0218]
Farmers Boy [B4540, Whipsnade end]: Village pub with good value food from sandwiches to good Sun roasts, generous and freshly made (so may be a wait), well kept Fullers, good house wines, cheerful staff, roaring fire, pleasant beamed lounge bar split into three areas, quaint nooks and crannies, good old-fashioned dining room (more restauranty evenings and Sun); children very welcome, and dogs, piped pop music, separate bar with pool, fruit machine and SkyTV; play area, maybe bouncy castle and rabbit hutches in big fenced-off back garden by fields with horses *(Bob and Maggie Atherton, George Atkinson, MP)*

Leighton Buzzard [SP9225]
Red Lion [North St]: Unpretentious traditional pub, fish tank in long comfortable intimate lounge, well priced Greene King Abbot and Tetleys, friendly service, separate chatty bar with piped music *(MP)*

Stag [Heath Rd]: Welcoming newish licensees in cosy, clean and comfortable pub, traditional home cooking inc some Scottish dishes, full Fullers beer range kept well, friendly efficient service, candles at night; quiz nights, plans for jazz *(MP)*

Melchbourne [TL0266]

St John Arms [Knotting Rd]: Unpretentious rambling country pub with food from lovely chunky sandwiches up, well kept Greene King ales, friendly landlord; peaceful cottagey garden *(Margaret and Roy Randle, LYM)*

Milton Bryan [SP9730]

Red Lion [Toddington Road, off B528 S of Woburn]: Beamed dining bar with some stripped brickwork, boards and flagstones, well kept Greene King IPA, Old Speckled Hen and Ruddles County, usual food inc OAP lunch; children welcome, plenty of tables in garden with terrace and climbing frame *(Ian Phillips, LYM)*

Northill [TL1546]

Crown [Ickwell Rd; village signed from B658 W of Biggleswade]: Busy black and white thatched pub with traditional food inc Sun lunch (and some interesting fashion plates) in extended restaurant, low-beamed main bar, huge open fire, well kept Greene King ales, good service; front seats by village pond, play area in huge back garden, tranquil village not far from the Shuttleworth Collection *(Bob and Maggie Atherton, Colin and Janet Roe, Michael Dandy, Pete Baker, Maysie Thompson)*

Old Warden [TL1343]

☆ *Hare & Hounds*: Welcoming rambling beamed pub under newish landlord, imaginative food, well kept Charles Wells Eagle and Bombardier and guest beers, simple but comfortable décor, case of aircraft memorabilia, open fire, dining room overlooking glorious garden stretching up to pine woods, play area; attractive thatched village, handy for Shuttleworth Collection, Swiss Garden and local walks *(BB, Colin and Janet Roe)*

Radwell [TL0057]

☆ *Swan* [Felmersham Rd]: Charming beamed and thatched pub, two spacious rooms joined by narrow passage, woodburner, lots of prints, wide choice of good food, service friendly even when very busy, well kept Charles Wells IPA and Eagle and a guest beer, decent coffee, popular evening restaurant (must book Fri/Sat); unobtrusive piped music; pleasant garden, attractive quiet village *(Stephen, Julie and Hayley Brown, Maysie Thompson)*

Ridgmont [SP9736]

☆ *Rose & Crown* [A507, 2 miles from M1 junction 13: follow Ampthill signs]: Relaxed motorway break, run by same unruffled landlord for 24 years, comfortable lounge with open fire, games in low-ceilinged public bar, no smoking dining area (children allowed), lots of Rupert Bear memorabilia and old english sheepdog china, usual food from sandwiches up, well kept Charles Wells Eagle and Bombardier and guests such as Adnams Broadside and Everards Tiger, up to 50 malt whiskies; piped music; good wheelchair access, long and attractive suntrap sheltered back garden, camping and caravanning *(Martin Jennings, Ian Phillips, Des and Jen Clarke, R T and J C Moggridge, Bob and Val Collman, LYM, Jim Bush)*

Sandy [TL1649]

☆ *Kings Arms* [London Rd; from bypass roundabout down Bedford Rd, left St Neots Rd, then left West Rd]: Attractive two-bar pub with friendly helpful staff, comfortable banquettes, lots of beams, open fire, wide choice of good reasonably priced food, no smoking eating area up steps, relaxed atmosphere, well kept Greene King IPA and Abbot and a guest beer, decent wines, friendly staff; restaurant, tiled courtyard, garden, bedrooms in well built chalets *(Robert Swanborough)*

Sharnbrook [TL0059]

Fordham Arms [SE of village]: New licensee doing wide range of enjoyable food, pleasant décor with lots of plates, copper and local paintings, Flowers IPA and Marstons Pedigree, quick friendly service even when busy; big garden with play area *(John Saul)*

Shefford [TL1438]

Brewery Tap [North Bridge St]: No-nonsense bare-boards L-shaped bar notable for its well kept B&T Bitter, Dark Mild and Dragon Slayer brewed nearby, with guests such as Everards Tiger and Wye Valley Princes Pride; beer bottle collection filling all the ledges, brewery posters and advertisements, friendly staff, cheap rolls or hot pies; frequent live music Fri, open all day *(Pete Baker, Ian Phillips)*

Shillington [TL1234]

Musgrave Arms [Apsley End Rd, towards Pegsdon and Hexton]: Low-beamed village local with settles, tables, prints and horsebrasses in friendly and civilised lounge, woodburner in comfortable public bar, small no smoking dining room, wide choice of generous home-made usual food inc Tues steak night and good Sun roast, Greene King IPA and Abbot and a guest beer tapped from cooled casks, cheerful service; big back garden with picnic-sets *(Len Banister, Phil and Heidi Cook)*

Silsoe [TL0835]

Star & Garter [High St]: Smart pub by village church, good range of home-made food for all tastes and pockets *(V Green)*

Souldrop [SP9861]

☆ *Bedford Arms* [High St; off A6 Rushden—Bedford]: Several bright and cheerful biggish room areas with large central stone fireplace, good range of interesting food esp fish, well kept Greene King ales, brasses, settles and prints; piped music; very peaceful village *(Bernie Adams, George Atkinson)*

Southill [TL1542]

☆ *White Horse* [off B658 SW of Biggleswade]: Country pub with comfortable lounge, dining room with large refurbished bar/eating area, wide choice of good value food, Fullers London Pride and Greene King IPA and Old Speckled Hen; lots of tables in large pleasant garden with good play area *(LYM, Michael Dandy)*

Steppingley [TL0135]

☆ *French Horn* [Church End]: Two-bar beamed pub, partly carpeted, part flagstones or bare boards, wide choice of enjoyable food in bar and fairly sizeable restaurant, Greene King IPA and Theakstons, woodburner, plenty of brass and pictures; small village, *(Michael Dandy)*

Stevington [SP9853]

Royal George [Silver St]: Well kept Charles Wells and guest beers such as Adnams and Wadworths, plenty of locals early evening, good Fri fish and chips, other events from theme nights to craft fairs *(B A Lord)*

Streatley [TL0728]

Chequers [just off A6 N of Luton; Sharpenhoe Rd]: Popular partly panelled open-plan local, mix of chairs and table sizes, old-fashioned prints and old local photographs, good value usual food (and doorstep sandwiches till late), Bass and Greene King IPA, Abbot, Old Speckled Hen and Ruddles County, cheerful staff, open fire; nostalgic piped music, Tues quiz night; garden with Sun lunchtime jazz *(Phil and Heidi Cook)*

Tebworth [SP9926]

Queens Head: No-frills village pub with friendly down-to-earth landlord, well kept Charles Wells beers and a guest such as Adnams Broadside, straightforward well priced food inc perfect chips, banquettes in light and airy small lounge bar with lots to look at and open fire, another in public bar; darts, fruit machine, may be quiet piped music; well spaced picnic-sets and swing in raised tree-sheltered garden *(MP)*

Thurleigh [TL0558]

Jackal [High St]: Friendly and welcoming, with good food under current regime, roaring winter fires in both bars, interesting wines, small dining room (booking recommended); dogs allowed in public bar; summer Sun barbecues in nice garden *(Karen and Steve Brine, John Saul)*

Upper Dean [TL0467]

Three Compasses: 17th-c beamed and thatched pub with good value food inc children's in L-shaped bar's dining area and neat separate dining room, well kept Charles Wells Eagle and Bombardier, polite service *(Michael and Jenny Back)*

'Children welcome' means the pub says it lets children inside without any special restriction. If it allows them in, but to restricted areas such as an eating area or family room, we specify this. Places with separate restaurants usually let children use them, hotels usually let them into public areas such as lounges. Some pubs impose an evening time limit – let us know if you find this.

Berkshire

Five new main entries here this year, or pubs back in the Guide *after a break, are the relaxing Elm Tree at Beech Hill (a fine all-rounder), the civilised Thatched Tavern at Cheapside (good if not cheap food, real character), the Crown & Horns at East Ilsley (this distinctive pub in horse-training country is back on top form, good all round), the Hobgoblin in Reading (a basic alehouse with a great choice of recherché real ales), and the well placed Two Brewers in Windsor (good beer, nice wines). Current favourites among the old guard are the Bell up on the downs at Aldworth (one of Britain's nicest pubs), the handsome old Bel & the Dragon in Cookham (popular imaginative food), the Horns at Crazies Hill (good all round, with appealing food), the Pot Kiln at Frilsham (charming country pub brewing its own beer), the Hare & Hounds near Lambourn (new landlord working out well), the Sweeney & Todd in Reading (much liked for its pies), the Bell at Waltham St Lawrence (another place thriving under a new landlord – with plans to start brewing his own beer), and the Winterbourne Arms at Winterbourne (proper home cooking). The restauranty Red House at Marsh Benham does excellent food, but our final choice as Berkshire Dining Pub of the Year is the George & Dragon in Swallowfield – in this generally upscale county, it's so nice to find a place doing really enjoyable meals yet still keeping a relaxed pubby atmosphere. In the Lucky Dip at the end of the chapter, current front-runners (all inspected and vouched for by the editorial team) are the Hinds Head at Aldermaston, Blackbird at Bagnor, Hinds Head in Bray, restauranty Bunk at Curridge, Star at East Ilsley, Pheasant at Great Shefford, Dundas Arms at Kintbury, Bird in Hand at Knowl Hill, Bull in Wargrave and Rowbarge at Woolhampton. Drinks prices in the county are well above the national average: the only main entries which undercut £2 for a pint were the Elm Tree at Beech Hill, Hobgoblin in Reading, Bell at Aldworth and Pot Kiln at Frilsham. It's worth looking out for the local beers from West Berkshire and Butts, which have low enough production to benefit from the new cut in beer tax.*

ALDWORTH SU5579 Map 2

Bell ★ 🍷 🍺 £

A329 Reading—Wallingford; left on to B4009 at Streatley

A huge favourite with walkers, cyclists and locals (the Ridgeway is nearby), this unchanging 14th-c country pub has been run by the same charming family for over 200 years. It is simply furnished with benches around the panelled walls, an ancient one-handed clock, a glass-panelled hatch rather than a bar counter for service, beams in the shiny ochre ceiling, and a woodburning stove. The timeless, welcoming atmosphere is helped by the ban on games machines, mobile phones and piped music. Apart from winter home-made soup (£2.50), appetising bar food is confined to exceptionally good value filled hot crusty rolls such as honey-roast ham, wild mushroom and port pâté, mature cheddar, stilton or brie (£1.70), turkey (£1.80), smoked salmon, crab, tuna or salt beef (£1.95), plus filled french bread (£2.50), and ploughman's (from £3); very good service. Particularly well kept and very cheap

Arkells BBB and Kingsdown, and from the local West Berkshire Brewery, Old Tyler, Dark Mild, and a monthly guest on handpump (they won't stock draught lager); good quality house wines. Darts, shove-ha'penny, dominoes, and cribbage. The quiet, old-fashioned garden by the village cricket ground is lovely in summer, and at Christmas, local mummers perform in the road by the ancient well-head (the shaft is sunk 400 feet through the chalk), and steaming jugs of hot punch and mince pies are handed round afterwards; occasional morris dancing in summer. It tends to get busy at weekends. *(Recommended by Jonathan Smith, Dick and Madeleine Brown, Peter B Brown, Guy Vowles, JP, PP, Paul Vickers, Catherine Pitt, the Didler, CMW, JJW, Susan and John Douglas)*

Free house ~ Licensee H E Macaulay ~ Real ale ~ Bar food (11-2.45, 6-10.45; 12-2.45, 7-10.15 Sun) ~ No credit cards ~ (01635) 578272 ~ Children must be well behaved ~ Dogs welcome ~ Open 11-3, 6-11; 12-3, 7-10.30 Sun; closed Mon exc bank hols

ASHMORE GREEN SU5069 Map 2

Sun in the Wood

NE of Newbury, or off A4 at Thatcham; off A34/A4 roundabout NW of Newbury, via B4009 Shaw Hill, then right into Kiln Road, then left into Stoney Lane after nearly ½ mile; or get to Stoney Lane sharp left off Ashmore Green Road, N of A4 at W end of Thatcham via Northfield Road and Bowling Green Road

It's hard to believe that this country pub, surrounded by tall trees, is just a few minutes away from the heart of Newbury. It's very popular locally for consistently good food, with lunchtime freshly baked baguettes, starters such as home-made soup (£3.35), hotpot of mushrooms in a creamy garlic and white wine sauce (£4.35), home-made thai fishcake with mango salsa (£4.65), and main dishes such as mille feuille of aubergine, beef tomato and halloumi cheese on a mixed salad (£7.95), chicken breast stuffed with ricotta cheese and spinach, wrapped in parma ham and topped with a white wine and cream sauce (£9.65), grilled filleted bass with lemon butter (£11.55) or roasted duck breast on creamy mash with a honey and orange sauce (£12.95); the puddings show some enjoyable variations on old favourites, such as chocolate bread and butter pudding with white chocolate ice cream. Two course Sunday lunch (£11.95; children £7.95). Part of the bar and the restaurant are no smoking. The high-beamed front bar has bare boards on the left, carpet on the right, with a mix of old bucket chairs, padded dining chairs and stripped pews around sturdy tables, and opens into a big back dining area with the same informal feel, candles on tables, and some interesting touches like the big stripped bank of apothecary's drawers. There is a small conservatory sitting area by the side entrance. Well kept Wadworths IPA and 6X, with a guest such as Badger Tanglefoot on handpump, decent house wines, and well organised friendly service. There are plenty of picnic-sets in the big woodside garden, which also has a play area with slide and climber. More reports please. *(Recommended by Mr and Mrs A Chandler, Edward Mason, Mike and Mary Carter)*

Wadworths ~ Tenant Philip Davison ~ Real ale ~ Bar food (12-2, 6.30-9.30; not Sun evening or Mon) ~ Restaurant ~ (01635) 42377 ~ Children welcome ~ Open 12-2.30(3 Sat), 6-11; 12-4, 7-10.30 Sun; closed Mon (exc Christmas)

BEECH HILL SU6964 Map 2

Elm Tree

3½ miles from M4 junction 11: A33 towards Basingstoke, turning off into Beech Hill Road after about 2 miles

Perhaps the nicest room at this relaxing country pub is the clock room on the left, where around 45 clocks of all types and ages tick away merrily, and regularly chime, though rarely all at once. Dotted around any gaps on the walls are signed photographs of Hollywood stars, and an antique fruit machine sits in the corner, opposite a woodburning stove. The whole place has been decorated with a great deal of care and thought, and each of the five rooms feels very different; a small snug has

a pastoral mural, while the restaurant is styled like an upmarket barn. Throughout are good furnishings and flowers (some especially nice orchids on our inspection visit), and even the lavatories are worth a look: the gents' has quite a collection of antlers around the walls, while the ladies' boasts a particularly ornate floral display. Close to most of the windows – especially in the conservatory – you'll find a pair of binoculars to better enjoy the view down the hill. Good generously served food might include toasted sandwiches, soup or filled baked potatoes (£3.95), seafood tagliatelle, grilled bass or slow-cooked ham hock on garlic mash (from £9.90), thai duck curry or chicken with noodles, bean sprouts, chillies and peppers (£9.95), and alluring puddings. Though there's quite an emphasis on food, drinkers are made very welcome, and the beers – Fullers London Pride, Greene King IPA and Old Speckled Hen, and a guest such as Morrells Oxford Blue – are particularly well kept. Service is friendly and attentive. There are a few benches and tables on a terrace in front.
(Recommended by Lucie Robson, Tony Beaulah)

Free house ~ Licensee Debra Walton ~ Real ale ~ Bar food (12-2, 7-9; 12-9 Sat, Sun) ~ (0118) 988 3505 ~ Children away from bar till 8.30 ~ Open 12-11; 12-10.30 Sun

BOXFORD SU4271 Map 2

Bell 🍷

Back road Newbury—Lambourn; village also signposted off B4000 between Speen and M4 junction 14

Most customers come to this civilised mock-Tudor inn to enjoy the popular food and impressive range of wines and champagnes by the glass, but there's still a relaxed, country local atmosphere as well. The bar is quite long but snug, with a nice mix of racing pictures, old Mercier advertisements, red plush cushions for the mate's chairs, some interesting bric-a-brac, and a coal-effect fire at one end. Bar food includes sandwiches and toasties (from £2.95), soup (£3.25; with a sandwich as well, £5.25), snacks to share such as potato dippers or spicy cajun prawns (from £4), welsh rarebit (£5.25), filled baked potatoes (from £5.50), omelettes (from £5.95), home-cooked ham and eggs (£6.95), pizzas made to order (from £7.25), curries (£8.50), and home-made pies (£8.95). Most people eat in the rather smart, no smoking restaurant area on the left, but you can also dine on the covered and heated terrace. Well kept changing beers might include Badger Tanglefoot, Courage Best, Fullers London Pride, and Morrells Oxford Blue on handpump, kept under light blanket pressure, and they stock a wide range of whiskies. Pool, pinball, shove-ha'penny, and dominoes, plus a fruit machine, TV, juke box, and piped music. A side courtyard has white cast-iron garden furniture. More reports please.
(Recommended by Martin and Karen Wake)

Free house ~ Licensee Paul Lavis ~ Real ale ~ Bar food (12-3, 7-9.30) ~ Restaurant (till 10) ~ (01488) 608721 ~ Children welcome ~ Dogs allowed in bar ~ Open 11-11; 12-10.30 Sun; 11-3, 6-11 winter ~ Bedrooms: £67.50S/£80S

BRAY SU9079 Map 2

Crown

1¾ miles from M4 junction 9; A308 towards Windsor, then left at Bray signpost on to B3028; High Street

Friendly and welcoming, this 14th-c pub is popular in winter with its three log fires, and in summer when you can sit at the tables and benches in an attractive and sheltered flagstoned front courtyard with a flourishing grape vine, or under cocktail parasols in a large back garden. The partly panelled main bar has a good mix of customers, oak tables, leather backed armchairs, and a good open fire. Throughout, there are lots of beams (some so low you have to watch your head), and plenty of old timbers conveniently left at elbow height where walls have been knocked through. One dining area has photographs of WWII aeroplanes. Reliable bar food is cooked to order and includes home-made soup (£3.60), pâté of the day (£5), tasty cumberland sausages with frites and onion gravy (£7.25), tagliatelle with sun-dried tomatoes, mushrooms and fresh basil or warm goats cheese salad (£7.50), home-made beef in Guinness pie or Scottish smoked salmon with lemon and garlic vinaigrette (£9.95), oriental warm chicken salad (£10.95), delicious fresh crab salad (£10.95), and Scotch sirloin steak with green peppercorn sauce (£14.80). Well kept Brakspears Special, and Courage Best and Directors on handpump and a fair choice of wines; helpful service. *(Recommended by Lesley Bass, Tom and Ruth Rees, John Robertson, J Hale, Jayne and Peter Capp, Ian Phillips, Robert Turnham, Susan and John Douglas)*

Scottish Courage ~ Tenants John and Carole Noble ~ Real ale ~ Bar food (not Sun or Mon evenings) ~ Restaurant ~ (01628) 621936 ~ Children in restaurant ~ Open 11-3, 6-11; 12-3, 7-10.30 Sun

BURCHETTS GREEN SU8381 Map 2

Crown

Side road from A4 after Knowl Green on left, linking to A404

New licensees have taken over this popular pub but, happily, have changed very little. The civilised main bar is clean and comfortable, with a restauranty layout and unobtrusive piped music; the very small plain bar has one or two tables for casual customers. Many people do come to eat, so it might be best to book a table at weekends: sandwiches, soup, smooth chicken liver parfait with home-made chutney, thai-style curried mushrooms, and baked avocado and prawn thermidor (all from £4.95), with main courses such as cumberland sausage and onion gravy, steak and kidney pudding, poached fillet of salmon with a prawn and herb cream, calves liver with bubble and squeak, bacon and caramelised onion jus, and roast rack of lamb with rosemary jus and dauphinoise potatoes (all from £9.95). Well kept Bass and Greene King IPA on handpump, kept under light blanket pressure, and a good range of wines by the glass. There are tables out in a pleasant quiet garden. *(Recommended by Brian Root, T R and B C Jenkins, Joan Thorpe, Paul Humphreys)*

Greene King ~ Lease David and Sarah Larner ~ Real ale ~ Bar food (till 9.30) ~ Restaurant ~ (01628) 822844 ~ Children in restaurant ~ Dogs allowed in bar ~ Open 12-2.30, 6-11

CHEAPSIDE SU9469 Map 2

Thatched Tavern

Off B383 at Village Hall sign; village signposted off A332/A329

Though this civilised dining pub is not actually thatched, it does keep a cottagey feel despite its extension and upgrading. The little bar has polished flagstones and very low gnarled beams, and there's an old cast-iron range in the big inglenook with comfortably padded seats and cushions built snugly around it; three smart dining rooms lead off here, with deep carpet, crisp linen and big church candles. Good bar food includes soup (£3.95), chicken liver and pistachio pâté with tomato and chilli chutney (£6.75), fried sardines with sun-dried tomatoes and capers (£6.95), open ravioli with queen scallops and spinach in a saffron sauce (£7.50), cumberland sausages with mustard mash and red wine and onion jus (£10.50), steak and kidney pudding or couscous, roasted peppers, asparagus, red onion, feta cheese and roquette tossed in fresh herb oil in a warm tortilla shell (£11.95), slow roasted half shoulder of lamb with rosemary and thyme jus (£13.75), and half a crispy duckling with a bitter orange sauce (£16.50); daily specials and fresh fish, too. Well kept Brakspears Bitter, Courage Best, and Fullers London Pride on handpump, lots of wines, daily papers, and no games or piped music. There are rustic seats and tables on the sheltered back lawn, and the pub is handy for Virginia Water walks, with the Blacknest car park a mile or so down the road. *(Recommended by Susan and John Douglas, Andy and Yvonne Cunningham, Simon and Laura Habbishow, John and Joyce Snell)*

4c Inns ~ Lease Laurence Coveney ~ Real ale ~ Bar food (12-2.30, 6-10) ~ Restaurant ~ 01344 620874 ~ Children in restaurant ~ Dogs allowed in bar ~ Open 12-4, 6-11; 12-11 Sat; 12-10.30 Sun

COOKHAM SU8884 Map 2

Bel & the Dragon

High Street; B4447 N of Maidenhead

It's the imaginative food that draws the many customers to this fine old pub: marvellous country breads with roast garlic, olive oil and olives or fresh mint and pea soup (£3.95), sautéed duck livers with bubble and squeak, topped with crispy pancetta and coated with sweet chilli jus or chargrilled halloumi on a basil and garlic crostini with green salad and a yoghurt and mint dressing (£7.95), smoked salmon and white crab with a warm potato cake on dressed rocket salad or battered fillet of cod with hand cut chips and lemon tartare sauce (£8.95), chargrilled pork fillet with an olive and sun-blush tomato, mashed potato and tarragon jus (£9.95), chargrilled tuna fish loin on sautéed spinach and roasted plum tomatoes with a pesto and aged balsamic dressing (£12.95), and roasted lamb rump sliced on basil mashed potato with sautéed green beans and sun-blushed tomato jus (£17.95); at lunchtime they serve sandwiches and baguettes. The three carefully furnished rooms have comfortable seats, heavy Tudor beams and open fires contrasting with the hand-painted cartoons on the pastel walls and up-to-date low voltage lighting; there's a small no smoking area. Well kept Brakspears Bitter, Courage Best, and Marstons Pedigree are served from the low zinc-topped bar counter, and there's a good choice of wines, whiskies, liqueurs and fruit juices; swift, friendly service. Street parking can be very difficult. The town's rewarding Stanley Spencer Gallery is almost opposite.

(Recommended by J and B Cressey, A F P Barnes, Guy Charrison, Mrs Ailsa Wiggans, Paul Humphreys, Ian Phillips, Susan and John Douglas)

Free house ~ Licensees Andrea Mortimer and Daniel Macdonald ~ Real ale ~ Bar food (12-2.30, 7-10) ~ Restaurant ~ (01628) 521263 ~ Children in eating area of bar and restaurant ~ Dogs allowed in bar ~ Open 11-11; 12-10.30 Sun

COOKHAM DEAN SU8785 Map 2

Uncle Toms Cabin

Hills Lane, Harding Green; village signposted off A308 Maidenhead—Marlow – keep on down past Post Office and village hall towards Cookham Rise and Cookham

Chatting customers – both locals and visitors – fill the mainly carpeted little rooms in this pretty and unpretentious cream-washed cottage. At the front are low beams and joists and lots of shiny dark brown woodwork, and furnishings such as old-fashioned plush-cushioned wall seats, beer advertisements, and old brass kitchen scales lend a nostalgic 1930s feeling. There's also quite a lot of breweriana, and some interesting gold discs. Tasty bar food includes baguettes or sandwiches (from £3.25), soup (£3.25), filled baked potatoes (from £3.95), rice, tomato and courgette gratin (£5.75), nice cheese-topped cottage pie (£5.95), steak and ale pie or chicken wrapped in bacon with blue cheese sauce (£6.95), chargrilled halibut with tomato sauce (£7.75), steaks (£10.95), and puddings such as home-made treacle tart and apple flan (£3.25). Well kept Brakspears Bitter, Fullers London Pride, and a guest such as Badger Tanglefoot, Butts Barbus Barbus, and Shepherd Neame Spitfire on handpump; darts, shove-ha'penny, cribbage, dominoes, TV, fruit machine, and piped music. The attractive, sheltered sloping back garden has picnic-sets, and there are a couple of old teak seats under a chestnut tree at the front. The two cats Jess (black and white) and Wilma (black) enjoy the winter coal fire, and Oggie the busy black and white dog welcomes other dogs (who get a dog biscuit on arrival).

(Recommended by Brian Root, Simon Chell, Mrs A Pantin, Ian Phillips, John and Glenys Wheeler, Tracey and Stephen Groves)

Punch ~ Lease Nick Ashman ~ Real ale ~ Bar food (12(12.30 wknds)-2(2.30 wknds), 7.30-10; not winter Sun) ~ Restaurant ~ (01628) 483339 ~ Children in eating area of bar and restaurant ~ Dogs allowed in bar ~ Open 11-3, 5.30-11; may open all day on summer Sats; 12-10.30 Sun

Tipping is not normal for bar meals, and not usually expected.

CRAZIES HILL SU7980 Map 2

Horns

From A4, take Warren Row Road at Cockpole Green signpost just E of Knowl Hill, then past Warren Row follow Crazies Hill signposts

By the time this book is published, the large garden here will have been landscaped and there will be access to it from a new garden bar. Inside the tiled, whitewashed cottage, the comfortable welcoming bars have rugby mementoes on the walls, exposed beams, open fires and stripped wooden tables and chairs. The no smoking barn room is opened up to the roof like a medieval hall, and the gentrified country atmosphere is helped by the fact that there is no juke box, fruit machine or piped music. Good, popular bar food includes lunchtime baguettes, bacon salad with avocado, stilton and mushrooms in a special dressing (£5.50), mozzarella wrapped in parma ham and breadcrumbs, deep-fried and served with chilli sauce or nice smoked tuna slices with an olive and mustard mayonnaise (£5.95), pasta with a creamy wild mushroom and cognac sauce (£7.25), wild boar and apple sausages with spring onion mash and gravy or beef, mushroom and Guinness pie (£7.95), chicken supreme with roasted almond, lemon and dill sauce (£10.95), calves liver with bacon and onions (£11.95), rack of lamb with redcurrant jelly, mint and rosemary gravy (£13.95), and an enjoyable fillet steak with creamy peppercorn sauce (£14.95). Fish comes daily from Billingsgate, and it is essential to book a table at weekends (it does get particularly busy on Sunday lunchtimes). Well kept Brakspears Bitter, Special, and seasonal ales on handpump, a thoughtful wine list, several malt whiskies, and they make a good bloody mary. *(Recommended by M Borthwick, T R and B C Jenkins, C A Hall, Paul Humphreys, Mike and Sue Richardson, Keith and Margaret Kettell, June and Robin Savage)*

Brakspears ~ Tenant A J Hearn ~ Real ale ~ Bar food (not Sun evening) ~ Restaurant ~ (0118) 940 1416 ~ Children in restaurant lunchtimes only ~ Open 11.30-2.30 (3 Sat), 6-11; 12-5.30, 7-10.30 Sun; closed winter Sun evening

EAST ILSLEY SU4981 Map 2

Crown & Horns

Just off A34, about 5 miles N of M4 junction 13

This welcoming old pub, in the heart of horse-training country, has interesting racing prints and photographs on the walls, and the side bar may have locals watching the latest races on TV; the chef may come out to discuss the form. A rambling set of beamed rooms is relaxed and cosy, with soft lighting, a blazing log fire, tables tucked into intimate corners and a no smoking snug with one big oval table that would be ideal for a small party. There is also a more formal dining room. Enjoyable bar food includes good sandwiches, toasties, french bread or baps (from £2.60), home-made soup (£3.25), lots of filled baked potatoes (from £4.50), ploughman's (from £5.50), steak and mushroom pie (£6.50), meaty or vegetable lasagne (£6.75), fish pie (£8.95), chicken in stilton and mushroom sauce or seafood pancake (£9.95), rump steak (£10.50), scampi flamed in rum in a coconut and cream sauce with pineapple (£12.95), puddings such as toffee apple cheesecake, chocolate mousse or treacle tart (£3.25), and daily specials. Among the wide range of regularly changing well kept real ales on handpump might be Boddingtons, Black Sheep, Brakspears, Hook Norton Old Hooky, Robinsons Best, and Wadworths 6X. They also stock an impressive collection of 160 whiskies from all over the world – even Morocco, Korea, Japan, China, Spain and New Zealand. Fruit machine and piped music. There are tables under two chestnut trees in the pretty paved stable yard. The surrounding countryside is laced with tracks and walks. *(Recommended by Ian Phillips, R Huggins, D Irving, E McCall, T McLean, Lynn Sharpless, Bob Eardley, SLC, Ann and Colin Hunt, Tom Clay, Mike and Mary Carter, Tom McLean, Dick and Madeleine Brown)*

Free house ~ Licensees Chris and Jane Bexx ~ Real ale ~ Bar food ~ Restaurant ~ (01635) 281545 ~ Children welcome ~ Dogs allowed in bar ~ Open 11-11; 12-10.30 Sun ~ Bedrooms: £50B/£60B

FRILSHAM SU5573 Map 2

Pot Kiln ★

From Yattendon take turning S, opposite church, follow first Frilsham signpost, but just after crossing motorway go straight on towards Bucklebury ignoring Frilsham signposted right; pub on right after about half a mile

In a lovely rural spot and surrounded by plenty of walks, this unassuming, well run brick pub is, not surprisingly, very popular – especially at weekends. The three basic yet comfortable bar areas have a lively, chatty atmosphere, wooden floorboards, bare benches and pews, and a good winter log fire. Well kept Brick Kiln Bitter and Resolution (from the pub's own microbrewery behind) is served from a hatch in the panelled entrance lobby – which has room for just one bar stool – along with well kept Arkells BBB, and Morlands Original on handpump; friendly, efficient staff. Decent straightforward food includes tasty filled hot rolls (from £2), home-made soup (£3.25), ploughman's (from £4.50), vegetable chilli (£7), salmon and broccoli fishcake (£7.50), and evening specials such as chicken lasagne with brandy and cream sauce (£8), fresh salmon fillet (£9.50), and venison casserole (£11); no chips, and vegetables are fresh. Rolls only on Sundays. The public bar has darts, dominoes, shove-ha'penny, table skittles, and cribbage. The pink candlelit back room/dining room is no smoking. There are picnic-sets in the big suntrap garden, with good views of the nearby forests and meadows. No credit cards. *(Recommended by JP, PP, Dick and Madeleine Brown, Mick Simmons, Richard Gibbs, the Didler, Simon Chell, Sheila Keene, J Hale, Mike and Sue Richardson)*

Own brew ~ Licensee Philip Gent ~ Real ale ~ Bar food (not Tues evening) ~ (01635) 201366 ~ Children in back room ~ Dogs allowed in bar ~ Irish music first Sun evening of month ~ Open 12-2.30(3 Sat), 6.30-11; 12-3, 7-10.30 Sun; closed Tues lunchtimes; 25 Dec

HAMSTEAD MARSHALL SU4165 Map 2

White Hart

Village signposted from A4 W of Newbury

On a sunny day, it's extremely pleasant to sit outside under the trees overlooking the pretty walled and flower-filled garden, and enjoy the good, popular Italian food. The much liked daily specials might include sogliole (fillet of lemon sole with olive oil, lemon juice and herbs, £12.50) or fegato (liver with onion, wine and fresh sage, £14.50), plus dishes from the menu such as home-made soup or mozzarella, tomato, basil and olive oil salad (£4.50), carpaccio of swordfish or Italian salami with olives (£5.50), fritatta omelette, spaghetti Napolitana or lasagne (£8.50), cottoletta di agnello (£14.50), steaks (from £14.50), and puddings (£4.50) like torta di mele or crespelle dolce (warm pancakes with poached plums and vanilla ice cream); the food boards are attractively illustrated with Mrs Aromando's drawings, many of the herbs and vegetables are home-grown, the bread is home-made, and their beef is from a local organic farm; no smoking restaurant. Hook Norton Best and Wadworths 6X are served on handpump alongside decent Italian wines in the L-shaped bar with red plush seats built into the bow windows, cushioned chairs around oak and other tables, a copper-topped bar counter, and a log fire open on both sides; piped music. There are quiet and comfortable beamed bedrooms in a converted barn across the courtyard. The pony in the paddock is called Solo, and his companion, Bertie. *(Recommended by James A Waller, Ian Phillips, Lynn Sharpless, Bob Eardley, Keith Allen, Mrs M Horgan)*

Free house ~ Licensees Nicola and Dorothy Aromando ~ Real ale ~ Bar food (not Sun) ~ Restaurant (not Sun) ~ (01488) 658201 ~ Children welcome ~ Open 12-2.30, 6-11; closed Sunday, 25, 26 Dec, 1 Jan, and two wks in summer ~ Bedrooms: £60B/£80B

Pubs brewing their own beers are listed at the back of the book.

HOLYPORT SU8977 Map 2
Belgian Arms

1½ miles from M4 junction 8/9 via A308(M), A330; in village turn left on to big green, then left again at war memorial (which is more like a bus shelter)

Much enjoyed by readers, this popular pub offers a friendly welcome from the staff, a varied choice of good food, and a relaxed atmosphere for those who just want a drink. The L-shaped, low-ceilinged bar has interesting framed postcards of Belgian military uniform and other good military prints, and some cricketing memorabilia on the walls, a china cupboard in one corner, a variety of chairs around a few small tables, and a roaring log fire. The daily specials are especially popular, and at lunchtime might include fresh smoked haddock with poached eggs, vegetarian shepherd's pie, steak in ale or fish pie, and chilli con carne or lasagne (from £5.95), with evening examples like grilled fresh salmon fillet with various sauces or breast of duck in orange sauce (£8.95). Other bar food includes sandwiches (the toasted 'special' is well recommended £3.50), a good ploughman's (£4.50), pizzas with different toppings (£5.50), steaks (from £9.95), and Sunday roast beef (£7.95). Well kept Brakspears Bitter and Special on handpump, and a few good malt whiskies. In summer, sitting in the charming garden looking over the duck pond towards the village green, it is hard to believe that you are so close to the M4. *(Recommended by Chris Glasson, Alyson and Andrew Jackson, Julie and Bill Ryan, Simon Collett-Jones, BKA, G S B G Dudley, June and Robin Savage, Mrs G R Sharman, B J Harding, Robert Turnham, Ian Phillips, Howard Dell)*

Brakspears ~ Tenant Alfred Morgan ~ Real ale ~ Bar food (12-2, 6.30-9.30; not Sun evening) ~ (01628) 634468 ~ Children in eating area of bar ~ Open 11-3, 5.30-11; 12-3, 7-10.30 Sun

INKPEN SU3564 Map 2
Swan

Lower Inkpen; coming from A338 in Hungerford, take Park Street (first left after railway bridge, coming from A4)

Those interested in organic produce would enjoy a visit to this beamed country pub. The licensees also have an organic beef farm, and their farm shop next door sells over 1,000 items including the owners' organic beef, sausages, burgers, cured meats and a new range of ready-to-cook organic meals. Naturally, you can expect to find plenty of home-grown ingredients among the decent bar meals, which include sandwiches, broccoli, mushroom and pasta bake or beef curry (£7.50), home-made salmon, cod and smoked haddock fishcakes or steak in ale pie (£7.95), steaks (from £10.50), and puddings such as bread and butter pudding, fresh fruit salad and pear tart (£4.25); they do cream teas in summer. The eating areas (and parts of the bar) are no smoking. Well kept Caledonian Golden Promise, Hook Norton Bitter and Mild, and a guest such as Butts Blackguard on handpump, and organic wines and champagne; local Lambourn Valley cider and home-made sloe gin. The rambling bar rooms have cosy corners, fresh flowers, polished furniture, and three open fires (there's a big old fireplace with an oak mantelbeam in the restaurant area). The games room has old paving slabs, bench seating and darts, shove-ha'penny, cribbage, and dominoes; piped music. Out in front there are flowers by the picnic-sets raised above the quiet village road on old brick terraces, and also a small quiet garden. *(Recommended by Lynn Sharpless, Bob Eardley, Peter and Jean Hoare, David Crook, Mrs A Pantin, Pat and Tony Martin, Betsy and Peter Little, John Robertson, John Parker)*

Free house ~ Licensees Mary and Bernard Harris ~ Real ale ~ Bar food ~ Restaurant ~ (01488) 668326 ~ Well behaved children in eating area of bar and restaurant ~ Occasional jazz/folk ~ Open 11-11; 11-11 Sat; 12-10.30 Sun; 11-2.30, 7-11(10.30 Sun) in winter; closed 25 and 26 Dec ~ Bedrooms: £40S/£70S

Pubs with outstanding views are listed at the back of the book.

LAMBOURN SU3175 Map 2

Hare & Hounds

Lambourn Woodlands, 3½ miles from M4 junction 14: A336 N, then first left on to B4000; pub is 2½ miles S of Lambourn itself

A new licensee again for this smart but friendly dining pub. There are several rooms leading off the narrow bar, with perhaps the nicest area being the mustard-coloured room off to the left as you head along the central passageway, with its attractive pine chairs and wooden tables and lovely fireplace; equine prints and pictures on the walls. The room next to that has a mix of simple wooden and marble-effect tables, a church-style pew, and neatly patterned curtains. Good bar food at lunchtime now includes home-made soup (£3.95), filled baguettes (£4.95), ploughman's (£6.50), grilled sausages with caramelised onion gravy or honey-roast ham with eggs (£6.95), and Aberdeen rump steak (£12.95). Also, creamed chicken liver pâté with onion marmalade (£4.95), grilled goats cheese on a chargrilled vegetable bruschetta (£5.95), seared king scallops, wrapped in pancetta, dressed mizuna salad, sweet pepper jam and parmesan crisps (£7.25), roast half local pheasant with crisp bacon and a port and game sauce (£13.50), baked fillet of monkfish with a sauce of poached shellfish in vermouth cream with chervil (£14.25), and rack of new season English lamb with rosemary jus and fondant potatoes (£14.95). Puddings such as caramelised lemon and lime tart with blackcurrant coulis and mango sorbet or home-made sticky toffee pudding with caramel sauce and rich cream custard (£4.50). Well kept Wadworths IPA or 6X, and a guest such as Arkells BBB or Boddingtons on handpump, and nice wines; piped music. Outside, there are new benches in the garden behind, and a decent children's play area. *(Recommended by Peter Wrobbel, John Saville, J Hale, Michael Sargent, M Hounsell)*

Free house ~ Licensee Anita Andrews ~ Real ale ~ Bar food ~ Restaurant ~ (01488) 71386 ~ Children welcome ~ Dogs allowed in bar ~ Open 12-3, 6-11; 12-3 Sun; closed Sun evening

MARSH BENHAM SU4267 Map 2

Red House

Village signposted from A4 W of Newbury

Although people do drop into this smartly renovated thatched dining pub for a casual pint, most customers come for the imaginative food. The comfortable bar has a light stripped wood floor and magenta walls, and a mix of Victorian and older settles. The library-style front restaurant (which is no smoking) is lined with bookcases and hung with paintings. From a modern, interesting (if not cheap) menu, dishes might include chilled gazpacho with olive tapenade and pesto swirl (£4.95), tian of avocado, cottage cheese, tomato and spring onion with sauce vierge (£6.25), chicken liver parfait with onion marmalade and warm brioche (£6.75), fried Cornish scallops on gruyère jersey royals with balsamic dressing (£9.75), risotto of mushrooms with parmesan basket and green salad (£9.95), shank of spicy lamb on ratatouille with flageolet and butter beans with mint pesto (£14), roast breast of duck with plantain purée and redcurrant sauce (£15), bouillabaisse with langoustine, razor clams and shi-itake mushrooms, croutons and aïoli (£17.50), and puddings like white chocolate and blueberry mousse with lavender rhubarb compote, lemon tart with red fruit coulis or chocolate tart with vanilla ice cream (£4.95); vegetables are £2 extra. Well kept Fullers London Pride and Greene King Ruddles County on handpump, good wines, lots of malt whiskies, and quite a few brandies and ports; piped music. A terrace with teak tables and chairs overlooks the long lawns that slope down to water meadows and the River Kennet. More reports please. *(Recommended by Jane and Graham Rooth, Ian Phillips, David Peakall, T R and B C Jenkins)*

Free house ~ Licensee Xavier Le-Bellego ~ Real ale ~ Bar food ~ Restaurant ~ (01635) 582017 ~ Children in eating area of bar and must be over 6 in restaurant ~ Open 12-11; 12-3.30 Sun; closed Sun evening and all day Mon

PEASEMORE SU4577 Map 2

Fox & Hounds

Village signposted from B4494 Newbury—Wantage

Perhaps the best time to visit this friendly local if you are after just a drink, is during their Happy Hour (5.30-7pm) when all pints are £1.50 and spirits just £1. But it's very much the place for everyone, whether it is just a drink you want, a quick snack or a more leisurely meal. The two bars have brocaded stripped wall settles, chairs and stools around shiny wooden tables, a new woodburning stove (open to both rooms), and piped music. One wall inside has a full set of Somerville's entertaining Slipper's *ABC of Fox-Hunting* prints, and another sports a row of flat-capped fox masks, reflecting the customs of the surrounding horse-training country. Enjoyable bar food includes filled baguettes, good home-made soup (£2.50), basket meals (from £2.75), home-made pizzas (from £3.95), hot garlic mushrooms (£3.95), asparagus and goats cheese tart, home-made pie of the day or speciality sausages with creamed potatoes and onion gravy (£5.50), home-made curry (£6.95), chicken breast with spinach, tomato and mozzarella (£8.75), and steaks (from £9.95); there's also a board dedicated to fish with dishes such as salmon supreme with honey, lime and ginger (£8.95), and casserole of monkfish with mushrooms, olive oil and tomatoes or swordfish steak with stilton mash and tomato and basil sauce (£9.25). The restaurant is no smoking. Well kept Fullers London Pride, Greene King IPA, and West Berkshire Good Old Boy on handpump, decent wines, and a good few malt whiskies. The pool bar has new comfortable leather chesterfields and chairs, plus darts, dominoes, cribbage, fruit machine, discreet juke box, and TV. The picnic-sets outside give views across rolling fields, and on a clear day you can look right over to the high hills of the Berkshire/Hampshire border about 20 miles southward. More reports please. *(Recommended by Stan Edwards, Richard Gibbs, Dick and Madeleine Brown)*

Free house ~ Licensees David and Loretta Smith ~ Real ale ~ Bar food (not Mon, not wkdy lunchtimes; 5.30-9.30) ~ Restaurant ~ (01635) 248252 ~ Children welcome ~ Dogs allowed in bar ~ Singer/guitarist monthly Fri or Sat ~ Open 5.30-11; 12-3, 6-11 Sat; 12-3.30, 7-10.30 Sun; closed Mon and Tues-Fri lunchtimes

READING SU7272 Map 2

Hobgoblin

2 Broad Street

The rapidly changing range of well kept esoteric real ales is what's earned this basic and characterful drinkers' pub such a loyal following. The choice can vary by the day, but a typical selection might include Wychwood Alchemy Gold, Fiddlers Elbow and Hobgoblin, and brews like Butts Barbus Barbus, Fisherrow Mick the Ticks 15,000th Tick, Hogs Back Tea, Oakleaf Yodel Weiss, Rebellion Round Avoider and West Berkshire Magnificent; the lively landlord can advise if you're stumped as to what to have. Also, a good range of bottled beers, Czech lager on tap, Inch's farm cider, and country wines. Beer mats cover practically every inch of the walls and ceiling of the simple bare-boards bar, a testament to the huge number of brews that have passed through the pumps over the last few years (3,576 when we last called). Up a step is a small seating area, but the best places to sit are the three or four tiny panelled rooms reached by a narrow corridor leading from the bar; cosy and intimate, each has barely enough space for one table and a few chairs or wall seats, but they're very appealing if you're able to bag one. The biggest also manages to squeeze in a fireplace. Popular with a good mix of locals, students and beer connoisseurs, this isn't the kind of place you'd want to take your mother for lunch – not least because they don't do lunch, nor indeed any food at all. It can get busy at weekends, but still keeps a friendly, cheery feel. Piped music (very much in keeping with the rough and ready feel of the place), TV; no mobile phones. They have weekly quiz nights. Note they don't allow children. *(Recommended by Catherine Pitt, Richard Lewis, Paul Hopton, Paul Vickers, Jonathan Smith)*

Wychwood ~ Manager Paul Campbell ~ Real ale ~ No credit cards ~ (0118) 950 8119 ~ Open 11-11; 12-10.30 Sun

Sweeney & Todd £

10 Castle Street; next to Post Office

The marvellous choice of pies continues to draw readers to this unique patisserie-cum pub, hidden behind the baker's shop. Behind the counter and down some stairs in the lively bar, a surprising number of tiny tables are squeezed into one long thin room, most of them in rather conspiratorial railway-carriage-style booths separated by curtains, and each with a leather-bound menu to match the leather-cushioned pews. Old prints line the walls, and the colonial-style fans and bare-boards floor enhance the period feel. Among the list of pies might be chicken, honey and mustard, hare and cherry, duck and apricot, goose and gooseberry, partridge and pear, or the rugby-influenced five nations – a medley of beef, Guinness, garlic, mustard and leeks (all £3.80), with other bar food such as soup (£2.95), lots of ploughman's (from £3.95), casseroles (£5.50), and roasts (£6.50). Helpings are huge, and excellent value. Well kept Adnams Best, Badger Tanglefoot, Wadworths 6X and a changing guest are served on handpump from the small bar, with various wines and a range of liqueurs and cigars. You can buy the pies in the shop to take away. *(Recommended by Andy and Yvonne Cunningham, Paul Vickers, Colin and Sandra Tann, D J and P M Taylor, R T and J C Moggridge, Paul Hopton)*

Free house ~ Licensee Mrs C Hayward ~ Real ale ~ Restaurant ~ (0118) 958 6466 ~ Children in restaurant ~ Open 11-11; closed Sun and bank hols

STANFORD DINGLEY SU5771 Map 2

Bull

From M4 junction 12, W on A4, then right at roundabout on to A340 towards Pangbourne; first left to Bradfield, and at crossroads on far edge of Bradfield (not in centre) turn left signposted Stanford Dingley; turn left in Stanford Dingley

The beamed tap room in this attractive 15th-c brick pub, now enlarged, is firmly divided into two parts by standing timbers hung with horsebrasses. The main part has an old brick fireplace, cushioned seats carved out of barrels, a window settle, wheelback chairs on the red quarry tiles, and an old station clock; a carpeted section has an exposed daub and wattle wall. The half-panelled lounge bar reflects the motorsport and classic car interests of the owners, and there are refectory-type tables. Bass, Brakspears Bitter, and Good Old Boy, Maggs Magnificent Mild, Resolution, and Skiff from the West Berkshire brewery are all well kept and cheap for the area. Lunchtime bar food includes a choice of home-made soups (£3.50), sandwiches or baguettes (from £3.50), ploughman's (£5), filled baked potatoes (£5), ham and egg (£6.95), sausage and mash with onion gravy (£8), and cajun-blackened cod (£11), as well as daily specials such as lasagne, irish stew, lancashire hotpot or lamb madras (all £8). In the evening, there might be seafood chowder or home-made gravadlax (£5.50), beef bourguignon or chicken and mushroom pie (£8), mignons of pork with calvados cream (£12.50), best end of lamb (£14.50), or magret of duck with Grand Marnier and cream (£15); home-made puddings (£3.50) and children's dishes (from £4.95). The dining room is no smoking. Ring-the-bull and piped music. In front of the building are some big rustic tables and benches, and to the side is a big new garden with many more seats. The Kennet Morris Men visit in August and on New Year's Day, and on summer Saturdays, owners of classic cars and bikes gather in the grounds. More reports please. *(Recommended by Lynn Sharpless, Bob Eardley, Klaus and Elizabeth Leist)*

Free house ~ Licensees Robert and Kate Archard, Robin and Carol Walker ~ Real ale ~ Bar food (12-2.30, 6.30(7 Sun)-9.30(9 Sun)) ~ Restaurant ~ (0118) 974 4409 ~ Children in eating area of bar and restaurant ~ Dogs allowed in bar ~ Folk music rehearsals 2nd Weds of month ~ Open 12-3, 6-11; 12-3, 7-10.30 Sun ~ Bedrooms: £55S/£70S(£80B)

> Food details, prices, timing etc refer to bar food – not to a separate restaurant if there is one.

Old Boot

Off A340 via Bradfield, coming from A4 just W of M4 junction 12

This stylish 18th-c place is a proper pubby pub where locals, visitors and children are all genuinely welcomed. The neatly kept and friendly beamed bar has fine old pews, settles, old country chairs, and tables smelling nicely of furniture polish, attractive fabrics for the old-fashioned wooden-ring curtains, some striking pictures and hunting prints, two welcoming fires (one in an inglenook), and bunches of fresh flowers. Well kept Brakspears, West Berkshire Good Old Boy, and Youngs Special on handpump, and generously poured good wine. Good tasty bar food might include super home-made soup with warmed bread (£3.50), various filled baguettes (£4.95), lambs liver and bacon or pork and beansprout curry (£7.95), steak and kidney pudding (£8.50), and fresh battered cod and chips (£8.95); no smoking dining conservatory. In summer, the peaceful sloping back garden and terrace – with their pleasant rural views – are popular places to sit, and there are more tables out in front. More reports please. *(Recommended by Dick and Madeleine Brown)*

Free house ~ Licensees John and Jeannie Haley ~ Real ale ~ Bar food ~ Restaurant ~ (0118) 974 4292 ~ Children welcome ~ Dogs allowed in bar ~ Open 11-3, 6-11; 12-3, 7-11 Sun

SWALLOWFIELD SU7364 Map 2

George & Dragon 🍴 🍷

Church Road, towards Farley Hill

Berkshire Dining Pub of the Year

Even though there's a strong emphasis in this attractive and cottagey dining pub on the delicious and very popular food, readers have been more than pleased to find that they are made just as welcome if they only want a drink and a chat. The atmosphere is cosily old-fashioned and relaxed, with rather a smart décor of stripped beams, red walls, rugs on flagstones and good solid wooden furnishings; there's a large log fire. Using fresh seasonal produce, the menu might include home-made soups such as carrot and ginger (£3.95), lunchtime ciabatta sandwiches (£5.50), wild boar liver and pistachio pâté (£5.65), a salad of queen scallops, smoked bacon and potato with a mango and lime dressing (£6.25), smoked salmon stack with red onions and crème fraîche (£6.75), five cheese and mushroom tortellini with sunblush tomato and pesto cream (£10.95), baked honey and thyme duck or fillet of venison in port, rosemary and juniper (£14.75), monkfish scallops with crab and spinach risotto (£15.95), puddings like chocolate and lime cheesecake or winter fruit compote with shortbread and crème fraîche (£4.95), and daily specials such as spinach and feta cheese roulade with pepper vinaigrette (£4.75), corn-fed supreme of chicken stuffed with goats cheese and coarse grain mustard and wrapped in pancetta with a wild mushroom sauce (£13.75), and puddings like mango and passion fruit pavlova (£4.95). It's probably best to book a table. Well kept Fullers London Pride and Wadworths 6X with a guest such as Youngs Bitter on handpump, and good wines. Service is friendly and prompt, and the staff bring drinks to your table. Piped music. *(Recommended by Andy and Debs Thorne, Robert F Smith, KC, Catherine Pitt, Ian Phillips, Susan and John Douglas)*

Free house ~ Licensee Paul Dailey ~ Real ale ~ Bar food (12-2, 6.30-9.30(10 Sat)) ~ Restaurant ~ (0118) 988 4432 ~ Well behaved children welcome ~ Dogs allowed in bar ~ Open 11.30-11; 11.30-3, 6-11 Sat; 12-4, 7-10.30 Sun; evenings 25 and 26 Dec and 1 Jan winter

WALTHAM ST LAWRENCE SU8276 Map 2

Bell

In village centre

Since our last edition, a friendly new licensee has taken over this timbered black and white pub in its pretty village setting, and readers are full of warm praise. The lounge bar has finely carved oak panelling, a cosy big sofa and a log fire, historical pictures of the pub, and newspapers to read; the public bar has heavy beams, an attractive seat in the deep window recess, and well kept Brakspears Bitter, Fullers London Pride, Timothy Taylors Landlord, and a beer brewed especially for them by the West Berkshire brewery called Brew No 1 on handpump; by the end of this year, they hope to have started their own microbrewery. Plenty of malt whiskies and good wine. The front snug is no smoking. Generous helpings of tasty bar food include sandwiches (from £2.50), home-made soup (£3.50), ploughman's (£4.50), ham and egg or bangers and mash (£5.50), fresh haddock, chips and mushy peas (Fridays, £6.50), steak and kidney pie (£7), vegetable curry (£7.50), salmon with a light lemon sauce or steaks (£8), and home-made puddings such as bakewell tart or walnut and treacle tart (£2.95). In summer, pretty flower baskets add colour to the front of the building, and there are seats in the garden and terrace behind. *(Recommended by Prof Chris Bucke, John Saville, Paul Humphreys, June and Robin Savage, Nick Holmes)*

Free house ~ Licensee I F Glenister ~ Real ale ~ Bar food (not Sun evening) ~ (0118) 934 1788 ~ Children in eating area of bar, in restaurant and family room ~ Dogs welcome ~ Open 12-3, 5-11; 12-11 Sat; 12-10.30 Sun

WEST ILSLEY SU4782 Map 2

Harrow 🍷

Signposted at East Ilsley slip road off A34 Newbury—Abingdon

In summer, this white-painted village pub is especially nice when you can sit at the picnic-sets either in the garden, or at seats under cocktail parasols looking out over the duck pond and cricket green. Inside, the open-plan bar has yellow walls, mainly hung with Victorian prints, and a mix of antique oak tables, unpretentious old chairs, and a couple of more stately long settles; there's also an unusual stripped twin-seated high-backed settle between the log fire and the bow window. Under the new licensee, the good bar food now includes home-made soup such as carrot and ginger with melted brie on croutons (£4.25), parfait of duck liver and wild mushroom, pigeon breast on lentil and pancetta salad with a raspberry vinaigrette or prawn and baby squid salad with garlic and ginger (£5.50), filled baguettes served with chips and salad (Tuesday-Saturday lunchtimes, from £5.50), ham and eggs (£6.50), bass with crab risotto, asparagus and grilled pancetta in lobster sauce with a cherry vinaigrette (£11.95), home-made pork and leek sausages with bubble and squeak and a dijon mustard sauce or lambs liver and bacon topped with black pudding with horseradish mash and a caramelised onion gravy (£9.95), chargrilled chicken with olive and potato croquettes, roast baby vegetables, and a lemon and tarragon dressing (£10.95), Aberdeen Angus fillet steak on a crouton in a port and stilton sauce with red onion marmalade (£15), and puddings like home-made chocolate brownie with caramel sauce or almond and black cherry tart (£5.50). Well kept Greene King Abbot, IPA, and Morlands Original on handpump, and decent wines. *(Recommended by Ian Phillips, Mr and Mrs T A Bryan, RB, Nick Holmes)*

Greene King ~ Lease Alan Berry ~ Real ale ~ Bar food (not winter Sun, not Mon) ~ (01635) 281260 ~ Well behaved children welcome ~ Dogs allowed in bar ~ Open 11-3, 6-11; 12-3, 7-10.30 Sun

WINDSOR SU9676 Map 2

Two Brewers 🍷 🍺

34 Park Street, off High Street next to Mews

A lovely old-fashioned pub, this former coffee house is next to the entrance to Windsor Great Park's Long Walk, which you could consider the Royal Family's driveway; one of the three cosy little rooms has photographs of the neighbours passing by on state occasions, when the normally quiet Georgian street swarms with flag-waving supporters. Rambling around a central servery, each of the quaint but snugly civilised bare-boards rooms has a different feel, but all share the same relaxed atmosphere and laid-back piped jazz. Perhaps most comfortable is the red room on the left, with a big armchair, sizeable piles of magazines, and a rarely used, discreetly tucked-away TV. Chalkboards record events of the day in history, and there are distinctive old pews and tables. The back bar leading off has something of a champagne theme; hundreds of corks line the walls, particularly around a big mirror above the fireplace. It's the kind of place where no space is wasted: around the bar are lots of tickets, for everything from Royal Ascot to the *Pop Idol* final. The bar on the right has stripped tables, and a good stack of daily papers. Good home-made food such as unusual lunchtime sandwiches (from £3), bangers and mash or ham, egg and chips (£6), and a choice of Sunday roasts (£7); most dishes have a £1 surcharge in the evening. It's worth booking at weekends if you're planning to eat. Well kept Courage Best, Wadworths 6X and a guest such as Charles Wells Bombardier on handpump, a fairly priced, wide-ranging wine list (several by the glass inc champagne), and good cappuccino; also a fine range of Havana cigars. There are a few tables out in front, under an array of hanging baskets. Note they don't allow children. You have to be nifty to secure one of Park Street's highly prized parking spaces, but there are plenty of big car parks nearby. *(Recommended by Val Stevenson, Rob Holmes, Simon Collett-Jones, Sue Demont, Tim Barrow, Chris Glasson, Dr Stuart Reed)*

Free house ~ Licensee Charles Gillespie ~ Real ale ~ Bar food (not Fri/Sat/Sun evening) ~ (01753) 855426 ~ Dogs welcome ~ Open 11-11; 12-10.30 Sun

WINTERBOURNE SU4572 Map 2

Winterbourne Arms

3½ miles from M4 junction 13; A34 N, first left through Chieveley and on to B4494, then left and right

Well run and friendly, this country pub has interestingly decorated bars with a collection of old irons around the fireplace, early prints and old photographs of the village, and a log fire; you can see the original bakers' ovens in the little no smoking restaurant area, which was once a bakery. Under the new licensee, the good food at lunchtime includes snacks like grilled goats cheese salad (£3.95 or £6.95), sandwiches and filled baked potatoes (£4.75), four bean chilli (£5.50), mixed cheese ploughman's or ham and eggs (£6.25), cumberland sausages with onion gravy (£6.95), and chef's salad of anchovies, croutons, avocado, bacon and poached eggs (£7.95). Also, home-made soup (£3.50), parma ham with poached egg and cheese sauce (£4.25), parfait of chicken livers with pistachios and cognac with toasted brioche (£4.75), moules marinière (£5.50), tagliatelle with wild mushrooms in white wine and cream sauce (£8.95), cajun roast salmon with wilted spinach and creamed leeks (£10.25), seared tuna loin with tabouleh and oriental spiced coconut sauce or herb-crusted rack of lamb with red cabbage and thyme gravy (£12.95), and steaks (from £12.95). Well kept Bass with a guest such as Fullers London Pride or West Berkshire Good Old Boy on handpump, and a decent wine list; prompt, friendly service, and piped music. The peaceful view over the rolling fields from the big bar windows cunningly avoids the quiet road, which is sunken between the pub's two lawns; bright flowering tubs and hanging baskets, and picnic-sets and a big weeping willow in the garden. There are nearby walks to Snelsmore and Donnington. *(Recommended by J Hale, John Saville, Philip Meek, Dr and Mrs A K Clarke, Chris Glasson, Alan and Paula McCully, David and Nina Pugsley)*

Free house ~ Licensee Gordon Fry ~ Real ale ~ Bar food (not Mon) ~ Restaurant ~ (01635) 248200 ~ Children welcome ~ Dogs allowed in bar ~ Open 12-2.30, 6-11; 12-3 Sun; closed Sun pm, all day Mon – exc bank hols

WOODSIDE SU9270 Map 2

Rose & Crown

Woodside Road, Winkfield; A332, over A330 cross at roundabout; after ½ mile, turn left down small lane and through village

This year, the low-beamed bar in this attractive white building has been extended and refurbished giving more seating in the no smoking dining area – most of these tables are set for diners. But there's still a thriving atmosphere with plenty of regulars dropping in for a drink, and as the pub is very handy for Ascot, on a big race day there may be a lively group in a corner around the TV. Well liked bar food at lunchtime includes sandwiches and filled baguettes (£3.50), home-made pie of the day (£5.95), lasagne (£6.95), and rib-eye steak (£7.95), with evening dishes such as chicken and bacon terrine on mixed leaves with a light mustard dressing or warm smoked haddock fillet on wilted spinach, a poached quails egg and creamed parsley sauce (£5.95), pasta with cherry tomatoes, pesto and parmesan (£7.50), seared calves liver with crispy bacon, bubble and squeak, and a light gratin jus or fried red mullet fillets with minted pea purée, gratin potatoes and a warm herb sauce (£13.95), and roast magret duck breast on caramelised apples and poached pears, dauphinois potatoes and baby fennel (£15.95). Well kept Greene King Abbot and Morlands Original, with a guest like Bass or Wadworths 6X on handpump; friendly licensees, piped music and fruit machine. The side garden has tables and a swing, and the setting backed by woodland is peaceful and pretty. *(Recommended by John and Glenys Wheeler, Nigel Williamson, Andy and Yvonne Cunningham, Richard Marjoram)*

Greene King ~ Tenant A Morris ~ Real ale ~ Bar food (12-2.30, 7-9.30; not Sun or Mon evenings) ~ Restaurant (evening) ~ (01344) 882051 ~ Children welcome ~ Open 11-11; 12-7 Sun; closed Sun evening ~ Bedrooms: £40B/£45B

YATTENDON SU5574 Map 2

Royal Oak 🍷 🛏

The Square; B4009 NE from Newbury; turn right at Hampstead Norreys, village signposted on left

Relaxed and friendly, this elegantly handsome and rather upmarket inn remains a fine place for an imaginative meal. You can eat in the panelled and prettily decorated brasserie/bar with its marvellous log fire, fresh flowers and relaxed atmosphere or in the no smoking (and more expensive) restaurant. With prices unchanged since last year, the menu includes roasted red pepper and tomato soup with a goats cheese dumpling (£4.25), tournedos of fresh poached salmon on a salad of marinated vegetables (£6.75), smoked haddock kedgeree with a poached egg and curry cream (£13.75), roast loin of pork with pomme fondant, carrot purée and a morel mushroom jus and chervil oil (£14.50), and corn-fed breast of chicken on a rösti with fennel, roasted onions and anchovy mayonnaise and red wine jus (£14.95), with puddings like warm chocolate brownie with white chocolate ice cream and pistachio tuile or vanilla crème brûlée with compote of rhubarb and shortcake biscuit (from £4.75); vegetables are extra. Well kept Wadworths 6X, and a good wine list; piped music. The restaurant is no smoking, and it is best to book. In summer, you can eat at tables in the pleasant walled garden – and there are more in front on the village square. Some of the attractive, well appointed bedrooms (not cheap) overlook the garden. The poet Robert Bridges once lived in the attractive village – one of the few still privately owned. *(Recommended by JP, PP, Simon Chell, W K Wood, Peter B Brown, the Didler, Derek Thomas)*

Regal-Corus ~ Manager Corinne Macrae ~ Real ale ~ Bar food ~ Restaurant ~ (01635) 201325 ~ Children in eating area of bar ~ Dogs allowed in bedrooms ~ Open 11-11; 11-10.30 Sun ~ Bedrooms: £105B/£130B

Post Office address codings confusingly give the impression that some pubs are in Berkshire, when they're really in Oxfordshire or Hampshire (which is where we list them).

Lucky Dip

Besides the fully inspected pubs, you might like to try these Lucky Dips recommended to us and described by readers (if you do, please send us reports: www.goodguides.com).

Aldermaston [SU5865]

☆ ***Hinds Head*** [Wasing Lane]: Interesting creeper-clad 17th-c village inn, refurbished but homely and comfortable, with good attractively presented home-cooked food, good friendly service, well kept ales such as Gales GB and HSB and a guest such as Fullers London Pride, some cosy corners away from main bar; children welcome (separate dining room with high chairs), fine enclosed garden; a good place to stay (the best bedrooms are in the main building) *(Ian Phillips, BB)*

Aldworth [SU5579]

☆ ***Four Points*** [B4009 towards Hampstead Norreys]: Tidy array of polished tables in long low carpeted main bar and dining area partly divided by standing timbers, generous enjoyable home-made food from baguettes up, Adnams and Wadworths 6X, helpful staff, no piped music, games room; neat garden over road *(LYM, Michael and Jenny Back)*

Aston [SU7884]

☆ ***Flower Pot*** [signed off A4130 Henley—Maidenhead at Crazies Hill]: Friendly old two-bar pub with nice orchard garden (dogs allowed there) looking over meadows to cottages and far side of Thames, side field with chickens, ducks and guinea fowl; well kept Brakspears inc Ted & Bens Organic, good unusual reasonably priced food from sandwiches to lots of fish and game in season, bare-boards public bar, lively and brightly lit, with lots of stuffed fish in glass cases, darts; unobtrusive piped music, friendly siamese cats and elderly dog, busy with walkers and families wknds, when service can slow *(Simon Collett-Jones, Michael Porter, Susan and John Douglas, Mike and Sue Richardson, M Borthwick)*

Bagnor [SU4569]

☆ ***Blackbird*** [quickest approach is from Speen on edge of Newbury]: Chatty traditional pub in very peaceful setting near Watermill Theatre – they do a pre-show menu; bar simple and unfussy with plates around walls, leaded lamps, plain wooden furnishings, old farm tools and firearms hanging from ceiling; more formal no smoking eating area opens off; changing beers such as Brakspears, Greene King Abbot and brews from West Berkshire Brewery, friendly staff, well prepared straightforward food, winter log fire; tables in pleasant side garden and on green in front; regular backgammon nights *(Klaus and Elizabeth Leist, BB)*

Binfield [SU8571]

Stag & Hounds [Forest Road (B3034)]: Comfortable 14th-c pub, often very busy, with interesting array of low-beamed bars, open fires, antiques, brass, wide changing food choice inc snacks such as hot ciabatta sandwiches, well kept ales such as Courage Best and Directors, Theakstons XB and Wadworths 6X, decent wines, friendly young staff, daily papers; piped music; children allowed in attractively redecorated partly no smoking eating area, tables out on front terrace and in back garden *(Andy and Yvonne Cunningham, David H T Dimock, LYM, Lesley and Peter Barrett)*

Bray [SU9079]

☆ ***Hinds Head*** [High St]: Handsome Tudor pub under new management, panelling and beams, sturdy oak furniture, leather porter's chairs and other comfortable seating, two blazing log fires, plenty of memorabilia and nice pictures, good helpings of decent food, well kept Greene King IPA and Ruddles and a guest such as John Smiths, good wines, friendly locals, helpful polite staff, upstairs restaurant; may be piped music; tables on suntrap front terrace *(Susan and John Douglas, Peter and Giff Bennett, George Atkinson, LYM, John and Glenys Wheeler)*

Chieveley [SU4774]

Blue Boar [3½ miles from M4 junction 13: A34 N North Heath, W of village]: Nicely placed thatched inn with high-backed settles and pleasant variety of other furnishings in three rambling rooms, bar food from sandwiches up, well kept Boddingtons, Fullers London Pride and Wadworths 6X, civilised oak-panelled restaurant; may be soft piped music; children welcome, tables out on front cobbled terrace, 17 bedrooms *(John Robertson, LYM, Comus and Sarah Elliott, John Saville, Christopher and Jo Barton, JCW, Sheila and Robert Robinson)*

Cippenham [SU9580]

Long Barn [Cippenham Lane]: Interesting and attractively converted old raftered barn dating from 17th c, well kept real ales, cheerful atmosphere – popular with young people; upstairs restaurant, large pleasant terrace *(Dr and Mrs A K Clarke)*

Cookham Dean [SU8785]

☆ ***Jolly Farmer*** [Church Rd, off Hills Lane]: Friendly, cosy and deliberately kept traditional by the village consortium which owns it, with small rooms, open fires, well kept ales such as Brakspears and Courage Best, enjoyable food, attractive dining room, pub games, no music or machines, good quiet garden with play area; well behaved children welcome away from bar *(Caroline and Anthony Skinner, LYM, Simon Chell)*

Curridge [SU4871]

☆ ***Bunk*** [3 miles from M4 junction 13: A34 towards Newbury, then first left to Curridge, Hermitage, and left into Curridge at Village Only sign]: More restaurant than pub, stylishly extended and refurbished, with wide choice of good interesting food (not cheap, not Sun evening), smart stripped-wood tiled-floor bar on left, wooded-meadow views and conservatory; four well kept ales inc Fullers London Pride, good choice of wines, buoyant atmosphere, welcoming efficient service, tables in neat garden, fine woodland walks nearby *(Angus and Rosemary Campbell, Lord Sandhurst, J Hale, BB)*

Datchet [SU9876]

Royal Stag [not far from M4 junction 5; The Green]: Above-average food and well kept Tetleys-related and guest beers in friendly and picturesque traditional local; beautiful beams, ecclesiastical windows overlooking churchyard, attractively carved armchairs (and bar), one wall panelled in claret case lids, log fire, daily papers, welcoming and entertaining old retriever; separate bar with TV and football posters, occasional juke box and a ghostly handprint is said to appear on the windowpane; open all day *(Chris Glasson, Susan and John Douglas)*

East Ilsley [SU4980]

☆ ***Star*** [leaving village southwards]: Comfortable and friendly partly 15th-c pub doing well under new management, good value traditional food in dining room, bar with beams and black woodwork, well kept Brakspears and Fullers London Pride, inglenook log fire, books and pub games; garden behind with picnic-sets and play area, good newly refurbished bedrooms *(Edward and Ava Williams, BB, Lisa-Marie Hunter)*

☆ ***Swan*** [High St]: Spacious, neat and well decorated, with a slightly formal look but pleasantly informal dining-pub feel; wide range of good bar food inc interesting vegetarian dishes (no sandwiches, though), friendly landlord, well kept Greene King beers, daily papers, perhaps a couple of welcoming dogs; no smoking restaurant, busy with families Sun – best to book; tables in courtyard and walled garden with play area, excellent bedrooms, some in house down road *(Mr and Mrs T A Bryan, LYM, Val and Alan Green, David Crook)*

Eton [SU9678]

☆ ***Gilbeys*** [High St]: Hardly a pub, but well worth knowing for good imaginative home-cooked light bar meals, nice sensibly priced house wines, friendly unstuffy family service; recently refurbished; can be very busy if there's an event at the school, best to book for back restaurant *(Mike and Sue Richardson, BB)*

New College [High St]: Well kept Badger ales with changing guest beers such as Gribble Fursty Ferret, popular food *(Mike and Sue Richardson)*

Finchampstead [SU7963]

Queens Oak [Church Lane]: Good value food in bar and separate restaurant (where children allowed), pleasant helpful staff, particularly well kept Brakspears; garden with play area and Sun lunchtime barbecues *(June and Robin Savage)*

Great Shefford [SU3673]

☆ ***Pheasant*** [less than ½ mile N of M4 junction 14 – B4000, just off A338]: Isolated country pub with National Hunt jockey landlord, four neat rooms, bistro atmosphere, lots of horse-racing pictures and cartoons and horsey customers; end dining area with emphasis on good tapas alongside other interesting dishes, well kept Butts Jester, log fires, no music; public bar with games inc ring the bull; attractive views from pleasant garden *(George Atkinson, John Davis, LYM, M J Park)*

☆ ***Swan*** [2 miles from M4 junction 14 – A338 towards Wantage]: Low-ceilinged bow-windowed pub under new management, horse-racing memorabilia, popular food (not Tues evening, and stops promptly at lunchtime) from baguettes to fish, steaks and good Sun lunch, well kept Bass and Courage Best and Directors, good wine choice, friendly attentive service, good log fire, daily papers and magazines, river-view restaurant; may be TV or piped music; children in eating areas, tables on quiet waterside lawn and terrace *(A and B D Craig, Sebastian Leach, M J Park, Jill McLaren, Gerald Wilkinson, Andy and Yvonne Cunningham, Tony Walker, Michael Cross, Mayur Shah, LYM, Dick and Madeleine Brown)*

Halfway [SU4068]

Halfway Inn [A4 Hungerford—Newbury]: Named for its position between London and Bath, with wide choice of enjoyable imaginative food inc Sun evenings, great attention to detail and colour, fresh veg, good children's dishes (and children's helpings of most main ones); good range of wines and beers, friendly helpful staff, real fire, partitions dividing dining room into cosy areas *(John Davis, Meg and Colin Hamilton)*

Hare Hatch [SU8077]

☆ ***Queen Victoria*** [Blakes Lane; just N of A4 Reading—Maidenhead]: Two relaxed and chatty low-beamed and panelled bars with nice décor and friendly local atmosphere, enjoyable food from sandwiches up, Brakspears Bitter, Special, Old and a seasonal beer, a fair choice of wines by the glass, cheerful service, pub games, flower-filled no smoking conservatory; children in eating area, one or two tables outside, open all day Sun *(Simon Collett-Jones, LYM, Colin and Sandra Tann, Doreen and Haydn Maddock , Rona Murdoch)*

Hungerford [SU3368]

John o' Gaunt [Bridge St (A338)]: Attractive pub with good choice of food, helpful staff and chef, decent wines *(Ken Flawn, LYM)*

Hurley [SU8283]

Rising Sun [High St]: Cottagey three-room pub, clean, light and airy despite its low beams, assorted chairs around scrubbed pine tables on flagstones, good well priced food esp fish (no sandwiches wknd lunchtimes), well kept Boddingtons, Brakspears and Fullers London Pride, friendly staff, pretty separate Shaker-style dining room; busy wknds, pool table, shame about the piped music; seats in tree-filled garden, attractive spot near Thames *(Susan and John Douglas, Tracey and Stephen Groves, Bill Sykes, BB)*

Hurst [SU8074]

☆ ***Green Man*** [Hinton Rd, just outside village]: Old-fashioned low-beamed pub nicely refurbished and extended, good atmosphere and mix of furnishings, cosy little areas, good value well prepared food (not Mon evening), well kept Brakspears, good choice of wines by the glass, pleasant service; pub games, piped music; pleasant sunny back garden *(LYM, Richard Endacott, D J and P M Taylor)*

Inkpen [SU3864]

☆ ***Crown & Garter*** [Great Common]: Three areas around central bar, oak settle by big log fireplace, old tables, attractive décor and relaxed atmosphere, good choice of good reasonably priced home-made food, imaginative without being too way-out, well kept Archers and West Berkshire Good Old Boy, friendly helpful service and a real welcome for families; play area in pleasant small garden, pretty bedrooms with own bathrooms, good downland walks, cl lunchtime Mon/Tues *(Philip Atkins, J V Dadswell)*

Kintbury [SU3866]

☆ ***Dundas Arms*** [Station Rd]: Clean and tidy, with good fresh home-made food (not Mon evening or Sun) from sandwiches up, well kept real ales such as Timothy Taylors Landlord, good coffee and wines by the glass, helpful staff, no piped music, fine range of clarets and burgundies in evening restaurant; tables out on deck above Kennet & Avon Canal, children welcome, pleasant walks; comfortable bedrooms with own secluded waterside terrace *(Keith Allen, Charles and Pauline Stride, LYM, Roger and Pauline Pearce, Mrs J H S Lang, Jim Bush)*

Knowl Hill [SU8178]

☆ ***Bird in Hand*** [A4, quite handy for M4 junction 8/9]: Relaxed atmosphere and good home-made food from sandwiches and baguettes up (two big bright menu boards, also fixed price buffet) in spacious beamed main bar and restaurant; splendid log fire, cosy alcoves, much older side bar; well kept Brakspears and Fullers London Pride, good wines by the glass, good choice of other drinks, friendly staff, no smoking buffet area – where children allowed; tables out on new front terrace, clean and tidy modern bedrooms *(Mrs E A Macdonald, Ron and Sheila Corbett, Simon Collett-Jones, June and Robin Savage, LYM)*

Littlewick Green [SU8379]

☆ ***Cricketers*** [not far from M4 junction 9; A404(M) then left on to A4, from which village signed on left; Coronation Rd]: Friendly pub in charming spot opp cricket green, well kept Brakspears and Fullers London Pride, freshly squeezed orange juice, good value food and good free Sun bar nibbles, neat housekeeping, lots of cricketing pictures, cosy local atmosphere; big-screen TV *(Chris Glasson, LYM, John and Glenys Wheeler)*

Ring o' Bells [A4, W of A404(M)]: Recently refurbished main road pub, wide choice of enjoyable food from some interesting snacks to steaks and Sun lunch, well kept beer *(Michael Porter)*

Newbury [SU4767]

Monument [Northbrook St]: Welcoming pub done out in old style, bar divided into several cubicles, four or five real ales such as Butts and Theakstons, board games *(SLC)*

Oakley Green [SU9276]

☆ ***Olde Red Lion*** [B3024 just W of Windsor]: Cosy old low-beamed dining pub with good interesting reasonably priced food, welcoming helpful staff, Bass, Courage Best and Flowers IPA in small bar; comfortable bedrooms, good breakfast, pleasant garden *(Simon Collett-Jones)*

Old Windsor [SU9874]

☆ ***Union*** [Crimp Hill Rd, off B3021 – itself off A308/A328]: Friendly old pub, good bar food from sandwiches up, well kept ales such as Brakspears and Courage Directors, consistently good service from long-serving staff, log fire in big fireplace, interesting nostalgic show-business photographs, good value attractive copper-decorated restaurant; fruit machine; white plastic tables under cocktail parasols on sunny front terrace (heated in cooler weather), country views; comfortable bedrooms with own bathrooms *(BB, Ian Phillips, Gordon Prince, R A Watson)*

Paley Street [SU8676]

☆ ***Royal Oak*** [B3024 W]: Stylishly refurbished, with good food and wines, well kept real ale, lots of photographs of celebrities with the landlord's father, Michael Parkinson, good lively buzz, nice service *(Bob and Maggie Atherton)*

Pangbourne [SU6376]

Swan [Shooters Hill]: Attractive 17th-c Thames-view pub with good range of bar food all day, relaxing modern interior, dining balcony and conservatory, Greene King ales inc Old Speckled Hen, decent wines, friendly cat; piped music, sports TV; picnic-sets overlooking the weir and moorings *(Mr and Mrs Hugh Spottiswoode, Jonathan Smith, Catherine Pitt)*

Reading [SU7273]

3Bs Bar [Town Hall, Blagrave St]: Light and airy bare-boards café-bar in town hall expansively redeveloped as arts/museum/concert centre, four well kept changing ales such as Butts Jester, Stonehenge Danish Dynamite and Youngs AAA, all-day side food servery with pastries and cakes as well as bar lunches, friendly staff, magazines and daily papers, plenty of posters about Reading's three Bs – beer, biscuits and bulbs; lots of tables out in pedestrian zone, open all day; young pubby atmosphere evenings, esp Tues blues night, also open mike Weds, indie Thurs *(Richard Lewis, Jonathan Smith, Catherine Pitt)*

☆ ***Fishermans Cottage*** [Kennet Side – easiest to walk from Orts Rd, off Kings Rd]: Good friendly backwater respite from Reading's bustle, by canal lock and towpath (gasometer view), with waterside tables, lovely big back garden and light and airy conservatory; modern furnishings of character, pleasant stone snug behind woodburning range, good value lunches inc lots of hot or cold sandwiches (very busy then but service quick), full Fullers beer range with perhaps a guest such as Brakspears, small choice of wines, small darts room, SkyTV; dogs allowed (not in garden) *(the Didler, Mark Percy, Lesley Mayoh, Jonathan Smith, Catherine Pitt)*

George [A329 Wokingham Rd, Earley]: Well kept beer and enjoyable food, waterside setting by River Loddon *(Andy and Yvonne Cunningham)*

Sandhurst [SU8461]

Wellington Arms [Yorktown Rd (A321)]: Recently refitted local with food inc good value sandwiches and usual bar meals, well kept Brakspears, pleasant staff; garden, new bedrooms *(Andy and Yvonne Cunningham)*

Shurlock Row [SU8274]

Royal Oak [Hungerford Lane]: Unpretentious décor like a homely dining room, well kept beer, very wide food choice inc all-year plum pudding *(Andy and Yvonne Cunningham)*

Sonning [SU7575]

☆ *Bull* [off B478, by church; village signed off A4 E of Reading]: Attractive old-fashioned inn in pretty setting near Thames, low heavy beams, cosy alcoves, cushioned antique settles and low-slung chairs, inglenook fireplaces, no smoking back dining area (children allowed), well kept Gales Best, HSB and Butser and a guest beer, lots of country wines, separate ordering for bar lunches from filled french sticks to seafood and steaks (they may try to keep your credit card, and may stop taking orders very promptly), charming courtyard; open all day summer wknds, bedrooms *(Paul Vickers, John and Glenys Wheeler, Karen and Graham Oddey, LYM, Val Stevenson, Rob Holmes, Paul Humphreys, Tim and Jane Charlesworth, Catherine Pitt)*

Theale [SU6168]

Winning Hand [A4 W, opp Sulhamstead turn]: Friendly, with good service, well kept Arkells and Hook Norton, varied wine list, wide choice of food, restaurant; bright gardens *(Geoff Palmer)*

Tidmarsh [SU6374]

Greyhound [A340 S of Pangbourne]: Old thatched pub with new management doing enjoyable fairly priced food, well kept Fullers inc seasonal beers; good walks nearby *(R C Wivesay)*

Twyford [SU7876]

Duke of Wellington [High St]: Congenial pub with lively bar and quiet lounge, wide choice of lunchtime food, well kept Brakspears, friendly staff *(Paul Humphreys)*

Waltham St Lawrence [SU8376]

☆ *Star* [Broadmoor Rd]: Clean and tidy old pub with enjoyable food inc substantial starters, stone-baked pizzas and restauranty dishes (a couple of tables straying into bar area, some no smoking), friendly licensees, beams, brasses, newspapers on hangers, open fire, full range of Wadworths beers *(J and B Cressey)*

Wargrave [SU7878]

☆ *Bull* [off A321 Henley—Twyford; High St]: Good friendly atmosphere in cottagey low-beamed pub popular for interesting and enjoyable food (now has second dining area) esp good value lunchtime filled baguettes and hot dishes, well kept Brakspears, good wine choice, friendly staff, good log fires; tables on pretty partly covered terrace, bedrooms *(Michael Porter, M Borthwick, LYM, Paul Humphreys)*

White Waltham [SU8577]

Beehive [Waltham Rd]: Friendly country local by cricket field, accent on food, well kept Brakspears, smallish front bar and larger back saloon *(Dr and Mrs A K Clarke)*

Windsor [SU9577]

Swan [Mill Lane, Clewer]: Unchanging traditional local, no music or machines, well kept Fullers IPA and London Pride, good choice of well priced wines by the glass; bedrooms *(Alistair Forsyth)*

Winnersh [SU7870]

Wheelwrights Arms [off A329 Reading—Wokingham at Winnersh crossroads by Sainsburys, signed Hurst, Twyford; then right into Davis Way]: Good friendly service, well kept Wadworths inc seasonal beers at sensible prices, enjoyable lunchtime bar food from sandwiches up, interesting décor, no smoking area; small family garden, disabled parking *(D J and P M Taylor)*

Wokingham [SU8068]

Broad Street Tavern [Broad St]: Old building smartly but not over-trendily done up with stripped wood, good range of filling lunchtime food, well kept Wadworths IPA, 6X and guest beers tapped from the cask, low prices, very friendly service, nice local atmosphere, quarterly beer festivals *(Dr and Mrs A K Clarke, Jonathan Smith)*

Crooked Billet [Honey Hill]: Busy country pub with pews, tiles, brick serving counter, crooked black joists, generous plain lunchtime food, well kept Brakspears inc Ted & Bens Organic, small no smoking restaurant area where children allowed; nice outside in summer, very busy wknds *(LYM, Dr and Mrs Jackson, Colin and Sandra Tann)*

Metropolitan [Rose St]: Friendly timbered high-street local, two small bars, well kept real ales *(Dr and Mrs A K Clarke)*

Plough [nr Coppid Beech A329 roundabout, London Rd]: Large pleasantly refurbished roadhouse with well kept Greene King Old Speckled Hen, good service, bar food inc children's, separate dining room; live music Thurs, booking advisable Sat/Sun evening *(Dr and Mrs A K Clarke)*

Woolhampton [SU5767]

☆ *Rowbarge* [Station Rd]: Big family dining place doing well under current management, attractive beamed bar with roaring log fire, panelled side room, small snug, large no smoking canal-view conservatory, wide choice of good freshly made food from lunchtime baked potatoes, ploughman's and baguettes to Sun lunch and curry nights, well kept Greene King ales inc Old Speckled Hen, plentiful pleasant staff; tables out by water and in big garden with fishpond, moorings not far *(Martin and Karen Wake, LYM, Roger and Pauline Pearce, Charles and Pauline Stride, Dick and Madeleine Brown, J V Dadswell)*

Buckinghamshire

This good county for pub-lovers has a fine choice of proper friendly country pubs in pretty walking country, as well as some very smart dining pubs with food that's good and imaginative – if not cheap. On the food side, the Mole & Chicken at Easington wins the accolade of Buckinghamshire Dining Pub of the Year (and it has new bedrooms this year – tempting for dinner and a stay over). Four pubs new to the Guide, *or making a reappearance in a new guise and after quite a few years, are the prettily placed Full Moon on Hawridge Common (doing well all round under its friendly new licensees), the White Horse at Hedgerley (great for good beer), the welcoming and civilised Swan at Ley Hill (another good all-rounder, with imaginative food), and the nicely placed Stag at Mentmore (good interesting food and helpful service in this pretty village pub). Other pubs currently doing particularly well include the Bell at Chearsley (proper home cooking in this friendly country pub), the cheerful Red Lion at Chenies (good home cooking here too), the nicely unpretentious Prince Albert at Frieth, the delightfully placed Stag & Huntsman at Hambleden, the Crooked Billet at Newton Longville (virtually unlimited choice of wines by the glass, alongside its interesting food), the bustling Polecat at Prestwood, the Frog at Skirmett (a fine all-rounder), the civilised Five Arrows in Waddesdon (a favourite), and the unaffected Chequers at Wheeler End (good food, happy balance between eaters and drinkers). The cheerful Dinton Hermit at Ford has new bedrooms this year (and its Sardinian chef is on great form). In the Lucky Dip section at the end of the chapter, we'd pick out the Pheasant at Brill, Blue Flag at Cadmore End, Chester Arms at Chicheley, Swan in Denham, Walnut Tree at Fawley, Chequers at Fingest, Crooked Billet at Flackwell Heath, Cross Keys in Great Missenden, Plough & Anchor in Kingswood, Blackwood Arms on Littleworth Common, Angel in Long Crendon (too restauranty for the main entries now, but excellent for a special meal out), Hare & Hounds near Marlow, Old Beams in Milton Keynes, Swan in Olney, Crown at Penn, Hit or Miss at Penn Street, White Hart at Preston Bissett (well worth a special trip, if you can get there before 10 December 2002), Cock in Stony Stratford, Old Swan at The Lee and Clifden Arms at Worminghall. We have inspected the great majority of these, and rate them all as good. Drinks prices here are generally very high. In our price survey this year independent brewers from outside the area, such as Fullers and Adnams, tended to be good value. And beers from even smaller local brewers such as Vale and Marlow Rebellion now benefit from the 14p a pint duty.*

BENNETT END SU7897 Map 4

Three Horseshoes

Horseshoe Road; from Radnage follow unclassified road towards Princes Risborough and turn left into Bennett End Road, then right into Horseshoe Road

By the time this book is published, new licensees will have taken over this unpretentious and hard-to-find old country inn. It is in such a lovely tranquil setting (with its surroundings made particularly distinctive by a red phone box rising inexplicably from the fenced-off duck pond) that we are keeping our fingers crossed that things will not change too much under the new regime. The more appealing room is the snug front bar, with flagstone floors, high wooden settles, and a few seats tucked around an antique range; the comfortable sitting-roomish lounge has some sofas. Brakspears, Flowers and Fullers London Pride on handpump, and bar food has included lunchtime sandwiches and macaroni cheese, with evening dishes such as chicken with cashew nuts. They do a roast on Sundays, when the pub can get busy; at other times you might have it almost to yourself. *(Recommended by Catherine and Richard Preston, Tim and Ann Newell)*

Free house ~ Real ale ~ Bar food ~ No credit cards ~ (01494) 483273 ~ Open 12-3, 7-11(10.30 Sun); closed Sun evening and Mon

CADMORE END SU7892 Map 4

Old Ship

B482 Stokenchurch—Marlow

Said to have been built in 1637, this carefully restored, tiled cottage has plenty of unpretentious character and charm. The tiny low-beamed two rooms of the bar are separated by standing timbers and simply furnished with brocaded banquettes and stools in the carpeted room on the right, and scrubbed country tables, bench and church chair seating (one still has a hole for a game called five-farthings), and bare boards on the left. Shove-ha'penny, cribbage, and dominoes. Bar food includes home-made soup (£3.25), sandwiches and baguettes (£4), garlic prawns or home-made chilli (£6.25), home-made bubble and squeak (£6.95), a vegetarian dish of the day (£7.50), a pie or casserole of the month (£8.95), and seasonal fish dishes (£7-£12). Monthly themed food evenings, two courses from £10. Well kept Brakspears Bitter, Old, Special, seasonal and Mild, and a guest like Fullers London Pride tapped from the cask. There are seats in the sheltered garden with a large pergola, and this year a new terrace at the end of the bar with cushioned seats and clothed tables has been opened for adults (children and families are welcome in the garden). Parking is on the other side of the road. More reports please. *(Recommended by Pete Baker, Brian Root, the Didler, Paul Vickers, Tracey and Stephen Groves)*

Free house ~ Licensee Ian Wingfield ~ Real ale ~ Bar food (12-2, 6.30-9.30; not Sun) ~ Restaurant ~ (01494) 883496 ~ Children at licensee's discretion ~ Dogs allowed in bar ~ Open 11-3, 5.30-11; 12-3, 7-10.30 Sun

CHEARSLEY SP7110 Map 4

Bell

The Green; minor road NE of Long Crendon and N of Thame

'What a lovely pub' is the comment several readers have made after visiting this bustling place. The cosy bar has a welcoming traditional fee, mugs and tankards hanging from the beams, a collection of plates at one end of the room, an enormous fireplace, and handsome counter; there are usually batches of local eggs for sale. Well kept Fullers Chiswick, London Pride and seasonal brews, and a small but well chosen choice of wines by the glass. Much of the simple good bar food is made from local ingredients and might include lunchtime sandwiches (from £3.45; bacon on chunky local bread topped with a local fried egg £3.95), leek and mushroom crumble (£5.95), generously served ham, egg and chips (£6.95), lamb casserole and minty dumpling (£7.55), lambs liver with smoked back bacon and mustard mash or thai-style green chicken curry (£7.95), tuna steak with coriander, lemon and white wine (£8.95), and puddings such as home-made bread pudding (£3.95). They sell ice pops and various drinks for children. You can't book tables, so there's ample space for drinkers, but it's best to get there early if you intend to eat. On Friday evenings you might find the licensees or one of the locals coming round the bar with sausages. Prompt friendly service; cribbage, dominoes. Play equipment such as slides, a rope bridge, wendy house, climbing frames and the like fill the spacious back garden, which has rabbits in one corner. There are plenty of tables out here, with more on a paved terrace, where there may be barbecues in summer. A couple of tables in front overlook the very grassy village green. More reports please. *(Recommended by John and Glenys Wheeler, Andrew Scarr, Gill and Keith Croxton, Jill McLaren, Richard Gibbs)*

Fullers ~ Tenants Peter and Sue Grimsdell ~ Real ale ~ Bar food (not winter Sun evening, not Mon (exc bank hols)) ~ (01844) 208077 ~ Children in eating area of bar ~ Dogs welcome ~ Open 12-2.30, 6-11; 12-11 Sat; 12-11 Sun; 12-2.30, 6-11 Sat in winter, 12-3, 7-10.30 Sun in winter; closed Mon lunchtime (exc bank hols)

CHENIES TQ0198 Map 3

Red Lion ★

2 miles from M25 junction 18; A404 towards Amersham, then village signposted on right; Chesham Road

Run by a cheerful, friendly landlord, this bustling place has a good, relaxed pubby atmosphere. The unpretentious L-shaped bar has original photographs of the village and traction engines, comfortable built-in wall benches by the front windows, and other traditional seats and tables; there's also a small no smoking back snug and a dining room. Highly enjoyable food (all made on the premises) includes home-made soup (£3.50), baguettes or soft baps with fillings such as bacon and turkish delight or chicken, celery and walnut in a blue cheese dressing (from £3.50), sardines marinated in lime and coriander with a tomato and onion salad (£4.95), three cheese terrine with olives and sunblush tomatoes (£5.25), ploughman's (from £5.25), grilled goats cheese on a crumpet with rocket and tomatoes (£5.50), pasta with salami and peppers in a tomato cream pesto sauce or bacon, mushroom and onion potato bake (£6.25), ratatouille and seafood gratin (£6.95), pork, chilli and lentil casserole (£7.50), curried steak and kidney with spinach (£7.95), spicy prawn and ham risotto (£8.95), home-made pies such as their very popular lamb one, mixed game or thai curry fish (from £8.95), chicken breast stuffed with bacon and mushroom and coated with a honey crust (£10.95); vegetables and salad are extra. Well kept Benskins Best, Marlow Rebellion Lion Pride (brewed for the pub), Wadworths 6X, and a guest beer on handpump. The hanging baskets and window boxes are pretty in summer, and there are picnic-sets on a small side terrace. No games machines or piped music; handy for the M25. *(Recommended by Mike and Jennifer Marsh, Peter Saville, John and Glenys Wheeler, Pat and Tony Martin, Peter and Giff Bennett, B N F and M Parkin, Tracey and Stephen Groves, Ian Phillips, Christopher and Elise Way, Angela Cerfontyn, Howard Dell)*

Free house ~ Licensee Mike Norris ~ Real ale ~ Bar food (12-2, 7-(9.30 Sun)10) ~ Restaurant ~ (01923) 282722 ~ Children welcome ~ Dogs allowed in bar ~ Open 11-2.30, 5.30-11; 12-3, 6.30-10.30 Sun; closed 25 Dec

EASINGTON SP6810 Map 4

Mole & Chicken 🍴 🍷 🛏

From B4011 in Long Crendon follow Chearsley, Waddesdon signpost into Carters Lane opposite the Chandos Arms, then turn left into Chilton Road

Buckinghamshire Dining Pub of the Year

This year, two cottages next door to this friendly dining pub, have been converted into attractive letting bedrooms with views over the rolling open countryside. This remains very much the place for a special meal out (they don't offer bar snacks), but they do keep three real ales and people do drop in for just a drink. Served by friendly staff, the imaginative food might include starters such as home-made soup (£3.50), chicken satay or grilled crostini of smoked fish and cream cheese (£5.95), and a bowl of chilli mussels (£6.95), with main courses like roasted butternut and spinach risotto with a basil dressing or popular duck and bacon salad with a warm plum sauce (£8.95), rack of pork ribs marinated and slow roasted in barbecue sauce (£9.95), whole roasted pheasant with bacon, mushroom and shallot gravy (£11.95), and thai prawn curry, calves liver with bacon, mushrooms and onions in brandy sauce or tender shoulder of lamb (all £12.95); daily specials and fish dishes are listed separately. Decent French house wines (and a good choice by the bottle), over 40 malt whiskies, and well kept Fullers London Pride, and Greene King IPA and Old

Speckled Hen on handpump. The open-plan layout is very well done, so that all the different parts seem quite snug and self-contained without being cut off from what's going on, and the atmosphere is chatty and relaxed. The beamed bar curves around the serving counter in a sort of S-shape, and there are pink walls with lots of big antique prints, flagstones, and (even at lunchtime) lit candles on the medley of tables to go with the nice mix of old chairs; good winter log fires. The garden, where they sometimes hold summer barbecues and pig and lamb roasts, has quite a few tables and chairs. More reports please. *(Recommended by Mike and Heather Watson, Karen and Graham Oddey, John Robertson)*

Free house ~ Licensees A Heather and S Ellis ~ Real ale ~ Bar food ~ Restaurant (12-2, 7-10; 12-9.30 Sun) ~ (01844) 208387 ~ Children in eating area of bar and restaurant ~ Open 12-3, 6-11; 12-10.30 Sun ~ Bedrooms: £50B/£65B

FORD SP7709 Map 4

Dinton Hermit

Village signposted between A418 and B4009, SW of Aylesbury

New bedrooms have been opened up in the converted barn by this 16th-c stone cottage, and other changes include church candles lit throughout the bar and restaurant, both at lunchtime and the evening, and the addition of hundreds of bottles of wine to decorate the walls and thick oak bar counter. There's also a huge inglenook fireplace with a very old print of John Bigg, the supposed executioner of Charles I and the man later known as the Dinton Hermit, hanging beside it, and the bar has kept its scrubbed tables on the original black and red tiled floor; well kept Adnams, Hook Norton, and Morrells Oxford Blue tapped from the cask, and decent wines. Very good food cooked by the Sardinian chef might consist of lunchtime sandwiches (£3.50) and (using their own eggs) lunchtime omelettes (from £4.95) or ham and egg (£5.95), plus home-made soup (£3.50), seared Scotch beef with a lime and ginger dressing (£5.95), fried quail with a fresh couscous salad or teriyaki sauce (£7.95), tagliatelle with red pepper and tomato pesto sauce (£8.50), guinea fowl with calvados and cream or fresh fish such as South African Kingclip grilled with black butter (£13.95), Scotch Orkney beef fillet (£17.95), and home-made puddings such as super banoffi pie, chocolate ganache or lemon tart (£4.50). Best to book for the cosy no smoking restaurant; piped music. Seats in the attractive courtyard, where they hold barbecues and live jazz events in summer, and there's an acre of garden. More reports please. *(Recommended by Tim and Ann Newell, Torrens Lyster, Karen and Graham Oddey, J Hale)*

Free house ~ Licensee Johnny Chick ~ Real ale ~ Bar food (not Sun evening or Mon) ~ Restaurant ~ (01296) 747473 ~ Children in restaurant ~ Dogs allowed in bar ~ Open 11-2.30, 6-11; 12-4 Sun; closed Sun evening, Mon ~ Bedrooms: £60B/£85B

FORTY GREEN SU9292 Map 2

Royal Standard of England

3½ miles from M40 junction 2, via A40 to Beaconsfield, then follow sign to Forty Green, off B474 ¾ mile N of New Beaconsfield; keep going through village

Until after the Battle of Worcester in 1651 (when Charles II hid in the high rafters of what is now the food bar), this ancient pub used to be called the Ship. The rambling rooms have lots to look at and much history: huge black ship's timbers, finely carved old oak panelling, roaring winter fires with handsomely decorated iron firebacks, and a massive settle apparently built to fit the curved transom of an Elizabethan ship, as well as rifles, powder-flasks and bugles, ancient pewter and pottery tankards, lots of brass and copper, needlework samplers, and stained glass. Two areas are no smoking. Enjoyable bar food includes sandwiches, home-made soup (£3.95), mushroom and egg florentine on spinach with a creamy cheese sauce or chicken liver pâté with a fruit coulis (£4.95), lunchtime ploughman's (£6.25), marinated tofu cutlets in a lemon and chilli sauce with rice noodles, chinese cabbage and cashews or beef in ale pie (£8.25), beef and herb battered haddock (£8.95), half an aylesbury crispy duck with a light orange and brown sugar sauce (£13.95), daily specials like home-made savoury tartlets (£7.95), sticky barbecued ribs or thai-seasoned fresh tuna and sweet potato fishcakes (£8.50), braised rump of lamb in cider and Guinness (£9.95), and puddings such as apple and cinnamon strudel or Eton mess (£3.95). Well kept Brakspears Bitter, Fullers London Pride, Greene King Old Speckled Hen, Marstons Pedigree, and Vale Notley Ale on handpump, and country wines and mead. There are seats outside in a neatly hedged front rose garden, or in the shade of a tree. *(Recommended by Tracey and Stephen Groves, Anthony Longden, Lesley Bass, Michael Porter, the Didler, Peter and Giff Bennett, JP, PP, Susan and John Douglas)*

Free house ~ Licensees Cyril and Carol Cain ~ Real ale ~ Bar food (12-2.15, 6.30-9.15) ~ (01494) 673382 ~ Children in family room until 9 (9.30 if eating) ~ Open 11-3, 5.30-11; 12-3, 7-10.30 Sun; closed evening 25 Dec

FRIETH SU7990 Map 2

Prince Albert

Village signposted off B482 in Lane End; turn right towards Fingest just before village

Readers enjoy this old-fashioned, cottagey country pub and you can be sure of a warm welcome from the friendly licensees. On the left, there are low black beams and joists, brocaded cushions on high-backed settles (one with its back panelled in neat squares), a big black stove in a brick inglenook, and a leaded-light built-in wall cabinet of miniature bottles. The slightly larger area on the right has more of a medley of chairs and a big log fire. Good bar food includes home-made soup (£3.25), sandwiches with a fresh green salad (from £3.25), filled baked potatoes (from £4.65), ploughman's or platters (from £4.85), butterfly prawns with garlic dip (£5.95), sausages with mustard and herb mash or lambs liver (£7.95), beef olives with tomato and herb tagliatelle, chicken in an asparagus and mushroom sauce or poached salmon in sweetcorn sauce (£8.95), and rib-eye steak (£10.95). Well kept Brakspears Best and Special on handpump. A nicely planted informal side garden has views of woods and fields, and there are plenty of nearby walks. *(Recommended by Tracey and Stephen Groves, the Didler, Charles Harvey, Pete Baker, Dennis Jenkin, Martin and Karen Wake, Mike and Kathryn Budd)*

Brakspears ~ Tenant Steve Anderson ~ Real ale ~ Bar food (12-3, 6-9.30) ~ No credit cards ~ (01494) 881683 ~ Children welcome ~ Dogs welcome ~ Open 11.30-3.30, 5.30-11; 12-11 Sat; 12-10.30 Sun

GREAT HAMPDEN SP8401 Map 4

Hampden Arms

Village signposted off A4010 N and S of Princes Risborough

Handy for good walks and cycling, this friendly place is in a lovely quiet spot opposite the village cricket pitch, and on the edge of Hampden Common. It's the good, reasonably priced food that most customers come to sample: home-made soup (£3.95), good value light lunches such as baked half avocado, cottage pie or cannelloni (£5.95) or lasagne (£6.95), as well as chicken and bacon pie, ham and eggs, vegetable curry, omelettes, mushroom pastingo, mussels or coquilles St Jacques (all £6.95), beef stroganoff (£13.95), mixed grill (£14.95), steak wellington (£15.95), and puddings such as treacle sponge or banana pancake (£3.50). A small corner bar has well kept Adnams and Brakspears on handpump, Addlestone's cider, and maybe winter mulled wine; service is quietly obliging. The green-walled front room has broad dark tables, with a few aeroplane pictures and country prints; the back room has a slightly more rustic feel, with its cushioned wall benches and big woodburning stove; one room is no smoking. There are tables out in the tree-sheltered garden. *(Recommended by Martin Burgess, Jack Clarfelt, John Branston, Mike and Sue Richardson, Peter Saville)*

Free house ~ Licensees Terry and Barbara Matthews ~ Real ale ~ Bar food (12-2, 6.30-9.30) ~ (01494) 488255 ~ Children welcome ~ Open 12-3, 6.30-11; 12-3, 6.30-10.30 Sun; may close some Sun or Mon evenings

HADDENHAM SP7408 Map 4

Green Dragon

Village signposted off A418 and A4129, E/NE of Thame; then follow Church End signs

This year there have been some alterations here. The whole pub has been opened up to reveal an open fireplace towards the back of the building, a new bar has been fitted, new furnishings added, and the colours are now pale olive and antique rose. The dining area now has an attractive mix of informal tables and chairs. Well liked, imaginative food includes sandwiches, home-made soup (£3.75), sardines on stir-fried vegetables with sweet chilli dressing (£5.50), tian of avocado with pine nuts grilled with goats cheese and served with a balsamic and port dressing (£5.75), smoked halibut on potato salad with crème fraîche (£6), crisp confit of duck glazed with clover honey and cracked black pepper served on pineapple chutney (£6.50), a daily vegetarian dish (£8.95), calves liver and bacon with baby onion sauce or home-made steak and kidney suet pudding with Notley ale (£9.50), fillets of pork glazed with soy and honey on braised bok-choi (£11), rump of English lamb with a tomato, haricot bean and chorizo sauce on olive mash (£12.50), fillets of monkfish wrapped in bacon, served on sweet potatoes, red onions and mustard dressing (£14), and puddings such as home-made lemon and lime tart with blackcurrant sorbet or home-made sticky toffee pudding with vanilla ice cream (£4.75); a plate of British and Irish organic cheeses (£6). The main eating area is no smoking. Well kept Timothy Taylors Landlord and Vale Wychert on handpump, and sensibly priced well chosen wines including a few by the glass. A big sheltered gravel terrace behind the pub has white tables and picnic sets under cocktail parasols, with more on the grass, and a good variety of plants. This part of the village is very pretty, with a duckpond unusually close to the church. *(Recommended by Tracey and Stephen Groves, Jestyn Phillips, Ian Phillips, Mike and Sue Richardson, Maysie Thompson, J Hale, Matthew Last, Patricia Purbrick)*

Whitbreads ~ Lease Peter Moffat ~ Real ale ~ Bar food ~ Restaurant ~ (01844) 291403 ~ Well behaved children over 7 only ~ Open 12-3, 6.30-11; 12-3, 7-10.30 Sun; closed 1 Jan

HAMBLEDEN SU7886 Map 2

Stag & Huntsman

Turn off A4155 (Henley—Marlow Road) at Mill End, signposted to Hambleden; in a mile turn right into village centre

At weekends especially, this attractive brick and flint pub is usually packed with walkers so it's best to get there early then – though staff cope well with the rush. The half-panelled, L-shaped lounge bar has a cheerful, lively atmosphere, low ceilings, a large fireplace, and upholstered seating and wooden chairs on the carpet. Popular and tasty, the home-made bar food includes home-made soup (£3.95), a bowl of chilli or ploughman's (£5.95), spicy vegetable goulash topped with goats cheese (£7.95), pork and leek sausages (£8.25), lambs liver and bacon or fresh salmon fishcakes (£8.50), ham and egg or moroccan-style lamb stew with couscous (£8.95), sirloin steak (£12.25), and puddings such as crumble of the day or summer pudding (£3.95); children's meals (from £3.50). Well kept Brakspears Bitter, Wadworths 6X and a guest beer on handpump, farm ciders, and good wines are served by friendly staff in the attractively simple public bar; darts, dominoes, cribbage, shove-ha'penny, and piped music. There's a dining room, and a cosy snug at the front. Seats in the spacious and neatly kept country garden are quickly snapped up in good weather. The pub is set opposite the church on the far edge of one of the prettiest Chilterns villages, and it's just a field's walk from the river. *(Recommended by Simon Collett-Jones, Eric Locker, T R and B C Jenkins, J Hale, Catherine and Richard Preston, Lesley Bass, Bob and Laura Brock, Tracey and Stephen Groves, June and Robin Savage, D and M T Ayres-Regan, Mike and Heather Watson)*

Free house ~ Licensees Hon. Henry Smith and Andrew Stokes ~ Real ale ~ Bar food (not winter Sun evenings) ~ (01491) 571227 ~ Children in eating area of bar and restaurant ~ Dogs allowed in bar ~ Open 11-2.30(3 Sat), 6-11; 12-3, 7-10.30 Sun; closed evenings 25 Dec and 1 Jan ~ Bedrooms: £58B/£68B

HAWRIDGE COMMON SP9406 Map 4

Full Moon

Hawridge Common; off A416 N of Chesham, then towards Cholesbury

Run by friendly, warmly welcoming licensees, this attractively set little 16th-c country local is doing particularly well these days. The low-beamed rambling bar is the heart of the building, with shiny black built-in floor-to-ceiling settles, ancient polished flagstones and flooring tiles, hunting prints, and an inglenook fireplace. They keep six well kept real ales on handpump, with regulars such as Bass, Boddingtons, Brakspears Special, and Fullers London Pride, and weekly changing guests like Hop Back Summer Lightning or Oakham JHB; good service. Enjoyable, reasonably priced food includes sandwiches (£3), home-made soup (£3.25), ploughman's (from £4.95), home-cooked ham and egg or chilli (£6.50), chicken breast stuffed with mango and caribbean fruits, fresh fish dish of the day or mushroom, leek and red onions in ale gravy in a pastry case (£7.25), steak pie or duck breast in chinese plum sauce (£7.95), salmon supreme with thai sauce (£8.25), steaks (from £9.95), and puddings like home-made lemon tart or chocolate mousse (£4). Both the restaurants are no smoking; piped music. There are seats on the terrace under a pergola, and more in the garden. *(Recommended by Marjorie and David Lamb, Peter and Giff Bennett, John Roots)*

Enterprise ~ Tenants Peter and Annie Alberto ~ Real ale ~ Bar food (12-2, 6-9) ~ Restaurant ~ (01494) 758959 ~ Children welcome ~ Dogs allowed in bar ~ Open 12-3, 5.30-11; 12-11 Sat; 12-10.30 Sun; closed evening 25 Dec

HEDGERLEY SU9686 Map 2

White Horse

2½ miles from M40 junction 2: at exit roundabout follow Hedgerley Lane alongside M40, turning right after about 1½ miles into Village Lane

The main draw at this pretty country local is the excellent changing range of seven or eight real ales, all tapped from the cask in a room behind the tiny hatch counter, alongside good farm cider; you might typically find Charles Wells Eagle, Greene King IPA and Marlow Rebellion, but the rest could be from anywhere in the country. Very busy at weekends, the cottagey main bar has plenty of beams, brasses and exposed brickwork, low wooden tables, some standing timbers, jugs, ball-cocks and other bric-a-brac, a log fire, and a good few leaflets and notices about future village events. At lunchtimes staff busily serve sandwiches and things like quiche, ploughman's and tandoori chicken from a food cabinet in the corner (all around £5.50), with a changing range of simple home-cooked hot dishes; service is cheery and relaxed. There is a little flagstoned public bar on the left. On the way out to the garden, which has tables and occasional barbecues, they have had a big sort of tent-like extension to help during busy periods. In front are lots of hanging baskets, with a couple more tables overlooking the quiet road. There are good walks nearby, and the pub is handy for the Church Wood RSPB reserve. *(Recommended by the Didler, LM, Simon Collett-Jones, J M Pitts, Paul Vickers, Kristian Brodie, Tracey and Stephen Groves)*

Free house ~ Licensees Dee Hobbs and Kevin Brooker ~ Real ale ~ Bar food (lunchtime only) ~ (01753) 643225 ~ Dogs allowed in bar ~ Open 11-2.30, 5.30-11; 11-11 Sat; 12-10.30 Sun

LEY HILL SP9802 Map 4

Swan

Village signposted off A416 in Chesham

Since this delightful 16th-c pub was last in the main entries, charming and very friendly licensees have taken over, and readers have been quick to voice their enthusiasm. The main bar has a good mix of customers, a cosy snug, black beams (mind your head) and standing timbers, an old working kitchen range, a log fire, and a collection of old local photographs. Good bar food at lunchtime includes open sandwiches or filled baguettes (from £3.25), filled baked potatoes (from £3.75), home-made soup (£3.90), warm mixed salads (from £4.95), warm cheese and vegetable tartlet (£5.50), spicy king prawns (£5.95), and home-baked ham and eggs (£6.95). In the evening, there might be chicken liver pâté (£4.95), sesame seed-battered scampi with chilli dip (£5.95), a vegetarian dish (from £7.95), fillet of pork stuffed with prunes and served with a prune and cognac reduction (£10.95), best end of new season's lamb on creamed onion sauce (£13.70), Aberdeen Angus steaks (from £11.95), and puddings such as home-made Grand Marnier cheesecake or sticky toffee pudding (£3.95). Fish is listed on a separate board: whitebait (£4.95), loin of cod wrapped in parma ham with a warm tomato and avocado vinaigrette (£11.20) or grilled fillets of sea bream with chargrilled asparagus (£11.40); Sunday roast beef (£8.45). Well kept Adnams, Brakspears, Fullers London Pride, Greene King Abbot, Marstons Pedigree, and Timothy Taylors Landlord on handpump, nine wines by the glass, and Addlestone's cider. Picnic-sets in front of the pub amongst the flower tubs and hanging baskets, with more in the large back garden. There's a cricket pitch, a nine-hole golf course, and a common opposite. *(Recommended by David and Ruth Shillitoe, Matthew Edworthy, Peter and Giff Bennett)*

Punch ~ Lease Joy and Carol Putland ~ Real ale ~ Bar food (Bar snacks lunchtime only) ~ Restaurant ~ (01494) 783075 ~ Children welcome lunchtime, but by arrangement only in evening ~ Open 12-3, 5.30-11; may open all day on summer wknds; 12-3, 7-10.30 Sun

LITTLE HAMPDEN SP8503 Map 4

Rising Sun

Village signposted from back road (ie W of A413) Great Missenden—Stoke Mandeville; pub at end of village lane; OS Sheet 165 map reference 856040

The secluded setting for this comfortable dining pub is delightful, with lots of tracks leading through the woods in different directions. The opened-up, mostly no smoking bar is dominated by dining tables, and there's a woodburning stove and log fire to add to the cosiness in winter. Quite a lot of our readers have enjoyed the very good meals here over the last few months: warm smoked chicken and bacon salad, mixed wild mushroom pancake with a creamy cheese sauce, warm smoked trout fillet with Irish soda bread or deep-fried vegetable samosas with mango chutney (all £4.95), charcoal-grilled rib-eye steak with béarnaise sauce, breadcrumbed breast of chicken filled with brie, roast guinea fowl with mango and orange sauce or fried calves liver with red wine and blackcurrant sauce (£8.95), and puddings such as rhubarb and ginger fool, chocolate toffee mousse with brandy soaked sultanas or bitter-sweet flummery with raspberries in syrup (£3.95). Well kept Adnams, Brakspears Bitter and Shepherd Neame Spitfire on handpump, with home-made mulled wine and spiced cider in winter, and a short but decent wine list. There are some tables on the terrace by the sloping front grass. Muddy boots must be left outside. *(Recommended by David and Michelle Bailey, Matthew Last, Brian Root, Mike and Sue Richardson, David and Ruth Shillitoe, Peter and Jan Humphreys, Peter and Giff Bennett, Dr M Owton, Mike and Heather Watson, Tracey and Stephen Groves)*

Free house ~ Licensee Rory Dawson ~ Real ale ~ Bar food (not Sun evening, not Mon) ~ Restaurant ~ (01494) 488360 ~ Children must be well behaved ~ Open 11.30-3, 6.30-10(11 Sat); 12-3 Sun; closed Sun and Tues evenings and all Mon (open bank hols) ~ Bedrooms: £40B/£70B

LITTLE MISSENDEN SU9298 Map 4

Crown ★

Crown Lane, SE end of village, which is signposted off A413 W of Amersham

The same family have been running this unspoilt country brick cottage now for over 90 years, and the present licensees (third generation) offer a traditional welcome, and keep the pub spotlessly clean. The bustling bars are more spacious than they might first appear, with old red flooring tiles on the left, oak parquet on the right, built-in wall seats, studded red leatherette chairs, a few small tables, and a complete absence of music and machines; a good mix of customers adds to the chatty relaxed atmosphere. Well kept Adnams, Brakspears Special, Fullers London Pride, and a guest from breweries such as Gales, Hop Back or Vale on handpump, and decent malt whiskies. Popular straightforward home-made bar food includes a decent choice of generous very good value sandwiches (from £2.75), as well as ploughman's and pasties (from £4.50), buck's bite (a special home-made pizza-like dish £4.50), and steak and kidney pie (£5.25); darts, shove-ha'penny, cribbage, dominoes, and table skittles. The attractive sheltered garden behind has picnic-sets and other tables, and may occasionally give a view of Fighter Command pilots practising startling aerobatics in small propellor aeroplanes overhead. The pretty village has an interesting church. No children. More reports please. *(Recommended by Simon Collett-Jones, Doug Sawyer, D and M T Ayres-Regan, Susan and John Douglas, Ian Phillips, Tracey and Stephen Groves)*

Free house ~ Licensees Trevor and Carolyn How ~ Real ale ~ Bar food (lunchtime only; not Sun) ~ No credit cards ~ (01494) 862571 ~ Open 11-2.30, 6-11; 12-3, 7-10.30 Sun

MENTMORE SP9119 Map 4

Stag

Village signposted off B488 S of Leighton Buzzard; The Green

This is a pretty village pub with seats out on the pleasant flower-filled front terrace looking across towards Mentmore House, and a charming, well tended, sloping garden. Inside, there's a relaxed atmosphere in the small civilised lounge bar, which has low oak tables, attractive fresh flower arrangements, and an open fire; the more simple public bar leading off has cribbage and dominoes. Well kept Wells Eagle, IPA and Bombardier, with a guest such as Fullers London Pride or Timothy Taylors Landlord on handpump; friendly service. Nicely presented, reasonably priced lunchtime bar food includes interesting sandwiches (£4; soup and a sandwich £5.50), salads (£5), and hot meals such as sausage, mash and onion gravy, trout with almonds, grilled chicken chasseur or tagliatelle with spinach, pine nuts and cream sauce (all £6). In the evening, there might be pasta with green vegetables, nuts and blue cheese, smoked cod kedgeree with poached egg or goats cheese bruschetta with marmalade onions (all £6.50), and curried coconut prawns, thai slow-cooked pork with sweet chilli and confit of duck with pak choi or 12oz grilled rump steak with rosemary potato wedges (all £9.50), with puddings like chocolate mousse cake with chocolate sauce, home-made bread and butter pudding or sticky toffee pudding with caramel ice cream (£4). Part of the restaurant is no smoking. *(Recommended by George Atkinson, MP, Marjorie and David Lamb, N J Dack)*

Charles Wells ~ Lease Jenny and Mike Tuckwood ~ Real ale ~ Bar food (not Mon evenings) ~ Restaurant ~ (01296) 668423 ~ Children in restaurant lunchtime only ~ Dogs allowed in bar ~ Occasional live jazz ~ Open 12-3, 6-11; 12-11 Sat; 12-10.30 Sun

NEWTON LONGVILLE SP8430 Map 4

Crooked Billet 🍷

Off A421 S of Milton Keynes; Westbrook End

All 250 wines on offer in this busily efficient and brightly modernised thatched pub are available by the glass, and they also keep Batemans XXXB, Greene King IPA, Wadworths 6X, and Wychwood Hobgoblin on handpump, and 30 malt whiskies. Most customers come to enjoy the imaginative food, which from a changing menu might include spring vegetable soup with parmesan crouton, sorrel and crème fraîche (£4.25), interestingly filled sandwiches like Morecambe Bay shrimp, cream cheese and rocket or toasted tuna and beaufort cheese melt (from £4.75; filled ciabattas from £5.25), black olive crostini, blood orange, red onion and mizuna salad and eight-year-old balsamic dressing (£4.75), honey roast ham with eggs (£6.50), pork and leek sausages with mustard mash and onion gravy (£7.50), salmon, prawn, green bean and parsley cream tagliatelle (£9), beer-battered cod or calves liver and double cream mash (£10), soft herb marinated chicken breast, little gem, leek, pea and mint cream (£11), and sea trout, sage and pea purée, avruga crème fraîche, and warmed artichoke hearts (£13.50), brace of quail stuffed two ways (£14), and puddings like an elaborate trifle or lemon tart with lemon sorbet and syrup (£4.75); the menu warns of a 25-minute wait for main courses. They don't take bookings at lunchtimes (except on Sundays), but in the evening restaurant tables need to be reserved well in advance – up to a month some weekends. The restaurant is no smoking. Though the focus is very much on the food, it still feels like a proper pub; the extended bar has beam and plank ceilings, some partly green-painted walls, sporting trophies on the shelves, and usually a few chatting locals. There are a few tables out on the lawn. *(Recommended by Simon Fisher, Ian Phillips, June and Malcolm Farmer, Karen and Graham Oddey, Andrea and Guy Bradley)*

Greene King ~ Lease John Gilchrist and Emma Sexton ~ Real ale ~ Bar food (not Sun evening or all Mon) ~ (01908) 373936 ~ Children in restaurant ~ Dogs allowed in bar ~ Open 12-2.30, 5.30-11; 12-11 Sat; 12-4, 7-10.30 Sun; closed Mon lunchtime

PRESTWOOD SP8700 Map 4

Polecat

170 Wycombe Road (A4128 N of High Wycombe)

Not surprisingly, this very well run pub is always full of cheerful customers keen to enjoy the particularly good food and decent choice of well kept beers and wines served by friendly staff. Several smallish rooms open off the low-ceilinged bar, with a medley of tables and chairs, all sorts of stuffed birds as well as the stuffed white polecats in one big cabinet, small country pictures, rugs on bare boards or red tiles, and a couple of antique housekeeper's chairs by a good open fire; the Gallery room is no smoking. At lunchtime there tend to be chatty crowds of middle-aged diners, with a broader mix of ages in the evening. As well as lunchtime snacks such as sandwiches (from £3.20), filled baked potatoes (from £4.60), and ploughman's (£4.95), there might be home-made soup (£3.50), baked field mushrooms with melting cheese, garlic and herb crust or pâté with red onion marmalade (£4.60), spiced lentil roast with onion purée (£7.50), home-made venison and rabbit pie, lancashire lamb hotpot or lasagne (£7.90), salmon fishcakes with tomato and herb sauce (£8.20), monkfish, pancetta, and rosemary baked in filo pastry with tomato and basil cordon (£9.80), sirloin steak with green peppercorn sauce (£10.80), daily specials like filo tartlet of smoked chicken, roast vegetables and mozzarella (£4.60), red bean roulade with smoked cheddar and chive sour cream (£7.50), seafood brochette with sweet and sour chilli dressing (£10.50), and puddings such as raspberry shortcake with raspberry coulis, chilled hazelnut soufflé with fudge sauce or apple bavarois with mango purée and almond biscuit (£3.90). Well kept Flowers IPA, Greene King Old Speckled Hen, Marstons Pedigree, and Wadworths 6X on handpump at the flint bar counter, nine wines by the glass, and a good few malt whiskies; piped music. The licensees take huge trouble with their attractive garden, with lots of bulbs in spring, and lovely summer hanging baskets, tubs, and herbaceous plants; there are quite a few picnic-sets under parasols on neat grass out in front beneath a big fairy-lit pear tree, with more on a big well kept back lawn. *(Recommended by Simon Collett-Jones, Matthew Last, Desmond Hall, D and M T Ayres-Regan, Mike and Heather Watson, Lesley Bass, Marion Turner, Kevin Thomas, Nina Randall, John and Glenys Wheeler, Ken Richards)*

Free house ~ Licensee John Gamble ~ Real ale ~ Bar food (12-2, 6.30-9; not Sun evening) ~ Restaurant ~ No credit cards ~ (01494) 862253 ~ Children in eating area of bar ~ Dogs welcome ~ Open 11.30-2.30, 6-11; 12-3 Sun; closed Sun evening, 25-26 Dec, evening 31 Dec, 1 Jan

Most pubs in this book sell wine by the glass. We mention wines if they are a cut above the average. Please let us know of any good pubs for wine.

SKIRMETT SU7790 Map 2

Frog

From A4155 NE of Henley take Hambleden turn and keep on; or from B482 Stokenchurch—Marlow take Turville turn and keep on

Readers enjoy this bustling country inn very much indeed – as somewhere to drop in for a drink after a walk along the many surrounding hiking routes, as a place to stay, and as a dining inn. Although brightly modernised, it still has something of a local feel with leaflets and posters near the door advertising raffles and so forth. The neatly kept beamed bar area has a mix of comfortable furnishings, a striking hooded fireplace with a bench around the edge (and a pile of logs sitting beside it), big rugs on the wooden floors, and sporting and local prints around the salmon painted walls. The function room leading off, with a fine-looking dresser, is sometimes used as a dining overflow. To be sure of a table, you must book in advance for the consistently good food: sandwiches, home-made soup (£2.95), watercress pancake filled with smoked haddock, glazed with saffron sauce (£5.75), smoked chicken, mango and mixed leaf timbale with a raspberry dressing (£6.25), lasagne of wild mushrooms and asparagus with chervil butter sauce (£8.95), turkey escalope in a tarragon cream sauce (£9.50), fillet of cod with a herb and prawn crust and parsnip mash (£10.95), braised and glazed shank of lamb in a port and redcurrant jus (£12.50), grilled rib-eye steak with red wine gravy and yorkshire pudding (£12.95), and interesting daily specials; they also offer a two-course (£13.95) and three-course (£17.50) menu. The restaurant is no smoking; piped music. Well kept Brakspears, Fullers London Pride and a weekly changing guest like Black Sheep or Hook Norton on handpump, a good range of wines, and various coffees. A side gate leads to a lovely garden, with a large tree in the middle, and unusual five-sided tables well placed for attractive valley views. The bedrooms are engaging, and it's a nice base for the area; Henley is close by, and just down the road is the delightful Ibstone windmill. *(Recommended by Mike and Sue Richardson, P G Plumridge, Boyd Catling, Phil and Sarah Kane, Peter Saville, Matthew Last, J V Dadswell)*

Free house ~ Licensees Jim Crowe and Noelle Greene ~ Real ale ~ Bar food ~ Restaurant ~ (01491) 638996 ~ Children welcome ~ Dogs allowed in bar ~ Open 11-3, 6-11; 12-10.30 Sun; closed Sun evening Nov-May ~ Bedrooms: £55B/£65B

TURVILLE SU7690 Map 2

Bull & Butcher

Valley road off A4155 Henley—Marlow at Mill End, past Hambleden and Skirmett

Set in a lovely Chilterns valley amongst ancient cottages, this civilised black and white timbered pub is a fine place to end up after a walk; there are seats on the lawn by fruit trees in the attractive garden. Good bar food might include warm crisp tart of spinach, black olives, feta cheese and sun-dried tomatoes with a chardonnay dressing (£5.95), thai-cured salmon with chilli, caramel and sweet soy (£6.50), home-smoked venison thinly sliced with rocket salad and truffle dressing (£8.75), wild mushroom risotto with parmesan crisp (£9.95), seared bass with warm new potato and bacon salad, stir-fried vegetables and a lime and spring onion dressing (£11.95), lamb with a herb crust and smoke-cooked with spiced couscous, roast mediterranean vegetables, and a hazelnut and mint pesto (£13.95), fillet steak with rösti potato, wild mushrooms and burgundy sauce (£15.50), and home-made puddings (£3.95). Very well kept Brakspears Bitter, Mild, Special and Old, and a couple of guest beers on handpump, Weston's cider, and 37 wines by the glass. There are two low-ceilinged, beamed rooms (one has a well), with cushioned wall settles and an inglenook fireplace. Once a month (Tuesday evenings) the MG car club meet here. It does get crowded at weekends. *(Recommended by the Didler, Mike and Sue Richardson, Martin and Karen Wake, Tim and Ann Newell, Mike and Jennifer Marsh, JP, PP, Lesley Bass, Mike and Heather Watson, Torrens Lyster, Tracey and Stephen Groves)*

Brakspears ~ Tenant Nicholas Abbott ~ Real ale ~ Bar food (12-2.30(4 Sun and bank hols), 7-9.45; not Sun evening/bank hols) ~ Restaurant ~ (01491) 638283 ~ Children welcome ~ Dogs welcome ~ Open 11-3, 6(6.30 Sat)-11; 12-5, 7-10.30 Sun

WADDESDON SP7417 Map 4

Five Arrows ★

A41 NW of Aylesbury

Part of the Rothschild Estate, this elegant and civilised place is somewhere that, once visited, draws you back again and again. A series of light and airy high-ceilinged rooms makes up the unstuffy open-plan pubby bar, with family portrait engravings, lots of old estate-worker photographs, heavy dark green velvet curtains on wooden rails, and mainly sturdy cushioned settles and good solid tables on parquet flooring. Newspapers and copies of *Country Life* are kept in an antique magazine rack. Exceptionally good food from an interesting menu might include tomato and basil soup or thai-marinated fillet of red mullet on a bed of soy noodles (£4.95), smoked duck breast with savoy cabbage, balsamic dressing and parmesan or spaghetti with a roquefort and walnut sauce (£5.25), baked goats cheese wrapped in parma ham on a garlic croute with baby pears (£5.50), salmon fishcakes with coriander jam or crayfish tail salad (£5.95, main course £11.95), herb pancake filled with wild rice biriani of spinach and mushrooms served with a tomato and onion raita or breast of chicken stuffed with sun-dried tomatoes, topped with mozzarella on pesto fettucine (£10.50), steamed hoki fish fillet served with ginger, spring onions and sesame (£12.50), confit of duck with a raspberry and red wine jus (£12.95), and fried boned quail with spring greens with a port and tarragon sauce or sirloin steak with stilton and roasted cherry tomatoes (£14), and specials such as grilled sardines with preserved lemons (£5), cajun swordfish with a tomato and chilli salsa (£10.50), calves liver with a caramelised onion mash and thyme jus (£12), and puddings such as apple crumble with cream (£4.15). The country-house-style restaurant is no smoking on one side; must book at busy times. The formidable wine list runs to Rothschild first-growth clarets as well as lesser-known Estate wines. Well kept Fullers London Pride on handpump, many malt whiskies, champagne by the glass, proper cocktails, and freshly squeezed orange juice; efficient service. The sheltered back garden has attractively grouped wood and metal furnishings. This is an ideal base for visiting Waddesdon Manor. No children. *(Recommended by Lesley Bass, Ian Phillips, Simon Reynolds, Val Stevenson, Rob Holmes, M A and C R Starling, Paul and Ursula Randall, Patricia Beebe, Dick and Penny Vardy, Andrew McHardy, Bob and Maggie Atherton)*

Free house ~ Licensees J A Worster and F Bromovsky ~ Real ale ~ Restaurant ~ (01296) 651727 ~ Open 11-3, 5.30(6 Sat)-11; 12-3, 7-10.30 Sun ~ Bedrooms: £60S/£80S(£80B)

WHEELER END SU8093 Map 4

Chequers

Off B482 in Lane End NW of Marlow, then first left also signposted Wheeler End

They've managed to strike a clever balance between drinkers and diners in this neatly kept and friendly 17th-c pub. Under the low ceiling, the bar has what might be called an inherently friendly layout: it's so small, and shaped in such a way, that you can't help but feel part of the general conversation. It angles back past the inglenook fireplace, and a little roomlet, to the bigger back newly refurbished, no smoking restaurant with its candlelit tables and hunting prints on the walls. Well kept Brakspears and Fullers London Pride, Chiswick, and ESB on handpump; dominoes and cribbage. Good bar food includes sandwiches (from £3; croque monsieur £5; ciabattas and baguettes £5), thai fishcakes with chilli dip or mussels in cumin, ginger, white wine and cream (£5), leek and asparagus pancake (£6), wild boar and apple sausages or lamb and coriander burgers with lime and tomato salsa (£7), seared calves liver on spring onion mash with a sage and smoked bacon jus (£10), and daily specials such as spinach and orange soup (£4.50), home-smoked pheasant salad (£6), goats cheese and onion marmalade tart (£8), braised shank of English lamb cooked in a red wine, rosemary and apricot sauce (£9), and puddings like honey and pine nut tart with fresh raspberries and clotted cream, milk chocolate tart or blueberry cheesecake (from £3.25); three-course Sunday lunch £17. There are two gardens, and Harvey the dog will share doggy biscuits and his water bowl.

(Recommended by Anthony Longden, John and Glenys Wheeler, J Hale, Ron and Val Broom, Tracey and Stephen Groves)

Fullers ~ Lease Anna Kaiser and Stephen Warner ~ Real ale ~ Bar food (12-2.30, 7-10; 12.30-8 Sun) ~ Restaurant ~ (01494) 883070 ~ Children in restaurant ~ Dogs allowed in bar ~ Open 11-3, 5.30-11; 11-11 Sat; 12-10.30 Sun

WOOBURN COMMON SU9187 Map 2

Chequers

From A4094 N of Maidenhead at junction with A4155 Marlow road keep on A4094 for another ¾ mile, then at roundabout turn off right towards Wooburn Common, and into Kiln Lane; if you find yourself in Honey Hill, Hedsor, turn left into Kiln Lane at the top of the hill; OS Sheet 175 map reference 910870

There's a good mix of customers in this bustling place – many are drawn from its thriving hotel and restaurant side. The low-beamed, partly stripped-brick bar has standing timbers and alcoves to break it up, comfortably lived-in sofas on its bare boards, a bright log-effect gas fire, and various pictures, plates, a two-man saw, and tankards; one room is no smoking. Good bar food includes sandwiches (from £4), celeriac soup (£3.95), ploughman's (£5.50), spaghetti with sun-dried tomatoes, olives and pesto (£7.95), home-made burger with bacon and cheese (£8.95), chicken curry (£9.95), chargrilled tuna loin with niçoise salad (£10.50), seared salmon with rocket salad (£10.95), calves liver (£11.50), chargrilled rib-eye steak with cep cream (£13.95), and puddings (£3.95); there's a more formal restaurant. Well kept Greene King IPA, Original, and Ruddles County on handpump, a sizeable wine list (champagne and good wine by the glass), and a fair range of malt whiskies and brandies; piped music. The spacious garden, set away from the road, has cast-iron tables. Attractive stripped-pine bedrooms are in a 20th-c mock-Tudor wing.
(Recommended by Mrs Ailsa Wiggans, Chris Glasson, Peter and Giff Bennett, Simon Chell, Desmond Hall, Simon Collett-Jones, Ian Phillips)

Free house ~ Licensee Peter Roehrig ~ Real ale ~ Bar food (all day on Sat/Sun) ~ Restaurant ~ (01628) 529575 ~ Children welcome ~ Open 11-11; 11-10.30 Sun ~ Bedrooms: £99.50B/£107.50B

Lucky Dip

Besides the fully inspected pubs, you might like to try these Lucky Dips recommended to us and described by readers (if you do, please send us reports: www.goodguides.com).

Adstock [SP7229]
Folly [A413 SE of Buckingham]: Roomy beamed bar, light and airy carpeted dining area, enjoyable food from baguettes to oriental specials, Brakspears and Tetleys, attentive staff, quick service; may be piped music; nice good-sized garden with fruit and other trees, ducks and poultry, play area; bedrooms, handy for Buckingham *(George Atkinson)*

☆ ***Old Thatched Inn*** [Main St, off A413]: Beams and flagstones, cosy corners and open fires, part pubby and part with easy chairs and settees; friendly and comfortable, with generous food from interesting sandwiches to game and theme nights, well kept Bass and Hook Norton Best, decent wines, welcoming staff; may be piped music; seats out in sheltered back garden, children in restaurant and eating area *(George Atkinson, LYM, Peter and Anne Hollindale, Arthur Baker, Karen and Graham Oddey)*

Amersham [SU9597]
Crown [Market Sq]: Small peaceful modernised bar in old hotel, beams and polished wood floors, neat tables all set for dining, interesting 16th-c features in comfortable lounge, good value food from baguettes up, afternoon teas, good restaurant, cheery helpful staff, Bass and Hancocks HB, good house wine; can be smoky, nearby parking may be difficult; attractive split-level outside seating area with cobbled courtyard and plant-filled garden, comfortable bedrooms *(BB, Reg J Cox, Howard Dell)*

☆ ***Saracens Head*** [Whielden St (A404)]: Friendly unspoilt 17th-c local, neat, clean and largely no smoking, with beams, gentle lighting, massive inglenook with roaring fire in ancient decorative fire-basket, interesting décor, enjoyable generous fresh food from baguettes to full meals, well kept Greene King IPA, Abbot, Old Speckled Hen and Ruddles Best, winter mulled wine, pleasant staff, cheery chatty landlord; soft piped music; little back terrace *(LYM, Betty Laker, Simon Collett-Jones)*

Aston Clinton [SP8811]
Duck In [London Rd]: Former Bell, now reworked as a Vintage Inn, with enjoyable

reasonably priced food inc lighter lunchtime dishes, nice variety of furnishings with flagstones and dark brown and dark cream paintwork; picnic-sets under trees in garden *(Mel Smith)*

Aylesbury [SP7510]

☆ ***Bottle & Glass*** [A418 some miles towards Thame, beyond Stone]: Friendly low-beamed thatched pub, tiled floor, attractive rambling layout, wide choice of good imaginative food inc good fresh fish and seafood range (best to book, two sittings wknds), lively atmosphere, attentive friendly service, well kept ales, good choice of wines, neat garden *(Brian Root, LYM, Iain and Joan Baillie)*

Ballinger [SP9103]

Wimpennys [off B485 NNE of Gt Missenden]: Former Pheasant, and as its name suggests restaurant rather than pub now – enjoyable innovative food, though not a place for just a drink *(Paul Coleman)*

Beaconsfield [SU9489]

Greyhound [a mile from M40 junction 2, via A40; Windsor End, Old Town]: Friendly new licensees in rambling two-bar former coaching inn with well kept Courage Best, Fullers London Pride, Wadworths 6X and a guest beer such as Marlow Rebellion, daily papers, food inc Sun lunches in partly no smoking back bistro area *(David and Ruth Shillitoe, Simon Collett-Jones, Tracey and Stephen Groves, LYM, Geoffrey Kemp)*

Bierton [SP8415]

Bell [Aylesbury Rd]: Consistently good honest food esp fresh fish, good service, well kept Fullers London Pride; traditional two-bar layout – can be busy lunchtime, best to book *(MP, Mel Smith, Brian Root)*

Red Lion [Aylesbury Rd]: Fullers pub with new licensees doing enjoyable food inc bargain lunchtime baguettes and hot dishes, well kept Chiswick, London Pride and ESB, two cosy bars; tables on small terrace *(Mel Smith)*

Bledlow [SP7702]

Lions of Bledlow [off B4009 Chinnor—Princes Risboro; Church End]: Low 16th-c beams, attractive oak stalls, antique settle, ancient tiles, inglenook log fires and a woodburner, and fine views from bay windows; well kept ales such as Courage Best, Marlow Rebellion and Wadworths 6X, bar food from sandwiches up, no smoking restaurant; well behaved children allowed, tables out on sheltered terrace and small sloping lawns, nice setting, good walks *(LYM, Tracey and Stephen Groves, the Didler, JP, PP, Torrens Lyster)*

Bolter End [SU7992]

Peacock [Just over 4 miles from M40 junction 5, via A40 then B482]: New tenants in pleasantly set pub, under its former tenants a main entry since the *Guide* started; brightly modernised bar with nice little bolt-hole down to the left, no smoking room, good log fire, well kept Brakspears and bar food; picnic-sets in garden, has been cl Sun evening and has not allowed children inside *(LYM, Tracey and Stephen Groves)*

Bovingdon Green [SU8286]

☆ ***Royal Oak*** [back rd Marlow—Frieth]: Country pub recently neatly redone in cream, green and terracotta, old beams, bare boards, parquet and flagstones, log fires, candles and flowers on nice mix of hand-picked tables, three rooms and a pretty back conservatory, new licensees putting emphasis on good food (best to book, evenings), Brakspears and Fullers London Pride, attentive helpful service; tables out on terrace and large grassed area, good walks *(T R and B C Jenkins, Susan and John Douglas)*

Brill [SP6513]

☆ ***Pheasant*** [off B4011 Bicester—Long Crendon; Windmill St]: Unpretentious simply furnished beamed pub in marvellous spot looking over to ancient working windmill, nearby view over nine counties, good choice of well presented food, well kept Marstons Pedigree and Tetleys, good value house wines, prompt friendly service, attractive dining room up a step; piped music, no dogs; children welcome, tables in verandah and garden, bedrooms, open all day wknds *(K H Frostick, LYM, C and G Fraser)*

Cadmore End [SU7892]

☆ ***Blue Flag*** [B482 towards Stokenchurch]: Comfortable beamed bar, well kept ales such as Fullers London Pride, Marlow Rebellion and Wadworths 6X, decent wines, wide choice of good value food esp fish, huge helpings, expert unobtrusive service, lots of proper big dining tables; vintage MG pictures; attractive little restaurant; bedrooms, good centre for walking *(BB, Betty Laker, Peter Saville)*

Cadsden [SP8204]

Plough: Mellow and comfortable, very popular with families and Chilterns ramblers, good range of well kept beers inc a Dark Mild, enjoyable food from reasonably priced sandwiches to hearty shoulder of lamb, sensible prices; lots of tables in delightful quiet front and back garden, pretty spot on Ridgeway Path *(Stephen Green)*

Chackmore [SP6835]

Queens Head [Main St]: Comfortable village pub by Stowe Gardens, with welcoming landlord, good value varied lunchtime food from toasties and baguettes up, well kept real ales, small separate dining room *(Brian Root)*

Cheddington [SP9217]

Old Swan [off B488 N of Tring; High St]: Pretty thatched pub, well kept Bass, Brakspears, Fullers London Pride and Tetleys, nice staff, usual food (not Sun evening) from sandwiches and baked potatoes to steaks, partly no smoking restaurant; beware of the very low beams; children welcome, good family garden with enclosed play area, furnished wendy house and child-size wooden bench and tables *(John Branston, LYM)*

Chesham [SP9501]

☆ ***Queens Head*** [Church St]: Good value Thai food, well kept ales inc Fullers London Pride, Hoegaarden on tap, sparkling brass, interesting pictures and paraphernalia, two coal fires, scrubbed tables, courteous Thai catering staff cope quickly even when very busy; tables in small courtyard, next to little River Chess *(Stephen Green)*

Chicheley [SP9045]
☆ ***Chester Arms*** [quite handy for M1 junction 14]: Cosy and pretty beamed pub with rooms off semicircular bar, log fire, comfortable settles and chairs, wide choice of good popular chef-served food from sandwiches to daily fresh fish and Aberdeen Angus beef, children's helpings, friendly service, Greene King IPA, Abbot and Ruddles, decent wines, sizeable back dining room down steps; darts, fruit machine, quiet piped music; picnic-sets in small back garden *(Gerry and Rosemary Dobson, Maysie Thompson, Ian Phillips, John Saul)*

Clifton Reynes [SP9051]
Robin Hood [off back rd Emberton—Newton Blossomville; no through road]: Friendly landlord, good range of decent food (inc Sun roasts) in pleasant stone-built pub, small and unpretentious, with inglenook, dark beams, good service, well kept Greene King IPA and Abbot, lots of *Robin Hood* film stills, nice grapevine conservatory; table skittles and juke box in plain public bar; very big garden with plenty of tables, grazing horses beyond, riverside walks to Olney. *(BB, George Atkinson, Mike Ridgway, Sarah Miles)*

Colnbrook [TQ0277]
Ostrich [1¼ miles from M4 junction 5 via A4/B3378, then 'village only' rd]: Striking Elizabethan pub, modernised but still signs of its long and entertaining history (even has a stuffed ostrich); good log fire, well kept Courage Best and Directors and Charles Wells Bombardier, prompt friendly service, though emphasis primarily on food side – good range of bar food, good upstairs restaurant; quiet piped music, and they may try to keep credit cards *(LYM, Susan and Nigel Wilson)*

Cublington [SP8322]
Unicorn [High St]: Relaxing and welcoming 16th-c beamed pub in centre of village, supposedly haunted, long rustic bare-boards room with wooden seating and attractive fireplace at one end, good generous reasonably priced food, four interesting changing real ales, prompt friendly service; picnic-sets in peaceful attractive enclosed garden behind *(MP, Marjorie and David Lamb)*

Cuddington [SP7311]
Crown [village signed off A418 Thame—Aylesbury; Spurt St]: Small convivial village pub, olde-worlde with candles and open fire, prompt friendly service, unusual choice of good food from interesting hot sandwiches up, Fullers Chiswick, London Pride and ESB, curry night Thurs, summer mediterranean nights *(Graham Parker, Neil and Jenny Dury, Marjorie and David Lamb)*

Denham [TQ0486]
Falcon [Village Rd]: Open-plan but old-fashioned, with bare boards and quarry tiles, old painted woodwork, coal-effect gas fires with inglenook fireside seats below ancient cupboards, well kept ales such as Brakspears, Marstons Pedigree and Timothy Taylors Landlord, polite service, lower back opened up by new landlord as no smoking dining area, wide range of food from lunchtime toasties, ploughman's and baked potatoes to fresh fish; steps up to entrance, lavatories upstairs; teak tables and comfortable chairs on cheerfully renovated extended terrace *(Helen Hazzard, Ian Phillips, John and Glenys Wheeler, Simon Collett-Jones, P J Keen)*

☆ ***Swan*** [¾ mile from M40 junction 1; follow Denham Village signs]: Pretty pub in lovely village, friendly and unassuming, comfortable mix of easy chairs and old drop-leaf tables, open fires, lots of plates, old bottles and prints on timbered walls, picture windows overlooking splendid floodlit back garden with picnic-sets and play area; pleasant licensees, well kept Courage Best and Directors and Marstons Pedigree, decent house wine, inexpensive popular food from sandwiches up; may be piped music *(John Branston, Helen Hazzard, Ian Phillips, John and Glenys Wheeler, LYM, Peter Saville, Dave Hess)*

Dinton [SP7611]
Seven Stars [signed off A418 Aylesbury—Thame, nr Gibraltar turn-off; Stars Lane]: New licensees in pretty pub with character inglenook bar, comfortable beamed lounge and spacious dining room, well kept Fullers London Pride, food (not Sun evening) from sandwiches and baked potatoes up, prompt service; cl Tues, tables under cocktail parasols in sheltered garden with terrace, pleasant village, handy for Quainton Steam Centre *(Andrea and Guy Bradley, LYM, Marjorie and David Lamb)*

Dorney [SU9278]
Palmer Arms [B3026, off A4, 2 miles from M4 junction 7]: Friendly renovated village pub with big dining room, smallish bar, well kept ales such as Courage Best, Greene King Old Speckled Hen, Rebellion and Theakstons Old Peculier, pleasant service, usual food from pricy sandwiches up; unobtrusive piped music, quiz machine; plenty of tables in garden behind, open all day Sat *(Simon Collett-Jones)*

Downley [SU8495]
☆ ***Le De Spencers Arms*** [The Common]: Unpretentious 18th-c Fullers local hidden away on common, fairy-lit loggia overlooking lawn with picnic-sets, prompt cheerful service, good bar food; woodland walks to nearby Hughenden Manor *(Tracey and Stephen Groves, LYM)*

Drayton Parslow [SP8328]
Three Horseshoes [Main Rd]: Friendly co-operative service, good well priced food inc some interesting puddings *(V Green)*

Fawley [SU7586]
☆ ***Walnut Tree*** [signed off A4155 or B480, N of Henley]: Relaxed and roomy Chilterns dining pub, friendly attentive service, wide choice from sandwiches and ciabattas up inc good fish in both smallish bars, restaurant (different menu) and no smoking conservatory, well kept Brakspears PA and SB, small but good range of wines, log fires; may be upmarket piped music; well spaced tables on big lawn, more in covered terrace extension; children welcome, open all day wknds *(Derek and Priscilla Coley, Simon Collett-Jones, LYM, Keith and Margaret Kettell, June and Robin Savage)*

Fingest [SU7791]

☆ ***Chequers*** [signed off B482 Marlow—Stokenchurch]: Proper traditional pub with several rooms around old-fashioned Tudor core, roaring fire in vast fireplace, sunny lounge by good-sized charming country garden with lots of picnic-sets, small no smoking room, interesting furniture, well kept Brakspears PA, SB, Old and Ted & Bens Organic, dominoes and cribbage, wholesome lunchtime food (not Mon) from sandwiches up, quick friendly service, attractive restaurant; children in eating area; interesting church opp, picture-book village, good walks – can get crowded wknds *(Tony Middis, Simon Collett-Jones, Mark Percy, Lesley Mayoh, Piotr Chodzko-Zajko, Martin and Karen Wake, the Didler, P G Plumridge, LYM, JP, PP, Howard Dell)*

Flackwell Heath [SU8889]

☆ ***Crooked Billet*** [off A404; Sheepridge Lane]: Cosily old-fashioned and comfortably worn in 16th-c pub with lovely views (beyond road) from flower-filled suntrap front garden, low beams, good choice of reasonably priced tasty lunchtime food (not Sun), eating area spread pleasantly through alcoves, charming considerate landlord, prompt service, well kept Brakspears, good open fire; juke box; good open walks *(BB, Tracey and Stephen Groves, Susan and John Douglas)*

Frieth [SU7990]

☆ ***Yew Tree*** [signed off B482 N of Marlow]: Enjoyable traditional food in peaceful bar and pleasant dining conservatory (service charge), well kept ales such as Brakspears PA and Fullers London Pride, friendly landlord and exemplary service, log fire, scrubbed tables; may be unobtrusive piped music, walkers with dogs welcome *(LYM, David and Michelle Bailey, Kerry and Tricia Thomas, Susan and John Douglas)*

Fulmer [SU9985]

Black Horse [Windmill Rd]: Appealing and unpretentious, popular for food but its several friendly bars include a good central one for drinkers, with well kept real ales; small garden, attractive village *(Dr and Mrs A K Clarke)*

Gawcott [SP6831]

Crown [Hillesden Rd]: Good cooking by Italian chef-landlord, from sandwiches and home-made pasta through intensely flavoured main dishes to exemplary tiramisu; well kept Adnams and a guest such as Greene King Old Speckled Hen, good Italian wines *(Howard and Margaret Buchanan)*

Cuckoos Nest [Back St]: Small pub with short choice of enjoyable food from cheap lunchtime snacks and sandwiches to local steaks, attractively priced house wine *(W J Taylor)*

Great Kimble [SP8106]

Swan & Brewer [Grove Lane (B4009, nr A4010)]: Attractive pub with beamed and tiled tap room, wide choice of good reasonably priced food, real ales such as Adnams, Fullers London Pride and Hook Norton Best, welcoming staff, pleasantly furnished end dining area; well behaved children allowed, tables out on village green *(Marjorie and David Lamb, J V Dadswell)*

Great Missenden [SP8901]

☆ ***Cross Keys*** [High St]: Buoyant atmosphere in old-fashioned beamed bar divided by standing timbers, bric-a-brac and traditional furnishings, big open fire, well kept Fullers Chiswick, London Pride and ESB, good wines, enjoyable modern food; may be piped music; children in restaurant, back terrace *(Kent Barker, LYM)*

Hawridge [SP9505]

Rose & Crown [signed from A416 N of Chesham; The Vale]: Roomy open-plan pub with wide choice of enjoyable food (they may be booked out), well kept Brakspears and good range of wines, attentive service, big log fire, peaceful country views from restaurant area; children allowed, broad terrace with lawn dropping down beyond, play area *(John and Glenys Wheeler, LYM, B Brewer)*

Hazlemere [SU8895]

Crown [Amersham Rd (A404)]: Quaint and cottagey outside, friendly inside, with stripped brick and dark wood in long narrow bar, well kept Greene King Abbot, close-set tables in eating area; games machines, quiet piped music *(Tracey and Stephen Groves)*

High Wycombe [SU8792]

Beech Tree [Amersham Rd]: Cosy little red brick local, roomy back conservatory eating area, well kept Courage Best and Directors, friendly staff, decent food all day; quiet piped music; nice grassy area out in front with excellent big children's play area and lots of picnic-sets, pleasant semi-rural setting *(Tony W Dickinson)*

Kingswood [SP6919]

☆ ***Plough & Anchor*** [Bicester Rd (A41 NW of Aylesbury)]: Very good food in plain but smart bar/restaurant, beams and flagstones, heavy tables, friendly staff, well kept ales such as Greene King Old Speckled Hen, Tetleys and Wadworths 6X, good wine list *(H O Dickinson, Brian Root)*

Lacey Green [SP8201]

☆ ***Pink & Lily*** [from A4010 High Wycombe—Princes Risboro follow Loosley sign, then Gt Hampden, Gt Missenden one]: Charming little old-fashioned tap room in much-extended Chilterns pub with warm welcome, airy and plush main dining bar (tables may all be reserved for diners), well presented good food; well kept ales such as Boddingtons, Brakspears PA, Courage Best and Glenny Hobgoblin, good well priced wines, friendly efficient service, open fire, dominoes, cribbage, ring the bull; piped music, children over 5 welcome if eating; conservatory, big garden *(JP, PP, LYM, Kerry and Tricia Thomas, the Didler)*

Lavendon [SP9153]

Green Man [A428 Bedford—Northampton]: Roomy and attractive thatched and beamed 17th-c pub in pretty village, enjoyable food from baguettes and interesting soups up, wkdy two-for-one lunches, snacks all afternoon, friendly attentive staff, relaxed atmosphere, lots of stripped stone, woodburner and hops around bar, Courage Directors, Greene King Ruddles and Theakstons Best and XB, big restaurant with no smoking area; children welcome, may be unobtrusive piped music; open all day, some seats out behind *(Mike Ridgway, Sarah Miles, George Atkinson)*

Horseshoe [A428 Bedford—Northampton; High St]: Big spotlessly kept beamed village pub with new tenant doing enjoyable food, esp fish, in bar and restaurant, well kept Charles Wells ales, small but interesting wine list, plush furnishings; appealing good-sized garden with play area. *(John Saul, BB, Chris Matthews)*

Ledburn [SP9022]

Hare & Hounds [off B488 Ivinghoe—Leighton Buzzard, S of Linslade]: Big country-style bar and adjoining restaurant now under same management as Cross Keys at Totternhoe (see Bedfordshire main entries), wide range of generous reasonably priced food, Greene King real ales with a guest such as Everards Tiger, quick friendly down-to-earth service even when busy, Great Train Robbery memorabilia; pleasant back garden, handy for Ascot (NT) *(Marjorie and David Lamb, MP)*

Little Marlow [SU8787]

Queens Head [Church Rd; cul de sac off A4155 nr Kings Head]: Small and attractive quietly placed pub with good generous unpretentious home cooking, well kept Marstons Pedigree and Charles Wells Bombardier, friendly helpful service, darts and TV in public bar; picnic-sets in pleasant front garden, a couple more tables on secluded terrace across lane – short walk from River Thames *(Howard Dell)*

Little Missenden [SU9298]

Red Lion: Small 15th-c pub, locals crowded around two coal fires, well kept Tetleys-related and other ales, decent wines, generous good value food from lots of sandwiches up (new eating area off bar), preserves for sale; piped music; tables (some under awning) and busy aviary in garden by river with ducks, swans and fat trout *(Ken and Jenny Simmonds, LM)*

Littleworth Common [SP9386]

☆ ***Blackwood Arms*** [3 miles S of M40 junction 2; Common Lane, OS Sheet 165 map ref 937864]: Simple rustic country interior, wide changing range of well kept ales on handpump or tapped from the cask, friendly atmosphere and prompt pleasant service, good home cooking inc game and lunchtime bargains, roaring log fire; quiet piped music, dogs welcome; tables outside, lovely spot on edge of beech woods – good walks *(John and Glenys Wheeler, Bob and Laura Brock, Simon Collett-Jones, LYM, Anthony Longden)*

Jolly Woodman [2 miles from M40 junction 2; off A355]: Busy Whitbreads pub by Burnham Beeches, beamed and cottagey, wide range of food, usual Whitbreads-related beers, quick pleasant service, bar billiards, useful tourist leaflets *(John and Glenys Wheeler, LYM)*

Long Crendon [SP6808]

☆ ***Angel*** [Bicester Rd (B4011)]: Partly 17th-c and now restaurant-with-rooms rather than pub – a place for a special treat, with most enjoyable interesting meals (lunchtime open sandwiches and baguettes too), friendly and crisply organised service, good no smoking dining areas inc a conservatory, comfortable pre-meal lounge with sofas; well kept Hook Norton and Ridleys, with an extensive wine list; may be piped music; tables in garden, good bedrooms *(J Hale, Patricia Purbrick, Douglas Smart, Roger Braithwaite, LYM)*

Churchill Arms [B4011 NW of Thame]: Neatly refurbished village local, long and low, with terracotta walls, end public bar, well kept Brakspears, Fullers London Pride, Greene King Abbot and maybe a guest such as Youngs Special, friendly service, good log fire in big fireplace, generous usual lunchtime bar food, evening restaurant; piped music; children welcome, pleasant garden *(John and Glenys Wheeler, LYM, Tim and Ann Newell)*

Maids Moreton [SP7035]

☆ ***Wheatsheaf*** [Main St, just off A413 Towcester—Buckingham]: Current management doing wide choice of good reasonably priced generous food in cosy thatched and low-beamed pub with lots of pictures and bric-a-brac in old part, two inglenooks, friendly atmosphere and service, large conservatory restaurant with woodburner, well kept Bass or Boddingtons, Hook Norton Best and a guest beer, good choice of wines; pleasant enclosed garden *(Graham and Elizabeth Hargreaves)*

Marlow [SU8586]

Chequers [High St]: Attractive Brakspears pub with heavily beamed cosy front bars, good range of well cooked and presented food from basic fish and chips to more exotic and expensive choices in bright and pleasant restaurant area, friendly service, homely tables on pavement; piped music; bedrooms, children welcome *(John and Glenys Wheeler)*

Claytons [Quoiting Sq, Oxford Rd]: Trendy tapas bar, good food, several beer taps (inc Brakspears – not on handpump), pleasant atmosphere, good mix of customers, friendly staff, smooth piped jazz; busy Fri/Sat night, heated terrace *(the Didler, Ian Hall)*

Crown [Market Sq]: Interesting 18th-c building with clock tower, former market hall, then jail and fire station; worth knowing for its good beers *(John and Glenys Wheeler)*

☆ ***Crown & Anchor*** [Oxford Rd]: Tap for Sam Trumans brewery with their changing ales and even a lager, maybe a guest beer, smallish local-feel bar with part set aside Fri/Sat for live music, friendly service, some tables set for the enjoyable food, more out behind; piped music, quiz night Weds, and several special events most weeks; comfortable bedrooms, pleasant back garden *(Richard Houghton, D and M T Ayres-Regan, John and Glenys Wheeler, Catherine Pitt, BB)*

Hand & Flowers [A4155 W]: Olde-worlde pub with wide choice of good value generous home-made food from sandwiches and baguettes up in big sympathetically lit dining area leading off bar, pleasant staff, good choice of well kept beers inc Bass and Marstons; boules pitch for hire *(John and Glenys Wheeler)*

☆ ***Hare & Hounds*** [Henley Rd]: Pretty ivy-clad

dining pub well worth knowing, cosy corners, inglenook log fire, comfortable armchairs, well kept ales such as Brakspears and Rebellion, good house wines in several glass sizes, friendly efficient staff, enjoyable food inc some early-evening bargains for two in comfortable no smoking restaurant, darts, cribbage, dominoes; piped music; children welcome; back garden *(John and Glenys Wheeler, Reg J Cox)*

Hogshead [High St]: Basic feel with rough bare wood, bare boards and beams, big room divided on different levels, old prints, good choice of real ale, wholesome food; piped pop, SkyTV, very popular with young people; tables out by pavement *(John and Glenys Wheeler)*

☆ ***Two Brewers*** [St Peter St, first right off Station Rd from double roundabout]: Busy low-beamed bar with shiny black woodwork, nautical pictures, gleaming brassware, well kept ales such as Brakspears and Fullers London Pride, good food and wines (unusual crypt-like dining area – may have to book Sun lunch), cheerful chatty service; children in eating area, unobtrusive piped music; tables in sheltered back courtyard, front seats with glimpse of the Thames (pub right on Thames Path) *(LYM, John and Glenys Wheeler)*

Milton Keynes [SP8739]

Barge [Newport Rd, Woolstone]: Large beamed Vintage Inn attractively set in untouched corner of an original village just off central Milton Keynes, with picnic-sets on spacious tree-dotted lawns, no smoking areas inc modern conservatory, well kept Bass, lots of wines by the glass, wide food choice, daily papers friendly staff, good food service (not in garden); piped music *(CMW, JJW)*

☆ ***Old Beams*** [Osier Lane, Shenley Lodge; in grounds tucked into curve of ridge-top Paxton Cres, off Fulmer St or Childs Way]: Sizeable and relaxing comfortably modernised and extended former farmhouse, lots of brick and wood, old photographs, paintings and brass, flagstoned bar with through fireplace, matching chairs around handsome candlelit tables, good choice of enjoyable food inc light dishes and Sun roasts, usually something available all day, well kept McMullens ales, keen and friendly young staff, speciality coffees, good pubby atmosphere, no smoking areas; business faxes sent and received free, very popular with local office staff; piped music; children in dining area; large pleasant garden perhaps with swans and ducks in former moat – a striking oasis in vast tracts of new red-brick housing *(George Atkinson, E J and M W Corrin, Dr and Mrs M E Wilson, John Saville, BB)*

Swan [Broughton Rd, Milton Keynes village]: Spacious dark-beamed thatched pub with big back dining extension, no smoking area; Boddingtons, Courage Best and Wadworths 6X, wide food choice, friendly service, attractive furnishings, log-effect gas fire in inglenook; popular with businesspeople lunchtime, very busy Sun; picnic-sets in back garden, footpaths to nearby lakes *(Brian Root)*

Moulsoe [SP9041]

☆ ***Carrington Arms*** [1¼ miles from M1, junction 14: A509 N, first right signed Moulsoe; Cranfield Rd]: Interesting pub featuring meats and fresh fish sold by weight from refrigerated display then cooked on indoor barbecue, with wide range of other food, even a lobster tank and separate oyster and caviar bar; well kept Bass, Caledonian Deuchars IPA and Theakstons Best, champagnes by the glass, friendly service, comfortable mix of wooden chairs and cushioned banquettes; open all day Sun, children allowed, long pretty garden behind *(Karen and Graham Oddey, W K Wood, Dr Alan Sutton, Tim Lawrence, Bob and Maggie Atherton, Colin Mason, Brian Root, Mike and Wendy Proctor, Prof M J Kelly, Ian Phillips, John Saville, LYM, Charlie Harris)*

Northall [SP9619]

Swan [Leighton Rd]: Bustling beamed village local with nicely prepared straightforward food, welcoming landlady, several well kept ales such as Brakspears and Fullers London Pride (popular happy hour from 5.30), good coffee, big stuffed pike, well placed pool table, no music; handy for Whipsnade *(MP)*

Olney [SP8851]

☆ ***Swan*** [High St S]: Cosy and civilised beamed and timbered pub, with good choice of excellent value generous food inc a bargain daily special, well kept real ales such as Adnams, Fullers London Pride, Hook Norton and Morrells, good value wines; very busy and popular at lunchtime, candles on pine tables, log fires, small no smoking back bistro dining room (booking advised for this); no under-10s; marsh views from roomy bedrooms, garden with tables in courtyard, one under cover *(Stephen, Julie and Hayley Brown, Michael Sargent, George Atkinson, O J Barlow, BB, Roger Braithwaite)*

Two Brewers [High St (A509)]: Large unpretentious double-fronted pub, clean and tidy lounge and snug, big dining area with plenty of different-sized tables, very wide choice of generous good value food from sandwiches through good home-made pies to Sun lunches, well kept beers, good coffee, friendly prompt service; attractive courtyard, tables in small garden too *(John Saville)*

Penn [SU9193]

☆ ***Crown*** [B474 Beaconsfield—High Wycombe]: Friendly and very carefully extended Chef & Brewer, very welcoming to children, with wide choice of good food from sandwiches up in three attractively furnished bars, one with medieval flooring tiles, interesting varied décor, well kept Courage Best, decent wine choice, prompt service even when packed; air conditioning, unobtrusive well chosen piped music, fruit machine, trivia; perched opp 14th-c church on high ridge with distant views, lots of tables in attractive gardens with good play area, wknd barbecues, open all day *(LYM, John and Glenys Wheeler, David and Michelle Bailey, Matthew Last, Peter Saville, Tracey and Stephen Groves, D J Mann, Jenny and Brian Seller, Simon Collett-Jones, B Brewer)*

Horse & Jockey [Church Rd]: New management doing interesting range of food inc imaginative dishes, good service, well kept beers *(Charles Moncreiffe)*

Penn Street [SU9295]

☆ ***Hit or Miss*** [off A404 SW of Amersham, then keep on towards Winchmore Hill]: Well laid out low-beamed pub with own cricket ground, pleasant atmosphere in three clean linked rooms, welcoming bustle and helpful service, well kept Badger ales, decent wines, log fire, charming décor inc interesting cricket and chair-making memorabilia, well behaved children over 5 allowed, good-sized no smoking area; may be soft piped music; picnic-sets out in front, pleasant setting *(Peter Saville, LYM, Tracey and Stephen Groves, Simon Collett-Jones, Mike Tucker)*

Pitstone Green [SP9216]

Duke of Wellington [Pitstone Wharf]: Unpretentious country pub with log fire, Flowers, Fullers London Pride and Marstons Pedigree, reasonably priced homely food, friendly obliging landlord, black beams, brasses, copper and decorative china; near Grand Union Canal *(Lynda Payton, Sam Samuells)*

Preston Bissett [SP6529]

☆ ***White Hart*** [Pound Lane; village can be reached off A421 Buckingham bypass via Gawcott, or from A4421 via Chetwode or Barton Hartshorn]: Charming little thatched and timbered 18th-c pub with three cosily traditional rooms (the biggest is no smoking), log fire and low beams; it's been a popular main entry, with welcoming service, good home cooking (they've been closed Mon/Tues lunchtimes), fine choice of wines by the glass, mulled wine and well kept Adnams and a guest beer, but the licensees leave on 10 Dec 2002 *(LYM)*

Saunderton [SU8198]

Rose & Crown [Wycombe Rd]: Pub/hotel with nice log fires, big winged leather chairs, good choice of wines and guest beers, friendly staff, restaurant with well presented food, coffee lounge; well placed for Chilterns walks; bedrooms *(David and Belinda Devine)*

Shabbington [SP6607]

☆ ***Old Fisherman*** [off A418 Oxford—Thame; Mill Rd]: Prettily placed riverside dining pub with three roomy and attractive areas, good range of generous reasonably priced good food inc good fish choice, enjoyable steaks and children's dishes, particularly popular Sun lunch and wknd evenings, friendly staff, well kept changing ales; waterside garden with play area, bedrooms, small camp site *(Brian Root, Tim and Ann Newell, Mr and Mrs A Mills, John and Glenys Wheeler)*

Sherington []

White Hart [off A509; Gun Lane]: Fair choice of good food from sandwiches up, four well kept real ales, two-room bar and pleasantly rustic restaurant; maybe quiet piped radio; children and dogs welcome, picnic-sets in garden with terrace *(CMW, JJW)*

Slapton [SP9320]

Carpenters Arms [signed off B488 S of Linslade, just N of Horton; or can be reached off A4146 S of Leighton Buzzard, via Billington]: This small country pub, which has combined interesting food with a fascinating secondhand bookshop, closed for refurbishment in 2002, but reopens soon – news please *(LYM)*

Soulbury [SP8827]

☆ ***Boot*** [High Rd]: Nicely reworked in modern style (owned by a brasserie firm), young well trained staff, good value well presented food inc interesting dishes, good atmosphere, real ales such as Greene King IPA, Ind Coope Burton and Youngs Special, sporting prints, brass and copper around inglenook fireplace, no smoking family room, restaurant *(J Iorwerth Davies, B H and J I Andrews)*

Speen [SU8399]

King William IV [Hampden Rd]: Now a pub again, after some years as more of a restaurant, with welcoming new licensees, enjoyable traditional bar food, well kept Brakspears and Greene King Old Speckled Hen, inglenook snug bar on left, log fire in second bar on right, separate no smoking restaurant with more elaborate food; children in eating areas, tables out on terrace, nice spot by cricket green; cl Sun evening *(David J Richardson)*

Old Plow [Flowers Bottom Lane, from village towards Lacey Green and Saunderton Station]: Restaurant not pub (they won't serve drinks unless you're eating), but friendly and relaxing, with good open fires, good if not cheap food and wines (you can have just one course), fine service, a real ale, log fires, children in eating area, pretty lawns, lovely countryside; cl Sun evening and Mon *(John and Glenys Wheeler, Mark Percy, Lesley Mayoh, R Isaacs, LYM)*

Stoke Goldington [SP8348]

☆ ***White Hart*** [High St (B526 NW of Newport Pagnell)]: Friendly thatched and beamed pub with two smartly modernised bars and restaurant, cheerful attentive landlord, good value well presented usual food from baguettes and baked potatoes up, quick service, Charles Wells Eagle and seasonal beers, decent coffee, comfortable banquettes, open fire, tiled bar with stripped stone, pictures and brasses; piped music; picnic-sets on sheltered back lawn with play area, footpath network starts just across road *(George Atkinson, LYM, CMW, JJW)*

Stoke Green [SU9882]

☆ ***Red Lion*** [off B416 signed Wexham and George Green]: Rambling and roomy refurbished Vintage Inn, lots of little separate areas, pleasant atmosphere, well presented good value food, Bass and Tetleys, good choice of decent wines, attentive helpful service, log fires, no smoking room, children welcome; tables outside, may be summer barbecues, open all day *(LYM, Bob and Laura Brock, June and Robin Savage, Dr and Mrs A K Clarke)*

Stone [SP7912]

Bugle Horn [Hartwell; A418 SW of Aylesbury]: Long low whitewashed stone-built Vintage Inn with lovely trees in large pretty garden; warm and friendly, with pleasant furnishings, decent food, usual choice of wines by the glass, log fire and conservatory *(Mel Smith)*

Stony Stratford [SP7840]

☆ ***Cock*** [High St]: Comfortable old-fashioned hotel, quiet at lunchtime but lively in the evenings, with leather settles and library chairs on bare boards, decent bar food from filled baps to chargrills, very friendly service, well kept ales inc Greene King Old Speckled Hen; tables in attractive courtyard, barbecues; bedrooms *(Ian Phillips, John Saville, LYM)*

Fox & Hounds [High St]: Friendly 17th-c two-bar pub with pictures and photographs, fresh flowers, well kept Greene King Abbot, decent cheap lunchtime food from sandwiches and burgers to bargain specials; piped radio, games area with hood skittles, darts, folk, blues or jazz Thurs, Sat and first Tues; tables in walled garden *(Pete Baker, CMW, JJW)*

Old George [High St]: Attractive and lively beamed and timbered inn, cosily pubby, with good value food at any time inc centrally placed roast of the day, quick attentive service, real ales such as Marstons Pedigree and Wadworths Roddys Best, good coffee; piped music, lavatories up rather awkward stairs; tables in courtyard behind, bedrooms *(George Atkinson)*

The Lee [SP8904]

☆ ***Old Swan*** [Swan Bottom, back rd ¾ mile N of The Lee]: Charming civilised 16th-c dining pub, with very good interesting food esp seafood cooked by long-serving landlord (sandwiches too); four simply but attractively furnished linked rooms, low beams and flagstones, cooking-range log fire in inglenook, particularly well kept Adnams and Brakspears, decent wines, friendly relaxed service; spacious prettily planted back lawns with play area, good walks *(LYM, J M Hunting, Mrs P J Pearce)*

Wendover [SP8607]

Firecrest [A413 about 2 miles S]: Large roadside Vintage Inn, cosy eating areas with settles and brocaded chairs around polished tables, turkey carpets, old fireplace, good choice of good value quickly served food; disabled parking *(Pam Adsley)*

☆ ***Red Lion*** [High St]: Bustling and friendly 17th-c inn with wide choice of good value changing food, inc fish specialities, Sun lunch and children's dishes in refurbished oak-beamed flagstoned bar and adjacent good value restaurant; four well kept ales such as Brakspears Ted & Bens Organic, Youngs Special and one brewed for the pub, good wines, many by the glass, efficient service; can get smoky, dogs allowed till 7; walker-friendly (on Ridgeway Long Distance Path), tables and heaters out behind, with colourful tubs; comfortable bedrooms *(BB, John and Glenys Wheeler)*

West Wycombe [SU8394]

☆ ***George & Dragon*** [High St; A40 W of High Wycombe]: Handsome and popular Tudor inn with comfortably worn-in rambling bar with massive beams, sloping rust-coloured walls, big log fire, well kept ales such as Fullers London Pride, Greene King Abbot and Charles Wells Bombardier, food from sandwiches to some exotic specials, small no smoking family dining room (wknd children's menu); spacious garden with fenced play area, bedrooms, handy for West Wycombe Park *(Desmond Hall, Piotr Chodzko-Zajko, Chris Glasson, LYM, Mr and Mrs A Mills, Ian Phillips, Susan and John Douglas)*

Weston Underwood [SP8650]

Cowpers Oak [signed off A509 in Olney; High St]: Charming old pub, beams, stripped stone and dark panelling, Adnams, Fullers London Pride, Greene King IPA, Marstons Pedigree and one or two unusual guest beers, farm cider, simple good value food (not Sun or Mon evenings) inc soup and sandwiches, no smoking back restaurant, open fire, good games room with darts, bar billiards, hood skittles and table football, daily papers; piped music, TV; children very welcome, dogs in main bar; small suntrap terrace, big orchard garden (no dogs) with play area and farm animals, open all day wknds, pretty thatched village near Flamingo Gardens *(Maysie Thompson, LYM, George Atkinson, Eric Locker, Ian Phillips)*

Whitchurch [SP8020]

☆ ***White Swan*** [High St]: Homely and pubby thatched two-bar local with well kept Fullers ales, good straightforward food, picnic-sets in big rambling back garden looking over fields *(LYM, Sue Demont, Tim Barrow)*

Wing [SP8822]

Cock [off A418 SW of Leighton Buzzard; High St]: Partly 16th-c, with good choice of well kept changing ales, decent wines, good coffee, friendly attentive service, cottage armchairs and roaring fire, lots of books, partly no smoking dining areas with good fresh food; may be unobtrusive piped music; garden with picnic-sets and play area *(John Poulter)*

Wooburn Common [SU9387]

☆ ***Royal Standard*** [about 3½ miles from M40 junction 2]: Thriving two-bar local with friendly and obliging staff, wide choice of enjoyable good value bar food, well kept ales such as Adnams, B&T Edwin Taylors Extra Stout, Fullers London Pride, Hook Norton Old Hooky and Hop Back Summer Lightning, well chosen wines, open fire, popular dining area; picnic-sets in garden *(LYM, Ian Phillips)*

Wooburn Moor [SU9189]

☆ ***Falcon*** [Old Moor Lane; SE edge of Loudwater]: Friendly and homely little low-beamed local doing well under newish management, three particularly well kept changing real ales, decent food, relaxing atmosphere; piped music, film/video machines; attractive garden *(Peter Kidson)*

Worminghall [SP6308]

☆ ***Clifden Arms*** [Clifden Rd]: A real visual treat, 16th-c beamed and timbered thatched pub in pretty gardens, old-fashioned seats and rustic memorabilia in lounge bar with roaring log fire, another in public bar, decent food inc bargain lunches, well kept Adnams Broadside, Boddingtons, Fullers ESB and London Pride, Hook Norton and interesting guest beers, traditional games, children allowed; good play area, aunt sally; attractive village *(LYM, Richard Fendick, John and Glenys Wheeler)*

Cambridgeshire

unusual décor, imaginative food), the friendly good value New Sun in Kimbolton (by contrast, very traditional), and the Three Tuns at Fen Drayton (back in the Guide *after a break of many years). Other pubs on fine form this year are the White Hart at Bythorn (good food in a warm and relaxed atmosphere), the simple and unspoilt Cambridge Blue in Cambridge (bargain food), the appealing Red Lion at Hinxton (enjoyable food, good staff), the Queens Head at Newton (an unspoilt classic, one of our favourites), the Brewery Tap in Peterborough (brewing some fine ales – but there's a redevelopment threat hanging over it), the welcoming George at Spaldwick (a good all-rounder), and the civilised and attractive old Bell at Stilton (gaining a Food Award this year). Five top-notch dining pubs, where a deeper pocket buys a really good meal in smart surroundings, stand out: the Chequers at Fowlmere, the Old Bridge Hotel in Huntingdon (great wine list), the Three Horseshoes at Madingley, the Pheasant at Keyston and the Anchor at Sutton Gault. From this exalted group we have chosen the Pheasant at Keyston as Cambridgeshire Dining Pub of the Year. Some particularly promising pubs in the Lucky Dip section at the end of the chapter are the Royal Oak at Barrington, Free Press and Mill in Cambridge, John Barleycorn in Duxford, Golden Pheasant at Etton, Blue Lion at Hardwick, Old Ferry Boat near Holywell and Fish & Duck at Little Thetford. We have inspected and can vouch for the appeal of all of these – as we can for the Navigator at Little Shelford and Red House at Longstowe, kept out of the main entries this year only by a lack of reports from readers. Drinks prices in the county are rather above the national average. The Brewery Tap and Charters, both in Peterborough, supplied by their own good Oakham brewery, have rock-bottom beer prices, and otherwise it's worth looking out for beers from smaller local breweries such as City of Cambridge or Milton, which benefit from the cut-rate duty and so can be cheaper.*

BARNACK TF0704 Map 5

Millstone

Millstone Lane; off B1443 SE Stamford; turn off School Lane nr the Fox

Run by a really welcoming hands-on landlord of the old school, this reliable old stone-built village local is a favourite with some of our readers for its enjoyable food, and you may need to get there early for a seat, even during the week. As well as home-made soup such as good carrot and coriander or broccoli and stilton (£2), sandwiches (from £2.95), freshly baked filled baguettes (£3.25), generous pâté (£3.85), ploughman's, stilton and vegetable crumble or liver and bacon hotpot (£6.95), and mixed grill (£8.95), they do delicious home-made pies such as steak in ale, chicken and bacon, minted lamb or pork with apple and cider (all £7.25); on Thursday and Friday there's fresh fish from Grimsby (battered haddock or plaice, £6.25). Puddings (some are home-made) may include white chocolate and rum torte or blackberry crumble (£2.95). They have smaller helpings for OAPs, a straightforward children's menu and sometimes marmalades, jams, pickles and fruit cakes on sale for charity. Well kept real ales include Adnams, Everards Old Original and Tiger and an interesting guest on handpump, and they also have a good choice of Gales country wines. The traditional timbered bar with high beams weighed down with lots of heavy harness is split into intimate areas with cushioned wall benches on the patterned carpet – look out for Stone the ancient pub dog who might be dozing in here. A little snug is decorated with a former regular's memorabilia (including medals from both World Wars), and leads through into their new wing: a conservatory, which has a TV, lots of plants and a wishing well (coins thrown into it go to charity), leads down into a recently converted cellar. The snug and dining room are no smoking. In summer the window baskets and window boxes are attractive, and there's a pleasant rockery and a few outside tables and chairs. *(Recommended by Michael and Jenny Back, Mr and Mrs J Glover, Kevin Thorpe, Norma and Keith Bloomfield, Eric Locker, Roger and Pauline Pearce, Michael J Gittins, Comus and Sarah Elliott)*

Everards ~ Tenant Aubrey Sinclair Ball ~ Real ale ~ Bar food (not Sun evening) ~ Restaurant ~ (01780) 740296 ~ Children in eating area of bar and restaurant ~ Open 11.30-2.30, 5.30(6 Sat)-11.30; 12-4, 7-10.30 Sun

BYTHORN TL0575 Map 5

White Hart

Village signposted just off A14 Kettering—Cambridge

Although the emphasis is very much on Bennett's Bistro, the informal pubby atmosphere, chatty landlord and friendly staff make this a nice place to come even if you just want a drink. As well as a thoughtfully chosen affordable wine list, they've well kept Everards Tiger, Greene King IPA and Abbot, and maybe a guest such as Old Speckled Hen on handpump; good strong coffee too. The generous helpings of interesting food could include crispy pork loin, game and Guinness casserole, king prawns in garlic butter, steak and mushroom pie, venison in red wine gravy, and wild boar sausages (all £8.50), and they also do steaks (from £10.95); the restaurant is no smoking. The homely main bar and several linked smallish rooms have a pleasant mix of furnishings, such as a big leather chesterfield, lots of silver teapots and so forth on a carved dresser and in a built-in cabinet, and wing armchairs and attractive tables. One particularly appealing area has a cosy log fire in a huge brick fireplace, soft pale leather studded chairs and stools, and rugs on stripped boards. There are cookery books and plenty of magazines for reading, and a good mix of customers. *(Recommended by Stephen, Julie and Hayley Brown, David and Mary Webb, Pat and Roger Fereday, Bob and Maggie Atherton)*

Free house ~ Licensee Bill Bennett ~ Real ale ~ Bar food (12-2, 6-10; not Sun evening, not Mon) ~ Restaurant ~ (01832) 710226 ~ Children welcome ~ Open 12-3, 6-11; 12-4 Sun; closed Sun evening, all day Mon

CAMBRIDGE TL4658 Map 5

Anchor

Silver Street (where there are punts for hire – with a boatman if needed)

In a marvellous setting right on the banks of the River Cam, with punts drifting past its suntrap terrace, this bustling pub is as popular as ever under the new licensees. It's at its liveliest in term time with plenty of students spreading around the four levels. The entrance area has some nooks and crannies with lots of bric-a-brac, church pews, and a brick fireplace at either end. Upstairs, the pubby bar (no smoking during food service times), has pews and wooden chairs and fine river and Mill Pond views, while the downstairs café-bar has enamel signs on the walls and a mix of interesting tables, settles, farmhouse chairs, and hefty stools on the bare boards. More steps take you down again, to a simpler flagstoned room with french windows leading out to the terrace (which is heated in the evenings). Simple but good value bar food includes home-made soup (£2.75), filled baked potatoes (£3.75), ploughman's (£4.95), salads (from £5.10), battered cod (£6.50), and usually four daily specials such as steak and ale pie, beef bourguignon, pasta with spinach in cream and white wine sauce (£5.75). The three real ales on handpump could be Boddingtons, Flowers Original and Wadworths 6X; they've also got internet access, video games, a juke box, fruit machines and TV. *(Recommended by Giles and Liz Ridout, Keith Jacob, Tim and Ann Newell, John Wooll, Michael and Marion Buchanan, Patricia Beebe, Laura and Stuart Ballantyne)*

Laurel Pub Company ~ Managers Anna and Steve Almond ~ Real ale ~ Bar food (12-8 Mon-Thurs; 12-5 Fri; 12-3 Sat; 12-3, 4-8 Sun) ~ (01223) 353554 ~ Children welcome in eating area of bar during food service hours ~ Open 11-11; 12-10.30 Sun

Cambridge Blue £

85 Gwydir Street

Readers are full of praise for this quiet backstreet pub (once they'd discovered it, one couple even returned here every night of their two-week holiday). Completely no smoking and free of piped music (mobile phones are discouraged too), it's run in a charmingly distinctive and friendly style. The two simple uncluttered rooms have old-fashioned bare-boards style furnishings with candles on the tables, a big collection of oars and such a nice selection of rowing photographs that you feel you're browsing through someone's family snaps. The regularly changing well kept real ales are picked from interesting, mostly East Anglian, small breweries such as Iceni, Milton and Potton (you can test them before you buy a pint) with a few from more usual brewers such as Adnams, Nethergate or Woodfordes; they also have a decent choice of wines and malt whiskies. Good value generous helpings of home-made food are served in an attractive little conservatory dining area, and might include filled ciabattas (from £2.50), two home-made soups (£2.95), a cold table with game or picnic pies, nut roast, various quiches and so forth (from £4.50), chilli (£4.75), chicken or vegetable burritos (£5), daily specials such as game casserole (£4.75), red pepper and mushroom stroganoff (£5) and steak, mushroom and ale pie (£5.50), with puddings such as carrot cake or apple pie with custard (£2.25). Children like the surprisingly large back garden, which has rabbits and a boules pitch. *(Recommended by John Wooll, the Didler, Michael and Marion Buchanan, Tina and David Woods-Taylor, Patricia Beebe, Sue Demont, Tim Barrow, Pat and Tony Martin, Peter J Holmes, Mike and Mary Carter, Dr and Mrs Jackson)*

Free house ~ Licensees Chris and Debbie Lloyd ~ Real ale ~ Bar food (12-2.30, 6-9.30) ~ (01223) 361382 ~ Children welcome in conservatory till 9pm ~ Dogs welcome ~ Open 12-2.30(3 Sat), 5.30-11; 12-3, 6-10.30 Sun

Eagle 🍷 £

Bene't Street

About to change hands as we go to press, the five rambling rooms of this lively old stone-fronted town centre coaching inn are interesting to explore. Keeping many charming original architectural features, they have lovely worn wooden floors and plenty of original pine panelling, two fireplaces dating back to around 1600, two medieval mullioned windows, and the remains of two possibly medieval wall paintings. The creaky old furniture is nicely in keeping. Don't miss the high dark red ceiling which has been left unpainted since World War II to preserve the signatures of British and American airmen worked in with Zippo lighters, candle smoke and lipstick. Readers warn us that it can get smoky, though there is a no smoking room. Promptly served from a counter in a small back room, the straightforward but enjoyable lunchtime food might include filled baguettes (from £4.95), vegetarian quiche (£4.50), lasagne or tasty fish and chips (£5.50), while in the evenings dishes cooked to order could include vegetable tikka (£5.75), tagliatelle with chicken and bacon or beef stroganoff (£6.95), 10oz sirloin steak (£9.45); puddings such as chocolate fudge cake or apple and rhubarb crumble (£2.45). Well kept Greene King IPA, Abbot and Old Speckled Hen and a guest such as Shepherd Neame Spitfire on handpump; friendly service from well dressed staff. An attractive cobbled and galleried courtyard, screened from the street by sturdy wooden gates and with heavy wooden seats and tables and pretty hanging baskets, takes you back through the centuries – especially at Christmas, when they serve mulled wine and you can listen to the choristers from King's College singing here. No children inside. *(Recommended by Terry Mizen, Eric Locker, Anthony Barnes, Keith and Janet Morris, John Wooll, Tim and Ann Newell, the Didler, Simon Chell, Patricia Beebe, Sue Demont, Tim Barrow, John Saville)*

Greene King ~ Real ale ~ Bar food (12-2.30, 5-8.45, not Sat evening) ~ (01223) 505020 ~ Open 11-11; 12-10.30 Sun

Live & Let Live £

40 Mawson Road; off Mill Road SE of centre

They have live music every Sunday evening at this welcoming and unpretentious little backstreet local. Friendly staff serve well kept Adnams, Everards Tiger and Nethergate Umbel, and there are three or four guests from independent brewers such as Milton, Oakham and Tring on handpump too, as well as 20 or so malts. The heavily timbered brickwork rooms have sturdy varnished pine tables with pale wood chairs on bare boards, real gas lighting, lots of interesting old country bric-a-brac, and posters about local forthcoming events; piped music, cribbage, dominoes. The eating area of the bar is no smoking until 9pm, and basic but good value food includes hot filled baguettes (£3.50), popular giant filled yorkshire puddings (£4.50, choose from beef, pork, lamb, sausage or chicken), one or two specials (£3.95-£5.95), a Saturday morning breakfast (£4.50), and a Sunday roast (£4.95). *(Recommended by Colin and Janet Roe, Patricia Beebe, John Brightley, Dr and Mrs Jackson)*

Burlison Inns ~ Lease Alan Kilker ~ Real ale ~ Bar food (12-2, 6-8.45, no food Sun evening) ~ (01223) 460261 ~ Children welcome in eating area of bar till 8pm ~ Dogs allowed in bar ~ Folk most Sun evenings ~ Open 11.30-2.30, 5.30-11; 11.30-3, 6-11 Sat; 12-3, 7-10.30 Sun; closed bank hol Mon

ELTON TL0893 Map 5

Black Horse

B671 off A605 W of Peterborough and A1(M); Overend

You'd never guess that this cheery village dining pub was once a morgue. It has a homely and comfortable mix of furniture (no two tables and chairs seem the same), roaring fires, hop-strung beams, antique prints, and lots of ornaments and bric-a-brac including an intriguing ancient radio set. Dining areas at each end of the bar have parquet flooring and tiles, and the stripped stone back lounge towards the restaurant has an interesting fireplace. Enjoyable food served by welcoming staff includes home-made soup (£3.75), sandwiches (from £3.65), filled baguettes such as emmental and red pepper (from £4.95), goats cheese salad or seafood medley (£5.95), mussels cassoulet (£6.95), ploughman's (from £7.25), roast chicken breast stuffed with black cherry and pork and served with an orange butter sauce (£12.50), rack of lamb with kidneys and a mustard sauce (£14.95), and six or seven fish dishes such as bass with garlic king prawns or monkfish with buttered spinach and crispy bacon (£13.95); home-made puddings could include lemon tart with citrus sorbet, banoffi pie or summer fruit pudding with mascarpone (£4.95). You'll find well kept Bass, Caledonian Deuchars IPA and a guest such as Nethergate Suffolk County on handpump, and the wines are good value; the family area is no smoking. There are tables, some shaded by horse chestnut trees, in a garden that's prettily divided into separate areas. Behind the low-built pub is Elton Hall, and this attractive bypassed village has a lovely Saxon church (and an oak which is said to have the widest spread in Europe). *(Recommended by Lorraine and Fred Gill, Stephen, Julie and Hayley Brown, Gerry and Rosemary Dobson)*

Free house ~ Licensee John Clennell ~ Real ale ~ Bar food (not Sun evening) ~ Restaurant ~ (01832) 280240 ~ Children welcome ~ Open 12-3, 6-11; 12-11 Sat; 12-5 Sun

If we know a pub does summer barbecues, we say so.

ELY TL5380 Map 5

Fountain

Corner of Barton Square and Silver Street

Even though this basic but genteel town corner pub is very close to the cathedral it still manages to escape the tourists. Very simple and traditional with no music, fruit machines or even food, it's the type of place that's nice to come to for a chat. You'll find a real mix of age groups, and the atmosphere is pleasant and inclusive. They serve well kept Adnams Bitter and Broadside, Fullers London Pride and a changing guest such as Black Sheep or Everards Tiger on handpump. Old cartoons, local photographs, regional maps and mementoes of the neighbouring King's School punctuate the elegant dark pink walls, and neatly tied-back curtains hang from golden rails above the big windows. Above one fireplace is a stuffed pike in a case, and there are a few antlers dotted about – not to mention a duck at one end of the bar; everything is very clean and tidy. A couple of tables are squeezed on to a tiny back terrace. Note the limited opening times; no credit cards. *(Recommended by Stephen, Julie and Hayley Brown, the Didler, C J Fletcher)*

Free house ~ Licensees John and Judith Borland ~ Real ale ~ No credit cards ~ (01353) 663122 ~ Children welcome until 8pm ~ Dogs welcome ~ Open 5-11; 12-2, 6-11 Sat; 12-2, 7-10.30 Sun; closed 25 Dec

FEN DITTON TL4860 Map 5

Ancient Shepherds

Off B1047 at Green End, The River signpost, just NE of Cambridge

Just the place for a restorative drink, the nicest room at this solidly beamed old place is the central one, with lots of fat dark red button-back leather settees and armchairs, low solid Indonesian tables, heavy drapes around a window seat with big scatter cushions, and a warm coal fire. Above a black dado the walls (and ceiling) are dark pink, and decorated with little steeplechasing and riding prints, and comic fox and policeman ones, and the lighting is soothing. On the right the smallish convivial bar serves Adnams and Greene King IPA on handpump, and there's another coal fire, while on the left is a pleasant restaurant (piped music in here). Bar food includes sandwiches (from £3.25), ploughman's (from £5.95) and steak baguettes (£6.25), as well as a menu that changes every six weeks or so but might include sausages and mash (£6.95), wild mushroom lasagne (£8.95) home-made steak and ale pie or calves liver and bacon (£9.95), and bass fillet with spinach and mash (£13.95). The friendly pub dog is called Hugo. More reports please. *(Recommended by Roy Bromell)*

Pubmaster ~ Lease J M Harrington ~ Real ale ~ Bar food (not Sun evening) ~ Restaurant ~ (01223) 293280 ~ Children in eating area of bar and restaurant ~ Dogs allowed in bar ~ Open 12-3(2.30 Sat), 6-11; 12-5 Sun; closed Sun evening

FEN DRAYTON TL3368 Map 5

Three Tuns

Signposted off A14 NW of Cambridge at Fenstanton; High Street

There's plenty of atmosphere in this well preserved ancient thatched building, which may have been the medieval guildhall for the pretty village. The relaxed and friendly bar has a pair of inglenook fireplaces, and heavy Tudor beams and timbers; the carving on the central boss suggests a former link with the corn industry. There are comfortable cushioned settles, and a nice variety of chairs here and in the appealing partly no smoking dining room. The enjoyable food, served by helpful well trained staff, includes lunchtime sandwiches (£2.95), baked potatoes (£3.50) and warm baguettes (from £4.25), ploughman's (£5.25), beef and Guinness pie, scampi, omelettes, and curry (from £5.95 to £7.25), with puddings such as blackcurrant cheesecake and sticky toffee pudding (£3.25). In the evening the more elaborate menu, which is served throughout, might include dishes such as calves liver and bacon (£8.95), poached salmon (£9.95) and duck leg (£10.95). They serve well kept Greene King IPA and Jubilation with a guest such as Brains SA or Wadworths 6X;

piped music, sensibly placed darts, and a fruit machine. A well tended lawn at the back has tables under cocktail parasols, apple and flowering cherry trees, and a good play area. *(Recommended by Steve Riches, Peter J Holmes, David and Ruth Hollands, JWAC, Ian Phillips)*

Greene King ~ Tenants Tim Cook and Darren Harris ~ Real Ale ~ Bar food (12-2, 7-9(6.30-9.30 Fri-Sat), not 25-26 Dec, 1 Jan) ~ Restaurant ~ (01954) 230242 ~ Children in eating area of bar and restaurant ~ Occasional live entertainment ~ Open 12-3, 6-11; 12-3, 7-10.30 Sun; closed evenings 25 and 26 Dec, lunchtime 1 Jan

FORDHAM TL6270 Map 5

White Pheasant

Market Street; B1085, off A142 and A11 N of Newmarket

The licensees who've recently taken over this pub have an excellent track record in the restaurant trade, and they look like doing really well here too. As well as home-made soup (£4.25), sandwiches (from £4.95), sausages and mustard mash or gammon steak with fried egg and sautéed new potatoes (£6.95), their interesting new menu includes dishes such as smoked salmon terrine with warm potato salad (£5.75), wild mushroom tortellini with basil butter sauce (£8.95), guinea fowl with mashed sweet potato (£13.95), grilled lamb cutlets with creamed leeks (£14.95), and specials such as baked bass stuffed with fennel, oyster mushrooms and red onion (£13.95); home-made puddings might include nutty apple crumble and lemon and passion fruit tart (£4.25). They plan gradual redecoration of the smallish but airy bar which, at the moment, has a mix of big farmhouse tables and chairs, a couple of turkey rugs on the bare boards, folded white napkins and flowers in bottles on the tables, prints and simple black iron candlelamps on white walls, some stripped brickwork and a cheery log fire at one end. One or two steps lead down to a small similarly furnished green-carpeted room. They serve three real ales such as Greene King Abbot, City of Cambridge Hobsons Choice and Woodfordes Wherry on handpump from the horseshoe bar that faces the entrance, and plan to introduce a fine wine list; piped jazz. They hope that redevelopment of the garden will be complete by the time this book goes to press. Reports please on the new regime. *(Recommended by J D M Rushworth, Ian and Nita Cooper, Ian Phillips, Stephen, Julie and Hayley Brown)*

Free house ~ Licensee Elizabeth Meads ~ Real ale ~ Bar food (12-2.30, 7-9) ~ Restaurant ~ (01638) 720414 ~ Children in eating area of bar ~ Open 12-3, 6-11.30(7-10.30 Sun); closed 25 and 26 Dec

FOWLMERE TL4245 Map 5

Chequers

B1368

Civilised and professionally run, this 16th-c dining pub is a great place to come for an imaginative, well cooked meal. Two warm and cosy comfortably furnished communicating rooms downstairs have an open log fire (there's a priest's hole above the bar), while upstairs there are beams, wall timbering and some interesting moulded plasterwork above the fireplace. The airy no smoking conservatory overlooks white tables under cocktail parasols among flowers and shrub roses in an attractive well tended floodlit garden – in summer overhead you might see historic aeroplanes flying from Duxford. The carefully chosen menu could include starters such as roast chicken soup (£3.40), mussels with white wine and cream (£5.40), haggis, faggots and black pudding (£5.60), spinach and walnut risotto (£5.80), with mains such as navarin of lamb with a herb scone and baked winter vegetables (£8.80), grilled venison with truffle oil salad (£12.20), fish stew (£12.80), and puddings such as rhubarb and almond crumble or date sponge with sticky toffee sauce, and English cheeses (£4.40); Sunday roast beef (£11.60). The thoughtful selection of attractively priced fine wines by the glass includes vintage and late-bottled ports. There's also a good list of malt whiskies, well kept Adnams with a guest such as Hop Back Summer Lightning or Timothy Taylors Landlord on handpump, freshly squeezed orange juice, and several brandies. *(Recommended by Ian Phillips, Alan Jones, JMC, Kay Vowles, Pat and Tony Hinkins, R C Wiles, Mary Anne Wright, WAH)*

Free house ~ Licensees Norman and Pauline Rushton ~ Real ale ~ Bar food (12-2, 7-10.30) ~ Restaurant ~ (01763) 208369 ~ Well behaved children allowed lunchtimes in the conservatory ~ Open 11.30-2.30, 6-11; 12-3, 7-10.30 Sun; closed 25 Dec

GODMANCHESTER TL2470 Map 5

Exhibition

London Road

Though it looks rather ordinary from the outside, this busy brick house scores highly for its very good unusual food – and the main bar's quite a surprise as well. The walls have been decorated with re-created shop-fronts – a post office, gallery, and wine and spirit merchant – complete with doors and stock in the windows. Some large plants have a few white fairy lights, and it's a cosy room, with big flagstones on the floor, cushioned wall benches, and fresh flowers and candles on each of the tables. Chalked up on a blackboard, the wide range of food might include imaginatively filled hot or cold lunchtime baguettes, steak sandwich (£5.95), roast pepper and goats cheese strudel (£7.95), citrus and herb marinated chicken supreme with fondant potato, pak choi, and orange and velouté sauce (£9.25), bass wrapped in vine leaves with pesto potatoes (£10.95), and balsamic dressed duck breast with mediterranean vegetables and egg noodles (£11.75); Sunday roasts, and children's menu. The dining room, with smart candelabra and framed prints, is no smoking. Well kept Fullers London Pride, Greene King IPA and a changing guest beer on handpump; good friendly service. There are picnic sets on the back lawn, and a couple in front as well, and they hold barbecues in summer. Every year the Exhibition and its sister pub, the nearby White Hart, organise a gathering of steam engines. *(Recommended by Robbie Dobson, Michael Dandy)*

Free house ~ Licensee Willem Middlemiss ~ Real ale ~ Bar food (12-2.15, 6.30-9.45; Sun 12.30-2.30, 6.30-9.30) ~ Restaurant ~ (01480) 459134 ~ Children in restaurant ~ Monthly live bands on Tues ~ Open 11.30-3, 5.30-11.30; 11.30-11 Fri/Sat; 12-10.30 Sun

HEYDON TL4340 Map 5

King William IV

Off A505 W of M11 junction 10

A good selection of interesting dishes means that even the most staunch meat-eater will be tempted to try something from the mouth-watering vegetarian menu here. About ten generous choices could include chestnut and leek cottage pie (£8.25), spicy three-bean chilli in a corn basket (£8.45), spinach and spring onion cakes with mustard cream sauce, brie, almond and oyster mushroom crumble or grilled portobello mushrooms with wild mushroom risotto (£8.95). Equally tasty meat dishes might be bangers and mash (£7.25), steak and kidney pie (£8.25), confit of duck with oriental spices with honey and ginger mash (£9.65), and chicken casserole or seafood kebab with coconut rice and citrus salsa (£9.95), with puddings such as brandy snap basket filled with strawberries and cream (£5.95) or rum and raisin cheesecake (£5.45). Part of the restaurant is no smoking. Warmed in winter by a log fire, the nooks and crannies of the beamed rambling rooms are crowded with a charming jumble of rustic implements like ploughshares, yokes and iron tools, as well as cowbells, beer steins, samovars, cut-glass, brass or black wrought-iron lamps, copper-bound casks and milk ewers, harness, horsebrasses, smith's bellows, and decorative plates and china ornaments. Half a dozen well kept real ales such as Adnams Regatta, Greene King IPA and Abbot, Everards Tiger and a guest beer on handpump; they also do cocktails. Fruit machine and piped music. A wooden deck has teak furniture and outdoor heaters, and there are more seats in the pretty garden. *(Recommended by Jack Clarfelt, M R D Foot, WAH, Keith and Janet Morris, George Atkinson, Sarah Davis, Rod Lambert, J D M Rushworth, Ian Arthur)*

Free house ~ Licensee Elizabeth Nicholls ~ Real ale ~ Bar food (12-2, 6.30(7 Sun)-10) ~ Restaurant ~ (01763) 838773 ~ Children in eating area of bar ~ Dogs allowed in bar ~ Open 12-2.30, 6.30-11; 12-3, 7-10.30 Sun; closed 25 Dec

HINXTON TL4945 Map 5

Red Lion

Between junctions 9 and 10 of M11; just off A1301 S of Great Shefford

In the tidy, attractive garden of this pretty pink-washed twin-gabled old pub, there's a pleasant terrace with picnic-sets. Inside, the dusky mainly open-plan bustling bar has leather chesterfields on wooden floors (occasionally you might see a chatty amazon parrot called George); TV, trivia and cribbage. The smart no smoking restaurant is filled with mirrors, pictures and grandfather and other clocks. It's a popular place to eat, with an enticing and well cooked menu, and friendly efficient staff. At lunchtime you might find sandwiches (from £2.50, not Sun), ploughman's (£5.75), ham, egg and chips (£6.95) and smoked salmon salad (£8.75), while other dishes could include home-made soup (£3.95), chargrilled jamaican jerk chicken with mango and papaya salad or stilton, port and cream cheese pâté (£4.75), chicken, smoked bacon and leek pie or salmon steak (£8.95), lamb steak with olive oil and cajun spices (£11.50), chargrilled bass with roasted red pepper sauce (£13.75), and desserts such as toffee pecan meringue cheesecake (£4.25) and home-made banoffi pie (£3.75). Real ales on handpump include Adnams, Woodfordes Wherry and perhaps guests such as Fullers London Pride and Oakham JHB, kept in good condition. The pub is not far from the Imperial War Museum, Duxford. *(Recommended by Mrs V Brown, Eric Locker, Patricia Beebe, Pat and Tony Martin, F M Craven, Jason Caulkin, Ian Phillips, John Wooll, Oliver and Sue Rowell)*

Free house ~ Licensees Jim and Lynda Crawford ~ Real ale ~ Bar food ~ Restaurant ~ (01799) 530601 ~ Children over 10 in eating area of bar ~ Open 11-2.30, 6-11; 12-2.30, 7-10.30 Sun; closed 25 and 26 Dec

HORNINGSEA TL4962 Map 5

Crown & Punchbowl

Just NE of Cambridge; first slip-road off A14 heading E after A10, then left at T; or via B1047 Fen Ditton road off A1303

This civilised and spacious low-beamed pub has four or five open-plan rooms which work their way around the central counter. It's fairly simply but appealingly furnished and decorated, with good solid stripped pine tables well spaced on the mainly bare boards, and some striking dark blue paintwork picking out the woodwork. The little bar area has a nice pulpit at one end, some stained glass and a big blue and white banner, with a few big prints and mirrors dotted around, simple black iron wall candles, and a big stag's head on the cream walls; piped classical music. There are two intimate and slightly separate-feeling little conservatory areas. Interesting skilfully cooked bar food includes dishes such as soup (£4.25), black pudding and apple salad or spicy cheddar cheese balls with tomato chutney (£6.15), sausages and mash (£6.25), mexican chicken and bacon salad (£9.95), and steak (£10.95), with specials such as cottage pie (£8.95), and home-made desserts (£4.25). A more formal menu, served throughout, could include prawn spaghetti (£5.85), smoked cod and crispy bacon bake (£6.75), or duck breast with plum spring onion and ginger sauce, and there are fresh fish specials. They have two well kept real ales on handpump from the local Milton Brewery, such as Pegasus or Constantine; also country wines and elderflower pressé. You can sit in the simple back garden. We haven't had any reports yet about the bedrooms. *(Recommended by Boyd Catling, Ian Phillips, John Wooll, Kevin Thorpe, D L Parkhurst, Brian Kneale, J D M Rushworth)*

Excalibur ~ Licensees Ian Hubert and Jonathan Gates ~ Real ale ~ Bar food (12-2.30, 6-10, 7-9 Sun) ~ Restaurant ~ (01223) 860643 ~ Children welcome ~ Open 12-2.30, 6-11(7-10.30 Sun); closed 25 Dec, and evenings 26 Dec and 1 Jan ~ Bedrooms: £45B/£75B

HUNTINGDON TL2371 Map 5

Old Bridge Hotel ★

1 High Street; ring road just off B1044 entering from easternmost A14 sliproad

Once a private bank, this elegant 18th-c hotel is tucked away in a pleasant spot by the River Great Ouse. The main emphasis here is on the excellent imaginative food, which you can eat in the big no smoking airy Terrace (an indoor room, but with lovely verdant murals suggesting the open air), or in the slightly more formal panelled no smoking restaurant. The menu changes monthly but could include sweet potato soup with red pepper, coriander and bacon salsa (£5), spinach, mascarpone, black truffle and parmesan lasagne (£6), king scallops with pea risotto and chervil (£8.50), shoulder of lamb with sweet red cabbage and hotpot potato with cumin (£12.50), and roast beef with fondant potato and wild mushroom. They also do sandwiches (from £4.50) and a very good cheese platter (£6). They excel too in their wine list which includes a fine choice by the glass; there's also freshly squeezed orange juice, smoothies, and good coffee, too. The bar, with its fine polished floorboards, good log fire, and quietly chatty atmosphere, serves well kept Adnams and a couple of guests such as City of Cambridge Hobsons Choice and Potton Shambles on handpump. You can sit outside in the neat garden (unfortunately there may be some traffic noise out here), and the hotel even has its own landing stage. *(Recommended by David R Crafts, David Stewart, Andy Sinden, Louise Harrington, Ian Phillips, Gordon Theaker, Mrs Thomas, Gordon Tong, R C Wiles, Pamela and Merlyn Horswell, Michael Sargent; also in the* Good Hotel Guide*)*

Huntsbridge ~ Licensee Martin Lee ~ Real ale ~ Bar food (12-2, 6.30-10; 12-2.30, 7-9.30 Sun) ~ Restaurant ~ (01480) 424300 ~ Children welcome ~ Dogs allowed in bar and bedrooms ~ Regular live music ~ Open 11-11; 12-10.30 Sun ~ Bedrooms: £80B/£125B

KEYSTON TL0475 Map 5

Pheasant

Village loop road; from A604 SE of Thrapston, right on to B663

Cambridgeshire Dining Pub of the Year

The exceptional food and service at this civilised dining pub make it a good choice for a special meal. People really like the courteous and efficient smart young staff, and the innovative changing menu might include leek and potato or squid and sweet corn soup, and pheasant salad (£4.95), crab with chilli, lime and coriander (£7.95), oak-smoked salmon (£6.75), lambs liver with red wine sauce (£11), steaks (from £14.25), red mullet with white beans (£16.95), and puddings such as lemon crème brûlée or hazelnut meringue (£5.95); they do a good set lunch (not Sun, £11.75 two courses, £14.95 three courses). The more formal little restaurant is no smoking. The excellent wine list includes an interesting choice of reasonably priced bottles and around 20 wines by the glass (plus two champagnes); fine port and sherry too. There's also well kept Adnams Bitter with changing guests such as Potton Village Bike and Nethergate Old Growler on handpump, and freshly squeezed juices. The atmosphere in the oak-beamed spreading bar is relaxing, and there are open fires, simple wooden tables and chairs, guns on the pink walls, and country paintings. Set out in front of the pub are wooden tables. *(Recommended by Ian and Jane Irving, J F M and M West, Gordon Theaker, O K Smyth, Brian Kneale, Michael Sargent, Dr Alan Sutton, Stephen, Julie and Hayley Brown, Marjorie and Bernard Parkin, Di and Mike Gillam, R C Wiles, Oliver and Sue Rowell)*

Huntsbridge ~ Licensee Clive Dixon ~ Real ale ~ Bar food (12-2, 6.30-10(7-9 Sun)) ~ Restaurant ~ (01832) 710241 ~ Children welcome ~ Dogs allowed in bar ~ Open 12-2, 6.30(6 Sat)-10.30; 12-2, 7-9.30 Sun; closed 25/26 Dec, 1 Jan evenings

If you know a pub's ever open all day, please tell us.

KIMBOLTON TL0967 Map 5

New Sun 🍷

High Street

A nice old pub fitting in well with Kimbolton's delightfully harmonious High Street, this is perhaps cosiest in its low-beamed front lounge, which has a couple of comfortable armchairs and a sofa beside the fireplace, standing timbers and exposed brickwork, books, pottery and brasses, and maybe mid-afternoon sun lighting up the wonkiest corners. This leads into a narrower locals' bar, with well kept Charles Wells Bombardier and Eagle, and a guest such as Greene King Old Speckled Hen; fruit machine, TV. Opening off here are a dining room and a bright, busy tiled conservatory, with wicker furniture, an unusual roof like a red and yellow striped umbrella, and plenty of tables for eating. Good bar food might include doorstep sandwiches (from £2.50), filled baked potatoes (from £2.95), soup (£3.25), mushroom stroganoff (£6.75), grilled pork cutlet with cider and sage gravy (£6.95), chicken supreme with caesar salad (£7.25), and lots of imaginative blackboard specials such as roast salmon on leek and potato crumble with gruyère and rocket pesto (£10.25), and rack of lamb or roast pigeon with chicken liver stuffing, celeriac mash and green peppercorn sauce (£12.95). Service is friendly and attentive. A wide choice of wines includes a dozen by the glass. There's a very pleasant garden behind, with plastic tables and chairs. Some of the nearby parking spaces have a 30-minute limit. *(Recommended by P Abbott, George Atkinson, John Picken)*

Charles Wells ~ Tenant Stephen Rogers ~ Real ale ~ Bar food (12-2.15, 7-9.30; not Sun, Mon evenings) ~ Restaurant ~ (01480) 860052 ~ Children in eating area of bar and restaurant ~ Dogs allowed in bar ~ Open 11-2.30, 6(6.30 Sat)-11; 12-10.30 Sun

MADINGLEY TL3960 Map 5

Three Horseshoes 🍴 🍷

Off A1303 W of Cambridge

The more adventurous diner will be hard pushed to choose from the innovative menu at this elegant thatched pub, and booking well in advance is a good idea if you want a table. Served in the bar or conservatory-restaurant, well cooked dishes change regularly and could include asparagus, baby leeks and dandelion salad with Cornish crab (£6.50), deep-fried anchovies with gremolata and rocket (£5.95), fried salmon with potato, leek and anchovy gratin, and green chilli and lemon peel salsa, roast chicken stuffed with mascarpone, rosemary and garlic with fennel, potato and parmesan gratin or chargrilled lamb chump with spinach and pine nut salad (£13.50), and fried beef fillet wrapped in parma ham with mustard mash (£18.50). Puddings might include passion fruit jelly with raspberries and crème fraîche (£5.50), or milk chocolate fondant with banana and malted milk ice cream (£6.50); they also do Sunday roasts. Not just the food but the wine list too is outstanding – it includes around 20 wines by the glass, plus sweet wines and ports. The pleasantly relaxed little no smoking airy bar has an open fire, simple wooden tables and chairs on the bare floorboards, stools at the bar and pictures on the green walls. There are two or three real ales on handpump such as Adnams, Batemans XXXB and Everards Tiger. *(Recommended by Penny Miles, Michael Sargent, Pamela Goodwyn, Keith and Janet Morris, Mr and Mrs J Glover, Michael Dandy, Maysie Thompson, Patricia Beebe, B N F and M Parkin, Richard Siebert, Terry Mizen, R C Wiles, Brian Root)*

Huntsbridge ~ Licensee Richard Stokes ~ Real ale ~ Bar food (12-2, 6.30-9.30; 12-7 Sun) ~ Restaurant ~ (01954) 210221 ~ Children welcome ~ Open 11.30-3, 6-11; 11.30-8 Sun

NEWTON TL4349 Map 5

Queens Head ★ 🍺 £

2½ miles from M11 junction 11; A10 towards Royston, then left on to B1368

Its simplicity is what makes this country pub so special. Unspoilt and friendly, with the same licensees for more than twenty-five years, it never seems to change much. An enjoyable place to bring visitors, it always has a good crowd of locals too. The well worn main bar has a low ceiling and crooked beams, bare wooden benches and seats built into the walls, paintings on the cream walls, and bow windows. A curved high-backed settle stands on yellow tiles, a loudly ticking clock marks the unchanging time, and a lovely big log fire cheerily warms the place. The little carpeted saloon is similar but even cosier. Adnams Bitter and Broadside are tapped straight from the barrel, with Regatta in summer, Old Ale in winter and Tally Ho at Christmas, Crone's and Cassell's ciders, and fresh orange and organic apple juice. Darts in a no smoking side room, with shove-ha'penny, table skittles, dominoes, cribbage, and nine men's morris. There's a limited range of hearty straightforward food which includes good value lunchtime sandwiches (from £1.90; they're thinking of adding some new varieties), and filled baked potatoes (£2.50), while another good bet is a mug of lovely home-made brown soup (£2.40), and they even do toast with delicious beef dripping; in the evening and on Sunday lunchtime you can get plates of excellent cold meat, smoked salmon, cheeses and pâté (from £3.50). There are seats in front of the pub, with its vine trellis. *(Recommended by Ian Phillips, Mr Biggs, Susan and Nigel Wilson, Keith and Janet Morris, Michael and Marion Buchanan, R C Wiles, JWAC, Minda and Stanley Alexander)*

Free house ~ Licensees David and Juliet Short ~ Real ale ~ Bar food (not 25 Dec) ~ No credit cards ~ (01223) 870436 ~ Very well behaved children in eating area of bar ~ Dogs welcome ~ Open 11.30-2.30, 6-11; 12-2.30, 7-10.30 Sun; closed 25 Dec

PETERBOROUGH TL1999 Map 5

Brewery Tap £

Opposite Queensgate car park

Although it's under threat of being turned into a parking complex, fingers crossed that this beer lovers' paradise will manage to stay open for a while longer. It's said to be one of the largest microbreweries in Europe, and a huge glass wall on one side of the pub gives a view of the massive copper-banded stainless brewing vessels that produce the very good Oakham beers. Up to a dozen real ales on handpump might include Bishops Farewell, Harlequin, Helterskelter, JHB and White Dwarf from the brewery here, with guests from other brewers like Bass, Elgoods, Nethergate and Newby Wyke. This American-style place is a striking conversion of an old labour exchange. Contemporary industrial décor continues throughout its vast open-plan areas, with blue-painted iron pillars holding up a steel-corded mezzanine level, light wood and stone floors, and hugely enlarged and framed newspaper cuttings on its light orange walls. It's stylishly lit by a giant suspended steel ring with bulbs running around the rim, and steel-meshed wall lights. A band of chequered floor tiles traces the path of the long sculpted light wood bar counter, which is boldly backed by an impressive display of uniform wine bottles in a ceiling-high wall of wooden cubes. The customers are surprisingly mixed (though the loud piped music might not be to everyone's taste), and it gets very busy in the evening; they have a DJ on Friday and Saturday nights, when there may be an entry fee. Thai bar food includes tempura vegetables (£2.75), tofu fries or spring rolls (£2.90), chicken balls or dim sum (£3.50), green, red or yellow curries or beef with oyster sauce, peppers, mushrooms and spring onions (£4.50), noodles stir-fried with sweet radish, spring onions, peanuts, egg and either tiger prawns or vegetables (£4.95), and aromatic duck stir-fried in tamarind sauce with cashew nuts (£5.50); they also do good value set menus. It's owned by the same people as Charters. *(Recommended by Peter H Stallard, Richard Lewis, the Didler, JP, PP, Pat and Tony Martin, Ian and Nita Cooper)*

Own brew ~ Licensee Neil Poulter ~ Real ale ~ Bar food (all day Fri/Sat) ~ (01733) 358500 ~ No children ~ DJ Fri/Sat evenings ~ Open 12-11(till 1.30 am Fri/Sat); 12-10.30 Sun; closed 25 and 26 Dec, 1 Jan

Charters £

Town Bridge, S side

Afloat on the River Nene, this lively pub is housed in a remarkable conversion of a sturdy 1907 commercial Dutch grain barge. Its uniqueness is not the pub's only attraction, though; manned by friendly staff, up to a dozen handpumps serve quickly changing ales such as well kept Archers, Bass, Fullers London Pride, Hop Back Summer Lightning and Newby Wyke, as well as Oakham beers from the owner's own nearby microbrewery (see the Brewery Tap entry above), like JHB (very cheap), Bishops Farewell and Old Tosspot, and guests from brewers such as Black Sheep, Cottage, Iceni and Fenland. There's plenty of seating in the well timbered sizeable nautically themed bar, which is down in the cargo holds, and above deck a glazed oriental restaurant replaces the tarpaulins that used to cover the hold; piped music. Good value lunchtime bar food includes tempura vegetables, crispy seaweed or spring rolls (£2.95), pitta bread filled with beef in black bean sauce or sweet and sour vegetables (£3.65), and singapore chicken curry or lamb rendang curry (£5.65). If you're not too keen on the water, the pub also boasts one of the biggest pub gardens in the city (it's often overrun with rabbits). *(Recommended by the Didler, Richard Lewis, Peter F Marshall, JP, PP)*

Free house ~ Licensee Paul Hook ~ Real ale ~ Bar food (12-2.30, 6-9.30; all day Fri/Sat) ~ Restaurant ~ (01733) 315700 ~ Dogs allowed in bar ~ Live bands Fri/Sat ~ Open 12-11(10.30 Sun); 12-2am Fri/Sat; closed 25 Dec and 1 Jan

SPALDWICK TL1372 Map 5

George

Just off A14 W of Huntingdon

'Like going into someone's home' is how one reader described a visit to this welcoming black-beamed pub. It's usually busy (so best to book if you want to eat here), but the staff and landlord are always friendly and helpful. Generous well cooked dishes include red thai chicken curry (£7.25), Grimsby battered cod, grilled sardines, and breaded pork with pepper sauce (all £6.95), chicken breast stuffed with salmon and watercress (£8.95), roast duck with apple sauce, rump steak or grilled lemon sole (£9.95) and baked bass (£11.95); the restaurant is no smoking. There's a chatty local atmosphere in the red-carpeted bar, which has pewter mugs hanging from the beams, a mix of understated comfortable seats grouped cosily around little tables, each with a posy of flowers in a vase on a lace doily and a candle, as well as nice little prints on the walls and some house plants; piped music, pool and fruit machine. Adnams Broadside, Charles Wells Bombardier and Eagle IPA are the three well kept real ales that they serve on handpump. *(Recommended by Margaret and Roy Randle, Mike and Mary Carter, Eric Locker, Charles and Pauline Stride, Michael Sargent, David and Mary Webb)*

Free house ~ Licensee Mr Watson ~ Real ale ~ Bar food (12-2, 7-10) ~ Restaurant ~ (01480) 890293 ~ Children in restaurant ~ Dogs allowed in bar ~ Open 12-3, 6-11 (7-10.30 Sun)

STILTON TL1689 Map 5

Bell

High Street; village signposted from A1 S of Peterborough

The generously served, enjoyable bar food at this elegant 16th-c stone coaching inn has won much praise from readers recently. The menu might include dishes such as stilton, celery and cider soup (£3.50), chicken liver and garlic pâté with red onion marmalade (£4.50), mussels in white wine, cream and garlic sauce (£5.50), spinach and ricotta lasagne with four-cheese sauce (£8.50), braised beef and ale with stilton dumplings or moroccan lamb tagine with buttered couscous (£9.25), rib-eye steak (£11.95) and grilled lemon sole; they do baguettes too. The eating area of the bar and lower part of the restaurant are no smoking; service is friendly and obliging (though it can sometimes be slow when they're busy). As well as a good choice of wines by the glass, they have well kept Fullers London Pride, Greene King IPA, Oakham JHB and a guest such as Bass on handpump. The two neatly kept and welcoming bars have bow windows, sturdy upright wooden seats on flagstone floors as well as plush button-back built-in banquettes, and a good big log fire in a handsome stone fireplace. The partly stripped walls have big prints of sailing and winter coaching scenes, and a giant pair of blacksmith's bellows hangs in the middle of the front bar; backgammon, dominoes, cribbage and piped music. Through the fine coach arch is a lovely sheltered courtyard with tables, and a well which supposedly dates back to Roman times; attractive chintzy bedrooms. *(Recommended by Gordon Theaker, David Peakall, B, M and P Kendall, Brian and Janet Ainscough, B N F and M Parkin, Anthony Barnes, Bob and Maggie Atherton, Tony Gayfer, Peter H Stallard, P R Morley, Mrs Joy Griffiths, Darly Graton, Graeme Gulibert)*

Free house ~ Licensee Liam McGivern ~ Real ale ~ Bar food ~ Restaurant ~ (01733) 241066 ~ Well behaved children in eating area of bar at lunchtime ~ Open 12-2 (3 Sat), 6-11; 12-3, 7-10.30 Sun; closed 25 Dec ~ Bedrooms: £69.50B/£89.50B

SUTTON GAULT TL4279 Map 5

Anchor ★

Village signed off B1381 in Sutton

Although most of our readers come here to enjoy the good imaginative food (and it's worth making a special effort to do so), you'll be made to feel welcome even if you've just popped in for a drink. The atmosphere in the four heavily timbered stylishly simple rooms is nicely pubby and informal, there are three log fires, antique settles and well spaced scrubbed pine tables on the gently undulating old floors, good lithographs and big prints on the walls, and lighting by gas and candles. Well set by the high embankment of the New Bedford River, it has pleasant seats outside, and good walks and bird-watching nearby. To be sure of a table here it's best to book, and the finely cooked (though not cheap) menu could include grilled dates with bacon and mustard sauce, home-made black pudding on crushed potatoes with poached egg or salmon terrine (£5.50), wild mushroom risotto (£11), poached smoked haddock or seared pigeon breasts with sweet potato and chorizo (£12.50), steak and kidney pudding (£13), and roast duck with braised red cabbage in orange and red wine sauce (£14.50); home-made puddings such as bread and butter pudding with poached apricots or apple and blackberry crumble tart (£4.50), and a particularly good changing British cheeseboard (£5.50). From Monday to Friday lunchtimes (not bank holidays), there's an exceptionally good value two-course menu (£7.95), and children can have most of their dishes in smaller helpings; three-course Sunday lunch (£18.50). The staff are friendly and helpful. As well as a thoughtful wine list (including a wine of the month and eight by the glass), winter mulled wine and freshly squeezed fruit juice, they have real ale tapped from the cask from brewers such as Black Sheep and City of Cambridge. *(Recommended by Derek Thomas, Michael Sargent, A J Bowen, Gordon Neighbour, DF, NMF, Alan Clark, Bob and Maggie Atherton, D L Parkhurst, Sharon and Alan Corper, Gordon Theaker, MDN, DC, Tina and David Woods-Taylor, Patricia Beebe)*

Free house ~ Licensee Robin Moore ~ Real ale ~ Restaurant ~ (01353) 778537 ~ Children welcome ~ Open 12-3, 7-11(10.30 Sun); closed 25 Dec evening, and 26 Dec ~ Bedrooms: £50S(£65B)/£66.50S(£95B)

SWAVESEY TL3668 Map 5

Trinity Foot

Right by A14 eastbound, NW of Cambridge, and accessible from that direction; from westbound carriageway take Swavesey, Fen Drayton turn

A regular stop-off for some of our readers, this busy pub gets its deliciously cooked fish fresh daily from the east coast ports. There's always a good choice and, depending on the catch, reasonably priced dishes could include smoked mackerel or soft herring roes on toast (£4.25), king scallops wrapped in bacon (£5.50), grilled cod, haddock, trout or scampi (£8), or monkfish medallions cooked in white wine and cream (£11); readers especially recommend the grilled lemon sole (£11). There are plenty of other options even if fish is not your thing, such as pâté or stuffed mushrooms (£4.25), sausage and mash or leek and stilton crumble (£6.50), and steaks (from £12). As well as decent wines, and freshly squeezed fruit juice, they may have Boddingtons, Elgoods Pageant Ale and Whitbreads kept under light blanket pressure. There are well spaced tables, fresh flowers, a light and airy flower-filled conservatory, and no smoking dining room. The big enclosed garden has shrubs and trees, though you may find the nearby A14 is too noisy for real relaxation. The pub owns a fresh fish shop next door, usually open Tues-Fri 11-2.30, 6-7.30, Sat 11.30-2.30. *(Recommended by Ian Phillips, Dr T E Hothersall, Mr and Mrs K J Morris, DF, NMF, Marjorie and Bernard Parkin, Jennie and Jim Wingate, Richard Marjoram, Sharon and Alan Corper)*

Whitbreads ~ Lease H J Mole ~ Real ale ~ Bar food (12-2, 6-9.30(Fri/Sat 6-10); 12-1.30 Sun, closed in evening) ~ Restaurant ~ (01954) 230315 ~ Children in eating area of bar ~ Open 11-2.30, 6-11; 12-3 Sun; closed Sun evenings

THRIPLOW TL4346 Map 5

Green Man

3 miles from M11 junction 10; A505 towards Royston, then first right; Lower Street

Since our last edition, new licensees have taken over this Victorian pub. They've made quite a few changes, though there's still a good mix of furniture, mostly sturdy stripped tables and attractive high-backed dining chairs and pews on a flowery red carpet, and shelves with pewter mugs and decorated china. To the right of the bar a sweet and cosy little room has comfortable sofas and armchairs, while two arches lead through to a no smoking dining area on the left. A very short lunchtime bar menu includes sandwiches (£4.50-£5.25) as well as a couple of specials such as crab and ginger tortellini or mozzarella, black olive and goats cheese ravioli (£5.95), while in the evening you can choose from four starters, mains and puddings, which could include mediterranean-style fish soup or home-cured bresaola (£4.50), braised lamb shank or salmon supreme with a herb crust (£14.50), and puddings such as strawberry cheesecake or sticky date pudding with toffee sauce and clotted cream (£4.50); they do two courses for £18, three courses for £21. Regularly changing real ales from brewers such as Buffys and Milton. You can sit outside (there's an outdoor heater). More reports on the new regime please. *(Recommended by Ian Phillips, Malcolm and Jennifer Perry, Neville and Anne Morley, Stephen, Julie and Hayley Brown, David R Crafts, P and D Carpenter, Kevin Thorpe, Roger Everett)*

Free house ~ Licensee Mary Lindgren ~ Real ale ~ Bar food (not Sun evening or Mon) ~ Restaurant ~ (01763) 208855 ~ Well behaved children over 4 welcome in eating area of bar ~ Open 12-2.30, 6-11; closed Sun evening and Mon

WANSFORD TL0799 Map 5

Haycock ★ 🍷 🛏

Village clearly signposted from A1 W of Peterborough

This handsome and much extended old coaching inn is a really refreshing place to take a break from the A1 – you may even be tempted to abandon your journey and stay the night. The main entrance hall has a fine flagstoned floor with antique hunting prints, seats and a longcase clock. This leads into a smart panelled main bar with dark terracotta walls, a sturdy rail above a mulberry dado, and old settles. Through two comely stone arches is another attractive area, while the comfortable front sitting room has some squared oak panelling by the bar counter, a nice wall clock, and a big log fire. The airy stripped brick Orchard Room by the garden has dark blue and light blue basketweave chairs, pretty flowery curtains and nice modern prints; doors open on to a big sheltered courtyard with lots of tables and cream Italian umbrellas; piped music. They only serve sandwiches (from £4.95), filled ciabattas (from £5.85), ploughman's (£6.95) and cream teas (£5.50) in the bar, but do full (though not cheap) meals in the Orchard Room; the restaurant is no smoking. Well kept Adnams and Bass on handpump and a good wine list. More reports please. *(Recommended by Derek Thomas, Mr and Mrs J Glover, Francis Johnston, Mr and Mrs T B Staples, Gordon Neighbour, Gordon Theaker, Norma and Keith Bloomfield, Barbara Wensworth)*

Free house ~ Licensee Shelby Neale ~ Real ale ~ Bar food (10-10) ~ Restaurant ~ (01780) 782223 ~ Children welcome ~ Dogs allowed in bedrooms ~ Open 11-11; 12-10.30 Sun ~ Bedrooms: £87.50B/£110B

Lucky Dip

Besides the fully inspected pubs, you might like to try these Lucky Dips recommended to us and described by readers (if you do, please send us reports: www.goodguides.com).

Abbotsley [TL2256]
Eight Bells [B1046]: 18th-c village pub with good value generous food, well kept Greene King IPA and Abbot; darts and TV in public bar; picnic-sets in garden with terrace and barbecues *(CMW, JJW)*
Jolly Abbot [High Street/St Neots Rd]: Roomy, relaxed and comfortable open-plan pub with chef/landlord doing good interesting food using carefully chosen ingredients, restaurant sectioned off by standing timbers, leather banquettes, chesterfields and stools, Greene King ales inc Ruddles organic, decent wines, nice atmosphere *(Anthony Barnes)*
Abington Pigotts [TL3044]
Pig & Abbot: Thriving L-shaped bar with four real ales inc Adnams and Fullers London Pride, food inc good hot beef baguettes *(JHBS)*
Alwalton [TL1396]
☆ ***Cuckoo*** [Oundle Rd, just off A1 W of Peterborough]: Big Vintage Inn with good service, enjoyable food all day, well kept Bass and Tetleys, good wine choice, some nice cosy corners *(Sally Anne and Peter Goodale, Tom Evans)*
Babraham [TL5150]
George [High St; just off A1307]: Popular beamed and timbered dining pub, old pictures and artefacts, good imaginative food in bar and restaurant inc pudding club, well kept Greene King and unusual guest beers, no smoking area, friendly efficient staff; very quiet piped music; tables on front grass, attractive setting on quiet road *(Keith and Janet Morris, Tony Middis)*
Barrington [ST3818]
☆ ***Royal Oak*** [from M11 junction 11 take A10 to Newton, turn right; West Green]: Rambling thatched Tudor pub with tables out overlooking classic village green, heavy low beams and timbers, lots of character, well kept Courage Best and Directors and Greene King IPA and Old Speckled Hen, prompt service, decent food in bar and pleasant no smoking dining conservatory; may be piped music, provision for children *(Gordon Theaker, LYM, Michael Dandy, Jim Bush)*
Boxworth [TL3464]
Golden Ball [High St]: Attractive pub/restaurant doing well under current helpful management, enjoyable food, well kept real ales; piped music; big well kept garden, nice setting *(Roche Bentley)*
Brampton [TL2170]
Grange [High St]: Imposing hotel with leatherette chairs and sofas in back bar used by locals, good food from sandwiches and more substantial bar meals (not Sun evening) to fine restaurant meals (not Sun evening or Mon), welcoming landlord, good service, Greene King IPA; comfortable bedrooms *(Gordon Theaker, BB)*
Broughton [TL2877]
Crown [off A141 opp RAF Wyton; Bridge Rd]: Good range of well kept guest beers in pub reopened by village syndicate, good food (book well ahead at night) *(Peter J Holmes)*
Buckden [TL1967]
☆ ***Lion*** [High St]: Lovely partly 15th-c coaching inn, oak beams and carvings in small comfortably pubby and relaxing bar, panelled restaurant, well presented generous food inc lots of fresh veg, appealing summer cold table, friendly attentive staff, roaring log fire, good choice of wines, Greene King Ruddles and John Smiths, no music or machines; bedrooms with own bathrooms *(Michael Sargent, David and Ruth Shillitoe, Gordon Theaker, Mr and Mrs J Glover, Susan Lee)*
Cambridge [TL4658]
☆ ***Castle*** [Castle St]: Large, airy and well appointed, with full Adnams range kept well and guests such as Wadworths Farmers Glory, generous quickly served food inc burgers, no smoking area with easy chairs upstairs, friendly staff; may be piped pop music; picnic-sets in good garden *(Brian and Anna Marsden, the Didler, Keith and Janet Morris)*
Champion of the Thames [King St]: Small and cosy local with plenty of character, wonderfully decorated windows, padded walls and seats, painted Anaglypta ceiling, lots of woodwork, no music, welcoming atmosphere, simple lunchtime sandwiches, particularly well kept Greene King IPA and Abbot *(the Didler, Keith and Janet Morris)*
Fort St George [Midsummer Common]: Picturesque pub noted for its charming waterside position on Midsummer Common, overlooking ducks, swans, punts and boathouses; extended around old-fashioned Tudor core, interesting bar food from open sandwiches to traditional Sun lunches, well kept Greene King ales with a guest such as Jennings Cockerhoop (but may be plastic glasses), decent wines, oars on beams, historic boating photographs, stuffed fish and bric-a-brac; can be very busy, when service may slow; lots of tables outside *(LYM, Kevin Blake, Mike and Mary Carter)*
☆ ***Free Press*** [Prospect Row]: Friendly and charmingly unpretentious, no smoking throughout, no piped music, machines or mobile phones; plain wooden tables and benches on bare boards, open fires, short changing choice of good value enjoyable generous food inc plenty of vegetarian dishes, well kept Greene King IPA, Abbot and Mild and a guest beer, decent wines, cribbage and dominoes; small sheltered paved back garden *(the Didler, Patricia Beebe, John Wooll, Terry Mizen, Sue Demont, Tim Barrow, LYM, Dr and Mrs Jackson, Geoffrey Plow, David Edwards, Michael and Marion Buchanan)*
Kingston Arms [Kingston St]: Doing well under friendly and helpful newish management, large U-shaped bar with several of their own

Lidstones ales and guests such as Hop Back and Timothy Taylors Landlord, good wine choice, decent choice of food, quick pleasant service, no music, machines or children inside; small enclosed torch-lit back garden *(Ged Lithgoe, David Edwards, John Wooll)*

☆ ***Mill*** [Mill Lane]: Sturdy scrubbed wooden tables and high-backed settles, well kept ales such as Adnams Best, Black Sheep, Fullers London Pride, Hop Back Summer Lightning, Greene King Old Speckled Hen and Theakstons XB, farm ciders, country wines, simple lunchtime bar food from sandwiches up; fruit machine, piped pop; children in eating area, open all day, overlooks mill pond where punts can be hired – very popular waterside garden *(Dr and Mrs Jackson, LYM)*

Red Bull [Barton Rd, Newnham; A603 SW edge]: Bare-boards real ale pub with good well kept range tapped into jugs at long counter, good value food inc Sun roasts, welcoming and obliging service even when very busy (near Rugby ground); seating limited, no children *(Jenny and Chris Wilson)*

Castor [TL1298]

Fitzwilliam Arms [signed off A47 just W of Peterborough]: This attractive thatched pub, a main entry in our previous edition, has now changed to an Italian restaurant (the Fratelli) *(LYM)*

Chatteris [TL3986]

Cross Keys [Market Hill]: Attractive 16th-c coaching inn opp church in fenland market town, relaxing open fire in long bar part public and part comfortable armchairs, pleasant back courtyard, good reasonably priced food in bar and restaurant inc good Sun lunches, warm friendly service, Greene King beers, inexpensive wine, tea and coffee; comfortable bedrooms *(Michael and Marion Buchanan, Robert Turnham)*

Chittering [TL4970]

☆ ***Travellers Rest*** [Ely Rd (A10)]: Roomy open-plan roadside dining pub done up in comfortable chain-pub style, all very neat and clean and largely no smoking, polite pleasant service, wide choice of good generous freshly prepared food (three-course bargains Mon and Weds), properly served coffee, may be well kept Greene King IPA, easy wheelchair access, spotless lavatories; may be soft piped music, but no mobile phones; children in family area, picnic-sets among fruit trees behind, camp site *(Michael and Jenny Back, BB, Peter J Holmes)*

Conington [TL3266]

White Swan [signed off A14 (was A604) Cambridge—Huntingdon; Elsworth Rd]: Friendly new management in attractive quietly placed country local with well kept Greene King IPA and Abbot and guest beers tapped from the cask, enjoyable straightforward food (not Sun evening) inc fish and children's, quick service, cheerful traditional bar, eating areas inc no smoking ones on right, games inc bar billiards and juke box on left; good big front garden with play area and play house *(Peter J Holmes, Keith and Janet Morris)*

Croydon [TL3149]

☆ ***Queen Adelaide*** [off A1198; High St]: Big beamed dining area full of people tucking into its wide range of attractively priced food, well kept ales such as Boddingtons and Greene King, impressive array of spirits, efficient friendly service, standing timbers dividing off part with settees, banquettes and stools; garden, play area *(P and D Carpenter, Keith and Janet Morris, Margaret and Roy Randle)*

Duxford [TL4745]

☆ ***John Barleycorn*** [off A1301; Moorfield Rd, pub at far end]: Useful food pub in thatched and shuttered early 17th-c cottage, good plain food all day (cooked to order, so may be a wait), Greene King IPA and Abbot and a guest such as Black Sheep, decent wines, good friendly service, softly lit spotless but relaxed bar with old prints, decorative plates and so forth; may be piped music; tables out among flowers, open all day *(David Twitchett, Charles Gysin, Mr and Mrs T B Staples, Stephen, Julie and Hayley Brown, LYM)*

Eaton Socon [TL1658]

☆ ***Crown*** [nr A1/A428 interchange]: Welcoming bustle in Chef & Brewer with low beams and separate areas, good choice of moderately priced food (not Sun) from sandwiches up, generous choice of changing ales kept well, two coal-effect gas fires, restaurant (good steaks); piped music, no T-shirts; garden *(John Saville)*

☆ ***White Horse***: Rambling, comfortable and interestingly furnished low-beamed rooms dating from 13th c, relaxing atmosphere, well kept real ales, decent wines, friendly service and enjoyable fresh food inc tender steaks; nice high-backed traditional settles around fine log fire in end room; play area in back garden, children in eating areas; bedrooms *(LYM, Bob and Maggie Atherton)*

Elsworth [TL3163]

☆ ***George & Dragon*** [off A14 NW of Cambridge, via Boxworth, or off A428]: Neatly furnished restauranty pub, very popular with older people for good range of reliable food and crisp professional service, now under new management – too soon for us to rate definitively, but first signs are promising; panelled main bar and back dining area, well kept Greene King ales, decent wines, open fire; nice terraces, play area in garden, restaurant; attractive village; has been cl Sun evening and Mon *(LYM)*

Eltisley [TL2659]

☆ ***Leeds Arms*** [signed off A428; The Green]: Knocked-through beamed bar overlooking peaceful village green, huge log fire, very friendly staff, close-set tables for substantial food from nicely presented sandwiches to enjoyable home-made hot dishes, well kept Adnams Broadside and Greene King IPA, Stowford Press cider, pleasant no smoking restaurant; unobtrusive piped music; children in eating area, pleasant garden with play area, simple comfortable bedrooms in separate block *(P and D Carpenter, Simon Mighall, Brian Root, LYM)*

Elton [TL0893]

☆ ***Crown*** [Duck St]: Carefully rebuilt stone pub

with above-average varied food from good chunky sandwiches (wknd baguettes instead) to enjoyable hot dishes and tempting puddings trolley, well kept ales such as Adnams, Brakspears, Greene King IPA and Woodfordes Wherry, cheerful helpful uniformed staff, banknotes on low beams, watercolours and drawings for sale, big log fire, large dining conservatory (cl Sun pm and Mon); steps up to no smoking restaurant and lavatories; opp green in beautiful small village *(Michael Sargent, Michael and Jenny Back)*

Ely [TL5380]

Cutter [Annesdale, off Station Rd just towards centre from A142 roundabout; or walk S along Riverside Walk from Maltings car park]: Lovely riverside setting, with plenty of tables outside and a genuine welcome for children, friendly series of unpretentious bars, well kept Courage Directors, Greene King IPA and Old Speckled Hen and John Smiths, good house wines; piped music can be obtrusive *(Michael and Marion Buchanan, Mike and Mary Carter, LYM)*

Lamb [Brook St (Lynn Rd)]: Good lunchtime bar food in impressively panelled hotel lounge bar (there's a different one at the far end), friendly staff, well kept Tetleys; bedrooms *(Stephen, Julie and Hayley Brown, Roger and Pauline Pearce)*

Prince Albert [Silver St]: Spotless traditional two-bar local with Greene King IPA, Abbot, XX Mild and Triumph kept well, good value straightforward food, friendly long-serving landlord, books for sale, no juke box; trim and attractive garden with two aviaries *(Keith and Janet Morris, the Didler, MDN, C J Fletcher)*

Etton [TF1406]

☆ ***Golden Pheasant*** [just off B1443 N of Peterborough, signed from nr N end of A15 bypass]: Looks like the 19th-c private house it once was, notable for consistently well kept ales usually inc Adnams Broadside, Batemans XXXB, Cottage Goldrush, Greene King IPA, Kelham Island Pale Rider, Timothy Taylors Landlord and six weekly guests; homely plush bar, airy glass-walled no smoking family side room, tasty food in bar and restaurant, quick friendly service, pub games; well reproduced piped music, friendly dogs; good-sized garden with soccer pitch, floodlit boules pitch, interesting aviary, adventure playground and marquee; bedrooms, open all day at least in summer *(Des and Jen Clarke, BB)*

Eye Green [TF2203]

Greyhound [A1073, nr A47 junction]: Well kept Adnams Broadside and Charles Wells Eagle and Bombardier, wide range of good value food inc bargain steak and children's dishes, quick service; very clean and bright *(C A Hall)*

Godmanchester [TL2470]

White Hart [Cambridge Rd]: Wide choice of traditional food, good-sized helpings, good beer range, pleasant atmosphere and décor, friendly attentive staff *(Chris and Trish Nye)*

Gorefield [TF4111]

Woodmans Cottage [Main St; off B1169 W of Wisbech]: Spacious bar with brocaded banquettes, well kept Greene King IPA and Abbot and a couple of guests from central servery, stripped brick side eating area, and pitched-ceiling restaurant, beams and open fires, games area, pubby food from sandwiches to vast array of home-made puddings; piped music; children in eating areas, tables on front verandah and sheltered back terrace, play area *(Michael and Jenny Back, LYM, R C Wiles)*

Grantchester [TL4355]

☆ ***Green Man*** [High St]: Attractively laid out and welcoming, with individual furnishings, lots of beams, good choice of food, two Adnams ales and a guest beer, no music or children in bar; plenty of tables in lovely garden behind, nice village, a short stroll from lovely riverside meadows *(Tim and Ann Newell, LYM)*

Great Chishill [TL4239]

☆ ***Pheasant*** [follow Heydon signpost from B1039 in village]: Good food choice in beamed split-level flagstoned and timbered bar with some elaborately carved though modern seats and settles, friendly staff, real ales such as Adnams, Courage Best and Directors and Theakstons, decent wine list, darts, cribbage, dominoes; piped music; children welcome, charming back garden with small play area *(Abi Benson, LYM)*

Hardwick [TL1968]

☆ ***Blue Lion*** [signed off A428 (was A45) W of Cambridge; Main St]: Enjoyably friendly and photogenic old local with lots of beams, open fire and woodburner, fairly priced food from lunchtime sandwiches and baguettes to enjoyable Sun lunch and fresh Whitby fish (good value fish and chips Mon night), extended restaurant area (evening booking recommended), well kept Greene King IPA and Abbot tapped from the cask, old farm tools, two cats, conservatory; piped music; pretty roadside front garden, car park; handy for Wimpole Way walkers *(Roy Bromell, Michael Sargent, Keith and Janet Morris, BB, Penny Miles)*

Helpston [TF1205]

Bluebell [Woodgate]: Real old-fashioned local, well kept beer inc Batemans and guests, cheese and onion rolls, darts, bar billiards; John Clare the 19th-c poet was born next door and originally worked here *(Des and Jen Clarke)*

Histon [TL4363]

King William IV [Church St]: Low beams, open fires, plenty of character, good food and atmosphere, friendly service, no piped music *(P and D Carpenter)*

Red Lion [High St]: Popular and friendly, with basic public bar, comfortably well used lounge, several real ales inc Greene King (holds beer festivals and other events), good value pub food; big garden *(Keith and Janet Morris)*

Holywell [TL3370]

☆ ***Old Ferry Boat*** [signed off A1123]: Roomy and congenial old thatched low-beamed Greene King inn doing well under newish management, sympathetically refurbished with several open fires and some other hints of antiquity, dozens of carpenter's tools, window seats overlooking Great Ouse, Greene King IPA, Abbot and

Ruddles County, enjoyable generous food from sandwiches to full meals (all day in summer), pleasant service, good no smoking areas; can get very busy; open all day wknds, children welcome, tables and cocktail parasols on front terrace and riverside lawn, moorings, bedrooms, conference facilities *(Sally and Philip Rose, Robert Turnham, LYM, Ian Phillips)*

Horningsea [TL4962]

Plough & Fleece [just NE of Cambridge: first slip-road off A14 heading E after A10, then left; or B1047 Fen Ditton road off A1303; High St]: Rambling country pub, low black beams, comfortably worn high-backed settles and other sturdily old-fashioned wooden furnishings, dark cool recesses in summer, log fires in winter, more modern no smoking back dining room and comfortable conservatory, well kept Greene King IPA and Abbot, some interesting light dishes; dominoes and cribbage; garden with nice mix of wild and cultivated flowers; can be busy lunchtime, handy for Cambridge Science Park; cl Mon evening *(J F M and M West, Patrick Hancock, LYM)*

Little Shelford [TL4451]

Navigator [2½ miles from M11 junction 11: A10 towards Royston, then left at Hauxton, The Shelfords signpost]: Friendly attractive village local with pews, beams, pine panelling and a hot coal fire, good generous authentic Thai food (not Sun evening), well kept Greene King ales, quick obliging service, reasonable prices; children welcome, some picnic-sets outside, cl Mon and Sat lunchtimes *(LYM)*

Little Thetford [TL5374]

☆ ***Fish & Duck*** [Holt Fen; track off A1123 Wicken—Stretham, by level crossing (well away from village)]: Neatly kept family pub in pretty spot by remote fenland marina where rivers Cam, Old West and Great Ouse join, big windows to enjoy the view, on one side stretching to Ely cathedral; good food all day inc Sun carvery, friendly service, interesting memorabilia and pictures everywhere, hardly an inch wasted, some stuffed birds and animal heads, daily papers on old pool table, lots of books, woodburner, Adnams and Shepherd Neame Spitfire, back dining room; piped music, dogs on leads allowed; nicely placed tables outside, good play area, moorings available *(Patricia Beebe, BB)*

Longstowe [TL3154]

☆ ***Red House*** [Old North Road; A1198 Royston—Huntingdon, S of village]: Relaxed rambling bar with big log fire, easy chairs and settees, horsey décor, well kept Greene King IPA and interesting changing guest beers, decent food from sandwiches to mixed grill, children welcome in neat restaurant area on left; may be quiet piped jazz; picnic-sets in sheltered and attractive little garden, cl Mon lunchtime *(LYM)*

Milton [TL4763]

Waggon & Horses [off A10 N of Cambridge; High St]: Welcoming mock-Tudor local with L-shaped lounge, good value food, faultlessly kept Elgoods ales, cheerful efficient service, games corner with darts and bar billiards, friendly dalmatian, lots of hats; attractive garden with slide and swing, apple trees, barbecues, picnic-sets and boules *(Pete Baker)*

Pampisford [TL4948]

Chequers [Town Lane]: Picturesque pub with lovely window boxes and hanging baskets, comfortable décor and atmosphere combining restaurant feel with traditional bar friendliness, good standard food inc fresh fish and Sun lunch, well kept Greene King IPA, helpful licensee; tables in pleasant garden, handy for M11 *(Tony Middis)*

Perry [TL1467]

Wheatsheaf [nr Grafham Water sailing club]: Clean and pleasant, with good food choice inc various baguettes, quick welcoming service, Greene King ales, quick cheerful service, good value coffee, flagstoned bar, no smoking dining area; piped music; plenty of tables in big pleasant garden with terrace, bedrooms *(George Atkinson, David and Mary Webb)*

Peterborough [TL1999]

Bogarts [North St]: Half a dozen well kept ales mainly from small breweries in friendly open-plan Victorian pub with central bar, good simple lunchtime food, daily papers, fine mix of customers, lots of Humphrey Bogart pictures; silent TV, games machine, quiz nights; handy for Westgate shopping centre, tables out on small terrace, open all day *(JP, PP, Richard Lewis)*

College Arms [Broadway]: Large open-plan Wetherspoons (converted technical college building) with well kept ales for cental bar, good value varied food inc bargains, friendly helpful staff, comfortable seating inc upstairs, side alcoves and no smoking areas, bookshelves and paintings; open all day, may be doormen Fri/Sat night *(Richard Lewis)*

Glass Onion [Burghley Rd]: Open-plan local with several well kept Payns ales (from landlord's Ramsey microbrewery) and others such as Everards Beacon and Tiger, low prices, pool, friendly staff; no children inside; open all day, picnic-sets and climber in back garden *(Richard Lewis)*

Palmerston Arms [Oundle Rd]: 16th-c stone-built pub with old tables, chairs, benches and a sofa in carpeted lounge, tiled-floor public bar, lots of well kept ales tapped from casks behind hop-hung counter, even organic lager, good pork pies, friendly landlord, no music or machines; step down into pub, steps to lavatory; small garden, open all day, but at busy times, esp wknds, they may lock doors and restrict access to locals only *(the Didler, JP, PP)*

Reach [TL5666]

☆ ***Dykes End*** [off A14 via B1102, and signed from Swaffham Prior; Fair Green]: Comfortable L-shaped bar and upstairs evening restaurant, tastefully redeveloped by village consortium; wide range of food from lunchtime sandwiches, baguettes and other bar food to local game, well kept Adnams, Greene King and guests such as Woodfordes Wherry, good atmosphere, friendly staff, quiz nights *(Chris Butt, Michael and Marion Buchanan, C J Fletcher, Pam and David Bailey)*

Shepreth [TL3947]

☆ ***Plough*** [signed just off A10 S of Cambridge; High St]: Neatly kept bright and airy local with popular generous home-made food from good sandwiches, baguettes and home-made soup up, quick service, well kept ales changing monthly such as Adnams, Greene King IPA, Tetleys and Wadworths 6X, decent wines, modern furnishings, family room, no smoking dining room; well tended back garden with fairy-lit arbour and pond, summer barbecues and play area *(Joy and Colin Rorke, Catherine and Richard Preston, Keith and Janet Morris, BB, Mr Biggs)*

St Neots [TL1859]

Chequers [St Marys St, Eynesbury]: Charming old beamed inn, interesting antique furnishings in small bar, well kept Tetleys and guest beers such as Greene King Old Speckled Hen, Nethergate Suffolk and Oakham JHB, good varied bar food from sandwiches and baked potatoes to steaks, welcoming staff, restaurant *(Michael Dandy)*

Stilton [TL1689]

Stilton Cheese [signed off A1; North St]: Well balanced choice of tasty food inc imaginative dishes in spacious dining areas with good tables, well kept real ales, decent wines, warm atmosphere, welcoming staff, interesting old interior inc unpretentious public bar; bedrooms, big back terrace and garden *(Suzanne McCarthy)*

Stow cum Quy [TL5159]

Quy Mill [Newmarket Rd]: Warm and relaxing, with neat friendly staff, wide choice of enjoyable food, well kept real ales, plenty of whiskies; comfortable bedrooms *(G Fairbairn, C Woodhams)*

☆ ***White Swan*** [just off B1102 – follow Bottisham sign]: Comfortable and cosy village local popular for good value generous food from hot or cold sandwiches to piping hot main dishes (may stop early lunchtime), no smoking dining room with fresh flowers, well kept Adnams, Greene King IPA, a house beer and interesting changing guests, friendly service; picnic-sets in garden, cl Mon *(BB, J D M Rushworth, Michael and Marion Buchanan, P and D Carpenter, Bill and Marian de Bass)*

Stretham [TL5174]

☆ ***Red Lion*** [High St (off A10)]: Neat village pub with wide daily-changing choice of good generous food inc children's and Sun lunch, solid pine furniture and old village photographs, friendly attentive service, five well kept real ales, marble-topped tables in pleasant no smoking dining conservatory; children welcome, picnic-sets in garden *(Joy and Colin Rorke)*

Swaffham Prior [TL5764]

Red Lion [B1102 NE of Cambridge; High St]: Attractive and interesting local in pleasant village, well kept Greene King Old Speckled Hen and Abbot, wide range of generous and reliable fresh food from sandwiches, baked potatoes and exemplary ploughman's to steaks, comfortably divided dining area, prompt friendly service *(Anthony Barnes, Ian Wilson, Jack Clarfelt, Michael and Marion Buchanan)*

Upware [TL5372]

Five Miles From Anywhere, No Hurry: Aptly named spacious modern pub in fine riverside site with elaborate play area, extensive moorings and public slipway (day boats for hire), seats on heated waterside terrace and in landscaped garden with play area; three real ales, open fire, restaurant, pool room, video games; live music Fri/Sat and bank hols; children welcome, disabled facilities *(LYM, Pam and David Bailey)*

Waresley [TL2454]

Duncombe Arms [Eltisley Rd (B1040, 5 miles S of A428)]: Comfortable and welcoming old pub, long main bar, fire one end, good range of generous reasonably priced food inc imaginative main dishes and good vegetarian options, consistently well kept Greene King IPA, Abbot and Ruddles, good service, restaurant; picnic-sets in garden *(Rev John Hibberd)*

Waterbeach [TL4965]

White Horse [Greenside]: Lounge bar with guest real ale one side of a bead curtain, Sappna good value curry house on the other; good friendly service *(David Bending)*

Wicken [TL5670]

Maids Head [High St]: Neatly kept dining pub in lovely village-green setting, huge helpings of reasonably priced good food in bar and no smoking restaurant, friendly local atmosphere, well kept Bass and related beers with a changing guest ale, fair-priced wines, quiet piped music; tables outside, handy for Wicken Fen nature reserve (NT) *(Stephen and Jean Curtis)*

Willingham [TL4070]

Three Tuns [Church St]: Welcoming old two-bar village local, attractively priced home cooking (not Mon) inc bargain steak and kidney pie, well kept Greene King ales inc Mild, darts, cards and dominoes; live music Fri *(Peter J Holmes, Pete Baker)*

Post Office address codings confusingly give the impression that some pubs are in Cambridgeshire, when they're really in the Leicestershire or Midlands groups of counties (which is where we list them).

Cheshire

Pubs on top form here this year are the Bhurtpore at Aston (great on the drinks side, and enjoyable food and surroundings too), the Cholmondeley Arms near Bickley Moss (a favourite for a meal out), the distinctive Albion in Chester, the spacious and appealing Fox & Barrel at Cotebrook (gaining a Food Award this year), the Nags Head at Haughton Moss (a fine all-rounder, new to the Guide*), the Leathers Smithy nicely placed near Langley (doing well under a new landlord), the Sutton Hall Hotel near Macclesfield (great atmosphere in this handsome old place), the Dog at Peover Heath (a good all-rounder), the Smoker at Plumley (a well run dining pub easily reached from the M6), and three pubs all in the same small group, and all doing nice civilised food yet keeping a good atmosphere for people just wanting a drink – the Grosvenor Arms at Aldford, Dysart Arms at Bunbury and Old Harkers Arms in Chester. The Fox & Barrel at Cotebrook, with all its attractively and distinctively furnished separate areas, is so nice for a meal out that it is our choice as Cheshire Dining Pub of the Year. The Lucky Dip section at the end of the chapter is full of interest this year, with no less than 43 promising newcomers. Pubs we'd particularly pick out in it (all already inspected and approved by us) are the Egerton Arms at Broxton, Boot and Mill in Chester, Harrington Arms at Gawsworth, restauranty Foxcote at Little Barrow, Roebuck at Mobberley, Highwayman at Rainow, Legs of Man at Smallwood, Setter Dog at Walker Barn, Boot & Slipper at Wettenhall and Crag at Wildboarclough. We'd also mention the Crown in Nantwich, kept out of the main entries this year only by a lack of readers' reports. Drinks prices in the county are well below the national average, with the Dog at Peover Heath and the Blue Bell at Bell o' th' Hill having particularly keen prices. Besides Burtonwood the major local brewery, there are quite a few good local microbreweries such as Weetwood, Storm, Coach House and Beartown – which now gain from the 14p a pint cut in beer duty for the smallest brewers.*

Pubs in the North Wirral (within the Merseyside boundary) and those around Stockport (within the Greater Manchester boundary) will be found in the Lancashire chapter, which includes both Merseyside and Greater Manchester.

ALDFORD SJ4259 Map 7

Grosvenor Arms ★

B5130 Chester—Wrexham

All sorts of customers come to this bustling pub to enjoy the delicious food and the well kept real ale. A pleasant place to spend a long summer evening, the airy terracotta-floored conservatory has lots of huge low hanging flowering baskets and chunky pale wood garden furniture, and opens on to a large elegant suntrap terrace and neat lawn with picnic-sets, young trees and a tractor. Inside, the spacious open-plan layout has a traditional feel, and a chatty atmosphere prevails in the huge panelled library, with tall book shelves along one wall, and lots of substantial tables well spaced on the handsome board floor. Several quieter areas are well furnished with good individual pieces, including a very comfortable parliamentary-type leather settle. Throughout are plenty of interesting pictures, and the lighting's exemplary;

cribbage, dominoes, Trivial Pursuit and Scrabble. Most people come here to eat the well presented and generous bar food, which might include curried parsnip soup (£3.50), sandwiches (from £3.75), leek and goats cheese tart with tomato and black olive dressing (£4.95), warm mushroom, artichoke and mussel salad with mustard cream (£5.75), ploughman's (£5.95), mushroom balti (£7.95), pork steak with stilton rarebit topping and creamed cabbage (£9.95), cold poached salmon with new potato and red onion salad (£10.45), and delicious puddings such as warm bakewell tart or vanilla truffle torte with raspberry coulis (from £3.95); best to book on weekend evenings. The five well kept real ales on handpump include Batemans XB, Flowers IPA and guests such as Caledonian Deuchars IPA, and Youngs Special. Another bonus is that all 20 wines (largely New World) are served by the glass, and their good choice of whiskies includes 75 malts, 30 bourbons, and 30 from Ireland. Dogs are welcome in the bar. *(Recommended by Revd D Glover, W K Wood, Denis and Dorothy Evans, Mike and Wendy Proctor, Lorraine and Fred Gill, Graham and Lynn Mason, Pat and Tony Hinkins, Mike and Wena Stevenson, Jean and Richard Phillips, Lorna and Howard Lambert, Mr and Mrs M Cooper, Paul Boot, Andrea and Guy Bradley)*

Brunning & Price ~ Licensees Gary Kidd and Jeremy Brunning ~ Real ale ~ Bar food (12-10(9 Sun); not 25 Dec) ~ (01244) 620228 ~ No children inside after 6pm ~ Dogs allowed in bar ~ Open 11.30-11; 12-10.30 Sun; closed 25 Dec evening

ASTBURY SJ8461 Map 7

Egerton Arms

Village signposted off A34 S of Congleton

Well run by friendly licensees, this popular village inn – originally a farmhouse – is in a pretty spot overlooking an attractive old church. The reasonably priced bar food (which you can have in either the bar or the restaurant) attracts locals and visitors alike, and at Sunday lunchtime you might struggle to get a place even though the car park is huge. There's a nice range of dishes on the unpretentious menu which includes generously filled sandwiches (from £2.70), hot baguettes (£3.65), baked potatoes (from £3.75), ploughman's (from £4.40), chicken, broccoli and stilton or beef and potato pie, haddock fillets, brie, courgette and almond crumble, sweet and sour chicken or lambs kidney, bacon and sausage casserole (£5.90), and steaks (from £10.75) as well as a few daily specials. They do good value OAP lunches Mon-Thurs (two courses £4.25, three £5.25). There's a cheerily pubby feel in the brightly yellow-painted rooms that ramble around the bar; some parts date back to the 14th c. Around the walls are the odd piece of armour, shelves of books, and mementoes of the Sandow Brothers, who performed as 'the World's Strongest Youths' (one of them was the landlady's father). In summer dried flowers fill the big fireplace. Parts of the bar and restaurant are no smoking. The well kept real ales on handpump are Robinsons Best, Frederics and Old Stockport; TV. There are a few well placed tables in front, and a play area with wooden fort. Though she's not made an appearance in a while, the ghost of a murdered neighbour is said to haunt the pub; look out too for the friendly pub dogs. We'd like to hear from readers who have tried the bedrooms here. *(Recommended by Andy Gosling, K M Crook, E G Parish, Mike and Wendy Proctor, Stephen Buckley)*

Robinsons ~ Tenants Alan and Grace Smith ~ Real ale ~ Bar food (11.30-2, 6.30-9; 12-2, 7-9 Sun) ~ Restaurant ~ (01260) 273946 ~ Children welcome away from bar ~ Open 11.30-11; 12-3, 6.45-10.30 Sun ~ Bedrooms: £25B/£50B

ASTON SJ6147 Map 7

Bhurtpore ★ 🍷 🍺

Off A530 SW of Nantwich; in village follow Wrenbury signpost

A fantastic place if you like real ale, this roadside inn has plenty to enjoy even if you don't. To complement up to a thousand different beers a year, they've a continually expanding wine list with a selection of fine wines (they've now added fruit wines too), and you can choose from 90 different whiskies. As for the beer – nine handpumps serve a rotating choice of really unusual and very well kept real ales which might include Derwent Doxy Brewer, Durham Magus, Hanbys Drawwell, Marston Moors Mongrel, Newby Wyke Sidewinder, Storm Beauforts, Salopian Shropshire Gold and Wye Valley Wholesome Stout, plus European beers such as Bitburger Pils or Timmermans Peach Beer. They also have dozens of good bottled beers, fruit beers and a changing farm cider and perry. The pub takes its name from the town in India where local landowner Lord Combermere won a battle, and the carpeted lounge bar bears some Indian influences, with an expanding collection of exotic artefacts (one turbaned statue behind the bar proudly sports a pair of Ray-Bans), as well as good local period photographs, and some attractive furniture. As well as a choice of about six very good home-made indian curries and baltis (£6.95-£7.75), enjoyable reasonably priced bar food includes sandwiches (from £2.25, hot filled baguettes £3.50), local sausages, egg and chips (£4.25), black pudding with mustard and apple sauce or smoked haddock in leek and cheese sauce (£4.25), steak, kidney and ale pie or quorn casserole with red wine and herb dumplings (£7.95), bass with coconut, lime and coriander sauce (£8.95), and maybe a seasonal game dish such as rabbit casserole (£8.50), and puddings such as baked blueberry cheesecake or bread and butter pudding (£3.25); changing specials board too. At weekends it can get extremely busy (the cheerful, sociable staff cope well under pressure), but at lunchtime or earlyish on a weekday evening the atmosphere is cosy and civilised. Tables in the comfortable public bar are reserved for people not eating, and the snug area and dining room are no smoking. Darts, dominoes, cribbage, pool, TV, fruit machine; dogs are allowed in the bar. Readers rave about their occasional beer festivals. *(Recommended by Mike and Wendy Proctor, Andy Chetwood, Rick Capper, E G Parish, the Didler, Nigel Woolliscroft, G Coates, Richard Lewis, JP, PP)*

Free house ~ Licensee Simon George ~ Real ale ~ Bar food (not 26 Dec) ~ Restaurant ~ No credit cards ~ (01270) 780917 ~ Well behaved children welcome in restaurant lunchtime and early evening ~ Dogs allowed in bar ~ Open 12-2.30(3 Sat), 6.30-11; 12-3, 7-10.30 Sun; closed 25 Dec and 1 Jan

BARTHOMLEY SJ7752 Map 7

White Lion ★ £

A mile from M6 junction 16; from the A500 towards Stoke-on-Trent, take B5078 Alsager road, then Barthomley signposted on left

The main bar of this lovely black and white thatched pub feels timeless, with its inviting open fire, heavy oak beams dating back to Stuart times, attractively moulded black panelling, Cheshire watercolours and prints on the walls, latticed windows, and wobbly old tables. Up some steps, a second room has another open fire, more oak panelling, a high-backed winged settle, a paraffin lamp hinged to the wall, and shove-ha'penny, cribbage and dominoes; local societies make good use of a third room. Having a drink outside is equally pleasant, and seats and picnic-sets on the cobbles have a charming view of the attractive village. From a short menu, the good value generous lunchtime bar food includes cheese and onion oatcakes with beans and tomatoes (£2.50), sandwiches (from £3.25), lemon and pepper chicken or sausages and mash (£4.50), daily roasts (£4.75), and stilton and local roast ham ploughman's (£5); best to arrive early at weekends to be sure of a table. Served by friendly and efficient staff, there's very well kept Burtonwood Bitter and Top Hat, and a monthly guest on handpump; no noisy games machines or music. The early 15th-c red sandstone church of St Bertiline across the road is worth a visit, and you can rent the cottage behind the pub. *(Recommended by MLR, JP, PP, E G Parish, John Robertson, the Didler, Mike Rowan, A C Stone, Dave Irving, Jim Bush, V N Stevenson, Karen Eliot, I H Saint, Tony Middis, Dr D J and Mrs S C Walker, Nigel Woolliscroft, Stephen Buckley, Jenny and Brian Seller, Hilary Forrest, Ewan and Moira McCall)*

Burtonwood ~ Tenant Terence Cartwright ~ Real ale ~ Bar food (lunchtime only, not Thursday) ~ (01270) 882242 ~ Children welcome away from public bar ~ Dogs welcome ~ Open 11.30-11(5-11 only Thurs); 12-10.30 Sun

You can send us reports through our web site: www.goodguides.com

BELL O' TH' HILL SJ5245 Map 7

Blue Bell £

Signposted just off A41 N of Whitchurch

If you like your pubs friendly and easy-going (and don't mind pets, which the welcoming Californian landlord positively encourages you to bring), then you're going to be very happy here. The entrance to this heavily beamed partly 14th-c country local – with its massive central chimney – is through a great oak door by a mounting-block; you then find yourself in a small quarry-tiled hallway, with stairs up, and another formidable oak door on your right. This leads into three communicating rooms, two served by hatch; the main bar is in an inglenook with an attractively moulded black oak mantelbeam. Comfortably plush wall seats among the cheerful mix of furnishings, lots of brass ornaments and newspapers to read on Sundays; several trophies reflecting the regulars' passion for dominoes. Very good value home-made bar food includes thick soup and sandwiches (£1.75), pâté (£2.50), cumberland sausage or gammon (£4.95), trout (£6.50), steaks (from £6.50), and daily specials including (with notice) vegetarian meals (mostly under £5); puddings (from £1.75). Very well kept Hanby Drawwell and an unusual guest from a small, independent brewery. There are picnic-sets among flowers on the front grass, and perhaps cows and a donkey or two in the adjoining field, where you can camp. *(Recommended by E G Parish, Nigel Woolliscroft, Derek and Sylvia Stephenson)*

Free house ~ Licensees Pat and Lydia Gage ~ Real ale ~ Bar food (12-2, 6-9) ~ Restaurant ~ No credit cards ~ (01948) 662172 ~ Children welcome ~ Dogs welcome ~ Open 12-3, 6-11(7-11 Sun)

BICKLEY MOSS SJ5650 Map 7

Cholmondeley Arms ★

Cholmondeley; A49 5½ miles N of Whitchurch; the owners would like us to list them under Cholmondeley Village, but as this is rarely located on maps we have mentioned the nearest village which appears more often

If it's your first visit to this imaginatively converted Victorian schoolhouse, you'll be torn between burying yourself in the enticing menu and soaking in your surroundings. The cross-shaped high-ceilinged bar is filled with eye-catching objects such as old school desks above the bar on a gantry, masses of Victorian pictures (especially portraits and military subjects), and a great stag's head over one of the side arches. A mix of seats runs from cane and bentwood to pews and carved oak settles, and the patterned paper on the shutters matches the curtains; gothic windows and huge old radiators too. Along with lunchtime sandwiches (£3.95), and dishes such as omelette and salad or steak baguette (£5.95), and stuffed pancakes (£6.25), the interesting, well cooked menu (which changes daily) might include home-made soup (£3.50), smoked haddock fishcakes with devilled tomato sauce or mushrooms with cream and stilton (£4.75), steak and kidney pie or leek and cheddar soufflé grilled with cheese (£7.95), oxtail braised in red wine (£9.25), bass fillets on buttered samphire with velouté sauce or pheasant in apple and calvados sauce (£9.95), and steak (£11.75), with puddings such as syrup tart or bakewell tart and cream (£4.25); children's menu (£3.95). You'll have to book at weekends for the bar food; friendly service. Well kept Adnams, Banks's, Marstons Pedigree, Weetwood Old Dog and perhaps a guest on handpump. An old blackboard lists ten or so interesting and often uncommon wines by the glass, and they do good coffees (liqueur ones too), and some speciality teas. The bedrooms are across the old playground in the headmaster's house; readers enjoy staying here, though we've heard that some of the rooms are in line for updating. There are seats out on a sizeable lawn, and Cholmondeley Castle and gardens are close by. Dogs are welcome. *(Recommended by Mike and Mary Carter, Revd D Glover, John Kane, Mike and Wendy Proctor, Kevin Blake, Ann and Max Cross, Ray and Winifred Halliday, Karen Eliot, Nigel Woolliscroft, Mike and Wena Stevenson)*

Free house ~ Licensees Guy and Carolyn Ross-Lowe ~ Real ale ~ Bar food (12-2.30, 6.30-10) ~ Restaurant ~ (01829) 720300 ~ Children in eating area of bar and

restaurant ~ Dogs welcome ~ Occasional jazz ~ Open 11-3, 6-11; closed 25 Dec ~ Bedrooms: £45B/£60B

BUNBURY SJ5758 Map 7

Dysart Arms ★

Bowes Gate Road; village signposted off A51 NW of Nantwich; and from A49 S of Tarporley – coming this way, coming in on northernmost village access road, bear left in village centre

Part of the excellent small pub group which includes the Grosvenor Arms at Aldford, this cheerful place makes both drinkers and diners feel at home, with nicely laid out spaces rambling around its pleasantly lit central bar. Under deep venetian red ceilings, the knocked-through cream-walled rooms have red and black tiles, some stripped boards and some carpet, a comfortable variety of well spaced big sturdy wooden tables and chairs, a couple of tall bookcases, some carefully chosen bric-a-brac, properly lit pictures, and warming fires in winter. One area is no smoking, and they have dominoes. They've lowered the ceiling in the more restauranty end room (with its book-lined back wall), and there are lots of plants on the window sills. Besides a short snack menu which includes sandwiches (from £3.95) and ploughman's (£5.50), interesting, popular food (which changes frequently) could include chinese marinated belly pork with stir-fried noodles (£4.95), smoked salmon with potato salad (£5.95), cheese, potato and leek hash cake with pepper dressing (£7.95), tuna steak with coriander mash and cajun onion rings (£10.95), peppered duck breast with sage and pistachio risotto or steak (£12.50), and puddings such as apple and almond tart or waffles with strawberries and ice cream (£3.95) as well as a good, changing selection of cheeses. Well kept Timothy Taylors Landlord and Thwaites Best, and a couple of guests such as Coach House Dick Turpin and Weetwood Eastgate on handpump, good interesting wines by the glass. Friendly, professional staff. The tables on the terrace and in the immaculately kept slightly elevated garden are very pleasant in summer, with views of the splendid church at the end of the picturesque village, and the distant Peckforton Hills beyond. *(Recommended by E G Parish, Joy and Peter Heatherley, Revd D Glover, SLC, Denis and Dorothy Evans, J G E Bell, Graham and Lynn Mason, Gill and Keith Croxton, Rita and Keith Pollard, Mr and Mrs M Cooper, Jim Bush, Nigel Woolliscroft, J C Temple, Mr and Mrs G Owens, Paul Boot)*

Brunning & Price ~ Managers Darren and Elizabeth Snell ~ Real ale ~ Bar food (12-2.15, 6-9.30; 12-9.30 Sat(9 Sun)) ~ (01829) 260183 ~ No children under 10 in eating area of bar after 6pm ~ Open 11.30-11; 12-10.30 Sun; closed 25 Dec

CHESTER SJ4166 Map 7

Albion ★

Park Street

Tucked away in a quiet part of town just below the Roman Wall, and with no piped music, noisy machines or children, this old-fashioned corner pub is an oasis of calm. The post-Edwardian décor is charmingly muted, with floral wallpaper, appropriate lamps, leatherette and hoop-backed chairs, a period piano, a large mangle, and cast-iron-framed tables; there's an attractive side dining room too. An interesting collection of World War I memorabilia is displayed throughout the rooms: you'll find big engravings of men leaving for war, similarly moving prints of wounded veterans, and other more expected aspects – flags, advertisements and so on. It's especially popular with older visitors: the atmosphere is friendly and chatty, and service is friendly (though they don't like people rushing in just before closing time, and discourage race-goers). Well kept Banks's Mild, Greene King IPA, Timothy Taylors Landlord and perhaps a couple of weekly guests such as Jennings Cocker Hoop and Titanic Best, up to 40 malt whiskies and fresh orange juice; the wines are non-French. It can get very busy at lunchtime, so arrive early to make the most of the generous home-made bar food, which includes Staffordshire oatcakes filled with black pudding, honey-roast gammon with cumberland sauce, roast turkey, vegetarian haggis, and lincolnshire sausages in red wine and shallot sauce (all £5.95, though this is in line for an increase), while puddings might include cold melted chocolate pudding, home-made brandy and apricot ice cream, and fresh lemon and lime cheesecake (£2.95); they also do hearty doorstep sandwiches. The landlord still plans to add a couple of bedrooms with bathrooms, and he's considering extending opening hours in 2003. *(Recommended by MLR, John Brightley, Joy and Peter Heatherley, E G Parish, Rob Fowell, SLC, JP, PP, the Didler, Darly Graton, Graeme Gulibert, Catherine Pitt, Tracey and Stephen Groves, Peter F Marshall, Joe Green, M Joyner)*

Pubmaster ~ Lease Michael Edward Mercer ~ Real ale ~ Bar food (12-2, 7-8) ~ Restaurant ~ No credit cards ~ (01244) 340345 ~ Dogs allowed in bar ~ Open 11.30-3, 5(6 Sat)-11; 12-2.30, 7-10.30 Sun

Old Harkers Arms

1 Russell Street, down steps off City Road where it crosses canal – under Mike Melody antiques

Right next to the canal (look out for boats drifting past the windows), this well converted Victorian warehouse is a great place to come for a chatty drink or a meal. Although the lofty ceiling and tall windows give a pleasant feeling of space and light, the tables are carefully arranged to create a sense of privacy. The nicely decorated bar has attractive lamps, interesting old prints on the walls, and newspapers and books to read from a well stocked library at one end. Apparently constructed from salvaged doors, the bar counter serves up to eight well kept real ales on handpump, such as Boddingtons, Fullers London Pride, Lees, Roosters Yankee, Salopian Golden Thread and Weetwood Best; around 50 malt whiskies too, and decent well described wines. The good food here is very popular, and from a frequently changing menu might include sandwiches (from £3.25), toasted ciabattas and baguettes (from £3.95), soup (£3.25), steamed mussels in cream and pink peppercorn sauce (£4.25), pork ravioli with spicy tomato sauce (£5.50), ploughman's (£5.95), chicken strips, noodles and spring onions in black bean sauce or salmon and dill fishcakes (£6.50), grilled bacon chop with bubble and squeak (£6.95) and steak (£12.95), with puddings such as apple fritters or steamed syrup sponge (£3.45); they do Sunday roast (£6.95), and on Monday evening two courses and half a bottle of wine are £12.95. It gets very busy Friday and Saturday evenings, when it's especially popular with younger visitors. *(Recommended by Kevin Blake, Darly Graton, Graeme Gulibert, Keith Fairbrother, Mrs Thomas, Peter F Marshall, SLC, Rob Fowell)*

Brunning & Price ~ Lease Barbie Hill and Catryn Devaney ~ Real ale ~ Bar food (11.30-2.30, 7-9(not Fri evening); 11.30-9 Sat/Sun) ~ (01244) 344525 ~ Children in eating area of bar till 8pm ~ Open 11.30-11; 12-10.30 Sun; closed 25 Dec and 1 Jan

COTEBROOK SJ5865 Map 7

Fox & Barrel

A49 NE of Tarporley

Cheshire Dining Pub of the Year

Despite an emphasis on enjoyable food, this well run bar and restaurant is still the kind of place where you'd be happy with just a drink. The uniformed staff (and there are plenty of them) are friendly and attentive, and the atmosphere is contagiously buoyant. The snug distinct areas are interestingly furnished, with a good mix of tables and chairs including two seats like Victorian thrones, an oriental rug in front of a very big log fireplace, a comfortable banquette corner, and a part with shelves of rather nice ornaments and china jugs; silenced fruit machine, unobtrusive piped music. Beyond the bar, there's a huge uncluttered candlelit dining area (no smoking) with varying-sized tables, comfortable dining chairs, attractive rugs on bare boards, rustic pictures above the panelled dado, and one more extensively panelled section. If you do decide to eat here make sure you're hungry, because the helpings are huge. The menu changes every few months, but you might find home-made soup (£3.25), sandwiches, and baguettes (from £3.50), tasty tandoori chicken salad (£7.25), ploughman's (£5.75), stir-fried shredded duck (£5.50), potted prawns and white crab meat (£6.25), home-made spinach, courgette and rosemary quiche (£8.50), steaks (from £12.45), fried pork fillet with honey and mustard sauce (£12.50), and roast cod with vanilla and ginger butter sauce (£14.95); best to book for Sunday lunch. Well kept John Smiths, Marstons Pedigree and a couple of guests such as Charles Wells Bombardier and Flowers Original are served (through a sparkler) by handpump, and there's a decent choice of wines. A traditional jazz band plays every Monday evening. *(Recommended by Revd D Glover, D Gaston, Ray and Winifred Halliday, E G Parish, Mr and Mrs M Cooper, Olive and Ray Hebson, Derek and Margaret Underwood, Mrs P J Carroll)*

Inn Partnership (Pubmaster) ~ Tenant Martin Cocking ~ Real ale ~ Bar food (12-2.30, 6.30-9.30; 12-2.30, 6-9.30 Sat and Sun) ~ Restaurant ~ (01829) 760529 ~ Children in restaurant ~ Trad jazz band Mon evening ~ Open 12-3, 5.30-11; 12-(11 Sat)10.30 Sun; closed 25 Dec

DARESBURY SJ5983 Map 7

Ring o' Bells

1½ miles from M56 junction 11; A56 N, then turn right on to B5356

Successfully combining a spacious and airy atmosphere with a cosy, homely feel, this welcoming pub has a good variety of places to sit in. On the right is a comfortable, down-to-earth part where walkers from the nearby canal can relax, while the left has more of a library style, and some reflection of its 19th-c use as a magistrates' court; there's a nice coal fire in winter. All rooms have wheelchair access. There are plenty of tables too out in a long partly terraced garden (as the village is an attractive place to stroll through this can get busy in the summer). The long bar counter has well kept Courage Directors, Greenalls Bitter and Mild, Theakstons, and perhaps two guests such as Batemans Miss Whiplash or Mauldons Black Adder on handpump; all their wines are available by the glass, and they've a dozen malt whiskies. They have enjoyable bar snacks including soup or sandwiches (from £2.95), hot baguettes or filled baked potatoes (from £3.95) and ploughman's (from £4.20), as well as more substantial meals such as beef and ale pie (£6.80), thai red curry (£7.85), ham hock with mash (£8.75), and half a roast duck with ginger and scallion sauce (£11.50); the dining rooms are no smoking. From the front of the pub you can see the church where Lewis Carroll's father was vicar – it has a window showing all the characters in *Alice in Wonderland*. This is now a Chef & Brewer pub, and has piped music and a fruit machine. *(Recommended by Marianne and Peter Stevens, David Field, E G Parish, Edward Leetham, Bernie Adams, Roy and Lindsey Fentiman, Graham and Lynn Mason, J Roy Smylie)*

Scottish Courage ~ Manager Martin Moylon ~ Real ale ~ Bar food (12-10(9.30 Sun)) ~ Restaurant ~ (01925) 740256 ~ Children in restaurant ~ Open 11-11; 12-10.30 Sun

FRODSHAM SJ5277 Map 7

Ring o' Bells £

Just over 2 miles from M56, junction 12; 2 Bellemonte Road – from A56 in Frodsham take B5152 and turn right (uphill) into Overton at Parish Church signpost

Festooned with a mass of colourful hanging baskets, in summer this early 17th-c pub is quite a sight. Inside it's charmingly old-fashioned – very much the sort of place where drinkers stand around the bar chatting. A couple of the little rambling rooms have pleasant views over a stone-built church and the Mersey far below, while the room at the back has some antique settles, brass-and-leather fender seats by the log fire, and old hunting prints on its butter-coloured walls; a beamed room with antique dark oak panelling and stained glass leads through to a darts room (there's also a TV, dominoes, cribbage, and other board games). An old-fashioned hatch-like central servery dispenses three very frequently changing real ales by handpump, such as Black Sheep Special, Coniston Bluebird and Greene King Ruddles County, and they stock about 85 malt whiskies. The straightforward lunchtime bar food is very reasonably priced. It could include sandwiches (from £1.60, toasties from £1.85), filled baked potatoes (£2.75), home-made beef and ale pie, chilli con carne, cumberland sausage and mash or tuna and pasta bake (£3.95), and puddings such as spotted dick; friendly staff. There's one no smoking room, and a secluded garden at the back has tables and chairs, a pond, and lots of trees. Look out for the friendly pub cats. *(Recommended by Bernie Adams, Joy and Peter Heatherley)*

Pubmaster ~ Tenant Shirley Wroughton-Craig ~ Real ale ~ Bar food (lunchtime only, not 25-26 Dec) ~ Restaurant ~ No credit cards ~ (01928) 732068 ~ Children welcome away from bar ~ Dogs welcome ~ Open 11.30-3, 5.30-11; 11.30-11 Fri; 12-4, 7-10.30 Sun

HANDLEY SJ4758 Map 7
Calveley Arms

Whitchurch Road, just off A41 S of Chester

First licensed in 1636, this cosy black and white country pub has enjoyable food and a pleasant atmosphere. Bound in the covers of old children's annuals, their changing menu could include home-made soup (£2.50), garlic mushrooms (£3.50), prawn cocktail (£3.95), home-made steak and kidney pie (£6.25), and scampi, gammon steak or apricot chicken (£7.25), with interesting specials (including at least four fresh fish dishes) such as black pudding with cream and mustard sauce (£3.95), plaice fillet with prawn and lobster sauce (£7.75), fried monkfish with bacon, cream and garlic or seared scallops with mange tout and ginger (£9.95), and crispy duck with sweet and spicy sauce (£10.25). If you're just after a snack they also do sandwiches and baguettes (£2.50-£4.50); service is courteous and welcoming. Well kept Boddingtons and Theakstons Black Bull, and they have occasional guests such as Everards Tiger and Wadworths 6X on handpump, as well as an interesting selection of soft drinks. The attractively furnished roomy beamed lounge has leaded windows, an open fire at one end, and some cosy alcove seating; piped music shove-ha'penny, dominoes, cribbage, and table skittles. In summer you can play boules in the secluded garden. More reports please. *(Recommended by A and B D Craig, Kevin Blake, Olive and Ray Hebson, Paul and Margaret Baker, Paul Boot, Mr and Mrs A H Young)*

Enterprise ~ Lease Grant Wilson ~ Real ale ~ Bar food (12-2.15, 6-9.30; 12-2.30, 7-9 Sun) ~ (01829) 770619 ~ Very well behaved children allowed ~ Open 12-3, 6-11 (7-10.30 Sun); closed 25 Dec evening

HAUGHTON MOSS SJ5855 Map 6
Nags Head

Turn off A49 S of Tarporley into Long Lane, at 'Beeston, Haughton' signpost

Very pretty, this immaculate black and white country pub greets you with a window-full of charmingly arranged collector's dolls. Inside, there are gleaming black and white tiles by the serving counter, with pews and a heavy settle by the fire in a small quarry-tiled room on the left, and button-back wall banquettes in the carpeted room on the right, which also has logs burning in a copper-hooded fireplace. There are heavy black beams, attractive Victorian prints, shelves of pewter mugs, and a few brass ornaments. The new American landlord has well chosen generous wines as well as Boddingtons and Fullers London Pride on handpump, and service is efficient. There may be very quiet piped music. As well as snacks (served till 4.30) such as sandwiches (£3.50), toasted baguettes or filled baked potatoes (£3.95), sausage and mash (£4.95), and ploughman's (£5.20), fresh food cooked to order could include roast chicken tagliatelle (£3.30), fishcakes (£3.80), mushroom stroganoff (£6.20), grilled trout (£7.20), pork fillet with chinese plum sauce (£8.50), steaks (from £9) and seafood provençale (£10.20); you can choose from various ice creams (£2.95), and there's a puddings trolley. Readers recommend their good value lunchtime buffet (Weds, Thurs and Fri); they also do an all-day brunch (£5.60, Mon-Sat), and Sunday roast (£7.95). On the right, the sizeable carpeted dining area looks out on a big neat garden with well spaced picnic-sets, and a good small adventure playground. This is a peaceful spot. *(Recommended by Mrs P J Carrol, E G Parish)*

Free house ~ Licensees Rory and Deborah Keigan ~ Real ale ~ Bar food (all day) ~ Restaurant ~ 01829 260265 ~ Children welcome in family area ~ Open 12-11(10.30 Sun)

HIGHER BURWARDSLEY SJ5256 Map 7

Pheasant

Burwardsley signposted from Tattenhall (which itself is signposted off A41 S of Chester) and from Harthill (reached by turning off A534 Nantwich—Holt at the Copper Mine); follow pub's signpost on up hill from Post Office; OS Sheet 117 map reference 523566

Well placed for the Sandstone Trail on the Peckforton Hills, this half-timbered and sandstone 17th-c pub gives spectacular views. On a clear day the telescope on the terrace lets you make out even the pier head and cathedrals in Liverpool, while from inside you can see right across the Cheshire plain. The bar has a bright modern feel, with wooden floors and light-coloured furniture; the see-through fireplace is said to house the largest log fire in the county. There's a pleasant no smoking conservatory and a restaurant. Staff are friendly, and the atmosphere is relaxed and pubby (walkers are welcome). Aside from sandwiches (from £3.50), tasty bar food includes soup (£3.50), shellfish terrine (£4.25), smoked chicken salad (£4.25), roast beef and horseradish sausages with chive mash and red wine gravy (£6.50), turkey, ham and leek pie (£7.25), smoked duck and spring onion stir fry (£8.95), scottish salmon kedgeree (£7.50), steaks (from £11.25), and puddings such as marmalade bread and butter pudding and chocolate truffle tart (£3.95). The three changing ales on handpump might include very well kept Timothy Taylors Landlord and Weetwood Eastgate, with a guest such as Wadworths 6X, and they stock over 30 malts. The big side lawn has picnic-sets, and they have barbecues on some summer weekends. There are bedrooms in the attractively converted sandstone barn. *(Recommended by Tracey and Stephen Groves, Rob Fowell, Graham and Lynn Mason, Mr and Mrs M Cooper)*

Free house ~ Licensee Simon McLoughlin ~ Real ale ~ Bar food (12-2.30, 6.30-9.30) ~ Restaurant ~ (01829) 770434 ~ Children welcome away from bar ~ Open 11-11; 12-10.30 Sun ~ Bedrooms: £55S(£55B)/£80S(£80B)

LANGLEY SJ9569 Map 7

Hanging Gate

Meg Lane, Higher Sutton; follow Langley signpost from A54 beside Fourways Motel, and that road passes the pub; from Macclesfield, heading S from centre on A523 turn left into Byrons Lane at Langley, Wincle signpost; in Sutton (half-mile after going under canal bridge, ie before Langley) fork right at Church House Inn, following Wildboarclough signpost, then 2 miles later turning sharp right at steep hairpin bend; OS Sheet 118 map reference 952696

Thought to have been built long before it was first licensed, nearly 300 years ago, this warmly welcoming pub is perched high on a Peak District ridge. Once frequented by drovers, the three cosy low-beamed rambling rooms are simply and traditionally furnished, and have big coal fires, and some attractive old prints of Cheshire towns. Readers really like the well cooked honest-to-goodness bar food, which includes soup (£2.45), black pudding or feta cheese salad (£3.95), fried cod (£7.25), steaks (from £8.95), and lamb cutlets (£9.95), and puddings such as bread and butter pudding (£2.95). Service is extremely helpful and friendly. Well kept Hydes Bitter, Jekylls Gold and a guest from the brewery on handpump, and there are quite a few malt whiskies; piped music. The blue room is no smoking. There's an airy garden room down some stone steps, and seats out on a crazy-paved terrace give spectacular views over a patchwork of valley pastures to distant moors, and the tall Sutton Common transmitter above them. *(Recommended by the Didler, Stephen Buckley, JP, PP, Nigel Woolliscroft, Doug Christian, R F Grieve, Mike and Wendy Proctor, Derek and Sylvia Stephenson, John Hillmer, Mr and Mrs Colin Roberts, Rob Fowell)*

Free house ~ Licensees Peter and Paul McGrath ~ Real ale ~ Bar food (not Sun evening) ~ Restaurant ~ (01260) 252238 ~ Children in family area ~ Open 12-3, 7-11; 12-11 Sat; 12-10.30 Sun

Pubs with attractive or unusually big gardens are listed at the back of the book.

Leathers Smithy

From Macclesfield, heading S from centre on A523 turn left into Byrons Lane at Langley, Wincle signpost; in Langley follow main road forking left at church into Clarke Lane – keep on towards the moors; OS Sheet 118 map reference 952715

There are good views of Ridgegate Reservoir from this popular walkers' pub. The cheerful, partly flagstoned right-hand bar has lots of traditional pubby character, with bow-window seats, wheelback chairs, and roughcast cream walls. On the left are more wheelback chairs around cast-iron-framed tables on a turkey carpet, and open fires give the place a lovely cosy feel in winter (when they serve glühwein from a copper salamander). They've a good collection of spirits including around 80 whiskies, as well as farm cider and well kept real ales such as Courage Directors, Marstons Pedigree, Storm Windgather and RCH Pitchfork. Enjoyable bar food includes sandwiches (from £2.50, baguettes from £4.50), black pudding and apple sauce (£2.25), steamed mussels (£5.75), ploughman's (£4.95), home-made steak and ale pie, cumberland sausage and mash or vegetable tagine (£5.95), wild mushroom risotto (£6.25), green thai chicken curry (£6.95), and good steaks (from £8.25), with specials such as pot roast lamb shank (£7.95); good service. The new landlord has added hanging baskets and traditional-looking wooden windows. The pub is close to Macclesfield Forest and Teggs Nose country park. *(Recommended by Mr and Mrs Colin Roberts, Stephen Buckley, Mike and Wena Stevenson, MLR)*

Free house ~ Licensee Paul McMahon ~ Real ale ~ Bar food (12-2, 7-9.30(10 Fri-Sat); 12-9 Sun) ~ Restaurant ~ (01260) 252313 ~ Children in family room ~ Open 12-3, 7-11; 12-10.30 Sun

LOWER PEOVER SJ7474 Map 7

Bells of Peover ★

The Cobbles; from B5081 take short cobbled lane signposted to church

Though we've heard less than we used to from readers since this attractive wisteria-covered pub became a Chef & Brewer, it's got so much going for it that we'd still rate it as one of Cheshire's star pubs. Nicely tucked away in a peaceful hamlet, it dates back in part some 750 years. The seats on the crazy-paved terrace in front overlook a fine black and white 14th-c church, and a spacious lawn beyond the old coachyard at the side spreads down through trees and under rose pergolas to a little stream. The cosy tiled bar has side hatches for its serving counter, toby jugs and comic Victorian prints, and the original lounge has antique settles, high-backed windsor armchairs and a spacious window seat, antique china in the dresser, pictures above the panelling, and two small coal fires; one room is no smoking. Swiftly served by friendly staff, bar food could include soup (£2.65), sandwiches and baguettes (from £2.95), filled baked potatoes (from £3.95), ploughman's (from £4.20), sausages with bubble and squeak (£5.95), beef and Theakstons pie (£6.80), and blackened cajun tuna with tomato and pepper sauce (£10.95). Well kept real ales such as Courage Directors, Greenalls and Theakstons on handpump; dominoes, cribbage and piped music. *(Recommended by Roger and Pauline Pearce, Revd D Glover, Simon and Laura Habbishow, Leo and Barbara Lionet, Mrs P J Carroll, Keith and Janet Eaton, the Didler, Denis and Dorothy Evans, Eric Locker, Lesley Bass, JP, PP)*

Scottish Courage ~ Manager Richard Casson ~ Real ale ~ Bar food (11-10; 12-9.30 Sun) ~ (01565) 722269 ~ Children till 7pm away from bar ~ Open 11-11; 12-10.30 Sun; closed 25 Dec evening

MACCLESFIELD SJ9271 Map 7

Sutton Hall Hotel ★

Leaving Macclesfield southwards on A523, turn left into Byrons Lane signposted Langley, Wincle, then just before canal viaduct fork right into Bullocks Lane; OS Sheet 118 map reference 925715

No wonder readers are charmed by this civilised but relaxed 16th-c baronial hall. Peacocks strut among the tables on the tree-sheltered lawn, and ducks and moorhens

swim in the pond; don't worry if it's raining, though – it's lovely inside too. The bar is divided into separate areas by tall black oak timbers, with some antique squared oak panelling, lightly patterned Art Nouveau stained-glass windows, broad flagstones around the bar counter (carpet elsewhere), and a raised open fire. Mostly furnished with straightforward ladderback chairs around sturdy thick-topped cast-iron-framed tables, it has a few unusual touches such as a suit of armour by a big stone fireplace, a longcase clock, a huge bronze bell for calling time, and a brass cigar-lighting gas taper on the bar counter itself. Generous bar food includes soup (£2.25), sandwiches (from £3.50), moules marinière (£4.75), broccoli and cheese bake (£5.75), tasty steak, kidney and oyster pie (£6.95), daily specials such as roast turkey with tarragon cream sauce (£6.45), grilled halibut in teriyaki marinade (£7.95), venison steak with cream, brandy and peppercorn sauce (£8.50), and puddings such as blueberry crème brûlée and chocolate, hazelnut and rum flan (£3). Well kept Bass, Greene King IPA, Marstons Pedigree and a guest beer on handpump, 40 malt whiskies, decent wines, freshly squeezed fruit juice, and proper Pimms. They can arrange clay shooting, golf or local fishing for residents, and there's access to canal moorings at Gurnett Aqueduct on the Macclesfield Canal 200 yards away.
(Recommended by the Didler, JP, PP, Wendy and Bob Needham, Dr W J M Gissane, Mr and Mrs B Hobden, Kevin Blake, Tracey and Stephen Groves, Mike and Wendy Proctor)

Free house ~ Licensee Robert Bradshaw ~ Real ale ~ Bar food (12-2.30(2 Sun), 7-10) ~ Restaurant ~ (01260) 253211 ~ Children in restaurant and family room wknd and bank hol lunchtimes only ~ Open 11-11(10.30 Sun) ~ Bedrooms: £75B/£90B

PEOVER HEATH SJ7973 Map 7

Dog

Off A50 N of Holmes Chapel at the Whipping Stocks, keep on past Parkgate into Wellbank Lane; OS Sheet 118 map reference 794735; note that this village is called Peover Heath on the OS map and shown under that name on many road maps, but the pub is often listed under Over Peover instead

The attractive garden of this friendly, civilised pub is nicely lit on summer evenings, and there are picnic-sets out on the quiet lane, underneath pretty hanging baskets. The main bar has comfortable easy chairs and wall seats (including one built into a snug alcove around an oak table), and two wood-backed seats built-in either side of a coal fire, opposite which logs burn in an old-fashioned black grate. Well kept Hydes, Moorhouses Black Cat and Weetwood Best and Old Dog are served on handpump, along with Addlestone's cider, over 50 malt whiskies, and freshly squeezed orange juice. They've got darts, pool, dominoes, TV, a juke box and piped music (children are welcome in the games area). Many people come here to eat, and they serve a good range of sandwiches (from £2.85), while other well cooked dishes could include home-made soup (£2.50), ploughman's (from £4.95), smoked scottish salmon, prawn and avocado salad or deep-fried whitebait (£4.95), ham shank with parsley sauce, haddock and prawn gratin or spinach and mushroom lasagne (£9.95), rack of lamb with apricot and ginger (£10.95), and puddings such as cheesecakes, fruit pies and pavlovas (£3.50). The dining room is no smoking, and it's best to book at weekends. Service is pleasant, and readers speak highly of the well equipped bedrooms, and good breakfasts. There's a nice walk from here along cross-country paths and quiet country lanes to the Jodrell Bank Centre and Arboretum.
(Recommended by Dr Paull Khan, Steve Whalley, Mr and Mrs Gordon Turner, JES, Doug Christian, R Pring, E G Parish, Denis and Dorothy Evans, Derek and Sylvia Stephenson)

Free house ~ Licensee Steven Wrigley ~ Real ale ~ Bar food (12-2.30, 7-9.30; 12-8.30 Sun) ~ Restaurant ~ (01625) 861421 ~ Children in eating area of bar and restaurant ~ Dogs allowed in bar ~ Theme night 2nd Friday in month ~ Open 11.30-3, 5(5.30 Sat)-11; 12-10.30 Sun ~ Bedrooms: £55B/£75B

Real ale to us means beer which has matured naturally in its cask – not pressurised or filtered.

PLUMLEY SJ7175 Map 7

Smoker

2½ miles from M6 junction 19: A556 towards Northwich and Chester

'Excellent' is a word that crops up frequently when readers write to us about this well run old pub. There's a pleasant atmosphere, and it's comfortably furnished inside with deep sofas, cushioned settles, windsor chairs, and some rush-seat dining chairs. The three well decorated connecting rooms have dark panelling, open fires in impressive period fireplaces, military prints, a collection of copper kettles, and an Edwardian print of a hunt meeting outside which shows how little the appearance of this partly thatched pub has changed over the centuries. The pub takes its name from a favourite racehorse of the Prince Regent. Well cooked food (the same menu covers the bar and restaurant) served by friendly staff includes home-made soup (£2.65), sandwiches and baked potatoes (from £3.55), brie wedges and cranberry sauce (£4.55), chicken liver pâté (£4.95), salmon and spinach or chicken, leek and stilton pie (£7.95), pork fillet with calvados (£8.95) and steaks (from £12.95), with puddings such as apple pie or treacle roly-poly; two-course Sunday set menu (£10.95). Well kept Robinsons Best and Old Stockport on handpump, 30 malt whiskies and a good choice of wines including around 11 by the glass. There are no smoking areas in the bar; piped music, fruit machine. The sizeable side lawn has roses and flower beds, and there's a children's play area in the extended garden. It's a good haven from the M6, and access to the pub has recently been improved. *(Recommended by Nigel and Sue Foster, Richard and Wendy Harris, Joy and Peter Heatherley, Stan and Hazel Allen, D S Jackson, R Mathews, Revd D Glover, M S Catling, Andrew Crawford)*

Robinsons ~ Tenants John and Diana Bailey ~ Real ale ~ Bar food (12-2, 6-9.30; 12-9 Sun) ~ Restaurant ~ (01565) 722338 ~ Children welcome ~ Open 11.30-3, 6-11; 12-10.30 Sun

TARPORLEY SJ5563 Map 7

Rising Sun

High Street; village signposted off A51 Nantwich—Chester

Set in a pretty village, this bustling pub appeals to both visitors and locals. The cosy rooms contain well chosen tables surrounded by eye-catching old seats including creaky 19th-c mahogany and oak settles; there's also an attractively blacked iron kitchen range (and three open fires), sporting and other old-fashioned prints on the walls, and a big oriental rug in the back room. Food prices haven't changed since last year, and enjoyable hearty dishes include sandwiches (from £2.50), toasties and filled baked potatoes (from £2.95), stuffed mushrooms (£3.45), home-made turkey and ham pie (£6.75), lasagne (£6.95), gammon steak (£7.95), a good vegetarian choice such as quorn and butter bean goulash or black bean sizzler (£8.10), mixed grill (£11.20), and 16oz rump steak (£11.95). Well kept Robinsons Best and Mild on handpump. It looks especially good in summer with its mass of hanging baskets and flowering tubs. *(Recommended by Mike and Wendy Proctor, Mike and Mary Carter, Rob Fowell, the Didler, Ken Richards)*

Robinsons ~ Tenant Alec Robertson ~ Real ale ~ Bar food (11.30-2, 5.30-9.30; 12-10.30 Sun) ~ Restaurant (evening) ~ (01829) 732423 ~ Children in lounge and eating area of bar, over 12s in restaurant only in evening ~ Open 11.30-3.30, 5.30-11; 11.30-11 bank hols and Sat; 12-10.30 Sun

WESTON SJ7352 Map 7

White Lion ⛟

3½ miles from M6 junction 16; A500 towards Crewe, then village signposted on right

The bustling low-beamed main room of this pretty black and white timbered inn is divided into smaller areas by very gnarled black oak standing timbers. There's a good variety of seats from cushioned modern settles to ancient oak ones, with plenty of smaller chairs, and in a smaller room on the left are three fine settles, carved in 18th-c style; the atmosphere is relaxed and friendly. You'll find well kept Bass and

Boddingtons on handpump, and a sizeable wine list; dominoes, TV and piped music. The hotel has its own bowling green by a sheltered lawn with picnic-sets behind. Courteous staff serve the simple bar food which includes home-made soup (£1.95), sandwiches (from £3.10), filled baguettes (from £3.95), chilli con carne or roast chicken (£5.95), and a daily special such as cottage pie or liver and onions (£5.50); they do a range of ice cream sundaes as well as puddings. It's worth noting that they stop serving lunch at 1.45 on Sunday. The two side rooms are no smoking. *(Recommended by K H Frostick, J Hale, D J Hulse)*

Free house ~ Licensee Alison Davies ~ Real ale ~ Bar food (not 25-26 Dec) ~ Restaurant ~ (01270) 500303 ~ Children in restaurant and family room till 9.30pm ~ Open 11-3, 5(6.30 Sat)-11; 12-3, 7-10.30 Sun; closed 25 Dec evening ~ Bedrooms: £58B/£68B

WILLINGTON SJ5367 Map 7

Boot

Boothsdale, off A54 at Kelsall

Looking out over the lush farmland and hedgerows of the Cheshire plain towards the Welsh hills, this dining pub is appealingly set on a wooded hillside. Converted from sandstone cottages, the inside has been carefully opened up, leaving small unpretentiously furnished room areas around the central bar with its woodburning stove; an extension with french windows overlooks the garden. The restaurant has wheelback chairs around plenty of tables on its flagstones, and a good log fire. As well as soup (£2.40), sandwiches (from £3.50) and baguettes (from £5.40), well cooked food includes warm smoked trout (£4.95), nut-roasted brie (£5.50), liver, bacon and onions with red wine gravy (£7.50), gammon and pineapple (£7.90), cheese and mushroom bake (£8.25), and steaks (from £10.95), there are tasty daily specials such as home-roast ham and parsley sauce (£7.50) and fisherman's pie (£7.95); puddings (£3.95). Well kept Cains, Flowers Original, Timothy Taylors Landlord and a guest from the local Weetwood brewery on handpump, 30 malt whiskies, and a decent wine list. Outside, the raised stone terrace with picnic-sets is a summer sun trap, and children will like the three donkeys, golden retriever H, and Sooty and Sweep the cats. *(Recommended by MLR, Joy and Peter Heatherley, John and Angela Main, Leo and Barbara Lionet)*

Pubmaster ~ Lease Mike Gollings and Liz Edwards ~ Real ale ~ Bar food (11-2.30, 6-9.30, all day wknds and bank hols) ~ Restaurant ~ (01829) 751375 ~ Children in restaurant and snug ~ Open 11-3, 6-11; 11-11 Sat; 11-10.30 Sun; closed 25 Dec

WINCLE SJ9666 Map 7

Ship

Village signposted off A54 Congleton—Buxton

Ask the friendly staff if you want advice on the best local walks through the picturesque countryside surrounding this cosy 16th-c pub. This is reputedly one of Cheshire's oldest pubs, and the two old-fashioned and simple little tap rooms (no piped music or games machines) have thick stone walls, and a coal fire. Carefully made with good quality ingredients, the bar food really appeals: it includes home-made soup (£2.95), home-made smoked salmon and dill pâté (£3.95), wild mushrooms with garlic and pesto cream sauce (£4.50), steak and ale pie, local trout with almonds sautéed in garlic butter or brie and leek parcels with mustard cream sauce (£7.95), chicken breast stuffed with mozzarella and sun-dried tomato with provençale sauce (£8.95), venison fillet with port and cranberry sauce £10.95), and home-made puddings such as rhubarb crumble or sticky chocolate pudding (£3.50). It can get busy Saturday evenings and Sunday lunchtimes (when you might have to park on the steep, narrow road outside), so it's a good idea to book. Well kept Boddingtons, Wye Valley and a constantly changing guest beer on handpump. There's a small garden with wooden tables and swings. They may stay open all day on summer weekends. *(Recommended by the Didler, Mike and Wendy Proctor, Nigel Woolliscroft, Rob Fowell, John Hillmer)*

Free house ~ Licensee Steven Mark Simpson ~ Real ale ~ Bar food (not Mon exc bank hols) ~ Restaurant ~ (01260) 227217 ~ Children in family room ~ Open 12-3, 7-11(10.30 Sun); closed Mon (exc bank hols)

WRENBURY SJ5948 Map 7

Dusty Miller

Village signposted from A530 Nantwich—Whitchurch

Peacefully set by the Shropshire Union Canal, this handsomely converted 19th-c mill gives a good view of the striking counter-weighted drawbridge going up and down, from a series of tall glazed arches. The comfortable modern main bar area has long low-hung hunting prints on terracotta walls, and the variety of seats flanking the rustic tables includes tapestried banquettes, an ornate church pew and wheelback chairs. If you go further in there's a quarry-tiled standing-only part by the bar counter, which has well kept Robinsons ales such as Best, Frederics, Hatters Mild, and in winter Old Tom on handpump; piped music, dominoes. In fine weather (when it can get very crowded) the picnic-sets on the gravel terrace among rose bushes by the water are a pleasant place to sit; they're reached either by the towpath or by a high wooden catwalk over the River Weaver. Readers like the fact that the good bar food is made largely from fresh local ingredients. Hearty dishes could include home-made soup (£2.95), mushrooms simmered in garlic, ginger and cream sauce (£4.25), deep-fried hot and spicy creel prawns with yoghurt dip (£5.75), roast local ham with hot potatoes or chargrilled vegetable lasagne (£8.75), chargrilled lamb steak marinated with coconut and lime or roast crispy salmon with buttered asparagus and tarragon mayonnaise (£10.95), and local steak (from £12.50); vegetables (£1.75); the restaurant and five tables in the bar are no smoking *(Recommended by E G Parish, Mike and Wendy Proctor, Dave Braisted)*

Robinsons ~ Tenant Mark Sumner ~ Real ale ~ Bar food (not Mon in winter) ~ Restaurant ~ (01270) 780537 ~ Children in restaurant ~ Dogs allowed in bar ~ Open 11.30-3(not Mon), 6.30-11; 12-3, 7-10.30 Sun

---

Lucky Dip

Besides the fully inspected pubs, you might like to try these Lucky Dips recommended to us and described by readers (if you do, please send us reports: www.goodguides.com).

Alderley Edge [SJ8478]

Drum & Monkey [Moss Rose; past Royal Oak off Heyes Lane (which is off A34)]: Cheerful friendly service, well kept Robinsons, open fire, wide choice of reasonably priced food from sandwiches up (but they may hang on to your credit card); big terrace overlooking bowling green *(Stephen Buckley)*

Alpraham [SJ5959]

Travellers Rest [A51 Nantwich—Chester]: Unchanging chatty four-room country local with veteran landlady (same family for three generations), particularly well kept Tetleys Bitter and Mild, leatherette, wicker and Formica, some flock wallpaper, fine old brewery mirrors, darts, back bowling green; no machines, piped music or food (apart from crisps and nuts), cl wkdy lunchtimes *(Pete Baker, the Didler, JP, PP)*

Bollington [SJ9377]

☆ *Church House* [Church St]: Small friendly village pub with wide choice of good value quickly served home-made lunchtime food such as bass in spring onion, ginger and garlic sauce (can book tables for busy lunchtimes), well kept Flowers, Theakstons and Timothy Taylors Landlord, furnishings inc pews and working sewing-machine treadle tables, roaring fire, separate dining room, provision for children; four bedrooms *(Stephen Buckley)*

Poachers [Mill Lane]: Friendly stone-built village local, good changing choice of well kept ales, decent wines, good value home-made food, helpful and attentive young licensees; attractive secluded garden and terrace behind, pretty setting, handy for walkers *(Stephen Buckley)*

Bottom of the Oven [SJ9872]

☆ *Stanley Arms* [A537 Buxton—Macclesfield, 1st left past Cat & Fiddle]: Isolated moorland pub, small, friendly and cosy, lots of shiny black woodwork, plush seats, dimpled copper tables, open winter fires, dining room, small choice of generous well cooked traditional food, well kept Marstons and guest beers; children welcome, piped music; picnic-sets on grass behind, may close Mon in winter if weather bad *(LYM, Stephen Buckley)*

Bradfield Green [SJ6859]

☆ *Coach & Horses* [A530 NW of Crewe]: Attractive and comfortably cottagey, good value properly cooked food inc moroccan specialities, children's dishes and OAP bargains, perfect veg, well kept ales inc Greenalls, decent wines, friendly helpful service, horse-racing pictures; discreet piped music *(E G Parish, Sarah Worth)*

Brereton Green [SJ7864]

☆ ***Bears Head*** [handy for M6 junction 17; set back off A50 S of Holmes Chapel]: Handsome old heavily timbered inn, welcoming warren of old rooms pleasantly refurbished as a comfortable brasserie-style Vintage Inn, with old-fashioned furniture, good choice of well prepared enjoyable fresh food, well kept Bass, Worthington BB and a guest such as Fullers London Pride, cheerful log fire, good service; open all day, good value bedrooms in modern block *(Roger Cass, LYM, Dorsan Baker, E G Parish)*

Broxton [SJ4858]

☆ ***Egerton Arms*** [A41/A534 S of Chester]: Large cheerfully efficient family pub, neatly kept and welcoming, with well polished old furniture, antique plates and prints in roomy dark-panelled bar, warmly decorated no smoking dining area off; wide choice of good ample food (all day wknds) from sandwiches up inc lots for children, helpful efficient staff, well kept Burtonwood and a guest beer, decent wines, children very welcome, colouring materials; discreet piped music; picnic-sets out under cocktail parasols, play area, balcony terrace with lovely views, open all day, comfortable bedrooms *(LYM, R Davies, E G Parish)*

Burleydam [SJ6042]

Combermere Arms [A525 Whitchurch—Audlem]: Brightly lit 16th-c beamed family-oriented pub with good generous food from sandwiches to restaurant meals, children's helpings and big indoor adventure play area, welcoming staff, Bass, Worthington and guest beers from unusual circular bar, pub games; piped music; open all day *(Edward Leetham, E G Parish, LYM)*

Chester [SJ4166]

☆ ***Boot*** [Eastgate Row N]: Down-to-earth and relaxed atmosphere in lovely 17th-c Rows building, heavy beams, lots of woodwork, oak flooring and flagstones, even some exposed Tudor wattle and daub, black-leaded kitchen range in lounge beyond good value food servery, no smoking oak-panelled upper area popular with families (despite hard settles), good service, cheap well kept Sam Smiths; piped music, children allowed *(Kevin Blake, Joe Green, the Didler, Rona Murdoch, LYM)*

☆ ***Falcon*** [Lower Bridge St]: Striking and substantial ancient building, with good bustling atmosphere, handsome beams and brickwork, well kept Sam Smiths, well thought out reasonably priced food (not Sun), fruit machine, piped music; children allowed lunchtime (not Sat) in airy upstairs room; open all day Sat (can get packed then, with lunchtime jazz), interesting tours of the vaults *(LYM, Tracey and Stephen Groves, E G Parish)*

☆ ***Mill*** [Milton St]: Up to 16 changing well kept and well priced ales from smaller breweries inc a Mild (and blackboard for real ale requests) in neat and comfortably carpeted sizeable bar off smart hotel reception, relaxed mix of customers from teenagers to older folk and ladies lunching (good value ciabattas and enjoyable hot dishes, till late evening), friendly efficient staff, restaurant overlooking canal (good value Sun lunch); quiet piped music, big-screen SkyTV, jazz Mon; good with children, waterside benches, boat trips; bedrooms *(the Didler, Sue Holland, Dave Webster, Andy Chetwood, Rick Capper, Joe Green, Tracey and Stephen Groves, BB)*

Olde Kings Head [Lower Bridge St]: Fine old timbered building, lots of woodwork, beams and bric-a-brac, coal fires, low lighting, friendly efficient bar service, well kept Greenalls, lunchtime bar food; upstairs restaurant and hotel part, comfortable bedrooms *(Kevin Blake)*

Pied Bull [Upper Northgate St]: Roomy open-plan carpeted bar, attractive mix of individual furnishings, divided inner area with china cabinet and lots of pictures, nice snug by pillared entrance, imposing intriguingly decorated fireplace; wide choice of generous reasonably priced food all day inc afternoon teas, real ales, attentive welcoming staff, no smoking area; fruit machines, maybe piped music; open all day, handsome Jacobean stairs up to bedrooms *(E G Parish, BB)*

Union Vaults [Francis St/Egerton St]: Traditional corner alehouse with three quietly interesting and friendly split-level rooms, enthusiastic staff, well kept and reasonably priced Greenalls, Plassey and unusual changing beers and stouts (guest beer suggestions book), bar billiards and bagatelle, back room with pool; may be sandwiches, piped music; open all day *(the Didler, Joe Green, Sue Holland, Dave Webster)*

Watergates [Watergate Sq]: Rambling candlelit medieval crypt, good wines by the glass, quickly served food; late evenings fills with young people and loud well reproduced music *(Kevin Blake, BB, Andy, Julie and Stuart Hawkins)*

Childer Thornton [SJ3678]

☆ ***White Lion*** [off A41 S of M53 junction 5; New Rd]: Low two-room whitewashed pub, old-fashioned and unpretentious, with well kept Thwaites Bitter and Mild, good value lunches, welcoming staff, open fire, framed matchbooks, no music or machines; tables out in sheltered area behind, swings in nice quiet front garden *(MLR)*

Christleton [SJ4465]

Cheshire Cat [Whitchurch Rd]: Large recently converted canalside Vintage Inn, food all day, good service; bedrooms *(SLC)*

Ring o' Bells: Spacious and well appointed village pub, good welcoming service, well presented food, Bass, decent house wines, reasonable prices; picnic-sets outside *(E G Parish)*

Church Minshull [SJ6660]

Badger [B5074 Winsford—Nantwich; handy for Shrops Union Canal, Middlewich branch]: Village pub redecorated and reopened after closure, friendly staff, food in bar and restaurant, roomy comfortable furnishings;

tables in garden behind, pretty village, open all day wknds *(E G Parish, LYM)*

Congleton [SJ8663]

Beartown Tap [Willow St]: Light and airy tap for nearby Beartown small brewery, their well priced beers from six handpumps, farm cider, bare boards in friendly bar and two pleasant rooms off, another upstairs *(Bernie Adams, Edward Leetham)*

Heath Farm [Padgbury Lane]: Popular open-plan country-theme family dining pub in converted farmhouse with animal pictures, no smoking and family areas inc attached indoor play area for younger children (but also a child-free dining area), usual food all day inc bargains for two and Sun carvery, plenty of choice for children, well kept Marstons Pedigree and Tetleys, maybe a guest such as Wadworths 6X, smart friendly staff; karaoke and disco nights; good disabled facilities, open all day *(Richard Lewis)*

Olde White Lion [High St]: Open-plan beamed black and white pub with several seating areas, good value food, real ales such as local Beartown Kodiak and Tolly Original; tables on back terrace with water feature, hanging baskets, pets corner and small aviary *(MLR)*

Cotebrook [SJ5765]

☆ ***Alvanley Arms*** [A49/B5152 N of Tarporley]: Handsome sandstone inn with three pleasant beamed rooms (two no smoking areas), big open fire, chintzy little hall, shire horse décor (plenty of tack and pictures – adjacent stud open in season), good generous food (they pride themselves on their steak pie); garden with pond and trout, seven bedrooms with own bathrooms *(LYM, E G Parish)*

Crewe [SJ7053]

Albion [Pedley St]: Refurbished backstreet local with well kept Tetleys Bitter and Dark Mild, friendly staff, lively bar with sports chat, darts, dominoes, TV and pool room, railway-theme lounge; piped music, quiz night Weds *(JP, PP, E G Parish)*

Borough Arms [Earle St]: Nine or ten interesting changing ales in top condition, four Belgian beers on draught and dozens in bottle, two real lagers, friendly licensees; railway theme, green décor, plans for basement microbrewery; games machine, TV, has been closed wkdy lunchtimes *(Richard Lewis, the Didler, E G Parish, Edward Leetham, Andy Chetwood, Rick Capper)*

Crewe Arms [Nantwich Rd (A534 nr railway station)]: Sedate Victorian businessmen's hotel with obliging friendly service, comfortable lounge with marble-topped tables, alabaster figurines, period pictures, curtained alcoves, ornate ceiling; good pubby public bar with pool, well kept Ind Coope Burton or Tetleys, powerful heating, bar food, restaurant; open all day, bedrooms *(E G Parish)*

Crown [Earle St]: Popular high-ceilinged local with welcoming landlady, well kept Robinsons, comfortable old-fashioned furnishings and wallpaper, 1940s snug with service bell pushes, back games area with pool and juke box; handy for Railway Heritage Centre *(E G Parish, Pete Baker)*

Express [Mill St]: Comfortable local with well kept ale, sports TV *(E G Parish)*

Monkey [West St]: Well renovated local tied to Slaters the Staffordshire microbrewery (see entry for George, Eccleshall), fine range of their beers and several guests, very reasonable prices; no food *(E G Parish, Edward Leetham)*

Rookery Wood [Weston Gate, Duchy Rd; A5020 SE, quite handy for M6 junction 16]: Plush and roomy Tom Cobleigh family dining pub with Grecian marble-effect lounge, big bar, lots of wood, prints and rustic bric-a-brac, good friendly service, well kept Bass and Theakstons XB, no smoking areas, log fire; good indoor supervised play barn, lots of tables and another play area outside; open all day, good disabled facilites *(Richard Lewis, Dr and Mrs A K Clarke)*

Three Lamps [Earle St, by town hall]: Very popular combination of good eating place with comfortably pubby bar, lots of woodwork and attractive prints, relaxed atmosphere, friendly staff; back food area, well kept Banks's ales inc Mild; piped music, games machines, live music some nights; open all day, overlooking Town Lawn and handy for Lyceum Theatre; very busy lunchtime, esp market days – Mon, Fri, Sat *(E G Parish)*

Duddon [SJ5164]

Headless Woman [A51 NW of Tarporley]: Neatly enlarged country pub, oak beams and gleaming brass, impression of several little rooms, old timbers worked into walls, wide choice of food from well filled baguettes up, real ale; play area, open for food all day wknds and bank hols *(E G Parish)*

Eaton [SJ5763]

Red Lion [the one nr Tarporley]: Nicely decorated comfortable country pub, pleasant restaurant, wide choice of good reasonably priced generous food inc unusual fresh fish, friendly landlord, efficient service, real ales, no smoking areas, separate bar with pool and darts; children welcome, floodlit bowling green, barbecues and play area, open all day *(Robert Colquhoun)*

Faddiley [SJ5753]

Thatch [A534 Wrexham—Nantwich]: Attractive cottagey thatched, low-beamed and timbered informal dining pub with carefully done new barn-style restaurant extension and charming country garden, friendly staff, well kept Courage-related beers with a local guest, food (all day Sun) from imaginatively filled baguettes to some interesting main dishes, children in restaurant, no smoking area; dominoes, fruit machine, piped music; open all day Sun *(E G Parish, LYM)*

Frodsham [SJ5177]

Golden Lion [Main St]: Good Sam Smiths pub with well kept low-priced real ale *(anon)*

Netherton Hall [A56 towards Helsby]: Large converted town-edge farmhouse popular for good imaginative well presented food all day, with well kept changing ales such as Jennings and Timothy Taylors Landlord, good choice of wine by the glass, friendly attentive young staff, no smoking rooms; well behaved children welcome, nice setting *(Mrs P J Carrol)*

Gawsworth [SJ8969]

☆ *Harrington Arms* [Church Lane]: One for the traditionalist's notebook – ancient farm pub with two small basic rooms (children allowed in one), bare boards and panelling, fine carved oak bar counter, well kept Robinsons Best and Hatters Mild served in big old enamelled jugs, friendly service, pickled eggs, freshly made sandwiches and pies; benches on small front cobbled terrace *(JP, PP, LYM, the Didler, Des and Jen Clarke)*

Goostrey [SJ7770]

Crown [off A50 and A535]: Extended neatly kept pub with open fires, pleasant furnishings and lots of beams and pictures in three-room bar side and spacious restaurant; good service, relaxed atmosphere, well kept Banks's and Marstons Pedigree, popular food; bedrooms, close to Jodrell Bank *(E G Parish, Michael Butler, LYM)*

☆ *Olde Red Lion* [Station Rd]: Comfortable open-plan bar and restaurant well reworked by new local landlord, increasingly popular for food inc OAP lunches, friendly efficient service, real ales; children welcome, nice garden with play area *(E G Parish, LYM)*

Great Budworth [SJ6778]

☆ *George & Dragon* [signed off A559 NE of Northwich; High St]: Attractive and unusual 17th-c building in delightful village, rambling panelled lounge, beams hung with copper jugs, interesting things to look at, red plush button-back banquettes and older settles, helpful service, sensibly priced bar food inc good Sun lunch, upstairs restaurant and (Weds-Sun – worth booking) family dining area, well kept Tetleys and two quickly changing guest beers (over a hundred a year), farm cider, decent coffee, no smoking area, games in public bar; open all day Sat/Sun *(E G Parish, LYM, John Hulme, Bernie Adams)*

Haslington [SJ7355]

Fox [Crewe Rd]: Large front family dining area, back bar and further dining area, pleasant décor, wide food choice inc children's, generous helpings with separate veg, well kept Boddingtons, Flowers Original and Marstons Pedigree, friendly helpful staff *(Richard Lewis)*

Hawk [A534 Crewe—Sandbach]: 16th-c coaching inn doing well under newish young landlord, several small rooms, oak beams, brasses, open fires, welcoming staff, Robinsons ales, good wkdy lunchtime bar food inc particularly good baguettes *(E G Parish)*

Hollins Green [SJ6991]

Black Swan [just off A57 Manchester—Warrington, 3 miles from M6 junction 21]: Attractively furnished low-ceilinged old building, with nooks and crannies on different levels, wide choice of enjoyable and generous good value fresh food inc OAP specials, Tetleys beers; may be piped music; notable Christmas decorations *(Norman Revell)*

Kelsall [SJ5268]

☆ *Morris Dancer* [Chester Rd (A54)]: Roomy and civilised yet cosy, with two bars, wine bar area and restaurant, wide choice of generous tasty food inc good fresh veg and game in season, attentive courteous service, pleasant relaxing atmosphere; well kept real ale, decent wines *(Derek and Margaret Underwood)*

Kingsley [SJ5474]

Horse Shoe [Hollow Lane]: Doing well under enterprising new tenants, warm and welcoming, with huge helpings of attractively priced food inc special nights, menu flexibility, well kept Burtonwood ales, fresh flowers; piped music; new garden *(F H Keens)*

Little Barrow [SJ4769]

☆ *Foxcote* [B5152, between A51 and A56 E of Chester]: Big largely no smoking L-shaped eating place specialising in good freshly cooked seafood (a separate board just for mussels dishes), early-evening bargains, good choice of wines by the glass, courteous efficient staff, relaxed and cheerful pubby atmosphere despite the gingham tablecloths on all tables and lack of real ales, seafood and country prints on hessian walls, classy flower arrangements, end tables with picture-window country views *(Mrs S Pritchard, Lynette and Stuart Shore, Jean and Douglas Troup, Mrs P J Carroll, BB, Mrs E Walker)*

Little Bollington [SJ7286]

☆ *Swan With Two Nicks* [2 miles from M56 junction 7 – A56 towards Lymm, then first right at Stamford Arms into Park Lane; use A556 to get back on to M56 westbound]: Welcoming bustle in refurbished beamed village pub full of brass, copper and bric-a-brac, snug alcoves, some antique settles, log fire, good choice of popular freshly made generous food from good value filling baguettes up, well kept ales inc Boddingtons, Greene King Old Speckled Hen and Timothy Taylors Landlord, decent wines, cheerful quick staff; tables outside, open all day, attractive hamlet by Dunham Hall deer park, walks by Bridgewater Canal *(Mr and Mrs Colin Roberts, LYM, Alun Howells, Stephen Buckley)*

Lymm [SJ6787]

☆ *Spread Eagle* [not far from M6 junction 20; Eagle Brow]: Long rambling recently refurbished beamed village pub, central bar serving big comfortable lounge, proper public bar with coal fire and games, separate dining room, cheery atmosphere, reasonably priced home-made food all day from sandwiches and baguettes to steak, particularly well kept Lees Bitter and Red Dragon; bedrooms, attractive village *(MLR, Pete Baker)*

Macclesfield [SJ9173]

Bate Hall [Chestergate]: Roomy open-plan pub with popular bar food, real ale, well spaced tables and fairly dark décor; may be piped music *(E G Parish)*

☆ *Castle* [Church St]: Deceptively large unchanging local in narrow cobbled street, two lounges, small public bar, plenty of character and lots of nooks and crannies inc end glass-roofed area up steps, well kept Courage Directors and Theakstons Bitter and Mild, simple lunchtime food inc proper chips *(E G Parish, the Didler, BB)*

Sun [Mill Lane/London Rd]: Beams and bare boards in two basic rooms off central servery, one with games, well kept Burtonwood, Cains and three changing guest beers, coal fires, friendly landlord may knock up a sandwich for you; open all day Sat *(Pete Baker)*

Marbury [SJ5645]

Swan [NNE of Whitchurch]: Old-fashioned unpretentious pub with seating around edges of partly panelled lounge, well presented fresh food from good lunchtime sandwiches to interesting dishes and game, genial staff, maybe winter fire in copper-canopied fireplace, decent wines, several dozen malt whiskies, no machines or piped music; venerable oak on green opposite, delightful village a half-mile's country walk from the Llangollen Canal, Bridges 23 and 24 *(LYM, Dr Phil Putwain)*

Marton [SJ8568]

Davenport Arms [A34 N of Congleton]: Clean and spaciously modernised, with generous good value home-made food in bar and restaurant inc popular Sun lunch, friendly service, well kept Courage, no smoking area; near ancient half-timbered church (and Europe's widest oak tree) *(Dr D J and Mrs S C Walker)*

Mobberley [SJ8079]

☆ ***Bird in Hand*** [Knolls Green; B5085 towards Alderley]: Cosy low-beamed rooms with comfortably cushioned heavy wooden seats, warm coal fires, small pictures on Victorian wallpaper, little panelled snug, good no smoking top dining area, good choice of promptly served reasonably priced food from enjoyable hot baguettes up, summer afternoon teas, helpful quietly friendly service, well kept Sam Smiths, lots of malt whiskies, decent house wines, pub games; occasional piped music; children allowed, open all day *(LYM, Mr and Mrs Colin Roberts, E G Parish)*

☆ ***Bulls Head*** [Mill Lane]: Comfortable low-beamed pub plushly opened up around central open fireplaces, with old pictures, soft lighting, friendly landlord, enjoyable straightforward food inc children's, well kept ales such as Boddingtons, Coach House Summer Sizzler, Timothy Taylors Landlord and Tetleys Bitter and Mild, games room; piped music; immaculate bowling green *(Michael and Jenny Back, BB)*

Chapel House [Pepper St; Ashley rd out towards Altrincham]: Small, clean and homely, nicely carpeted, darkish woodwork, upholstered stools and wall settles, good cheap food (not Mon) from generous filled barm cakes, club sandwiches and baked potatoes to chilli and curries etc, good friendly service, well kept Boddingtons, two open fires, small games room; courtyard seats *(Mr and Mrs Colin Roberts)*

Church Inn [opp church]: Popular lunchtime for enjoyable food from good baguettes up, well kept real ales, big log fire, cheerful service, friendly atmosphere; children welcome, tables outside, play area, own bowling green *(Pat and Robert Watt, Mrs P J Carroll)*

Plough & Flail [Paddock Hill; small sign off B5085 towards Wilmslow]: Friendly and relaxed three-room pub, well kept Bass, Boddingtons and perhaps a seasonal beer from Robinsons, log fire, food all day from snacks to restaurant dishes; children welcome, good garden with play area *(Brian and Anna Marsden)*

Railway [Station Rd]: Clean and comfortable, with wide choice of food from sandwiches up in large bar and side dining room, well kept Greenalls *(Doug Christian)*

☆ ***Roebuck*** [Mill Lane; down hill from sharp bend on B5085 at E edge of 30mph limit]: Spacious and appealing open-plan bar with brasses, pews, polished boards, panelling and alcoves; good fresh food from lunchtime sandwiches to interesting modern hot dishes, good friendly young staff, well kept real ales, upstairs restaurant; children welcome, can get busy Sat night; pretty outside, with tables in cobbled courtyard and garden behind, play area, handy for Hillside Bird Park *(Doug Christian, LYM, Suzanne Miles)*

Nantwich [SJ6552]

☆ ***Black Lion*** [Welsh Row]: Three atmospheric little rooms alongside main bar, old-fashioned nooks and crannies, beams and bare floors, big grandfather clock; four changing real ales inc well kept local Weetwood brews and a guest such as Titanic, farm cider, cheap sandwiches, very friendly cat, chess; occasional live music; heated marquee outside, open all day *(Pete Baker, Edward Leetham, BB)*

☆ ***Crown*** [High St, free public parking behind]: Striking three-storey timbered Elizabethan hotel with overhanging upper galleries, cosy rambling beamed bar with antique tables and chairs on sloping creaky floors, decent bar lunches from sandwiches and baked potatoes to steak, Italian evening restaurant (and all day Sat), Boddingtons and Flowers IPA, helpful service; very busy wknd evenings, piped music, fruit machine and TV; children welcome, open all day, comfortable bedrooms *(M Joyner, LYM)*

Globe [Audlem Rd]: Traditional home cooking (all day wknds) inc lunchtime and early evening bargains, Flowers real ale, good wine choice, very welcoming and helpful staff, comfortable seating inc some small room areas, good civilised pub atmosphere, quaint rooms with old prints; tables in garden, pretty floral displays *(E G Parish)*

Peacock [Crewe Rd (A534)]: Popular chain family dining pub, roomy and comfortable, with separate attractively decorated areas inc no smoking, good reasonably priced food inc bargain offers, well spaced tables, friendly helpful service, well kept changing ales inc interesting guests, decent wines, games room with pool and big-screen sports TV; facilities for disabled, big lawn with lots of picnic-sets and excellent play area, open all day; bedrooms in back Travelodge *(Edward Leetham, Richard Lewis)*

Red Cow [Beam St]: Well renovated low-ceilinged former Tudor farmhouse, well kept Robinsons real ales, smallish lounge and bar, coal fire, relaxed atmosphere, home-made food inc lots of vegetarian, no smoking dining area, back pool table; terrace with pergola and play area, bedrooms *(E G Parish, MLR, Edward Leetham)*

☆ *Vine* [Hospital St]: Popular town pub, dates from 17th c though sympathetically modernised inside, stretching far back with dimly lit quiet corners (seem to get better the deeper you penetrate), good value plain food from hearty sandwiches up, well kept Hydes beers inc seasonal ones, chatty landlord and friendly staff, dog and locals, pub games; piped music may be loud; children welcome, open all day Sat, cl Mon lunchtime *(E G Parish, BB)*

Wickstead Arms [Mill St]: Nice new refurbishment, Boddingtons and Cains real ale, bar lunches cooked by landlord's Italian wife, prints in roomy carpeted bar, separate pool room *(Edward Leetham)*

Ness [SJ3076]

Wheatsheaf [Neston Rd]: Large Thwaites roadhouse by Ness Gardens, overlooking Dee Estuary, sturdy comfortable furnishings in open-plan L-shaped bar with spacious alcoves, 1940s stained glass, well kept real ale, low-priced straightforward lunchtime home cooking inc children's meals, charming young managers; TV, games; picnic-sets on lawn, play area, open all day *(MLR, E G Parish)*

Neston [SJ2976]

☆ *Harp* [Quayside, SW of Little Neston; keep on along track at end of Marshlands Rd]: Well kept real ales such as Fullers London Pride, Greene King Abbot, Holts, Ind Coope Burton, Morrells Blustering Bursar and Timothy Taylors Landlord, good malt whiskies, woodburner in pretty fireplace, local atmosphere, pale quarry tiles and simple furnishings (children allowed in room on right), lunchtime food; picnic-sets up on grassy front sea wall look out over the Dee marshes to Wales, glorious sunsets with wild calls of wading birds; open all day from noon *(MLR, Sue and Keith Campbell, BB)*

Oakgrove [SJ9169]

Fools Nook [A523 S of Macclesfield]: Welcoming, lots of brass plates and pewter, attractive fireplace and longcase clock, settles, good choice of food (not cheap) and beers inc Boddingtons and guests, several dozen whiskies; cottagey garden *(Kevin Blake)*

Over Peover [SJ7674]

Olde Park Gate [Stocks Lane; off A50 N of Holmes Chapel at the Whipping Stock]: Sam Smiths country pub which has been a popular main entry for its good food, warm welcome and individuality, but the landlady who brought it that appeal over her six years there has recently left; reports on new regime, please *(LYM)*

Parkgate [SJ2878]

Boathouse [village signed off A540]: Black and white timbered dining pub with several interesting connecting rooms and big conservatory (booking needed wknds), spectacular views to Wales over silted grassy estuary behind, generous if not cheap food inc children's and popular Sun lunch, well spaced tables, busy young staff, well kept real ales; nearby marshes good for birdwatchers *(E G Parish)*

☆ *Red Lion* [The Parade (B5135)]: Comfortable and neatly kept local on attractive waterfront, big windows look across road to silted grassy estuary with Wales beyond, typical pub furnishings, shiny brown beams hung with lots of china, copper and brass, chatty macaw called Nelson, good value sandwiches and home-cooked lunchtime main dishes, well kept Adnams, Ind Coope Burton and Tetleys, flame-effect fire in pretty Victorian fireplace, good games room off public bar; picnic-sets out on small front terrace, open all day *(BB, MLR, Sue and Keith Campbell)*

Poynton [SJ9483]

☆ *Boars Head* [Shrigley Rd, Higher Poynton, off A523]: Welcoming Victorian country pub next to Middlewood Way (ex-railway walk and cycle route) and Macclesfield Canal, well refurbished with button-back leather seats (and darts) in bar, lounge with enjoyable home-made food (all day wknds) inc speciality pies, well kept reasonably priced Boddingtons with a guest such as Bass, coffee etc, big open fire; handy for Lyme Park *(Adam Wainwright, Doug Christian, Brian and Anna Marsden)*

Rainow [SJ9576]

☆ *Highwayman* [A5002 Whaley Bridge—Macclesfield, NE of village]: Timeless unchanging moorside pub with small rooms, low 17th-c beams, well kept Thwaites ales, bar food inc good sandwiches and ideal black pudding, good winter fires (electric other times), plenty of atmosphere, lovely views *(LYM, the Didler, Dr D J and Mrs S C Walker)*

Shavington [SJ6951]

Elephant & Castle [A52 E of Nantwich]: Smart and comfortable, good range of food and of beers such as Marstons Pedigree, friendly staff *(Richard Greenwood)*

Shocklach [SJ4349]

Bull [off A534 from Wrexham at crossrds with Farndon]: Good food inc interesting dishes and wide range of puddings, changing daily, good value house wines, conservatory; can be very busy *(Rita and Keith Pollard)*

Smallwood [SJ7861]

☆ *Legs of Man* [A50 S of Sandbach]: Comfortable roadside pub with carefully matched chairs, banquettes, carpet, curtains and wallpaper, fin de siècle tall white nymphs on columns, lush potted plants, big helpings of good home-cooked food inc some imaginative dishes (and they try to suit special diets), well kept Robinsons Best, Frederics and Hatters Mild, staff friendly and effective even when very busy; restaurant, children truly welcome; well spaced tables on side lawn with play area *(BB, E G Parish)*

Swettenham [SJ8067]

☆ *Swettenham Arms* [off A54 Congleton—Holmes Chapel or A535 Chelford—Holmes Chapel]: Attractive and prettily placed old country pub very popular for wide choice of good food efficiently served in charming series of individually furnished rooms from sofas and easy chairs to no smoking dining area (must book Sun), well spaced tables, well kept ales such as Beartown, Hydes, Jennings and Tetleys, farm cider, picnic-sets on quiet side lawn; children welcome, live music Weds *(Doug Christian, LYM, Mike and Wendy Proctor)*

Tarporley [SJ5563]

☆ *Swan* [High St, off A49]: Tastefully modernised Georgian inn with cosy little spaces, well kept Greene King and guest beers, bottled Belgian beers, dozens of malt whiskies, civilised informal brasserie with rather smart food from lunchtime sandwiches and snacks up, separate restaurant, polite service; tables outside, provision for children; comfortable well equipped bedrooms *(LYM, Mike and Wendy Proctor)*

Tattenhall [SJ4958]

Sportsmans Arms [Burwardsley Rd]: Enjoyable food at reasonable prices *(A and B D Craig)*

Tiverton [SJ5660]

☆ *Shady Oak* [Bates Mill Lane]: Canalside family pub looking up to Beeston Castle (telescope available), with comfortable bar, airy lounge with leather chesterfields, small carpeted heated no smoking conservatory, well kept Courage with a guest such as Greene King Ruddles or local Weetwood, reasonably priced food from good sandwiches to enjoyable blackboard dishes inc light meals all day, pleasant service; plenty of tables in waterside garden and terrace, good play area and pets corner, summer barbecues, moorings *(MLR, LYM, E G Parish)*

Walker Barn [SJ9573]

☆ *Setter Dog* [A537 Macclesfield—Buxton]: Warm, clean and civilised stone-built pub in great moorland setting with windswept Pennine views, two real ales such as Bass and local Storm in small low-beamed pubby bar, good friendly service, high-backed settles, roaring fire, small separate restaurant with appetising sensibly priced food inc good value Sun lunch; tables in car park across road (watch for fast traffic), handy for Teggs Nose Country Park, open all day (but has been cl Tues/Weds lunchtime), camping barn available *(MLR, BB, Dave Irving, JP, PP)*

Warmingham [SJ7161]

☆ *Bears Paw* [School Lane]: Attractive pub with wide choice of well prepared food from enormous filled baguettes to substantial main courses, reasonable prices, plush seating around marble-top tables in raised areas, well kept Bass, Boddingtons and Worthington BB, relaxed atmosphere, friendly helpful staff, charming restaurant, pool room, children very welcome; good spot by river and ancient church in picturesque village, seats in front garden, bedrooms *(E G Parish)*

Warrington [SJ5686]

☆ *Ferry Inn* [leave A562 in Penketh – park in Station Rd off Tannery Lane]: Pretty building in lovely isolated spot between St Helens Canal and River Mersey, four well kept real ales inc very quickly changing guest beers, over 100 whiskies, good home-cooked food (not Sun evening) inc fresh fish, friendly service, cosy low-beamed bar, coal or log fire in lounge eating area, games room, provision for children, nice upstairs dining room; tables outside with play area, pets corner, pony paddock *(LYM, Lyn and Geoff Hallchurch, MLR)*

Wettenhall [SJ6261]

☆ *Boot & Slipper* [off B5074 just S of Winsford; Long Lane – OS Sheet 118 map ref 625613]: Attractive layout and décor in immaculate tucked-away country pub, hard-working cheerful landlady and charming staff, convivial atmosphere, good generous fresh food from sandwiches to inventive main dishes, well kept Marstons Pedigree and Tetleys, good choice of malt whiskies, decent wine list, children welcome in eating areas inc cottagey restaurant; picnic-sets on front cobbles, play area, comfortable bedrooms, open all day wknds *(A and B D Craig, LYM, E G Parish)*

Wheelock [SJ7559]

Commercial [off new A534 bypass; Game St]: Old-fashioned unspoilt local, two smaller rooms (one no smoking) off high-ceilinged main bar, unaltered décor, Boddingtons, Marstons Pedigree, Thwaites and an occasional guest beer, real fire, firmly efficient service, no food; pool in games room, may be Thurs folk night, open from 8 evenings only, and Sun lunchtime *(Pete Baker, the Didler)*

Whitegate [SJ6268]

Plough [Foxwist Green, OS Sheet 118 map ref 624684; off A556 just W of Northwich, or A54 W of Winsford]: Two rooms, simple but comfortable and interesting, with cosy fire, small dining room, well kept Robinsons Best, Hatters Mild and Old Stockport, cheerful efficient service, wide choice of home-made food (all day summer Sun) from sandwiches and baked potatoes to steak; piped music, TV, Mon quiz night; no children inside, garden with play area, popular walks nearby, open all day (cl Sun afternoon in winter) *(LYM)*

Whiteley Green [SJ9278]

Windmill [Hole House Lane; village signposted off A523 a mile N of B5091 Bollington turn-off]: Roomy open-plan pub extended from heavy-beamed core, good-sized no smoking area, well kept Greene King Old Speckled Hen, Tetleys and a guest beer, food from sandwiches and ploughman's to steak and Sun lunch; TV, piped music; children in eating areas, big attractive garden with plenty of picnic-sets and summer bar, handy for Middlewood Way and other walks, open all day wknds *(Andrew Scarr, Doug Christian, Roger and Pauline Pearce, LYM, Stephen Buckley)*

Wildboarclough [SJ9868]

☆ *Crag*: Welcoming old stone-built pub hidden in charming little sheltered valley below the moors, enjoyable home cooking using local ingredients, well kept beer; tables on pretty terrace *(LYM, J A Lewis, Stephen Buckley)*

Wincle [SJ9467]

Wild Boar: Traditional moorland pub with new licensees doing food lunchtimes and evenings from sandwiches to steaks, Robinsons Bitter, coal fire in comfortable bar, separate restaurant; open all day wknds, cl Tues, two newly done bedrooms *(MLR, BB)*

Winterley [SJ7557]

Forresters Arms [A534]: Cosy and friendly low-beamed village pub with warmly welcoming attentive landlord, good value lunches, well kept Marstons Pedigree, Tetleys and Weetwood Eastgate; pleasant garden with dovecote and retired tractor *(John Hulme)*

Wrenbury [SJ5948]

Cotton Arms [Cholmondeley Rd]: Welcoming beamed and timbered pub in popular spot by canal locks and boatyard, with good value food in two large comfortable dining areas, friendly staff, well kept real ales inc a guest beer, lots of brass, open fire, side games room *(E G Parish, Andy Chetwood, Rick Capper, Mike and Wendy Proctor)*

Paradise Brewery [Creamery Industrial Estate, Station Rd]: Microbrewery with bar open 3-11 Fri, 12-2 Sat/Sun, their own interesting ales, breweriana and bric-a-brac, darts, real fire; visible brewing equipment *(Martin Grosberg, Richard Lewis)*

Wybunbury [SJ6950]

☆ ***Swan*** [B5071]: Spotless family-friendly bow-windowed pub with nooks and crannies in homely rambling lounge, snug dining areas inc no smoking one, pleasant public bar, well kept ales inc Jennings, good house wines, good popular home-made food, reasonable prices, efficient helpful service, plenty of bric-a-brac; tables in garden by beautiful churchyard; bedrooms *(Mike and Wendy Proctor, Edward Leetham, LYM)*

Post Office address codings confusingly give the impression that some pubs are in Cheshire, when they're really in Derbyshire (and therefore included in this book under that chapter) or in Greater Manchester (see the Lancashire chapter).

Cornwall

A good crop of new Cornish main entries (or pubs reappearing in the Guide after an absence) consists of the Cadgwith Cove Inn at Cadgwith (just the sort of pub you'd hope to find in this lovely spot), the smartly decorated Heron perched above its creek at Malpas, the attractive thatched New Inn in the waterside village of Manaccan, the stylish Old Coastguard with its garden going down to the sea on the edge of Mousehole, the Crown at St Ewe (enjoyable food using local produce) and the friendly White Hart in St Teath. Other pubs on great form here this year are the Old Ferry at Bodinnick (gaining its Place to Stay Award this year), the friendly and relaxed Napoleon at the top of Boscastle, the Trengilly Wartha at Constantine (a great all-rounder), the well run Olde Plough House at Duloe, the Halzephron near Helston (almost too popular in high season), the nicely individual Crown at Lanlivery, the Plume of Feathers at Mitchell (now has nice bedrooms, along with the good imaginative food which this year earns it a Food Award), the Roseland at Philleigh (a particular favourite), the friendly Falcon at St Mawgan (a nice all-rounder), the Springer Spaniel at Treburley (a sister pub of the Roseland, also much enjoyed) and the New Inn on Tresco (which gains its Beer Award this year – a great achievement considering its isolation, which of course is part of its charm). The county's four pubs with Food Awards are the Trengilly Wartha near Constantine, the Halzephron near Helston, the Plume of Feathers at Mitchell and the Springer Spaniel at Treburley. Another place for a special meal out is the Old Coastguard in Mousehole – as a new entry, it doesn't yet have its Food Award (which depends partly on the flow of reader reports), but we enjoyed it so much that it is our choice as Cornwall Dining Pub of the Year. The Lucky Dip section at the end of the chapter has such rich pickings this year that there are simply too many hot prospects to list individually. There are several dozen which have the star that signifies a main-entry standard of appeal. We have ourselves inspected over two-thirds of these, and have reports from trusted reader-reporters on all those not yet inspected, so can confidently recommend them all. A word of warning about Cornish pubs in general, and the seaside ones in particular: they do get very busy indeed in the summer holidays. Drinks here are a bit cheaper than the national average. The local beers from Sharps, St Austell and Skinners often score on price over beers from further afield.

BODINNICK SX1352 Map 1

Old Ferry ★ 🛏

Across the water from Fowey; coming by road, to avoid the ferry queue turn left as you go down the hill – car park on left before pub

From most of the bedrooms, tables by the windows in the restaurant, and from the terrace in front of this friendly 16th-c inn, there are lovely views of the pretty Fowey river; the lane beside the pub, in front of the ferry slipway, is very steep, so make sure your brakes work well if you park there. The three simply furnished little rooms have quite a few bits of nautical memorabilia, a couple of half model ships mounted on the wall, and several old photographs, as well as wheelback chairs, built-in plush pink wall seats, and an old high-backed settle; there may be several friendly cats and a dog. The family room at the back is actually hewn into the rock; piped music (maybe a bit loud in the attractive, no smoking restaurant) and TV. Decent bar food includes home-made soup (£3.25), sandwiches (from £2.25; toasties 30p extra), ploughman's (from £5.50), quite a few dishes with chips (from £3.95; home-cooked ham and egg £4.75), home-made cream cheese and broccoli pasta bake (£6.25), curry of the day (£6.50), home-made steak and kidney pie (£6.75), fresh smoked haddock with scrambled egg (£7.95), puddings (from £2.95), good daily specials like fresh scallop and prawn au gratin £4.95), grilled loin of pork in tandoori sauce on coconut rice (£9.75), and fresh Cornish fish platter topped with prawns in a creamy white wine sauce (£10.95), and children's menu (from £2.75). Sharps Own on handpump, kept under light blanket pressure. *(Recommended by David and Anthea Eeles, Dr M W A Haward, Sue Demont, Tim Barrow, Prof and Mrs Tony Palmer, Peter Salmon, Dennis Jenkin, Charlie Harris, Simon, Jo and Benjamin Cole, M Benjamin, Nick Lawless, M Joyner, Jayne Capp, John Saville, B, M and P Kendall)*

Free house ~ Licensees Royce and Patricia Smith ~ Real ale ~ Bar food (12-2.30, 6-9 (12-2, 6.30-8.30 in winter)) ~ Restaurant ~ (01726) 870237 ~ Children in eating area of bar and in family room ~ Dogs welcome ~ Open 11-11; 12-10.30 Sun; 12-2.30, 6.30-10.30 winter; closed 25 Dec ~ Bedrooms: /£55S(£65B)

BOSCASTLE SX0990 Map 1

Napoleon

High Street; up at the top of the village

Run by friendly, welcoming licensees, this 16th-c thick-walled white cottage is at the top of this steep, quaint village, and there are splendid views on the way up. Several little flagstoned rooms ramble around up and down, with oak beams, slate floors, log fires, an exposed oven, an interesting and unusual collection of Napoleon prints and memorabilia, pottery boots, walking sticks and lots of other knick-knacks. Well kept Bass and St Austell Tinners, HSD and seasonal ales tapped from casks behind the bar, and decent wines. Good bar food includes tasty home-made soup with herb scones, hummus with pitta bread or calamari (from £2.25), grilled local mackerel, cheese and onion tart, lamb rogan josh, local pork and leek sausages with onion gravy, chicken, leek and bacon pie, and steak (£5.95-£8.75), and puddings like treacle tart or apple and rhubarb crumble (£2.95); it's best to book for the evening restaurant. Table skittles, darts, shove-ha'penny, cribbage, dominoes, and toad-in-the-hole. There are seats (and boules) out on a small sheltered terrace. *(Recommended by David Cartwright, G Walsh, Dr M W A Haward, Jonathan Gibbs, Bob and Sue Hardy, Chris and Elaine Lyon, the Didler, Canon and Mrs Michael Bourdeaux, George Atkinson)*

St Austell ~ Tenant Mike Mills ~ Real ale ~ Bar food (12-2, 6.30-9(9.30 in summer)) ~ Restaurant ~ (01840) 250204 ~ Children in eating area of bar ~ Dogs allowed in bar ~ Live acts Tues evening and jazz Fri evening ~ Open 11-2.30, 5.30-11; 11-11 Sat; 12-10.30 Sun

CADGWITH SW7214 Map 1

Cadgwith Cove Inn

Down very narrow lane off A3083 S of Helston; no nearby parking

This is the friendly and old-fashioned local for a charming steep thatched working fishing cove, with lots of local photographs including gig races, cases of Naval hat ribands and of fancy knot-work, a couple of compass binnacles, and ship's shields on some of its dark beams – others have spliced blue rope hand-holds. Its two snugly dark front rooms have plain pub furnishings on their mainly parquet flooring, a log fire in one stripped stone end wall, and plenty of locals chatting around the serving counter, which has well kept Everards Tiger, Flowers IPA, Marstons Pedigree, Sharps Own, and Wadworths 6X on handpump. A plusher pink back room has a huge and colourful fish mural. The daily specials tend to be the things to go for in the food line: ones we or readers have enjoyed include local crab soup (£4.95), moules marinière (£5.95 or £8.95), grilled garlic mackerel fillets (£6.95), skate wing with capers (£7.95), monkfish tail in a light creamy curry sauce (£8.95), and hake in a tangy cheese sauce (£9.95). Other dishes include sandwiches and baguettes (from £3.55; the crab are particularly good), filled baked potatoes (from £3.95), ploughman's (£4.95), sausage and mash (£6.25), home-made curry (£6.45), home-made lasagne (£6.50), steak (£9.95), and puddings like home-made blackberry and apple pie with clotted cream (£3.50). The left-hand room has darts. There may be 1960s piped music, and a wide range of entertainment runs from impromptu shanty singing through Irish folk music and karaoke to Christmas mummers. A good-sized front terrace has green-painted picnic-sets, some under a fairy-lit awning, looking down to the fish sheds by the bay. Coast Path walks are superb in both directions. *(Recommended by Lawrence Pearse, Mike and Alison Stevens, Nigel Hopkins, Jeanne and Paul Silvestri, Martin and Karen Wake, Cathy Robinson, Ed Coombe, Mr and Mrs McKay, Sue Holland, Dave Webster, R G Price, Mrs B M Smith)*

Pubmaster ~ Lease David and Lynda Trivett ~ Real ale ~ Bar food ~ Restaurant ~ (01326) 290513 ~ Children allowed away from main bar ~ Dogs welcome ~ Folk club Tues, Cornish singing Fri ~ Open 12-11; 12-11 Sat; 12-10.30 Sun; 12-3, 7-11 Mon-Thurs in winter ~ Bedrooms: £19.85/£39.50

CALLINGTON SX3669 Map 1

Coachmakers Arms

Newport Square (A388 towards Launceston)

A new licensee has taken over this imposing 18th-c pub, has re-decked the balcony of one of their letting bedrooms, and added a growing collection of horsebrasses and money from around the world to the burgeoning collection of antique clocks, prints of coach making and transport on the walls of the irregularly shaped, comfortable beamed and timbered bar. Lots of fresh flowers, little winged settles and stools made from polished brass-bound casks, and well kept Sharps Own and Doom Bar (kept under light blanket pressure), and Skinners Cornish Knocker on handpump. Good home-made food in the bar and open-plan restaurant area includes home-made soup (£2.50), garlic egg mayonnaise (£2.95), sizeable sandwiches or chargrilled burgers (from £4.25), and daily specials such as home-made quiches (£4.95), home-made pies (£5.50), lasagne, pork in cider or lamb in red wine (£5.95), cod fillet topped with cheddar and tomato (£8.95), and fillet steak with pepper sauce (£11.95); nice breakfasts. Euchre on Monday evenings, quiz night on Wednesdays, fruit machine, and piped music. *(Recommended by Bryan Robinson, Mr and Mrs N Smith, Mrs E Hayes)*

Free house ~ Licensee Les Elliott ~ Real ale ~ Bar food ~ (01579) 382567 ~ Children in eating area of bar and restaurant ~ Dogs welcome ~ Open 11-3, 6-11; 12-3, 7-10.30 Sun ~ Bedrooms: £30S/£55S(£45B)

CONSTANTINE SW7229 Map 1

Trengilly Wartha ★ 🍴 🍷 🍺 🛏

Constantine signposted from Penryn—Gweek road (former B3291); in village turn right just before Minimarket (towards Gweek); in nearly a mile pub signposted left; at Nancenoy, OS Sheet 204 map reference 731282

Much enjoyed by readers, this tucked-away inn appeals to a wide range of customers. It's a nice place to stay, the conservatory welcomes families, there are well kept real ales and excellent wines, and highly enjoyable food. The long low-beamed main bar has a woodburning stove and attractive built-in high-backed settles boxing in polished heavy wooden tables, and at one end, shelves of interesting wines with drink-in and take-out price labels (they run their own retail wine business, Cochonnet Wines). The bright no smoking conservatory has an area leading off that houses pool, darts, shove-ha'penny, dominoes, cribbage, and shut-the-box; they run their own cricket team. Popular bar food includes soup (£2.60), local feta cheese, bean and tomato salad (£5.20), lunchtime ploughman's with home-made breads, pickles and chutneys (some of which are for sale behind the bar, from £6.50), good local meaty or vegetarian pasties (£4), devon blue cheese and walnut pâté (£5.20), sausages with mustard mash and onion gravy (£6.40), leek and cheese soufflé (£7.80), thai pork (£8.80), crab cakes (£12.50), specials like tagliatelle with a cream cheese, mushroom and garlic sauce (£7), half a dozen Helford oysters or seared local scallops with pak choy in a chilli and garlic sauce (£8), ham hock braised with an anise and sherry sauce (£8.90), and roast gressingham duck breast with a damson sauce (£11), with proper food for children. Well kept Skinners Knocker, Sharps Cornish, and maybe a local guest on handpump or tapped from the cask. Over 50 malt whiskies (including several extinct ones), 20 wines by the glass (from a fine list of over 200), and around 10 armagnacs. The pretty landscaped garden has some tables under large parasols, an international sized piste for boules, and a lake; lots of surrounding walks. *(Recommended by Sue Demont, Tim Barrow, Martin and Karen Wake, Mike Gorton, Andy and Yvonne Cunningham, the Didler, Dr Paull Khan, Mike and Sue Loseby, M G Hart, Joy and Peter Heatherley, Charlie Harris, Ruth and Andrew Crowder, Mr and Mrs M Cooper, JP, PP, M A Borthwick, Lorna and Howard Lambert, Mr R P Brewer, R and S Bentley, T A Smith, Mike and Alison Stevens, Dr and Mrs M E Wilson, Mr and Mrs M A Cook, Eamonn and Natasha Skyrme, Patrick Hancock, Nigel Long, Joyce and Maurice Cottrell, Jenny and Brian Seller, Ner, Neil and Angela Huxter, Bernard Stradling, Simon and Laura Habbishow, Ian Wilson)*

Free house ~ Licensees Nigel Logan and Michael Maguire ~ Real ale ~ Bar food (12-2.15(2 Sun), 6.30(7 Sun)-9.30; not 25 or evening 31 Dec) ~ Restaurant ~ (01326) 340332 ~ Children welcome ~ Dogs welcome ~ Open 11-3, 6.30-11; 12-3, 7-10.30 Sun ~ Bedrooms: £48B/£77B

DULOE SX2358 Map 1

Olde Plough House

B3254 N of Looe

This neatly kept place is so popular, it's best to book to be sure of a table. The two communicating rooms have a lovely dark polished Delabole slate floor, some turkey rugs, a mix of pews, modern high-backed settles and smaller chairs, foreign banknotes on the beams, three woodburning stoves, and a restrained décor – some prints of waterfowl and country scenes, a few copper jugs and a fat china pig perched on window sills. The public side (just as comfortable) has darts; piped music. Well liked and reasonably priced food at lunchtime includes home-made soup (£2.45), filled baguettes (from £3.15; sausage, bacon and egg £4.25), a roast of the day (£4.95), ploughman's (from £4.95), home-cooked ham and egg (£5.45), vietnamese sweet chilli chicken (£5.65), vegetable lasagne (£5.95), and scallops in garlic butter (£6.95), with evening dishes such as duck confit (£4.65), crevettes and moules or scallops with spinach and bacon (£4.95), medallions of pork in a citrus and whisky sauce (£9.25), and breast of duck with a vegetable galette on a port sauce with a red fruit compote (£9.95), and daily specials like fried strips of chicken with a sweet and sour sauce (£7.25), baked swordfish steak garnished with scallops and caper butter (£10.45), and medley of seafood with saffron, ginger and sweet pepper cream sauce (£10.85). Bass and Sharps Doom Bar on handpump, sensibly priced wines, and good attentive service. There is a small more modern carpeted dining room, and a few picnic-sets out by the road. The two friendly jack russells are called Jack and Spot, and the cat, Willow. *(Recommended by Prof and Mrs Tony Palmer, Nick Lawless, Mayur Shah, John and Shelia Brooks, Peter and Anne-Marie O'Malley, R G Price, Mrs B M Smith, P R and S A White, Mrs M E Lewis, Mrs June Wilmers, J A Lewis, M Joyner, Glenys and John Roberts, B J Harding, Robert Turnham)*

Free house ~ Licensees Gary and Alison Toms ~ Real ale ~ Bar food (not 25 Dec) ~ (01503) 262050 ~ Children in eating area of bar ~ Dogs allowed in bar ~ Open 12-2.30, 6.30-11; 12-2.30, 7-10.30 Sun; closed evenings 25-26 Dec

The symbol shows pubs which keep their beer unusually well or have a particularly good range.

EDMONTON SW9672 Map 1

Quarryman

Village signposted off A39 just W of Wadebridge bypass

This interesting pub is built around a carefully reconstructed slate-built courtyard of former quarrymen's quarters, and is part of an attractively understated small health and holiday complex. The three beamed rooms (one is no smoking) have simple pleasant furnishings, a set of interesting old brass spirit optics above the fireplace nestling among some fine old whisky advertising figurines, fresh flowers on tables, a woodburner, and a couple of bow windows (one with a charming stained-glass quarryman panel) looking out to a distant wind farm; there's some interesting sporting memorabilia – particularly the Roy Ullyett menu cartoons for British Sportsman's Club Savoy lunches for visiting cricket and rugby international teams. Served by friendly staff, the good bar food includes lunchtime sandwiches (from £2.90; ciabatta with cajun chicken, avocado and sour cream £3.50), home-made soup (£2.90), warm goats cheese salad with pears and walnut (£4.90), tiger prawns in tempura batter with a sweet chilli dip (£5.50), vegetarian cannelloni (£6.50), Aberdeen Angus steaks (from £10.50), and specials such as toad-in-the-hole with shallot and red wine jus (£7.50), chargrilled loin of pork topped with red onion and chilli marmalade and welsh rarebit with cider sauce (£10.50), and roast cod wrapped in parma ham on a bed of bubble and squeak with a light parsley sauce (£10.90). They have four well kept beers on handpump such as Sharps Eden, Skinners Coastliner and Cornish, and maybe Timothy Taylors Landlord, decent house wines and some interesting good value bottles, and 10 malt whiskies; pool, fruit machine, cribbage and dominoes. The dog is called Floyd. There's a cosy no smoking bistro on the other side of the courtyard. *(Recommended by Geoff Calcott, Simon, Jo and Benjamin Cole, Joy and Peter Heatherley, Dr S J Shepherd, Mike and Sue Loseby, Pete and Rosie Flower, Kevin Thorpe)*

Free house ~ Licensees Terry and Wendy De Villiers Kuun ~ Real ale ~ Bar food (12-2.30, 6-9) ~ Restaurant ~ (01208) 816444 ~ Well behaved children away from bar area ~ Dogs allowed in bar ~ Open 12-11; 12-10.30 Sun

EGLOSHAYLE SX0172 Map 1

Earl of St Vincent £

Off A389, just outside Wadebridge

Tucked away in a narrow quiet back street behind the church, this pretty pub has over 162 antique clocks, all in working order – as well as golfing memorabilia, Art Deco ornaments, and all sorts of rich furnishings. Well kept St Austell Tinners, Trelawnys Pride, HSD, and a guest on handpump; piped music. Enjoyable, good value food such as sandwiches, soup or ploughman's (from £2.50), lunchtime specials such as liver and bacon (£4.50), and ham and egg, steak pie or chicken cordon bleu (all £5), and evening dishes like fresh fish dishes (from £8.50), and speciality steaks (£13.50). The snug is no smoking. In summer, there are picnic-sets in the lovely garden and marvellous flowering baskets and tubs. *(Recommended by the Didler, M A Borthwick, Kevin Thorpe, James Nunns, Ted George, Dr M W A Haward, Jayne Capp, George Atkinson, Terry Mizen, Mrs M Griffin, John and Sarah Perry, Mr and Mrs B Hobden, Pete and Rosie Flower, P and M Rudlin)*

St Austell ~ Tenants Edward and Anne Connolly ~ Real ale ~ Bar food (not Sun evening) ~ Restaurant ~ (01208) 814807 ~ Children in eating area of bar ~ Open 11-3, 6.30-11; 12-3, 7-10.30 Sun

HELFORD SW7526 Map 1

Shipwrights Arms

Off B3293 SE of Helston, via Mawgan

The position here is lovely, and seats on the terrace overlook the pretty wooded creek (at its best at high tide); there are plenty of surrounding walks and a long distance coastal path goes right past the door – so in good weather, this thatched pub does get very busy. There's quite a nautical theme inside, with navigation lamps, models of ships, sea pictures, drawings of lifeboat coxswains and shark fishing photographs – as well as a collection of foreign banknotes behind the bar counter. A dining area has oak settles and tables; winter open fire. Well kept Castle Eden and Sharps Doom Bar on handpump, and bar food such as home-made soup (£3.25), buffet lunch platters (from £4.95), summer evening barbecue dishes such as marinated lamb fillet (£9.25), steaks (from £9.40), and monkfish marinated with chilli, lime and coriander (£12.25), and home-made puddings (£4.50); piped music. The pub is quite a walk from the nearest car park but there's also a foot ferry from Helford Passage. *(Recommended by Tim and Jan Dalton, Andrea Rampley, R J Herd, Mr and Mrs M Cooper, Alan and Paula McCully, Geoff Pidoux, Mrs B Rogers, P R and S A White, Simon and Laura Habbishow, Brian Skelcher, the Didler, JP, PP, Jenny and Brian Seller)*

Greenalls ~ Lease Charles Herbert ~ Real ale ~ Bar food (not Sun or Mon evenings in winter) ~ (01326) 231235 ~ Children in eating area of bar and restaurant ~ Dogs welcome ~ Open 11-2.30, 6-11; 12-3, 7-10.30 Sun; closed winter Sun evening

HELSTON SW6527 Map 1

Blue Anchor £

50 Coinagehall Street

Probably the oldest brewing house in the country, this 15th-c thatched pub was once a monks' hospice. It remains as it always has been, a basic drinkers' tavern and they still brew their own Middle, Spingo Special, and Easter and Christmas Special; also, farm cider. A series of small, low-ceilinged rooms opening off the central corridor has simple old-fashioned furniture on the flagstones, interesting old prints, some bared stone walls, and in one room a fine inglenook fireplace. A family room has darts; dominoes and cribbage. Bar food includes home-made soup (£1.80), rolls and sandwiches (from £1.90), ham and eggs (£3.95), ploughman's (from £4.25), liver and bacon hotpot (£4.75), steak and kidney pie (£5.50), and daily specials (£3.50). Past an old stone bench in the sheltered little terrace area is a skittle alley which you can hire. At lunchtimes you can usually go and look round the brewery and the cellar. *(Recommended by the Didler, Andrea Rampley, P J Holdsworth, Su and Bob Child, Roger and Jenny Huggins, Kevin Thorpe, Giles Francis, Sue Holland, Dave Webster, M G Hart, JP, PP)*

Own brew ~ Licensee Simon Stone ~ Real ale ~ Bar food (12-4) ~ No credit cards ~ (01326) 565765 ~ Children in own room ~ Dogs welcome ~ Jazz 1st Mon of month, folk Thurs, live bands wknds ~ Open 10.30-11; 12-10.30 Sun ~ Bedrooms: £27S(£29B)/£44S

Halzephron

Gunwalloe, village about 4 miles S but not marked on many road maps; look for brown sign on A3083 alongside perimeter fence of RNAS Culdrose

As this former smugglers' haunt does get incredibly busy during the summer holidays, many of our readers prefer it during the quieter months. There's a really friendly feeling in the bustling, spotlessly clean bar, with comfortable seating, copper on the walls and mantelpiece, and a warm winter fire in the big hearth; there's also a quite a small no smoking family room. Particularly good, popular bar snacks at lunchtime include sandwiches (from £3; super crab £7.90), home-made soup (£4.10), freshly made pâté or mushrooms sautéed with herbs in a cream sauce with garlic bread (£5), ploughman's (from £5.25), and platters such as crab, prawn or smoked salmon (from £11.25), with evening choices like breast of chicken marinated in herbs and dijon mustard, breadcrumbed and deep fried (£10), and chargrilled sirloin steak (£12.25); lunchtime specials might include duck liver and orange pâté with toasted brioche (£5), seafood chowder with basil aïoli (£6.95), lasagne or mushroom and nut stroganoff (£8.50), and hot baked prawns and crab (£11), with evening choices like duck leg confit on oriental cabbage with sweet and sour sauce (£6.50), sweet and sour pork with egg fried rice (£11.50), roast saddle of lamb with an apricot and rosemary stuffing on garlic pomme purée, with a date compote and red wine sauce (£11.90), pasta with mediterranean vegetables, artichokes, olives and sun-dried tomatoes with olive oil and basil, topped with parmesan (£12.50), and caramelised gressingham duck on butternut squash purée with redcurrant juniper jus (£13.90). Puddings are home-made: lemon mousse, hot chocolate fudge cake or caramel cream pots (from £4); all the eating areas are no smoking. Well kept Sharps Cornish, Own and Doom Bar, and St Austell Tribute on handpump, a good wine list, lots of malt whiskies, and around 25 liqueurs; dominoes and cribbage. There are lots of lovely surrounding unspoilt walks with fine views of Mount's Bay, Gunwalloe fishing cove is just 300 yards away, and there's a sandy beach one mile away at Church Cove. The church of St Winwaloe (built into the dunes on the seashore) is only a mile away, and well worth a visit. *(Recommended by Dr D J and Mrs S C Walker, D and H Broodbank, Mr and Mrs M Cooper, Brian Skelcher, John and Sarah Perry, Andrea Rampley, Andy and Yvonne Cunningham, Jayne Capp, Eamonn and Natasha Skyrme, Sue Demont, Tim Barrow, John Saville, Cliff Blakemore, Joyce and Maurice Cottrell, M G Hart, Stuart Turner, Dr Phil Putwain, John Bodycote, Sue Holland, Dave Webster, James Nunns, Mrs Caroline Siggins, Jenny and Brian Seller, Jacquie and Jim Jones, Dr P Brown, David Crook, Mrs Romey Heaton, Nick Lawless, Cathy Robinson, Ed Coombe)*

Free house ~ Licensee Angela Thomas ~ Real ale ~ Bar food (not 25 Dec) ~ Restaurant ~ (01326) 240406 ~ Children in family room ~ Open 11-2.30, 6(6.30 winter)-11; 12-2.30, 6-10.30 Sun; closed 25 Dec ~ Bedrooms: £40B/£70B

KINGSAND SX4350 Map 1

Halfway House

Fore Street, towards Cawsand

The name of this attractive old inn comes from the fact that the stream behind once marked the border between Devon and Cornwall – it is now the point where the twin villages of Kingsand and Cawsand meet. The simply furnished but quite smart bar is mildly Victorian in style, and rambles around a huge central fireplace, with low ceilings, soft lighting, and plenty of locals – though there's a warm welcome for the many summer visitors. Decent bar food includes daily specials such as marinated sardines (£3.95), warm tomato, red onion and mozzarella salad (£4.50), fish pie, pork tenderloin with apple, rosemary and garlic or chicken stuffed with cream cheese, wholegrain mustard and cider sauce (all £9.95), monkfish with green thai sauce (£12.95), and mixed fish grill with seafood paella (£13.95); from the menu, there might be filled baguettes (from £2.50), filled baked potatoes (from £3.85), locally made pasty (£5.25), ploughman's (from £5.25), home-cooked ham and egg (£6.35), red pepper and spinach lasagne (£6.95), curry of the day (£7.50), and steaks (from £10.40). Well kept Courage Best, Sharps Doom Bar, and maybe Wadworths 6X on handpump kept under light blanket pressure, and decent wines. Service is quick and friendly, and the bar staff add a lot to the enjoyable atmosphere. The piped music is generally unobtrusive; cribbage, dominoes. The village is well placed for visiting Mount Edgcumbe House and Country Park, and there are marvellous surrounding walks, especially on the cliffs at Rame Head. More reports please. *(Recommended by M Joyner, Stephen and Judy Parish)*

Free house ~ Licensees Sarah and David Riggs ~ Real ale ~ Bar food ~ Restaurant ~ (01752) 822279 ~ Children in eating area of bar and restaurant ~ Dogs allowed in bar ~ Choir Weds evenings ~ Open 12-3(3.30 Sat), 6.30-11; 12-4, 6.30-10.30 Sun ~ Bedrooms: £27.50S/£55S

LANLIVERY SX0759 Map 1

Crown

Signposted off A390 Lostwithiel—St Austell (tricky to find from other directions)

You can be sure of a warm welcome from the friendly licensees in this bustling, newly redecorated pub, and it's a popular place with both locals and visitors. The small, dimly-lit public bar has heavy beams, a slate floor, built-in wall settles and an attractive alcove of seats in the dark former chimney; darts. A much lighter room leads off here with beams in the white boarded ceiling, some new settees in one corner, cushioned black settles, a small cabinet with wood turnings for sale, owl and badger pictures, and a little fireplace with an old-fashioned fire; there's another similar small room. No noisy games machines or music. Enjoyable bar food includes sandwiches (from £1.85), good meaty or vegetarian pasties (from £2), home-made soup (£3), ploughman's (from £4.15), local scallops in garlic, tomatoes and herbs (£6), home-made curries (from £6.15), home-made nut roast (£7.95), daily specials such as liver and bacon casserole (£5.95), steak in stout pie (£8.15), cajun-style chicken or lamb shank with port and redcurrant sauce (£8.95), and fresh bass with citrus sauce (£11.95), and puddings (from £3.50); good service. Well kept Sharps Own, Doom Bar, Eden, and a beer named for the pub called Glory on handpump; darts, dominoes, cribbage, table skittles, and shove-ha'penny. The slate-floored porch room has lots of succulents and a few cacti, and wood-and-stone seats, and at the far end of the restaurant is a no smoking sun room, full of more plants, with tables and benches. There's a sheltered garden with granite faced seats and white cast-iron furniture. The Eden Project is only 10 minutes away. *(Recommended by Andy and Yvonne Cunningham, R M Corlett, Dennis Jenkin, J Davidson, Terry Mizen, George Atkinson, Dr M W A Haward, BKA, Mrs June Wilmers, Joy and Peter Heatherley, Richard and Margaret Peers, R J Herd, Robyn Turner, Anne and David Robinson, P R and SA White, David Crook, Roger and Jenny Huggins, Jayne Capp, Prof and Mrs Tony Palmer)*

Free house ~ Licensees Ros and Dave Williams ~ Real ale ~ Bar food ~ Restaurant ~ (01208) 872707 ~ Children welcome ~ Dogs allowed in bar ~ Trad jazz once a month ~ Open 11-3, 6-11; 11.30-3, 7-10.30 Sun ~ Bedrooms: £30S/£50S

LOSTWITHIEL SX1059 Map 1

Royal Oak

Duke Street; pub just visible from A390 in centre – best to look out for Royal Talbot Hotel

There's always a good mix of customers in this long-standing *Guide* entry, and the landlord offers a friendly welcome to all. Good, popular bar food includes lunchtime snacks such as sandwiches (from £1.60; toasties 25p extra), ploughman's (from £4.25), and fried chicken (£5.25), as well as soup (£2.50), stuffed mushrooms (£3.95), vegetarian lasagne (£6.95), fresh local trout (£8.75), steaks (from £9.50), daily specials such as a curry or steak and kidney in ale pie (£7.95), fresh salmon in a cucumber and cream sauce (£9.45), and garlic king prawns (£9.95), and puddings like home-made treacle tart or cherry pie (£2.50). Well kept Bass, Fullers London Pride, Marstons Pedigree, Sharps Own, and a couple of changing guests on handpump – as well as lots of bottled beers from around the world. The neat lounge is spacious and comfortable, with captain's chairs and high-backed wall benches on its patterned carpet, and a couple of wooden armchairs by the log-effect gas fire; there's also a delft shelf, with a small dresser in one inner alcove. The flagstoned and beamed back public bar has darts, fruit machine, TV, and juke box, and is liked by younger customers; piped music. On a raised terrace by the car park are some picnic-sets. *(Recommended by Stuart Turner, George Atkinson, John and Pat Horne, David Crook, Lee Potter, Jayne Capp, Dr and Mrs M E Wilson, David and Kay Ross, Mayur Shah, Brian and Diane Mugford)*

Free house ~ Licensees Malcolm and Eileen Hine ~ Real ale ~ Bar food (not 25 Dec) ~ Restaurant ~ (01208) 872552 ~ Children in eating area of bar and restaurant ~ Dogs allowed in bar ~ Open 11-11; 12-10.30 Sun ~ Bedrooms: £38B/£65B

MALPAS SW8442 Map 1

Heron

Trenhaile Terr, off A39 S of Truro

Since this pub was last in our *Guide*, a new licensee has taken over and totally refurbished the inside. It's now light and airy, with pale oak floors and furniture, smart sky-blue colours, and local artefacts and modern art on the walls; there's a large no smoking area. Good bar food includes locally smoked salmon and crème cheese baguette (£4.50), local crab sandwich (£5.25), locally smoked mackerel with horseradish, apple and crème fraîche dip (£5.50), home-made steak in ale pie (£5.95), home-made smoked haddock and prawn fish pie (£6.95), gammon (£8.75), lamb chop with honey and tomatoes (£8.95), and steaks (from £10.50). Well kept St Austell HSD, Trelawnys Pride, and Tribute on handpump, and several malt whiskies; piped music. The setting is outstanding with seats on the suntrap slate-paved front terrace looking down over the wooded creek far below, and the summer hanging baskets are lovely. *(Recommended by Dr and Mrs M E Wilson, Norman and Sarah Keeping, Robert Turnham, Gloria Bax, Alan M Pring, Patrick Hancock)*

St Austell ~ Tenant F C Kneebone ~ Real ale ~ Bar food ~ (01872) 272773 ~ Children welcome ~ Open 11-3, 6-11; 12-3, 7-10.30 Sun; 11.30-2.30, 6.30-10.30 winter

MANACCAN SW7625 Map 1

New Inn

Down hill signed to Gillan and St Keverne

Charming old thatched village pub, comfortably olde-worlde and neatly kept, with a friendly landlady and courteous staff. The double-room bar has a beam and plank ceiling, individually chosen chairs, traditional built-in wall seats, and maybe fresh flowers. Good bar food at lunchtime includes a marvellous choice of up to 30 sandwiches such as crispy bacon and avocado, hot sausage and onion, and cheddar and mango (from £3.50), home-made soup (£4), smoked salmon or stilton and walnut pâté (£4.95), fresh fish in their own beer batter (£7), steak in ale pie (£8), and kedgeree or lamb in redcurrant pie (£8.50), with evening dishes like vegetable stir fry with egg-fried rice or mushroom stroganoff (£7), chicken breast stuffed with stilton and wrapped with parma ham or crab cakes with chive butter sauce (£10), roasted lamb loin with redcurrant and thyme sauce or roasted trio of local fish with hollandaise (£10.50), and puddings such as treacle tart, Eton mess or crème brûlée (£3.75); lots of fresh fish, and a fine Sunday lunch. Well kept Flowers IPA and Wadworths 6X on handpump; board games and cards. There are picnic-sets in the rose-filled garden. This is a lovely setting in a pretty waterside village. *(Recommended by Nicholas Pope, Mike and Linda Boxall, Richard Nicholson, Michael Pashby, Andrea Rampley, the Didler, P and M Rudlin)*

Pubmaster ~ Tenant Penny Williams ~ Real ale ~ Bar food (12-2.30, 6.30-9.30) ~ (01326) 231323 ~ Children welcome ~ Dogs welcome ~ Open 12-3, 6-11; 12-3, 7-10.30 Sun

MITCHELL SW8654 Map 1

Plume of Feathers

Just off A30 Bodmin—Redruth, by A3076 junction; take the southwards road then turn first right

The bedrooms in the refurbished barns at the back of this friendly pub have now opened, and readers have enjoyed staying there. The attractive bars have stripped old beams, an enormous open fire and pastel-coloured walls, and a natural spring well has been made into a glass-topped table. There's a no smoking restaurant with interesting paintings, and an eating area near the main bar for the minority who want to smoke. Good, interesting and well presented, the lunchtime bar specials might include spiced lentil and cumin soup (£2.30), crispy bacon and black pudding salad (£3.95), roasted crab claws in fresh herb butter (£4.25), steak in ale pie (£5.95), thai chicken curry (£7.50), chargrilled lamb cutlets on a chick pea and chorizo salsa (£7.95), and grilled whole plaice with lemon grass butter (£8); in the evening, there are choices such as fish soup with rouille and parmesan (£2.30), fresh asparagus with gazpacho sauce (£4.50), steamed shellfish with lemon, garlic and olive oil (£4.95), roasted cod with leek, potato and shellfish broth (£12), john dory with sunblush tomato and rocket mash, crispy prosciutto, and tapenade (£12.95), roasted breast of duck with onions and a red wine jus (£13.25), and fillet of beef with seared scallops and basil oil (£14.50). Puddings like chocolate and mint truffle torte, bakewell tart with clotted cream or glazed Italian meringue with wild berry soup (£3.25); friendly, fast service. Well kept Courage Directors, Sharps Doom Bar and Skinners on handpump, a comprehensive wine list, freshly squeezed orange juice and good fresh Italian coffees. Piped music, darts, and fruit machine. The raised lawn at the back has an adventure playground for children. *(Recommended by Patrick Hancock, Jack and Rosalin Forrester, Karen Hands, Mr and Mrs A M Marshall, Simon Priestman, Dr Phil Putwain)*

Free house ~ Licensees M F Warner and J Trotter ~ Real ale ~ Bar food (12-10; not evening 25 Dec) ~ Restaurant ~ (01872) 510387 ~ Children welcome ~ Dogs allowed in bar ~ Open 11-11; 12-10.30 Sun ~ Bedrooms: £56.25S(£66.75B)/£75S(£89B)

MITHIAN SW7450 Map 1

Miners Arms

Just off B3285 E of St Agnes

In one of Cornwall's oldest villages, this 16th-c pub has plenty of character and history. There are several cosy little rooms and passages warmed by winter open fires, and the small back bar has an irregular beam and plank ceiling, a wood block floor, and bulging squint walls (one with a fine old wall painting of Elizabeth I); another small room has a decorative low ceiling, lots of books and quite a few interesting ornaments. The Croust Room is no smoking; piped music. Bar food includes home-made soup (£3), open sandwiches (from £3.75), wild boar and apple sausages (£6.95), steak and oyster pie (£7.75), seared scallops on sautéed cabbage and smoked salmon (£11.25), medley of seafood (around £11.50), and rosemary-roasted monkfish with warm potato salad (£11.95). Bass, Courage Best and Sharps Doom Bar on handpump, and several wines by the glass. Shove-ha'penny, cribbage, and dominoes. There are seats on the back terrace, with more on the sheltered front cobbled forecourt. *(Recommended by Patrick Hancock, Peter Salmon, Brian Skelcher, Pete and Rosie Flower, David Crook, JP, PP, Robert Turnham, Ted George, Andrea Rampley, W F C Phillips, Su and Bob Child, Joe and Marion Mandeville)*

Inn Partnership (Pubmaster) ~ Lease Andrew Bown ~ Real ale ~ Bar food ~ Restaurant ~ (01872) 552375 ~ Children welcome ~ Dogs allowed in bar ~ Open 12-11(10.30 Sun); 12-2.30, 6-11 in winter

MOUSEHOLE SW4726 Map 1

Old Coastguard 🍷 🛏

The Parade (edge of village, coming in on coast road from Newlyn – street parking just before you reach the inn); village also signposted off B3315

Cornwall Dining Pub of the Year

Attached to a comfortable hotel but a few steps down from a separate entrance, this stands on its own two feet as a notable seaside bar of considerable character. Light, airy and spacious yet cosy and relaxed, the main area has modern metal and wicker seats around well spaced matching tables on wood strip flooring, good cheerful modern sea and fish pictures on butter-coloured walls, and palms, potted plants and fresh flowers. Its lower dining part has a glass wall giving a great view out over the garden to Mounts Bay. A quiet back area is darker, with comfortable Art Deco leatherette tub chairs. The neat and attractive sizeable garden, with palms and dracaenas, has marble-look tables on decking, and you can walk straight down through it to the water's-edge rock pools. Service is friendly, attentive and helpful, and besides well kept real ales such as Bass and Sharps Doom Bar they have a good choice of wines by the glass, good value house wines by the bottle, and a thoughtful choice of fresh juices and pressés. Good enterprising mainly modern food using fresh produce (and a strong emphasis on fish) includes sandwiches (from £3, smoked chicken and horseradish £4, local crab with lemon mayonnaise £7), home-made soup (£3.50; the crab and fish is delicious £4.50), ceviche of mixed fish with crispy noodles (£5), smoked haddock fishcake with a lemon butter sauce (£8), butternut squash and parmesan risotto on artichoke, fennel, olive and leek compote (£9), grilled salmon steak with crab butter and lemon and coriander risotto (£9.50), steaks (from £11.50), duck breast with honey, soy sauce and egg noodles, toasted coconut and stir-fried vegetables or mussels and scallops on spaghetti with herbs and salsa verde (£12), daily specials, and puddings such as chocolate and rum torte or chilled stem ginger and orange pudding (from £3.50); children's menu (from £4.50), light breakfasts (served between 11 and 12; if you stay, the full breakfasts are good), afternoon tea (from £3), and lots of coffees. The piped music is quite appealing (understated jazz on our inspection), and they stage lots of musical events. *(Recommended by Mrs M Griffin, Angela Thomas, Janet Edwards, Tamsyn Bond, Mrs W Frost)*

Free house ~ Licensee Amanda Wood ~ Real ale ~ Bar food (11-9.30; winter 11-3, 6-9.30) ~ Restaurant ~ (01736) 731222 ~ Children in eating area of bar and restaurant ~ Dogs allowed in bedrooms ~ Open 11-11; 11-10.30 Sun; 11-3, 6-11(10.30 Sun) in winter; closed 25 Dec ~ Bedrooms: £35S/£85B

Ship

Harbourside

This is a bustling harbourside local just across the road from the harbour and set in a lovely village. The opened-up main bar has black beams and panelling, built-in wooden wall benches and stools around the low tables, photographs of local events, sailors' fancy ropework, granite flagstones, and a cosy open fire. Under the new licensee bar food includes soup (£3.50), filled baguettes (from £3.50), steak and kidney pudding (£5.50), chargrilled vegetables with pasta (£6.25), and steaks. Well kept St Austell IPA, Tinners, HSD and Tribute on handpump, and several malt whiskies. The elaborate harbour lights at Christmas are worth a visit; best to park at the top of the village and walk down. More reports please. *(Recommended by Patrick Hancock, Andrea Rampley, Kevin Flack, Jayne Capp, John and Annabel Hampshire , Alan and Paula McCully, Roger and Jenny Huggins, Mr and Mrs P Eastwood)*

St Austell ~ Manager Geoff Burns-Sweeney ~ Real ale ~ Bar food ~ Restaurant ~ (01736) 731234 ~ Children welcome away from bar ~ Open 11-11; 12-10.30 Sun ~ Bedrooms: £42.50S/£55S

MYLOR BRIDGE SW8137 Map 1

Pandora ★★ 🍷

Restronguet Passage: from A39 in Penryn, take turning signposted Mylor Church, Mylor Bridge, Flushing and go straight through Mylor Bridge following Restronguet Passage signs; or from A39 further N, at or nr Perranarworthal, take turning signposted Mylor, Restronguet, then follow Restronguet Weir signs, but turn left down hill at Restronguet Passage sign

The position of this lovely medieval thatched pub is very special, and in fine weather you can sit with your drink on the long floating pontoon and watch children catching buckets of crabs and visiting dinghies pottering about in the sheltered waterfront; showers for yachtsmen. Inside, the several rambling, interconnecting rooms have low wooden ceilings (mind your head on some of the beams), beautifully polished big flagstones, cosy alcoves with leatherette benches built into the walls, a kitchen range, and a log fire in a high hearth (to protect it against tidal floods); half the bar area is no smoking – as is the restaurant. Good, well liked bar food includes home-made soup (£3.50), sandwiches (from £3.50, good local crab £6.75), sausages with apple chutney (£6.25), chicken curry (£6.95), home-made pies, mediterranean fish stew or good spicy bean goulash (£7.25), crab cakes (£8.50), puddings, and children's menu (from £3.50); swift, friendly staff. Well kept Bass, St Austell Tinners, HSD, Trelawnys Pride, and Tribute on handpump from a temperature controlled cellar, lots of good wines by the glass, and local cider; winter bar billiards. It does get very crowded in summer, and parking is difficult at peak times. Good surrounding walks. *(Recommended by JP, PP, Dr and Mrs M E Wilson, Andy and Yvonne Cunningham, J Davidson, Dennis Jenkin, Simon and Laura Habbishow, Mr and Mrs K Box, Martin and Karen Wake, Kevin Macey, Emma Kingdon, the Didler, Charlie Harris, Anne and Paul Horscraft, Geoff Pidoux, Robert Turnham, Val Stevenson, Rob Holmes, Andrea Rampley, P R and S A White, Peter Meister, Patrick Hancock, Brian Skelcher, Joy and Peter Heatherley, Ian Arthur, S Horsley, J Forbes, Joyce and Maurice Cottrell, Mike Rowan)*

St Austell ~ Tenant John Milan ~ Real ale ~ Bar food ~ Restaurant ~ (01326) 372678 ~ Children welcome ~ Dogs welcome ~ Open 11-11; 12-10.30 Sun; 12-2.30, 7-11 in winter

PENZANCE SW4730 Map 1

Turks Head

At top of main street, by big domed building (Lloyds TSB), turn left down Chapel Street

Happily, this reliably friendly pub remains unchanging. The bustling bar has old flat irons, jugs and so forth hanging from the beams, pottery above the wood-effect panelling, wall seats and tables, and a couple of elbow rests around central pillars; piped music. Bar food includes soup, lunchtime sandwiches, vegetarian nut roast (£5.50), a daily roast (£5.95), pie of the day (£6.95), cajun chicken (£8.95), tuna steak (£9.50), steaks (from £9.95), pork tenderloin (£10.95), and a trio of local fish (£11.95). Well kept Black Sheep Special, Greene King IPA, Sharps Doom Bar, and Youngs Special on handpump; helpful service. The suntrap back garden has big urns of flowers. There has been a Turks Head here for over 700 years – though most of the original building was destroyed by a Spanish raiding party in the 16th c. *(Recommended by Dr Phil Putwain, Theocsbrian, Ken Flawn, Andrea Rampley, Gloria Bax, Val Stevenson, Rob Holmes, P R and S A White)*

Inn Partnership (Pubmaster) ~ Lease William Morris ~ Real ale ~ Bar food (11 (12 Sun)-2.30, 5.30-10) ~ Restaurant ~ (01736) 363093 ~ Children in family room ~ Open 11-3, 5.30-11; 12-3, 5.30-10.30 Sun; closed 25 Dec

PHILLEIGH SW8639 Map 1

Roseland ★ 🍷

Between A3078 and B3289, just E of King Harry Ferry

This is a smashing little pub and much enjoyed by both locals and visitors. The two bar rooms (one with flagstones and the other carpeted) have wheelback chairs and built-in red-cushioned seats, open fires, old photographs and some giant beetles and butterflies in glasses, and a relaxed chatty atmosphere; the little back bar is used by locals. Good, interesting bar food includes home-baked pasty (£2.95), home-made soup (£3.95), sandwiches (from £3.95; bocatta bread with bacon and brie £5.95), filled baked potatoes (from £4.60), ploughman's or smoked haddock topped with Cornish yarg on a roasted tomato and balsamic salad (£6.50), fresh local mussels in garlic, ginger and spring onion cream sauce (£7.50; large £12), stir-fried vegetables in a satay sauce on egg noodles (£9), ham on wholegrain mustard mash with a creamy cheese sauce (£9.25), chicken and roasted sweet potato risotto (£10.50), fillets of seabream on a squid ink risotto with saffron sauce (£13.95), and daily specials such as fillets of mackerel on a confit of cherry tomatoes with a basil dressing (£9.50), wild boar steak on wild rice and mushrooms with a redcurrant dressing (£13), cockle and mussel linguini in a cream, ginger and mirin sauce (£13.50), and whole bass stuffed with their own-grown herbs and wild garlic butter (£14.50); children's meals (£4.50). You must book to be sure of a table; the restaurant is no smoking. Well kept Greene King Old Speckled Hen, Ringwood Best, and Sharps Cornish and Doom Bar on handpump, a good wine list with quite a few by the glass, and several malt whiskies; friendly, helpful young staff. Shove-ha'penny, chess, cards, dominoes and cribbage. The pretty paved front courtyard is a lovely place to sit in the lunchtime sunshine beneath the cherry blossom, and the back garden has a small outdoor children's play area. Handy for Trelissick Gardens and the King Harry ferry. *(Recommended by Walter and Susan Rinaldi-Butcher, Dr Phil Putwain, Geoff Palmer, the Didler, M Joyner, Jenny and Brian Seller, Kevin Macey, Patrick Hancock, Deborah Taylor, Mayur Shah, JP, PP, D S Jackson, Stuart Turner, Andrea Rampley, Robert Turnham, Nick Lawless, MDN, Mike Gorton, Joy and Peter Heatherley, Paul Boot, Joe and Marion Mandeville)*

Authentic Inns ~ Lease Colin Philips ~ Real ale ~ Bar food ~ Restaurant ~ (01872) 580254 ~ Children welcome ~ Dogs allowed in bar ~ Open 11-11; 12-10.30 Sun; 11-3, 6-11 winter

If we know a pub has a no smoking area, we say so.

POLKERRIS SX0952 Map 1

Rashleigh

Signposted off A3082 Fowey—St Austell

The position of this popular pub is splendid. It's just a few steps from an isolated beach with a jetty, and there are seats on the stone terrace in front of the building that enjoy the views towards the far side of St Austell and Mevagissey bays. The bar is snug and cosy, and the front part has comfortably cushioned seats and half a dozen well kept real ales on handpump such as St Austell HSD, Sharps Doom Bar, Timothy Taylors Landlord, a beer named after the pub, and a couple of changing guests; Addlestone's farm cider and a good wine list with quite a few by the glass. The more simply furnished back area has local photographs on the brown panelling, and a winter log fire. Under the new licensee, bar food includes sandwiches (from £2.25; open ones from £5.75), ploughman's (from £4.75), vegetarian shepherd's pie (£5.50), cottage pie (£5.95), daily specials, and puddings (£3.20). Though parking space next to the pub is limited, there's a large village car park, and there are safe moorings for small yachts in the cove. This whole section of the Cornish Coast Path is renowned for its striking scenery. *(Recommended by Simon, Jo and Benjamin Cole, Charlotte Latham, Jenny and Brian Seller, Joy and Peter Heatherley, David Crook, the Didler, JP, PP, Mayur Shah, Jayne Capp, DAV, M Benjamin, Prof and Mrs Tony Palmer, Brian Skelcher)*

Free house ~ Licensees Jon and Samantha Spode ~ Real ale ~ Bar food (12-2, 6-9; snacks on summer afternoons) ~ Restaurant ~ (01726) 813991 ~ Children in eating area of bar and restaurant ~ Pianist Sat evening in summer ~ Open 11-11; 12-10.30 Sun; 11-3, 6-11 in winter; 12-3, 6-10.30 Sun in winter

PORT ISAAC SX0080 Map 1

Golden Lion

Fore Street

As you sit on the terrace and look down over the lovely steep village, you can just imagine the tunnel that used to run from here to a harbourmouth cave in smuggling days. The same view can be enjoyed from window seats in the cosy rooms inside this friendly local. There's a bustling, chatty atmosphere, and a bar with a fine antique settle among other comfortable seats, and decorative ceiling plasterwork. Bar food (with prices unchanged as we went to press) includes sandwiches (lunchtime only, from £2.30), filled baked potatoes (from £3.25), proper fish and chips or home-made vegetable korma (£6.95), home-made fish pie (£7.95), home-made steak in ale pie (£8.25), chargrilled sirloin steak (£11.95), and daily specials like fresh crab sandwich (£4.95) or warm goats cheese and bacon salad (£7.95); during the summer, evening meals are also served in the no smoking bistro. Well kept St Austell Tinners, HSD and Tribute on handpump and several malt whiskies. Darts, shove-ha'penny, dominoes, cribbage, a fruit machine in the public bar, and piped music. You can park at the top of the village unless you are lucky enough to park on the beach at low tide. *(Recommended by Nigel Pittman, George Atkinson, Joy and Peter Heatherley, the Didler, Tom Evans, R J Walden, MDN, Kevin Macey, Sue Demont, Tim Barrow, DAV)*

St Austell ~ Tenants Mike and Nikki Edkins ~ Real ale ~ Bar food ~ Restaurant (evening) ~ (01208) 880336 ~ Children in eating area of bar and restaurant ~ Dogs allowed in bar ~ Open 11.30-11; 12-10.30 Sun; closed evening 25 Dec

Port Gaverne Inn 🍷 🛏

Port Gaverne signposted from Port Isaac, and from B3314 E of Pendoggett

An enthusiastic new licensee has taken over this well liked 17th-c inn but little has changed so far, and the chef has stayed on – which readers are happy about. The bar has big log fires and low beams, flagstones as well as carpeting, some exposed stone, and lots of chatty locals. In spring, the lounge is usually filled with pictures from the local art society's annual exhibition, and at other times there are interesting antique local photographs. Bar food now includes soup (£3.95), sandwiches (from £4; local crab £5), ploughman's (£5), shepherd's pie (£5.95), ham and free range eggs or vegetable lasagne (£6), beef in ale pie or fish pie (£6.50), crab salad (£7.95), chargrilled steak (£10.95), puddings (£2.50), Sunday lunch (£7.95), and children's meals (£3.50); you can eat in the bar, the 'Captain's Cabin' – a little room where everything is shrunk to scale (old oak chest, model sailing ship, even the prints on the white stone walls) or on a balcony overlooking the sea; the restaurant is no smoking. Well kept St Austell HSD, and Sharps Doom Bar and Cornish on handpump, a good wine list, and several whiskies. There are seats in the garden close to the sea. There are splendid surrounding clifftop walks, and plenty of bird life. More reports please. *(Recommended by MDN, Tony and Valerie Marshall, Kevin Macey, Anthony Barnes, Joy and Peter Heatherley, Sue Demont, Tim Barrow, Charles Gysin)*

Free house ~ Licensee Graham Sylvester ~ Real ale ~ Bar food ~ Restaurant ~ (01208) 880244 ~ Children in eating area of bar ~ Dogs welcome ~ Open 11-11; 12-10.30 Sun; 11-2.30, 5.30-11 winter; closed mid Jan-mid Feb ~ Bedrooms: £35B/£70B

PORTHLEVEN SW6225 Map 1

Ship

Village on B3304 SW of Helston; pub perched on edge of harbour

To reach this old fisherman's pub, you have to climb a flight of rough stone steps – it's actually built into the steep cliffs, and there are marvellous views over the pretty working harbour and out to sea; at night, the harbour is interestingly floodlit. The knocked-through bar has log fires in big stone fireplaces and some genuine character, and the family room is a conversion of an old smithy and has logs burning in the huge open fireplace. Popular bar food includes sandwiches (from £3.95; fine toasties from £4.75; excellent crusties from £4.75), filled baked potatoes (from £4.95), moules marinière or grilled goats cheese on a pesto crouton with gooseberry sauce (£4.95), ploughman's (from £5.95), home-made chilli (£8.75), half barbecue chicken (£8.95), crab and prawn mornay (£10.95), steaks (from £10.95), local crab claws (£11.95), daily specials like home-made crab soup (£4.25), roasted duck legs in orange sauce (£7.95), home-made steak and kidney pie (£8.50), steak au poivre or cajun salmon (£10.95), and monkfish wrapped in bacon with hollandaise sauce (£12.95); the candlelit dining room also enjoys the good view. Well kept Courage Best, Greene King Abbot, and Sharps Doom Bar and Own on handpump, and several malt whiskies; good, friendly service. Dominoes, cribbage, fruit machine and piped music. There are seats out in the terraced garden. *(Recommended by M G Hart, Mrs Caroline Siggins, the Didler, Brian Skelcher, Cliff Blakemore, James Nunns, Mr and Mrs P Eastwood, R J Herd, Mr and Mrs McKay, Tim and Jan Dalton, Joyce and Maurice Cottrell, P and M Rudlin, Mike Gorton, Andrea Rampley, P R and S A White, Cathy Robinson, Ed Coombe, Mike and Sue Loseby)*

Free house ~ Licensee Colin Oakden ~ Real ale ~ Bar food ~ (01326) 564204 ~ Children in family room ~ Dogs welcome ~ Open 11.30-3, 6.30-11; all day in summer; 12-3.30, 6.30-10.30 Sun

RUAN LANIHORNE SW8942 Map 1

Kings Head

Village signposted off A3078 St Mawes road

New licensees have taken over this attractive, neatly kept pub, set opposite a fine old church in a pleasant out-of-the-way village. The beamed bar has a welcoming local atmosphere, and is decorated with hanging china and framed cigarette cards, and there's an attractive family room with lots of mirrors next door. Bar food has become much more pubby now: lunchtime sandwiches (from £2.50), sausage, egg and beans (£3), and scampi (£3.50), as well as soup (£2.50), brie, potato, courgette and almond crumble (£5.25), chicken and chips (£5.50), steaks (from £6.95), home-made daily specials like steak and kidney or ham and turkey pie (from £4.95), curries (£5.25), and mussels in white wine and garlic (£5.95), children's meals (from £2.75), and Sunday roast (£5.25). The dining room is no smoking. Well kept Sharps Cornish, a beer brewed for the pub by Skinners, and two guest beers on handpump;

darts, dominoes, piped music, and cards and games for children. There are seats in the suntrap, sunken garden and views down over the pretty convolutions of the River Fal's tidal estuary. More reports please. *(Recommended by Dr Phil Putwain, Bernard Stradling, Dr P Brown, Mike Gorton, Patrick Hancock, Gordon Stevenson, John and Sarah Perry, Jenny and Brian Seller, Mrs J Anderton, P R and S A White, Jackie McCarthy, Joy and Peter Heatherley, Paul Boot)*

Free house ~ Licensee Ruth Carpenter ~ Real ale ~ Bar food ~ Restaurant ~ (01872) 501263 ~ Children welcome away from bar area ~ Open 12-2.30, 6.30-11; 12-2.30, 7-10.30 Sun; closed Mon in winter, Mon lunchtime in summer

ST AGNES SV8807 Map 1

Turks Head

The Quay

As well as the real ale that arrives in St Agnes via a beer supplier in St Austell and two boat trips, this little slate-roofed white cottage now serves a couple of ales brewed by the new local microbrewery, Ales of Scilly Scuppered and Maiden Voyage on handpump; decent house wines, a good range of malt whiskies, and hot chocolate with brandy. The simply furnished but cosy and very friendly pine-panelled bar has quite a collection of flags, helmets and headwear and banknotes, as well as maritime photographs and model ships. At lunchtime, the decent bar food includes open rolls (from £2.95; local crab £4.95), ploughman's (from £4.65), salads (from £5.75; local crab £8.25), cold roast beef with chips (£5.70), vegetable pasta bake (£6.50), and puddings (£3), with evening fish dishes like crab cakes with dip (£6.50) cod (£7.25), and hake (£8.75); children's meals (from £2.75). Ice cream and cakes are sold through the afternoon, and in good weather they may do evening barbecues. The dining extension is no smoking, and the cats are called Taggart and Lacey, and the collie, Tess. Darts, cribbage, dominoes and piped music. From the tables on the extended outside area across the sleepy lane are wonderful views, and there are steps down to the slipway so you can walk down with your drinks and food and sit right on the shore. In spring and autumn opening hours may be shorter, and winter opening is sporadic, given that only some 70 people live on the island; see below. *(Recommended by Theocsbrian, Dr and Mrs M E Wilson, Pete and Rosie Flower, P and M Rudlin, Jonathan Smith)*

Free house ~ Licensees John and Pauline Dart ~ Real ale ~ Bar food (12-2.30, 6.30-9) ~ (01720) 422434 ~ Children welcome if well behaved ~ Dogs allowed in bar ~ Open 11-11; 12-11 Sun; Best to phone for limited opening hours in winter ~ Bedrooms: /£57B

ST BREWARD SX0977 Map 1

Old Inn

Old Town; village signposted off B3266 S of Camelford, also signed off A30 Bolventor—Bodmin

To get here, just head for the church which is a landmark for miles around – the pub was originally built to house the monks who built it. It's a friendly, welcoming place, and the spacious middle bar has plenty of seating on the fine broad slate flagstones, banknotes and horsebrasses hanging from the low oak joists that support the ochre upstairs floorboards, and plates on the stripped stonework; two massive granite fireplaces date back to the 11th c. Generous helpings of bar food include filled baps or sandwiches (from £2.50), home-made soup (£2.75), filled baked potatoes (from £4.95), local ham and eggs and home-made chicken curry or a pie of the day (£5.95), ploughman's (from £5.95), all-day breakfast (£6.95), mixed grill (£11.50), home-made puddings (£3.50), and children's meals (from £3.95). The restaurant and family room are no smoking. Well kept Bass, Sharps Doom Bar and Special Ale, and a guest beer on handpump, decent wines, and a huge range of malt whiskies; sensibly placed darts, piped music, TV, and fruit machine. Picnic-sets outside are protected by low stone walls. There's plenty of open moorland behind, and cattle and sheep wander freely into the village. In front of the building is very worn carved stone; no one knows exactly what it is but it may be part of a Saxon cross. *(Recommended by Sheila and Phil Stubbs, Joy and Peter Heatherley, Roger and Jenny Huggins, the Didler)*

Free house ~ Licensee Darren Wills ~ Real ale ~ Bar food ~ Restaurant ~ (01208) 850711 ~ Children welcome ~ Dogs allowed in bar ~ Monthly live entertainment at weekends ~ Open 11-11; 12-10.30 Sun; 11-3, 6-11 Mon-Thurs in winter

ST DOMINICK SX3967 Map 1

Who'd Have Thought It

Village signposted a mile E of A388, S of Callington

Comfortable and friendly with a great deal of individuality, this country pub has lovely views which can best be appreciated from the spacious no smoking conservatory. The lounge bars have plush stools and solid antique furniture on the turkey carpet, high shelves of Staffordshire pottery, gleaming copper jugs and lamps, and a winter open fire. The Silage Bar has darts, pool, juke box and TV. Good reasonably priced food includes soup (£1.90), sandwiches (from £2.90), pasty (£3.15), basket meals (from £4.50), filled baked potatoes (from £4.95), mushroom stroganoff (£5.95), platters (from £6.10; smoked fish platter £7.45; warm smoked duck breast £7.95), steak and kidney pie or gammon and pineapple (£7.05), fish pie (£7.35), steaks (from £9.80), daily specials, and puddings such as spotted dick or fruit crumble with clotted cream (£2.95); children's menu. Part of the dining area is no smoking. Well kept Bass, St Austell HSD, Skinners Betty Stogs and Worthington Best on handpump, and decent wines. There are seats in the garden; Cotehele House (NT) is nearby. *(Recommended by Ted George, Jacquie and Jim Jones, Dennis Jenkin, Robert Turnham, Ian Phillips)*

Free house ~ Licensee J D Potter ~ Real ale ~ Bar food (12-1.45, 7-9.45) ~ (01579) 350214 ~ Children in family conservatory ~ Dogs allowed in bar ~ Open 11.30-2.30, 6.30-11; 12-3, 7-10.30 Sun

ST EWE SW9746 Map 1

Crown

Signed from B3287

Handy for the Lost Gardens of Heligan (which Mr Nelson helped restore), this attractive cottagey dining pub is doing well under its new licensees. The traditional bar has 16th-c flagstones, a very high-backed curved old settle, long shiny wooden tables, an ancient weight-driven working spit, and a relaxed atmosphere; the large no smoking dining area is up steps at the back. Lovely log fire and a parrot in a large cage. Good, quickly served food using all local produce, includes sandwiches and filled baguettes, ploughman's (from £3.95), home-cooked ham and egg or giant yorkshire pudding with home-cooked beef in ale (£5.95), giant stuffed mushrooms (£7.60), and lots of local fish such as mackerel with gooseberry sauce (£8.60), bass, lemon sole or bream (from £11.95), and a huge seafood platter for two (£40), and puddings like home-baked cherry and Amaretto crumble (£3.75). Well kept St Austell HSD, Tinners, Trelawnys Pride, and Tribute on handpump. There are picnic-sets on the raised back lawn. *(Recommended by Christopher Wright, JDM, KM, Dr M W A Haward, Jenny and Brian Seller, Kevin Thorpe, Brian Skelcher, June and Ken Brooks)*

St Austell ~ Tenant Lyn Nelson ~ Real ale ~ Bar food ~ Restaurant ~ (01726) 843322 ~ Children in eating areas ~ Dogs allowed in bar ~ Open 11-11; 12-10.30 Sun; 11-3, 5-11 winter Mon-Sat, 12-3, 7-10.30 Sun in winter ~ Bedrooms: /£50

ST KEW SX0276 Map 1

St Kew Inn

Village signposted from A39 NE of Wadebridge

This rather grand-looking old stone building has a neatly kept bar with winged high-backed settles and varnished rustic tables on the lovely dark Delabole flagstones, black wrought-iron rings for lamps or hams hanging from the high ceiling, a handsome window seat, and an open kitchen range under a high mantelpiece decorated with earthenware flagons. At lunchtime, the good, popular bar food includes soup (£2.50), sandwiches (from £2.50), filled baked potatoes or good ploughman's (£5.50), leeks and bacon in a cheese sauce or plaice and chips (£5.95), and sirloin steak (£11.95), but it's the daily specials (lunchtime and evening) that people enjoy most: grilled goats cheese with grilled red peppers (£3.75), New Zealand green-lipped mussels (£4.25), roasted red pepper and aubergine au gratin or roasted tomato, parmesan and basil tart (£6.25), chicken tikka masala (£6.75), fish or steak and kidney pies or fresh haddock (£7.50), and fillet of brill with a tomato and basil sauce (£10.95). Well kept St Austell Tinners, HSD, and a summer guest tapped from wooden casks behind the counter (lots of tankards hang from the beams above it), a couple of farm ciders, a good wine list, and several malt whiskies; darts, cribbage, dominoes, and shove-ha'penny. The big garden has seats on the grass and picnic-sets on the front cobbles. Parking is in what must have been a really imposing stable yard. The church next door is lovely. *(Recommended by Dennis Jenkin, Andrea Rampley, R J Walden, the Didler, Michael and Ann Cole, MDN, Brian Skelcher, Jacquie and Jim Jones, M A Borthwick, Kevin Thorpe, George Atkinson)*

St Austell ~ Tenant Desmond Weston ~ Real ale ~ Bar food ~ Restaurant ~ (01208) 841259 ~ Children in restaurant ~ Open 11-2.30, 6-11; 12-3, 7-10.30 Sun

ST MAWGAN SW8766 Map 1

Falcon

NE of Newquay, off B3276 or A3059

Neatly kept and friendly, this comfortable pub is set in a pretty village, and is very popular for its good food. The big bar has a log fire, small modern settles and large antique coaching prints and falcon pictures on the walls, and plenty of space to enjoy the generously served, interesting meals: crab soup (£3.35), home-made smoked salmon mousse served in a parmesan pastry basket (£3.75), fresh cannelloni filled with spinach and cheese and cooked in a tomato sauce (£5.75), fresh cod fillet in their own beer batter (£6.25), prawn and garlic pasta filled with tomato and apricot sauce (£6.95), caribbean chicken in a spicy coconut milk sauce (£7.25), venison casserole (£8.95), steaks (from £9.65), daily specials such as home-made lamb and apricot curry (£6.95), salmon steak with fresh basil and olive oil dressing (£7.50), and red snapper with caper and dill sauce (£8.95), with puddings like home-made chocolate ginger cheesecake or apple pie (from £2.65); hearty breakfasts, served promptly. The restaurant is no smoking and has paintings and pottery by local artists for sale. Well kept St Austell Tinners, HSD and Tribute on handpump, and a decent wine list; efficient service even when busy; darts, dominoes, quiz nights, and euchre. Particularly when the fine wisteria is flowering, the cobbled courtyard in front, with its stone tables, is a lovely spot to relax. The peaceful, attractive garden has plenty of seats, a wishing well, and play equipment for children. *(Recommended by Robert Turnham, Suzanne Stacey, Helen Hazzard, Theo, Anne and Jane Gaskin, John Crafts, Ian and Deborah Carrington, David and Julie Glover, Robyn Turner, John Saville, P J Holdsworth, Patrick Hancock, Mrs Caroline Siggins, Mike and Sue Loseby, W Ruxton)*

St Austell ~ Tenant Andy Banks ~ Real ale ~ Bar food ~ Restaurant ~ (01637) 860225 ~ Children in restaurant ~ Dogs welcome ~ Open 11-3, 6-11; 12-3, 7-10.30 Sun ~ Bedrooms: £21/£50(£64S)

ST TEATH SX0680 Map 1

White Hart

B3267; signed off A39 SW of Camelford

You can be sure of a warm welcome in this unpretentious flagstoned village pub from the landlord and his friendly staff. The main bar and lounge are decorated with sailor hat-ribands and ship's pennants from all over the world, swords and a cutlass, and a coin collection embedded in the ceiling over the serving counter in the main bar – which also has a fine Delabole flagstone floor. Between the counter and the open fire is a snug little high-backed settle, and leading off here is a neat dining room. Well kept Bass, Sharps Doom Bar, and Greene King Ruddles County on handpump. The games bar has darts, pool, fruit machine, TV, dominoes and piped music. Reasonably priced bar food includes soup or burgers (£2.50), garlic mushrooms (£4.95), filled baked potatoes (from £4.95), ploughman's (from £5.50), vegetable or meaty lasagne, salmon and prawn fishcakes or home-cooked ham and egg (all £5.95), and good steaks (from £8.95); the breakfasts are good, Sunday roast lunch (£4.95). *(Recommended by Dr and Mrs Nigel Holmes, Sue and Dave Harris, Dr Paull Khan, Roger and Jenny Huggins, Gloria Bax)*

Free house ~ Licensee Barry Burton ~ Real ale ~ Bar food (12-2, 6-9.30) ~ Restaurant ~ (01208) 850281 ~ Children welcome ~ Dogs welcome ~ Live entertainment at weekends ~ Open 11-3, 5-11; 11-11 Sat; 12-10.30 Sun ~ Bedrooms: £50S/£80S

TREBURLEY SX3477 Map 1

Springer Spaniel

A388 Callington—Launceston

'A first class find' is an apt quote from one of our many readers describing this bustling, popular pub. The relaxed, friendly bar has a lovely, very high-backed settle by the woodburning stove in the big fireplace, high-backed farmhouse chairs and other seats, and pictures of olde-worlde stage-coach arrivals at inns; this leads into a room with chintzy-cushioned armchairs and a sofa in one corner, and a big solid teak table. Up some steps from the main bar is the beamed, attractively furnished, no smoking restaurant. Particularly good, well presented food includes sandwiches (from £3.95; crab £6.50), home-made soup, mushroom pots (with bacon in a cream and brandy sauce, £4.95), mediterranean tart (£5.95), pies such as super steak and kidney (£6.95) or venison and game (£9.95), lemon and cashew nut risotto (£7.95), smoked haddock and salmon fishcakes with parsley sauce (£9.75), shank of lamb braised with red wine and herbs (£9.95), steaks (from £10), local crab pasty with a mild wholegrain mustard sauce (£11.50), duck breast on a blackberry and cassis sauce (£12.95), daily specials such as pasta with tomato and pine nuts (£6.50) or pheasant casserole (£9.95), and puddings like chocolate tart or fresh lemon mousse (£4.50). Well kept Sharps Doom Bar and a beer named for the pub on handpump, a good wine list, and 20 malt whiskies; cribbage and dominoes. *(Recommended by Jacquie and Jim Jones, Dr M W A Haward, Richard and Margaret Peers, John Kirk, W F C Phillips, Basil Minson, Mrs J A Taylar, Brian and Diane Mugford, John and Sarah Perry, Mike and Sue Loseby, DAV, Mr and Mrs J Brown, Martin and Karen Wake, John and Elizabeth Thomason)*

Authentic Inns ~ Licensee Colin Phillips ~ Real ale ~ Bar food ~ Restaurant ~ (01579) 370424 ~ Children welcome ~ Dogs allowed in bar ~ Open 11-3, 6-11; 12-3, 7-10.30 Sun

TREGADILLETT SX2984 Map 1

Eliot Arms

Village signposted off A30 at junction with A395, W end of Launceston bypass

The series of little softly lit rooms in this creeper-covered house is full of interest; 72 antique clocks (including 7 grandfathers), 400 snuffs, hundreds of horsebrasses, old prints, old postcards or cigarette cards grouped in frames on the walls, quite a few barometers, and shelves of books and china. Also, a fine old mix of furniture on the Delabole slate floors, from high-backed built-in curved settles, through plush Victorian dining chairs, armed seats, chaise longues and mahogany housekeeper's chairs, to more modern seats, and open fires; piped music. Straightforward bar food, and well kept Courage Best, and Sharps Doom Bar and Eden on handpump; darts, fruit machine. There are seats in front of the pub and at the back of the car park; more reports please. *(Recommended by Mike and Sue Loseby, JP, PP, P R and S A White, Brian Skelcher, Helen Hazzard, the Didler, Joan and Michel Hooper-Immins, David Crook, W W Burke, Jacquie and Jim Jones, Mr and Mrs D Lloyd, Kevin Blake, DAV, W F C Phillips, Mr and Mrs K Box, Liz and Tony Colman)*

J P Leisure ~ Managers Jamie Player and Debbie Cooper ~ Real ale ~ Bar food (12-2.30, 6.30-9.30) ~ (01566) 772051 ~ Children in eating area of bar ~ Dogs allowed in bar ~ Open 11-3, 6-11; 11-11 Sat; 12-10.30 Sun ~ Bedrooms: /£55S(£45B)

TRESCO SV8915 Map 1

New Inn

New Grimsby; Isles of Scilly

The first beer festival to be held on the Isles of Scilly was about to take place here as we went to press, and they were hoping to have 24 Cornish and Scillonion ales from 10 breweries. The locals' bar has a good chatty atmosphere, while visitors enjoy the main bar room or the light, airy dining extension. There are some comfortable old sofas, banquettes, planked partition seating, and farmhouse chairs and tables, a few standing timbers, boat pictures, a large model sailing boat, a collection of old telescopes, and plates on the delft shelf. The Pavilion extension has plenty of seats and tables on the blue wooden floors, cheerful yellow walls; it looks over the terrace where there's plenty of teak furniture. Well liked bar food served by friendly staff includes home-made soup (£2.95), sandwiches (from £4.25; soup and a sandwich from £6.25), home-made pâté with scrumpy apple chutney (£4.75), pasties (from £4.95), ploughman's (from £5.25), house potted prawns (£5.95), lunchtime dishes like potato, leek and cheddar bake (£5.95) or beef casserole with suet dumplings (£6.95), quite a choice of breakfasts (served from 9am to midday, from £5.95), evening pizzas (from £6.50), pasta with garlic sausage, chorizo and mozzarella (£7.95), evening chargrills (from £9.25), local crab claws with sweet chilli dipping sauce (£10.95), daily specials like thai-fried local squid (£4.95), local scallops with tarragon butter sauce (£12.50), and roasted local john dory (£14.25), and a children's menu; they also offer home-made cakes and pastries during the afternoon. The five well kept real ales are all Cornish: the new microbrewery Ales of Scilly Maiden Voyage and Scuppered, Skinners Betty Stogs Bitter and Tresco Tipple, and St Austell IPA on handpump; interesting wines (by the large glass), up to 25 malt whiskies, and 10 vodkas; real espresso and cappuccino coffee. Darts, pool, cribbage, dominoes, and euchre. Note that the price below is for dinner, bed and breakfast. *(Recommended by BKA, Gloria Bax, Jonathan Smith, Dr and Mrs M E Wilson, P and M Rudlin, John and Jackie Chalcraft, R J Herd, Bernard Stradling)*

Free house ~ Licensee Robin Lawson ~ Real ale ~ Bar food (all day) ~ Restaurant ~ (01720) 423006 ~ Children welcome ~ Dogs allowed in bar ~ Irish band or rock and roll every 10 days in winter ~ Open 11-11; 12-10.30 Sun; 12-2.30, 6-11 in winter ~ Bedrooms: /£172B

TREVAUNANCE COVE SW7251 Map 1

Driftwood Spars

Quay Road, off B3285 in St Agnes

There are plenty of coastal walks surrounding this popular 17th-c inn, set just up the road from the beach and dramatic cove. It was originally a marine warehouse and fish cellar and is constructed from local slate and granite, and timbered with massive ships' spars – the masts of great sailing ships, many of which were wrecked along this coast. There's said to be an old smugglers' tunnel leading from behind the bar, up through the cliff. The two bustling lower bars have a good mix of locals and visitors, with a variety of wooden tables and chairs, old ship prints and lots of nautical and wreck memorabilia, and a winter log fire; one bar has a juke box, pool, fruit machine and TV. Upstairs, the comfortable dining areas offer plenty of space (and residents have the use of a gallery bar). Well liked bar food includes sandwiches (from £2.30), filled baked potatoes (from £3.10), ploughman's (from £4), chilli crab cakes (£5.20), ham and eggs (£5.55), steaks (from £7.75), and daily specials like steak in ale pie, honey mustard chicken, fish pie or lamb and mint casserole (all £6.25), a lunchtime carvery on summer evenings and winter Sundays, and puddings. They have their own microbrewery where they produce Cuckoo Ale, and keep five guests from Bass, Sharps, Skinners and St Austell on handpump; over 100 malt whiskies, and friendly helpful staff. There are seats in the garden, and the summer hanging baskets are pretty. *(Recommended by Mrs M Furness, David Crook, the Didler, Peter Salmon, Val Stevenson, Rob Holmes)*

Own brew ~ Licensees Gordon and Jill Treleaven ~ Real ale ~ Bar food (12-2.30, 6.30-9.30; all day during summer school hols) ~ (01872) 552428 ~ Children welcome ~ Dogs welcome ~ Live music Fri/Sat evenings ~ Open 11-11(12 Fri and Sat); 12-10.30 Sun ~ Bedrooms: £34B/£68B

TRURO SW8244 Map 1

Old Ale House £

Quay Street

There's a good bustling atmosphere and a pleasant welcome for all in this chatty, relaxed pub. One of the draws are the 12 regularly changing real ales on handpump or tapped from the cask from breweries such as Bass, Batemans, Courage, Exmoor, Fullers, Sharps, Skinners, John Smiths, and Theakstons; 21 country wines. Decent bar food prepared in a spotless kitchen in full view of the bar includes doorstep sandwiches (from £2.65; hot baked garlic bread with melted cheese from £2.70), filled oven-baked potatoes (from £3.25), ploughman's (from £3.65), hot meals served in a skillet pan like five spice chicken, sizzling beef or vegetable stir fry (small helpings from £4.95, big helpings from £6.25), daily specials such as sausage or vegetable hotpot (from £2.50), and puddings (£2.30). The dimly lit bar has a good mix of customers, an engaging diversity of furnishings, some interesting 1920s bric-a-brac, beer mats pinned everywhere, matchbox collections, and newpapers and magazines to read. Dominoes, giant Jenga, giant Connect Four, and piped music. *(Recommended by Joyce and Maurice Cottrell, Dr and Mrs M E Wilson, Patrick Hancock, JP, PP, Tim and Ann Newell, Ted George, the Didler, Brian Skelcher, Jonathan Gibbs)*

Enterprise ~ Tenant Mark Jones ~ Real ale ~ Bar food (12-2.45(5 Sat), 7-8.45; no food Sat or Sun evenings) ~ (01872) 271122 ~ Children in eating area of bar until 9 ~ Live music Mon, Thurs, Sat ~ Open 11-11; 12-10.30 Sun

Lucky Dip

Besides the fully inspected pubs, you might like to try these Lucky Dips recommended to us and described by readers (if you do, please send us reports):

Altarnun [SX2182]

Rising Sun [NW, towards St Clether]: Basic 16th-c local in attractive spot, with two small traditional flagstoned or tiled-floor rooms, coal fire, six well kept changing ales, good value simple food, friendly staff and locals, restaurant; open all day wknds and summer, tables outside, bedrooms *(the Didler, P J Holdsworth)*

Blisland [SX0973]

☆ ***Blisland Inn*** [signed off A30 and B3266 NE of Bodmin]: Five well kept changing ales (hundreds each year, and one at a bargain price), really friendly welcome, masses of old pictures and clocks, efficient service, log fire in no smoking lounge, family room, sensibly priced food inc local fish, small helpings for children or a spare plate to share; dogs welcomed (there's a huge pub poodle), pool room, no music or machines; very peaceful setting with tables out by big village green *(Peter Salmon, D and M T Ayres-Regan, Dr and Mrs M E Wilson, P and M Rudlin, P R and S A White, Anthony Barnes, the Didler, Joan and Michel Hooper-Immins)*

Bolventor [SX1876]

Jamaica Inn [signed just off A30 on Bodmin Moor]: Lots of character in oak-beamed stripped stone original core, clean, comfortable and cosy, with log fire, welcoming service, well kept Wadworths 6X and a beer brewed for the pub, and pretty secluded garden with play area; bedrooms, properly bleak moorland setting (if you forget about the big side cafeteria, souvenir shop and tourist museums) *(Steve Whalley, Nick Lawless)*

Boscastle [SX0990]

Cobweb [B3263, just E of harbour]: Well worn in, with hundreds of old bottles hanging from heavy beams, two or three high-backed settles, dark stone walls, cosy log fire, real ales such as Dartmoor, St Austell, even a wheat beer, no smoking area; darts, dominoes, cribbage, pool, fruit machine and juke box, more machines and another fire in sizeable family room; live music Sat, open all day *(P R and S A White, LYM, DAV, Mike and Sue Loseby, JP, PP, Ian and Deborah Carrington, the Didler)*

Botusfleming [SX4061]

Rising Sun [off A388 nr Saltash]: Untouched low-ceilinged rural local in same family for many years, rather spartan but cosy, with great atmosphere, welcoming landlord, well kept Bass and an ever-changing guest beer, good coal fire, no food; cl Mon-Thurs lunchtimes, open all day wknds *(the Didler)*

Bugle [SX0158]

Bugle Inn [Fore St]: Village local with three or four real ales, food all day inc children's and takeaways; pool, games machine, piped music (some live), pub alsatian and white chow; bedrooms *(CMW, JJW)*

Camborne [SW6438]

☆ ***Old Shire*** [Pendarves; B3303 towards Helston]: Largely extended family dining pub with decent generous food inc popular carvery, well kept Bass, pleasant wines, friendly ever-present landlady, attentive young staff, modern back part with lots of easy chairs and sofas, pictures for sale and roaring coal fire, conservatory; picnic-sets on terrace, summer barbecues *(David Crook, P and M Rudlin, Mr and Mrs P Eastwood)*

Canons Town [SW5335]

Lamb & Flag [A30 Hayle—Penzance; half a mile Penzance side of St Erth station]: Some concentration on good value generous food from lunchtime baguettes, ploughman's and baked potatoes through usual hot dishes to evening restaurant strong on fish, well kept Bass and Flowers, warm welcome; tables in courtyard and garden *(Peter Salmon)*

Chapel Amble [SW9975]

Maltsters Arms [off A39 NE of Wadebridge]: Attractively knocked-together rooms with stripped stone, panelling, big stone hearth, oak joists, heavy furnishings on partly carpeted flagstones, well kept Bass, Greene King Abbot, Sharps Coaster and a beer brewed by them for the pub by Sharps, food in bar and restaurant, quick service; dogs welcome in bar, children confined to plain upstairs family room, piped pop music may be loud; benches out in sheltered sunny corner *(MDN, Liz and Tony Colman, David and Julie Glover, LYM)*

Charlestown [SX0351]

Harbour Inn [part of Pier House Hotel]: Small well managed somewhat hotelish bar, good value traditional food, well kept Bass and Flowers Original, good wine choice; first-class location alongside and looking over the classic little harbour, interesting film-set conservation village with shipwreck museum *(Duncan Cloud, Myke and Nicky Crombleholme)*

Constantine [SW7329]

Queens Arms [Fore St]: Friendly and unpretentious, with good value simple food from sandwiches up, Sharps Eden, veritable museum of ancient tools; handy for 15th-c church, good walks *(Jenny and Brian Seller)*

Coverack [SW7818]

Paris [The Cove]: Friendly old-fashioned pub above harbour in beautiful fishing village, spectacular bay views, well kept Bass and Boddingtons, enjoyable generous food esp local fish and seafood, also children's, good Sun lunch and maybe teas, nautical items inc large model of namesake ship, interesting wooden moulds from Falmouth churchyard, no mobile phones; garden, bedrooms *(Sue Holland, Dave Webster, Eamonn and Natasha Skyrme)*

Crackington Haven [SX1396]

☆ ***Coombe Barton***: Beautifully placed open-plan pub in tiny village, welcoming and good for families with young children; spectacular sea view from roomy and spotless partly no smoking lounge/dining area, good value food inc plenty of local fish, good puddings and nice choice for children, well kept Sharps Doom Bar and another local guest ale, good coffee and service, tables on big terrace, games room with pool tables; bedrooms, on Coast Path *(Mrs C Noble, P and M Rudlin, Tim and Sue Halstead, Brian, Dill, Jenni and Kate Hughes, Mr and Mrs R B Hayman)*

Crafthole [SX3654]

☆ ***Finnygook***: Clean and comfortable much-modernised lounge bar, light and airy, with good baguettes and ploughman's, lots of blackboard dishes, well kept St Austell beers, reasonably priced wines, friendly helpful staff, restaurant; discreet piped music, one car park is steep, and beware of the high pressure taps in the lavatories; tables in yard, good sea views from residents' lounge, low-priced bedrooms *(Dennis Jenkin, BB)*

Crantock [SW7960]

☆ ***Old Albion*** [Langurroc Rd]: Pleasantly placed photogenic thatched village pub, low lighting, low beams and flagstones, old-fashioned small bar with brasses and open fires, larger more open room with local pictures, informal local feel despite all the summer visitors (and the souvenirs sold here), generous basic home-made bar lunches inc giant ploughman's, well kept Sharps and Skinners ales, farm cider; open all day, tables out on terrace *(Patrick Hancock, Brian Skelcher, David and Carole Chapman, LYM, P R and S A White, Peter Salmon, JP, PP, Colin Gooch)*

Cremyll [SX4553]

Edgcumbe Arms: Super setting by foot-ferry to Plymouth, with good Tamar views and seats out by water; attractive layout and décor, with slate floors, big settles and other old-fashioned furnishings, old pictures and china, no smoking area, well kept St Austell ales; usual food from sandwiches up, games area; children in eating area, bedrooms *(Ralph and Gloria Maybourn, Angela, LYM, Carole and John Smith)*

Cubert [SW7858]

☆ ***Smugglers Den*** [village signed off A3075 S of Newquay, then brown sign to pub (and Trebellan holiday park) on left]: Newly thatched 16th-c pub, hugely extended and open-plan – nicely done, with lots of well ordered tables, dim lighting, stripped stone and heavy beam and plank ceilings, west country pictures and seafaring memorabilia, small barrel seats, steps down to no smoking area with enormous inglenook woodburner, another step to big side family dining room; neat helpful friendly staff, fresh generous quickly served enjoyable food inc local seafood, well kept ales such as Sharps Eden, Skinners Betty Stogs and St Austell HSD and Tribute, farm cider; well lit pool area, darts; fruit machine, may be loud piped music; picnic-sets in small courtyard and on lawn below car park; has been cl winter Mon-Weds lunchtime *(John Saville, JP, PP, BB, Pete and Rosie Flower, P R and S A White, the Didler, Patrick Hancock)*

Devoran [SW7938]

Old Quay House [Quay Rd – brown sign to pub off A39 Truro—Falmouth]: Old local with welcoming young licensees, more like being among friends than a customer; two small unpretentious rooms, one with food inc good baguettes and some interesting specials, the other with daily papers and coal fire, boating bric-a-brac, well kept ales such as Fullers London Pride, quick service; no dogs, good value bedrooms, steep garden making the most of the idyllic spot – creekside village, lovely views *(Alan M Pring, David Crook)*

Falmouth [SW8033]

Boathouse [Trevethan Hill/Webber Hill]: interesting two-level local with plenty of atmosphere, lots of woodwork, nautical theme, log fire, well kept beer, friendly staff; jam nights, deck with great estuary views *(Dr and Mrs M E Wilson)*

☆ ***Chain Locker*** [Custom House Quay]: Fine spot with lots of tables out by inner harbour, welcoming atmosphere and interesting strongly nautical bare-boards décor, well kept ales such as Sharps Doom Bar and Skinners, well priced food from sandwiches to fresh local fish, good separate darts alley; fruit machine, piped music; well behaved children welcome, open all day; self-catering accommodation *(Kevin Blake, LYM, Patrick Hancock, Dr and Mrs M E Wilson)*

Flynns [Killigrew St/Market St]: Big curved windows looking out on the main street bustle, dark woodwork, warm fire; Guinness etc, juke box, fruit machine *(Dr and Mrs M E Wilson)*

Grapes [Church St]: Spacious refurbished pub with fine harbour view (beyond car park) from the back, beams, comfortable armchairs, sofas, lots of ships' crests and nautical memorabilia, plenty of tables, wide range of cheap food esp fish from adjoining servery, helpful friendly staff, local real ales, games room; piped music, steep stairs to lavatories *(Geoff Pidoux)*

Masons Arms [Killigrew St]: Friendly local with St Austell HSD, Tribute and a seasonal beer, local marine photographs, nautical flags on ceiling, roaring woodburner, pub and board games *(Dr and Mrs M E Wilson, Peter and June Tysoe)*

☆ ***Quayside Inn & Old Ale House*** [ArwenackSt/Fore St]: Bustling bare-boards dark-panelled bar with half a dozen well kept ales inc Skinners and lots of pub games (also juke box or piped music, fruit machine, TV), upstairs harbour-view lounge with armchairs and sofas one end, reasonably priced unpretentious food (all day in summer) from doorstep sandwiches to Sun roasts; good mix of visitors and locals, children welcome; live music Fri/Sat (packed then with young people), open all day, picnic-sets out by Custom House Dock *(Alan M Pring, Patrick Hancock, Jenny and Brian Seller, Dr and Mrs M E Wilson, LYM, David Crook, Ted George, Andy and Yvonne Cunningham)*

Seaview [Wodehouse Terr]: Convivial maritime local above 111-step Jacob's Ladder, lots of appropriate bric-a-brac, stunning harbour view from picture windows and a couple of tables outside, good range of well kept ales inc Bass; big-screen sports TV, can be smoky; bedrooms *(Dr and Mrs M E Wilson)*

☆ ***Seven Stars*** [The Moor (centre)]: Classic unchanging and unsmart 17th-c local with wonderfully entertaining vicar-landlord, no gimmicks, warm welcome, Bass, Sharps Own and Skinners tapped from the cask, home-made rolls, chatty regulars, big key collection, quiet back snug; tables on roadside courtyard *(the Didler, Patrick Hancock, Kevin Thorpe, BB)*

Star & Garter [High St]: Thriving two-room local with fine high views over harbour and estuary, friendly service, reasonably priced bar food, well kept Flowers Original and interesting guest ales, huge collection of teapots, local murals; theme and music nights *(Kevin Blake)*

Flushing [SW8033]

Royal Standard [off A393 at Penryn (or foot ferry from Falmouth); St Peters Hill]: Trim and traditional waterfront local with veteran welcoming landlord, plenty of genuine characters, great views from front terrace, neat bar with pink plush and copper, alcove with pool and darts, simple well done food inc good baked potatoes and home-made pasties, well kept Bass, Flowers IPA and Sharps Doom Bar; outside gents' *(the Didler)*

Fowey [SX1252]

Galleon [Fore St; from centre follow Car Ferry signs]: Superb spot overlooking harbour and estuary, well refurbished with solid pine and modern nautical décor, dining areas off, well kept and priced Bass, Flowers IPA, Sharps Coaster and changing guest beers, fast friendly service; jazz Sun lunchtime; tables out on attractive extended waterside terrace, good estuary-view bedrooms *(D and M T Ayres-Regan, Andy and Yvonne Cunningham, Peter and Audrey Dowsett, Keith and Suzie Stevens, BB)*

☆ ***King of Prussia*** [Town Quay]: Upstairs bar in handsome quayside building, large, clean and neatly refurbished, with bay windows looking over harbour to Polruan, St Austell ales, sensibly priced wines, good friendly service, side family food bar with good value food inc fish and seafood; maybe piped music, occasional live; seats outside, open all day at least in summer, bedrooms *(Will Evans, Nick Lawless, LYM, Val Stevenson, Rob Holmes, M Benjamin)*

Lugger [Fore St]: Unpretentious locals' bar, comfortable small dining area, very family-friendly but popular with older people too for good inexpensive food inc lots of seafood, cheap well kept St Austell ales, friendly service, big waterfront mural; piped music; tables outside, bedrooms *(BB, Nick Lawless)*

☆ ***Ship*** [Trafalgar Sq]: Friendly, clean and tidy local, good choice of good value generous food from sandwiches up inc fine local seafood, lots of sea pictures, coal fire, pool/darts room, family dining room with big stained-glass window, well kept St Austell beers; juke box or piped music may be loud, small TV for sports, dogs allowed; bedrooms old-fashioned, some oak-panelled *(Nick Lawless, LYM, Peter Meister, BB)*

Golant [SX1155]

☆ ***Fishermans Arms*** [Fore St (B3269)]: Plain but charming waterside local, nice garden, lovely views from terrace and window; warm welcome, good generous straightforward home-made food all day in summer (cl Sun afternoon), well kept real ales, log fire, interesting pictures, tropical fish *(Rob Thorley, Julia Turner, M Benjamin, the Didler)*

Goldsithney [SW5430]

☆ ***Crown*** [B3280]: Roomy and comfortable local with good value food inc bargain Thurs lunches, local fresh fish and Sun roasts, well kept St Austell ales, decent house wines, good friendly service, L-shaped beamed bar and small attractive no smoking dining room; pretty suntrap glass-roofed front loggia and pavement tables, masses of hanging baskets *(Dr Phil Putwain, P and M Rudlin)*

Gorran Haven [SX0141]

☆ ***Llawnroc*** [Chute Lane]: Comfortable and relaxed family-friendly granite hotel overlooking harbour and quiet fishing village, good choice of home-made food inc local fish and good value Sun lunch in expanded dining area, Scottish Courage and local ales, prompt friendly service; sunny tables out in front, barbecues; good value bedroom block *(Pete and Rosie Flower, John Brightley, Christopher Wright, Geoff Palmer, Peter Salmon)*

Grampound [SW9348]

☆ ***Dolphin*** [A390 St Austell—Truro]: Unpretentious village pub with good value generous food from crab sandwiches up, Weds OAP lunch, well kept Dartmoor and Sharps Doom Watch, decent house wines, friendly helpful staff, two-level bar with comfortable chintzy settees and easy chairs, interesting prints, log fire; children allowed, pool, fruit machine, piped music; handy for Trewithen Gardens; bedrooms *(D and S Price, Jenny and Brian Seller, Dr and Mrs R Booth)*

Gurnards Head [SW4338]

☆ ***Gurnards Head Hotel*** [B3306 Zennor—St Just]: Well placed isolated hotel with unpretentiously pubby bar, log and coal fires each end, masses of local pictures (some for sale) on plank panelling, well kept ales such as Flowers Original, Fullers London Pride and Skinners Betty Stogs, good wine list, friendly licensees and staff, imaginative good value food (not Mon evening) esp fish soup, seafood and vegetarian, two-room carpeted dining bar; plain family room, may be piped music, folk nights Weds and Fri; tables in garden behind, well equipped comfortable bedrooms with own bathrooms, glorious walks in outstanding NT scenery, inland and along the cliffy coast *(Annette Morley, David Whittaker, John and Gillian Scarisbrick, BB, David Crook)*

Gweek [SW7027]

Gweek Inn [back roads E of Helston]: Happy and comfortable family chain pub, large open-plan low-ceilinged bar with woodburner, quick good-humoured service, well kept Greene King Old Speckled Hen and Wadworths 6X, reasonably priced standard food inc good puddings choice, decent wines, lots of motoring trophies (enthusiast licensees), roomy pleasant restaurant; live music Fri, children welcome, tables on grass (safe for children), summer kiosk with all-day snacks, short walk from seal sanctuary *(Cliff Blakemore, Ian and Deborah Carrington)*

Helford Passage [SW7627]

☆ ***Ferry Boat*** [signed from B3291]: Extensive family bar in great – and popular – summer spot by sandy beach with swimming, small boat hire, fishing trips and summer ferry to Helford, full St Austell range kept well, very good range of wines by the glass, separate servery with good generous food from sandwiches to fresh fish and afternoon teas, comfortable no smoking restaurant, efficient cheerful helpful service; may be piped music, games area with pool, juke box and SkyTV; suntrap waterside terrace with covered area, barbecues, usually open all day summer (with cream teas and frequent live entertainment); about a mile's walk from gate at bottom of Glendurgan Garden (NT); steep walk down from the overflow car park; bedrooms *(P and M Rudlin, David Crook, LYM, Jenny and Brian Seller, Martin and Karen Wake)*

Hessenford [SX3057]

Copley Arms [A387 Looe—Torpoint]: Emphasis on bar and restaurant food, with pleasant alcoves in modernised eating area, well kept St Austell ales; piped music, dogs allowed in one small area, big plain family room; sizeable and attractive streamside garden and terrace, play area, bedrooms *(Peter Salmon)*

Kingsand [SX4350]

Rising Sun [The Green]: Welcoming civilised local, quite smart, with generous food from sandwiches and pasties to local seafood, well kept ales such as Bass, Courage Best and Sharps Wills Resolve, good coffee, open fire; on one of Cornwall's best walks *(Ian Phillips)*

Lamorna [SW4424]

Lamorna Wink [off B3315 SW of Penzance]: Unspoilt no-frills country local short stroll above pretty cove, with good coast walks; good collection of warship mementoes, sea photographs and nautical brassware, Sharps Own and Doom Bar and Skinners Cornish Knocker, simple food from sandwiches up (may not be available out of season), coal fire, pool table; children in eating area, benches outside, open all day in summer *(LYM, Mike and Sue Loseby, Paul and Penny Rampton, Peter Wrobbel)*

Langdon [SX3091]

Countryman [Boyton, B3254 N of Launceston]: Comfortably refurbished, with well kept Bass, Fullers London Pride and St Austell Strong, reasonably priced food inc good toasties and baguettes, friendly service, dining area, restaurant and family room; very busy Sun lunchtime and school hols; tables and swings outside, handy for Tamar Otter

Sanctuary *(Dennis Jenkin)*
Lanivet [SX0364]
Lanivet Inn [Truro Rd]: Long L-shaped bar with woodburner in no smoking dining end, good value food inc children's, three real ales; games end with darts, pool, juke box and TV *(CMW, JJW)*
Lanner [SW7240]
☆ ***Fox & Hounds*** [Comford; A393/B3298]: Relaxed rambling bar with very friendly helpful staff, low black beams, stripped stone, dark panelling, high-backed settles and cottagey chairs on flagstones, warm fires, good choice of generous reasonably priced food from sandwiches through lunchtime ad lib buffet to duck, shark or guinea fowl, well kept Bass and St Austell ales tapped from the cask, children welcome in no smoking dining room; pub games, piped music; great floral displays in front, neat back garden with pond and play area; open all day wknds *(P R and S A White, Andy and Yvonne Cunningham, LYM)*
Lelant [SW5437]
☆ ***Badger*** [village signed off A30 W of Hayle; Fore St]: Spaciously extended dining pub with large new kitchen doing very wide range of food from sandwiches to fresh fish and lavish home-made puddings, OAP carvery bargain, attractively softly lit modern L-shaped interior, partly no smoking, with panelled recesses, some high-backed settles, airy back conservatory, well kept St Austell ales, cheerful efficient service; may be piped music; children welcome, bedrooms good value, prettily decorated; wonderful breakfast *(Mrs Pat Crabb, Ian and Nita Cooper, A J Bowen, Mr and Mrs M Cooper)*
Old Quay House [Griggs Quay, Lelant Saltings; A3047/B3301 S of village]: Extensively refurbished large pub in marvellous spot overlooking estuary, car park shared with RSPB; good value usual food, real ales; new bedrooms *(John and Jackie Chalcraft)*
☆ ***Watermill*** [Lelant Downs; A3074 S]: Neatly kept former mill, working waterwheel behind with gearing in dark-beamed dim-lit downstairs bar opening into brighter airy front extension and gallery restaurant area – some emphasis on the food side; relaxed chatty atmosphere, well kept Sharps Wills Resolve and Skinners Cornish Blonde, decent wines (off-sales too), good coffee, cheerful young managers, attentive service; dark pink pool room, may be piped nostalgic pop music; tables out under pergola and among trees in pretty streamside garden *(BB, R J Howdle, Andy Sinden, Louise Harrington, Joyce and Maurice Cottrell, C Jones, John and Gillian Scarisbrick)*
Lerryn [SX1457]
☆ ***Ship*** [signed off A390 in Lostwithiel; Fore St]: Lovely spot esp when tide's in, near famous stepping-stones and three well signed waterside walks, picnic-sets and pretty play area outside; wide food choice from proper pasties and good sandwiches to masses of main courses and popular Sun carvery, well kept ales such as Bass, Skinners and Sharps Eden, local farm cider, fruit wines and malt whiskies, efficient service even when busy, no smoking area, huge woodburner; games room with pool, dogs on leads and children welcome; nice bedrooms in adjoining building, wonderful breakfast *(David Crook, Simon, Jo and Benjamin Cole, Robert Turnham, Dr and Mrs B D Smith, Nick Lawless, Dennis Jenkin, Peter and Audrey Dowsett, LYM)*
Linkinhorne [SX3173]
☆ ***Church House*** [off B3257 NW of Callington]: Neatly modernised bar, part rustic furniture and flagstones, part plush and carpet, with customer snapshots, some decorative china etc, woodburner, darts; well kept Sharps Doom Bar and Skinners Cornish Knocker, low mark-ups on wine, popular home-made food inc vegetarian and some bargains for children, also plush no smoking restaurant; piped music; nice spot opp church, has been cl Mon *(BB, John and Sarah Perry)*
Lizard [SW7012]
☆ ***Top House*** [A3083]: Spotless well run pub particularly popular with older people, in same friendly family for over 40 years; lots of interesting local sea pictures, fine shipwreck relics and serpentine craftwork (note the handpumps) in neat bar with generous good value bar food from sandwiches to local fish and seafood specials, ales such as Flowers IPA, Sharps Doom Bar and Wadworths 6X, reasonably priced wines, roaring log fire, big no smoking area, no piped music (occasional live); tucked-away fruit machine, darts, pool; tables on terrace, interesting nearby serpentine shop *(Eric George, Nigel Hopkins, Sue Holland, Dave Webster, Mr and Mrs McKay, P and M Rudlin, Alan and Paula McCully, BB, Edward Jago)*
Looe [SX2553]
Olde Salutation [Fore St, E Looe]: Big squarish beamed and tiled bar popular locally as The Sal, red leatherette seats and neat tables, nice old-fashioned fireplace, lots of local fishing photographs, side snug with olde-worlde harbour mural and fruit machine, step down to simple family room; good value usual food from notable crab sandwiches to Sun roasts, fast friendly service, well kept real ale; piped music may be obtrusive, forget about parking; open all day, handy for coast path *(BB, Joyce and Maurice Cottrell, Dr and Mrs B D Smith)*
Lostwithiel [SX1059]
Globe [North St]: Rambling traditional pub with cheerful bustle in roomy front bar and cosier back part, friendly landlady and staff, open fire, pleasant plain décor, good food choice, well kept Cotleigh Tawny; tables in attractive garden *(Dr and Mrs B D Smith, David and Kay Ross)*
Ludgvan [SW5033]
White Hart [Churchtown; off A30 Penzance—Hayle at Crowlas – OS Sheet 203 map reference 505330]: Unpretentious and well worn in beamed and small-roomed 19th-c pub with much appeal to the many readers who like things truly unspoilt; great atmosphere, paraffin lamps, masses of mugs, jugs and pictures, rugs on bare boards, two big woodburners, well

kept Bass, Flowers IPA and Marstons Pedigree tapped from the cask, sensibly priced home cooking (not winter Mon evenings) from sandwiches up, no piped music – a successful attempt to hold on to the past (WCs in period, too, which may not be so popular) *(Joy and Peter Heatherley, Joyce and Maurice Cottrell, Brian Skelcher, the Didler, Andrea Rampley, P and M Rudlin, P R and S A White, P J Holdsworth, DAV, Su and Bob Child, Mrs Romey Heaton, LYM)*

Madron [SW4532]

King William IV: Attractive local brightened up by newish licensees, plenty of horsebrasses and other country effects (but not overdone), enjoyable home-made food from sandwiches to Sun lunch, well kept Ushers, warm fire; handy for Trengwainton (NT) *(Dennis Jenkin)*

Mawgan Porth [SW8467]

Merrymoor [nr Newquay]: Very welcoming modern bar with picture-window views of glorious surfing beach, real ales, enjoyable food inc particularly good value specials; picnic-sets out in neat garden, comfortable bedrooms with own bathrooms *(Pete and Rosie Flower)*

Riviera Lodge: Fantastic bay views, lots of little alcoves so wouldn't look busy even if it was, very welcoming, with enjoyable food inc plenty of seafood and bargain Sun lunch; just yards from glorious surfing beach *(Pete and Rosie Flower)*

Mawnan Smith [SW7728]

☆ ***Red Lion*** [W of Falmouth, off former B3291 Penryn—Gweek; The Square]: Attractive old thatched pub with open-view kitchen doing wide choice of enjoyable food inc seafood (should book summer evening), welcoming helpful service, fresh flowers, dark woodwork, pictures, plates and bric-a-brac in cosy softly lit interconnected beamed rooms inc no smoking room behind restaurant, lots of wines by the glass, well kept real ales inc Bass, good coffee; piped music, children welcome, handy for Glendurgan and Trebah Gardens *(LYM, Alan and Paula McCully)*

Mevagissey [SX0145]

☆ ***Fountain*** [Cliff St, down alley by Post Office]: Welcoming unpretentious low-beamed and slate-floored harbourside local with good value simple food inc good crab sandwiches and fresh fish, well kept St Austell ales, lovely coal fire, friendly obliging service, plenty of atmosphere, lots of old local prints and photographs, cosy back bar with glass-topped cellar; local artist does piano sing-song Fri (may be trombone accompaniment), good fish in popular upstairs restaurant; SkyTV sports in back room; open all day, bedrooms, pretty frontage *(Christopher Wright, the Didler, Bob and Margaret Holder, Colin McKerrow, Pete and Rosie Flower, Mayur Shah, Tim and Ann Newell)*

Kings Arms [Fore St]: Small welcoming local, cheap cheerful food, well kept Bass and Sharps Doom Bar; good local male voice choir Mon, often music Sat too *(Pete and Rosie Flower, Patrick Hancock)*

Ship [Fore St, nr harbour]: Lively 16th-c pub with small interesting areas in big comfortable bar and two rooms off, low ceilings, flagstones, nice nautical décor, open fire, friendly helpful staff, good range of generous quickly served food, full St Austell range kept well; fruit machines, juke box or piped music, regular live music; comfortable bedrooms *(Pete and Rosie Flower, Christopher Wright, Nick Lawless)*

Morwenstow [SS2015]

☆ ***Bush*** [signed off A39 N of Kilkhampton; Crosstown]: One of Britain's oldest pubs, quiet, individual and unchanging; part Saxon, with serpentine Celtic piscina in one wall, ancient built-in settles, beams and flagstones, and big stone fireplace, upper bar with interesting bric-a-brac, well kept St Austell HSD and Worthington BB tapped from the cask, Inch's cider, friendly service, darts, no piped music; limited lunchtime food (not Sun), no children or dogs, seats out in yard; lovely setting, interesting village church with good nearby teashop, great cliff walks; cl Mon in winter *(the Didler, Mr and Mrs McKay, Martin and Karen Wake, Basil Minson, LYM, DAV, Debbie and Neil Hayter)*

Mount Hawke [SW7147]

Old School: Unusual building (ex 19th-c primary school), largely open-plan, with Skinners Cornish Knocker, Tetleys, a beer brewed for the pub and a guest ale, good cheap food (landlord catches fish); live music Sat, family skittles Sun, Tues, Thurs, cl Tues/Weds lunchtime *(Alan Bowker)*

Mullion [SW6719]

Mounts Bay Hotel [Churchtown (B3296)]: Pleasant and spacious genuine two-bar local, very welcoming, with well kept Courage Directors, Marstons Pedigree and Skinners, interesting jug collection, well integrated family room, good value food in simple dining area; good play area, bedrooms *(Alan and Paula McCully)*

Mullion Bay [Churchtown (B3296)]: Wonderful clifftop position, access to cove and coastal walks, airy bistro-style bar and food inc good crab cakes, pleasant atmosphere, friendly staff; keg St Austell beers, tables out on lawns, open all day (cream teas etc), bedrooms *(Alan and Paula McCully)*

☆ ***Old Inn*** [Churchtown]: Thatched and beamed family food pub with central servery doing generous good value food (all day July/Aug) from good doorstep sandwiches to pies and evening steaks, extensive eating areas with lots of brasses, nautical items and old wreck pictures, big inglenook fireplace, no smoking room, well kept Sharps Doom Bar, Skinners Cornish Knocker and John Smiths, friendly attentive staff; children welcome, open all day Sat/Sun and Aug; can be very busy (esp on live music nights), darts, fruit machine; picnic-sets in pretty orchard garden; good bedrooms *(LYM, Lawrence Pearse, Sue Holland, Dave Webster, Kevin Blake, Alan and Paula McCully)*

Polurrian [Polurrian Rd]: Comfortable hotel bar, but friendly staff and plenty of locals inc fishermen and RNLI members banish any stuffiness; good lunchtime bar food inc local crab sandwiches, spectacular coast views; clifftop terrace, bedrooms *(Alan and Paula McCully)*

Newlyn [SW4629]

Tolcarne [Tolcarne Pl]: Clean and well kept traditional pub, good value food, well kept Greene King Old Speckled Hen and Sharps Doom Bar; new terrace by sea wall, good parking – useful here *(Mrs W Frost)*

Newquay [SW8061]

☆ ***Fort*** [Fore St]: Massive newish pub in magnificent setting high above surfing beach and small harbour, decent food all day from sandwiches, hot baguettes and baked potatoes up, open-plan areas well divided by balustrades and surviving fragments of former harbourmaster's house, good solid furnishings from country kitchen to button-back settees, soft lighting and one panelled area, friendly service, well kept St Austell HSD and Tribute (but they may not have any ginger beer or tomato juice!), games area with two well lit pool tables, excellent indoor play area; great views from long glass-walled side section and from sizeable garden with terrace and play areas, good bedrooms, open all day *(Mike and Lynn Robinson, BB, David and Carole Chapman)*

Lewinnick Lodge [Pentire headland, off Pentire Rd]: This pub, previously highly praised for its interesting food, well kept local real ales, friendly staff and outstanding position built into the bluff just above the beach, was being entirely rebuilt in 2002 – news please *(Brian Skelcher)*

Skinners Ale House [East St]: Open-plan bar well refurbished in bare boards and sawdust style, steps up to back part, good choice of Skinners ales with some guests tapped from the cask, good value food; live music wknds inc trad jazz Sun night; small front terrace, open all day *(Mike and Lynn Robinson, JP, PP, the Didler)*

Padstow [SW9175]

☆ ***Golden Lion*** [Lanadwell St]: Pleasant black-beamed front bar, high-raftered back lounge with plush banquettes against ancient white stone walls; cheerful local bustle, reasonably priced simple lunches inc very promptly served good sandwiches, evening steaks and fresh seafood, well kept real ales, coal fire; pool in family area, piped music or juke box, fruit machines; bedrooms *(P R and S A White, the Didler, P J Holdsworth, Joyce and Maurice Cottrell, Harry Thomas, BB)*

☆ ***London*** [Llanadwell St]: Kindly down-to-earth fishermen's local a bit off the beaten track, impressive hanging baskets out in front, lots of pictures and nautical memorabilia, good buzzing atmosphere (get there early for a table), well kept and well priced St Austell beers, decent choice of malt whiskies, good choice of wknd lunchtime bar food inc good value crab sandwiches and fresh local fish, more elaborate evening choice (small back dining area), great real fire; can be smoky, games machines but no piped music – home-grown live music Sun night; open all day, bedrooms good value *(Harry Thomas, Steve Crooke, Ted George, LYM, Val Stevenson, Rob Holmes, M Joyner, Charles Eaton, John Saville, Sue Demont, Tim Barrow, Brian Skelcher, Joyce and Maurice Cottrell, P R and S A White)*

Old Custom House [South Quay]: Large airy open-plan seaside bar with conservatory and big family area, St Austell ales, food from sandwiches and baguettes up, pool; good spot by harbour, attractive sea-view bedrooms *(BB, John Saville)*

Shipwrights [North Quay; aka the Blue Lobster]: Stripped brick, lots of wood, flagstones, lobster pots and nets in big popular low-ceilinged quayside bar with quick food, St Austell ales, attractive prices, friendly service, upstairs restaurant; popular with young people evenings; a few tables out by water *(BB, Edward Jago, David and Carole Chapman, MDN)*

Par [SX0853]

Ship [Polmear Hill (A3082 towards Fowey)]: Good friendly atmosphere, chatty locals and staff, nice shipping décor, big stove, good food choice using fresh produce, back dining area still in keeping with dark furniture, big conservatory opening to tables in garden; near holiday camps *(Jayne Capp)*

Penelewey [SW8240]

Punch Bowl & Ladle [B3289]: Much extended thatched dining pub in picturesque setting, cosy Victorian-feel bar with big settees and rustic bric-a-brac, wide choice of reasonably priced generous food from good sandwiches up (Thurs is very popular with elderly lunchers – at 76, one of our readers felt among the youngest there), St Austell ales and Sharps Doom Bar; unobtrusive piped music, children and dogs on leads welcome; handy for Trelissick Gardens, small back sun terrace, open all day summer *(R and S Bentley, Pat and Robert Watt, Dennis Jenkin, LYM, Joe and Marion Mandeville)*

Pentewan [SX0147]

Ship [just off B3273 St Austell—Mevagissey; West End]: Friendly 17th-c local opp harbour, comfortable and clean, with three separate areas and dining room, four well kept St Austell ales, fair-priced usual food from good local pasties to Sun lunch, open fire; pool room, nostalgic piped music; views from tables outside, near good sandy beach and caravan park *(Peter Meister)*

Penzance [SW4730]

Cocos [Chapel St]: Not a pub but worth knowing for wide range of creative Spanish tapas dishes, good value, good service *(Andy Sinden, Louise Harrington)*

☆ ***Dolphin*** [The Barbican; Newlyn road, opp harbour after swing-bridge]: Roomy welcoming pub with attractive nautical décor, good harbour views, quick bar food inc good pasties, well kept St Austell ales, good service, great fireplace, children in room off main bar; big pool room with juke box etc, no obvious nearby parking *(A J Bowen, LYM, the Didler)*

☆ ***Globe & Ale House*** [Queen St]: Well kept Bass, Sharps Own and Skinners Betty Stogs and Bettys Mild with guest beers, some tapped from the cask, in small low-ceilinged tavern, lots of old pictures and artefacts, bare boards and dim lighting, enthusiastic helpful landlord, enjoyable prompt food *(Jonathan Smith, the Didler, A J Bowen)*

Mounts Bay Inn [Promenade, Wherry Town]: Small busy pub near seafront, welcoming landlord, straightforward food inc local meat and fish, well kept ales inc Sharps Doom Bar and Skinners, pool; no children *(Dr B and Mrs P B Baker, the Didler)*

Perranarworthal [SW7738]

☆ ***Norway*** [A39 Truro—Penryn]: Large pub done up in traditional style, half a dozen areas, beams hung with farm tools, lots of prints and rustic bric-a-brac, old-style wooden seating and big tables on slate flagstones, open fires, tropical fish tank; big helpings of popular food, well kept Sharps and Tetleys, decent wines, quick friendly service, attractive restaurant; games machine and piped music; tables outside, open all day *(BB, Dr and Mrs A K Clarke)*

Perranuthnoe [SW5329]

☆ ***Victoria*** [signed off A394 Penzance—Helston]: Comfortable and relaxed L-shaped local, cosy low-beamed bar, some stripped stonework, coastal and wreck photographs, freshly baked lunchtime baguettes and doorstep sandwiches, interesting evening specials inc seafood and home-made gravadlax, friendly efficient service, well kept ales such as Flowers and Wadworths 6X, nice wine choice, neat coal fire, no smoking and family areas; quiet piped music; good bedrooms, handy for Mounts Bay *(Kevin McEleny, Bob and Ann Westbrook, Jeanne and Paul Silvestri, LYM, Clare McLaughlin, Sally McEleny, Simon Carter)*

Perranwell [SW7739]

☆ ***Royal Oak*** [off A393 Redruth—Falmouth and A39 Falmouth—Truro]: Welcoming village pub with large black-beamed bar, nice décor, cosy seats, buoyant atmosphere, good value food inc sandwiches, well kept Whitbreads-related ales and good wines by the glass, good log fire; provision for children, garden with picnic-sets *(LYM)*

Pillaton [SX3664]

☆ ***Weary Friar*** [off Callington—Landrake back road]: Pretty tucked-away 12th-c pub with four spotless and civilised knocked-together rooms (one no smoking), appealing décor, comfortable seats around sturdy tables, easy chairs one end, log fire, well kept Bass, Greene King Old Speckled Hen and Sharps Eden, farm cider, nicely presented bar food inc lunchtime sandwiches, children's helpings and good puddings, quick cheerful helpful service; big back restaurant (not Mon), children in eating area; maybe piped radio; tables outside, Tues bell-ringing in church next door; comfortable bedrooms with own bathrooms *(Richard and Margaret Peers, LYM, Ted George, Jacquie and Jim Jones)*

Polperro [SX2051]

☆ ***Blue Peter*** [Quay Rd]: Dark and cosy, in great setting up narrow steps above harbour; unpretentious little low-beamed wood-floored friendly local with nautical memorabilia, well kept St Austell and guest beers such as Sharps Doom Bar, farm cider, quick service, log fire, traditional games, some seats outside, family area upstairs with video game; open all day, can get crowded, and piped music – often jazz or nostalgic pop – can be loudish; often live music Sat, no food (you can bring in pasties) *(Val Stevenson, Rob Holmes, the Didler, S Creeson, Ted George, LYM, Jackie Evans, Prof and Mrs Tony Palmer, Roger and Jenny Huggins, Dave Irving)*

Noughts & Crosses [Lansallos St; bear right approaching harbour]: Steps down to cosy and cheerful little beamed terraced pub with flagstoned woody servery, small food bar, more steps to bigger tiled-floor stripped stone streamside bar, upstairs family room; Ushers seasonal ale, good choice of good value food inc local crab sandwiches, good specials and cheap children's food, quick pleasant service; children welcome, open all day wknds *(Helen Hazzard, BB, Peter Salmon)*

☆ ***Old Mill House*** [Mill Hill; bear right approaching harbour]: Stripped pine, bare boards and flagstones, nautical décor, big log fireplace, well kept Sharps Cornish Coaster and Eden Ale, usual bar food, no smoking dining room; quiz nights, games area with darts and pool, piped music, no nearby parking; children in eating areas, picnic-sets out in streamside garden, good value bedrooms, open all day *(Mayur Shah, Roger and Jenny Huggins, R J Walden, Dave Irving, Rona Murdoch, Mike and Sue Loseby, Bob Broadhurst, LYM)*

☆ ***Three Pilchards*** [Quay Rd]: Welcoming low-beamed fishermen's local high over harbour, lots of black woodwork, dim lighting, simple furnishings, enjoyable food from good crab sandwiches and pasties to lots of local seafood, open fire in big stone fireplace, well kept real ales; piped music, can get very busy; tables on upper terrace up steep steps, open all day *(John and Vivienne Rice, Val Stevenson, Rob Holmes, BB, Jackie Evans)*

Polruan [SX1251]

☆ ***Lugger*** [back roads off A390 in Lostwithiel, or passenger/bicycle ferry from Fowey]: Beamed waterside pub with high-backed wall settles, big model boats etc, open fires, good views from upstairs partly no smoking family room, bar food inc children's and local fish, wider evening choice, restaurant, well kept St Austell ales, pub games; piped music (occasional live), games machine, children and well behaved dogs welcome; good walks, open all day *(the Didler, Nick Lawless, Jayne Capp, M Benjamin)*

Russell [West St]: New licensee in genuine local, friendly and lively, good simple popular food inc fresh fish, full St Austell beer range kept well; may be piped music *(Simon, Jo and Benjamin Cole, Jayne Capp, Nick Lawless)*

Porthallow [SW7923]

☆ ***Five Pilchards*** [SE of Helston; B3293 to St Keverne, then village signed]: Sturdy stone-built local right by the shingle beach, lots of salvaged nautical gear, interesting shipwreck memorabilia, reasonable range of lunchtime food (not winter), well kept Greene King Abbot and Sharps Doom Bar, Coaster and Eden Ale, good wines, quick friendly service, children in eating area; conservatory with waterfall, seats out in sheltered yard, cl Sun evening/Mon in winter *(LYM, Andrea Rampley, Ian Wilson, P and M Rudlin, Mrs Caroline Siggins, Roger and Jenny Huggins)*

Porthleven [SW6225]

Harbour Inn [Commercial Rd]: Large well looked-after pub/hotel notable for outstanding setting with tables out on big harbourside terrace; good value simple food in dining area off expansive lounge and bar, quick friendly service, well kept St Austell ales, comprehensive wine list, restaurant; decent bedrooms, some with harbour view *(P R and S A White, Dr and Mrs A K Clarke, Sue Demont, Tim Barrow, Alan Johnson, Charlie Harris)*

Portloe [SW9339]

Ship: Comfortable L-shaped bar smartly refurbished under friendly new tenants, lots of nautical and local memorabilia, good choice of sensibly priced well cooked food inc good pasties, curries and pizzas, well kept St Austell ales; sheltered streamside garden over road, pretty village, handy for coast path *(Christopher Wright, Jenny and Brian Seller, Pete and Rosie Flower)*

Portmellon Cove [SX0144]

☆ ***Rising Sun*** [just S of Mevagissey]: New landlord doing well, with wider choice of well kept ales such as Sharps and Shepherd Neame Spitfire, flagstoned bar with unusual open fire, big upper family/games room, enjoyable bar lunches and good evening restaurant with upmarket dishes; tables outside, fine spot overlooking quiet sandy cove *(BB, Pete and Rosie Flower)*

Portreath [SW6545]

Basset Arms [Tregea Terr]: Welcoming village pub at end of Devoran cycle path, enjoyable food inc fresh fish in comfortable bar, no smoking dining room and big bright conservatory, friendly caring service, well kept beers inc a local one; unobtrusive piped music; tables on sunny terrace and grass with play area, short stroll from beach, open all day Sun and summer *(P and M Rudlin, David Crook)*

Portscatho [SW8735]

Plume of Feathers [The Square]: Comfortable pub in pretty fishing village, side locals' bar (can be very lively in the evening), well kept St Austell and other ales, good value usual food inc popular Fri fish night, restaurant; dogs allowed, very popular with summer visitors but perhaps most welcoming out of season *(Jenny and Brian Seller, P R and S A White, Dr D J and Mrs S C Walker, Kevin Macey, LYM)*

Praze An Beeble [SW6336]

St Aubyn Arms [The Square]: Traditional two-bar country pub, well kept Sharps and Skinners ales, wide choice of enjoyable food inc children's (who are warmly welcomed), two restaurants, one upstairs; public bar with fruit machines and piped music; large garden *(John and Glenys Wheeler, P and M Rudlin, Colin Gooch)*

Redruth [SW6842]

☆ ***Tricky Dickys*** [Tolgus Mount; OS Sheet 203 map ref 686427]: Spotless and well run modern conversion of isolated former tin-mine smithy, dark inside, with forge bellows, painting of how it might have looked; buoyant atmosphere, well kept Sharps, decent wines, good value food, courteous service; piped music, games machines; children welcome, partly covered terrace with barbecues, aviary, jazz Tues, other entertainment Thurs; bedroom block, squash and fitness centre *(P and M Rudlin, David Crook)*

Scorrier [SW7244]

Fox & Hounds [B3298, off A30 just outside Redruth]: Long partly panelled well divided bar, big log or coal fires each end, red plush banquettes, hunting prints, stripped stonework and creaky joists, large no smoking section, wide choice of food inc lots of vegetarian dishes, well kept Sharps Special; unobtrusive piped music; picnic-sets out in front *(David Crook, LYM)*

Sennen Cove [SW3526]

☆ ***Old Success***: Great spot by clean beach with glorious view along Whitesand Bay, especially from upper terrace; big bustling nautical-theme bar, perhaps best out of season, old photographs, well kept Sharps Doom Bar and Special, efficient friendly staff, enjoyable bar food from good crab sandwiches to interesting main dishes, carvery restaurant; piped music, gents' past car park; children welcome, attractive bedrooms with good breakfasts in hotel part *(Mr and Mrs McKay, Lawrence Pearse, Stuart Turner, Dr and Mrs A K Clarke)*

St Agnes [SW7250]

☆ ***Railway Inn*** [Vicarage Rd, via B3277]: Village local with fascinating shoe collection, also splendid original horsebrasses, interesting naval memorabilia and photographs; decent cheap bar food from lunchtime sandwiches to steaks and OAP specials, well kept Bass, Boddingtons and Flowers IPA, friendly cat, no smoking restaurant; juke box; children in eating area, open all day summer, tables on terrace *(Trevor Swindells, Terry Mizen, Val Stevenson, Rob Holmes, John and Glenys Wheeler, P R and S A White, LYM)*

St Anns Chapel [SX4170]

☆ ***Rifle Volunteer*** [A390]: Good food choice inc interesting dishes, fresh fish and tasty sauces, great Tamar estuary views, good garden eating area below restaurant, well kept real ales, decent wines; very popular, most tables booked in summer; bedrooms *(John Kirk, Joan York)*

St Austell [SX0152]

Stag [Victoria Pl]: Small friendly bare-boards local, five real ales, good choice of other drinks and of good value food inc children's helpings; piped music, TV, games machine; bedrooms *(CMW, JJW)*

St Erth [SW5535]

Star [Church St]: Low-beamed 17th-c pub, well worn in and deceptively spacious, with lots of bric-a-brac, wide blackboard food choice using local produce and fresh local fish, Bass, Banks's Mild and guest beers, good wine list, friendly service; dogs welcome, particularly good play garden for children, comfortable bedrooms, open all day *(Ken Flawn)*

St Issey [SW9271]

☆ ***Ring o' Bells*** [Churchtown; A389 Wadebridge—Padstow]: Neatly modernised cheerful village local with consistently good freshly made food in bustling bar or quieter restaurant inc children's helpings, well kept Bass and Courage Directors, welcoming service, open fire, no piped music; darts, no dogs, some tables in flowery courtyard; can get packed in summer; bedrooms *(CMW, JJW, Sheila and Phil Stubbs, LYM)*

St Ives [SW5441]

Castle [Fore St]: Cosy and spotless local, low ceilings and lots of dark panelling in one long room, stained-glass windows, old local photographs, maritime memorabilia, well priced wholesome bar food, well kept ales such as Bass and Wadworths 6X tapped from the cask, good value coffee, friendly staff; unobtrusive piped music; bustling in summer, relaxing out of season *(Ted George)*

Golden Lion [High St]: Lively atmosphere, standard lunchtime food, and well kept beers such as Courage Best and Sharps Doom Bar; live bands *(Kevin Blake)*

☆ ***Pedn Olva*** [The Warren]: Tasteful modern décor, with some emphasis on the handsome restaurant's good modern cooking, particularly in the evenings; large bar with well kept St Austell Bitter and Tribute, exemplary friendly service, great views of sea and Porthminster beach, esp from tables on rooftop terrace; comfortable bedrooms *(Alan Johnson, Ken Flawn)*

☆ ***Sloop*** [The Wharf]: Low-beamed and flagstoned front bar with bright St Ives School pictures and attractive portrait drawings, booth seating in beamed and panelled back bar, well cooked down-to-earth food from sandwiches and baguettes to lots of fresh local fish, well kept Bass, John Smiths, Greene King Old Speckled Hen and Sharps Doom Bar, good coffee, friendly staff coping well with the summer crowds; juke box or piped music, TV, can get packed summer; children in eating area, a few seats out on cobbles, open all day, bedrooms, handy for Tate Gallery *(A J Bowen, the Didler, Dr and Mrs M E Wilson, Emma Kingdon, Patrick Hancock, Joyce and Maurice Cottrell, Edward Jago, N H E Lewis, Liz and John Soden, John Saville, P R and S A White, John and Annabel Hampshire , Mr and Mrs P Eastwood, LYM)*

Union [Fore St]: Spotless friendly pub, roomy but cosy dark interior, low beams, small fire, masses of old local photographs, neatly ordered tables, food from filled baguettes to local fish, well kept ales inc Bass and John Smiths, decent wines, coffee; piped music, can get very crowded *(Liz and John Soden, Tim and Ann Newell, Ted George)*

St Just in Penwith [SW3631]

Kings Arms [Market Sq]: Friendly local, comfortable and clean, with plenty of character, good value bar meals, well kept St Austell ales, some tapped from the cask; popular live music nights, Sun quiz; reasonably priced bedrooms with own bathrooms, prodigious breakfast *(Jeanne and Paul Silvestri, the Didler)*

☆ ***Star*** [Fore St]: Harking back to the 60s in customers, style and relaxed atmosphere; interesting and informal dimly lit low-beamed local with good value home-made food from sandwiches and pasties up, well kept St Austell ales, farm cider in summer, mulled wine in winter; traditional games inc bar billiards, nostalgic juke box, local male voice choir usually in late Fri; tables in attractive back yard, simple bedrooms, good breakfast *(Jeanne and Paul Silvestri, LYM, Brian Skelcher, the Didler)*

Wellington [Market Sq]: Unpretentious, busy and friendly, with good ample food, well kept St Austell beers, polite cheerful service, good local atmosphere, decent wines; bedrooms, good breakfast *(Mr and Mrs McKay)*

St Keverne [SW7921]

☆ ***Three Tuns*** [The Square]: Friendly and relaxing village pub by church, consistently good generous honest food, well kept Sharps Doom Bar, quick helpful service even when packed, lots of old photographs; piped music; picnic-sets out by square, bedrooms, attractive sea-view garden with pitch and putt *(BB, Helen White, Nicholas Pope)*

St Mabyn [SX0473]

St Mabyn Inn: Cheerful bustling country pub, appetising restaurant food inc lots of good fish, pleasant service, attractive décor, good choice of real ales inc Sharps and Skinners, farm cider, interesting wines; darts *(the Didler)*

St Mawes [SW8433]

Idle Rocks [Tredenham Rd (harbour edge)]: Waterfront hotel with good bar lunches inc good sandwiches (evening restaurant only, must book), Skinners Betty Stogs, good house wines, attentive welcoming service, superb sea view; tables on terrace, bedrooms *(MDN, Dennis Jenkin)*

☆ ***Rising Sun*** [The Square]: Tidy and roomy open-plan hotel bar, the locals' current favourite, dozens of old Cornwall prints, interesting choice of reasonably priced good food in bar and restaurant inc proper sandwiches and hugely popular Fri fish and chip night, well kept ales inc Sharps Doom Bar, decent wines, good coffee, efficient, welcoming and helpful staff; pleasant conservatory, slate-topped tables on sunny terrace just across lane from harbour wall of this pretty seaside village; open all day summer, good value attractive bedrooms *(Jenny and Brian Seller, Pamela and Merlyn Horswell, Mike Gorton, Dennis Jenkin, Andy Sinden, Louise Harrington, MDN, LYM)*

Victory [Victory Hill]: Our former Fish Pub of the Year now under new management, with more usual food, though there's still some emphasis on that side of things; homely and comfortable long narrow bar with ales such as Marstons Pedigree and Sharps Doom Bar, upstairs overflow area *(Jenny and Brian Seller, LYM, David Pennington, Mayur Shah, Geoff Palmer)*

St Merryn [SW8874]

☆ ***Cornish Arms*** [Churchtown (B3276 towards

Padstow)]: Well kept St Austell ales, pleasant service and usual bar food at reasonable prices inc good pasties in spotless local with fine slate floor and some 12th-c stonework; good games room, picnic-sets out under cocktail parasols; children over 6 may be allowed in eating area *(LYM, Alan M Pring)*

St Neot [SX1867]

☆ ***London*** [N of A38 Liskeard—Bodmin]: Spotless 16th-c beamed country pub on Bodmin Moor, comfortable and airy, with cheerful efficient staff, good home-made food from sandwiches (normal or doorstep) up, well kept Sharps Own and Doom Bar tapped from the cask, decent house wines (choice of glass sizes), two log fires, dining area behind trellis; unobtrusive piped music; attractive village in wooded valley, 15th-c church with outstanding stained glass *(R G Price, Mrs B M Smith, Dennis Jenkin)*

Sticker [SW9750]

Hewas [just off A390]: Ivy-covered pub in pleasant village, flower-filled heated front terrace, genuinely warm welcome, good-sized bar with dining area each end (one no smoking), popular reasonably priced food, St Austell beers; pool room, weekly entertainment *(Alan Bowker)*

Stratton [SS2406]

☆ ***Tree*** [just E of Bude; Fore St]: Rambling and interesting 16th-c pub with cheerful family service, lovely old furniture, great log fires, very friendly bar rooms, well kept ales inc Greene King Abbot, well priced generous food from soup and sandwiches to Sun carvery, character evening restaurant; children welcome in back bar; seats alongside unusual old dovecot in attractive ancient coachyard, bedrooms *(BB, Tom Evans)*

Tintagel [SX0588]

Tintagel Arms [Fore St]: Good generous food inc children's and Greek specialities (Greek-leaning décor, too), good service, clean and spacious plush bar, restaurant, Sharps Doom Bar; back terrace, good bedrooms, may close winter *(Joan and Michel Hooper-Immins)*

Trebarwith [SX0586]

☆ ***Mill House*** [signed off B3263 and B3314 SE of Tintagel]: Marvellously placed in steep streamside woods above sea, darkish bar with fine Delabole flagstones and interesting local pictures, enjoyable rather upmarket food, well kept real ales, restaurant; may be piped music; tables out on terrace and by stream, comfortable bedrooms, open all day *(MB, Nick Farrow, BB)*

Treen [SW3824]

Logan Rock [just off B3315 Penzance—Lands End]: Cheerful relaxed local near fine coast walks, fine low-beamed traditional bar with high-backed modern oak settles, wall seats, inglenook seat by hot coal fire, well kept St Austell ales, lots of games in family room, friendly dogs (others allowed on leads); food (all day in summer) from sandwiches and pasties up inc children's, local fish and cream teas, may be juke box or piped music; tables in small sheltered garden *(Mr and Mrs McKay, Nigel Hopkins, Gloria Bax, LYM, the Didler)*

Tregony [SW9245]

☆ ***Kings Arms*** [Fore St (B3287)]: Well run old local, two chatty comfortable bars, dining area with no smoking room, good value quickly served food inc fresh fish and good Sun lunch, well kept Sharps Doom Bar and Wadworths 6X, decent wine, friendly licensees; tables in pleasant garden, charming village *(Geoff Palmer, M G Hart, Christopher Wright)*

Trematon [SX3959]

☆ ***Crooked Inn*** [off A38 just W of Saltash]: A tucked-away surprise, relaxed and friendly, down a long bumpy drive: lots of animal drawings and photographs, a good mix of furnishings in the big stepped bar, conservatory, generous bar food using local produce, well kept Bass, Sharps Own and Doom Bar, Skinners Cornish Knocker and St Austell HSD, decent wines, friendly service; great for children, with tame sheep, hens, ducks and rabbits, courtyard tables and more out on the grass with a good play area and far views; open all day wknds, good bedrooms and breakfast *(David and Sarah Gilmore, George Little, Peter Salmon, LYM, Ian Phillips)*

Tresillian [SW8646]

Wheel [A39 Truro—St Austell]: Neatly thatched, steps between two cosy main areas with plush seating, timbering, stripped stone and low ceiling joists, good value food inc children's dishes, well kept Bass, pleasant service; piped music; play area in neat garden stretching down to tidal inlet *(Geoff Pidoux, BB)*

Truro [SW8244]

Barley Sheaf [Old Bridge St, behind cathedral]: Stretches back through linked beamed areas, lots of wood, two chesterfields by the fire, well kept Boddingtons, Sharps Doom Bar and Skinners Cornish Knocker, decent low-priced food, good quick service, conservatory; piped music, TVs; pleasant terrace *(Patrick Hancock, Ted George, James Nunns)*

☆ ***City*** [Pydar St]: Rambling bar with enjoyable food inc light lunchtime dishes, well kept Courage Best, Skinners Betty Stogs, Sharps Doom Bar and a guest beer, genuine character, cosy atmosphere, attractive bric-a-brac, cheerful helpful service, pool in room off; sheltered back courtyard *(P and M Rudlin, Patrick Hancock)*

Roundhouse [St Austell St]: Bare boards, small simply furnished raised areas, well kept Bass, cheery service *(Ted George)*

Tywardreath [SX0854]

New Inn [off A3082; Fore St]: Friendly, informal and busy conversion of private house in nice village setting, well kept Bass tapped from the cask and St Austell ales on handpump, food (till 8 evening), games and children's room; secluded garden, bedrooms *(the Didler, BB)*

Veryan [SW9139]

☆ ***New Inn*** [village signed off A3078]: Good value nourishing food inc popular Sun lunch in neat and homely one-bar beamed local, no smoking dining area, leisurely atmosphere, genial landlord, well kept St Austell ales, good value house wines, good coffee, inglenook woodburner; friendly alsatian and burmese cat; quiet garden behind the pretty house, bedrooms, interesting partly thatched village – nearby parking unlikely in summer *(the Didler, Bernard Stradling, Christopher Wright, P R and S A White, Jenny and Brian Seller, BB, John and Joan Calvert)*

Widemouth [SS2002]

Bay View [Marine Drive]: Open-plan, with fine views over beach, good value food, well kept Sharps Doom Bar and Own, Skinners Betty Stogs and a beer brewed for the pub; open all day in summer, bedrooms *(the Didler)*

Zelah [SW8151]

Hawkins Arms [A30]: Cosy, warm and comfortable 18th-c beamed stone-built local, log fire, generous well priced fresh food inc Sun roast, half a dozen real ales inc Skinners, farm cider, copper and brass in bar and dining room; quiet piped music, TV, can be smoky; children and dogs welcome, pub golden retriever, bedrooms *(CMW, JJW, Dr and Mrs M E Wilson)*

Zennor [SW4538]

☆ *Tinners Arms* [B3306 W of St Ives]: Unaffected country local in lovely windswept setting by church near coast path, limited food (all day in summer inc cream teas), usually ales such as Sharps and Wadworths 6X kept well in casks behind bar, Lane's farm cider, decent coffee, relaxed local atmosphere, friendly licensees, flagstones, lots of granite and stripped pine, real fires each end (may be papered over in mild weather), back pool room (where children may be allowed), no music; cats and friendly dogs, tables in small suntrap courtyard, fine long walk from St Ives; parking space has been increased *(Jacquie and Jim Jones, S Horsley, Peter and Anne Hollindale, the Didler, Mr and Mrs McKay, LYM, Kevin Flack, Gloria Bax)*

ISLES OF SCILLY

St Martin's [SV9215]

Seven Stones [Lower Town]: St Austell real ales, enjoyable freshly made food inc pizzas, pasta, steaks and local crab; doubles as village hall and looks it, but once you've climbed the 11 steps it has a decent interior and superb view, with tables outside; limited winter opening *(D and M T Ayres-Regan, P and M Rudlin, Jonathan Smith)*

St Mary's [SV9010]

☆ *Atlantic Inn* [The Strand; next to but independent from Atlantic Hotel]: Spreading rather dark bar with nice little room at one end, low beams, hanging boat and lots of nautical bits and pieces, flowery-patterned seats, usual bar food (local fish is good), reasonably priced St Austell ales inc XXXX Mild, friendly landlord, efficient service, mix of locals and tourists, sizeable brighter dining area overlooking harbour; darts, pool, fruit machines; little terrace with green cast-iron furniture and wide views, good bedrooms *(P and M Rudlin, John Knighton, Theocsbrian, BB, Jonathan Smith)*

We accept no free drinks or payment for inclusion. We take no advertising, and are not sponsored by the brewing industry – or by anyone else. So all reports are independent.

Cumbria

Cumbria has a good many lovely pubs – warmly welcoming places for walkers, nice places to stay in, smashing food, great scenery. And this year our inspections have turned up several most attractive new entries: the Shepherds Arms at Ennerdale Bridge (simple but civilised, nice all round and great for walkers), the Mill Inn at Mungrisdale (lovely spot, very friendly), the Swan at Newby Bridge (good spreading bar in this smart well run hotel), the Sandford Arms at Sandford (an appealingly homely all-rounder, usefully placed), the Santon Bridge Inn at Santon Bridge (a friendly Lakeland inn, with good bar and popular restaurant), the Langstrath at Stonethwaite (stylishly simple, in a great Borrowdale location – looks set to become quite a favourite), and the welcoming Blacksmiths Arms at Talkin (good local produce, comfortable bedrooms). Other pubs doing really well here this year are the Dukes Head in Armathwaite (warmly welcoming licensees making the most of the area's fresh produce), the Wheatsheaf at Beetham (good imaginative food, rather more restauranty than in the past), the pleasantly pubby little White Hart at Bouth, the Britannia at Eltwerwater (one of our all-time favourites – but it does get packed in summer), the civilised Drunken Duck near Hawkshead (good food and bedrooms), the Watermill at Ings (marvellous collection of real ales, but much enjoyed by all), the Three Shires in Little Langdale (particularly nice to stay in), the Queens Head at Tirril (hugely popular with readers, and just finishing some careful upgrading), the interesting Queens Head at Troutbeck (new bedrooms and more dining space for its good imaginative food), the Bay Horse just outside Ulverston (great for food and as a place to stay), and the Gate Inn at Yanwath (lovely welcoming combination of unpretentious atmosphere and very good food). Our choice as Cumbria Dining Pub of the Year is the Drunken Duck near Hawkshead: expect restaurant prices here now, especially at night, but the imaginative cooking makes it worth while. Front-runners in the Lucky Dip section at the end of the chapter (almost all already inspected and approved by us) are the Hole in t' Wall in Bowness-on-Windermere, Kings Arms in Cartmel, Trout in Cockermouth, Royal at Dockray, Highland Drove at Great Salkeld, Swinside near Keswick, Croglin Castle in Kirkby Stephen, Farmers Arms at Lowick Green, Herdwick at Penruddock and Brown Horse at Winster. Drinks prices in the county are rather lower than the national average. Half a dozen of the main entries now brew their own beer, often at particularly attractive prices, though much the cheapest beer we found was the Sam Smiths at the Blue Bell in Heversham. Jennings is the main local brewer, and supplies the cheapest beer in many Lakeland pubs. Other smaller brewers such as Coniston, Hesket Newmarket and Yates are also well worth looking out for, particularly with the benefit of the 14p small-brewer cut in beer duty.

We say if we know a pub allows dogs.

AMBLESIDE NY3804 Map 9

Golden Rule

Smithy Brow; follow Kirkstone Pass signpost from A591 on N side of town

Run by a jovial landlord who welcomes all his customers – including walkers and their dogs – this honest Lakeland local remains unchanged over the years. The bar has plenty of friendly regulars to chat to, lots of local country pictures and a few fox masks decorating the butter-coloured walls, horsebrasses on the black beams, built-in leatherette wall seats, and cast-iron-framed tables; dominoes and cribbage. The room on the left has darts, TV, and a fruit machine, and the one down a few steps on the right is a quieter sitting room. Well kept Hartleys XB and Cumbrian Way, and Robinsons Best, Frederics, Hatters Mild, and Old Tom on handpump; pork pies (50p), and filled rolls (£1.50). There's a back yard with tables, and especially colourful window boxes. The golden rule referred to in its name is a brass measuring yard mounted over the bar counter. *(Recommended by MLR, Mike and Sue Loseby, P Abbott, H K Dyson, Margaret and Roy Randle)*

Robinsons ~ Tenants John Lockley and Alan Risdon ~ Real ale ~ No credit cards ~ (015394) 32257 ~ Children welcome until 9pm ~ Dogs welcome ~ Open 11-11; 12-10.30 Sun

APPLEBY NY6921 Map 10

Royal Oak

B6542/Bongate is E of the main bridge over the River Eden

A new licensee has taken over this old-fashioned coaching inn, but early reports from readers suggest that little has changed. The oak-panelled public bar has a chatty, relaxed atmosphere and a good open fire, and the beamed lounge has old pictures on the timbered walls, some armchairs and a carved settle, and a panelling-and-glass snug enclosing the bar counter; dominoes and cribbage. Bar food now includes filled baguettes (the rare beef ones are liked, £4.95), chicken and spinach pancake or prawn st jacques (£3.95), queenie scallops, chorizo and smoked duck (£4.95), local sausages (£5.95), beef in ale pie or gammon and egg (£7.25), home-made vegetable lasagne (£7.95), braised lamb shank (£9.95), and steaks (from £11.45). Part of the restaurant is no smoking. Well kept Black Sheep and John Smiths, with a couple of guests from Brakspears or Shepherd Neame on handpump, and a good range of wines and malt whiskies; TV. There are seats on the front terrace, and masses of flowering tubs, troughs and hanging baskets. You can get here on the scenic Leeds/Settle/Carlisle railway (best to check times and any possible delays to avoid missing lunch). *(Recommended by MLR, Guy Vowles, Susan and John Douglas, Greta and Christopher Wells, Anthony Barnes, Paul A Moore, JWAC, Steve Whalley, Ian S Morley, Richard J Holloway, Vicky and David Sarti, C A Hall, Tony Middis, Linda Reiterbund, Ron and Mary Nicholson, Mr and Mrs T B Staples, Angus Lyon, Brian and Janet Ainscough)*

Mortal Man Inns ~ Manager Tim Collins ~ Real ale ~ Bar food (12-3, 6-9) ~ Restaurant ~ (01768) 351463 ~ Children in eating area of bar and restaurant ~ Dogs allowed in bar ~ Open 11-11; 12-10.30 Sun ~ Bedrooms: £39/£78B

ARMATHWAITE NY5146 Map 10

Dukes Head ★ 🛏

Off A6 a few miles S of Carlisle; turn right at T-junction

The licensees of this unpretentious village pub really go out of their way to make visitors feel warmly welcomed, and work very hard to make the best of local (and their own) produce. They only use local meat, all their wine is supplied locally, they sell (over the counter) excellent farmhouse sausages and their own blend of coffee, and make their own ginger beer, damson gin and blackcurrant liqueur. The civilised lounge bar has oak settles and little armchairs among more upright seats, oak and mahogany tables, antique hunting and other prints, and some brass and copper powder-flasks above its coal fire. Consistently good bar food includes home-made soup with croutons (£2.75), sandwiches (from £2.95), lovely hot potted Solway shrimps (£4.15), home-made pork, venison and apricot terrine (£4.25), omelettes (£6.45), salad platters (from £6.85), lentil, carrot and cashew nut loaf (£6.90), home-made salmon and coley fishcakes (£7.75), chicken breast in a creamy tarragon and lemon sauce (£8.25), grilled venison with a mushroom, red wine and redcurrant sauce (£9.90), and roast duckling with apple sauce (£11.45), with daily specials such as smoked duck and mango salad (£4.35), braised pheasant with apple, chestnuts and cider (£8.35), baked bream with vermouth and leeks (£8.95), and fillet steak on rösti potato with a port sauce (£12.75). Nice touches such as real butter, their own tartare sauce, and free coffee top-ups; good breakfasts. The restaurant is no smoking. Well kept Tetleys, and a guest such as Courage Directors or Thwaites Thoroughbred on handpump; dominoes and cribbage; separate public bar with darts and table skittles. There are tables out on the lawn behind; boules. You can hire bicycles. *(Recommended by Helen Maynard, Richard J Holloway, Helen Flaherty, Nick and Pam Hancock, Mr and Mrs J McRobert, JWAC, Dave Braisted, R Davies, Robin Lord, Keith Mould, Dr T E Hothersall, Joan Thorpe, Brian and Anna Marsden, D S Jackson, John and Christine Lowe, Christopher Ross, John and Sylvia Harrop, Michael Sargent, P R Morley)*

Pubmaster ~ Tenant Henry Lynch ~ Real ale ~ Bar food (12-2, 6.15-9) ~ Restaurant ~ (016974) 72226 ~ Children welcome ~ Dogs allowed in bedrooms ~ Open 12-3, 5.30-11; 12-10.30 Sun ~ Bedrooms: £32B/£52.50B

BARBON SD6282 Map 10

Barbon Inn

Village signposted off A683 Kirkby Lonsdale—Sedbergh; OS Sheet 97 map reference 628826

In a charming village setting below the fells, this friendly 17th-c coaching inn has plenty of surrounding tracks and paths to walk along. Several small rooms lead off the simple bar with its blackened range, each individually and comfortably furnished: carved 18th-c oak settles, comfortable sofas and armchairs, a Victorian fireplace. Reasonably priced bar food includes sandwiches or home-made soup (£2.50), home-made pâté (£2.95), Morecambe Bay shrimps (£4.50), cod and chips (£5.95), cumberland sausage or steak in ale pie (£6.95), gammon steak (£7.95), and rib-eye steak (£8.50); the restaurant is no smoking. Well kept Theakstons Best and a guest such as Greene King Old Speckled Hen on handpump; dominoes and piped music. The lovely sheltered garden here is prettily planted and neatly kept. *(Recommended by Mr and Mrs W D Borthwick, R M Corlett, Jayne and Peter Capp)*

Free house ~ Licensee Lindsey MacDiarmid ~ Real ale ~ Bar food ~ Restaurant ~ (015242) 76233 ~ Children welcome ~ Dogs allowed in bar ~ Open 12-2.30(3 Sat), 6.30-11(10.30 Sun) ~ Bedrooms: £30(£40B)/£65B

BASSENTHWAITE LAKE NY1930 Map 9

Pheasant ★

Follow Pheasant Inn sign at N end of dual carriageway stretch of A66 by Bassenthwaite Lake

Surrounded by attractive woodlands and with plenty of walks in all directions, this rather smart and civilised hotel is a lovely place to stay. Its little bar remains as pleasantly old-fashioned and pubby as ever, with mellow polished walls, cushioned oak settles, rush-seat chairs and library seats, hunting prints and photographs, and well kept Bass, Jennings Cumberland, and Theakstons Best on handpump; a dozen good wines by the glass and 40 malt whiskies. Several comfortable lounges have log fires, fine parquet flooring, antiques, and plants; one is no smoking – as is the restaurant. Enjoyable lunchtime bar food includes soup with home-made bread (£2.95), salmon mousse (£5.25), open sandwiches (from £5.25), potted Silloth shrimps (£5.35), ploughman's (£5.95), spaghetti napolitana (£6.75), lambs liver and black pudding with red onion gravy (£7.25), fillets of smoked haddock on a bed of spinach with a light cheese sauce and topped with a poached egg (£7.85), and puddings (from £3.25). There are seats in the garden. *(Recommended by Peter Burton, Nigel Woolliscroft, J Hale, Tina and David Woods-Taylor, Nick Lawless, Ben and Sheila Walker, John and Sheila Lister; also in the* Good Hotel Guide*)*

Free house ~ Licensee Matthew Wylie ~ Real ale ~ Bar food (not in evening – restaurant only) ~ Restaurant ~ (017687) 76234 ~ Children in eating area of bar and in restaurant if over 8 ~ Dogs allowed in bar ~ Open 11-2.30, 5.30-10.30(11 Sat); 12-2.30, 6-10.30 Sun ~ Bedrooms: £75B/£140B

BEETHAM SD5079 Map 7

Wheatsheaf

Village (and inn) signposted just off A6 S of Milnthorpe

The very good, enjoyable food continues to draw customers to this 16th-c coaching inn. As well as sandwiches (from £4.40), there might be home-made soup (£2.95), grilled polenta with roasted peppers and spiced plum chutney (£5.05), gateau of black pudding and goats cheese with smoked bacon and sage gravy (£5.25), steamed mussels in a tomato and herb broth (£5.50), pork, leek and stilton pie (£7.95), caramelised onion tart with basil crème fraîche (£9.50), chillied salmon confit with cucumber and mint sauce (£10.95), roast breast of duck with carrot, orange and cashew nut stir fry (£12.95), and puddings like bitter chocolate mousse with Baileys-coffee sauce, key lime pie with cardamom syrup or ginger and banana sponge (from £4.75); nice breakfasts. The opened-up front lounge bar has lots of exposed beams and joists and is decorated in warm ochre shades and gingham fabrics; the main bar is behind on the right, with well kept Jennings Bitter and Cumberland and a changing guest beer on handpump, and a fine choice of New World wines by the glass; there's also a cosy and relaxing smaller room for drinkers, a roaring log fire, and daily newspapers and magazines to read. The upstairs no smoking dining room is candlelit at night; piped music. *(Recommended by Steve Whalley, Karen Eliot, Gerald Wilkinson, Chris and Duncan Grant, Maurice and Gill McMahon, Revd D Glover, Geoff and Angela Jaques, Jean and Douglas Troup, Arby, Roger Everett, Gordon Neighbour, Mike Green, DC, G P McGovern, David Cooke, Margaret Dickinson, Jim Bush)*

Free house ~ Licensee Emma Lamb ~ Real ale ~ Bar food ~ Restaurant ~ (015395) 62123 ~ Children in restaurant ~ Dogs allowed in bar ~ Open 11-3, 6-11; 12-3, 7-10.30 Sun ~ Bedrooms: £50B/£65B

BOUTH SD3386 Map 9

White Hart

Village signposted off A590 nr Haverthwaite

Though popular with locals, you can be sure of a down-to-earth Lakeland welcome for visitors as well in this little village inn. The sloping ceilings and floors show the building's age, and there are lots of old local photographs and bric-a-brac – farm tools, stuffed animals, a collection of long-stemmed clay pipes – and two log fires, one in a woodburning stove. The games room has darts, pool, dominoes, fruit machine,TV, and juke box; piped music. Daily specials use local produce such as fresh Fleetwood haddock (mainly Friday evening, £7.25) and Herdwick lamb cutlets or chicken breast with napoli sauce (£7.95), and there's a fair choice of other bar food such as sandwiches, good soups, pizzas (from £5.45), salads (from £6.45), five bean chilli (£7.25), sirloin steak (£9.95), home-made puddings (£3.25), and children's dishes (from £3.45); the restaurant is no smoking. Well kept Black Sheep, Jennings Cumberland, and Tetleys, with guests such as Barngates Cracker, Timothy Taylors Landlord, and Yates Bitter on handpump, and 40 malt whiskies. There are plenty of surrounding walks, and tables out in the attractively planted garden. *(Recommended by JDM, KM, Michael Doswell, Dr B and Mrs P B Baker, Mrs Romey Heaton)*

Free house ~ Licensees Nigel and Peter Barton ~ Real ale ~ Bar food (12-2, 6-8.45; not Mon or Tues lunchtime) ~ Restaurant ~ No credit cards ~ (01229) 861229 ~ Children welcome until 8.30 ~ Dogs allowed in bar ~ Open 12-2, 6-11; 12-11 Sat; 12-10.30 Sun; closed Mon and Tues lunchtimes ~ Bedrooms: £20(£25B)/£40(£50B)

There are report forms at the back of the book.

BROUGHTON MILLS SD2190 Map 9

Blacksmiths Arms

Off A593 N of Broughton-in-Furness

The enjoyable food in this charming little pub is very popular, and even on a midweek evening, customers will be queuing for a table. The four simply but attractively decorated small rooms have open fires in three of them, ancient slate floors, and well kept Coniston Bluebird, Dent Aviator, and Jennings Cumberland on handpump, summer farm cider, and interesting bottled beers. From quite a choice, the menu might include lunchtime sandwiches and baked potatoes as well as home-made soup (£2.25; fresh fish chowder £3.25), tasty beer-battered lancashire cheese (£3.25), home-made pâté (£3.65), steak in ale pie, cumberland sausage with apple sauce and egg or vegetable goulash (all £6.95), thai chicken (£7.25), cajun pork fillet (£7.45), chicken in a creamy stilton sauce (£7.95), local lamb chops (£8.45), and steaks (from £8.50). There are three smallish dining rooms (the back one is no smoking). Darts, dominoes, and children's books and games. The hanging baskets and tubs of flowers in front of the building are very pretty in summer. *(Recommended by Derek Harvey-Piper, BKA, JP, PP, Margaret Dickinson, Kevin Thorpe, Dave Braisted)*

Free house ~ Licensee Philip Blackburn ~ Real ale ~ Bar food (not winter Mon lunchtime) ~ Restaurant ~ (01229) 716824 ~ Children welcome ~ Dogs allowed in bar ~ Occasional Irish music in bar ~ Open 12-11; 12-10.30 Sun; 5-11 Mon (cl winter Mon), 12-2.30, 5-11 Tues-Fri in winter; closed 25 Dec

BUTTERMERE NY1817 Map 9

Bridge Hotel

Just off B5289 SW of Keswick

This chatty, friendly inn is set in some of the best steep countryside in the county, and Crummock Water and Buttermere are just a stroll away – so it's not surprisingly popular with walkers. The flagstoned area in the beamed bar is good for walking boots, and has built-in wooden settles and farmhouse chairs around traditional tables, a panelled bar counter and a few horsebrasses, and there's a dining bar with brocaded armchairs around copper-topped tables, and brass ornaments hanging from the beams; the restaurant and guest lounge are no smoking. Good bar food includes soup with home-made bread (£3.45), interesting sandwiches such as brie and sun-dried tomato or barbecue spiced chicken and mayonnaise (£2.95; toasties £3.60), ploughman's or warm bacon, onion, chopped egg, and seasonal salad with parmesan cheese croutons (£4.50), butterbean casserole (£6.50), tasty cumberland hotpot, home-made steak and kidney pie or crispy duck stir-fried with vegetables and soy sauce (£6.95), poached Borrowdale trout (£7.75), and steaks (from £11). Well kept Black Sheep, Flowers IPA, and Theakstons Old Peculier on handpump, quite a few malt whiskies, and a decent wine list. Outside, a flagstoned terrace has white tables by a rose-covered sheltering stone wall. The views from the bedrooms are marvellous; please note, the bedroom prices are for dinner, bed and breakfast; self-catering, too. *(Recommended by Jim Abbott, David Field, Michael and Ann Cole, Dick and Madeleine Brown, Meg and Colin Hamilton, Tracey and Stephen Groves, Filip Lemmens, H K Dyson)*

Free house ~ Licensee Peter McGuire ~ Real ale ~ Bar food (12-2.30, 5.30-9.30) ~ Restaurant ~ (017687) 70252 ~ Children in eating area of bar and, if over 7, in restaurant ~ Dogs allowed in bedrooms ~ Open 10.30-11; 10.30-10.30 Sun ~ Bedrooms: £70B/£150B

CASTERTON SD6279 Map 10

Pheasant

A683 about a mile N of junction with A65, by Kirkby Lonsdale; OS Sheet 97 map reference 633796

This civilised inn is run by warmly friendly licensees who work hard at making their customers feel genuinely welcome and relaxed. The neatly kept and attractively modernised beamed rooms of the main bar have padded wheelback chairs, newly cushioned wall settles, newspapers and magazines to read, a woodburning stove surrounded by brass ornaments in a nicely arched bare stone fireplace with polished brass hood, and well kept Theakstons Bitter and guests such as Black Sheep Bitter, Coniston Bluebird or Dent Bitter on handpump; over 30 malt whiskies, and a good wine list offering 12 by the glass. There's a further room (which is no smoking) across the passage with a piano. Good bar food includes home-made soup (£2.75), lunchtime sandwiches (from £2.95) and smoked salmon and scrambled eggs (£5.95), home-made chinese vegetable spring rolls with a mild chilli dip (£4.95), local cumberland sausage with apple and sultana chutney (£6.75), steak in ale pie or spinach, feta cheese and mushroom strudel with salsa sauce (£6.95), Aberdeen Angus steaks (from £12.95), and daily specials such as goats cheese with onion marmalade and salad (£4.75), dressed crab with lemon mayonnaise (£4.95), mixed game casserole (£8.95), Loch Fyne mussels in white wine and garlic (£9.95), roast Lunesdale duckling with an apple and pear sauce (£11.95), and chargrilled fresh tuna steak (£13.95); hearty breakfasts. The restaurant is no smoking. Darts, dominoes, chess, cards, draughts, and piped music. There are some tables with cocktail parasols outside by the road, with more in the pleasant garden. The nearby church (built for the girls' school of Brontë fame here) has some attractive pre-Raphaelite stained glass and paintings. *(Recommended by Mr and Mrs C J Frodsham, Brian Randall, Jayne and Peter Capp, Pierre and Pat Richterich, Ken Richards, Mr and Mrs R Barclay, Mrs V Goldie, John Watson, Malcolm Taylor)*

Free house ~ Licensees Melvin and May Mackie ~ Real ale ~ Bar food ~ Restaurant ~ (015242) 71230 ~ Children welcome ~ Dogs welcome ~ Open 11-3, 6-11(10.30 Sun); closed 25 and 26 Dec ~ Bedrooms: £40B/£76B

COCKERMOUTH NY1231 Map 9

Bitter End £

Kirkgate, by cinema

From a tiny Victorian-style shop window in this interestingly refurbished place, there's a view of the little brewery where the landlord brews his own Cockersnoot and Cuddy Luggs and two new ones, Old Neddy and Farmers Ale; he also keeps Caledonian Deuchars IPA and Hesket Newmarket Doris's 90th Birthday Ale as guests on handpump, in good condition; quite a few bottled beers from around the world. The three main rooms have a different atmosphere in each – from quietly chatty to sporty, with the décor reflecting this, such as unusual pictures of a Cockermouth that even Wordsworth might have recognised, to more up-to-date sporting memorabilia, and framed beer mats. Some tables in the front bar are no smoking. As well as simple lunchtime snacks, the bar food includes cumberland sausage or five bean casserole (£5.50), fish and chips (£5.60), chicken tikka masala (£5.70), lasagne or steak and mushroom in ale pie (£5.75), and daily specials. Service is very welcoming; piped music; the public car park round the back is free after 6. *(Recommended by MLR, Edward Mirzoeff, G Coates, Gerald and Wendy Doyle, Christine and Neil Townend, Richard Lewis, David and Rhian Peters, Rona Murdoch, David Field)*

Own brew ~ Licensee Susan Askey ~ Real ale ~ Bar food ~ No credit cards ~ (01900) 828993 ~ Children in eating area of bar ~ Open 12(11.30 Sat)-2.30(3 Sat), 6-11; 12-3, 7-10.30 Sun; closed 25 Dec

CONISTON SD3098 Map 9

Sun

Pub signposted from centre

A welcome sight after a hard day on the fells, this friendly and comfortable place manages to cleverly combine the 16th-c pubby part with its informal 10 bedroom Edwardian hotel side. This year, there has been a lot of refurbishment in the bedrooms (most have fine views), the kitchen has been completely overhauled, and the old dining room has become a public lounge next to the conservatory. The old-fashioned, classic Lakeland bar has walls stripped back to the stonework, ceiling beams, a nice flagstoned floor, and a 19th-c range with leaping hare tiles; also, cask seats and cast-iron-framed tables, old Victorian settles, and Donald Campbell photographs (this was his HQ during his final attempt on the world water speed record). Well liked bar food includes home-made soup (£2.95), ciabatta sandwiches with fillings like pork and leek sausage with caramelised onion (£5.50), creamed mussel hotpot or roasted peppers stuffed with herb tomatoes and mozzarella (£6.75), pasta with pesto cream and sunblush tomatoes (£7.50), yorkshire pudding filled with casserole (£7.95), salmon with stir-fried vegetables and a prawn vinaigrette (£9.95), braised lamb shank (£10.95), daily specials such as chicken and crab pâté with tangy beetroot chutney (£5.25), mushroom and walnut cream risotto (£7.95), ham shank braised in sherry sauce (£10.95), and chargrilled crevettes (£12.75), puddings such as home-made apple crumble or sticky toffee pudding with butterscotch sauce (£4.95), and children's meals (from £3.95); the children's area in the bar is no smoking. Five well kept real ales on handpump: Barngates Tag Lag, Black Sheep, Coniston Bluebird, Moorhouses Black Cat, and Yates Spring Fever, a decent wine list, a growing number of malt whiskies, and friendly staff. Darts, table skittles, cribbage, dominoes, and occasional piped music. There are seats and tables in front of the building and in the big tree-sheltered garden, which make the most of the lovely views, and more on the front terrace. Fishing, riding and shooting can all be arranged for residents. *(Recommended by Tina and David Woods-Taylor, Mike and Sue Loseby, Lorraine and Fred Gill, Neil and Anita Christopher, John Foord, JDM, KM, Kevin Flack, David Whitehead, Ewan and Moira McCall)*

Free house ~ Licensee Alan Piper ~ Real ale ~ Bar food (12-2, 6-9) ~ Restaurant ~ (015394) 41248 ~ Children in eating area of bar and restaurant ~ Dogs allowed in bar ~ Open 11-11; 12-10.30 Sun ~ Bedrooms: £35S/£70S(£80B)

CROSTHWAITE SD4491 Map 9

Punch Bowl

Village signposted off A5074 SE of Windermere

The emphasis in this idyllically placed 16th-c inn is very much on the excellent, imaginative food, but the beer is good, and people do just drop in for a drink. It's also a nice place to stay. There are several separate areas carefully reworked to give a lot of space, and a high-raftered central part by the serving counter with an upper minstrel's gallery on either side; all areas are no smoking except the bar. Steps lead down into a couple of small rooms on the right, and there's a doorway through into two more airy rooms on the left. It's all spick and span, with lots of tables and chairs, beams, pictures by local artist Derek Farman, and an open fire. As well as a set-price lunch (two courses £9.95, three courses £12.95), the imaginative food might include sandwiches, home-made cream of broccoli and stilton soup (£2.75), smooth chicken liver parfait with piccalilli dressing and toasted brioche (£5.25), oven baked beetroot tart with crumbled goats cheese and a basil orange vinaigrette (£5.50), chargrilled fresh tuna niçoise (£5.95), three-cheese polenta with baked field mushrooms and chargrilled aubergine (£8.50), chargrilled breast of chicken on crushed new potatoes with a tomato, herb, tarragon and olive oil dressing (£11.25), chargrilled breast of duck on ginger braised cabbage with melting leeks, a honey sauce, and oyster mushrooms (£13.50), and roast fillet of cod served with prawns, mussels and queenie scallops and a creamy curried leek sauce (£13.95), with puddings like home-made mango and summer strawberry sorbet with a raspberry sauce, honey and Drambuie crème brûlée or chocolate and ginger tart with home-made honey ice cream and chocolate sauce (from £4.25). Good British cheeses (£4.95), and popular Sunday lunch (two courses £13.95). Well kept Barngates Tag Lag, Black Sheep, and Coniston Bluebird on handpump, a carefully chosen wine list with 20 by the glass, and several malt whiskies; there's a new espresso coffee machine in the bar. There are some tables on a terrace stepped into the hillside. Most visitors have been very pleased with the service here too, but in the last year there have been occasions when readers have felt that some staff have lost sight of the fact that the customer is always more important than the establishment. We imagine that the Dohertys will be stamping this attitude out pretty smartly. *(Recommended by RDK, Derek and Margaret Underwood, Joan Yen, A Preston, Margaret and Roy Randle, Maurice and*

Gill McMahon, Tracey and Stephen Groves, Revd D Glover, Roger Stock, D J Hulse, Gwyneth and Salvo Spadaro-Dutturi, John Saul)

Free house ~ Licensee Steven Doherty ~ Real ale ~ Restaurant ~ (015395) 68237 ~ Children welcome ~ Open 11-11; 12-4 Sun; closed Sun evening, all day Mon ~ Bedrooms: /£55B

DALTON-IN-FURNESS SD2376 Map 7

Black Dog £

Holmes Green, Broughton Road; a mile N of town, beyond A590

The cheery couple who run this simple, comfortable local lift it right out of the ordinary, and you are quite likely to be entertained, quite spontaneously, by some local singing or brass band rehearsals. The unpretentious bar has beer mats and brasses around the beams, two log fires, partly tiled and flagstoned floor, and plain wooden tables and chairs; there may be several dried hams hanging above the bar counter. A side terrace has a few plastic tables and chairs. Good value hearty bar food – all home-made – includes soup (£1.75), sandwiches (from £1.95), omelettes (from £3.50), cumberland sausage or chick pea and lentil curry (£4.50), beef stew (£5.25), smoked haddock cutlet with parsley sauce (£5.95), steaks (£7.95), daily specials like chicken, leek and pasta bake (£4.25), lamb cutlets with garlic and mushroom sauce (£4.95), and roast pork shank with cabbage and apple (£5.50), with puddings such as blackberry and apple crumble or chocolate sponge (£1.80), and children's meals (£2.50). The six real ales change constantly but might include Black Dog Special, Brysons Mild, Hart Squirrel Hoard or Roosters Yankee on handpump; they also have two or three farm ciders and quite a few country wines. Table skittles, shove-ha'penny, cribbage, and dominoes. The pub is handy for the South Lakes Wild Animal Park. More reports please. *(Recommended by Richard Gibbs)*

Free house ~ Licensees Jack Taylor and Julia Walker ~ Real ale ~ Bar food (12-2.30, 5-8; all day weekends) ~ No credit cards ~ (01229) 462561 ~ Children welcome ~ Dogs welcome ~ Occasional local singing, brass band rehearsals, morris men ~ Open 12-2.30, 5-11; 12-11(10.30 Sun) Sat; closed weekday lunchtimes Oct-end April ~ Bedrooms: £15/£35S

DENT SD7187 Map 10

Sun

Village signposted from Sedbergh; and from Barbon, off A683

This bustling pub brews its own real ales in the Dent Brewery (actually a few miles up in the dale); well kept on handpump, there's Bitter, T'Owd Tup, Kamikazee, and Aviator Ale, and monthly guests. The bar has a pleasant traditional atmosphere, simple furniture, a coal fire, some timbers and beams, and several local snapshots; one room to the left of the bar is no smoking. Straightforward bar food includes sandwiches (£2.25), home-made soup (£2.50), ploughman's or three bean chilli (£5.25), and home-made steak and kidney pie or cumberland sausage (£5.50). Darts, pool, dominoes, fruit machine, and juke box (in the pool room). There are rustic seats and tables outside. More reports please. *(Recommended by Dr Paull Khan, Jane Taylor, David Dutton, JP, PP)*

Own brew ~ Licensee Martin Stafford ~ Real ale ~ Bar food (12-2, 6.30-8.30) ~ (015396) 25208 ~ Children welcome ~ Open 11-11; 12-10.30 Sun; 11-2.30, 6-11 weekdays in winter ~ Bedrooms: £25B/£37B

ELTERWATER NY3305 Map 9

Britannia ★

Off B5343

There's so much about this smashing pub that everybody loves. It's very well run by the friendly, efficient licensees and their staff (though there is inevitably a wait at peak times when the pub does get packed), the little rooms have a lot of character and a very relaxed, informal atmosphere, and the food and beer are very good indeed. As well as a small and traditionally furnished back bar, there's a front one with a couple of window seats looking across to Elterwater itself through the trees on the far side: cosy coal fires, oak benches, settles, windsor chairs, a big old rocking chair, and well kept Coniston Bluebird, Dent Aviator, Jennings Bitter, and two guest beers such as Fraoch Heather Ale and Timothy Taylors Landlord on handpump, lots of malt whiskies, a few country wines, and winter mulled wine; the lounge is comfortable. Good, popular bar food (with prices little changed since last year) includes lunchtime filled rolls (from £2.50; beef with onion gravy £3), home-made soup (£2.65), filled baked potatoes (£3.75), home-made quiche (£4.95) or home-made cumberland pie (£6.50), with evening dishes such as home-made pâté with cumberland sauce or deep-fried brie wedges with fruit coulis (£3.95), home-made lamb rogan josh or steak and mushroom pie (£8.25), poached fresh salmon steak with lemon and dill butter (£8.95), and puddings like hot banana with butterscotch pancakes or bread and butter pudding (£3.50); super breakfasts and home-baked fruit scones for afternoon cream teas. The restaurant and residents' lounge are no smoking; dominoes and cribbage. In summer, people flock to watch the morris and step and garland dancers. *(Recommended by Arby, SLC, Tina and David Woods-Taylor, Dr Bob Bland, Mr and Mrs W D Borthwick, Richard Lewis, W W Burke, David Cooke, Jayne and Peter Capp, Dave Irving, Trevor Hosking, Mrs S E Griffiths, Roger and Jenny Huggins, David Carr, Steve and Liz Tilley, Ewan and Moira McCall)*

Free house ~ Licensees Judith Fry and Christopher Jones ~ Real ale ~ Bar food (all day) ~ Restaurant ~ (015394) 37210 ~ Children welcome ~ Dogs allowed in bar ~ Quiz Sun evenings ~ Open 11-11; 12-10.30 Sun; closed 25 and 26 Dec ~ Bedrooms: /£78S(£72B)

ENNERDALE BRIDGE NY0716 Map 9

Shepherds Arms

Ennerdale signposted off A5086 at Cleator Moor E of Egremont; it's on the scenic back road from Calder Bridge to Loweswater

This is a wonderful place for walks, as there are really no cars in Ennerdale, and the simple convivial bar has a detailed pictorial display of the off-road footpath plans. It also has a frequently updated weather-forecast blackboard, and a shelf of Wainwright books – it's on his popular coast-to-coast path. Service is always cheerful and obliging, and they couldn't be more welcoming and helpful to walkers, however wet and miserable. The bar has its serving counter in a bare-boards inner area up three steps, with a woodburning stove below a big beam hung with copper coffee pots. Its carpeted main part has a coal fire and a homely variety of comfortable seats; it opens into a small brick-floored extension with director's chairs around teak tables. Substantial bar food – using local meat and fish and only fresh vegetables – includes sandwiches (from £2.20), home-made chicken liver pâté (£3), omelettes (from £4.75), cumberland sausage with a fried egg (£5), quite a lot of vegetarian dishes such as mixed bean casserole (£5), cheese and broccoli pasta bake (£5.25), and home-made spinach and wensleydale tart (£5.50), home-made lasagne (£6), home-made steak in ale pie (£6.25), sirloin steak (£9.25), daily specials like thai vegetable bake (£6.50), venison casserole (£7.75), and rack of fellside lamb (£8.50), puddings (£2.75), and children's menu (£2.80). Well kept Courage Directors, Jennings, Timothy Taylors Landlord, Theakstons Black Bull and York Stonewall on handpump, decent coffee, and a good choice of wines by the glass; a couple of daily papers. There's a piano, and may be piped music. An entrance lounge has a sofa and a longcase clock. *(Recommended by Geoff and Angela Jaques, Tina and David Woods-Taylor, Lord Sandhurst)*

Free house ~ Licensee Norman Stanfield ~ Real ale ~ Bar food ~ Restaurant ~ (01946) 861249 ~ Children welcome ~ Dogs allowed in bar ~ Jazz, blues and folk in winter and spring ~ Open 11-11; 12-10.30 Sun ~ Bedrooms: £32S/£59B

We say if we know a pub has piped music.

GRASMERE NY3406 Map 9

Travellers Rest

Just N of Grasmere on A591 Ambleside—Keswick; OS Sheet 90 map reference 335089

The bedrooms in this 16th-c inn have been refurbished this year, and the chef now bakes his own bread, scones and cakes for full afternoon tea – which is proving popular. The lounge area has settles and upholstered armchairs and sofa benches, there are newspapers and magazines to read, a warming log fire, local watercolours and suggested walks and coast-to-coast information on the walls, and a relaxed atmosphere; piped classical music. From quite a choice, bar food includes home-made soup (£2.95), sandwiches (from £3.50; open ones £6.50), cumberland sausage, bacon and mushroom skillet (£5.25), steak and kidney in ale pie (£7.95), chick pea, aubergine and mushroom tagine (£8.95), steaks (from £12.95), daily specials such as seared Shetland scallops or chilli crab cakes (£3.95), wild mushroom risotto (£6.95), herb-crusted rack of Herdwick lamb with redcurrant and rosemary jus (£9.95), and puddings such as seville orange bread and butter pudding or lemon tart (£3.95). Well kept Greene King Boot, Jennings Bitter, Cumberland, and Sneck Lifter, and a guest such as Coniston Bluebird or Theakstons Old Peculier on handpump, and up to 20 malt whiskies. The games room is popular with families: darts, pool, fruit machine, TV, and dominoes. This is a lovely spot with wonderful surrounding scenery and good walks. As well as the telephone number listed below, they have a reservations number – 0870 0112152. *(Recommended by Richard Lewis, Maurice and Gill McMahon, Dr Paull Khan, Jim Abbott, Tina and David Woods-Taylor, Derek and Margaret Underwood, Michael Doswell, W W Burke, Stephen Buckley, Walter and Susan Rinaldi-Butcher, Mrs Romey Heaton, G J French)*

Free house ~ Licensees Lynne, Derek and Graham Sweeney ~ Real ale ~ Bar food (12-9.30; 12-3, 6-9.30 in winter) ~ Restaurant ~ (015394) 35604 ~ Children in eating area of bar and in family room ~ Dogs allowed in bar ~ Open 11-11; 12-10.30 Sun ~ Bedrooms: £48S/£68S

HAWKSHEAD NY3501 Map 9

Drunken Duck ★

Barngates; the hamlet is signposted from B5286 Hawkshead—Ambleside, opposite the Outgate Inn; or it may be quicker to take the first right from B5286, after the wooded caravan site; OS Sheet 90 map reference 350013

Cumbria Dining Pub of the Year

New bedrooms have been opened in a house behind this civilised and friendly 17th-c inn, and others across the courtyard are to have a private garden with lovely views. Many people do come to stay overnight and enjoy the restaurant-style evening meals, but at lunchtime it is at its pubbiest, the food is simpler, and there's a more informal, chatty atmosphere. The bar and snug are traditional beamed rooms with good winter fires, cushioned old settles and a mix of chairs on the fitted turkey carpet, pictures, cartoons, cards, fox masks, and cases of fishing flies and lures. All of the pub is no smoking except the bar. From the lunchtime menu, there might be feta cheese with plum tomato and fennel seed salad and mint dressing or smoked chicken breast with potatoes, beetroot and mustard salad and honeycomb mayonnaise (£4.95), duck and spring onion confit with chilli jam and coriander dressing (£5.95), toasted open sandwiches (from £5.95), thin crispy tartlet of leek purée, asparagus and goats cheese (£7.95), guinea fowl breast on prune and garlic risotto (£8.75), and grilled lemon sole and sautéed Flookburgh shrimps and leeks (£13.95). Evening choices run to smoked mackerel with roquefort rarebit served on caramelised red onion and truffle oil (£5.25), baked asparagus wrapped in cumbrian air-dried ham served with hollandaise sauce (£5.95), layers of grilled pasta, aubergine, sautéed spinach, chargrilled red pepper and chestnut served with pesto and boscaiola olives (£9.95), duck breast with roast shallots and chestnuts, shi-itake mushrooms and potatoes with garlic jus (£12.95), and fillet of venison marinated in espresso on sautéed green cabbage and chestnuts with a fig and vanilla confit or cod with grilled parsley crust on fenugreek sautéed potatoes, asparagus and roast red pepper hollandaise (£13.95). Puddings might include warm rhubarb and custard tart with crumble ice cream or ginger and walnut pudding with toffee sauce and lemon cinnamon ice cream (from £4.25). As well as their own Barngates Chesters Strong & Ugly, Cracker, and Tag Lag, they keep Jennings Bitter and Yates Bitter on handpump; over 20 malt whiskies, 20 wines by the glass, and foreign bottled beers. Dominoes. There are seats on the front verandah with stunning views and quite a few rustic wooden chairs and tables at the side, sheltered by a stone wall with alpine plants along its top; the pub has fishing in a private tarn behind. *(Recommended by M and C Lovatt, John and Gillian Scarisbrick, John and Joan Calvert, Edward Jago, Mrs Romey Heaton, Nick Lawless, John Saul, Dominic Epton, Tracey and Stephen Groves, Lorraine and Fred Gill, B H and J I Andrews, Richard Lewis, Sally Anne and Peter Goodale, Ian S Morley, Maurice and Gill McMahon, Mike and Sue Loseby, Giles and Liz Ridout, Arby, Olive and Ray Hebson, David Field, SLC, G J French)*

Own brew ~ Licensee Steph Barton ~ Real ale ~ Bar food (12-2.30, 6-9; not 25 Dec) ~ Restaurant ~ (015394) 36347 ~ Children welcome ~ Dogs allowed in bar ~ Open 11.30-11; 12-10.30 Sun ~ Bedrooms: £67.50B/£110B

Kings Arms

The Square

When one of the original beams in the bar of this Elizabethan inn began to sag and surveyors told the licensees it had to be replaced, they asked a local wood-carver to help them, and there's now the figure of a medieval king holding up the ceiling. The atmosphere is relaxed and friendly, there's a good mix of both locals and visitors, traditional pubby furnishings, and well kept Black Sheep, Coniston Bluebird, Tetleys and Theakstons, and a guest such as Fraoch Heather Ale or Barngates Tag Lag on handpump, several malt whiskies, summer cider, and winter mulled wine. Piped music, fruit machine, dominoes and cribbage. Good straightforward lunchtime bar food includes home-made soup (£2.75), filled baked potatoes (£4.25), filled rolls or baguettes (from £4.25), sausages and mash (£5.95), and steak in ale pie or vegetable lasagne (£6.50), with evening choices like mushrooms in creamy garlic sauce (£3.50), quiche of the day (£5.75), chicken curry (£6.25), minted lamb steaks (£8.50), and chargrilled sirloin steak (from £11.95). The restaurant is no smoking. As well as comfortable bedrooms, they offer self-catering cottages. The square on which this pub sits is glorious. *(Recommended by R C Vincent, Mr and Mrs S Mason, Nick Lawless)*

Free house ~ Licensee Rosalie Johnson ~ Real ale ~ Bar food (12-2.30, 6-9.30; not evening 25 Dec) ~ Restaurant ~ (0153 94) 36372 ~ Children in eating area of bar and restaurant ~ Dogs allowed in bar ~ Occasional one-man band or folk group ~ Open 11-11; 12-10.30 Sun; closed evening 25 Dec ~ Bedrooms: £34(£40S)/£60(£70S)

HESKET NEWMARKET NY3438 Map 10

Old Crown

Village signposted off B5299 in Caldbeck

The particularly good, own-brewed real ales on handpump continue to draw customers to this relaxed and unfussy local: Hesket Newmarket Blencathra Bitter, Great Cockup Porter, Helvellyn Gold, Skiddaw Special Bitter, Old Carrock Strong Ale, and Catbells Pale Ale. You can arrange to see the brewery on Wednesdays; also, traditional cider, and quite a few wines. Also popular are the well liked evening curries (meaty ones £7.50 and vegetarian £6.50) – though they also offer sandwiches, mushroom, parsley and garlic soup with home-made bread (£2.30), chicken, pheasant and apricot pie (£4.50), ham and egg (£5), lamb casserole (£6.50), and roast Sunday lunch (£5.50). The dining room is no smoking. The little bar has a few tables, a coal fire, and shelves of well thumbed books, and a friendly atmosphere; piped music, darts, pool, fruit machine, cribbage and dominoes. They have a self-catering cottage. The pub is in a pretty setting in a remote, attractive village. More reports please. *(Recommended by MLR, David Cooke, Tina and David Woods-Taylor)*

Own brew ~ Licensee Kim Mathews ~ Real ale ~ Bar food (12-2, 6.30-8.30; not Mon or Tues, not Sun evening) ~ Restaurant ~ No credit cards ~ (016974) 78288 ~ Children in eating area of bar and restaurant ~ Dogs welcome ~ Folk 1st Sun of month ~ Open 12-3, 5.30-11; 12-3, 7.30-10.30 Sun; closed Mon and Tues lunchtimes

HEVERSHAM SD4983 Map 9

Blue Bell

A6 (now a relatively very quiet road here)

Once a vicarage, this partly timbered 15th-c country hotel is a civilised and comfortable place. The lounge bar has warm winter fires, pewter platters hanging from the beams, an antique carved settle, cushioned windsor armchairs and upholstered stools, and small antique sporting prints and a display cabinet with two stuffed fighting cocks on the partly panelled walls. One big bay-windowed area is divided off as a no smoking room where children are allowed, and the long, tiled-floor public bar has darts, pool, cribbage, dominoes, fruit machine, TV, and piped music. Tasty bar food includes home-made soup (£2.95), sandwiches (£2.95; open ones from £3.95), filled baked potatoes (from £3.95), lovely Morecambe Bay potted shrimps (£4.95), daily specials such as battered haddock (£5), chicken and lamb kebabs or steak and kidney pie (£6.95), grilled fresh salmon in prawn sauce or roast beef and yorkshire pudding (£7.45), sirloin steak (£10.95), and children's dishes (£4.95); they also do morning coffee and afternoon tea. The restaurant is no smoking. Well kept Sam Smiths OB on handpump kept under light blanket pressure, quite a few malt whiskies, and a fair wine list. Crossing over the A6 into the village itself, you come to a picturesque church with a rambling little graveyard; if you walk through this and on to the hills beyond, there's a fine view across to the estuary of the River Kent. The estuary itself is a short walk from the pub down the country road that runs by its side. *(Recommended by Ray and Winifred Halliday, MLR, Maurice and Gill McMahon, Ruth and Paul Lawrence, David Carr, W W Burke, Michael Doswell, Dr Paull Khan, SLC)*

Sam Smiths ~ Managers Susan and Richard Cowie ~ Real ale ~ Bar food (11-3, 6-9; all day during holidays) ~ Restaurant ~ (015395) 62018 ~ Children welcome ~ Dogs allowed in bar ~ Open 11-11; 12-10.30 Sun ~ Bedrooms: £52.50B/£70B

INGS SD4599 Map 9

Watermill

Just off A591 E of Windermere

'A smashing all-rounder' is how one reader describes this particularly well run pub. It's a very apt description, too, as they keep a fantastic range of 16 real ales, serve good, popular food at very reasonable prices, and offer a genuinely warm welcome to all their customers – and their dogs as well, who get a biscuit and bowl of water. Perfectly kept on handpump, the beers might include Black Sheep Special and Best, Coniston Bluebird, Jennings Cumberland, Lees Moonraker, and Theakstons Best and Old Peculier, with changing guests like Adnams Regatta, Batemans XXXB, Dent Ramsbottom, Fullers London Pride, Hop Back Summer Lightning, Hughes Dark Ruby Mild, Isle of Skye Young Pretender, Moorhouses Pendle Witches Brew, and Tomintoul Caillie; also, Hoegaarden wheat beer and Old Rosie scrumpy on draught, bottled beers, and up to 50 malt whiskies. The bars have a very friendly, bustling atmosphere, and a happy mix of chairs, padded benches and solid oak tables, bar counters made from old church wood, open fires, and amusing cartoons by a local artist on the wall. The spacious lounge bar, in much the same traditional style as the other rooms, has rocking chairs and a big open fire; two areas are no smoking. Enjoyable bar food (they tell us prices have not changed since last year) includes lunchtime sandwiches, splendid home-made soup (£2.30), deep-fried crispy vegetables with a garlic dip (£3.85), home-made pâté (£3.95), Whitby haddock (£6.50), beef in ale pie (£6.95), cajun chicken (£7.80), lamb cutlets roasted in honey and coarse grain mustard (£9.95), steaks (from £11.25), and home-made daily specials such as thai fishcakes or spinach filled pancakes with a wild mushroom sauce glazed with mozzarella (£4), moroccan-style lamb and apricot tagine (£6.60), chicken, leek and smoked bacon pie (£6.80), sweet and sour pork (£6.95), and braised venison and chestnut casserole (£7). Darts, cribbage, and dominoes. There are seats in the front garden. Lots of climbing, fell-walking, fishing, boating of all kinds, swimming and pony-trekking within easy reach. Note that even residents cannot book a table for supper. *(Recommended by MLR, Mr and Mrs D W Mitchell, Richard Lewis, David and Barbara Knott, Lee Potter, Stephen, Julie and Hayley Brown, Mike Pugh, Jayne and Peter Capp, Peter F Marshall, Tracey and Stephen Groves, John and Gillian Scarisbrick, Maurice and Gill McMahon, SLC, Paul Boot)*

Free house ~ Licensees Alan and Brian Coulthwaite ~ Real ale ~ Bar food (12-4.30, 5-9) ~ (01539) 821309 ~ Children in family room ~ Dogs allowed in bar ~ 1st Tues of month story telling club ~ Open 12-11(10.30 Sun); closed 25 Dec ~ Bedrooms: £25S/£50S

KESWICK NY2623 Map 9

Dog & Gun

Lake Road; off top end of Market Square

Little changes in this bustling and unpretentious pub. There's a good, relaxed atmosphere, low beams, a partly slate floor (the rest are carpeted or bare boards), some high settles, a fine collection of striking mountain photographs by the local firm G P Abrahams, brass and brewery artefacts, coins in beams and timbers by the fireplace (which go to the Mountain Rescue Service), and log fires. Well kept Theakstons Best and Old Peculier, and Yates Bitter on handpump, and well liked, simple bar food such as home-made soup (£2.50), sandwiches (from £2.60), five bean chilli with garlic bread (£5.50), lamb curry, goulash or baked Borrowdale trout (£6.75), and puddings (from £2.75). 25 malt whiskies, piped music. *(Recommended by Karen and Graham Oddey, Jim Abbott, SLC, Eric Locker, David Carr, Mr and Mrs G Clay, Gerald and Wendy Doyle, Richard Lewis)*

Scottish Courage ~ Manager Peter Ede ~ Real ale ~ Bar food (12-9) ~ (017687) 73463 ~ Children welcome until 9 ~ Open 11-11; 12-10.30 Sun

George

3 St Johns Street, off top end of Market Street

The poet Southey used to wait by the good log fire for Wordsworth to arrive from Grasmere in the attractive traditional black-panelled side room of this fine old inn. There's also an open-plan main bar with old-fashioned settles and modern banquettes under Elizabethan beams, pleasant efficient staff, and daily papers. Under the new licensees, bar food now includes home-made soup (£2.25), sandwiches or filled baguettes (from £3.25), home-made chicken liver pâté (£4.45), cold meat platters (from £5.95), fresh breaded haddock (£6.25), home-made steak and mushroom pie (£6.95), cumberland sausage or gammon and pineapple (£7.95), and wild mushroom stroganoff (£8.95). Well kept Jennings Bitter, Cumberland, and Sneck Lifter on handpump. The restaurant is no smoking; piped music, fruit machine, and dominoes. *(Recommended by Gerald and Wendy Doyle, Jim Abbott, Lesley Bass, David Carr, H K Dyson, Chris Kent, Stephen Buckley)*

Jennings ~ Lease Ian Pettifrew, Ian Dixon and John Ward ~ Real ale ~ Bar food (12-2.30, 6-9) ~ Restaurant ~ (017687) 72076 ~ Children welcome away from bar ~ Open 11-11; 12-10.30 Sun ~ Bedrooms: £30S/£60S

KIRKBY LONSDALE SD6278 Map 7

Snooty Fox

Main Street (B6254)

There's a good bustling atmosphere in this rambling pub and a happy mix of locals and visitors. The various rooms have lots of interesting items on the walls: eye-catching coloured engravings, stuffed wildfowl and falcons, mounted badger and fox masks, guns and a powder-flask, stage gladiator costumes, and horse-collars and stirrups. The bar counters are made from English oak, as is some panelling, and there are also country kitchen chairs, pews, one or two high-backed settles and marble-topped sewing-trestle tables on the flagstones, mugs hanging from the beams, and two coal fires. Good bar food includes sandwiches such as chargrilled vegetables with mascarpone cheese or home-roasted turkey on home-baked walnut and date bread with cranberry dressing (from £3.75), crab cakes with citrus and sour cream dressing (£4.95), home-made pie of the day or fresh cod fillet in beer batter (£6.25), pasta with mushrooms and mixed peppers or spicy Greek lamb salad (£7.25), steaks (from £10.25), daily specials like pork loin steak with a coarse grain mustard and cream sauce (£8.25) or chargrilled venison steak with a green peppercorn and wild mushroom sauce (£11.25), and puddings (from £3.25); they also offer a set two-course lunch (£7.95). The dining annexe is partly no smoking. Well kept Theakstons Best, Timothy Taylors Landlord, and a guest such as Hook Norton Best or Oakham JHB on handpump, and several country wines; piped music, dominoes, and fruit machine in the back bar. There are tables out in the pretty garden. *(Recommended by Angus Lyon, Ray and Winifred Halliday, Steve Whalley, Michael and Lesley Fell, David Carr, Julian Heath)*

Mortal Man Inns ~ Manager Stuart Rickard ~ Real ale ~ Bar food (12-2.30, 6.30-9.30) ~ Restaurant ~ (01524) 271308 ~ Children in eating area of bar and restaurant ~ Dogs allowed in bar ~ Open 11-11; 12-10.30 Sun ~ Bedrooms: £36S/£56S

LANGDALE NY2906 Map 9

Old Dungeon Ghyll

B5343

The whole feel of this dramatically set inn is basic but cosy – and once all the fell walkers and climbers crowd in, full of boisterous atmosphere. There's no need to remove boots or muddy trousers, and you can sit on the seats in old cattle stalls by the big warming fire, and enjoy the seven well kept real ales such as Black Sheep, Jennings Cumberland, Theakstons XB and Yates Bitter with guests such as Coniston Bluebird or Hop Back Summer Lightning on handpump. The pub is in a marvellous position at the heart of the Great Langdale Valley and surrounded by fells including the Langdale Pikes flanking the Dungeon Ghyll Force waterfall; there are grand views of the Pike of Blisco rising behind Kettle Crag from the window seats cut into the thick stone walls; part of the bar is no smoking. Straightforward food includes sandwiches (£2.50, lunchtime), home-made soup (£2.50), filled baked potatoes (£3.75), evening pizzas (from £4.40), cumberland sausage (£6.30), steak pudding or home-made chilli (£7), puddings (£2.50), and children's meals (£3.50); if you are not a resident and want to eat in the restaurant you must book ahead; friendly, helpful staff, and darts. It can get really lively on a Saturday night (there's a popular National Trust campsite opposite). *(Recommended by SLC, Dave Irving, Sarah and Peter Gooderham, H K Dyson, John Wooll, Lorraine and Fred Gill, Dr Bob Bland, Nigel Woolliscroft)*

Free house ~ Licensee Neil Walmsley ~ Real ale ~ Bar food (12-2, 6-9) ~ Restaurant ~ (015394) 37272 ~ Children in eating area of bar ~ Dogs allowed in bar ~ Folk music 1st Weds of month ~ Open 11-11; 12-10.30 Sun; closed Christmas ~ Bedrooms: £34.75/£75.50S

LITTLE LANGDALE NY3204 Map 9

Three Shires

From A593 3 miles W of Ambleside take small road signposted The Langdales, Wrynose Pass; then bear left at first fork

This is a particularly nice place to stay and residents are made to feel genuinely welcomed and looked after. The comfortably extended back bar has stripped timbers and a beam-and-joist stripped ceiling, antique oak carved settles, country kitchen chairs and stools on its big dark slate flagstones, Lakeland photographs lining the walls, and a warm winter fire in the modern stone fireplace with a couple of recesses for ornaments; an arch leads through to a small, additional area. Well liked bar food at lunchtime includes soup (£3), sandwiches (£3.25; baguettes £5), terrine of the day or cherry tomato, brie and basil tart (£4.95), ploughman's (£5.50), and cumberland sausage or beef in ale pie (£6.95); in the evening, there might be salmon and crab parfait with dill and caper dressing or venison and pistachio terrine with home-made chutney (£4.95), baked baby goats cheese marinated in chilli and thyme, with a roasted sweet pepper salad (£8.25), fresh salmon fillet en croûte with currants and ginger, wrapped in puff pastry with a lemon grass butter sauce or honey-glazed pork loin chop with apple, sage and apricot risotto (£9.95), and sirloin steak or roast rack of Lakeland lamb (£11.25). The restaurant and snug are no smoking. Well kept Coniston Old Man, Jennings Bitter and Cumberland, and a guest such as Coniston Bluebird or Theakstons XB on handpump, 40 malt whiskies, and a decent wine list; darts, cribbage and dominoes. From seats on the terrace there are lovely views over the valley to the partly wooded hills below Tilberthwaite Fells, with more seats on a well kept lawn behind the car park, backed by a small oak wood. *(Recommended by Dave Irving, Roger and Jenny Huggins, Tina and David Woods-Taylor, SLC, Ewan and Moira McCall)*

Free house ~ Licensee Ian Stephenson ~ Real ale ~ Bar food (12-2, 6-8.45; no evening meals midweek in Dec or Jan) ~ Restaurant ~ (015394) 37215 ~ Children welcome ~ Dogs allowed in bar ~ Open 11-10.30(11 Sat); 12-10.30 Sun; 11-3, 8-10.30 midweek in winter; closed 25 Dec ~ Bedrooms: £40B/£70B

LOWESWATER NY1222 Map 9

Kirkstile Inn

From B5289 follow signs to Loweswater Lake; OS Sheet 89 map reference 140210

The smartened up bedrooms in this 16th-c country inn are proving popular with readers and the breakfasts are very good indeed. There are plenty of outdoor pursuits on the surrounding peaks and fells, and the pub is situated between Loweswater and Crummock Water. The bar is low-beamed and carpeted, with a roaring log fire, comfortably cushioned small settles and pews, and partly stripped stone walls. Tasty bar food includes home-made soup (£2.75), baguettes (£3.95), filled baked potatoes (£4.25), ploughman's (£4.95), vegetarian lasagne (£5.95), home-made steak and mushroom in Guinness pie or gammon with pineapple and mozzarella (£6.50), grilled tuna steak with peppers, olives and feta cheese or lamb cobble with a warm herb scone (£7.25), and home-made puddings such as sticky toffee pudding or fruit crumble (£3); children's dishes (£3.25). Well kept Coniston Bluebird, Jennings Bitter and Cumberland, and Yates Spring Fever on handpump; cribbage, dominoes, and a slate shove-ha'penny board. You can enjoy the view from picnic-sets on the lawn, from the very attractive covered verandah in front of the building, and from the bow windows in one of the rooms off the bar. *(Recommended by John and Christine Lowe, Simon and Caroline Turner, J Hale, H K Dyson, Dr Paull Khan)*

Free house ~ Licensees Roger and Helen Humphreys ~ Real ale ~ Bar food ~ Restaurant ~ (01900) 85219 ~ Children welcome ~ Dogs allowed in bar ~ Jazz 1st Fri of month Apr-Dec ~ Open 11-11; 11-10.30 Sun ~ Bedrooms: £35B/£60B

MELMERBY NY6237 Map 10

Shepherds ♀

About half way along A686 Penrith—Alston

A new licensee has taken over this red sandstone pub since our last edition, so we'd be grateful for any feedback on the changes. The bar is divided up into several areas, with a heavy beamed, no smoking room to the left of the door which is carpeted and comfortable, and has bottles on the mantelbeam over the warm open fire, sunny window seats, and sensible tables and chairs; to the right is a stone-floored drinking part with a few plush bar stools and chairs. At the end is a spacious room with a high-raftered ceiling and pine tables and farmhouse chairs, a woodburning stove, and big wrought-iron candelabra, and steps up to a games area with pool; darts, dominoes, shove-ha'penny, fruit machine and juke box. Bar food at lunchtime now includes snacks such as soup (£3.15), hot filled ciabatta sandwiches (from £5.20), various platters (from £5.30), a quiche of the day (£5.60), and freshly battered haddock (£6.80), as well as garlic mushrooms (£4.95), cumberland sausage hotpot (£6.55), stilton and mushroom pie or baked local trout (£7.40), chicken korma (£7.90), and steaks (from £10.80), with daily specials like baked baby squid (£6.50) or beef casserole (£7.20). Much of the main eating area is no smoking. Well kept Badger IPA, Black Sheep Riggwelter, Hesket Newmarket Blencathra Bitter, Jennings Bitter, and Wychwood Hobgoblin on handpump, and quite a few malt whiskies. Hartside Nursery Garden, a noted alpine and primula plant specialist, is just over the Hartside Pass. *(Recommended by David Cooke, Richard J Holloway, R Davies, Michael Doswell, Andy and Jill Kassube, Dr Adam Roberts, Keith Mould, Guy Vowles)*

Free house ~ Licensee Nick Baucutt ~ Real ale ~ Bar food (11-2.30, 6-9.45) ~ Restaurant ~ (017687) 79632 ~ Children welcome ~ Dogs allowed in bar ~ Occasional live entertainment Fri evening in winter ~ Open 12-11(10.30 Sun); closed 25 Dec

MUNGRISDALE NY3630 Map 10

Mill Inn

Off A66 Penrith—Keswick, a bit over a mile W of A5091 Ullswater turn-off

Since taking over a couple of years ago, the friendly family running this delightfully placed pub have made several changes. The simply furnished and neatly kept main bar has been refurbished, and there's a wooden bar counter with an old millstone by it, a warm fire in the stone fireplace, and a warm welcome to both locals and visitors. They now offer morning coffee and afternoon teas and make their own scones and cakes, and have a writers' club, a luncheon club, and teams for darts and dominoes. Using local lamb and beef, the enjoyable bar food now includes home-made soup (£2.10), grilled black pudding on herb mash with a grain mustard and bacon sauce (£3.35), Whitby scampi or good home-made steak and kidney pie (£6.35), grilled fresh salmon with a mushroom, white wine and cream sauce (£8.25), duck breast with honey, port and fresh coriander (£9.15), steaks (from £9.95), daily specials such as roasted vegetable lasagne (£6.95), lamb curry (£7.45), game pie (£8.25), and grilled fresh haddock with parsley, chive and lemon butter (£8.65). The restaurant is no smoking. Well kept Jennings Bitter and Cumberland, and guests like Black Sheep or Jennings Cocker Hoop on handpump, and quite a few malt whiskies; games room with darts, pool, dominoes, and piped music.There are tables on the gravel forecourt and neat lawn sloping to a little river. Please note that there's a quite separate Mill Hotel here. *(Recommended by Peter and Pat Frogley, Mike and Penny Sutton, Dr Alan Sutton)*

Jennings ~ Tenants Jim and Margaret Hodge ~ Real ale ~ Bar food (12-2.15, 6-8.30) ~ Restaurant ~ (017687) 79632 ~ Children welcome ~ Dogs allowed in bar ~ Open 12-11; 12-10.30 Sun; closed 25-26 Dec ~ Bedrooms: £35B/£55B

NEAR SAWREY SD3796 Map 9

Tower Bank Arms

B5285 towards the Windermere ferry

As Beatrix Potter's Hill Top Farm (owned by the National Trust) backs onto this little country inn (and the pub features in *The Tale of Jemima Puddleduck*), it does get very busy at peak times. The low-beamed main bar has a fine log fire in the big cooking range, high-backed settles on the rough slate floor, local hunting photographs and signed photographs of celebrities on the walls, a grandfather clock, and good traditional atmosphere. Tasty bar food includes home-made soup (£2.35), lunchtime filled rolls (from £3) or ploughman's (from £4.50), Morecambe Bay potted shrimps (£4.75), cumberland sausage, home-made flan or a vegetarian dish of the day (£5.95), Whitby scampi (£6.95), and wild boar and pheasant or game pies or duckling à l'orange (£7.75). Well kept Theakstons Best and Old Peculier, and weekly changing guest beers like Barngates Tag Lag, Wells Bombardier, Yates Bitter, and York Yorkshire Terrier on handpump, as well as lots of malt whiskies, and Belgian fruit beers and other foreign beers; darts, shove-ha'penny, cribbage, and dominoes.

Seats outside have pleasant views of the wooded Claife Heights. This is a good area for golf, sailing, birdwatching, fishing (they have a licence for two rods a day on selected waters in the area), and walking, but if you want to stay at the pub, you'll have to book well in advance. More reports please. *(Recommended by Giles and Liz Ridout, Mike Pugh, Tina and David Woods-Taylor, Mrs Romey Heaton, Gerald and Wendy Doyle)*

Free house ~ Licensee Philip Broadley ~ Real ale ~ Bar food (not 25 Dec) ~ Restaurant ~ (015394) 36334 ~ Children in eating area of bar lunchtime but in restaurant only, in evenings ~ Open 11-3, 5.30(6 in winter)-11; 12-10.30 Sun; 12-3, 7-10.30 Sun in winter; closed evening 25 Dec ~ Bedrooms: £37B/£52B

NEWBY BRIDGE SD3786 Map 9

Swan

Just off A590

This is a substantial hotel rather than a pub, but in the best Lakeland hotel tradition this former coaching inn includes a very welcoming bar round to the left. Immaculately kept, it rambles around through various nooks and corners, with flagstones here, carpet there, and bare boards in one inner recess, and has some heavy black beams, Lakeland and country pictures, and a mix of comfortably cushioned seating from country-kitchen to easy chairs and settees; two alcoves off the bar and a lounge are no smoking. They have well kept Boddingtons and Wadworths 6X on handpump and good cafetière coffee, and the uniformed staff are friendly and obliging; there may be very faint piped music. They do nicely presented bar snacks such as home-made soup (£2.95), filled ciabattas (from £3.25), sandwiches (from £4.50), and toasties (from £5.95), as well as proper meals which are taken in the adjoining brasserie (just a couple of steps from the bar) which has some stripped stone and a raised balustraded bare-boards area: garlic mushrooms (£3.95), a terrine of lancashire cheese, sausage, black pudding and potato wrapped in bacon with a spicy tomato chutney (£4.25), cherry tomato and red onion tart (£7.65), beef in ale pie, braised cumberland sausage or Italian cheese and wild mushroom ravioli in a creamy sauce (£7.75), cod in beer batter or lemon pepper chicken (£7.95), and chargrilled steaks (from £12.75). Outside, picnic-sets under cocktail parasols line a pretty inlet at the foot of Lake Windermere (the main body of the lake is just a short stroll away); it's a lovely spot. *(Recommended by Meg and Colin Hamilton, Michael Doswell, Eddie Edwards)*

Free house ~ Licensee Paul Roebuck ~ Real ale ~ Bar food (all day snacks and food all day weekends) ~ Restaurant ~ (015395) 31681 ~ Children in bar until 9; welcome in brasserie and restaurant ~ Open 11-11; 12-10.30 Sun ~ Bedrooms: £77.50B/£155B

PENRITH NY5130 Map 10

Agricultural

Castlegate; ¾ mile from M6 junction 40 – A592 into town, just off entrance roundabout

There's a bustling market town atmosphere in this Victorian pub, and many original features have been kept. The comfortable L-shaped beamed lounge has partly glazed panelling, plenty of seating, a lovely log fire, curved sash windows over the bar, and a good down-to-earth local feel with a thorough mix of customers. Jennings Bitter, Dark Mild, Cumberland, Cocker Hoop and Sneck Lifter on handpump are particularly well kept, and service from the chatty staff is prompt and helpful; over 30 malt whiskies, and darts, dominoes, and piped music. Enjoyable bar food includes home-made soup (£1.95), sandwiches (from £2.20; toasties from £2.60; baguettes from £3.05), baked potatoes (from £2.75), and specials such as chargrilled chicken breast on a cassoulet of pulses and smoked sausage (£6.75), pork fillet medallions with a sweet cider sauce and spiced apple chutney or grilled fresh salmon fillet with a mushroom and chive cream sauce (£7.95), calves liver and bacon with sage butter and red onion marmalade (£9.50), and chargrilled fillet steak (£10.95). The restaurant is no smoking. There are good views from the picnic-sets out at the side. Some readers feel a lick of paint might not go amiss. *(Recommended by Andy*

Rudge, Peter Salmon, Richard Gibbs, W W Burke, MLR, Geoff and Angela Jaques, Ian and Nita Cooper)

Jennings ~ Tenants Jim and Margaret Hodge ~ Real ale ~ Bar food (12-2, 6-8.30 (9 Fri, Sat and Sun)) ~ Restaurant ~ (01768) 862622 ~ Children in restaurant ~ Dogs allowed in bar ~ Open 11-11; 12-10.30 Sun; closed 25 and 26 Dec ~ Bedrooms: £25/£40

SANDFORD NY7316 Map 10

Sandford Arms

Village and pub signposted just off A66 W of Brough

Tucked away in a very small village by the River Eden (where it has fishing), this neat and welcoming little inn was once an 18th-c farmhouse. The friendly family who run it are fairly new to pub-keeping, which may be why you get the feeling that you're almost a family guest rather than a paying customer. The landlady's husband is a professional classical guitarist, and for once the piped music doesn't jar at all. The two sons do the cooking, and the food is good, using local organic ingredients where possible. It might include home-made soup (£2.10), grilled black pudding with mustard sauce (£2.85), sandwiches (from £3.20), huntsman's platter with cheese, pâté and ham (£6.20), home-made pie of the day (£6.95), chicken with mushrooms and bacon in a creamy sauce or gammon with egg or pineapple (£7.50), salmon fillet with parsley sauce (£7.95), minted lamb Henry (£8.75), steaks (from £11.50), and puddings like sticky toffee pudding or highland trifle (from £2.85). The compact and comfortable no smoking dining area is on a slightly raised balustraded platform at one end of the L-shaped carpeted main bar, which has stripped beams and stonework, homely pub furnishings, and maybe the clatter of dominoes as George licks his team into shape for the local league. Well kept changing ales such as Black Sheep Best and Special and Theakstons Best on handpump, a good range of malt whiskies, and nice New World house wines (including ones from the Sandford Estate – no connection). There's also a more formal separate dining room (not always in use), and a second bar area with broad flagstones, charming heavy-horse prints, an end log fire, and darts and a TV; piped music. There are a few picnic-sets outside. *(Recommended by Michael Doswell, Phil and Sally Gorton)*

Free house ~ Licensee Susan Stokes ~ Real ale ~ Bar food ~ Restaurant ~ (017683) 51121 ~ Children welcome ~ Dogs allowed in bar ~ Open 12-1.45, 7(6.30 Weds-Sat)-11; closed Mon lunchtime in winter; may close all winter lunchtimes depending on trade – best to phone ~ Bedrooms: £40B/£60B

SANTON BRIDGE NY1101 Map 9

Santon Bridge Inn

Off A595 at Holmrook or Gosforth

This traditional small black and white Lakeland inn is nicely placed in a quiet riverside spot, with fell views, and run by cheerful, hardworking licensees. The turkey-carpeted bar has stripped beams, joists and standing timbers, a coal and log fire, and three rather unusual timbered booths around big stripped tables along its outer wall, with small painted school chairs and tables elsewhere. Bar stools line the long concave bar counter, which has well kept Jennings Bitter, Cumberland, Cocker Hoop, and Sneck Lifter and a guest such as Adnams Broadside on handpump; good big pots of tea, speciality coffees, welcoming service; fruit machine, well reproduced piped nostalgic pop music, and separate room with TV. Bar food, with a big colourful specials board, includes baguettes (from £3.95), filled baked potatoes (from £4.50), steak and kidney pie (£6.95), cumberland sausage (£7.25), curry of the day (£7.50), vegetarian chilli (£7.95), lemon and garlic chicken (£8.95), a fish dish of the day (£9.95), steaks (from £11.95), and daily specials such as pork champignon (£8.95), sizzling beef satay (£9.95), and duck à l'orange (£10.50). The small reception hall has a rack of daily papers, and a comfortable more hotelish lounge on the left; one room is no smoking. There are picnic-sets out in front by the quiet road, with more in the garden. *(Recommended by Nigel and Sue Foster)*

Jennings ~ Tenants John Morrow and Lesley Rhodes ~ Real ale ~ Bar food (12-2.30, 6-9.30) ~ Restaurant ~ (01946) 726221 ~ Children welcome ~ Dogs allowed in bar and bedrooms ~ Open 11-11; 12-10.30 Sun ~ Bedrooms: £40(£45B)/£55(£60B)

SEATHWAITE SD2396 Map 9

Newfield Inn

Duddon Valley, near Ulpha (ie not Seathwaite in Borrowdale)

Tables out in the nice garden here have good hill views and the pub is popular at weekends with climbers and walkers. Inside, the slate-floored bar has a genuinely local and informal atmosphere, with wooden tables and chairs, and some interesting pictures, and well kept real ales such as Coniston Bluebird, Jennings Bitter, J W Lees Bitter, and Theakstons Old Peculier on handpump. There's a comfortable side room and a games room with darts, shove-ha'penny, cribbage, and dominoes. Good value bar food includes sandwiches (£2.25), good home-made soup (£2.45), filled baked potatoes (from £3.45), spicy bean casserole or cumberland sausage (£5.85), home-made steak pie or lasagne (£6.35), gammon and egg (£7.85), steaks (from £9.15), and puddings such as sticky toffee pudding (£2.25). The restaurant and one bar are no smoking; piped music. The pub owns and lets the next-door self-catering flats. *(Recommended by Derek Harvey-Piper, M Tempest, Karen and Graham Oddey, Rona Murdoch)*

Free house ~ Licensee Paul Batten ~ Real ale ~ Bar food (12-9) ~ Restaurant ~ (01229) 716208 ~ Children in eating area of bar and restaurant ~ Dogs allowed in bar ~ Open 11-11; 11-10.30 Sun

SEDBERGH SD6692 Map 10

Dalesman

Main Street

The various rooms of this nicely modernised pub have quite a mix of decorations and styles – lots of stripped stone and beams, cushioned farmhouse chairs and stools around dimpled copper tables, and a raised stone hearth with a log-effect gas fire; also, horsebrasses and spigots, Vernon Stokes gundog pictures, various stuffed animals, tropical fish, and a blunderbuss. Through stone arches on the right, a no smoking buttery area serves tasty food such as big breakfast (£6.90), home-made cumberland sausages, steak and kidney pie or 12oz gammon and egg (£7), and lots of daily specials priced at £8.95 like chargrilled lambs liver with black pudding mash and rosemary gravy, duck breast with roasted plums and celeriac mash, chicken fillet with cream cheese, sun-dried tomatoes and coriander, fresh cod fillet deep-fried in lager batter with dill mayonnaise, and chargrilled marlin with avocado and cherry tomato salsa. Well kept Black Sheep and Tetleys Bitter on handpump, and several malt whiskies; dominoes and piped music. Some picnic-sets out in front, and a small car park. The Dales Way and Cumbrian Cycle Way pass the door, and there are lots of walks of varying difficulty all around. *(Recommended by Edward Jago, Brian and Pat Wardrobe)*

Free house ~ Licensees Michael and Judy Garnett ~ Real ale ~ Bar food (12-2, 6(5.30 weekends)-9(9.30 weekends)) ~ Restaurant ~ (015396) 21183 ~ Children welcome ~ Open 11-11; 12-10.30 Sun ~ Bedrooms: £30S/£60B

STAINTON NY4928 Map 10

Kings Arms

1¾ miles from M6 junction 40: village signposted from A66 towards Keswick, though quickest to fork left at A592 roundabout then turn first right

Being so close to the M6, this pleasantly modernised, friendly pub makes a good lunchtime stop. The neatly kept open-plan bar has a rather cosy feel, leatherette wall banquettes, stools and armchairs around wood-effect tables, brasses on the black beams, and prints and paintings of the Lake District on the swirly cream walls; one room is no smoking during mealtimes. Enjoyable traditional bar food includes lunchtime snacks such as sandwiches (from £2.35; toasties from £2.90; open ones from £3.70), filled baked potatoes (from £3.90), and ploughman's (£4.45); also, home-made soup (£2.05), crispy mushrooms with garlic dip (£3.20), bacon chop with egg (£4.25), beef in ale casserole in yorkshire pudding (£5.45), lemon and ginger chicken or steak and kidney pie (£5.75), vegetarian lasagne (£6.35), sirloin steak (£9.95), daily specials, roast Sunday lunch, and puddings (£2.80). Well kept Flowers IPA, Greene King Old Speckled Hen, and Tetleys on handpump, and 21 malt whiskies; welcoming staff. Sensibly placed darts, dominoes, scrabble, and piped music. There are tables on the side terrace, with more on a small lawn. *(Recommended by John and Sylvia Harrop, Alistair Forsyth, Mrs P Gregory, Brian and Lynn Young)*

Pubmaster ~ Tenants James and Anne Downie ~ Real ale ~ Bar food (not Mon) ~ No credit cards ~ (01768) 862778 ~ Children in eating area of bar if dining until 9 ~ Open 11.30-3, 6.30-11; 12-4, 7-10.30 Sun; open 7pm evenings in winter; closed Mon exc bank hols

STONETHWAITE NY2613 Map 9

Langstrath

Off B5289 S of Derwent Water

Beautifully surrounded by the steep fells above Borrowdale, this small and civilised inn is quietly placed in a tiny village. The first thing you see in the neat and simple bar, largely no smoking, is the welcoming coal and log fire in a big stone fireplace; it has just a handful of cast-iron-framed tables, plain chairs and cushioned wall seats, and on its textured white walls quite a few walking cartoons and attractive Lakeland mountain photographs. They have well kept Black Sheep and Jennings on handpump with a couple of guest beers such as Durham Magus and Timothy Taylors Landlord, and quite a few malt whiskies. A little oak-boarded room on the left reminded us almost of a doll's house living room in style. Enjoyable bar food includes home-made soup (£2.95), sandwiches (from £3.25), mushrooms in creamy garlic sauce (£4.25), Morecambe Bay potted shrimps (£4.95), mushroom, broccoli and stilton pasta bake (£7.95), local trout poached with tarragon (£8.95), local roast lamb with mint (£10.25), roast fillet of barbary duck breast with a raspberry coulis (£10.95), daily specials like roast rib of local beef (£8.95) or fresh tuna fillet with a mango salsa or chicken supreme stuffed with wild mushrooms and cream cheese (£9.95), and home-made puddings (£2.75). There is also a separate back restaurant, by the residents' lounge. Outside, a big sycamore shelters a few picnic-sets. *(Recommended by Jane Taylor, David Dutton, H K Dyson, Alan Thomas)*

Free house ~ Licensees Donna and Gary MacRae ~ Bar food (12-2, 6-8.30; not Sun lunchtime) ~ Restaurant ~ (017687) 77239 ~ Children in restaurant ~ Open 11-11; 5.30-10.30 Sun; closed Sun lunchtime, weekdays during Jan, and for 2 weeks prior to Christmas ~ Bedrooms: £26/£52(£62S)(£72B)

TALKIN NY5557 Map 10

Blacksmiths Arms

Village signposted from B6413 S of Brampton

Extended from an early 18th-c blacksmith's, this welcoming inn is set by the green of a pretty village, with good surrounding walks. On the right is a warm, neatly kept lounge with upholstered banquettes, tables and chairs, an open fire, and country prints and other pictures on the walls. Well kept Black Sheep, Jennings Cumberland, and Tetleys on handpump, and several good wines by the glass; piped music, fruit machine, and dominoes. Using local produce, the popular food might include sandwiches, deep-fried brie (£3.95), smoked fish platter or asparagus spears in ham with cheese sauce (£4.45), chicken breast topped with pesto, herbs and smoked cheese (£7.95), venison casserole in Guinness and juniper sauce (£8.95), supreme of pheasant in a bacon, garlic and madeira sauce (£9.25), barbary duck breast in an orange and Grand Marnier sauce (£9.85), shoulder of lamb marinated in mint and honey (£10.45), and lots of puddings. The restaurant on the left is pretty. The bedrooms have been recently upgraded, and breakfasts are good. There are seats outside in the garden. *(Recommended by Ken Richards, Alan Clark, Mrs Phoebe A Kemp, JWAC, Michael Doswell)*

Free house ~ Licensees Donald and Anne Jackson ~ Real ale ~ Bar food (12-2, 6-9) ~ Restaurant ~ (016977) 3452 ~ Children in eating area of bar and restaurant ~ Open 12-3, 6-11(10.30 Sun) ~ Bedrooms: £30S/£45B

TIRRIL NY5126 Map 10

Queens Head ★

3½ miles from M6 junction 40; take A66 towards Brough, A6 towards Shap, then B5320 towards Ullswater

By the time this book is published, the brewery belonging to this very popular, well run inn will have moved a couple of miles away to Brougham Hall, and they will add an extra beer to their existing three. All the bedrooms will have been refurbished and have their own bathrooms, and the bars and restaurants will have had a facelift. The oldest parts of the bar have original flagstones and floorboards, low bare beams, black panelling, high-backed settles, and a roomy inglenook fireplace (once a cupboard for smoking hams); the little back bar has a lot of character; piped music. Their own beers include Bewshers Best (after the landlord in the early 1800s who bought the inn from the Wordsworths and changed its name to the Queens Head in time for Victoria's coronation), Academy Ale, Brougham Hall, and Old Faithful, and they keep guest beers from other local breweries on handpump. During the Cumbrian Beer & Sausage Festival in August, there are 20 local real ales. Over 40 malt whiskies, a good choice of brandies and other spirits, a carefully chosen wine list. As well as lunchtime bar snacks, the enjoyable food includes home-made soup (£2.75), caramelised onion tart with lemon crème fraîche (£3.25), home-made chicken liver pâté or garlic mushrooms (£3.50), a daily fresh pasta dish or home-made pie (£7.75), mediterranean risotto (£8.50), chicken curry (£8.75), braised shoulder of lamb in redcurrant gravy (£9.95), steaks (from £12.95), daily specials like mushroom ragoût on toasted tomato bread (£3.25), butterfish steak on a thai-spiced coconut sauce (£9.25), Solway salmon and mango en croûte with lime butter (£9.75), szechuan stir-fried beef on noodles (£10.75), and puddings such as orange mousse cake or dark chocolate tuile filled with white chocolate mousse and strawberry coulis (from £2.95). The restaurant is no smoking. Pool, juke box, and dominoes in the back bar. The pub is very close to a number of interesting places, such as Dalemain House at Dacre. *(Recommended by Dr Terry Murphy, Tony Middis, Dr Paull Khan, Mike Pugh, Gwyneth and Salvo Spadaro-Dutturi, Karen and Graham Oddey, Andy and Jill Kassube, A White, J Roy Smylie, Guy Vowles, Steve Whalley, Trish Carter, P Abbott, Maurice and Gill McMahon, David Cooke, Dr B and Mrs P B Baker, Sally Anne and Peter Goodale, Richard Lewis, Christine and Neil Townend, David Heath, Brian and Anna Marsden, Karen Eliot, Michael Doswell, D S Jackson, Mr and Mrs J Curtis, Paul Boot, Ian and Nita Cooper)*

Own brew ~ Licensee Chris Tomlinson ~ Real ale ~ Bar food (12-2, 6-9.30) ~ Restaurant ~ (01768) 863219 ~ Children in eating area of bar and in restaurant until 9.30; over 13 for accommodation ~ Dogs allowed in bar and bedrooms ~ Open 12-3, 6-11; 12-11 Fri and Sat; 12-10.30 Sun ~ Bedrooms: £35B/£60B

TROUTBECK NY4103 Map 9

Queens Head ★

A592 N of Windermere

For 400 years, this civilised inn has been offering hospitality to travellers, and now that the new bedrooms are up and running, it is an even more pleasant place to stay. Most of the rooms have fine views, and breakfasts are very good. The big rambling original U-shaped bar has a little no smoking room at each end, beams and flagstones, a very nice mix of old cushioned settles and mate's chairs around some sizeable tables (especially the one to the left of the door), and a log fire in the raised stone fireplace with horse harness and so forth on either side of it in the main part, with a woodburning stove in the other; some trumpets, cornets and saxophones on one wall, country pictures on others, stuffed pheasants in a big glass case, and a stag's head with a tie around his neck, and a stuffed fox with a ribbon around his neck. A massive Elizabethan four-poster bed is the basis of the finely carved counter where they serve Boddingtons, Coniston Bluebird, and Jennings Bitter, with guests such as Barngates Cracker, Black Sheep Special or Dent Ramsbottom on handpump. The newer dining rooms (where you can also drop in for just a drink) are similarly decorated to the main bar, with oak beams and stone walls, settles along big tables, and an open fire. Imaginative bar food includes light lunches such as a bowl of fresh mussels steamed with garlic and herbs and finished with cream (£5.25), mixed bean and wild mushroom cassoulet on pasta with a rich butter sauce or pork schnitzel fried onto creamy garlic noodles (£5.95), and peppered venison and redcurrant casserole with a timbale of braised rice (£6.25), as well as home-made soup with home-made bread (£2.75), home-smoked pork loin with pickle (£5.25), steak and mushroom in ale cobbler (£7.25), chicken marinated in ginger and coriander with bean sprouts (£9.25), saffron scented risotto cakes on a mixed bean and tomato compote (£9.50), fillet of cod baked onto marinated fennel with a citrus butter (£12.95), breast of barbary duck on a kumquat risotto with lime and garlic dressing (£13.95), and puddings such as cinnamon and apple brûlée, orange parfait with an orange syrup or sticky toffee pudding (£3.75). They also have a three-course menu £15.50, and good children's choices (from £3); piped music and dominoes. Seats outside have a fine view over the Trout valley to Applethwaite moors. *(Recommended by Ray and Winifred Halliday, Malcolm Taylor, Dominic Epton, Derek and Margaret Underwood, John and Christine Lowe, John and Gillian Scarisbrick, Tina and David Woods-Taylor, Tim and Beryl Dawson, Richard Lewis, Derek Thomas, Phil and Heidi Cook, Tracey and Stephen Groves, RJH, Lorraine and Fred Gill, Maurice and Gill McMahon, Ian and Jane Irving, R N and M I Bailey, Hugh Roberts, Revd D Glover, Paul Boot, Pat and John Morris)*

Free house ~ Licensees Mark Stewardson and Joanne Sherratt ~ Real ale ~ Bar food ~ Restaurant ~ (015394) 32174 ~ Children welcome ~ Dogs allowed in bar ~ Open 11-11; 12-10.30 Sun; closed 25 Dec ~ Bedrooms: £57.50B/£80B

ULVERSTON SD2978 Map 7

Bay Horse

Canal Foot signposted off A590 and then you wend your way past the huge Glaxo factory

Originally a brewery, inn, and fishermen's cottages, this civilised small hotel has commanding views of both the Lancashire and Cumbrian fells, and stands on the water's edge of the Leven Estuary. It's at its most informal at lunchtime when the good, imaginative bar food might include home-made soup (£3.25), sandwiches (from £3.70; smoked chicken with curry mayonnaise and toasted coconut £3.95; hot smoked pork loin on caramelised apple, apricot and shallots £6.25), home-made herb and cheese pâté, rich chicken liver pâté with cranberry and ginger purée or button mushrooms in a tomato, cream and brandy sauce on a peanut butter crouton (£6.25), smoked haddock and sweetcorn chowder served with hot garlic and paprika bread (£6.75), braised lamb, apricot and ginger puff pastry pie (£8.50), grilled cumberland sausage with date chutney, cranberry and apple sauce (£9), spiced lasagne (£9.25), fresh crab and salmon fishcakes on white wine and herb cream sauce or Aberdeen Angus burgers with caramelised onions (£9.50), and home-made puddings (£4.50). Well kept Jennings and Thwaites and a guest on handpump, a decent choice of spirits, and a carefully chosen and interesting wine list with quite a few from South Africa. The bar, notable for its huge stone horse's head, has a relaxed atmosphere despite its smart furnishings: attractive wooden armchairs, some pale green plush built-in wall banquettes, glossy hardwood traditional tables, blue plates on a delft shelf, and black beams and props with lots of horsebrasses. Magazines are dotted about, there's a handsomely marbled green granite fireplace, and decently reproduced piped music; darts, bar billiards, shove-ha'penny, cribbage, and dominoes. The no smoking conservatory restaurant has fine views over Morecambe Bay (as do the bedrooms) and there are some seats out on the terrace. Please note, the bedroom price includes dinner as well. *(Recommended by Ray and Winifred Halliday, John and Christine Lowe, JDM, KM, Derek Harvey-Piper, Revd D Glover,*

Philip Vernon, Kim Maidment, Jenny and Chris Wilson, Tina and David Woods-Taylor; also in the Good Hotel Guide*)*

Free house ~ Licensee Robert Lyons ~ Real ale ~ Bar food (bar food lunchtime only; not Mon) ~ Restaurant ~ (01229) 583972 ~ Children in eating area of bar and in restaurant if over 12 ~ Dogs allowed in bar and bedrooms ~ Open 11-11; 12-10.30 Sun ~ Bedrooms: /£165B

Farmers Arms

Market Place

A wide range of customers enjoys this particularly welcoming town pub, and there's a good choice of real ales, and a popular, varied menu. The building dates back to the 16th c, and is pretty much unchanged from the outside, but has been appealingly modernised and extended inside. The original fireplace and timbers blend in well with the more contemporary furnishings in the front bar – mostly wicker chairs on one side, comfortable sofas on the other; the overall effect is rather unusual, but somehow it still feels like the most traditional village pub. A table by the fire has newspapers, glossy magazines and local information, then a second smaller bar counter leads into a big raftered eating area, part of which is no smoking; piped music. Six swiftly changing well kept real ales on handpump, some chosen because they're local brews, others simply because they have amusing names: Broughton Greenmantle, Courage Directors, Eccleshall Slaters, Flowers IPA, Moorhouses Pendle Witches Brew, Theakstons Best, and Timothy Taylors Landlord. They specialise in carefully chosen New World wines, with around a dozen by the glass. The very good food includes super sandwiches or hot baguettes (usually available all day and made with their own bread), New Zealand green lipped mussels topped with garlic (£3.25), chicken strips marinated in lemon and ginger, stir-fried with crunchy vegetables and finished in cajun and oyster sauce or peppered pork steak with cajun wild mushrooms, served with a sweet pepper and paprika glaze (£6.95), fillet of fresh coley marinated in thai spices, served on a bed of fresh mussels in a blue cheese and chive cream sauce or beef marinated in chilli and ginger with oriental vegetables and finished with honey and cracked black pepper (£7.95), and seared salmon fillet on mediterranean roasted vegetables with a buttered lime sauce (£8.95). They open early for a good choice of breakfasts and coffees. It's worth booking at busy times. In front is a very attractive terrace with plenty of good wooden tables looking on to the market cross, big heaters, and lots of colourful plants in tubs and hanging baskets (the landlord is a keen gardener). If something's happening in town, the pub is usually a part of it: events range from weekly quiz nights to the world's largest gathering of pantomime ponies. They can be busy on Thursday market day. *(Recommended by Ray and Winifred Halliday, David Field, Mrs M Granville-Edge)*

Free house ~ Licensee Roger Chattaway ~ Real ale ~ Bar food (10-3, 5.30-8.30) ~ (01229) 584469 ~ Children in eating area of bar and restaurant ~ Open 11(9.30 for breakfast)-11(10.30 Sun)

WASDALE HEAD NY1808 Map 9

Wasdale Head Inn

To NE of lake; long detour off A595 from Gosforth or Holmrook

They've opened their own microbrewery at this three-gabled hotel, the Great Gable Brewing Company and brew Great Gable and Wasd' Ale. Also well kept on handpump, there might be Derwent Kendal Pale Ale and Bitter, Hesket Newmarket Keen Knotts Crack, Jennings Dark Mild, and Yates Bitter on handpump. The high-ceilinged, spacious no smoking main bar has an old-fashioned country-house feel with its shiny panelling, cushioned settles on the polished slate floor, great George Abraham early mountaineering photographs on the walls, and a log fire. It's named for the first landlord, Will Ritson, who by his death in 1890 had earned the reputation of being the World's Biggest Liar for his zany tall stories. There's a comfortably old-fashioned residents' bar and lounge (the oak-panelled walls covered with photographs of ground-breaking climbs), snug and restaurant. Popular bar food includes soup (£2), a vegetarian dish (£6), and cumberland sausage, good rabbit pie, local Herdwick lamb, and steak in ale pie (£6.50); a decent choice of malt whiskies, and good wine list; dominoes, cribbage, chess and quoits. The drive below the plunging majestic screes by England's deepest lake is quite awesome. Besides the comfortable bedrooms, they offer well equipped self-catering accommodation; nice breakfasts. *(Recommended by Peter Burton, H K Dyson, Nigel Woolliscroft, Paul Thompson, Anna Blackburn, Mike Pugh, Dr Bob Bland, Nigel and Sue Foster, Mrs Jane Wyles; also in the* Good Hotel Guide*)*

Own brew ~ Licensee Howard Christie ~ Real ale ~ Bar food (11-8.30(8 in winter)) ~ Restaurant ~ (019467) 26229 ~ Children in eating area of bar and in family room ~ Dogs allowed in bar ~ Open 11-11(10 in winter); 12-10.30 Sun ~ Bedrooms: £45B/£90B

WINTON NY7810 Map 10

Bay Horse

Just off A685, N of Kirkby Stephen

Unassuming and very popular, this low white building has a bustling, friendly atmosphere. The two simple, low-ceilinged rooms have old village photographs and well kept Black Sheep and beers from local breweries such as Border, Daleside, Hambleton, and Rudgate on handpump. Served by quick, friendly staff, the good, reasonably priced bar food includes home-made soup (£1.65), filled baguettes or wraps (from £2.50), pâté (£2.50), cold buffet (£5.50), home-made steak and kidney pie or cumberland sausage (£5.95), vegetarian dishes, hot spiced chicken breast (£6.50), sirloin steak (£9.50), and daily specials such as curries (from £5.75), marinated lamb chop (£7.50), and duck breast (£10.50). Juke box, pool, darts, and dominoes. From the garden behind the inn (which is surrounded by farms and faces the village green), there are tables looking up to Winton and Hartley fells. *(Recommended by Karen Eliot, Comus and Sarah Elliott, Dr Paull Khan, Geoffrey and Brenda Wilson)*

Free house ~ Licensee Derek G Parvin ~ Real ale ~ Bar food (not Tues lunchtime) ~ Restaurant ~ (017683) 71451 ~ Children in eating area of bar and restaurant ~ Dogs allowed in bar ~ Open 1.30-11 Mon, Weds, Thurs Fri; 7-11 Tues; 12-11 Sat; 12-10.30 Sun; closed afternoons in winter; closed Tues lunchtimes ~ Bedrooms: /£40B

YANWATH NY5128 Map 9

Gate Inn

2¼ miles from M6 junction 40; A66 towards Brough, then right on A6, right on B5320, then follow village signpost

Although this is an unpretentious village local it does have qualities that lift it right out of the ordinary. The staff are particularly helpful and friendly, the atmosphere is welcoming and relaxed, and the food is exceptionally good. The simple turkey-carpeted bar, full of chatting regulars, has a log fire in an attractive stone inglenook and one or two nice pieces of furniture and middle-eastern brassware among more orthodox seats; or you can go through to eat in a two-level no smoking restaurant. Carefully prepared, the imaginative dishes might include home-made soup (£2.50), good 'black devils' (sliced black pudding with cream and peppercorn sauce £3.40), seafood pancake (£3.95), pies such as sweet potato or chicken and leek or good fish (£6.95), much enjoyed steak baguette (£6.95), salmon and monkfish wrapped in parma ham with a creamy prawn sauce (£9.95), steaks (from £9.95), daily specials such as venison steak with mushroom and red wine sauce (£9.75) and breast of barbary duck with cranberry and orange sauce (£11.75), and puddings like sticky toffee pudding or cappuccino coffee cup mousse (£3.50). Well kept Hesket Newmarket Helvelyn Gold and Jennings Cumberland on handpump, and a decent wine list; darts, dominoes, cribbage, chess, backgammon, and shove-ha'penny; the friendly border collie is called Domino and is good with children. There are seats on the terrace and in the garden. *(Recommended by Christine and Neil Townend, JWAC,*

Richard J Holloway, Roger and Jenny Huggins, B, M and P Kendall, Marcus Byron, David and Julie Glover, Roy and Margaret Jones, Tina and David Woods-Taylor)

Free house ~ Licensees Ian and Sue Rhind ~ Real ale ~ Bar food ~ Restaurant ~ (01768) 862386 ~ Children welcome ~ Dogs allowed in bar ~ Open 12-3, 6-11(10.30 Sun); evening opening 6.30 in winter

Lucky Dip

Besides the fully inspected pubs, you might like to try these Lucky Dips recommended to us and described by readers (if you do, please send us reports: www.goodguides.com).

Alston [NY7146]

☆ ***Angel*** [Front St]: Friendly 17th-c local on steep cobbled street of charming small Pennine market town, beams, timbers, big log and coal fire, traditional furnishings, good value generous quickly served food (not Tues evening) from well filled sandwiches to steaks, well kept Flowers IPA and Wadworths 6X, decent house wines; children welcome in eating area, tables in sheltered back garden; cheap bedrooms *(R T and J C Moggridge, LYM)*

☆ ***Turks Head*** [Market Pl]: Comfortable and convivial old-world local with good value food, well kept Boddingtons, cheerful landlord, bar counter dividing big low-beamed front room into two areas, cosy back lounge, log fires; at top of steep cobbled street *(P and D Carpenter)*

Ambleside [NY3703]

Wateredge [Borrans Rd]: Hotel rather than pub, recently refurbished in pleasant modern style, great views from bar and lakeside garden, Coniston Bluebird and Bluebird XB, good food and service; comfortable bedrooms *(D J Hulse)*

Armathwaite [NY5045]

Fox & Pheasant: Cosy, comfortable and neatly kept 18th-c coaching inn, enjoyable food, helpful staff, Theakstons ales, attractive beamed bar, shining brass, roaring fire; tables outside, bedrooms *(Jean and Douglas Troup)*

Askham [NY5123]

Punch Bowl: This nice pub, a former main entry, has closed (a victim of the downturn in trade following 2001 foot & mouth restrictions); we hope it will be reopened *(LYM)*

Queens Head [lower green; off A6 or B5320 S of Penrith]: Two-room lounge with open fire, lots of beams, copper and brass, good choice of well served food inc good fresh fish and veg, well kept ale, wide choice of wines; children welcome, pleasant garden; bedrooms comfortable with creaking floorboards, good breakfast *(LYM, Peter and Giff Bennett)*

Baycliff [SD2872]

Fishermans Arms [A5087 Barrow—Ulverston]: Large hotel bar with slightly raised eating area, Tetleys and a quickly changing guest beer, enjoyable food from lunchtime bar snacks to restaurant dishes, wknd high teas, efficient service; garden with play area, comfortable bedrooms *(MLR)*

Boot [NY1700]

☆ ***Brook House***: Obliging family service in converted small Victorian hotel with wide choice of good generous home-cooked food on solid timber tables, small no smoking plush bar, comfortable hunting-theme lounge, log fires, four well kept ales inc Black Sheep and Theakstons, decent wines, peaceful dining room, good views; handy for Ravenglass railway and great walks, eight good bedrooms with own bathrooms – and good drying room *(Christine and Neil Townend, S C Cowell, David and Rhian Peters)*

☆ ***Burnmoor*** [signed just off the Wrynose/Hardknott Pass rd]: 16th-c inn in peaceful hamlet, comfortable beamed bar with ever-burning fire, well kept Black Sheep, Jennings Bitter and Cumberland and a guest beer, thoughtful wine list, Islay malt whiskies, good mulled wine all year, enjoyable lunchtime bar food from sandwiches and baked potatoes up using carefully chosen ingredients, no smoking restaurant; games room with pool, TV and juke box; children welcome, seats out on sheltered front lawn with play area, good walks, open all day, bedrooms, lovely surroundings *(Roger Braithwaite, Dr Paull Khan, Nicholas Paint, H K Dyson, LYM, David and Julie Glover)*

Borwick Rails [SD1879]

Duddon Pilot [just outside Millom]: No smoking throughout, interesting local iron industry memorabilia in comfortably modern nautical-theme bar, enjoyable food inc shellfish here or in dining room; bedrooms with own bathrooms *(Dave Braisted)*

Bowland Bridge [SD4189]

Hare & Hounds [signed from A5074]: Pleasantly set and handy for Sizergh Castle, with decent food maybe inc Sun carvery, open fires in comfortably modernised carpeted bar, helpful staff, Tetleys, children welcome; picnic-sets in spacious side garden, comfortable bedrooms *(RDK, LYM)*

Bowness-on-Windermere [SD4097]

☆ ***Hole in t' Wall*** [Lowside]: Ancient beams and flagstones, stripped stone, lots of country bric-a-brac and old pictures, splendid log fire under vast slate mantelpiece, upper room with attractive plasterwork (and dominoes and juke box), reasonably priced generous food from sandwiches to steak and good curries, well kept Robinsons Frederics, Best and Hartleys XB, may be home-made lemonade or good winter mulled wine; very busy in tourist season; no dogs or prams, sheltered picnic-sets in tiny flagstoned front courtyard *(Mike and Sue Loseby, Ian S Morley, Richard Lewis, J G E Bell, Jayne and Peter Capp, Alan*

Thomas, Edward Jago, LYM, Val Stevenson, Rob Holmes)

Olde John Peel [Rayrigg Rd]: Attractively refurbished lounge, panelled bar, country artefacts, good value family bar food, well kept Theakstons Best, mulled wine, friendly staff; upstairs games rooms with darts, pool and machines; handy for World of Beatrix Potter, open all day *(Richard Lewis)*

Brampton [NY6723]

New Inn [the different smaller Brampton, off A66 or B6542 N of Appleby]: Two comfortably traditional unpretentious bar rooms with stripped and polished old pine furnishings, interesting low-beamed and flagstoned dining room with ancient cooking range by massive old oak settle, well kept ales such as Black Sheep and Theakstons, decent wines, good choice of malt whiskies, enjoyable food with plentiful veg, friendly service, darts, dominoes; piped music; tables out on grass with barbecue *(LYM, Tony and Katie Lewis)*

Brigsteer [SD4889]

☆ ***Wheatsheaf***: Cosy traditional pub in quiet pretty village, comfortable atmosphere, good food from sandwiches and early-week bargains to plenty of fish, good value Sun lunch, welcoming efficient staff, Boddingtons, Theakstons and guests, good wines; country views *(Malcolm Taylor, Michael Doswell, Mrs B Cadman, John Foord, Margaret and Roy Randle, Margaret Dickinson)*

Broughton-in-Furness [SD2187]

Black Cock [Princes St]: Olde-worlde pub dating from 15th c, good new tenants doing enjoyable food (helped by landlady's mother who has great track record), good service, well kept Theakstons, step down to lounge bar with convivial atmosphere and cosy fireside, spacious comfortable dining room, juke box in games room up steps in former back stables; pleasantly decorated bedrooms *(Derek Harvey-Piper, G Coates)*

☆ ***Manor Arms*** [The Square]: Changing well kept ales such as Burton Bridge Spring, Cambrinus Deliverance, Coniston Bluebird, Harviestoun Bitter & Twisted, Nethergate Priory Mild, Timothy Taylors Landlord and Yates in neatly kept and comfortable open-plan pub on quiet sloping square, flagstones and bow window seats, coal fire in big stone fireplace, chiming clocks, good sandwiches, pizzas and bockwurst sausages, winter soup, pool table; children allowed, stairs down to lavatories (ladies' has baby-changing); well appointed good value bedrooms, big breakfast, open all day *(BB, Derek Harvey-Piper, H K Dyson, G Coates)*

Caldbeck [NY3239]

☆ ***Oddfellows Arms*** [B5299 SE of Wigton]: Comfortable bar, well kept Jennings Bitter and Cumberland, decent generous food from baked potatoes and lunchtime sandwiches up, good-sized no smoking dining room; piped music, games area with pool, juke box and TV; children welcome, open all day wknds and summer, bedrooms, nice village *(Mike and Penny Sutton, Mr and Mrs W D Borthwick, P and M Rudlin, Tina and David Woods-Taylor, Dr Paull Khan, Steve and Liz Tilley, Dave Braisted)*

Cark-in-Cartmel [SD3676]

Engine [follow Holker Hall signs]: Comfortable and welcoming low-beamed bar with thriving local atmosphere, good home-made food from lunchtime sandwiches up, Theakstons real ales, quick friendly service, good fire, games room, restaurant; tables out by little stream, has been open all day; self-contained holiday flats *(D W Stokes, LYM)*

Carlisle [NY4056]

Kings Head [Fishergate]: Enjoyable cheap bar snacks, well kept Jennings and Yates, upstairs restaurant *(MLR)*

Cartmel [SD3778]

Cavendish Arms [Cavendish St, off main sq]: Civilised and friendly, with open fire, well kept Theakstons, good varied menu, no smoking restaurant, children welcome; tables out in front and behind by stream, comfortable bedrooms, good walks, open all day *(R T and J C Moggridge, LYM)*

☆ ***Kings Arms*** [The Square]: Picturesque and inviting, nicely placed at the head of the attractive town square – rambling and neatly kept heavy-beamed bar, mix of furnishings from traditional settles to banquettes, up to half a dozen or more well kept real ales, wide choice of generous usual bar food, reasonable prices, all-day scones, cakes and so forth, good friendly service and attentive landlord, nice view from no smoking restaurant; children welcome, sunny seats out on square and in attractive back courtyard by beck, craft and gift shop upstairs *(Mary Belshaw, John Foord, JDM, KM, LYM)*

Pig & Whistle: Friendly well run local, well kept beers, good adjoining bistro *(David Field)*

Royal Oak [The Square]: Tastefully refurbished, with low ceilings, cosy nooks, generous good value food from baguettes up, well kept real ales such as Wadworths 6X, friendly helpful service; nice big garden, bedrooms *(Margaret Dickinson, Gerald and Wendy Doyle, BB)*

Cartmel Fell [SD4288]

Masons Arms: This moorland pub, previously a very popular main entry, changed hands in 2002 *(LYM)*

Chapel Stile [NY3205]

☆ ***Wainwrights*** [B5343]: Roomy slate-floored bar welcoming walkers and dogs, old kitchen range, cushioned settles, well kept Jennings Bitter, Cumberland, Sneck Lifter and a guest beer, food from sandwiches and baked potatoes up inc children's dishes, no smoking family dining area, darts and dominoes; piped music; good views from front picnic-sets, good walks, open all day wknds and summer *(B H and J I Andrews, LYM, W W Burke, Dave Braisted, Ewan and Moira McCall)*

Cockermouth [NY1231]

☆ ***Trout*** [Crown St]: Solid and civilised old fishing hotel as used by Bing Crosby, pink plush sofas, captain's chairs and open fire in comfortable and friendly bar reached through other public rooms, good bar food from good sandwiches up (large or small helpings), well kept Jennings Cumberland, Marstons Pedigree and Theakstons Best, over 50 malt whiskies, decent wines, freshly squeezed juices, friendly helpful staff; coffee lounge and comfortable restaurant (best to book Sun lunch) both no smoking; piped music; children welcome, nice gardens down to river, good bedrooms, fishing courses in season *(Peter and Pat Frogley, LYM, Edward Jago, David Field)*

Coniston [SD3098]

☆ ***Black Bull*** [Yewdale Rd (A593)]: The beers brewed at the pub are what earn the star here: Old Man, Coniston and Bluebird (lots of Donald Cambell water-speed memorabilia); cheery flagstoned back area (dogs allowed), banquettes and open fire in partly no smoking lounge bar (no smoking restaurant too), usual food inc children's, farm ciders, quite a few bottled beers and malt whiskies; children welcome in eating areas, tables out in former coachyard, bedrooms, open all day *(John and Gillian Scarisbrick, Mike and Sue Loseby, Neil and Anita Christopher, JDM, KM, Jayne and Peter Capp, Karen and Graham Oddey, J Roy Smylie, Dr D J and Mrs S C Walker, Richard Lewis, Kevin Thorpe, Edward Jago, LYM)*

Crook [SD4795]

☆ ***Sun*** [B5284 Kendal—Bowness]: Wide choice of ambitious food (all day wknds), sensibly priced, in partly no smoking open-plan dining pub with welcoming atmosphere, well kept Coniston and other ales, good value wines, cheerful helpful service; piped music *(David and Julie Glover, L W L Horton, Karen Eliot, LYM, Les and Barbara Owen, Maurice and Gill McMahon, Dominic Epton, John Foord, Tina and David Woods-Taylor)*

Culgaith [NY6029]

☆ ***Black Swan*** [off A66 E of Penrith]: Well run clean and cheerful 17th-c inn in Eden Valley village, open fire, jovial landlord, enjoyable food inc Sun lunch, nice no smoking dining area, real ales inc Black Sheep; bedrooms *(Dr D Parker, Tony and Katie Lewis)*

Dalston [NY3650]

Blue Bell [The Square]: Good generous food (not Mon) inc interesting sandwiches, good friendly service, attractive small village *(C A Hall)*

Dean [NY0725]

Royal Yew [just off A5086 S of Cockermouth]: Busy modernised village local in nice spot, good range of good value food from sandwiches to steaks, efficient service, well kept ales inc Jennings and Theakstons; best to book *(Mr and Mrs G Clay)*

Dockray [NY3921]

☆ ***Royal*** [A5091, off A66 or A592 W of Penrith]: Bright and immaculate open-plan bar in great spot away from the summer crowds, wide choice of good food from lunchtime rolls and baked potatoes up, children's helpings, friendly helpful service, well kept Black Sheep, Boddingtons, Castle Eden, Jennings Cumberland, Theakstons and Timothy Taylors Landlord, decent wines by the glass, two dining areas (one no smoking), walkers' part with stripped settles on flagstones; darts, cribbage and dominoes; piped music; picnic-sets in garden; open all day, comfortable bedrooms, good breakfast *(P Abbott, Ken Richards, Richard J Holloway, Brian Wall, LYM, Mr and Mrs Richard Osborne, Jim Abbott)*

Dufton [NY6825]

☆ ***Stag***: Small, basic pub in lovely unspoilt village on Pennine Way; friendly licensee, good value food inc good lunchtime sandwiches, well kept Black Sheep Best and a guest beer, good coffee, sensible prices, splendid early Victorian kitchen range in main bar, room off on left, back dining room; children, walkers and dogs welcome; open all day summer (cl winter Mon lunchtime), garden with shetland ponies, bedrooms in next-door cottage, big breakfast *(Guy Vowles)*

Eskdale Green [NY1300]

☆ ***Bower House*** [½ mile W]: Civilised old-fashioned stone-built inn with good log fire in main lounge bar extended around beamed and alcoved core, well kept Coniston Bluebird, Hesket Newmarket Cat Bells, Jennings and Theakstons XB, friendly staff, bar food, no noisy machines (but may be piped music), no smoking restaurant; nicely tended sheltered garden by cricket field, charming spot with great walks, bedrooms, open all day *(Rona Murdoch, David and Rhian Peters, Bob and Val Collman, Pat and Clive Sherriff, Tina and David Woods-Taylor)*

☆ ***King George IV*** [E of village]: Cheerful bustling beamed and flagstoned bar, comfortable lounge, back games room, wide choice of quickly served good generous food from sandwiches to steaks, well kept Bass, Jennings Cumberland and Theakstons Best, XB and Old Peculier, good collection of malt whiskies, restaurant; friendly staff, log fire, fine views from garden tables (road nearby), lots of good walks; children and dogs very welcome, open all day summer; good value bedrooms *(LYM, David and Rhian Peters)*

Foxfield [SD2185]

Prince of Wales [opp station]: Friendly and simple, with wide choice of well kept ales inc beers brewed in the former stables here and at the Tigertops brewery down in Wakefield (same owners), bottled imports and regular beer festivals, enthusiastic licensees, enjoyable simple home-made food, open fire, pub games inc bar billiards, papers and beer-related reading matter; children very welcome, games for them; cl Mon/Tues, opens 5 Weds/Thurs, open all day Fri-Sun, reasonably priced new bedrooms with own bathrooms *(Gill and David Weild, Dr B and Mrs P B Baker, Richard Lewis)*

Garrigill [NY7441]

George & Dragon [Village signposted off B6277 S of Alston]: Nicely set small 17th-c village inn with great log fire in flagstoned bar and pleasant stone-and-panelling dining room, which has been a popular main entry for well kept ales and good value food and bedrooms, but we have no reports yet on the new licensees *(LYM)*

Grasmere [NY3406]
Swan [A591]: Upmarket hotel but individual and relaxed even when busy, with lively little public bar, quieter old-fashioned lounge popular with older people (children allowed here), oak beams, armchairs, velvet curtains, prints and swords, inglenook log fires; varied reasonably priced well prepared food in bar and restaurant, polite service, keg beers but good malt whiskies and coffee, terrace tables in garden, picturesque surroundings; easy parking, open all day, comfortable bedrooms *(Tina and David Woods-Taylor, Richard Lewis, LYM)*

Great Salkeld [NY5536]
☆ ***Highland Drove*** [B6412, off A686 NE of Penrith]: Neatly kept 18th-c inn with surprisingly inventive food from unusual sandwiches to innovative main dishes based on local produce, fish and game, also great vegetarian mezze; straightforward bar and plain pool room, large orthodox dining lounge, new hunting-lodge style upstairs dining room with woodburner and Pennine views, Black Sheep, Theakstons and a monthly guest beer such as Ridleys, good wine and whisky choice, proper soft drinks, friendly and helpful father-and-son licensees; stone tables out in garden with water feature, good value comfortable bedrooms with own bathrooms *(Michael Doswell, Kevin Tea, David Cooke, Janette, BB)*

Grizebeck [SD2385]
Greyhound: Large warmly welcoming 17th-c local, beams and flagstones, good value food inc good home-made pies, well kept John Smiths, Greene King Old Speckled Hen and Theakstons XB, good service, woodburners, no smoking dining room; well behaved dogs welcome, tables in pleasant garden behind, good value smart bedrooms with big breakfast *(Brian Dickinson)*

Hawkshead [SD3598]
Queens Head [Main St]: Bustling dining pub with bow-tied barmen in red plush low-beamed and panelled bar, open fire, shiny brasses, no smoking snug, well kept Robinsons Best, Mild, Frederics and Hartleys XB, dominoes, cribbage; piped music; children in eating areas and snug, open all day, good bedrooms *(Mrs J Walker, Margaret Dickinson, LYM, Bernard Stradling, SLC, Derek and Margaret Underwood)*
Sun [Main St]: Lots of brass, brickwork and beams, reasonably priced bar food, sizeable restaurant with good more enterprising food, well kept Bass; children and dogs welcome, tables out in front by small courtyard; bedrooms *(B H and J I Andrews)*

Hayton [NY5157]
☆ ***Lane End*** [A69 Carlisle—Brampton]: Well run stone-built pub usefully placed for wide choice of good value generous food all day from sandwiches up, pleasant softly lit low-beamed bar, rugs on flagstones, banquettes and settles, roaring log fire, good bustling atmosphere, welcoming service, well kept Jennings, good coffee, dining room and attractive conservatory; pool room, piped music; open all day, play area *(Audrey and Derek Lambert, Michael Doswell)*

High Newton [SD4082]
Crown [just off A590 Lindale—Newby Bridge, towards Cartmel Fell]: Friendly, well run and attractive former 18th-c coaching inn with changing well kept beers inc Jennings and Yates, enjoyable food inc quickly served Sun lunch, spacious bars and dining area; children welcome, cl Mon/Tues lunchtimes, all day Weds, comfortable bedrooms with own bathrooms *(Clive Boucher, David Field)*

Kendal [SD5392]
Alexanders [Castle Green Hotel, Castle Green Lane]: Separate building off substantial hotel, medieval décor, hideaway bar, terrace high over town with great Lakeland views; kind bar staff, enjoyable food inc good home-made specials, real ales inc Dent; comfortable bedrooms, separate restaurant and fitness/leisure centre with swimming pool *(Margaret Dickinson)*
Olde Fleece [Highgate]: Much refurbished beamed 17th-c pub, pleasant child-friendly split-level bar, well kept Tetleys and guest beers, inexpensive generous food all day with children's menu, efficient staff; piped music may obtrude; open all day *(Ian and Nita Cooper)*

Keswick [NY2623]
Four in Hand [Lake Rd]: Neatly refurbished cosy back lounge, panelling, stage-coach bric-a-brac, lots of brasses and old photographs, decent-sized tables in dining room, full Jennings range kept well, varied food from unusual sandwiches up, wider evening choice; very busy in summer *(David Carr)*
Lake Road Inn [Lake Rd]: Straightforward two-room Victorian town pub with well kept Jennings Bitter, Cumberland and Sneck Lifter, usual food, informal service; tables in small sheltered courtyard with converted stables, open all day wknds and summer wkdys *(Peter and Pat Frogley, Gerald and Wendy Doyle)*
☆ ***Pheasant*** [Crosthwaite Rd (A66, a mile out)]: Small friendly beamed local with lots of customer cartoons, good value sandwiches and generous simple food (esp ham and eggs) lunchtime and early evening, consistently well kept Jennings beers, fast service, log fire, no smoking dining room; children if eating; bedrooms, near ancient church of St Kentigern *(P Abbott, Olive and Ray Hebson)*
☆ ***Swinside Inn*** [only pub in Newlands Valley, just SW; OS Sheet 90 map ref 242217]: Attractive neatly modernised but rustic and rambling pub very popular for good value tasty and substantial fresh food from sandwiches, baguettes or soup and warm rolls up in bar and restaurant, no smoking area, welcoming obliging service, well kept Jennings beers, decent wines, good log fires, family room; dogs allowed, plenty of tables outside with play area, open all day Sat and summer; bedrooms, peaceful valley setting, stunning views of crags and fells *(Dick and Madeleine Brown, D J Hulse, Jim Abbott, LYM, H K Dyson, David Cooke, Tina and David Woods-Taylor)*

Kirkby Lonsdale [SD6178]
Royal [Main St]: Cosy bar with roaring fire, large relaxing main room with sofas, young friendly staff, enjoyable food inc evening restaurant, well kept real ales; bedrooms *(Julian Heath)*

Sun [Market St (B6254)]: Low-beamed and partly stripped-stone bar, one room no smoking, cosy pews, good winter fires, well kept Black Sheep, Boddingtons, Dent and a guest beer, lots of malt whiskies, bar food; piped music; bedrooms *(MLR, Julian Heath, LYM)*

Kirkby Stephen [NY7707]

☆ ***Croglin Castle*** [South Rd]: Stone-built local with basic décor in large comfortable bar, remarkably good interesting food in dining room, friendly staff, good wines, Theakstons Best *(Guy Vowles, Marcus Byron)*

Langdale [NY2906]

New Dungeon Ghyll [B5343]: Large dim-lit barn (now called the Langdale Inn) with plain tables on functional stone floor, open fire, Theakstons Best and XB from small counter, simple food all day in summer – useful for walkers down from the Langdale Pikes; picnic-sets outside, restaurant in adjoining Victorian hotel with good views *(Sarah and Peter Gooderham)*

Stickle Barn [by car park for Stickle Ghyll]: Lovely views from busy café-style walkers' and climbers' bar, generous good value food inc packed lunches, well kept Scottish Courage beers, quick service, small no smoking area, mountaineering photographs; fruit machines, TV, piped music; big pleasant terrace with inner verandah, open all day; bunkhouse accommodation, live music in loft *(Brian and Lynn Young, John Wooll)*

Levens [SD4785]

Gilpin Bridge Inn [on cut-off from A590, nr A5074 junction]: Popular for good reasonably priced food in bar and restaurant (wider choice here, booking advised), well trained cheerful service, Robinsons real ales *(John Foord)*

Lowick Green [SD3084]

☆ ***Farmers Arms*** [just off A5092 SE of village]: Charming cosy public bar with heavy beams, huge slate flagstones, big open fire, cosy corners and pub games (also piped music, TV; this part may be closed in winter), some interesting furniture and pictures in plusher hotel lounge bar across yard, tasty reasonably priced food in bar and restaurant inc daily roast, well kept John Smiths and Theakstons, friendly attentive staff; unobtrusive piped music; children welcome, open all day, comfortable bedrooms *(LYM, Margaret and Roy Randle)*

Metal Bridge [NY3564]

Metal Bridge Hotel [off A74 Carlisle—Gretna, nr Rockcliffe]: Friendly staff, enjoyable bar food, good choice of Scottish Courage beers, nice river view from sun lounge *(Mike and Lynn Robinson, Michael and Marion Buchanan)*

Milnthorpe [SD4981]

Cross Keys [Park Rd]: Roomy and nicely refurbished crossroads pub, spotlessly clean, with attentive staff; pleasant outdoor sitting area, attractive bedrooms with own bathrooms (quieter at the back) *(Margaret Dickinson)*

Outgate [SD3599]

☆ ***Outgate Inn*** [B5286 Hawkshead—Ambleside]: Attractively placed and very hospitable country pub with three pleasantly modernised rooms, well kept Robinsons Best, Frederics and Hartleys XB, popular food inc sandwiches; trad jazz Fri, open all day wknds, comfortable bedrooms, good breakfast, nice walks *(SLC, BB)*

Penruddock [NY4327]

☆ ***Herdwick*** [off A66 Penrith—Keswick]: Pleasantly refurbished cottagey 18th-c inn, neat and well cared for, with enjoyable well priced food, good cosy atmosphere, quick obliging service, well kept Tetleys from unusual curved bar, stripped stone, nice dining room with upper gallery (worth booking evenings), pool room; five bedrooms *(Mike and Penny Sutton, Maurice and Gill McMahon, Mike and Sue Loseby, BB)*

Pooley Bridge [NY4724]

Sun: Panelled village pub with good choice of food from sandwiches to nicely cooked main dishes, friendly service, several well kept Jennings ales, good wine choice, small lounge bar, steps past servery to bigger bar with games and piped music, restaurant; tables in garden *(David Heath)*

Ravenglass [SD0894]

☆ ***Ratty Arms***: Extended former waiting room a 200-metre walk over the footbridge from the Ravenglass & Eskdale terminus and rail museum, well kept Jennings ales, interesting food, good value restaurant, service friendly and efficient even when busy; pool table in busy public bar; children very welcome, open all day wknds and summer, big courtyard *(LYM, Mr and Mrs G Sadie, Gordon Neighbour, Christine and Neil Townend, Nick Holding)*

Red Dial [NY2546]

Sun [A595 Cockermouth—Carlisle]: Clean and comfortable functional main-road pub/restaurant with well kept Jennings Cumberland and Crag Rat, wide choice of very generous food from good sandwiches up, young obliging staff, big dining room; may be piped pop music *(Steve Whalley)*

Rosthwaite [NY2615]

Scafell [B5289 S of Keswick]: Plain slate-floored bar in back extension, a few tables out overlooking beck, well kept Theakstons Best and XB, log fire, usual food from sandwiches up, fast friendly service even when packed with walkers (weather forecasts up on a board); afternoon teas, piped music, pool; separate entrance to rather plush hotel with appealing cocktail bar/sun-lounge and dining room, bedrooms not big but good *(BB, David Heath, H K Dyson)*

Satterthwaite [SD3392]

☆ ***Eagles Head***: Small and unpretentious but very welcoming, with imaginative vegetarian menu alongside more conventional good value generous home-made lunchtime food esp soup, sandwiches and home-made pies (also Fri/Sat summer evenings), big log fire, helpful entertaining landlord, well kept Jennings, pool, darts; papers and guidebooks for sale; handy for Grizedale Forest; a real welcome for small children; bedrooms comfortable and clean, shared bathroom; may be some closures winter esp Mon, but usually open all day at least Thurs-Sat in summer *(Maeve Brayne)*

Shap [NY5615]

☆ ***Greyhound*** [A6, S end]: Friendly, bustling and unpretentious, with good unfussy food esp slow-cooked meats in bar or restaurant, copious helpings, real ales inc Wadworths 6X, good wine list, really quick attentive service; bedrooms, popular with coast-to-coast walkers *(David Cooke, D and B M Clark)*

St Bees [NX9712]

Queens [Main St]: Two softly lit bars, well kept beers inc Jennings and Yates, lots of whiskies, friendly locals, good very generous home-made food from sandwiches to some local specialities, dining area with large tables, sizeable conservatory, garden behind; bedrooms *(Peter and Pat Frogley)*

Staveley [SD4798]

☆ ***Eagle & Child*** [off A591 Windermere—Kendal]: L-shaped open-plan bar with well kept Jennings Cumberland and a guest such as Coniston Bluebird from small bar counter, good home-made food inc fresh fish and veg, imaginative dishes, thoughtful provision for children and generous Sun lunch, farm cider, coal fire, upstairs restaurant; small neat riverside garden, comfortably renovated bedrooms, good breakfast *(MLR, BB, Jackie Moffat)*

Temple Sowerby [NY6127]

☆ ***Kings Arms*** [A66]: Handsome red sandstone inn doing well under new owners, good log fire and lots of window seats in roomy L-shaped lounge bar, cosily comfortable hotelish lounge, enjoyable food from good home-cooked ham and beef sandwiches to restaurant dishes; bedrooms *(Moira Steven, LYM)*

Thirlspot [NY3217]

☆ ***Kings Head*** [A591 Grasmere—Keswick]: Well refurbished beamed bar, long and low, with inglenook fires, wide choice of food in no smoking eating area, well kept Jennings, Theakstons Best, XB and Mild, Yates and a guest ale, fast polite service, games room with pool and big-screen TV; piped music; walkers and children welcome, with toy box; tables in garden, good spot, good value bedrooms (the hotel part and restaurant are separate) *(LYM, P and J Shapley, Ann and Max Cross, Jim Abbott, Tina and David Woods-Taylor)*

Threlkeld [NY3325]

Salutation [old main rd, bypassed by A66 W of Penrith]: New licensees in low-beamed old-fashioned walkers' local below Blencathra, good log fire, well kept Theakstons, quite a few malt whiskies, substantial home-made food from sandwiches and baguettes up; piped music, TV, spacious upstairs children's room with pool and juke box *(Christopher J Darwent, Tina and David Woods-Taylor, LYM)*

Torver [SD2894]

☆ ***Church House*** [A593/A5084 S of Coniston]: Big rambling place with fine log fire in cheerfully civilised low-beamed flagstoned bar, another in beamed lounge with dark red walls, splendid hill views (if weather allows), reasonably priced food from good baguettes to interesting main dishes, decent house wines, Castle Eden and Greene King Old Speckled Hen; friendly alsatian, children welcome, attractive evening restaurant; open all day at least in summer; nice big garden, small caravan/camp site, bedrooms *(Christine and Neil Townend, Lord Sandhurst, Lorraine and Fred Gill, Neil and Anita Christopher)*

Troutbeck [NY4103]

☆ ***Mortal Man*** [A592 N of Windermere; Upper Rd]: Neatly kept partly panelled beamed hotel bar with big log fire, mix of seats inc a cushioned settle, copper-topped tables, cosy eating room, no smoking picture-window restaurant, enjoyable generous food from sandwiches to steaks with some tempting specials, well kept ales such as Jennings, John Smiths and Theakstons Best, friendly young staff, darts, dominoes; piped music may obtrude,TV room, Sun folk/blues night; children welcome, open all day, good bedrooms – lovely village, great scenery *(Peter Heaton, Kevin Thorpe, B H and J I Andrews, IHR, LYM, Tim and Beryl Dawson)*

Troutbeck Hotel [A5091/A66 – the 'other' Troutbeck, nr Penrith]: Recently refurbished, with two bars and dining room, good reasonably priced food choice (handy for nearby caravan site users), well kept Jennings ales and perhaps a guest beer, good friendly service; children welcome, seven bedrooms with own bathrooms, self-catering cottages *(P Abbott, Jim Abbott)*

Wetheral [NY4654]

Crown [off A69 at Warwick Bridge]: Country hotel's plain back public bar, with Thwaites real ales, good service, some interesting food; good bedrooms, attractive village-green setting near river in pleasant village *(Christine and Neil Townend)*

Winster [SD4193]

☆ ***Brown Horse*** [A5074 S of Windermere]: Roomy open-plan dining place, light and comfortable, with well spaced tables inc no smoking dining room, popular esp with older people for attractively priced food inc interesting dishes, prompt caring cheery service, well kept Jennings Cumberland and Theakstons, decent wines, good log fire; children welcome (own menu, toys) *(Dr R G J Telfer, LYM)*

If you see cars parked in the lane outside a country pub have left their lights on at night, leave yours on too: it's a sign that the police check up there.

Derbyshire

Three new entries here this year span an interesting range that sums up the rich variety in Derbyshire's good pubs. The Black Swan at Idridgehay is an airy freshly decorated dining pub, even calling itself a bistro; the Dead Poets in Holbrook, dark and simple, has particularly good real ales and bargain food, in a buoyant atmosphere; and the relaxed and rambling Bear at Alderwasley is a memorable find, with masses of character – a great all-rounder. Other pubs here on top form these days include the Waltzing Weasel at Birch Vale (good food, a nice place to stay), the Druid at Birchover (a dining pub with a very broad repertoire), the classic old-fashioned Olde Gate at Brassington, the Alexandra and the Brunswick in Derby (both magnets for beer lovers), the Hardwick Inn fitting perfectly with a visit to Hardwick Hall, the bustling Plough near Hathersage (imaginative food, and gains its Place to Stay Award this year), the Red Lion at Hognaston (good food in a properly pubby atmosphere – it too gains a Place to Stay Award), the timelessly spartan Barley Mow at Kirk Ireton (excellent beer, cheap rolls), the inviting and very welcoming Red Lion at Litton, the John Thompson at Ingleby near Melbourne (it brews good beer, and the home cooking is good), the cheerful Old Crown near Shardlow (an enjoyable food break from the M1), and the White Horse at Woolley Moor (good food, good value, nice views). The Waltzing Weasel, such a nice place for a special meal out, is Derbyshire's Dining Pub of the Year – the fifth time it has won our top award. Current favourites in the Lucky Dip section at the end of the chapter, expanded with some 40 new entries this year, are the Lamb at Chinley, Standing Order in Derby, Scotsmans Pack in Hathersage, Lantern Pike at Hayfield, Packhorse at Little Longstone, Holly Bush in Makeney, Bulls Head at Monyash, Bell at Smalley and George at Tideswell. Drinks prices here are lower than the national average. As always, pubs brewing their own beers are particularly good news on price, and others we found very cheap were the Navigation at Buxworth, the Cheshire Cheese at Hope, the Alexandra in Derby, the Derby Tup in Whittington Moor and the Barley Mow at Kirk Ireton. Local beers to look out for include Leatherbritches, Whim, Shardlow and (from the John Thompson near Melbourne) Lloyds.

ALDERWASLEY SK3153 Map 7

Bear ★ 🍷

Village signposted with Breanfield off B5035 E of Wirksworth at Malt Shovel; inn ½ mile SW of village, on Ambergate—Wirksworth high back road

There's no obvious front door here, and the plain back entrance from the wind-swept car park doesn't at all prepare you for the quite delightful interior – worth a special trip for anyone who likes unspoilt pubs that conjure up past centuries. Several small dark rooms, with low beams, bare boards and ochre walls throughout, have a great variety of old tables, with seats running from brocaded dining chairs and old country-kitchen chairs to high-backed settles and antique oak chairs carved with traditional Derbyshire motifs. One little room is filled right to its built-in wall seats by a single vast table. There are log fires in huge stone fireplaces, candles galore, antique paintings and engravings, plenty of Staffordshire china ornaments, and no fewer than three grandfather clocks. Despite the treasures, this is a proper easy-going and unpretentious country local, with dominoes players clattering about beside canaries trilling in a huge Edwardian-style white cage (elsewhere are talkative cockatoos, an african grey parrot, and budgerigars). Unpretentious, yes; but they also have a fine range of interesting wines, as well as Bass, Greene King Old Speckled Hen and Marstons Pedigree on handpump. And, mainly made with ingredients from local suppliers, the blackboard food (served in only two of the rooms) is good and imaginative. It changes every few days but might include soup (£2.95), sandwiches (£3.25), home-made ham, egg and chips or liver and onions (£6.95), popular scampi (£7.95), duck breast with caramelised onion and peppers (£10.95), fried prawns with garlic butter or lamb shank with rosemary and mint gravy (£12.95) and fillet steak (£14.95), with puddings such as treacle sponge or banana fritter (£3.75); they have a Sunday carvery (£6.95). Service is friendly and enthusiastic, and there are peaceful country views from well spaced picnic-sets out on the side grass. We have not yet heard from any readers who have stayed in this interesting inn. *(Recommended by Mrs J Hinsliff, A Preston)*

Free house ~ Licensee Nicola Fletcher-Musgrave ~ Real ale ~ Bar food (12-9.30, not 25 Dec) ~ Restaurant ~ (01629) 822585 ~ Children welcome in family area ~ Open 12-11 ~ Bedrooms: £40S/£65S

ASHBOURNE SK1846 Map 7

Smiths Tavern

St Johns Street; bottom of market place

The atmosphere in this neatly kept traditional pub, just at the foot of the town's market place, is chatty and relaxed, though if you're not feeling sociable there's a good choice of newspapers to read. The attractive bar stretches back a lot further than you might think from the relatively narrow shop-front entrance, with horsebrasses and tankards hanging from heavy black beams, a delft shelf of antique blue and white china, old cigarette and drinks advertisements, and a plush wall seat facing the bar counter (it can get smoky down here). Steps lead up to a middle room with more plush seating around solid tables, a piano and log-effect gas fire, and beyond that a light and airy end no smoking dining room. Enjoyable hearty food includes home-made soup (£2.50), garlic breaded mushrooms or deep-fried brie wedges (£3.50), a popular home-made steak and kidney pie (£5.25), leek and mushroom crumble or spinach, mozzarella and basil lasagne (£5.50), steaks (from £8.95), and good daily specials such as pork casserole with apple and thyme dumpling (£5.25) and minted roast lamb shank (£6.25); good value pensioners' special (£4.95). They serve Banks's, Marstons Pedigree and a guest such as Morrells Varsity on handpump, over 30 whiskies, and a range of vodkas; very friendly obliging service; darts, dominoes and cribbage. *(Recommended by JP, PP, David Carr, Sue Holland, Dave Webster, T J W Hill, P Abbott)*

Union Pub Company ~ Tenant Paul Mellor ~ Real ale ~ Bar food (12-2.45, 6-9(9.30 wknds)) ~ Restaurant ~ (01335) 342264 ~ Children welcome ~ Quiz night every second Sun ~ Open 11-11; 12-10.30 Sun; 11-3, 5-11 winter

BEELEY SK2667 Map 7

Devonshire Arms

B6012, off A6 Matlock—Bakewell

Handy for Chatsworth House, this handsome old stone pub is beautifully set in a pretty Peak District estate village. The building was successfully converted from three early 18th-c cottages, to become a prosperous coaching inn by the 19th c – when Dickens is said to have been a regular. These days big log fires cheerfully warm its charming black-beamed rooms, which have comfortably cushioned stone seats along stripped walls, and antique settles and simpler wooden chairs on flagstoned floors. The restaurant and cocktail bar are no smoking. They serve Black Sheep Best and

Special, Theakstons XB and Old Peculier, and a guest such as Jennings on handpump, and you'll find decent good value house wine, and about three dozen malt whiskies; shove-ha'penny, cribbage and dominoes. There's a big emphasis on the bar food, which is served all day, and could include soup (£3), baguettes (from £4.25), roasted pepper and mozzarella terrine (£5.75), steak and ale pie (£7.20), chicken breast with stilton sauce (£8.25), grilled halibut with orange and lemon butter (£9.95) and steak (from £12.25), with puddings (from £2.95). They have a Friday fish night, and on Sundays they do a Victorian breakfast (£11.25); you'll need to book for both, and at weekends. The Duchess of Devonshire's excellent produce shop is nearby, at Pilsley. *(Recommended by Ian S Morley, Mike and Sue Loseby, Roger and Maureen Kenning, Dr S J Shepherd, Derek and Sylvia Stephenson, Darly Graton, Graeme Gulibert, Steven and Sally Knight, JP, PP, W W Burke, the Didler, June and Malcolm Farmer, Bob and Valerie Mawson, Peter F Marshall, Jenny and Peter Lowater, Keith and Chris O'Neill, Annette and John Derbyshire, Kevin Thorpe, Mr and Mrs J McRobert, O K Smyth)*

Free house ~ Licensee John A Grosvenor ~ Real ale ~ Bar food (12-9.30) ~ (01629) 733259 ~ Children welcome ~ Open 11-11; 12-10.30 Sun; closed 25 Dec

BIRCH VALE SK0286 Map 7

Waltzing Weasel

A6015 E of New Mills

Derbyshire Dining Pub of the Year

Readers are full of praise for the consistently delicious food at this friendly dining pub, and it's a lovely place to stay too. The menu includes lots of dishes that reflect the landlord's passion for Italy, and home-made bar food might include soup (£3.30), sandwiches (from £3.50), black olive pâté (£4.75), scallops in cream sauce (£5.75), pizzas (from £5.75), crayfish tails (£6.25), vegetable crêpe (£8.50), seafood tart (£9.50), a casserole of the day (£9.75), a fish dish such as bass or halibut (from £10.50), and the Italian platter (£11.75), with irresistible puddings such as bread and butter pudding or brandy snap baskets with fruit and ice cream (£3.95); on weekday evenings they do a slightly different set menu (£22 for two courses), and there's a Sunday roast (£10.50). The building is high on a hill with fine views of Kinder Scout and the Peak District from its charming back restaurant, pretty garden and terrace. There's a good pubby atmosphere in the comfortable bar, which has a cheerful fire, plenty of houseplants on corner tables, and daily papers on sticks. The licensees' interest in antiques (they're former dealers) is reflected in some of the furnishings, with handsome oak settles and tables among more usual furniture; there are lots of nicely framed mainly sporting Victorian prints, and a good longcase clock. Well kept Marstons Best and Timothy Taylors on handpump, perhaps with a guest beer on handpump, and a good choice of decent wines and malt whiskies. The spacious bedrooms are comfortably furnished, and lovely breakfasts include home-made marmalade. Bess, the friendly pub dog, is eager to greet visitors. *(Recommended by A S and M E Marriott, David Heath, Mike and Wendy Proctor, Mike and Lynn Robinson, B, M and P Kendall, Dr T E Hothersall, Mike and Linda Hudson, Richard Fendick, Peter F Marshall, Glenys and John Roberts, Bob Broadhurst, Robin and Joyce Peachey, Mike and Mary Carter, Eddie Edwards, Mr A Wright, Revd D Glover, M N Carey, Mrs P J Carroll)*

Free house ~ Licensee Michael Atkinson ~ Real ale ~ Bar food ~ Restaurant ~ (01663) 743402 ~ Children in eating area of bar ~ Dogs allowed in bar and bedrooms ~ Open 12-3, 5.30-11 ~ Bedrooms: £45S/£75B

BIRCHOVER SK2462 Map 7

Druid

Village signposted off B5056

The amazingly wide choice of well cooked food at this popular creeper-clad dining pub includes around ten vegetarian dishes. Besides the blackboards displaying lots of daily specials, the menu includes home-made soup (£3), spicy lamb meatballs or mussels with tomato, garlic and mozzarella (£4.90), steak and potato pie (£6.50), mediterranean roasted vegetables (£8), vegetable curry or vegetable wellington

(£8.50), poached chicken breast with bacon and stilton sauce (£9.60), salmon fillet with orange and ginger (£10.60) and steaks (from £11.50), with a good selection of puddings such as date and ginger pudding with butterscotch sauce or lime and chocolate chip mousse (£3.50). As the emphasis here is firmly on food, it's best to book for evening and weekend meals. Candlelit at night, the spacious and airy two-storey dining extension is really the heart of the place, with pink plush seats on an olive-green carpet. The small plain bar has plush-upholstered wooden wall benches around straightforward tables, and a big coal fire; the well kept real ales could include Marstons Pedigree and John Smiths, and they've a good collection of malt whiskies. The Garden Room, tap room and part of the bar are no smoking; there may be a couple of animals roaming around. There are picnic-sets in front, and good walks in the area. *(Recommended by Darly Graton, Graeme Gulibert, John and Christine Lowe, Mrs P J Carroll, John Close, A Preston, Mike and Wendy Proctor, Wendy Dye, T J W Hill, JP, PP, Richard Cole, Roy and Margaret Jones, Keith and Chris O'Neill, Patrick Hancock, Keith and Di Newsome, Bob and Valerie Mawson, Roger Bridgeman, Cliff Blakemore, Stephen and Judy Parish)*

Free house ~ Licensee Brian Bunce ~ Real ale ~ Bar food (not Mon; 12-2, 7-8.30 winter, till 9.30 in summer) ~ Restaurant ~ (01629) 650302 ~ Children welcome in restaurant till 8 ~ Open 12-2.30, 7-11; they may close earlier in winter; closed Mon (exc bank hols), 25 Dec and evening 26 Dec

BRASSINGTON SK2354 Map 7

Olde Gate ★

Village signposted off B5056 and B5035 NE of Ashbourne

Although the date etched outside this appealing village pub is 1874, it was originally built in 1616, of magnesian limestone and timbers salvaged from Armada wrecks, bought in exchange for locally mined lead. Furnishings in the relaxing public bar are nice and traditional, and there's a lovely ancient wall clock, rush-seated old chairs, antique settles, including one ancient black solid oak one, and roaring log fires. Gleaming copper pots sit on a lovely 17th-c kitchen range, pewter mugs hang from a beam, and a side shelf boasts a collection of embossed Doulton stoneware flagons. On the left of a small hatch-served lobby, another cosy beamed room has stripped panelled settles, scrubbed-top tables, and a roaring fire under a huge mantelbeam. Stone-mullioned windows look across lots of tables in a pleasant garden to small silvery-walled pastures. The largely home-made changing bar food is good, though not cheap, and might include open sandwiches and tasty baguettes (from £4.95), omelette with monterey jack cheese and crispy bacon (£5.95), ploughman's (£6.15), and home-made pies such as ham, leek and stilton or salmon and asparagus (from £7.50), while more elaborate evening dishes could include chicken curry (£10.50), lamb tagine (£10.95) or fried halibut (£14.95), with puddings such as chocolate fudge cake or strawberry pavlova (£3.50); in summer they often have a variety of barbecued dishes. The dining room is no smoking. Marstons Pedigree and a guest on handpump, and a good selection of malt whiskies; cribbage and dominoes. In summer, the small front yard with a few benches is a nice spot to listen to the village bell-ringers practising on Friday evenings. Ideal for water sports and activities, Carsington reservoir is a five-minute drive away. *(Recommended by Mr and Mrs S Oxenbury, Pat and Roger Fereday, Peter F Marshall, Anthony Barnes, Stephen and Judy Parish, Di and Mike Gillam, P Abbott, Rob Fowell, Keith and Di Newsome, Darly Graton, Graeme Gulibert, JP, PP, John and Christine Lowe, Roger Bridgeman, the Didler, Kevin Blake, Mike and Wendy Proctor)*

Marstons (W & D) ~ Tenant Paul Burlinson ~ Real ale ~ Bar food (12-1.45(2 Fri/Sat), 7-8.45(9 Fri/Sat); Sun 12-2.15 – and in summer 7-8.30) ~ (01629) 540448 ~ Children over 10 ~ Open 12-2.30(3 Sat), 6-11; 12-3, 7-10.30 Sun; closed Mon lunchtime except bank hols

BUXTON SK1266 Map 7

Bull i' th' Thorn

Ashbourne Road (A515) 6 miles S of Buxton, near Hurdlow

Handy for the High Peak Trail, this is a curious cross between a medieval hall, interesting to look around, and a straightforward roadside pub. Among the lively old carvings that greet you on your way in is one of the eponymous bull caught in a thornbush, and there are also images of an eagle with a freshly caught hare, and some spaniels chasing a rabbit. In the hall, which dates from 1471, a massive central beam runs parallel with a forest of smaller ones, there are panelled window seats in the embrasures of the thick stone walls, handsome panelling, and old flagstones stepping gently down to a big open fire. It's furnished with fine long settles, an ornately carved hunting chair, a longcase clock, a powder-horn, and armour that includes 17th-c German helmets, swords, and blunderbusses and so forth. Stuffed animals' heads line the corridor that leads to a candlelit hall, used for medieval themed evening banquets. Bar food includes soup (£2.25), filled baguettes (from £3.95), cod or haddock (£6.60), beef, mushroom and ale pie (£6.95), oriental sizzler (£7.25), various curries (£7.50) and citrus chicken (£7.95); puddings such as caramel and apple pie (£3.25). An adjoining room has pool and dominoes, and there's piped music. Robinsons Best on handpump. A simple no smoking family room opens on to a terrace and big lawn with swings, and there are more tables in a sheltered angle in front. The pub's name comes from a hybrid of its 15th-c and 17th-c titles, the Bull and Hurdlow House of Hurdlow Thorn. *(Recommended by G B Longden, Mike and Wendy Proctor, the Didler, Kevin Blake, Dr Paull Khan, Mike and Lynn Robinson, JP, PP)*

Robinsons ~ Tenant Peter Atkins ~ Real ale ~ Bar food (12-2.30, 6-9; 12-8 Sun) ~ (01298) 83348 ~ Children welcome ~ Dogs allowed in bar and bedrooms ~ Open 12-3, 6-11; 12-10.30 Sun ~ Bedrooms: /£60B

BUXWORTH SK0282 Map 7

Navigation

Minor road S of village towards Silkhill, off B6062, which itself leads off the A6 just NW of Whaley Bridge roundabout

Right next to the restored canal basin, this extended early 18th-c free house lets you watch the barges chugging past, and is a good base for towpath walks. Interesting prints and other canal memorabilia inside recall the days when the old Peak Forest Tramway ran from what is now the car park, connecting the canal with limestone quarries in nearby Dove Holes. A clutter of brassware and china brightens up the cosy low-ceilinged and flagstoned linked rooms, which have plenty of snug corners, and good coal and log fires (it can sometimes get smoky). In summer it's pleasant to sit out on the sunken flagstoned terrace and enjoy the attractive surroundings, and there's a play area and pets corner. Bar food includes soup (£2.25), nachos (£4.25), steak and kidney pie or broccoli and cheese bake (£6.50), scampi (£6.95), thai chicken curry (£7.75), and 8oz rump steak (£9.95); children's dishes (from £2.95). They serve reasonably priced Marstons Pedigree, Timothy Taylors Landlord, Websters Yorkshire and a guest such as Abbeydale Moonshine on handpump, farm ciders in summer and mulled wine in winter. A games room has pool, darts, shove-ha'penny, cribbage, dominoes, and TV; quiet piped music. *(Recommended by Kevin Blake, David Carr, Bob Broadhurst, Bob and Lisa Cantrell, Dr Paull Khan, Richard Fendick, Bernie Adams, Rob Fowell, Mike and Lynn Robinson, Stephen Buckley)*

Free house ~ Licensees Alan and Lynda Hall ~ Real ale ~ Bar food (12-3, 6-9.30; 12-9 Sat/Sun) ~ Restaurant ~ (01663) 732072 ~ Children welcome away from bar ~ Dogs allowed in bar ~ Open 11-11; 12-10.30 Sun ~ Bedrooms: £32B/£49.50B

If we don't specify bar meal times for a main entry, these are normally 12-2 and 7-9; we do show times if they are markedly different.

CASTLETON SK1583 Map 7

Castle Hotel

High Street at junction with Castle Street

A good day to visit this neatly kept historic hotel is 29 May, when the colourful Garland Ceremony procession, commemorating the escape of Charles II, passes by. The inviting bar has stripped stone walls with built-in cabinets, lovely open fires, finely carved early 17th-c beams and, in one room, ancient flagstones. Served by pleasant and efficient staff, the popular good value bar food includes lunchtime sandwiches (from £3.60), breaded mushrooms (£3.25), chicken, leek and ham pie (£6.50), cod and chips (£6.75), lamb shank in thyme and butterbean sauce or poached salmon salad (£8.50), and puddings. They have well kept Bass and Tetleys on handpump. A good part of the pub is no smoking, and there's a fruit machine and piped music. The many spooky tales associated with this pub include one about the ghost of a bride who, instead of enjoying her planned wedding breakfast here, died broken-hearted when she was left at the altar. You can sit in the pretty garden, and there are good views from the new heated terrace. *(Recommended by Duncan Cloud, Simon Woollacott, John Hulme, JP, PP, Emma Napper, Ian S Morley, Kevin Blake, Mike and Wendy Proctor, John and Christine Lowe, Lorraine and Fred Gill, D J and P M Taylor, Stephen Buckley)*

Vintage Inns ~ Manager Glen Mills ~ Real ale ~ Bar food (12-10; 12-9.30 Sun) ~ Restaurant ~ (01433) 620578 ~ Children in eating area of bar and restaurant ~ Open 11-11; 12-10.30 Sun ~ Bedrooms: £60B/£75S(£50B)

DERBY SK3435 Map 7

Alexandra £

Siddals Road, just up from station

Just a couple of minutes from Derby Station, this cheerful two-roomed Victorian town pub is a great place to decide to miss your train, especially if you like real ale. The friendly landlord's pride and joy, the interesting range of beers changes continually, and as well as Bass, Batemans XB, Castle Rock and Timothy Taylors Landlord, you'll find around half a dozen or so interesting guests from all sorts of breweries such as Caledonian, Cottage and Skinners. They also have up to five continental beers on tap, country wines, cider tapped from the cask, around two dozen malt whiskies and, as in all Tynemill pubs, their soft drinks are very good value too. There's a cheerfully chatty atmosphere in the simple bustling bar, which has good heavy traditional furnishings on dark-stained floorboards, shelves of bottles, and lots of railway prints and memorabilia; the lounge is no smoking. Darts, dominoes and piped music. At lunchtime they serve good value rolls (from £1.60), and on Sundays they do a bargain roast (£3.25, two for £6). *(Recommended by the Didler, Richard Lewis, C J Fletcher, JP, PP, David Carr, Patrick Hancock)*

Tynemill ~ Manager Mark Robins ~ Real ale ~ Bar food (lunchtimes only) ~ No credit cards ~ (01332) 293993 ~ Dogs allowed in bar ~ Open 11-11; 12-3, 7-10.30 Sun ~ Bedrooms: £25S/£35S

Brunswick £

1 Railway Terrace; close to Derby Midland railway station

Said to be the first railwaymen's hostelry in the world, this beer lover's paradise is situated at the apex of a row of preserved railway cottages. Of the incredible range of up to 17 beers on handpump or tapped straight from the cask, six are from the Brunswick Brewery, produced in the purpose-built brewery tower which you can see from a viewing area at the back of the pub. Alongside Father Mikes Dark Rich Ruby, Old Accidental, Second Brew, the highly praised Railway Porter, Triple Hop and Old Accidental, changing guests chosen by the sociable hands-on landlord are from far and wide but could include Bass, Batemans XB, Everards Original, Hook Norton Old Hooky, Marstons Pedigree and Timothy Taylor Golden Best and Landlord; farm cider is tapped from the cask. The welcoming high-ceilinged serving bar has heavy well padded leather seats, whisky-water jugs above the dado, and a dark blue ceiling and upper wall, with squared dark panelling below. The no smoking room is decorated with little old-fashioned prints and swan's neck lamps, and has a high-backed wall settle and a coal fire; behind a curved glazed partition wall is a quietly chatty family parlour narrowing to the apex of the triangular building. Darts, dominoes, cribbage, fruit machine and TV. From a short lunchtime menu, the reasonably priced home-made bar food includes filled rolls (from £1.65), soup (£1.95), hot beef, cheese and bacon or sausage cobs (from £2.10), quiche, ploughman's, chilli and a vegetarian dish (£3.50) and lasagne (£3.95); on Sunday they do rolls only. There are seats on the terrace behind. *(Recommended by Richard Lewis, Kevin Flack, JP, PP, Mike Pugh, the Didler, C J Fletcher, Keith and Chris O'Neill, John and Gillian Scarisbrick, David Carr, Kevin Blake, Patrick Hancock)*

Own brew ~ Licensee Trevor Harris ~ Real ale ~ Bar food (11.30-2.30 Mon-Sat) ~ No credit cards ~ (01332) 290677 ~ Children in family room ~ Dogs welcome ~ Jazz Thurs evenings ~ Open 11-11; 12-10.30 Sun

Olde Dolphin £

Queen Street; nearest car park King Street/St Michaels Lane

Dating from 1530 and just a stroll from the cathedral, this quaint little place is Derby's oldest pub. Friendly and well run, its four snug old-fashioned rooms (two with their own separate street doors) have big bowed black beams, shiny panelling, cast-iron-framed tables, opaque leaded windows, lantern lights, and coal fires; there are varnished wall benches in the tiled-floor public bar, and a brocaded seat in the little carpeted snug. There's no piped music or noisy fruit machines to spoil the pleasant chatty atmosphere, and they get the newspapers every day. Ten handpumps dispense the well kept real ales, which include Adnams, Bass, Black Sheep, Caledonian Deuchars IPA, Greene King Abbot, Marstons Pedigree and guests such as Hook Norton Old Hooky and Hop Back Summer Lightning; there's a beer festival in the last week in July. The hearty bar food is very good value, and includes soup (£1.50), sandwiches (from £1.90), hot filled baguettes (£2.95), spinach and mushroom pancakes (£3.50), fish and chips or lasagne (£3.75), and 8oz rump steak (£4.50); they do a bargain three-course Sunday lunch (£3.50). A no smoking upstairs restaurant serves reasonably priced steaks. Good-humoured service from the helpful uniformed staff. The beer garden is a nice place to escape the bustle of the city centre. *(Recommended by David Carr, the Didler, JP, PP, Richard Lewis, Hazel Morgan)*

Six Continents ~ Tenant Janina Holmes ~ Real ale ~ Bar food (11-10) ~ Restaurant (6-11pm) ~ (01332) 267711 ~ Children welcome ~ Open 10.30-11; 12-11 Sun

EARL STERNDALE SK0967 Map 7

Quiet Woman £

Village signposted off B4053 S of Buxton

You can buy free-range bantam and goose eggs, local cheese, local poetry books and even silage at this unspoilt stone cottage. A joy for those who like their pubs really basic and old-fashioned, it's very simple inside, with hard seats, plain tables (including a sunken one for dominoes or cards), low beams, quarry tiles, lots of china ornaments and a lovely winter coal fire; pool table in the family room, table skittles and darts. Served by friendly staff, Marstons Best and Pedigree and Mansfield on handpump are well kept, as are guest beers from brewers such as Adnams, Everards and Whim. Refurbishment of the kitchen is almost complete, but at the moment they just serve very good value sandwiches and toasties (from £1.60), various pies and occasional winter hotpots. There are picnic-sets out in front, and budgies, hens, turkeys, ducks and donkeys will help to keep children entertained. They have a caravan for hire in the garden, and you can also arrange to stay at the small campsite next door. *(Recommended by Ann and Colin Hunt, Bernie Adams, Barry Collett, Dr D J and Mrs S C Walker, the Didler, L Davenport, JP, PP, Patrick Hancock)*

Free house ~ Licensee Kenneth Mellor ~ Real ale ~ No credit cards ~ (01298) 83211 ~ Children in family room ~ Jamming sessions most Sun lunchtimes ~ Open 12-3(4 Sat), 7-11; 12-5, 7-10.30 Sun

EYAM SK2276 Map 7

Miners Arms

Signposted off A263 Chesterfield—Chapel-en-le-Frith

The village around this popular pub is a good base for exploring the Peak District, and there are decent walks nearby, especially below Froggatt Edge. The chatty staff and landlord are very welcoming; the pleasantly relaxed atmosphere becomes more lively in the evening, when locals drop in for the well kept Bass, Stones and a guest such as Theakstons on handpump. Cosy in winter, the three little plush beamed rooms each have their own stone fireplace. Home-made bar food includes good value tasty sandwiches (from £2.35), soup (£2.50), smoked chicken salad, cumberland sausages with onion gravy or ploughman's (£4.95), steak and ale pie £6.95) and salmon in white wine and ceam sauce (£8.95), with specials such as lasagne (£6.95) and fisherman's pie (£7.95); puddings could include bakewell tart and bread and butter pudding (£3.95). Readers like the breakfasts here, and we've heard that the bedrooms have recently been redecorated. Eyam is famous for the altruism of its villagers, who isolated themselves during the plague to save the lives of others in the area. *(Recommended by Revd John E Cooper, Ann and Colin Hunt, JP, PP, Roy Morrison, the Didler, DC, Tim and Jane Shears)*

New Century Inns ~ Tenants John and Michele Hunt ~ Real ale ~ Bar food (12-6.30; 12-5 Sun) ~ Restaurant ~ (01433) 630853 ~ Children welcome until 9pm ~ Dogs allowed in bedrooms ~ Open 12-11(10.30 Sun) ~ Bedrooms: £30S(£30B)/£60S(£60B)

FENNY BENTLEY SK1750 Map 7

Coach & Horses

A515 N of Ashbourne

This pleasant 17th-c rendered stone house has a comfortable front bar with handmade flowery-cushioned wall settles and library chairs around the dark tables on its flagstone floor, waggon wheels hanging from the black beams, horsebrasses, pewter mugs, and prints on the walls. There are more prints on the stained pine panelling in the little back room, with country cottage furnishings, and a lovely old fireplace (one of three). The dining room and back bar are no smoking. Readers like the reasonably priced bar food here: the changing blackboard might include home-made soup (£2.75), lunchtime sandwiches (from £3.25), baked avocado with tomatoes, mushrooms and brie or thai prawns in filo pastry with sweet chilli sauce (£3.95), ploughman's (£5.95), roasted vegetable pancake with brie (£6.50), game casserole with potato gratin or smoked haddock with lemon butter and mash with cheese (£7.50), pork medallions with black pudding in brandy, cream and mushroom sauce (£8.50), and tasty puddings (£2.95). There's a nicely relaxed atmosphere, and the licensees are quietly friendly. They've very well kept Marstons Pedigree, and a couple of guests such as Timothy Taylors Landlord and Whim Hartington, and 24 whiskies; cribbage, dominoes and piped music. There are views across fields from picnic-sets in the side garden by an elder tree, and wooden tables and chairs under cocktail parasols on the front terrace. *(Recommended by Duncan Cloud, Eric Locker, Derek and Sylvia Stephenson, A Preston, Mr and Mrs S Oxenbury, JP, PP, Bernie Adams, the Didler, Kevin Blake, John and Christine Lowe, Ian and Jane Irving, John and Gillian Scarisbrick)*

Free house ~ Licensees John and Matthew Dawson ~ Real ale ~ Bar food (12-2.30, 6-9; 12-9 Sat/Sun) ~ (01335) 350246 ~ Children in eating area of bar and restaurant ~ Open 11-3, 5-11; 11-11 Sat; 12-11 Sun

FOOLOW SK2077 Map 7

Barrel

Bretton; signposted from Foolow, which itself is signposted from A623 just E of junction with B6465 to Bakewell; can also be reached from either the B6049 at Great Hucklow, or the B6001 via Abney, from Leadmill just S of Hathersage

On the edge of an isolated ridge in excellent walking country, this unspoilt old stone turnpike inn gives views over five counties. The cosy and peaceful oak-beamed bar, its old-fashioned charm still very much intact, has flagstones, studded doors in low doorways, lots of pictures, antiques and a collection of bottles. Stubs of massive knocked-through stone walls divide it into several areas: the cosiest is at the far end, with a log fire, a leather-cushioned settle, and a built-in corner wall-bench by an antique oak table. There are seats out on the front terrace, and a new courtyard garden gives good shelter from the breeze. As well as soup (£2.25) and sandwiches (from £2.95, toasted from £3.20), bar food includes creamy garlic mushrooms (£4.25), cumberland sausage and mustard mash or cheese and leek crumble (£7.95) and steaks (from £11.95), with daily specials such as lamb shank braised with redcurrant, red wine and rosemary (£9.95), seafood kebabs (£11.95) and fried venison steak (£12.95); children's meals (£3.95). Four real ales on handpump could include Greene King Abbot, Marstons Pedigree, Tetleys and Timothy Taylors Landlord, and they've over 20 malts. It's handy for Chatsworth. In the summer school holidays it may be open all day – phone to check. *(Recommended by the Didler, Patrick Hancock, Nigel Woolliscroft, IHR, Keith and Chris O'Neill, David Carr, Gareth and Toni Edwards, Jack Morley, JP, PP, DC, Bill Sykes)*

Free house ~ Licensee Paul Rowlinson ~ Real ale ~ Bar food (12-2.30, 6.30-9.30) ~ Restaurant ~ (01433) 630856 ~ Children welcome ~ Dogs allowed in bar ~ Open 11-3, 6-11; 11-11 Sat; 11-10.30 Sun; closed 25 Dec ~ Bedrooms: £45B/£65B

FROGGATT EDGE SK2477 Map 7

Chequers

B6054, off A623 N of Bakewell; OS Sheet 119 map reference 247761

This prettily set country inn is usually busy with customers enjoying the good interesting bar food. The bar is fairly smart, with library chairs or small high-backed winged settles on the well waxed floorboards, an attractive richly varnished beam-and-board ceiling, antique prints on white walls that are partly stripped back to big dark stone blocks, and a big solid-fuel stove; one corner has a nicely carved oak cupboard. Continually changing, the menu might feature soup (£2.95), generous tasty sandwiches (£3.50-£5.50), goats cheese, potato and black olive salad (£6.95), vegetable paella (£6.50), salmon and cod fishcakes (£8.25), beef goulash (£8.50) and grilled marinated pork chop with creamed leeks and stilton butter or roast salmon fillet (£9.95), with tempting specials such as fried venison steak with onion marmalade in walnut, whisky and peppercorn sauce (£12.95) or grilled lemon sole with capers, parsley and lemon butter (£14.95); puddings could be banana pancakes or bakewell pudding (£3.25). The dining area is partly no smoking. The staff are efficient and helpful. Well kept Charles Wells Bombardier and Greene King IPA, a good range of malt whiskies and a changing wine board; piped music. There are seats in the pleasant peaceful back garden, and Froggatt Edge is just up through the woods behind the pub. *(Recommended by Andrew Stephenson, Darly Graton, Graeme Gulibert, John and Sheila Lister, Mike and Wendy Proctor, B C Hammond, Dr S J Shepherd, Steven and Sally Knight, B, M and P Kendall, June and Malcolm Farmer, James A Waller, Emma Napper, Ian S Morley, Mike and Karen England, D L Parkhurst, David Carr, Hilary Forrest, Mrs M Shardlow)*

Pubmaster ~ Tenants Jonathan and Joanna Tindall ~ Real ale ~ Bar food (12-2, 6-9.30; 12-9.30 Sat; 12-9 Sun) ~ (01433) 630231 ~ Children welcome ~ Dogs allowed in bedrooms ~ Open 12-3, 5-11; 12-11 Sat; 12-10.30 Sun; closed 25 Dec ~ Bedrooms: /£64B

HARDWICK HALL SK4663 Map 7

Hardwick Inn

2¾ miles from M1 junction 29: at roundabout A6175 towards Clay Cross; after ½ mile turn left signed Stainsby and Hardwick Hall (ignore any further sign for Hardwick Hall); at sign to Stainsby follow road to left; after 2½ miles turn left at staggered road junction

This 17th-c golden stone house was originally built as a lodge for the nearby Elizabethan Hall, and is also owned by the National Trust. As it's handy for the M1, it can get very crowded (especially at weekends), but readers assure us that the friendly efficient staff cope well, and the atmosphere is cheerful. Its cosy rooms – one has an attractive 18th-c carved settle – have stone-mullioned latticed windows. The carpeted lounge is the most comfortable, with its upholstered wall settles, tub chairs and stools around varnished wooden tables. Served all day in huge helpings, the reasonably priced enjoyable bar food includes soup (£2.25), sandwiches (from £2.85), ploughman's (from £4.55), home-made steak and kidney or turkey and mushroom pie (£5.95), roast of the day (£6.65) and grilled trout with prawns (£6.95), with daily specials such as rabbit and cider pie or cajun chicken (£6.75); puddings such as damson crumble (£2.75). They also do a children's menu (from £2.90). The carvery restaurant is no smoking. As well as more than 160 malt whiskies, they've well kept Greene King Old Speckled Hen and Ruddles County, John Smiths and Theakstons XB and Old Peculier on handpump; they play piped music, and it can get smoky. The view from the tables in the garden is pleasant. *(Recommended by the Didler, June and Ken Brooks, W W Burke, Walter and Susan Rinaldi-Butcher, Ian and Nita Cooper, Jayne and Peter Capp, Roger and Maureen Kenning, Bill Sykes, Susan and Nigel Wilson, Michael Lamm, Peter F Marshall, Keith and Chris O'Neill, Simon and Laura Habbishow, JP, PP, IHR, Mr and Mrs J E C Tasker, BKA, Peter and Anne Hollindale, Stephen, Julie and Hayley Brown, John and Christine Lowe, Irene and Ray Atkin)*

Free house ~ Licensees Peter and Pauline Batty ~ Real ale ~ Bar food (11.30-9.30; 12-9 Sun) ~ Restaurant ~ (01246) 850245 ~ Open 11.30-11; 12-10.30 Sun

HASSOP SK2272 Map 7

Eyre Arms

B6001 N of Bakewell

Colourful hanging baskets, and in autumn the virginia creeper, brighten up the outside of this peaceful 17th-c stone-built inn. The Eyre coat of arms, painted above a stone fireplace (which has a coal fire in winter), dominates the beamed dining bar. There's also a longcase clock, cushioned settles around the walls, comfortable plush chairs, and lots of brass and copper. A smaller public bar has an unusual collection of teapots, dominoes and another fire; the snug is no smoking too, and there's another small dining area; there may be quiet piped classical music. The good food might include soup (from £2.65), lunchtime sandwiches (from £2.45), sliced duck and mango (£4.40), aubergine and mushroom lasagne (£6.25), steak and kidney pie (£7.45), salmon with orange and basil sauce (£7.65), chicken stuffed with leeks and stilton in a creamy sauce (£8.95), puddings such as bread and butter pudding or brandy snap basket filled with coffee ice cream (£2.75), and daily specials such as braised pheasant (£9.75) or halibut steak with asparagus sauce (£10.25). The cheerful staff are efficient and helpful, and you'll find Black Sheep Special, John Smiths and Marstons Pedigree on handpump. There's a fountain in the small garden, which has tables looking out over beautiful Peak District countryside; there are good walks near here. *(Recommended by Mike and Karen England, JP, PP, the Didler, Patrick Hancock)*

Free house ~ Licensee Lynne Smith ~ Real ale ~ Bar food ~ Restaurant ~ (01629) 640390 ~ Well behaved children in restaurant ~ Open 11.30-2.30(3 Sat), 6.30-11(10.30 Sun); 11.30-2.30, 7-11(10.30 Sun) winter; closed 25 Dec

HATHERSAGE SK2380 Map 7

Plough 🍷 🛏

Leadmill; B6001 (A625) towards Bakewell, OS Sheet 110 map reference 235805

With over 40 main dishes on the menu, you're sure to find something you want to eat at this very popular former farmhouse. Their good imaginative food is carefully prepared using fresh ingredients (the landlord, who used to be a butcher, is proud of his sources), and could include soup (£3.75), duck and ham hock terrine (£4.95), crab and artichoke salad (£5.25), steak and kidney pie or sautéed lambs liver and bacon with mash (£7.95), artichoke and wild mushroom lasagne (£9.95), roast pheasant glazed with maple syrup, portuguese beef piri piri or fried swordfish

(£12.95), grilled monkfish with tomato and herb crust (£14.95), and puddings such as ginger and lemon pudding or warm chocolate brioche (from £3.25). It's worth booking for Sunday lunch. Everything is spotlessly kept, and the attractive cosy-feeling bar, furnished with solid comfort, is on two levels, with a big log fire at one end and a woodburning stove at the other. Service is cheerful and hospitable, and so well organised that things go smoothly even at very busy times; piped music and no smoking restaurant. Along with around nine good value wines by the glass, they serve well kept Tetleys and Theakstons and a couple of guests such as Adnams, Black Sheep and Theakstons Old Peculier on handpump; good cafetière coffee. The pub is beautifully placed just south of the village, by the River Derwent, and tables in the pleasant garden run down to the water. *(Recommended by Sue and John Harwood, E E Atkins, W W Burke, Christine and Neil Townend, IHR, Susan Jeanes, Mike and Linda Hudson, Ian S Morley, Tom and Ruth Rees, Kathy and Chris Armes, Darly Graton, Graeme Gulibert, Terry Mizen, Jo Rees)*

Free house ~ Licensee Bob Emery ~ Real ale ~ Bar food (11.30-2.30, 6.30-9.30; 11.30-9.30 Sat/Sun) ~ Restaurant ~ (01433) 650319 ~ Children welcome until 7pm in eating area of bar ~ Open 11-11; 12-10.30 Sun ~ Bedrooms: £49.50B/£69.50S (£99.50B)

HOGNASTON SK2350 Map 7

Red Lion

Village signposted off B5035 Ashbourne—Wirksworth

'A hidden gem' is how one reader described this welcoming pub. Handy for Carsington Reservoir, it's in a lovely peaceful spot, and, despite an emphasis on the deservedly popular bar food, it remains the type of place where locals drop in just for a drink. The open-plan oak-beamed bar has a good relaxed atmosphere, with almost a bistro feel around the attractive mix of old tables (candlelit at night) on ancient flagstones, and copies of *Country Life* to read. There are old-fashioned settles among other seats, three open fires, and you'll find a growing collection of teddy bears among other bric-a-brac. Delicious, generous bar meals could include home-made soup (£3.95), filled baguettes or garlic mushrooms (£4.95), mussels or prawns (£5.95), three-cheese lasagne or half a lobster (£8.95), and sirloin steak (£11.95), and specials such as warm smoked chicken salad (£8.95), lamb shank in garlic and mint gravy with mashed potatoes (£9.95) and seafood medley (10.95), with puddings such as lemon and marmalade bread and butter pudding (£3.95); it's a good idea to book on the weekend, especially for their good Sunday lunch. On handpump they've well kept Bass, Greene King Old Speckled Hen and Marstons Pedigree, with a guest such as Leatherbritches Bespoke; country wines. Excellent, friendly service; piped music, dominoes. Readers tell us their hearty breakfasts are very good. *(Recommended by Mr and Mrs G Owens, Bernard Stradling, M Joyner, John and Gillian Scarisbrick, Jan and Alan Summers, John Kane, Ron and Sheila Corbett, June and Malcolm Farmer, JP, PP, Andrew Scarr)*

Free house ~ Licensee Pip Price ~ Real ale ~ Bar food (12-2, 6-9; not Sun evening, not Mon) ~ Restaurant ~ (01335) 370396 ~ Children over 9 welcome in eating area of bar ~ Dogs allowed in bar ~ Open 12-3, 6-11(7-10.30 Sun); closed Mon lunchtime except bank hols ~ Bedrooms: £45S/£75S

HOLBROOK SK3644 Map 7

Dead Poets £

Village signposted off A6 S of Belper; Chapel Street

Tucked into a quiet street, this low white-painted pub seems dark as a cellar when you first go in, with low black beams in its ochre ceiling, stripped stone walls with some smoked plaster, and broad flagstones. Candles burn on scrubbed tables, there's a big log fire in the end stone fireplace, high-backed winged settles form snug cubicles along one wall, and there are pews and a variety of chairs in other intimate corners and hide-aways. The décor makes a few nods to the pub's present name (it used to be the Cross Keys), and adds some old prints of Derby. Our inspection visit coincided unexpectedly with one of their regular beer festivals: 41 different brews, most of them rarities, from three temporary serveries as well as the regular bar, which even at normal times has a good well kept choice such as Batemans Salem Porter, Brains Rev James, Greene King Abbot, Marstons Pedigree and Whim Hartington, alongside Dead Poets (brewed specially for the pub by Shardlow) on handpump or served by the jug from the cellar, also farm cider and several country wines. Alongside cobs (from £1.50), good value bar food includes home-made soup (£2), chilli con carne or casserole (£3.25) and chicken jalfrezi (£3.75). There's a great atmosphere, with a good easy mix of customers, male and female; well reproduced piped music, and you can borrow the chess set drinking game made for the pub by a local potter. There's a sort of verandah room outside, with lanterns, fairy lights and a few plants, and more seats out in the yard, with outdoor heaters. *(Recommended by Bernie Adams, JP, PP, the Didler, Alan Bowker)*

Free house ~ Licensee David Brown ~ Real ale ~ Bar food (lunchtime only) ~ No credit cards ~ 01332 780301 ~ Well behaved children in snug ~ Fortnightly live music session, and poetry night 1st Tues in month ~ Open 12-2.30, 5-11; 12-11Fri/Sat; 12-10.30 Sun

HOPE SK1783 Map 7

Cheshire Cheese

Edale Road – off A625 at W end of village

Originally built on the salt-carrying route from Cheshire across the Pennines to Yorkshire, this 16th-c village pub takes its name from the payments that were made in the form of cheese for an overnight stop – you can still see the original cheese hooks in the lower room. Handy in summer, it's close to the Pennine Way and well placed for a walk in the lovely Edale Valley, while in winter it's lovely and cosy as each of the three very snug oak-beamed rooms has its own coal fire. Tasty bar food includes soup (£2.50), sandwiches (from £3.50), baked potatoes (from £4.75), filled yorkshire puddings (from £4.95), cumberland sausage or scampi and chips (£6.95) and grilled cod in lime and ginger butter (£7.95), with puddings such as cherry cheesecake (£3.50), and daily specials; the lower dining room is no smoking. Well kept Barnsley Best, Wentworth PA and a couple of guest beers such as Black Sheep and Timothy Taylors Landlord on handpump, a good choice of house wines and malt whiskies; piped music. The bedrooms are attractively furnished. When it's busy, parking can be a problem. *(Recommended by John Hulme, John Close, Steven and Sally Knight, James Woods, A C and E Johnson, Patrick Hancock, Kevin Blake, Brian and Anna Marsden, Gordon Tong, Jean Kendrick, JP, PP, Mike and Lynn Robinson, Hilary Forrest)*

Free house ~ Licensee David Helliwell ~ Real ale ~ Bar food (12-2(2.30 Sat/Sun), 6.30-9) ~ Restaurant ~ (01433) 620381 ~ Children in eating area till 9pm ~ Dogs allowed in bar ~ Open 12-3, 6.30-11; 12-11 Sat; 12-4, 6.30-10.30 Sun ~ Bedrooms: /£60S

IDRIDGEHAY SK2848 Map 7

Black Swan

B5023 S of Wirksworth

Reworked in 1998 as more of a restaurant than a pub, this does still have a little sitting area by the big bow window on the left, with a rack of daily papers and magazines, a few bar stools, wicker armchairs and padded seats, and snapshots of some very cheery customers; and they have Bass, Marstons Pedigree and John Smiths on handpump here. Most of the open-plan space (and indeed the feel of the place) is given over to eating, though: well spaced tables with wicker chairs comfortably cushioned in a mix of colours, and a bright and airy simple décor – white ceiling, ragged yellow walls with a few pictures of French restaurants, wine bottles and local scenes. The bare floors make for cheerful acoustics (not too clattery), and on our inspection visit they had fairly quiet piped light jazz. Down steps is a similarly furnished no smoking area, given a slight conservatory feel by its high pitched roof light (with rattan blinds) and two narrow floor-to-ceiling windows at the far end, looking out over the neat and pleasant garden to rolling tree-sheltered pastures. The generous enjoyable lunchtime bar food, generally colourful and well presented, could include home-made soup (£3.25), filled ciabattas (from £3.95), mediterranean vegetables and haloumi cheese (£6.55), scottish smoked salmon with marinated olives and sour cream (£6.55), chargrilled chicken breast with teriyaki sauce (£7.25), grilled haddock fillet with watercress dressing (£7.50) and 10oz steak with green peppercorn sauce (£10.95), with puddings (£3.50); a popular good value two-course lunch gives plenty of choice (£8.95, Mon-Fri). Service is prompt and polite, they do good coffees, and there's a relaxed and unhurried atmosphere. *(Recommended by A Preston, Mrs Kathy Barkway, R P and L E Booth, John and Christine Lowe)*

Free house ~ Licensees Michael Buckland and Steve Williams ~ Real ale ~ Bar food (lunchtime, not Sun) ~ Restaurant ~ (01773) 550249 ~ Children welcome ~ Dogs allowed in bar ~ Jazz and Irish music nights a few times a month ~ Open 11-11; 12-6 Sun

KIRK IRETON SK2650 Map 7

Barley Mow

Village signed off B5023 S of Wirksworth

Traditional furnishings and civilised old-fashioned service create a charmingly timeless atmosphere at this tall gabled Jacobean brown sandstone inn. Dimly lit passageways and narrow stairwells open into a small main bar, which has a pubby feel, with antique settles on the tiled floor or built into the panelling, a roaring coal fire, four slate-topped tables, and shuttered mullioned windows. Another room has built-in cushioned pews on oak parquet flooring and a small woodburner, and a third has more pews, tiled floor, beams and joists, and big landscape prints. One room is no smoking. Instead of games machines and other gadgets, you'll find only an occasional game of cards or dominoes. Kept in their casks behind a modest wooden counter are well kept (and good value) Hook Norton Best and Old Hooky, Leatherbritches, Marstons Pedigree, Whim Hartington and possibly a guest from another small brewery such as Black Sheep or Cottage; farm ciders too. Food consists of lunchtime filled rolls (75p); the good home-made imaginative evening meals are for residents only. The pub is home to good-natured ancient pugs and a newfoundland. There's a decent-sized garden, and a couple of benches out in front, and they've now opened a post office in what used to be the pub stables. In good walking country, the pretty hilltop village is handy for Carsington Water. *(Recommended by JP, PP, John and Gillian Scarisbrick, Bernard Stradling, Pete Baker, Rob Webster, P Abbott, Mike Rowan, Tim Lawrence, the Didler, MLR)*

Free house ~ Licensee Mary Short ~ Real ale ~ No credit cards ~ (01335) 370306 ~ Children welcome lunchtimes away from bar ~ Dogs welcome ~ Open 12-2, 7-11(10.30 Sun); closed 25 Dec and 1 Jan ~ Bedrooms: £25S/£45B

LADYBOWER RESERVOIR SK1986 Map 7

Yorkshire Bridge

A6013 N of Bamford

Attractively placed near lots of pleasant countryside walks, this fine roadside hotel has a nicely bustling atmosphere. As this is such a popular part of the world, it's a good idea to get here early in summer for the generous bar food. The enjoyable menu, which contains lots of traditional dishes, could include soup (£2.60), lunchtime sandwiches (from £3), filled baked potatoes (from £3.25), lunchtime ploughman's (£6.25), spring rolls with plum sauce (£4), home-made steak and kidney pie or roast chicken with sausage, stuffing and yorkshire pudding (£6.75) and barbecued lamb chops (£8.50); readers particularly recommend the steaks (from £10.25). Specials could be pork and apple sausages with crispy bacon and mashed potatoes (£6.80) and fresh crab salad (£7.95), with puddings such as blackberry and apple crumble (from £3.10); all three dining rooms are no smoking. One area has a country cottage atmosphere, with floral wallpaper, sturdy cushioned wall settles, Staffordshire dogs and toby jugs on a big stone fireplace with a warm coal-effect gas fire, china on delft shelves, a panelled dado and so forth. Another extensive area, with another fire, is lighter and more airy with pale wooden furniture, good big black and white photographs and lots of plates on the walls. The Bridge Room has yet another coal-effect fire and oak tables and chairs, and the small no smoking conservatory gives pleasant views across a valley to steep larch woods. Bass, Stones and Theakstons Best and Old Peculier are well kept on handpump, and you get real cream with the good coffee; darts, dominoes, fruit machine, and piped music; disabled lavatories. Comfortable bedrooms. Immortalised by the World War II Dambusters, the Ladybower, Derwent and Howden reservoirs are nearby. *(Recommended by A Preston, Keith and Chris O'Neill, Kevin Blake, Richard Gibbs, Mike and Wena Stevenson, Alan J Morton, Revd D Glover, Annette and John Derbyshire, Irene and Ray Atkin, John and Christine Lowe)*

Free house ~ Licensees Trevelyan and John Illingworth ~ Real ale ~ Bar food (12-2, 6-9(9.30 Fri/Sat); 12-8.30 Sun) ~ Restaurant ~ (01433) 651361 ~ Children in eating area of bar and restaurant ~ Dogs welcome ~ Open 11-11; 12-10.30 Sun ~ Bedrooms: £45B/£62B

LITTLE HUCKLOW SK1678 Map 7

Old Bulls Head

Pub signposted from B6049

The neatly tended garden of this friendly old country pub boasts lovely views over to the Peak District, and if you get tired of looking at that, there's an unusual collection of well restored and attractively painted old farm machinery here too. A little low door takes you into the two neatly kept, heavily oak-beamed pub rooms; one room is served from a hatch, the other over a polished bar counter. The low ceilings and walls are packed with brasses, tankards and mining equipment, local photographs, thickly cushioned built-in settles, and a coal fire in a neatly restored stone hearth; darts, dominoes. For years a shaft in the cellar led down to a mine, until an explosion in the shaft blew off a piece of the cellar roof to create the unusual little 'cave' room at the back. There may be a wait for the generous home-made bar food, which includes hot smoked mackerel (£3.75), scampi, lasagne or stilton and vegetable bake (£7.95) and steaks (from £12.95), with traditional puddings such as rice pudding or treacle sponge (from £2.95). Well kept John Smiths and Tetleys are served from carved handpumps, and they keep several malt whiskies. *(Recommended by Patrick Hancock, Ann and Colin Hunt, Richard Gibbs, Mike and Lynn Robinson, Doug Christian, JP, PP, John and Christine Lowe)*

Free house ~ Licensee Julie Denton ~ Real ale ~ Bar food (not Mon/Tues) ~ (01298) 871097 ~ Children welcome ~ Open 12-3(not Mon/Tues), 6-11; 12-3, 6.30-10.30 Sun ~ Bedrooms: £40B/£50B

LITTON SK1675 Map 7

Red Lion

Village signposted off A623, between B6465 and B6049 junctions; also signposted off B6049

The exceptionally friendly staff make visitors feel genuinely welcome at this 17th-c village pub, although it's also very much a proper community local. The two homely linked front rooms are immediately inviting, with low beams and some panelling, and blazing log fires. There's a bigger no smoking back room with good-sized tables, and large antique prints on its stripped stone walls. The small bar counter has well kept Barnsley Bitter, Black Sheep, Jennings Cumberland and a guest such as Shepherd Neame Spitfire on handpump, with decent wines and 30 malt whiskies; shove-ha'penny, cribbage and dominoes. Apart from very good value hot and cold sandwiches (from £2), enjoyable bar food includes soup (£2.50), breaded garlic mushrooms (£2.85), steak and ale pie, gammon or battered cod (£5.95), 8oz sirloin (£7.50) and daily specials such as thai chicken curry (£5.85) or garlic lamb knuckle or salmon in white wine sauce or salmon in dill hollandaise (£6.95); puddings (£2.50). The quiet tree-studded village green in front is attractive, and there are good walks nearby. It's lovely at Christmas when a brass band plays carols, and bustling during the annual village well-dressing carnival (usually the last weekend in June), when villagers create a picture from flower petals, moss and other natural materials. *(Recommended by Mike and Wendy Proctor, Peter F Marshall, the Didler, JP, PP, Eric Locker, David Atkinson, John Watson, Patrick Hancock, Andrew Pashley, Mrs P J Carroll, Ian S Morley, B, M and P Kendall)*

Free house ~ Licensees Terry and Michele Vernon ~ Real ale ~ Bar food (12-2, 6-8(8.30 Thurs-Sat); not Sun evenings) ~ (01298) 871458 ~ Well behaved children over 6 till 8pm ~ Dogs welcome ~ Open 12-3, 6-11; 12-11 Sat; 12-10.30 Sun

MELBOURNE SK3427 Map 7

John Thompson £

Ingleby, which is NW of Melbourne; turn off A514 at Swarkestone Bridge or in Stanton by Bridge; can also be reached from Ticknall (or from Repton on B5008)

Brewed by the enthusiastic landlord, the splendid real ales are the main draw at this converted 15th-c farmhouse. Very attractively priced, they include JT Bitter, Summer Gold and Winter Porter. The straightforward lunchtime carvery too has won much praise from readers, and includes sandwiches or rolls (from £1.40, nothing else on Sundays), home-made soup (£1.50), salads with cold ham or beef (£4), excellent roast beef with yorkshire puddings and tasty gravy (£6, not Mondays), and delicious puddings such as bread and butter pudding or rhubarb crumble (£2). This is a simple but comfortable place, with a big, pleasantly modernised lounge with ceiling joists, some old oak settles, button-back leather seats, sturdy oak tables, antique prints and paintings, and a log-effect gas fire; a couple of smaller cosier rooms open off, with a piano, pool, fruit machine and a juke box in the children's room. There's a no smoking area in the lounge; piped music. There are lots of tables by flowerbeds on the well kept lawns, and on a partly covered outside terrace with its own serving bar. *(Recommended by the Didler, MLR, Bernie Adams, C Herbert, Peter and Patricia Burton, Mrs Kathy Barkway, Dr S J Shepherd, Keith and Chris O'Neill, Peter and Carol Heaton, Rosemary Kennell)*

Own brew ~ Licensee John Thompson ~ Real ale ~ Bar food (lunchtime) ~ No credit cards ~ (01332) 862469 ~ Children in eating area of bar and family room ~ Dogs allowed in bar ~ Open 10.30-2.30, 7-11; 12-2.30, 7-10.30 Sun

MILLTOWN SK3561 Map 7

Miners Arms

Off B6036 SE of Ashover; Oakstedge Lane

Although the emphasis in this impeccably kept stone-built pub is firmly on the restaurant-style food, they do serve two interesting constantly rotating real ales, usually from smaller brewers such as Grainstore and Oakham. Booking in advance is recommended if you do want to enjoy the particularly good value home-made food. Tasty changing dishes are listed on a board; although they're not that unusual the quality is high, and things come with particularly good vegetables. There might be home-made soup (from £1.95), spinach stuffed mushrooms (£3.35), pork terrine (£3.65), pork, apple and sausage pie (£7.10), turkey escalope with herb butter (£8.25), chicken breast with mustard ceam sauce (£8.35) and grilled cod (£8.0), with puddings such as chocolate crumble cheesecake and crème brûlée (£3.10). The layout is basically L-shaped, with a local feel up nearer the door; the dining room is no smoking. They serve good value wines, service is friendly and efficient, and there may be quiet piped classical music. Virtually on the edge of Ashover, the pub is in former lead-mining country, with vestiges of the old workings adding interest to attractive country walks right from the door. Please take note of their opening times. *(Recommended by the Didler, John and Christine Lowe)*

Free house ~ Licensees Andrew and Yvonne Guest ~ Real ale ~ Restaurant ~ (01246) 590218 ~ Children welcome ~ Open 12-3, 7-11.30 Weds-Sat; 12-3 Sun; closed Weds evening winter; closed Mon/Tues, and Sun pm

MONSAL HEAD SK1871 Map 7

Monsal Head Hotel

B6465

The cosy stable bar of this busy extended hotel perched high above Monsal Dale once housed the horses that used to pull guests and their luggage up from the station at the other end of the steep valley; the stripped timber horse-stalls, harness and brassware, and lamps from the disused station itself, all hint at those days. There's a big warming woodburning stove in the inglenook, and cushioned oak pews around the tables on the flagstones. Served by friendly staff, the eight well kept real ales might include Abbeydale Moonshine and Absolution, Kelham Island Easy Rider and Pale Rider, Monsal Best (brewed for them by Lloyds), Theakstons Old Peculier and Best, Timothy Taylors Best, and a couple of guests such as Abbeydale and Barnsley Bitter on handpump (you may be allowed a little taster before you commit yourself to a pint). There's also a very good choice of bottled German beers, and sensibly priced wines. Good reasonably priced bar food is served all day, and might include home-made soup (£2.90), filled baked potatoes (from £3.20), chicken liver pâté (£3.90), cod in beer batter or couscous salad (£6.90), game pie (£8.90), grilled lamb chump chop with garlic, rosemary and orange (£10.50), and puddings such as sticky toffee (£3.90); children's meals (from £2.90). The restaurant is no smoking; piped music. The boundary of the parishes of Little Longstone and Ashford runs through the hotel, and the spacious restaurant and smaller lounge are named according to which side of the line they sit; beer garden. The best place to admire the view is from the big windows in the lounge, and from four of the seven bedrooms; the generous breakfasts come in for particular praise. *(Recommended by Ian S Morley, Keith and Chris O'Neill, John and Gillian Scarisbrick, JP, PP, Nigel Woolliscroft, the Didler, Mike and Lynn Robinson, G B Longden, Richard Fendick, Dr*
S J Shepherd, Andrew Wallace, Sue Demont, Tim Barrow, Mike and Wendy Proctor, Professor John Hibbs, A C and E Johnson, Patrick Hancock)

Free house ~ Licensees Christine O'Connell and Philip Smith ~ Real ale ~ Bar food (12-9.30) ~ Restaurant ~ (01629) 640250 ~ Children in eating area of bar and restaurant ~ Dogs allowed in bar and bedrooms ~ Open 11-11; closed 25 Dec ~ Bedrooms: £45.53B/£50.66B

OVER HADDON SK2066 Map 7

Lathkil

Village and inn signposted from B5055 just SW of Bakewell

Lathkil Dale, one of the quieter dales with a harmonious landscape of pastures and copses, lies steeply down below this unpretentious and welcoming hotel, and the views are terrific. It's understandably very popular with walkers, who can leave their muddy boots in the pub's lobby. The airy room on the right as you go in has a nice fire in the attractively carved fireplace, old-fashioned settles with upholstered cushions or plain wooden chairs, black beams, a delft shelf of blue and white plates, original prints and photographs, and big windows. On the left, the spacious and sunny dining area – partly no smoking – doubles as a restaurant in the evenings; it's not quite as pubby as the bar, but there isn't a problem with shorts or walking gear at lunchtime. The changing hearty blackboard menu could include home-made soup (£2.30), filled rolls (from £2.40), smoked mackerel (£5.25), beef and black peppercorn crumble (£6.15), chicken stuffed with apricot (£6.50), dressed crab salad (£6.95), venison casserole (£7.50) and puddings (from £2.75). You'll find Charles Wells Bombardier, Whim Hartington and a couple of guests such as Marstons Pedigree and Timothy Taylors Landlord well kept on handpump (samples are offered in sherry glasses); select malt whiskies and a good range of new world wines. Darts, bar billiards, shove-ha'penny, backgammon, dominoes, cribbage, and piped music. It does get very busy, so it's best to get here early in good weather. *(Recommended by the Didler, Andrew Stephenson, JP, PP, W K Wood, Anthony Barnes, Dr and Mrs M Locker, Dr A McCormick, Rob Fowell, Lorraine and Fred Gill,*

James A Waller, Eric Locker, Peter F Marshall, Mike and Wendy Proctor, Doug Christian, Cliff Blakemore, Catherine and Richard Preston, Sue Holland, Dave Webster, Mike and Heather Watson, Derek and Sylvia Stephenson, Nigel Woolliscroft, Mike Ridgway, Sarah Miles, Paul and Margaret Baker)

Free house ~ Licensee Robert Grigor-Taylor ~ Real ale ~ Bar food (lunchtime, not 25 Dec) ~ Restaurant ~ (01629) 812501 ~ Children in dining room ~ Dogs allowed in bar ~ Open 11.30-3, 6.30(7 winter)-11; 11.30-11 Sat; 12-10.30 Sun ~ Bedrooms: £37.50S/£55S(£70B)

SHARDLOW SK4330 Map 7

Old Crown

3 miles from M1 junction 24, via A50: at first B6540 exit from A50 (just under 2 miles) turn off towards Shardlow – pub E of Shardlow itself, at Cavendish Bridge, actually just over Leics boundary

Once a deportation point for convicts bound for the colonies, this welcoming 17th-c coaching inn (handy for the A6 as well as the M1) is well worth a visit. The cheerful bar is packed with hundreds of jugs and mugs hanging from the beamed ceiling, and brewery and railway memorabilia and advertisements and other bric-a-brac cover the walls (even in the lavatories). Served by friendly staff, about half a dozen well kept real ales on handpump include Bass, Everards Tiger, Fullers London Pride, Marstons Pedigree and Tower Malty Towers, with guests such as Everard Beacon or Exmoor Gold; there's also a nice choice of malt whiskies. Shove-ha'penny, cribbage, fruit machine and piped music. The popular bar food is a hit with readers, including soup (£1.70), sandwiches (from £2), a good range of baguettes (from £3.25), omelettes (from £4.25), mediterranean vegetable lasagne (£4.95), cod (£6.95) and steaks (from £8.25), with good specials such as tasty beef and kidney pie (£5.95), chicken with mustard and cider sauce or grilled lamb chops topped with blue cheese sauce (£6.95), and puddings such as chocolate sponge and spotted dick (from £2.25); best to book for Sunday lunch. The cellar restaurant has a terrace overlooking the garden. They may close early in winter. *(Recommended by Michael and Marion Buchanan, the Didler, John Beeken, MLR, Mike and Heather Watson, A C and E Johnson, Darly Graton, Graeme Gulibert, John Saville, Dick and Penny Vardy, Kevin Blake, JHBS, JP, PP, Roger and Maureen Kenning)*

Free house ~ Licensees Peter and Gillian Morton-Harrison ~ Real ale ~ Bar food (lunchtime) ~ (01332) 792392 ~ Children in eating area of bar ~ Dogs allowed in bar ~ Open 11.30-3.30, 5-11; 12-4.30, 7-10.30 Sun; closed 25 and 26 Dec ~ Bedrooms: £30S/£40S

WARDLOW SK1875 Map 7

Three Stags Heads

Wardlow Mires; A623 by junction with B6465

We've known this simple white-painted cottage for some 20 years, and like many readers are delighted that its robustly traditional character remains unchanged. It certainly doesn't aim to attract a smart dining crowd, but beer lovers happy to swap stories with the friendly locals and landlord over a hearty home-made meal will have a great time here. The tiny flagstoned parlour bar, warmed right through the winter by a cast-iron kitchen range, has old leathercloth seats, a couple of antique settles with flowery cushions, two high-backed windsor armchairs and simple oak tables – look out for the petrified cat in a glass case. The well kept beers on handpump are Abbeydale Absolution, Black Lurcher (brewed for the pub at a hefty 8% ABV) and Matins, and Broadstone Charter, and they've lots of bottled continental and English beers (the stronger ones can be quite pricy). They also do a roaring trade in mugs of tea, and in winter there might be free hot chestnuts on the bar. They try to vary the seasonal menu to suit the weather, so dishes served on hardy home-made plates (the barn is a pottery workshop) might include leek and stilton hotpot or pasta with mushroom and tomato sauce (from £7), cottage pie or curry (£8.50) and roast squirrel, fried pigeon breasts or hare casserole (£10.50). You can book the tables in the small no smoking dining parlour, with another open fire. Cribbage and dominoes, nine men's morris and backgammon. It's situated in a natural sink, so don't be surprised to find the floors muddied by boots in wet weather (and the dogs even muddier). The front terrace looks across the main road to the distant hills. The pub opens on weekday evenings in high summer only, or when there's sufficient demand, so it's best to phone before visiting. *(Recommended by JP, PP, Pete Baker, Nigel Woolliscroft, Mike and Wendy Proctor, the Didler, Mike and Lynn Robinson, Andrew Stephenson, John Hulme, A C and E Johnson, L Davenport)*

Free house ~ Licensees Geoff and Pat Fuller ~ Real ale ~ Bar food ~ No credit cards ~ (01298) 872268 ~ Dogs welcome ~ Folk music most Sat evenings ~ Open 7-11 Fri; 12-11 Sat; 12-10.30 Sun; closed wkdys exc Fri evenings and bank hols

WHITTINGTON MOOR SK3873 Map 7

Derby Tup £

387 Sheffield Road; B6057 just S of A61 roundabout

At this down-to-earth corner house, you'll find well kept Batemans XXXB, Black Sheep Bitter, Greene King Abbot, Theakstons Old Peculier, Timothy Taylors Landlord and Whim Hartington on handpump, alongside four rotating guest beers such as Archers Golden, Fullers London Pride, Exmoor Gold and Kelham Island Pale Rider. They also have a nice variety of continental and bottle-conditioned beers, fruit beers, farm ciders and perry, and decent malt whiskies; good value soft drinks too. The plain but sizeable rectangular bar, with frosted street windows and old dark brown linoleum, has simple furniture arranged around the walls (including a tremendously long green plastic banquette), leaving lots of standing room. There are two more small no smoking rooms; daily papers, darts, dominoes and cribbage. The wide choice of good value food, which changes regularly, might include tasty sandwiches made with fresh bread from the neighbouring bakery (from £2), home-made soup (£2), chilli, mushroom goulash or tuscan bean stew (£4.25), steak and ale pie or thai curry (£4.50) and lasagne (£4.95). Despite the remote-sounding name, Whittington Moor is on the northern edge of Chesterfield, and the pub can get very busy on weekend evenings. *(Recommended by the Didler, Patrick Hancock, JP, PP, Darly Graton, Graeme Gulibert, Keith and Chris O'Neill)*

Tynemill ~ Tenant Peter Hayes ~ Real ale ~ Bar food (lunchtime) ~ (01246) 454316 ~ Children in two side rooms ~ Dogs welcome ~ Open 11.30-3, 5-11 Mon-Tues; 11.30-11 Weds-Sat; 12-4, 7-10.30 Sun

WOOLLEY MOOR SK3661 Map 7

White Horse

Badger Lane, off B6014 Matlock—Clay Cross

This attractive old pub is not only delightfully situated with fine views of the Ogston reservoir and the Amber Valley (particularly from the no smoking conservatory), it also has a good chatty bar, and serves beautifully cooked food too. Changing with the season and using fresh local produce, reasonably priced dishes include soup (£2.95), sandwiches (from £3.95), toasted panini (from £3.95), leek, stilton and tomato quiche or sausage and mash (£5.95), fish and chips (£6.75) and game and ale pie (£7.25); you can also choose from slightly more elaborate dishes such as goats cheese and apple filo parcel (£3.95), peking duck pancakes (£4.95), leek, chestnut and stilton wellington (£7.95), roast salmon fillet with prawn and dill hash brown in tomato sauce (£8.95), and steaks (£11.95). The good children's meals come with a puzzle sheet and crayons. It's best to book for the restaurant. The bustling tap room, still very much in its original state, serves well kept Greene King Ruddles with a couple of guests such as Adnams Broadside, Jennings Cumberland and Theakstons Old Peculier; decent wines too, and good efficient service. There is piped classical music in the lounge. A sign outside shows how horses and carts carried measures of salt along the toll road in front – the toll bar still stands at the entrance of the road. Picnic-sets in the garden share the lovely views, and there's a very good play area with a wooden train, climbing frame and swings; boules too. *(Recommended by the*

Didler, Richard Cole, Bernie Adams, A Preston, Peter and Audrey Dowsett, Norma and Keith Bloomfield, Ms J Davidson, Keith and Chris O'Neill, Steven and Sally Knight)

Musketeers ~ Managers Graeme Jones and Keith Hurst ~ Real ale ~ Bar food (12-2, 6-9; 12-8 Sun) ~ Restaurant ~ (01246) 590319 ~ Children in restaurant ~ Dogs allowed in bar ~ Open 12-3, 6-11; 12-10.30 Sun

Lucky Dip

Besides the fully inspected pubs, you might like to try these Lucky Dips recommended to us and described by readers (if you do, please send us reports: www.goodguides.com).

Apperknowle [SK3878]

☆ ***Yellow Lion*** [High St]: 19th-c stone-built village local, comfortable banquettes in L-shaped lounge, no smoking dining room; has been very popular for wide choice of good value food from sandwiches up, five well kept ales inc Timothy Taylors Landlord, and good choice of wines by glass, but the long-serving licensees retired earlier in 2002 – news please; garden with play area, Mon and Weds quiz nights, children welcome, attractively priced bedrooms *(Keith and Chris O'Neill, JP, PP, Patrick Hancock, the Didler)*

Ashford in the Water [SK1969]

☆ ***Bulls Head*** [Church St]: Cosy and homely comfortable lounge, busy bar, well kept Robinsons Best, Old Stockport and Hartleys XB, well prepared food from good sandwiches to adventurous main dishes, prompt friendly service; may be piped music or radio; children in public bar, tables out behind and by front car park *(MLR, Darly Graton, Graeme Gulibert, Patrick Hancock, Annette and John Derbyshire)*

Ashover [SK3463]

Black Swan [Church St]: Decent cheap food inc good range of sandwiches, prompt cheerful service, well kept Bass and another real ale *(Darly Graton, Graeme Gulibert)*

Aston-upon-Trent [SK4129]

Malt Shovel [off A6 SE of Derby; The Green (one-way st)]: Comfortably chatty Victorian pub with lots of copper, plates and pictures, basic fresh lunchtime food (not Sun) from sandwiches up, five or six real ales inc Marstons Pedigree and Tetleys, pool room with big-screen TV, back terrace; quiz night Thurs, open all day Sat *(Tony and Wendy Hobden)*

Bakewell [SK2168]

Peacock [Bridge St]: Clean, bright and cheerful, well kept Theakstons and guests such as Adnams Bitter and Broadside, popular food (not Mon-Weds evenings), good prices and service *(Darly Graton, Graeme Gulibert, Roger Bridgeman)*

Rutland Arms [The Square]: Handsome stone-built Georgian hotel with welcoming young staff, enjoyable food in bar and restaurant; comfortable bedrooms *(Christine and Neil Townend)*

Barlow [SK3375]

Trout [Valley Road, Common Side; B6051 NW of Chesterfield]: Popular beamed dining pub under new management, decent food from sandwiches and baguettes to steak, inviting partly no smoking layout with comfortable banquettes and good-sized tables, old-world prints, Bass, Boddingtons and a guest beer, decent wines; unobtrusive piped music; tables out on terrace *(Ian S Morley, LYM)*

Baslow [SK2572]

Devonshire Arms [A619]: Small hotel in pleasant surroundings, footpath to Chatsworth; long L-shaped bar with nice mix of different-sized tables and various seats inc leather chairs, Bass and Marstons Pedigree, well trained young staff, food from decent sandwiches to carvery meals, fish nights and evening restaurant with attractive draped ceiling, end games area; may be quiet piped music; bedrooms *(Stephen, Julie and Hayley Brown)*

Bonsall [SK2858]

Barley Mow [off A6012 Cromford—Hartington; The Dale]: Friendly tucked-away pub with particularly well kept Whim Hartington and two or three guest beers, fresh sandwiches and other food, character furnishings; live music wknds inc landlord playing accordion, organises local walks; cl wkdy lunchtimes (may open Fri by arrangement, open all day Sat) *(the Didler, JP, PP)*

Buxton [SK0572]

Bakers Arms [West Rd]: Homely family-run terraced local with well kept Greene King Abbot, Tetleys and guest beers, welcoming comfortable atmosphere, good mix of customers *(the Didler)*

Old Sun [33 High St]: Relaxing traditional pub, several small softly lit areas off central bar, open fires, low beams, bare boards or tiles, stripped wood screens, old local photographs, well kept Marstons Best and Pedigree with a guest from that group, lots of bottled beers and malt whiskies, farm cider, good choice of wines by the glass, friendly staff, usual bar food from sandwiches up; piped music, TV; children in back bar, open all day *(Dr W J M Gissane, Barry Collett, the Didler, Andrew Crawford, Mike and Wendy Proctor, LYM)*

Calver [SK2474]

Bridge Inn [Calver Bridge, off A623 N of Baslow]: Unpretentious two-room stone-built village local, welcoming if hardly quiet, quick good value plain food (not Mon evening or winter Sun evening), particularly well kept Hardys & Hansons ales, good friendly service, lots of areas and cosy corners, coal fires, bank notes on beams, local prints and bric-a-brac; picnic-sets in nice big garden by River Derwent *(R A Watson, Gill Waller, Tony Morriss, DC, CMW, JJW)*

Castleton [SK1583]
☆ ***George*** [Castle St]: Relaxed atmosphere, friendly South African licensees doing good food from nourishing sandwiches to imaginative main dishes, two good-sized rooms, one mainly for eating, with beams and stripped stone, well kept Wadworths 6X, no music; tables on wide forecourt, lots of flower tubs; popular with young people – near YHA; dogs, children and muddy boots welcome *(JP, PP, Steven and Sally Knight, Liz and John Soden, Lorraine and Fred Gill)*
Olde Cheshire Cheese [How Lane]: Two communicating family-friendly beamed areas, cosy, welcoming and spotless, lots of photographs, cheery landlord, well kept real ales, back lounge set for wide choice of usual reasonably priced food all day, open fire, toby jugs and local paintings, sensibly placed darts; piped music may obtrude; bedrooms *(BB, Rona Murdoch, Lorraine and Fred Gill)*
Chellaston [SK3729]
Bonnie Prince [A50/A514]: Dining pub with comprehensive food choice, well kept Hardys & Hansons, restaurant *(Tony and Wendy Hobden)*
Chelmorton [SK1170]
Church Inn [between A6 and A515 SW of Buxton]: Comfortable split bar, ample space for diners, good range of reasonably priced generous food inc fresh veg and delicious puddings, friendly landlord and golden labrador, well kept Adnams and Marstons with a guest such as Mansfield; piped music, outside lavatories; tables out in sloping garden with terrace, well tended flower boxes, superb walking country *(Mrs P J Carroll, JP, PP)*
Chesterfield [SK3871]
Barrow Boy [Low Pavement]: After several name changes, now a real ale pub with well kept Black Sheep and several changing guest beers, enjoyable food *(Keith and Chris O'Neill)*
Rutland [Stephenson Pl]: Very old L-shaped pub next to crooked spire church, well kept real ales inc Greene King Abbot, farm cider, rugs and assorted wooden furniture on bare boards, good value food, pleasant service, darts, pinball machine, old photographs; piped music; children welcome, open all day *(Keith and Chris O'Neill, R T and J C Moggridge)*
Chinley [SK0482]
☆ ***Lamb*** [just off A624 S of Hayfield]: Friendly new chef/landlord doing interesting cheffy dishes as well as good value generous more standard food from lunchtime sandwiches and (not Fri/Sat evening) baguettes to fresh fish inc very popular OAP lunch and some children's dishes (all day wknds and bank hols), in profusely decorated three-room stone-built pub tucked below road, well kept Bass and other ales; children welcome, lots of tables out in front with good views *(Greta and Christopher Wells, Dr and Mrs R E S Tanner, BB, Mrs P J Carroll)*
Coxbench [SK3743]
Fox & Hounds [off B6179 N of Derby; Alfreton Rd]: Entirely no smoking village local with long partly flagstoned bar, attractive raised restaurant area, wide choice of good interesting fresh food, reasonable prices, well kept changing ales such as Fullers London Pride, Marstons Pedigree and Tetleys, good welcoming service; may be piped music *(the Didler, John Beeken, David and Helen Wilkins)*
Crich [SK3554]
Cliff [Cromford Rd, Town End]: Cosy and unpretentious two-room pub with real fire, well kept Hardys & Hansons ales, good value generous standard bar food; great views, handy for National Tramway Museum *(Gill Waller, Tony Morriss, the Didler, JP, PP)*
Cromford [SK2956]
☆ ***Boat*** [Scarthin, off Mkt Pl]: Attractive traditional 18th-c waterside local doing well under newish licensees, good range of well kept changing ales such as Leatherbritches and Springhead, friendly relaxed atmosphere, log fire, good value basic food, long narrow low-beamed bar with stripped stone, bric-a-brac and books, darts; TV may be on for sports; children welcome, garden, quaint village *(JP, PP, the Didler, Anne and Steve Thompson, Derek and Sylvia Stephenson)*
Crowdecote [SK1065]
Packhorse: Small 16th-c two-bar local, food from sandwiches up, real ale; tables in back garden, beautiful views, on popular walking route *(Doug Christian)*
Derby [SK3438]
☆ ***Abbey Inn*** [Darley St, Darley Abbey]: Notable for massive stonework remnants of 11th-c abbey; brick floor, studded oak doors, big stone inglenook, stone spiral stair to upper bar with handsome oak rafters; well kept cheap Sam Smiths, decent lunchtime bar food, children allowed; opp Derwent-side park, pleasant riverside walk out from centre *(JP, PP, the Didler, Anthony Barnes, LYM)*
Babington Arms [Babington Lane]: Large open-plan Wetherspoons, usual style and comfortable seating, friendly staff, well kept real ales, 20 whiskies *(Richard Lewis)*
Capt Blake [Agard St]: Comfortably reworked open-plan local with enjoyable food, Adnams, Bass and Marstons Pedigree, flame-effect gas fire; open all day Sat *(the Didler)*
Exeter Arms [Exeter Pl]: Several comfortable and friendly areas inside, inc super little snug with black-leaded and polished brass range, black and white tiled floor, two built-in curved settles, lots of wood and bare brick, HMS *Exeter* and regimental memorabilia and breweriana; friendly staff, well kept Banks's and Camerons Strongarm, fresh rolls and pork pies, daily papers, well reproduced piped music; open all day *(Kevin Blake, the Didler, Richard Lewis, JP, PP, David Carr, Richard Houghton)*
Falstaff [Silver Hill Rd, off Normanton Rd]: Lively and friendly three-room former coaching inn, basic and unsmart, with changing well kept ales such as Greene King Abbot and Marstons Pedigree; right-hand bar with coal fire usually quieter; open all day *(the Didler)*
☆ ***Flower Pot*** [King St]: Extended real ale pub with well kept changing beers such as Brakspears Bee Sting, Burton Bridge Polar

Eclipse, Oakham Bishops Farewell, Ossett Hercules, Ventnor SunFire and Whim Arbor Light and Hartington IPA – glazed panels show cellarage, regular beer festivals; friendly staff, three linked rooms inc comfortable back bar with lots of books, side area with old Derby photographs and brewery memorabilia, good value food till early evening, daily papers, pub games; piped music, good live bands wknds; open all day, tables on cherry-tree terrace; same small group runs the Smithfield *(Richard Lewis)*

Liversage Old Ale House [Nottingham Rd]: Well kept Leadmill Wild Weasel, Sidewinder and Saigon and John Smiths from central servery, helpful friendly landlord, comfortable lounge, bar with darts, games and TV; opens 4 wkdys, open all day wknds *(Richard Lewis)*

Old Silk Mill [Full St]: Attractively decorated and welcoming two-room 1920s pub with old prints and full-scale mural of 1833 Derby turnout, good interesting range of beers under light carbon dioxide blanket, lots of country wines, good value cheap food from sandwiches to steaks all day (back dining area, breakfasts from 9am), daily papers, real fires, SkyTV sports; open all day, handy for cathedral and Industrial Museum *(Richard Lewis, the Didler, David Carr, JP, PP)*

Rowditch [Uttoxeter New Rd (A516)]: Popular good value roadside pub, friendly atmosphere, well kept Mansfield, Marstons Pedigree and guest beers, country wines, attractive small snug on right, coal fire, quiz and food nights *(the Didler)*

☆ ***Smithfield*** [Meadow Rd]: Friendly and comfortable bow-fronted pub with big bar, snug, back lounge full of old prints, curios and breweriana, well kept changing ales such as Fullers London Pride, Hook Norton Best, Oakham JHB, Ossett Silver King and Wicked Hathern Hawthorn Gold, filled rolls and hearty lunchtime meals, real fires, daily papers; piped music, pub games inc table skittles, board games, TV and games machines, quiz nights, live music; open all day, children welcome, riverside garden *(Richard Lewis, the Didler, JP, PP, David Carr)*

☆ ***Standing Order*** [Irongate]: Vast Wetherspoons conversion of imposing bank, central bar, booths down each side, elaborately painted plasterwork, pseudo-classical torsos, high portraits of mainly local notables; usual popular food all day, good range of well kept ales, reasonable prices, daily papers, neat efficient young staff, no smoking area; rather daunting acoustics; good disabled facilities *(the Didler, JP, PP, Richard Lewis, BB)*

Station Inn [Midland Rd]: Friendly and bustling basic local with good food lunchtime and early evening in large back lounge, particularly well kept Bass in jugs from cellar, M&B Mild and Marstons Pedigree on handpump, tiled floor bar, side room with darts, pool and TV, ornate façade; piped music, open all day Fri *(Richard Lewis, the Didler)*

Dronfield [SK3378]

Jolly Farmer [Pentland Rd/Gorsey Brigg, Dronfield Woodhouse; off B6056]: Extensive bar done as comfortably rustic ale house, old pine, bare bricks, boards and carpets, alcoves and cosy corners, bric-a-brac and fresh flowers, very friendly staff and atmosphere, no smoking dining area, daily papers, comfortable seats, open fire, real ales from glazed cellarage such as Black Sheep, Jennings, Greene King, Tetleys and Timothy Taylors Landlord, good wine choice, reasonably priced food inc choice of Sun roasts, daily papers; piped music, games area with pool and TV, quiz nights Tues and Sun; children allowed if eating, open all day *(Andrew Crawford, CMW, JJW)*

Edale [SK1285]

☆ ***Old Nags Head*** [off A625 E of Chapel-en-le-Frith; Grindsbrook Booth]: Popular well used pub at start of Pennine Way, flagstoned area for booted walkers, food from basic hearty sustenance to more interesting dishes and wknd restaurant, well kept Scottish Courage and other ales, open fire; children in airy back family room, tables on front terrace and in garden – short path down to pretty streamside cottages; open all day *(JP, PP, C J Fletcher, LYM, Richard Fendick, John Hulme)*

Ednaston [SK2442]

Yew Tree: Unusual and attractive village pub with four rooms served from central bar, best one with lots of copper and brass, dark beams hung with whisky-water jugs, bay window overlooking garden, wall seats, large round table and open fire; good range of well cooked food, friendly efficient service, Bass beers with a guest such as Charles Wells Bombardier, separate games room out by car park *(Norma and Keith Bloomfield, Kevin Blake)*

Elmton [SK5073]

Elm Tree: Softly lit and popular low-ceilinged rural pub handy for M1 junction 30, with good value bar food, restaurant Fri/Sat evening and for good Sun lunch, well kept Bass; open all day Weds-Sun *(Gerry and Rosemary Dobson)*

Elton [SK2261]

☆ ***Duke of York*** [village signed off B5056 W of Matlock; Main St]: Unspoilt old-fashioned local in charming Peak District village, like stepping back in time, lovely little quarry-tiled back tap room with coal fire in massive fireplace, glazed bar and hatch to corridor, two front rooms – one like private parlour with piano and big dining table (no food, just crisps); Mansfield and occasional guest beer such as Adnams, friendly character landlady, welcoming regulars, darts; lavatories out behind by the pig sty; open 8.30-11, and Sun lunchtime *(John Brightley, the Didler, JP, PP, RWC, Pete Baker)*

Fenny Bentley [SK1750]

Bentley Brook [A515 N of Ashbourne]: Big open-plan bare-boards bar/dining room, log fire, communicating restaurant, one or two changing own-brewed Leatherbritches ales and well kept guest beers, food inc some unusual dishes, well reproduced piped music; picnic-sets on terrace with barbecue area, skittles, kitchen shop; marquee for spring bank hol beer festival, open all day, handy for Dovedale; bedrooms

(BB, the Didler, JP, PP, Dr B and Mrs P B Baker, Alun Howells)

Foolow [SK1976]

☆ ***Bulls Head***: Attractive moorland village pub with friendly flagstoned bar, prompt cheerful service, well kept changing ales such as Black Sheep, enjoyable food from generous sandwiches up in bar and pleasant no smoking restaurant area, interesting photographs inc good collection of Edwardian naughties; bedrooms, fine views, cl Sun evening *(LYM, David Carr, Roy Morrison, A Preston)*

Ford [SK4080]

Bridge Inn [off B6054 S of Sheffield]: Good service, four real ales, popular food (not Sun/Mon evenings) inc good sandwiches, log fire; no dogs, machines or piped music; TV in front lobby; children welcome, picnic-sets in garden, pretty millpond village, walks *(Patrick Hancock)*

Froggatt Edge [SK2577]

Grouse [B6054 NE of Froggatt]: Plush front bar, open fire and wooden benches in back bar, big dining room, good home cooking, Adnams and Banks's beers, friendly service, handsome views; verandah and terrace, clean bedrooms, good gritstone moorland walking country *(G B Longden)*

Great Hucklow [SK1878]

Queen Anne: Friendly family atmosphere, beams and gleaming copper, well kept Mansfield and guest beers such as Adnams, open fire, french windows to small back terrace and charming garden with lovely views, walkers' bar, unpretentious blackboard food (maybe just soup and sandwiches, winter lunchtimes); unobtrusive piped music; two quiet bedrooms, good walks *(CMW, JJW, the Didler, Peter F Marshall, Rona Murdoch, Trevor Swindells)*

Great Longstone [SK1971]

White Lion [Main St]: Friendly and helpful new management, reasonably priced enjoyable and imaginative home-made food, bistro-style dining room with stylishly simple décor, well kept Robinsons; charming stone-built village, beautiful countryside *(Susan Lee)*

Grindleford [SK2478]

Maynard Arms [Main Rd]: Spacious high-ceilinged hotel bar with dark panelling, local and autographed cricketing photographs, generous food from sandwiches to steaks and extremely rare roast beef (may take a while at busy times), well kept Boddingtons and Castle Eden, well chilled white wines, no smoking restaurant overlooking neat gardens with water feature; piped music; children in eating areas, open all day Sun, comfortable bedrooms, nice setting *(David Carr, LYM, D J and P M Taylor)*

Hardstoft [SK4463]

Shoulder of Mutton [B6039]: Country inn with two comfortable and attractive lounges, snug bar and (mainly oriental) restaurant, well kept Hardys & Hansons beers, lots of pictures and plates, soft lighting; handy for Hardwick Hall and Five Pits Trail *(Kevin Blake)*

Hartington [SK1561]

Jug & Glass [A515 Ashbourne—Buxton just N of B5054 junction]: Low-beamed moorland pub at long last reopened after restoration following 1994 fire, short choice of nicely prepared straightforward food, Bass and sometimes a guest beer *(Derek and Sylvia Stephenson)*

Hathersage [SK2680]

☆ ***Fox House*** [A6187/A625 3 miles towards Sheffield – just inside S Yorks]: Handsome 18th-c stone-built Vintage Inn with several linked rooms on different levels, oak-framed open fireplaces, good range of good value well presented food from sandwiches up, Bass and Stones real ale, good wine choice, quick friendly service; nice moorland location, good views from back terrace, bedrooms with own bathrooms *(BB, Eric Locker, Richard Fendick, Keith and Chris O'Neill)*

☆ ***George*** [Main Rd (A625 W of Sheffield)]: Substantial old hotel, civilised and restful, with old-fashioned attentive service but not at all stuffy, good value well presented food, keg beer but decent wine; a nice place to stay *(John and Christine Lowe, Paul A Moore, LYM)*

Millstone [Sheffield Rd (A625)]: Cosy pub with very friendly landlord and staff, lots of knick-knacks and antiques, many for sale, side brasserie, good bar meals and carvery; good choice of well kept beers, wines and whiskies; tables outside with good views, bedrooms *(Patrick Hancock)*

☆ ***Scotsmans Pack*** [School Lane, off A625]: Big clean welcoming open-plan local very popular with walkers, huge choice of generous nicely presented imaginative food inc wide vegetarian choice (best to book Sun lunch), reasonable prices, well kept Burtonwood beers inc Top Hat, decent wines, good service even when very busy; some seats in pleasant side courtyard by trout stream; four good value bedrooms, huge breakfast (may be piped radio then) *(David Carr, Patrick Hancock, Paul A Moore, DC, Steven and Sally Knight, D I Lucas, C J Fletcher, Gill Pennington)*

Hayfield [SK0388]

☆ ***Lantern Pike*** [Glossop Rd (A624 N)]: Cosily unpretentious and welcoming, with plush seats, lots of brass, china and toby jugs, well kept Boddingtons, Flowers IPA and Timothy Taylors Landlord, good choice of malt whiskies, decent fresh bar food from sandwiches and splendid filled oatcakes up inc children's and OAP wkdy lunches; no smoking back dining room, darts, dominoes, maybe piped nostalgic music; back terrace looking up to Lantern Pike, great spot for walkers; children welcome, open all day wknds, good value bedrooms (quieter at back) *(Kevin Blake, John Hulme, LYM)*

Pack Horse [off A624 Glossop—Chapel-en-le-Frith; Market St]: Busy nicely furnished dining pub open all day, proper food cooked to order from baguettes to steaks; great decorations for Christmas and other festivals *(Mike and Wendy Proctor, John and Christine Lowe, Mike and Linda Hudson)*

Heath [SK4467]

Elm Tree [just off M1 junction 29; A6175

towards Clay Cross, then first right]: Large lounge and public bar area, good value food inc children's, Banks's, Mansfield and Marstons beers, friendly efficient service; children welcome, quiz nights; views from attractive garden to Bolsover and beyond *(Roy and Lindsey Fentiman)*

Holbrook [SK3644]

Spotted Cow [Town St]: Traditional pub extended behind, Jennings, good value food inc generous help-yourself veg, comfortable no smoking eating area *(Bernie Adams)*

☆ ***Wheel*** [Chapel St]: Friendly beamed country local with well kept Courage Directors, Marstons Pedigree, Theakstons Best and Black Bull, Whim Hartington and a guest beer, some in jugs from the cellar, interesting whiskies and brandies, good value home-made food (not Sun evening or Mon) from sandwiches and baguettes up, good log fire, cheerful attentive staff, snug, family room, attractive separate restaurant; tables on terrace and in pleasant secluded garden with hawk in aviary, open all day Sat, cl Mon lunchtime *(Bernie Adams, Geoff and Tricia Alderman, Alan Bowker, the Didler, JP, PP)*

Holmesfield [SK3277]

George & Dragon [Main Rd]: Very comfortable and friendly; opp church *(Alison Keys)*

Horns [Main Rd]: Sensitively renovated, roomily comfortable, well kept ales inc Timothy Taylors Landlord, decent wines, new landlord doing wide choice of food inc imaginative fish dishes *(Alison Keys)*

Holymoorside [SK3469]

Lamb [Loads Rd, just off Holymoor Rd]: Small, cosy and spotless two-room village pub in leafy spot, Bass, Theakstons XB and up to six guest beers inc one from Adnams, pub games, tables outside; cl lunchtime Mon-Thurs *(the Didler)*

Ilkeston [SK4643]

Bridge Inn [Bridge St, Cotmanhay; off A609/A6007]: Two-room local by Erewash Canal, popular with fishermen and boaters for early breakfast and sandwich lunches; extremely well priced well kept Hardys & Hansons Best and Best Mild; well behaved children allowed, nice back garden with play area, open all day *(the Didler)*

☆ ***Dewdrop*** [Station St, Ilkeston Junction, off A6096]: Large welcoming three-room Victorian pub in old industrial area, two blazing coal fires, pictures and plates, friendly new beer-enthusiast landlord, interesting well kept guest beers from countrywide microbreweries, good value bar snacks inc huge cheap sandwiches, darts and TV in small public bar and impromptu piano sessions in lounge; sheltered outside seating, barbecue; has been cl Sat lunchtime, good value bedrooms *(JP, PP, Kevin Blake, James and Laura Newton, the Didler)*

Observatory [Market Pl]: Useful Wetherspoons, their usual features inc food all day; upstairs roof garden *(anon)*

Rutland Cottage [Heanor Rd]: Attractive pastel-décor lounge with lots of mining pictures and plates, jugs hanging from beams, friendly service, well kept ales such as Marstons Pedigree, Tetleys and Worthington, flowers on tables, long corridor to games room; big garden with play area *(Kevin Blake)*

Little Longstone [SK1971]

☆ ***Packhorse*** [off A6 NW of Bakewell via Monsal Dale]: Snug unchanging 16th-c cottage, a pub since 1787, with old wooden chairs and benches in two homely well worn in beamed rooms, well kept Marstons Best and Pedigree, simple but most enjoyable food lunchtime and evening, informal service, pub games, terrace in steep little back garden, hikers welcome; Weds folk night, opens 5 wkdys *(LYM, the Didler, JP, PP, Andrew Stephenson, Patrick Hancock)*

Makeney [SK3544]

☆ ***Holly Bush*** [from A6 heading N after Duffield, take 1st right after crossing River Derwent, then 1st left]: Unspoilt two-bar village pub, cosy and friendly, well kept changing ales such as Anglo Dutch Grizzly Ghost, Bass, Brains SA, Flowers Original, Greene King Old Speckled Hen and Otter Bright (may be brought from cellar in jugs), beer festivals, lots of brewing advertisements; three roaring open fires (one in old-fashioned range by snug's curved settle), flagstones, beams, black panelling and tiled floors; cheap food from lunchtime rolls up inc Thurs steak night; games lobby; children allowed in rough and ready hatch-served back conservatory, picnic-sets outside, dogs welcome *(the Didler, Bernie Adams, JP, PP, BB)*

Matlock [SK2959]

☆ ***Boat House*** [Dale Rd, Matlock Bridge – A6 S edge of town]: Friendly old-fashioned three-room Hardys & Hansons pub by River Derwent, between road and cliff of old limestone quarry; their ales and guest beers kept well and priced reasonably, blackboard food with seafood specialities inc great seafood platter for two served with moules marinière, family room; pool, traditional games, old juke box; open all day – tea at teatime; some seats outside, interesting walks, bedrooms *(Peter F Marshall, Derek and Sylvia Stephenson, JP, PP, the Didler)*

Matlock Bath [SK2958]

Princess Victoria [South Parade]: Small pub recently bought by Batemans, three of their beers and a guest, coal fire, good value food in comfortable long beamed bar and upstairs restaurant; open all day, busy wknds *(the Didler, Kevin Blake)*

Milford [SK3545]

William IV [Milford Bridge]: Stone-built pub with beams, bare boards and quarry tiles, relaxing atmosphere, Bass, Fullers London Pride, Timothy Taylors Landlord, Charles Wells Bombardier and Whim Hartington tapped from casks in back room, blazing coal fire, cheap food inc sandwiches and pork pies most evenings *(the Didler)*

Millers Dale [SK1473]

Anglers Rest [just down Litton Lane; pub is PH on OS Sheet 119 map ref 142734]: Friendly and comfortable creeper-clad pub with wonderful gorge views, good value food in cosy lounge, ramblers' bar and candlelit no smoking dining room, well kept Marstons Pedigree, Tetleys and changing guest beers such as Coach House Posthorn and Greene King Ruddles County, lots of toby jugs, plates and teapots, pool room; attractive village, good riverside walks *(A and B D Craig, Roy and Margaret Jones, JP, PP, the Didler)*

Monyash [SK1566]

☆ *Bulls Head* [B5055 W of Bakewell]: Homely and friendly high-ceilinged two-room local with oak wall seats and panelled settle, horse pictures, shelf of china, roaring log fire, mullioned windows, good value unpretentious home cooking using local ingredients, sandwiches too, Tetleys Bitter and Mild, Theakstons Black Bull and Whim Hartington, efficient staff; nicely set tables in plush two-room dining room, darts, dominoes, pool in small back bar, may be quiet piped music; long pews outside facing small green, friendly ginger cat, children and muddy dogs welcome; simple bedrooms, attractive village *(A G Thompson, BB, Bruce M Drew)*

Moorwood Moor [SK3656]

White Hart [nr South Wingfield]: Good choice of reasonably priced food, welcoming licensees, log fires, attractive décor, spacious and comfortable dining area; tables in garden *(Jan and Jerry Harwood)*

New Mills [SJ9886]

Fox [Brookbottom; OS Sheet 109 map ref 985864]: Friendly and unchanging old country pub cared for well by long-serving landlord, open fire, well kept Robinsons, plain good value food inc sandwiches, darts, pool; children welcome, handy for walkers (can get crowded wknds); splendid tucked-away hamlet down single-track lane *(the Didler, John Hulme)*

Newhaven [SK1660]

Carriages [A515/A5012]: Smart bar and restaurant, two Pullman dining carriages linked by attractive lounge with fresh flowers and railway memorabilia, lots of wines, well kept beers, with food choice from bar snacks to italian dishes *(Kevin Blake)*

Newton Solney [SK2825]

Unicorn [Repton Rd]: Friendly pub with good value food in bar and small restaurant; good bedrooms, huge breakfast *(Theo, Anne and Jane Gaskin, the Didler)*

Oakerthorpe [SK3856]

Peacock [B6013 Belper—Clay Cross]: Spacious and attractive dining pub, nooks and crannies, plenty of character, lots of pictures and plates, shelves of tasteful bric-a-brac, smart separate restaurant, enjoyable food, well kept beers such as Mansfield and Marstons Pedigree; play area, open all day *(Kevin Blake)*

Ockbrook [SK4236]

☆ *Royal Oak* [village signed off B6096 just outside Spondon; Green Lane]: Quiet 18th-c village local run by same family for 48 years, small unspoilt rooms (one no smoking), well kept Bass and guest beers such as Boggart Hole Clough Common Elf, Hobsons Mild and Springhead Roaring Meg, Oct beer festival, tiled-floor tap room, turkey-carpeted snug, inner bar with Victorian prints, larger and lighter side room, nice old settle in entrance corridor, open fires, cheap popular lunches from good sandwiches up, evening rolls, traditional games inc darts, no music or machines; band night Sun; tables in sheltered cottage garden, separate play area, more tables on cobbled front courtyard *(Pete Baker, BB, the Didler, JP, PP)*

Owler Bar [SK2978]

Peacock [A621 2 miles S of Totley]: Chef & Brewer in attractive moorland setting with panoramic views of Sheffield and Derbyshire Peak District, good food from extensive blackboard menu, helpful attentive staff; open all day *(Frank Gorman)*

Parwich [SK1854]

Sycamore: Fine old welcoming unspoilt pub, jovial landlady, lively chat and roaring log fire in simply furnished but comfortable main bar, lots of old local photographs, hatch-served tap room with games and younger customers; plain wholesome fresh food lunchtimes and Weds-Sat evenings, big helpings, well kept Robinsons inc seasonal Old Tom, and Theakstons; tables out in front and on grass by car park, quiet village not far from Tissington *(John Foord, A C and E Johnson, JP, PP, Pete Baker, the Didler)*

Repton [SK3026]

Bulls Head [High St]: Beams and open fires, ex-stables dining area with original flagstones and boards, wide food choice (not Mon) from good baguettes up inc children's, well kept Bass, Marstons Pedigree and a guest such as Adnams Broadside, helpful staff; families welcome; garden with terrace and play area, attractive village *(Dr S J Shepherd)*

Ripley [SK3851]

Excavator [Buckland Hollow; A610 towards Ambergate, junction B6013]: Welcoming open-plan pub recently refurbished in clean modern style, family dining area and no smoking area, wide choice of good value food (all day Sun) inc good children's menu, friendly efficient staff, well kept Marstons Pedigree and other ales *(Darly Graton, Graeme Gulibert)*

Rowarth [SK0189]

Little Mill [off A626 in Marple Bridge at Mellor sign, sharp left at Rowarth sign, then pub signed]: Beautiful tucked-away setting, unusual features inc working waterwheel; cheap cheerful plentiful bar food all day, big open-plan bar with lots of little settees, armchairs and small tables, Banks's, Marstons Pedigree and a guest beer, big log fire, busy upstairs restaurant; pub games; children welcome, pretty garden dell across stream great for them, with good play area; vintage Pullman-carriage bedrooms, open all day *(LYM, Eddie Edwards)*

Sandiacre [SK4737]

Blue Bell [Church St]: Friendly tucked-away 1700s former farmhouse, beams and breweriana, well kept Ind Coope Burton, Mallard, Marstons Pedigree, Oldershaws and a Mild *(Kevin Blake, Tony and Wendy Hobden, JP, PP, the Didler)*

Sawley [SK4833]

Harrington Arms [Derby Rd (B6540)]: Open-plan pub with beams and panelling, well kept Hardys & Hansons inc Mild (also Aug beer festival), fresh food strong on adventurous sauces; piped music may obtrude; tables outside, open all day *(Darly Graton, Graeme Gulibert, Niall Radford)*

Shardlow [SK4330]

☆ ***Malt Shovel*** [3½ miles from M1 junction 24, via A6 towards Derby; The Wharf]: Warm and friendly old-world beamed pub in 18th-c former maltings attractively set by canal, pretty hanging baskets etc, interesting odd-angled layout, well kept Banks's Best and Marstons Pedigree, quick service, cheap lunchtime food from baguettes and baked potatoes up (meal orders stop 2 sharp), good central open fire, farm tools and bric-a-brac; no small children, lots of tables out on waterside terrace *(JP, PP, John Beeken, Tony and Wendy Hobden, the Didler, Roger and Maureen Kenning, LYM, Kevin Douglas, Kevin Blake, Kevin Flack)*

Sheldon [SK1768]

Cock & Pullet: Light and cheerful cottage conversion, small and cosy, with helpful staff, good local atmosphere, well kept beer, busy dining area with good value tasty food inc Sun roasts and home-made puddings, morning coffee, open fire and scrubbed oak tables, pool in adjacent room; welcomes ramblers; tables outside *(Anne and Steve Thompson, Keith and Di Newsome)*

Shottlegate [SK3247]

☆ ***Hanging Gate*** [A517 W of Belper]: Charming Vintage Inn dining pub, above-average sensibly priced food all day, well kept Bass and Tetleys, decent choice of sensibly priced wines esp New World, friendly helpful staff, pleasant tidily kept rooms with attractive settles and lovely views; garden *(Stephen, Julie and Hayley Brown)*

Smalley [SK4044]

☆ ***Bell*** [A608 Heanor—Derby]: Two-room village pub with atmosphere all the better for being both small and popular, dining area with good reasonably priced changing food, well kept cheap real ales such as Adnams Broadside, Fullers London Pride, Whim IPA and Hartington and one or two guest beers, good choice of wines, pots of tea or coffee, smart efficient friendly staff; post office annexe, tables out in front and on big relaxing lawn with play area, beautiful hanging baskets, open all day wknds, attractive bedrooms behind *(JP, PP, Derek and Sylvia Stephenson, Bernie Adams, the Didler, A Preston)*

Smisby [SK3419]

Smisby Arms [Nelsons Sq]: Friendly beamed pub with good interesting food, shortish menu (good point), delicious puddings, well kept Marstons Pedigree; handy for specialist nursery *(Donald and Nesta Treharne)*

South Normanton [SK4457]

Castlewood [just off M1 junction 28, via A38; Carter Lane E]: Busy family Brewers Fayre with large friendly collection of rooms and dining nooks, good choice of beers and wines, big good value menu inc children's, quick service, huge indoor play area; piped music; attached Travel Inn *(Keith and Chris O'Neill, Peter and Audrey Dowsett)*

South Wingfield [SK3755]

Old Yew Tree [B5035 W of Alfreton; Manor Rd]: Cosy and convivial local thriving under new owners, good value food esp steaks and Sun lunch, well kept Marstons Pedigree and a couple of interesting guest beers, log fire, panelling, kettles and pans hanging from beams, separate restaurant area *(Kevin Blake, Derek and Sylvia Stephenson)*

Sparklow [SK1265]

Royal Oak [off A515 S of Buxton]: Relaxed country atmosphere in civilised open-plan pub popular for its enjoyable food inc interesting specials and busy Thurs steak night; two bar areas, well kept ales inc local Whim Hartington, good wine range, quick friendly service, chatty landlord, log fire, restaurant; children welcome, on Tissington Trail *(Mike and Wendy Proctor, Doug Christian, Peter Edwards, Dr W J M Gissane)*

Spondon [SK3935]

Malt Shovel [off A6096 on edge of Derby, via Church Hill into Potter St]: Cheap food, well kept Bass and a guest such as Alcazar or Orkney Red MacGregor from hatch in tiled corridor with cosy panelled and quarry-tiled or turkey-carpeted rooms off, old-fashioned décor, gas heater in huge inglenook, steps down to big games bar with full-size pool table, friendly efficient staff; lots of picnic-sets, some under cover, in big well used back garden with rabbit pens and good play area *(L Davenport, the Didler, JP, PP, Brian and Halina Howes, John Beeken, BB)*

Stanton in Peak [SK2464]

Flying Childers [off B5056 Bakewell—Ashbourne; Main Rd]: Cool in summer, warm in winter with coal fire in cosy and unspoilt right-hand room, well kept changing ales usually from Bass, Batemans, Fullers and/or Whim, very welcoming old-fashioned landlord, chatty locals, dominoes and cribbage, good value ready-made filled lunchtime rolls; in delightful steep stone village overlooking rich green valley; cl Mon and perhaps Thurs lunchtimes *(the Didler, Peter F Marshall, JP, PP)*

Staveley [SK4374]

☆ ***Speedwell*** [Lowgates]: Former typical industrial local attractively reworked in late 1990s, brewing its own Townes beers, all good with distinctive flavours and served cheaply in top condition, friendly staff, no smoking area, no juke box or machines (nor food); cl wkdy lunchtimes, open all day wknds *(Keith and Chris O'Neill, Derek and Sylvia Stephenson)*

Stoney Middleton [SK2375]

Moon [Townend]: Good sensibly priced food, well kept beer, friendly staff, nice décor with old photographs; handy for dales walks *(Sue Wheeler)*

Tansley [SK3259]

Tavern [A615 Matlock—Mansfield]: Dining pub with good value well prepared English cooking inc good Sun lunch, friendly relaxed atmosphere, well kept Marstons Pedigree, Tetleys and another real ale, reasonably priced wines *(Keith and Chris O'Neill)*

Tideswell [SK1575]

☆ *George* [Commercial Rd (B6049, between A623 and A6 E of Buxton)]: Traditional unpretentious L-shaped bar/lounge (partly no smoking), friendly newish licensees and quick happy staff, good value generous food inc children's, three well kept Hardys & Hansons ales, decent wines, open fires; piped music, games room with darts, pool, juke box and machines; children and dogs welcome, 60s music Fri; by remarkable church, tables in front overlooking pretty village, sheltered back garden; good value simple bedrooms (church clock strikes the quarters), pleasant walks *(BB, the Didler, CMW, JJW, Roy Morrison, Mike and Penny Sutton, Patrick Hancock, Ann and Colin Hunt, Steven and Sally Knight, JP, PP)*

Wardlow [SK1874]

☆ *Bulls Head*: Plushly comfortable country dining pub with short menu of decent food, good specials and steaks, real ale, helpful landlord and welcoming staff, provision for children; no dogs or walking boots, no credit cards *(LYM, G B Longden)*

Wensley [SK2661]

Red Lion [B5057 NW of Matlock]: Virtually a pub with no beer (may not even have bottles now), but worth a visit for its unspoilt appeal; friendly two-room no smoking farmhouse with chatty brother and sister owners, an assortment of 1950s-ish furniture, piano in main bar (landlord likes sing-songs), unusual tapestry in second room (usually locked, so ask landlady), no games or piped music, just tea, coffee, soft drinks and filled sandwiches or home-baked rolls maybe using fillings from the garden; outside lavatories; open all day *(John Brightley, JP, PP, Kevin Thorpe, Pete Baker, the Didler)*

Whatstandwell [SK3255]

Homesford Cottage [Homesford; A6 towards Cromford]: Friendly and comfortable, good helpings of fair-priced lunchtime bar food from good filled rolls up (they sell their home-made relishes to take away), jolly landlord, well kept Hardys & Hansons Best and Best Mild, separate restaurant; car park over road *(Andrew Crawford)*

Whittington Moor [SK3873]

Red Lion [Sheffield Rd (B6057)]: Small 19th-c stone-built pub tied to Old Mill with their Bitter, Bullion and a seasonal beer kept well, thriving atmosphere, old local photographs in two rooms, very friendly landlady *(Keith and Chris O'Neill, the Didler)*

Whitwell [SK5276]

Mallet & Chisel [Hillside]: Well kept real ales inc a Mild and cheap food inc bargain Sun lunch (popular, so best to book), pleasant bar with TV and linked dining room, children welcome; pool room, quiet piped music *(CMW, JJW)*

Winster [SK2460]

Bowling Green [East Bank, by NT Market House]: Refurbished but bar still pleasantly traditional and local-feeling, with friendly staff, well kept beers such as Whim Hartington, wide choice of enjoyable generous home cooking inc good Sun lunch, log fire, dining area and family conservatory; has been cl wkdy lunchtimes, open all day wknds *(Darly Graton, Graeme Gulibert, the Didler, Anthony Barnes, Theocsbrian, JP, PP)*

Miners Standard [Bank Top (B5056 above village)]: Welcoming 17th-c local, friendly family service, well kept Boddingtons and Marstons Pedigree, attractively priced generous food inc huge pies, big open fires, lead-mining photographs and minerals, ancient well; children allowed away from bar; restaurant, attractive view from garden, interesting stone-built village below; open all day (at least Sun) *(Anthony Barnes, JP, PP, the Didler, L Davenport)*

Woodthorpe [SK4574]

Albert [Woodthorpe Rd/Seymour Lane, off A619]: Old village local with three or four real ales inc low-priced Barnsley, enjoyable reasonably priced food inc choice of bargain Sun roasts; pool, games machines, piped music, TV; picnic-sets outside *(CMW, JJW)*

Youlgreave [SK2164]

☆ *George* [Alport Lane/Church St]: Handsome yet unpretentious stone-built 17th-c inn opp church, quick friendly service, welcoming locals, good straightforward home cooking inc game, comfortable banquettes, well kept John Smiths, Theakstons Mild and a guest such as Hartington; flagstoned locals' and walkers' side room, dogs welcome, games room, juke box; attractive village handy for Lathkill Dale and Haddon Hall, roadside tables, open all day *(Darly Graton, Graeme Gulibert, the Didler, JP, PP)*

Bedroom prices normally include full English breakfast, VAT and any inclusive service charge that we know of. Prices before the '/' are for single rooms, after for two people in double or twin (B includes a private bath, S a private shower). If there is no '/', the prices are only for twin or double rooms (as far as we know there are no singles). If there is no B or S, as far as we know no rooms have private facilities.

Devon

Up to now Devon, with Yorkshire, has been one of Britain's two best areas for pubs: interesting and attractive buildings, often in beautiful places, with good food and drink, and that essential factor, a buoyant and friendly atmosphere. But this year – we're sure as a depressing result of the foot & mouth restrictions keeping visitors away – a lot of the spark seems to have gone out of many Devon pubs. So those on really good form at the moment stand out even more prominently than usual: the Sloop near the sea at Bantham (a great all-rounder), the Drewe Arms at Broadhembury (wonderful fish cooking, a charming bar), the unspoilt and friendly Butterleigh Inn at Butterleigh, the well run Old Thatch Inn at Cheriton Bishop (popular as an A30 food stop), the Five Bells at Clyst Hydon (a favourite, with very helpful staff and a lovely garden), the Anchor at Cockwood (seafood's the thing here), the Wild Goose at Combeinteignhead (nice food, half a dozen west country beers), the interesting and welcoming old Cherub in Dartmouth (good fresh fish), the Drewe Arms at Drewsteignton (nice food in a classic thatched village pub), the Double Locks on the edge of Exeter (pleasing an extraordinarily wide variety of people), the Rock beautifully placed at Haytor Vale (good all round), the well run Hoops at Horns Cross (interesting food, half a dozen real ales), the cheerful old Masons Arms at Knowstone (keeping much of its character after careful alterations), the Church House at Marldon (once they've found it, people hunt for excuses to return), the friendly Peter Tavy Inn at Peter Tavy (good food and drink), the ancient and interesting Church House at Rattery, the Blue Ball at Sidford (in the same family for five generations, still going strong), the intriguing old Tower at Slapton (current regime doing well, with imaginative food), the individually run Kings Arms at Stockland (a nice all-rounder), the Green Dragon at Stoke Fleming (lots of character, a favourite for many), the smart Tradesmans Arms at Stokenham (good for an evening meal), the Passage House in Topsham (lots of fish, nice shoreside terrace), the Start Bay at Torcross (immensely popular for its good value fish), the Maltsters Arms at Tuckenhay, the Kings Arms at Winkleigh (nice food, friendly atmosphere), and the charming unspoilt Northmore Arms at Wonson. To add to these, we have six new main entries: the Merry Harriers at Clayhidon (food that looks to be in line for a Food Award, attractive and individual décor), the Dartmoor Inn at Lydford (exceptionally good food, charming décor), the London at Molland (wonderful country tavern), the Mountpleasant at Nomansland (another nice country pub, good all round), the Jack in the Green at Rockbeare (reliably good food, good drinks), and the Hare & Hounds near Sidbury (very popular all-rounder, nice layout). Unusually, one of these new entries wins our top accolade of Devon Dining Pub of the Year: the Dartmoor Inn at Lydford. There's a good choice of places in the Lucky Dip section at the end of the chapter: over 200, with several dozen added this year. Front-runners, most of them already inspected and approved by us, are the Awliscombe Inn, Ship at Axmouth, White Hart in Buckfastleigh, Exeter Inn at Chittlehamholt, Globe at Frogmore, Rock at Georgeham, Hartland Quay Hotel, Forest Inn at Hexworthy, Church House at Holne, Bickley Mill at Kingskerswell, Rising Sun in Lynmouth, Chichester Arms at Morteboe, Ring of Bells at North Bovey, Kings Arms at Tedburn St Mary, Globe in Topsham, Hole in the Wall in Torquay, Black Horse in Torrington, Whitchurch Inn, Old Inn at Widecombe, and the Marisco on Lundy Island. The Diggers Rest at Woodbury Salterton, long a popular main entry, changed hands too late for us to get a line on the new people, but we hope it will rejoin the main entries when we can. Drinks prices here are close to the national average, with some bargain exceptions, most notably the Imperial in Exeter. The Fountain Head at Branscombe (brewing its own Branoc ales), and the Dolphin in Beer, George at Blackawton, Cherub in Dartmouth, Hare & Hounds near Sidbury and Oxenham Arms at South Zeal also had cheap beer – always from small breweries. Small local breweries to look out for include Otter, Teignworthy, Exe Valley, Princetown, Branscombe Vale, Barum, Scattor Rock, Sutton, Clearwater and Jollyboat. The widely available Dartmoor Best actually comes from St Austell in Cornwall.

ASHPRINGTON SX8156 Map 1

Durant Arms

Village signposted off A381 S of Totnes; OS Sheet 202 map reference 819571

Beautifully kept and popular, this welcoming place is in a pretty village opposite the church. The beamed open-plan bar has several open fires, lamps and horsebrasses, fresh flowers, and a mix of seats and tables on the red patterned carpet; there's a lower carpeted lounge too, with another open fire. Using fresh local produce and totally home-made, the good, enjoyable bar food includes soup (£3.25), sandwiches (from £3.25), home-cooked ham and eggs (£6.25), chicken in brandy lasagne, good liver and onions, tasty spinach and mushroom risotto or cottage pie (all £6.95), steak and kidney pie (£7.45), fish dishes such as grilled salmon steak with a tomato and cucumber salsa (£10.50) or scallops and monkfish in a bacon and cream sauce (£13.45), gressingham duck breast (£13.95), and puddings such as blackberry and apple pie or home-made brûlée (£3.75); best to book if you want to be sure of a table. The no smoking dining room has lots of oils and watercolours by local artists on the walls. Good, attentive service. Well kept Flowers Original and Wadworths 6X on handpump, and local Pigsqueal cider; no games machines but they do have piped music. There is some wooden garden furniture on the back terrace. We'd expect this to be a very nice place to stay and would be grateful for feedback from readers. *(Recommended by Mrs J L Wyatt, Mr and Mrs D Barlow, Mrs Thomas, John Glaze, Richard and Margaret Peers, Bob and Ann Westbrook)*

Free house ~ Licensees Graham and Eileen Ellis ~ Real ale ~ Bar food ~ Restaurant ~ (01803) 732240 ~ Children in family room ~ Dogs allowed in bar ~ Open 11.30-2.30, 6.30-11; 12-2.30, 7-10.30 Sun ~ Bedrooms: £35B/£60B

AVONWICK SX7157 Map 1

Avon

Off A38 at W end of South Brent bypass; village signposted from exit

Mr Velotti's enjoyable Italian cooking continues to draw customers to this busy pub; best to book to be sure of a table. Listed on boards in the small back bar, there might be home-made soup (£2.50), filled ciabatta (from £3.50), penne with gorgonzola and artichokes (£6.25), wild mushroom risotto or fettucine with smoked salmon and mushrooms (£6.50), stir-fried monkfish, veal escalopes with wild mushrooms and red wine sauce, rack of lamb, duck stuffed with sun-dried tomatoes and olives or bass baked with ginger (all £12.50), beef with stilton (£13.50), and home-made puddings; espresso coffee. Some decent Italian wines alongside the well kept Badger Best and Bass on handpump; fruit machine and piped music. Décor and furnishings are comfortable and pleasant in a fairly modern style, and there's a woodburning stove. Tables out in an attractive garden by the River Avon; adventure playground. *(Recommended by Ian Phillips, John Evans, Dudley and Moira Cockroft)*

Free house ~ Licensees Mario and Marilyn Velotti ~ Real ale ~ Bar food (not Sun) ~ Restaurant (closed Sun) ~ (01364) 73475 ~ Children in restaurant ~ Open 11.30-2.30, 6.30-11; 7-10.30 Sun; closed Sun lunchtime

AXMOUTH SY2591 Map 1

Harbour Inn

B3172 Seaton—Axminster

The friendly licensees and their cheerful staff make this prettily set thatched pub an enjoyable place to visit. The Harbour Bar has black oak beams and joists, fat pots hanging from pot-irons in the huge inglenook fireplace, brass-bound cask seats, a high-backed oak settle, and an antique wall clock. A central lounge has more cask seats and settles, and over on the left another room is divided from the no smoking dining room by a two-way log fireplace. At the back, a big flagstoned lobby with sturdy seats leads on to a very spacious and simply furnished family bar. Well kept Flowers IPA and Original, Otter Ale, and Wadworths 6X on handpump; pool, and winter skittle alley. Good bar food includes sandwiches (from £2), soup (£2.75, home-made pâté (£3.50), ploughman's (from £4.25), sausages (£5), half a roast chicken or home-cooked ham (£5.75), good local lamb (curry or lasagne £6.90, cutlets in red onion and rosemary £7.50), popular fresh local fish like plaice (£7) or lemon sole (£8), steak (£8.25), puddings (from £3), and children's menu (£2.75); cheerful service even when busy, and friendly cat. They have a lavatory for disabled people, and general access is good. There are some tables in the neat back flower garden. The handsome church opposite has some fine stone gargoyles. *(Recommended by Alan and Paula McCully, Basil Minson, Michael and Marion Buchanan, Peter Burton, John and Vivienne Rice, Chris Reeve)*

Free house ~ Licensees Dave and Pat Squire ~ Real ale ~ Bar food (not winter Sun evenings) ~ (01297) 20371 ~ Children in eating area of bar and in summer family room ~ Dogs welcome ~ Live entertainment every 2nd Sat ~ Open 11-2.30(3 Sat), 6-11; 12-3, 7-10.30 Sun; closed Sun evenings end Oct-Easter

BANTHAM SX6643 Map 1

Sloop 🍷 🛏

Off A379/B3197 NW of Kingsbridge

'A smashing all-rounder' is how one reader describes this popular 16th-c pub – and it is a rather apt phrase. It's a nice place to stay and most bedrooms have views down to the beach or across the Avon estuary, there's a warm welcome for the good mix of customers, service is friendly, and the food and drink are most enjoyable. The black-beamed bar has a good bustling atmosphere, country chairs around wooden tables, stripped stone walls and flagstones, a woodburning stove, and easy chairs in a quieter side area with a nautical theme. From a wide choice, the interesting bar food includes pasties (from £2.10), sandwiches (from £2.60), tasty home-made soups (from £2.60), basket meals (from £3.10), home-made chicken liver pâté (£3.95), ploughman's (£4.60), fresh crab salad (£10.25), daily specials such as laver bread with ham and cockles (£4.45), tagliatelle with sun-dried tomato pesto (£5.65), seared scallop salad (£5.95), steamed fillet of local haddock with a cream and spinach sauce (£7.90), breast of chicken stuffed with apricot mousse (£8.45), deep-fried squat lobster with a lemon and tarragon mayonnaise (£9.25), and puddings like home-made summer pudding, treacle tart or hot chocolate fudge cake (£3.65); hearty breakfasts. Part of the dining room is no smoking. Well kept Bass, and Palmers IPA and Copper Ale on handpump, Luscombe farm cider, 25 malt whiskies, 14 wines by the glass from a carefully chosen wine list (including some local ones), and a good choice of liqueurs and West Country drinks like rum and shrub or brandy and lovage. Darts, dominoes, cribbage, and table skittles. There are some seats at the back. The bedrooms in the pub itself have the most character; they also have self-catering cottages. Plenty of surrounding walks. *(Recommended by Roger Wain-Heapy, Hugh Roberts, R and D Gray, David Crook, Chris Butt, Lynda and Trevor Smith, Lorna and Howard Lambert, H L Dennis, Pete and Jo Cole, Alan and Paula McCully, Geoff and Tricia Alderman, Nick Lawless, Michael Porter, Steve Whalley, Geoff Calcott, Derek and Caroline Earwood, C A Hall, Mr and Mrs J Curtis)*

Free house ~ Licensee Neil Girling ~ Real ale ~ Bar food (12-2, 7-10; not 25-26 Dec) ~ Restaurant ~ No credit cards ~ (01548) 560489 ~ Children welcome ~ Dogs welcome ~ Open 11-2.30, 6-11; 12-2.30, 6.30-10.30 Sun; closed evenings 25 and 26 Dec ~ Bedrooms: £35B/£70B

BEER SY2389 Map 1

Dolphin

Fore Street, off B3174 W of Seaton

Just up the steep lane from the beach, this seaside local has a good-sized friendly open-plan bar with a lively and bustling atmosphere (especially in summer), old-fashioned décor, and oak panelling and interesting nooks. You soon find yourself looking past the other customers, and spotting all sorts of bric-a-brac and memorabilia, not just nautical hardware (though there's plenty of that, too); piped music, darts, dominoes, cribbage, and fruit machine. Particular favourites are the giggly old fairground distorting mirrors, and the antique prize-fighting prints on the way through to the back (where there are sometimes antique stalls). Well kept Bass and Cotleigh Tawny and Barn Owl on handpump, and decent wine. As well as good local fish such as scallops, skate, lemon sole, and crab (from £8.25), enjoyable bar food includes sandwiches (from £1.95; fresh crab £5.25), soup (£2.25), ploughman's (from £3.75), roast beef or lamb (£5.75), generous home-made steak and kidney pie (£6), with daily specials such as king prawns in garlic butter (£6), chicken curry (£9.25), and scallop thermidor (£10.25), and puddings like home-made fruit pie or spotted dick with custard (£3.25). There's a dining room, and one or two tables out by the pavement keeping an eye on the high street action. More reports please. *(Recommended by John Couper, AL and Gill, Basil Minson)*

Free house ~ Licensee Mrs Lee Gibbs ~ Real ale ~ Bar food ~ Restaurant ~ No credit cards ~ (01297) 20068 ~ Children welcome ~ Dogs welcome ~ Open 11-3, 6-11; 12-3, 6.30-11 Sun ~ Bedrooms: £26S/£42(£52B)

BERRYNARBOR SS5646 Map 1

Olde Globe £

Village signposted from A399 E of Ilfracombe

New licensees have taken over this rambling 13th-c pub and are keen to change as little as possible – though they will open up a dining room, and the menu will be different. The series of dimly lit homely rooms has low ceilings, curved deep-ochre walls, and floors of flagstones or of ancient lime-ash (with silver coins embedded in them). There are old high-backed oak settles (some carved) and plush cushioned cask seats around antique tables, and lots of cutlasses, swords, shields and fine powder-flasks, a profusion of genuinely old pictures, priests (fish-coshes), thatcher's knives, sheep shears, gin-traps, pitchforks, antlers, and copper warming pans; the partly no smoking family room has a ball pool and other play equipment. Well kept Bass, Courage Directors, and Dartmoor Best on handpump; sensibly placed darts, pool, skittle alley, dominoes, fruit machine, and piped music. Bar food includes sandwiches (from £1.60), home-made soup (£1.75), ploughman's (from £2.95), home-made vegetable lasagne (£4.75), steak and kidney pie (£5.30), steaks (from £7.20), daily specials such as local lamb and mint sausages (£3.95), liver and onions (£4.50), and home-made curries (from £4.85), puddings (from £2.20), and children's dishes (£2.25). The crazy-paved front terrace has some old-fashioned garden seats, and there is a children's activity house. *(Recommended by Dr D J and Mrs S C Walker, Pat and Tony Martin, Boyd Catling, George Atkinson, Mr and Mrs I Bennett, Paul and Ursula Randall)*

Unique Pub Co ~ Lease Don and Edith Ozelton and family ~ Real ale ~ Bar food (not 25 Dec) ~ (01271) 882465 ~ Children in own room ~ Dogs allowed in bar ~ Open 12-2.30, 6-11; 12-2.30, 7-10.30 Sun; evening opening 7 in winter

BLACKAWTON SX8050 Map 1

George

Main Street; village signposted off A3122 W of Dartmouth, and off A381 S of Halwell

New licensees have taken over this traditional and friendly local but early reports from readers are warmly enthusiastic. The main bar has some timbering, a mix of cushioned wooden chairs, cushioned wall benches, and wheelbacks on the bare boards, local pictures, horsebrasses, and a collection of beer mats and pump clips, and hop bines above the bar; another bar has old pictures of the village. On one wall is a quaint old bow-windowed panel with little drawings of customers scratched on the glass. There's also a cosy end lounge with a woodburning stove and big bow window with a pleasant view. Bar food includes garlic mushrooms with bacon and cream (£3.25), ciabatta with bacon and brie or sun-dried tomatoes and basil (£4.95), liver and bacon (£5.95), a choice of sizzling skillets (£6.95), daily specials like rabbit and tarragon casserole (£6.50) or fresh fish dishes, and puddings such as sticky toffee pudding (£2.70). Well kept Teignworthy Spring Tide and Martha's Mild, and a guest such as Brakspears Bee Sting on handpump, three draught Belgian beers, and quite a few bottled Belgian beers; they hold a beer festival around the early May bank holiday, and another in August with live bands. Darts, cribbage, dominoes and euchre. The garden, set below the pub, has several picnic-sets and nice views. *(Recommended by Steve Dark, Paul Boot)*

Free house ~ Licensees Heather Gates, Ruth Coe, Vic Hall ~ Real ale ~ Bar food (till 10; not Mon lunchtime) ~ No credit cards ~ (01803) 712342 ~ Children in lounge or family room ~ Dogs welcome ~ Live musicians monthly ~ Open 12-2.30, 6(7 in winter)-11; 12-3, 7-10.30 Sun; closed Mon lunchtime except bank hols ~ Bedrooms: £20S/£40S

Normandy Arms

Signposted off A3122 W of Dartmouth; OS Sheet 202 map reference 807509

This friendly pub's name refers to the time the whole village was commandeered as a training ground to prepare for the Normandy landings. The main bar has an interesting display of World War II battle gear, a good log fire, and well kept Blackawton Bitter from the West Country Brewery, and a guest like Ind Coope Burton or Youngs on handpump. Well liked bar food includes home-made soup (£2.10), sandwiches (from £2.10; the crab is good, £3.35), devilled mushrooms (£3.65), ploughman's (£3.95), omelettes (£4.25), steak and kidney pie (£4.95), pork in cider and cream (£8.95), steaks with quite a choice of sauces (from £8.95), whole lemon sole (£9.25), and home-made puddings like tipsy cake or apple pie (from £2.95). The restaurant is no smoking. Sensibly placed darts, pool, shove-ha'penny, cribbage, dominoes, and piped music. Some tables out in the garden. *(Recommended by C A Hall, Richard and Margaret Peers, G R Taylor)*

Free house ~ Licensees Jonathan and Mark Gibson ~ Real ale ~ Bar food (12-1.45, 7-9; not winter Sun evenings) ~ Restaurant ~ (01803) 712316 ~ Children in restaurant ~ Dogs allowed in bar ~ Open 12-2.30, 7-11; 12-11 Sat; 12-10.30 Sun; 12-3, 7-10.30 Sun in winter; closed 25 Dec, 1 Jan ~ Bedrooms: /£56B

BRANSCOMBE SY1888 Map 1

Fountain Head

Upper village, above the robust old church; village signposted off A3052 Sidmouth—Seaton, then from Branscombe Square follow road up hill towards Sidmouth, and after about a mile turn left after the church; OS Sheet 192 map reference SY188889

This is a friendly, old-fashioned place with a lot of real character, and has the added attraction of brewing its own beers in the Branscombe Vale Brewery: Branoc, Jolly Geff (named after Mrs Luxton's father, the ex-licensee), summer Summa That, winter Hells Belles, Christmas Yo Ho Ho, and summer guest beers; they also hold a midsummer weekend beer festival which comprises three days of spit roasts, barbecues, live music, morris men, and over 30 real ales; farm cider, too. The room on the left – formerly a smithy – has forge tools and horseshoes on the high oak beams, a log fire in the original raised firebed with its tall central chimney, and cushioned pews and mate's chairs. On the right, an irregularly shaped, more orthodox snug room has a another log fire, white-painted plank ceiling with an unusual carved ceiling-rose, brown-varnished panelled walls, and rugs on its flagstone-and-lime-ash floor; the children's room is no smoking, the airedale is called Max, and the black and white cat, Casey Jones. Bar food such as sandwiches, filled baked potatoes or ploughman's, scallops au gratin (£4.50), sausage and mash with onion gravy (£4.95), good ham and egg, fresh battered cod (£5.95), home-made moussaka, and sole meunière (£8.95). Darts, shove-ha'penny, cribbage, and dominoes. There are seats out on the front loggia and terrace, and a little stream rustling under the flagstoned path. They offer self-catering. *(Recommended by A C and E Johnson, Joan and Michel Hooper-Immins, Dr and Mrs M E Wilson, JP, PP, Dr D E Granger, Brian and Bett Cox, the Didler, Basil Minson, June and Malcolm Farmer, Mrs Jean Clarke, David Holloway, Frank Smith)*

Own brew ~ Licensee Mrs Catherine Luxton ~ Real ale ~ Bar food (not 25 Dec) ~ (01297) 680359 ~ Children in own room; must be over 10 in evening restaurant ~ Dogs welcome ~ Folk/Irish summer Thurs ~ Open 11.30-3, 6-11; 12-3, 6-10.30 Sun; 11.30-2.30, 6.30-11 in winter

Masons Arms

Main Street; signed off A3052 Sidmouth—Seaton, then bear left into village

For nearly seven centuries this fine old inn has been welcoming travellers, and the long-standing present licensees continue working very hard to ensure that visitors are still made to feel at home – though probably now in a lot more comfort. The rambling low-beamed main bar has a massive central hearth in front of the roaring log fire (spit roasts on Tuesday and Sunday lunch and Friday evenings), windsor chairs and settles, and a good bustling atmosphere. The no smoking Old Worthies bar has a slate floor, a fireplace with a two-sided woodburning stove, and woodwork that has been stripped back to the original pine. The no smoking restaurant (warmed by one side of the woodburning stove) is stripped back to dressed stone in parts, and is used as bar space on busy lunchtimes. The same good, seasonally changing food is served in both bar and restaurant, and might include sandwiches (from £2.75, local crab £4.50; hot rolls with spicy chicken or toasted ciabatta with roasted vegetables, mozzarella and pesto £5.85), crab bisque (£4.50), ploughman's with home-made preserve or pickle (from £4.85), chinese-style confit of duck pancakes (£5.50), cod in beer batter (£7.95), steamed pudding filled with roasted vegetables, served with a tomato, lemon and garlic coulis (£8.95), steak and kidney pudding (£9.25), spicy chicken (£9.50), local pork in cider and cream with caramelised apple or king prawns in dijon mustard and cream (£11.50), roast half duck with honey (£13.50), and puddings such as baked rice pudding with raspberries, dark chocolate cheesecake marinated in orange and pineapple or peach and strawberry crumble, and children's menu (£3.95); several good value set meals (from £10). Well kept Bass, Otter Ale and Bitter, and two guest beers on handpump; they held their 10th beer festival in July and keep 30 malt whiskies, 14 wines by the glass, and farm cider; polite, attentive staff. Darts, shove-ha'penny, dominoes, and a lovely 200-year-old shove-ha'penny board. Outside, the quiet flower-filled front terrace has tables with little thatched roofs, extending into a side garden. As well as comfortable bedrooms, there are three cottages across the road which can be let with full hotel facilities or as self-catering units. *(Recommended by Phyl and Jack Street, David Peakall, P and J Shapley, Shaun Pinchbeck, Dr and Mrs M E Wilson,,B and F A Hannam, Cathy Robinson, Ed Coombe, Mike and Wendy Proctor, Steve Whalley, Howard and Margaret Buchanan, Lynn Sharpless, Bob Eardley, Charlie Harris, the Didler, Dr S J Shepherd, Andy Sinden, Louise Harrington, A C and E Johnson, Mrs Thomas, Peter Craske, Michael Doswell, Alan and Paula McCully)*

Free house ~ Licensees Murray Inglis and Mark Thompson ~ Real ale ~ Bar food ~ Restaurant ~ (01297) 680300 ~ Children welcome but must be well behaved ~ Dogs allowed in bar ~ Open 11-11; 12-10.30 Sun; 11-3, 6-11 in winter ~ Bedrooms: £24(£45B)/£48(£65B)

BROADHEMBURY ST1004 Map 1

Drewe Arms ★ 🍴 🍷

Signposted off A373 Cullompton—Honiton

Despite the emphasis on the excellent, really fresh fish dishes here, the small bar area has kept its lovely local chatty atmosphere so that anyone walking in for just a drink would not feel at all out of place. The bar has neatly carved beams in its high ceiling, and handsome stone-mullioned windows (one with a small carved roundabout horse), and on the left, a high-backed stripped settle separates off a little room with flowers on the three sturdy country tables, plank-panelled walls painted brown below and yellow above with attractive engravings and prints, and a big black-painted fireplace with bric-a-brac on a high mantelpiece; some wood carvings, walking sticks, and framed watercolours for sale. The flagstoned entry has a narrow corridor of a room by the servery with a couple of tables, and the cellar bar has simple pews on the stone floor; the dining room is no smoking. Most people do come to enjoy the unfailingly good food: open sandwiches (from £5.25; gravadlax £5.95; sirloin steak and melted stilton £7.25), daily specials such as spicy tomato soup (£5), griddled sardines (£7 small helping, £10.50 large helping), smoked haddock and stilton rarebit (£7 small helping, £11 large helping), wing of skate with black butter and capers (£11.50), fillet of brill with horseradish hollandaise (£16.75), sea bream with orange and chilli (£14.50), half lobster (£16), and puddings such as spiced pears with stem ginger ice cream or rhubarb compote with vanilla ice cream (£4.50); they also offer a three-course meal (£27.25) with choices such as marinated herring with a glass of aquavit, fillet of turbot, and St Emilion chocolate pudding. Best to book to be sure of a table. Well kept Otter Bitter, Ale, Bright and Head tapped from the cask, and a very good wine list laid out extremely helpfully – including 12 by the glass; shove-ha'penny, dominoes and cribbage. There are picnic-sets in the lovely garden which has a lawn stretching back under the shadow of chestnut trees towards a church with its singularly melodious hour-bell. Thatched and very pretty, the 15th-c pub is in a charming village of similar cream-coloured cottages. *(Recommended by the Didler, Kevin Blake, Mr and Mrs H D Brierly, Alan and Paula McCully, Anthony Longden, Basil Minson, Shaun Pinchbeck, Patrick Hancock, Howard and Margaret Buchanan, Charlie Harris, Peter Craske, Ian Phillips, R T and J C Moggridge, David and NinaPugsley, David and Elizabeth Briggs, JP, PP, B H and J I Andrews)*

Free house ~ Licensees Kerstin and Nigel Burge ~ Real ale ~ Bar food (not Sun evening) ~ Restaurant ~ (01404) 841267 ~ Well behaved children in eating area of bar and in restaurant ~ Dogs allowed in bar ~ Open 11-3, 6-11; 12-3 Sun; closed Sun evening, 31 Dec

BUCKLAND BREWER SS4220 Map 1

Coach & Horses ★

Village signposted off A388 S of Monkleigh; OS Sheet 190 map reference 423206

Carefully preserved, this 13th-c thatched house has a bustling pubby atmosphere, and a good mix of customers. The attractively furnished and heavily beamed bar has comfortable seats (including a handsome antique settle), a woodburning stove in the inglenook, and maybe Harding the friendly cat; a good log fire also burns in the big stone inglenook of the cosy lounge. A small back room has darts and pool. Good bar food includes sandwiches (from £2.95), home-made pasty (£3.75), filled baked potatoes (from £3.50), ploughman's (£4.75), ham and egg (£6.50), five home-made curries (£7.75), daily specials such as steak and mushroom in ale pie (£7.25), pork in honey and mustard sauce (£7.50), whole prawns sautéed in garlic (£7.95), duck strips in honey and ginger sauce (£8.50), braised lamb wrapped in bacon with rosemary and wine sauce (£8.95), fried fillets of bream in chilli sour cream (£10.95), and whole bass baked with orange and sage butter (£13.95); Sunday roasts (£5.50). The restaurant is no smoking. Well kept Bass and Flowers London Pride on handpump; dominoes, cribbage, fruit machine, skittle alley, and piped music. There are tables on a terrace in front, and in the side garden. They have a cottage to let. *(Recommended by Jill Thomas, Harry Thomas, Steve and Liz Tilley, Dr Paull Khan, R M Corlett, R J Walden, the Didler)*

Free house ~ Licensees Oliver Wolfe and Nicola Barrass ~ Real ale ~ Bar food (not evenings 25 or 26 Dec) ~ Restaurant ~ (01237) 451395 ~ Children welcome ~ Dogs welcome ~ Open 12-3, 6-11; 12-3, 7-10.30 Sun; closed evening 25 Dec ~ Bedrooms: £30B/£60B

BUCKLAND MONACHORUM SX4868 Map 1

Drake Manor

Off A386 via Crapstone, just S of Yelverton roundabout

This quietly relaxed and friendly pub was originally built to house the masons constructing the church in the 12th c; it was rebuilt in the 16th c. The heavily beamed public bar on the left has brocade-cushioned wall seats, prints of the village from 1905 onwards, some horse tack and a few ship badges on the wall, and a really big stone fireplace with a woodburning stove; a small door leads to a low-beamed cubby hole where children are allowed. The snug Drakes Bar has beams hung with tiny cups and big brass keys, a woodburning stove in an old stone fireplace hung with horsebrasses and stirrups, a fine stripped pine high-backed settle with a partly covered hood, and a mix of other seats around just four tables (the oval one is rather nice). On the right is a small, beamed no smoking dining room with settles and tables on the flagstoned floor. Shove-ha'penny, darts, euchre, and dominoes. Enjoyable bar food includes soup (£2.75), lunchtime baguettes (from £3.50), ploughman's (from £4.25), and sausage, ham and chips (£4.25), as well as tasty crispy coated ginger and garlic prawns (£4.25), vegetable tagine or home-made lasagne (£5.95), home-made steak and kidney in ale pie (£6.25), steaks (from £9.25), and daily specials such as pork fillet with wholegrain mustard, brandy and cream or grilled whole lemon sole (£8.95), duck breast with Grand Marnier and tangy orange sauce (£9.25), and fresh grilled halibut with lemon butter (£10.25). Well kept Courage Best, Greene King Abbot and Sharps Doom Bar on handpump, and they keep nearly 100 malt whiskies, a decent wine list, and Inch's dry cider. There are picnic-sets in the prettily planted and sheltered back garden. The pub is handy for Garden House. *(Recommended by Gordon Stevenson, Jacquie and Jim Jones, DAV, Lynn Sharpless, Bob Eardley)*

Innspired Inns ~ Lease Mandy Robinson ~ Real ale ~ Bar food (12-2, 7-10(9.30 Sun)) ~ Restaurant ~ (01822) 853892 ~ Children in eating area of bar and in restaurant ~ Dogs allowed in bar ~ Open 11.30-2.30(3 Sat), 6.30-11; 12-3, 7-10.30 Sun

BUTTERLEIGH SS9708 Map 1

Butterleigh Inn

Village signposted off A396 in Bickleigh; or in Cullompton take turning by Manor House Hotel – it's the old Tiverton road, with the village eventually signposted off on the left

Well worth seeking out, this bustling and unspoilt village pub is run by a warmly friendly landlady and has plenty to look at in its little rooms: pictures of birds and dogs, topographical prints and watercolours, a fine embroidery of the Devonshire Regiment's coat of arms, and plates hanging by one big fireplace. One room has pine dining chairs around country kitchen tables, another has an attractive elm trestle table and sensibly placed darts, and there are prettily upholstered settles around the three tables that just fit into the cosy back snug. Tasty bar food includes filled lunchtime rolls or home-made soup (£2.50), lunchtime ploughman's (£4.25), popular home-made burger or asparagus, mushroom and tomato tartlet (£5.25), tuna steak with a hot tomato salsa (£7.75), bacon chops with a plum sauce (£8.25), steaks (from £9.25), and daily specials. Well kept Cotleigh Tawny and Barn Owl, and a guest such as Exe Valley Spring or RCH East Street Cream on handpump;

darts, shove-ha'penny, cribbage, dominoes, chess, backgammon, and piped music; jars of snuff on the bar. Outside are tables on a sheltered terrace and neat lawn. *(Recommended by Mrs Sylvia Elcoate, Jacquie and Jim Jones, Ian Phillips, P J Ridley, George Atkinson, Jane and Adrian Tierney-Jones, Tom Evans, Richard and Margaret Peers, Bryan Robinson, B H and J I Andrews)*

Free house ~ Licensee Jenny Hill ~ Real ale ~ Bar food (not Sun evening) ~ (01884) 855407 ~ Children in eating area of bar lunchtime only ~ Dogs welcome ~ Open 12-2.30, 6(5 Fri)-11; 12-3, 7-10.30 Sun

CHAGFORD SX7087 Map 1

Ring o' Bells

Off A382 Moretonhampstead—Whiddon Down

Quietly civilised with no noisy games machines or piped music, this old black and white pub is liked by more mature customers – though families with well behaved children are certainly welcome. The oak-panelled bar has black and white photographs of the village and local characters past and present on the walls, comfortable seats, a choice of newspapers, a big fireplace full of copper and brass, and a log-effect gas fire; newspapers to read and no noisy games machines or piped music. There's a small no smoking candlelit dining room. Generous helpings of good food using local game, meat, and fresh fish include home-made soup such as parsnip and sage (£3.50), sandwiches (from £3), filled baked potatoes (from £5.50), home-cooked ham ploughman's (£5.95), Italian vegetarian bean salad (£7), daily specials using local produce, such as egg and prawn mayonnaise (£5), cold meats and cheese with pickles and chutney, rabbit and bacon pie, herb-roasted chicken with fruit stuffing, roast Dartmoor lamb with fresh rosemary and redcurrant gravy and sweet mint or two cheese and red onion tart (all £7.95), whole sardines or local mussels (£8.50), half a fresh roast duckling with port and orange cumberland sauce (£13.95), and home-made puddings like boozy chocolate orange mousse, bread and butter pudding made with home-made marmalade or fresh lime meringue pie (£3.95). Well kept Butcombe Bitter, Exmoor Ale, and St Austell HSD on handpump, Addlestone's cider, and quite a few malt whiskies. Shove-ha'penny, cribbage, dominoes, and darts (if the pub is not busy). The sunny walled garden behind the pub has seats on the lawn; there are dog biscuits on the corner of the bar, though the pub cat Coriander keeps visiting dogs under control. There are walks on the nearby moorland. *(Recommended by DAV, John and Annabel Hampshire, Gartlen and Wally Rogers, Michael Lamm, Mrs Jean Clarke, Nigel Williamson, B H and J I Andrews)*

Free house ~ Licensee Mrs Judith Pool ~ Real ale ~ Bar food (they serve breakfast and snacks from 8.30am) ~ (01647) 432466 ~ Children over 10 in eating area of bar; younger children in restaurant but no pushchairs ~ Dogs welcome ~ Open 11-3, 5-11; 12-3, 6-10.30 Sun; may close early on quiet evenings in winter ~ Bedrooms: £20/£40(£45S)

CHERITON BISHOP SX7793 Map 1

Old Thatch Inn

Village signposted from A30

This bustling pub – so handy for the A30 – is always full of contented diners, and at peak times it is worth booking a table. The rambling beamed bar is separated from the lounge by a large open stone fireplace (lit in the cooler months), and has well kept Branscombe Vale Branoc, and a couple of guests such as Otter Ale or Skinners Figgys Brew on handpump; fresh flowers on the tables, and polite, hard-working staff. At the end of May, they hold a weekend beer festival featuring mainly west country ales from small independent breweries. Enjoyable bar food includes sandwiches, home-made soup (£2.95), home-made chicken liver pâté with cumberland sauce (£3.25), spicy garlic and herb mushrooms in cream sauce (£3.50), pasta with creamed smoked haddock au gratin (£6.50), generous fish and chips (£6.95), pork with prunes and a cream sauce (£7.95), steaks (from £8.95), daily specials such as smoked chicken and bacon salad with raspberry vinaigrette (£4.50), poached chicken breast with brandy and green peppercorn sauce (£7.95), fried pork tenderloin in a mustard and smoked bacon sauce (£9.95), grilled whole bass with lime and ginger butter (£8.95), and puddings such as delicious raspberry and cinnamon torte with raspberry coulis and clotted cream (£3.50). The family room is no smoking, and leads onto the terrace with a thatched water well; piped music. *(Recommended by Esther and John Sprinkle, Peter and Audrey Dowsett, M Hounsell, R J Walden, Dr and Mrs J Lakic, Geoff Pidoux, David Crook, Michael Lamm, Tracey and Stephen Groves, Peter Meister, Ian and Deborah Carrington, Jenny and Brian Seller, Peter and Margaret Lodge, Mrs I Charles, M H Lendrum, Peter Wrobbel, Laura Wilson, Colin McKerrow, Anthony Barnes, Cath Donne)*

Free house ~ Licensee Stephen James Horn ~ Real ale ~ Bar food ~ Restaurant ~ (01647) 24204 ~ Children in restaurant and family room ~ Dogs allowed in bar ~ Open 11.30-3, 6-11; 12-3, 7-10.30 Sun; closed winter Sun evenings ~ Bedrooms: £35B/£49B

CLAYHIDON ST1615 Map 1

Merry Harriers

3 miles from M5 junction 26: head towards Wellington; turn left at 1st roundabout signposted Ford Street and Hemyock, then after a mile turn left signposted Ford Street; at hilltop T-junction, turn left towards Chard – pub is 1½ miles on right

Reopened a couple of years ago, this is now a warmly welcoming and charmingly laid out dining pub, with good restauranty food using local venison, lamb, and duck, organic chicken, fresh fish from Brixham, and local cheeses and cream; it's already best to book at weekends. The food might include parmesan, tomato and olive salad drizzled with basil olive oil (£3.50; main course £6.50), west country brie roasted in nibbed hazelnuts with home-made chutney (£4; main course £6.75), lunchtime sandwiches (from £4), deep-fried king prawns in oriental pastry with sweet chilli dipping sauce (£4.50; main course £8.25), lunchtime main courses such as lightly smoked carved ham with free range eggs (£6.50), fresh haddock in beer batter (£7.50), tagliatelle with fresh pesto (£9.50), and local venison steak with cranberry jus (£14), with evening choices like mixed game and wild mushroom casserole with herb dumplings (£11), confit of Quantock duck with home-made onion marmalade (£12.50), griddled tuna loin and vintage balsamic vinegar (£14), and Brixham scallops with white wine and chive sauce (£16). Home-made puddings may include steamed chocolate pudding with rich chocolate sauce or fresh raspberry shortbread with whipped cream (£4). Several small linked green-carpeted areas have comfortably cushioned pews and farmhouse chairs, lit candles in bottles, a couple of warm woodburning stoves (one with a sofa beside it), and plenty of horsey and hunting prints and local wildlife pictures. One snug little extension has a sloping ceiling, William Morris curtains and ragged pink walls; another slightly larger one has a brighter feel with its quarry tiles and lightly timbered white walls. You can only smoke in the bar area. They have Bollhaye's farm cider and well kept Juwards, Otter Head and Wadworths 6X on handpump, and 10 enjoyable wines by the glass. There are two dogs, Annie who likes real ale, and Nipper who only has three legs. There are picnic-sets on a small terrace, with more in a sizeable garden sheltered by shrubs and the old skittle alley; this is a good walking area. *(Recommended by Patrick Darley, Nick and Lesley Warboys, Brian and Bett Cox)*

Free house ~ Licensees Barry and Chris Kift ~ Real ale ~ Bar food ~ Restaurant ~ (01823) 421470 ~ Children over 6 in bar eating area lunchtime; no children in evening ~ Dogs allowed in bar ~ Open 12-3, 7-11; 12-3 Sun; closed Mon, lunchtime Tues, Sun evening

CLYST HYDON ST0301 Map 1

Five Bells

West of the village and just off B3176 not far from M5 junction 28

On many people's list of 'must go backs', this is a most attractive thatched pub run by particularly friendly and helpful licensees. The partly no smoking bar is spotlessly kept, has a bustling, chatty atmosphere, and is divided at one end into different seating areas by brick and timber pillars; china jugs hang from big horsebrass-studded beams, there are many plates lining the shelves, lots of sparkling copper and brass, and a nice mix of dining chairs around small tables (fresh flowers and evening candles in bottles), with some comfortable pink plush banquettes on a little raised area; the pretty no smoking restaurant is up some steps to the left. Past the inglenook fireplace is another big (but narrower) room they call the Long Barn with a pine dresser at one end and similar furnishings. Popular, enjoyable daily specials might include mussels in cider with cream (£4.95; main course £9.95), lambs liver with bacon and thyme and red wine gravy, pork in cider and apple sauce or much loved steak and kidney pudding (£8.95), platters (around £7.50; smoked fish platter (£10.25), lamb shank with rosemary and honey (£10.95), vegetarian choices, and steaks (from £10.95); also, sandwiches (from £3.75; crab £5.95), jumbo sausages (£4.75), prawn and egg mayonnaise (£4.95), courgette provençale (£5.75), and cold home-cooked ham (£7.75). Well kept Cotleigh Tawny, O'Hanlon's Blakeley's Best, and Otter Bitter on handpump, a thoughtful wine list, and several malt whiskies; piped music. The cottagey front garden is a fine sight with its thousands of spring and summer flowers, big window boxes and pretty hanging baskets; up some steps is a sizeable flat lawn with picnic-sets, a play frame, and pleasant country views.

(Recommended by Anne and David Robinson, Alan and Paula McCully, R J Herd, Jacquie and Jim Jones, Brian and Genie Smart, R J Walden, Dr and Mrs M E Wilson, Nigel and Sue Foster, Tony Dyer, Comus and Sarah Elliott, Joan E Hilditch, Barry Smith, Haydn Jones, James Flory, Les and Barbara Owen)

Free house ~ Licensees Robin Bean and Charles Hume Smith ~ Real ale ~ Bar food (till 10pm) ~ Restaurant ~ (01884) 277288 ~ Well behaved children in eating area of bar ~ Open 11.30-2.30, 6.30-11; 12-2.30, 6.30-10.30 Sun; evening opening 7 (6.30 Sat) in winter

COCKWOOD SX9780 Map 1

Anchor

Off, but visible from, A379 Exeter—Torbay

Even in mid-winter, this former ex-seaman's mission remains immensely popular, and you must arrive early to be sure of a table – and even a parking space. From a large menu, there are 30 different ways of serving mussels (£6.50 normal size helping, £11.50 for a large one), 12 ways of serving scallops (from £5.95 for a starter, from £13.95 for a main course), 10 ways of serving oysters (from £7.95 for a starter, from £14.95 for a main course), and 5 'cakes' such as crab cakes or mussel cakes (£5.95 for a starter, £9.95 for a main course), as well as tuna steak in tomato and garlic (£6.50), locally caught cod or whole grilled plaice (£6.95), and a shellfish selection (£15.50), and lots of daily specials. Non-fishy dishes feature as well, such as home-made soup (£2.85), sandwiches (from £2.95), home-made chicken liver pâté (£3.85), cheese and potato pie (£4.50), home-made steak and kidney pudding (£5.95), rump steak (£8.95), and children's dishes (£2.50). But despite the emphasis on food, there's still a pubby atmosphere, and they keep six real ales on handpump or tapped from the cask: Bass, Flowers Original, Fullers London Pride, Greene King Old Speckled Hen, Otter Ale and Youngers. Also, a rather good wine list (10 by the glass – they do monthly wine tasting evenings September-June), 25 brandies, 70 malt whiskies, and west country cider. The small, low-ceilinged, rambling rooms have black panelling, good-sized tables in various alcoves, and a cheerful winter coal fire in the snug; the cosy restaurant is no smoking. Darts, dominoes, cribbage, fruit machine, and piped music. From the tables on the sheltered verandah you can look across the road to the bobbing yachts and crabbing boats in the harbour.

(Recommended by Basil Minson, Richard and Margaret Peers, Meg and Colin Hamilton, Bob and Ann Westbrook, R J Walden, Peter and Jenny Quine, Canon and Mrs Michael Bourdeaux, Darly Graton, Graeme Gulibert, Mike Gorton, Susan and Nigel Wilson, John Beeken, Jayne and Peter Capp)

Heavitree ~ Tenants Mr Morgan and Miss Sanders ~ Real ale ~ Bar food (12-3(2.30 Sun), 6.30-10(9.30 Sun)) ~ Restaurant ~ (01626) 890203 ~ Children in eating area of bar and in restaurant ~ Dogs allowed in bar ~ Open 11-11; 12-10.30 Sun; closed evening 25 Dec

COLEFORD SS7701 Map 1

New Inn

Just off A377 Crediton—Barnstaple

At 600 years old, this is one of the oldest 'new' inns in the country. There are several interestingly furnished areas that spiral around the central servery, with ancient and modern settles, spindleback chairs, plush-cushioned stone wall seats, some character tables – a pheasant worked into the grain of one – and carved dressers and chests; also, paraffin lamps, antique prints and old guns on the white walls, and landscape plates on one of the beams, with pewter tankards on another; the resident parrot Captain is chatty and entertaining. The servery itself has settles forming stalls around tables on the russet carpet, and there's a winter log fire. Good, interesting food, using good local produce, includes soup (£3.95), filled baguettes (from £3.95; ciabatta with warm goats cheese and tapenade £4.95), ploughman's (from £5.95), duck and orange pâté with onion marmalade (£4.50), king prawns in thai butter or omelettes (£4.95), salads (from £6.95; smoked chicken and pineapple £7.95), roasted mediterranean vegetables on couscous with yoghurt dressing (£7.50), pork and leek sausages with cider sauce or liver, bacon and onion gravy (£7.95), seafood platter or pork tenderloin with bubble and squeak, cider sauce and caramelised apples (£9.95), seared tuna steak with tomato salsa (£10.95), steaks (from £13.95), and daily specials. The restaurant is no smoking. Well kept Badger Best and Exmoor Gold, with a guest such as Greene King Abbot and Otter Ale on handpump, and quite a range of malt whiskies, ports and cognacs. Fruit machine (out of the way up by the door) and piped music. There are chairs, tables and umbrellas on decking under the willow tree along the stream, and more on the terrace. *(Recommended by Steve Harvey, Jed and Virginia Brown, R J Walden, Richard and Margaret Peers, Mrs Sylvia Elcoate, G C Buckle, Sarah and Simon House, Pat and Tony Martin, DAV, Peter and Jenny Quine)*

Free house ~ Licensees Paul and Irene Butt ~ Real ale ~ Bar food (till 10(9.30 Sun)) ~ Restaurant ~ (01363) 84242 ~ Children in eating area of bar and in restaurant ~ Dogs allowed in bar ~ Open 12-3, 6-11; 12-3, 7-10.30 Sun; closed 25 and 26 Dec ~ Bedrooms: £60B/£70B

COMBEINTEIGNHEAD SX9071 Map 1

Wild Goose

Just off unclassified coast road Newton Abbot—Shaldon, up hill in village

There's a good mix of visitors and locals in this bustling pub. The spacious back beamed lounge has wheelbacks, red plush dining chairs, a decent mix of tables, and french windows to the garden, with nice country views beyond; the front bar has some red Rexine seats in the window embrasures of the thick walls, flagstones in a small area by the door, some beams and standing timbers, and a step down on the right at the end, with dining chairs around the tables and a big old fireplace with an open log fire. In the main part are standard lamps in corners, a small carved oak dresser with a big white goose, and a fruit machine; darts, pool, cribbage, dominoes, fruit machine, and shove-ha'penny; there's also a cosy section on the left with an old settee and comfortably well used chairs. Six well kept west country ales like Bath, Exe Valley, Otter Ale, Princetown, Scattor Rock, Skinners, and Teignworthy on handpump, over 30 malt whiskies, and local Luscombe cider. Good bar food includes lunchtime snacks such as jumbo sausage and onions in a baguette (£2.95), filled granary rolls (from £3.50), and omelettes (from £4.95), as well as home-made soup (£2.95), home-made pâté such as smoked mackerel or duck with port or king prawns in filo pastry with a dip (£4.95), cashew nut paella (£6.75), game sausages (£6.95), smoked chicken and bacon (£9.95), popular rack of ribs, fresh fish dishes like cod in dill batter or whole lemon sole (from £9.95), and puddings such as home-made bread and butter pudding, cheesecakes or banoffi pie (£3.45); they have a Thursday curry evening. Some picnic-sets in the garden. *(Recommended by Mrs Sylvia*

Elcoate, Dr and Mrs M E Wilson, David and Elizabeth Briggs, Neil and Beverley Gardner, Bob and Ann Westbrook, JP, PP, Mike and Mary Carter, Owain Ennis, Phil and Heidi Cook, the Didler, Ian and Nita Cooper, B H and J I Andrews)

Free house ~ Licensees Jerry and Kate English ~ Real ale ~ Bar food (till 10(9.30 Sun)) ~ (01626) 872241 ~ Well behaved children in eating area of bar and in restaurant ~ Dogs allowed in bar ~ Open 11.30-2.30, 6.30-11; 12-2.30, 7-10.30 Sun

CORNWORTHY SX8255 Map 1

Hunters Lodge

Off A381 Totnes—Kingsbridge ½ mile S of Harbertonford, turning left at Washbourne; can also be reached direct from Totnes, on the Ashprington—Dittisham road

Run by genuinely friendly, welcoming licensees, this spotlessly kept little pub has a small low-ceilinged bar with two rooms, and a combination of wall seats, settles, and captain's chairs around heavy elm tables; there's also a small and pretty no smoking cottagey dining room with a good log fire in its big 17th-c stone fireplace. Well presented, popular food at lunchtime includes sandwiches, roasted tomato and fresh basil soup (£2.50), chicken, pork and duck liver pâté with cointreau (£3.75), ploughman's (£4.50), scrambled egg, smoked salmon and mushrooms on toast or local sausages and mash (£5.25), steak and kidney pie (£7.50), and lamb and rosemary casserole (£7.75), with evening dishes such as grilled goats cheese with apple sauce (£3.95), liver and bacon (£6.50), mushroom tortellini (£7), breast of chicken with camembert and bacon on a tarragon and mushroom sauce (£9.95), and roast aromatic duckling on hot raspberry coulis (£12.95), daily specials like grilled cod with herb and cheese topping (£8.45) or monkfish and scallops in cream and garlic sauce (£10.45), and puddings such as treacle tart or sherry trifle (£3.25). Well kept Teignworthy Reel Ale and Beachcomber, and a guest such as Orkney Dark Island on handpump, 45 malt whiskies, country wines, and a decent wine list. Dominoes, cribbage, Jenga, shut the box, and piped music. In summer, there is plenty of room to sit outside, either at the picnic-sets on a big lawn or on the flower-filled terrace closer to the pub, and they hold barbecues, weather permitting. They have two cats, Ollie and Alex, the huge ginger tom. *(Recommended by David and Elizabeth Briggs, Doreen and Haydn Maddock, Mark and Amanda Sheard, Mr and Mrs R Reece, Brian Lynch, Mrs A Maslen, Glen Hamill, Jeffrey Stackhouse)*

Free house ~ Licensees Elizabeth and Roger Little ~ Real ale ~ Bar food ~ Restaurant ~ (01803) 732204 ~ Children welcome ~ Dogs allowed in bar ~ Jazz/acoustic/Irish music 4th Thurs of month ~ Open 11.30-2.30, 6.30-11; 12-3, 7-10.30 Sun

DALWOOD ST2400 Map 1

Tuckers Arms

Village signposted off A35 Axminster—Honiton

The summer hanging baskets, flowering tubs and window boxes in front of this pretty thatched 13th-c longhouse are lovely, and inside, the fine flagstoned bar has lots of beams, a random mixture of dining chairs, window seats, and wall settles (including a high-backed winged black one), and a log fire in the inglenook fireplace. The back bar has an enormous collection of miniature bottles. Popular, well liked bar food includes soup (£2.95), filled granary rolls or baguettes (from £3.95), ploughman's (£4.95), tossed green salad topped with grilled goats cheese with walnut (£6.95), seafood medley (£8.95), and a trio of salmon (gravadlax, smoked and roasted, £9.95), sweet potato and pine nut roulade on a coulis of sweet peppers and tomato topped with yoghurt and chives (£9.95), steaks (from £12.95), finnan haddock with prawns and a sauce of fresh rosemary with cream and vermouth (£14.95) and a two-course menu with starters like tomato and mozzarella cheese, broccoli and stilton soup or pork rillette with home-made chutney, and main courses such as fillet of cod with herb and nut crust, chicken with spinach and sage or sirloin steak with artichoke purée (£14.95). Half the restaurant is no smoking. Well kept Courage Directors, and Otter Ale and Bitter on handpump kept under light blanket pressure; skittle alley and piped music. *(Recommended by Jenny Cridland, Gordon Cooper,*

Basil Minson, Mike Gorton, Alan and Paula McCully, Bob and Margaret Holder, Laura Wilson, Andy Sinden, Louise Harrington, Esther and John Sprinkle)

Free house ~ Licensees David and Kate Beck ~ Real ale ~ Bar food ~ Restaurant ~ (01404) 881342 ~ Children in restaurant and family room ~ Open 12-3, 6.30-11; 12-3, 7-10.30 Sun ~ Bedrooms: £32.50S/£55S

DARTMOUTH SX8751 Map 1

Cherub

Higher Street

As good as ever, this Grade II* listed, 14th-c pub is run by friendly, welcoming licensees. The bustling bar has tapestried seats under creaky heavy beams, leaded-light windows, and a big stone fireplace; upstairs is the low-ceilinged no smoking restaurant. Four well kept real ales on handpump: Batemans, Brakspears, Robinsons, and a beer named for the pub, 20 malt whiskies, and 10 wines by the glass; piped music. Good, popular bar food includes soup (£2.50), sandwiches (from £2.75; the crab ones are delicious), filled baked potatoes (£4.50), deep-fried stilton mushrooms (£5), smoked haddock in white wine sauce and topped with cheese (£6), steak, mushroom and Guinness pie (£7.25), fish pie or curry of the day (£7.25), and steak and chips (£8.50); the fresh fish dishes are highly recommended by readers. In summer particularly, the building is a striking sight with each of the two heavily timbered upper floors jutting further out than the one below, and the hanging baskets are at their best. *(Recommended by Pete and Jo Cole, Gordon Stevenson, Christine and Neil Townend, Charles Eaton, Alan Thomas, Derek and Sylvia Stephenson, Emma Kingdon, Betsy and Peter Little, Ken Flawn, JP, PP, Neil and Beverley Gardner, John Knighton, Geoff Calcott, Julie and Bill Ryan, Graham Lynch-Watson)*

Free house ~ Licensees Charles Veals and Laurie Scott ~ Real ale ~ Bar food ~ Restaurant ~ (01803) 832571 ~ Children in restaurant only and must be over 10 ~ Dogs allowed in bar ~ Open 11-11; 12-10.30 Sun; 11-2.30, 5-11 Mon-Thurs in winter

Royal Castle Hotel

11 The Quay

This year, the Harbour Bar on the left of the flagstoned entrance hall in this friendly place has been refurbished with leather and chrome seats, and lots of light wood – they tell us the local fishermen and sailors are happy with the new look; TV, cribbage, dominoes, and piped music. There are two ground floor bars, each with its own atmosphere. On the right is the Galleon bar which is more lounge-like, and has some fine antiques, a Tudor fireplace, and a no smoking area. Well kept Courage Directors, Exe Valley Dob's Best Bitter, and Wadworths 6X on handpump. Well liked bar food (with prices unchanged since last year) includes home-made soup (£2.50), sandwiches (from £2.85; smoked chicken and avocado £3.65; crab £3.95), baked potatoes (from £3.95), good deep-fried brie with a port and orange sauce (£4.45), broccoli, mushroom and tomato bake with a stilton and garlic crumble (£4.95), ploughman's (from £4.95), home-baked ham with eggs (£5.25), local venison sausages with cumberland sauce or popular home-made steak and kidney in ale pie (£6.25), braised lamb shank in a rich mint and rosemary sauce (£7.95), fresh crab (£9.95), steaks (from £11.75), and puddings (£2.95); on winter lunchtimes, they serve spit roasts from their 300-year-old Lidstone range – pork, lamb and beef, all from local suppliers. The inn was originally two Tudor merchant houses (but has a Regency façade), and overlooks the inner harbour and the river beyond. *(Recommended by Rona Murdoch, Neil and Beverley Gardner, JP, PP, Pete and Jo Cole, Joyce and Maurice Cottrell, Gill and Keith Croxton, George Atkinson, Tracey and Stephen Groves)*

Free house ~ Licensees Nigel and Anne Way ~ Real ale ~ Bar food (all day) ~ Restaurant ~ (01803) 833033 ~ Children in restaurant and family room ~ Dogs allowed in bar ~ Open 11-11; 12-10.30 Sun ~ Bedrooms: £67.95S/£115.90B

DODDISCOMBSLEIGH SX8586 Map 1

Nobody Inn ★★

Village signposted off B3193, opposite northernmost Christow turn-off

The wine list in this extremely popular inn is probably the best in the country. There are 900 well cellared wines by the bottle and 20 by the glass kept oxidation-free, and they hold monthly tutored tastings (they also sell wine retail, and the good tasting-notes in their detailed list are worth the £3.50 it costs – anyway refunded if you buy more than £30-worth). Also, a choice of 250 whiskies, local farm ciders, and well kept Nobody's (brewed by Branscombe), Otter Ale, and a guest such as Scattor Rock Teign Valley Tipple on handpump. The two rooms of the lounge bar have handsomely carved antique settles, windsor and wheelback chairs, benches, carriage lanterns hanging from the beams, and guns and hunting prints in a snug area by one of the big inglenook fireplaces. Good bar food includes tasty home-made soups or ciabatta bread filled with tomatoes, mushrooms and pesto (£3.50), well liked Brixham crab pâté, leek and chestnut tarts or pork meat balls with sweet and sour sauce (£3.90), ploughman's (£5.50), spicy lentil cakes with red onion salsa and yoghurt or super cumberland-style sausages with mash and onion gravy (£5.90), breast of chicken with coconut and ginger sauce or fillet on salmon with mediterranean vegetables (£7.90), barbary duck breast in a rum and honey sauce (£8.50), and puddings such as baked cheesecake with blackcurrant compote or local organic rhubarb and ginger crumble (£3.90); half a dozen good west country cheeses from an incredible choice of around 50 (£5; you can buy them to take away as well). The restaurant is no smoking. There are picnic-sets on the terrace with views of the surrounding wooded hill pastures. The medieval stained glass in the local church is some of the best in the West Country. No children are allowed inside the pub.

(Recommended by C A Hall, David Peakall, Basil Minson, MDN, Duncan Cloud, Sarah and Simon House, Mr and Mrs Thomas, Mrs J H S Lang, Lynn Sharpless, Bob Eardley, Shaun Pinchbeck, V N Stevenson, Paul Thompson, Anna Blackburn, Jenny and Chris Wilson, Richard and Margaret Peers, Mr and Mrs S Oxenbury, the Didler, P and J Shapley, Charlie Harris, P R and S A White, Andy and Katie Wadsworth, Anne and Barry Coulton, Steve Whalley, Hugh Roberts, Kevin Blake, Peter B Brown, C M Miles, J B Towers, JP, PP, Andrea Rampley, Nick Lawless, Ann and Colin Hunt, Dr and Mrs M E Wilson, Dr S J Shepherd, Dr T E Hothersall, Haydn Jones; also in the Good Hotel Guide*)*

Free house ~ Licensee Nick Borst-Smith ~ Real ale ~ Bar food (till 10) ~ Restaurant ~ (01647) 252394 ~ Open 12-2.30, 6-11; 12-3, 7-10.30 Sun; closed 25 and 26 Dec ~ Bedrooms: £23(£38B)/£66(£70B)

DOLTON SS5712 Map 1

Union

B3217

Freshly decorated outside in a warm cream colour with black paintwork, this comfortable village inn offers a warm welcome for all. The little lounge bar has a cushioned window seat, a pink plush chesterfield, a nicely carved priest's table and some dark pine country chairs with brocaded cushions, and dagging shears, tack, country prints, and brass shell cases. On the right, and served by the same stone bar counter, is another bar with a chatty atmosphere and liked by locals: heavy black beams hung with brasses, an elegant panelled oak settle and antique housekeeper's chairs, a small settle snugged into the wall, and various dining chairs on the squared patterned carpet; the big stone fireplace has some brass around it, and on the walls are old guns, two land-felling saws, antlers, some engravings, and a whip. Using local produce, tasty bar food includes grilled sardines or lamb or beef burgers (£4.75), omelettes (£5.15), king prawns or local sausages with bubble and squeak and an egg (£5.50), daily specials like toasted ciabatta with smoked chicken and dill pickle (£4.95), fresh clams cooked in sherry and prosciutto or local mussels steamed with wine, cream and shallots (£5.25), and spinach and feta pie or smoked salmon fishcakes (£5.95), and lunchtime snacks such as filled baguettes (£4) or cold platters (£4.95). The restaurant is no smoking. Well kept St Austell HSD and a guest such as

Clearwater Cavalier, Jollyboat Freebooter or Sharps Doom Bar on handpump, and decent wines. Outside on a small patch of grass in front of the building are some rustic tables and chairs. More reports please. *(Recommended by Mrs M Bagnall, Dr M W A Haward, P and J Shapley, Jed and Virginia Brown, R J Walden, Anthony Longden)*

Free house ~ Licensees Ian and Irene Fisher ~ Real ale ~ Bar food (not Weds) ~ Restaurant ~ (01805) 804633 ~ Children in eating area of bar (until 9) and in restaurant ~ Dogs allowed in bar and bedrooms ~ Open 12-2.30, 6-11; 12-2.30, 7-10.30 Sun; closed Wednesdays and 1st 2 wks Feb ~ Bedrooms: /£55S(£65B)

DREWSTEIGNTON SX7390 Map 1

Drewe Arms

Signposted off A30 NW of Moretonhampstead

Both locals and visitors enjoy this unpretentious and friendly old thatched pub, and a new lick of paint and colourful hanging baskets have made it even prettier. The small, unchanging room on the left still has its serving hatch and basic seats; the room on the right with its assorted tables and chairs has a log fire, and is not much bigger. Well kept Bass, Gales HSB, and a guest such as Brakspears kept on racks in the tap room behind, and local cider. At the back is a sizeable eating area, with good, popular food such as a huge bowl of soup with a loaf of bread (£3.50), delicious (if pricy) sandwiches (from £4.50), a proper ploughman's (£5.95), pork and sage sausage with bubble and squeak, a vegetarian dish or crispy belly of pork on tatties and leeks with apple sauce (£6.95), big cod fillet in beer batter (£7.95), and shank of lamb with an orange and red wine sauce £10). The restaurant is no smoking. Dominoes, darts, shove-ha'penny, and skittle alley. Castle Drogo nearby (open for visits) looks medieval, though it was actually built earlier last century. *(Recommended by Peter Meister, Jason Caulkin, Eddie Edwards, Peter Craske, Di and Mike Gillam, JP, PP, Robert Gomme, the Didler, David Biggins, G and A Wall, Mr and Mrs McKay, Jane Parsons, Jenny and Brian Seller, D I Lucas, Steve Crooke, John and Vivienne Rice, Julie and Bill Ryan)*

Whitbreads ~ Lease Janice and Colin Sparks ~ Real ale ~ Bar food (not 25 Dec) ~ Restaurant ~ (01647) 281224 ~ Children in eating area of bar and in restaurant ~ Dogs allowed in bar ~ Open 11-3, 6-11; 12-3, 7-10.30 Sun ~ Bedrooms: /£60B

EXETER SX9190 Map 1

Double Locks

Canal Banks, Alphington; from A30 take main Exeter turn-off (A377/396) then eventually right at traffic lights into Marsh Barton Industrial Estate and follow Refuse Incinerator signs; when road bends round in front of the factory-like incinerator, take narrow dead end track over humpy railway bridge, cross narrow canal swing bridge, then turn sharp right and follow track along canal; much quicker than it sounds, and a very worthwhile diversion from the final M5 junction

It's always heartening to come across a pub where a real mix of customers all feel at home and genuinely welcomed. This isolated, converted lock-keeper's cottage is just such a place, with students, business people, boat keepers, families with children, and ladies on their own, enjoying themselves in the consistently friendly and very relaxed, laid-back atmosphere. The ten real ales on handpump or tapped from the cask are quite a draw: Adnams Broadside, Badger Tanglefoot, Branscombe Branoc and Summa That, Exmoor Ale, Greene King Abbot, Shepherd Neame Spitfire, and Youngs Bitter, Special, and Waggle Dance. Local cider and quite a few Irish whiskeys. Well liked bar food includes sandwiches (£2.95; garlic bread with goats cheese £3.70), filled baked potatoes (from £4.70), bangers and mash, ham and eggs or feta cheese and spinach pie (£5.45), ploughman's (£5.50), Wednesday evening curries (from £5.50), breakfast special (plus a pint of beer, £6.25), daily specials (from £5.50), and puddings like treacle tart; barbecues in fine weather. There's quite a nautical theme in the bar – with ship's lamps and model ships, and darts, shove-ha'penny, cribbage, and piped music. The decking by the canal is a fine place to sit on a warm evening, and there's a large children's play area with rope walk, swings, slides and climbing area; cycle paths along the ship canal. *(Recommended by Joan and Michel Hooper-Immins, John and Vivienne Rice, Esther and John Sprinkle, John Beeken, JP, PP, Jayne Capp, Mike Gorton, Ruth and Andrew Crowder, Jonathan Smith, Geoff and Linda Dibble, Michael and Marion Buchanan, John Wilson, R T and J C Moggridge, Dave Irving, the Didler, Kerry Law, Simon Smith)*

Youngs ~ Managers Tony Stearman and Mike Wilkins ~ Real ale ~ Bar food (11-10.30; 12-10 Sun) ~ Restaurant ~ (01392) 256947 ~ Children in eating area of bar and restaurant ~ Dogs welcome ~ Trad jazz Thurs evening, soft rock/folk weekends; lots on bank hols ~ Open 11-11; 12-10.30 Sun

Imperial £

Crediton/Tiverton road near St Davids Station

In fine weather, the attractive cobbled courtyard with its elegant garden furniture at the front of this splendid early 19th-c building is a restful place to sit, and there are plenty of picnic-sets in the surrounding 6-acre hillside park, too. Inside, it's quite spread out with various different areas including a couple of little clubby side bars, a left-hand bar looking into a light and airy former orangery – the huge glassy fan of its end wall is lightly mirrored – and a glorious ex-ballroom filled with elaborate plasterwork and gilding brought here in the 1920s from Haldon House (a Robert Adam stately home that was falling on hard times). One area is no smoking. The furnishings give Wetherspoons' usual solid well spaced comfort, and there are plenty of interesting pictures and other things to look at. Well kept and very cheap Greene King Abbot, Shepherd Neame Spitfire, Theakstons Best, and a couple of guest beers tapped from the cask. Decent bar food includes filled baps (from £2.89), filled baked potatoes (from £3.39), ham and eggs (£4.39), quite a few burgers (from £5.09), spinach and red pepper lasagne (£5.29), Aberdeen Angus pie (£5.49), and puddings like treacle sponge (from £2.39); there's also an all day every day offer of two meals for £5.99. Silenced fruit machines and video game. *(Recommended by Dr and Mrs A K Clarke, JP, PP, Mike Gorton, the Didler, Tony and Wendy Hobden, C J Fletcher)*

Wetherspoons ~ Manager Val Docherty ~ Real ale ~ Bar food (11-10; 12-9.30 Sun) ~ (01392) 434050 ~ Children in family area until 5pm ~ Open 11-11; 12-10.30 Sun

EXMINSTER SX9487 Map 1

Turf Hotel ★

Follow the signs to the Swan's Nest, signposted from A739 S of village, then continue to end of track, by gates; park, and walk right along canal towpath – nearly a mile; there's a fine seaview out to the mudflats at low tide

A new barbecue and decking area has been built outside this isolated, friendly pub, and there's now an outdoor rotisserie for chicken and pig roasts; the licensees have applied for an outdoor licence, too. Inside, the pleasantly airy bar has church pews, wooden chairs and alcove seats on the polished bare floorboards, and pictures and old photographs of the pub and its characters over the years on the walls; woodburning stove and antique gas fire. From the bay windows there are views out to the mudflats (full of gulls and waders at low tide). Good bar food includes chicken with sweet chilli sauce in ciabatta bread or duck breast with spring onion and plum salad wrapped in a tortilla (£5.95), aubergine and lentil moussaka (£6.95), prawns with parsley, garlic, ginger and chilli (£7.50), and lamb tagine with couscous (£8.50); the very popular cook-your-own-barbecue menu (which operates in spring and autumn as well as summer) has meaty or vegetable burgers, various sausages, mint and orange lamb steak, gammon with pineapple, and marinated chicken (from £3.50). The dining room is no smoking. Well kept Otter Bitter, Bright and Otter Ale on handpump, Green Valley farm cider, freshly squeezed orange juice, local apple juice, and cappuccino and espresso coffee; cribbage, dominoes, and piped music. The garden has a children's play area built using a lifeboat from a liner that sank off the Scilly Isles around 100 years ago. To get to the pub, you can either walk (which takes about 20 minutes along the ship canal) or cycle, or take a 40-minute ride from Countess Wear in their own boat, the Water Mongoose (bar on board; £5 adult, £2 child return, charter for up to 56 people £200). They also operate a 30-seater boat which brings people down the Exe estuary from Topsham quay (15 minute trip, adults £3, child £2). For those arriving in their own boat there is a large pontoon as well as several moorings. *(Recommended by Mike Gorton, John and Vivienne Rice, Esther and John Sprinkle, Keith and Suzie Stevens, James Flory, John Beeken, the Didler, Canon and Mrs Michael Bourdeaux, Alan and Paula McCully)*

Free house ~ Licensees Clive and Ginny Redfern ~ Real ale ~ Bar food (12-2.30(3 Sat and Sun), 7-9) ~ (01392) 833128 ~ Children welcome ~ Dogs welcome ~ Open 11.30-11; 11.30-10.30 Sun; closed Nov-Feb ~ Bedrooms: £30/£60

HARBERTON SX7758 Map 1

Church House

Village signposted from A381 just S of Totnes

Part of this ancient pub may actually be Norman, as it was probably used as a chantry-house for monks connected with the church. The open-plan bar has some magnificent medieval oak panelling, and the latticed glass on the back wall is almost 700 years old and one of the earliest examples of non-ecclesiastical glass in the country. Furnishings include attractive 17th- and 18th-c pews and settles, candles, and a large inglenook fireplace with a woodburning stove; one half of the room is set out for eating. The family room is no smoking. Enjoyable bar food using local produce includes home-made soup (£2.95), sandwiches (from £2.95), home-made chicken liver pâté or devilled whitebait (£3.95), locally made sausages (£4.25), ploughman's (from £4.50), omelettes (£6.75), local lamb steak with a port, rosemary and redcurrant sauce (£9.95), steaks (from £8.95), daily specials such as mussel and prawn chowder (£3.75), anchovies on a garlic crouton sprinkled with parmesan (£3.95), vegetarian lasagne (£7.50), chicken and spinach balti (£8.50), pork tenderloin in apple and calvados sauce (£9.95), and thai duck curry (£10.50), and puddings like bread and butter pudding or chocolate Amaretto torte (from £3.75). Well kept Bass and Wells Bombardier and a guest such as Greene King Abbot or Palmers IPA on handpump, farm cider, a dozen wines by the glass, and several malt whiskies; darts and dominoes. Tabitha the cat is very friendly. *(Recommended by June and Ken Brooks, Basil Minson, John and Sarah Perry, Alan and Paula McCully, Richard and Margaret Peers, Brian and Bett Cox, Bob and Ann Westbrook)*

Free house ~ Licensees David and Jennifer Wright ~ Real ale ~ Bar food (not 25 or 26 Dec or 1 Jan) ~ (01803) 863707 ~ Children in family room ~ Dogs allowed in bar ~ Open 12-3, 6-11; 12-3.30, 6(7 winter Sun)-11(10.30 Sun) Sat; closed evenings 25 and 26 Dec and 1 Jan ~ Bedrooms: £30/£40

HATHERLEIGH SS5404 Map 1

George

A386 N of Okehampton

In summer, the window boxes and hanging baskets in the courtyard of this black and white timbered old pub are particularly pretty, and there are rustic wooden seats and tables on the cobblestones; there's also a walled cobbled garden. The little front bar in the original part of the building has huge oak beams, stone walls two or three feet thick, an enormous fireplace, and easy chairs, sofas and antique cushioned settles. The spacious L-shaped bar was built from the wreck of the inn's old brewhouse and coachmen's loft, and has more beams, a woodburning stove, and antique settles around sewing-machine treadle tables; piped music. The Mad Monk bar has amusing murals of monks on its light gold walls, and a mix of country tables and chairs, and there's another dining area. Well kept Bass, St Austell Dartmoor Best and a beer named for the pub on handpump, lots of malt whiskies, and farm cider. Decent bar food includes sandwiches (£2.50), home-made soup (£2.95), filled baked potatoes (from £3.95), ploughman's (£4.95), daily specials (around £5.50), beef and vegetable pie (£5.95), salmon in a creamy dill and tarragon sauce (£9.75), and steaks (from £10.95). More reports please. *(Recommended by the Didler, Geoff and Linda Dibble, R J Walden, JP, PP)*

Free house ~ Licensees Janice Anderson and J Pozzetto ~ Real ale ~ Bar food (12-2.30, 6.30-9.30) ~ Restaurant ~ (01837) 810454 ~ Children in eating area of bar and in family room ~ Dogs allowed in bar ~ Occasional live music ~ Open 11-11; 12-10.30 Sun ~ Bedrooms: £48S/£69.50S(£79.50B)

HAYTOR VALE SX7677 Map 1

Rock ★

Haytor signposted off B3387 just W of Bovey Tracey, on good moorland road to Widecombe

As well as being a very nice place to stay, this neatly kept and civilised inn welcomes both locals and visitors for a drink after a hike (its location makes it a very good centre for walking) or for an enjoyable meal. The two communicating, partly panelled bar rooms have polished antique tables with candles and fresh flowers, old-fashioned prints and decorative plates on the walls, and good winter log fires (the main fireplace has a fine Stuart fireback); the restaurant, lounge and children's area are no smoking. Served by friendly staff, the impressive choice of first class bar food at lunchtime might include home-made soup (£2.95), sandwiches (from £3.75), wild boar and apple sausages with onion gravy (£6.50), smoked mackerel fillet with elderflower chutney (£5.25), local mussels in garlic butter or ploughman's (£6.25), and salmon fishcakes with dill dressing, steak and kidney pudding or wild mushroom and rocket risotto with olive oil and lemon (£8.95), with evening choices such as duck liver parfait with pickled mushrooms (£5.95), roasted vegetable lasagne (£8.95), roast breast of pheasant (£12.95), fillet of john dory with pea risotto and confit tomatoes or well liked provençale daube of venison with celeriac mash and croutons (£13.95), and puddings like banoffi pie or chocolate pot (£3.85). Well kept Bass, Greene King Old Speckled Hen, and St Austell Dartmoor Best on handpump, and several malt whiskies. In summer, the pretty, large garden opposite the inn is a popular place to sit and there are some tables and chairs on a small terrace next to the pub itself. *(Recommended by B J Harding, Di and Mike Gillam, Mr and Mrs S Oxenbury, Mr and Mrs J McRobert, Patrick Hancock, Basil Minson, Suzanne Stacey, Ann and Colin Hunt, Chris and Joan Woodward, Sue Demont, Tim Barrow, Mike Gorton, Andrea Rampley, Julie and Bill Ryan, Richard and Margaret Peers, Neil and Beverley Gardner, Jane and Adrian Tierney-Jones, H L Dennis, R J Walden, M G Hart, Ian Wilson)*

Free house ~ Licensee Christopher Graves ~ Real ale ~ Bar food (not 25 Dec) ~ Restaurant ~ (01364) 661305 ~ Children in restaurant ~ Dogs allowed in bedrooms ~ Open 11-11(10.30 in winter); 12-10.30 Sun; closed 25 Dec ~ Bedrooms: £65B/£75S (£85B)

HOLBETON SX6150 Map 1

Mildmay Colours

Signposted off A379 W of A3121 junction

Neatly kept and friendly, this off-the-beaten-track pub is set in a quiet village. The bar has various horse and racing pictures, and the framed racing colours of Lord Mildmay-White on the partly stripped stone and partly white walls, plenty of bar stools as well as cushioned wall seats and wheelback chairs on the turkey carpet, and a tile-sided woodburning stove; an arch leads to a smaller, similarly decorated family area. Though the brewery has moved away, they still offer Mildmay SP and Colours, and a guest beer such as Greene King Old Speckled Hen and Sharps Eden Ale on handpump; local farm cider. There's a decent, carpeted family area with pool, TV, pinball, and fruit machine. Bar food includes sandwiches (from £2.95; baguettes from £3.95), home-made soup (£2.99), home-made chicken liver pâté (£3.55), ham and egg (£3.95), ploughman's (from £4.95), mushroom stroganoff (£5.60), liver and bacon with onion gravy (£7.15), steaks (from £9.95), daily specials, home-made puddings (£3.10), and children's meals (£2.50). The well kept back garden has picnic-sets, a swing, and an aviary, and there's a small front terrace. More reports please. *(Recommended by Dr Paull Khan, Martin Jennings, John Evans, G R Taylor, Geoff and Tricia Alderman)*

Free house ~ Licensee Louise Price ~ Real ale ~ Bar food ~ Restaurant ~ (01752)

830248 ~ Children in family room ~ Dogs welcome ~ Open 11-3, 6-11; 12-3, 7-10.30 Sun ~ Bedrooms: £32.50B/£50B

HORNDON SX5280 Map 1

Elephants Nest

If coming from Okehampton on A386 turn left at Mary Tavy Inn, then left after about ½ mile; pub signposted beside Mary Tavy Inn, then Horndon signposted; on the Ordnance Survey Outdoor Leisure Map it's named as the New Inn

Benches on the spacious lawn in front of this 400-year-old place look over dry-stone walls to the pastures of Dartmoor's lower slopes, and the rougher moorland above; plenty of walks. The bar has a good log fire, large rugs and flagstones, a beams-and-board ceiling, and cushioned stone seats built into the windows, with captain's chairs around the tables; the name of the pub is written up on the beams in 80 languages. What was once an old beer cellar is another bar with views over the garden and beyond to the moors. Decent home-made bar food includes soup (£2.10), filled rolls (from £2.30), home-made crab or chive and cashew nut pâté (£3.95), half a dozen burgers (from £4.20), ploughman's (from £4.20), ratatouille (£6.20), sweet and sour pork or beef curry (£6.80), local game pie (£7.80), and steaks (from £10.80). Well kept Boddingtons, Palmers IPA, St Austell HSD, and two changing guest beers on handpump. Sensibly placed darts, cribbage, dominoes, shut-the-box, and piped music. They have quite a few animals. More reports please. *(Recommended by Esther and John Sprinkle, JP, PP, Dr and Mrs Nigel Holmes, Peter Craske, Jacquie and Jim Jones)*

Free house ~ Licensee Nick Hamer ~ Real ale ~ Bar food (11.30-2, 6.30-10(9.30 Sun)) ~ Restaurant ~ (01822) 810273 ~ Children in family room ~ Dogs welcome ~ Open 11.30(12 Sun)-2.30, 6.30-11(10.30 Sun)

HORNS CROSS SS3823 Map 1

Hoops

A39 Clovelly—Bideford

As well as a good choice of half a dozen real ales, this friendly 13th-c inn serves popular, enjoyable food, quickly brought to you by cheerful staff. The oak-beamed bar has an ancient well set into the floor, paintings and old photographs of the pub on the walls, cushioned window seats and oak settles, and logs burning in big inglenook fireplaces; leading off here is a small similarly furnished room with another fireplace. Generous helpings of good bar food include home-made soup (£3.50), mushrooms grilled with somerset brie and served with onion marmalade (£4.50), grilled chicken livers wrapped in pancetta with garlic crostini (£5.30), bangers and mash with onion gravy (£8.95), fresh spinach pancakes filled with creamed leeks in a local stilton sauce (£9.50), huge steak and kidney pie (£9.75), lamb fillet of rosemary and lemon couscous with port and redcurrant jus (£11.50), fillet of local venison on celeriac with blueberry and ginger sauce (£12.50), daily fish specials such as whitebait with paprika (£3.90), beer-battered fish (£6.90), skate wing with black butter (£8.50), and grilled lemon sole (£11.50), and puddings like banana pancakes with white chocolate and rum sauce or banoffi pie (£4.25). There are several no smoking areas. Well kept Bass, Clearwater Cavalier, Greene King Old Speckled Hen, Jollyboat Buccaneers and Mainbrace Bitter, Marstons Pedigree, and Otter Ale tapped from the cask, farm cider, lots of malt whiskies, and 20 wines by the glass (including champagne); piped music, darts, dominoes, cribbage, table skittles, and TV. Outside, it is particularly pretty in summer with lots of flowering tubs and baskets and picnic-sets in a sheltered central courtyard. *(Recommended by Tom Evans, David Carr, the Didler, George Atkinson, Derek Thomas, Steve and Liz Tilley, John Saville, Barry Smith, Barbara and Brian Best)*

Free house ~ Licensee Gay Marriott ~ Real ale ~ Bar food (12-3, 6-9.30; 12-9.30 Sat and Sun) ~ Restaurant ~ (01237) 451222 ~ Well behaved children in eating area of bar but not in evening restaurant ~ Dogs allowed in bar ~ Open 11-11; 12-10.30 Sun; closed 25 Dec ~ Bedrooms: £55B/£90B

IDDESLEIGH SS5708 Map 1

Duke of York ★

B3217 Exbourne—Dolton

The bar in this old thatched pub, run by friendly licensees, has a lot of character, with rocking chairs by the roaring log fire, cushioned wall benches built into the wall's black-painted wooden dado, stripped tables, and other homely country furnishings, and well kept Adnams Broadside, Cotleigh Tawny, and a guest such as Sharps Doom Bar or Teignworthy Reel Ale tapped from the cask; freshly squeezed orange and pink grapefruit juice. Good bar food includes sandwiches, two home-made soups (£2.75 small, £3.25 large), stilton and port pâté (£4.50), scallops wrapped in smoked bacon or crab mayonnaise (£4.50 small, £7.50 large), grilled or battered fish and chips (£5.50), vegetable curry, beef in Guinnesss casserole or liver and bacon (£6.50), leg of lamb steak with minted gravy or pork chop with apple gravy (£7.50), steak and kidney pudding (£8), sirloin steak (£11), and home-made puddings (£3.50). Cribbage, dominoes, shove-ha'penny, and darts. Through a small coach arch is a little back garden with some picnic-sets. Fishing nearby. More reports please. *(Recommended by JP, PP, the Didler, Mike Gorton, R J Walden, Theo, Anne and Jane Gaskin, Anthony Longden, Jed and Virginia Brown, Guy Consterdine, George Atkinson, Jane and Adrian Tierney-Jones)*

Free house ~ Licensees Jamie Stuart and Pippa Hutchinson ~ Real ale ~ Bar food (all day) ~ Restaurant ~ (01837) 810253 ~ Children welcome ~ Dogs allowed in bar ~ Open 11-11; 12-10.30 Sun ~ Bedrooms: £25B/£50B

KINGSTON SX6347 Map 1

Dolphin

Off B3392 S of Modbury (can also be reached from A379 W of Modbury)

After a drink or a meal in this charming, shuttered 16th-c inn, it's well worth the walk down to the lovely estuary below; plenty of other surrounding walks, too. Several knocked-through beamed rooms have a good mix of customers, a relaxed, welcoming atmosphere (no noisy games machines or piped music), amusing drawings and photographs on the walls, and rustic tables and cushioned seats and settles around their bared stone walls; one small area is no smoking. Served by friendly staff, the good honest bar food includes sandwiches (from £2.50; crab £4.95), home-made soup (£2.95), jumbo sausage and chips (£3.95), ploughman's or ham and chips (£4.95), lasagne (£5.50), spinach, potato and cashew nut curry or caribbean chicken (£6.50), pheasant in port and orange sauce (£8.95), salmon with hazelnut dressing (£9.95), steaks (from £9.95), and home-made puddings like banana and walnut pudding with caramel sauce or treacle tart (£3); children's meals (from £1.50), and nice breakfasts.Well kept Bass and Courage Best with a guest from Palmers or Ushers on handpump. Outside, there are tables and swings. *(Recommended by John Wilson, R and D Gray, Eric Locker, David and Helen Wilkins, Geoff Calcott, Darren Le Poidevin, James and Penny Abell, G R Taylor, Simon, Jo and Benjamin Cole, P and J Shapley, Nick Lawless, Malcolm Taylor)*

InnSpired ~ Lease Neil and Annie Williams ~ Real ale ~ Bar food (not 25 Dec) ~ (01548) 810314 ~ Children in no smoking room ~ Open 11-3(2.30 in winter), 6-11; 12-3, 6(7 in winter)-10.30 Sun ~ Bedrooms: £39.50B/£55B

KNOWSTONE SS8223 Map 1

Masons Arms ★

Off A361 Tiverton—South Molton (brown sign to pub), or B3227 Bampton—South Molton

Run by a jovial, helpful licensee, this 13th-c thatched inn is doing well after its alterations, and most readers feel the character has been preserved. The simple little main bar has heavy medieval black beams, farm tools on the walls, pine furniture on the stone floor, and a fine open fireplace with a big log fire and side bread oven – there is always a fire lit, whatever the weather. Good bar food includes soups such as cream of broccoli and stilton (£2.95), prawn and red pepper pâté or avocado and goats cheese bake (£4), pork and leek sausages with onion gravy or potato, onion, herbs and cream pie (£6.50), steak, kidney and Guinness pie (£6.95), game and red wine pie (£7.50), chargrilled cajun chicken breast with pesto butter (£7.95), substantial lamb shank with lentils and beans or smoked haddock and egg pie (£8.50), rib-eye steak (£10.50), and puddings like warm chocolate pudding with chocolate sauce or banana and coffee crème brûlée (£3.50). Well kept Cotleigh Tawny tapped from the cask; piped music. Although they don't offer bedrooms in the pub itself, they have a very popular cottage a walk from the pub, with an ensuite bedroom and downstairs sitting room with an inglenook fireplace and woodburning stove, and breakfast supplied from the pub. *(Recommended by A Hawkes, Mrs M S Porter, Shaun Pinchbeck, Mrs S Matthews, the Didler, Jed and Virginia Brown, R H Down, JP, PP, P Dash, J C Brittain-Long, Bob and Margaret Holder, Paul and Karen Cornock, Debbie and Neil Hayter, Hazel Boundy, Tom Evans, Anne Westcott, Mr and Mrs J M Lefeaux, David Carr)*

Free house ~ Licensees Paul and Jo Stretton-Downes ~ Real ale ~ Bar food ~ Restaurant ~ (01398) 341231 ~ Children in restaurant and family room if over 10 ~ Dogs allowed in bar ~ Open 12-3, 6-11.30; 12-3, 7-10.30 Sun; closed 25 Dec ~ Bedrooms: £40S/£60S

LITTLEHEMPSTON SX8162 Map 1

Tally Ho!

Signposted off A381 NE of Totnes

The neatly kept and cosy rooms of this friendly little pub are full of interest, and the bare stone walls are covered with porcelain, brass, copperware, stuffed wildlife, old swords, and shields and hunting horns and so forth; there's also an interesting mix of chairs and settles (many antique and with comfortable cushions), two coal fires, low beams and panelling, and fresh flowers and candles on the tables. Well liked bar food includes home-made soup (£2.75), sandwiches (from £2.95), home-made chicken liver pâté (£4.25), lasagne (£6.95), steak and kidney pie (£7.95), pork fillet with an apricot cream sauce (£9.95), steaks (from £10.95), whole local plaice with dill and lemon butter (£9.50), escalope of turkey layered with smoked bacon and camembert and a rich cranberry and port sauce or duck with black cherry and kirsch sauce (£11.95), and home-made puddings (from £3.25). Well kept Bass and a guest such as Robinsons or Wells Bombardier on handpump. The two cats are called Monica and Thomas. The terrace is full of flowers in summer. More reports please. *(Recommended by Mrs J Ekins-Daukes, P G Wooler, Derek and Margaret Underwood)*

Free house ~ Licensees P Saint, G Waterfield ~ Real ale ~ Bar food ~ Restaurant ~ (01803) 862316 ~ Children in eating area of bar and restaurant ~ Dogs welcome ~ Open 12-3, 6-11; 12-3, 7-10.30 Sun ~ Bedrooms: £50S/£60S

LOWER ASHTON SX8484 Map 1

Manor Inn

Ashton signposted off B3193 N of Chudleigh

A most enjoyable place to visit, this creeper-covered pub is set in a charming valley, and has pretty summer hanging baskets. There's a good mix of customers, although the left-hand room with its beer mats and brewery advertisements on the walls is more for locals enjoying the well kept Princetown Jail Ale, RCH Pitchfork, Teignworthy Reel Ale, and a constantly changing guest on handpump; local cider and decent wines by the glass. On the right, two rather more discreet rooms have a wider appeal, bolstered by the good, popular home-made food which might include home-made soup (£2.75), sandwiches (from £2.40), lots of filled baked potatoes (from £3.50), home-made burgers with various toppings (from £3.95), ploughman's (from £5.25), vegetable bake (£5.75), home-cooked ham and egg (£6.50), steak, mushroom and ale pie (£6.95), and steaks (from £8.95), with a good choice of changing specials such as mixed bean chilli (£5.50), lamb, leeks and mushrooms cooked in local cider, beef and red wine casserole or venison sausage with a creamy onion and butter sauce (all £6.95), and chicken breast with a stilton, bacon and cream sauce or salmon and prawn au gratin (£7.95). Shove-ha'penny. The garden has lots of picnic-sets under cocktail parasols (and a fine tall Scots pine). No children inside. *(Recommended by R J Walden, JP, PP, the Didler, Mike Gorton, Jeanne and Paul Silvestri, G and A Wall, Alan and Paula McCully)*

Free house ~ Licensees Geoff and Clare Mann ~ Real ale ~ Bar food (12-1.30, 7-9.30; not Mon) ~ (01647) 252304 ~ Dogs allowed in bar ~ Open 12-2(2.30 Sat and Sun), 6.30(7 Sun)-11; closed Mon (except bank hols)

LUSTLEIGH SX7881 Map 1

Cleave

Village signposted off A382 Bovey Tracey—Moretonhampstead

In summer, this old thatched pub looks lovely, with its pretty hanging baskets and flower-filled sheltered garden; seats outside and a wendy house for children. Inside, the low-ceilinged lounge bar has granite walls, attractive antique high-backed settles, cushioned wall seats, and wheelback chairs around the tables on its patterned carpet, and a roaring log fire. A second bar has similar furnishings, a large dresser, harmonium, an HMV gramophone, and prints, and the no smoking family room has crayons, books and toys for children. Decent bar food (they tell us examples and prices have not changed since last year) includes home-made soup (£3.50), lunchtime sandwiches (from £3.95; hot sardines £4.95), home-made chicken liver and brandy pâté (£4.95), home-made cheese and onion flan or local butcher's sausages (£6.50), roast beef and yorkshire pudding (£8.95), half a honey-roasted duckling with an orange and Grand Marnier sauce (£11.95), and daily specials such as home-made lasagne (£6.95), chilli con carne (£7.50), and monkfish stroganoff (£11.45); the dining room is no smoking. Well kept Bass, Otter Ale, and Wadworths 6X on handpump kept under light blanket pressure, quite a few malt whiskies, and several wines by the glass. *(Recommended by Wally and Irene Nunn, Di and Mike Gillam, Neil and Beverley Gardner, Andrea Rampley, Ann and Colin Hunt, John and Vivienne Rice)*

Heavitree ~ Tenant A Perring ~ Real ale ~ Bar food (all day Sat and Sun in summer) ~ Restaurant ~ (01647) 277223 ~ Children in family room and in restaurant if over 8 ~ Dogs welcome ~ Open 11.30-3, 6-11; 11-11 Sat; 12-10.30 Sun; closed Mon Nov-Feb

LYDFORD SX5184 Map 1

Castle Inn

Village signposted off A386 Okehampton—Tavistock

This pink-washed Tudor inn is next to the village's daunting, ruined 12th-c castle and close to a beautiful river gorge (owned by the National Trust; closed Nov-Easter). The twin-roomed bar has country kitchen chairs, high-backed winged settles and old captain's chairs around mahogany tripod tables on big slate flagstones. One of the rooms has low lamp-lit beams, a sizeable open fire, masses of brightly decorated plates, some Hogarth prints, and, near the serving counter, seven Lydford pennies hammered out in the old Saxon mint in the reign of Ethelred the Unready, in the 11th c. The bar area has a bowed ceiling with low beams, a polished slate flagstone floor, and a stained-glass door with the famous Three Hares; there's a snug with high-backed settles which is used by families. Under the new licensee, bar food now includes sandwiches or soup (£4), stilton and plum tart or chicken liver and green peppercorn pâté (£5), warm crispy shredded duck or grilled goats cheese with tapenade and walnut oil and herb dressing (£6), wild mushroom and nut risotto (£8), confit of duck on herb mash or chicken breast on creamed leeks with a wholegrain mustard sauce (£9), lemon sole with lemon parsley butter and capers (£10), rump steak (£11), and puddings (£4). Well kept Flowers IPA, Fullers London Pride, and Greene King Old Speckled Hen on handpump, organic ciders, and lovage or shrub cordials; darts, cribbage and dominoes. *(Recommended by Tony Walker, Peter Rogers, R M Corlett, Mrs J H S Lang, Peter Meister, Simon, Jo and Benjamin Cole, Jason Caulkin, Andrea Rampley, Richard Gibbs, DAV, Pat and Tony Martin, Karen and Steve Wilson, Mrs Ursula Hofheinz, Miss Diana Lewis, Duncan and Lisa Cripps, Paul Boot)*

Heavitree ~ Manager Terence Jackson ~ Real ale ~ Bar food ~ Restaurant ~ (01822) 820241 ~ Children in eating area of bar and in restaurant ~ Dogs welcome ~ Open 11-11; 12-11 Sun ~ Bedrooms: £70B/£95B

Dartmoor Inn 🍴 🍷

A386

Devon Dining Pub of the Year

Though a few walkers may drop in at weekends for a pint of the well kept Bass or St Austell Dartmoor Best on handpump, and in the evening you might find a local drinking in the bar, usually virtually everyone in this small room is pondering a menu or the interesting and helpfully short wine list, before moving off to eat in one of the other four rooms. There is a limited choice of lunchtime bar snacks such as goats cheese salad or a 4oz steak and chips (£7.50), but the main emphasis is on more restauranty food, creatively cooked using top-notch ingredients from named local suppliers (melt-in-mouth devon black beef, for instance), and presented most stylishly by the polite young staff in their crisp black and white. It might include seafood soup of mussels, crab and scallops with garlic and parsley toasts (£4.75), terrine of chicken livers, pork and duck with pistachio nuts and quince paste (£5), a selection of Italian salami and ham with a red onion and artichoke salad (£5.50), fillet of cod deep fried in saffron batter or roasted sweet peppers with creamed leeks, basil breadcrumbs and parmesan sauce (£11), grilled fillet of organic chicken with bacon, celeriac and herb relish (£12.75), charcoal grilled loin of pork with bacon and black pudding couscous (£13.50), and roasted fillet of monkfish with fennel and a béarnaise sauce (£14.75); there's a two-course light supper (£14.50) and several themed food evenings. Puddings, such as banana fritters or kumquat toffee pudding (£4.75), are delicious. Six good wines by the glass and excellent coffee. The overall feel is of civilised but relaxed elegance: matt pastel paintwork in soft greens and blues, naïve farm and country pictures, little side lamps supplemented by candles in black wrought-iron holders, basketwork, dried flowers, fruits and gourds, maybe an elaborate bouquet of fresh flowers. There are tables out on the terrace, with a track straight up on to the moors. *(Recommended by Robin and Clare Hosking, Robin and Nicky Barthorp, Jacquie and Jim Jones, John and Vivienne Rice, Mike Gorton)*

Free house ~ Licensees Philip Burgess and Ian Brown ~ Real ale ~ Bar food (not Sun evening, not Mon) ~ Restaurant ~ (01822) 820221 ~ Children in restaurant ~ Dogs allowed in bar ~ Open 11.30-2.30, 6.30-11; 12-2.30 Sun; closed Sun evening, Mon

MARLDON SX8663 Map 1

Church House 🍴 🍷

Just W of Paignton

Many customers come back to this charming, attractive inn again and again – it's that sort of rewarding place. The welcome is friendly, the food and drink very good, and service remains efficient even when they are busy (which they usually are). There's a good relaxed atmosphere in the spreading bar, and several different areas radiating off the big semicircular bar counter. The main bar has interesting windows, some beams, dark pine chairs around solid tables on the turkey carpet, and green plush-seated bar chairs; leading off here is a cosy little candlelit room with just four tables on the bare-board floor, a dark wood dado, and stone fireplace, and next to this is the attractive, no smoking restaurant with a large stone fireplace. At the other end of the building is a characterful room split into two parts with a stone floor in one bit and a wooden floor in another (with a big woodburning stove). Good, interesting bar food includes soup (£3.50; fish soup £6), sandwiches (from £4; bruschetta topped with tomato, cheese and prosciutto £6), braised beef with lemon and thyme potatoes (£8.50), lamb shank cooked with cumin and orange (£11), breast of chicken filled with feta and spinach (£10.50), whole lemon sole or grilled bass (£12.50), monkfish wrapped in bacon (£14), and puddings like chocolate bread and butter pudding or summer pudding (£4.50). Well kept Bass, Boddingtons, Flowers IPA , and Fullers London Pride with a guest such as Greene King Abbot or

Shepherd Neame Spitfire on handpump, and 10 wines by the glass; skittle alley. There are three grassy terraces with picnic-sets behind. *(Recommended by Mr and Mrs Colin Roberts, P R and S A White, James Woods, Ken Arthur, Pamela and Merlyn Horswell, Alan and Paula McCully, B J Harding, David Hoare)*

Whitbreads ~ Lease Julian Cook ~ Real ale ~ Bar food (12-2, 6.30-9.30) ~ Restaurant ~ (01803) 558279 ~ Children in eating area of bar and restaurant ~ Dogs allowed in bar ~ Open 11.30-2.30, 5-11; 12-3.30, 6-10.30 Sun

MOLLAND SS8028 Map 1

London

Village signposted off B3227 E of South Molton, down narrow lanes

This is real old Exmoor: a water-bowl by the good log fire for the working dogs which come in with keepers from one of the country's top shoots, lots of local stag-hunting pictures, proper farm cider and well kept Cotleigh and Exmoor tapped from casks, and an easy chatty mix of what used to be called all levels of society. The two small linked rooms by the old-fashioned central servery have tough carpeting or rugs on flagstones, cushioned benches and plain chairs around rough stripped trestle tables, a table of shooting and other country magazines, ancient stag and otter trophies, and darts, table skittles, and dominoes. On the left an attractive beamed room has accounts of the rescued stag which lived a long life at the pub some 50 years ago (and is still remembered by at least one reader, from childhood visits); on the right, a panelled dining room with a great curved settle by its fireplace has particularly good hunting and gamebird prints, including ones by McPhail and Hester Lloyd. Good value honest home cooking includes sandwiches, home-made soup (£2.20), filled baked potatoes, smoked trout pâté (£3.20), fish and chips (£3.80), filled savoury pancake (£4.90), pork curry and game pie (£5.45), and superb omelettes, with evening choices like gratin of seafood (£3.50), guinea fowl with red wine sauce and black cherries or steak, pigeon and mushroom pie (£7.80), and chargrilled tuna with salsa or steaks (£8.50); the cheerful licensees are very welcoming. A small hall with stuffed birds and animals and lots of overhead baskets has table skittles and a box of toys, and there are good country views from a few picnic-sets out in front. The low-ceilinged lavatories are worth a look, with their Victorian mahogany and tiling (and in the gents' a testament to the prodigious thirst of the village cricket team). And don't miss the next-door church, with its untouched early 18th-c box pews – and a spring carpet of Tenby daffodils in the graveyard. *(Recommended by Shaun Pinchbeck, Richard and Anne Ansell, Dr and Mrs M E Wilson)*

Free house ~ Licensees M J and L J Short ~ Real ale ~ Bar food ~ Restaurant ~ No credit cards ~ (01769) 550269 ~ Children in family room ~ Dogs welcome ~ Open 11.30-2.30, 6-11; 12-2.30, 7-10.30 Sun ~ Bedrooms: /£46B

NEWTON ABBOT SX8468 Map 1

Two Mile Oak

A381 2 miles S, at Denbury/Kingskerswell crossroads

Friendly new licensees for this old coaching inn, though happily little has changed. There's a relaxed atmosphere, a beamed lounge and an alcove just for two, a mix of wooden tables and chairs, and a fine winter log fire. The beamed and black-panelled bar is traditionally furnished, again with a mix of seating, lots of horsebrasses, and another good log fire. Well kept Bass, Flowers IPA, Greene King Abbot and Otter Ale tapped from the cask, and decent wines. Enjoyable bar food includes home-made soup (£3.25), filled baguettes (from £4.25), ploughman's (from £5.75), goats cheese coated in pink peppercorns and couscous served with a honey and dill dressing (£5.95), hot thai chicken curry (£8.95), roasted lamb shank with sweet redcurrant and ginger sauce or chicken supreme filled with rosemary and mascarpone cheese (£10.95), daily specials such as venison in red wine and chocolate sauce or skate wing with capers and black butter (£11.95), and home-made puddings like banoffi pie, raspberry brûlée or chocolate bread and butter pudding (£3.45). Piped music, darts, and cribbage. There are picnic-sets on the terrace where

they hold summer barbecues, and a lawn with shrubs and tubs of flowers.
(Recommended by the Didler, Mr and Mrs Colin Roberts, Neil and Beverley Gardner, JP, PP)

Heavitree ~ Manager Melanie Matthews ~ Real ale ~ Bar food ~ (01803) 812411 ~ Children welcome ~ Dogs allowed in bar ~ Open 11-11; 11-11 Sat; 12-10.30 Sun

NEWTON ST CYRES SX8798 Map 1

Beer Engine

Sweetham; from Newton St Cyres on A377 follow St Cyres Station, Thorverton signpost

Run by friendly, genuinely helpful licensees, this old station hotel brews its own good beers – as well as drinking them here, you can also take them home with you: Rail Ale, Piston Bitter, and the strong Sleeper on handpump. There's a cheerful, bustling atmosphere, and the no smoking eating area of the spacious bar has partitioning alcoves, and windsor chairs and some cinnamon-coloured button-back banquettes around dark varnished tables on the brown carpet. Good bar food includes ploughman's (served any time during opening hours), speciality sausages (£4.95), vegetarian dishes (from £4.95), chicken in barbecue sauce (£5.95), steak in their own ale pie (£6.50), and rump steak; roast Sunday lunch (£5.95 one course, £7.90 two courses). Darts, shove-ha'penny, dominoes, cribbage, chess, and Trivial Pursuit. The hanging baskets and window boxes are very pretty in summer, and in the large sunny garden, there are plenty of seats; popular summer barbecues.
(Recommended by G and A Wall, John and Bryony Coles, Gene and Kitty Rankin, Tony and Wendy Hobden, Jane and Adrian Tierney-Jones, Dr B and Mrs P B Baker)

Own brew ~ Licensee Peter Hawksley ~ Real ale ~ Bar food (12-2, 6.30-9.30) ~ Restaurant ~ (01392) 851282 ~ Children in eating area of bar ~ Dogs allowed in bar ~ Open 11-11; 12-10.30 Sun

NOMANSLAND SS8313 Map 1

Mountpleasant

B3131 Tiverton—South Molton

One sister runs the front-of-house and the other the kitchen in this cosy country pub, its long bar divided into three, with huge fireplaces each end, one with a woodburning stove under a low dark ochre black-beamed ceiling, the other with a big log fire. A nice informal mix of furniture on the patterned carpet includes an old sofa with a turquoise throw, old-fashioned leather dining chairs, pale country kitchen chairs and wall pews, and the tables all have candles in attractive metal holders; there are country prints and local photographs including shooting parties. The bar, with plenty of bar stools, has well kept Cotleigh Tawny, Flowers Original and Wadworths 6X and decent wines, and coffee is particularly well served. A good choice of good inexpensive freshly made food (using carefully sourced local produce) runs from huge sandwiches, home-made soup (£2.50), proper burgers (from £3.50), whitebait (£4.25), smoked chicken and bacon salad (£4.50), all-day breakfast (£5.25), pasta with various toppings, steak and kidney pie or vegetable curry (£6.95), chicken with cranberries, mushrooms, garlic and cream (£8.95), steaks (from £9.95), and half a honey-roast duck with plum and pear sauce (£11.95); children's meals (from £2.95). On the left a high-beamed stripped stone dining room with a stag's head over the sideboard was once a smithy, and still has the raised forge fireplace. Games machines, darts, TV, cribbage, dominoes, and maybe piped radio; picnic-sets under smart parasols in the neat back garden, out past the stables – which are still in use. Samuel the spaniel comes in to say hello at closing time.
(Recommended by Richard and Anne Ansell)

Free house ~ Licensees Anne and Karen Butler and Charles Gore-Lloyd ~ Real ale ~ Bar food (all day) ~ Restaurant ~ (01884) 860271 ~ Children welcome ~ Dogs allowed in bar ~ Open 11.30-11; 12-10.30 Sun; closed 25 Dec pm, 1 Jan

NOSS MAYO SX5447 Map 1

Ship

Off A379 via B3186, E of Plymouth

This is a very pretty spot on a tidal inlet, and visiting boats can tie up alongside – with prior permission; parking is restricted at high tide. Inside, the two thick-walled bars have a happy mix of dining chairs and tables on the wooden floors, log fires, bookcases, dozens of local pictures, newspapers to read, and a friendly, chatty atmosphere. All of the first floor is no smoking; Scrabble, dominoes, cribbage, and chess. Good food (which can be eaten anywhere in the pub) features much local produce which includes home-made soup (£3.95), sandwiches (from £4.50; cornish crab £5.25), smooth liver pâté with red onion marmalade and brioche (£4.95), local mussels (£6; main course £9), ploughman's (£6.50), turkey and sage sausages with black pudding, herb mash and gravy (£7.25), layered roasted aubergine, goats cheese, herbs and shallots (£7.50), cod tail deep fried in real ale batter with minted mushy peas (£8.50), chicken supreme on pasta with a smoked bacon and mushroom sauce (£9.50), braised shoulder of local lamb (£10.95), and roast fillet of wild bass on sunblushed tomato and spring mash (£13.50); helpful staff. Well kept Exmoor Gold, Summerskills Tamar, and Shepherd Neame Spitfire, and a guest such as Batemans, Everards Beacon or Timothy Taylors Landlord on handpump, lots of malt whiskies, and quite a few wines by the glass. There are seats outside. *(Recommended by Mr and Mrs C Derry, John Evans, Frances Capel, Stephen Archer, Andy and Katie Wadsworth)*

Free house ~ Licensees Lesley and Bruce Brunning ~ Real ale ~ Bar food (12-9.30) ~ Restaurant ~ (01752) 872387 ~ Children in eating area of bar until 7.30 ~ Dogs allowed in bar ~ Open 11.30-11; 12-10.30 Sun

PETER TAVY SX5177 Map 1

Peter Tavy Inn

Off A386 near Mary Tavy, N of Tavistock

As well as serving good, very popular food in this attractive old stone inn, the friendly licensees have quite a few well kept real ales, too. The low-beamed bar has high-backed settles on the black flagstones by the big stone fireplace (a good log fire on cold days), smaller settles in stone-mullioned windows, a snug, no smoking side dining area, and efficient service. At lunchtime, the menu might include home-made soup such as parsnip and apple (£2.95), filled baguettes or baked potatoes (from £3.95; hot spicy chicken £5.45), ham and egg (£5.50), roast beef and yorkshire pudding (£6.25), thai chicken, steak and kidney pie or avocado and sundried tomato tartlets (£6.50), and game casserole with stilton dumpling (£7.95), with evening choices like seared scallops with Noilly Prat dressing (£4.50), vegetable curry (£6.95), monkfish in creamy garlic sauce (£9.95), mexican fajita with a meaty or vegetarian filling (£10.95), lamb shank on garlic mash (£11.45), and super 12oz rump steak or roast duck with peking sauce (£12.45), daily specials, and home-made puddings such as sticky toffee pudding, chocolate truffle torte or apple and apricot crumble (£3.50). Well kept Bass, Princetown Jail Ale, Summerskills Tamar Best, and a guest such as Cottage Hop 'n' Drop or Wells Bombardier on handpump, kept under light blanket pressure; 30 malt whiskies and 10 wines by the glass; piped music. From the picnic-sets in the pretty garden, there are peaceful views of the moor rising above nearby pastures. *(Recommended by Neil and Beverley Gardner, Richard and Margaret Peers, Jacquie and Jim Jones, John Evans, Dr M W A Haward, JP, PP, DAV)*

Free house ~ Licensees Graeme and Karen Sim ~ Real ale ~ Bar food (not 25 Dec) ~ Restaurant ~ (01822) 810348 ~ Children in restaurant ~ Dogs welcome ~ Open 12-2.30(3 Sat), 6.30(6 Sat)-11; 12-3, 6-10.30 Sun; closed 25 Dec

The details at the end of each main entry start by saying whether the pub is a free house, or if it's tied to a brewery or pub group (which we name).

POSTBRIDGE SX6780 Map 1

Warren House

B3212 1¾ miles NE of Postbridge

After a hike on Dartmoor, this no-frills, friendly place is a valuable refuge and remains something of a focus for the scattered moorland community. The cosy bar has a fireplace at either end (one is said to have been kept almost continuously alight since 1845), and is simply furnished with easy chairs and settles under a beamed ochre ceiling, wild animal pictures on the partly panelled stone walls, and dim lighting (fuelled by the pub's own generator); there's a no smoking family room. Good no-nonsense home cooking includes locally made meaty or vegetable pasties, home-made soup, sandwiches and filled baked potatoes, good ploughman's, home-made rabbit pie or home-made vegetable curry (£7), home-made steak in ale pie (£7.20), tenderloin of pork with wild mushroom sauce (£9.75), venison with a red wine sauce (£12), and home-made puddings such as chocolate truffle torte or lime posset. Well kept Badger Tanglefoot, Moor Old Freddy Walker, Sharps Doom Bar, and a guest like Butcombe Gold or Sharps Special on handpump, local farm cider, and malt whiskies. Darts, pool, cribbage, and dominoes; maybe piped music. *(Recommended by Robert Gomme, Doreen and Haydn Maddock , Anthony Longden, Eddie Edwards, Charles Eatof, Pat and Robert Watt, Neil and Beverley Gardner, P J Holdsworth)*

Free house ~ Licensee Peter Parsons ~ Real ale ~ Bar food (all day summer) ~ Restaurant ~ (01822) 880208 ~ Children in family room ~ Dogs welcome ~ Open 11-11; 12-10.30 Sun; 11-3, 6-11 Mon-Thurs in winter

RATTERY SX7461 Map 1

Church House

Village signposted from A385 W of Totnes, and A38 S of Buckfastleigh

This is one of Britain's oldest pubs, and the spiral stone steps behind a little stone doorway on your left as you come in date from about 1030. There are massive oak beams and standing timbers in the homely open-plan bar, large fireplaces (one with a little cosy nook partitioned off around it), windsor armchairs, comfortable seats and window seats, and prints on the plain white walls; the no smoking dining room is separated from this room by heavy curtains. Good bar food includes generously filled rolls (from £3.35), ploughman's with local cheeses (from £4.95), and daily specials such as chicken and cranberry curry (£7.50), steak and stilton or fish pie (£8.95), chicken jambalaya (£9.25), fresh fish such as salmon with lime and parsley sauce (£8.95) or large bass or grilled brill (£10.95), peppered steak (£9.50), and half a roast guinea fowl (£10.50). Well kept Greene King Abbot, Marstons Pedigree, and St Austell Dartmoor Best on handpump, lots of malt whiskies, and a decent wine list; friendly staff. Outside, there are peaceful views of the partly wooded surrounding hills from picnic-sets on a hedged courtyard by the churchyard. *(Recommended by Dudley and Moira Cockroft, D S Jackson, Ted George, Bob and Ann Westbrook, John and Vivienne Rice, MP, Neil and Beverley Gardner, Ian Phillips, Dr and Mrs M E Wilson, Wally and Irene Nunn, B J Harding, Bob Broadhurst, Lee Potter, JP, PP)*

Free house ~ Licensees Brian and Jill Evans ~ Real ale ~ Bar food ~ Restaurant ~ No credit cards ~ (01364) 642220 ~ Children in eating area of bar and restaurant ~ Dogs allowed in bar ~ Open 11-2.30, 6-1(10.30 in winter); 12-2.30, 7-10.30 Sun

ROCKBEARE SY0295 Map 1

Jack in the Green 🍷

Signposted from new A30 bypass E of Exeter

A reliable dining place, this still has the friendly helpful service, relaxed atmosphere and good drinks choice of a proper pub – Branscombe Vale labelled as JIG for the pub, Otter Ale and Theakstons Best on handpump, and 10 good wines by the glass. The neat and comfortable good-sized bar has wheelback chairs, sturdy cushioned wall pews and varying-sized tables on its dark blue carpet, with sporting prints, nice decorative china and a dark carved oak dresser; on our inspection visit the piped music was Tom Jones and Sandie Shaw. The larger dining side, extended in 2001, is air-conditioned but similarly traditional in style: some of its many old hunting and shooting photographs are well worth a close look, and it has button-back leather chesterfields by its big woodburning stove. Consistently enjoyable food using fresh local produce includes bar snacks such as tomato and pepper soup (£3.50), ploughman's (£4.95), bangers and mash with onion gravy (£7.50), grilled goats cheese salad with raspberry dressing (£7.95), good steak and kidney pie (£8.25), smoked haddock fishcakes (£8.95), fresh cod and parsley pie or smoked seafood (£9.50), chargrilled calves liver with sage and mascarpone (£10.50), and roast saddle of venison with fresh vegetables and chocolate jus (£10.95); Sunday lunch (two courses £13.25, three courses £16.75) and vegetarian choices like wild mushroom omelette and truffle sabayon or stuffed aubergine with grilled goats cheese, couscous and roasted pine nuts. You may get truffles with your coffee. There are some tables out behind, by a back skittle alley that doubles as a summer children's room, with more in a fairly new garden area. *(Recommended by Richard and Margaret Peers, Dr and Mrs M E Wilson, Oliver and Sue Rowell, Lucien, Brian and Bett Cox, Mrs Sylvia Elcoate, Basil Minson)*

Free house ~ Licensee Paul Parnell ~ Real ale ~ Bar food ~ Restaurant ~ (01404) 822240 ~ Well behaved children in eating area of bar ~ Open 11-2.30(3 Sat), 5.30 (6 Sat)-11; 12-10.30 Sun; closed 25 Dec-3 Jan

SHEEPWASH SS4806 Map 1

Half Moon 🍷 £ 🛏

Off A3072 Holsworthy—Hatherleigh at Highampton

This is still the place to stay if you love fishing as they have 10 miles of private fishing on the River Torridge (salmon, sea trout and brown trout) as well as a rod room, good drying facilities and a small shop stocking the basic necessities. The white walls of the neatly kept carpeted main bar are covered in fishing pictures, there's solid old furniture under the beams, and a big log fire fronted by slate flagstones. Lunchtime bar snacks are traditionally simple and include sandwiches (£1.75, toasties £2.50), home-made pasties (£3.75), ploughman's or home-cooked ham salad (£4.25), home-made lasagne (£5.50), and puddings (from £2.25). Well kept Courage Best, Greene King Ruddles County, and a guest such as Sharps Doom Bar on handpump (well kept in a temperature-controlled cellar), a fine choice of malt whiskies, and an extensive wine list; darts, cribbage, dominoes, shove-ha'penny, and separate pool room. Several bedrooms in the annexe have been recently refurbished. *(Recommended by S G N Bennett, Bob and Ann Westbrook)*

Free house ~ Licensees Lee and Nathan Adey ~ Real ale ~ Bar food (12-1.45; no evening bar food (restaurant only)) ~ Restaurant ~ No credit cards ~ (01409) 231376 ~ Children in eating area of bar and restaurant ~ Dogs allowed in bar ~ Open 11.30-2.30, 6-11; 12-2.30, 7-10.30 Sun; closed no accommodation 20-27 Dec ~ Bedrooms: £40B/£80B

SIDBURY SY1595 Map 1

Hare & Hounds

3 miles N of Sidbury, at Putts Corner; A375 towards Honiton, crossroads with B3174

This useful isolated roadside pub surprises in two ways: first, it seems so much bigger inside than you could have guessed from outside, rambling all over the place; and secondly, even on a winter weekday that leaves other much smaller pubs pretty empty, it manages to fill that space with a comfortable bustle of happy customers. It's well divided inside, with two good log fires (and rather unusual wood-framed leather sofas complete with pouffes), heavy beams and fresh flowers throughout, some oak panelling, plenty of tables with red leatherette or red plush-cushioned dining chairs, window seats and well used bar stools too; it's mostly carpeted, with bare boards and stripped stone walls at one softly lit no smoking end. At the opposite end of the pub, on the left, another big dining area has huge windows looking out over the garden. As you come in, the first thing you see is the good popular daily carvery counter, with a choice of joints, and enough turnover to keep up a continuous supply of fresh vegetables (lunchtime £5.95, evening £6.75, children £3.95). Other food includes sandwiches (from £2.20), filled baked potatoes (from £2.60), home-made soup (£2.75), home-made chicken liver pâté (£3.65), vegetarian pie (£5.65), ploughman's (£5.75), lasagne (£5.85), pie of the day or home-made curry (£5.95), steaks (from £10.25), and daily specials such as minted lamb hotpot topped with cripsy potatoes and cheese (£5.65), duck and vegetable stir fry (£7.25), chicken breast with jalapeno glaze or pork medallions with cider, apples and cream (£9.85), skate wing with caper butter (£10.15), and whole pink bream (£10.45). Well kept changing ales such as Branscombe Branoc, Fullers London Pride and Otter Bitter and Ale on handpump or tapped from the cask, good cheerful service; pool in one side room, another with big-screen sports TV. The big garden, giving good valley views, has picnic-sets, a play area enlivened by a pensioned-off fire engine, and a small strolling flock of peafowl. *(Recommended by Dr and Mrs M E Wilson, Joyce and Maurice Cottrell, Paul and Annette Hallett, Michael and Marion Buchanan, John Couper)*

Free house ~ Licensee Peter Cairns ~ Real ale ~ Bar food (all day) ~ Restaurant ~ (01404) 41760 ~ Children welcome ~ Dogs allowed in bar ~ Open 11-11; 12-10.30 Sun

SIDFORD SY1390 Map 1

Blue Ball ★

A3052 just N of Sidmouth

Since 1912, this popular and friendly 14th-c thatched inn has been run by the same family (five generations in all). The low, partly panelled and neatly kept lounge bar has heavy beams, upholstered wall benches and windsor chairs, three open fires, and lots of bric-a-brac; the family room and part of the restaurant are no smoking. Well liked bar food includes sandwiches (from £2.50; fresh Lyme Bay crab £4.25), home-made soup (£2.95), local sausages (£3.95), ploughman's or omelettes (£5.50), wild mushroom lasagne (£6.25), steak and kidney pudding (£7.75), grilled fillet of fresh salmon with prawns in a white wine, tarragon and mushroom sauce (£8.50), steaks (from £9.50), and daily specials such as chicken, game or steak and mushroom pies or fresh local fish and crab (from £8.50). Bass, Flowers IPA, Greene King Old Speckled Hen, Otter Ale, and a guest from Brakspears, J W Lees or Smiles on handpump, kept well in a temperature-controlled cellar, and a weekly choice of special wines plus their standard list; helpful staff. A plainer public bar has darts, dominoes, cribbage, shove-ha'penny, and a fruit machine; maybe piped music in the evening. Tables on a terrace look out over a colourful front flower garden, and there are more seats on a bigger back lawn – as well as in a covered area next to the barbecue; seesaw and play house for children. *(Recommended by Mike Tucker, A and B D Craig, PB, JB, R T and J C Moggridge, S Palmer, Alan and Paula McCully, P R and S A White, David Peakall, Rod Stoneman, Joyce and Maurice Cottrell, Ian and Deborah Carrington, Mrs Joy Griffiths, the Didler, Eric Locker)*

Pubmaster ~ Lease Roger Newton ~ Real ale ~ Bar food (12-2(3 Sun), 6.30-9.30) ~ Restaurant ~ (01395) 514062 ~ Children in restaurant and family room ~ Dogs allowed in bar ~ Occasional live entertainment ~ Open 11-11; 12-10.30 Sun ~ Bedrooms: £28(£40B)/£45(£70B)

SLAPTON SX8244 Map 1

Tower ★

Signposted off A379 Dartmouth—Kingsbridge

The picnic-sets on the neatly kept back lawn here are overlooked by the ivy-covered ruin of a 14th-c chantry – this atmospheric old place was built around 1347 to house the men working on it. The low-ceilinged beamed bar has armchairs, low-backed settles and scrubbed oak tables on the flagstones or bare boards, open log fires, and up to five well kept real ales such as Adnams Best, Badger Tanglefoot, and St Austell Dartmoor Best with guests like Black Sheep, Butcombe Gold, Exmoor Gold or Wells Bombardier on handpump; farm cider and decent wines. Good, imaginative food at lunchtime includes home-made soup (£2.95), sandwiches (from £3.95), home-made chicken and duck liver pâté with spiced pears (£4.75), antipasti or local pork sausages with wholegrain mustard mash and onion gravy (£5.95), liver and bacon or lightly spiced crab cakes on noodles with warm citrus dressing and tomato and chilli jam (£6.95), and braised lamb shank with mash and rich mint gravy (£7.95), with evening choices such as a warm tartlet of dolcelatte, spinach and cherry tomatoes (£4.65), sautéed king prawns and scallops with chilli jam and crème fraîche (£6.95), vegetable crisp-top pie with vichyssoise sauce (£6.95), salmon with wilted lettuce and cucumber salad and a split tomato dressing (£8.95), duck breast on celeriac and orange mash (£12.95), and chargrilled beef fillet with watercress purée and mushroom and red wine jus (£14.95), and daily specials like rabbit braised with orange and rosemary (£10.95), monkfish with cherry tomatoes, olives and parma ham (£11.50), and partridge with calvados, baby pears and lentils or venison steak with balsamic and red wine jus (£11.95); lovely puddings – treacle tart, crème brûlée with rhubarb, ginger and raspberry compote or frozen white chocolate and orange terrine with honeycomb and cherries (£3.75). Cribbage, dominoes, chess, backgammon, Scrabble, draughts, and piped music. The lane up to the pub is very narrow and parking is not easy. *(Recommended by the Didler, Roger Wain-Heapy, John Brightley, Lynda and Trevor Smith, B J Harding, Derek and Caroline Earwood, Brian and Bett Cox, Bob and Ann Westbrook, Tracey and Stephen Groves)*

Free house ~ Licensees Nicola and Josh Acfield ~ Real ale ~ Bar food (not winter Sun evening or Mon) ~ Restaurant ~ (01548) 580216 ~ Children in room next to bar ~ Dogs allowed in bar ~ Occasional live folk and jazz ~ Open 12-3, 6-11; 12-3, 7-10.30 Sun; closed 25 Dec and evening 26 Dec ~ Bedrooms: /£50S

SOURTON SX5390 Map 1

Highwayman ★

A386, S of junction with A30

The meticulous workmanship, unrestrained imagination and sheer eccentricity of this pub's remarkable design will take your breath away. For over 40 years, Mrs Thomson's parents put huge enthusiasm into this extraordinary décor, and Sally and Bruce are carefully continuing to add to it. The porch (a pastiche of a nobleman's carriage) leads into a warren of dimly lit stonework and flagstone-floored burrows and alcoves, richly fitted out with red plush seats discreetly cut into the higgledy-piggledy walls, elaborately carved pews, a leather porter's chair, Jacobean-style wicker chairs, and seats in quaintly bulging small-paned bow windows; the ceiling in one part, where there's an array of stuffed animals, gives the impression of being underneath a tree, roots and all. The separate Rita Jones' Locker is a make-believe sailing galleon, full of intricate woodwork and splendid timber baulks, with white antique lace-clothed tables in the embrasures that might have held cannons. They only sell keg beer, but specialise in farm cider and organic wines, and food is confined to a range of meaty and vegetarian pasties (from £1.50) or platters and cheeses; service is warmly welcoming and full of character; old-fashioned penny fruit machine, and 40s piped music; no smoking at the bar counters. Outside, there's a play area in similar style for children with little black and white roundabouts like a Victorian fairground, a fairy-tale pumpkin house and an old-lady-who-lived-in-the-shoe house. You can take children in to look around the pub but they can't stay inside. The period bedrooms with four-posters and half-testers are attractive. A cycle route which incorporates the disused railway line now passes the inn, and there are bunk rooms available for walkers and cyclists. *(Recommended by Kevin Blake, Mayur Shah, the Didler, JP, PP)*

Free house ~ Licensees Sally and Bruce Thomson ~ Bar food (12-1.45, 6-10.15) ~ No credit cards ~ (01837) 861243 ~ Dogs allowed in bar ~ Open 11-2, 6-10.30; 12-2, 7-10.30 Sun ~ Bedrooms: /£35S(£55B)

Please let us know of any pubs where the wine is particularly good.

SOUTH POOL SX7740 Map 1

Millbrook

Village off A379 from Frogmore, E of Kingsbridge

By the time this new edition of the *Guide* is published, this tiny pub will have opened letting bedrooms and a small dining area. The charming little back bar has handsome windsor chairs, a chintz easy chair, drawings and paintings (and a chart) on its cream walls, clay pipes on the beams, and fresh flowers; there's also a top bar. Tasty bar food includes sandwiches (from £2; crab £4,75), home-made soup (£2.50), ploughman's (from £4.50), cottage pie, potato, leek and cheese bake or chilli (£4.95), fish pie (£5.95), salads (from £5.95; seafood platter £10.95), daily specials, and puddings like treacle tart or sticky toffee pudding (£3.25). Well kept Bass, Fullers London Pride, Wadworths 6X, and a changing guest on handpump, and local farm cider. Darts in the public bar in winter. You can sit outside even in poor weather as both the front courtyard and the terrace by the stream (where you can watch the aylesbury ducks) are covered by canopies and there are now outside heaters. Parking can be difficult. More reports please. *(Recommended by Mark and Amanda Sheard, Roger Wain-Heapy, B J Harding, Mrs J Ekins-Daukes, P R and S A White, Nick Lawless, Mr and Mrs J Curtis)*

Free house ~ Licensees Liz Stirland and Rod Seymour ~ Real ale ~ Bar food (not winter Sun evening) ~ Restaurant ~ No credit cards ~ (01548) 531581 ~ Children in family room ~ Open 11.30-2.30, 5.30(6 in winter)-11; 12-2.30, 6.30(7 in winter)-10.30 Sun ~ Bedrooms: /£50B

SOUTH ZEAL SX6593 Map 1

Oxenham Arms ★ 🍷 🛏

Village signposted from A30 at A382 roundabout and B3260 Okehampton turnoff

As we went to press, we heard that this friendly place had been sold. It's been a very popular main entry for many years so we are keeping our fingers crossed that the new people won't change too much. What will not change, of course, is the fact that it's a marvellous building with great character and a real sense of history. It was first licensed in 1477 – though it has grown up around the remains of a Norman monastery, built here to combat the pagan power of the neolithic standing stone that still forms part of the wall in the family room behind the bar (there are actually twenty more feet of stone below the floor). It later became the Dower House of the Burgoynes, whose heiress carried it to the Oxenham family. And Charles Dickens, snowed up one winter, wrote a lot of *Pickwick Papers* here. The beamed and partly panelled front bar has elegant mullioned windows and Stuart fireplaces, and windsor armchairs around low oak tables and built-in wall seats. The small family room has beams, wheelback chairs around polished tables, decorative plates, and another open fire. Well liked bar food has included home-made soup (£2.50), sandwiches (from £2.50), good ploughman's (£4.75), fish and chips (£5.50), nice local farm sausages with mustard and leek mash and onion gravy (£5.75), steak, kidney, mushroom and Guinness pie or daily curry (£6.25), daily specials such as cauliflower cheese (£4.95), moussaka or prawn creole (£6.25), and salmon and broccoli mornay (£7.25), and children's menu (£2.95). The dining room is no smoking. Well kept Princetown IPA and Sharps Doom Bar and Eden Ale on handpump or tapped from the cask, and an extensive list of wines including good house claret; darts, shove-ha'penny, dominoes, and cribbage. Note the imposing curved stone steps leading up to the garden where there's a sloping spread of lawn. *(Recommended by Jenny Cridland, Gordon Cooper, Mrs Ursula Hofheinz, Andrea Rampley, Nick Lawless, MB, M G Hart, the Didler, Di and Mike Gillam, Ian and Deborah Carrington, Bernard Stradling, John and Sarah Perry, Richard Endacott, Pete Baker, Dennis Jenkin, Richard and Margaret Peers, Peter Craske, Brian Skelcher, Walter and Susan Rinaldi-Butcher, Tony and Wendy Hobden, Jacquie and Jim Jones, Dr Brian and Mrs Anne Hamilton, Neil and Angela Huxter, R J Walden, Mayur Shah, Jane and Adrian Tierney-Jones, Peter and Margaret Lodge, Stuart Turner, Rita Horridge, Mrs Sylvia Elcoate, JP, PP, Dr D G Twyman)*

Free house ~ Licensee James Henry ~ Real ale ~ Bar food ~ Restaurant ~ (01837)

840244 ~ Children welcome ~ Dogs allowed in bar ~ Open 11-2.30, 6-11; 12-2.30, 7-10.30 Sun ~ Bedrooms: £45B/£60S(£70B)

STAVERTON SX7964 Map 1

Sea Trout

Village signposted from A384 NW of Totnes

This was known as the Church House for several hundred years until a previous landlord caught a sea trout in the River Dart and renamed it. There's always a good crowd of visitors and locals, and the neatly kept rambling beamed lounge bar has sea trout and salmon flies and stuffed fish on the walls, cushioned settles and stools, and a stag's head above the fireplace; the main bar has low banquettes, soft lighting and an open fire, and there's also a public bar with darts, pool, TV, table skittles, shove-ha'penny, and dominoes. Using top quality produce from the best local producers, good bar food includes lunchtime sandwiches, home-made soup (£2.95), cream and garlic mushrooms (£3.95), avocado and prawns in a lemon salsa (£4.85), oriental vegetable stir fry (£6), home-cooked ham and egg or pork and herb sausages with onion gravy (£6.25), home-made steak in ale pie (£7.95), whole grilled local trout filled with prawns and a lemon butter sauce (£8.95), steaks (from £11.95), daily specials such as confit of duck leg or a changing curry, puddings like crème brûlée or bread and butter pudding (£3.45), and children's menu (from £2.85). The restaurant and most eating areas are no smoking. Well kept Palmers Best, Copper Ale, and 200 on handpump, a decent range of wines, quite a few whiskies, and farm cider; efficient, helpful staff. There are seats under parasols on the attractive paved back garden. A station for the South Devon Steam Railway is not too far away.

(Recommended by Ron and Sheila Corbett, the Didler, JP, PP, Joyce and Maurice Cottrell, Dr Paull Khan, Roger Bridgeman, John Wilson, Jonathan Smith, Neil and Beverley Gardner, Richard and Margaret Peers, Dennis Jenkin, Chris Butt)

Palmers ~ Tenants Nicholas and Nicola Brookland ~ Real ale ~ Bar food ~ Restaurant ~ (01803) 762274 ~ Children in eating area of bar and restaurant ~ Dogs allowed in bar ~ Open 11-3, 6-11; 12-4, 7-10.30 Sun ~ Bedrooms: £47.50B/£68B

STOCKLAND ST2404 Map 1

Kings Arms

Village signposted from A30 Honiton—Chard; and also, at every turning, from N end of Honiton High Street

Despite the emphasis on the enjoyable food and the fact that many customers stay overnight in this spotlessly kept and individually run 16th-c inn, there's a proper pubby atmosphere and plenty of locals. The dark beamed, elegant dining lounge has solid refectory tables and settles, attractive landscapes, a medieval oak screen (which divides the room into two), and a great stone fireplace across almost the whole width of one end; the cosy restaurant has a huge inglenook fireplace and bread oven. Bar food is served at lunchtime only: sandwiches or home-made soup (£2.50), smoked mackerel or chicken liver pâté (£4), omelettes (from £4), various pasta dishes (small £4.50, large £7.50), and steak and kidney pie (£6.50), there might be Portuguese sardines (£4), moules marinière or confit of duck with a plum sauce (£5), mushroom stroganoff or pasta carbonara (£7.50), king prawn madras (£9.50), supreme of guinea fowl (£10.50), Cotley rack of lamb (£11.50), and puddings such as apple and treacle crumble, crème brûlée or chocolate truffle torte (£4). In the evening, only the restaurant menu is available and diners are invited to the Cotley Bar to listen to the landlord recite the menu while you enjoy a free sherry. Well kept Courage Directors, Exmoor Ale and Gold, and Otter Ale on handpump, over 40 malt whiskies (including island and west coast ones; large spirit measures), a comprehensive wine list, and farm ciders. At the back, a flagstoned bar has cushioned benches and stools around heavy wooden tables, and leads on to a carpeted darts room with two boards, another room with dark beige plush armchairs and settees (and a fruit machine), and a neat ten-pin skittle alley; dominoes, quiz machine, TV, and quiet mainly classical piped music. There are tables under cocktail parasols on the terrace in front of the white-faced thatched pub and a lawn enclosed by trees and shrubs. The bedrooms are newly refurbished. *(Recommended by Pat and Robert Watt, Giles and Liz Ridout, Steve Whalley, John and Glenys Wheeler, Jenny and Chris Wilson, Wally and Irene Nunn, Brian and Bett Cox, Shirley Mackenzie, Derek and Sylvia Stephenson, Dr and Mrs M E Wilson, Muriel and Peter Gleave, Derek and Margaret Underwood, Francis Johnston, TOH, Mrs Jean Clarke, Mrs Sylvia Elcoate, Peter Burton)*

Free house ~ Licensees Heinz Kiefer and Paul Diviani ~ Real ale ~ Bar food (lunchtime only 12-1.45; not Sun) ~ Restaurant ~ (01404) 881361 ~ Children in eating area of bar and restaurant ~ Dogs allowed in bar ~ Live music Sat and Sun evenings ~ Open 12-3, 6.30-11(10.30 Sun); closed 25 Dec ~ Bedrooms: £30B/£50B

STOKE FLEMING SX8648 Map 1

Green Dragon 🍷

Church Road

Peter Crowther, the long-distance yachtsman, runs this interesting local and there are cuttings about him, maps of his races, and accounts of his sinking 800 miles out in the Atlantic on the walls. The atmosphere is very relaxed and, while obviously popular with regulars, it is a favourite with many visitors, too. The main part of the flagstoned and beamed bar has two small settles, bay window seats and stools, boat pictures, and maybe Maia the burmese cat or Rhea the relaxed german shepherd; down on the right is a wooden-floored snug (recently decorated) with throws and cushions on sofas and armchairs, a few books (30p to RNLI), adult board games, and a grandfather clock. Down some steps is the Mess Deck decorated with old charts and lots of ensigns and flags, and there's a playbox of children's games; piped music, shove-ha'penny, cribbage, and dominoes. Enjoyable home-made bar food includes soup (£2.30), freshly cooked filled baguettes (£3.50), baked crab and mushrooms in a creamy anchovy sauce, topped with cheese (£4.20), prawn platter (£4.90), steak in ale or fish pies (£6.30), and daily specials such as thai crab cakes (£5.80), field mushrooms with sun-dried tomato and pepper pesto topped with local goats cheese (£6.20), venison and cranberry daube (£6.80), marinated tuna steak (£7.50), local rump steak (£9), and Friday night fish and chips (£5); winter Sunday lunch. Well kept Bass, Flowers IPA, Otter Ale, and Wadworths 6X on handpump (all except Bass kept under light blanket pressure), big glasses of good house wines, Luscombe's slightly alcoholic ginger beer and organic apple juice, and a decent range of spirits; you can take the beer away with you. There's a back garden with swings, a climbing frame and picnic-sets and a front terrace with some white plastic garden tables and chairs under a new awning. The church opposite has an interesting tall tower. Parking can be tricky at peak times. *(Recommended by Barry Smith, Rona Murdoch, Alan Vere, Dennis Jenkin, J M Law, Charles Eatof, Val Stevenson, Rob Holmes, Pete and Jo Cole, Eric Locker, Alan and Paula McCully, Paul Boot)*

Heavitree ~ Tenants Peter and Alix Crowther ~ Real ale ~ Bar food (12-2.30, 6.30-9) ~ (01803) 770238 ~ Children in eating area of bar and in restaurant ~ Dogs allowed in bar ~ Occasional summer folk or Irish music ~ Open 11-3, 5.30-11; 12-3, 6(6.30 in winter)-10.30 Sun; closed 25 Dec

STOKE GABRIEL SX8457 Map 1

Church House

Village signposted from A385 just W of junction with A3022, in Collaton St Mary; can also be reached from nearer Totnes

This is a bustling local with friendly regulars and staff, and plenty of history and unspoilt character. The lounge bar has an exceptionally fine medieval beam-and-plank ceiling, a black oak partition wall, window seats cut into the thick butter-coloured walls, decorative plates and vases of flowers on a dresser, and a huge fireplace still used in winter to cook the stew; darts. The mummified cat in a case, probably about 200 years old, was found during restoration of the roof space in the verger's cottage three doors up the lane – one of a handful found in the West

Country and believed to have been a talisman against evil spirits. Straightforward bar food includes home-made soup (£2.75), a big choice of sandwiches and toasties (from £2.75; ham, cheese, pineapple and onion toastie £3.75), filled baked potatoes (from £3.95), ploughman's (from £4.50), steak and kidney in ale pie, chicken curry or stilton and leek bake (£6.50), and puddings (£3.25). Well kept Bass, Worthington Best, and a weekly guest ale on handpump, and 20 malt whiskies. Euchre in the little public locals' bar. There are picnic-sets on the little terrace in front of the building, and see if you can spot the priest hole, dating from the Reformation. No children inside. *(Recommended by Dr and Mrs M E Wilson, P Duffield, Mike and Mary Carter, Richard and Margaret Peers, Emma Kingdon, James Woods, P R and S A White, Derek and Margaret Underwood)*

Free house ~ Licensee T G Patch ~ Real ale ~ Bar food (12-2.30, 6.30-9.30) ~ (01803) 782384 ~ Dogs welcome ~ Open 11-3, 6-11; 11-11 Fri and Sat; 12-3.30, 7-10.30 Sun

STOKENHAM SX8042 Map 1

Tradesmans Arms

Just off A379 Dartmouth—Kingsbridge

Now only open in the evenings (though they do open for Sunday lunch), this charming thatched village pub is extremely popular for the very good food cooked by the licensee, and the warm welcome from the hard-working landlady. The little beamed bar has a relaxed, friendly atmosphere, plenty of nice antique tables and neat dining chairs – with more up a step or two at the back – window seats looking across a field to the village church, and a big fireplace; the no smoking room to the left of the door offers the same food as the bar. They specialise in local game and fish and the landlord shoots in season to provide rabbit, pigeon and venison; you must book to be sure of a table. Changing regularly, the interesting dishes might include soup (£2.95; the fish soup is lovely, £3.75), home-made pâté or devilled mushrooms (£3.75), home-made fishcakes with spicy tomato sauce (£4.25), scallops flamed in brandy and served with a light onion sauce (£4.95), baked lentil, courgette and mushroom layer (£7.75), wild rabbit with smoked bacon in a red wine sauce (£9.25), local pheasant braised in wine sauce (£9.95), flash fried venison garnished with juniper flavoured swede and bacon (£11.25), baked hake with citrus sauce (£11.50), wild pigeon breast finished with cream and chorizo (£11.75), and rod caught local baked bass (£12.50); home-made puddings, local cheese, and Sunday roast local lamb or beef (£6.95). Well kept Adnams Southwold and a guest such as Butcombe or Exmoor Ale on handpump, local cider, a shortish, well chosen wine list, and quite a few malt whiskies. There are some seats outside in the garden. *(Recommended by Tracey and Stephen Groves, Mr and Mrs I Jones, Rev E D Coombes, Pete and Jo Cole, Roger Wain-Heapy, Michael and Marianne Tann, Nick Lawless, C A Hall, Mr and Mrs J Curtis, Paul Boot)*

Free house ~ Licensees John and Elizabeth Sharman ~ Real ale ~ Bar food (not Mon, Tues to Sat lunchtimes; not Sun or Mon evenings) ~ (01548) 580313 ~ Children allowed only Sun lunchtime ~ Dogs allowed in bar ~ Open 6.30-11; 6.30-11 Sat; 12-3 Sun; closed Sun evening, Mon, Tues to Sat lunch

TOPSHAM SX9688 Map 1

Bridge

2¼ miles from M5 junction 30: Topsham signposted from exit roundabout; in Topsham follow signpost (A376) Exmouth on the Elmgrove Road, into Bridge Hill

The utterly old-fashioned layout and character of this 16th-c ex-maltings remains unchanged over the years (to the relief of a good many readers), and the fifth generation of the same family helps to run it. There are fine old traditional furnishings (true country workmanship, not just bought-in stuff) in the little lounge partitioned off from the inner corridor by a high-backed settle; log fire. A bigger lower room (the old malthouse) is open at busy times. The cosy regulars' no smoking inner sanctum keeps up to 10 real ales tapped from the cask: Adnams Broadside, Badger Tanglefoot, Bath Old Gem, Blackawton Wheal Dream, Branscombe Vale

Branoc and Hells Belles, Exe Valley Exeter Old Bitter and Winter Glow, Moor Old Freddy Walker, amd RCH Firebox. Local farm cider and elderberry and gooseberry wines; friendly service. Simple, tasty bar food such as pasties (£1.95), winter home-made soup (£2.95), sandwiches (from £2.70; the smoked chicken with elderflower and gooseberry pickle is liked), and various ploughman's (from £4.70); no noisy music or machines – just a chatty, relaxed atmosphere. There are riverside picnic-sets overlooking the weir. *(Recommended by Steve Harvey, Canon and Mrs Michael Bourdeaux, the Didler, Jane and Adrian Tierney-Jones, JP, PP, Pete Baker, Jenny and Brian Seller, June and Ken Brooks, Tom McLean, Keith and Suzie Stevens, Dr and Mrs M E Wilson, Hugh Roberts)*

Free house ~ Licensee Mrs C Cheffers-Heard ~ Real ale ~ Bar food ~ No credit cards ~ (01392) 873862 ~ Children in room without bar ~ Dogs allowed in bar ~ Open 12-2, 6(7 Sun)-10.30(11 Fri/Sat)

Passage House 🍷

Ferry Road, off main street

At any time of year, this attractive waterside pub is a pleasant, popular place to visit. It's cosy and warm on wet, windy days, and in good weather, the wooden tables and chairs on the quiet shoreside terrace are quickly snapped up. The traditional bar has wall pews and bar stools, and is decorated with electrified oil lamps hanging from big black oak beams in the ochre ceiling; the lower dining area with its slate floor is no smoking. The lure for most is the good, fresh fish dishes; they have a fine choice of up to ten a day. Other bar food includes sandwiches (from £2.25), ploughman's (from £4.75), ham and eggs (£4.95), a pie of the day, lasagne or chicken curry (£5.95), and popular cod and fries (£6.95). Well kept Bass, Flowers IPA, Otter and Wadworths 6X on handpump, and good wines; piped music. *(Recommended by the Didler, Comus and Sarah Elliott, John and Vivienne Rice, Howard and Margaret Buchanan, Andy and Yvonne Cunningham, P R and S A White, Richard and Margaret Peers, D J Hulse, Dr and Mrs M E Wilson)*

Heavitree ~ Manager Richard Davies ~ Real ale ~ Bar food ~ Restaurant ~ (01392) 873653 ~ Children in restaurant ~ Dogs allowed in bar ~ Open 11-11; 12-10.30 Sun; 11-3, 5-11 weekdays in winter

TORCROSS SX8241 Map 1

Start Bay

A379 S of Dartmouth

Almost as soon as this immensely popular dining pub opens, it is full, and there are often queues – so it does make sense to get there early to be sure of a table. A local trawler catches the fish, a local crabber drops the crabs at the back door, and the landlord enjoys catching plaice, scallops, and bass: cod (medium £4.50; large £6.10; jumbo £8.30) and haddock (medium £4.60; large £6.20; jumbo £8.40), whole lemon sole (from £6.90), skate (£7.20), whole dover sole (in three sizes from £8.20), brill (from £8.70), and whole bass (small £9.50; medium £10.50; large £11.50). Other food includes sandwiches (from £2.50), ploughman's (from £3.90), filled baked potatoes (from £2.90), vegetable lasagne (£5.90), gammon and pineapple (£6.90), steaks (from £8.60), and children's meals (£3.90); they do warn of delays at peak times. Well kept Bass and Flowers Original or Otter Ale on handpump, and maybe Heron Valley cider and fresh apple juice, and local wine from the Sharpham Estate. The unassuming main bar (which has a small no smoking area) is very much set out for eating with wheelback chairs around plenty of dark tables or (round a corner) back-to-back settles forming booths; there are some photographs of storms buffeting the pub and country pictures on its cream walls, and a winter coal fire; a small chatty drinking area by the counter has a brass ship's clock and barometer. The winter games room has darts and shove-ha'penny; there's more booth seating in a no smoking family room with sailing boat pictures. There are seats (highly prized) out on the terrace overlooking the three-mile pebble beach, and the freshwater wildlife lagoon of Slapton Ley is just behind the pub. *(Recommended by Charlie Harris, Tracey and Stephen Groves, Neil and Beverley Gardner, Michael Porter, Alan Kilpatrick, Derek and Margaret Underwood, Pete and Jo Cole, Alan and Paula McCully, Eric Locker, John Brightley, Charles Eatof, Betsy and Peter Little)*

Whitbreads ~ Tenant Paul Stubbs ~ Real ale ~ Bar food (11.30(12 Sun)-2(2.15 Sun), 6-10; will serve snacks all day in summer) ~ (01548) 580553 ~ Children in family room ~ Dogs welcome ~ Open 11.30-11; 12-10.30 Sun; 11.30-2.30, 6-11 wkdys and Sat, and 12-2.45, 6-10.30 Sun in winter

TUCKENHAY SX8156 Map 1

Maltsters Arms

Take Ashprington road out of Totnes (signed left off A381 on outskirts), keeping on past Watermans Arms

Many people arrive at this popular pub by boat and they offer free overnight moorings. It's in a lovely spot by a peaceful wooded creek with tables by the water, and in summer there are regular live music concerts on the quayside and barbecues. Inside, there's been some gentle redecoration this year and the walls are now apricot and jade. The long, narrow bar links two other rooms – a little snug one with an open fire, and plenty of bric-a-brac, and another with red-painted vertical seats and kitchen chairs on the wooden floor. They keep a smashing range of drinks including well kept Princetown Dartmoor IPA and up to three changing guest beers on handpump from Blackawton, Robinsons, Teignworthy, and Youngs, 17 good wines by the glass, local farm cider, a serious bloody mary, summer kir and kir royale, organic apple juice and spicy ginger beer, and items in the freezer like buffalo grass vodka and various eau de vies. And the daily changing bar food also continues to draw customers, with lunchtime dishes such as chilli, tomato and pepper or creamy cauliflower and cumin soups (£3.50), sandwiches (from £3.95), chicken livers in onion and white wine (£4.50), field mushrooms stuffed with chestnut, artichoke and mozzarella (£4.75), ploughman's (from £4.95), smoked meat platter (£5.95), cottage pie, ratatouille topped with smoked cheddar or gammon and egg (£7.95), half a roast pheasant (£10.50), and whole baked bass (£13.95); in the evening, there might be spinach, halloumi and herb tart (£4.25), octopus and red wine stew (£4.95), scallops flash-fried in onion and saffron (£6.50), tacos stuffed with five bean chilli and crème fraîche (£7.75), lamb, apricot, date and cumin pie (£9), casserole of rump steak with red wine and mushrooms (£10), grilled whole lemon sole (£13), roast half duck with honey, five spice and pineapple (£14.95), puddings such as banana and papaya crème brûlée, warm chocolate fudge cake or rhubarb and clotted cream crunch fool (from £3.95), and proper food for children (£4.50); nice home-made bar nibbles, too. Darts, shove-ha'penny, cribbage, dominoes, chess, backgammon, and TV for sports. There may be a minimum stay of two nights at weekends.

(Recommended by Rebecca Nicholls, JP, PP, Jonathan Smith, Norman and Sheila Davies, John Evans, John and Vivienne Rice, Mike Gorton, Lynda and Trevor Smith, Richard and Margaret Peers, J M Law, Brian and Bett Cox, Catherine Pitt, MP, Suzanne Stacey, the Didler, Roger Wain-Heapy, Mr and Mrs M Cooper, R Mathews, Mr and Mrs M Dalby, Tracey and Stephen Groves, Bernard Stradling, Simon, Jo and Benjamin Cole, John and Elizabeth Thomason)

Free house ~ Licensees Denise and Quentin Thwaites ~ Real ale ~ Bar food (12-3, 7-9.30) ~ Restaurant ~ (01803) 732350 ~ Children in eating area of bar and restaurant ~ Dogs allowed in bar ~ Jazz 1st and 3rd Fri of month; outside music in summer ~ Open 11-11; 12-10.30 Sun; closed evening 25 Dec ~ Bedrooms: /£85S

UGBOROUGH SX6755 Map 1

Anchor

Off A3121 – signed from A38 W of South Brent

While the oak-beamed public bar of this bustling pub with its log fire in the stone fireplace, and wall settles and seats around wooden tables on the polished woodblock floor is where the locals gather, visitors tend to head for the comfortable restaurant with its windsor armchairs (the lower area is no smoking). You can eat from either the bar or restaurant menus and sit anywhere in the pub (apart from Saturday night when there are no bar snacks in the restaurant): home-made soup

(£2.95), filled baguettes (from £3), whitebait (£3.50), ploughman's (£4.50), omelettes (from £4.50), fennel bake (£5.50), steak and kidney pie or fish bake (£6.95), salads such as crab (from £7), and daily specials such as a trio of fishcakes (£6.95). Well kept Bass, Shepherd Neame Spitfire, and Suttons XSB on handpump or tapped from the cask; darts, cribbage, TV, and fruit machine. There's a small outside seating area. More reports please. *(Recommended by John Evans, Trevor Owen, Bob and Ann Westbrook, P R and S A White, Roger and Jenny Huggins, Alan and Paula McCully)*

Free house ~ Licensee Sheelagh Jeffreys-Simmons ~ Real ale ~ Bar food ~ Restaurant ~ (01752) 892283 ~ Children welcome ~ Dogs allowed in bar ~ Live entertainment every 2nd Sat ~ Open 11-3, 5.30-11; 10-11.30 Sat; 11-3, 5.30-10.30 Sun ~ Bedrooms: £35B/£50B

WIDECOMBE SX7176 Map 1

Rugglestone £

Village at end of B3387; pub just S – turn left at church and NT church house, OS Sheet 191 map reference 720765

Just up the lane from the bustling tourist village, this is an unspoilt, tucked away local. The small bar has a strong rural atmosphere, just four small tables, a few window and wall seats, a one-person pew built into the corner by the nice old stone fireplace, and a rudimentary bar counter dispensing well kept Butcombe Bitter and Dartmoor Best tapped from the cask; local farm cider and a decent little wine list. The room on the right is a bit bigger and lighter-feeling, and shy strangers may feel more at home here: another stone fireplace, beamed ceiling, stripped pine tables, and a built-in wall bench. There's also a little no smoking room which is used for dining; cribbage, euchre, and dominoes. Good simple bar food includes home-made soup or pasties (£2.50), filled baked potatoes (from £2.95), ploughman's (£4.20), cottage pie or a vegetarian dish of the day (£4.40), chicken pie (£4.60), local beef casserole with dumplings (£5.20), and home-made puddings such as treacle tart or fruit crumble (£2.95); friendly service, and espresso and cappuccino coffee. The cat is called Elbi, the two terriers, Tinker and Belle, and the retriever, Spring. Outside across the little moorland stream is a field with lots of picnic-sets. No children inside (though there is a large shelter with tables and chairs in the garden). *(Recommended by R J Walden, Joy and Colin Rorke, Andrea Rampley, David and Nina Pugsley, JP, PP, Mike Gorton, the Didler, Neil and Beverley Gardner, Mr and Mrs J McRobert, Bob and Ann Westbrook, Mr and Mrs McKay)*

Free house ~ Licensees Lorrie and Moira Ensor ~ Real ale ~ Bar food ~ (01364) 621327 ~ Dogs welcome ~ Open 11-2.30(3 Sat), 6-11; 12-3, 6-10.30 Sun; evening opening 7 in winter

WINKLEIGH SS6308 Map 1

Kings Arms

Village signposted off B3220 Crediton—Torrington; Fore Street

This thatched pub, set on the edge of the little village square, is the sort of place you come back to on a regular basis. It has an attractive main bar with beams, some old-fashioned built-in wall settles, scrubbed pine tables and benches on the flagstones, and a woodburning stove in a cavernous fireplace; another woodburning stove separates the bar from the no smoking dining room. Good bar food includes home-made soup (£2.95), sandwiches (from £2.95; filled baguettes from £3.50), creamy garlic mushrooms (£4.25), ploughman's or filled baked potatoes (£4.50), ham and eggs (£5.50), salmon fishcakes (£6), steak and kidney pie, italian-style meatballs in rich tomato sauce or vegetable shepherd's pie (£6.50), lamb chops with rosemary and redcurrant gravy or chicken breast wrapped in bacon with a chasseur sauce (£7), steaks (from £7.95), and whole bass with lemon parsley butter (£10.95). Well kept Bass, Butcombe Bitter, and Wells Bombardier on handpump, local cider, and decent wines; darts, shove-ha'penny, cribbage, and dominoes. There are seats out in the garden. *(Recommended by R J Walden, Pamela and Merlyn Horswell, Ann and Colin Hunt)*

Free house ~ Licensees Heather Williams, Jamie Stuart and Pippa Hutchinson ~ Real ale ~ Bar food (all day) ~ (01837) 83384 ~ Children welcome ~ Dogs allowed in bar ~ Open 11-11; 12-10.30 Sun; closed 25 Dec

WONSON SX6789 Map 1

Northmore Arms

Off A382 half mile from A30 at Whiddon Down; turn right down lane signposted Throwleigh/Gidleigh. Continue down lane over hump back bridge; turn left to Wonson; OS Sheet 191 map reference 674903

An ideal place for the curious traveller, this is a delightful secluded cottage run by a charming, friendly landlady. The two small connected beamed rooms – modest and informal but civilised – have wall settles, a few elderly chairs, five tables in one room and just two in the other. There are two open fires (only one may be lit), and some attractive photographs on the stripped stone walls; darts and cribbage. Besides well kept ales such as Adnams Broadside, Cotleigh Tawny and Exe Valley Dobs, they have good house wines, and most enjoyable home-made food (with prices unchanged since last year) such as sandwiches (from £1.50; toasties from £1.95), garlic mushrooms (£2.65), ploughman's (£4.25), filled baked potatoes (from £4.25), ham and egg or liver and bacon (£4.75), roast lamb with garlic potatoes (£5.95), steak (£7.95), and puddings such as home-made treacle tart with clotted cream (£2.25); Sunday roast beef (£5.95); Tuesday curries (£6.95), and huge breakfasts. The ladies' lavatory is up steep steps. Tables and chairs sit precariously in the steep little garden – all very peaceful and rustic; excellent walking from the pub (or to it, perhaps from Chagford or Gidleigh Park). *(Recommended by Lorna and Howard Lambert, Andrea Rampley, the Didler, Karen and Steve Wilson, MP)*

Free house ~ Licensee Mrs Mo Miles ~ Real ale ~ Bar food (12-9; 12-2.30, 7-9 Sun) ~ (01647) 231428 ~ Well behaved children away from bar ~ Dogs allowed in bar ~ Open 11-11; 12-10.30 Sun ~ Bedrooms: /£30

WOODLAND SX7968 Map 1

Rising Sun

Village signposted off A38 just NE of Ashburton – then keep eyes peeled for Rising Sun signposts

Readers enjoy staying at this bustling and friendly Dartmoor inn, and the hearty breakfasts are most enjoyable. Quite an emphasis is placed on the good interesting bar food – though plenty of customers do drop in for just a drink. Changing frequently, the dishes might include sandwiches and ploughman's, home-made soup (£3.25), home-made chicken liver pâté with bramley apple chutney or leek and devon blue cheese tart with tomato and balsamic vinegar dressing (£4.50), home-cooked ham with local free range egg and home-made chips or ploughman's with four west country cheeses and home-made chutney (£5.95), local venison sausages (£6.50), popular home-made pies (£6.95), lambs liver with bacon, mash and onion gravy (£7.95), fillet of gurnard with a herb crust and cream sauce (£8.95), rib-eye steak with caramelised red onions and balsamic dressing (£11.95), and home-made puddings with local clotted cream such as treacle tart, chocolate marquise or rhubarb crème brûlée (£3.25); they have children's dishes (£2.50) or will do small helpings of some of the main courses. The dining area is no smoking. There's an expanse of softly lit red plush button-back banquettes and matching studded chairs, partly divided by wooded banister rails, masonry pillars and the odd high-backed settle. A forest of beams is hung with thousands of old doorkeys, and a nice part by the log fire has shelves of plates and books, and old pictures above the fireplace. Well kept Princetown Jail Ale and Dartmoor IPA, and Teignworthy Reel Ale on handpump; cheerful service. The family area has various toys (and a collection of cookery books). There are some picnic-sets in the spacious garden, which has a play area including a redundant tractor. *(Recommended by Dr and Mrs A K Clarke, Andy Sinden, Louise Harrington, Mrs M E Lewis, Dr and Mrs M E Wilson, Neil and Beverley Gardner, Colin and Sandra Tann, Mrs J L Wyatt, D and H Broodbank, Ian and Nita Cooper)*

Free house ~ Licensee Heather Humphreys ~ Real ale ~ Bar food (12-2.15(3 Sun), 6(7 Sun)-9.15) ~ Restaurant ~ (01364) 652544 ~ Children in eating area of bar and restaurant ~ Dogs allowed in bar ~ Open 11.45-3, 6-11; 12-3, 7-10.30 Sun; closed Mon lunchtime (except bank hols) and all day Mon in winter ~ Bedrooms: £30B/£53B

Lucky Dip

Besides the fully inspected pubs, you might like to try these Lucky Dips recommended to us and described by readers (if you do, please send us reports: www.goodguides.com).

Abbotsham [SS4226]
Thatched Inn: Extensively refurbished family pub, friendly staff, Bass, Butcombe, Courage Directors and John Smiths, attractive food inc good value Sun lunch, families welcome, mix of modern seats and older features; tables outside; handy for the Big Sheep *(R J Walden, Mr and Mrs I Bennett)*
Abbotskerswell [SX8569]
☆ *Court Farm* [Wilton Way; look for the church tower]: Attractive neatly extended 17th-c former farmhouse catering for Torbay's affluent retired folk, various rooms off long crazy-paved main beamed bar, partly no smoking, good mix of furnishings, Bass, Castle Eden, Flowers IPA and Fullers London Pride, farm cider, decent wines, woodburners, good helpings of good unpretentious waitress-served food (can take a time when busy) from sandwiches to steaks and bargain Sun lunch, half helpings for children, friendly helpful service; piped music; children in eating area, tables in pretty garden, open all day *(Andrew Hodges, Ian Mcintyre, John Braine-Hartnell, LYM, John and Vivienne Rice, Mrs Sylvia Elcoate, John Wilson, Derek Allpass)*
Appledore [SS4630]
Beaver [Irsha St]: Great estuary views from raised area in thriving well worn in harbourside pub, good value food esp fish, friendly staff, well kept Bass with changing guest beers from Cornwall and afar, decent house wines, great range of whiskies; can be smoky, pool in smaller games room; tables on sheltered terrace, children really welcome, disabled access *(Andy Marks, Christine and Neil Townend, Paul and Ursula Randall)*
☆ *Royal George* [Irsha St]: Simple but good fresh food inc local fish in no smoking dining room with superb estuary views, well kept ales such as Bass, Greene King Old Speckled Hen and Ind Coope Burton, decent wines, good friendly service, cosy unspoilt front bar (dogs allowed), attractive pictures, fresh flowers; disabled access, picnic-sets outside, picturesque street sloping to sea *(Christine and Neil Townend, Helen Hazzard)*
Ashprington [SX8156]
☆ *Watermans Arms* [Bow Bridge, on Tuckenhay road]: Bustling quarry-tiled heavy-beamed pub at the head of Bow Creek, comfortable and roomy, with high-backed settles and other sturdy furnishings, stripped stonework, partly no smoking eating area, log fire, wide food choice inc children's, welcoming service, well kept Bass, Theakstons XB and a beer brewed for the pub, local wine and farm cider, darts, dominoes, cribbage; piped music, TV; children and dogs welcome, open all day, comfortable bedrooms, pretty flower-filled garden, more tables over road by creek *(John Evans, Lynda and Trevor Smith, LYM, Norman and Sheila Davies, Jonathan Smith, Catherine Pitt, Mike and Mary Carter)*
Awliscombe [ST1301]
☆ *Awliscombe Inn* [A373 just NW of Honiton]: Recently comfortably refurbished by new owners, good chunky elm tables, flowery-cushioned pews and high-backed wall banquettes in big-beamed main bar, attractive three-room dining extension with William Morris fabrics and rockery conservatory, good reasonably priced food inc children's, friendly helpful family service, well kept Otter and decent wines; piped music, silenced fruit machine, back public bar with pool; good tables out in garden with small terrace, quiet village *(Basil Minson, BB, J P Shucksmith)*
Axminster [SY2998]
Hunters Lodge [A35 nr B3165 junction]: Friendly and well run, with a welcome for coach parties, good value bar and restaurant food inc carvery, pleasant staff, well kept Bass and Worthington; big garden with children's play area, well behaved dogs welcome *(I R Fourmy, Prof and Mrs Tony Palmer)*
Axmouth [SY2591]
☆ *Ship* [Church St]: Comfortable and civilised, good fresh local fish and other food using their own herbs inc children's and interesting vegetarian speciality, well kept Bass and Otter, good wine and coffee, lots of embroidered folk dolls, one room devoted to Guinness memorabilia, friendly staff and samoyeds, computer for customers, no smoking restaurant; skittle alley full of nostalgiamenta, tables in attractive garden with long-established owl rescue home *(LYM, David Peakall)*
Bampton [SS9520]
☆ *Exeter Inn* [A396 some way S, at B3227 roundabout]: Well run long low stone-built pub under steep hill overlooking River Exe, several friendly and bustling linked rooms, mainly flagstoned, huge choice of good food inc cold cabinet, local crab and fish (may be a wait when very busy in summer), large pleasant carvery restaurant, well kept Cotleigh Tawny and Exmoor Ale and Gold tapped from the cask, log fire, friendly landlord, daily papers, no piped music, free-range eggs for sale (lots of double-yolkers); tables out in front, bedrooms with own bathrooms, open all day, fairly handy for Knightshayes Court *(Dr and Mrs M E*

Wilson, Peter and Audrey Dowsett, Stan Edwards, BB)

Barnstaple [SS5533]

Panniers [Boutport St]: Wetherspoons, fast efficient service, well kept beers and cider, low prices, simple appetising food all day, no smoking area, no piped music *(Pat and Tony Martin, R J Walden)*

Beer [ST2289]

Anchor [Fore St]: Nice old local photographs in simply furnished bow-windowed front public bar, sizeable no smoking restaurant and back lounge bar, friendly prompt service, real ales inc Otter, pricy food; reasonably priced bedrooms, lots of tables in garden opp, balcony harbour views, delightful seaside village – parking may not be easy *(Ken Flawn, T J and J D Fitzgerald, John Saville, LYM)*

Barrel of Beer [Fore St]: Small pub with reasonably priced generous food from simple dishes like pizzas to good fresh local seafood, real ales such as Exe Valley Devon Glory and Wadworths 6X; open all day *(Kevin Stokes, Barry and Verina Jones, Paul and Annette Hallett, Jeanne and Paul Silvestri)*

Beesands [SX8140]

Cricket: Friendly local by sea wall, with tables outside; softly lit bar with local photographs, enjoyable food under new chef, well kept Whitbreads-related and other ales such as Wadworths 6X, log fire, family room; unobtrusive piped music; bedrooms, at start of coast path to Hallsands and Start Point *(Tracey and Stephen Groves)*

Belstone [SX6293]

Tors [a mile off A30]: Austere granite building with good choice of reasonably priced generous food from good big baguettes up, friendly local licensees, well kept Flowers IPA, Sharps Doom Bar and Timothy Taylors Landlord, decent wines and malt whiskies, good winter mulled wine, woodburner, old settles nicely dividing bar; picnic-sets outside (you can make more of the view by crossing the road to sit on the moor), bedrooms, attractive village well placed for N Dartmoor walks *(John and Vivienne Rice, Dr and Mrs M E Wilson, R J Walden, Tony and Wendy Hobden)*

Bickleigh [SS9406]

Fishermans Cot: Greatly extended thatched fishing inn with lots of tables on acres of turkey carpet broken up with pillars, plants and some panelled parts, charming view over shallow rocky race below 1640 Exe bridge, more tables out on terrace and waterside lawn, pleasant service; huge food choice inc carvery, chilled beers such as Courage Directors on sparkler, piped music; bedrooms looking over own terrace to river *(Ian Phillips, Alan Kilpatrick, BB, John Wilson)*

Bolberry [SX6939]

☆ ***Port Light***: Former radar station alone on dramatic NT clifftop, bright, clean, spacious and busy, with superb picture-window views, decent food, well kept Dartmoor, friendly efficient service, restaurant and conservatory; well behaved children allowed, tables in garden, good play area; five bedrooms, near fine beaches, right on the coast path *(MDN)*

Bovey Tracey [SX8178]

Cromwell Arms [Fore St]: Attractive old local, popular and friendly, with reasonably priced generous food inc good value Sun lunch, quick service, well kept well priced Marstons Pedigree and other beers, good wine choice, high-backed settles, no piped music *(Joyce and Maurice Cottrell, Neil and Beverley Gardner)*

Riverside [Fore St]: New regime in cottagey hotel on River Bovey (no children now), L-shaped bar with food from sandwiches up, real ales such as Ind Coope Burton, internal mill race and waterside garden; piped pop music; comfortable bedrooms *(Dennis Jenkin)*

Bow [SS7101]

White Hart [A3072 W of Crediton]: Unchanging beamed bar with cosy settles and logs blazing in huge inglenook, well kept Scattor Rock Kingfisher, welcoming service, reasonably priced food, charming small dining room; games room with pool, skittle alley; tables in neat garden *(Tom Evans)*

Bradworthy [SS3213]

Bradworthy Inn [The Square]: Two-bar local with good straightforward food in family dining room, attractive prices, friendly service; comfortable bedrooms *(Keith John Ryan)*

Braunton [SS4836]

Mariners Arms [South St]: Busy pleasantly untouristy local, friendly and comfortable, lots of nautical prints and bric-a-brac, well kept Exmoor ales, cheerful service, dining area with good range of good value meals (not Mon), enthusiasm for shove-ha'penny; unobtrusive piped music, skittle alley; back terrace safe for children *(Des and Jen Clarke)*

Brendon [SS7648]

Staghunters: Idyllic setting with garden by East Lyn river, welcoming licensees, traditional furnishings, enjoyable freshly prepared food from delicious filled baguettes up, good helpings, well kept Wadworths 6X and Addlestone's cider, woodburner, family room with pool table, restaurant; walkers and dogs welcome, can get very busy, good value bedrooms *(Lynda and Trevor Smith)*

Brixham [SX9255]

Blue Anchor [Fore St/King St]: Warm and friendly harbourside pub with good mix of locals and visitors, two or three well kept real ales, well kept Dartmoor Best and Greene King Abbot, plenty of nautical hardwear, decent usual food inc local fish in two small dining rooms – one a former chapel, down some steps; live music Fri/Sat, open all day *(Steve Whalley, Bryan Robinson, Emma Kingdon)*

Vigilance [Bolton St]: Wetherspoons shop conversion, very busy with locals and families all day, sizeable open-plan bar with no smoking area, their usual inexpensive menu, no music; nearby parking difficult *(Emma Kingdon, David and Pam Wilcox)*

Broadclyst [SX9897]

Red Lion [B3121, by church]: Peaceful old local with fine wisteria, long dark bar with heavy beams, cushioned window seats, some nice chairs around a mix of oak and other tables, flagstoned area with cushioned pews and low tables by old woodburner, collection of carpenters' planes, generous bar food from doorstep sandwiches up inc children's dishes, separate dining area with longer menu, real ales inc Bass and Fullers London Pride; picnic-sets on front cobbles, more in small enclosed garden across quiet lane, not far from Killerton (NT – they own the pub too) *(Ian and Nita Cooper, Pamela and Merlyn Horswell, Alan and Paula McCully, James Flory, LYM)*

Broadhempston [SX8066]

☆ ***Monks Retreat*** [The Square]: Black beams, massive old walls, lots of copper, brass and china, log fire in huge stone fireplace, well kept Bass, Butcombe and a guest beer, new chef doing good attractively priced food with interesting specials, lunchtime sandwiches and wide children's choice too, sizeable no smoking dining area a couple of steps up (best to book), cheerful service; by arch to attractive churchyard, a few picnic-sets out in front *(BB, Mr and Mrs Christopher Warner)*

Buckfastleigh [SX7366]

☆ ***Dartbridge*** [Totnes Rd, handy for A38]: Big bustling family pub, prettily placed opp Dart Valley Railway, good range of generous food with some emphasis on fish, choice of Sun roasts, well kept guest beers inc Otter, good house wines, efficient friendly service even under summer pressure; reasonable disabled access, tables in roadside garden, 10 letting chalets *(John Evans, Joyce and Maurice Cottrell)*

Kings Arms [Fore St]: Friendly well run local, real ales, farm cider, wholesome food; beautiful garden, bedrooms *(Neil and Beverley Gardner)*

☆ ***White Hart*** [Plymouth Rd]: Simple but attractive comfortably carpeted open-plan bar with cheerful homely feel, woodburner one end, huge log fire the other, stone walls, lots of pictures, horsebrasses, plates, jugs and so forth; particularly well kept ales such as Ash Vine One Way Traffic, Greene King Abbot and Teignworthy Beachcomber, with a beer brewed for them by Teignworthy, also Sam's local farm cider, lots of pumpclips above bar, friendly licensees, home cooking with good changing choice, side family dining room; dogs welcome; bedrooms, tables in pretty back courtyard with barbecues; open all day, cl Sun afternoon and Mon lunchtime *(Catherine Pitt, Neil and Beverley Gardner, Jonathan Smith)*

Budleigh Salterton [SY0682]

Salterton Arms [Chapel St]: Attractive bar with well kept Bass, Butcombe and Charles Wells Bombardier, expert new chef, helpful efficient staff, small open fires, upper dining gallery; can get very busy summer; children welcome, has been open all day wknds *(Dr and Mrs M E Wilson, Dennis and Janice Chaldecott, John Beeken, Betsy and Peter Little, LYM)*

Burgh Island [SX6444]

Pilchard [300 yds across tidal sands from Bigbury-on-Sea; walk, or take summer Tractor – unique bus on stilts]: Great setting high above sea on tidal island with unspoilt cliff walks; decidedly unsmart, but with ancient beams and flagstones, lanterns, nets and (when it's lit) blazing fire; Courage Best and Directors; piped music, dogs welcome but not children; some tables down by beach *(the Didler, Keith and Suzie Stevens, JP, PP, LYM)*

Challacombe [SS6941]

☆ ***Black Venus*** [B3358 Blackmoor Gate—Simonsbath]: Good varied home-made food inc choice of Sun roasts, fair prices, well kept Exmoor and St Austell Tribute, friendly efficient staff, low 16th-c beams, pews, decent chairs, stuffed birds, woodburner and big open fire, attractive big dining area (children over 5 allowed), separate games room; seats in garden, attractive countryside; bedrooms *(Christopher Tull, BB, Stan Edwards, Paul and Ursula Randall)*

Chillington [SX7942]

☆ ***Open Arms*** [A379 E of Kingsbridge]: Roomy modernised open-plan turkey-carpeted bar with well kept ales such as Badger Tanglefoot, Bass, Beer Seller Mild, Exmoor and Wadworths 6X, good wines and choice of spirits, inexpensive hearty home-made food, good local atmosphere, back games room with pool *(John Brightley, BB)*

Chittlehamholt [SS6521]

☆ ***Exeter Inn*** [off A377 Barnstaple—Crediton, and B3226 SW of South Molton]: Friendly old inn, matchbox, bottle and banknote collections, open stove in the huge fireplace, side area with booth seating, enjoyable food from sandwiches, baguettes and baked potatoes to good local steaks and Sun roast, no smoking restaurant, well kept Dartmoor Best, Greene King Abbot and a guest beer, farm ciders; traditional games, piped music, dogs allowed (pub dog called Alice); children in eating areas, benches out on terrace, decent bedrooms with showers *(Eddie Edwards, Dr and Mrs A K Clarke, Shaun Pinchbeck, LYM, Crystal and Peter Hooper)*

Christow [SX8385]

☆ ***Teign House*** [Teign Valley Rd (B3193)]: Attractive former farmhouse in country setting, open fire in beamed bar, good fresh food (all day Sat) using local produce here and in partly no smoking family dining room, friendly staff, well kept Devonian ale brewed in the village, decent wines; pretty garden, cl Tues lunchtime *(Mrs B Davies, Mrs L Hopkinson)*

Chudleigh [SX8679]

Bishop Lacey [Fore St, just off A38]: Quaint partly 14th-c church house with good service, well kept Branscombe Vale, Flowers IPA, Fullers London Pride and a guest such as Princetown Jail, some tapped from casks in back bar, good strong coffee, good value food, no smoking dining room; tables in garden, winter beer festival, open all day *(JP, PP, the Didler, Dr and Mrs A K Clarke, John Saville)*

Old Coaching House [Fore St]: Popular flagstoned country pub with attractively priced food inc good curries and mixed grill in bar or restaurant, well kept Greene King Abbot and Worthington, friendly staff *(the Didler, JP, PP)*

Chudleigh Knighton [SX8477]

Claycutters Arms [just off A38 by B3344]: Friendly 17th-c thatched two-bar village pub with well kept Bass and Marstons Pedigree, decent wines, good service, stripped stone, interesting nooks and crannies, pleasant restaurant; tables on side terrace and in orchard *(LYM, D S Jackson, John and Vivienne Rice, A D Marsh, Neil and Beverley Gardner, John Wilson)*

Chulmleigh [SS6814]

Globe [Church St]: Attractive little pub by large church, true local atmosphere, good nicely priced home cooking, friendly staff, well kept Butcombe and Marstons Pedigree, two fish tanks and comfortable labrador – dogs allowed; good bedrooms *(Eddie Edwards)*

Churchstow [SX7145]

Church House [A379 NW of Kingsbridge]: Generous food from sandwiches to mixed grill and (Weds-Sat nights, Sun lunch) popular carvery in long character pub with heavy black beams (dates from 13th c), stripped stone, cushioned settles, back conservatory with floodlit well feature; well kept Bass, Fullers London Pride, Greene King Old Speckled Hen and changing guest ales, decent wines, no piped music; well behaved children and dogs welcome, tables outside *(R and D Gray, Michael Porter, LYM, Mrs W Boast, J A Elllis, P R and S A White)*

Churston Ferrers [SX9056]

☆ *Churston Court* [off A3022 S of Torquay; Church Rd]: Attractive Elizabethan former manor house in lovely setting next to ancient church near Elbury Cove, nicely furnished beamed bar with oil paintings and large sofa by log fire (the pub cat has its own chair), good food inc carvery, good fresh fish and home-made puddings; bedrooms *(Roland Curtis, Elaine Thompson, Bob and Ann Westbrook)*

Clearbrook [SX5265]

☆ *Skylark* [village signed down dead end off A386 Tavistock—Plymouth]: Welcoming old two-room pub in pretty cottage row tucked right into Dartmoor, relaxed and chatty, with plenty of locals, well kept Bass, Courage Best and Greene King Old Speckled Hen, wide choice of good value food from sandwiches up inc good vegetarian dishes, good service, simple furnishings, log fire; quite separate children's room in big back garden with plenty of picnic-sets and other seats, small adventure play area, wandering ponies *(BB, Mike and Linda Boxall, Jacquie and Jim Jones, Mayur Shah)*

Clovelly [SS3225]

New Inn [High St]: Attractive old inn halfway down the steep cobbled street, simple easy-going lower bar with friendly efficient service (front part has more character than back room), good choice of inexpensive bar food and of beers inc a local one brewed for the pub; quiet piped music, dogs allowed; bedrooms *(Peter and Audrey Dowsett, Eddie Edwards)*

Clyst St Mary [SX9791]

☆ *Half Moon* [under a mile from M5 junction 30 via A376]: Attractive and genuine old pub next to multi-arched bridge over Clyst, well kept Bass and Otter, good value generous home-made food inc some local dishes and local produce, friendly unpretentious local atmosphere, red plush seating, log fire; wheelchair access, bedrooms *(Dr and Mrs M E Wilson)*

Cockwood [SX9780]

☆ *Ship* [off A379 N of Dawlish]: Comfortable 17th-c inn overlooking estuary and harbour, partitioned beamed bar with big log fire and ancient oven, decorative plates and seafaring prints and memorabilia, small no smoking restaurant, good value food from open crab sandwiches up inc imaginative evening fish dishes and good puddings (freshly made so takes time), well kept Bass and Greene King IPA and Abbot, friendly efficient staff; piped music; good steep-sided garden *(Peter Salmon, John Beeken)*

Colyton [SY24943]

Gerrard Arms [St Andrews Sq]: Good value open-plan local with well kept Bass and guests such as local Otter, good value home-made food inc Sun roasts; nice garden *(the Didler)*

☆ *Kingfisher* [off A35 and A3052 E of Sidmouth; Dolphin St]: Village local with hearty popular food from good crab sandwiches and baked potatoes up, stripped stone, plush seats and elm settles, beams and big open fire, well kept Badger Best and Tanglefoot and changing guest beers, low-priced soft drinks, friendly family service; pub games, upstairs family room, skittle alley, tables out on terrace, garden with water feature, colourful inn sign *(LYM, the Didler)*

Combe Martin [SS5747]

Fo'csle [Seaside]: Waterside pub with Dartmoor Best and Ind Coope Burton, sports TV, good local fish in harbour-view restaurant; good value bedrooms with own bathrooms *(C J Fletcher)*

Countisbury [SS7449]

Exmoor Sandpiper [A39, E of Lynton]: Beautifully set rambling and cheery heavy-beamed pub with antique furniture, several good log fires, well kept Bass and two Exmoor ales tapped from the cask, pewter mugs on old beams, lots of stuffed animals (and two sandpipers); hearty food in bar and restaurant, children in eating area, garden tables, open all day; comfortable bedrooms, good nearby cliff walks *(LYM, Richard Gibbs)*

Crediton [SS8300]

Crediton Inn [Mill St (follow Tiverton sign)]: Small friendly straightforward local with particularly well kept Sharps Doom Bar and two constantly changing guest beers (150 different ones a year), cheap well prepared food, back games room; open all day Mon-Sat, free skittle alley can be booked *(Pete Baker)*

Croyde [SS4439]

Manor House Inn [St Marys Rd, off B3231 NW of Braunton]: Friendly family pub opened up a bit under new management, well kept Bass, Wadworths 6X and a house beer, good value food from baguettes and baked potatoes to a few less common dishes, cheerful efficient service, no smoking restaurant and dining conservatory; piped music, games end with darts, pool, juke box, big-screen TV and fruit machine, piped music may be intrusive; skittle alley, disabled facilities, attractive terraced garden and good play area *(Mr and Mrs*

D J Nash, Paul and Ursula Randall)

☆ ***Thatched Barn*** [B3231 NW of Braunton; Hobbs Hill]: Lively rambling thatched pub near great surfing beaches, with cheerful efficient young staff, laid-back feel and customers to match (can get packed in summer); wide choice of generous food from sandwiches and baguettes up, well kept Bass, St Austell HSD and Tetleys, morning coffee, teas; restaurant, children in eating area; piped music; open all day, bedrooms simple but clean and comfortable, tables outside *(Mr and Mrs D J Nash, LYM, BKA, Des and Jen Clarke, Andy Marks)*

Dartington [SX7762]

Cott [Cott signed off A385 W of Totnes, opp A384 turn-off]: Picturesque long thatched 14th-c managed pub, heavy beams, steps and flagstones, big log fires, food from lunchtime sandwiches, big ploughman's, baked potatoes and buffet to more elaborate evening dishes, well kept real ales; children welcome, picnic-sets in garden and on pretty terrace, bedrooms with own bathrooms, open all day at least in summer *(LYM, MDN, Tony and Katie Lewis, Neil and Beverley Gardner)*

White Hart Bar [Dartington Hall]: Light bright modern décor and open fires in the college's bar (open to visitors), good low-priced food here and in baronial hall, real ales such as Exmoor; very special atmosphere sitting out in the famously beautiful grounds *(Dr and Mrs A K Clarke, Catherine Pitt)*

Dartmouth [SX8751]

George & Dragon [Mayors Ave]: Cosy traditional pub with naval theme, enjoyable food at sensible prices, enterprising landlord, well kept Bass and Flowers Original; children catered for, fishing parties arranged, back terrace with barbecue, good value well equipped bedrooms *(Pete and Jo Cole)*

Gunfield [Castle Rd]: Hotel with bright fresh young-feeling bar, modern trendy restaurant with good food, comfortable lounge, lovely harbour views; tables out on terrace, bedrooms *(Pete and Jo Cole)*

Windjammer [Victoria Rd]: Family-run pub with good home cooking using fresh produce, local ales and cider, no juke box or machines *(Mrs J L Wyatt)*

Dawlish Warren [SX9778]

Boathouse [seafront, opp lifeguard hut]: Good value family pub in big complex; free soft play area, decent food choice inc two-for-one winter bargains, lower eating area called Fishermans Wharf, upstairs sea views, lots of tables outside *(Meg and Colin Hamilton)*

East Budleigh [SY0684]

☆ ***Sir Walter Raleigh*** [High St]: Chattily convivial and attractive local near interesting church in lovely village, neat and clean, with faultless friendly service, reliable good value food inc help-yourself salad bar and good Sun lunch, charming large no smoking dining room, well kept Flowers IPA, Marstons Pedigree and local brews, good house wine; no children; bedrooms, handy for Bicton Park gardens *(Dr and Mrs M E Wilson, Pat and Robert Watt, LYM, Basil Minson, Pam Adsley)*

East Prawle [SX7836]

Freebooter [off A379 E of Kingsbridge]: This nice small pub has closed *(LYM)*

Ermington [SX6353]

Crooked Spire [The Square]: Open-plan pub recently refurbished in bright colours, well kept Bass and Otter, enjoyable straightforward food inc Sun roasts with good veg, pleasant service; theme and quiz nights; good heated back courtyard, comfortable bedrooms with shared bathroom *(Keith Richard Waters)*

First & Last [Church St]: Beautifully set local, lots of well tended hanging baskets, friendly chatty landlord, limited choice of reliably good cheap food with ample veg, Bass *(John Evans)*

Exeter [SX9292]

☆ ***Great Western*** [St Davids Hill]: Great choice of well kept changing real ales usually inc Adnams, Bass, Exmoor, Fullers London Pride and Teignworthy in large hotel's small sociable public bar, with plenty of regulars, attractively priced honest food all day from sandwiches up (also a restaurant), daily papers, peanuts in the shell, no music; bedrooms *(JP, PP, the Didler, Phil and Sally Gorton, Catherine Pitt, Dr and Mrs A K Clarke, C J Fletcher, Jane and Adrian Tierney-Jones)*

Jolly Porter [St Davids Hill]: Attractive and airy, lively with students and locals, with big windows, raised seating, well kept changing ales from small breweries, cheap plentiful food all day, bare boards, bric-a-brac and books, snooker room, family room; jazz Weds, open all day *(Catherine Pitt, JP, PP, the Didler)*

Mill on the Exe [Bonhay Rd (A377)]: Good spot by weir with heated waterside terrace, bar comfortably done out with bare boards, old bricks, beams and timbers, recent extension into large airy river-view conservatory restaurant, good sensibly priced food, well kept St Austell Tinners and HSD, good house wines, friendly young staff; children welcome *(BB, John and Vivienne Rice, Dr and Mrs A K Clarke)*

Old Fire House [New North Rd]: Superb collection of Fire Service memorabilia in small flagstoned pub with three real ales, red check tablecloths and further eating area upstairs; through high arched wrought-iron gates to block of flats or offices *(Dr and Mrs M E Wilson)*

Prospect [The Quay]: Good waterfront spot, with comfortable upper river-view dining area (food from doorstep sandwiches up, prepared to order – so can be a wait), well kept ales inc Otter; lower beamed bar with games machines, piped music – live some evenings *(Alan M Pring, John and Vivienne Rice)*

☆ ***Ship*** [Martins Lane]: Pretty 14th-c pub with substantial furniture in bustling heavy-beamed bar, well kept Boddingtons, Flowers, Greene King Old Speckled Hen and Marstons Pedigree, farm cider, speedy friendly service, generously filled sandwiches only down here, enjoyable meals in comfortable upstairs restaurant with feel of below-decks man-o'-war; can get crowded; handy for town centre and cathedral *(Mr and Mrs Colin Roberts, Dr and Mrs*

M E Wilson, P G Plumridge, LYM)
Welcome [Canal Banks, off Haven Rd]: Old pub overlooking basin on Exeter Ship Canal, gas lighting and flagstones, very friendly old-school landlady, well kept Castle Eden or a guest beer such as RCH PG Steam, nostalgic 60s/70s juke box *(the Didler)*
Well House [Cathedral Yard, attached to Royal Clarence Hotel]: Big windows looking across to cathedral in open-plan bar with rows of tables divided by inner walls and partitions, lots of interesting Victorian prints, well kept real ales, quick service, popular bar lunches inc good sandwiches and salads, daily papers; Roman well beneath (can be viewed when pub not busy); piped music *(Mike Gorton, P G Plumridge, John Saville, BB, Ian Phillips)*
White Hart [South St]: Still worth knowing for its old-fashioned no smoking rambling bar (heavy beams, oak flooring and antiques), and as a handy central place to stay, with free parking; Bass, Courage Directors and John Smiths, good wines, choice of places to eat in *(JP, PP, Nigel Williamson, Dr and Mrs M E Wilson, Neil and Beverley Gardner, David and Nina Pugsley, LYM)*
Exminster [SX9487]
☆ ***Swans Nest*** [Station Rd, just off A379 on outskirts]: Has had huge choice of reasonably priced self-service food from sandwiches and children's dishes up from long attractive carvery/buffet in very popular high-throughput food pub, Bass and Dartmoor, helpful staff, well arranged rambling dining bar with no smoking areas; especially good for family groups, handy for M5; pub found closed in spring 2002, perhaps for refurbishment – news please *(LYM, Dr and Mrs M E Wilson, S F Wakeham)*
Exmouth [SY0080]
Grove [Esplanade]: Roomy panelled Youngs pub set back from beach with large seafront garden and play area, their beers kept well with a guest such as Smiles, decent house wines, good coffee, good value food inc plenty of local fish and children's menu, young efficient staff, simple furnishings, caricatures and local prints, attractive fireplace at back, sea views from upstairs restaurant; live music Fri *(John Beeken, Dr and Mrs M E Wilson)*
Powder Monkey [The Parade]: Wetherspoons with long bar, armchairs in two smaller front rooms (children allowed in one), reasonably priced food and five real ales; very popular with young people wknds; a few tables on courtyard facing roundabout *(Alan Wilson)*
Exton [SX9886]
Puffing Billy: Wide choice of good inventive food inc seafood in friendly recently renovated restauranty dining pub *(Peter Burton, Samantha Simonitsch)*
Fairmile [SY0897]
Fairmile Inn [A30 Honiton—Exeter]: Refurbished two-bar pub with log fires, well kept ales inc Bass and Tetleys, pleasant staff, food from good value sandwiches up inc popular weekly OAP lunch, beamed inglenook dining room; quiz nights, tables in garden, good value simple bedrooms, big breakfast *(Dr and Mrs M E Wilson, Philip Howes, K W Dabney)*
Frogmore [SX7742]
☆ ***Globe*** [A379 E of Kingsbridge]: Walls papered with maritime charts, lots of ship and yacht paintings, some built-in settles creating corner booths, mix of simple tables, generous usual food from sandwiches to steak inc children's, well kept Exmoor Ale and Greene King Abbot, local farm cider in summer, country wines, friendly helpful staff, good log fire, games and TV in flagstoned locals' bar; piped radio may be loud; tables out on pretty terraces with play area and a bit of a creek view, plenty of walks, bedrooms; cl Mon lunchtime in winter *(Tracey and Stephen Groves, C A Hall, Caroline Raphael, Dr and Mrs Allen, LYM, John and Vivienne Rice)*
Georgeham [SS4639]
☆ ***Rock*** [Rock Hill, above village]: Well restored oak-beamed pub with well kept ales such as Barum Breakfast, Cotleigh Golden Eagle, Greene King IPA and Abbot and St Austell, local farm cider, decent wines, good value food from giant baps up, fast attractive service, old red quarry tiles, open fire, pleasant mix of rustic furniture, lots of bric-a-brac, pleasant vine-adorned back conservatory great for children; piped music, darts, fruit machine, pool room and juke box; tables under cocktail parasols on front terrace, pretty hanging baskets *(Paul and Ursula Randall, Mr and Mrs I Bennett, Steve Harvey, Boyd Catling, BB, Derek Harvey-Piper)*
Grenofen [SX4971]
Halfway House [on A386 nr Tavistock]: Welcoming, clean and attractive, good choice of reasonably priced home-made food inc local beef, four real ales such as Bass and Sharps, farm cider, decent wines, lounge, restaurant and traditional bar with pool and darts; tables out overlooking Dartmoor, good value bedrooms *(Wally Parson)*
Halwell [SX7853]
☆ ***Old Inn*** [A381 Totnes—Kingsbridge, junction with B3207]: Good atmosphere, warm welcome, chatty landlord, good value interesting food cooked by his Filipino wife, well kept RCH IPA, Premium and East St Cream; bedrooms *(Dudley and Moira Cockroft, D G T Horsford)*
Hartland Quay [SS2224]
☆ ***Hartland Quay Hotel*** [off B3248 W of Bideford, down toll road (free Oct–Easter); OS Sheet 190 map ref 222248]: Unpretentious and relaxed old hotel in stunning cliff scenery, rugged coast walks, real maritime feel with fishing memorabilia and interesting shipwreck pictures; down-to-earth helpful staff, small no smoking bar, lots of tables outside – very popular with holidaymakers; maybe well kept Sharps Doom Bar (often keg beer only), basic good value generous food, dogs welcome, good value bedrooms, seawater swimming pool; cl midwinter *(Helen Hazzard, Mr and Mrs McKay, Tony and Valerie Marshall)*
Hatherleigh [SS5404]
☆ ***Tally Ho*** [Market St (A386)]: Attractive heavy-

beamed and timbered linked rooms, sturdy furnishings, big log fire and woodburner, usual food from lunchtime sandwiches up, good real ales brewed for them locally by Clearwater (they no longer brew themselves), no smoking restaurant, traditional games; piped music; tables in nice sheltered garden, three cosy and prettily furnished bedrooms *(the Didler, Tony and Wendy Hobden, Christine and Neil Townend, Tom Evans, JP, PP, LYM)*

Hexworthy [SX6572]

☆ ***Forest Inn*** [signed off B3357 Tavistock—Ashburton, E of B3212]: Welcoming hotel in gorgeous Dartmoor setting, roomy plush-seated open-plan bar and back walkers' bar, short daily-changing choice of good generous bar and restaurant food using fresh local produce, prompt friendly service, well kept local ales inc Teignworthy, local cider, relaxing atmosphere, real fire, daily papers; comfortable bedrooms, bunkhouse; fishing permits on sale, good walking and horse riding *(LYM, Jeanne and Paul Silvestri, Ann and Colin Hunt, Karen Scott)*

Holne [SX7069]

☆ ***Church House*** [signed off B3357 W of Ashburton]: Ancient and interesting country inn well placed for attractive walks, log fires in both rooms, nicely served well cooked food from good lunchtime sandwiches up, children's helpings, well kept Butcombe, Dartmoor and Wadworths 6X, Gray's farm cider, country wines, decent house wines, no smoking areas, traditional games in public bar; well behaved children in eating area; comfortable bedrooms, some newly refurbished, dogs welcome *(D and M T Ayres-Regan, LYM, Simon and Rachel Dowdy, Richard and Margaret Peers, Mr and Mrs J McRobert)*

Holsworthy [SS3408]

Kings Arms [Fore St/The Square]: 17th-c inn with Victorian fittings, etched windows and coal fires in three interesting traditional bars, old pictures and photographs, 40s and 50s beer advertisements, lots of optics behind ornate counter, particularly well kept Bass and Sharps Doom Bar, friendly locals; open all day, Sun afternoon closure *(the Didler, JP, PP)*

Honiton [SY1198]

Greyhound [Fenny Bridges, 4 miles W]: Big busy thatched family dining pub with wide food choice from good open sandwiches and baked potatoes up, quick friendly service, well kept Otter beers, old-fashioned heavy-beamed décor, attractive restaurant with no smoking area; bedrooms *(Dr and Mrs M E Wilson, LYM)*

☆ ***Red Cow*** [High St]: Welcoming local, very busy on Tues and Sat market days, scrubbed tables, pleasant alcoves, log fires, well kept Bass, Courage Directors and local Otter, decent wines and malt whiskies, wide choice of good value home-made food inc excellent sandwiches and good puddings, fast service from friendly Welsh licensees (may have Radio Wales), loads of chamber-pots and big mugs on beams, pavement tables; bedrooms *(BB, R G Price, Mrs B M Smith, John Oates)*

Hope Cove [SX6640]

Hope & Anchor: Simple seaside inn, friendly and comfortable, with good open fire, kind efficient staff, good value straightforward food, well kept Wadworths 6X, reasonably priced wines, flagstone floor, no piped music; children and dogs welcome in family room, games room with pool; good views from tables outside, bedrooms, open all day *(Geoffrey and Karen Berrill, LYM, Norma and Keith Bloomfield, June and Ken Brooks)*

Horsebridge [SX3975]

☆ ***Royal*** [off A384 Tavistock—Launceston]: Cheerful slate-floored rooms, interesting bric-a-brac and pictures, tasty food from baguettes and baked potatoes through good chilli con carne to steak, Bass, Sharps Doom Bar, Wadworths 6X and guest beers, farm cider, bar billiards, cribbage, dominoes, no smoking café-style side room, no music or machines; no children in evening, tables on back terrace and in big garden *(Andrea Rampley, LYM, DAV, Dr and Mrs Nigel Holmes, John Wilson)*

Ide [SX9090]

Huntsman [High St]: Straightforward jolly local with well kept Bass, Greene King Old Speckled Hen and Ringwood, good value food from baguettes to home-made hot dishes, friendly helpful staff *(John and Vivienne Rice, Dr and Mrs M E Wilson)*

☆ ***Poachers*** [3 miles from M5 junction 31, via A30; High St]: Good welcoming atmosphere, inventive reasonably priced generous food inc good fish choice, well kept Branscombe Vale Branoc and Otter, good value house wines, prompt friendly service, sofas and open fire; blues night, attractively decorated bedrooms *(Eamonn and Natasha Skyrme, John and Vivienne Rice, Dr and Mrs M E Wilson)*

Ideford [SX8977]

☆ ***Royal Oak*** [2 miles off A380]: Friendly, dark and cosy unspoilt thatched and flagstoned village local, vast and interesting collection of mainly marine memorabilia from Nelson to World War II, well kept Flowers IPA and Original, log fire, perhaps occasional sandwiches; may be a vociferous jack russell *(the Didler, JP, PP)*

Ilfracombe [SS5247]

☆ ***George & Dragon*** [Fore St]: Oldest pub here, handy for harbour, with decent food inc Sun lunch, helpful friendly staff, well kept real ale, decent wines, attractive olde-worlde décor, soft lighting; may be piped music *(Gene and Kitty Rankin, Ken Flawn)*

Ilsington [SX7876]

Carpenters Arms: Unspoilt 18th-c local next to church in quiet village, friendly licensees, wholesome cheap food, well kept Bass and guest beers on handpump or tapped from the cask, log fire, parlour off main public bar; no music, good walks *(Neil and Beverley Gardner)*

Instow [SS4730]

☆ ***Boat House*** [Marine Parade]: Airy modern high-ceilinged café/bar with huge tidal beach just across lane and views to Appledore, big old-fashioned nautical paintings on stripped stone wall, well kept Bass, Flowers IPA and a local guest beer, good choice of popular food from sandwiches to steaks inc plentiful fish,

open fire, friendly prompt service even when crowded, lively family bustle – children welcome; piped music; roof terrace *(John Saville, Andy Marks, Ken Flawn, LYM, Eamonn and Natasha Skyrme)*
Commodore [Marine Parade]: Smart hotel with outstanding estuary views, decent if not cheap bar meals, well kept Barum Breakfast and Dartmoor Best, restaurant; tables on terrace, bedrooms *(Paul and Ursula Randall)*
Kenton [SX9583]
☆ ***Dolphin*** [Fore St]: Attractive and welcoming, with old black range and carved oak counter in public bar, beams, pews and settles in alcovey dining area, soft lighting, generous food inc fresh veg and good puddings, Weds lunchtime and Sat night carvery (OAP discount), well kept ales such as Dartmoor Best, Youngs and bargain Otter, reasonably priced wines, no music; dogs allowed, pretty village *(Dr and Mrs M E Wilson, David and Elizabeth Briggs, Canon and Mrs Michael Bourdeaux)*
Kilmington [SY2797]
☆ ***Old Inn*** [A35]: Thatched pub with pleasant local atmosphere, small character polished-floor front bar (dogs allowed here), back lounge with leather armchairs by inglenook fire, good value food inc local fish and good Sun lunch, well kept Boddingtons, Flowers IPA, Wadworths 6X and Worthington BB, traditional games, small no smoking restaurant; children welcome, two gardens *(Andrea Rampley, Ian Phillips, A D Marsh, LYM, A and B D Craig, R T and J C Moggridge)*
Kingsbridge [SX7343]
Crabshell [Embankment Rd, edge of town]: Lovely waterside position, charming when tide in, with big windows and tables out on the hard; simple bar with plainly furnished eating area, friendly staff, Bass, Worthington and a house beer, good farm cider, warm fire, wide choice of food from good fresh lunchtime shrimp or crab sandwiches to local fish and shellfish (this may be confined to upstairs restaurant, with good views) *(Ken Flawn, Dr and Mrs M E Wilson, BB)*
Kingskerswell [SX8767]
Barn Owl [Aller Mills; pub signed just off A380 Newton Abbot—Torquay]: 16th-c converted farmhouse, large panelled bar with ornamental plaster ceiling, other softly lit rooms with low black beams, flagstones, stripped stone and inglenook fireplace, one room with lots of sportsman and celebrity pictures; decent food, well kept Bass, Courage Best and Cotleigh Tawny, no smoking area; piped music and SkyTV sports; picnic-sets in small sheltered garden, bedrooms in adjoining Holiday Express *(LYM, Mr and Mrs Colin Roberts, Richard and Margaret Peers)*
☆ ***Bickley Mill*** [Stoneycombe, on road from Abbotskerswell to Compton and Marldon]: Tucked-away pub currently on top form, wide choice of good food from sandwiches or baguettes to fine main dishes, sensible prices, well kept real ales, faultless service, buoyant atmosphere in rambling beamed rooms with lots of copper and brass, log fire; children welcome, tables in courtyard, subtropical-style hillside garden, bedrooms *(LYM, Richard and Margaret Peers, Christine and Neil Townend, Andrew Hodges, Martyn Canevali)*
Sloop [Newton Rd (A380)]: Modern pub with good value generous food in big bustling dining area, Sun carvery, quick cheerful helpful service, well kept Greene King Old Speckled Hen; piped music, games machines; attractive hanging baskets, big terrace with splendid views, play area *(anon)*
Kingsteignton [SX8773]
☆ ***Old Rydon*** [Rydon Rd]: Dining pub with big log fire in small cosy heavy-beamed bar, upper gallery seating, no smoking restaurant with well planted conservatory, food from baked potatoes and toasted muffins to chargrills, children's dishes, well kept Bass, Fullers London Pride and a guest beer such as Greene King Abbot or Otter; piped music, recent management and staff changes; tables on terrace and in nice sheltered garden *(Mike and Mary Carter, LYM)*
Ten Tors [Exeter Rd]: Large extended 1930s pub doing well under newish landlord, wide choice of good food from doorstep sandwiches to OAP specials, end restaurant, well kept Courage and local beers *(Alain and Rose Foote, Ian and Nita Cooper)*
Kingswear [SX8851]
Ship [Higher St]: Attractive old inn with quiet atmosphere, well kept Bass, nice wines, friendly service, usual food; one table with Dart views, a couple outside *(James Woods)*
Knowle [SS4938]
☆ ***Ebrington Arms*** [A361 2 miles N of Braunton]: Lots of bric-a-brac and relaxed olde-worlde atmosphere in comfortable main bar, good interesting food in bar and attractive candlelit evening restaurant, well kept real ales *(LYM, Steve Harvey)*
Lapford [SS7308]
Old Malt Scoop: Cosy, old-fashioned and friendly, with huge log fire, good choice of good food; bedrooms *(DAV)*
Lee [SS4846]
☆ ***Grampus*** [signed off B3343/A361 W of Ilfracombe]: Attractive and welcoming 14th-c pub short stroll from sea, simple furnishings, wide range of good simple home-made food, well kept real ales, woodburner, pool in family room, dogs very welcome; two bedrooms, lots of seats in quiet sheltered garden, superb coastal walks *(BB, Lynda and Trevor Smith, Natalie and Chris Sharpe)*
Longdown [SX8691]
☆ ***Lamb***: Attractive stone-built pub with settees and light wood in open-plan bar, smart upper dining area, Bass and Badger IPA, wide choice of enjoyable reasonably priced food from good sandwiches up, friendly landlord, big sleepy pub dog *(John and Vivienne Rice, Alan Wilson)*
Lundy [SS1344]
☆ ***Marisco***: One of England's most isolated pubs (yet full every night), great setting, atmospheric galleried interior with lifebelts and other paraphernalia from local shipwrecks; brews its own tasty beer, also others and Lundy spring

water on tap, good value house wines, welcoming staff, good if not cheap range of home-cooked food using island produce, with lots of seafood; children welcome, tables outside, self catering and camping available; souvenir shop, and doubles as general store for the island's few residents *(Richard Gibbs)*

Luppitt [ST1606]

Luppitt Inn [back roads N of Honiton]: Unspoilt little basic farmhouse pub, friendly chatty landlady who keeps it open because she (and her cats) like the company; one room with corner bar and one table, another with fireplace and not much else, Otter tapped from the cask, no food or music, lavatories across the yard; a real throwback, may be closed some lunchtimes *(the Didler, RWC, JP, PP)*

Lutton [SX5959]

Mountain [pub signed off Cornwood—Sparkwell rd]: Simply furnished beamed pub with log fires, some stripped stone, a high-backed settle, dogs and cats (no visiting dogs), generous straightforward food, well kept ales such as Exmoor, Ind Coope Burton and Wadworths 6X, local farm cider; seats on verandah and vine-arbour terrace, children in eating area and small family room *(LYM, John Poulter)*

Lympstone [SX9984]

☆ ***Globe*** [off A376 N of Exmouth; The Strand]: Roomy dining area and bar, popular with locals for food from sandwiches to fresh fish, four real ales, decent house wines; children welcome, some live entertainment, open all day in summer *(LYM, Mrs Jean Clarke, John Wooll, Chris Parsons, Dr and Mrs M E Wilson, Pam Adsley)*

Saddlers Arms [A376 N of Exmouth]: Steak & Ale pub reopened after major refurbishment, cheapish standard pub food, Courage and Theakstons; tables and play area in garden *(Dr and Mrs M E Wilson, Geoffrey Hart)*

Lynmouth [SS7249]

☆ ***Rising Sun*** [Mars Hill, by harbour]: Wonderful position overlooking harbour, good immaculate bedrooms (one very small) in cottagey old thatched terrace stepped up hill; concentration on the upmarket hotel side and the attractive cosy no smoking restaurant (where residents come first – no supper bookings taken for others till 6.30), but they normally have well kept ales such as Courage Directors and Exmoor Gold and Fox, good lunchtime bar food, friendly chatty helpful staff, good fire and a nice dog called Sophie; may be faint piped music; bedrooms, charming gardens up behind, children may be allowed in eating areas *(RB, Dave Irving, Mr and Mrs Matt Binns, John Saville, George Atkinson, LYM, Adam and Tracy Bradbery , Keith and Margaret Kettell, Theocsbrian, C J Fletcher)*

Lynton [SS7148]

☆ ***Bridge Inn*** [B3234 just S]: Former Olde Cottage renamed by new owner, good sensibly priced home-made food and decent wines at attractive prices, warm welcoming service, well kept ales, pleasant straightforward décor, churchy Victorian windows, dining room overlooking West Lyn gorge; glorious coast views from terrace, footbridge to wooded NT walks up to Watersmeet or even the Rockford Inn at Brendon – and there's a lovely short walk from Lynton centre, on the Lynway *(Derek Orgill)*

Crown [Market St/Sinai Hill]: Clean and comfortable hotel lounge bar, good relaxed atmosphere, friendly and chatty staff and locals, open fire, decent reasonably priced food here and in small restaurant, well kept beer and cider; good bedrooms *(Miss Jo Ford)*

Hunters [Martinhoe, Heddon's Gate – which is well signed off A39 W of Lynton]: Popular for its glorious Heddon Valley position beside NT information centre, great walks inc one, not too taxing, down to the sea; enjoyable freshly prepared food from soup and baguettes to local seafood (may be a wait when crowded), cheerful young staff, real ale; garden with peacocks *(Diana Brumfit, Dr D J and Mrs S C Walker)*

Maidencombe [SX9268]

Thatched Tavern [Steep Hill]: Spotless hugely extended three-level thatched pub with lovely coastal views, well kept Bass in pubby bar, well priced food inc local fish (can be a wait), hospitable service, big family room, no smoking areas, attractive restaurant; children allowed, nice garden with small thatched huts (dogs allowed out here but not in pub); pleasant bedrooms in annexe, good breakfast; small attractive village above small beach *(E G Parish, Bob and Ann Westbrook)*

Manaton [SX7580]

Kestor: Welcoming modern Dartmoor-edge inn in splendid spot near Becky Falls, attractive dining room with good range of food inc adventurous children's menu, friendly Yorkshire landlord, good mix of locals and visitors, well kept real ales, farm cider, open fire; piped music; attractive bedrooms *(Joan York)*

Marsh [ST2510]

☆ ***Flintlock*** [pub signed just off A303 Ilminster—Honiton]: Long open-plan dining pub popular for wide choice of good varied reasonably priced food inc well cooked Sun lunches, friendly Spanish landlord, well kept Fullers London Pride and Otter, neat furnishings, woodburner in stone inglenook, beamery and mainly stripped stone walls, plenty of copper and brass; piped music; cl Mon *(Brian and Bett Cox, BB, D and M T Ayres-Regan)*

Mary Tavy [SX5078]

☆ ***Mary Tavy Inn*** [A386 Tavistock—Okehampton]: Warmly welcoming unpretentious old pub, good reasonably priced home-made food inc popular OAP lunch Thurs, wknd front carvery, well kept Bass, Otter and St Austell HSD and Mild, woodburner; good value bedrooms, big breakfast *(DAV)*

Royal Standard: Spotlessly comfortable traditional pub with lounge at one end and bar at the other, good choice of well kept ales inc Otter, good generous home-made food inc popular steak nights, friendly staff, open fire; dogs welcome *(Dr and Mrs Nigel Holmes)*

Meavy [SX5467]

☆ ***Royal Oak*** [off B3212 E of Yelverton]: Pews, red plush banquettes, old agricultural prints and church pictures (the pub's owned by the parish), new licensees with good catering background doing good value food from lunchtime sandwiches or baguettes up, well kept Bass, Princetown IPA and Jail Ale and a guest beer, friendly service, big fireplace in flagstoned locals' bar with dominoes and euchre; piped music; picnic-sets outside, no children *(LYM, B J Harding, Joan York)*

Meeth [SS5408]

☆ ***Bull & Dragon*** [A386 Hatherleigh—Torrington]: 16th-c beamed and thatched village pub, well kept Fullers London Pride, decent wines, good freshly made food, friendly professional staff, interesting early 20th-c photographs; unobtrusive piped music; children and dogs welcome, handy for Tarka Trail *(Ron and Sheila Corbett)*

Merrivale [SX5475]

☆ ***Dartmoor Inn*** [B3357, 4 miles E of Tavistock]: Refurbished yet unchanging pub in tranquil spot with high Dartmoor views; generous lunchtime food from sandwiches and good ploughman's up, well kept ales inc Bass and one labelled for the pub, good choice of country wines, water from their 36-metre (120-ft) deep well, open fire, tables outside – very popular summer evenings; good walks, near bronze-age hut circles, stone rows and pretty river *(Mayur Shah, DAV)*

Miltoncombe [SX4865]

☆ ***Who'd A Thought It*** [village signed off A386 S of Yelverton]: Attractive 16th-c black-panelled bar with interesting bric-a-brac, woodburner, barrel seats and high-backed winged settles, separate lounge, big dining conservatory with Plymouth Sound views, decent usual food, well kept Blackawton, Cornish Rebellion, Exmoor, Princetown Jail and Wadworths 6X; piped music, tables may be reserved for coach parties; children welcome, well planted garden with water feature (flaming torches may light your way from the car park on summer nights), more tables out in front; folk club Sun *(Ted George, LYM)*

Monkleigh [SS4520]

Bell: Warm-hearted village pub with good Civil War prints by local artist, log fire, well kept Barum, bargain down-to-earth home-made food inc some interesting variations; Fri music night, attached shop with organic meats and local food *(Kevin Beer)*

Morchard Bishop [SS7707]

London [signed off A377 Crediton—Barnstaple]: Open-plan low-beamed 16th-c coaching inn, big carpeted red plush bar with woodburner in large fireplace, big helpings of good simple home-made food in bar or small dining room, friendly engaging service, real ales inc Fullers London Pride and Sharps Doom Bar, pool, darts and skittles *(Peter Craske)*

Moreleigh [SX7652]

New Inn [B3207, off A381 Kingsbridge—Totnes in Stanborough]: Busy country local with character old furniture, nice pictures, candles in bottles; limited choice of wholesome and generous home cooking (book if you want a table near the big inglenook log fire), reasonable prices, well kept Palmers tapped from the cask; may be cl Sat lunchtime/race days *(Alan Vere, LYM)*

Mortehoe [SS4545]

☆ ***Chichester Arms*** [off A361 Ilfracombe—Braunton]: Cheerful young staff, lots of old village prints in busy plush and leatherette panelled lounge and comfortable no smoking dining room, wide choice of good value generous food (not Sun night or Mon, in winter, and not always available other days then) cooked by landlord inc local fish and meat and good veg and puddings, well kept Badger Best and Tanglefoot, local Barum Original and a guest beer, reasonably priced wine, speedy service even on crowded evenings; pubby locals' bar with darts and pool, no piped music; skittle alley and games machines in summer children's room, tables out in front and in small garden, good walks *(Roger S Kiddier, Keith and Margaret Kettell, Pat and Tony Martin, Paul and Ursula Randall, Peter and Audrey Dowsett)*

Newton Abbot [SX8571]

Dartmouth [East St]: Relaxing three-room pub with good choice of well kept ales from the area's small breweries, farm cider, log fire; children welcome till 7, tables and barbecues in nice outside area *(the Didler)*

☆ ***Olde Cider Bar*** [East St]: Heady atmosphere fuelled by casks of eight interesting farm ciders and a couple of perries, with more in bottles, in unusual basic cider house, no-nonsense dark stools, barrel seats and wall benches, flagstones and bare boards, pre-war-style décor; good country wines, baguettes, heated pies and venison pasties etc, very low prices; small games room with machines *(JP, PP, Jonathan Smith, the Didler, Catherine Pitt)*

Newton Poppleford [SY0889]

Cannon [High St]: Bustling 16th-c two-bar inn with full-blown maritime décor, friendly service, reasonably priced food inc speciality steaks and lunchtime bargain, good choice of beers tapped from the cask, log fires; good garden, bedrooms *(Pat and Robert Watt, the Didler)*

Newton Tracey [SS5226]

Hunters [B3232 Barnstaple—Torrington]: Friendly 15th-c pub with massive low beams, four well kept ales inc local Bideford Bootlegger, decent wines and malt whiskies, log fire, enjoyable home-made food inc huge puddings and children's dishes, evening restaurant; skittle alley/games room, juke box and machines; tables outside, play area *(Andy Marks, Peter Bakker, E B Ireland)*

North Bovey [SX7483]

☆ ***Ring of Bells*** [off A382/B3212 SW of Moretonhampstead]: Attractive bulgy-walled 13th-c thatched inn, low-ceilinged bar with well kept real ales inc Butcombe, Gray's farm cider and good log fire, enjoyable bar food inc good ploughman's and freshly prepared specials, restaurant, longer more functional room with pool and TV; seats out by lovely tree-covered village green below Dartmoor, big bedrooms with four-posters *(John Crafts, LYM, Mark Percy, Lesley Mayoh, Esther and John Sprinkle, Nick Lawless)*

North Molton [SS7933]

Sportsmans [Sandyway Cross, up towards Withypool]: Remote yet popular unspoilt country pub fairly handy for Landacre beauty spot, with two rooms, good generous food, well kept Exmoor tapped from the cask, local farm ciders, friendly landlord and regulars, restaurant *(Michael Lamm, Francis Johnston)*

Okehampton [SX5895]

Plymouth [West St]: Pretty pub with friendly helpful landlord and staff, local-feel bar with surprisingly enterprising food, well kept mainly local ales tapped from the cask (May and Nov beer festivals), no smoking area, provision for children; open all day wknds *(Dr and Mrs A K Clarke, Derek Allpass)*

Paignton [SX8960]

☆ ***Inn on the Green*** [Esplanade Rd]: Big brightly comfortable unpubby bar open all day, useful lunchtime for enormous choice of popular sensibly priced quick food, well kept real ales, good soft and hot drinks, friendly service; out-of-the-way family room, live music and dancing nightly, restaurant, big terrace looking out over green to sea *(LYM, Mr and Mrs Colin Roberts)*

Ship [Manor Rd, Preston]: Large yet homely mock-Tudor pub with comfortable furnishings inc leather settees, soft lighting, well kept Fullers London Pride from very long bar, enjoyable generous low-priced food (dining areas on three floors), efficient smiling service; a minute's walk from Preston beach *(Mr and Mrs Colin Roberts, Jo Miller)*

Parracombe [SS6644]

☆ ***Fox & Goose*** [off A39 Blackmoor Gate—Lynton]: Rambling pub with attractive wine bar feel and wide range of good freshly made food from sandwiches to Exmoor lamb and venison or local fish, well kept local ales, decent wines; children welcome *(David Jones, Miss E Holmes, P Hill, Stan Edwards, Paul and Ursula Randall)*

Petrockstowe [SS5109]

Laurels [signed off A386 N of Hatherleigh]: Former coaching inn with proficient and hospitable licensees, good freshly made food, well kept St Austell HSD and a guest beer *(R J Walden)*

Plymouth [SX4755]

China House [Sutton Harbour, via Sutton Rd off Exeter St (A374)]: Conversion of Plymouth's oldest warehouse, listed for its super views day and night over harbour and Barbican; newly done up spacious bar with great beams and flagstones, bare slate and stone walls, good log fire, great choice of wines by the glass (it's been taken over by Vintage Inns), well kept Bass and Tetleys, food from ciabattas and filled baguettes up; piped music; open all day *(R T and J C Moggridge, LYM)*

Dolphin [Barbican]: Well worn in lively and unspoilt local, good range of beers inc particularly well kept Bass and Worthington Dark tapped from the cask, coal fire; colourful green and orange décor, Beryl Cook paintings inc one of the friendly landlord; open all day *(John Poulter, David Crook, JP, PP, the Didler)*

Kings Head [Breton Side]: Unpretentious beamed pub with reasonably priced food, real ales inc Bass and Courage, friendly service; pool *(George Atkinson)*

Lounge [Stopford Pl, Stoke]: Unspoilt basic backstreet pub, two rooms, friendly landlord, Bass and a guest beer from oak-panelled counter, popular lunchtime food *(the Didler)*

Notte [Notte St]: Thriving local atmosphere, single long bar (can get crowded) with barrel seats below windows, well kept Fullers London Pride and Wadworths 6X tapped from the cask, 20 single malts, wide range of enjoyable food inc seafood, friendly landlord; free 50s/60s juke box *(David Crook, Steve Whalley, Keith and Suzie Stevens)*

Queens Arms [Southside St, Barbican]: Small cosily Victorian local, spotless and smartly decorated, with comfortable banquettes, well kept Bass, excellent sandwiches inc fresh crab, good friendly service *(Steve Whalley)*

Thistle Park [Commercial Rd]: Welcoming pub near National Maritime Aquarium, good range of well kept beers inc some from next-door Sutton brewery, tasty food all day, friendly landlady, children welcome; open all day, live music wknds *(the Didler, JP, PP)*

Portgate [SX4185]

☆ ***Harris Arms*** [Launceston Rd (old A30)]: Warmly friendly, bright and comfortable, good food inc superb South Devon steaks and mixed grill, well kept Bass and guest ales such as Sharps Doom Bar, prompt informal service with good attention to detail, wonderful view from dining room *(DAV, Dr and Mrs Nigel Holmes, Mr and Mrs Frank Greenwood, John and Sarah Perry)*

Postbridge [SX6579]

☆ ***East Dart*** [B3212]: Central Dartmoor hotel by pretty river, doing well under current generation of the family which built it in 1861; roomy and comfortable open-plan bar with promptly served enjoyable food from large crisp filled rolls up, cheerful helpful service, well kept real ale, good fire, hunting murals and horse tack, pool room; children welcome, bedrooms, some 30 miles of fishing *(Di and Mike Gillam, Dennis Jenkin, BB)*

Princetown [SX5973]

☆ ***Plume of Feathers*** [Plymouth Hill]: Much-extended local doubling as hikers' pub, unpretentious and individual, with good value food inc good pasties, service quick and friendly even with crowds, well kept ales inc Princetown Jail, two log fires, solid slate tables, live music Fri night, Sun lunchtime – can be lively then; big family room with a real welcome for children, play area outside; good value bedrooms, also bunkhouse and camping; open all day *(David and Nina Pugsley)*

Prixford [SS5436]

Ring o' Bells: Neat and comfortable, with good home-made food, real ales, hospitable service, coal-effect gas fires; piped music, shove-

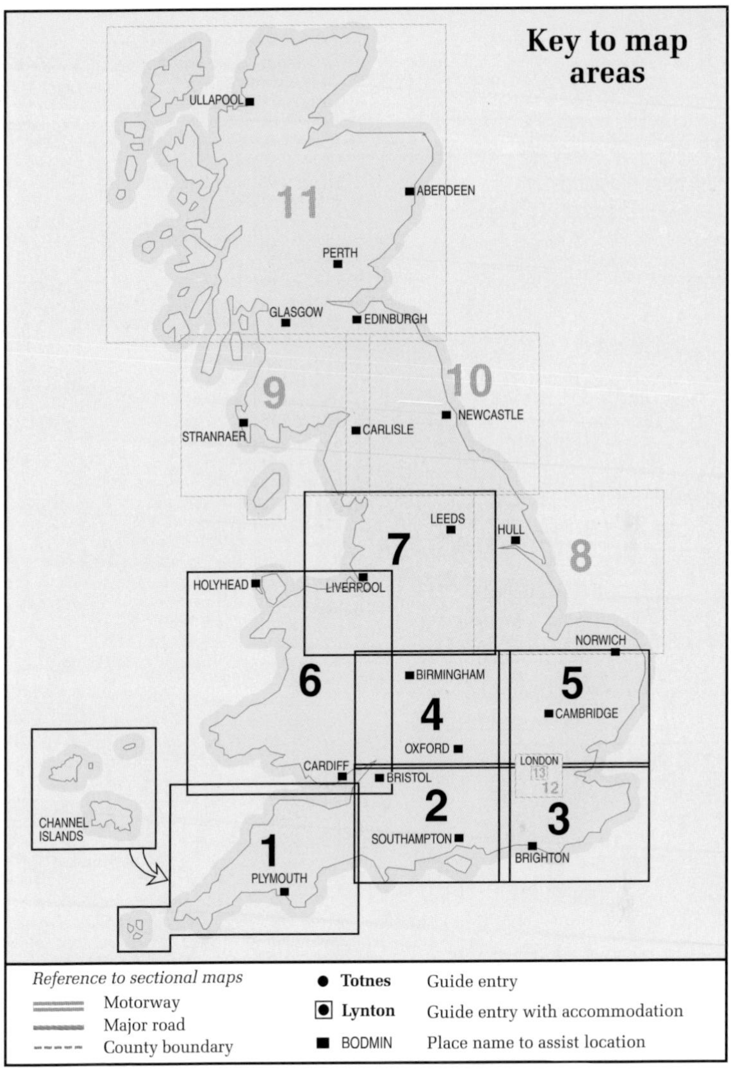

MAPS IN THIS SECTION

The South-West and Channel Islands	Map 1
Southern England	Map 2
The South-East	Map 3
Central and Western England	Map 4
Central England and East Anglia	Map 5
Wales	Map 6
The North-West	Map 7

For Maps 8 – 13 see later colour section

1

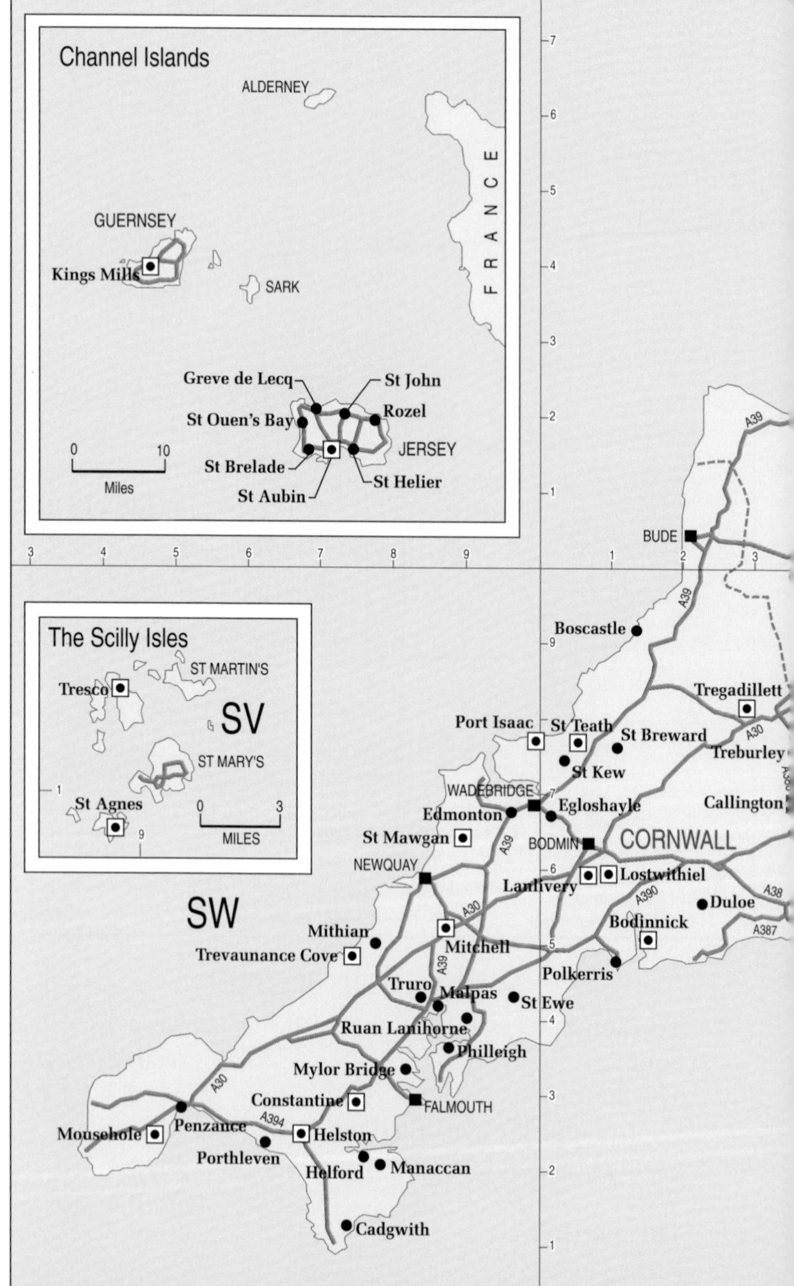

Channel Islands
ALDERNEY
GUERNSEY
Kings Mills
SARK
FRANCE
Greve de Lecq
St John
St Ouen's Bay
Rozel
JERSEY
St Brelade
St Helier
St Aubin
0
10
Miles
The Scilly Isles
ST MARTIN'S
Tresco
SV
ST MARY'S
St Agnes
0
3
MILES
SW
BUDE
A39
Boscastle
Tregadillett
Port Isaac
St Teath
St Breward
A30
Treburley
St Kew
WADEBRIDGE
Egloshayle
Callington
Edmonton
St Mawgan
BODMIN
CORNWALL
NEWQUAY
Lanlivery
Lostwithiel
A390
Duloe
A38
Bodinnick
A387
Mithian
Mitchell
Trevaunance Cove
Polkerris
Truro
Malpas
St Ewe
Ruan Lanihorne
Philleigh
Mylor Bridge
Constantine
FALMOUTH
Penzance
A394
Mousehole
Helston
Porthleven
Helford
Manaccan
Cadgwith

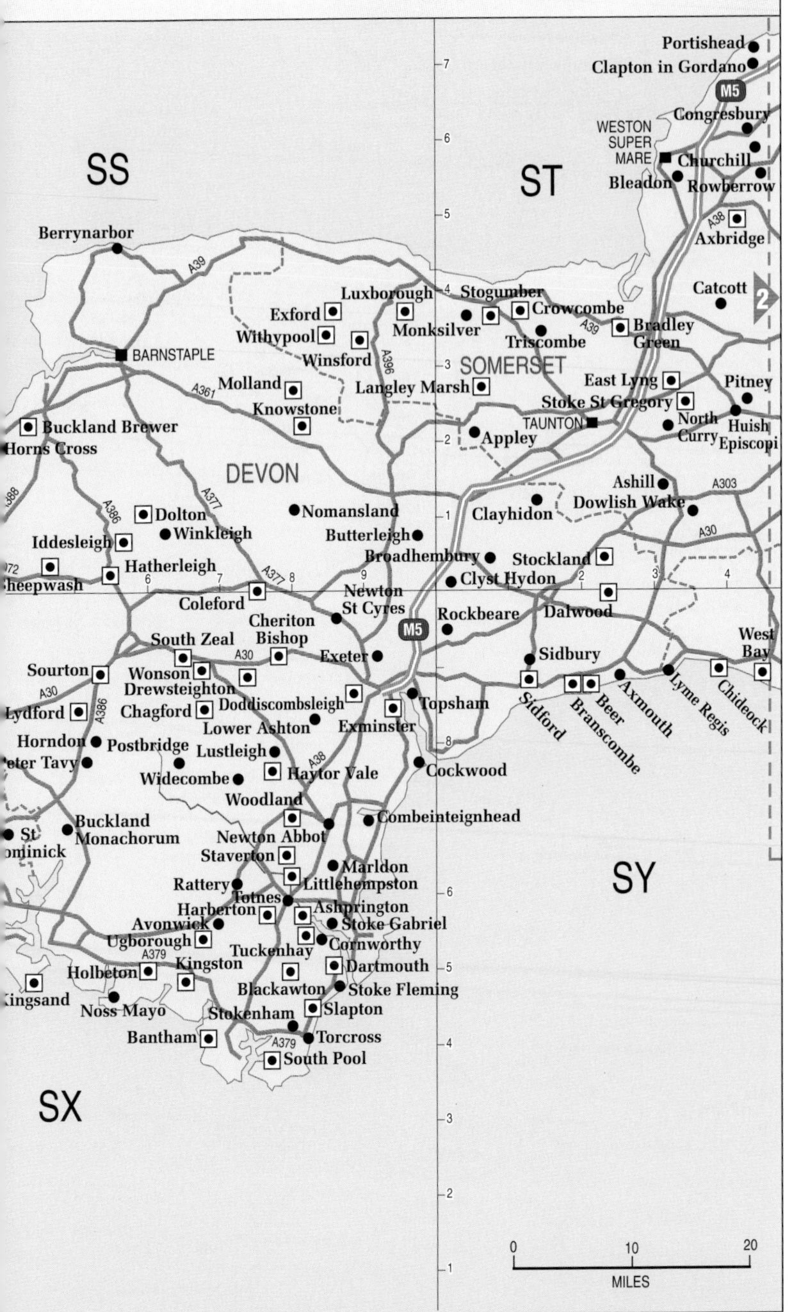
SS
ST
SX
SY
DEVON
SOMERSET
BARNSTAPLE
TAUNTON
WESTON SUPER MARE
Portishead
Clapton in Gordano
Congresbury
Churchill
Bleadon
Rowberrow
Axbridge
Catcott
Berrynarbor
Luxborough
Stogumber
Crowcombe
Exford
Monksilver
Withypool
Winsford
Triscombe
Bradley Green
Molland
Langley Marsh
East Lyng
Pitney
Knowstone
Stoke St Gregory
North Curry
Huish Episcopi
Buckland Brewer
Horns Cross
Appley
Ashill
Dowlish Wake
Clayhidon
Nomansland
Dolton
Winkleigh
Butterleigh
Iddesleigh
Broadhembury
Stockland
Hatherleigh
Sheepwash
Clyst Hydon
Coleford
Newton St Cyres
Rockbeare
Dalwood
Cheriton Bishop
South Zeal
Exeter
West Bay
Sourton
Wonson
Drewsteighton
Sidbury
Lydford
Chagford
Doddiscombsleigh
Topsham
Sidford
Branscombe
Beer
Axmouth
Lyme Regis
Chideock
Lower Ashton
Exminster
Horndon
Postbridge
Lustleigh
Peter Tavy
Widecombe
Haytor Vale
Cockwood
Woodland
Combeinteignhead
Buckland Monachorum
St Dominick
Newton Abbot
Staverton
Marldon
Rattery
Littlehempston
Totnes
Harberton
Ashprington
Avonwick
Stoke Gabriel
Ugborough
Cornworthy
Tuckenhay
Kingston
Dartmouth
Holbeton
Blackawton
Stoke Fleming
Kingsand
Noss Mayo
Stokenham
Slapton
Bantham
Torcross
South Pool
M5
A39
A361
A396
A377
A386
A30
A38
A379
A303
A388
2
0
10
20
MILES

2

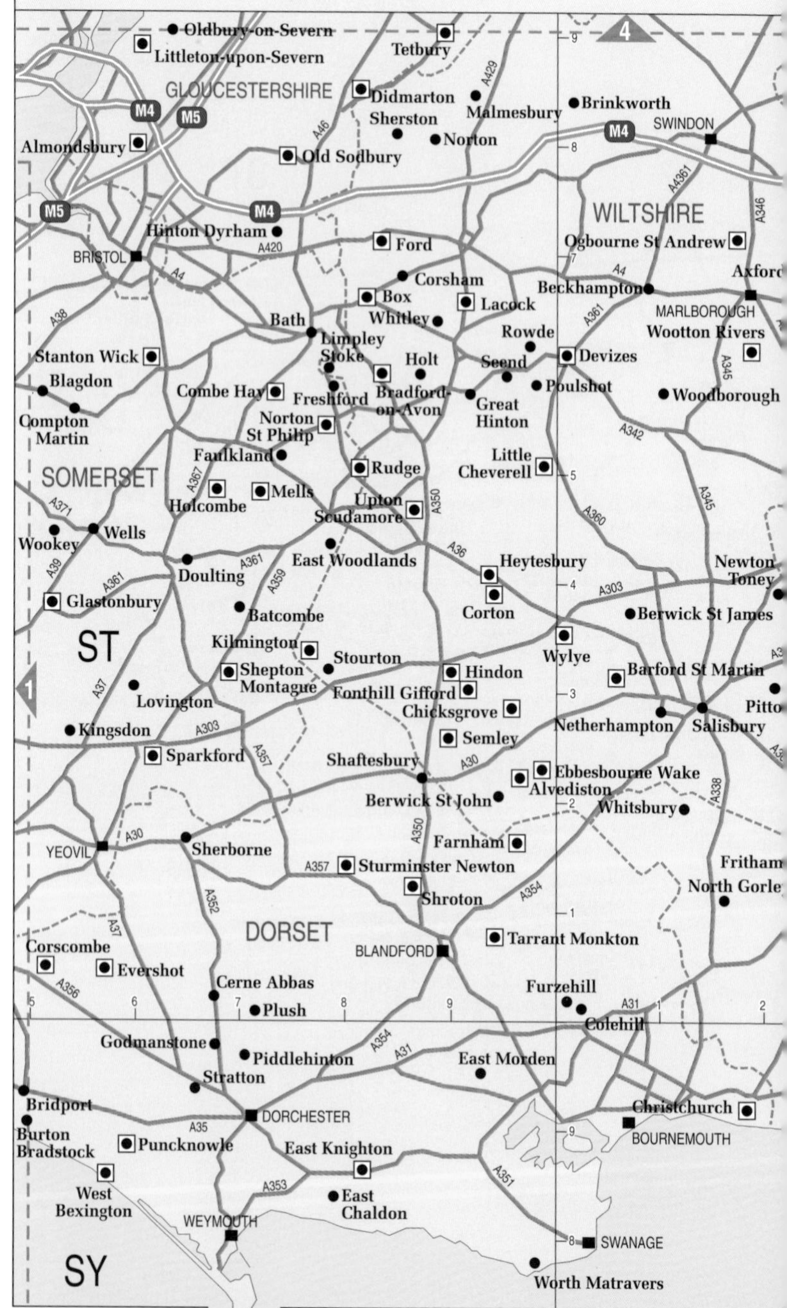

Oldbury-on-Severn
Littleton-upon-Severn
GLOUCESTERSHIRE
Tetbury
Didmarton
Sherston
Malmesbury
Norton
Brinkworth
SWINDON
Almondsbury
Old Sodbury
WILTSHIRE
Hinton Dyrham
BRISTOL
Ford
Ogbourne St Andrew
Axford
Corsham
Box
Lacock
Beckhampton
MARLBOROUGH
Whitley
Wootton Rivers
Bath
Limpley Stoke
Rowde
Stanton Wick
Holt
Seend
Devizes
Blagdon
Bradford-on-Avon
Poulshot
Woodborough
Combe Hay
Freshford
Great Hinton
Compton Martin
Norton St Philip
Faulkland
Little Cheverell
Rudge
SOMERSET
Holcombe
Mells
Upton Scudamore
Wookey
Wells
East Woodlands
Heytesbury
Newton Toney
Doulting
Glastonbury
Batcombe
Corton
Berwick St James
ST
Kilmington
Wylye
Stourton
Shepton Montague
Hindon
Barford St Martin
Fonthill Gifford
Lovington
Chicksgrove
Salisbury
Netherhampton
Kingsdon
Semley
Sparkford
Shaftesbury
Ebbesbourne Wake
Alvediston
Berwick St John
Whitsbury
YEOVIL
Sherborne
Farnham
Fritham
Sturminster Newton
North Gorley
Shroton
DORSET
Tarrant Monkton
BLANDFORD
Corscombe
Evershot
Cerne Abbas
Furzehill
Plush
Colehill
Godmanstone
Piddlehinton
East Morden
Stratton
Bridport
Christchurch
DORCHESTER
Burton Bradstock
Puncknowle
East Knighton
BOURNEMOUTH
West Bexington
East Chaldon
WEYMOUTH
SWANAGE
SY
Worth Matravers
M4
M5
A420
A4
A38
A46
A429
A4361
A346
A361
A345
A342
A367
A371
A350
A360
A36
A39
A359
A303
A37
A357
A30
A338
A354
A352
A356
A31
A35
A353
A351
1
4

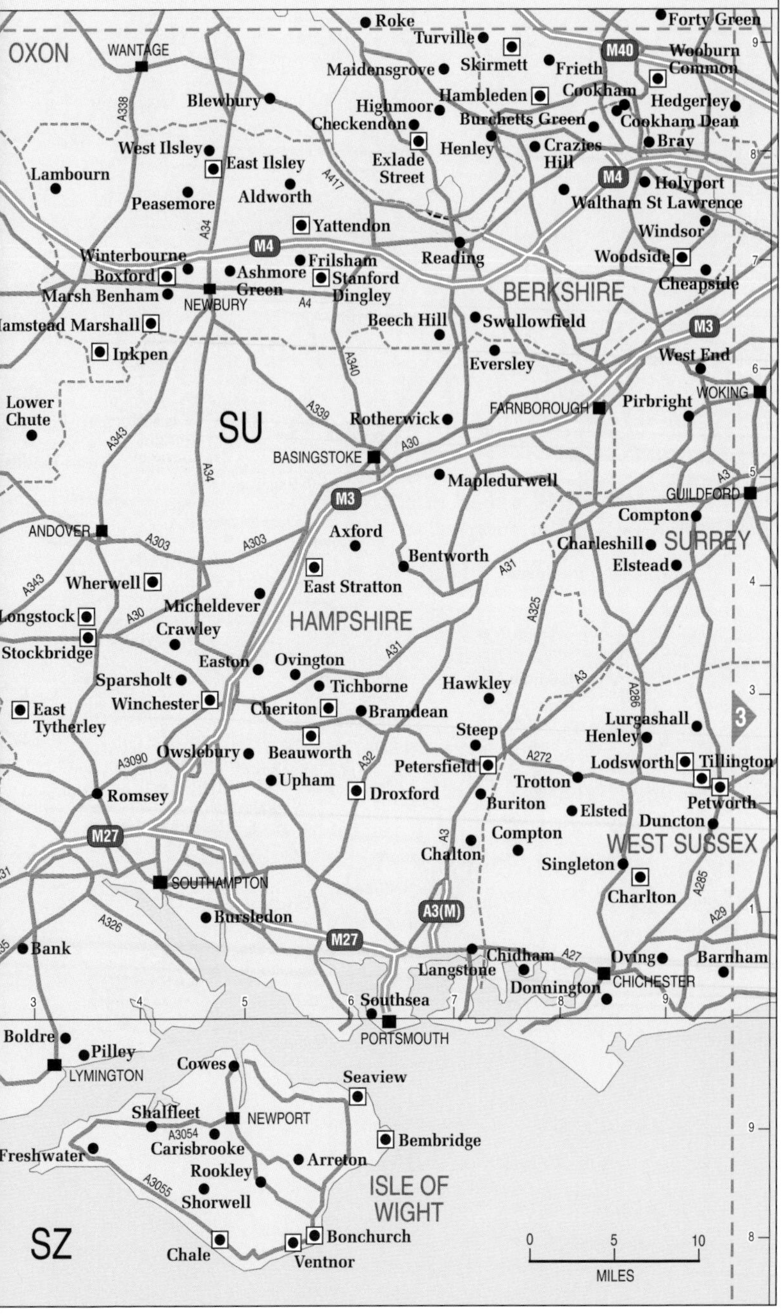

OXON
WANTAGE
Roke
Turville
Skirmett
Frieth
Forty Green
Wooburn Common
Maidensgrove
Hambleden
Cookham
Hedgerley
Blewbury
Highmoor
Checkendon
Burchetts Green
Cookham Dean
Bray
West Ilsley
East Ilsley
Exlade Street
Henley
Crazies Hill
Holyport
Lambourn
Aldworth
Waltham St Lawrence
Peasemore
Yattendon
Windsor
Winterbourne
Frilsham
Reading
Woodside
Boxford
Ashmore Green
Stanford Dingley
Cheapside
Marsh Benham
NEWBURY
BERKSHIRE
Hamstead Marshall
Beech Hill
Swallowfield
Inkpen
Eversley
West End
WOKING
Lower Chute
SU
Rotherwick
FARNBOROUGH
Pirbright
BASINGSTOKE
Mapledurwell
GUILDFORD
Compton
ANDOVER
Axford
Charleshill
SURREY
Bentworth
Elstead
Wherwell
East Stratton
Micheldever
Longstock
HAMPSHIRE
Crawley
Stockbridge
Easton
Ovington
Sparsholt
Tichborne
Hawkley
East Tytherley
Winchester
Cheriton
Bramdean
Lurgashall
Steep
Henley
Owslebury
Beauworth
Petersfield
Lodsworth
Tillington
Upham
Trotton
Romsey
Droxford
Buriton
Elsted
Petworth
Duncton
Compton
Chalton
WEST SUSSEX
Singleton
SOUTHAMPTON
Charlton
Bursledon
Bank
Chidham
Oving
Barnham
Langstone
Donnington
CHICHESTER
Southsea
PORTSMOUTH
Boldre
Pilley
LYMINGTON
Cowes
Seaview
Shalfleet
NEWPORT
Bembridge
Carisbrooke
Freshwater
Arreton
Rookley
ISLE OF WIGHT
Shorwell
Bonchurch
SZ
Chale
Ventnor
0 5 10
MILES

3

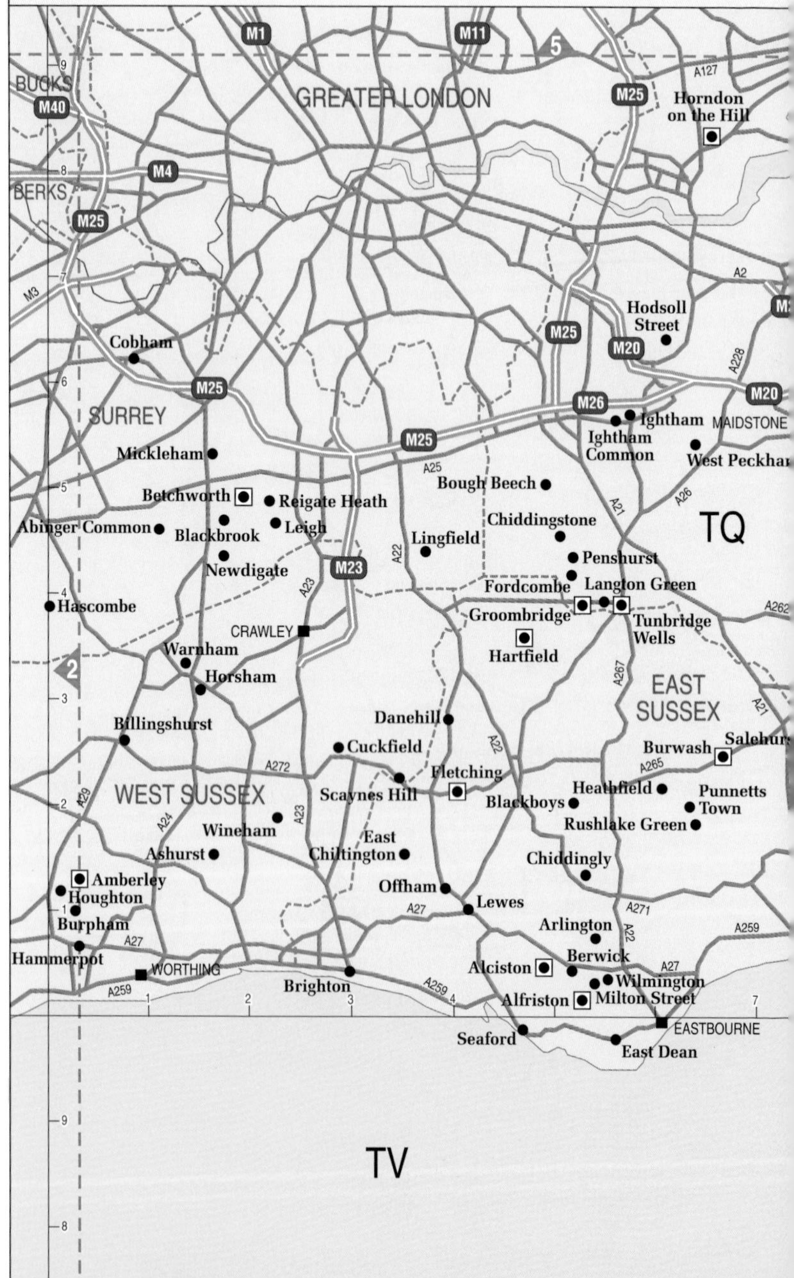

M1
M11
5
BUCKS
M40
GREATER LONDON
M25
A127
Horndon on the Hill
M4
BERKS
M25
M3
A2
Hodsoll Street
M25
M20
Cobham
A228
M20
M25
SURREY
M26
Ightham
MAIDSTONE
M25
Ightham Common
West Peckham
Mickleham
A25
Bough Beech
Betchworth
Reigate Heath
A21
A26
Abinger Common
Blackbrook
Leigh
Chiddingstone
TQ
Lingfield
Newdigate
A22
M23
Penshurst
A23
Fordcombe
Langton Green
Hascombe
Groombridge
Tunbridge Wells
A262
CRAWLEY
Hartfield
Warnham
2
Horsham
A267
EAST SUSSEX
A21
Billingshurst
Danehill
A22
Cuckfield
Burwash
A265
A272
Fletching
Heathfield
Punnetts Town
WEST SUSSEX
Scaynes Hill
Blackboys
A29
A24
A23
Wineham
Rushlake Green
East Chiltington
Ashurst
Chiddingly
Amberley
Houghton
Offham
Lewes
A271
A27
Burpham
Arlington
A22
A259
A27
Berwick
Hammerpot
WORTHING
Alciston
A27
Wilmington
A259
Brighton
A259
Alfriston
Milton Street
Seaford
EASTBOURNE
East Dean
TV

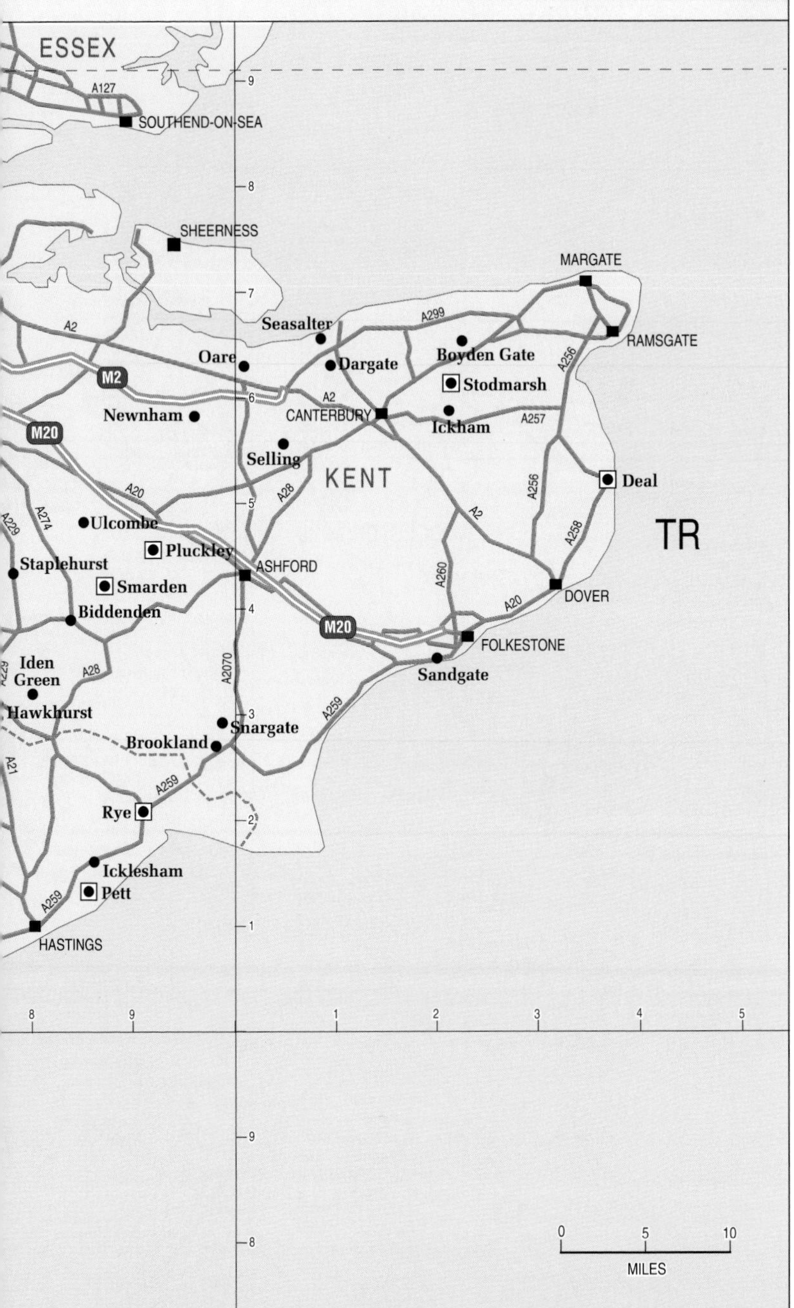
ESSEX
A127
SOUTHEND-ON-SEA
SHEERNESS
MARGATE
RAMSGATE
A299
A2
Seasalter
Oare
Dargate
Boyden Gate
Stodmarsh
A256
M2
A2
CANTERBURY
Ickham
A257
Newnham
M20
Selling
KENT
Deal
A20
A28
A256
A2
Ulcombe
A274
A229
Pluckley
A258
TR
Staplehurst
ASHFORD
Smarden
A260
DOVER
Biddenden
A20
M20
FOLKESTONE
Iden
Green
A28
A2070
Sandgate
Hawkhurst
A259
Snargate
Brookland
A21
A259
Rye
Icklesham
Pett
A259
HASTINGS
9
8
7
6
5
4
3
2
1
8
9
1
2
3
4
5
9
8
0
5
10
MILES

4

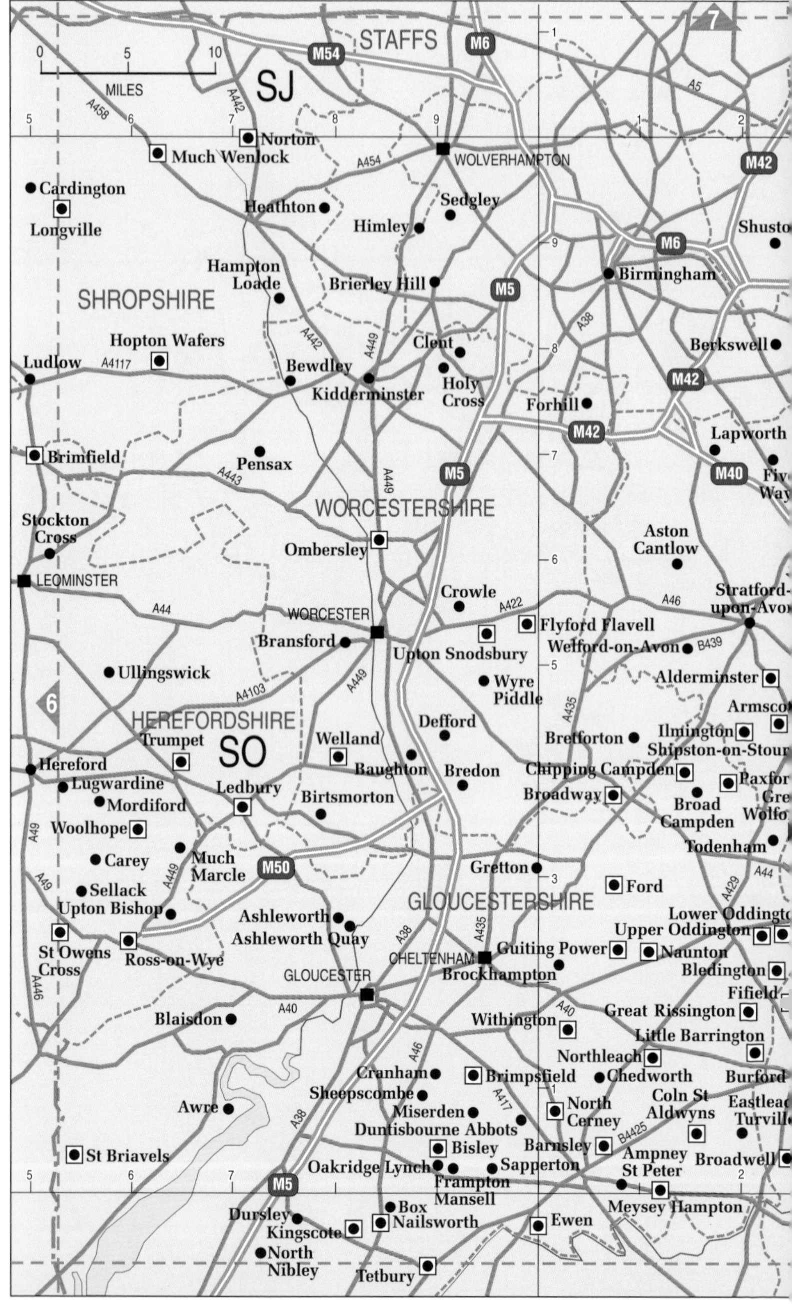

STAFFS
M54
M6
0 5 10
MILES
SJ
A442
A458
A454
Norton
Much Wenlock
WOLVERHAMPTON
M42
A5
Cardington
Longville
Heathton
Sedgley
Himley
Shuston
M6
Birmingham
Hampton Loade
Brierley Hill
M5
SHROPSHIRE
A442
A449
A38
Hopton Wafers
Clent
Berkswell
Ludlow
A4117
Bewdley
Kidderminster
Holy Cross
M42
Forhill
M42
Lapworth
Brimfield
Pensax
A443
A449
M5
M40
Stockton Cross
WORCESTERSHIRE
Aston Cantlow
Ombersley
LEOMINSTER
Crowle
A46
Stratford-upon-Avon
A44
WORCESTER
A422
Flyford Flavell
Bransford
Welford-on-Avon
B439
Upton Snodsbury
Ullingswick
Wyre Piddle
Alderminster
A4103
A449
A435
Armscote
6
HEREFORDSHIRE
Defford
Ilmington
Trumpet
SO
Welland
Bretforton
Shipston-on-Stour
Hereford
Baughton
Bredon
Chipping Campden
Paxford
Lugwardine
Ledbury
Broadway
Mordiford
Birtsmorton
Broad Campden
Woolhope
A49
Todenham
Carey
Much Marcle
M50
Gretton
A44
A49
A449
Ford
Sellack
GLOUCESTERSHIRE
A429
Upton Bishop
Ashleworth
Lower Oddington
Ashleworth Quay
Upper Oddington
A38
A435
Guiting Power
St Owens Cross
Ross-on-Wye
CHELTENHAM
Naunton
Brockhampton
Bledington
GLOUCESTER
A446
Fifield
Blaisdon
A40
Withington
A40
Great Rissington
Little Barrington
A46
Northleach
Cranham
Brimpsfield
Chedworth
Burford
Sheepscombe
A417
Coln St Aldwyns
Eastleach Turville
Awre
Miserden
North Cerney
A38
Duntisbourne Abbots
Barnsley
B4425
Bisley
St Briavels
Ampney St Peter
Broadwell
Oakridge Lynch
Sapperton
Frampton Mansell
M5
Box
Meysey Hampton
Dursley
Nailsworth
Ewen
Kingscote
North Nibley
Tetbury
7

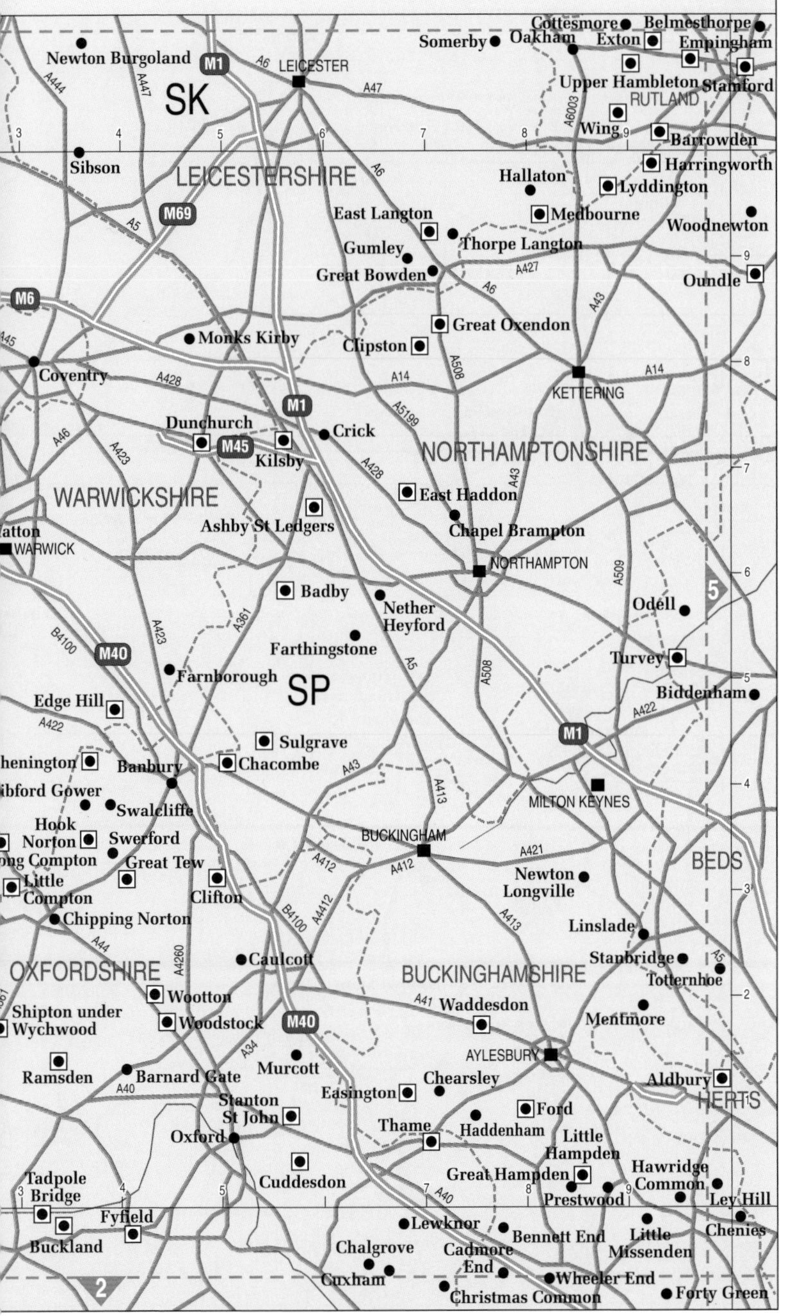

SK
SP
LEICESTER
LEICESTERSHIRE
RUTLAND
NORTHAMPTONSHIRE
WARWICKSHIRE
OXFORDSHIRE
BUCKINGHAMSHIRE
BEDS
HERTS
Newton Burgoland
Sibson
Somerby
Oakham
Cottesmore
Exton
Belmesthorpe
Empingham
Upper Hambleton
Stamford
Wing
Barrowden
Harringworth
Lyddington
Hallaton
Medbourne
Woodnewton
East Langton
Thorpe Langton
Gumley
Great Bowden
Oundle
Great Oxendon
Clipston
Monks Kirby
Coventry
KETTERING
Dunchurch
Crick
Kilsby
East Haddon
Chapel Brampton
Ashby St Ledgers
WARWICK
NORTHAMPTON
Badby
Nether Heyford
Farthingstone
Odell
Turvey
Farnborough
Biddenham
Edge Hill
Sulgrave
Chacombe
Banbury
Swalcliffe
Hook Norton
Swerford
Great Tew
Little Compton
Clifton
Chipping Norton
MILTON KEYNES
BUCKINGHAM
Newton Longville
Linslade
Stanbridge
Totternhoe
Caulcott
Wootton
Woodstock
Shipton under Wychwood
Waddesdon
Mentmore
AYLESBURY
Ramsden
Barnard Gate
Murcott
Chearsley
Easington
Aldbury
Stanton St John
Ford
Thame
Haddenham
Oxford
Little Hampden
Cuddesdon
Great Hampden
Hawridge Common
Tadpole Bridge
Prestwood
Ley Hill
Fyfield
Buckland
Lewknor
Bennett End
Little Missenden
Chenies
Chalgrove
Cadmore End
Cuxham
Wheeler End
Christmas Common
Forty Green
M1
M6
M69
M45
M40
A6
A47
A444
A447
A5
A427
A43
A508
A14
A428
A5199
A46
A423
A361
A509
B4100
A422
A413
A421
A412
A4412
A44
A4260
A41
A34
A40
5
2

5

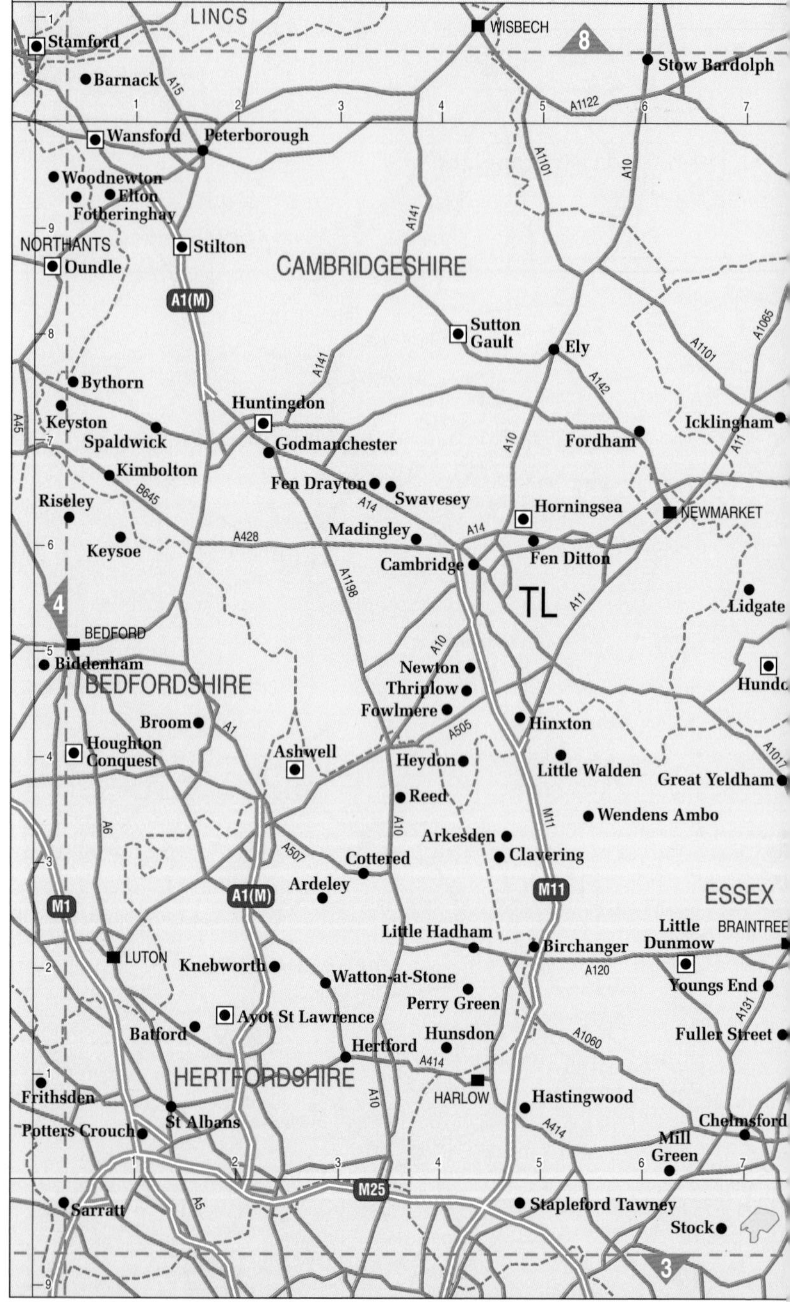

LINCS
Stamford
Barnack
WISBECH
8
Stow Bardolph
Wansford
Peterborough
Woodnewton
Elton
Fotheringhay
NORTHANTS
Stilton
Oundle
CAMBRIDGESHIRE
A1(M)
Sutton Gault
Ely
Bythorn
Huntingdon
Keyston
Spaldwick
Godmanchester
Fordham
Icklingham
Kimbolton
Fen Drayton
Swavesey
Riseley
Horningsea
NEWMARKET
Madingley
Keysoe
Fen Ditton
Cambridge
TL
Lidgate
4
BEDFORD
Biddenham
BEDFORDSHIRE
Newton
Thriplow
Fowlmere
Broom
Hinxton
Houghton Conquest
Ashwell
Heydon
Little Walden
Great Yeldham
Reed
Wendens Ambo
Arkesden
Clavering
Cottered
Ardeley
A1(M)
M1
M11
ESSEX
Little Hadham
Little Dunmow
BRAINTREE
Birchanger
LUTON
Knebworth
Watton-at-Stone
Youngs End
Perry Green
Ayot St Lawrence
Batford
Hunsdon
Fuller Street
Hertford
HERTFORDSHIRE
HARLOW
Frithsden
Hastingwood
St Albans
Potters Crouch
Chelmsford
Mill Green
M25
Sarratt
Stapleford Tawney
Stock
3

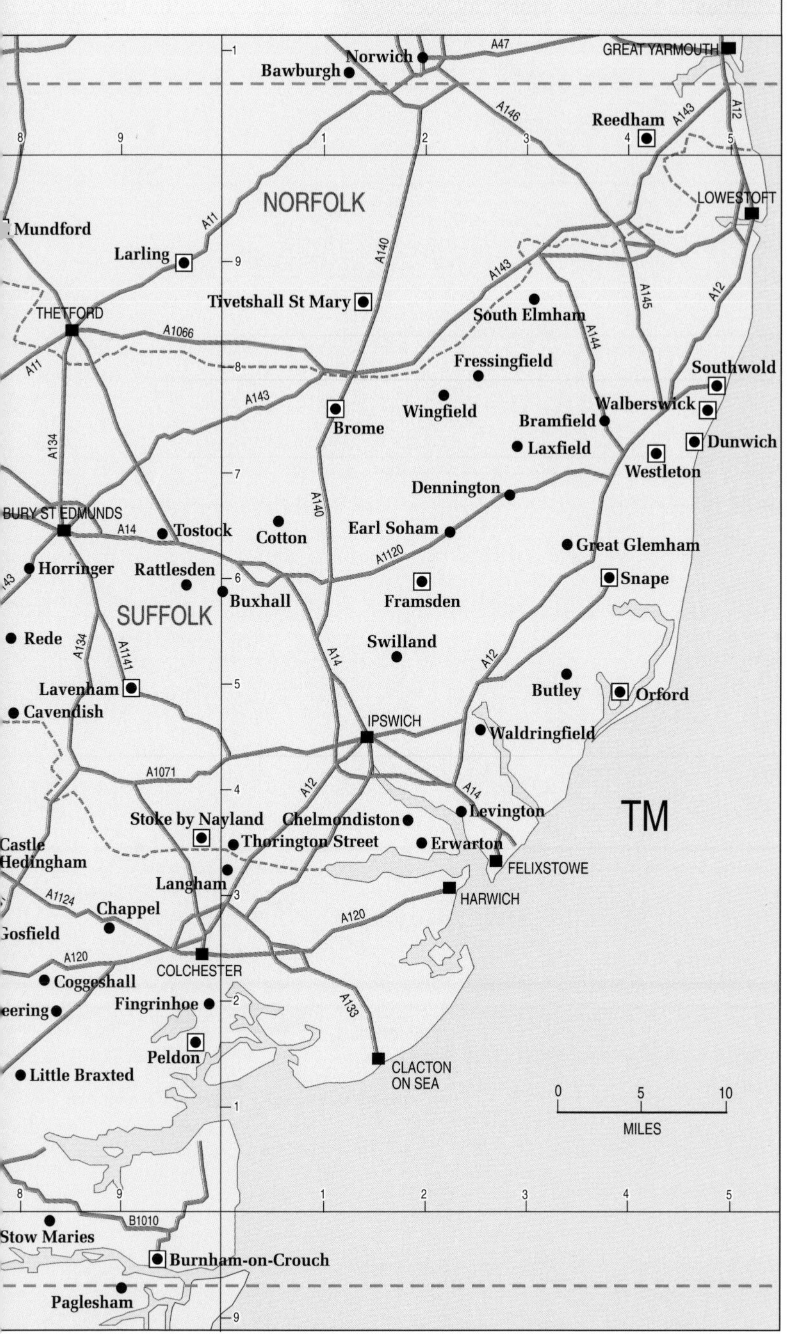
GREAT YARMOUTH
Norwich
Bawburgh
A47
A146
Reedham
A143
A12
NORFOLK
LOWESTOFT
Mundford
Larling
A11
A140
A143
Tivetshall St Mary
South Elmham
A145
A12
THETFORD
A1066
A144
Fressingfield
Southwold
A11
A143
Brome
Wingfield
Walberswick
Bramfield
Dunwich
Laxfield
Westleton
A134
Dennington
BURY ST EDMUNDS
A14
Tostock
Cotton
A140
Earl Soham
Great Glemham
Horringer
Rattlesden
A1120
Snape
Buxhall
Framsden
SUFFOLK
Rede
Swilland
A134
A1141
A14
A12
Lavenham
Butley
Orford
Cavendish
IPSWICH
Waldringfield
A1071
A12
A14
Levington
TM
Stoke by Nayland
Chelmondiston
Castle Hedingham
Thorington Street
Erwarton
FELIXSTOWE
Langham
HARWICH
A1124
Chappel
A120
Gosfield
A120
COLCHESTER
Coggeshall
Fingrinhoe
A133
Peldon
CLACTON ON SEA
Little Braxted
0
5
10
MILES
B1010
Stow Maries
Burnham-on-Crouch
Paglesham

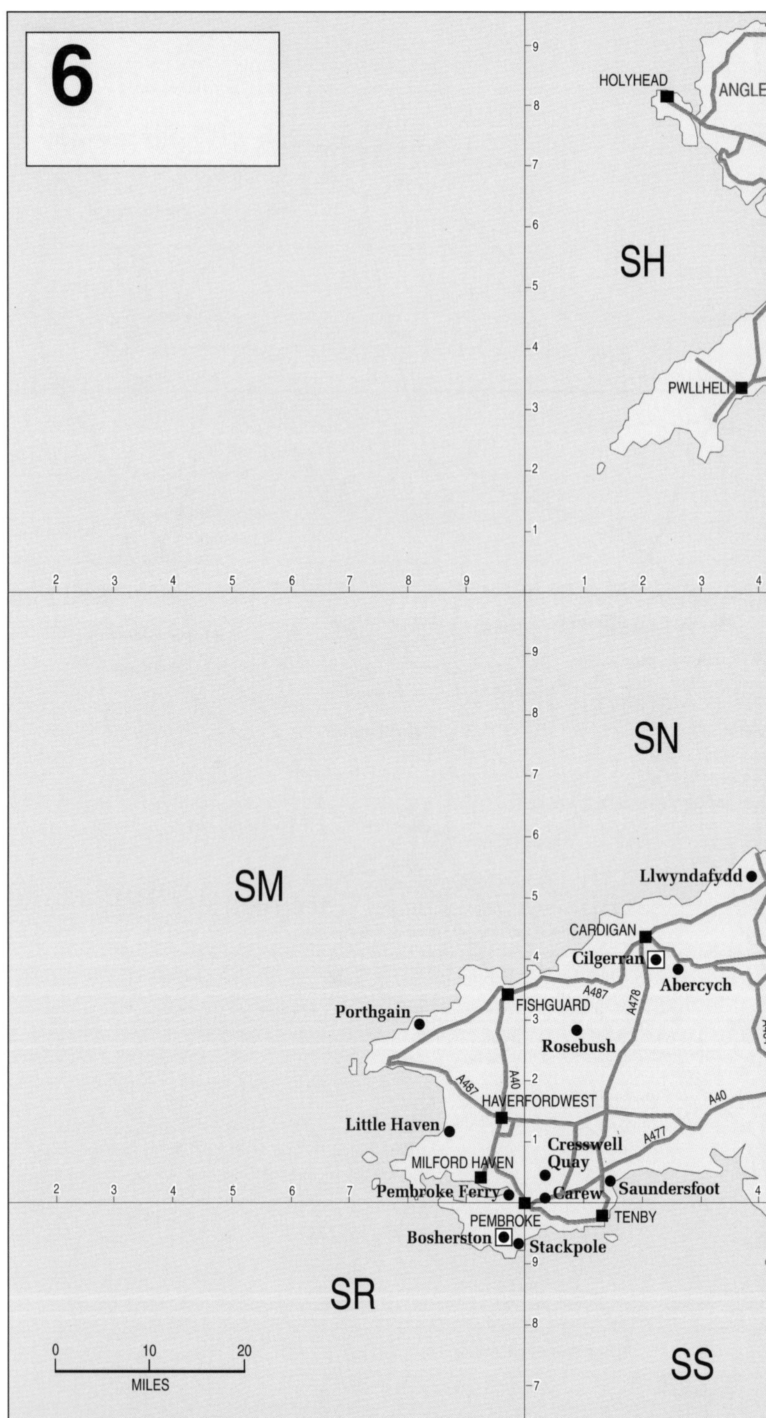

6
HOLYHEAD
ANGLESE
SH
PWLLHELI
SN
SM
Llwyndafydd
CARDIGAN
Cilgerran
Abercych
FISHGUARD
Porthgain
Rosebush
HAVERFORDWEST
Little Haven
Cresswell Quay
MILFORD HAVEN
Pembroke Ferry
Carew
Saundersfoot
PEMBROKE
TENBY
Bosherston
Stackpole
SR
SS
A487
A478
A484
A40
A477
MILES

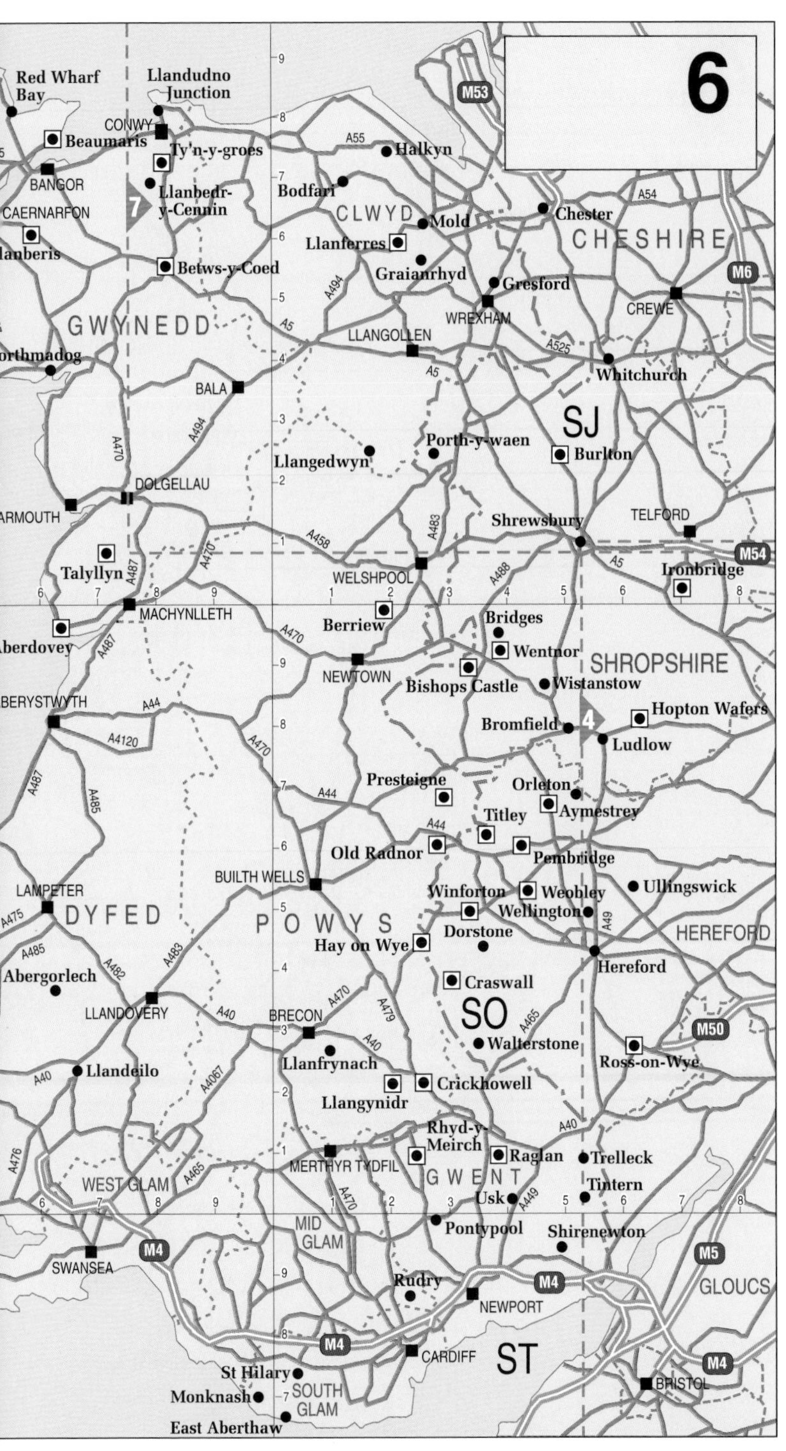
6
Red Wharf Bay
Llandudno Junction
CONWY
Beaumaris
Ty'n-y-groes
BANGOR
Llanbedr-y-Cennin
CAERNARFON
Llanberis
Betws-y-Coed
GWYNEDD
Porthmadog
BALA
DOLGELLAU
BARMOUTH
Talyllyn
MACHYNLLETH
Aberdovey
ABERYSTWYTH
LAMPETER
DYFED
Abergorlech
LLANDOVERY
Llandeilo
WEST GLAM
SWANSEA
Halkyn
Bodfari
CLWYD
Mold
Llanferres
Graianrhyd
Gresford
WREXHAM
LLANGOLLEN
Llangedwyn
Porth-y-waen
WELSHPOOL
Berriew
NEWTOWN
Bishops Castle
Presteigne
Old Radnor
BUILTH WELLS
POWYS
Hay on Wye
BRECON
Llanfrynach
Llangynidr
Crickhowell
MERTHYR TYDFIL
MID GLAM
Rudry
CARDIFF
St Hilary
Monknash
SOUTH GLAM
East Aberthaw
Chester
CHESHIRE
CREWE
Whitchurch
SJ
Burlton
Shrewsbury
TELFORD
Ironbridge
Bridges
Wentnor
SHROPSHIRE
Wistanstow
Hopton Wafers
Bromfield
Ludlow
Orleton
Aymestrey
Titley
Pembridge
Ullingswick
Winforton
Weobley
Wellington
Dorstone
HEREFORD
Hereford
Craswall
SO
Walterstone
Ross-on-Wye
Rhyd-y-Meirch
Raglan
Trelleck
GWENT
Usk
Tintern
Pontypool
Shirenewton
NEWPORT
ST
GLOUCS
BRISTOL
M53
M6
M54
M50
M5
M4
A55
A54
A5
A525
A494
A470
A458
A483
A488
A487
A44
A4120
A485
A475
A482
A40
A4067
A465
A479
A49
A449
A476

7

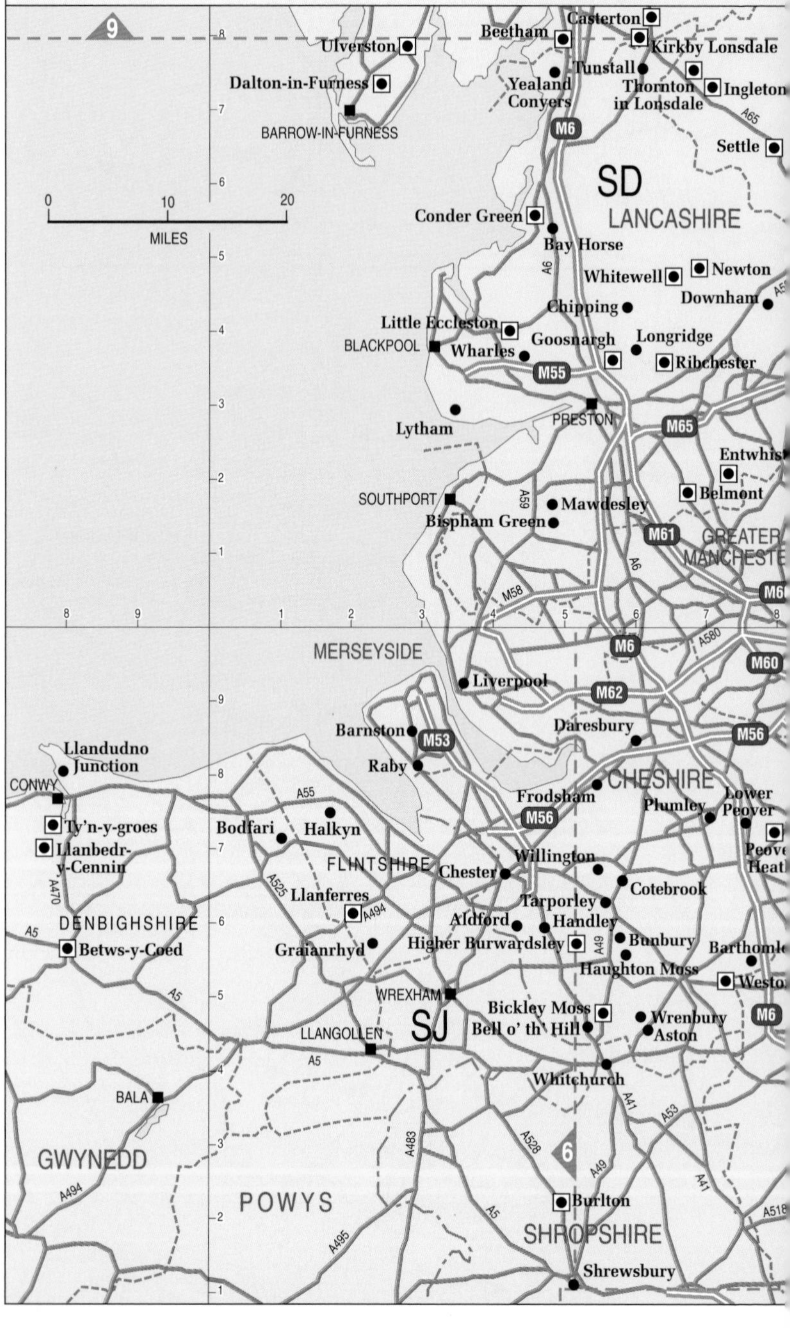
9
Ulverston
Dalton-in-Furness
BARROW-IN-FURNESS
Beetham
Casterton
Kirkby Lonsdale
Tunstall
Yealand Conyers
Thornton in Lonsdale
Ingleton
A65
M6
Settle
SD
LANCASHIRE
0
10
20
MILES
Conder Green
Bay Horse
A6
Whitewell
Newton
Downham
Chipping
Little Eccleston
BLACKPOOL
Goosnargh
Longridge
Wharles
Ribchester
M55
PRESTON
Lytham
M65
Entwhistle
Belmont
SOUTHPORT
A59
Mawdesley
Bispham Green
M61
GREATER MANCHESTER
A6
M58
M60
MERSEYSIDE
A580
Liverpool
M62
Barnston
M53
Daresbury
M56
Llandudno Junction
CONWY
Raby
CHESHIRE
Frodsham
Lower Peover
Plumley
A55
Ty'n-y-groes
Bodfari
Halkyn
Llanbedr-y-Cennin
Willington
FLINTSHIRE
Chester
A525
Cotebrook
Llanferres
A470
A494
Tarporley
DENBIGHSHIRE
Aldford
Handley
A5
Graianrhyd
Higher Burwardsley
A49
Bunbury
Betws-y-Coed
Barthomley
Haughton Moss
Weston
WREXHAM
A5
Bickley Moss
Wrenbury
SJ
Bell o' th' Hill
Aston
LLANGOLLEN
A5
Whitchurch
BALA
A41
A53
A528
A483
6
GWYNEDD
A49
A41
A494
POWYS
Burlton
A518
A5
A495
SHROPSHIRE
Shrewsbury

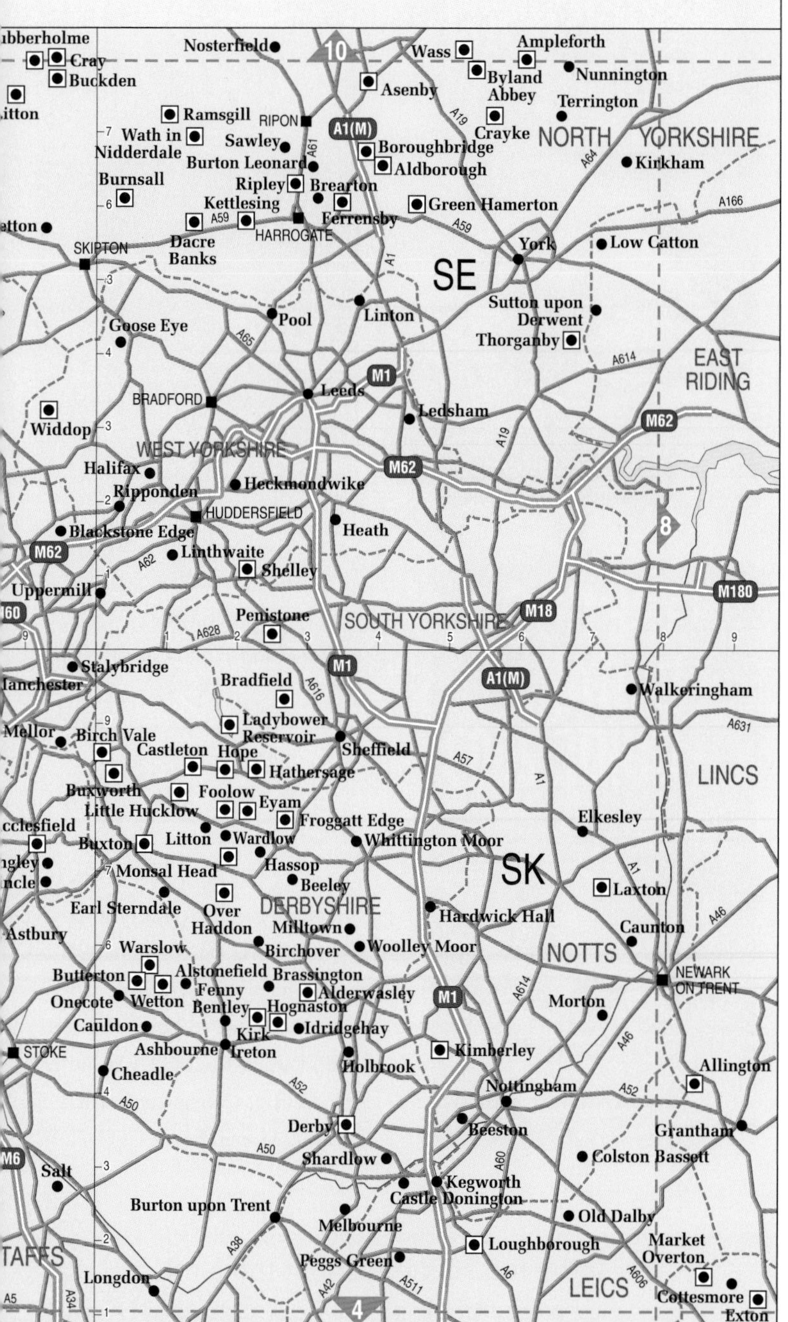
Nosterfield
10
Wass
Ampleforth
Cray
Buckden
Byland Abbey
Nunnington
Asenby
Terrington
Ramsgill
RIPON
A1(M)
Crayke
NORTH YORKSHIRE
Wath in Nidderdale
Sawley
Boroughbridge
Burton Leonard
Aldborough
Kirkham
Burnsall
Ripley
Brearton
Kettlesing
Green Hamerton
A166
A59
HARROGATE
Ferrensby
Dacre Banks
SKIPTON
York
Low Catton
SE
Pool
Linton
Sutton upon Derwent
Goose Eye
Thorganby
A614
EAST RIDING
M1
Leeds
BRADFORD
Ledsham
Widdop
M62
WEST YORKSHIRE
Halifax
Heckmondwike
Ripponden
HUDDERSFIELD
8
Blackstone Edge
Heath
Linthwaite
Shelley
M180
Uppermill
Penistone
SOUTH YORKSHIRE
M18
Stalybridge
Bradfield
A1(M)
Walkeringham
Ladybower Reservoir
Mellor
Birch Vale
Sheffield
Castleton
Hope
Hathersage
LINCS
Buxworth
Foolow
Little Hucklow
Eyam
Froggatt Edge
Elkesley
Litton
Wardlow
Whittington Moor
Buxton
Hassop
SK
Monsal Head
Beeley
Laxton
Earl Sterndale
Over Haddon
DERBYSHIRE
Hardwick Hall
Caunton
Milltown
Astbury
Warslow
Birchover
Woolley Moor
NOTTS
Alstonefield
Brassington
NEWARK ON TRENT
Butterton
Fenny Bentley
Alderwasley
Onecote
Wetton
Hognaston
Morton
Cauldon
Kirk Ireton
Idridgehay
STOKE
Ashbourne
Kimberley
Holbrook
Allington
Cheadle
Nottingham
A52
A50
Derby
Beeston
Grantham
Shardlow
Colston Bassett
Salt
Kegworth
Castle Donington
Burton upon Trent
Old Dalby
Melbourne
Loughborough
Market Overton
Peggs Green
Longdon
LEICS
Cottesmore
Exton
STAFFS
4

ha'penny, pool, skittle alley *(Trevor Swindells, Peter and Audrey Dowsett)*

Pyworthy [SS3102]

☆ ***Molesworth Arms***: Popular flagstoned country pub with enjoyable food in bar or restaurant, well kept real ales and decent wines, friendly staff *(M Etherington)*

Rackenford [SS8518]

Stag [pub signed off A361 NW of Tiverton]: New licensees yet again in this interesting 13th-c low-beamed thatched pub, with lots of character and atmosphere, huge fireplace flanked by ancient settles, original flagstoned and cobbled entry passage, well kept Cotleigh Tawny and local guest beers, farm cider, cottagey dining room; children in eating areas, simple bedrooms *(LYM)*

Ringmore [SX6545]

☆ ***Journeys End*** [signed off B3392 at Pickwick Inn, St Anns Chapel, near Bigbury; best to park up opp church]: Old village inn with character panelled lounge, well kept changing ales such as Adnams Broadside, Badger Tanglefoot, Exmoor and Otter, some tapped from casks in back room, local farm cider, log fires; varied interesting food inc good fresh fish (lunchtime menu may be limited, but helpful about special diets), friendly locals and staff, pleasant big terraced garden, sunny back add-on family dining conservatory; piped radio may obtrude; attractive setting near thatched cottages, not far from the sea; bedrooms antique but comfortable and well equipped *(Mike and Wena Stevenson, Rona Murdoch, JP, PP, Nick Lawless, the Didler, LYM, Steve Pocock)*

Salcombe [SX7438]

☆ ***Ferry Inn*** [off Fore St nr Portlemouth Ferry]: The star is for the fine estuary position, with tiers of stripped-stone bars rising from sheltered flagstoned waterside terrace, inc top one opening off street, and middle dining bar; well kept Palmers and farm cider; piped music can be loud, can get busy, may be closed part of winter *(MDN, LYM)*

Fortescue [Union St, end of Fore St]: Sizeable pub near harbour, popular and welcoming, nautical theme in five interlinked rooms, lots of old local black and white shipping pictures, three well kept changing beers, decent wines, enjoyable promptly served food, reasonable prices, pleasant service, relaxing atmosphere, good woodburner, restaurant, big games room, no piped music; picnic-sets in courtyard *(Keith and Suzie Stevens, Peter Salmon, Geoff Calcott)*

Victoria [Fore St]: Well placed, smartly attractive and tidy yet unpretentious, with bare-boards bar, comfortable lounge, well kept St Austell Tinners and Dartmoor Best, good coffee, generous bar food, cosy stone-walled dining room downstairs; may be unobtrusive piped music, segregated children's room; bedrooms, large sheltered terrace garden behind *(Dr and Mrs M E Wilson, John Brightley, Pete and Jo Cole)*

Sandy Park [SX7087]

☆ ***Sandy Park Inn*** [A382 S of Whiddon Down]: Thatched country local with old-fashioned small bar, stripped pine tables, built-in high-backed wall seats, big black iron fireplace, good food with copious veg here or in small cosy dining room (children allowed there), friendly staff, well kept ales inc Blackawton Bitter and Dobs Best, decent wines and farm cider; simple clean bedrooms *(LYM, Philip Crawford, Mark Percy, Lesley Mayoh)*

Sandygate [SX8674]

Sandygate Inn: Popular cosy local with wide choice of low-priced generous food with potatoes, rice or salad, Bass and Wadworths 6X, farm cider, friendly landlady; tables in garden *(Jeanne and Paul Silvestri)*

Seaton [SY2490]

George [The Square]: Pleasant seaside pub under new management, usual food and special curry menu *(Ken Flawn)*

Shaldon [SX9372]

Clifford Arms [Fore St]: Friendly and attractive two-bar open-plan 18th-c local in pleasant seaside village, good value home-made usual food, well kept Fullers London Pride, Greene King Abbot and Teignworthy Reel from fine copper-topped bar, chamber-pots hanging from low beams, huge tropical fish tank, local photographs and sailing paintings, woodburner; games area with darts and pool, family room; colourful little front courtyard, pleasant back terrace *(Phil and Heidi Cook)*

London [The Green]: Friendly village pub with enjoyable food inc good crab baguettes, kind staff and particularly well kept Greene King Abbot; children welcome, good value bedrooms with wholesome breakfast, pretty waterside village *(Simon Harris, Meg and Colin Hamilton)*

Shiphay [SX8865]

☆ ***Devon Dumpling*** [Shiphay Lane, off A380/A3022 NW edge of Torquay]: Open-plan farmhouse pub, comfortable and clean, with plenty of space inc atmospheric cosy corners, aquarium and lots of decorations at Christmas; popular locally for good value quick generous food, real ales such as Courage Best, Fullers London Pride and Wychwood Hobgoblin, quick cheerful service; children in plainer upper barn loft, occasional live music, no dogs inside *(Mr and Mrs Colin Roberts)*

Sidmouth [ST1287]

Anchor [Old Fore St]: Friendly high-ceilinged local with good generous cheap food inc unusual daily specials in no smoking dining area, second bar downstairs, Bass-related beers; tables in good outdoor area, open all day – full of folk music in festival week *(Neil and Beverley Gardner)*

☆ ***Old Ship*** [Old Fore St]: Partly 14th-c, with low beams, mellow black woodwork and panelling, sailing ship prints, good food from open sandwiches to local fish, well kept Flowers Original, Wadworths 6X and a guest beer, prompt courteous service even when busy, friendly atmosphere; close-set tables but roomier raftered upstairs bar with family room, dogs allowed; in pedestrian zone just moments from the sea (note that around here parking is limited to 30 mins) *(Barry Smith, John Beeken, BB, Bob and Ann Westbrook)*

Swan [York St]: Nice small flower-filled garden, well kept Branscombe Vale beer, food inc good crab sandwiches *(June and Malcolm Farmer)*

Silverton [SS9502]

☆ ***Three Tuns*** [Exeter Rd]: Wide choice of well prepared food inc fine vegetarian dishes in 17th-c or older inn's old-fashioned beamed bars or cosy restaurant (where children welcome), comfortable settees, friendly staff, well kept ales inc local ones; tables in pretty inner courtyard, handy for Killerton *(Sheila and Phil Stubbs, Tim and Ann Newell)*

Smallridge [ST3000]

☆ ***Ridgeway*** [signed off A358 N of Axminster]: Charming décor, fresh flowers, comfortable seating, good value food prepared to order (so may be a wait), well kept Branscombe and Otter, very friendly attentive service, open fire, welcoming family atmosphere; pleasant quiet terrace and garden, lovely spot *(John and Ann Colling, R T and J C Moggridge)*

South Brent [SX6958]

Woodpecker [A38]: Recently reopened, with pleasant décor, booth tables, no smoking area, very wide choice of enjoyable food at attractive prices (should book in season), Bass and Blackawton 44, reasonably priced wines *(Dudley and Moira Cockroft)*

Sparkwell [SX5857]

Treby Arms: Warm atmosphere, reliable modestly priced food with some enterprising specials, friendly helpful service, good range of beers inc unusual guests and one brewed locally for the pub, decent house wines, small dining room; disabled facilities *(John Evans)*

Sticklepath [SX6494]

Devonshire [off A30 at Whiddon Down or Okehampton]: Well used 16th-c thatched village inn next to foundry museum, easy-going low-beamed slate-floored bar with big log fire, longcase clock and friendly old furnishings, sofa in small snug, well kept St Austell ales tapped from the cask, farm cider, informal welcoming service, magazines to read, sandwiches, bookable Sun lunches and evening meals, hopeful pub dog, games room with piano and bar billiards; lively folk night 1st Sun in month, open all day Fri/Sat, bedrooms *(Nick Lawless, the Didler, JP, PP, LYM)*

Stokeinteignhead [SX9170]

☆ ***Church House*** [signed from Combeinteignhead, or off A379 N of Torquay]: 13th-c pub with thatch, heavy beams, inglenook fireplace, antique furnishings, relaxed, informal atmosphere, some emphasis on food from sandwiches up, well kept Adnams, Bass, and Greene King Abbot or Otter Ale, farm cider, good coffee, no smoking dining room, simple public bar with traditional games and TV; quiet piped music; children in eating area, neat back garden with dracaenas, unspoilt village *(Pamela and Merlyn Horswell, M G Hart, Nick Lawless, David and Elizabeth Briggs, LYM)*

Stokenham [SX8042]

☆ ***Church House*** [opp church, N of A379 towards Torcross]: Comfortable open-plan pub, hard-working long-serving landlord, enjoyable food from filled baked potatoes to fresh local seafood and good steaks, well kept ales inc Bass and Flowers Original, farm cider, good wines, no smoking dining room; unobtrusive piped music; front children's room with writing/drawing materials, attractive garden with enjoyably individual play area and fishpond *(LYM, C A Hall, Geoff and Tricia Alderman, Lynn Sharpless, Bob Eardley)*

Tedburn St Mary [SX8193]

☆ ***Kings Arms*** [off A30 W of Exeter]: Attractive traditional pub, open-plan but comfortable, with heavy-beamed and panelled L-shaped bar, lantern lighting and snug stable-style alcoves, big log fire, lots of brass and hunting prints, good choice of nicely priced food (all day Sun) from good sandwiches and interesting hot baguettes to unusual dishes, well kept Bass, Sharps Doom Bar and St Austell Bodmin Boar, local farm cider, pleasant painstaking service, modern restaurant, end games area; shame about the piped pop music; children in eating area, tables on back terrace, bedrooms *(John and Vivienne Rice, Gloria Bax, LYM, John Beeken, Alan Wilson)*

Teignmouth [SX9372]

Queensbury Arms [Northumberland Ave]: Welcoming beamed pub with bargain food inc local fish, alcove seating, keg beers *(Joyce and Maurice Cottrell)*

☆ ***Ship*** [Queen St]: Upper and lower decks like a ship, good friendly atmosphere, nice mix of locals, families and tourists, good reasonably priced food (all day in summer) esp simply cooked local fish and good Sun lunch, good service from obliging staff, well kept ales inc Bass and Greene King Abbot, interesting wine list, fresh coffee, gallery restaurant; open all day, fine floral displays, lovely riverside setting, beautiful views *(Peter J Holmes, Crystal and Peter Hooper)*

Thelbridge Cross [SS7912]

Thelbridge Cross Inn [B3042 W of Tiverton]: Welcoming lounge bar with log fire and plush settees, good generous food inc some unusual dishes in extensive dining area and separate restaurant, friendly helpful service, particularly well kept Bass and Butcombe; reasonable disabled access, bedrooms smallish but good breakfast *(BB, John Evans)*

Tipton St John [SY0991]

☆ ***Golden Lion*** [signed off B3176 Sidmouth—Ottery St Mary]: Enjoyable food from baked potatoes and ploughman's to good fish and some interesting dishes, well kept Bass, Greene King Old Speckled Hen, Otter and Wadworths 6X, roaring log fire, attractive décor and mix of furnishings, no smoking restaurant; piped music; children in eating areas, open all day wknds, seats out on terrace and in garden, two comfortable bedrooms with showers *(Basil Minson, R J Walden, Richard Fendick, Barry Smith, Dr and Mrs M E Wilson, LYM)*

Topsham [SX9688]

☆ ***Globe*** [Fore St; 2 miles from M5 junction 30]: Substantial traditional inn dating from 16th c, good solid furnishings and log fire in heavy-beamed bow-windowed bar, good interesting home-cooked food at reasonable prices, well kept Bass, Hancocks HB and Sharps Doom Bar, decent reasonably priced wine, prompt friendly service, plenty of locals, snug little dining lounge, good value separate restaurant, back extension; children in eating area, open all day, good value attractive bedrooms *(David Peakall, D J Hulse, Andrew Woodgates, LYM, the Didler, Dr and Mrs M E Wilson)*

☆ ***Lighter*** [Fore St]: Spacious and comfortably refurbished, with panelling and tall windows looking out over tidal flats, more intimate side room, nautical décor, welcoming efficient staff, well kept Badger Best and Tanglefoot, food from good sandwiches to mildly upmarket dishes inc local fish, central log fire, good children's area; games machines, piped music; tables out in lovely spot on old quay, handy for big antiques centre *(Dr and Mrs M E Wilson, E G Parish, P R and S A White, Mike Tucker, Pam Adsley, R J Walden, Dr and Mrs A K Clarke, Mrs Sylvia Elcoate, BB, Comus and Sarah Elliott)*

Lord Nelson [High St]: Lots of sea prints and nautical memorabilia inc sails over big dining area, smaller side one up steps (both no smoking), wide choice of reasonably priced bar meals, very attentive friendly service, Bass and Flowers Original; may be piped pop music; useful car park *(the Didler, C J Farr)*

Salutation [Fore St]: Victorian pastiche complete with flagstoned period courtyard; clean, comfortable, warm and welcoming, with good low-priced food, happy obliging staff, well kept Bass and Worthington BB *(Jo Foster)*

Steam Packet [Monmouth Hill]: Well priced bar food, several well kept ales, dark flagstones, scrubbed boards, panelling, stripped masonry, a lighter dining room; on boat-builders' quay *(the Didler, LYM)*

Torbryan [SX8266]

Old Church House [most easily reached from A381 Newton Abbot—Totnes via Ipplepen]: Early 15th-c inn by part-Saxon church, quaint bar on right with benches built into Tudor panelling, high-backed settle and big log fire, also rambling series of comfortable and discreetly lit lounges, one with a splendid inglenook fireplace; well kept Bass, Flowers IPA and Original, Marstons Pedigree, Wadworths 6X and a beer brewed for the pub, good choice of malt whiskies and wines, decent food from sandwiches up; piped music; children welcome, well equipped bedrooms, roomy and immaculate *(John and Glenys Wheeler, R T and J C Moggridge, LYM)*

Torquay [SX9175]

Crown & Sceptre [Petitor Rd, St Marychurch]: Friendly two-bar local in 18th-c stone-built coaching inn, eight real ales inc guests, bar food, interesting naval memorabilia and chamber-pot collection, good-humoured landlord, jazz Tues and Sun, folk first Thurs of month, bands Sat *(the Didler, JP, PP)*

☆ ***Hole in the Wall*** [Park Lane, opp clock tower]: Ancient unpretentious two-bar local near harbour, consistently good value usual food, well kept Courage and guest beers, Blackawton cider, friendly service, flagstones, low beams and alcoves, lots of naval memorabilia, old local photographs, chamber-pots; band nights, open all day *(Joseph Cairns, Kevin Blake)*

London [Strand]: Vast Wetherspoons bank conversion overlooking harbour and marina, no smoking upper mezzanine bar, big local ship paintings and a couple of reproduction ship's figureheads, good value food all day, bargain coffee as well as usual real ales, no piped music; can be very busy *(George Atkinson, Pamela and Merlyn Horswell, Andrew Hodges)*

Torrington [SS4919]

☆ ***Black Horse*** [High St]: Pretty twin-gabled inn dating from 15th c, overhanging upper storeys, beams hung with stirrups, solid furniture, oak bar counter, no smoking lounge with striking ancient black oak partition wall and a couple of attractive oak seats, oak-panelled restaurant with aquarium, enjoyable food inc OAP wkdy lunchtime bargains, friendly service, well kept Courage Best and Directors, John Smiths and changing guest beers, darts, shove-ha'penny, cribbage, dominoes; well reproduced piped music, friendly cat and dogs; open all day Sat, handy for RHS Rosemoor garden and Dartington Crystal *(D and S Price, LYM, Gordon Tong)*

Totnes [SX8060]

King William IV [Fore St]: Warm, spacious and comfortably carpeted Victorian pub, popular (esp with older people) for sensibly priced home-made food from sandwiches to bargain steak and huge mixed grill; Boddingtons, Flowers, Tetleys and Wadworth 6X, friendly service; bedrooms with own bathrooms *(Mr and Mrs Colin Roberts, Neil and Beverley Gardner, C M Miles, J B Towers)*

☆ ***Kingsbridge Inn*** [Leechwell Street]: New female management in attractive rambling bar, neat and tidy, with black beams, timbering and some stripped stone; two log fires, plush seats, small no smoking upper area (children allowed here), home-made food from lunchtime sandwiches and baked potatoes to some good interesting hot dishes, well kept Bass, Cotleigh Tawny, Theakstons Old Peculier and two changing guest beers; may be piped music; children in eating area, some live music and readings *(LYM, David M Cundy, John Wilson)*

Steam Packet [St Peters Quay]: Well refurbished under current welcoming licensees, staff cheerful and efficient even when it's crowded, enjoyable food from lunchtime sandwiches up, real ales inc two guest beers, good coffee, log fire, restaurant with spectacular river view from no smoking conservatory; children welcome (books and games for them in leather-seated side area), jazz Sun lunchtime; tables outside, bedrooms, open all day *(J G S Widdicombe)*

Turnchapel [SX4952]

☆ ***Boringdon Arms*** [off A379 via Plymstock and Hooe; Boringdon Terr]: 18th-c pub at foot of cliffs and built back into them, eight interesting well kept ales such as Butcombe, Oakham JHB, RCH Pitchfork and Sharps, farm cider, good value freshly made food all day esp curries and pies, cheerful landlord and welcoming staff, roaring log fire in massive fireplace, RN, RM and other nautical memorabilia, shelves of bottled beers; monthly beer festivals, Sat folk nights; dogs welcome, tables outside, shortish water-taxi ride from central Plymouth; open all day, cheap bedrooms *(the Didler, JP, PP)*

Two Bridges [SX6175]

☆ *Two Bridges Hotel* [B3357/B3212 across Dartmoor]: Rambling 18th-c hotel in protected central Dartmoor hollow, relaxed L-shaped beamed back bar full of interesting pictures, comfortable old-fashioned entrance lounge with roaring log fire, well kept Boddingtons, Flowers IPA and Princetown Jail, bar food, no smoking area, restaurant, pianist Fri/Sat; children in eating areas, picnic-sets out on riverside grass, attractive bedrooms, good walks – a romantic winter hideaway, but very busy with tourists and their children in summer; open all day *(Rod Stoneman, Ann and Colin Hunt, LYM)*

Umberleigh [SS6023]

☆ *Rising Sun* [A377 S of Barnstaple]: Comfortable and civilised fishing inn with five River Taw salmon and sea trout beats, lots of stuffed fish and fishing memorabilia in pleasant partly no smoking divided bar with woodburner and flagstones; has had well kept Bass, Clearwater Cavalier, Cotleigh Tawny and Jollyboat Mainbrace, good wines by the glass and farm cider, and good food inc lunchtime sandwiches, but sold in 2002 – reports please; children in eating areas, tables outside, good bedrooms *(LYM)*

Walkhampton [SX5369]

Walkhampton Inn: 17th-c Dartmoor-edge village pub recently reopened after refurbishment by new licensees, stripped stone and beams, well kept Princetown and St Austell ales, good choice of food inc good steaks, friendly staff, no smoking area; dogs welcome *(Dr and Mrs Nigel Holmes)*

Wembworthy [SS6609]

Lymington Arms [Lama Cross]: Clean and bright, with wide choice of good food (not Mon) from new chef, well kept beers inc Sharps, Inch's cider, decent wines, agreeable restaurant; children welcome, tables in garden, pleasant setting *(R J Walden, Val Davies)*

Westcott [ST0204]

Merry Harriers [B3181 S of Cullompton]: Small country pub with very wide range of enjoyable food cooked by landlord, welcoming service by wife and daughter, big log fire, good choice of beers and wines, attractive restaurant *(John Close, Ken Flawn)*

Whitchurch [SX4972]

☆ *Whitchurch Inn* [village signed off A386 just S of Tavistock; then keep straight on up over crossroads – opp Old School Children's Centre]: Beamed local owned by the church, all neat and warm with woodburner each end, long sparklingly kept bar for the good Bass, Blackawton 44, Fullers London Pride and St Austell HSD, nice choice of wines by the glass, particularly good service, good food choice, comfortable furnishings inc no smoking dining end, butter-coloured plaster crisply cut away to show stonework, plenty of chatty regulars and their dogs *(BB, Jacquie and Jim Jones)*

Widecombe [SX7176]

☆ *Old Inn* [B3387 W of Bovey Tracey]: Busy, friendly and comfortable, with 14th-c stonework, big log fires, olde-worlde pubby front bar, some concentration on large restaurant area with wide choice of good value hearty food from well filled granary rolls up, well kept ales inc Wadworths 6X, local farm cider, decent wines, good friendly service, family room; in pretty moorland village – get there before about 12.30 in summer to miss the tourist coaches; room to dance on music nights, good big garden with pleasant terrace; great walks – the Grimspound one gives spectacular views *(LYM, J C Brittain-Long, Neil and Beverley Gardner, David and Nina Pugsley, M W Turner, Bob and Ann Westbrook)*

Woodbury [SY0187]

White Hart [3½ miles from M5 junction 30; A376, then B3179; Church St]: Unpretentious local with well kept Bass and Worthington BB, decent wines, good value food, plain public bar, comfortable quieter dining lounge, log fire; attractive small walled garden with aviary, skittle alley, nice spot by church in peaceful village *(Dr and Mrs M E Wilson)*

Woodbury Salterton [SY0189]

☆ *Diggers Rest* [3½ miles from M5 junction 30, off A3052 towards Sidmouth]: Interesting heavy-beamed thatched village pub with log fire, comfortable antique furnishings, dark oak Jacobean screen; has been a very long-standing main entry, with enjoyable food from sandwiches up, and well kept Bass and Sharps Doom Bar, but sold just as we go to press, and things may change after the departure of the charming landlady – though most of the helpful staff are staying on; children allowed away from serving bar, darts and dominoes in small public bar, views from terrace garden *(LYM)*

Woolacombe [SS4543]

Captain Jacks [West Rd]: Touristy place on site of 12th-c farm building, with well kept St Austell HSD and friendly staff; dogs allowed *(Eddie Edwards)*

Wrafton [SS4935]

Williams Arms [A361 just SE of Braunton]: Attractive modernised thatched family dining pub giving children free rein, two big bars divided into several cosy areas, interesting wall hangings, wide bar food choice, unlimited self-service carvery in separate restaurant, children's helpings, quick friendly helpful service, Bass and Courage, decent house wines; pool, darts, piped music, discreet TV; picnic-sets outside with play area and aviary *(Andy Marks, David Carr)*

Yealmpton [SX5751]

Volunteer [Fore St]: Surprisingly good interesting unusual food in simple pub with very helpful friendly staff, local beer; stairs up to lavatories; views from lovely garden *(Roy and Margaret Jones)*

Dorset

Pubs scoring particularly highly with readers in the last few months are the Royal Oak in Cerne Abbas (nice all round, hard-working licensees gaining a Food Award this year), the Anchor near Chideock (great seaside position), the picturesque Fox at Corscombe (good food using local sources), the Cock & Bottle at East Morden (very popular dining pub), the Museum Hotel at Farnham (interesting food, good wines), the Thimble at Piddlehinton (nice all-rounder, pretty garden), the attractive thatched Brace of Pheasants at Plush (good food), the Two Brewers in Shaftesbury (a new entry, good all round), the Digby Tap in Sherborne (a down-to-earth traditional town pub), the Cricketers at Shroton (another new entry, with new licensees doing interesting food, and a good range of real ales), the West Bay Hotel in West Bay (yet another new entry – good local fish and a nice atmosphere in this quite individual seaside pub), the Manor Hotel at West Bexington (hotel and restaurant, but very welcoming, with a nice bar), and the unspoilt and idiosyncratic Square & Compass looking towards the coast at Worth Matravers. The pub which gains our award of Dorset Dining Pub of the Year is the Brace of Pheasants at Plush. Dorset must go down as one of England's most dog-friendly counties (despite its muddy paths), with about three-quarters of the main entries allowing dogs in their bars. In the Lucky Dip section at the end of the chapter, pubs to note particularly are the White Hart at Bishop's Caundle, Saxon at Child Okeford, Dolphin in Gillingham, Pilot Boat in Lyme Regis, Crown at Marnhull, Marquis of Lorne at Nettlecombe, Smugglers at Osmington Mills, European at Piddletrenthide, Inn in the Park in Poole, Red Lion at Sturminster Marshall, Greyhound at Sydling St Nicholas, Old Ship and Riverhouse at Upwey and Wise Man at West Stafford. The Spyway at Askerswell, Shave Cross Inn, and Crown at Uploders are the most notable of several old favourites, normally main entries, which figure this year in the Lucky Dip while we wait to see how new licensees turn out in them. The county's drinks prices are if anything a shade more expensive than the national average. The main local brewers are Badger and Palmers; and it's worth looking out for beers from Quay and Poole (gaining from the 14p small brewery cut in beer duty).

BRIDPORT SY4692 Map 1

George £

South Street

The buoyant informal atmosphere in this happily well worn town pub gives an engaging appeal to its two bars. Dating from Georgian times, they're divided by a coloured tiled hallway, and the smaller one on the left is served by a hatch. There are nicely spaced ageing dining tables, country seats and wheelback chairs, big mats on tiled floors, usually flowers on the mahogany bar counter along one side, and a winter log fire. Enjoyable bar food, cheerfully whistled up from the end open-view kitchen in big helpings (one reader found this the only pub where he's ever needed a doggy bag for the butter) includes sandwiches (from £2.95), welsh rarebit (£3.50), garlic mushrooms, kedgeree or lentil and courgette bake (£3.95), pies such as rabbit or game (from £3.95), casserole or liver and bacon (£4.95), sausage and mash (£5.25) and lamb chops (£6.50); puddings (£2.95). Palmers IPA and Dorset Gold on handpump, and a decent wine list. *(Recommended by W W Burke, Jasmine Utteridge, Ann and Colin Hunt, Jean and Douglas Troup)*

Palmers ~ Tenants Jacqueline King and Ann Halliwell ~ Real ale ~ Bar food (not Sun) ~ (01308) 423187 ~ Children in family room ~ Dogs welcome ~ Open 10-11(9am for coffee); 12-10.30(9.30am for coffee) Sun

BURTON BRADSTOCK SY4889 Map 1

Anchor (food award)

B3157 SE of Bridport

This bustling little seafood pub is in an attractive village. Although there's a lunchtime snack menu with filled baguettes (from £2.95), baked ham and egg, mackerel or salmon fishcakes (£6.95), chicken and vegetable cajun stir fry (£7.95), and puddings (£3.95), most people come for the excellent fresh fish. Up on blackboards, the wide (though not cheap) selection could include mussels (£6.95), salmon (£13.95), scallops (£14.95), brill (£16.95), monkfish in parma ham (17.95), lobster thermidor (£24) and, good for an expensive treat, a shellfish platter (£50 for two); you can also choose from dishes such as peppered pork loin (£13.95) or leg of lamb or duck (£14.95); on Sunday they do a choice of roasts (£6.95). The restaurant is no smoking, and it's best to book well ahead at weekends. The lounge bar has pink plush cushioned wall seats and some fishy décor, and there's a public bar with big windows, more cushioned seats, usually a good crowd of locals and well kept Marstons Pedigree and Ushers Best on handpump; the Scottish landlord also has over 40 malt whiskies; darts, table skittles, bar billiards, TV, shove-ha'penny, cribbage and dominoes. *(Recommended by TOH, Basil Minson, Philip Bardswell, Comus and Sarah Elliott)*

InnSpired ~ Lease J R Plunkett ~ Real ale ~ Bar food ~ Restaurant ~ (01308) 897228 ~ Children welcome ~ Dogs allowed in bar ~ Open 11-3.30, 6-11; 11-11 Fri-Sun

CERNE ABBAS ST6601 Map 2

Royal Oak (food award) (wine award)

Long Street

The delicious bar food is a good reason for visiting this picturesque creeper-covered Tudor inn, though it's also pleasant to drop in just for a drink. Its stone walls and the ceilings are packed with an incredible range of small ornaments from local photographs to antique china, brasses and farm tools, and a nice touch is the candles and pots of herbs on the tables. The three flagstoned communicating rooms have sturdy oak beams, lots of shiny black panelling, an inglenook with an oven, and warm winter log fires. From the uncommonly long bar counter, they serve five well kept real ales on handpump (you can have a taste beforehand to see which one you like best): Butcombe, Greene King Old Speckled Hen and Wadworths IPA, with a couple of guests from small breweries such as Quay. They also have around 10 wines by the glass, and 15 malt whiskies. It's well run by the enthusiastic licensees, and the staff are friendly. Skilfully prepared using good ingredients, mostly local, the bar food includes sandwiches (from £2.95), soup (£3.25), fish and chips or ham, egg and chips (£6.25), lasagne (£7.25), around half a dozen tasty vegetarian dishes such as wild mushroom strudel or caribbean wellington (£8.65), and interesting specials (which include a good choice of seafood and game) such as seafood chowder or local rabbit saddle (£7.25), smoked pigeon breast with mashed potatoes and brie (£9.25) and portuguese hake fillet with sweet potato rösti and provençale sauce (£10.45). Popular home-made puddings include blackberry and apple crumble and crème brûlée; smaller meals are available for children. The enclosed back garden is very pleasant, with Purbeck stone terracing and cedarwood decking, comfortable chairs, and tables under cocktail parasols; it also has outdoor heaters. If the weather is nice, they may serve drinks and snacks out here on summer afternoons. *(Recommended by Paul Vickers, W W Burke, the Didler, Tracey and Stephen Groves, Jess and George Cowley, Stephen Bonarjee, Ian and Deborah Carrington)*

Free house ~ Licensees David and Janice Birch ~ Bar food (till 9.30 Mon-Sat) ~ (01300) 341797 ~ Children in eating area of bar ~ Dogs allowed in bar ~ Folk last Weds in month ~ Open 11.30(11 Sat)-3, 6-11; 12-3; 7-10.30 Sun

CHIDEOCK SY4292 Map 1

Anchor

Seatown signposted off A35 from Chideock

Nestling dramatically beneath the 188-metre (617-ft) Golden Cap pinnacle, this well liked pub is just a few steps from the cove beach. Seats and tables on the spacious front terrace are ideally placed for the lovely sea and cliff views, though to bag a place in summer you'll have to get here pretty early. Out of season, when the crowds have gone, the recently refurbished cosy little bars feel especially snug, with warming winter fires, some sea pictures and lots of interesting local photographs, a few fossils and shells, simple but comfortable seats around neat tables, and low white-planked ceilings; the family room and a further corner of the bar are no smoking, and the cats are friendly (one of them is over 20 years old). The sweet-natured black labrador is called Oliver. The friendly hard-working licensees have run this pub for more than 16 years, and there's a good welcoming atmosphere, even when it's really busy. Efficient helpful staff serve bar food which includes lunchtime sandwiches (from £2.25), filled baked potatoes (from £3.65), and ploughman's (from £4.65), as well as soup (£3.25), burgers (from £5.25), plaice and chips (£6.45), avocado bake (£6.95), home-made beef curry (£8.45), and daily specials including fresh fish and lobster from the beach; the puddings are home-made. Well kept Palmers 200, IPA, and Copper on handpump (under light blanket pressure in winter only), freshly squeezed orange juice, and a decent little wine list. Shove-ha'penny, cribbage, dominoes, and piped, mainly classical, music. There are fridges and toasters in the bedrooms (which are simple, and share a bathroom); you make your own breakfast while enjoying the sea views. The Dorset Coast path is nearby. *(Recommended by Doreen and Haydn Maddock, Heather and Dick Martin, Peter Meister, Val and Alan Green, Linda Norsworthy, John Mitchell, Tracey and Stephen Groves, Alan and Paula McCully, Robert Mitchell, Marianne and Peter Stevens, Peter Salmon, R and D Gray, Richard Martin, Lynn Sharpless, Bob Eardley, John and Vivienne Rice)*

Palmers ~ Tenants David and Sadie Miles ~ Real ale ~ Bar food (12-9.30 Whitsun-early Sept, not Sun evening Nov-Feb) ~ (01297) 489215 ~ Well behaved children welcome ~ Dogs allowed in bar ~ Jazz, folk and blues Sat evening, some summer Weds evenings ~ Open 11-11; 12-10.30 Sun; 11-2.30, 6-11 winter; closed 25 Dec evening ~ Bedrooms: £25/£50

CHRISTCHURCH SZ1696 Map 2

Fishermans Haunt

Winkton: B3347 Ringwood road nearly 3 miles N of Christchurch

This big, well run hotel is not far from the New Forest. The very neat bar, partly no smoking, is divided into various areas, with brocaded chairs around tables, stools at a pine-panelled bar counter, and a few pictures on brown wallpaper. At one end big windows look out on the neat front garden, and there are attractive views of the River Avon from the restaurant (open Saturday and Sunday only). Well kept Bass, Gales HSB and GB and Ringwood Fortyniner on handpump, and lots of country wines. The straightforward bar food is reasonably priced, and includes sandwiches (from £2.60; toasties from £3.10), filled baked potatoes (from £4.55), ham, egg and chips (£5.75), steak and kidney pie, or lasagne (£6.25), and a couple of specials such as curry (£6.50) and sausage and pasta bake (£6.75). The quiet back garden has tables among the shrubs, roses and other flowers; disabled lavatories. Readers tell us this is a pleasant place to stay. More reports please. *(Recommended by Sue and Mike Todd, W W Burke, Ian Phillips)*

Gales ~ Manager Kevin A Crowley ~ Real ale ~ Bar food ~ Restaurant ~ (01202) 477283 ~ Children welcome ~ Dogs allowed in bar and bedrooms ~ Open 10.30-2.30, 5-11; 10-11 Sat; 12-10.30 Sun ~ Bedrooms: £49.50B/£66B

COLEHILL SU0302 Map 2

Barley Mow

From roundabout junction of A31 Ferndown bypass and B3073 Wimborne road, follow Colehill signpost up Middlehill Road, pass Post Office, and at church turn right into Colehill Lane; OS Sheet 195 map reference 032024

This fine thatched former drovers' cottage is especially attractive in summer, when colourful flowers in tubs and hanging baskets are set off vividly against the whitewash. Sheltered by oak trees, there's a pleasant, enclosed big lawn at the back with a boules pitch. Inside, the cosy low beamed main bar has a good winter fire in the huge brick inglenook, attractively moulded oak panelling, some Hogarth prints and a relaxed dining atmosphere; the cat is called Misty. A no smoking extension has another log fire; there's piped music and a fruit machine. The home-made bar food is served generously by attentive staff, and includes soup (£2.50), sandwiches (from £3.95), prawn cocktail (£4.95), ham and egg, salmon fishcakes or ploughman's (£5.50), mushroom crumble or turkey, gammon and leek pie (£6.95), smoked haddock with creamy leek sauce and grilled cheese (£7.95), chicken piri piri (£8.50) and rump steak (£9.95), and puddings such as chocolate fudge cake (£3.75); specials could include tuna steak (£9.95) and cajun chicken (£8.50). Well kept Badger Best, Tanglefoot and a seasonal ale on handpump, and a dozen fruit wines. There are good walks nearby. More reports please. *(Recommended by Colin Draper)*

Badger ~ Manager Bruce Cichocki ~ Real ale ~ Bar food ~ (01202) 882140 ~ Children allowed in family dining area ~ Dogs allowed in bar ~ Open 11-3, 5.30-11; 12-3, 7-10.30 Sun

CORSCOMBE ST5105 Map 2

Fox

On outskirts, towards Halstock

In a lovely country setting, this picturesque old thatched pub with roses over the door serves really good food. They source their supplies carefully using the best local produce (free range and organic where possible), and interesting, though not cheap, dishes might be roast augergines baked with mozzarella, garlic, tomato and cream (£4.95), lovely fish soup with cod, mussels and prawns or warm pigeon breast and bacon salad (£5.50), chicken in a creamy sauce with celery and red pepper (£8.25), duck breast with red wine and cranberry sauce (£13.50) and monkfish fillets with red pepper salsa (£16). Keep your eyes open for the specials, often delicious: grilled sardines with chilli, lemon and coriander dressing (£5.50), salmon and haddock kedgeree (£8.95), perhaps roast guinea fowl stuffed with goats cheese with creamy mashed potatoes (£12.95); they also do baguettes (from £4). As well as making their own ice cream and sorbets, they produce tempting puddings such as treacle tart or plum crumble (£3.50). A flagstoned room on the right has lots of lovely polished copper pots, pans and teapots, harness hanging from the beams, small Leech hunting prints and Snaffles prints, Spy cartoons of fox hunting gentlemen, a long scrubbed pine table, and two open fires with large inglenooks. In the left-hand room (partly no smoking) there are built-in settles, candles on the blue-and-white gingham tablecloths or barrel tables, an assortment of chairs, lots of horse prints, antlers on the beams, two glass cabinets with a couple of stuffed owls in each, and an L-shaped wall settle by the inglenook fireplace; darts, dominoes and backgammon. The no smoking dining room (which is open when they're busy and for winter breakfast) has an Aga, pine cupboards, a welsh dresser, and lots of personal memorabilia. In summer, breakfast is taken in the conservatory with its maturing vine, orchids, and huge oak table. They've a very good thoughtful wine list, alongside well kept Exmoor Ale and Fullers London Pride and a summer guest such as Exmoor Fox on handpump; also local cider and home-made elderflower cordial, damson vodka, and sloe gin. There are seats across the quiet village lane on a lawn by the little stream, and this is a nice area for walks. You'll probably meet their sociable black labrador Bramble, her friend Cracker and her son Rayburn. The Acorn at Evershot is under the same management. *(Recommended by Mr and Mrs Bruce Jamieson, C J Langdon, Jane Legate, David Frost, Ron*

Shelton, Mrs J H S Lang, J Hale, Pat and Robert Watt, John and Jane Hayter, W W Burke, Simon and Jane Williams, Ann and Colin Hunt, Tracey and Stephen Groves, R M Corlett, Peter Neate, S G N Bennett, Marianne and Peter Stevens, Miss G Irving, R Styles, OPUS)

Free house ~ Licensees Martyn and Susie Lee ~ Real ale ~ Bar food (till 9.30 Fri and Sat) ~ Restaurant ~ (01935) 891330 ~ Well behaved children ~ Open 12-2.30, 7-(10.30 Sun)11; closed 25 Dec ~ Bedrooms: £55.75B/£65(£80B)

EAST CHALDON SY7983 Map 2

Sailors Return

Village signposted from A352 Wareham—Dorchester; from village green, follow Dorchester, Weymouth signpost; note that the village is also known as Chaldon Herring; OS Sheet 194 map reference 790834

Close to Lulworth Cove, this well extended thatched pub is tracked down by a lot of people, especially in fine weather, even though it's in an isolated spot. Picnic-sets, benches and log seats on the grass in front look down over cow pastures to the village, and you can wander to the interesting little nearby church or enjoy a downland walk from the pub. From nearby West Chaldon, a bridleway leads across to join the Dorset Coast Path by the National Trust cliffs above Ringstead Bay. The convivial flagstoned bar still keeps much of its original country-tavern character, while the newer part has unfussy furnishings, old notices for decoration, and open beams showing the roof above. They serve straightforward bar food, and the dining area has solid old tables in nooks and corners; service is good even when it's busy. Well kept Hampshire Strongs Best and Ringwood and around four guests such as Badger Tanglefoot, Hop Back Summer Lightning, Marstons Pedigree and Shepherd Neame Spitfire on handpump, country wines, and several malt whiskies; darts, cribbage, dominoes and piped music. *(Recommended by Marjorie and David Lamb, R J Davies, Pat and Robert Watt, Joan and Michel Hooper-Immins, Brian and Bett Cox, Paul and Penny Rampton, W W Burke, Paul Vickers, Charlie Harris)*

Free house ~ Licensees Mike and Sue Pollard ~ Real ale ~ Bar food (12-2, 6.30-9; 12-9 summer) ~ Restaurant ~ (01305) 853847 ~ Children in restaurant ~ Dogs allowed in bar ~ Open 11-11; 12-10.30 Sun; 11-2.30, 6.30-11 winter; closed 25 Dec

EAST KNIGHTON SY8185 Map 2

Countryman

Just off A352 Dorchester—Wareham; OS Sheet 194 map reference 811857

This big bustling pub is welcoming to families, with play equipment in the garden, toys inside, and now baby-changing facilities too. There's a buoyant atmosphere in the neat and comfortable long main bar, with its mix of tables, wheelback chairs and comfortable sofas, and fires at either end. This room opens into several other smaller areas, including a no smoking family room, a games bar with pool and darts, and a carvery (£12.95 for a good roast and pudding; not Monday, nor lunchtime on Tuesday). They serve well kept real ales such as Courage Best and Directors, Greene King Old Speckled Hen and Ringwood Best and Old Thumper on handpump, as well as farm cider, and a good choice of wines; piped music. Generous tasty dishes include sandwiches or filled rolls (from £2.65), home-made soup (£3.25), omelettes (from £4.50), ploughman's (from £5.25), lemon and pepper chicken breast or fried plaice (£7.95), and a handful of daily specials such as home-made quiche (£6.95) and dover sole fried with herbs and lemon (£15.75), and the home-made puddings include apple pie and treacle tart (from £2.95); best to book on Sunday, when they have two lunchtime sittings. They also do children's meals (from £3.25). Disabled lavatories are a new addition here. *(Recommended by Mike and Heather Watson, Peter Neate, Jeff and Wendy Williams, Miss G Irving, R Styles, Dr Paull Khan, Joyce and Maurice Cottrell, Ian and Deborah Carrington, Guy Masdin, Brian and Bett Cox, Charles Moncreiffe, MDN, M N Pledger, Rod Stoneman, OPUS)*

Free house ~ Licensees Jeremy and Nina Evans ~ Real ale ~ Bar food (till 9.30) ~ Restaurant ~ (01305) 852666 ~ Children welcome ~ Dogs welcome ~ Open 11 (12 Sun)-2.30, 6-11; closed 25 Dec ~ Bedrooms: £48S/£65S

EAST MORDEN SY9195 Map 2

Cock & Bottle

B3075 between A35 and A31 W of Poole

For an enjoyable meal in pleasant surroundings, this pub is a reliable and popular choice. Warm and welcoming, it's divided into several communicating areas (mostly laid out for dining) with heavy rough beams, some stripped ceiling boards, squared panelling, a mix of old furnishings in various sizes and degrees of antiquity, small Victorian prints and some engaging bric-a-brac. There's a roaring log fire, and intimate corners each with just a couple of tables, and although the emphasis is on dining there's a pubby wood-floored public bar with piped music, a fruit machine, and a sensibly placed darts alcove. This in turn leads on to yet another individually furnished dining room. Booking is recommended if you do want to eat, and, as well as lunchtime ploughman's (£5.50) and filled baguettes (from £5.55), the good changing bar menu might include wild mushroom tartlet with mustard hollandaise (£5.25), duck spring rolls with chilli jam (£5.75), grilled plaice with parsley butter (£8.95), pheasant breast braised in cider, apple and chestnut sauce (£10.95), pork with a stilton and apple crust with mustard sauce (£11.25), and puddings such as soft chocolate pudding with raspberry cream, or coffee or Tia Maria crème brûlée (£3.95); children's dishes (£3.50). Most of the restaurant is no smoking, and they have some disabled facilities. Well kept Badger Best, K&B and Tanglefoot on handpump, and a good choice of decent house wines including half a dozen by the glass; service is pleasant, though when it's busy food might take a while to come. There are a few picnic-sets outside, a garden area, and an adjoining field with a nice pastoral outlook. *(Recommended by W W Burke, M G Hart, Rod Stoneman, Mr and Mrs Thomas, Mr and Mrs S Oxenbury, W A Evershed, Lord Sandhurst, Howard and Margaret Buchanan, Dr Phil Putwain, Colin Draper, Ian Phillips)*

Badger ~ Tenant Peter Meadley ~ Real ale ~ Bar food (12-2, 6(7 Sun)-9) ~ Restaurant ~ (01929) 459238 ~ Children in restaurant ~ Dogs welcome ~ Open 11-3, 6-11; 12-3, 7-10.30 Sun

EVERSHOT ST5704 Map 2

Acorn

Village signposted from A37 8 miles S of Yeovil

Handily open all day, this prettily placed former coaching inn (like its sister-pub, the Fox at Corscombe) puts emphasis on its imaginative restaurant-style food. In a nice village with lots of good surrounding walks, the pub is full of character, with thoughtful touches and helpful pleasant service. There's a very short pubby bar menu with good sandwiches (made with bread from the village bakery) and filled baguettes (from £3.50), ploughman's (from £4.50) and burger and chips (£6.95), but you'll probably be tempted by the more imaginative specials which might include marinated pigeon breast and bacon salad or fish soup (£5.50), vegetable gateau with chive butter sauce (£7.95), local game casserole with port and junipers (£10.85), cajun spiced chicken breast with lime yoghurt dressing (£11.95), turbot with crème fraîche and cherry tomatoes (£16.50) and bass with fennel and chilli salsa (£16.95); puddings such as lemon tart and sticky toffee pudding (£3.50). The dining room and restaurant are no smoking. The Hardy Bar has oak panelling and two Hamstone fireplaces carved by local craftsmen, a fine carved and gilded oak sconce, pictures by local artists, re-upholstered chairs, and copies of the inn's deeds going back to the 17th c. Another lounge has a woodburning stove. Their well kept beers might be Butcombe Bitter, Fullers London Pride and Otter Bright on handpump, and they have home-made elderflower cordial, damson vodka and sloe gin, and an interesting wine list; pool, darts, skittle alley, dominoes, cribbage, backgammon, chess, and juke box. Outside, there's a terrace with dark oak furniture. The pub is immortalised as the Sow & Acorn in Thomas Hardy's *Tess of the d'Urbervilles*. *(Recommended by Marianne and Peter Stevens, John Saville, Dr Paull Khan, Peter Neate, W A Evershed, R J Davies, Ann and Colin Hunt, S G N Bennett, Richard and Jean Green)*

Free house ~ Licensees Martyn and Susie Lee ~ Real ale ~ Bar food (till 9.30 Fri/Sat) ~

Restaurant ~ (01935) 83228 ~ Children welcome ~ Dogs allowed in bedrooms ~ Open 12-11(10.30 Sun) ~ Bedrooms: £60B

FARNHAM ST9515 Map 2

Museum Hotel

Village signposted off A354 Blandford Forum—Salisbury

Effortlessly civilised, the various areas of this attractively converted 17th-c thatched building have a bright, fresh feel thanks both to the cheery yellow paint on the walls and the plentiful windows. The flagstoned bar has a big inglenook fireplace, light beams and good comfortably cushioned furnishings; there's a little posy on every table. To the right is a dining room with plates on an antique dresser, while off to the left is a cosier hunt-themed room, with a very jolly 3-D tableau and a seemingly sleeping stuffed fox curled in a corner. Another room feels rather like a contemporary version of a baronial hall, soaring up to a high glass ceiling, with dozens of antlers and a stag's head looking down on to a long wooden table and church-style pews. It leads to an outside terrace with more wooden tables. The choice of wines is excellent, and the three real ales, which come from independent local brewers, could be Exmoor Gold, Hop Back Summer Lightning and Ringwood Best. Promptly served by professional staff, the very good, interesting bar food might include red pepper and tomato soup (£3.95), duck confit terrine, celeriac remoulade and brioche (£5.95), roast pork belly with lentil du puy and red wine (£9.95), lamb shank with buttered spinach and sauté potatoes (£10.25), and john dory done with capers and basil (£13.95), with puddings such as dark chocolate mousse and apple and cinnamon crumble with honey (from £4.95). Wherever possible they use local and organic produce, and make their own bread, jams, chutney and marmalades. The attractive restaurant is open only for Friday and Saturday dinner and Sunday lunch; it's a good idea to book. Please note that you have to give them five days' warning for a bedroom cancellation or you'll be charged in full. *(Recommended by John and Vivienne Rice, Peter Neate, J R Ringrose, W W Burke; also in the* Good Hotel Guide*)*

Free house ~ Licensees Vicky Elliot and Mark Stephenson ~ Real ale ~ Bar food (till 3 Sun) ~ Restaurant (Fri and Sat evening and Sun lunch) ~ (01725) 516261 ~ Well behaved children over 8 in eating area of bar ~ Dogs allowed in bar and bedrooms ~ Open 12-3, 6-11(7-10.30 Sun); closed 25 Dec, and evenings 26 Dec and 1 Jan ~ Bedrooms: £55B/£85B

FURZEHILL SU0102 Map 2

Stocks

Village signposted off B3078 N of Wimborne Minster

Although it's about to gain a new manager, this welcoming pub, popular with older customers, should continue to satisfy readers, as the plan is to continue much as before – including their good value two-course lunch on Tuesdays and Thursdays (£5.50). The rest of their popular menu includes home-made soup (£2.95), lunchtime ciabatta sandwiches (from £2.95), breaded plaice (£6.95), home-made curry or mushroom and stilton bake (£7.95), home-made steak and ale pie or seafood mornay (£8.95), and steaks (from £9.95), with puddings (from £2.95); most of the restaurant is no smoking. The thatched part of this extended place has the most character: two long rooms divided into rather snug sections, each with an open fire (brick in one and stone in the other), plush wall and window seats and stools, and timbered ochre walls. A dining area leads off here, with lots of copper and earthenware, an area with nets and a crab pot, and a big wall mirror cleverly creating an illusion of even more space. There are other dining areas with more mirrors, solid farmhouse chairs and tables, low ceilings and soft lighting, and good New Forest black and white photographs, old prints, farm tools, hay sleds, and so forth – even a Rayburn range in one place; piped music and darts. They serve well kept Ringwood Best and Fortyniner on handpump; as so often, there's a tale that the original cellar had a tunnel which came out in Smugglers Lane. There are some green plastic seats out in front, and solid teak furniture under a fairy-lit arbour by the car park at the back. *(Recommended by Nick and Pam Hancock, Peter Neate)*

Scottish Courage ~ Real ale ~ Bar food (12-2, 6-9.30; 12-9 Sun) ~ Restaurant ~ (01202) 882481 ~ Children welcome ~ Dogs allowed in bar ~ Open 11-11; 12-10.30 Sun

GODMANSTONE SY6697 Map 2

Smiths Arms £

A352 N of Dorchester

Measuring only 12 by 4 metres, this old-fashioned 15th-c thatched inn is one of the smallest pubs in the country. There are just six tables in the quaint little bar, which is traditionally furnished with long wooden stools and chunky tables, antique waxed and polished small pews and an elegant little high-backed settle, all tucked against the walls. There are National Hunt racing pictures and some brass plates on the walls, and an open fire; dominoes and cribbage. The home-made food is simple but tasty, and might include sandwiches (from £2.10), giant sausage (£3.75), ploughman's (from £3.90), quiche or chilli (£4.95), and daily specials such as curried prawn lasagne or steak and kidney pie (£5.45), and puddings (from £2.25). Seats and tables are very pleasantly set out on a crazy-paved terrace and on the grassy mound by the narrow River Cerne. There's a nice walk over Cowdon Hill to the River Piddle. Note the limited opening times. *(Recommended by the Didler, Peter Neate)*

Free house ~ Licensees John and Linda Foster ~ Bar food (12-3.30) ~ No credit cards ~ (01300) 341236 ~ Open 11-5.30; closed Nov-Mar

PIDDLEHINTON SY7197 Map 1

Thimble

B3143

Attractively floodlit at night, the flower-filled garden of this pretty partly thatched streamside pub is a pleasant place for lunch too. Simpler than the exterior suggests, the neatly kept low-beamed bar is nicely spacious, so that in spite of attracting quite a lot of people in the summer, it never feels too crowded. There's a handsome stone fireplace, a deep glassed-over well, and a collection of thimbles. Popular reasonably priced bar food served generously might include home-made soup (£2.55), sandwiches (from £2.35), filled baked potatoes (from £3.30), deep-fried whitebait or tasty home-made chicken liver pâté (£4), battered haddock (£5.80), steak and kidney pie (£6.50), and steak (from £9.95), with daily specials such as lasagne or chicken curry (£5.95), and grilled venison chops with cranberry and red wine sauce (£7.25), and puddings such as damson crumble (£3.90). They do a Sunday roast (£6.10) and have a children's menu (from £2.20). The staff are friendly and helpful even when it's busy. Well kept Badger Best and Tanglefoot, Palmers Copper and IPA, and Ringwood Old Thumper on handpump, along with quite a few malt whiskies and farm cider. Darts, shove-ha'penny, dominoes, cribbage, and piped music. *(Recommended by Greta and Christopher Wells, Joan and Michel Hooper-Immins, Mr and Mrs Thomas, H D Wharton, Pat and Robert Watt, Peter Bell, Michael and Ann Cole, Tony and Wendy Hobden)*

Free house ~ Licensees N R White and V J Lanfear ~ Real ale ~ Bar food ~ Restaurant ~ (01300) 348270 ~ Children welcome ~ Dogs welcome ~ Open 12-2.30, 7-11(10.30 Sun); closed 25 Dec and evening 26 Dec

PLUSH ST7102 Map 2

Brace of Pheasants 🍴

Village signposted from B3143 N of Dorchester at Piddletrenthide

Dorset Dining Pub of the Year

One couple described a visit to this handsome 16th-c thatched pub as the highlight of their holiday. Charmingly placed in a fold of hills surrounding the Piddle Valley, it used to be two cottages and the village smithy. The comfortably airy beamed bar has

good solid tables, windsor chairs, fresh flowers, a huge heavy-beamed inglenook at one end with cosy seating inside, and a good warming log fire at the other. There's also a decent-sized garden and terrace with a lawn sloping up towards a rockery. From an interesting menu, the very good food could include goats cheese with caramelised pear (£5.25), twice-baked smoked haddock and cheddar soufflé (£4.75), baked salmon with a garlic and herb crust, pork tenderloin medallions with stilton and sherry sauce or delicious pheasant with calvados and apple cream (£10.95), and ginger and honey roasted bass with stir-fried vegetables (£12.50), with tempting daily specials such as venison and orange pie (£7.75), calves liver with bacon and onions (£8.75), and seared salmon with chilli oil and lemon (£10.75). We've heard very good things about the home-made puddings, which could include chocolate and rum pot or raspberry and cream cheese tart (£3.75). The restaurant and family room are no smoking. They serve well kept Fullers London Pride and a guest such as Butcombe Bitter tapped from the cask. The friendly black labrador is called Bodger, and the golden retriever Molly. The pub lies alongside Plush Brook, and an attractive bridleway behind goes to the left of the woods and over to Church Hill.
(Recommended by the Didler, B H and J I Andrews, Mike and Sue Loseby, Joan and Michel Hooper-Immins, Glenys and John Roberts, W W Burke, Mrs Hilarie Taylor, Michael and Ann Cole, Rod Stoneman, Dr and Mrs J F Head, Phyl and Jack Street, Simon Mighall, Pat and RobertWatt, OPUS)

Free house ~ Licensees Jane and Geoffrey Knights ~ Real ale ~ Bar food (not winter Mon) ~ Restaurant ~ (01300) 348357 ~ Children in restaurant and family room ~ Dogs allowed in bar ~ Open 12-2.30, 7-11; 12-3, 7-10.30 Sun; closed Winter Mon and 25 Dec

PUNCKNOWLE SY5388 Map 2

Crown

Church Street; village signposted off B3157 Bridport—Abbotsbury; or reached off A35 via Chilcombe

A nice place for a drink after a walk, the heavily beamed interior of this comfortable 16th-c thatched and flint inn has welcoming log fires in big stone fireplaces. There's a pleasantly informal mix of furnishings, darts and table skittles in the neatly kept rambling public bar, with a comfortable no smoking family room opening off. The inviting stripped stone lounge bar has red plush banquettes and stools, and there are paintings by local artists for sale. The staff are friendly and cheerful. The reasonably priced menu is quite a draw: it includes generous sandwiches (from £1.70), home-made soup (£2.60), filled baked potatoes (from £3.95), faggots, chips and peas (£4.30), Quorn, tomato and garlic casserole with red wine (£6.40), home-made steak, kidney and Guinness pie (£6.85), trout with toasted almonds (£7.85), and rump steak (£9.90), and puddings such as coconut and cherry cake (£2.80); children's meals (£3.20). Well kept Palmers Copper, IPA and 200 on handpump, and country wines. There's a nice view from the partly paved back garden, which has tables under two venerable fairy-lit apple trees. Prettily set opposite a partly Norman church (and its rookery), the pub was originally built as a home for the monks; the village is pronounced Punnell. *(Recommended by Lynn Sharpless, Bob Eardley, W W Burke, Ian and Deborah Carrington, David Carr, Pat and Tony Martin, Elizabeth Pickard, Ian and Joan Blackwell, Ann and Colin Hunt, Chris Mawson, W A Evershed, Alan and Paula McCully, OPUS)*

Palmers ~ Tenant Michael Lawless ~ Real ale ~ Bar food (not 25 Dec) ~ No credit cards ~ (01308) 897711 ~ Children in family room ~ Dogs allowed in bar and bedrooms ~ Open 11-3, 6.30(7 in winter)-11; 12-3, 7-10.30 Sun; closed 25 Dec evening ~ Bedrooms: /£42(£46S)

Post Office address codings confusingly give the impression that some pubs are in Dorset, when they're really in Somerset (which is where we list them).

SHAFTESBURY ST8622 Map 2

Two Brewers £

St James Street, 150 yards from bottom of Gold Hill

Down steep and famously photogenic Gold Hill (remember those Hovis TV advertisements?), this proper pub combines comfort, good drink, good value food and a friendly atmosphere. The open-plan turkey-carpeted bar is well divided for a cosily chatty feel, with plush banquettes in small bays, masses of decorative plates running along a delft shelf with more on the walls, and two nicely carved modern fireplaces. A good collection of pump clips shows how often they change the two guest beers, alongside their particularly well kept Courage Best and Directors, Greene King Ruddles County and Theakstons XB on handpump; the house wines are good value. The very wide choice of low-priced fresh and enjoyable bar food includes sandwiches (from £1.55), soup (£1.95), ploughman's (from £3.75), vegetarian specials or ham and eggs (£4.75), pasta dishes or meat pie (£4.95), a casserole such as minty lamb (£5.25), and a huge mixed grill (£8.95). They do cheap children's helpings of most dishes, as well as the usual burgers, fish fingers and so forth; good puddings such as apple cake or hot chocolate fudge cake (£2.45) and Sunday roasts. The back eating area, with stripped pews, lots of engravings, prints and other pictures, is no smoking. The landlord is chatty and welcoming, and service is good; they have a skittle alley. The attractive good-sized back garden has lovely views from its picnic-sets, some under cocktail parasols. There is a companion Two Brewers, over in Street (Leigh Road). *(Recommended by Dr and Mrs M E Wilson, Ron Shelton, John and Joan Calvert, Colin and Janet Roe)*

Free house ~ Licensees Richard and Maggie Pearce ~ Real ale ~ Bar food (12-2, 6-9(10 Fri/Sat); 12-2, 7-9 Sun) ~ (01747) 854211 ~ Children welcome ~ Open 11-3, 6-11; 12-3, 7-10.30 Sun

SHERBORNE ST6316 Map 2

Digby Tap £

Cooks Lane; park in Digby Road and walk round corner

Handy for the glorious golden stone abbey, this old-fashioned town ale house pleases everyone who likes their pubs down-to-earth. It has four or five interesting real ales on handpump, and they work through around 20 different beers a week, most from fairly local brewers such as Cottage, Exmoor, Goldfinch and Otter. There's a relaxed and friendly atmosphere in the simple stone-flagged main bar, which attracts a good mix of customers; several small games rooms have pool, cribbage, fruit machine, TV, and piped music. The enjoyable food, like the beer, is very reasonably priced. In huge helpings, it includes tasty soup (£1.95), sandwiches or baguettes (from £1.75, toasted from £1.80), filled baked potatoes (from £2.80) and lasagne, sausage casserole, liver and bacon and steak, kidney and mushroom pie (£3.95). There are some seats outside. *(Recommended by B H and J I Andrews, Stephen, Julie and Hayley Brown, W W Burke, Evelyn and Derek Walter, R M Corlett, Dennis Jenkin, Dr and Mrs M E Wilson, Basil Minson, Mick Simmons)*

Free house ~ Licensees Peter Lefevre and Nick Whigham ~ Real ale ~ Bar food (not evenings, not Sun) ~ No credit cards ~ (01935) 813148 ~ Children welcome in eating area of bar at lunchtime ~ Open 11-2.30, 5.30-11; 11-3, 6-11 Sat; 12-3, 7-10.30 Sun

SHROTON ST8512 Map 2

Cricketers

Off A350 N of Blandford (village also called Iwerne Courtney); follow signs

This prettily set red brick pub, facing the peaceful village green, has been given quite a boost since the Cowies took it over in 2001. Mrs Cowie shares the cooking with Tom the new head chef and his team: besides good baguettes (blue vinney with bacon is £4.75, cajun chicken with mango mayonnaise is £4.95), filled baked potatoes (from £3.95), lots of home-made soups and light meals from the blackboard such as red onion and goats cheese tartlet (£4.50), beetroot risotto with toasted pecans, feta and watercress or hoisin duck tortilla wrap with cucumber and spring onion (£4.75), and oak-smoked sausages with mustard mash and onion gravy (£4.95), there are main dishes such as venison pie (£6.95), red mullet with cheese sauce (£7.95), gammon and egg (£8.25), and lamb hock in red wine and wild mushroom sauce (£8.95). The comfortable back restaurant has been updated, with a fresh neutral décor; the bright divided bar, with a big stone fireplace, alcoves and cricketing memorabilia, has well kept changing ales such as Brakspears PA, Greene King IPA, Abbot and Old Speckled Hen, Otter Bright, Ringwood True Glory, Charles Wells Bombardier and Youngs Waggledance served from pumps made into little cricket bats, eight wines by the glass and quite a few malt whiskies. Mr Cowie is welcoming and attentive, as are his neatly uniformed staff. A sizeable games area has pool, darts and a fruit machine, and there's a no smoking area on the way to the restaurant. The attractive secluded garden, with big sturdy tables under cocktail parasols and some outdoor heaters, has a fairy-lit clematis arbour, well tended shrubs, and a well stocked – and well used – herb garden by the kitchen door. We've not yet had reports from readers on the single well equipped bedroom, which opens on to the garden. *(Recommended by Pat and Robert Watt, B and K Hypher, Dr A Abrahams, J Conti-Ramsden)*

Free house ~ Licensees George and Carol Cowie ~ Real ale ~ Bar food ~ Restaurant ~ (01258) 860421 ~ Children in eating area of bar and restaurant ~ Open 11.30-2.30, 6.30-11; 12-3, 6.30-10.30 Sun ~ Bedrooms: /£80S

STRATTON SY6593 Map 2

Saxon Arms

Village signposted off A37 bypass NW of Dorchester; The Square

Although it's thatched and made with traditional materials such as oak, flint and natural stone, don't be fooled: this well run and welcoming pub was built only in 2001. The bright open-plan room has plenty of space, with a fireplace and drinking area to the left, and a large no smoking dining section on the right. The floor is made with big flagstones, and there are smart curtains, fresh flowers on the light oak tables, and comfortable cushioned settles. Readers enjoy the reasonably priced food, which includes soup (£2.75), filled ciabatta or baked potatoes (from £3.50), prawn cocktail (£4.25), deep-fried camembert (£4.50), chicken, bacon and tarragon pie (£6.75), roasted vegetable lasagne (£7.25), breaded scampi (£7.50) and sirloin steak (£10.25), with daily specials such as beef stroganoff (£8.50), roast duck with cumberland sauce (£9.95), and scallop and tiger prawn brochette (£10.25), while puddings could be apple and ginger sponge with custard or almond and apricot strudel (£3.50). Friendly staff serve well kept Fullers London Pride, Palmers IPA, Saxon Ale and a guest such as Timothy Taylors Landlord on handpump; the very reasonably priced wine list includes about eight wines by the glass, and there are a dozen malt whiskies; soft piped music, cribbage, dominoes, table skittles. The chocolate labrador is called Ed. There are lots of tables outside, overlooking a clutch of similarly well constructed new buildings and the village green. *(Recommended by Brian and Bett Cox, Martyn and Nicola Wyatt, Dr C D and Mrs S M Burbridge, Mr and Mrs J R Lyons)*

Free house ~ Licensees Ian and Anne Barrett ~ Real ale ~ Bar food (11.30-2, 6.30-9) ~ (01305) 260020 ~ Children in eating area of bar ~ Dogs allowed in bar ~ Open 11-2.30, 5.30(6 Sat)-11; 12-3, 6.30-10.30 Sun

STURMINSTER NEWTON ST7814 Map 2

Swan

Town signposted off A357 Blandford—Sherborne, via B3092; Market Place

This friendly 18th-c coaching inn is handily open all day. Traditional and very neatly kept, the busy beamed bar has a particularly interesting brick fireplace at one end, its tiny grate sitting incongruously next to an old safe. Close by is a comfortable green leatherette sofa, as well as wooden corner seats, a table with newspapers to read, and the odd stuffed fish or bird in glass cases. Elsewhere there's lots of exposed brickwork, including sturdy brick pillars dividing the room, plenty of panelling, and a good number of tables leading through into a couple of eating areas. Like everything else at the bar, the well kept Badger Best and Tanglefoot have their prices displayed with admirable clarity; fruit machine, TV and soft piped music. There are many more tables out on a terrace and lawn behind. As well as sandwiches (from £2.45, baguettes from £2.95) and filled baked potatoes (from £4.45), the good value bar food, served in generous helpings, might include spicy cajun shrimps (£3.75), breaded plaice or lasagne (£5.95), steak and kidney or chicken, gammon and leek pie (£6.85), and tasty steaks (from £9.45), with specials such as spinach, mushroom and pepper parcel (£6.75), gammon steak (£8.75) and roasted duck breast with port, cranberry and orange sauce (£10.75); service is polite and friendly (though it may slow at busy times). The particularly nice bedrooms are individually decorated, and they go down in price after you've stayed the first night. More reports please. *(Recommended by Andrew York)*

Badger ~ Tenants Roger and Marion Hiron ~ Real ale ~ Bar food (10-9(8.30 Sun), not 25 Dec) ~ Restaurant ~ (01258) 472208 ~ Children in restaurant ~ Dogs allowed in bar ~ Open 10-11; 11.30-10.30 Sun ~ Bedrooms: £44.95S(£44.95B)/£59.95S (£59.95B)

TARRANT MONKTON ST9408 Map 2

Langton Arms

Village signposted from A354, then head for church

Whether you're a family looking for a good lunch or a dog-walker after a quick well kept pint, this pretty 17th-c thatched pub owned by a farming couple should enjoyably fit the bill (and your dog may be lucky enough to be offered a free sausage). Alongside Hop Back Best they serve four quickly changing guests from interesting small brewers such as Cannon Royall, Federation, Moor and Tring on handpump. The fairly simple beamed bar has a huge inglenook fireplace, settles, stools at the counter and other mixed dark furniture, and the public bar has a juke box, darts, pool, a fruit machine, TV, cribbage, and dominoes; piped music. There's a no smoking bistro restaurant in an attractively reworked barn, and the skittle alley doubles as a no smoking family room during the day. The interesting, though mostly traditional, bar menu includes home-made soup (£2.95), four-bean stew or broccoli, brie and mushroom lasagne (£6.25), braised wild rabbit with tarragon and mustard (£7.20), game pie with red wine and redcurrant gravy, breaded scampi or pigeon breast in cranberry and red wine sauce (£7.95), and puddings such as treacle tart or local ice creams (from £3); specials such as turkey faggots in redcurrant and apple gravy (£6.45) and pork fillet with mushrooms in a thai sauce (£7.95). The garden has a very good wood-chip play area, the village is pretty, and there are good nearby walks. They hold two beer festivals a year. *(Recommended by John Robertson, Ron Shelton, T J and J D Fitzgerald, Dr Paull Khan, Ian Wilson)*

Free house ~ Licensees Barbara and James Cossins ~ Real ale ~ Bar food (all day Sat and Sun, not 25 Dec) ~ Restaurant ~ (01258) 830225 ~ Children welcome in family room and restaurant ~ Dogs allowed in bar and bedrooms ~ Open 11.30-11; 12-10.30 Sun ~ Bedrooms: £50B/£70B

WEST BAY SY4690 Map 1

West Bay

Station Road

A find for this low-key resort: in the three years they've been here, the friendly licensees have brought this seaside pub's food so firmly into the reckoning that even on a winter midweek evening it can get very busy with those locals who are in the know. Making the most of freshly landed seafood (they always have at least 10 fish dishes available), and using local suppliers wherever possible, the interesting menu might include good crab sandwiches (£4.25), salmon fishcakes (£9.50), halibut steak with a welsh rarebit crust and red onion salsa or monkfish fillets fried with cumin with green bean salad and a tomato and crème fraîche dip (£13.95). They also have a good choice of dishes for those who aren't keen on fish, such as steak and kidney casserole with Guinness and mustard dumplings or roasted peppers stuffed with couscous, mixed vegetables and nuts with a spicy tomato sauce (£7.95), and lamb shank with herb mash and red wine sauce (£10.95), as well as lunchtime snacks such as baked potatoes (from £3.50), and ploughman's (from £5.25); children's meals (from £3.25). They have occasional gourmet evenings. An island servery separates the bare-boards front part with its coal-effect gas fire and mix of sea and nostalgic prints from a cosier carpeted no smoking dining area with more of a country kitchen feel. Well kept Palmers BB, Copper and 200 on handpump, good house wines and whiskies, cheerful service, and a very pleasantly relaxed atmosphere, with decent piped music (Bryan Ferry's nostalgic *As Time Goes By* CD on our inspection visit); they've also a skittles alley, and the local team meets here. There are tables outside, and they have plans for a new dining terrace in the garden; there's plenty of parking. We have not yet heard from readers who have stayed here, but would expect it to be a nice place to stay in. *(Recommended by Bob and Margaret Holder, Prof and Mrs S Barnett)*

Palmers tenancy ~ Licensees John Ford and Karen Trimby ~ Real ale ~ Bar food ~ Restaurant ~ (01308) 422157 ~ Children in eating area of bar and restaurant ~ Dogs allowed in bar ~ Open 11-2.30, 6-11; 11-11 Sat; 12-10.30 Sun; 11-2.30, 6-11; 12-3, closed Sun evening winter ~ Bedrooms: /£70B

WEST BEXINGTON SY5387 Map 2

Manor Hotel

Village signposted off B3157 SE of Bridport; Beach Road

Readers really enjoy staying at this relaxing and well run old stone hotel, just a short stroll from Chesil beach and within earshot of the waves breaking. The helpful, courteous staff go out of their way to make visitors feel welcome, and are accommodating to families with young children. You can see the sea from the smart no smoking Victorian-style conservatory (which has airy furnishings and lots of plants), from the bedrooms, and from the garden, where there are picnic-sets on a small lawn with flower beds lining the low sheltering walls; a much bigger side lawn has a children's play area. The bustling downstairs cellar bar (on the same level as the south-sloping garden) has small country pictures and good leather-mounted horsebrasses on the walls, red leatherette stools and low-backed chairs (with one fat seat carved from a beer cask) under the black beams and joists, as well as heavy harness over the log fire. The bar food is very good, but not cheap, and includes sandwiches (from £3.15), soup (£3.45), ploughman's (from £5.55), cottage pie and sausage and mash (£6.95), crab cakes (£7.55), vegetable moussaka (£8.55), peppered salmon (£12.65), and steaks (from £12.95), with puddings such as chocolate roulade (£3.95); there's a good restaurant too, and breakfasts are much enjoyed. Well kept Butcombe Gold and Oakhill Charioteer on handpump, quite a few malt whiskies and several wines by the glass. *(Recommended by Alan and Paula McCully, W A Evershed, Mr and Mrs D S Price, R Michael Richards, P J and Avril Hanson, OPUS)*

Free house ~ Licensees Richard and Jayne Childs ~ Real ale ~ Bar food ~ Restaurant ~ (01308) 897616 ~ Children welcome ~ Open 11-11; 12-11 Sun ~ Bedrooms: £70B/£110B

WORTH MATRAVERS SY9777 Map 2

Square & Compass

At fork of both roads signposted to village from B3069

Run by the Newman family for more than 90 years, the pub remains completely unspoilt, basic and unique – hardly anything has changed during that time. So it's a joy for lovers of simple slightly idiosyncratic places. On a winter's evening with the rain lashing the windows, you wouldn't be that surprised if a smuggler, complete with parrot and wooden leg, suddenly materialised. Well kept Badger Tanglewood, Ringwood Best and an interesting changing guest such as Hop Back Thunderstorm are tapped from a row of casks and passed to you in the hall through two serving hatches – there's no bar as such. A couple of rooms opposite have simple furniture on the flagstones, a woodburning stove, and a staunch band of friendly locals (service is friendly too). The only bar food you can get is home-made pasties (£2.20, served all day); cribbage, shove-ha'penny and dominoes. There's a free little museum displaying local fossils and artefacts, mostly collected by the current landlord and his father. It's in a lovely peaceful hilltop setting, and on a clear day gives a fantastic view from benches out in front, looking down over the village rooftops to the sea between the East Man and the West Man (the hills that guard the coastal approach) and out beyond Portland Bill. You may find free-roaming hens, chickens and other birds clucking around your feet. There are good walks from the pub – but limited parking, so it's usually best to park in the public car park 100 yards along the Corfe Castle road. *(Recommended by Mary and Dennis Jones, R J Davies, Mike and Sue Loseby, Andrea Rampley, JP, PP, the Didler, Pete Baker, R M Corlett, JDM, KM, Paul Vickers, Hazel and Michael Duncombe, Michael and Ann Cole, M S Catling, Patrick Hancock, James Woods, Ron Shelton)*

Free house ~ Licensee Charlie Newman ~ Real ale ~ No credit cards ~ (01929) 439229 ~ Children welcome ~ Dogs welcome ~ Open 12-3, 6-11; 12-11 Sat; 12-3, 7-10.30 Sun; may close Sun evening winter

Lucky Dip

Besides the fully inspected pubs, you might like to try these Lucky Dips recommended to us and described by readers (if you do, please send us reports: www.goodguides.com).

Abbotsbury [SY5785]
Ilchester Arms [B3157]: Busy rambling stone inn done out as themed servants' quarters from cook's sitting room to potting shed, with old pine furniture and lots to look at inc prints of the famous swans; decent food from sandwiches or baked potatoes up, attractive no smoking conservatory restaurant, quick service, Courage Directors, Quay Weymouth JD and a guest such as Theakstons tapped from the cask, good house wines in three glass sizes, nice views from terrace tables; darts, winter pool, fruit machine, TV and piped music; children in eating areas, bedrooms, open all day *(Paul Vickers, OPUS, Dennis Jenkin, Tracey and Stephen Groves, David Carr, LYM, Ann and Colin Hunt, Mrs Thomas)*

Almer [SY9097]
☆ ***Worlds End*** [B3075, just off A31 towards Wareham]: Big open-plan thatched family dining pub, beams, panelled alcoves and soft lighting, very wide choice of food all day (you can choose generous or smaller helpings), well kept Badger ales, good quick service (but so popular you may have to wait for a table), restaurant with no smoking area; open all day, picnic-sets out in front and behind, outstanding play area *(BB, D and S Price, Ian and Deborah Carrington)*

Ansty [ST7603]
☆ ***Fox*** [NW of Milton Abbas]: The original home of the Hall & Woodhouse brewers (now trading under the name of Badger), more hotel than pub, with interesting family history in the high-ceilinged partly no smoking main bar; lots of toby jugs, well kept Badger Best and Tanglefoot, good wines by the glass, interesting bar food and Sun carvery, children welcome in restaurant; piped music, separate bar with pool and TV, skittle alley; bedrooms, attractive countryside, open all day *(Mrs June Victor, LYM, Dr and Mrs J F Head, B and K Hypher, Andy Sinden, Louise Harrington, Dr C D and Mrs S M Burbridge)*

Askerswell [SY5292]
☆ ***Spyway*** [off A35 Bridport—Dorchester]: Charming country pub with old-fashioned high-backed settles, cushioned wall and window seats, cosy old-world décor, no smoking beamed dining area; new licensees have taken over too recently for us to gauge quality, but they're doing quite a lot of bar food, with several real ales; marvellous views from back terrace and garden, good walks; children in eating areas, no longer open all day; reports please *(LYM)*

Beaminster [ST4701]
Hine Bar [Hogshill St]: Enjoyable well served food, well kept beer, decent wine; renamed and themed some years ago for local brandy family *(Peter Neate)*

☆ ***Pickwicks*** [The Square]: Quaint and comfortable restaurant with bar attached, popular for wide choice of good well presented home-cooked food; good atmosphere, interesting real ales, friendly landlord; may be piped opera; bedrooms *(Peter Neate)*

Bishop's Caundle [ST6913]
☆ ***White Hart*** [A3030 SE of Sherborne]: Nicely moulded dark beams, ancient panelling, attractive furnishings, sizeable no smoking family area with french windows to big prettily floodlit garden with fine play area and all sorts of games; friendly helpful service, well kept Badger Best, K&B and Tanglefoot, wide choice of generous food from reasonably priced lunchtime sandwiches to steaks inc smaller and children's helpings; darts, skittle alley, fruit machine, muted piped music; reasonably priced bedrooms *(LYM, Marjorie and David Lamb, Pat and Robert Watt)*

Bournemouth [SZ0991]
Goat & Tricycle [West Hill Rd]: Comfortable and friendly two-level pub, with well kept beers such as Bass, Gales HSB and Wadworths IPA, 6X, JcB and Malt & Hops, Cheddar Valley farm cider, good coffee, coal fire, lots of bric-a-brac inc hundreds of hats, simple generous food *(Joan and Michel Hooper-Immins, Anthony Barnes, Ian Phillips)*
Bourton [ST7430]
White Lion [High St, off old A303 E of Wincanton]: Plushly refurbished stripped stone dining pub, nicely lit beamed bars with sporting equipment, well kept beers such as Bass, Courage Best and Dr Thirstys, well prepared food from generous sandwiches or baguettes to steaks, good range of home-made puddings, friendly service, restaurant; dogs welcome, well spaced tables in pleasant garden, live music wknds *(LYM, R J Davies)*
Bradford Abbas [ST5814]
Rose & Crown [Church Rd]: Popular country local with four linked rooms, pleasant up-to-date furnishings and décor, well kept Courage Directors and Theakstons, enjoyable food; charming sheltered garden by fine medieval church, bedrooms *(W W Burke)*
Bridport [SY4692]
Greyhound [East St]: Old pub smartly converted by Wetherspoons (smaller than most of theirs), with three changing real ales, good coffee, food till 9pm, polite friendly young staff *(Ann and Colin Hunt, Pat and Tony Martin)*
Ropemakers [West St]: Warm and friendly country-feel pub with cheap enjoyable bar lunches, free shell-on peanuts *(Cheryl Burden)*
Woodman [South St]: Friendly pub with decent food, even on Sun *(Graham Parsons)*
Broadmayne [SY7286]
Black Dog [Main St]: Comfortably modernised village pub with reasonably priced popular food inc good sandwiches and Sun lunch, pleasant staff *(LYM, R J Davies)*
Burton [SZ1793]
Manor Arms [the one on B3347 just N of Christchurch]: Simple and friendly, with well kept Courage Directors, obliging service, good value food in bar and roomy back room; good jazz nights, bedrooms *(John and Vivienne Rice)*
Cattistock [SY5999]
☆ *Fox & Hounds*: Hidden-away unspoilt village local, looks Tudor in parts; current licensees doing good value food inc bargain no-choice Thurs OAP lunch, two well kept real ales, decent wines, log fires *(Peter Neate, BB)*
Cerne Abbas [ST6601]
☆ *New Inn* [14 Long Street]: Handsome Tudor inn with comfortably relaxed oak-beamed lounge bar, mullioned window seats, three well kept real ales, and no smoking dining room; the tenants are changing again, but the last ones had decent food from ploughman's to generous fish; children welcome, tables on sheltered lawn behind old coachyard, comfortable well decorated bedrooms, open all day wknds and summer *(LYM)*
Charlton Marshall [ST9003]
☆ *Charlton Inn* [A350 Poole—Blandford]: Comfortably extended beamed pub with wide choice of good honest food (may take a while) from doorstep sandwiches up inc fresh fish and plenty of vegetarian dishes, very big helpings, particularly good veg, several carpeted country-style areas inc snug and plenty of dining tables, Badger Best and Tanglefoot, several wines by glass, quick service, no smoking area, unobtrusive piped music; small garden *(BB, David and Elizabeth Briggs)*
Charmouth [SY3693]
George [off A35 W of Bridport]: Friendly and comfortable open-plan pub, cheerful Yorkshire landlord, big helpings of good value food, well kept Otter and John Smiths, pool, table skittles; garden with play area, dogs welcome *(John and Glenys Wheeler, BB)*
Chickerell [SY6480]
Red Barn [Bagwell Farm]: Good freshly made food in converted building on working farm, stripped brick, roaring fire, neat tables; big terrace with walled tent *(Howard and Margaret Buchanan)*
Chideock [SY4292]
George [A35 Bridport—Lyme Regis]: Thatched 17th-c pub, welcoming and relaxed, with neat rows of tables in simple front bar, plusher lounge, hundreds of banknotes on beams, lots of ephemera and bric-a-brac, big log fire, well kept Palmers, decent wines, good value food inc fresh fish (may take a while), family room and big restaurant (two no smoking areas); may be quiet piped music; tables in back garden with terrace, bedrooms *(Bruce Bird, Peter Salmon, LYM, W A Evershed)*
Child Okeford [ST8313]
☆ *Saxon* [signed off A350 Blandford—Shaftesbury and A357 Blandford—Sherborne; Gold Hill]: Cosy and friendly old village meeting place, quietly clubby snug bar with log fire and more spacious side room (where children allowed), well kept changing ales such as Butcombe, Hampshire Strongs Best and Morrells, country wines, traditional games, reasonably priced food (not Tues evening, not winter Sun evening) inc sandwiches and children's dishes; piped music, dry dogs on leads welcome; quite a menagerie in attractive back garden, may be friendly golden retrievers and cats; good walks on neolithic Hambledon Hill *(LYM, Ian Phillips)*
Christchurch [SZ1592]
Olde George [Castle St]: Bustling old character pub, low beams, cosy bar, friendly staff, well kept ales such as Black Sheep, Gales HSB and Ringwood Fortyniner, good choice of home-made food with different evening menu; some music nights, tables in large courtyard *(Charlotte Brittain, W W Burke)*
Church Knowle [SY9481]
☆ *New Inn* [off A351 just N of Corfe Castle]: Partly thatched pub with some emphasis on daily fresh fish, other food from sandwiches up (not cheap), well kept Flowers Original, Greene King Old Speckled Hen and Wadworths 6X, farm cider, good wines (inc off sales), friendly long-serving landlord, log fires each end of the two main areas, attractive furnishings, relaxed

atmosphere, no smoking part, some stripped stone and high rafters, separate children's room; disabled facilities, nice garden with country views, bookable camping, cl Mon evening Jan-Mar *(LYM, W W Burke, Tony and Katie Lewis, Jayne and Peter Capp, Mike and Sue Richardson, John and Enid Morris, JDM, KM, Eric Locker, R J Davies)*

Corfe Castle [SY9681]

Castle Inn [East St]: Friendly smallish pub mentioned in Hardy's *Hand of Ethelberta*, new landlady doing good value home cooking inc Sun lunches, well kept Ringwood Best and Fortyniner, two smartly refurbished yet unpretentious rooms with flagstoned floors shown to good effect *(Robert Newton)*

☆ ***Fox*** [West St]: Old-fashioned take-us-as-you-find-us stone-built local with ancient origins inc pre-1300 stone fireplace, hatch service, tiny front bar, glassed-over well in lounge (many tables reserved for eaters), well kept ales such as Greene King Abbot, Fullers London Pride or Wadworths 6X tapped from the cask, food from sandwiches and baguettes up; informal garden *(Paul Vickers, Dr D E Granger, Mary and Dennis Jones, Patrick Hancock, David Carr, Mr and Mrs Thomas, JP, PP, R J Davies, Andrea Rampley, Des and Jen Clarke, the Didler)*

☆ ***Greyhound*** [A351]: Bustling old pub in centre of tourist village, three small low-ceilinged panelled rooms, well kept Adnams, Hampshire Strong, Ringwood Best and several guest beers, traditional games inc Purbeck shove-ha'penny on 5ft board, no smoking family room, food (all day in summer) from filled rolls and baked potatoes up; live music Fri; garden with fine castle and countryside views, pretty courtyard opening on to castle bridge, bedrooms, open all day wknds and summer *(LYM, Des and Jen Clarke, JDM, KM, Philip and June Caunt, David Carr, Derek and Sylvia Stephenson, Esther and John Sprinkle, Dr D E Granger, Patrick Hancock, W W Burke, Paul Vickers, Tracey and Stephen Groves, the Didler, Andrew York, Martin and Jane Wright)*

Cranborne [SU0513]

☆ ***Fleur-de-Lys*** [B3078 N of Wimborne]: 17th-c inn nicely set on the edge of Cranborne Chase, subject of a witty Rupert Brooke poem about going to the wrong pub (framed above fire in panelled lounge); friendly landlord, simpler beamed public bar with well kept Badger Best and Tanglefoot, farm cider, bar food from good baguettes and sandwiches up inc children's, evening restaurant; pub games, piped music, TV; pretty bedrooms *(LYM, H D Wharton, David Surridge, John Saville, Mike and Shelley Woodroffe, Dr D E Granger)*

Dorchester [SY6890]

Blue Raddle [Church St]: Lively unpretentious sidestreet local with good very attractively priced lunchtime food inc game, well kept ales such as Greene King Abbot, Otter Head and Sharps Cornish Coaster, obliging landlord; maybe quiet piped jazz; disabled access, but one step *(John Beeken, Ian and Joan Blackwell, G Coates, David Carr, the Didler)*

Borough Arms [High East St]: Cosy and friendly bar, with several beers inc a guest such as Mansfield, separate bare-floored pool room; some steps *(G Coates)*

Kings Arms [High East St]: Hotel bar with well kept Bass and Courage Directors, decent wines, food from sandwiches up, pleasant helpful service, open fire; close associations with Nelson and Hardy's *Mayor of Casterbridge*; bedrooms (the Lawrence of Arabia suite and the Tutenkhamen have to be seen to be believed) *(the Didler, David Carr, LYM, Ian Phillips)*

Tom Browns [High East St]: Small plain bare-boards L-shaped bar notable for very well kept Goldfinch beers such as Tom Browns Best, Flashmans Clout and Midnight Blinder brewed in back microbrewery, wholesome reasonably priced lunchtime bar food (not Sun); welcoming staff, friendly locals, traditional games; nostalgic juke box, outside lavatories; open all day Thurs-Sun *(G Coates)*

Trumpet Major [Alington Ave (A352 towards Wareham, just off bypass)]: Bright and airy big-windowed modern lounge bar with easy chairs in raised area and peaceful dining conservatory, well kept real ales such as Courage Directors, good choice of wines by the glass, second bar with games machines, TV and games room with two pool tables; handy for Max Gate (Thomas Hardy's house, now open to the public); children welcome, spacious tree-lined garden with aviaries and adventure play area, very busy lunchtime *(B and K Hypher)*

East Burton [SY8387]

Seven Stars: Old country pub refurbished with dining conservatory, good choice of generous food, well kept ales such as Itchen Valley, friendly welcome for families, tables outside, play area inc summer bouncy castle; handy for Bovington Tank Museum and Monkey World, parking for caravans – can be packed in summer *(Jenny and Brian Seller)*

East Lulworth [SY8581]

Weld Arms [B3070 SW of Wareham]: Cheerful yet relaxed, with nice mix of individual furnishings, attractive little snug, well kept Greene King IPA and Abbot, pleasant service, food from well filled rolls up; shame about the piped music; tables out in big garden, fairly cheap bedrooms *(LYM, R J Davies)*

Fiddleford [ST8013]

☆ ***Fiddleford Inn*** [A357 Sturminster Newton—Blandford Forum]: Comfortable and spacious, good generous quickly served food from sandwiches up in lounge bar, restaurant area and back family area, well kept real ales, friendly service, three linked smartly refurbished areas, ancient flagstones and some other nice touches; unobtrusive piped music; big pleasant garden with play area *(David Rawlins, B and K Hypher, LYM)*

Gillingham [ST8027]

☆ ***Dolphin*** [Peacemarsh (B3082)]: Popular dining pub with good choice of particularly good value food esp fish all freshly cooked to order (so can take a while), regular themed menus, friendly helpful staff, partly no smoking restaurant area, well kept Badger beers in pleasant beamed bar for drinking; garden with climbing frame *(Mr and Mrs Thomas, P Goldman, R M Wickenden, Colin and Janet Roe, BB, Pat and Robert Watt)*

Kingston [SY9579]

Scott Arms [West St (B3069)]: Busy holiday pub with rambling warren-like rooms, panelling, stripped stone, beams, open fires and some fine antique prints, attractive room overlooking garden, decent family extension, well kept Courage Directors and Ringwood Best, lots of wines, generous if not cheap standard food inc summer cream teas, no smoking dining area; darts, dominoes and fruit machine, piped music; well kept garden with superb views of Corfe Castle and the Purbeck Hills *(the Didler, W W Burke, Paul Thompson, Anna Blackburn, LYM, Joan and Michel Hooper-Immins, M G Hart)*

Langton Herring [SY6182]

☆ ***Elm Tree*** [signed off B3157]: Low black beams, lots of copper, brass and bellows, cushioned window seats, windsor chairs and scrubbed pine tables, inglenook, and traditionally furnished extension, wide range of food from sandwiches up inc some interesting dishes (may be a long wait), decent house wine, Bass and Flowers or Marstons Pedigree, friendly staff; no dogs inside; pretty flower-filled sunken garden, track down to Coast Path which skirts Chesil lagoon *(Irene and Derek Flewin, Jean and Douglas Troup, Eric Locker, Peter Neate, James Woods, Dave Braisted, LYM, Dennis Jenkin, W A Evershed, Joan and Michel Hooper-Immins)*

Langton Matravers [SY9978]

Kings Arms [High St]: Popular old-fashioned village pub with fine local marble fireplace in simple beamed main bar, well kept Ringwood with a guest such as Wychwood Dogs Bollocks, friendly locals and staff, food inc good Sun roasts, splendid antique Purbeck longboard for shove-ha'penny; tables outside *(Richard Burton, LYM)*

Litton Cheney [SY5590]

☆ ***White Horse***: Palmers pub with three well kept ales, good home-made food using fresh local ingredients, pictures on stripped stone walls, country kitchen chairs in dining area, table skittles, friendly efficient staff; good spot on quiet lane into quaint village, picnic-sets on pleasant streamside front lawn *(BB, Ian Phillips, R J Davies, W A Evershed)*

Loders [SY4994]

Loders Arms [off A3066 just N of Bridport]: Well worn in local, welcoming and relaxed, log fire, Palmers real ales, good choice of house wines, good value changing food from huge baguettes to interesting main dishes, no smoking dining room, skittle alley; may be piped music; children in eating areas, pleasant views from tables in small back garden, pretty thatched village, open all day Sun *(LYM, OPUS, Esther and John Sprinkle, Ian Phillips, Stephanie and Kamal Thapa)*

Longham [SZ0698]

White Hart [A348 Ferndown—Poole]: Small friendly traditional pub with pine furniture, quickly fills lunchtime for good home-made food from sandwiches and baked potatoes up, well kept Badger beers, bright log fire, old tools and newspapers; soft piped music *(A J Martin)*

Lyme Regis [SY3492]

Angel [Mill Green]: Two-bar local refurbished under welcoming newish licensees and doing well, Badger beers tapped from the cask, relaxing atmosphere; bedrooms *(David Pott)*

Cobb Arms [Marine Parade, Monmouth Beach]: Spaciously refurbished, with wide range of reasonably priced generous bar food, quick service even when busy, good value cream teas, well kept Palmers, decent wines, interesting ship pictures and marine fish tank; popular with local young people till late; next to harbour, beach and coastal walk, children welcome, open all day, tables on small back terrace, bedrooms, good breakfast *(Bruce Bird, Leigh and Gillian Mellor)*

☆ ***Pilot Boat*** [Bridge St]: Handy food spot, nicely set near waterfront, plenty of tables in cheery nautically themed bars with no smoking dining area, cheap quickly served generous food all day from sandwiches to steak, Palmers real ales, several wines by the glass, skittle alley; piped music; children and dogs welcome, tables out on terrace, open all day *(Peter Salmon, Quentin and Carol Williamson, Joan and Michel Hooper-Immins, Martin and Jane Wright, Tracey and Stephen Groves, Mike and Wendy Proctor, Prof Kenneth Surin, JDM, KM, Bruce Bird, Derek, Hazel and Graeme Lloyd, LYM)*

Royal Standard [Marine Parade, The Cobb]: Right on broadest part of beach, with suntrap courtyard (own servery and wendy house); lively bar serving area dominated by pool table and piped pop, but has some fine built-in stripped high settles, and there's a quieter no smoking area with stripped brick and pine; well kept Palmers IPA, BB, 200 and Gold, good value food inc sensibly priced sandwiches, plenty of local crab and fish, good cream teas, darts; children welcome *(Ian Phillips, Esther and John Sprinkle, BB)*

Lytchett Minster [SY9693]

St Peters Finger [Dorchester Rd]: Well run beamed two-part Badger pub with good value standard food from sandwiches and baguettes up, well kept beer inc Tanglefoot, cottagey mix of furnishings and end log fire giving a cosy feel despite its size; good skittle alley, tables on big terrace, part covered and heated *(B and K Hypher)*

Manston [ST8115]

Plough [B3091 Shaftesbury—Sturminster Newton, just N]: Current landlord doing well, with good choice of popular food from sandwiches up, well kept changing ales, quick helpful welcoming service; richly decorated plasterwork, ceilings and bar front, tables in garden *(Pat and Robert Watt)*

Marnhull [ST7718]

☆ ***Crown*** [about 3 miles N of Sturminster Newton; Crown Rd]: Part-thatched 17th-c dining pub, good generous food with nice blackboard choice, oak beams, huge flagstones, old settles and elm tables, window seats cut into thick stone walls, logs burning in big stone hearth, Badger Best and Tanglefoot, welcoming service, small more modern lounge; skittle alley, may be piped music; tables in peaceful enclosed garden, children welcome *(Pat and Robert Watt, LYM, Charles and Pauline Stride)*

Milton Abbas [ST8001]

☆ ***Hambro Arms*** [signed off A354 SW of Blandford]: In beautiful late 18th-c thatched landscaped village, good log fire, well kept Bass, Boddingtons and Tetleys, good generous food from sandwiches to steak, fish and Sunday carvery, friendly prompt service even when busy, bright décor; darts, pool and TV in cosy back public bar, children in restaurant; no dogs, tables out on terrace, comfortable bedrooms *(LYM, John and Glenys Wheeler, J P Humphery, R Halsey, Simon and Laura Habbishow)*

Moreton [SY7889]

Frampton Arms [B3390 nr station]: Quiet, relaxed and very neatly kept, with good choice of good value food from sandwiches and crisp baguettes up inc good fish and seafood, Boddingtons and Flowers IPA, log fire, friendly landlord, steam railway pictures in lounge bar, Warmwell Aerodrome theme in public bar, bright and airy conservatory restaurant; tables on front terrace, comfortable bedrooms *(D J Ferrett)*

Mudeford [SZ1891]

☆ ***Haven House*** [beyond huge seaside car park at Mudeford Pier]: Much-extended and smartly refurbished, best in winter for old-fashioned feel in quaint little part-flagstoned core and lovely seaside walks (dogs banned from beach May-Sept), good value food from good crab sandwiches and winter soup up, well kept Boddingtons, Flowers Original and Wadworths 6X, cheerful service; very popular wknds and summer for position on beach with family cafeteria, tables on sheltered terrace *(Derek and Sylvia Stephenson, JDM, KM, LYM)*

☆ ***Ship in Distress***: Dining pub very popular for good fresh carefully cooked fish and seafood, and classy puddings, in restaurant (best to book) and bar – two rooms, one plain, one cosy with fun décor inc hops, plants and nautical memorabilia; well kept Bass, Greenalls Original, Marstons Pedigree and Ringwood Best, good house wines, friendly service (the fresh cooking takes a time, of course) *(A D Marsh, Julian and Linda Cooke)*

Nettlecombe [SY5195]

☆ ***Marquis of Lorne*** [off A3066 Bridport—Beaminster, via W Milton]: Tucked away in lovely countryside, neat and comfortable panelled main bar, pleasant décor, two smarter dining areas, one no smoking, log fires, friendly helpful tenants doing enjoyable food from sandwiches up with some emphasis on fresh fish, well kept Palmers real ales, decent wines, public bar with cribbage, dominoes and table skittles; children in eating areas, bedrooms, big pretty garden with rustic-style play area *(Ann and Colin Hunt, Cathy Robinson, Ed Coombe, Roger Braithwaite, Mike Gorton, Tracey and Stephen Groves, R M Corlett, Elizabeth Pickard, Denis and Dorothy Evans, Dominic and Christiane Zwemmer, Paul and Annette Hallett, Anthony Barnes, Evelyn and Derek Walter, LYM)*

North Wootton [ST6514]

Three Elms [A3030 SE of Sherborne]: Lively country pub with enormous collection of Matchbox and other model cars and other vehicles, half a dozen or more well kept ales such as Fullers London Pride, Potton Shambles, Shepherd Neame Spitfire and one brewed by Ash Vine for the pub, hearty usual food from sandwiches up; seaside postcard collection in gents'; three comfortable bedrooms, shared bathrooms, good breakfast, big garden *(W W Burke, Stephen, Julie and Hayley Brown)*

Okeford Fitzpaine [ST8011]

☆ ***Royal Oak*** [Lower St]: Well kept Ringwood Best, Wadworths 6X and weekly changing guest beer, farm cider, promising food from traditional pub dishes to more upmarket things, huge fireplace with copper-hooded stove in small traditional beamed and flagstoned front bar, no smoking green-painted L-shaped eating area with three very small cottagey interconnected rooms off, steps up to newly refurbished skittle alley, pool; quiz night, beer festival first wknd in July, tables on back lawn with play area, charming village *(BB)*

Osmington Mills [SY7381]

☆ ***Smugglers*** [off A353 NE of Weymouth]: Pretty part-thatched pub in fine position a short stroll up from the sea, with good cliff walks; much extended but done well, with cosy dark corners, log stove, shiny black panelling and nautical decorations; well kept Badger Best, Tanglefoot and a guest such as Firsty Ferret, quickly served generous enjoyable food from good filled baps to full meals, partly no smoking restaurant; discreet games area, piped music; children in eating areas, streamside garden with good play area and thatched summer bar, open all day, can be very crowded in summer (holiday settlement nearby); comfortable bedrooms, big breakfast, on Coast Path *(Paul Vickers, LYM, the Didler, Pat and Tony Martin, Eric Locker, Alan and Ros Furley, Esther and John Sprinkle, Kerry and Tricia Thomas)*

Piddletrenthide [SY7099]

☆ ***European***: Unpretentiously old-fashioned oak-beamed pub locally favoured for good generous reasonably priced fresh food inc fine home-cooked ham and very good value lamb shanks (should book wknds), well kept Courage Directors and Ringwood Best, genuinely friendly and helpful cheery staff, log fire in attractive copper-hooded fireplace, willow-pattern china, stylish chairs; piped music; tables in neatly kept front garden, three bedrooms with own baths and good views *(Dennis Jenkin, BB, Marianne and Peter Stevens, R J Townson)*

☆ ***Piddle*** [B3143 N of Dorchester]: Friendly plain-speaking landlord, emphasis on good food esp fish, with whole board of imaginative fish specials, most tables set for eating, but comfortable leatherette sofas in refurbished bar;

good range of beers, children's room, dining room and pool room; informal streamside garden with picnic-sets and play area; bedrooms planned; village and pub named after the river here *(Peter Neate, Rita and Keith Pollard, B H and J I Andrews, Ian Jones, BB)*

Poole [SZ0493]

Crown [Market St]: Warm and friendly, with linked open-plan areas inc comfortable end eating area with military uniform prints, low-priced plentiful food, two-for-one bargains some days, good evening fresh fish choice, four well kept ales inc Courage Directors, generous house wines, very helpful service *(Keith and Suzie Stevens, Joyce and Maurice Cottrell)*

☆ *Guildhall Tavern* [Market St]: Largely French fish restaurant rather than pub now, good (if not cheap), with friendly service; small front bar, well kept Ringwood and decent house wine, thorough-going bright nautical décor, good atmosphere *(LYM, Joyce and Maurice Cottrell, D Cairns)*

Hogshead [Ashley Rd]: Large reliable L-shaped pub with usual Hogshead décor, six well kept ales such as Greene King Abbot and Old Speckled Hen, Hop Back Summer Lightning, Ringwood Best and Timothy Taylors Landlord, farm cider, good range of other drinks inc Costa coffee, popular modestly priced pub food with bargains for two, speedy pleasant service *(W W Burke)*

☆ *Inn in the Park* [Pinewood Rd, off A338 towards Branksome Chine – via The Avenue]: Pleasantly decorated and cheerful open-plan bar in substantial Edwardian villa (now a small hotel), popular with local residents and business people for well kept Adnams Broadside, Bass and Wadworths 6X and good value generous bar food (not Sun evening) from good 'sandwedges' (sandwiches with chips) up; polite young staff, attractive dining room (children allowed), log fire, tables on small sunny terrace; comfortable bedrooms, quiet pine-filled residential area above sea *(W W Burke, Pam Adsley, LYM, JDM, KM)*

Kings Head [High St]: Enjoyable bar food, friendly staff, large no smoking area; tables in garden behind *(D J and P M Taylor)*

Shah of Persia [Longfleet Rd/Fernside Rd (A35)]: Spacious roadhouse pleasantly decorated with William Morris wallpaper and Art Deco lighting, lots of old posters and advertisements, well kept real ales such as Courage Best, wide choice of generous food (not Sat or Sun evening) from lunchtime sandwiches and baguettes (not Sun) to carvery dishes and full meals (occasional half-price bargains), big no smoking eating area, bright friendly service; piped music; modern bedroom block *(Joan and Michel Hooper-Immins, Ian Phillips, JDM, KM)*

Portland [SY6872]

George [Reforne]: Particularly well kept Ringwood Best and Fortyniner and good value food (not Weds lunchtime) from sandwiches to cheap hot dishes in 17th-c stone-built pub mentioned by Thomas Hardy and reputed to have smugglers' tunnels running to the cliffs; low beams, flagstones, small rooms, interesting prints *(Joan and Michel Hooper-Immins)*

Powerstock [SY5196]

Three Horseshoes [off A3066 Beaminster—Bridport via W Milton]: Friendly pub with good fires and stripped panelling, well kept Palmers real ales, quite a few wines by the glass, enjoyable food from generous baguettes to full meals, chatty locals, children welcome in no smoking restaurant; open all day, pleasant bedrooms, lovely views towards the sea from tables in garden behind *(OPUS, LYM, Ann and Colin Hunt, Barry and Verina Jones, Richard Gibbs)*

Preston [SY7083]

Bridge Inn [A353 Weymouth—Osmington]: Cottagey ivy-covered stone-built pub with enjoyable blackboard food, Bass and Ringwood Best and Fortyniner, very busy in summer, homely out of season; attractive sun-trap front garden with swings etc, stream alongside *(Joan and Michel Hooper-Immins)*

Spyglass [Bowleaze Coveway]: Busy family dining pub, great views over Weymouth from top of Furzy Cliff, wide choice of enjoyable food with plenty for children, real ales such as Boddingtons, Courage Directors and Ringwood Fortyniner; piped music; side adventure play area *(Joan and Michel Hooper-Immins)*

Shaftesbury [ST8622]

Half Moon [Salisbury Rd (A30, by roundabout)]: Roomy comfortable restaurant area, wide choice of well prepared generous food inc popular Sun lunch, reasonable prices, quick welcoming service, Badger beers; garden with adventure playground *(B and K Hypher, Marjorie and David Lamb)*

Shapwick [ST9302]

☆ *Anchor* [off A350 Blandford—Poole; West St]: Attractive décor, varnished pine tables on quarry tiles, warm atmosphere, good freshly cooked food changing monthly (not Mon; may take a while), three real ales, good wine list, several small rooms with pleasant end dining room; piped music, occasional live; in heart of pretty thatched village, brightly painted tables in front, more on terrace behind, children welcome (small garden has play area); handy for Kingston Lacy *(BB, B and K Hypher)*

Shave Cross [SY4198]

☆ *Shave Cross Inn*: This charming partly 14th-c thatched pub, with country antiques, flagstones, enormous inglenook, stylish dining room and pretty garden, has long been a main entry, but the owners, who have had well kept real ales, decent wines and good imaginative food, are selling and there is a risk that it may become a private house – news please *(LYM)*

Sherborne [ST6316]

☆ *Skippers* [Horsecastles (A352 link rd)]: Comfortable extended pub with long stripped-stone bar partly laid for eating, immense choice of good generous food from sandwiches and baked potatoes to local venison and daily fresh fish, pleasant local bustle, jolly landlord, quick warm-hearted service in spite of crowds, well kept Wadworths IPA, JcB and 6X with a guest such as Butcombe, interesting pictures and bric-a-brac; tables outside *(Joan and Michel Hooper-Immins)*

Stoke Abbott [ST4500]

☆ ***New Inn*** [off B3162 and B3163 2 miles W of Beaminster]: 17th-c thatched pub very popular for generous food inc fresh fish; beams, brasses, stripped stone alcoves on either side of one big log fireplace, another with handsome panelling, no smoking dining room; friendly family service, well kept Palmers ales, neat and attractive sizeable garden with play area, nice setting in unspoilt quiet thatched village; children welcome, bedrooms; cl Mon in July/Aug *(LYM, Mr and Mrs A H Young, Basil Minson, Marjorie and David Lamb)*

Studland [SZ0382]

Bankes Arms [off B3351, Isle of Purbeck; Manor Rd]: Very popular spot above fine beach, outstanding country, sea and cliff views from huge pleasant garden with masses of seating; comfortably basic, friendly and easy-going big bar with raised drinking area, plentiful decent food (at a price) all day from baguettes to local fish, well kept beers such as Palmers, Poole, Wadworths 6X and unusual guest beers (shame about the plastic glasses), local farm cider, attractive log fires, big-screen sports TV, darts and pool in side games area; children welcome, just off Coast Path; can get very busily trippery wknds and in summer, parking in season can be complicated or expensive if you're not a NT member; big comfortable bedrooms *(Ron Shelton, David and Elizabeth Briggs, Jayne and Peter Capp, Tony and Katie Lewis, JDM, KM, Jenny and Brian Seller)*

Sturminster Marshall [SY9499]

☆ ***Red Lion*** [N end of High St, opp church; off A350 Blandford—Poole]: Attractive flower-decked and creeper-clad old-fashioned pub, clean and pleasant, with low beams, welcoming atmosphere, good value home-made food inc substantial interesting starters, bargain OAP two-course lunch, sandwiches on Sun too, friendly prompt service, well kept Badger ales, log fire, quiet end round corner, no smoking restaurant extension, skittle alley doubling as family room *(Ron Shelton, Marjorie and David Lamb, Michael and Ann Cole, David M Cundy, B and K Hypher)*

Sturminster Newton [ST7813]

Bull [A357 just W of Bridge]: Low-beamed 16th-c country inn by River Stur, good hearty home cooking from interesting sandwiches up, pleasant landlord, well kept Badger beers, key-ring collection, big corner bookcases in bar and side room; well behaved dogs welcome, pleasant garden *(Andrew York)*

Swanage [SZ0378]

Mowlem [Shore Rd]: Bright and comfortable theatre café and restaurant, not a pub, but has good value food (all day in summer) inc children's menu, well kept Badger Best and Tanglefoot, good service, and great views to Isle of Wight *(Joan and Michel Hooper-Immins)*

Red Lion [High St]: Low beams, shelves and walls densely hung with hundreds of keys, mugs and lots of highly polished brass blow lamps, decent inexpensive food, well kept Flowers, Greene King Old Speckled Hen and Ringwood, prompt friendly service, separate locals' bar; children's games in large barn, garden with partly covered back terrace *(the Didler, R J Davies)*

Sydling St Nicholas [SY6399]

☆ ***Greyhound*** [High St]: Wide choice of particularly good food from filled crusty rolls to main dishes with plentiful properly cooked veg, good fish and delicious puddings, friendly family service, chatty locals, well kept Palmers and Youngs Special, long brick bar counter, some stripped stonework and flagstones, pool, piped music; pleasant bistro-style flagstoned conservatory, restaurant; good tables in nice small garden with play area, very pretty village *(Anthony Barnes, BB, Cynthia and Stephen Fisher, Vivian T Green)*

Symondsbury [SY4493]

☆ ***Ilchester Arms*** [signed off A35 just W of Bridport]: Attractive and popular old thatched inn in peaceful village, snugly traditional open-plan low-ceilinged bar with high-backed settle built in by big inglenook, cosy no smoking dining area with another fire, good food choice concentrating on local produce, well kept Palmers beers, friendly service; pub games, skittle alley; children welcome, tables by pretty brookside back garden, good walks nearby *(LYM, Tracey and Stephen Groves)*

Tarrant Keynston [ST9204]

True Lovers Knot: Village pub with friendly licensees, good food served quickly, well kept Badger ales, woodburner; big garden behind with play area, donkey and chickens *(Frank Smith, Marjorie and David Lamb)*

Three Legged Cross [SU0904]

Old Barn Farm [Ringwood Rd, towards Ashley Heath and A31]: Large quaint thatched Vintage Inn with good value usual food presented well, pleasant restaurant, friendly and attentive young staff, Bass and Worthington, decent wines; lots of tables on attractive front lawn by pond, some children's amusements, enormous dovecote; handy for Moors Valley Country Park *(Phyl and Jack Street, I R Fourmy)*

Tolpuddle [SY7994]

Martyrs [former A35 W of Bere Regis]: Good freshly cooked food in bar and busy attractively laid out restaurant, hard-working friendly staff, well kept Badger beers; well used by locals, children welcome, nice garden with ducks, hens and rabbits; open all day, quiet bypassed village *(Tony and Wendy Hobden, Martin and Jane Wright, Ann and Colin Hunt, R T and J C Moggridge, Mr and Mrs R G Spiller, Mr and Mrs A P Lawrence)*

Uploders [SY5093]

☆ ***Crown*** [signed off A35 E of Bridport]: Homely brightly furnished low-beamed village pub, mainly no smoking; the friendly Jameses who made it a popular main entry with their good value home cooking, and filled it with all sorts of entertaining bric-a-brac and pictures by local artists, left in Sept 2002; we hope their successors will turn out just as well, with well kept Palmers and good service; log fires, table skittles; tables in attractive two-tier garden, bedrooms *(LYM)*

Upwey [SY6785]

☆ ***Old Ship*** [off A354; Ridgeway]: Relaxed and attractive linked beamed rooms, log fires each end, traditional furnishings, china, copper pans and old clocks, enjoyable food from good choice of lunchtime baguettes to fresh fish in bar and no smoking restaurant, well kept Bass, Greene King Old Speckled Hen and Ringwood Best, decent wines, friendly attentive staff; piped music; colourful hanging baskets, picnic-table sets in garden with terrace *(Mrs Thomas, John Beeken, Sean Odell, Peter Neate, JDM, KM, Alan and Paula McCully, LYM)*

☆ ***Riverhouse*** [B3159, nr junction A354]: Coal-effect gas fireplace dividing flagstoned bar side from neat carpeted no smoking dining side, main emphasis on wide range of good food from lunchtime baguettes through familiar dishes to Italian specialities, children's dishes, well kept Wadworths 6X and a beer brewed for the pub, adventurous wine choice, good Gaggia coffee, efficient service; well reproduced piped pop music; disabled access, sizeable garden with play area, cl Sun evening *(Peter Neate, BB)*

Wareham [SY9287]

Black Bear [South St]: Bow-windowed 18th-c hotel with old local prints and lots of brass in convivial well worn in bar off through corridor, lounge with settees and easy chairs, well kept Courage Directors, good choice of keenly priced usual food inc vegetarian and children's, decent coffee, back eating room and restaurant; piped classical music; picnic-sets in pleasant flower-filled back yard, open all day; bedrooms *(BB, W W Burke)*

Quay Inn [The Quay]: Comfortable, light and airy stripped-stone bars in great spot right by the water, food from soup and sandwiches up, open fire, well kept Whitbreads-related and other ales, children allowed away from main bar; picnic-sets out on quay; bedrooms, open all day summer, parking nearby can be difficult *(Des and Jen Clarke, R J Davies, Joyce and Maurice Cottrell)*

West Bay [SY4590]

Bridport Arms: Cheerfully unpretentious 16th-c thatched local on beach of Bridport's low-key holiday village (was the Bridehaven pub in TV's *Harbour Lights*), generous good value food esp soups and fish, well kept Palmers IPA, Copper and 200, two-room lounge and separate basic flagstoned summer bar, back family room facing beach, bright dining room, no music; tables in adjoining hotel with own entrance; tables outside, paying public car park *(Joan and Michel Hooper-Immins, E G Parish, BB)*

George [George St]: Red plush banquettes, mate's chairs, masses of shipping pictures, some model ships and nautical hardware, roomy L-shaped public bar with games and juke box, separate no smoking back restaurant; food inc lots of good value local fish from prawn and crab sandwiches up, well kept Palmers IPA and Gold, cheery helpful service; tables outside, bedrooms *(Ken Flawn, BB, Joan and Michel Hooper-Immins)*

West Knighton [SY7387]

☆ ***New Inn*** [off A352 E of Dorchester]: Biggish neatly refurbished pub doing well under current licensees, interesting generous food inc tempting puddings, friendly attentive staff, real ales, country wines, small restaurant, skittle alley, good provision for children; big colourful garden, pleasant setting in quiet village with wonderful views *(Bill and Doreen Sawford)*

West Lulworth [SY8280]

☆ ***Castle Inn*** [B3070 SW of Wareham]: Pretty thatched inn in lovely spot near Lulworth Cove, good walks and lots of summer visitors; flagstoned bar concentrating on usual food inc children's, decent house wines, farm cider, Flowers Original and Marstons Pedigree, chatty staff, maze of booth seating divided by ledges for board games and jigsaws; piped music (may be loud), video game; cosy more modern-feeling lounge bar, pleasant dining room, splendid ladies', popular garden with giant chess boards, boules, barbecues *(Jayne and Peter Capp, LYM, R J Davies, J and B Cressey)*

West Parley [SZ0897]

☆ ***Curlew*** [Christchurch Rd]: Attractively reworked and civilised Vintage Inn with nicely mixed furnishings in half a dozen linked room areas inc no smoking ones, hops on beams, extensive wine racks and old bric-a-brac, two log fires, good food inc interesting dishes, plenty of good value wines, well kept Bass, very friendly well trained service; no under-21s unless eating *(John and Vivienne Rice, W W Burke)*

West Stafford [SY7289]

☆ ***Wise Man*** [signed off A352 Dorchester—Wareham]: Comfortable 16th-c village local near Hardy's cottage, very busy in summer; thatch, beams, toby jugs and masses of old pipes, wide choice of good value generous home-made food (not Sun evening) from good baguettes to local fish and shellfish, friendly landlord and good service from happy staff, well kept Fullers London Pride, Ringwood Best and Youngs Special, farm cider, decent wines and country wines, coal and log fire, sensibly placed darts, cottagey stripped-stone restaurant; piped music; dogs on leads welcome (biscuits on bar), solid tables out in front, picnic-sets in small back garden, lovely walks nearby *(J G Dias, BB, R J Davies)*

West Stour [ST7822]

Ship: Good value generous food cooked by landlord, friendly landlady, well kept local beer, spotless attractive furnishings, big log fire, lovely views from chatty bar, intimate split-level restaurant; garden behind, comfortable bedrooms *(Pat and Robert Watt, M Chapman)*

Weymouth [SY6778]

Boot [High West St]: Largely 18th-c beamed pub near harbour, stone-mullioned windows even older, well kept Ringwood ales with a guest beer, farm cider, good value filled rolls and cold snacks, welcoming bearded landlord *(Joan and Michel Hooper-Immins, Bryan Robinson)*

Dorothy [Esplanade]: Neatly kept real-ale pub in outstanding seafront spot, great views from pavement tables; big plain open-plan bar, carpet and bare boards, interesting changing ales such as Bass, Cotleigh Golden Eagle, Otter Head, local Quay Bitter and Old Rott, Wadworths 6X and Wye Valley Butty Bach, Inch's cider, good value straightforward food (all day in summer) inc crab sandwiches and variety sausages, friendly landlady, daily papers; children welcome, some tables outside, open all day (may stay open as nightclub after 11) *(Joan and Michel Hooper-Immins, the Didler, Tracey and Stephen Groves)*

☆ ***Nothe Tavern*** [Barrack Rd]: Roomy and comfortable well run local with good atmosphere, wide range of food inc local fresh fish specialities and children's dishes, friendly service, well kept real ales, decent wines; maybe quiet piped music; distant harbour glimpses from garden *(BB, Peter and Audrey Dowsett)*

☆ ***Red Lion*** [Hope Sq]: Lively unsmart bare-boards pub with four well kept beers such as Courage Best and Weymouth Organic Gold, quickly served cheap simple meals from good crab sandwiches up (not Fri-Sun evenings), interesting RNLI and fishing stuff all over the walls and ceiling (even two boats), open fires, daily papers, friendly family atmosphere, good staff; plenty of tables outside (more than inside), open all day in summer (food all day then too), opp smart touristy Brewers Quay complex in former brewery *(the Didler, BB, Liz and John Soden)*

Ship [Custom House Quay]: Neat and spacious modern open-plan waterfront pub with several real ales from long bar, good value usual food; piped music may obtrude; pleasant back terrace *(LYM, Peter and Audrey Dowsett)*

Spa [Dorchester Rd, Radipole; off A354 at Safeway roundabout]: Large open-plan family pub, new licensees doing some ambitious dishes esp fresh fish alongside good value straightforward things (all day Sun), good helpings, attentive service, Courage Best and Directors, peaceful restaurant and back conservatory; good garden with play area *(Joan and Michel Hooper-Immins)*

Wellington Arms [St Alban St]: Homely and peaceful panelled L-shaped bar with etched windows, good value lunchtime food (all day summer wkdys) from toasted sandwiches and baguettes to sensibly priced hot dishes inc daily roasts, Courage Best, Ind Coope Burton and Tetleys, no smoking back dining room *(Joan and Michel Hooper-Immins)*

Wimborne Minster [SZ0199]

☆ ***Dormers***: Mainly 18th/19th-c town house, open-plan but keeping handsome panelling and ceilings, pleasant furnishings, big conservatory dining area, well kept Badger Best and Tanglefoot, wide range of good food, helpful staff, boxed games; may be piped classical music; picnic-sets on lawn running down to small river *(W W Burke)*

Green Man [Victoria Rd, W of town]: Splendid flower-draped façade, three linked areas with nooks and alcoves, usual pub furnishings, brasses and prints, well kept Wadworths ales from back bar, good value food with wider evening choice, relaxed atmosphere, efficient welcoming service; no dogs, lavatories up steps, occasional live music; benches out under ivy trellis *(Mrs M Hughes, G Coates, Nick and Pam Hancock)*

White Hart [Corn Market]: Welcoming new licensees in old-fashioned low-beamed bar in pedestrian precinct a few steps from Minster, well kept real ales, wide range of good fresh reasonably priced bar food from good warm baguettes up in eating area, OAP bargains, good friendly service *(P Michelson, Derek, Hazel and Graeme Lloyd, JDM, KM)*

Winterborne Kingston [SY8697]

Greyhound [North St]: Good range of food, efficient service, Badger ales, plenty of room; piped radio *(Marjorie and David Lamb)*

Winterborne Zelston [SY8997]

Botany Bay [A31 Wimborne—Dorchester]: Roomy and attractive restaurant-oriented pub with good range of food, well kept Ringwood, lots of books, friendly service, decent coffee; tables on back terrace *(Marjorie and David Lamb)*

Wool [SY8486]

Ship [A352 Wareham—Dorchester]: Roomy open-plan thatched and timbered family pub doing well under new licensees; well decorated and furnished, with good choice of generous food all day inc children's in long low-ceilinged lounge bar and plush back restaurant, friendly quick service, well kept Badger Best, K&B and Tanglefoot; quiet piped music; picnic-sets overlooking railway in attractive fenced garden with terrace and play area, handy for Monkey World and Tank Museum, pleasant village *(Jenny and Brian Seller, W W Burke, Joan and Michel Hooper-Immins, Mrs Pat Crabb)*

Looking for a pub with a really special garden, or in lovely countryside, or with an outstanding view, or right by the water? They are listed separately, at the back of the book.

Essex

Two new entries here are the Alma in Chelmsford, imaginatively redesigned in a friendly traditional style, with imaginative food too; and the Rose at Peldon, a nice old place subtly smartened up and doing well under new owners, with good locally sourced food and a great choice of wines by the glass. Four old favourites, all doing particularly well these days, also have good food: the pretty thatched Axe & Compasses at Arkesden (nice all round), the plush Cricketers at Clavering (elaborate imaginative cooking), the handsome old White Hart at Great Yeldham (enterprising cooking, especially in the evenings, with good wines by the glass and a good guest beer policy), and the Bell in Horndon-on-the-Hill (a great all-rounder and always busy – food, beer, wine and welcome all choice, and a nice place to stay). We've known and liked the Bell for a long time, and it just seems to go on getting better and better: the Bell in Horndon-on-the-Hill is Essex Dining Pub of the Year. Other pubs deserving a special mention are the chatty and easy-going Sun in Feering (good changing beers), the Square & Compasses at Fuller Street (tasty food, buoyant atmosphere), the Green Man at Gosfield (kind service and good food, with an enjoyable lunchtime cold table), the pretty Viper at Mill Green (a nice all-rounder), the tucked-away Mole Trap near Stapleford Tawney (good no-nonsense food and drink), the lively and unspoilt Hoop at Stock (good beer), and the Green Dragon at Youngs End (a pleasantly extended dining pub, with very fairly priced fresh fish). In the Lucky Dip section at the end of the chapter, we'd pick out the Black Bull at Fyfield, Crooked Billet in Leigh-on-Sea, Duck at Newney Green, Plough at Radwinter and Cats at Woodham Walter – all inspected and approved by the editorial team. Drinks prices in Essex are slightly higher than the national average, and are now typically just over the £2 mark. The regional brewer Greene King tends to dominate the beer scene here: smaller Essex brewers to look out for include Ridleys, Crouch Vale and Mighty Oak.

ARKESDEN TL4834 Map 5

Axe & Compasses ★ 🍷

Village signposted from B1038 – but B1039 from Wendens Ambo, then forking left, is prettier

There's warm praise from readers for this rambling, thatched country pub, which has a welcoming and relaxed atmosphere – a well run place with a cheery landlord and friendly staff who cope well when it gets busy. Dating back to the 17th c, the cosy carpeted lounge bar is the oldest part, and has beautifully polished upholstered oak and elm seats, easy chairs and wooden tables, a warming fire, and lots of gleaming brasses. A smaller quirky public bar (which can get a bit smoky) is uncarpeted, with cosy built-in settles and a dart board. Popular home-made bar food changes daily but might include carrot and coriander soup (£3), sandwiches (from £3, weekdays only), prawn and smoked mackerel roulade (£4.95), moussaka and greek salad (£8.95), chicken supreme with lemon and tarragon butter or spaghetti and meatballs (£9.95), half a dozen fresh fish dishes such as cod fillet (£8.95) and monkfish on roasted red pepper sauce (£12.95), and a tempting puddings trolley with things like chocolate roulade or raspberry and hazelnut meringue (£3.50). The no smoking restaurant has a more elaborate menu. Well kept Greene King IPA, Old Speckled Hen and perhaps Ruddles County on handpump, a very good wine list and over 20 malt whiskies; cheerful, helpful service. There are seats out on a side terrace with pretty hanging baskets; parking at the back. It's in a very pretty village, with a crafts centre in the post office opposite. *(Recommended by David R Crafts, Peter Baggott, H O Dickinson, Jack Clarfelt, Marjorie and Bernard Parkin, Mr and Mrs Thomas, Mrs M Thomas, John and Patricia White, John Saville)*

Greene King ~ Lease Themis and Diane Christou ~ Real ale ~ Bar food (12-2, 6.45-9.30) ~ Restaurant ~ (01799) 550272 ~ Children in restaurant ~ Open 12-2.30, 6-11; 12-3, 7-10.30 Sun

BIRCHANGER TL5022 Map 5

Three Willows £

Under a mile from M11 junction 8: A120 towards Bishops Stortford, then almost immediately right to Birchanger Village; don't be waylaid earlier by the Birchanger Services signpost!

What draws so many people here is the good choice of fresh simply cooked fish served generously with chunky chips and plain salads, at hard-to-beat prices: £7.95 for most fish including paella, £9.95 for whole lemon sole or bass. There's also a fairly wide choice of usual food including sandwiches (from £2), filled baked potatoes (from £3), chilli con carne (£4.95), and roast duck breast (£9.95). The roomily extended carpeted main bar is filled with dark chairs and tables laid for dining; above a puce dado, the buff and brown ragged walls have a plethora of cricketing prints, photographs, cartoons and other memorabilia – the pub's name refers to cricket bats of the last three centuries. Well kept Greene King IPA, Abbot and Ruddles County on handpump, decent house wines, friendly and very informal family service. A small public bar has pool and sensibly placed darts, and there's a fruit machine. It's advisable to book if you want to eat in their restaurant. There are picnic-sets out on a terrace with heaters and on the lawn behind, with a sturdy climbing frame, swings and a basketball hoop (you can hear the motorway out here). No children are allowed inside. *(Recommended by Stephen and Jean Curtis, David and Pauline Loom, Joy and Peter Heatherley, Charles Gysin)*

Greene King ~ Tenants Paul and David Tucker ~ Real ale ~ Bar food (12-2, 7-9, not Sun evening) ~ Restaurant ~ 01279 815913 ~ Dogs allowed in bar ~ Open 11.30-3, 6-11; 12-3, 7-11 Sun

BURNHAM-ON-CROUCH TQ9596 Map 5

White Harte

The Quay

This friendly old hotel has a great outlook over the yachting estuary of the River Crouch – you can hear the water lapping against its private jetty and rigging slapping against the masts of boats on moorings beyond, and in summer it's popular with boaty types. Throughout the partly carpeted bars, with cushioned seats around oak tables, you'll find replicas of Royal Navy ships, and assorted nautical hardware such as a ship's wheel, a barometer, even a compass in the hearth. The other traditionally furnished high-ceilinged rooms have sea pictures on panelled or stripped brick walls. In winter, the enormous welcoming log fire fuels a cheerful atmosphere. Straightforward bar food includes sandwiches (from £2.10), soup (£2.80), locally caught skate, plaice or cod (£7.80), a handful of daily specials (all £5.60) such as chicken and sweetcorn pie, vegetable lasagne or pork in blackbean sauce, and puddings such as apple crumble and fruit pies (£2.80). Well kept Adnams, Crouch Vale Best and Tolly on handpump; friendly prompt service. *(Recommended by Lisa Lewis, George Atkinson, Mr and Mrs M Hayes, Theocsbrian)*

Free house ~ Licensee G John Lewis ~ Real ale ~ Bar food ~ Restaurant ~ (01621) 782106 ~ Children in eating area of bar and restaurant ~ Dogs welcome ~ Open 11-11; 12-10.30 Sun; closed 25 Dec afternoon ~ Bedrooms: £19.80(£44B)/£37(£59B)

CASTLE HEDINGHAM TL7835 Map 5

Bell

B1058 E of Sible Hedingham, towards Sudbury

There's loads of character at this fine old coaching inn, run by the same family for over 35 years. The unchanging beamed and timbered saloon bar has Jacobean-style seats and windsor chairs around sturdy oak tables, and beyond the standing timbers left from a knocked-through wall, some steps lead up to an unusual little gallery. Behind the traditionally furnished public bar, a games room has dominoes and cribbage. One bar is no smoking, and each of the rooms has a warming log fire; piped music. Straightforward bar food includes home-made soup (£2.95), ploughman's (£5), vegetarian chilli (£7.25), steak and Guinness pie (£7.25), red thai chicken curry (£7.95), and Monday night fish barbecue: sardines £6.50, swordfish £9; puddings such as treacle tart or apple and blackberry pie (from £3.25). Adnams, Greene King IPA and Old Speckled Hen, Shepherd Neame Spitfire and a guest such as Fullers London Pride are tapped from the cask. The big walled garden behind the pub is a pleasant place to sit in summer, with its acre or so of grass, trees and shrubs as well as a sandpit and toys for children; there are more seats on a vine-covered terrace. An acoustic guitar group plays on Friday evenings, they have live jazz on the last Sunday of the month, and there's a Sunday night pub quiz. The nearby 12th-c castle keep is worth a visit. *(Recommended by MLR, Bernie Adams, Mark Percy, Lesley Mayoh)*

Grays ~ Tenants Penny Doe and Kylie Turkoz-Ferguson ~ Real ale ~ Bar food (12-2(2.30 wknds), 7-9(9.30 wknds)) ~ (01787) 460350 ~ Children away from public bar ~ Traditional jazz last Sun lunchtime of month, acoustic guitar group Fri evening ~ Open 11.30-3(3.15 Sat), 6-11; 12-3.30, 7-10.30 Sun; closed 25 Dec evening

CHAPPEL TL8927 Map 5

Swan

Wakes Colne; pub visible just off A1124 Colchester—Halstead

Fresh fish is the speciality at this old timbered pub, with daily catches bringing in fried rock eel (£7.25, large £9.75), plaice (£7.95, large £11.95), haddock (£7.95, large £11.95), skate (£8.95), and a mixed fish platter (£12.95). Other good value popular bar food includes filled baguettes or sandwiches (from £1.75), ploughman's (from £3.75), gammon with pineapple or home-made pies (from £6.45), sirloin steak (£10.95), and good puddings (from £3.25); a simple children's menu. It's splendidly set, with the River Colne running through the garden on its way to an impressive Victorian viaduct. Big overflowing flower tubs and French street signs lend the sheltered suntrap cobbled courtyard a continental feel, and gas heaters mean that you can sit out even on cooler evenings. Inside, the spacious and low-beamed rambling bar has standing oak timbers dividing off side areas, plenty of dark wood chairs around lots of dark tables for diners, one or two swan pictures and plates on the white and partly panelled walls, and a few attractive tiles above the very big fireplace (which is filled with lots of plants in summer). The central bar area keeps a pubbier atmosphere, with regulars dropping in for a drink; piped music and fruit machine. The lounge bar is no smoking. Well kept Greene King IPA, Abbot and a guest such as Nethergate on handpump, a good choice of wines by the glass, and just under two dozen malt whiskies, served by cheery helpful staff; cribbage. Just a few minutes walk away is the Railway Centre (a must for train buffs). *(Recommended by Judy Wayman, Bob Arnett, David J Bunter, Colin and Dot Savill, Ian Phillips, B N F and M Parkin, Malcolm and Jennifer Perry, Richard Siebert)*

Free house ~ Licensee Terence Martin ~ Real ale ~ Bar food (12-2.30(3 Sun), 7(6.30 Sat)-10.30) ~ Restaurant ~ (01787) 222353 ~ Children in eating area of bar and restaurant ~ Dogs allowed in bar ~ Open 11-3, 6-11; 11-11 Sat; 12-10.30 Sun

It is illegal for bar staff to smoke while handling your drink.

CHELMSFORD TL7006 Map 5

Alma

Arbour Lane, off B1137 (Springfield Road)

A new Chelmsford oasis, this has been transformed by its current owners – attractive layout and décor, a civilised country-pub feel, and good food. The beamed bar, mainly carpeted, has a comfortable mix of tables and brocade-cushioned chairs and stools, a central brick fireplace with a club fender, a piano nearby, and a big mirror over another prettily tiled fireplace flanked by bookcases. One cosy alcove has a deeply cushioned button-back leather sofa and armchair, and above a dark dado there's a nice collection of old advertising posters on the puce rough-cast walls. There are red-cushioned bar stools on flagstones by the brick-built serving counter – look out for the trompe l'oeil on the wall opposite – which has well kept Greene King IPA and a couple of guests such as Nethergate Suffolk County and Shepherd Neame Spitfire on handpump, and decent house wines; good friendly service; a TV in one corner, piped music and fruit machine. Besides the no smoking bar dining area, there's a comfortable restaurant prettily decorated in creams and blues, with an inglenook fireplace. The food, changing seasonally, might include courgette and lemon grass soup with oriental pork wontons (£2.95), fried pigeon breast with sweet red cabbage and smoked bacon lardons (£4.75), open mediterranean vegetable and dolcelatte ravioli with roquefort and chard salads (£7.95), steamed lamb, rosemary and onion pudding (£9.50), fillet of bass with fried garlic scampi tails (£12.95), fruits de mer (£25, with 24 hours' notice), and puddings such as summer pudding with wild berry coulis and blackcurrant sorbet or orange bread and butter pudding with chocolate sauce (£3.95); Sunday roast (£6.95). They do a couple of special offers including a two-course lunch for £5, and 25% off your meal if you eat between six and seven. There are picnic-sets out on a crazy-paved terrace at the front and in a small garden at the back. *(Recommended by Robert Swanborough, Rebecca Nicholls)*

Free house ~ Licensees David and Sheila Hunt ~ Real ale ~ Bar food (12-2.30, 6-9.30) ~ Restaurant ~ (01245) 256783 ~ Children in eating area of bar and restaurant ~ Dogs allowed in bar ~ Open 11-11; 12-10.30 Sun; closed 26 Dec

CLAVERING TL4731 Map 5

Cricketers

B1038 Newport—Buntingford, Newport end of village

This smart, immaculately modernised 16th-c dining pub is run by the parents of TV chef Jamie Oliver, and the imaginative cooking lives up to expectations. It attracts a well heeled set as prices are not cheap, but helpings are generous. There can be a really lively atmosphere during busy lunchtimes, when you might have to wait for the freshly prepared and fairly elaborate bar food. As well as sandwiches (from £3.50), the seasonally changing menu might include starters such as carpaccio of salmon (£6), roast boned quail with a chicken stuffing and quails egg with a shallot and honey sauce (£6.50), and main courses such as medallions of veal on braised savoy cabbage with blue cheese sauce (£12.75), duck breast with apricot and lemon sauce (£15.25) or fried king scallops and prawns with saffron, fried potatoes and pasta (£17.75). There's an enticing puddings trolley (£4.50); children's meals (£3.50), or they can have a half helping of some main meals. Service is friendly and professional. The spotlessly kept and roomy L-shaped beamed bar has standing timbers resting on new brickwork, and pale green plush button-backed banquettes, stools and windsor chairs around shiny wooden tables on a pale green carpet, gleaming copper pans and horsebrasses, dried flowers in the big fireplace (open fire in colder weather), and fresh flowers on the tables; one area and the restaurant are no smoking; piped music. Adnams, Tetleys and a guest on handpump; specialist teas. The attractive front terrace has picnic-sets and umbrellas among colourful flowering shrubs. The pretty traditionally furnished bedrooms are in the adjacent cottage. *(Recommended by Terry Mizen, Derek Thomas, Joy and Peter Heatherley, David Twitchett, Mrs A Chesher, Gordon Theaker, D Moore Brooks, Brian and Pat Wardrobe)*

Free house ~ Licensee Trevor Oliver ~ Real ale ~ Bar food (12-2, 7-10) ~ Restaurant ~

(01799) 550442 ~ Children in family room, eating area of bar and restaurant ~ Open 10.30-3, 6-11 ~ Bedrooms: £70B/£100B

COGGESHALL TL8224 Map 5

Compasses

Pattiswick; signposted from A120 about 2 miles W of Coggeshall

Surrounded by rolling farmland, this friendly pub is a quiet spot to eat outside in the summer, with seats in an orchard and on the lawns, and an adventure play area to keep the children happy. Inside, the attractive, spacious beamed bars are neatly kept and comfortable, with tiled floors and lots of brass ornaments. The atmosphere is welcoming and the staff friendly. Under new licensees, bar food includes soup (£3.75), sandwiches (from £3.95), scampi (£7.95), steak and ale pie (£8.95), daily specials such as garlic mushrooms (£3.95), prawns and smoked salmon (£5.95), sirloin steak or chilli (£7.95), and puddings such as toffee and praline cheesecake or toffee and banana pudding (£3.95); the three-course weekday lunchtime special (£12.95) includes a bottle of wine for each couple. More elaborate dishes are served in the adjacent, partly no smoking barn restaurant. Well kept Adnams and Greene King IPA and Abbot on handpump. *(Recommended by Gordon Neighbour, John W Allen, Charles Gysin, Ian Phillips)*

Free house ~ Licensees Daryl and Melissa Heffer ~ Real ale ~ Bar food ~ Restaurant ~ (01376) 561322 ~ Children welcome ~ Open 12-11; 12-3, 6-11.30 Mon-Fri winter

FEERING TL8720 Map 5

Sun

Feering Hill; before Feering proper, B1024 just NE of Kelvedon

Up to 30 mostly unusual real ales might pass through the six handpumps every week at this very friendly easy-going old place, and the bar staff are happy to chat to you about their range; a typical clutch might be Blanchfields Bull Best and Raging Bull, Crouch Vale FPA, Shepherd Neame Masterbrew and St Peters Best. Their Easter and August bank holiday beer festivals have a regional theme, when they'll stock ales from a particular county or area. They also keep one or two weekly changing farm ciders, and over 40 malt whiskies. This gabled inn was originally part of a 16th-c mansion, and carvings on the beams in the lounge are reputedly linked with Catherine of Aragon. Standing timbers break up the several areas, with plenty of neatly matching tables and chairs, green-cushioned stools and banquettes around the walls, and a handsome canopy with a sun motif over the woodburning stove; newspapers, backgammon, chess, dominoes, fruit machine. Well presented good value bar food includes sandwiches (from £1.90), ploughman's (from £4.50), scampi (£5.50), daily specials such as garlic mushrooms (£3.50), roast of the day (£4.95), steak and kidney pudding (£6.90), spicy chicken in a peanut and tomato sauce (£7.50), and puddings such as bread and butter pudding (from £2.40). Behind the pub is a partly covered paved terrace with quite a few seats and tables; there are more in an attractive garden beyond the car park. They sometimes have barbecues on sunny weekends. *(Recommended by Mrs V Brown, Joy and Peter Heatherley, Michael and Jeanne Shillington, Ian Phillips, Peter Saville)*

Free house ~ Licensees Charles and Kim Scicluna ~ Real ale ~ Bar food (12-2(3 Sun), 6-9.30) ~ Restaurant ~ No credit cards ~ (01376) 570442 ~ Well behaved children allowed ~ Dogs welcome ~ Open 12-3, 6-11(10.30 Sun)

FINGRINGHOE TM0220 Map 5

Whalebone

Follow Rowhedge, Fingringhoe signpost off A134, the part that's just S of Colchester centre; or Fingringhoe signposted off B1025 S of Colchester

It's well worth a trip off the beaten track to find this very civilised and relaxing pub. The pale yellow washed interior has been very nicely done out, its three room areas airily opened together, leaving some timber studs, and there's a pleasant mix of chairs and cushioned settles around stripped tables on the unsealed bare boards. Roman blinds with swagged pelmets, neat wall lamps, a hanging chandelier and local watercolours (for sale) are good finishing touches. The main focus is the genuinely inventive cooking and stylish food presentation. Dishes are listed on a blackboard over the small but warming coal fire. Starters might include asparagus and dill soup (£3.50), spiced bean patties with mango chutney and nan bread (£4.75), griddled tiger prawns with lemon and garlic (£4.95), baby aubergine and chilli casserole with couscous (£8.95), rack of lamb on carrot and parsnip purée with caramelised onions and port sauce (£9.50), skate wing with black butter and capers (£9.75), sautéed pigeon breasts on celeriac and walnut rösti with port glaze (£9.95), and puddings such as toffee and banana crumble and custard (£3.95), or cheesecake with red berry coulis (£4). They also do a wide and interesting choice of lunchtime sandwiches and baguettes (from £2.95), a good value set menu (two courses £8.95, three £10.95), and good breakfasts 10-11.30am. Well kept Greene King IPA, Abbot and Old Speckled Hen and a guest such as Mauldons Cuckoo Old on handpump, decent house wines and coffee; good service; piped music. The back garden, with gravel paths winding through the grass around a sizeable old larch tree, has picnic-sets with a peaceful valley view. *(Recommended by Jane Hunt)*

Free house ~ Licensee Vivien Steed ~ Real ale ~ Bar food (10-2.30, 6.30-9.30) ~ Restaurant ~ (01206) 729307 ~ Children in separate family room ~ Dogs allowed in bar ~ Occasional plays ~ Open 10-3, 5.30-11; 10-11 summer Sat/Sun

FULLER STREET TL7416 Map 5

Square & Compasses

From A12 Chelmsford—Witham take Hatfield Peverel exit, and from B1137 there follow Terling signpost, keeping straight on past Terling towards Great Leighs; from A131 Chelmsford—Braintree turn off in Great Leighs towards Fairstead and Terling

Cheerily individualistic licensees, a welcoming atmosphere, and enjoyable interesting food have won many friends for this small, civilised country pub. Along with the stuffed birds, traps and brasses which adorn the L-shaped beamed bar, you'll find otter tails, birds' eggs and old photographs of local characters, many of whom still use the pub. Comfortable and well lit, this carpeted bar has a woodburning stove as well as a big log fire; shove-ha'penny, table skittles, cribbage, dominoes and a fruit machine. Very well kept Nethergate Suffolk County and Ridleys IPA tapped from the cask, decent French regional wines. The wide choice of home-made bar food ranges from filled rolls and sandwiches (from £3), soup (£3.60), ham and eggs (£7.25), and fish pie (£8.75) to regularly changing and rewarding specials such as pigeon breast with crispy bacon croutons (£6.50), garlic sausages with bubble and squeak or goats cheese and red onion tart (£8.75), home-made quiche (£9), and fresh fish such as swordfish with roasted peppers (£13.50), and chargrilled butterfish with asparagus (£14), home-made puddings (from £4). There are gentle country views from tables outside; disabled lavatories. *(Recommended by Roger and Pauline Pearce, Adrian White, John and Enid Morris, Peter Baggott, Tina and David Woods-Taylor, Charles and Pauline Stride, B N F and M Parkin, Colin and Dot Savill, Paul and Ursula Randall, Bob and Maggie Atherton)*

Free house ~ Licensees Howard Potts and Ginny Austin ~ Real ale ~ Bar food (12-2, 7-9(10 Fri/Sat); light snacks at any time) ~ Restaurant ~ (01245) 361477 ~ Well behaved children welcome in eating area of the bar ~ Dogs welcome ~ Open 11.30-3, 6.30(7 in winter)-11; 12-3, 7-10.30 Sun; closed Mon

GOSFIELD TL7829 Map 5

Green Man

3 miles N of Braintree

Readers really enjoy the help-yourself lunchtime cold table at this smart dining pub, where you can choose from a tempting display of home-cooked ham and pork, turkey, tongue, beef and poached or smoked salmon, as well as game pie, salads and home-made pickles (from £7.15). There's a good choice of generous, mostly traditional English bar food too, including soups such as game with sherry (from £2.85), sandwiches (from £2.65), filled baked potatoes (from £2.75), soft roe on toast (£3.75), steak and kidney pudding (£7.35), trout baked with almonds (£7.50), calves liver and bacon or pork chops marinated in dill and mustard (£8.25), chicken breast filled with crab, cream cheese and prawns (£8.95), swordfish steak (£9.35), and half a roast duck with orange and red wine sauce (£11.50). Mouth-watering home-made puddings include fruit pies, pavlovas and treacle tart (£3.30), vegetables are fresh, and the chips home-made. The landlady is welcoming and you can expect kind, friendly and efficient service. There's a laid-back sociable atmosphere in the two little bars, which have well kept Greene King IPA and Abbot on handpump. Many of the decent nicely priced wines are by the glass; darts, pool, fruit machine and juke box. Booking is advisable even midweek. *(Recommended by I D Greenfield, George Atkinson, John and Patricia White, Richard Siebert, B N F and M Parkin, Richard and Margaret Peers)*

Greene King ~ Lease Janet Harrington ~ Real ale ~ Bar food (12-2, 6.45-9, not Sun evening) ~ Restaurant ~ (01787) 472746 ~ Children in eating area of bar and restaurant ~ Dogs allowed in bar ~ Open 11-2.30, 6.15-11; 12-2.30, 7-10.30 Sun

GREAT YELDHAM TL7638 Map 5

White Hart 🍴 🍷

Poole Street; A1017 Halstead—Haverhill

Recent interior restoration after flood damage to this black and white timbered dining pub was supervised by English Heritage to ensure that it was in keeping with its Grade I* listing. The main areas have stone and wood floors with some dark oak panelling, especially around the fireplace; watch your head – the door into the bar is very low. The food is what most people come here for, so booking is recommended; cooked by the landlord, the same ambitious imaginative menu is available in the bar or in the no smoking restaurant. At lunchtime you can enjoy soup (£3.75), ploughman's (£5.95), pasta with creamy wild mushrooms, spinach and parmesan (£6.75), smoked salmon brioche with chive crème fraîche (£7.25), cod and chips (£9.50), and steamed venison and onion pudding (£11.95). Meals on the more sophisticated evening menu might include starters such as coarse venison terrine with runner bean chutney (£5.25) and seared scallops on a bok choy and oyster mushroom stir fry with sweet pepper sauce (£8.50), main courses such as baked oyster mushroom, plum tomato and dolcelatte cheese tart with warm french bean, rocket and almond salad (£9.95), medallion of beef on roast cocotte potatoes with wild mushroom, mustard and tarragon jus (£11.95), grilled calves liver on buttered leeks and lentils with crispy pancetta and sage jus (£13.75), and puddings such as blackberry and pear sorbet or sticky toffee pudding with fudge sauce (£3.95-£5.25); smaller helpings available for children. Vegetables are extra, and service can be slow at times. As well as Adnams Bitter, one or two very regularly changing real ales on handpump could be Blue Moon Dark Island and Moorhouses Black Cat. They also stock a good range of Belgian bottled beers, organic fruit juices and cider, and have a very good wine list with about 10 by the glass. The already attractive garden with well tended lawns and pretty seating has been landscaped and replanted. *(Recommended by Marjorie and Bernard Parkin, Peter Baggott, Tina and David Woods-Taylor, I D Greenfield, Richard Siebert, Ray and Jacki Davenport, Pam and David Bailey)*

Free house ~ Licensee John Dicken ~ Real ale ~ Bar food (12-2, 6.30(7 Sun)-9.30) ~ Restaurant ~ (01787) 237250 ~ Children in eating area of bar and restaurant ~ Open 11-3, 6-11; 12-3, 7-10.30 Sun

HASTINGWOOD TL4807 Map 5

Rainbow & Dove £

¼ mile from M11 junction 7; Hastingwood signposted after Ongar signs at exit roundabout

It's well worth knowing this comfortable 17th-c rose-covered cottage as it makes such a handy break from the motorway, but it's very much a favourite in its own right too. There are cosy fires in the three homely little low-beamed rooms which open off the main bar area; the one on the left is particularly snug and beamy, with the lower part of its wall stripped back to bare brick and decorated with brass pistols and plates. A small function room is no smoking. The atmosphere is relaxed, even when it's busy. Reasonably priced bar food includes sandwiches (from £2.25), baked potatoes (from £2.50), crab (£3.95), ploughman's (from £4.25), local sausages and mash (£4.95), turkey, ham and mushroom pie (£5), vegetable crumble (£5.75), and two or three fresh fish dishes such as skate wing, sea bream with mushroom sauce and swordfish (from £4.95). Well kept Courage Directors, Greene King IPA and a guest such as Youngs Special on handpump; piped music. Hedged off from the car park is a stretch of grass with picnic-sets under cocktail parasols. Being so close to the motorway, the pub does sometimes come under pressure from floods of visitors; one or two readers have suggested that housekeeping might need to be beefed up to cope with this, but the great majority have found no problem. *(Recommended by Joy and Colin Rorke, Colin and Janet Roe, David Twitchett, B N F and M Parkin, Tony Beaulah, Peter Meister, Ian Phillips, Mrs A Chesher, Roy and Lindsey Fentiman, Patricia Beebe, Michael Butler, Tony Middis, Adrian White, Gordon Neighbour)*

Punch ~ Tenants Jamie and Andrew Keep ~ Real ale ~ Bar food (12-2.30, 7-9.30) ~ (01279) 415419 ~ Children in eating area of bar ~ Open 11.30-3, 6-11; 12-3, 7-10.30 Sun

HORNDON-ON-THE-HILL TQ6683 Map 3

Bell

M25 junction 30 into A13, then left into B1007 after 7 miles, village signposted from here

Essex Dining Pub of the Year

Centuries ago, many important medieval dignitaries would have stayed at this ancient place, as it was the last inn before travellers heading south could ford the Thames at Highams Causeway. Doing as well these days as then, it's still a welcoming and refreshing stop with almost everything you need for a fulfilling visit. The heavily beamed bar has some antique high-backed settles and benches, rugs on the flagstones or highly polished oak floorboards, and a curious collection of ossified hot cross buns hanging from a beam. Food is prepared to a high standard, and the very popular menu (you may need to book), which changes twice a day, is available in the bar and no smoking restaurant. Prettily presented dishes might include butternut soup with curried garlic (£3.95), sandwiches such as smoked salmon with dill and mayonnaise (from £4.50), chicken caesar salad (£5.50), grilled cod fillet with white beans and watercress (£7.50), red wine and tradivo risotto with balsamic poached egg and sage (£11.50), roast rabbit saddle with tea-smoked sweetbreads and parsley (£12.50), and puddings such as glazed banana and lime tart with praline ice cream or passion fruit panna cotta with coffee marshmallow and cardamom ice cream (£5). They have a good list of over 100 well chosen wines from all over the world, including over a dozen by the glass, and you can buy very fairly priced bottles off-sales. They are keen on supporting local brewers and stock a good range of well kept real ales, with quickly rotating guests such as Burntwood Mighty Oak, Mauldons White Adder and Ridleys Rumpus joining Bass and Greene King IPA on handpump; occasional beer festivals. The beamed bedrooms are very attractive. *(Recommended by Malcolm and Jennifer Perry, Suzie Gibbons, Simon Pyle, John and Enid Morris, Stephen, Julie and Hayley Brown, Kevin Flack, Evelyn and Derek Walter, Pat and Tony Martin, Bruce M Drew, R T and J C Moggridge, John Saville, Adrian White, Mrs A Mager, Thomas Neate, Kay Vowles, Ian Phillips, Len Banister, Bernie Adams)*

Free house ~ Licensee John Vereker ~ Real ale ~ Bar food (12-1.45, 6.45-9.45; not bank hols) ~ Restaurant ~ (01375) 642463 ~ Children in eating area of bar and restaurant ~ Dogs allowed in bar and bedrooms ~ Open 11-2.30(3 Sat), 5.30(6 Sat)-11; 12-4, 7-10.30 Sun; closed 25, 26 Dec ~ Bedrooms: /£65B

Prices of main dishes usually include vegetables or a side salad.

LANGHAM TM0233 Map 5

Shepherd & Dog 🍷

Moor Road/High Street; village signposted off A12 N of Colchester

The spick and span L-shaped bar at this welcoming village pub is made up of an engaging hotch-potch of styles, with interesting collections of continental bottled beers and brass and copper fire extinguishers, and there are usually books on sale for charity. Made wherever possible from fresh local produce (all the meat is British), good hearty home-cooked food which changes daily is chalked on boards around the bar, and might include sandwiches (from £2.30), starters (all £3.95) such as fresh sardines, garlic mushrooms or crab cakes with plum and lemon sauce, 10 fresh fish dishes such as tuna, salmon and squid kebabs or grilled halibut with thai coconut sauce (£8.95), skate with ginger butter (£9.95) as well as grilled ox tongue with madeira (£6.95), confit of duck with couscous (£8.95), and puddings such as apple and apricot crumble or chocolate parfait (£3.25); Sunday roast (from £6.50). Well kept Greene King IPA, Abbot and Ruddles County with a weekly changing guest such as Nethergate Suffolk County on handpump, and a short but thoughtful wine list; pleasant obliging service. In summer, there are very pretty window boxes, and a shaded bar in the enclosed side garden; tables outside. They now have regular (and very popular) theme weeks and activity nights. *(Recommended by Peter Baggott, John McDonald, Ian Phillips, B N F and M Parkin, Sarah Lomas, R J Walden)*

Free house ~ Licensees Paul Barnes and Jane Graham ~ Real ale ~ Bar food (12-2.15, 6-10) ~ Restaurant ~ (01206) 272711 ~ Children welcome ~ Dogs allowed in bar ~ Folk jam sessions every fourth Sun ~ Open 11-3, 5.30(6 Sat)-11; 12-3, 7-10.30 Sun

LITTLE BRAXTED TL8314 Map 5

Green Man

Kelvedon Road; village signposted off B1389 by NE end of A12 Witham bypass – keep on patiently

Keep on driving down a fairly long isolated lane to find this pretty tucked away brick house, which is a great place to come for a quiet drink. The welcoming, cosy little lounge has an open fire and an interesting collection of bric-a-brac, including 200 horsebrasses, some harness, mugs hanging from a beam, and a lovely copper urn. The more spartan tiled public bar has darts, shove-ha'penny, cribbage, dominoes and fruit machine; well kept Ridleys IPA and Old Bob, along with several malt whiskies. The sheltered garden behind the pub has picnic-sets and a pond, and the new licensees plan summer Sunday barbecues out here. Reasonably priced and enjoyably straightforward home-made bar food is served in generous helpings, and includes sandwiches (from £2.35), ploughman's (£5.25), cottage pie (£3.75), a couple of daily specials such as steak and ale pie (£6.95), minted lamb shank (£7.95), and puddings such as treacle tart or apple pie (£2.95); friendly service. *(Recommended by Ian Phillips, John and Elspeth Howell, Mary and Dennis Jones, Joy and Peter Heatherley)*

Ridleys ~ Tenant Neil Pharaoh ~ Real ale ~ Bar food ~ (01621) 891659 ~ Dogs allowed in bar ~ Open 11.30-3, 6(5 Fri) -11; 11.30-11 Sat; 12-10.30 Sun

LITTLE DUNMOW TL6521 Map 5

Flitch of Bacon 🛏

Village signposted off A120 E of Dunmow, then turn right on village loop road

The Caldwells give an uplifting Scottish welcome at this unchanging country pub, with its easy-going mix of locals and visitors gathering in the small timbered bar. It's simply but attractively furnished, with flowery-cushioned pews and ochre walls, and while quietly relaxing on weekday lunchtimes, in the evenings it can get quite bustling; piped music. From a short menu, the straightforward reasonably priced bar food might include sandwiches (from £2.30), scampi (£5.95), liver and bacon (£6.50), smoked haddock and spinach bake (£6.75), and sirloin steak (£9.50); the back eating area is no smoking. Well kept Greene King IPA with a couple of guests from brewers such as Crouch Vale and Nethergate on handpump, several wines by the glass, and 10 or so malt whiskies. There are views across a quiet lane to a broad expanse of green with a few picnic-sets on the edge, and a back room has french windows looking out on to the terrace. The nearby church of St Mary is well worth a visit (the pub has a key). Basic, but clean and comfortable bedrooms. Handy for Stansted Airport. *(Recommended by Stephen and Jean Curtis, Ian Phillips, Tony Beaulah)*

Free house ~ Licensees David and Teresa Caldwell ~ Real ale ~ Bar food (not Sun evening) ~ Restaurant ~ No credit cards ~ (01371) 820323 ~ Children in family room ~ Dogs allowed in bar ~ Open 12-3, 6-11(7-10.30 Sun) ~ Bedrooms: £40S/£55S

LITTLE WALDEN TL5441 Map 5

Crown

B1052 N of Saffron Walden

The warm, cosy atmosphere in the low-beamed bar of this 18th-c low white cottage is helped along by a good log fire in the brick fireplace, bookroom-red walls, flowery curtains and a mix of bare boards and navy carpeting. Seats, ranging from high-backed pews to little cushioned armchairs, are spaced around a good variety of closely arranged tables, mostly big, some stripped. The small red-tiled room on the right has two little tables, and darts. You can expect to find up to six very well kept real ales tapped from the cask by friendly, chatty staff. Alongside Greene King IPA and Abbot, there could be Adnams Regatta, City of Cambridge Boathouse and Hook Norton. Generously served bar food includes sandwiches (from £2.25), soup (£3.50), ploughman's (from £4.25), home-made lasagne (£6.95), steak and ale pie (£7.95), and changing daily specials on blackboards such as vegetable curry (£7.50), smoked haddock mornay (£7.95), chicken cacciatore (£8.95), cold seafood platter (£9.75), and beef stroganoff (£10.25), with puddings such as bread and butter pudding (from £3.50); piped local radio. The walk from the car park in the dark can be tricky. *(Recommended by Kevin Thorpe, Stephen, Julie and Hayley Brown, MLR, Joy and Peter Heatherley, Peter Baggott)*

Free house ~ Licensee Colin Hayling ~ Real ale ~ Bar food (not Sun/Mon evening) ~ (01799) 522475 ~ Children welcome ~ Dogs allowed in bar ~ Trad jazz Weds evening ~ Open 11-3, 6-11; 12-10.30 Sun

MILL GREEN TL6401 Map 5

Viper £

The Common; from Fryerning (which is signposted off north-east bound A12 Ingatestone bypass) follow Writtle signposts

Quietly set in the middle of a wood, this charmingly uncomplicated, friendly little pub is well worth a visit in summer, when its front is almost hidden by overflowing hanging baskets and window boxes; tables on the lawn overlook a carefully tended cottage garden which is an absolute mass of colour. There's an easy-going welcoming atmosphere in the two timeless cosy lounge rooms, which have spindleback seats, armed country kitchen chairs, and tapestried wall seats around neat little old tables, and there's a log fire. Booted walkers are directed towards the fairly basic parquet-floored tap room, which is more simply furnished with shiny wooden traditional wall seats, and beyond that another room has country kitchen chairs and sensibly placed darts; shove-ha'penny, dominoes, cribbage and a fruit machine. From an oak-panelled counter they serve very well kept Ridleys IPA and five weekly changing guests from breweries such as Nethergate and local Mighty Oak on handpump, as well as farm cider. The simple bar snacks are served only at lunchtime, and include good sandwiches (from £2, toasted from £2.50), soup (£2.50), hawaiian toast (£2.75), chilli con carne (£3.50) and ploughman's (from £4.75). Cheerful service even when busy; no children in pub. The friendly dog is called Ben. *(Recommended by Peter Baggott, Ian Phillips, Phil and Sally Gorton, John and Enid Morris, Sarah Davis, Rod Lambert, Kay Vowles, Pete Baker, Len Banister)*

Free house ~ Licensee Roger Beard ~ Real ale ~ Bar food (12-2(2.30 Sat/Sun) only) ~ No credit cards ~ (01277) 352010 ~ Dogs allowed in bar ~ Open 12-3, 6-11(7-10.30 Sun)

PAGLESHAM TQ9492 Map 5

Plough & Sail

East End; on the Paglesham road out of Rochford, keep right instead of heading into Church End

Clad in white weatherboarding (like many of the older buildings around here), this beautifully kept 17th-c dining pub is in a pretty spot and so can get very busy on warm summer evenings. It's friendly and cosy inside, with big log fires, pine tables and seats under its rather low beams, lots of brasses and pictures, and pretty flower arrangements. Good food includes sandwiches (from £2.75), soup (£2.75), ploughman's (£4.25), lasagne (£7.50), and steak and kidney pie (£7.95), with interesting daily specials such as field mushrooms topped with brie (£3.95), fresh prawns, crab and salmon on mixed leaves with balsamic dressing (£6.25), home-made curries (£6.95), and fresh fish such as fried skate or monkfish (from £8.95); home-made puddings such as fruit crumble and coconut and lime pudding with coconut ice cream (£3.25). The staff are friendly and attentive. Well kept Greene King IPA and and a guest such as Shepherd Neame Spitfire on handpump; decent house wines; cribbage, dominoes and unobtrusive piped music. There are tables and an aviary in the attractive and neatly kept garden. *(Recommended by George Atkinson)*

Free house ~ Licensee M Oliver ~ Real ale ~ Bar food ~ Restaurant ~ (01702) 258242 ~ Open 12-3(11.30-3.30 Sat), 6.30-11; 12-11 Sun

Punchbowl 🍷

Church End; from the Paglesham road out of Rochford, Church End is signposted on the left

In a secluded spot away from it all down long country lanes, the cosy beamed bar of this pretty white weatherboarded pub is beautifully kept, with pews, barrel chairs and other seats, and lots of bric-a-brac. Enjoyable good value bar food includes rolls (from £2), sandwiches and filled baguettes (from £2.30), soup (£2.25), filled baked potatoes or prawn cocktail (£3.50), ploughman's (£4.25), vegetable jambalaya or battered haddock (£5.25), cajun chicken or gammon steak (£6.95), daily specials such as lamb with rosemary (£6.75), beef stroganoff (£6.95), and good fresh fish such as grilled skate, plaice or dover sole (from £5.95); puddings such as raspberry pavlova and bread pudding (from £2.75). Well kept Adnams and Ridleys Old Bob and a couple of guests such as Elgoods Double Swan and Nethergate Woodmans on handpump; piped music. There are some tables in the small garden, with a couple out by the quiet road. *(Recommended by Richard Gibbs)*

Free house ~ Licensees Bernie and Pat Cardy ~ Real ale ~ Bar food ~ Restaurant ~ (01702) 258376 ~ Children in restaurant if eating ~ Open 11.30-3, 7- 11; 12-3, 7-10.30 Sun

PELDON TL9916 Map 5

Rose 🍷

B1025 Colchester—Mersea, at junction with southernmost turn-off to Peldon

Quite recently taken under promising new management, and we have high hopes for this huge pastel-washed inn, which has been bought by the well known family-owned Essex wine merchant Lay & Wheeler as their first and only pub. They have gently smartened it up, without disturbing the fine sense of history in its dark alcoves that conjure up smugglers discussing bygone contraband. In the cosy bar one or two standing timbers support the low ceiling with its dark bowed 17th-c oak beams; there are creaky close-set tables, some antique mahogany, leaded-light windows, and brass and copper on the mantelpiece of the gothick-arched brick fireplace. The very spacious airy conservatory has a much more modern feel, and is no smoking. Not surprisingly they have a very good wine list, with over 20 by the glass listed with helpful descriptions on a blackboard, alongside well kept Adnams Best and Broadside, Greene King IPA and a guest from a local brewer such as Mauldons. Changing bar food, home-made and where possible locally sourced, might include sandwiches (from £3.25, smoked salmon £5), marinated herring fillets on potato salad (£4.50), aubergine filled with mediterranean vegetables and brie (£6.95), steak and mushroom pie or sausage and mash (£7.25), sweet and sour chicken or braised shoulder of lamb (£8.50), very good local Mersea fish such as grilled cod, plaice or skate (from £8.95), and puddings such as warm apricot sponge with toffee sauce and vanilla ice cream or baked lemon cheesecake (£3.50). They do smaller helpings of main courses for children (from £4.25), and do their best to suit special wishes. Staff are friendly and efficient, though as it does get very busy you may need to book. The spacious garden is very relaxing, with good teak seats and a nice pond with white ducks. *(Recommended by Gordon Neighbour, Chris Pearson, Hazel Morgan, Robb Tooley, Rona Murdoch)*

Lay & Wheeler ~ Licensees Alex Scarf, John Riddlestone, Richard Solomans ~ Real ale ~ Bar food (12-2(sandwiches till 3), 6.30-9(9.30 Fri, Sat)) ~ (01206) 735248 ~ Children welcome away from bar ~ Open 11-11; 12-10.30 Sun ~ Bedrooms: £45B/£60B

STAPLEFORD TAWNEY TL5501 Map 5

Mole Trap £

Tawney Common, which is signposted off A113 just N of M25 overpass; OS Sheet 167 map reference 550013

It's quite a treat when you open the door (mind your head as you go in!) to this lovely country pub, which is tucked away in what seems like the back of beyond, to find it simply humming with customers – a true sign of quality in such a peaceful and isolated spot. The smallish carpeted bar has black dado, beams and joists, brocaded wall seats, library chairs and bentwood elbow chairs around plain pub tables, and steps down through a partly knocked-out timber stud wall to a similar area; keeping those three coal fires blazing must be nearly a full-time job. There are a few small pictures, 3-D decorative plates, some dried-flower arrangements and (on the sloping ceiling formed by a staircase beyond) some regulars' snapshots, with a few dozen beermats stuck up around the serving bar. The beers on handpump include Fullers London Pride and a couple of interesting guests such as Caledonian Deuchars IPA and Timothy Taylors Landlord; the piped radio tends to be almost inaudible under the gentle wash of contented chatter. In the food line, the lamb curry is strongly tipped, and other home-made dishes include sandwiches (£2.50), liver and bacon, chicken and ham pie, quiche or fresh fish (£5.50), and steaks (£6.95). Beware if your children or dogs don't behave here, as we wouldn't put it past the kindly but no nonsense landlady, and very friendly landlord, to ask you to leave. There are some plastic tables and chairs and a picnic-set outside, and quite a tribe of resident animals, many rescued and most wandering around outside, including very friendly cats, rabbits, a couple of dogs, hens, geese, a sheep, goats and horses. *(Recommended by H O Dickinson, Stephen Jeal, Ian Phillips, Bernie Adams)*

Free house ~ Licensees Mr and Mrs Kirtley ~ Real ale ~ Bar food (not Sun evening) ~ No credit cards ~ (01992) 522394 ~ Well behaved children in family room ~ Dogs allowed in bar ~ Open 11.30-3, 6.30(perhaps 7 in winter)-11; 12-4, 7-10.30 Sun

STOCK TQ6998 Map 5

Hoop £

B1007; from A12 Chelmsford bypass take Galleywood, Billericay turn-off

The cheerful unspoilt atmosphere makes this refreshingly unmodern village pub most enjoyable. Another main draw is the bank of splendidly kept changing real ales, usually six tapped from the cask or on handpump, from breweries such as Adnams, Crouch Vale, Fullers, Hop Back, Mighty Oak and Woodfordes. They also serve changing farm ciders and perries, and mulled wine in winter. The atmosphere in the cosy, bustling bar is inclusive, and the staff are friendly. Traditional consistently good value bar food includes soup (£3), sandwiches (from £2), omelettes (from £3), ploughman's (from £5), home-baked ham and eggs (£5.50), sausage pie (£6.50), a couple of daily specials such as cod fillet, pork and cider sauce or beef and tomato ragoût (£5.50) and home-made puddings such as apple pie or crème brûlée (£2.50).

There's a coal-effect gas fire in the big brick fireplace, brocaded wall seats around dimpled copper tables on the left, and a cluster of brocaded stools on the right; sensibly placed darts (the heavy black beams are pitted with stray flights), dominoes and cribbage. Prettily bordered with flowers, the large sheltered back garden has picnic-sets, a covered seating area, and in fine weather an outside bar and weekend barbecues. Over-21s only in the bar; they hold a popular beer festival in May with up to 150 different real ales. The two collies are called Colly and Boots. *(Recommended by Ian Phillips, John and Enid Morris, T A S Halfhide, Kay Vowles, Mr and Mrs A P Lawrence, B, M and P Kendall, Adrian White)*

Free house ~ Licensees Albert and David Kitchin ~ Real ale ~ Bar food (11-9; 12-8.30 Sun; not 25/26 Dec) ~ (01277) 841137 ~ Open 11-11; 12-10.30 Sun

STOW MARIES TQ8399 Map 5

Prince of Wales

B1012 between S Woodham Ferrers and Cold Norton Posters

Genuine inspiring character marks this welcoming laid-back marshland pub out from the rest. The landlord is a real ale enthusiast and has five or six very well kept weekly changing beers on handpump, from varied brewers such as Brakspears, Dark Star, Hop Back, Mauldons and Titanic, two draught Belgian wheat beers and several bottled beers, as well as farm cider, and vintage ports. He also puts on the odd beer festival. Summer Sundays, when they barbecue unusual fish – the very cheery easy-going barman told us they even have fish with three eyes here – such as saupe, mahimai and black barracuda, and steaks (from £7.95), are a fun time to visit. In winter try going on a Thursday evening, when they fire up the old bread oven to make pizzas in the room that used to be the village bakery. Seemingly unchanged since the turn of the century, the cosy and chatty low-ceilinged rooms have in fact been renovated in a genuinely traditional style. Few have space for more than one or two tables or wall benches on the tiled or bare-boards floors, though the room in the middle squeezes in quite a jumble of chairs and stools. Enjoyable well cooked food with lots of fresh fish specials might include whitebait (£4.50), chilli wrap (£5.95), swordfish or marlin (£6.95), smoked haddock (£7.25), and puddings such as spotted dick and sticky toffee pudding (£2.50). There are seats and tables in the back garden and, in the gap between the white picket fence and the pub's weather-boarded frontage, there's a terrace with herbs in Victorian chimney pots. *(Recommended by Adrian White, John and Enid Morris, Sarah Davis, Rod Lambert)*

Free house ~ Licensee Rob Walster ~ Real ale ~ Bar food (12-2.30, 7-9.30, 12-9.30 Sun) ~ No credit cards ~ (01621) 828971 ~ Children in family room ~ Live music most bank hol wknds ~ Open 11-11; 12-10.30 Sun

WENDENS AMBO TL5136 Map 5

Bell

B1039 just W of village

The small cottagey low-ceilinged rooms at this jolly village local are spotlessly kept, with brasses on ancient timbers, wheelback chairs around neat tables, comfortably cushioned seats worked into snug alcoves, quite a few pictures on the cream walls, and a welcoming open fire. Bar food includes filled rolls (from £2.50), ploughman's (£4.25), chicken, bacon and avocado salad, steak and kidney pie, leek and mushroom pasta or plaice (£6.95), seafood platter (£8.25), and home-made puddings such as apple pie, sherry trifle or spotted dick (£2.50); the dining room is no smoking. Well kept real ales on handpump include Adnams, Greene King Old Speckled Hen and a couple of guests, and they have an annual beer festival; darts, cribbage, dominoes and piped music. The extensive back garden and terrace have plenty to keep children entertained. After they've had fun meeting the goats Reggie and Ronnie, and Gizmo the 14-stone bernese mountain dog, there's a wooden wendy house, proper tree swing, crazy golf (£2), a sort of mini nature-trail wandering off through the shrubs, a pets corner, and a big tree-sheltered lawn. Handy for Audley End. *(Recommended by Ian Wilson, Eddie Edwards)*

Free house ~ Licensees David and Sheila Thorp ~ Real ale ~ Bar food (not Sun or Mon evenings) ~ Restaurant ~ (01799) 540382 ~ Children in restaurant ~ Dogs allowed in bar ~ Open 11.30-3, 6-11; 11.30-11 Sat

YOUNGS END TL7319 Map 5

Green Dragon

A131 Braintree—Chelmsford, just N of Essex Showground

The very fairly priced fresh fish is one of the main draws at this bustling unpretentious dining pub. A good range of seafood specials might include potted shrimps (£4.75), Loch Fyne smoked salmon (£5.75), scottish clams in garlic butter or cajun red snapper with yoghurt dressing (£8.50), swordfish steak with garlic butter (£10), lobster salad (half £10.95), and fruits de mer for two (£40). Other reasonably priced bar food, served by cheerful staff, includes sandwiches (from £2.95, filled baguettes from £3.95), home-made soup (£2.75), ploughman's (from £4.95), cottage pie (£5), curry of the day or steak, kidney and mushroom pie (£7.50) and greek-style lamb shank (£8); weekday fixed price set menu (two courses £10.50), and at lunchtime (not Sunday) you can have bar food in part of the restaurant, where the tables are bigger than in the bar. There's quite a pubby atmosphere in the two bar rooms, which have ordinary pub furnishings, and in the little extra low-ceilinged snug just beside the serving counter. Greene King IPA, Abbot and perhaps Ruddles County on handpump; unobtrusive piped jazz music. The no smoking restaurant area has an understated barn theme with stripped brick walls, a manger at one end, and a 'hayloft' part upstairs. The neat back garden has lots of picnic-sets under cocktail parasols, a budgerigar aviary, a climbing frame, and a big green play dragon. *(Recommended by Paul and Ursula Randall, Mrs P J Pearce, Ian Phillips)*

Greene King ~ Lease Bob and Mandy Greybrook ~ Real ale ~ Bar food (12-2.15, 6-9; 12-9.30(6 Sun) Sat) ~ Restaurant ~ (01245) 361030 ~ Children in eating area of bar and restaurant ~ Open 12-3, 5.30-11; 12-11(10.30 Sun) Sat

Lucky Dip

Besides the fully inspected pubs, you might like to try these Lucky Dips recommended to us and described by readers (if you do, please send us reports: www.goodguides.com).

Abridge [TQ4696]

Maltsters Arms [London Rd (A113)]: Snug and friendly weatherboarded pub, partly 16th c, low beams and timbering dividers, lots of china jugs and small plates, bargain food from doorstep sandwiches up, well kept Greene King IPA and Abbot, friendly interested staff, open fires, back pool table in one bar; popular with young people evenings; picnic-sets on small back terrace *(LM)*

Battlesbridge [TQ7894]

Hawk [Hawk Hill]: Extensive Vintage Inn attractively laid out with rugs, settles and oak tables on flagstones, log fire, hanging baskets, farm tools and dried hops; well kept Bass and Tetleys, good choice of wines by the glass, daily papers, three no smoking areas, usual food all day from separate servery; piped music, packed wknds with antiques enthusiasts visiting the centre here; open all day, children welcome, good tables out on front grass *(Colin and Dot Savill, George Atkinson, BB, Adrian White)*

Lodge [Hayes Chase, just off A132]: Doing well under current licensees, popular bargain lunchtime specials, separate restaurant; big lawn with bouncy castle, bedrooms *(Adrian White)*

Billericay [TQ6893]

Duke of York [Southend Rd, South Green]: Pleasant beamed local with real fire, longcase clock, local photographs, upholstered settles and wheelback chairs, good value food in bar and modern restaurant, long-serving licensees, Greene King and occasional guest beers; may be unobtrusive piped 60s pop music, monthly quiz night, fortnightly ladies' darts *(David Twitchett)*

Blackmore [TL6001]

☆ ***Bull*** [off A414 Chipping Ongar—Chelmsford; Church St]: Very hospitable old timbered dining pub, cosy and pleasantly decorated, with tempting choice of tasty if not cheap food, well kept ales such as Adnams and Mauldons, brasses; may be quiet piped music, fruit machine in public bar; near church in quietly attractive village with big antiques and crafts shop *(Marjorie and Bernard Parkin, Roy and Lindsey Fentiman, Mary and Dennis Jones)*

Prince Albert [The Green]: Several linked areas around central servery, wide choice of generous food from filled baked potatoes to good fresh fish, well kept real ales, friendly obliging service; attractive village *(Roy and Lindsey Fentiman)*

Blackmore End [TL7430]

☆ ***Bull*** [off A131 via Bocking Church Street and

Beazley End; towards Wethersfield]: Comfortable tucked-away dining pub, red plush built-in button-back banquettes, low black beams, further cottagey restaurant area, lots of blackboards for very wide choice of enjoyable food from sandwiches to set lunches, well kept Adnams, Greene King IPA and perhaps a guest, decent wines; children welcome, cl Mon, picnic-sets outside *(D S Cottrell, LYM, Richard Siebert)*

Boreham [TL7509]

☆ *Six Bells* [B1137]: Thriving dining pub with enjoyable straightforward fresh food in comfortable bar and restaurant, cheerful efficient service even when busy, well kept Greene King IPA and Abbot and a guest beer, friendly locals; play area in garden *(John Saville, Paul and Ursula Randall, Quentin and Carol Williamson)*

Braintree [TL7522]

Boars Head [High St]: Lunchtime food inc nice ploughman's and children's menu, friendly landlady; piped music, fruit machine, disco some nights *(Alan M Pring)*

Brentwood [TQ5993]

Nags Head [A1023, just off M25 junction 28]: Wide choice of enjoyable food in recently refurbished old pub, prompt, friendly and attentive service *(John Saville)*

Swan [High St]: Pleasantly unspoilt, with well priced food inc good choice of baguettes, good range of well kept ales such as local Mighty Oak Burntwood, good staff *(Andy and Jill Kassube)*

Canfield End [TL5821]

Lion & Lamb [A120 Bishops Stortford—Dunmow]: Neat and comfortable, with friendly staff, good atmosphere, wide choice of enjoyable food inc children's in open-plan bar and spacious restaurant, well kept Ridleys, decent wines and coffee; piped music; back garden with terrace, barbecue and play area *(Linda Lewis)*

Chelmsford [TL6807]

Horse & Groom [Roxwell Rd (A1060)]: Attractive mock-Tudor Chef & Brewer family dining pub, well kept Courage Directors and Theakstons, decent wines, cheerful friendly staff, spacious bar, big pine tables in roomy no smoking dining area, several log fires; unobtrusive piped music; tables outside with country views *(Tina and David Woods-Taylor, D P and J A Sweeney)*

Partners [Lower Anchor St]: Well kept Adnams, Greene King, Ridleys and perhaps guest beers, bar food; near county cricket ground – its popularity with players and supporters gives it rather an unusual sports-club atmosphere sometimes *(Bruce M Drew)*

Chignall Smealy [TL6711]

☆ *Pig & Whistle* [NW of Chelmsford, just S of village]: Two attractively opened up bar areas, beams, brasses and stripped brick, solid furniture and soft lighting, good value generous freshly made food from sandwiches and light bar meals to restaurant dishes inc OAP midweek lunch, well kept Shepherd Neame ales (décor includes their idiosyncratic advertisements), good house wines, helpful friendly staff, nice no smoking restaurant (best to book wknds); fruit machine, piped music; children welcome away from bar, tables out on terrace with wide views, climbing frame *(Tony Beaulah, Mr and Mrs Youngs, Colin and Dot Savill, Paul and Ursula Randall)*

Chigwell [TQ4493]

☆ *Kings Head* [High Rd (A113)]: Handsome weatherboarded 17th-c Chef & Brewer with interesting Dickens memorabilia (it features in *Barnaby Rudge*), some antique furnishings, quick friendly service, well kept Courage Best and Directors, John Smiths and Theakstons, popular food inc upstairs carvery restaurant, conservatory; piped music, can get very crowded weekend evenings; attractive garden *(Robert Lester)*

Coggeshall [TL8522]

☆ *White Hart* [Bridge St]: Civilised dining pub with multitude of neat waiters, cosy front bar with lots of low 15th-c beams, antique settles among other thoroughly comfortable seats, prints and fishing trophies, wide choice of food from sandwiches up, well kept Adnams or Greene King IPA, decent wines and coffee, restaurant; service may be slow; good recently refurbished bedrooms *(BB, Michael Dandy, Kevin Flack, George Atkinson)*

Colchester [TM0025]

Dragoon [Butt Rd (B1026)]: Welcoming unpretentious L-shaped local with lounge and public ends, limited very cheap bar food (fry-up recommended), well kept Adnams and a guest beer, friendly staff *(Pete Baker)*

Copthall Green [TL4200]

Good Intent: Open-plan roadside pub with plush wall banquettes, friendly and efficient Italian landlord and family doing enjoyable bar food inc good value sandwiches, ciabatta, pasta and pizzas, upstairs restaurant, well kept McMullens; may be piped radio; some picnic-sets outside *(Roger and Pauline Pearce, Joy and Peter Heatherley)*

Danbury [TL7704]

Cricketers Arms [Penny Royal Rd]: Cheerful country local overlooking common, three beamed areas and restaurant, friendly bar staff, generous food, Shepherd Neame beers, appropriate prints and autographed bat of 2000 West Indian team; may be piped music *(Robert Lester)*

Dedham [TM0533]

☆ *Marlborough Head* [Mill Lane]: Handsome medieval timbered inn with easy chairs, pictures, log fires and beautiful carving in beamed central lounge, well kept Adnams Broadside and Greene King IPA and Abbot, pleasant young staff, no smoking family room, lots of tables in dining bar; piped music; tables on terrace and in back garden, open all day wknds, comfortable bedrooms, charming village *(P Beeby, Ian Phillips, Mr and Mrs Thomas, LYM, Quentin and Carol Williamson)*

Dunmow [TL6221]

Dunmow Inn [High St]: Open-plan bar with some armchairs and red plush, dark wood tables and chairs, musical instruments and copper hanging from beams, enjoyable reasonably priced blackboard food inc fresh fish, two real ales such as Worthington Best, friendly atmosphere *(Paul and Ursula Randall)*

Earls Colne [TL8528]

Carved Angel: [Upper Holt Street] Refitted a couple of years ago, with big fireside sofas, pine tables in eating area, good fresh food, good changing wine list, well kept beers, welcoming atmosphere *(Humphrey Bull)*

East Hanningfield [TL7701]

Windmill [The Tye]: Pleasant beamed bar, good standard food from baguettes to Sun roasts, several real ales inc Crouch Vale and a guest beer, restaurant Thurs-Sat evenings and Sun lunch, good prompt service – landlord and staff try hard to please; seats out on front terrace opp green (fairly busy road) *(Gordon Neighbour, George Atkinson)*

Fiddlers Hamlet [TL4701]

☆ *Merry Fiddlers* [Stewards Green Rd, a mile SE of Epping]: Long low-beamed and timbered 17th-c country pub, lots of copper and brass, chamber-pots, beer mugs and plates, real ales such as Adnams, Bass and Greene King IPA and Old Speckled Hen, good helpings of reasonably priced sensible home-cooked food inc substantial Sun roast and fresh veg, family dining area, attentive friendly staff; may be unobtrusive piped music, occasional live sessions; big garden with good play area (motorway can be heard) *(Roger and Pauline Pearce, Robert Lester)*

Finchingfield [TL6832]

☆ *Red Lion* [Church Hill]: Good choice of sensibly priced food inc some interesting dishes and no-nonsense two-course roast Sun lunch, well kept Adnams and Ridleys, interesting wine choice, cosy local atmosphere, Tudor beams, small dining area; three comfortable bedrooms with own bathrooms, nice spot opp churchyard and 15th-c guild hall *(MDN)*

Fyfield [TL5606]

☆ *Black Bull* [B184, N end]: Welcoming 15th-c pub with heavy low beams and standing timbers, comfortably modernised pubby bar, wide range of sensibly priced generous food from baguettes through traditional dishes to more spicy ones, no smoking country-style dining area, well kept Courage Directors, Greene King Ruddles and Marstons Pedigree, good service, open fire, traditional games; quiet piped music; tables outside, lots of flower-filled barrels, aviary with budgerigars and cockatiels *(LYM, Colin and Janet Roe, Mrs A Chesher, Bernie Adams, Roy and Lindsey Fentiman, Mary and Dennis Jones, Ian Phillips)*

Gestingthorpe [TL8138]

Pheasant [off B1058]: Country views, enjoyable food (not Sun evening or Mon) from sandwiches and other bar dishes to more restauranty things, well kept ales such as Adnams and Greene King IPA and Old Speckled Hen, interesting old furnishings and log fire in lounge, another in beamed public bar; children welcome, picnic-sets in garden, cl Mon lunchtime; no reports at all from readers recently on this nice pub, so news please *(LYM)*

Great Horkesley [TL9732]

☆ *Rose & Crown* [Nayland Rd (A134)]: Friendly and spotless old two-floored pub with good food in bars and restaurant (the chef/landlord does well in competitions), well kept Greene King and other ales, good log fire *(Gilly Gutteridge, John Prescott, Charles and Pauline Stride)*

Hatfield Heath [TL5115]

Thatchers [A1005 towards Bishop's Stortford]: Neatly refurbished beamed and thatched pub with woodburner, copper kettles, jugs and brasses in L-shaped bar, well kept Greene King ales and decent house wines from long bar, wide choice of decent food; may be piped music; tables out under cocktail parasols *(Marjorie and Bernard Parkin)*

Hatfield Peverel [TL7911]

Wheatsheaf [The Green]: Friendly old weatherboarded pub with accent on food, well kept Ridleys; tables outside, busy aviary *(Dr and Mrs A K Clarke)*

Herongate [TQ6391]

Boars Head [Billericay Rd, just off A128]: Picturesque low-beamed Chef & Brewer with pleasant nooks and crannies, Courage Best and Marstons Pedigree, reliable sensibly priced usual food all day inc good choice of lunchtime baguettes; can get crowded wknds; garden tables overlooking big attractive reed-fringed pond with ducks and moorhens *(Roy and Lindsey Fentiman)*

Heybridge Basin [TL8707]

Old Ship [Lockhill]: Well kept Greene King IPA, Abbot and Old Speckled Hen, malt whiskies, good choice of standard food in bar with blond wooden furniture (window tables reserved for diners), more ambitious upstairs restaurant with estuary views, good friendly service, daily papers; well behaved dogs welcome, no children; seats outside, some overlooking water by canal lock – lovely views of the saltings and across to Northey Island, pretty window boxes; can be very busy, esp in summer when parking nearby impossible (but public park five mins' walk) *(Robert Turnham, Pam and David Bailey)*

Hockley [TQ8392]

☆ *Bull* [Main Rd]: Attractive 17th-c beamed pub, one of the better Chef & Brewers, in nice spot by ancient woods, so very popular with walkers; lots of pictures and bric-a-brac, stable area with well, well kept beers inc a guest such as Adnams Fisherman, good wine range, cafetière coffee, hospitable service, usual food; piped music; big garden with own servery, animals, pond and play area; vast car park *(Tina and David Woods-Taylor)*

Inworth [TL8817]

Prince of Wales [Kelvedon Rd]: Friendly old-world country local currently popular for its food, two well kept ales such as Greene King Abbot, decent house wines; tables out on attractive front lawn *(Adrian White)*

Kelvedon Hatch [TQ5798]

☆ *Eagle* [Ongar Rd (A128)]: Clean and friendly local with no smoking dining area, good food esp fresh fish specials Thurs/Fri, good value early summer shellfish, choice of four all day Sun roasts (worth booking), good choice of children's meals, well kept Fullers London Pride, large play area with children's tables; unobtrusive piped music, TV football, live music Thurs, Sat and Sun *(Joy and Colin Rorke)*

Layer de la Haye [TL9619]

Donkey & Buskins [B1026 towards Colchester]: Old-fashioned country pub with good range of reasonably priced straightforward food in bar and dining room esp fresh fish and good Sun roasts, decent helpings, Adnams and Greene King, pleasant service; handy for Abberton Reservoir's fishermen and birders *(J Strain, Gordon Neighbour, Jane Hunt)*

Leigh-on-Sea [TQ8385]

☆ ***Crooked Billet*** [High St]: Homely old pub with waterfront views from big bay windows, local fishing pictures and bric-a-brac, beams and bare boards, well kept changing ales such as Adnams, Bass and Theakstons, spring and autumn beer festivals, home-made lunchtime food (not Sun) inc seafood, friendly service, woodburner; piped music, live music nights; open all day, side garden and terrace, seawall seating over road shared with Osbornes good shellfish stall; pay-and-display parking (free Sat/Sun) by fly-over *(Tina and David Woods-Taylor, Lynn Sharpless, Bob Eardley, John and Enid Morris, Ian Phillips, LYM)*

Smack [High St, Old Leigh, nr station and opp footbridge]: Three life-size wooden sailors and fishermen leaning on the bar, small booths made from rowing boats, simple good value food from sandwiches up, Courage Directors and Greene King IPA, friendly staff, good estuary views; children welcome, harbourside terrace and pleasant conservatory *(Tina and David Woods-Taylor)*

Little Waltham [TL7012]

☆ ***Dog & Gun*** [E of village, back rd Great Leighs—Boreham]: Long L-shaped timbered dining lounge refurbished with stripped woodwork and pastel walls, good generous food from lunch snacks to enterprising but unpretentious restauranty dishes and Sun family lunches, friendly informal atmosphere and cheerful helpful staff, well kept Adnams and Greene King IPA, decent wine, suntrap conservatory; may be piped music; picnic-sets in good-sized garden with floodlit heated terrace, elegant pondside willow, tidy play area *(Paul and Ursula Randall, Peter Baggott)*

Loughton [TQ4296]

Last Post [High Rd]: Wetherspoons post office conversion, good warming atmosphere, sensibly priced Courage Directors, Marstons Pedigree and Theakstons, decent cheap coffee, food all day, no smoking area, old Loughton prints, no music *(Robert Lester)*

Maldon [TL8506]

Jolly Sailor [Church St/The Hythe]: Charming quayside timber-framed pub, three Archers ales, meals served, tables out overlooking Thames barges etc *(Quentin and Carol Williamson)*

Rose & Crown [High St]: Good choice of reasonably priced food, good helpings, friendly staff *(Abi Benson)*

Manningtree [TM1031]

☆ ***Crown*** [High St]: Bustling 16th-c pub, lots of beams, old photographs, maps and fishing gear, real fires, well kept Greene King IPA, Abbot and XX Mild, impressive landlord and bright cheerful staff, usual food inc interesting sandwiches and plenty for children, two bars and new no smoking room, back glazed gable ends overlooking Stour estuary; super Christmas decorations; picnic-sets in back yard, attractively priced bedrooms *(Rona Murdoch, Ian Phillips, Bernie Adams, Ian and Nita Cooper)*

Station Buffet [Manningtree Station, out towards Lawford]: Clean and warm, with coal stove, nostalgic early 1950s long marble-topped bar, three little tables and a handful of unassuming seats with adjoining eating area, well kept ales such as Adnams and Greene King IPA and Triumph, bargain pubby food from good sandwiches to simple hot dishes, friendly helpful service, no piped music (though Rachmaninov's 2nd piano concerto springs to mind) *(Ian Phillips, Tony Hobden)*

Margaretting [TL6701]

Red Lion [B1002 towards Mountnessing]: Relaxed beamed and timbered local, all tables laid for good choice of enjoyable food from good fish and chips to more elaborate dishes, no smoking dining area, well kept Ridleys IPA, Bob and Prospect, efficient unrushed service, attractive floral displays; piped radio; good wheelchair access, picnic-sets and play area in garden *(John Saville, Joy and Peter Heatherley, Ian Phillips)*

Margaretting Tye [TL6801]

White Hart: L-shaped bar with wide choice of good value promptly served straightforward food from sandwiches up, well kept Adnams Bitter and Broadside, Mighty Oak IPA and guest beers (lots at occasional beer festivals), cheerful service, comfortable new conservatory-roofed family dining room; may be piped music; robust play area and pets corner in attractive garden by quiet village green, good walks *(Paul and Ursula Randall, Paul and Penny Rampton, Evelyn and Derek Walter)*

Mill Green [TL6401]

☆ ***Cricketers***: Cheerfully well worn in dining pub in picturesque setting, plenty of tables out in front, interesting cricketing memorabilia, some farm tools, popular freshly cooked traditional food, well kept Greene King ales tapped from the cask, decent wines, no smoking area, friendly attentive service; children welcome, no music, cl winter Sun evenings *(Eddie Edwards, M A and C R Starling)*

Moreton [TL5307]

☆ ***White Hart*** [off B184, just N of A414]: Comfortable divided L-shaped lounge bar with log fire, soft lighting, old-fashioned prints and lots of woodwork, well kept Adnams and Greene King IPA and Abbot, decent house wines, new chef specialising in Italian food, attractive small timbered dining room, pool and darts in public bar; picnic-sets on small back terrace and in informal garden with play area *(LYM)*

Mountnessing [TQ6397]

Prince of Wales [Roman Rd (B1002)]: Popular rambling beamed pub opp windmill, good atmosphere, friendly staff, food inc fish specialities, well kept Ridleys IPA and Rumpus, good wine list *(Roy and Lindsey Fentiman)*

Newney Green [TL6506]

☆ ***Duck*** [off A1060 W of Chelmsford via Roxwell, or off A414 W of Writtle – take Cooksmill Green turnoff at Fox & Goose, then bear right]: Comfortable and welcoming dining pub with attractive rambling bar full of hop-hung beams, timbering, panelling and interesting bric-a-brac, comfortable furnishings, enjoyable food inc good value set lunches, well kept ales such as Ridleys Rumpus and Shepherd Neame Spitfire, decent wines by the glass, attentive willing young staff; well laid tables out on attractive terrace *(LYM, John and Enid Morris, Mary and Dennis Jones)*

Newport [TL5234]

Coach & Horses [Cambridge Rd (B1383)]: Big helpings of enjoyable good value food, Adnams, Greene King and a guest beer, friendly landlord; tables outside *(Tony and Shirley Albert, B N F and M Parkin)*

North Fambridge [TQ8597]

☆ ***Ferry Boat*** [village signed from B1012 E off S Woodham Ferrers; keep on past railway to quay]: Unpretentious 15th-c weatherboarded pub tucked prettily down by the marshes, warmly welcoming chatty landlord, simple traditional furnishings, nautical memorabilia, log fire one end, woodburner the other, good value honest food from sandwiches up, well kept Shepherd Neame Bitter, Spitfire and Bishops Finger, traditional games, children in family room and partly no smoking restaurant; piped music, fruit machine, TV; tables in garden with pond (ducks and carp), bedrooms in barn-like building behind, good lonely walks *(John Saville, LYM)*

Nounsley [TL7910]

Sportsmans Arms [off B1019; Sportsman Lane]: This proper country local, with well kept Adnams Broadside and Greene King IPA and picnic-sets and swings in a big garden, has lost the landlady who made it a popular main entry for its unusual oriental cooking *(LYM)*

Old Harlow [TL4711]

Marquis of Granby [Market St]: Comfortable and interesting two-level local with wide choice of well kept changing ales from far and wide, friendly staff, usual food, old gas cigar lighter on bar; pool, piped music, TV; attractive old tiled building *(Ian Phillips, Dr and Mrs A K Clarke)*

Pleshey [TL6614]

☆ ***White Horse*** [The Street]: 15th-c beams and timbers, cheerful tablecloths and flower posies, big back extension with two dining rooms, one no smoking (should book wknds), friendly service, good range of enjoyable bar food from sandwiches to imaginative full meals (freshly made, so may take a while), well kept Youngs Bitter and AAA, decent wines; may be piped Richard Clayderman; luncheon club and theme nights, children welcome, tables out on terrace and in garden with small safe play area, pretty village with ruined castle *(LYM, Richard Trim, Paul and Ursula Randall)*

Radwinter [TL6137]

☆ ***Plough*** [Sampford Rd (B1053 E of Saffron Walden)]: Congenial and neatly kept red plush open-plan black-timbered beamed bar with some concentration on generous home-made food esp good fresh fish, well kept Greene King IPA and a guest such as Adnams, good coffee, friendly landlord, no music; children, and dogs on lead, welcome; very attractive terrace and garden, open countryside; comfortable bedrooms *(DC, Andrew and Samantha Grainger, BB)*

Rickling Green [TL5029]

Cricketers Arms [just off B1383 N of Stansted Mountfichet]: Beams, timbers and lots of cricketing memorabilia, wide choice of bar food esp fish and seafood, well kept Flowers IPA, Fullers ESB, Wadworths 6X and a guest beer tapped from the cask, good wines by the glass, open fires; piped music; picnic-sets in sheltered front courtyard *(Kevin Thorpe, R T and J C Moggridge, Charles Gysin, Clive Petts, LYM, Peter and Jean Hoare, Adrian White)*

Ridgewell [TL7341]

☆ ***Kings Head*** [A1017 Haverhill—Halstead]: Much modernised unpretentious local with newish tenants doing good food choice at sensible prices, well kept Greene King IPA and Abbot, decent wines, some signs of Tudor origins, interesting local World War II memorabilia; pool and other games in airy public bar, may be subdued piped music, a few tables in roadside garden *(Fred Nicholls, BB)*

Saffron Walden [TL5438]

☆ ***Eight Bells*** [Bridge St; B184 towards Cambridge]: Large handsomely timbered Tudor pub with wide choice of enjoyable food in open-plan rambling bar and appealing partly no smoking medieval-theme tapestried and timbered restaurant, children allowed here and in family room with open fire, well kept Adnams, good wines, good friendly service; games machines; open all day, tables in garden, handy for Audley End, good walks *(Alain and Rose Foote, LYM, John Brightley, Geoffrey and Brenda Wilson)*

South Weald [TQ5793]

Tower Arms [off A1023; handy for M25 junction 28]: Good choice of enjoyable food, friendly prompt service, pleasant furnishings and conservatory; big garden, nice village *(John Saville)*

St Osyth [TM1215]

White Hart [The Bury (signed to Point Clear)]: Small family-run pub in row of pretty weatherboarded houses, friendly and welcoming, with wide choice of good value food and good range of well kept ales; muted piped music; small garden and barbecue *(Bernard Patrick)*

Stanford-le-Hope [TQ6882]

Inn on the Green [Wharf Rd, The Green]: Comfortable creeper-covered pub opp church, Greene King IPA and Abbot *(Ian Phillips)*

Stifford [TQ6080]

Dog & Partridge [High Rd, North Stifford]: Magnificent play area, very extensive; inside well divided for intimacy despite its large size, well kept beer, enjoyable food *(Dr and Mrs A K Clarke)*

Stisted [TL7924]

☆ ***Dolphin*** [A120 E of Braintree, by village turn]: Well kept Ridleys tapped from the cask in heavily beamed and timbered properly pubby locals' bar on right, popular well priced straightforward food (not Tues or Sun evenings) inc steak bargains Sat evening, log fire, bright eating area on left (children allowed here); tables outside *(Pete Baker, LYM)*

Stock [TQ6998]

☆ ***Bakers Arms*** [Common Rd, just off B1007 Chelmsford—Billericay]: Busy open-plan low-beamed pub with smart banquettes, well kept Adnams Broadside and Greene King IPA, enjoyable fairly priced home-made food, good salads, attractive airy dining room with french windows to charming small garden, pictures by local artists for sale, no piped music *(George Atkinson, David Twitchett)*

Tolleshunt Major [TL9011]

☆ ***Bell*** [off B1026 NE of Maldon; Beckingham St]: Country pub with beams and timbers, comfortable banquettes and bay windows in L-shaped saloon with woodburner, quietly friendly service, well kept Greene King and a guest beer, good house wine and coffee, good value dining area (daily fresh fish exc Mon), no music, public bar with fruit machine; children welcome, verandah and garden with big rustic pond, barbecue and play area, disabled facilities *(Adrian White)*

Toot Hill [TL5102]

☆ ***Green Man*** [off A113 in Stanford Rivers, S of Ongar, or A414 W of Ongar]: Pleasantly laid out much as a simply furnished country pub with a long plush dining room alongside the colourful front terrace, but best thought of as a restaurant both in price and in style (meals rather than bar food); very good wine list, Fullers London Pride, Youngs Bitter and guest beers such as Mighty Oak IPA and Smiles; piped music may obtrude, no under-10s, tables in back garden *(Keith and Janet Morris, David and Ruth Shillitoe, LYM, Ian Phillips, Len Banister, Adrian White, John Saville, Neil Hogg, Grahame McNulty, John and Enid Morris, Mrs Jill Silversides, Barry Brown, R F Ballinger)*

Waltham Abbey [TL3800]

☆ ***Volunteer*** [½ mile from M25 junction 26; A121 towards Loughton]: Roomy family pub extensively refurbished under new management, but still does good value generous chinese food alongside other dishes; prompt friendly service, attractive conservatory, McMullens Country and Mild; piped music; some tables on side terrace, pretty hanging baskets, nice spot by Epping Forest *(Charles and Pauline Stride, John Saville, BB, Tony Middis)*

Woodbine [handy for M25 junction 26, via A121; Honey Lane]: Friendly open-plan local with well kept Greene King IPA and Abbot from central servery, reasonably priced food esp curries, old piano, plates on walls, large conservatory; piped music may obtrude; by Epping Forest, good walks from forest car park opp *(Ian Phillips)*

White Roding [TL5613]

Black Horse [Chelmsford Rd]: Sprucely well kept Ridleys pub, beams and plush seating, old photographs and brasses, generous home cooking (not Sun evening; lots of fresh fish Thurs), well kept IPA, Old Bob and Rumpus, decent house wines, welcoming attentive service, relaxing atmosphere, two-part dining room; may be quiet piped music; small enclosed garden behind *(George Atkinson)*

Wivenhoe [TM0321]

Black Buoy [off A133]: 16th-c behind its more recent façade, unpretentious open-plan partly timbered bar, upper dining area glimpsing river over roofs, wide choice of good generous food (stops by 2) inc sandwiches, local fish and interesting vegetarian dishes, well kept Adnams, Courage Directors and Greene King IPA, open fires; piped music; own parking, pleasant village *(Peter Meister, James Nunns, BB)*

Rose & Crown [The Quay]: Unpretentious Georgian pub on River Colne barge quay, low beams, lots of ship pictures, scrubbed floors and log fires, well kept Adnams Broadside with several guest beers, good house wines, wide choice of good value straightforward food all day from fresh baguettes up (next-door bakery), friendly and helpful young staff, local and nautical books and maps, no piped music; open all day Sun, lots of waterside picnic-sets *(George Atkinson, Charles Gysin, BB, John and Elizabeth Cox, Kevin Flack)*

Woodham Mortimer [TL8004]

Royal Oak [Chelmsford Road (A414 Danbury—Maldon)]: Comfortably toney décor of pinks, greens and greys, corner banquettes, a mix of chairs, stripped and sealed sturdy pub tables with candles in bottles, decent food, Greene King IPA and Abbot, separate smartly pink restaurant; may be piped music; tables on small side terrace and in the garden behind, with playhouse and climbing frame. *(Adrian White, BB)*

Woodham Walter [TL8006]

☆ ***Cats*** [back rd to Curling Tye and Maldon, from N end of village]: Relaxed and chatty country cottage, low black beams and timbering in timeless rambling bar with interesting nooks and crannies, roaring log fire each end, shelves of china cats, well kept Adnams, Greene King and beer brewed for them, good doorstep sandwiches, friendly service, no children or piped music; pretty garden with farmland views *(Peter Baggott, LYM, Phil and Sally Gorton)*

Post Office address codings confusingly give the impression that some pubs are in Suffolk, when they're really in Essex (which is where we list them).

Gloucestershire

This county's fine variety of good pubs – from friendly and unpretentious country locals with nice views and walks to smart and civilised dining pubs with imaginative food and good wines – is reflected in the new entries here this year. (And they typify Gloucestershire pubs' relaxed approach to dogs, in that six out of the seven allow them in.) There's the Victoria looking down on pretty Eastleach Turville (a friendly rambling village pub, good all round), the White Horse at Frampton Mansell (a fine new dining pub), the interesting old Bull at Hinton Dyrham (good all round, a quiet break from the M4), the Weighbridge near Nailsworth (in the Guide *some years ago under different licensees – the current team are very good), the Wheatsheaf in Northleach (a handsome old inn well reworked as a civilised up-to-date dining pub), the Trouble House near Tetbury (also redone as a good gastropub and gaining a Food Award, but keeping a companionable small-roomed layout), and the Horse & Groom at Upper Oddington (transformed by very welcoming newish owners, enjoyable food and drink, great atmosphere). Other pubs on top form here these days are the Queens Arms at Ashleworth (attractive décor, good food and drink including South African specialities), the delightful old Boat at Ashleworth Quay (in the same family for centuries, a favourite for traditionalists), the Village Pub at Barnsley (imaginative food), the friendly and unpretentious Bear in Bisley (interesting home cooking, nice bedrooms), the well run Seven Tuns in pretty Chedworth (a haven for walkers and cyclists, enjoyable food), the New Inn at Coln St Aldwyns (plenty of character and atmosphere, nice bedrooms, and the new chef's good), the Five Mile House at Duntisbourne Abbots (showing that a pub can aim high on the food side without losing its character or appeal to drinkers), the Lamb at Great Rissington (good bedrooms, enterprising newish chef, locals and visitors feeling happily at home), the Fox at Lower Oddington (though as we go to press the team who have made it so good are thinking of moving on), the relaxed and friendly Masons Arms at Meysey Hampton (good all round), the attractively unpretentious Carpenters Arms in idyllic Miserden, the Churchill at Paxford (good dining pub, one of the first in the county's current mode of stylish simplicity), the Bell at Sapperton (a very successful reworking – good imaginative food, lots of wines by the glass, but plenty of local real ales too, and buoyant atmosphere), the cosy and civilised Farriers Arms at Todenham (nice food and drink), and the charmingly set and attractive old Mill Inn at Withington (good friendly new manager). Especially in a county where so many pubs do such good food, it's most unusual for a newcomer to be picked out in this way, but it is the White Horse at Frampton Mansell which gains the title of Gloucestershire Dining Pub of the Year. In the Lucky Dip section at the end of the chapter, pubs to note particularly are the Sherborne Arms at Aldsworth, Black Horse at Amberley, Kings Arms in Chipping Campden, Twelve Bells in Cirencester, Tunnel House at Coates, Bell at Frampton on Severn, Glasshouse Inn at Glasshouse, Fox at Great Barrington, Ostrich at Newland, Rose & Crown at Nympsfield, Falcon in Painswick, Boat at Redbrook, Snowshill Arms at Snowshill, Coach & Horses near Stow-on-the-*

Wold and Queens Head in that town, and Ram at Woodchester. Drinks prices are a little lower than the national average. The Mill Inn at Withington had the cheapest beer among the main entries (Sam Smiths, from Yorkshire). Lots of other pubs here do stock good value local beers. Ones to look out for include Donnington, Uley, Wickwar, Goffs, Freeminer and Stanway, with Hook Norton (from over the Oxfordshire border) often turning out cheap.

ALMONDSBURY ST6084 Map 2

Bowl

1¼ miles from M5 junction 16 (and therefore quite handy for M4, junction 20; from A38 towards Thornbury, turn first left signposted Lower Almondsbury, then first right down Sundays Hill, then at bottom right again into Church Road

In good weather you have to get to this bustling pub almost as soon as they open if you want to bag a seat outside; it all looks very pretty with the church next door and the lovely flowering tubs, hanging baskets, and window boxes. Inside, the long neatly kept beamed bar has quite a mix of customers, blue plush-patterned modern settles, pink cushioned stools and mate's chairs around elm tables, horsebrasses on stripped stone walls, and big winter log fire at one end, with a woodburning stove at the other. Well liked bar food includes filled baguettes (from £3.95; sausage and caramelised onion £4.95), interesting salads such as mozzarella, roasted red peppers and artichokes or warm beef with sweet chilli sauce (from £4.50 for starter helpings, and from £8.50 for main courses), ploughman's (£4.95), pasta with wild mushrooms, parmesan and crème fraîche (£4.95; main course £8.95), battered cod and chips or sausage and mash with onion gravy (£6.95), roast loin of pork with a wholegrain mustard and cider sauce (£8.50), steak and mushroom pie (£8.95), rib-eye steak (£11.95), and puddings such as lemon tart with raspberry coulis and clotted cream or sticky toffee pudding (£3.95); they will serve half helpings for children under 12, and breakfasts are good. Well kept Courage Best, Moles Best, Smiles Best, and Wickwar BOB plus a couple of seasonal guests on handpump; piped music and fruit machine. *(Recommended by Hugh Roberts, S H Godsell, Ian Phillips, Joy and Peter Heatherley, Dr D J and Mrs S C Walker, Richard Fendick, Bob and Ann Westbrook, Peter and Jenny Quine, R Mathews, Susan and Nigel Wilson, Rev Michael Vockins, Paul Hopton, Mrs Jane Kingsbury)*

Free house ~ Licensee Mrs P Alley ~ Real ale ~ Bar food ~ Restaurant ~ (01454) 612757 ~ Children welcome ~ Dogs allowed in bar ~ Open 11.30-3, 5(6 Sat)-11; 12-3, 7-10.30 Sun; closed 25 Dec ~ Bedrooms: £41.50S/£67S

AMPNEY ST PETER SP0801 Map 4

Red Lion

A417, E of village

As delightful and as splendidly traditional as ever, this little roadside pub remains a great place for a friendly chat, with a fine mix of locals and visitors, and a charming, courteous landlord. A central stone corridor, served by a hatch, gives on to the little right-hand tile-floor public bar. Here, one long seat faces the small open fire, with just one table and a wall seat, and behind the long bench an open servery (no counter, just shelves of bottles and – by the corridor hatch – handpumps for the well kept Hook Norton Best and summer Haymaker, and maybe Flowers IPA). There are old prints on the wall, and on the other side of the corridor is a small saloon, with panelled wall seats around its single table, old local photographs, another open fire, and a print of Queen Victoria one could believe hasn't moved for a century – rather like the pub itself. There are seats in the side garden. *(Recommended by the Didler, Peter and Audrey Dowsett, R Huggins, D Irving, E McCall, T McLean, JP, PP, Giles Francis, Richard Stancomb, Roger and Jenny Huggins, RWC)*

Free house ~ Licensee John Barnard ~ Real ale ~ No credit cards ~ (01285) 851596 ~

Children in the tiny games room ~ Dogs allowed in bar ~ Open 6-10.30; 12-2.30, 6-10.30 Sat; 12-2.30, 7-10.30 Sun; closed weekday lunchtimes

ASHLEWORTH SO8125 Map 4

Queens Arms

Village signposted off A417 at Hartpury

This year, the hard-working and courteous licensees in this attractive low-beamed country pub have divided the long dining room into two cosier rooms with wood panelling, which is proving popular with customers. They've also added larger wrought-iron tables to the sunny courtyard and are planning to put in a water feature. The comfortably laid out main bar, softly lit by fringed wall lamps and candles at night, is neatly kept and civilised with faintly patterned wallpaper and washed red ochre walls, big oak and mahogany tables and a nice mix of farmhouse and big brocaded dining chairs on a red carpet. Good, imaginative bar food includes lunchtime dishes such as freshly baked baguettes (from £5.50), salad niçoise (£5.95), a pasta of the day (£6.50), South African sausage with tomato and onion gravy or Irish stew (£6.95), chicken, ham and leek pie (£7.50), and grilled salmon with cherry tomatoes and thyme butter (£7.95), with evening dishes like pork and duck liver terrine (£3.95), whitebait (£4.50), deep-fried brie and stilton croquettes (£4.95), steak and kidney pie or home-cooked ham and eggs (£8.95), and steaks (from £10.95), and specials such as bobotie (a spicy South African beef dish with egg custard, almonds and raisins, £10.50), potjeikos (another South African speciality cooking venison in a three-legged cast-iron pot, £10.75), pork tenderloin with a brandy and apricot sauce (£10.95), roast partridge (£11.50), and bass fillets with asparagus and mushroom risotto topped with a prawn and white wine sauce (£12.25). Puddings are well liked: raspberry crème brûlée, sticky fudge and walnut pudding, and chocolate truffle tart (from £3.95). They keep three real ales from a rotating choice of 20 on handpump: Archers Village, Badger Best, Brains Reverend James Original Ale, Brakspears Special, Donnington BB, Shepherd Neame Spitfire, Timothy Taylors Landlord, and Youngs Special. A thoughtful wine list with quite a few South African choices (the friendly licensees hail from there), and 21 malt whiskies. Piped music, shove-ha'penny, cribbage, dominoes, and winter skittle alley. The little black pub cat Bonnie charms customers with her ping-pong football antics. Two perfectly clipped mushroom shaped yews dominate the front of the building. *(Recommended by Roy and Lindsey Fentiman, B Knowles, Gill Waller, Tony Morriss, EML, Bernard Stradling, Brian and Bett Cox, Guy Vowles, P J G Nicholl, Di and Mike Gillam, Mrs A Vilsoen, Mr and Mrs P Slatter, Neil and Debbie Cook, Mrs Pam Vanden Bergh, Mrs A Willis, Mike and Mary Carter, P J G Nicoll, Rodney and Norma Stubington, Stephen and Jean Curtis, Ian and Nita Cooper)*

Free house ~ Licensees Tony and Gill Burreddu ~ Real ale ~ Bar food ~ Restaurant ~ (01452) 700395 ~ Well behaved children welcome ~ Open 12-3, 7-11(10.30 Sun); closed 25 Dec

ASHLEWORTH QUAY SO8125 Map 4

Boat ★

Ashleworth signposted off A417 N of Gloucester; quay signed from village

The same family have run this charming, quite unspoilt pub since it was originally licensed by Royal Charter in the 17th c – we believe this is a record for continuous pub ownership. It's set in an idyllic spot on the banks of the River Severn, and there's a front suntrap crazy-paved courtyard, bright with plant tubs in summer, with a couple of picnic-sets under cocktail parasols; more seats and tables under cover at the sides. The little front parlour has a great built-in settle by a long scrubbed deal table that faces an old-fashioned open kitchen range with a side bread oven and a couple of elderly fireside chairs; there are rush mats on the scrubbed flagstones, houseplants in the window, fresh garden flowers, and old magazines to read. One small lounge is no smoking; shove-ha'penny, dominoes and cribbage (the front room has darts). A pair of flower-cushioned antique settles face each other in the back room where Arkells BBB and Kingsdown Ale, Dark Horse Fallen Angel, Eccleshall Slaters Original, and RCH Pitchfork, and guests from Bath Ales, Church End, and Malvern Hills are tapped from the cask, along with a full range of Weston's farm ciders. They usually do good lunchtime rolls (from £1.35) during the week. The striking medieval tithe barn nearby is being renovated; some readers prefer to park here and walk to the pub. *(Recommended by Di and Mike Gillam, P R and S A White, Pete Baker, JP, PP, the Didler, Keith Jacob, Theocsbrian, Richard Stancomb, Derek and Sylvia Stephenson, Peter Scillitoe, Ian and Nita Cooper)*

Free house ~ Licensees Jacquie and Ron Nicholls ~ Real ale ~ Bar food (lunchtime only) ~ No credit cards ~ (01452) 700272 ~ Children welcome until 8pm ~ Open 11-2.30(3 Sat), 6-11; 12-3, 7-10.30 Sun; evening opening 7pm in winter; closed Mon and Weds lunchtimes Oct-Apr

AWRE SO7108 Map 4

Red Hart

Village signposted off A48 S of Newnham

Tucked away in a remote Severnside farming village, this tall, red-tiled 15th-c pub has a friendly, relaxed atmosphere. The neat L-shaped bar, the main part of which has a deep glass-covered illuminated well, has an antique pine bookcase filled with cookery and wine books, an antique pine display cabinet with Worcester china, and pine tables and chairs. The bottom end of the bar has old prints of the village and surrounding area, and the restaurant has some exposed wattle and daub. Good, totally home-made bar food includes sandwiches, home-made soup (£2.95), button mushrooms in a brandy, cream and pepper sauce (£4.25), spanish-style sardines or welsh rarebit (£4.50), chargrilled gloucestershire old spot pork chop with apple sauce and onion gravy, steak in ale pie or liver and bacon with grain mustard sauce (£6.95), several vegetarian choices, lamb curry (£7.25), chargrilled barracuda with chilli and coriander pesto or chicken gruyère (£9.95), and skate wing with lemon and caper butter (£11.95). The eating part of the bar is no smoking, as is the restaurant. Well kept Fullers London Pride, plus changing guests such as Badger Tanglefoot, Freeminer Speculation or Goffs Jouster on handpump, several malt whiskies, and decent house wine; piped music. In front of the building are some picnic-sets. *(Recommended by Mike and Lynn Robinson, Clare and Paul Howes, Bob and Margaret Holder, Theocsbrian, Guy Vowles, Revd John E Cooper, Lucien, Mike and Mary Carter, David Jeffreys, Tim and Ann Newell, S H Godsell)*

Free house ~ Licensee Jeremy Bedwell ~ Real ale ~ Bar food ~ Restaurant ~ (01594) 510220 ~ Children in eating area of bar until 8 ~ Open 12-3, 6.30-11; 12-3, 7-10.30 Sun

BARNSLEY SP0705 Map 4

Village Pub

B4425 Cirencester—Burford

Although many locals do drop into this popular place for a casual drink, the emphasis for most visitors is on the very good, imaginative food. The low-ceilinged communicating rooms (one is no smoking) have oil paintings, plush chairs, stools, and window settles around polished candlelit tables, and country magazines and newspapers to read. The menu changes twice a day and might include game consommé (£3.50), prawn, mango and coconut salad, steamed mussels with cider, onion and sage, poached duck with pickled fig or suckling pig and cabbage terrine with mustard celeriac (all £5.25), tomato, avocado and bacon sandwich with chips or fried chicken livers, grilled polenta and mushrooms (£5.50), chicken breast with caraway spiced cabbage or salmon fillet with creamed beans and polenta (£10.75), barnsley chop, sauté potatoes and rosemary roast carrots (£11.50), grilled peppered halibut steak with tomato and coriander salsa (£12.50), and grilled rib of beef, roquefort glazed mushrooms and roast sweet potatoes (£14.50), with puddings such as chocolate brownie with peanut butter ice cream, rice pudding with apple jelly or apricot and almond tart with crème fraîche (£4.50). Well kept Donnington BB,

Hook Norton Bitter, and Wadworths 6X on handpump, local cider and apple juice, and malt whiskies; good coffee. Dominoes, chess, and draughts. The sheltered back courtyard has plenty of tables, and its own outside servery. *(Recommended by Stuart Turner, John Kane, Anna and Martyn Carey, Alec and Barbara Jones, Maysie Thompson, Kate and Michael Colgrave, Jennifer Lamburn, Peter Meister, Dr and Mrs A S C Calder, Joanne Boissevain, R Huggins, D Irving, E McCall, T McLean, A L and L R Barnes, Wendy and Bob Needham, Guy Vowles, RJH, Di and Mike Gillam, John Robertson)*

Free house ~ Licensees Tim Haigh and Rupert Pendered ~ Real ale ~ Bar food (12-2.30(3 Sat/Sun), 7-9.30(10 Fri/Sat) ~ Restaurant ~ (01285) 740421 ~ Children welcome ~ Dogs allowed in bar ~ Open 11-3.30(4 Sat), 6-11; 12-4, 7-10.30 Sun; closed 25 Dec ~ Bedrooms: £65S/£95B

BISLEY SO9006 Map 4

Bear

Village signposted off A419 just E of Stroud

For the first 300 years of its life this elegantly gothic 16th-c place was a courthouse and you can still see the nearby two-cell lockup, the iron-grill doors of which opened on to the road, leaving the unfortunate prisoners open to public jeers – or worse. This is a favourite with readers, and there's a good, relaxed pubby atmosphere and a warm welcome from the helpful staff. The meandering L-shaped bar has a long shiny black built-in settle and a smaller but even sturdier oak settle by the front entrance, and an enormously wide low stone fireplace (not very high – the ochre ceiling's too low for that); the separate no smoking stripped-stone area is used for families. Enjoyable home-made bar food includes soup (£3.50), goats cheese toasties (£3.75), lots of baguettes interestingly filled with tuna salad niçoise, brie and grape, roasted ratatouille or lamb steak with redcurrant jelly (mostly £4.75), sautéed potatoes and onions on lettuce with tomato and garlic (£5.50), provençale vegetables (£5.85) or smoked salmon and leek (£6.25), home-made rabbit or steak, kidney and Guinness pies, moroccan spiced lamb or vegetable pasty (from £7.50), and daily specials like pasta carbonara (£6.95), spicy meatloaf with wine gravy or mild and creamy chicken curry (£7.25), sausages casseroled with bacon, onions and sage (£7.95), and chunky cod roasted with red peppers and cherry tomatoes (£8.95). Well kept Courage Directors, Flowers IPA, Tetleys, Wells Bombardier, and a guest such as Brains SA on handpump; dominoes, cribbage, and table skittles. A small front colonnade supports the upper floor of the pub, and the sheltered little flagstoned courtyard made by this has a traditional bench; the garden is across the quiet road, and there's quite a collection of stone mounting-blocks. The steep stone-built village is attractive. *(Recommended by Richard Gibbs, Guy Vowles, J A Cheverton, P R and S A White, Mike and Lynn Robinson, Nick and Meriel Cox, Prof H G Allen, Paul Oneill, Jill Hurley, Martin Jennings, Mr and Mrs P Higgins, Dave Irving)*

Pubmaster ~ Tenants Simon and Sue Evans ~ Real ale ~ Bar food (not Sun evening) ~ (01452) 770265 ~ Children in family room ~ Dogs welcome ~ Occasional Weds evening jazz ~ Open 11.30-3, 6-11; 12-3, 7-10.30 Sun ~ Bedrooms: /£40

BLAISDON SO7017 Map 4

Red Hart

Village signposted off A4136 just SW of junction with A40 W of Gloucester; OS Sheet 162 map reference 703169

This bustling pub is set in a quiet village tucked away in the Forest of Dean. The flagstoned main bar has a thoroughly relaxing atmosphere – helped along by well reproduced piped bluesy music, and maybe Spotty the perky jack russell – as well as cushioned wall and window seats, traditional pub tables, and a big sailing-ship painting above the log fire. Well kept Hook Norton Best, Tetleys, and three guests such as Timothy Taylors Landlord, Uley Bitter, and Wickwar Brand Oak Bitter on handpump, and a decent wine list. On the right, there's an attractive beamed two-room no smoking dining area with some interesting prints and bric-a-brac, and on the left, additional dining space for families. Well liked bar food includes home-made soup (£2.75), sandwiches (from £3.75), fried sardines (£4.25), salmon and coriander fishcakes (starter £4.25, main course £6.50), fresh scallops (£4.75), ham, egg and bubble and squeak (£5.75), lemon chicken stir fry (£9.50), roast monkfish (£10), and fillet of lamb with red wine and rosemary sauce (£10.50). Cribbage, dominoes, and table skittles. There are some picnic-sets in the garden and a children's play area, and at the back of the building is a large space for barbecues. *(Recommended by Clare and Paul Howes, Geoff and Brigid Smithers, R Marshall, Theocsbrian, Mr and Mrs F J Parmenter, W Ruxton, Rod Stoneman)*

Free house ~ Licensee Guy Wilkins ~ Real ale ~ Bar food ~ Restaurant ~ (01452) 830477 ~ Children in eating area of bar and restaurant ~ Dogs allowed in bar ~ Open 11.30-3, 6-11; 12-3.30, 7-10.30 Sun

BLEDINGTON SP2422 Map 4

Kings Head

B4450

Overlooking the village green, this stone-built house looks a classic Cotswold village pub. Inside, it has more the feel of an efficiently run pub-cum-brasserie. This year, the restaurant has been redone to create a large, airy room with heavy country-style modern oak tables and chairs on the flagstones, and a large painting of foxhounds on one of the butter-yellow walls. The main bar is full of ancient beams and other atmospheric furnishings (high-backed wooden settles, gateleg or pedestal tables), and there's a warming log fire in the stone inglenook (with a big black kettle hanging in it). To the left of the bar a drinking space for locals has benches on the wooden floor, a woodburning stove, and darts, cribbage, dominoes, TV, piped music; on Sunday lunchtimes it is used by families. The lounge looks on to the garden. Ambitious food which usually hits the mark might include ciabattas filled with bacon or brie, or chicken with roast tomato and basil (from £3.95), spicy thai chicken and noodle soup or roasted chick pea and aubergine salad with mint yoghurt dressing (£4.50), duck spring rolls with sweet and sour dressing (£5.50), goats cheese tart on rocket salad, tomato and parsley dressing (£7.50), home-made fish pie (£8), scallops with spaghetti, spinach, roasted red pepper and lime and garlic dressing (£10.95), fillet of bass, dill and potato cake with lemon crème fraîche (£11.25), pork cutlet marinated in honey and ginger with parsley and mustard mash and roasted courgette (£11.50), pepper-crusted fillet of beef with sautéed wild mushrooms, caramelised shallots and parmentier potatoes (£15.95), puddings such as warm fudge brownie, key lime pie or banoffi pie (£3.50), and interesting cheeses (a choice of three for £4.95). An antique bar counter dispenses well kept Hook Norton Best and Wadworths 6X with a couple of guests such as Archers Village, Goffs Jouster or Shepherd Neame Spitfire, an excellent extensive wine list, with 11 by the glass (champagnes also), 25 malt whiskies, organic cider and perry, and local apple juice. The restaurant is no smoking. There are seats in the back garden; aunt sally. At weekends, you are encouraged to stay two nights. *(Recommended by Richard Greaves, Stephen Buckley, R Halsey, A S and M E Marriott, David and Anthea Eeles, Felicity Stephens, Les Trusler, David and Nina Pugsley, Stephen, Julie and Hayley Brown, Colin Fisher, Victoria Simon, Dr K Roger Wood, Maysie Thompson)*

Free house ~ Licensees Nicola and Archie Orr-Ewing ~ Real ale ~ Bar food ~ Restaurant ~ (01608) 658365 ~ Children in restaurant ~ Dogs allowed in bar ~ Open 11-3, 6-11; 12-3, 6.30-10.30 Sun; closed 25 and 26 Dec ~ Bedrooms: £50B/£70B

BOX SO8500 Map 4

Halfway Inn

Edge of Minchinhampton Common; from A46 S of Stroud follow Amberley signpost, then after Amberley Inn turn right towards Box, then left along common edge as you reach Box; OS Sheet 162 map reference 856003; can also be reached from Brimscombe on A419 SE of Stroud

A new licensee took over this extended tall house a few weeks before we went to press, and we are keeping our fingers crossed that the blip the pub seemed to have gone through over the recent months will have been smoothed out. The light and airy open-plan upstairs bars wrap around the central serving bar, and there are simple rush seated sturdy blond wooden chairs around good wooden tables, a built-in wall seat and long pew, a woodburning stove, fresh flowers and other plants, and stripped wood floors. The bar has yellowy cream walls and ceiling, the dining area is mainly a warm terracota, there are windows with swagged curtains and views to the common, and an unusual pitched-roof area with a vast mirror and a big wrought-iron candelabrum; it's all most inviting and attractive. Good, interesting bar food now includes sandwiches or baguettes (from £4.25), pigeon breast with baby artichokes, sautéed spinach and chutney sauce (£5.25), salad of guinea fowl and grapes, truffle oil and shallots (£5.75), honey-glazed goats cheese salad (£5.95), a plate of British cheese with ham and chutney (£6.25), aubergine and potato cannelloni with spinach, carrot and cardamom sauce (£8.95), slow-roasted duck leg with chorizo cassoulet and fondant potato (£10.50), tuna spring roll with a spiced avocado salad and aïoli sauce (£12.95), halibut fillet, lemon grass broth, braised endive and mussels (£13.25), fillet steak with rösti potatoes, glazed baby vegetables and port sauce (£15.50), and puddings such as home-made sticky toffee pudding with butterscotch and toffee ice cream, spiced pear tart tatin or home-made chocolate brownie (from £4.25). Well kept Bass, Hook Norton Best, Uley Bitter, and Wickwar BOB on handpump, kept under light blanket pressure, and good wines; piped music. There are seats in the landscaped garden. *(Recommended by Brian and Pat Wardrobe, Charles and Pauline Stride, Mary Kirman and Tim Jefferson, R Huggins, D Irving, E McCall, T McLean)*

Red Rose ~ Licensee Matt Walker ~ Real ale ~ Bar food ~ Restaurant ~ (01453) 832631 ~ Children welcome ~ Dogs welcome ~ Open 11-11; 12-10.30 Sun; 11-3, 6-11 in winter

BRIMPSFIELD SO9413 Map 4

Golden Heart 🍷 🍺

Nettleton Bottom; A417 Birdlip—Cirencester, by start of new village bypass

Run by a welcoming, knowledgeable landlord, this is an enjoyable pub that sees return visitors again and again. The main low-ceilinged bar is divided into three cosily distinct areas, with a roaring log fire in the huge stone inglenook fireplace in one, traditional built-in settles and other old-fashioned furnishings throughout, and quite a few brass items, typewriters, exposed stone, and wood panelling. A comfortable parlour on the right has another decorative fireplace, and leads into a further room that opens onto the terrace; two rooms are no smoking. Well presented, popular bar food includes home-made soup (£3.25), sandwiches (from £3.25), home-made pâté (£4.25), filled baked potatoes (from £4.50), ploughman's (from £4.95), omelettes (£6.95), chicken curry (£7.50), mushroom stroganoff (£8.25), steaks (from £9.95), daily specials like sweet thai chicken pieces or smoked ham, leek and onion terrine (£4.95), hazelnut and mushroom nut roast (£8.25), lasagne or bubble and squeak with pork and stilton sausages (£9.25), steak and kidney pudding (£9.75), shark steak in garlic butter (£10.25), and puddings such as chocolate and kumquat truffle, chunky caramel cheesecake or lemon and lime bavarois (£3.50); Sunday roast (from £7.50). Well kept Archers, Bass, Timothy Taylors Landlord, and Youngs on handpump; decent wines. They hold beer festivals during the May and August bank holidays with live entertainment. There are pleasant views down over a valley from the rustic cask-supported tables on its suntrap gravel terrace, and good nearby walks. *(Recommended by Dr and Mrs James Stewart, R Huggins, D Irving, E McCall, T McLean, Dorsan Baker, Guy Vowles, Charles Moncreiffe, Stan and Hazel Allen, Rev Michael Vockins, James Woods, David Edwards, JP, PP, Dave Irving, Lesley and Peter Barrett)*

Free house ~ Licensee Catherine Stevens ~ Real ale ~ Bar food (12-3, 6-10) ~ Restaurant ~ (01242) 870261 ~ Children in eating area of bar and in family room ~ Dogs welcome ~ Open 11-3, 5.30-11; 11-11 Sat; 12-10.30 Sun ~ Bedrooms: £35S/£55S

BROAD CAMPDEN SP1637 Map 4

Bakers Arms

Village signposted from B4081 in Chipping Campden

A new terraced area with seats has been built by the play area behind this traditional village pub; more seats under parasols by flower tubs on other terraces and in the back garden. Inside, there's a chatty, relaxed atmosphere undisturbed by noisy games machines or piped music. The part with the most character is the tiny beamed bar with its pleasant mix of tables and seats around the walls (which are stripped back to bare stone), and inglenook fireplace at one end. The oak bar counter is attractive, and there's a big framed rugwork picture of the pub. Bar food includes lunchtime sandwiches (from £3.25), ploughman's (£4.25), and filled yorkshire puddings (£4.75), as well as home-made soup (£2.75), smoked haddock bake (£5.95), chicken curry (£5.75), cheese, leek and potato bake (£5.95), pie of the day or liver and bacon (£6.25), puddings (£2.95), daily specials, and children's menu (£3.25). Well kept Donningtons BB, Hook Norton Best, Stanway Stanney Bitter, and Wells Bombardier with a guest such as Badger Best or Fullers London Pride on handpump. Darts, cribbage, dominoes. This is a tranquil village. More reports please. *(Recommended by Yvonne Iley, John Brightley, Martin and Karen Wake, E V Walder, P R and S A White)*

Free house ~ Licensees Ray and Sally Mayo ~ Real ale ~ Bar food (all day in summer) ~ No credit cards ~ (01386) 840515 ~ Children in eating area of bar ~ Folk music 3rd Tues evening of month ~ Open 11.30-11; 12-10.30 Sun; 11.30-2.30, 4.45-11 weekdays in winter; closed 25 Dec, evening 26 Dec

BROCKHAMPTON SP0322 Map 4

Craven Arms ♀

Village signposted off A436 Andoversford—Naunton – look out for inn sign at head of lane in village; can also be reached from A40 Andoversford—Cheltenham via Whittington and Syreford

After a walk or even a morning's shopping, this attractive 17th-c inn, set in a pleasant gentrified hillside village with lovely views, is a pleasant and relaxed place to be. There are low beams, thick roughly coursed stone walls and some tiled flooring, and though much of it has been opened out to give a sizeable (and spotlessly kept) eating area off the smaller bar servery, it's been done well to give a feeling of several communicating rooms; the furniture is mainly pine, with some wall settles, tub chairs and a log fire. Well liked bar food using fresh local produce includes home-made crab cakes with salsa (£4.75), salad of goats cheese and bacon (£4.95), smoked salmon with dill mayonnaise (£4.95; main course £7.50), big ploughman's (from £4.95), cumberland sausage with onion and wine sauce (£6.95), mushrooms and nuts in ale under a puff pastry topping (£7.50), steak, mushroom and Guinness pie (£7.95), confit of duck leg with redcurrant and port sauce or seared salmon slice on a champagne and dill dressing (£9.25), slow roasted belly of pork with lemon and chilli marmalade (£9.50), steaks (from £11.75), whole bass gently roasted with fresh herbs (£12.95), and home-made puddings like sticky toffee pudding or apple crumble (from £3.50); popular Sunday roasts. Well kept Fullers London Pride, Hook Norton Best and a weekly guest on handpump; shove-ha'penny. *(Recommended by Tom and Ruth Rees, Martin Jennings, Neil and Anita Christopher, Guy Vowles, Mike and Mary Carter, Peter Burton, Dr and Mrs James Stewart, Mr and Mrs B J P Edwards)*

Free house ~ Licensee Dale Campbell ~ Real ale ~ Bar food ~ Restaurant ~ (01242) 820410 ~ Children in eating area of bar and restaurant ~ Live entertainment every 2nd Sun evening – jazz or blues ~ Open 11-3, 6-11; 12-4, 7-10.30 Sun

Post Office address codings confusingly give the impression that some pubs are in Gloucestershire, when they're really in Warwickshire (which is where we list them).

CHEDWORTH SP0511 Map 4

Seven Tuns

Village signposted off A429 NE of Cirencester; then take second signposted right turn and bear left towards church

There's a really good mix of customers in this bustling 17th-c pub from walkers, cyclists, locals wanting just a drink, and those after a good meal. The cosy little lounge on the right has a good winter log fire in the big stone fireplace, comfortable seats and decent tables, sizeable antique prints, tankards hanging from the beam over the serving bar, and a partly boarded ceiling. The public bar on the left down a couple of steps has an open fire, and this opens into a no smoking dining room with another open fire; the upstairs skittle alley also acts as the games room with pool, darts, bar billiards, cribbage, shove-ha'penny, and dominoes. Enjoyable bar food includes sandwiches or baguettes (from £3.75; back bacon and fried mushrooms £4.50; Scotch sirloin steak £4.75), filled baked potatoes or ploughman's (£5.95), ham and egg (£6.25), beef or vegetarian lasagne (£6.95), and daily specials such as prawn curry (£6.75), salmon fishcakes (£7.95), pigeon breast on black pudding topped with smoked streaky bacon and red wine sauce (£8.75), whole bass with a pesto crust and crispy leeks (£10), local wild venison fillet steaks with a port, cream and redcurrant jelly sauce (£10.95), and roast Sunday lunch (£6.75). Well kept Smiles Best and IPA, and Youngs Bitter and IPA on handpump; lots of malt whiskies, and prompt service. Across the road is a little walled raised terrace with a waterwheel and a stream, and there are plenty of tables both here and under cocktail parasols on a side terrace. The famous Roman villa is closeby. *(Recommended by Susan and Peter Davies, Des and Jen Clarke, Peter and Audrey Dowsett, Trevor Owen, R Huggins, D Irving, E McCall, T McLean, George Atkinson, Lynn Sharpless, Patricia A Bruce, J M Law)*

Youngs ~ Tenant Kevin Dursley ~ Real ale ~ Bar food (all day in summer; 11-2.30, 6-10 in winter) ~ (01285) 720242 ~ Children welcome ~ Dogs welcome ~ Open 11-11; 12-10.30 Sun; 11-3, 6-11 in winter

CHIPPING CAMPDEN SP1539 Map 4

Eight Bells

Church Street (which is one way – entrance off B4035)

Some careful refurbishments and a new lavatory block for this handsome old inn over the last year. There are heavy oak beams with massive timber supports, stripped stone walls, cushioned pews and solid dark wood furniture on the broad flagstones, daily papers to read, and log fires in up to three restored stone fireplaces. Part of the floor in the no smoking dining room has a glass inlet showing part of the passage from the church by which Roman Catholic priests could escape from the Roundheads. Bar food includes lunchtime (not Sunday) filled baguettes, home-made soup (£3.75), tomato and mozzarella tartlet (£5.25), steamed Cornish mussels with a thai broth (£5.95), braised faggots with sage polenta and onion gravy (£8), pasta with peppers, olives, spring onion and diced tomatoes in a green sauce (£9), Irish stew with dumplings (£10.25), rib-eye steak (£12.50), tuna marinated in chilli, coriander and ginger with warm potato salad and niçoise dressing (£13.75), and home-made puddings such as citrus mousse with shortbread fingers, chocolate tart with raspberry coulis or sticky toffee pudding with caramel sauce (£3.95); children's menu (£4.75). Well kept Goffs Jouster, Hook Norton Best and Old Hooky, and a guest such as Fullers London Pride or Wyre Piddle Piddle in the Hole on handpump from the fine oak bar counter; country wines. Piped music, cribbage, and dominoes. Plenty of seats in the large terraced garden with striking views of the almshouses and church. Handy for the Cotswold Way walk to Bath. *(Recommended by P R and S A White, Desmond O'Donovan, Stuart Turner, Pat and Roger Fereday, John Mitchell, J A and R M Ashurst, Di and Mike Gillam, Dave Braisted, Martin Jones, Jenny and Chris Wilson, Rodney and Norma Stubington)*

Free house ~ Licensee Neil Hargreaves ~ Real ale ~ Bar food (12-2(2.30 Fri-Sun), 6.30-9.30(7-10 Fri/Sat)) ~ Restaurant ~ (01386) 840371 ~ Children in eating area of

bar and restaurant ~ Dogs welcome ~ Open 11-3, 5.30-11; 11-11 Fri- Sat; 12-10.30 Sun; closed 25 Dec ~ Bedrooms: £40B/£70B

Volunteer

Lower High Street

They have up to half a dozen well kept real ales on handpump in this friendly old local: Hook Norton Best, North Cotswold Brewery Genesis, Stanway Stanney Bitter, and guests such as Goffs Jouster, Wells Bombardier, and Wickwar Cotswold Way; quite a few malt whiskies. The little bar by the street has cushioned seats in bay windows, a log fire piled with big logs in the golden stone fireplace with hops, helmets and horse bits above it, proper old dining chairs with sage green plush seats and some similarly covered stools around a mix of tables, old army (Waterloo and WWI) paintings and bugles on the walls, with old local photographs on the gantry, and quite a few brass spigots dotted about. The public bar has modern upholstered wing settles, juke box, darts, pool, fruit machine, cribbage, dominoes. Tasty bar food includes soup (£2.75), home-roasted honey glazed ham with egg and chips or battered cod (£6), steak and kidney pie (£6.50), calves liver and bacon with balsamic gravy (£7.50), chicken breast flamed with calvados and finished with cream and almonds (£8.50), and 10oz rib-eye pepper steak (£10.75); Sunday roast (£6.25). There are picnic-sets in a small brick-paved ivy courtyard with an arch through to the back garden where there are more seats; maybe pig roasts and barbecues on some bank holidays. *(Recommended by Dr Paull Khan, Di and Mike Gillam, Steve Whalley)*

Free house ~ Licensee Hilary Mary Sinclair ~ Real ale ~ Bar food ~ (01386) 840688 ~ Children in eating area of bar ~ Dogs allowed in bar ~ Open 11.30-3, 5(6 Sat)-11; 12-3, 7-10.30 Sun ~ Bedrooms: £30B/£55B

COLN ST ALDWYNS SP1405 Map 4

New Inn

On good back road between Bibury and Fairford

This civilised, friendly inn is a lovely place for a quiet weekend, and if you enjoy fishing, they now have day tickets for trout fishing in season on the pretty River Coln. And although many customers do come to enjoy the particularly good food both at lunchtime and in the evening, there is just as warm a welcome for those who only want a drink and a chat. The two neatly kept main rooms are attractively furnished and decorated, and divided by a central log fire in a neat stone fireplace with wooden mantelbeam and willow-pattern plates on the chimney breast; there are also low beams, some stripped stonework around the bar servery with hops above it, oriental rugs on the red tiles, and a mix of seating from library chairs to stripped pews. Down a slight slope, a further room has a coal fire in an old kitchen range at one end, and a white pheasant on the wall. Many of the starters can also be taken as main courses: soup (£3.25 or £5.50), steamed mussels or fresh pasta with sweet red pepper and marjoram (£4.50 or £8.50), chicken liver and madeira pâté with toasted onion bread (£5 or £8.50), and cured meats, salami, manchego and marinated olives (£5.75 or £9.75). Also, lunchtime sandwiches and filled baguettes, pork and honey and mustard sausages with roast garlic mash and sweet onions or herb risotto with local mushrooms and parmesan (£9.50), finnan smoked haddock, poached egg and mustard (£9.75), calves liver and bacon with parsley mash and red wine sauce (£11.20), lamb kleftiko (£11.25), chargrilled tiger prawns (£11.50), peppered rib-eye steak with béarnaise sauce (£13.25), and steamed date and apricot pudding with butterscotch sauce, crème brûlée with red fruits or vanilla ice cream profiteroles with chocolate sauce (from £4.25). The restaurant is no smoking. Well kept Hook Norton Best, and Wadworths 6X with a guest such as Butcombe Best or Smiles on handpump, eight good wines and champagne by the glass, and several malt whiskies; shove-ha'penny and dominoes. The split-level terrace has plenty of seats. The peaceful Cotswold village is most attractive, and the riverside walk to Bibury is not to be missed. *(Recommended by A E Brace, Tony Baldwin, Doreen and Haydn Maddock, John Bramley, Paul Humphreys, R Huggins, D Irving, E McCall, T McLean, Lawrence Pearse, John*

Kane, Simon Collett-Jones, Peter Sutton, Philip Vernon, Kim Maidment, Ted George, Lesley and Peter Barrett, Peter Meister, Peter D B Harding, G T Brewster, S H Godsell, John Bowdler, Philip and Jenny Grant; also in the Good Hotel Guide*)*

Free house ~ Licensee Brian Evans ~ Real ale ~ Bar food (12-2.30, 7-9(9.30 Fri/Sat)) ~ Restaurant ~ (01285) 750651 ~ Children in eating area of bar; must be over 10 in restaurant ~ Dogs allowed in bar ~ Occasional jazz ~ Open 11-11; 12-10.30 Sun ~ Bedrooms: £80S/£110B

CRANHAM SO8912 Map 4

Black Horse

Village signposted off A46 and B4070 N of Stroud; look out for small sign up village side turning

Popular locally – though there's a warm welcome for visitors too – this old-fashioned 17th-c inn is tucked away down narrow lanes. A cosy little lounge has just three or four tables, and the main bar is quarry-tiled, with cushioned high-backed wall settles and window seats, and a good log fire. Generous helpings of well liked bar food include sandwiches and toasties (from £2), ploughman's (£5), omelettes using their own free range eggs (£5.25), vegetarian moussaka (£7.25), salmon fishcakes (£7.95), chicken with stilton (£8.25), pies such as fish or steak and kidney (from £8.25), pork and bean cassoulet (£8.50), tuna with salsa verde (£9.50), and lamb kleftiko or half roast duck with apple sauce and stuffing (£10.50); roast Sunday lunch (£7.95). You can eat the same menu in the upstairs no smoking dining rooms (best to book at weekends). Well kept Boddingtons, Flowers Original, Greene King IPA, Hook Norton Best, and Wickwar BOB on handpump. Shove-ha'penny and piped music. Tables in the sizeable garden behind have a good view out over the steep village and wooded valley, and they keep chickens and rabbits; the jack russell is called Baxter and the cocker spaniel, Biscuit. Morris dancers in summer. More reports please. *(Recommended by Pete Baker, Nigel and Sue Foster, Mike and Wendy Proctor, James Nunns)*

Free house ~ Licensees David and Julie Job ~ Real ale ~ Bar food (not Sun evening) ~ Restaurant ~ (01452) 812217 ~ Children welcome ~ Dogs allowed in bar ~ Open 11.45-2.30, 6.30-11; 12-3, 7-11 Sun

DIDMARTON ST8187 Map 2

Kings Arms

A433 Tetbury road

This attractively restored and decorated 17th-c coaching inn has knocked-through rooms that work their way around a big central counter: deep terracotta walls above a dark green dado, a pleasant mix of chairs on bare boards, quarry tiles and carpet, hops on beams, a big stone fireplace, and a nice old upright piano. Everything is neat and tidy, with good attention to detail. You can eat the same menu in the bar or restaurant which might include soup (£3), filled baguettes (from £3.75; cheese, bacon and mushroom £4.25), grilled smoked goats cheese and nectarines with baby spinach and a honey and pink peppercorn sauce (£4.50 or £8.25), monkfish and salmon terrine with a tarragon chantilly mayonnaise (£4.95 or £8.50), pigeon breast with celeriac remoulade (£5.25 or £8.25), lamb and coriander sausages on minted pea mash and gravy (£7.95), haddock in beer batter (£8.95), beef in ale stew with thyme dumplings (£9.95), wild mushrooms, sweet pepper and rice strudel with cajun sauce (£10.95), hare tagine with apricots and saffron and mustard seed rice (£12.95), and pecan butter tart with crème fraîche or sticky toffee pudding with toffee sauce (£4.50). The restaurant is no smoking. Well kept John Smiths, Uley Bitter, and a couple of guests (changing four or five times a week) from small brewers or microbreweries on handpump, a good wine list with half a dozen by the glass, farm cider in summer, and several malt whiskies; darts, cribbage, and dominoes. Seats in the pleasant back garden, and they have self-catering cottages in a converted barn and stable block. *(Recommended by Peter and Audrey Dowsett, Hugh Roberts, Derek Carless, Tom and Ruth Rees, Gaynor Gregory, MRSM, Philip and Jenny Grant,*

KC, Martin and Karen Wake, Stephen and Jean Curtis, Mr and Mrs A H Young)

Free house ~ Licensees Nigel and Jane Worrall ~ Real ale ~ Bar food ~ Restaurant ~ (01454) 238245 ~ Children in eating area of bar and restaurant ~ Dogs allowed in bar ~ Open 12-2.30, 6-11; 12-3, 7-10.30 Sun; closed 25 Dec ~ Bedrooms: £45S/£70S

DUNTISBOURNE ABBOTS SO9709 Map 4

Five Mile House

Approaching from Cirencester on A417 take exit marked Duntisbourne Abbots, Winstone and services; take 3 consecutive right turns; pub on left just before dead end

Although the original part of this popular old place is 17th-c and used to be a toll station (the bay window was the look-out post for the toll-keeper), this quiet country lane was once Ermine Street, the main Roman road from London to Wales. It's a favourite pub with many customers, and the front room has a companionable bare-boards drinking bar on the right, with wall seats around the big table in its bow window and just one other table; on the left is a flagstoned hallway tap room snug formed from two ancient high-backed settles by a woodburning stove in a tall carefully exposed old fireplace; newspapers to read. There's a small cellar bar, a back restaurant down steps, and a family room on the far side; cribbage and dominoes. The lounge and cellar bar are no smoking. Well kept Archers Village, Donningtons BB and Timothy Taylors Landlord on handpump (the cellar is temperature-controlled), and interesting wines (strong on New World ones). Generous helpings of good, popular bar food (cooked by the landlord and with prices unchanged since last year) include, at lunchtime, open sandwiches (from £3.95), ploughman's (from £4.95), free range egg omelette (£5.95), home-cooked ham with eggs or deep-fried cod and chips (£6.95), and whole local trout with a prawn and lemon butter (£8.50), with evening dishes such as home-made soup (£3.25), home-made chicken liver pâté (£4.50) or chicken breast fillet stuffed with stilton, wrapped in bacon and served with a mushroom and brandy cream sauce (£9.95), and daily specials like home-made faggots or hot avocado filled with apricots, figs, celery, apple and grapes and topped with toasted brie (£7.50), pork loin steaks glazed with honey and mustard (£9.50), and barbary duck breast with a mulled wine and orange glaze (£12.50); puddings such as white chocolate cheesecake, crème brûlée, treacle tart or fruit crumble (£3.50), children's helpings where possible, and roast Sunday lunch (£8.50). You may have to book some time ahead. Service is thoughtful and friendly. The gardens have nice country views. *(Recommended by Roger and Jenny Huggins, Debbie and Neil Hayter, R Huggins, D Irving, E McCall, T McLean, Phil and Sally Gorton, Dave Irving, R T and J C Moggridge, GL, JP, PP, Helen Eastwood, Di and Mike Gillam, Rob Webster, Giles Francis, the Didler, Dennis Jenkin, Rev Michael Vockins, Patricia A Bruce, Guy Vowles, Richard Stancomb, Helen Gazeley)*

Free house ~ Licensees Jo and John Carrier ~ Real ale ~ Bar food (12-2.30, 6-9.30; not evenings 25 Dec or 1 Jan) ~ Restaurant ~ (01285) 821432 ~ Children welcome if well behaved ~ Dogs allowed in bar ~ Open 12-3, 6-11; 12-3, 7-10.30 Sun

DURSLEY ST7598 Map 2

Old Spot

By bus station

With plenty of character and a lively bunch of customers, this unassuming town pub has a good range of ales and a friendly atmosphere. The front door opens into a deep pink little room with stools on shiny quarry tiles along its pine boarded bar counter, and old enamel beer advertisements on the walls and ceiling; there's a profusion of porcine paraphernalia. Leading off here there's a little room on the left with a bar billiards table, cribbage and dominoes, and the little dark wood floored room to the right has a stone fireplace. From here a step takes you down to a cosy Victorian tiled snug and (to the right) the no smoking meeting room. Well kept Moles Barleymole, Shepherd Neame Spitfire, Uley Old Ric, and Wychwood Shires XXX and England's Ale (named for the World Cup Football) on handpump, and several malt whiskies. Bar food (they tell us prices have not changed since last year) includes sandwiches (from £2.75), filled baked potatoes (from £3.75), ploughman's (from £4.75), stir-fries such as vegetarian or chicken (from £4.95), sausages such as lamb and mint or pork, leek and ginger, all served with red onion gravy (from £5.25), beef in ale pie (£5.50), smoked trout fillets (£5.15), and puddings (from £2.25). More reports please. *(Recommended by Comus and Sarah Elliott, Theocsbrian)*

Free house ~ Licensees Steve and Belinda Herbert ~ Real ale ~ Bar food (lunchtime only) ~ (01453) 542870 ~ Children in family room ~ Dogs welcome ~ Local musicians Weds evenings ~ Open 11-3, 5.30-11; 11-11 Sat; 12-10.30 Sun

EASTLEACH TURVILLE SP1905 Map 4

Victoria 𝕐

Village signposted off A361 S of Burford

Up at the top of the delightful streamside village, this low-ceilinged old pub has picnic-sets out in front, looking down over a steep bank of daffodils at the other stone-built houses and a couple of churches. It's open-plan inside, but nicely divided, rambling cosily around a central bar, with sturdy pub tables of varying sizes, and some attractive seats – particularly those built in beside the log fire in the stripped stone chimneybreast. There are some unusual engravings and lithographs of Queen Victoria around the back. Enjoyable freshly made food includes filled baguettes, home-made chicken liver parfait, moules marinière or field mushrooms baked with stilton (£3.95), warm smoked chicken, bacon and brie salad (£6.95), salmon fishcakes with prawn and dill sauce or steak and mushroom pie (£7.25), and calves liver and bacon with red wine sauce (£8.25), with evening extras such as chicken breast with creamy stilton sauce (£8.25), pork medallions with grape, mushroom and tarragon sauce or poached smoked haddock and egg coated with mustard sauce (£8.95), and lamb shank on minty mash topped with caramelised onion and jus (£10.50); part of the restaurant is no smoking. Arkells 2B and 3B on handpump, six or seven nice New World wines by the large glass, well served cafetière coffee, good drinks prices, welcoming service; may be unobtrusive piped local radio. It can get very busy on warm days, with cyclists and longer-distance walkers as well as the parties of older folk who come to enjoy a short stroll in this lovely spot. The right-hand area has more of a public bar feel, with darts, cribbage and dominoes and more standing room. There are some more picnic-sets on grass behind the car park. *(Recommended by Dr and Mrs M E Wilson, Patrick Hancock, Peter and Audrey Dowsett, Marjorie and David Lamb, R Huggins, D Irving, E McCall, T McLean, John Bowdler, Ted George)*

Arkells ~ Tenants Stephen and Susan Richardson ~ Real ale ~ Bar food ~ Restaurant ~ (01367) 850277 ~ Children in eating area of bar and restaurant ~ Dogs allowed in bar ~ Open 12-3(4 Sat), 7-11; 12-4. 7-10.30 Sun; closed evening 25 Dec

EWEN SU0097 Map 4

Wild Duck 𝕐

Village signposted from A429 S of Cirencester

Handy for Cirencester and so always busy, this civilised 16th-c inn has a high-beamed main bar with a nice mix of comfortable armchairs and other seats, paintings on the red walls, crimson drapes, a winter open fire, candles on tables, and magazines to read; the residents' lounge has a handsome Elizabethan fireplace and antique furnishings, and looks over the garden; piped music. Bar food includes lunchtime choices such as lightly spiced kedgeree with tomato salsa (£5.50), ploughman's (£5.95), and wild boar and apple sausages or pasta with roquefort, walnuts and parsley (£6.95), as well as leek and haddock pot (£5.95), seared tuna layered with guacamole and toasted tortilla (£6.25), goats cheese and asparagus tart with roast pepper salad and black pepper dressing (£8.95), and lamb chump on feta cheese and black olive salad with a greek-style dressing (£10.95), with daily specials like cream of watercress soup (£3.50), prawn salad with crab dressing (£6.95), salmon steak with basil butter or black bream with a mango and coconut dressing (£8.95), half a guinea fowl with a tomato and tarragon sauce or pork steak topped with a cheesy crust and a smoked bacon and mushroom sauce (£9.95), and chargrilled steaks (from £12.95). As well as Duckpond Bitter, brewed especially for the pub, real ales might include Wells Bombardier and Youngs Special on handpump, kept under light blanket pressure. Good wines, several malt whiskies, and shove-ha'penny. There are green painted cast-iron tables and seats in the neatly kept and sheltered garden. More reports please. *(Recommended by KC, Ian Phillips, Di and Mike Gillam, Richard Gibbs, Bernard Stradling, R Huggins, D Irving, E McCall, T McLean, John Robertson, Rob Webster, Kevin Blake, Christopher Harrowe, Mr and Mrs J McRobert, P R and S A White)*

Free house ~ Licensees Tina and Dino Mussell ~ Real ale ~ Bar food (till 10pm) ~ Restaurant ~ (01285) 770310 ~ Children welcome ~ Dogs allowed in bar ~ Open 11-11; 12-10.30 Sun; closed evening 25 Dec ~ Bedrooms: £60B/£80B

FORD SP0829 Map 4

Plough

B4077

This pretty pub used to be the local courthouse, and what is now the cellar was the gaol. It's a friendlier place nowadays and as it is set opposite a well known racehorse trainer's yard, there's a bustling atmosphere and racing prints and photos on the walls in the beamed and stripped-stone bar; also, old settles and benches around the big tables on its uneven flagstones, oak tables in a snug alcove, four welcoming log fires (two are log-effect gas), and dominoes, cribbage, shove-ha'penny, fruit machine, TV (for the races), and piped music. Under the new licensee, home-made bar food includes lunchtime sandwiches or chicken liver and brandy pâté (£3.95), filled baguettes (from £4.95), mustard baked ham and free range eggs (£6.95), wild mushroom risotto or fish and chips (£7.95), and chicken breast in a wine and herb sauce or lamb shank in red wine and cumberland sauce (£8.25); they still offer breakfasts for travellers on the way to the Gold Cup meeting at Cheltenham, and continue with their traditional asparagus feasts – every May-June the first asparagus spears to be sold at auction in the Vale of Evesham usually end up here. Well kept Donnington BB and SBA on handpump, and Addlestone's cider; polite, helpful service. There are benches in the garden, pretty hanging baskets, and a play area at the back. The Llama Farm and Cotswold Farm Park are nearby. More reports please. *(Recommended by Tom Evans, Mike and Wena Stevenson, M G Hart, P and J Shapley, the Didler, Peter and Audrey Dowsett, Guy Vowles, Ian Phillips, JP, PP, Mike Horler)*

Donnington ~ Tenant Craig Brown ~ Real ale ~ Bar food ~ (01386) 584215 ~ Children only in one bar area ~ Occasional live entertainment ~ Open 11-11; 12-10.30 Sun ~ Bedrooms: £25S/£55S

FRAMPTON MANSELL SO9201 Map 4

White Horse

A491 Cirencester—Stroud

Gloucestershire Dining Pub of the Year

The licensees have transformed what had been a run-down – and indeed closed – pub into a smart, friendly dining place with attractive furnishings. Alongside the pine tables, rush matting and clean up-to-date décor of the main part, they have also included a cosy bar area with a large sofa and comfortable chairs for those who want to pop in just for a relaxing drink. As well as Hook Norton, Uley Bitter and a guest such as Arkells Summer Ale or Wadworths 6X on handpump, they have a well chosen wine list helpfully split into different style sections, and they give a choice of half a dozen white and red wines by the glass or 50cl pot. The menu changes daily, and only carefully sourced ingredients are used for the excellent modern English dishes. As well as lunchtime baguettes, home-glazed ham and egg (with home-made chips) or smoked chicken, avocado and bacon salad, there might be pea and pear soup (£3.50), lamb sweetbreads with lardons of pancetta, roasted baby onions and a port and thyme jus (£4.95), whole grilled monkfish tail with guacamole, spicy chorizo and a coriander and lime yoghurt (£5.75), tomato and leek risotto with grilled goats cheese and crispy leeks (£8.95), slow-braised pork belly with pak choi and a balsamic jus (£9.75), chicken breast with caramelised onion mash and a sherry and ginger jus (£10), seared tuna loin with chilli and coriander couscous and red pepper pesto (£11), and puddings such as rhubarb fool with sweet cherry ice cream, warm rice pudding with mixed berry compote or hot sweet beignets with butterscotch sauce (£4); a good choice of coffee or tea; friendly staff. There are tables out in the attractive garden. *(Recommended by Mike Snelgrove, Eleanor Taylor, John Kane, Guy Vowles, R Huggins, D Irving, E McCall, T McLean)*

Free house ~ Licensees Shaun and Emma Davis ~ Real ale ~ Bar food (12-2.45; not evenings) ~ Restaurant ~ (01285) 760960 ~ Children in restaurant ~ Dogs welcome ~ Open 11-3, 6-11; 12-4 Sun; closed Sun evening

GREAT RISSINGTON SP1917 Map 4

Lamb

Turn off A40 W of Burford to the Barringtons; keep straight on past Great Barrington until Great Rissington is signed on left

The hard-working licensees are keen that both locals and visitors should feel welcome in this partly 17th-c inn – and they seem to be succeeding. The rather civilised two-roomed bar has peach coloured walls, cushioned seats covered in an orange and burgundy brocade with curtains to match, wheelback and tub chairs grouped around polished tables on the beige carpet, and an open fire in the stone fireplace. Some interesting things to look at include part of a propeller from the Wellington bomber that crashed in the garden in October 1943, a collection of old cigarette and tobacco tins (along a beam in the restaurant), photographs of the guide dogs the previous staff and customers raised money to buy – plus the Gabriels' first one – a history of the village, and various plates and pictures. Under the new chef, good bar food now includes home-made soup with cream and croutons (£3.50), chicken and duck liver pâté with mediterranean vegetable pickle or cheese and nut terrine with tomato coulis (£4.75), tiger prawns with garlic, ginger, chilli and lemon (£5.95), well liked devilled lambs kidneys with chive mash and crispy leeks (£8.50), casseroles such as venison and pigeon or cajun-asian ratatouille (from £8.50), pithivier of leeks and puy lentils, blue cheese gratin and herb butter (£8.95), tasty pork tenderloin with caramelised apples and sage jus (£9.50), half a gressingham duck with a black cherry and port sauce (£11.95), popular roast half shoulder of lamb with a rich redcurrant and red wine gravy (£12.95), and daily specials; helpful service. The no smoking restaurant has another open fire. Well kept Hook Norton Best or Shepherd Neame Spitfire on handpump, a decent wine list, and several malt whiskies. Piped classical music, darts, dominoes, and cribbage. You can sit out in the sheltered hillside garden or really take advantage of the scenery and walk (via gravel pits now used as a habitat for water birds) to Bourton-on-the-Water. *(Recommended by Simon Collett-Jones, Michael and Jenny Back, Mike and Wena Stevenson, John and Jackie Chalcraft, Jill Small, Pam Adsley)*

Free house ~ Licensees Paul and Jacqueline Gabriel ~ Real ale ~ Bar food ~ Restaurant ~ (01451) 820388 ~ Children welcome ~ Dogs allowed in bedrooms ~ Open 11.30-2.30, 6.30-11; 12-2.30, 7-10.30 Sun ~ Bedrooms: £35S(£40B)/£60S(£65B)

GRETTON SP0131 Map 4

Royal Oak

Village signposted off what is now officially B4077 (still often mapped and even signed as A438), E of Tewkesbury; keep on through village

At the bottom of the garden runs the private Gloucestershire—Warwickshire Railway and a stop is being opened right here to allow travellers on the steam trains to visit the pub. The series of bare-boarded or flagstoned rooms has beams hung with tankards, hop bines and chamber-pots, old prints on dark ochre walls, a medley of pews and various chairs, candles in bottles on the mix of stripped oak and pine tables, and a friendly bustle. The no smoking dining conservatory has stripped country furnishings, and a broad view over the countryside. New licensees again this year, and bar food now includes soup (£2.95), filled baguettes (from £3.25), ploughman's (£3.75), chicken liver pâté or smoked salmon and prawns (£3.95), feta cheese salad (£4.95), tandoori vegetables or lamb tagine (£6.95), home-made steak, onion and leek in ale pie (£7.25), chicken and wild mushrooms (£8.95), and puddings (£3.50). Well kept Goffs Jouster, White Knight, a beer named for the pub, Grettons Glory, a weekly changing guest or two on handpump, and a decent wine list; piped music and cribbage. They still hold a beer and music festival in June. From seats on the flower-filled terrace you can enjoy the fine views over the village and across the valley to Dumbleton Hills and the Malverns. There are more seats under a giant pear tree, a neatly kept big lawn running down to a play area (with an old tractor and see-saw), and even a bookable tennis court. *(Recommended by Ian Phillips, Will Hayes, David Rule, Bernard Stradling, Norman and June Williams, Hugh Roberts, Ted George, P and M Rudlin, Edward Jago, R J Herd, M Mainwaring)*

Free house ~ Licensee Roger Barlow ~ Real ale ~ Bar food (not winter Sun evening) ~ Restaurant ~ (01242) 604999 ~ Children in eating area of bar and restaurant ~ Live entertainment Weds or Thurs ~ Open 11-3, 6-11; 12-3, 7-10.30 Sun

GUITING POWER SP0924 Map 4

Hollow Bottom

Village signposted off B4068 SW of Stow-on-the-Wold (still called A436 on many maps)

Friendly and relaxed, this snug 17th-c inn has a comfortable beamed bar full of racing memorabilia including racing silks, tunics and photographs (it is owned by a small syndicate that includes Peter Scudamore and Nigel Twiston-Davies), and there's a winter log fire in an unusual pillar-supported stone fireplace. The public bar has flagstones and stripped stone masonry and racing on TV. Enjoyable bar food includes home-made soup (£3.75), filled baguettes (from £4.75), filled baked potatoes (from £5.75), ploughman's or home-made burger (£7.50), home-made cottage pie or lasagne (£7.95), steaks (from £13.50), and daily specials like stuffed red pepper and mushrooms (£9.95), calves liver or kangaroo (£11.95); Sunday carvery. Well kept Hook Norton, Wadworths 6X, and a guest such as Timothy Taylors Landlord on handpump, and helpful, pleasant service; piped music, darts, cribbage, dominoes, spoof, and putting competitions. From the pleasant garden behind are views towards the peaceful sloping fields. Decent walks nearby. *(Recommended by Guy Vowles, Dr A Y Drummond, Terry Mizen, Michael and Jenny Back, David Musgrove, Chris Glasson, Stephen, Julie and Hayley Brown)*

Free house ~ Licensees Hugh Kelly and Charles Pettigrew ~ Real ale ~ Bar food (12-9.30) ~ Restaurant ~ (01451) 850392 ~ Children welcome ~ Dogs allowed in bar ~ Live entertainment during Cheltenham Races ~ Open 11-11; 12-10.30 Sun ~ Bedrooms: £30B/£50B

HINTON DYRHAM ST7376 Map 2

Bull

2½ miles from M4 junction 18; A46 towards Bath, then first right (opp the Crown)

On a very quiet country lane, this pretty 16th-c stone-built pub has plenty of picnic-sets (and plenty of play equipment) out in a sizeable sheltered upper garden, with more on its sunny front terrace. Inside, two huge fireplaces with good coal and log fires face each other across the ancient pitted flagstones of the main bar, with a nice window seat and some massive built-in oak settles and pews as well as dark captain's chairs, and one or two big oriental rugs; even by day candles burn in wall sconces – no surprise the low ceiling is so smoky. A stripped stone back area has some unusual cushioned cast-iron chairs, and there's a stripped stone family room on the left; darts. All is glisteningly well kept, as is the Bass and Wadworths IPA and 6X on handpump; service is friendly, as are the local regulars. Enjoyable food includes sandwiches, beef in ale pie (£7.95), thai red chicken curry or smoked fish and seafood pie (£8.95), rib-eye steak with salsa verde (£11.95), and various seafood dishes. The restaurant is no smoking. *(Recommended by John and Joan Nash)*

Wadsworth tenancy ~ Licensees Martyn and Phyllida Williams ~ Real ale ~ Bar food (12-2, 6-9(9.30 weekends)) ~ (0117) 937 2332 ~ Children in eating area of bar and restaurant ~ Dogs welcome ~ Open 11.30-3, 6-11; 12-3, 6.30-10.30 Sun

KINGSCOTE ST8196 Map 4

Hunters Hall

A4135 Dursley—Tetbury

This is a consistently well run and civilised, creeper-covered old inn that readers enjoy very much. It has held a continuous licence for 500 years, and there is quite a series of bar rooms and lounges with fine high Tudor beams and stone walls, a lovely old box settle, sofas and miscellaneous easy chairs, and sturdy settles and oak tables on the flagstones in the lower-ceilinged, cosy public bar. An airy end room serves the good, changing bar food which includes sandwiches (not Sunday lunch), home-made soup (£3.25), chicken and duck liver pâté with a red onion and orange chutney (£4.50), tian of crab, avocado and prawns (£4.75), pork and leek sausages (£7.25), liver and bacon (£7.35), steak, kidney and Guinness pie (£7.45), roasted loin of cod with lemon butter sauce (£8.25), tasty ginger stir fry of vegetables with mozzarella (£8.95), steaks (from £10.95), roast rack of lamb with a rosemary and redcurrant jus (£12.95), and daily specials such as smoked chicken and red pepper terrine (£4.95), fresh garlic and herb tagliatelle with a wild mushroom and herb cream sauce (£8.95), and fried baramundi on pesto mash (£10.95); there's more space to eat in the Gallery upstairs; the Retreat Bay and restaurant (where there is piped music) are no smoking. Well kept Greene King IPA, Ruddles Best, Uley Hogs Head and a guest such as Everards Tiger or Wadworths 6X on handpump; friendly, helpful staff. A back room – relatively untouched – is popular with local lads playing pool; darts, dominoes, cribbage, shove-ha'penny, and juke box. The garden has seats, and a wooden fortress, play house, and swings for children. *(Recommended by S H Godsell, Neil and Anita Christopher, Hugh Roberts, Steve Godfrey, Dr Paull Khan, R Huggins, D Irving, E McCall, T McLean, Peter and Audrey Dowsett)*

Old English Inns ~ Tenant Stephanie Ward ~ Real ale ~ Bar food ~ Restaurant ~ (01453) 860393 ~ Children welcome ~ Dogs allowed in bar ~ Open 11-11; 12-10.30 Sun ~ Bedrooms: £55B/£85B

LITTLE BARRINGTON SP2012 Map 4

Inn For All Seasons 🍴 🍷

On the A40 3 miles W of Burford

They specialise in fresh fish in this civilised and comfortable old inn, and some of the delicious dishes might include flash-fried squid (£6.50), Irish rock oysters (£7.50), red thai fish curry (£9.95), fillet of River Dart salmon with a vermouth, smoked bacon and spinach sauce or whole cock crabs with a glass of Chablis (£10.50), wing of skate with baby caper and shallot butter sauce (£11.50), seared scallops with crisp smoked bacon (£14.50), and whole grilled dover sole (£15). Other non-fishy dishes include sandwiches (from £3.50), home-made soup (£3.75), fresh Cornish crab and chive pâté with lemon dressing (£4.95), hand-raised pork pie with home-made chutney or ploughman's (£5.75), ricotta cheese and spinach pancakes in parmesan cheese sauce (£7.95), free range roast chicken on braised spring greens with a herb butter sauce (£10.95), grilled Cotswold lamb on roasted vegetables (£11.95), and puddings such as fresh lemon tart with raspberry coulis or hot sticky toffee and date pudding (£4.25). The attractively decorated, mellow lounge bar has a relaxed, friendly atmosphere, low beams, stripped stone, and flagstones, old prints, leather-upholstered wing armchairs and other comfortable seats, country magazines to read, and a big log fire (with a big piece of World War II shrapnel above it); maybe quiet piped classical music. Well kept Wadworths 6X, Wychwood Shires XXX, and maybe a guest such as Bass or Badger Best on handpump, a good wine list with 100 bin ends, and over 60 malt whiskies; cribbage and dominoes. The pleasant garden has tables and a play area, and there are walks straight from the inn. It's very busy during Cheltenham Gold Cup Week – when the adjoining field is pressed into service as a helicopter pad. *(Recommended by Nick Holmes, Peter and Audrey Dowsett, John Bramley, Rod Stoneman, Mr and Mrs J McAngus, Dr R J Rushton, Simon Collett-Jones, Barry Smith, Mrs N W Neill, Les and Barbara Owen, Felicity Stephens, David and Brenda Tew, I D Greenfield, Pat and Tony Martin, Dick and Madeleine Brown, M A and C R Starling, Jim Bush, Mike Horler)*

Free house ~ Licensees Matthew and Heather Sharp ~ Real ale ~ Bar food ~ Restaurant ~ (01451) 844324 ~ Children welcome ~ Dogs allowed in bar ~ Singer monthly Fri evening ~ Open 11-2.30, 6-10.30(11 Sat); 12-2.30, 7-10.30 Sun ~ Bedrooms: £51.50B/£89B

LITTLETON-UPON-SEVERN ST5990 Map 4

White Hart

3½ miles from M4 junction 21; B4461 towards Thornbury, then village signposted

The three atmospheric main rooms in this 17th-c farmhouse have some fine furnishings: long cushioned wooden settles, high-backed settles, oak and elm tables, and a loveseat in the big low inglenook fireplace. There are flagstones in the front, huge tiles at the back, and smaller tiles on the left, plus some old pots and pans, and a lovely old White Hart Inn Simonds Ale sign. By the black wooden staircase are some nice little alcove seats, there's a black-panelled big fireplace in the front room, and hops on beams. A no smoking family room, similarly furnished, has some sentimental engravings, plates on a delft shelf, and a couple of high chairs, and a back snug has pokerwork seats and table football; darts, cribbage, fruit machine, chess, backgammon and Jenga. Bar food includes filled baguettes (from £2.50), popular battered haddock (£6.95), mushroom and nut stroganoff, barbecued chicken or summer salads (£7.95), and puddings (from £3.95). Youngs Bitter and Special, and a guest such as Smiles Best on handpump. Picnic-sets on the neat front lawn with interesting cottagey flowerbeds, and by the good big back car park are some attractive shrubs and teak furniture on a small brick terrace. Several walks from the pub itself. *(Recommended by Ian Phillips, Paul Hopton, Mr and Mrs Thomas, Rob Webster, George Little, Di and Mike Gillam, W F C Phillips, A C and E Johnson, Bob Broadhurst, Mrs B M Spurr, Theocsbrian)*

Youngs ~ Managers Howard and Liz Turner ~ Real ale ~ Bar food ~ (01454) 412275 ~ Children in family room ~ Dogs welcome ~ Open 12-2.30, 6-11; 11-2.30, 6-11 Sat; 12-3, 7-10.30 Sun ~ Bedrooms: £45B/£55B

LOWER ODDINGTON SP2325 Map 4

Fox

Near Stow-on-the-Wold

As we went to press, we heard that this smart, popular inn was up for sale. Obviously we are keeping our fingers crossed that when it does get sold, things won't change too much as it has been a super place to stay with good, enjoyable food. The Red Room houses a collection of wine related antiques and corkscrews, and the other simply and spotlessly furnished rooms have fresh flowers and flagstones, an inglenook fireplace, hunting scene figures above the mantelpiece, a display cabinet with pewter mugs and stone bottles, daily newspapers, and hops hanging from the ceiling; dominoes and cribbage. Served by staff in uniform shirts, the interesting food might include potato, leek and parsley soup (£3.95), weekday sandwiches (from £4.75), warmed goats cheese on a tapenade croûte (£5.50), sautéed tiger prawns with chilli and coriander butter (£6.95), fresh pasta with tomato and greek olive concasse (£7.50), steak and kidney pie (£8.75), confit of duck with date and onion marmalade (£8.90), rib-eye steak (£10.95), and puddings such as sticky toffee pudding or cherry and almond tart (£4.10); on Tuesdays there are fish specials at lunchtime and in the evening, and on Sunday, rare roast sirloin (£9.75). The wine list is excellent (they have daily and monthly specials), and they keep Badger Tanglefoot, Hook Norton Best, and a changing guest like Shepherd Neame Spitfire or Wyre Piddle Piddle in the Wind on handpump. The terrace has a custom-built awning and outdoor heaters, and the cottagey garden is pretty. A good eight-mile walk starts from here (though a stroll around the pretty village might be less taxing). *(Recommended by D J Hayman, P R and S A White, R J Chenery, Bernard Stradling, Pat and Roger Fereday, John Saville, Howard Gregory, Eric Locker, Andrew Barker, Claire Jenkins, Martin Jones, Peter Burton, John Kane, John Smither, Rod Stoneman, Robert Gomme, Mrs S White, M A and C R Starling, Dr and Mrs James Stewart, Patricia A Bruce, Mark Norton, Ian and Joan Blackwell, John Bramley, Guy Vowles, R Mathews, Ben Tatham, Mike Green, C A Hall, Di and Mike Gillam, Jeff and Wendy Williams, Mike Gorton, Dr K Roger Wood, Mid, Michael Sargent, Karen and Graham Oddey, Mrs G Delderfield, John Bowdler, Paul Boot)*

Free house ~ Licensees Sally and Kirk Ritchie ~ Real ale ~ Bar food (till 10pm) ~ Restaurant ~ (01451) 870555 ~ Children welcome if quiet and well behaved ~ Dogs allowed in bedrooms ~ Open 12-3, 6.30-11; 12-3, 7-10.30 Sun; closed 25 Dec, evenings 26 and 31 Dec, 1 Jan ~ Bedrooms: /£75S(£85B)

MEYSEY HAMPTON SU1199 Map 4

Masons Arms

High Street; just off A417 Cirencester—Lechlade

All – including dogs and muddy boots – are made welcome by the dedicated licensees in this neatly kept 17th-c stonebuilt inn. The longish open-plan bar has a bustling, chatty atmosphere, painted brick walls, carefully stripped beams with some hops, solid part-upholstered built-in wall seats with some matching chairs, good sound tables, a big inglenook log fire at one end, daily newspapers, and a few steps up to the no smoking restaurant. Well kept Bass, Hook Norton Best, and a couple of guests from breweries like Archers, Bartrams, Freeminer, Goffs or Wickwar on handpump, and decent wines including several ports; dominoes, cribbage, TV and piped music. Well liked bar food includes sandwiches (from £2.15; filled baguettes from £4.25;BLT £5.95), home-made soup (£2.65), filled baked potatoes (from £4.25), caesar salad with spicy chicken (£4.95), ploughman's (from £5.65), honey-roasted ham with two eggs (£5.95), liver and bacon in rich onion gravy (£6.55), masons pie (£6.75), spinach and mushroom filo parcels or red snapper Italian style (£7.95), duck breast grilled with cherries or lamb shank (£8.95), and sirloin steaks (from £9.95). *(Recommended by Charles Gysin, Rod Stoneman, Geoff Palmer, Dennis Jenkin, James Woods, Simon Collett-Jones, R Huggins, D Irving, E McCall, T McLean, Des and Jen Clarke, Peter and Audrey Dowsett)*

Free house ~ Licensees Andrew and Jane O'Dell ~ Real ale ~ Bar food (not Sun evening) ~ Restaurant ~ (01285) 850164 ~ Children in restaurant until 9 ~ Dogs welcome ~ Open 11.30-2.45, 6-11; 12-4, 7-10.30 Sun; closed Sun evening in winter ~ Bedrooms: £45B/£65B

MISERDEN SO9308 Map 4

Carpenters Arms

Village signposted off B4070 NE of Stroud; also a pleasant drive off A417 via the Duntisbournes, or off A419 via Sapperton and Edgeworth; OS Sheet 163 map reference 936089

The licensees in this friendly local – set in an idyllic Cotswold estate village – are very keen that their pub should remain just that, and welcome those who want a pint and a snack just as much as customers wanting a special meal out. The two open-plan bar areas have low beams, nice old wooden tables, seats with the original little brass name plates on the backs and some cushioned settles and spindlebacks on the bare boards; also, stripped stone walls with some interesting bric-a-brac, and two big log fires; The small no smoking dining room has dark traditional furniture. The sizeable collage (done with Laurie Lee) has lots of illustrations and book covers signed by him. Well kept Goffs Jouster, Wadworths 6X, and a guest such as Greene King IPA on handpump, country wines, darts, cribbage, and dominoes. At lunchtime, bar snacks include filled rolls (£3.95), filled baked potatoes (from £4.25), and ploughman's (£4.95); there's also soup (£3.25), crispy whitebait (£4.50), spinach and ricotta tortellini in a creamy white wine sauce (£6.95), swordfish steak with chilli oil dressing, a pie of the day or cajun chicken (£7.25), sirloin steak (£8.95), and daily specials like leek and parmesan quiche (£5.95), pork, apple and cider casserole (£6.50), lambs liver and bacon (£6.75), baked trout with almonds (£7.25), and crispy duck breast with a brandy and orange sauce (£10.95). There are seats out in the garden and occasional summer morris men. The nearby gardens of Misarden Park, open midweek summer, are well worth visiting. *(Recommended by BKA, Giles Francis, Bernard Stradling, Keith Allen, Austin and Lisa Fleming)*

Free house ~ Licensees Johnny Johnston and Ted Isaac ~ Real ale ~ Bar food (12-2.30, 7-9.30) ~ Restaurant ~ (01285) 821283 ~ Children in eating area of bar and in restaurant until 9pm ~ Dogs allowed in bar ~ Occasional country music ~ Open 11-2.30(3 Sat), 6-11; 12-3, 7-10.30 Sun

NAILSWORTH ST8599 Map 4

Egypt Mill

Just off A46; heading N towards Stroud, first right after roundabout, then left

Most customers do come to this popular place either to enjoy the good food or to stay overnight. It's a stylish conversion of a three-floor stonebuilt mill, which still has working waterwheels and the millstream flowing through. The brick-and-stone-floored split-level bar gives good views of the wheels, and there are big pictures and lots of stripped beams in the comfortable carpeted lounge, along with some hefty yet elegant ironwork from the old mill machinery. Although it can get quite crowded on fine weekends, it's actually spacious enough to feel at its best when it's busy – with good service to cope, and the atmosphere is almost bistro-ish; piped music. There's a civilised upstairs no smoking restaurant. Well kept Adnams and Ind Coope Burton on handpump, and a wide choice of nicely presented good food such as lunchtime sandwiches or filled baguettes (from £3.25) or omelettes (£5.95), as well as soup (£3.85), field mushrooms topped with stilton rarebit (£5.50), mediterranean prawns with ginger and lemongrass butter with a tomato and chilli relish (£6.95), fishcakes (£7.25), local sausages with rich onion gravy (£7.50), a daily suet pudding (£8.95), mushroom and roast shallot tart with goats cheese and red pesto dressing or crispy confit of duck leg on a cassoulet of beans topped with black pudding (£10.50), sirloin steak (£11.95), daily specials with an emphasis on fish like baked cornish cod with spring vegetable and chervil broth (£11.50), whole grilled lemon sole with herby butter (£13.25), and grilled halibut steak with chargrilled artichokes and a lime and coconut sauce (£13.50), and puddings such as rich chocolate brownie with hot fudge sauce, baked Irish coffee cheesecake or lemon and rhubarb fool with lemon shortbread biscuits (£4.50). The floodlit terrace garden by the millpond is pretty, and there's a little bridge over from the car park; no dogs. *(Recommended by Lesley and Peter Barrett, John and Patricia White, Rod Stoneman, R Mathews, Andrew Barker, Claire Jenkins, J G E Bell, Philip and Jenny Grant, Christopher and Mary Thomas, Michael Doswell, P R and D Thomas)*

Free house ~ Licensee Stephen Webb ~ Real ale ~ Bar food ~ Restaurant ~ (01453) 833449 ~ Children welcome ~ Open 10.30-2.30, 6.30-11; 10.30-11 Sat; 12-10.30 Sun; 10.30-2.30, 6.30-11 in winter ~ Bedrooms: £54.50B/£75B

Weighbridge

B4014 towards Tetbury

Particularly friendly, chatty licensees run this bustling pub, and they create a really good atmosphere. The relaxed bar has three cosily old-fashioned rooms with stripped stone walls, antique settles and country chairs, and window seats. The black beamed ceiling of the lounge bar is thickly festooned with black ironware – sheepshears, gintraps, lamps, and a large collection of keys, many from the old Longfords Mill opposite the pub. Upstairs is a raftered no smoking hayloft with an engaging mix of rustic tables; no noisy games machines or piped music. Their speciality are the very popular 2in1 pies which are served in a large bowl – half the bowl contains the filling of your choice and the other is full of home-made cauliflower cheese, and then topped with pastry: steak and mushroom, turkey and trimmings, salmon in a creamy sauce, roast root vegetables, pork, bacon and celery in stilton sauce or chicken, ham and leek in a cream and tarragon sauce (from £7.80; you can also have mini versions from £5.90 or straightforward pies without the cauliflower cheese, from £7). Other choices include sandwiches, filled baked potatoes and salad, soup (£2.75), coarse chicken liver pâté with red onion chutney or freshly made scotch egg (£3.95), cottage pie (£4.75), bangers and mash with rich onion gravy and garlic and rosemary mash (£6.95), honey roast duck on an orange and water chestnut salad (£8.45), daily specials like seafood ravioli (£3.95 or £5.95), pork paprika (£7.95), and lamb shank (£8.45), and puddings such as banana crumble, crème brûlée or lemon cheesecake (£3.75). Well kept Uley Old Spot, Wadworths 6X, and a couple of guests like Black Sheep or Uley Hogshead on handpump, 16 wines (and champagne) by the glass, and Thatcher's cider. Behind is a sheltered landscaped garden with picnic-sets under umbrellas. By the time this book is published, there will be good disabled access. Some years back, the landlord also operated the weighbridge from which the inn took its name. *(Recommended by Mike Snelgrove, Tom and Ruth Rees, Bruce Adams, Chris and Jan Phillips, R Huggins, D Irving, E McCall, T McLean, Sylvia and Tony Cooper, Paul Weedon, R Telfer)*

Free house ~ Licensees Jane and Simon Hudson ~ Real ale ~ Bar food (all day) ~ (01453) 832520 ~ Children in restaurant ~ Dogs welcome ~ Open 12-11; 12-10.30 Sun

NAUNTON SP1123 Map 4

Black Horse

Village signposted from B4068 (shown as A436 on older maps) W of Stow-on-the-Wold

After a walk on the blowy hills, this busy and friendly old inn is the place to head for, and there's always a good mix of customers. The comfortable, neatly kept bar has black beams, stripped stonework, simple country-kitchen chairs, built-in oak pews, polished elm cast-iron-framed tables, and a warming open fire. Well liked, straightforward bar food includes home-made soup (£3.30), huge baguettes, ploughman's or filled baked potatoes (from £5.50), mushroom stroganoff (£7.25), ham and egg (£7.50), steak and kidney suet pudding or popular chicken curry (£7.95), rack of lamb (£8.95), and daily specials; they offer a two-course OAP meal for £4.95. The dining room is no smoking. Well kept and well priced Donnington BB and SBA on handpump, and sensibly placed darts, cribbage, dominoes, and piped music. Some tables outside. *(Recommended by E V Walder, Mike and Mary Carter, Norman and June Williams, Di and Mike Gillam, Patricia A Bruce, John Bowdler, Guy Vowles, Catherine and Richard Preston, Lynn Sharpless, Pete Baker, James Oakley)*

Donnington ~ Tenant Martin David Macklin ~ Real ale ~ Bar food ~ (01451) 850565 ~ Children in eating area of bar and restaurant ~ Open 11.30-3, 6-11; 12-3, 7-10.30 Sun ~ Bedrooms: /£45B

NORTH CERNEY SP0208 Map 4

Bathurst Arms

A435 Cirencester—Cheltenham

Over the years, this handsome, welcoming old place has, happily, changed very little. The beamed and panelled bar has a fireplace at each end (one quite huge and housing an open woodburner), a good mix of old tables and nicely faded chairs, old-fashioned window seats, and some pewter plates. There are country tables in a little carpeted room off the bar, as well as winged high-backed settles forming a few booths around other tables; one of the small dining rooms is no smoking. At lunchtime, good bar food includes filled baguettes (£3.95), ploughman's (£5.50), a burger (£6.50), and home-made salmon fishcakes (£7.50), as well as home-made soup (£3.50), seafood and spinach terrine with fresh herb dressing (£4.50), grilled goats cheese on fresh beetroot salad (£4.95; main course £8.50), roasted vegetable tart tatin topped with mozzarella or organic sausages with bubble and squeak and a caramelised red onion sauce (£8.50), pork medallions on celeriac mash with apple and sage gravy (£9.95), sirloin steak (£10.95), daily specials such as home-made steak and mushroom pie (£7.95), bass with couscous and basil oil (£11.95), and herb-crust fillet of lamb with rosemary sautéed potatoes and a port and redcurrant sauce (£12.50), and puddings like rhubarb crème brûlée or banoffi pie (£3.50). Well kept Fullers London Pride, Hook Norton Best, Wadworths 6X, and a guest beer on handpump, and 11 good wines (including champagne) by the glass; piped music. There are picnic-sets outside sheltered by small trees and shrubs; lots of surrounding walks. *(Recommended by Mrs Mary Walters, Neil and Anita Christopher, Andrew Barker, Claire Jenkins, R Huggins, D Irving, E McCall, T McLean, Lorna and Howard Lambert, P and L Hope-Lang, Dave Irving, J A Cheverton, Simon Collett-Jones, KC, Peter and Anne-Marie O'Malley)*

Free house ~ Licensee Mike Costley-White ~ Real ale ~ Bar food ~ Restaurant ~ (01285) 831281 ~ Well behaved children welcome ~ Dogs allowed in bar ~ Open 11-3, 6-11; 12-3, 7-10.30 Sun; closed 25 Dec ~ Bedrooms: £45B/£65B

NORTH NIBLEY ST7596 Map 4

New Inn

Waterley Bottom, which is quite well signposted from surrounding lanes; inn signposted from the Bottom itself; one route is from A4135 S of Dursley, via lane with red sign saying Steep Hill, 1 in 5 (just SE of Stinchcombe Golf Course turn-off), turning right when you get to the bottom; another is to follow Waterley Bottom signpost from previous main entry, keeping eyes skinned for small low signpost to inn; OS Sheet 162 map reference 758963; though this is the way we know best, one reader suggests the road is wider if you approach directly from North Nibley

In a peaceful secluded setting in lovely South Cotswold walking country, this rural pub has plenty of seats on the lawn for warm days, and at the end of the garden is a small orchard with swings and slides; there's a neat terrace, and boules. Inside, the lounge bar has cushioned windsor chairs and varnished high-backed settles against the partly stripped stone walls, and dominoes, cribbage, TV, and sensibly placed darts in the simple public bar. A short choice of home-made bar food includes toasties, filled baguettes and ploughman's (£1.90-£4.50), goats cheese and red onion flan, steak and kidney pie or pork stroganoff (all £6.50), beef and mushroom casserole (£8), and poached plaice with prawn sauce (£8.50). Well kept Bath Gem Bitter and SPA, Cotleigh Tawny, Greene King Abbot, and a guest like Wickwar Cotswold Way or Wye Valley Bitter are dispensed from Barmaid's Delight (the name of one of the antique beer engines) or tapped from the cask; they import their own French wines. *(Recommended by PB, JB, Patrick Hancock, the Didler, Guy Vowles, JP, PP, Mrs C McNulty, Keith Allen, BKA)*

Free house ~ Licensees Jackie and Jacky Cartigny ~ Real ale ~ Bar food (not Mon except bank hols) ~ (01453) 543659 ~ Children welcome ~ Dogs allowed in bar ~ Live music 2nd Fri evening ~ Open 12-2.30, 6(7 Mon)-11; 12-11 Sat; 12-10.30 Sun; closed Mon lunchtime except bank hols

NORTHLEACH SP1114 Map 4

Wheatsheaf

West End; the inn is on your left as you come in following the sign off the A429, just SW of its junction with the A40

This handsomely proportioned 16th-c stone-built inn stands on a quiet street of similarly attractive buildings, in a lovely little town with plenty to see (including a fascinating collection of musical boxes and clocks, polyphons and automata). It's been reworked as a civilised modern-feeling dining pub, light and airy, with the three big-windowed rooms lining the street now run together. The central bar part has flagstones, the dining area open to it on the right has bare boards, and both have quite high ceilings – so the acoustics are bright and lively. The room on the left, with comfortable red or green semi-easy chairs on matching carpet matting, has a less exposed atmosphere which some might prefer. There are modern horse-racing oil paintings for sale, and log fires. The Australian couple in charge are very helpful and friendly, the Hook Norton Best, Wadworths 6X and Youngs Special on handpump well kept, and the changing selection of wines by the glass good and interesting (we found free nuts on the bar, too). The short choice of good bar food is equally appealing (and carefully sourced), and at lunchtime might include soup (£3.95), croque monsieur or madame (£4.95), potted prawns (£5.95), sausages of the day with herb mash and onion gravy (£7.95), and a meaty, fishy or vegetarian dish of the day (from £8.95), with evening choices such as ham hock, lentil and foie gras terrine with apricot dressing (£6.95), Pernod cured gravadlax with roast beetroot and spring onion salad (£7.45), smoked chicken, bacon, avocado and olive salad (£8.95), roast cod with peppered new potatoes and caper butter or crispy pork belly with rösti potato and plum jus (£9.95), duck breast with wild mushroom and orange berry jus (£10.95), and puddings like orange crème brûlée, chocolate bread and butter pudding or apple tart with cinnamon ice cream (£4.50); several teas and coffees. Behind is a pretty garden with picnic-sets on tiers of grass among flowering shrubs; the black labrador is called Tolly. They do a good breakfast. *(Recommended by Dr W J M Gissane, Richard Greaves, Dr J J H Gilkes)*

Free house ~ Licensee Nick Elliott ~ Bar food (12-2.30, 7-10; not 25 Dec) ~ Restaurant ~ (01451) 860244 ~ Children welcome ~ Dogs allowed in bar ~ Open 12-3, 6-11; 12-11 Fri/Sat; 12-10.30 Sun; closed 25 Dec ~ Bedrooms: £45B/£55B

OAKRIDGE LYNCH SO9103 Map 4

Butchers Arms

Village signposted off Eastcombe—Bisley road, E of Stroud, which is the easiest approach; with a good map you could brave the steep lanes via Frampton Mansell, which is signposted off A419 Stroud—Cirencester

Particularly in good weather, this white-painted pub is a popular place to be. It is set above a particularly steep and twisty village, with seats on the neatly kept lawn looking down over the valley and very pretty summer flowering tubs and hanging baskets; good walks in the valley along the old Thames & Severn canal. Inside, the spacious rambling bar has a few beams in its low ceiling, some walls stripped back to the bare stone, old photographs, comfortable, traditional furnishings like wheelback chairs around the neat tables on its patterned carpet, and three open fires. Bar food includes burgers (from £4.25), interestingly filled hot baguettes (£4.95), home-made cottage pie or cauliflower cheese (£5.50), potato wedge dishes (from £5.95), omelettes (£6.50), brunch (£6.95), fillet of haddock with celery sauce or beef, kidney, and mushroom in ale pie (£7.75), and rib-eye steak (£9.95). Best to book at the weekend; the restaurant is no smoking. Well kept Archers Best, Greene King Abbot, Tetleys Bitter, and Wickwar BOB on handpump; a little room off the main bar has a fruit machine and TV. *(Recommended by R Huggins, D Irving, E McCall, T McLean, Nick and Meriel Cox, Mike and Lynn Robinson, Dave Irving, Bernard Stradling)*

Free house ~ Licensees Peter and Brian Coupe ~ Real ale ~ Bar food (not Sun evening or Mon except bank hols) ~ Restaurant ~ (01285) 760371 ~ Children welcome away from main bar ~ Dogs allowed in bar ~ Open 11.30-3, 6-11; 12-4, 7-10.30 Sun

OLD SODBURY ST7581 Map 2

Dog

Not far from M4 junction 18: A46 N , then A432 left towards Chipping Sodbury

This year, the skittle alley of this bustling village pub has been turned into ensuite bedrooms. It's a bustling place with quite a mix of customers, and the two-level bar and smaller no smoking room both have areas of original bare stone walls, beams and timbering, low ceilings, wall benches and cushioned chairs, and open fires. From a huge menu, the choice of food might include fresh fish dishes like sole, plaice, halibut, cod, trout, scallops, shark or tuna, giant prawns, and several different ways of serving mussels and squid, as well as sandwiches (from £2.50), smoked mackerel pâté (£3.95), ploughman's (£4.95), vegetarian moussaka (£6.75), cheese and onion flan or lasagne (£6.95), home-made steak and kidney pie, prawn curry or mexican tacos (£7.45), creamy seafood tagliatelle (£7.95), steaks (from £7.95), puddings like home-made fruit pie, jam roly poly or rhubarb crumble (from £2.75), and children's meals (from £2.25); service does slow down when pushed and they have a sign in the bar which says that if you cannot spare an hour to eat, don't stay. Well kept Marstons Pedigree, Wadworths 6X, Wickwar BOB, and a guest beer on handpump, several malt whiskies, and quite a few wines. Dominoes, fruit machine, and juke box. There's a large garden with lots of seating, a summer barbecue area, climbing frames, swings, slides, and football net. Lots of nearby walks. *(Recommended by Sebastian Leach, Roy and Lindsey Fentiman, Ian Phillips, John and Enid Morris, Keith Allen, Christopher and Mary Thomas, Tom Evans, Joy and Peter Heatherley, Dr and Mrs A K Clarke, Matthew Shackle, Graham and Lynn Mason, R T and J C Moggridge, Colinand Stephanie McFie, W W Burke)*

Whitbreads ~ Lease John and Joan Harris ~ Real ale ~ Bar food (11-10; 12-3, 7-9.30 Sun) ~ (01454) 312006 ~ Children in eating area of bar ~ Dogs allowed in bedrooms ~ Open 11-11; 12-10.30 Sun ~ Bedrooms: £26(£45B)/£40(£60B)

OLDBURY-ON-SEVERN ST6292 Map 2

Anchor

Village signposted from B4061

In fine weather, customers very much enjoy eating in the pretty garden here and watching a game of boules; the hanging baskets and window boxes are lovely. The neatly kept lounge has modern beams and stone, a mix of tables including an attractive oval oak gateleg, cushioned window seats, winged seats against the wall, oil paintings by a local artist, and a big winter log fire. Diners can eat in the lounge or bar area or in the no smoking dining room at the back of the building (good for larger groups) and the menu is the same in all rooms. All the food is home-made using local produce, and although they don't do chips, they do offer dauphinois potatoes, and new and baked ones. From the light menu, for those with smaller appetites or in more of a hurry, there might be home-made soup (£2.80), wholemeal bread with pâté, home-cooked beef and ham, sliced smoked chicken breast and fresh orange, and cheeses (from £3.60), and quite a few salads (from £4.95). There's also home-made faggots with onion gravy (£5.75), spinach and mushroom parcel (£6.25), beef curry (£6.60), chicken breast in a rich creamy stilton sauce (£7.45), pasta with salmon, prawns, crab and mussels in a creamy white wine sauce (£7.95), swordfish à la portugaise (£8.25), lamb shank with mint and red wine (£7.95), and puddings like treacle tart or sticky toffee pudding (£3.30). Well kept Bass, Butcombe Bitter, and Theakstons Best and Old Peculier on handpump or tapped from the cask, all well priced for the area. Also over 75 malts, and a decent choice of good quality wines (12 by the glass); darts and cribbage; they have wheelchair access and a disabled lavatory. Plenty of walks to the River Severn and along the many footpaths and bridleways, and St Arilda's church nearby is interesting, on its odd little knoll with wild flowers among the gravestones (the primroses and daffodils in spring are lovely). *(Recommended by George Little, Mr and Mrs Colin Roberts, Christopher and Mary Thomas, Mike and Mary Carter, Theocsbrian, Mrs M Albery, Tom Evans, Desmond Hall, John and Patricia White, Charles and Pauline Stride)*

Free house ~ Licensees Michael Dowdeswell, Alex de la Torre ~ Real ale ~ Bar food ~ Restaurant ~ (01454) 413331 ~ Children in restaurant only ~ Dogs allowed in bar ~ Open 11.30-2.30, 6.30-11; 11.30-11 Sat; 12-10.30 Sun; closed evenings 25 and 26 Dec

PAXFORD SP1837 Map 4

Churchill

B4479, SE of Chipping Campden

Although you cannot book a table in advance here – your name goes on a chalked waiting list if all the tables are full – customers certainly feel the good, imaginative food is worth the wait. The simply furnished atmospheric flagstoned bar has low ceilings, assorted old tables and chairs, and a snug warmed by a good log fire in its big fireplace; there's also a dining extension. Well kept Hook Norton and a couple of guests such as Arkells Summer Ale, Goffs Jouster or Wychwood Shires XXX on handpump, and eight good wines by the glass; dominoes. From a constantly changing menu, dishes might include interesting soup (£3.50), hot cheese soufflé with grain mustard sauce (£4.75), chicken and chorizo ravioli with fennel purée and roast tomatoes (£5), smoked haddock terrine with avocado relish or soft boiled egg served in a tartlet of spinach, crisp parma ham, duck livers and juniper sauce (£5.50), salmon poached in red wine with shallots, mushrooms and crab sauce (£10), escalope of veal with a julienne of ham, tongue and tomato concasse with tarragon and madeira sauce (£11), whole cold poached stuffed trout (£11.50), peppered monkfish with roast butternut squash, lime, capers and puy lentils or breast of guinea fowl with an apricot and herb stuffing and curried aubergine (£12), saddle of lamb with sautéed kidneys, crisp sweetbreads and rosemary sauce (£12.50), and super puddings; vegetarian dishes are made to order. There are some seats outside; aunt sally. *(Recommended by Canon and Mrs Michael Bourdeaux, Geoff Palmer, John Bowdler, W W Burke, Patricia A Bruce, John and Christine Lowe, Martin Jones, Stephen and Judy Parish, George Atkinson, John and Enid Morris, Pat and Roger Fereday, Don Mather, Mr and Mrs A H Young)*

Free house ~ Licensees Leo and Sonya Brooke-Little ~ Real ale ~ Bar food ~ (01386) 594000 ~ Children in eating area of bar ~ Open 11.30-3, 6-11; 12-3, 7-10.30 Sun ~ Bedrooms: £40B/£70B

SAPPERTON SO9403 Map 4

Bell

Village signposted from A419 Stroud—Cirencester; OS Sheet 163 map reference 948033

While there is obviously emphasis on the very good food in this sensitively refurbished, 250-year-old pub, the friendly licensees are pleased to note that the local real ales are selling better and better. There are three separate, cosy rooms with a nice mix of wooden tables and chairs, country prints on stripped stone walls, one or two attractive rugs on the flagstones, log fires and woodburning stoves, fresh flowers, and newspapers and guidebooks to browse. Using local produce whenever possible and no frozen food at all (except ice cream), the very popular and imaginative food might include terrine of duck livers and foie gras with a plum and orange confit (£5.50), warm meguez sausages with a salad of cannellini beans, lime and coriander (£5.75), seared scottish scallops, sesame oil, soy, honey and pak choi (£6.95), frittata of sweet peppers and spinach (£8.75), chargrilled spicy lamb burger (£9.50), crisp beer battered cod with home-made tartare sauce (£10.75), braised shank of lamb on puy lentils, pancetta and red wine (£12.75), roast breast and confit of guinea fowl marinated in lime and ginger with a potato and bacon cake (£12.75), daily specials such as roast mediterranean vegetable soup (£3.50), smoked chicken and avocado salad with honey and mustard dressing (£5.50), chargrilled spring lamb cutlets with aubergine, tomato and red onion stack (£11.75), and whole roast black bream with rosemary and garlic (£12.50), and puddings like rich chocolate torte, banoffi pie or bread and butter pudding (£4.50); take-away fish and chips, and Sunday roasts (£10.75). A basket of home-made bread and butter and olives accompanies every meal. Well kept Hook Norton Best, Uley Old Spot and Hogshead, and Wickwar Cotswold Way on handpump, up to 16 wines by the glass, champagne by the glass, and Weston's cider. Harry the springer spaniel likes to greet everyone. There are tables out on a small front lawn and in a partly covered and very pretty courtyard, for eating outside. Good surrounding walks, and horses have their own tethering rail. *(Recommended by R Huggins, D Irving, E McCall, T McLean, John and Kay Grugeon, Di and Mike Gillam, Michael Doswell, Cyrus I Harvey, Jr, Ronald Harry, Colin McKerrow, Philip and Jenny Grant, Guy Vowles, Keith Allen, RJH, Andrew Carter, Ian Arthur, Martin Jennings, Charles and Pauline Stride, Giles Francis, John Kane, Mr and Mrs J Curtis)*

Free house ~ Licensees Paul Davidson and Pat Le Jeune ~ Real ale ~ Bar food (not Mon except bank hols) ~ Restaurant ~ (01285) 760298 ~ Children allowed but under 10 to leave by 6.30 ~ Dogs welcome ~ Open 11-2.30, 6.30-11; 12-3, 7-10.30 Sun

Pubs close to motorway junctions are listed at the back of the book.

SHEEPSCOMBE SO8910 Map 4

Butchers Arms 🍷

Village signed off B4070 NE of Stroud; or A46 N of Painswick (but narrow lanes)

Locals, groups of walkers and visitors from the nearer towns and cities all mingle happily in this bustling 17th-c pub. They still have their popular policy of not reserving tables in the bar so casual diners and drinkers have a relaxed area in which to enjoy their drinks. The bar has log fires, seats in big bay windows, flowery-cushioned chairs and rustic benches, and lots of interesting oddments like assorted blow lamps, irons, and plates. As well as filled rolls, baked potatoes and bar snacks, the well liked, constantly changing bar food includes home-made basil tagliatelle with mixed Italian cream cheeses (£6.25), salmon fishcakes or local sausages (£7.25), smoked haddock with mash and poached eggs (£7.50), chicken breast stuffed with a leek and brie mousse (£8.25), pork fillet with apricot and cider stuffing and wrapped in bacon (£8.75), shellfish chowder with sun-dried tomato ciabatta (£9.95), venison barnsley chop marinated in shallots, redcurrants and red wine (£10.95), and steaks with various home-made sauces. The restaurant and a small area in the bar are no smoking. Well kept Hook Norton Best, and two changing guests such as Goffs Jouster or Wye Valley Dorothy Goodbodys on handpump, eight wines by small or large glasses, and country wines; darts, cribbage, cards, and dominoes. The views are marvellous and there are teak seats below the building, tables on the steep grass behind, and a cricket ground on such a steep slope that the boundary fielders at one end can scarcely see the bowler. This pub is part of their little Blenheim Inns group. *(Recommended by BKA, David and Rhian Peters, Martin Jennings, Mike and Lynn Robinson, Bernard Stradling, Pat and Roger Fereday, Brian, Dill, Jenni and Kate Hughes, Austin and Lisa Fleming, Tom Evans, Hugh Roberts, P R and S A White, Paul Oneill, Paul Boot)*

Free house ~ Licensees Johnny and Hilary Johnston ~ Real ale ~ Bar food (12-2.30, 7-9.30) ~ Restaurant ~ (01452) 812113 ~ Children in eating area of bar and restaurant ~ Occasional morris men and folk music ~ Open 11.30-3, 6-11; 12-3.30, 7-10.30 Sun

ST BRIAVELS SO5605 Map 4

George

High Street

Seats on the flagstoned terrace behind this attractive white painted pub overlook a grassy former moat to the silvery 12th-c castle built as a fortification against the Welsh. There's an ancient escape tunnel connecting the castle to the pub, and a ghost called George. The three rambling rooms have old-fashioned built-in wall seats, some booth seating, cushioned small settles, toby jugs and antique bottles on black beams over the servery, and a large stone open fireplace; a Celtic coffin lid dating from 1070, discovered when a fireplace was removed, is now mounted next to the bar counter. The restaurant is no smoking. Enjoyable home-made bar food includes sandwiches and filled baked potatoes, soup (£2.95), garlic tiger prawns (£4.95), steak baguette (£5.95), vegetarian quiche or lasagne (£6.95), curries (£7.95), beef in Guinness, mushroom, leek and nut stroganoff or chargrilled lamb steak with honey and mint sauce (£8.95), pork tenderloin in mustard, cream and brandy sauce (£9.95), and puddings (£3.45). The dining room is no smoking; piped music. Well kept Bass, Bath SPA, Marstons Pedigree, RCH Pitchfork, and a guest beer on handpump, and country wines. Lots of walks start nearby but muddy boots must be left outside; outdoor chess. *(Recommended by Theocsbrian, Mr and Mrs P Talbot, Bob and Margaret Holder, Rob Holt, Desmond Hall, Mr and Mrs F J Parmenter, A S and M E Marriott, Mike and Lynn Robinson, Keith Allen, Catherine and Richard Preston, Les Trusler, Clare and Paul Howes)*

Free house ~ Licensee Bruce Bennett ~ Real ale ~ Bar food ~ Restaurant ~ (01594) 530228 ~ Children in restaurant if well behaved ~ Dogs welcome ~ Open 11-2.30, 6.30-11; 12-2.30, 7-10.30 Sun ~ Bedrooms: £35S/£50S

TETBURY ST8394 Map 4

Gumstool

Part of Calcot Manor Hotel; A4135 W of town, just E of junction with A46

This civilised place is certainly not a pub and it is attached to a well thought of country hotel, but they do keep Courage Best and Directors, Shepherd Neame Spitfire and Wickwar BOB on handpump (under light blanket pressure), and many customers do drop in for just a drink. The layout is well divided to give a feeling of intimacy without losing the overall sense of contented bustle, the lighting is attractive, and materials are old-fashioned (lots of stripped pine, flagstones, gingham curtains, hop bines) though the style is neatly modern; well chosen pictures and drawings; beyond one screen there are a couple of marble-topped pub tables and a leather armchair by the big log fire, and daily papers. 60 malt whiskies, and a dozen interesting wines by the glass, spanning a wide price range. Good, imaginative food includes several dishes that sensibly come in two sizes: caramelised red onion tart with slow baked tomatoes and tallegio on a rocket salad (£5.50; generous £7.50), thai-spiced crab cakes with cucumber and crème fraîche (£5.75; generous £8), devilled lambs kidney in a crisp pastry case (£6; generous £8.20), and locally smoked salmon and trout with cucumber salad and horseradish cream (£6.50; generous £8.50). They also offer soup (£3.50), baked smoked cheddar cheese soufflé (£5.50), sweetcorn and potato fritters with spiced brown shrimps (£6.25), organic old spot pork and sage sausages with colcannon (£8.75), breast of chicken with parma ham, tomato and gruyère (£9.25), battered cod and chips with home-made tartare sauce (£9.50), braised beef and onions with herb dumplings (£10.20), smoked haddock fillet on buttered greens, topped with a poached egg and grain mustard sauce (£10.75), chargrilled rib-eye steak with tarragon shallot butter (£11.50), and puddings such as warm chocolate and orange tart with vanilla ice cream, crème brûlée or waffles with bananas in hot toffee sauce and coconut ice cream (from £4); a plate of local cheeses with celery, grapes and pickle (£5.50). Extra vegetables £1.75, and several coffees; professional, friendly service. To be sure of a table, you must book beforehand. Most of the restaurant is no smoking; piped music. Westonbirt Arboretum is not far away. *(Recommended by Karen and Graham Oddey, Jason Caulkin, Ian and Joan Blackwell, John Kane, Geoff and Brigid Smithers, John Robertson, Donald Godden, Mike Green, Alec and Barbara Jones, B and F A Hannam, Bernard Stradling, KC, Tom and Ruth Rees, Eric Markland, Rod Stoneman, Carol and Dono Leaman, Neil and Debbie Cook)*

Free house ~ Licensees Paul Sadler and Richard Ball ~ Real ale ~ Bar food ~ Restaurant ~ (01666) 890391 ~ Children in eating area of bar and restaurant ~ Open 11-2.30, 6-11; 11-11 Sat; 12-10.30 Sun; 12-2.30, 6-10.30 Sun in winter ~ Bedrooms: £130B/£160B

Trouble House

A433 towards Cirencester, near Cherington turn

Very foody under its newish young owners, this is still a nice place to drop in for a drink – perhaps sitting on the chesterfield by the good log and coal fire in the big stone fireplace in the parquet-floor room on the left, with its hop-girt mantelpiece and more hops hung from one of its two big black beams. Or you could commandeer one of the bar stools in the small saggy-beamed middle room, where they have well kept Wadworths IPA and 6X on handpump, and a nice selection of wines by the glass. But there's no doubt that the good cooking is the main attraction now: salt cod and potato soup (£3.75; large £5.50), fried sardines with tomato and red peppers (£5.50), potted pork and foie gras pâté (£6), roasted scallops with broad bean and tomato salad (£7.50), home-made pasta with pesto, stewed tomatoes and red onions (£8.50), calves liver and bacon with onion gravy (£10.75), roasted gloucester old spot pork cutlet with mushy peas and black pudding (£11.50), salmon poached in thai spices with lime pickle potato (£12), ox cheeks braised in red wine with wild mushrooms and creamed potato (£12.40), rib-eye steak with béarnaise sauce (£14), and puddings such as dark chocolate cheesecake, rhubarb and custard or black cherry frangipane (£5). They do smaller helpings for children, and sell quite a few of their own preserves such as tapenade or preserved tomatoes with onions (the homely packaging would easily let you pass them off as your own work, for point-scoring presents); service is friendly. Furnishings are mainly stripped pine or oak tables with chapel chairs, some wheelback chairs and the odd library chair, and there are attractive mainly modern country prints on the cream or butter-coloured walls. The rush-matting room on the right is no smoking. There's a little noise from the traffic rushing past, perhaps quiet piped pop music, and (more engagingly) some enticing kitchen noises off. You can sit out at picnic-sets on the gravel behind, or in a back paddock where we saw wild rabbits hopping around. *(Recommended by Dr and Mrs M E Wilson, Richard Stancomb)*

Wadworths ~ Tenants Michael and Sarah Bedford ~ Real ale ~ Bar food (not Mon) ~ (01666) 502206 ~ Children in restaurant only and not in evening ~ Dogs allowed in bar ~ Open 11-3, 6.30-11; 12-3, 7-10.30 Sun; closed Mon except bank hols; last wk Aug, first 2 wks Jan

TODENHAM SP2436 Map 4

Farriers Arms 🍷 ◼

Between A34 and A429 N of Moreton-in-Marsh

A new garden with fine views over the surrounding countryside has been opened at this tucked-away pub, and there are a couple of tables with views of the church on a small terrace by the quiet little road. Inside, there's a cosy, friendly atmosphere, and the main bar has nice wonky white plastered walls, hops on the beams, lovely old polished flagstones by the stone bar counter and a woodburner in a huge inglenook fireplace. A tiny little room off to the side is full of old books and interesting old photographs. Good bar food includes home-made soup (£3.25), grilled goats cheese on a pesto crouton with salad and sun-dried tomatoes (£4.95), sandwiches (from £4.25), ploughman's (£5.95), ham and eggs or home-made steak and kidney pie (£6.95), daily specials such as chicken liver parfait (£5.25), crayfish and avocado salad (£5.50), stuffed peppers (£7.95), roast vegetable couscous topped with feta cheese and olives or gloucester old spot sausages with red wine and onion gravy (£8.95), whole grilled plaice with caper butter (£9.95), chicken breast on buttered leeks with a mushroom and chardonnay sauce (£10.95), and home-made puddings like chocolate mousse, bread and butter pudding or fruit crumble (£3.75). Well kept Hook Norton Best, and a couple of guests such as North Cotswold Genesis or Timothy Taylors Landlord on handpump, and quite a few wines by the glass. Piped music, and aunt sally. *(Recommended by Martin and Karen Wake, Adam and Joan Bunting, Ted George, Ian and Nita Cooper, S Evans, John and Hazel Williams, K H Frostick, H O Dickinson, Mike Gorton)*

Free house ~ Licensees Sue and Steve Croft ~ Real ale ~ Bar food (not winter Mon) ~ Restaurant ~ (01608) 650901 ~ Children in restaurant ~ Open 11-3, 6.30-11; 12-3, 7-10.30 Sun; closed Mon in winter

UPPER ODDINGTON SP2225 Map 4

Horse & Groom

Village signposted from A436 E of Stow-on-the-Wold

Now a free house, this 16th-c pub is run by a delightful and warmly welcoming couple who always have time for a chat, no matter how busy they are. The bar has pale polished flagstones, a handsome antique oak box settle among other more modern seats, dark oak beams in the ochre ceiling, stripped stone walls, and an inglenook fireplace. Good, enjoyable bar food includes sandwiches, home-made soup (£3), chicken liver and mushroom parfait (£3.50), leek and bacon tartlet (£4), cajun spiced chicken (£7.50), sausage and mash (£7), salmon fishcake with parsley sauce (£7.95), baked goats cheese and beef tomato on creamy spinach (£8), breast of guinea fowl with pickled red cabbage and grilled mozzarella (£8.50), peppered pork fillet (£9.50), grey mullet provençale (£10.50), daily specials such as fish terrine (£3.95), gammon and pineapple (£7), and fish pie (£8), puddings like toffee and apple crumble or tropical cheesecake (£3.75), and children's menu; Wednesday evening half crispy duck with rosemary and black pepper sauce (£12.50), and good coffee. The no smoking candlelit dining room is pretty. Well kept Hook Norton Best and Wadworths 6X on handpump. There are seats in the pretty garden, and there's a fine play area. *(Recommended by Richard Greaves, Mrs N W Neill, Sam Merton, Ted George, John Bramley, John Bowdler, Colin McKerrow, Andrew Carter, Christopher White, Mr and Mrs Richard Osborne, E J and M W Corrin, Pam and Gareth Turner, Adrian and Nicky Hall, Stuart Turner, Mike Green, Rosie Farr, P and J Shapley, John Saville, Mr and Mrs R Tate, Martin Jones, Steve and Karen Holland)*

Free house ~ Licensees Peter and Assumpta Golding ~ Real ale ~ Bar food ~ Restaurant ~ (01451) 830584 ~ Children welcome ~ Irish nights every 2 nights ~ Open 11-11; 12-10.30 Sun; closed 25 Dec ~ Bedrooms: £45S/£60S

WITHINGTON SP0315 Map 4

Mill Inn

Village signposted from A436, and from A40; from village centre follow sign towards Roman villa (but don't be tempted astray by villa signs before you reach the village!)

The setting for this mossy-roofed and friendly old stone inn is charming – it stands virtually alone in a little valley surrounded by beech and chestnut trees and a rookery, and the garden is pretty with the River Coln running through it and a bridge to a small island where there are seats and tables; more seats on the main lawn. Inside, the beamed and flagstoned bar and other wooden floored rooms have little nooks and corners with antique high-backed settles, a happy bustling atmosphere, and large stone fireplaces; the old dining room is no smoking. Under the friendly new manager, bar food includes soup (£2.95; large bowl £4.95), baguettes or filled baked potatoes (from £3.95), ploughman's (from £4.75), salad bowls (from £5.75), mushroom and nut fettuccine (£6.25), and grilled salmon with a white wine and spring onion sauce (7.25). Well kept Sam Smiths OB on handpump, a decent wine list, and quite a few malt whiskies; piped music, darts, and dominoes. This attractive village is surrounded by splendid walks. *(Recommended by Rod Stoneman, Mike and Wena Stevenson, Nick and Meriel Cox, Dr and Mrs James Stewart, Lawrence Pearse, Martin Jennings, R Huggins, D Irving, E McCall, T McLean, Anne and Leuan Williams, Susan and Nigel Wilson, Mary Rayner, Dorsan Baker, Eddie Edwards, Roger and Pauline Pearce, Austin and Lisa Fleming, Mike and Mary Carter)*

Sam Smiths ~ Manager Karl Phillips ~ Real ale ~ Bar food ~ (01242) 890204 ~ Children welcome ~ Dogs welcome ~ Open 11.30-3, 6-11; 12-3, 6-10.30 Sun ~ Bedrooms: £45B/£55B

Lucky Dip

Besides the fully inspected pubs, you might like to try these Lucky Dips recommended to us and described by readers (if you do, please send us reports: www.goodguides.com).

Alderton [SP0033]

Gardeners Arms [Beckford Rd, off B4077 Tewkesbury—Stow]: Thatched Tudor pub modernised under new licensees, hospitable landlady, decent food from baked potatoes to attractively priced two- and three-course lunches, theme nights and good puddings, well kept Castle Eden, Flowers IPA, Greene King Old Speckled Hen and Marstons Pedigree, above-average wines, log fire; piped music (turned down on request); dogs and children welcome, tables on sheltered terrace, well kept garden *(George Atkinson, LYM, Michael and Christine Halls, Mr and Mrs J Williams)*

Aldsworth [SP1510]

☆ ***Sherborne Arms*** [B4425 Burford—Cirencester]: Cheerful extended wayside pub very popular for wide choice of good fresh food from baked potatoes and ploughman's up, esp fish; log fire, beams, some stripped stone, smallish bar, big dining area and attractive no smoking conservatory, friendly obliging service and attentive landlord, well kept ales such as Greene King IPA, Abbot and Ruddles County; games area with darts, lots of board games, fruit machine, piped music; pleasant front garden, lavatory for disabled *(Marjorie and David Lamb, Derek Carless, Michael and Jenny Back, Robert and Patricia Battarbee, R Huggins, D Irving, E McCall, T McLean, BB, Michael Gray)*

Amberley [SO8401]

☆ ***Black Horse*** [off A46 Stroud—Nailsworth; Littleworth]: Comfortably refitted dining pub, spectacular views, open fire and daily papers, conservatory, no smoking family bar, games room, usual food inc Mon-Thurs bargains, well kept ales such as Archers Best and Golden, Greene King Abbot, Ind Coope Burton, Marstons Pedigree and guests (special prices Tues), farm cider, interesting murals; tables on back terrace with barbecue and spit roast area, more on lawn (sometimes a parrot out here); open all day summer wknds, has been cl Mon *(LYM, Dave Irving, Louise English, Mike and Heather Watson, David and Carole Chapman, J Davidson)*

Andoversford [SP0219]

Royal Oak [signed just off A40; Gloucester Rd]: Cosy and attractive beamed village pub, lots of stripped stone, nice galleried dining room beyond big central open fire, well kept ales inc Goffs Jouster, reasonably priced food, obliging service; popular quiz night, tables in garden *(R Huggins, D Irving, E McCall, T McLean, BB)*

Apperley [SO8628]

☆ ***Coal House*** [Gabb Lane; village signed off B4213 S of Tewkesbury]: Airy bar in splendid riverside position and well restored after flooding; welcoming chatty landlord, well kept Bass, Wickwar Brand Oak and a guest beer, wide-ranging substantial enjoyable food from baguettes up; front terrace with Severn views, play area, moorings; walkers welcome *(Theocsbrian, BB, Mrs Mary Walters)*

Aust [ST5789]

Boars Head [½ mile from M48, junction 1; follow Avonmouth sign and keep eyes peeled for sign off]: Useful creeper-covered motorway break, nice mix of old furnishings, some stripped stonework, log fires, children allowed in partly no smoking eating area, bar food from baguettes up inc Sun roast, well kept Courage Best and Directors, good house wines; piped music; pretty sheltered garden, dogs allowed on a lead *(Charles and Pauline Stride, R Mathews, LYM, Mr and Mrs Thomas, Ian Phillips, Peter Neate, Rob Webster, John and Enid Morris)*

Bibury [SP1106]

Catherine Wheel [Arlington; B4425 NE of Cirencester]: Well used open-plan main bar, quieter smaller back rooms, low beams, stripped stone, good log fires, no smoking dining area (children allowed), well kept Bass, Courage Best and Wadworths 6X, limited generous if not cheap food from sandwiches up, traditional games; fruit machine, piped music; picnic-sets in attractive quiet and spacious garden with play area, famously beautiful village, handy for country and riverside walks; open all day, children welcome, quiet comfortable bedrooms in former stable block *(P R and S A White, BKA, Richard Gibbs, LYM, Di and Mike Gillam)*

Swan [B4425]: Hotel in lovely spot on River Coln, well kept beer in roomy and very comfortable relaxing bar used by locals, reasonably priced food in nice adjoining brasserie, good service; tables out by pergola with masses of flowers, comfortable bedrooms *(Guy Vowles, Des and Jen Clarke)*

Birdlip [SO9316]

Air Balloon [A417/A436 roundabout]: Much extended dining pub, standard value food, good-sized no smoking area, pubbier front corner with open fire, stone walls and flagstones, real ales; tables on terrace and in garden *(Neil and Anita Christopher, Darren Le Poidevin)*

Royal George: Big comfortable two-level bar beyond hotel reception, beams hung with chalked sayings from such savants as Hemingway and Homer Simpson, large tables, well kept Greene King, soft lighting; quiet piped music; wide range of reasonably priced bar and restaurant food from sandwiches up; fine garden, pleasant setting, bedrooms *(R Huggins, D Irving, E McCall, T McLean)*

Bishop's Cleeve [SO9527]

Crown & Harp [Cheltenham Rd]: Large extended family pub, relaxed and friendly, cheerful efficient staff good with children, decent food choice inc OAP specials and Sat steak night, Smiles and Wadworths 6X; pleasant tables in big garden, play area *(Ian and Nita Cooper)*

Bisley [SO9006]

☆ ***Stirrup Cup*** [Cheltenham Rd]: Long rambling well furnished local with cheerful, enthusiastic and helpful new landlord, good modestly priced food from sandwiches and tasty baguettes to generous Sunday roasts inc children's meals, well kept real ales, decent wines, friendly bustle, no music; dogs welcome *(Matthew Shackle, Dave Irving)*

Blockley [SP1634]

☆ ***Great Western Arms*** [Station Rd (B4479)]: Convivial and comfortable village local with straightforward modern-style lounge/dining room, cheery landlord, wide choice of promptly served good value home-cooked food, three well kept Hook Norton ales and Gales HSB, no piped music, busy public bar with games room; attractive village, lovely valley view *(George Atkinson, Christopher and Jo Barton, Giles Francis, G W A Pearce)*

Bourton-on-the-Water [SP1620]

Mousetrap [Lansdown, W edge]: Small comfortable stone pub with well kept Hook Norton and Wadworths 6X in long narrow partly beamed bar, good food inc imaginative dishes and particularly good steaks in separate attractive kitchen-style dining area, attentive friendly service, welcoming fire; picnic-sets out in front, bedrooms *(Helen White)*

Old Manse [Victoria St]: Front garden and one end of long turkey-carpeted beamed bar overlooking River Windrush, big log fire, attractive old prints, bookshelves, some stripped stone, friendly attentive staff, well kept real ales, decent food from sandwiches up inc afternoon teas and good steaks, pretty restaurant; piped music; good bedrooms, open all day *(George Atkinson, BB)*

☆ ***Old New Inn***: Old hotel next to 1:9 scale model of village built here in 1930s by present landlord's father, banquettes and plush chairs on varnished boards of refurbished lounge bar, plainer back bar (where children welcome if eating) with big painted panels, well kept changing real ales, good value home-made food, quick friendly service, lovely dining room overlooking ford through River Windrush; good bedrooms *(Pam Adsley)*

Bream [SO6005]

Rising Sun [High St; Forest of Dean]: Large rambling pub with great views to Severn Estuary, four or five well kept changing ales, good value home-made food from bar snacks through plenty of fish (esp Thurs night) and vegetarian to pheasant, Tues curry night, log fire restaurant; tables outside *(T N Bywater, Guy Vowles)*

Broadwell [SP2027]

☆ ***Fox*** [off A429 2 miles N of Stow-on-the-Wold]: Attractive and welcoming small pub opp broad green in pleasant village, generous straightforward food from good ploughman's up, well kept Donnington BB, SB and SBA, Addlestone's cider, decent wines, stripped stone and flagstones, beams hung with jugs, log fire, darts, dominoes and chess, plain public bar with pool room extension, nice separate restaurant (locally popular for Sun family lunches); may be piped jazz; tables out on gravel, good big back garden with aunt sally, field behind for Caravan Club members; bedrooms *(George Atkinson, Roger and Jenny Huggins, Mr and Mrs Richard Osborne)*

Brockweir [SO5401]

Brockweir Inn [signed just off A466 Chepstow—Monmouth]: Well placed Wye Valley walkers' pub (no muddy boots) with beams and stripped stonework, quarry tiles, sturdy settles, woodburner, snugger carpeted alcoves with brocaded seats, country décor, food inc sandwiches, well kept Adnams, Bass, Hook Norton Best, Smiles and Worthington BB, Stowford Press cider; upstairs restaurant, pool, machines and piped music in public bar, dogs allowed; conservatory, small garden with interesting covered terrace; open all day Sat, children in eating area; bedrooms *(Bob and Margaret Holder, LYM, Anne and Leuan Williams, Desmond Hall)*

Bussage [SO8804]

Ram: Well kept and friendly Cotswold stone village pub, generous good value wholesome food in dining area, several well kept ales, decent wines, pleasant flagstoned bar extension, good valley view esp from deck outside *(June and Ken Brooks, Dave Irving)*

Cambridge [SO7403]

George [3 miles from M5 junction 13 – A38 towards Bristol]: Big, busy and welcoming, with two spacious dining extensions, good value food from filled rolls and baked potatoes up inc bargain lunches, well kept Greene King Old Speckled Hen, helpful staff; garden with barbecues, aviaries and play area, also camp site; open all day Sun *(M G Hart)*

Chalford [SO9003]

Kings Head [France Lynch]: Friendly and attractive old country local, long room with brasses and jugs on beams, well kept beers, decent wines, wide range of good food inc Sun roast, helpful service, cosy atmosphere, no juke box or fruit machine; garden, great views *(Tom and Ruth Rees)*

Charfield [ST7292]

Railway Tavern [Wotton Rd]: Real ales such as Adnams Broadside, Greene King Abbot and Old Speckled Hen, Flowers IPA and Thwaites Reward, decent food, separate entrance to games room *(Ian Phillips)*

Charlton Kings [SO9819]

Waterside [A40 about a mile E]: Generous enjoyable food from filled rolls and baked potatoes to choice of Sun roasts; play area *(Mr and Mrs J Brown)*

Chedworth [SP0609]

☆ ***Hare & Hounds*** [Fosse Cross – A429 N of Cirencester, some way from village]: Interestingly furnished rambling dining pub, low beams, soft lighting, cosy corners, nice furnishings, two big log fires, small conservatory; good food with some inventive dishes, well kept Arkells 2B, 3B and Kingsdown, good house wines, happy staff; children welcome away from bar; disabled facilities *(KC, LYM, P R and S A White, R Huggins, D Irving, E McCall, T McLean)*

Cheltenham [SO9422]

Belgian Monk [Clarence St]: Themed as Belgian-style bar with six helpfully described Belgian beers on tap each served in its characteristic glass, lots more in bottles, good home-made soup, baguettes and largely Belgian food inc lots of seafood (the chips seem more English), hot chocolate etc, pleasant service; may be cl Sun *(R T and J C Moggridge, Dave Irving)*

Kemble Brewery [Fairview St]: Small backstreet Archers local, all their beers inc Porter kept well at low prices, charming landlady, basic food; can get quite smoky; small back garden *(Theocsbrian, Guy Vowles)*

☆ ***Tailors*** [Cambray Pl]: Friendly pub in substantial town house, attractive flight of steps to main bar with lots of dark wood, old clocks and prints, two fireplaces and comfortable armchairs, good basic lunchtime food inc plenty of ploughman's and baked potatoes, well kept Wadworths 6X and guest ales; cosy snug, cellar bar Fri/Sat evenings; piped music, two discreet TVs; some tables outside *(Ian and Nita Cooper)*

Tavern in the Town [Bath Rd]: Bay-windowed local comfortably refurbished and renamed after closure, snug friendly atmosphere, original fireplace and wooden dado; piped music, TV *(Chris Rutherford)*

Chipping Campden [SP1539]

☆ ***Kings Arms*** [High St]: Small hotel reopened after extensive alterations and doing well under same management as Village Pub at Barnsley, inventive modern changing food, friendly staff and good log fire in charmingly refurbished bar with widened eating areas; secluded back garden, open all day Sat, bedrooms *(Martin Jones, Susan and John Douglas, LYM, Mrs Gillian Lewis, John and Patricia White, K H Frostick)*

☆ ***Lygon Arms*** [High St]: Stripped-stone bar with lots of horse pictures, open fires, well kept

Hook Norton Best, Wadworths 6X and several guest beers, helpful friendly service, very wide choice of enjoyable reasonably priced food till late evening in bar and small back dining room, raftered evening restaurant beyond shady courtyard with tables; children welcome, open all day exc winter wkdys; good bedrooms *(Klaus and Elizabeth Leist, Michael Porter, LYM, Peter Meister)*

Noel Arms [High St]: Old inn with polished oak settles, attractive old tables, armour, casks hanging from beams, tools and traps on stripped stone walls, well kept Bass and Hook Norton Best, decent food from sandwiches to some interesting dishes, no smoking restaurant, coal fire; piped music; children welcome, tables in enclosed courtyard, bedrooms *(A E Brace, Patricia A Bruce, LYM, Marjorie and Bernard Parkin, Susan and John Douglas)*

Chipping Sodbury [ST7282]

George [Broad St]: Old coaching inn with interesting interior, stimulating choice of food, Courage Best, Tetleys and Wickwar BOB, reasonably priced wine, enthusiastic and obliging young staff, also new café-bar with tea, coffee, lagers and wines, separate Chinese restaurant (takeaways); lots of picnic-sets in huge back garden with own bar and barbecue, attractive old town *(Ian Phillips)*

Royal Oak [Broad St]: Real ales such as Courage Best, Hampshire Glory, Timothy Taylors Landlord and Charles Wells Bombardier, big fireplace, pleasant staff, good value restaurant *(Rebecca Gould)*

Cinderford [SO6512]

White Hart [St Whites Rd (B4226/A4151)]: Good food with enterprising choice of menus at varying price levels inc bargain lunches Mon-Sat, well kept real ales, good friendly service *(Revd John E Cooper)*

Cirencester [SP0201]

Bear [Dyer St]: Long lively bar with cheap well kept Moles, juke box, TV; nice pavement table area *(R Huggins, D Irving, E McCall, T McLean)*

☆ ***Corinium Court*** [Dollar St/Gloucester St]: Cosy, civilised and relaxed character inn, recently opened up a little by newish owners, with big log fire, attractive antique coaching prints, good mix of tables, sofas and small armchairs, well kept changing ales, decent wines, food from sandwiches, baguettes and baked potatoes up in bars and nicely decorated restaurant; no piped music; entrance through charming courtyard with tables, attractive back garden, large car park; good bedrooms *(R Huggins, D Irving, E McCall, T McLean, BB, Guy Vowles)*

Golden Cross [Black Jack St, between church and Corinium Museum]: Popular 1920s backstreet local with good pubby atmosphere, simple very cheap generous food, well kept reasonably priced Arkells 2B and 3B, nice wine, friendly licensees, quick service, hanging jugs and beer mugs; pool, skittle alley, tables in back garden, open all day wknds, bedrooms *(R Huggins, D Irving, E McCall, T McLean, Dave Braisted, Peter and Audrey Dowsett)*

Somewhere Else [Castle St]: Two light and airy rooms with pastel walls and café tables, well kept Archers and a guest such as Youngs, decent house wine – bistro-feel café/restaurant by day, with small interesting choice of quickly served food, lively bar (with tapas available) and more of a pub mood evenings; lots of tables on heated terrace, games room off with pool *(R Huggins, D Irving, E McCall, T McLean, Betsy and Peter Little)*

☆ ***Twelve Bells*** [Lewis Lane]: Cheery well worn in backstreet pub with particularly well kept Abbey Bellringer and five changing beers, small low-ceilinged three-roomed bar, small back dining area with sturdy pine tables and rugs on quarry tiles, coal fires, pictures for sale, clay pipe collection, friendly forthright landlord, good food inc local produce and fresh fish lunchtime and early evening; can get smoky, piped music may be loud; small sheltered back terrace with fountain *(Pete Baker, R Huggins, D Irving, E McCall, T McLean, Guy Vowles, Ian and Nita Cooper, Giles Francis, Di and Mike Gillam, Mike Pugh, Peter and Audrey Dowsett, BB, Frank Willy)*

Waggon & Horses [London Rd]: Cosy and comfortably cottagey stone-built pub recently remodelled to give more space, lots of bric-a-brac, good choice of well kept changing ales; back dining room *(R Huggins, D Irving, E McCall, T McLean)*

Wheatsheaf [Cricklade St]: Friendly, roomy and neat, good range of real ales, wide choice of cheapish food until 4pm inc OAP bargains, quick friendly service, no piped music but corner TV; well used skittle alley, back car park, open all day *(R Huggins, D Irving, E McCall, T McLean, Peter and Audrey Dowsett)*

Clearwell [SO5708]

Butchers Arms [High St]: Large, friendly and attractive old stone-built dining pub with particularly well kept ales inc Smiles and Wadworths 6X, subdued red upholstery, dark woodwork, hops, big log fire, popular food inc Sun lunch and half-price helpings for children; tables in neat little back courtyard with pond and flowers *(Mike and Lynn Robinson, Keith Allen, Piotr Chodzko-Zajko)*

Cleeve Hill [SO9826]

Rising Sun [B4632]: Worth knowing for the view over Cheltenham to the Malvern Hills from the terrace and lawn, esp as the evening lights come on; usual food, friendly staff, Greene King beers *(Di and Mike Gillam)*

Coates [SO9600]

☆ ***Tunnel House*** [follow Tarleton signs (right then left) from village, pub up rough track on right after railway bridge; OS Sheet 163 map ref 965005]: Idiosyncratic beamed country pub idyllically placed by interesting canal tunnel (now being restored; good walk to Daneway at Sapperton), very relaxed management style, mix of comfortably worn armchairs, sofa, rustic benches, enamel advertising signs, stuffed mustelids, race tickets, real ales such as Archers Best, Greene King Old Speckled Hen, Smiles and Wadworths 6X, good food inc bargain lunches and authentic Indonesian curries, Sunday barbecues, log fire, pub games, juke box; children welcome (plenty of room to run around outside, too), camping facilities *(Richard Stancomb, Guy Vowles, LYM, R Huggins, D Irving, E McCall, T McLean)*

Cold Aston [SP1219]

Plough [aka Aston Blank; off A436 (B4068) or A429 SW of Stow-on-the-Wold]: Tiny 17th-c village pub under new licensees, low black beams, flagstones, old-fashioned simple furnishings, open fire, well kept Donnington Best and Hook Norton Best, enjoyable food; piped music; well behaved children welcome, picnic-sets under cocktail parasols on small side terraces, has been cl Mon *(Martin Jones, LYM)*

Colesbourne [SO9913]

☆ ***Colesbourne Inn*** [A435 Cirencester—Cheltenham]: Gabled grey stone 18th-c coaching inn, beams, candlelight and log fires, spacious bar with heavy dark wooden chairs, settles and tables on bare boards, well kept Wadworths IPA, 6X and Farmers Glory, lounge with chintzy sofas and armchairs and big stripped stone fireplace, no smoking restaurant; traditional games, no dogs, piped music; views from attractive back garden and terrace, well appointed bedrooms in converted stable block *(LYM, Jo Rees, P R and S A White, David and Higgs Wood)*

Compton Abdale [SP0616]

Puesdown Inn [A40 outside village]: Former coaching inn with comfortable leather chesterfields by huge log fire, well kept Hook Norton beers, wide choice of reliable food from generous ploughman's to good evening meals, attractive no smoking restaurant, no piped music, public bar with big woodburner and games room with pool; good base for walking, tables in garden behind, open all day Fri-Sun *(Peter and Audrey Dowsett, Anthony Gill)*

Cowley [SO9614]

☆ ***Green Dragon*** [off A435 S of Cheltenham at Elkstone, Cockleford signpost]: Two-bar country dining pub in nice spot, good value food from sandwiches up, friendly service, beams, cream or stripped stone walls, log fires, fresh flowers and candles, tasteful oak furniture and fittings from Thompsons of Kilburn, pine boards or limestone composition floor, Courage Best, Hook Norton Best, Theakstons Old Peculier and Wadworths 6X, reasonably priced wines, espresso machine; piped music; children allowed in public bar, restaurant; big car park, two terraces, one heated, comfortable bedrooms off courtyard, good breakfast – good walking area *(Jo Rees, Sue and Jeff Evans, Guy Vowles, LYM, JP, PP, A and M Worth)*

Eastcombe [SO8904]

Lamb: Dignified stone building recently much extended to take advantage of fine views towards Lypiatt Park, two bars and sunken conservatory-style dining room, three or four well kept ales such as Batemans XXXB, Greene King Abbot and Charles Wells Bombardier, Stowford Press cider, well priced wines, good imaginative inexpensive food from varied menu, friendly landlord, slightly Bohemian décor; lovely terrace *(Prof H G Allen, Christopher Mobbs, Miss W Reynolds, R Huggins, D Irving, E McCall, T McLean, Guy Vowles)*

Ebrington [SP1840]

☆ ***Ebrington Arms*** [off B4035 E of Chipping Campden or A429 N of Moreton-in-Marsh]: Recently renovated village pub with low beams, stone walls, flagstones and inglenooks, decent food from good sandwiches up, well kept Donnington SBA, Hook Norton Best and a guest beer; children welcome, no dogs at meal times, picnic-sets on sheltered terrace, handy for Hidcote and Kiftsgate, bedrooms *(John Kane, LYM, Terry Mizen, E V Walder, Mr and Mrs Richard Osborne)*

Edge [SO8509]

☆ ***Edgemoor*** [Gloucester Rd]: Tidy modernised dining place, ideal for grandma's birthday lunch, with wide choice of good value food inc fine home-made puddings, friendly landlord and quick helpful service, picture-window panoramic valley view, relaxing atmosphere, well kept Smiles, Uley Old Spot and Wickwar BOB, good coffee; no smoking area, children welcome, pretty terrace, good walks nearby; cl Sun evening *(LYM, Dave Irving, Alun Jones, Mrs Sheela Curtis)*

Elkstone [SO9610]

☆ ***Highwayman*** [Beechpike; off northbound A417 6 miles N of Cirencester]: Rambling 16th-c warren of low beams, stripped stone, cosy alcoves, antique settles among more modern furnishings, big log fires, rustic decorations, well kept Arkells ales, good house wines, big back eating area (wide affordable choice inc vegetarian), quick friendly service; maybe quiet piped music; disabled access, good family room, outside play area *(P R and S A White, David and Rhian Peters, Peter and Audrey Dowsett, the Didler, LYM)*

Fairford [SP1501]

Bull [Market Pl]: Friendly beamed hotel, large comfortably old-fashioned timbered bar with enormous blackboard choice of good value food, good helpful service, well kept Arkells 2B and 3B, two coal-effect gas fires, local RAF memorabilia, charming restaurant, no smoking areas, no piped music; children welcome, bedrooms small but fresh and bright, charming village, church has UK's only intact set of medieval stained-glass windows *(Peter and Audrey Dowsett, Des and Jen Clarke, Guy Vowles, Peter Meister)*

Forest of Dean [SO6212]

Speech House [B4226 nearly 1m E of junction with B4234]: Hotel superbly placed in centre of Forest, lovely warm interior with lots of oak panelling, substantial reasonably priced bar food, well kept Bass, afternoon teas, plush restaurant; comfortable bedrooms, tables outside *(Neil and Anita Christopher)*

Frampton Mansell [SO9102]

☆ ***Crown*** [brown sign to pub off A491 Cirencester—Stroud]: Emphasis on food, with some good unusual dishes from sandwiches up (but rather an irritating ordering system), well kept Courage and Wadworths 6X, good choice of wines by the glass, nice atmosphere in heavy-beamed bar with two log fires, stripped stone and rugs on bare boards, friendly helpful staff, daily papers, turkey-carpeted restaurant; piped music; picnic-sets in sunny front garden with terrace and pretty views over village and steep wooded valley; decent bedrooms, good breakfast *(R Huggins, D Irving, E McCall, T McLean, Mrs J L Wyatt, Giles Francis, Roger Everett, Dave Irving, LYM, Lawrence Pearse)*

Frampton on Severn [SO7407]

☆ ***Bell*** [The Green]: Georgian dining pub by huge village cricket green, pleasant staff, three well kept real ales inc interesting guests, log fire and plush seats, steps up to L-shaped family dining room, separate locals' bar with pool; good small back play area, now open all day *(Nick and Meriel Cox, Meg and Colin Hamilton, Prof H G Allen, Dave Irving)*

Frocester [SO7831]

George [Peter St]: Traditional welcoming two-bar coaching inn now owned by a village consortium, log fires, well kept real ales, good food, welcoming service, daily papers, bistro, no machines; courtyard with boules, huge shuttered bedrooms *(R Huggins, D Irving, E McCall, T McLean)*

Glasshouse [SO7121]

☆ ***Glasshouse Inn*** [first right turn off A40 going W from junction with A4136; OS Sheet 162 map ref 710213]: Charming country tavern with well kept ales such as Bass and Butcombe tapped from the cask, beams and flagstones, log fire in vast fireplace, good generous honest home cooking from thick sandwiches up, friendly staff, interesting decorations, recent extension carefully toning in; darts and quoits, lovely hanging baskets, seats on fenced lawn with interesting topiary inc yew tree seat, fine walks in nearby Newent Woods *(Guy Vowles, Clare and Paul Howes, LYM, the Didler, Gill Waller, Tony Morriss, Mr and Mrs F J Parmenter)*

Gloucester [SO8218]

Black Swan [Southgate St]: Fine early Victorian building handy for docks tourist attractions, six well kept mainly local ales (friendly staff may give small samples), good well priced standard food (not Sun), lots of tables in large comfortably smart room, fireplace and chandelier giving character; open all day (Sun afternoon closure) tables outside, bedrooms *(Dave Irving, Gill Waller, Tony Morriss)*

☆ ***Fountain*** [Westgate St/Berkeley St]: Friendly licensees in 17th-c pub's civilised L-shaped bar, plush seats and built-in wall benches, helpful service, cheap freshly made usual food inc good range of curries, well kept Brakspears, Boddingtons, Fullers London Pride, Greene King Abbot and Wickwar BOB, good range of whiskies, attractive prints, handsome stone fireplace, log-effect gas fire; tables in pleasant courtyard, good disabled access, handy for cathedral, open all day *(BB, Mike and Mary Carter, Sue and Mike Todd, Dave Irving)*

Linden Tree [Bristol Rd; A350 about 1½ miles S of centre, out past docks]: Lively unpretentous terraced local with low beams and stripped stone, well kept Wadworths and several interesting guest beers, usual good value lunchtime food, coal fire, back skittle alley; bedrooms, open all day Sat *(the Didler)*

Windmill [Eastgate St]: Doing well under new management, friendly and helpful, with short choice of carefully cooked food, good house wine *(Ken Flawn)*

Great Barrington [SP2013]

☆ ***Fox*** [off A40 Burford—Northleach; pub towards Little Barrington]: Charming spot in summer, enlarged area with heated terrace by River Windrush (private fishing), orchard with pond, river views from dining area; low-ceilinged small bar with stripped stone and simple country furnishings, well kept Donnington BB and SBA, farm cider, promptly served food from sandwiches (not Sun) up – all day Sun and summer Sat, not winter Mon night, restaurant in former skittle alley; darts, shove-ha'penny, cribbage, dominoes, juke box, fruit machine, TV; children welcome, open all day *(David and Kay Ross, LYM, Pete Baker, Ted George, Stephen, Julie and Hayley Brown, R M Gibson, Les Trusler, the Didler, Colin McKerrow)*

Greet [SP0230]

Harvest Home [B4078 N of Winchcombe]: Well spaced tables, bay window seats, hop bines on beams, wide choice of enjoyable food inc wkdy OAP lunches in bar or big beamed pitched-roof side restaurant (no smoking), decent beers and house wines, log fires, good service; sizeable garden, not far from medieval Sudeley Castle *(Christopher and Jo Barton, LYM, R Mathews, John and Enid Morris)*

Gretton [SP0131]

Bugatti: Stylish yet laid-back and comfortable, sofas, log fire, pleasant Australian staff, good interesting well served food with good veg; cats and dogs *(Jo Rees, Patricia A Bruce)*

Guiting Power [SP0924]

Farmers Arms [Fosseway (A429)]: Stripped stone, mix of carpet and flagstones, well kept Donnington BB and SBA, wide range of unpretentious food from sandwiches up inc children's dishes, good coal or log fire; skittle alley, games area with darts, pool, cribbage, dominoes, fruit machine; piped music; seats (and quoits) in garden, good walks; children welcome, bedrooms, lovely village *(Derek Carless, P R and S A White, LYM, Mike and Wena Stevenson, the Didler)*

Hawkesbury Upton [ST7786]

Beaufort Arms [High St]: Friendly landlord and staff, good choice of low-priced bar food in extended uncluttered dining lounge on right, well kept local Wickwar ales and others such as Bath and Fullers London Pride, local farm cider, darts in stripped-brick bare-boards bar, plenty of brewery and local memorabilia; skittle alley, seats outside, on Cotswold Way *(R Huggins, D Irving, E McCall, T McLean)*

Fox [High St]: Friendly attentive service, interested landlord, well kept beer, lots of local photographs *(R Huggins, D Irving, E McCall, T McLean)*

Kemble [ST9897]

☆ ***Thames Head*** [A433 Cirencester—Tetbury]:

Well served decent food inc wide puddings choice, well kept Arkells 2B and 3B, welcoming helpful staff, stripped stone, timberwork, cottagey back area with pews and log-effect gas fire in big fireplace, country-look dining room with another big gas fire, real fire in front area; skittle alley, seats outside, children welcome, good value four-poster bedrooms, nice walk to nearby source of River Thames *(Gerald Wilkinson, I A Herdman, A B and G S Dance , LYM)*

Kilkenny [SP0018]

Kilkeney Inn [A436 W of Andoversford]: Spacious modernised dining pub with log fire and comfortable no smoking conservatory, well kept Bass and Hook Norton; well behaved children allowed in eating areas, tables outside, attractive Cotswold views, open all day wknds *(Mike and Mary Carter, Rita Horridge, Bernard Stradling, LYM)*

Kineton [SP0926]

☆ ***Halfway House*** [signed from B4068 and B4077 W of Stow-on-the-Wold]: Traditional unpretentious country local with helpful friendly licensees, simple food inc baguettes and sensibly priced hot dishes using local ingredients, well kept cheap Donnington BB and SBA from nearby brewery, pub games (and juke box), restaurant; children allowed lunchtime, no visiting dogs; attractive sheltered back garden, tables on narrow front terrace too, simple comfortable bedrooms, good walks *(LYM)*

Knockdown [ST8388]

Holford Arms: Popular and comfortable, real ales inc Bass, huge fireplace, dining area (decent choice of food), no piped music; neat side garden, handy for Westonbirt *(Peter and Audrey Dowsett)*

Lechlade [SU2199]

New Inn [Market Sq (A361)]: Big comfortably unpretentious lounge with huge log fire, good range of changing well kept ales and very wide choice of generous well cooked food, not expensive, games machine and TV at one end; back restaurant; piped music; play area and a few tables in big garden extending to Thames, good walks; comfortable bedrooms *(Peter and Audrey Dowsett)*

☆ ***Trout*** [A417, a mile E]: Low-beamed three-room pub dating from 15th c, with some flagstones, beams, stuffed fish and fishing prints, spill-over bar out in converted boathouse, big Thamesside garden with boules, aunt sally; well kept Courage Best, John Smiths and Wadworths 6X, popular well presented if pricy food from ploughman's to steaks and plenty of fish, no smoking dining room, two fires; children in eating areas, jazz Tues and Sun, no piped music, fishing rights; may be long waits in summer (open all day Sat then), when very busy, with bouncy castle and fairground swings; large car park, camping *(SLC, Keith and Suzie Stevens, JCW, LYM, P R and S A White)*

Longborough [SP1729]

Coach & Horses: Unpretentious largely flagstoned L-shaped local, good log fire, welcoming service, particularly well kept Donnington inc XXX Mild, walkers and dogs welcome; tables outside *(Pete Baker, Mrs N W Neill)*

Longford [SO8320]

Queens Head [Tewkesbury Rd]: Attractive open-plan bar with no smoking restaurant area, good value lunches from baguettes and baked potatoes up, slightly more upmarket evening meals, well kept ales such as Bass, Fullers London Pride, Greene King Old Speckled Hen and Hook Norton, pleasant efficient service *(Neil and Anita Christopher, Peter Jones)*

Lower Swell [SP1725]

☆ ***Golden Ball*** [B4068 W of Stow-on-the-Wold]: Sprucely unspoilt local with well kept Donnington BB and SBA from the pretty nearby brewery, good range of ciders and perry, very friendly landlady, well presented generous home-made food, log fire, games area with fruit machine and juke box behind big chimneystack, small evening restaurant (not Sun evening), small garden with occasional barbecues, aunt sally and quoits; may be piped classical music, no dogs or children; decent simple bedrooms, pretty village, good walks *(the Didler, LYM)*

Marshfield [ST7773]

☆ ***Catherine Wheel*** [High St; signed off A420 Bristol—Chippenham]: Recently bought by three local couples, plates and prints on stripped stone walls, medley of settles, chairs and stripped tables, open fire in impressive fireplace, cottagey back family bar, charming no smoking Georgian dining room, flower-decked back yard; cheerful service, wide choice of food (not Sun) inc imaginative dishes, well kept Archers, Bass, Courage and Wadworths 6X, farm cider, decent wines; darts, dominoes; provision for children, unspoilt village *(LYM, Dr and Mrs M E Wilson, Dr and Mrs A K Clarke)*

Mickleton [SP1543]

☆ ***Kings Arms*** [B4632 (ex A46)]: Comfortable, clean, relaxed and civilised family lounge bar, friendly considerate service, popular food inc notable ploughman's and Sun roasts, nice puddings, well kept real ales, farm cider, small log fire, no piped music; welcoming locals' bar with darts, dominoes and cribbage; some tables outside, handy for Kiftsgate and Hidcote *(BB, John Brightley)*

Minchinhampton [SO8500]

☆ ***Old Lodge*** [Nailsworth—Brimscombe – on common fork left at pub's sign; OS Sheet 162 map ref 853008]: Relaxed and welcoming dining pub now owned by Youngs, three of their real ales kept well, small snug central bar opening into eating area with beams and stripped brick, no smoking area, friendly efficient staff; tables on neat lawn with attractive flower border, looking over common with grazing cows and horses; has been cl Mon *(LYM, James Morrell, Bernard Stradling, R Huggins, D Irving, E McCall, T McLean, PB, JB, Neil and Anita Christopher)*

Moreton-in-Marsh [SP2032]

Bell [High St]: Comfortable divided beamed

and flagstoned bar with lots of china, brass and photographs, solid-fuel stove, no smoking family area, real ales such as Bass, Boddingtons, Flowers IPA, Fullers London Pride, Greene King IPA and Marstons Pedigree, plenty of wines by the glass, good value standard food inc afternoon tea, friendly mix of all ages, good uniformed staff; live music Weds, tables (some under cover) in attractive courtyard, open all day, bedrooms *(JHBS, Chris Glasson)*

Black Bear [High St]: Unpretentious beamed pub, stripped stone with hanging rugs and old village pictures, well kept local Donnington XXX, BB and SBA, good coffee, good value pub food inc fresh fish, friendly service; public bar with lots of football memorabilia, darts, sports TV and games machine, large airy dining lounge (not Sun evening); may be piped radio; tables outside, big bedrooms sharing bathrooms *(Joan and Michel Hooper-Immins, Joyce and Maurice Cottrell, the Didler, Ted George, BB)*

☆ ***Inn on the Marsh*** [Stow Rd]: Good reasonably priced restaurant-style food in beamed bar and attractive candlelit dining conservatory, artist landlord's Dutch wife cooks excellent puddings and interesting Dutch snacks too, friendly attentive service, buoyant atmosphere, well kept Mansfield and Marstons Bitter and Pedigree, comfortable armchairs and sofa, pink walls giving bistro look, log fire; bedrooms *(Pat and Robert Watt, Joyce and Maurice Cottrell, Mrs N W Neill)*

☆ ***Redesdale Arms*** [High St]: Fine old coaching inn with prettily lit alcoves and big stone fireplace in solidly furnished comfortable panelled bar on right, well kept ales such as Courage Directors and Wye Valley, quickly served generous food, friendly staff, back restaurant and dining conservatory, darts in flagstoned public bar; piped music, fruit machine, TV; tables out on heated decking in courtyard, comfortable well equipped bedrooms beyond *(George Atkinson, BB, Ted George)*

Swan [High St]: Friendly welcome in bright and comfortable lounge with flowered wallpaper and old photographs, good choice of low-priced generous food inc pies and children's, well kept Boddingtons and Wadworths 6X, decent wine, staff friendly and efficient even when coachloads roll in on Tues market day; attractive restaurant *(Joyce and Maurice Cottrell, Peter and Audrey Dowsett)*

Newland [SO5509]

☆ ***Ostrich***: Unspoilt and dating from 13th c, plenty of atmosphere, unpretentious mix of furnishings, fine range of real ales such as Hook Norton Best, Monmouth Rebellion, RCH Pitchfork, Shepherd Neame Spitfire, Timothy Taylors Landlord and one brewed for them by Freeminer, enjoyable good value thoroughly home-made food, friendly landlady, candles on tables, big log fire, children now allowed; unobtrusive piped jazz and 50s/60s music; small garden, dogs allowed on lead; two bedrooms (nearby church clock strikes on the quarter) *(Phil and Heidi Cook, Mr and Mrs F J Parmenter, Bob and Margaret Holder, Mike and Mary Carter, LYM)*

North Nibley [ST7495]

Black Horse [Barrs Lane]: Friendly village pub refurbished by new owners, wide range of generous good value home-made food, well kept Flowers Original and Marstons Pedigree, good log fire, restaurant; tables in pretty garden, good value cottagey bedrooms, good breakfast; useful for Cotswold Way walkers *(Mrs S A Brooks, LYM)*

Northleach [SP1114]

Sherbourne Arms [Market Pl]: Friendly pub doing well under new management, good interesting food from unusual sandwiches up, partly no smoking restaurant, good wines by the glass; open from 10 for coffee and pastries *(John and Kay Grugeon)*

Nympsfield [SO8000]

☆ ***Rose & Crown*** [The Cross; signed off B4066 Stroud—Dursley]: Bright well decorated stone-built dining pub with good value generous food from sandwiches to interesting restauranty dishes and things for children, well kept Archers, Timothy Taylors and Uley, decent wines, helpful friendly staff, daily papers, log fire and beams in front part with serving bar, pews and other seats in large back area; unobtrusive piped music, children welcome, picnic-sets in side yard and on sheltered lawn with good play area; bedrooms, handy for Cotswold walks *(BB, Lawrence Pearse, Tom Evans, Mike Burke, Patrick Hancock, A and M Worth, Tom and Ruth Rees)*

Oldbury-on-Severn [ST6092]

Ship [Camp Rd]: Recently expanded and refurbished, with enjoyable freshly made food from sandwiches and baked potatoes up, popular dining area, pleasant service; tables in garden with play area *(Charles and Pauline Stride, BB)*

Painswick [SO8609]

☆ ***Falcon*** [New St]: Sizeable old stone-built inn opp churchyard famous for its 99 yews; open-plan, largely panelled, with high ceilings, bare boards bar on right, mainly carpeted dining area with lots of prints on left, high bookshelves and shelves of ornaments by coal-effect fire, relaxing atmosphere, lots of wines by the glass, well kept Boddingtons and Wadworths 6X, with Hook Norton Best and Old Hooky in the public bar, good coffee, wide range of good value food inc lunchtime snacks, pleasant efficient service, daily papers, carpeted L-shaped dining area; big comfortable bedrooms, good breakfast *(Di and Mike Gillam, John Brightley, John Holroyd, Martin Jennings, Chris Parsons, BB, David Biggins, Sue and Mike Todd)*

☆ ***Royal Oak*** [St Mary's St]: Old-fashioned partly 16th-c town pub carefully restored under new ownership (same as Butchers Arms, Sheepscombe – see main entries), some attractive old or antique seats, enjoyable food from filled rolls to interesting main dishes, well kept real ales, decent wines, friendly efficient service, open fire, small sun lounge by suntrap pretty courtyard; children in eating area *(LYM)*

Parkend [SO6208]

Fountain [just off B4234]: Homely and

welcoming, with assorted chairs and settles, real fire, old local tools and photographs, good freshly made usual food inc good range of curries, efficient landlord, well kept local Freeminer and guest beers; children welcome *(Pete Baker)*

☆ ***Woodman*** [Whitecroft]: Roomy and relaxed stripped-stone bar, two open fires, heavy beams, forest and forestry decorations, mix of furnishings inc some modern seats, smaller back bar and dining room, well presented food (not Sun or Mon evenings) inc good vegetarian range, children's meals and Sun lunch, well kept Greene King Old Speckled Hen and Wadworths 6X, decent wines, pleasant service, evening bistro (Thurs-Sat); picnic-sets on front terrace facing green, more out behind, good walks into Forest of Dean; bedrooms *(Neil and Anita Christopher, BB)*

Perrotts Brook [SP0105]

Bear [A435 Cirencester—Gloucester]: Beamed roadside pub doing well under new management, plenty of atmosphere, comfortable seating, well kept real ales, popular food *(R Huggins, D Irving, E McCall, T McLean)*

Pillowell [SO6306]

Swan Cheesehouse [off B4234 Lydney—Parkend; Corner Rd]: Small carefully run pub, its bar food confined to ploughman's but with choice of several dozen unusual mainly local cheeses, good chutneys and pickles, also remarkable range of bottle-conditioned ales, and local and west country wines; attentive licensees, cheese/beer shop; no children or dogs, cl lunchtimes Mon/Tues and winter Weds *(Bernard Stradling)*

Poulton [SP1001]

Falcon [London Rd]: Clean and smart, with good choice of inexpensive food, well kept ales such as Arkells 3B, Hook Norton Best and Theakstons XB, friendly landlord, big fireplace; quiet piped music; pretty village with ancient church *(Peter and Audrey Dowsett)*

Prestbury [SO9624]

☆ ***Plough*** [Mill St]: Well preserved thatched village local, cosy and comfortable front lounge, service from corridor counter in basic but roomy flagstoned back taproom with oak panelling, grandfather clock and big log fire, consistently friendly service, well kept Flowers Original, Greene King Abbot and Tetleys tapped from the cask, homely food;, delightful back garden *(R Huggins, D Irving, E McCall, T McLean)*

Redbrook [SO5410]

☆ ***Boat*** [car park signed on A466 Chepstow—Monmouth, then 100-yard footbridge over Wye]: Beautifully set laid-back Wyeside walkers' pub, friendly landlord, changing well kept ales such as Greene King IPA and Abbot, Robinsons Best, Stonehenge Bodyline, Wadworths 6X and Wye Valley Butty Bach tapped from casks, good range of country wines and hot drinks, roaring woodburner, a couple of cats and beautiful old english sheepdog, reasonably priced usual food inc good value baked potatoes, baguettes and children's dishes; dogs and children welcome, live music Tues and Thurs, rough home-built seats in informal garden with stream spilling down waterfall cliffs into duck pond, open all day wknds *(Keith and Suzie Stevens, LYM, LM, Dave and Meg Richards, Mike and Lynn Robinson, Mr and Mrs P Talbot, Phil and Heidi Cook, Theocsbrian)*

Rodborough [SO8404]

☆ ***Bear*** [Rodborough Common]: Comfortably cosy and pubby beamed and flagstoned bar in smart hotel, friendly staff, pleasant window seats, welcoming log fire, hops hung around top of golden stone walls, interesting paintings, well kept Bass and Uley, good value food (bar and restaurant); children welcome, bedrooms *(R Huggins, D Irving, E McCall, T McLean)*

Ruardean [SO6117]

☆ ***Malt Shovel***: Carefully restored and furnished giving a homely time-warp feel, stripped stone, oak and mahogany, plenty of collectables, central fire, good choice of home-made seasonal food and of real ales, farm cider, roomy interestingly furnished restaurant, lively local feel in public bar on Sat night – local entertainment; attractively furnished well equipped bedrooms *(Boyd Catling)*

Sapperton [SO9403]

Daneway Inn [Daneway; off A419 Stroud—Cirencester]: Sleepy flagstone-floored local worth tracking down for its tables on terrace and lovely sloping lawn in charming quiet wooded countryside near derelict canal (£80 million restoration starting) with good walks and interesting tunnel; amazing floor-to-ceiling carved oak Dutch fireplace, sporting prints, well kept Wadworths IPA, 6X and a guest such as Adnams, Weston's farm cider, food from filled baps up (may be a wait), small no smoking family room, traditional games in inglenook public bar; camping possible *(Roger and Jenny Huggins, Richard Gibbs, Dave Irving, Keith Allen, Richard Stancomb, Jonathan Smith, LYM)*

Selsley [SO8304]

Bell [B4066, just SW of Stroud]: Quietly attractive little 17th-c village pub perched on hillside common overlooking Stroud valley, wide range of reasonably priced home-cooked bar food, three changing real ales, decent wines, friendly landlord and staff; good walks inc Cotswold Way *(Tom Evans, Guy Vowles)*

Shipton Moyne [ST8989]

Cat & Custard Pot [off B4040 Malmesbury—Bristol; The Street]: Enormous good value food choice from sandwiches up, well kept Fullers London Pride, Wadworths 6X and guest beers, Thatcher's cider, good service, reasonable prices, hunting prints in divided bar/dining room, cosy back snug; picturesque village *(J Wedel, BB)*

Siddington [SU0399]

Greyhound [Ashton Rd; village signed from A419 roundabout at Tesco]: Two unpretentious linked rooms full of copper, brass and bric-a-brac, two big log fires, informal mix of tables and chairs, public bar with slate floor, darts and cribbage, extended function room doubling as skittle alley; friendly licensees, decent straightforward bar food, well kept Badger Tanglefoot, Wadworths IPA and seasonal beers; seats out in well planted garden *(LYM, P R and S A White, R Huggins, D Irving, E McCall, T McLean)*

Slad [SO8707]

Woolpack [B4070 Stroud—Birdlip]: Small unpretentious hillside village local with particularly friendly landlord, lovely valley views, several linked rooms with Laurie Lee photographs, some of his books for sale, good value food (not Sun evening) from sandwiches and baguettes to simple hot dishes, Weston's Old Rosie cider, well kept Bass and Uley Old Spot, log fire, games and cards *(Pete Baker)*

Slimbridge [SO7303]

Tudor Arms [Shepherds Patch]: Well kept Tetleys, Wadworths 6X and a guest such as Timothy Taylors Landlord, good choice of generous basic food from sandwiches and ploughman's up inc children's dishes, typical modernised lounge, bar with billiards and TV, skittle alley, family room, evening restaurant; handy for Wildfowl Trust and canal boat trips, snacks all day wknd; bedrooms in small annexe *(Dave Irving)*

Snowshill [SP0934]

☆ ***Snowshill Arms***: Handy for Snowshill Manor and for Cotswold Way walkers, with friendly service, good choice of good value generous food served quickly (fill in your own order form), well kept Donnington BB and SBA, spruce and airy carpeted bar, neat array of tables, local photographs, stripped stone, log fire; skittle alley, charming village views from bow windows and from big back garden with little stream and good play area, friendly local feel midweek winter and evenings, can be very crowded other lunchtimes – get there early; children welcome if eating, nearby parking may be difficult *(LYM, Martin Jennings, David and Anthea Eeles, C A Hall)*

Somerford Keynes [SU0195]

Bakers Arms: Pretty stone-built pub now under same management as Wild Duck at Ewen (see main entries), two knocked-together rooms with stripped stone, pine tables and hop bines, decent food from baguettes and ciabattas up, well kept Wadworths 6X, Charles Wells Bombardier and a beer brewed for the pub, good house wine, two log fires; can be smoky; children welcome, big garden, lovely Cotswold village *(R Huggins, D Irving, E McCall, T McLean, Rob Webster)*

South Cerney [SU0497]

Eliot Arms [signed off A419 SE of Cirencester; Clarks Hay]: Smart pub/hotel under new management, interesting décor in relaxed and comfortable little rooms, some emphasis on attractive choice of enjoyable food, well kept Boddingtons, Flowers Original, Marstons Pedigree and Wadworths 6X, 120 malt whiskies, interesting foreign bottled beers, fast service; children welcome, restaurant, comfortable bedrooms *(LYM, Dr John Lunn)*

Southrop [SP2003]

☆ ***Swan***: Attractively refurbished low-ceilinged dining lounge with log fire, well spaced tables and good generous interesting food, friendly helpful staff, real ales such as Greene King IPA and Marstons Pedigree, good wines, no smoking restaurant (not Sun evening); stripped stone skittle alley, public bar, children welcome; pretty village esp at daffodil time *(LYM, R Huggins, D Irving, E McCall, T McLean)*

Stanton [SP0734]

☆ ***Mount*** [off B4632 SW of Broadway; no through road up hill, bear left]: Gorgeous spot up steep lane from golden-stone village, with views to Welsh mountains – it attracts all sorts; heavy beams, flagstones and big log fire in original core, horseracing pictures and trappings and plenty of locals, roomy picture-window extensions, one no smoking with cricket memorabilia; Donnington BB and SBA under light blanket pressure, farm cider, bar food (not Sun evening) from sandwiches up; open all day Sat and summer Sun, well behaved children allowed, tables outside *(Di and Mike Gillam, Martin Dormer, Christopher and Jo Barton, Paul and Penny Rampton, LYM, Terry Mizen, KN-R, Martin Jennings, John and Joan Calvert, Pam Adsley)*

Stow-on-the-Wold [SP1729]

☆ ***Coach & Horses*** [Ganborough (A424 N)]: Very wide choice of good generous sensibly priced food (all day summer Fri/Sat) from baguettes to popular Sun lunch in warmly welcoming beamed and flagstoned roadside pub alone on former coaching road, central coal fire, steps up to carpeted dining area with high-backed settles; cheerful relaxed service, good value Donnington BB and SBA, no smoking area; popular skittle alley, children welcome, tables in garden, open all day Sun too *(Mrs N W Neill, Brian and Bett Cox, LYM, Joan and Michel Hooper-Immins, Les and Barbara Owen)*

Fosse Manor [A429 S]: Hotel, but with civilised local feel in bar with stripped stone, beamery and local pictures, good value generous food, friendly staff; good garden seating with chessboard game for children, bedrooms *(Mr and Mrs J Curtis)*

☆ ***Queens Head*** [The Square]: Good chatty old local with heavily beamed and flagstoned traditional back bar, high-backed settles, big log fire, horse prints, piped classical or opera, usual games; lots of tables in civilised stripped stone front lounge, good value straightforward fresh food (not Mon evening or Sun), well kept Donnington BB and SBA, mulled wine, friendly helpful service, nice dogs; children welcome, tables outside, occasional jazz Sun lunchtime *(LYM, the Didler, Klaus and Elizabeth Leist, D J Hayman)*

Stroud [SO8504]

Golden Fleece [Nelson St, just E of centre]: Cosy old terrace pub, fairly dark inside, with well kept beer, daily papers, cheerfully musical décor, unobtrusive piped jazz, separate smaller upstairs room *(Dave Irving)*

Lord John [Russell St]: Big airy split-level conversion of former PO sorting office, striking décor with something of a railway theme, tables in alcoves; usual Wetherspoons good value food and wide choice of sensibly priced beers; no children, silenced fruit machines *(Dave Irving)*

Tetbury [ST8993]

Snooty Fox [Market Pl]: Good unusual food in welcoming high-ceilinged hotel lounge with medieval-style chairs and elegant fireplace, restaurant; bedrooms good value *(Patricia A Bruce)*

Tewkesbury [SO8932]

☆ ***Olde Black Bear*** [High St]: County's oldest pub, rambling unpretentious rooms with heavy low beams, lots of timbers, armchairs in front of open fires, bare wood and ancient tiles, plenty of pictures and bric-a-brac, well kept beers inc Courage Directors and Wadworths 6X, friendly staff, enjoyable food all day from lunchtime baguettes up; piped music, quiz nights Weds and Sun; children welcome, picnic-sets and play area in pleasant riverside garden, open all day *(the Didler, Theocsbrian, Gordon Tong, Sue and Mike Todd, Muriel and Peter Gleave, Alan and Paula McCully, LYM)*

Thornbury [ST6390]

Wheatsheaf [Chapel St]: 1930s pub remodelled by friendly youngish licensees, enjoyable generous fresh home cooking inc children's helpings, obliging service, well kept local real ales *(James Morrell)*

Tockington [ST6186]

Swan: Clean, bright and spacious, with beams, standing timbers, bric-a-brac on stripped stone walls, log fire, friendly staff, Bass and Boddingtons, guests such as Greene King or Smiles tapped from the cask, country wines, good range of reasonably priced food; piped music; tables in tree-shaded garden, quiet village *(Charles and Pauline Stride)*

Toddington [SP0432]

Pheasant [A46 Broadway—Winchcombe, junction with A438 and B4077]: Much enlarged, with no smoking area, emphasis on good choice of decent food, Bass and Tetleys; handy for nearby preserved Gloucestershire Warwickshire Railway *(Martin Jennings)*

Tolldown [ST7577]

☆ ***Crown*** [under a mile from M4 junction 18 – A46 towards Bath]: Tidy and attractively pubby heavy-beamed stripped stone bar, good value honest food, quick friendly service, well kept Badger Tanglefoot and Wadworths IPA and 6X, woodburner and coal fire, no smoking area; dominoes, darts, fruit machine, piped music; children in eating area and restaurant, no dogs, good garden with play area; comfortable bedrooms *(Susan and Nigel Wilson, LYM)*

Twyning [SO8737]

☆ ***Fleet*** [Fleet Lane, Twyning Green]: Superb setting at end of quiet lane, with good river views from roomy high-ceilinged bars, interesting boating-theme décor, snug styled as cosy kitchen with Aga, light and airy restaurant, friendly pub atmosphere, good value standard food inc all-day baguettes and burger bar, Whitbreads-related ales and others such as Adnams Regatta, Banks's and Greene King Old Speckled Hen, pleasant staff; tables on terrace and lawn, pets corner; disabled access, boat shop, stop on Tewkesbury—Bredon summer boat run, even own ferry across from Worcs bank (it's a long walk from the B4080); bedrooms *(Martin Jennings, BB, Dave Braisted)*

Tytherington [ST6688]

Swan [Duck St]: Big well furnished family food pub with good choice (all day Sun) from sandwiches, baguettes and baked potatoes to some interesting specials, no smoking area, children's room; huge car park, very busy wknds *(Mr and Mrs P Cowley)*

Upton Cheyney [ST6969]

Upton Inn [signed off A431 at Bitton]: Stripped stone with wall hangings and archways, interesting choice of home-made food, pleasant service, well kept beer, small smart restaurant; tables outside *(Neil and Anita Christopher)*

Westbury on Severn [SO7114]

☆ ***Red Lion*** [A48, corner Bell Lane]: Substantial half-timbered building on busy road but by quiet church-side lane to river, welcoming and well managed; generous interesting home cooking in big dining room with old pews, comfortable bar with button-back wall seats, velvet curtains, baseball cap collection on beams, coal stove, well kept ales such as Bass, Fullers London Pride and SP Doves Delight, decent wine, very friendly service; evening opening 7; handy for Westbury Court gardens (NT) *(BB, Neil and Anita Christopher)*

Westonbirt [ST8690]

Hare & Hounds [A433 SW of Tetbury]: Substantial inn with separate entrance for end turkey-carpeted bar, with high-backed settles, good food (the alternative restaurant menu), Smiles Best and Wadworths 6X, central log-effect gas fire, sporting prints, games in public bar on left; small tweedy more central cocktail bar, pleasant gardens, good value bedrooms, handy for Arboretum *(BB, Meg and Colin Hamilton, Derek and Sylvia Stephenson)*

Whitminster [SO7708]

Fromebridge Mill [A38 nr M5 junction 13]: Large recently renovated mill with attractively extended bar and dining areas, decent reasonably priced food from sandwiches and baked potatoes up inc carvery, friendly helpful staff; picnic-sets out behind with play area, lovely setting overlooking weir *(Charles and Pauline Stride, Mike and Mary Carter, Pauline and Philip Darley, M G Hart)*

Old Forge [A38 1½ miles N of M5 junction 13]: Simple L-shaped beamed pub, part set aside for dining (good inexpensive food); happy staff, four well kept real ales, decent wines; children welcome *(R Huggins, D Irving, E McCall, T McLean)*

Wick [ST7072]

Rose & Crown [High St (A420)]: Busy and roomy Chef & Brewer, plenty of character with dark oak and linked rooms, well kept Courage, Greene King Old Speckled Hen and Wadworths 6X, daily papers, very wide food range (only main meals on Sun); pleasant tables facing village green *(Nigel Long, Dr and*

Mrs M E Wilson, MRSM)

Willersey [SP1039]

Bell [B4632 Cheltenham—Stratford, nr Broadway]: Attractive 14th-c golden stone dining pub, carefully prepared home-made food, good friendly service, well kept ales such as Boddingtons and Wadworths 6X; overlooks delightful village's green and duck pond, lots of tables in big garden *(Alan Cowell)*

Winchcombe [SP0228]

☆ ***Old Corner Cupboard*** [Gloucester St]: Attractive golden stone pub, comfortable stripped-stone lounge bar with heavy-beamed Tudor core, traditional hatch-service lobby, small side smoke room with woodburner in massive stone fireplace, some nice old furnishings and buoyant local atmosphere; enjoyable fresh food inc children's, well kept Boddingtons, Flowers IPA and Original, Fullers London Pride and seasonal local Stanway ales, decent wines, cheerful service, traditional games, partly no smoking restaurant; soft piped music; children in eating areas, tables in back garden, open all day *(John and Jackie Chalcraft, Martin Jennings, Di and Mike Gillam, Martin Jones, BB, B A Dale, LYM)*

☆ ***Plaisterers Arms*** [Abbey Terr]: 18th-c pub with stripped stonework, beams, Hogarth prints and open fire, two front bars both with steps down to dim-lit lower back dining area with tables in stalls, real home cooking, well kept Goffs Jouster; good play area in attractive garden, long and narrow; good value comfortable bedrooms, handy for Sudeley Castle *(BB, John Whitehead, Martin Jones, Neil and Anita Christopher)*

White Hart [High St (B4632)]: Comfortable beamed and timbered stone-built inn with pleasant largely Swedish staff and modern Swedish-style back restaurant, interesting generous food inc all-day bar food and Fri lunchtime smorgasbord buffet, well kept ales such as Flowers Original, Greene King Old Speckled Hen, Stanway and Wadworths 6X, decent wines, daily papers; bedrooms spacious with good facilities *(Guy Vowles, Peter King, Di and Mike Gillam)*

Withington [SP0315]

Kings Head [Kings Head Lane]: Unpretentious local, well kept Hook Norton Best and a changing Wickwar beer tapped from the cask, friendly service, long narrow bar with darts, shove-ha'penny, table skittles and pool, lounge with piano, may be pork pies and pickled eggs; pleasant garden behind *(Pete Baker)*

Woodchester [SO8403]

☆ ***Old Fleece*** [Rooksmoor; A46 a mile S of Stroud – not to be confused with Fleece at Lightpill a little closer in]: Informal bare-boards décor in open-plan line of several big-windowed room areas, largely no smoking, bar on right, restaurant on left (nice rooms), wide choice of good interesting freshly made bar food from unusual lunchtime sandwiches up, well kept Bass, Boddingtons and Greene King Abbot, good wines, local non-alcoholic drinks, good cheerful service once they get to you (tills ready for euros), big log fire, candles, daily papers, stripped stone or dark salmon pink walls; children welcome, two roadside terraces, one with heater *(BB, Carol and Dono Leaman)*

☆ ***Ram*** [Station Rd, South Woodchester]: Attractively priced well kept ales such as Archers Best, John Smiths, Theakstons Old Peculier, Uley Old Spot and several interesting guest beers, in relaxed L-shaped beamed bar with friendly staff, nice mix of traditional furnishings, stripped stonework, bare boards, three open fires, darts, varied menu from sandwiches to steaks, restaurant; children welcome, open all day Sat/Sun, spectacular views from terrace tables *(LYM, R Huggins, D Irving, E McCall, T McLean, Tom and Ruth Rees)*

☆ ***Royal Oak*** [off A46; Church Road, N Woodchester]: Big log fire in huge fireplace, well kept ales such as Bath and Uley, tables in several pleasant areas inc upstairs dining room with great valley view, appealing food (not Sun evening or Mon lunchtime) inc baguettes and some interesting specials; big-screen TV, piped music; children and dogs welcome, open all day Sat *(Derek and Sylvia Stephenson, R Huggins, D Irving, E McCall, T McLean, LYM)*

Woolaston Common [SO5900]

Rising Sun [village signed off A48 Lydney—Chepstow]: Unpretentiously old-fashioned village pub on fringe of Forest of Dean, friendly and welcoming, reasonably priced fresh food (not Weds evening) inc curries, well kept Fullers London Pride, Hook Norton and usually a guest beer, darts and piano in side area (folk nights alternate Tues); seats outside, cl Weds lunchtime *(Pete Baker)*

'Children welcome' means the pub says it lets children inside without any special restriction. If it allows them in, but to restricted areas such as an eating area or family room, we specify this. Places with separate restaurants usually let children use them, hotels usually let them into public areas such as lounges. Some pubs impose an evening time limit – let us know if you find this.

Hampshire

A fat crop of new entries in this favoured county consists of the Crown at Axford (a well run tucked-away country pub with nice food), the Red Lion at Chalton (Hampshire's oldest pub, back in these pages after a break of some years, and currently in fine fettle), the Northbrook Arms nicely placed at East Stratton (a good all-rounder, pleasantly unassuming), the Chestnut Horse at Easton (charming décor, good food, drink and service – likely to become quite a favourite), the cheerful Three Tuns in Romsey (an attractive and very welcoming town pub), the pleasantly opened-up Falcon at Rotherwick (an appealing all-rounder), and the snug and interestingly decorated Three Cups in Stockbridge (again, good all round). Among the wide choice of other good pubs in the county, current favourites include the Oak at Bank in the New Forest (new licensee should do well), the very welcoming Sun at Bentworth (lots of good beers, nice food, charming décor), the Red Lion at Boldre (good interesting food, lots to look at), the Jolly Sailor at Bursledon (lovely waterside position), the Fox & Hounds at Crawley (an engaging all-rounder in an interesting building), the Star at East Tytherley (good often imaginative food, and nice to stay at), the cheerfully rustic Royal Oak surrounded by the New Forest at Fritham, the Hawkley Inn at Hawkley (interesting beers, well liked food), the prettily placed and attractive Bush at Ovington (it earns a Food Award this year), the Ship at Owslebury (good for families in summer), the charmingly run Trooper above Petersfield (this year gaining a Food Award and Place to Stay Award, along with its existing Beer Award – enjoyable food, too), the friendly Fleur de Lys at Pilley (nice food), the marvellously unchanging and unpretentious Harrow at Steep, the Brushmakers Arms at Upham (a consistently enjoyable and well run all-rounder), and the Wykeham Arms in Winchester (delightful atmosphere, good food and drink, and a nice place to stay in). For a rewarding meal out, the Star at East Tytherley takes the title of Hampshire Dining Pub of the Year. The Lucky Dip section at the end of the chapter is a very strong one this year: some 200 entries, 80 of them new. Ones to note particularly are the Tally Ho at Broughton, White Buck at Burley, Hampshire Arms at Crondall, Queens Head at Dogmersfield, Hampshire Bowman at Dundridge, Turf Cutters Arms at East Boldre, George at East Meon, Cricketers at Easton, New Forest at Emery Down, Ship at Langstone, Red Shoot at Linwood, Jolly Farmer in Locks Heath, Yew Tree at Lower Wield (too predominantly a restaurant for the main entries, but well worth knowing), Fishermans Rest in Lymington, Trusty Servant at Minstead, Alice Lisle at Rockford, Castle Inn at Rowlands Castle, Greyhound, Grosvenor and White Hart in Stockbridge, Cricketers Arms at Tangley, Bear & Ragged Staff at Timsbury, Crown at Upton, Hoddington Arms at Upton Grey, George at Vernham Dean and Chequers at Well. Drinks in Hampshire pubs are generally more expensive than the national average: the Brushmakers Arms at Upham and Chestnut Horse at Easton both undercut the average by a very comfortable margin, as does the Flower Pots at Cheriton (brewing its own good beer, available elsewhere as Cheriton). Gales and Ringwood, the county's two best-known brewers, are too big to benefit from the 14p cut in

beer duty. Other smaller local brewers which can pass this on to customers include Itchen Valley, fff, Hampshire and Becketts. Hampshire pubs tend to be extraordinarily dog-friendly: 90% of the main entries allow dogs in the bar.

AXFORD SU6043 Map 2

Crown 🍷

B3046 S of Basingstoke

This tucked-away country pub rambles around a central servery which has well kept Adnams Best and Flowers IPA on handpump, a good interesting wine list with a nice choice by the glass, and staff who keep a friendly watchful eye out for their customers' enjoyment. The three compact rooms open together enough to build a cheerfully chatty atmosphere, but each keeps its own character – appealing late 19th-c local villager photographs, cream walls, patterned carpet and stripped boards on the left, for instance, abstract prints on pale terracotta walls and rush carpeting on the right; the black labrador is called Screwball. Furnishings are largely stripped tables and chapel chairs, and each room has a small log fire. Enjoyable food might include broccoli and stilton soup (£3.75), grilled sardines (£4.50), filled baguettes (from £4.50), pâté with mango and cranberry chutney or ploughman's (£4.75), tomato, mozzarella and pesto salad (£4.95), tiger prawns sautéed in garlic butter (£6.50), cod or cumberland sausage (£7.50), pecorino and asparagus ravioli with pesto (£7.95), crispy marinated duck breast (£10.95), sirloin steak (£11.95), and puddings such as crème brûlée (£3.75); daily papers; may be unobtrusive piped music. There are picnic-sets out on the front terrace, others on the sloping shrub-sheltered grass behind – and they grow some herbs for the kitchen. *(Recommended by Andy and Jill Kassube, Tony and Wendy Hobden, Phyl and Jack Street, Lynn Sharpless)*

Mercury Taverns ~ Manager Simon Sheasby ~ Real ale ~ Bar food (12-2.30, 7-9.30; not Sun evening) ~ Restaurant ~ (01256) 389492 ~ Children welcome ~ Dogs welcome ~ Open 12-3, 6-11; 12-3, 7-10.30 Sun

BANK SU2807 Map 2

Oak

Signposted just off A35 SW of Lyndhurst

In a forest and pony setting, this friendly pub always has a good mix of customers – ramblers, lunching couples, and plenty of locals. On either side of the door in the bay windows of the L-shaped bar are built-in green-cushioned seats, and on the right, two or three little pine-panelled booths with small built-in tables and bench seats. The rest of the bar has more floor space, with candles in individual brass holders on a line of stripped old and blond newer tables set against the wall on bare floorboards, and more at the back; some low beams and joists, fishing rods, spears, a boomerang, and old ski poles on the ceiling, and on the walls are brass platters, heavy knives, stuffed fish, and guns; a big fireplace. Cushioned milk churns along the bar counter, and little red lanterns among hop bines above the bar and country wines; piped music. Well kept Bass, Holdens Black Country Special, Ringwood Best, and a couple of guests like Black Sheep or Hop Back Summer Lightning on handpump; darts, shove-ha'penny, and dominoes. Bar food includes good lunchtime sandwiches (from £3.95), filled baked potatoes (from £4.25), and ploughman's (from £4.95), as well as home-made soup (£3.95), deep-fried brie with raspberry coulis (£4.75), home-cooked ham and eggs or roasted vegetable couscous with harissa-style dressing (£6.95), local sausages cooked in onion sauce (£7.45), fresh cornish cod in beer and lemon batter (£7.95), home-made steak, kidney and ale pie (£8.95), steaks (from £12.50), daily specials, and puddings like fruit crumble or sticky ginger bread pudding with ginger wine and brandy sauce (£3.95). The side garden has picnic-sets and long tables and benches by the big yew trees. *(Recommended by Diana Brumfit, M Joyner, Jess and George Cowley, D Lamping, I Sachdev, Dennis Jenkin, Alan and Paula McCully, Lynn Sharpless)*

Free house ~ Licensee Tom Finlay ~ Real ale ~ Bar food ~ (023) 8028 2350 ~ Children in eating area of bar and restaurant ~ Dogs welcome ~ Open 11.30-2.30 (3 Sat), 6-11; 12-3, 7-10.30 Sun

BEAUWORTH SU5624 Map 2

Milbury's ■

Turn off A272 Winchester/Petersfield at Beauworth ¾, Bishops Waltham 6 signpost, then continue straight on past village

There are plenty of reminders here of the great age of this pub. One is a 600-year-old well with a massive 250-year-old treadmill – if you drop an ice cube into the spotlit shaft it takes eight full seconds to reach the bottom, which apparently means it is 300 feet deep. There are also sturdy beams and panelling, stripped masonry, interesting old furnishings, and massive open fireplaces (with good winter log fires). Well kept Cheriton Diggers Gold and Best, fff Altons Pride, Hop Back Summer Lightning, Theakstons Old Peculier, and a beer named for the pub on handpump, Addlestone's cider, 20 malt whiskies, and country wines. Decent bar food at lunchtime includes sandwiches (from £2.95), home-made soup (£3.50), filled tortilla wraps (from £4.25), ploughman's (£4.95), daily specials, and steaks (from £12.95), with evening dishes such as grilled goats cheese with a herb crust (£4.25), vegetarian chilli (£7.95), strips of chicken in cajun spices (£8.95), chargrilled venison steak with berry jus (£9.25), and half a crispy aromatic duck with pancakes (£10.50); children's menu (£3.95). A black mark is that they may try to get you to leave a credit card with them while you eat. One area is no smoking (but is not always open); piped music, fruit machine, skittle alley. The name of this pub was at first only a nickname, coming from the Millbarrow, a Bronze Age cemetery surrounding it, briefly famous back in 1833 when a Norman hoard of 6,000 silver coins was found here. The garden has fine views over rolling downland countryside, and there are plenty of surrounding walks – the South Downs Way passes the door, the Wayfarers Walk is nearby, and there's a strenuous walk around Old Winchester Hill. *(Recommended by Charles and Pauline Stride, S G N Bennett, Mrs Thomas, Val and Alan Green, Klaus and Elizabeth Leist, Ann and Colin Hunt, Tracey and Stephen Groves, S F Parrinder, Martin and Karen Wake, Susan and John Douglas)*

Free house ~ Licensee Lenny Larden ~ Real ale ~ Bar food ~ (01962) 771248 ~ Children in eating area of bar and restaurant ~ Dogs welcome ~ Open 12-11(10.30 Sun)

BENTWORTH SU6740 Map 2

Sun ■

Sun Hill; from the A339 coming from Alton the first turning takes you there direct; or in village follow Shalden 2¼, Alton 4¼ signpost

On a miserable weekday lunchtime, one reader was delighted to find a roaring fire and candles lit on all the tables in this tucked away and especially friendly pub. There's a good chatty, cosy atmosphere (not spoilt by any noisy games machines or piped music), in the two little traditional communicating rooms, high-backed antique settles, pews and schoolroom chairs, olde-worlde prints and blacksmith's tools on the walls, and bare boards and scrubbed deal tables on the left; big fireplaces. An arch leads to a brick-floored room with another open fire and hanging baskets. Tasty home-made bar food includes sandwiches, chicken in ginger (£6.95), chicken fajitas, sweet and sour pork or haddock bake with cheese (£7.25), steak and kidney pie or liver and bacon with onion gravy (£7.95), poached salmon (£8.25), venison in Guinness (£9.95), and minted lamb steak (£10.95). They have around eight well kept real ales on handpump such as Brakspears Bitter, Bunces Pigswill, Cheriton Pots Ale, Courage Directors, Gales HSB, Ringwood Best, Youngs Special, and a beer from Hampshire named after the pub; several malt whiskies. There are seats out in front and in the back garden, and pleasant nearby walks. *(Recommended by Martin and Karen Wake, Lynn Sharpless, J Hale, Ann and Colin Hunt, K Brewster, Simon Fox, R Lake, the Didler, Ian Phillips, Mark and Liz Wallace, Andrew Scarr)*

Free house ~ Licensee Mary Holmes ~ Real ale ~ Bar food ~ (01420) 562338 ~ Children in eating area of bar ~ Dogs welcome ~ Open 12-3, 6-11; 12-10.30 Sun

BOLDRE SZ3198 Map 2

Red Lion ★ 🍷

Village signposted from A337 N of Lymington

Very well run, this popular New Forest pub has ponies strolling by, and is a fine area for walking with 1,000 acres of Royden Wood Nature Reserve. The neatly kept four black-beamed rooms are filled with heavy urns, platters, needlework, rural landscapes, and so forth, taking in farm tools, heavy-horse harness, needlework, gin-traps and even ferocious-looking man-traps along the way; the central room has a profusion of chamber-pots, and an end room has pews, wheelback chairs and tapestried stools, and a dainty collection of old bottles and glasses in the window by the counter; most of the pub is no smoking. There's a fine old cooking range in the cosy little bar, and two good log fires. Enjoyable, if not cheap, bar food includes sandwiches (from £3.95; club sandwich £6), home-made soup (£4), game pâté with cranberry sauce (£5.60), home-made salmon and crab fishcakes with a mild anchovy sauce (£5.80), ploughman's (£6.50), salad bowls (from £7.20), sausages of the day with rich gravy (£8.90), home-made steak and kidney pie or prawn and asparagus pasta in a lemon pepper and garlic cream sauce (£9.90), salmon fillet with a grape, paprika and white wine sauce (£10.20), half a crispy duckling (£10.90), daily specials like creamy fish pie (£9.60), coq au vin (£10.10), and grilled fillet of hake wrapped in bacon on a bed of leeks and squid laced with white wine and garlic sauce (£11.30), and puddings like spotted dick or whisky bread and butter pudding (£4.25). Well kept Bass and Flowers IPA on handpump, and an extensive wine list. In summer, the flowering tubs and hanging baskets are pretty, and there are seats in the back garden. No children inside. *(Recommended by Phyl and Jack Street, Sally and Aidan Vine, Martin and Karen Wake, D Lamping, I Sachdev, M Joyner, Nigel and Anna Boden, Lynn Sharpless, G L Carlisle, Alan and Paula McCully, Mrs J L Wyatt, Miss J F Reay, Michael and Marion Buchanan, Joan and Michel Hooper-Immins, Martin Weinberg, Mr and Mrs W D Borthwick, Peter Saville, A D Marsh)*

Eldridge Pope ~ Tenant Vince Kernick ~ Real ale ~ Bar food (12-2.30, 6.30-9.30) ~ Restaurant ~ (01590) 673177 ~ Open 11-11; 12-10.30 Sun

BRAMDEAN SU6127 Map 2

Fox

A272 Winchester—Petersfield

Mr and Mrs Inder are a good team – he is in the kitchen cooking the very good food, and she keeps a friendly and watchful eye over everything in the bar. It's a civilised dining pub with a relaxed atmosphere, and the open-plan and carefully modernised bar has black beams, tall stools with proper backrests around the L-shaped counter, and comfortably cushioned wall pews and wheelback chairs; the fox motif shows in a big painting over the fireplace, and on much of the decorative china. At least one area is no smoking. Much emphasis is placed on the popular food, which at lunchtime includes sandwiches, soup (£2.95), pâté, fresh grilled sardines or baked brie in filo pastry with redcurrant jelly (£4.95), poached pear, blue cheese and crispy bacon salad (£5.95), fresh dressed crab (£6.95), deep-fried fillet of cod in beer batter (£8.95), and grilled lamb cutlets, calves liver and bacon or fresh grilled fillet of plaice (£10.95), with evening dishes like scallops with bacon or king prawns (£6.95), breast of chicken with coarse grain mustard sauce (£10.95), fresh whole grilled bass (£13.95), steaks (from £13.95), and half a duck with orange gravy (£14.95); Sunday roast (£10.95). Well kept Greene King Abbot on handpump. At the back of the building is a walled-in terraced area, and a spacious lawn spreading among the fruit trees, with a good play area – trampoline as well as swings and a seesaw. No children inside. Good surrounding walks. *(Recommended by Colin and Janet Roe, W A Evershed, Phyl and Jack Street, Michael and Robin Inskip, John and Joan Calvert, Betty Laker, Charles and Pauline Stride, Geoffrey and Brenda Wilson)*

Greene King ~ Tenants Ian and Jane Inder ~ Real ale ~ Bar food (not winter Sun or Mon evenings) ~ Restaurant ~ (01962) 771363 ~ Open 11-3, 6-11; 12-3, 7-10.30 Sun; closed winter Sun and Mon evenings

BURITON SU7320 Map 2

Five Bells

Village signposted off A3 S of Petersfield

New licensees have taken over this country pub and have gently refurbished the bars. There are several interesting rooms, and the low-beamed lounge on the left with its terracotta walls, hops on beams, new curtains, and chunky white candles on the tables, is dominated by a big log fire; the public side has some ancient stripped masonry, a woodburning stove, and old-fashioned tables; an end alcove has cushioned pews and board games. Bar food now includes home-made soup (£3.75), ploughman's (from £4.50), filled baguettes (from £4.95), interesting summer salads (snack or starter £4.95, main course £8.95), roasted vegetable or meaty lasagne (£6.95), home-made steak and kidney pie (£7.95), red bream fillets with caramelised onions and pesto sauce (£10.95), half a roast shoulder of lamb (£12.95), puddings such as banoffi pie or bread and butter pudding, and children's dishes (from £3.50); the dining room is no smoking. Well kept Badger Best, Fursty Ferret, Tanglefoot, and K&B Sussex on handpump, and decent wines with several by the glass. Fruit machine, and piped music. There are seats on the informal lawn that stretches back above the building, with more on sheltered terraces. The converted stables are self-catering cottages. *(Recommended by Mark Percy, Lesley Mayoh, Lynn Sharpless, W A Evershed, Val and Alan Green, Mike and Alison Stevens, Sheila Rowell, Geoffrey Johns, Lord Sandhurst, P R and S A White, Shirley Mackenzie, Ian Phillips)*

Badger ~ Managers Joyce and Hughen Riley ~ Real ale ~ Bar food (12-2(2.30 Sun), 6-9(8 Mon, 9.30 Sat) ~ Restaurant (Fri/Sat evenings and Sun lunch) ~ (01730) 263584 ~ Children in eating area of bar and restaurant ~ Dogs allowed in bar ~ Live band every Weds ~ Open 11-3, 5.30-11; 12-3, 7-10.30 Sun

BURSLEDON SU4809 Map 2

Jolly Sailor ♀

2 miles from M27 junction 8; then A27 towards Sarisbury, then just before going under railway bridge turn right towards Bursledon Station; it's best to park round here and walk as the lane up from the station is now closed to cars

In a lovely spot overlooking the River Hamble and all the boats, this very popular, well run pub has tables and chairs in the courtyard under the big yew tree or on the covered wooden jetty looking over the harbour. The airy front bar has ship pictures, nets and shells, as well as windsor chairs and settles on the floorboards, and there are views of the water from the window seat. The atmospheric beamed and flagstoned back bar, with pews and settles by its huge fireplace, is a fair bit older. Enjoyable bar food includes good home-made soup (£3.40), sandwiches (from £3.95; popular crab and prawn with lemon and dill mayonnaise £5), greek salad (£4.95), cheese platter ploughman's (£6.50), home-cooked ham with real ale pickle (£5.50), sausages with onion gravy (£8.50), seafood pie (£8.95), minted lamb shoulder (£10.95), sirloin steak (£11.95), and children's menu (£3.50), with daily specials such as moroccan lamb casserole with herby couscous (£8.95), whole trout fillets with crab topped with toasted almonds (£9.95), and steamed whole bass with tomato butter and vanilla dressing (£12.95). The dining area is no smoking. Well kept Badger Best, Golden Champion, and Tanglefoot, and K&B Sussex, and Gribble Fursty Ferret on handpump, eight wines by the glass, freshly squeezed juice, and country wines; fruit machine, Jenga, Connect Four, and piped music. The path down to the pub (and of course back up again) from the lane is steep. *(Recommended by JP, PP, Ian Phillips, the Didler, Colin McKerrow, Alan Thomas, John Saville, J A Cheverton, George Little, Stephen, Julie and Hayley Brown, Nigel and Sue Foster, Ann and Colin Hunt, Tom and Ruth Rees, Betsy and Peter Little, Charles and Pauline Stride, Roger and Pauline Pearce, Tony and Wendy Hobden, Jess and George Cowley)*

Badger ~ Managers Adrian Jenkins and Jackie Cosens ~ Real ale ~ Bar food (12-9.30) ~ (023) 8040 5557 ~ Children in no smoking area ~ Dogs allowed in bar ~ Open 11-11; 12-10.30 Sun; closed 25 Dec

CHALTON SU7315 Map 2

Red Lion

Village signposted E of A3 Petersfield—Horndean

Particularly pretty – especially in summer with its colourful hanging baskets – this timbered, newly thatched pub is Hampshire's oldest and was first licensed in 1503. The most characterful part is the heavy-beamed and panelled front bar with high-backed traditional settles and elm tables and an ancient inglenook fireplace with a frieze of burnished threepenny bits set into its mantelbeam; the lounge and dining room are no smoking. Good bar food includes sandwiches or filled baguettes (from £3.30), filled baked potatoes (from £4.20), and ploughman's (from £4.75), plus lots of daily specials such as home-made stilton and broccoli soup (£3.75), home-made oyster mushroom stroganoff (£6.75), braised lambs kidneys with sausage and mushrooms in mustard sauce (£8.40), home-made steak in ale pie (£8.55), venison stew or roasted lamb shank (£8.75), baked whole bass with ginger and spring onions (£10.30), grilled skate wing with caper butter (£10.95), beef wellington (£13.75), and puddings like coffee chocolate log, treacle tart or strawberry shortbread (£3.50). You are offered a choice of potatoes: colcannon (creamed potato with leeks, cabbage and butter), dauphinoise, cheesy, baked or chips. There are also various toppings for fish: lime, coconut and coriander mayonnaise, tomato, cucumber and onion salsa, tangy lemon chutney or ginger and sweet pepper glaze. Well kept Gales Butser, GB, HSB, Winter Brew, and a guest like Shepherd Neame Old Spitfire or Wells Bombardier on handpump, country wines, and over 50 malt whiskies; piped music. The garden is pretty in summer and the pub is popular with walkers and riders as it is fairly close to the extensive Queen Elizabeth Country Park and about half a mile down the lane from an Iron Age farm and settlement; it's only about 20 minutes to the car ferry, too. *(Recommended by Ann and Colin Hunt, Ian Phillips, Tony and Wendy Hobden)*

Gales ~ Managers Mick and Mary McGee ~ Real ale ~ Bar food (not Sun evening) ~ Restaurant ~ (023) 9259 2246 ~ Children in restaurant ~ Dogs welcome ~ Open 11-3, 6-11; 12-3, 7-10.30 Sun; closed evenings 25 and 26 Dec

CHERITON SU5828 Map 2

Flower Pots ★

Pub just off B3046 (main village road) towards Beauworth and Winchester; OS Sheet 185 map reference 581282

The unusual name of this unspoilt village local comes from the fact that it once belonged to the retired head gardener of nearby Avington Park. There are two little rooms with a wide mix of customers and no noisy games machines or piped music, and the one on the left feels almost like someone's front room, with pictures of hounds and ploughmen on its striped wallpaper, bunches of flowers, and a horse and foal and other ornaments on the mantelpiece over a small log fire; it can get smoky in here. Behind the servery there's disused copper filtering equipment, and lots of hanging gin-traps, drag-hooks, scaleyards and other ironwork. Good value straightforward bar food includes sandwiches (from £2.20; toasties from £2.50; big baps from £3), winter home-made soup (£2.80), filled baked potatoes (from £3.90), and hotpots such as lamb and apricot, chilli or beef stew (from £5.20); popular Indian dishes on Wednesday evenings. The menu may be restricted at weekend lunchtimes. From the Cheriton Brewhouse, they offer their own Diggers Gold, Pots Ale and Cheriton Best Bitter tapped from casks behind the bar. The neat extended plain public bar (where there's a covered well) has cribbage, shove-ha'penny and dominoes. On the pretty front and back lawns are some old-fashioned seats – very useful in fine weather as it can quickly fill up inside; they sometimes have morris dancers out here in summer. The pub is near the site of one of the final battles of the

Civil War. No children inside. *(Recommended by Jenny Cridland, Gordon Cooper, Ann and Colin Hunt, Pamela and Merlyn Horswell, Charlie Harris, T G Thomas, Val and Alan Green, Lynn Sharpless, Basil Cheesenham, Peter Meister, S G N Bennett, Dave Holmes, Jess and George Cowley, Tony and Wendy Hobden, JP, PP, Patrick Hancock, the Didler, Les Trusler, Colin and Janet Roe, Mark Percy, Lesley Mayoh, P R and S A White, Carol and Dono Leaman, Ron Shelton, Simon Collett-Jones, John and Annabel Hampshire)*

Own brew ~ Licensees Jo and Patricia Bartlett ~ Real ale ~ Bar food (not Sun evening or bank hol Mon evenings) ~ No credit cards ~ (01962) 771318 ~ Dogs welcome ~ Open 12-2.30, 6-11; 12-3, 7-10.30 Sun ~ Bedrooms: £40S/£60S

CRAWLEY SU4234 Map 2

Fox & Hounds

Village signposted from A272 and B3420 NW of Winchester

In a village of fine old houses (and a pretty duck pond), this solidly constructed building is one of the most striking with its steep and elaborately carved gable ends, and not one but two jettied and timbered upper storeys, each in turn jutting further out. It's a very popular pub and much enjoyed by many of our readers. The beamed rooms are warmed by three log fires, there's a relaxed atmosphere, evening candlelight, a mix of attractive wooden tables and chairs, helpful and friendly staff, well kept Wadworths IPA, 6X, and seasonal ales, and a guest such as Adnams or Bass on handpump; interesting wines. Using fresh local produce, the very good bar food might include sandwiches, cream of broccoli and watercress soup (£3.95), chicken liver pâté with home-made pickle (£5.25), chargrilled pepper, tomato and brie crostini (£5.50), pork and leek sausages with onion gravy (£6.95), marinated salmon with black tagliatelle (£6.25), smoked haddock in a grain mustard sauce (£7.45), liver and bacon (£7.95), thai chicken curry or home-made faggots (£8.50), wild mushroom tortellini with garlic and herb sauce (£8.95), seared tuna with herb oil (£12.50), duck breast with plum and apple sauce on rösti potatoes (£13.25), and chargrilled sirloin steak with peppercorn sauce topped with blue cheese (£13.95). Summer barbecues in the garden. *(Recommended by John and Joan Calvert, Madeleine and Keith Bright, Mr and Mrs A G Leece, Phyl and Jack Street, Peter Jacobs, Peter B Brown, T Leeson, Mr and Mrs R Porter, Mrs J Purry, Lynn Sharpless)*

Free house ~ Licensees Richard and Kathryn Crawford ~ Real ale ~ Bar food (12-2, 6-9(9.30 Fri/Sat) ~ Restaurant ~ (01962) 776006 ~ Children in eating area of bar ~ Dogs welcome ~ Open 11-3, 6-11; 12-3, 6-10.30 Sun; closed 25 Dec

DROXFORD SU6018 Map 2

White Horse

4 miles along A32 from Wickham

Set in good rolling country for walks, this rambling 16th-c inn is run by friendly licensees. The atmospheric lounge bar is made up of several small cosy rooms – low beams, bow windows, alcoves, and log fires, while the public bar is larger and more straightforward: pool, darts, table football, TV, cribbage, dominoes, shove-ha'penny, and CD juke box. At lunchtime, well liked bar food might include sandwiches (from £2), baguettes (from £2.50), filled baked potatoes (from £2.50), and ploughman's (from £3.75); there's also good home-made soup (£2.50), duck in Cointreau pâté (£4), portuguese sardines in garlic butter (£7), greek-style feta cheese salad, vegetable curry or spicy cumberland sausages (£7.25), steaks (from £9), daily specials such as pork hock in cider or beef roulade stuffed with bacon and sausage (£8), and puddings like rhubarb crumble or black cherry cheesecake (from £2.50). Two dining rooms are no smoking. Well kept Greene King IPA, Abbot, Old Speckled Hen, and Ruddles Best on handpump; several malt whiskies. One of the cubicles in the gents' overlooks an illuminated well. There are tables in a secluded flower-filled courtyard comfortably sheltered by the building's back wings. *(Recommended by Phyl and Jack Street, Ann and Colin Hunt, Dr Paull Khan, Lynn Sharpless, Prof and Mrs Tony Palmer, W A Evershed, Esther and John Sprinkle, Charlie Harris, Ian Phillips, Simon Collett-Jones)*

Greene King ~ Tenant Paul Young ~ Real ale ~ Bar food (all day Sun; not 25/26 Dec)

~ Restaurant ~ (01489) 877490 ~ Children welcome ~ Dogs allowed in bar ~ Open 11-11; 12-10.30 Sun ~ Bedrooms: £25(£40B)/£35(£50B)

EAST STRATTON SU5339 Map 2

Northbrook Arms

Brown sign to pub off A33 4 miles S of A303 junction

A substantial brick inn with outbuildings (one at the back now a nearly new clothes shop), this looks across a quiet lane to a neat lawn with picnic-sets by an old horse-drawn plough – a nice spot, in a small thatched village. Inside has been opened into an unpretentious L-shaped area: blond wheelback chairs and solid square pale-varnished tables on quarry-tiles on the right, with a log fire, and a carpeted dining area on the left. Big windows, cream walls, a large mirror and fresh flowers give an airy, uncluttered atmosphere, and the friendly traditional licensees (and dog) make everyone feel at home. The enjoyable food might include soup (£2.95), sandwiches (£3.50), pâté (£4.25), ploughman's (£5.95), toad in the hole or mushroom and watercress lasagne (£6.95), spicy beef with onion and pepper strips on salad with a lemon and yoghurt dressing or vegetable pasta bake (£7.95), steak and kidney pie or chicken in a mild fruity curry sauce (£8.95), rolled plaice on shredded vegetables with tagliatelle and a lemon and parsley sauce (£9.95), and sirloin steak with a creamy mushroom sauce (£12.95). There is also a separate restaurant. Well kept Cottage Best, Gales GB and HSB and Otter Bitter on handpump, nice bottled beers and decent house wines. The piped radio didn't seem annoying in this setting; silenced fruit machine, darts, shove-ha'penny, cribbage and dominoes, and skittle alley. We haven't yet heard from readers who have stayed here, but would expect this to be a nice place to stay in. *(Recommended by Lynn Sharpless)*

Free house ~ Licensees Maurice and Jean Caine ~ Restaurant ~ (01962) 774150 ~ Children in eating area of bar until 7pm ~ Dogs allowed in bar ~ Open 12-3, 6-11; 12-3, 7-10.30 Sun; closed evenings 25 and 26 Dec ~ Bedrooms: £35/£50

EAST TYTHERLEY SU2927 Map 2

Star

Off B3084 N of Romsey, via Lockerley – turn off by railway crossing near Mottisfont Abbey

Hampshire Dining Pub of the Year

Readers enjoy staying in this popular 16th-c pub and the comfortable cottage-style bedrooms overlook the village cricket pitch (which is used every Saturday through the summer); good nearby walks. The bar has a mix of comfortable furnishings, log fires in attractive fireplaces, and horsebrasses and saddlery; there's a lower lounge bar, and a cosy and pretty no smoking restaurant. Good, interesting bar food includes home-made soup (£3.25), sandwiches or toasted focaccia (from £3.50; focaccia with mozzarella, parma ham and pesto £5.95), filled baked potatoes (from £3.90), linguini with artichokes, french beans, mange tout and roasted tomato oil (£5; main course £11.50), smooth liver pâté with onion confit (£5.25), beef, roquefort and juniper pie (£7.50), millefeuille of scallops with café de paris butter and sweet peppers (£7.50; main course £15), faggots with pea and potato purée (£7.95), lambs liver, mash and bacon (£8.95), steaks (from £12), venison steak and braised red cabbage with blood orange sauce (£14), and fried emperor fish with a peanut crust and bok choi (£14.50). You can eat the same menu in the bar or restaurant; kind, attentive staff. Well kept Ringwood Best, and a guest beer, several malt whiskies, and a thoughtful wine list with 12 by the glass; piped music, shove-ha'penny, and a newly decorated skittle alley for private dining. There are seats on the smartly furnished terrace, and a children's play area with new play equipment using local reclaimed wood. *(Recommended by Phyl and Jack Street, Angela Cerfontyn, Prof H G Allen, Prof and Mrs Tony Palmer, A D Marsh, Nick and Meriel Cox, Mike and Heather Watson, Derek Harvey-Piper, Mrs J Purry, Val and Alan Green)*

Free house ~ Licensees Paul and Sarah Bingham ~ Real ale ~ Bar food ~ Restaurant ~ (01794) 340225 ~ Children in eating area of bar ~ Dogs allowed in bar ~ Open

11-2.30, 6-11; 12-2.30, 7-10.30 Sun; 11-2.30, 6-11 Sat in winter; closed Mon except bank hols; 26 Dec ~ Bedrooms: £45S/£60S

EASTON SU5132 Map 2

Chestnut Horse 🍷

Village signposted off B3047 Kings Worthy—Itchen Abbas; bear left in village

All opened together, this gently up-market 16th-c pub has kept the cosy feel of small separate rooms, with a really snug décor: candles burning on all the tables even at lunchtime, dark comfortable furnishings, black beams and joists hung with all sorts of jugs, mugs and chamber-pots, lots of attractive waterfowl and other country pictures on the cream or dusky green walls, some panelling, log fires in cottagey fireplaces. Good generous creative food (cooked to order, so there may be a wait) might include home-made soup (£3.95), sandwiches or grilled open sandwiches on ciabatta (from £4.50), deep-fried brie with summer fruit coulis (£4.95), hot crispy duck with mango dressing or ploughman's (£6.95), local ham and free range eggs (£8.95), pork and leek sausages on wholegrain mustard mash with deep-fried leeks and rich onion and red wine jus (£9.95), popular fish in beer batter (£9.95; massive £12.95), steaks (from £12.95), daily specials such as baked scallops with spinach and cheese (£6.95), baked cod rarebit (£11.95), calves liver on crispy bacon and black pudding (£14.95), and confit of duck with bacon and apple mash and port jus or grilled fillets of sea bream with sweet chilli dressing and fresh lime (£15.95), and puddings like home-made sticky toffee pudding, chocolate mouse or crème brûlée (£4.95); you must book to be sure of a table at weekends. They also do a Sunday brunch, from 10am; the restaurant areas are no smoking. Courage Best, Fullers London Pride, Youngs Special and a beer brewed locally for the pub on handpump, decent wines including champagne by the glass, good nicely served coffee, a buoyant yet relaxed atmosphere, friendly licensees and efficient young staff; on our visit, piped radio was fairly unobtrusive; cribbage. There are good tables out on a smallish sheltered back terrace with pretty flower tubs and baskets; this sleepy village is handy for Itchen Valley walks. *(Recommended by Cynthia and Stephen Fisher, Lynn Sharpless, Prof H G Allen, Keith and Sheila Baxter, Phyl and Jack Street, Ron Shelton, Sheila and Robert Robinson, Susan and John Douglas)*

Free house ~ Licensee John Holland ~ Real ale ~ Bar food (12-2.30, 7-9.30; 12-8 Sun) ~ Restaurant ~ (01962) 779257 ~ Children in eating area of bar and restaurant ~ Dogs allowed in bar ~ Open 11-3, 5.30-11; 12-10.30 Sun

EVERSLEY SU7861 Map 2

Golden Pot

Eversley Centre; B3272

The masses of colourful flowering tubs, pots and window boxes in front of this little brick building carry on through the summer and right into autumn. Inside, there's a comfortable atmosphere in the different spreading areas, bowls of lilies, candles in bottles on the tables, and one particularly snug part by the log-effect gas fire, with two armchairs and a sofa; piped music. From quite a choice, the bar food might include baked field mushrooms with melted stilton (£4.75), warm goats cheese and lentil salad or bacon and onion rösti with eggs or cheese (£6.50), ham and eggs or lambs kidneys with a mustard and brandy sauce (£6.95), salmon kedgeree or wild venison and red wine sausages on horseradish mash with onion gravy (£7.50), cajun chicken (£7.75), pork schnitzel (£8.95), tiger prawns in garlic, chilli and ginger (£9.95), steaks (from £10.75), and puddings such as chocolate, banana and toffee mousse or profiteroles (from £4.25); on Monday they hold a rösti evening (from £6.75). Well kept Greene King IPA and Ruddles Best, and a guest such as Wadworths 6X or Wychwood Hobgoblin on handpump, and 12 wines by the glass; piped music. The pretty restaurant is no smoking. There are some picnic-sets under a pergola overlooking fields as well as in front by the car park. *(Recommended by Martin and Karen Wake, KC, Ian Phillips, P J Ridley, Philip and June Caunt, Lynn Sharpless)*

Greene King ~ Lease Justin Winstanley ~ Real ale ~ Bar food (not winter Sun evening) ~ Restaurant ~ (0118) 973 2104 ~ Pianist/vocalist/guitarist Mon evening ~ Dogs allowed in bar ~ Open 11-3(3.30 Sat), 6-11; 12-3.30, 7-10.30 Sun

FRITHAM SU2314 Map 2

Royal Oak

Village signed from exit roundabout, M27 junction 1; quickest via B3078, then left and straight through village; head for Eyeworth Pond

The bar staff in this charming cob and brick-built thatched pub always offer a cheery welcome to the good mix of customers, and there's a proper traditional atmosphere. The three neatly kept, simple bar rooms have antique wheelback, spindleback, and other old chairs and stools with colourful seats around solid tables on the new oak flooring, prints and pictures involving local characters on the white walls, restored panelling and black beams, and two roaring log fires. The simple lunchtime food consists of freshly made soup (£3) and ploughman's with home-made pâté and quiche, and home cooked ham (£4), and sometimes home-made scotch eggs or sausage parcels; they do evening meals on Mondays or by arrangement. Well kept Ringwood Best and Fortyniner plus Cheriton Pots, Hop Back Summer Lightning, and Palmers Dorset Gold tapped from the cask; darts, dominoes, and cribbage, and the back bar has quite a few books. There are lovely views across forest and farmland and regular summer weekend barbecues and hog roasts in the neatly kept big garden (they have a marquee for bad weather); it's also part of a working farm, and there are animals at close quarters – plus ponies and pigs on the nearby green. Fine surrounding walks. *(Recommended by the Didler, Philip and Susan Philcox, Pete Baker, Lynn Sharpless, George Atkinson, R J Walden, Ann and Colin Hunt, JP, PP, Keith and Suzie Stevens, Tracey and Stephen Groves)*

Free house ~ Licensees Neil and Pauline McCulloch ~ Real ale ~ Bar food (lunchtime – though see text) ~ No credit cards ~ (023) 8081 2606 ~ Children welcome but must be well behaved ~ Dogs welcome ~ Occasional local folk ~ Open 11-3, 6-11; 11-11 Sat; 12-10.30 Sun

HAWKLEY SU7429 Map 2

Hawkley Inn

Take first right turn off B3006, heading towards Liss ¾ mile from its junction with A3; then after nearly 2 miles take first left turn into Hawkley village – Pococks Lane; OS Sheet 186 map reference 746292

The half a dozen real ales kept well on handpump in this unpretentious country local are always from small breweries, and readers have often never heard of them: Arundel Gauntlet, Becketts Old Town Bitter, Goffs Fallen Knight, Kelham Island Pale Rider, Oakleaf Bitter, and Ringwood Best. They have their own cider, too. There's a chatty, friendly atmosphere and a good mix of customers, and the opened-up bar and back dining room have simple décor – big pine tables, a moose head, dried flowers, and prints on the mellowing walls; parts of the bar can get a bit smoky when it's busy, but there is a no smoking area to the left of the bar. Promptly served, tasty bar food (they tell us prices have not changed since last year) includes filled rolls, good soups such as stilton and celery or ham, tomato and watercress (£4.85), cheese, leek and potato pie (£7.95), philippine lamb and olive stew (£8.25), beef stew (£8.50), and puddings such as spotted dick (£3.50). There are tables and a climbing frame in the pleasant garden. At weekends, this is a popular spot for walkers to relax, and the pub is on the Hangers Way Path. *(Recommended by Martin and Karen Wake, the Didler, Tony and Wendy Hobden, Francis Johnston, Stephen Kiley, JP, PP, Lynn Sharpless, Ian Phillips, W A Evershed, Simon Collett-Jones, Simon Fox, Len Banister)*

Free house ~ Licensee A Stringer ~ Real ale ~ Bar food (not Sun evening) ~ (01730) 827205 ~ Well behaved children in eating area of bar until 8pm ~ Dogs welcome ~ Live music every second winter Sat ~ Open 12-2.30(3 Sat), 6-11; 12-3, 7-10.30 Sun

LANGSTONE SU7105 Map 2

Royal Oak

High Street (marked as cul-de-sac – actually stops short of the pub itself); village is last turn left off A3023 (confusingly called A324 on some signs) before Hayling Island bridge

You need to arrive at this charmingly placed pub early if you want to bag a window seat – though in warm weather you can always sit on the wall and watch the boats arriving at high tide or the wading birds when the tide is out. It really is a lovely spot. Inside, the spacious flagstoned bar has windows from which you can see the ancient wadeway to Hayling Island, simple furnishings like windsor chairs around old wooden tables on the parquet and ancient flagstones, photographs of local scenes, and two winter open fires. Bar food includes soup (£2.95), brie and bacon melt (£4.75), roast vegetables and plum tomatoes with pasta (£5.75), steak in ale pie (£7.75), grilled salmon fillets (£7.95), chicken in a cheese and creamy mushroom sauce (£8.45), and popular summer sizzlers; there are two linked dining areas looking over the water. Well kept Boddingtons, Flowers Original, Gales HSB, and a guest on handpump, and decent wines; no noisy piped music or games machines. Morris dancers in summer; good coastal paths nearby. *(Recommended by Ian Phillips, Jess and George Cowley, Ann and Colin Hunt, Martin and Karen Wake, Val and Alan Green, Irene and Derek Flewin, Charles and Pauline Stride, Tracey and Stephen Groves, Esther and John Sprinkle, D P and J A Sweeney, Stephanie Smith, Leigh Hughes)*

Whitbreads ~ Manager Simon Courtley ~ Real ale ~ Bar food (12-2.30, 6-9; snacks served all day) ~ Restaurant ~ (023) 9248 3125 ~ Children in eating area of bar and restaurant ~ Dogs allowed in bar ~ Folk club 3rd Sun of month ~ Open 11-11; 12-10.30 Sun

LONGSTOCK SU3537 Map 2

Peat Spade

Village signposted off A30 on W edge of Stockbridge, and off A3057 Stockbridge—Andover

Although locals do drop in for a pint and a chat, most visitors come to this popular dining pub to enjoy the good, interesting food. The roomy and attractive squarish main bar is airy and high-ceilinged, with pretty windows, well chosen furnishings and a nice show of toby jugs and beer mats around its fireplace. A rather elegant no smoking dining room leads off, and there are doors to a big terrace. From a sensibly short menu, there might be creamed watercress soup (£4.25), pork and sweet red pepper terrine (£4.75), roquefort and hazelnut pâté (£4.90), salmon and smoked haddock tartlet (£5.50), moroccan organic vegetables on couscous in lemon and cumin sauce (£6.95), organic lamb curry with coconut and lime (£7.10), organic steak and kidney pie (£7.25), roasted cod fillet with herb crust and sauce vierge (£11.75), duo of duck breast and red bream with orange sauce (£13.25), organic somerset lamb noisettes stuffed with rosemary (£13.50), organic hereford steak (£13.75), and puddings such as butterscotch and apple flan, organic rhubarb fool or organic pear, mincemeat and almond crumble (£4.50). Well kept Ringwood Fortyniner and Best, and a guest such as Hampshire King Alfreds on handpump, and a decent wine list with several by the glass. There are teak seats on the terrace, with more in the not large but pleasant garden, and maybe free range chickens, two cats and Mollie the diabetic dog (who is not allowed to be fed). This attractive village is on the 44-mile Test Way long-distance path and there are bracing downland walks up around the Danebury hillfort path; the River Test is only about 100 yards away. *(Recommended by J R and J Moon, Alan and Ros Furley, Dennis Jenkin, John Robertson, J M and P M Carver, Lynn Sharpless, Margaret Ross)*

Free house ~ Licensees Bernie Startup and Sarah Hinman ~ Real ale ~ Bar food (not Sun evening, not Mon) ~ Restaurant ~ No credit cards ~ (01264) 810612 ~ Children welcome ~ Dogs welcome ~ Open 11.30-3, 6.30-11; 12-3 Sun; closed Sun evening, all Mon ~ Bedrooms: /£62.75B

Soup prices usually include a roll and butter.

MAPLEDURWELL SU6851 Map 2

Gamekeepers

3½ miles off M3 junction 6: A339 towards Basingstoke, then right signposted Old Basing, Hatch (A30 towards Hartley Wintney), then village and pub signed off on right; OS Sheet 185 map reference 686514

Handy for Basingstoke but nicely tucked away, this busy dining pub is popular for its ambitious restaurant-style food. There are dark beams, joists, and standing timbers throughout, and a pleasant, relaxed atmosphere. The bar has brocaded heavy dark long seats and wheelbacks around tables prettily set with gingham tablecloths and candles in the eating part, hunting, fish, military, and country pictures on the partly stripped brick and partly cream and timber effect walls, and a log-effect gas fire in a slightly raised brick two-way fireplace; the flagstoned small part in the middle has wood panelling, horse tack and fox masks, and a large no smoking dining room with a glass-topped stone well with carp at the bottom. There's also a back bar with cushioned winged wooden settles and wheelbacks on the turkey carpet. Changing constantly, dishes might include tasty filled baguettes, game soup (£5.25), smoked trout mousse wrapped in smoked salmon and served with lemon chutney or caesar salad (£5.95), smoked duck breast slices on couscous with a raspberry and balsamic vinaigrette (£6.25), parsnip and sun-dried tomato bake topped with creamed gruyère cheese (£11.50), queen scallops, ginger, spring onions and coriander together in a fresh local trout wrapped in bacon and steamed (£12.95), breast of gressingham duck on a black cherry sauce (£14.75), venison steak marinated in port on sweetened red cabbage with port and cream (£14.95), and fillet steak or fillet of lamb on cumberland sauce (£16.95); they have a lobster week in May and a game week in November. Well kept Badger Best and Tanglefoot on handpump; piped music. The lhasa apso dog is called Barney and she has a daughter called Pebbles. There are picnic-sets on the terrace and back grassy area. *(Recommended by Martin and Karen Wake, Phyl and Jack Street, Derek Harvey-Piper, Ian Phillips, Mrs M Webster, KC, Francis Johnston)*

Badger ~ Tenants Shaun and Tracey Nother ~ Real ale ~ Bar food (12-2.30, 6.30-9.30 or 10) ~ Restaurant ~ (01256) 322038 ~ Children in restaurant ~ Dogs allowed in bar ~ Open 12-3, 6-11; 12-4, 7-10.30 Sun

MICHELDEVER SU5138 Map 2

Half Moon & Spread Eagle

Village signposted off A33 N of Winchester; then follow Winchester 7 signpost almost opposite hall

Bustling and friendly with a good mix of locals and visitors, this country local has a simply decorated and beamed bar with heavy tables and good solid seats – a nice cushioned panelled oak settle and a couple of long dark pews as well as wheelback chairs – and a woodburning stove at each end; a no smoking area with lighter-coloured furniture opens off. Good bar food includes sandwiches, ploughman's, ham and eggs or stir-fried vegetables and rice (£6.95), cajun chicken (£7.50), fresh mussels in cream and garlic sauce (£7.95), half shoulder of lamb or duck breast with blackberries (£9.95), and steaks (from £11.95), gammon and egg (£6.50), lasagne (£6.95), cod in beer batter or fresh crab salad (£7.95), grilled local bass (£9.95), and surf and turf (£11.95); fresh local shellfish (when available), and daily specials. Well kept Greene King Abbot, IPA, and Mild, and a guest such as Archers Gold or Batemans on handpump; darts, pool, fruit machine, cribbage, and piped music. The landlord plays the saxophone, and they have an alsatian called Brew, and four cats. There are seats on a small sheltered back terrace, and some more widely spaced picnic-sets and a play area on the edge of a big cricket green behind; also, rabbits and chickens and a pony. This is a good starting point for exploring the Dever Valley (there are lots of good walks nearby). *(Recommended by D S Jackson, Geoff Palmer, Charles Moncreiffe, Val and Alan Green, Prof and Mrs Tony Palmer, Dennis Jenkin, Mike Gorton, Richard and Judy Winn, Phyl and Jack Street)*

Greene King ~ Tenants Ray Douglas and Belinda Boughtwood ~ Real ale ~ Bar food

(12-2, 6-9) ~ Restaurant ~ (01962) 774339 ~ Children welcome ~ Dogs allowed in bar ~ Live music Fri evening ~ Open 12-3, 6-11; 12-3, 7-10.30 Sun

NORTH GORLEY SU1611 Map 2

Royal Oak

Ringwood Road; village signposted off A338 S of Fordingbridge

With a relaxed atmosphere and particularly friendly, helpful staff, it's not surprising that this 17th-c thatched pub is so popular. There's a quiet, comfortable and neatly refurbished no smoking lounge on the left, though our own preference is for the busier main bar on the right: carpeted too, with pews, mate's chairs, a corner woodburning stove, old engravings and other pictures, with steps down to an attractive L-shaped eating area. This has a mix of dark pine tables and pleasant old-fashioned chairs, with big rugs on bare boards, and a further no smoking part with pine booth seating. There are french windows to a neatly kept sheltered back garden, with a play area. Good bar food includes soup (£2.75; the home-made leek and potato is recommended), well presented sandwiches (from £2.75; baguettes £4.25), ploughman's (from £4.95), cumberland sausages with onion gravy (£5.65), spinach and mushroom bake (£6.25), steak and kidney pie or chicken curry (£6.50), gammon with egg or pineapple (£6.95), fresh grilled mackerel or salmon (£7.25), and rump steak (£9.25). Well kept Fullers London Pride, Greene King IPA, and Ringwood Best on handpump, decent wines, and several malt whiskies; sensibly placed darts, CD juke box, fruit machine, cribbage, dominoes, and skittle alley. Across the road is a big pond with ducks, and there are usually ponies roaming around. More reports please. *(Recommended by Colin and Sandra Tann, Ann and Colin Hunt, Mrs Sally Kingsbury, Mr and Mrs Thomas)*

Whitbreads ~ Lease David Catt ~ Real ale ~ Bar food (12-2. 6-9) ~ Restaurant ~ (01425) 652244 ~ Children in restaurant and family room ~ Dogs welcome ~ Open 11-11; 12-10.30 Sun

OVINGTON SU5531 Map 2

Bush

Village signposted from A31 on Winchester side of Alresford

As this charming little cottage is in a lovely spot with nearby walks, many of the customers in good weather are cyclists and walkers, and there are plenty of seats in the back garden which runs down to the River Itchen. The rooms have nice old-fashioned décor, and the low-ceilinged bar has cushioned high-backed settles, elm tables with pews and kitchen chairs, masses of old pictures in heavy gilt frames on the walls, and a roaring fire on one side with an antique solid fuel stove opposite. Quickly served, good (if not cheap) bar food includes home-made wild mushroom and madeira soup (£4.40), home-made smoked Loch Fyne trout mousse (£6.25), thai spiced crab cake with chilli peanut dressing (£6.60), a vegetarian dish of the day or chargrilled chicken and chilli cheese salad (£9.90), king prawns in garlic, chilli and ginger butter (£9.75), chargrilled rib-eye steak with garlic and anchovy butter or tempura shrimp, salad and jerk seasoned chips (£11.50), grilled bass with mushroom sauce and wild mushrooms (£12.80), home-made venison casserole with red wine and juniper or duck breast with chargrilled marinated vegetables and honey cider sauce (£13.50), and puddings such as chocolate and black cherry bread and butter pudding with white chocolate sauce, hot spiced pineapple with coconut ice cream or rum and banana crumble with banana ice cream (£4.20); two rooms are no smoking. Even when not busy, they ask you to leave your credit card behind the bar. Well kept Wadworths IPA, 6X, and JCB and a couple of guest beers on handpump, and several country wines and malt whiskies; cribbage, dominoes, Monopoly and Scrabble. The friendly scottish springer spaniel is called Paddy. *(Recommended by Michael and Ann Cole, A R Hawkins, Ian Phillips, Sylvia and Tony Cooper, Ann and Colin Hunt, Michael and Robin Inskip, Martin and Karen Wake, W A Evershed, Lynn Sharpless)*

Wadworths ~ Managers Nick and Cathy Young ~ Real ale ~ Bar food (not Sun

evening) ~ (01962) 732764 ~ Well behaved children in eating area of bar until 9 ~ Dogs welcome ~ Open 11-3, 6-11; 12-2.30, 7-10.30 Sun; closed 25 Dec

OWSLEBURY SU5123 Map 2

Ship

Whites Hill; village signposted off B2177 between Fishers Pond and Lower Upham; can also be reached from M3 junction 10 via Morestead, or from A272 2½ miles SE of A31 junction

On fine weekends and during school holidays, this busy place is well liked by families. There's a children's play area and new toddler zone, a weekend bouncy castle, a pets corner, and a summer marquee; both garden areas have fine views – one side looks right across the Solent to the Isle of Wight, the other gives a view down to Winchester. Lots of good surrounding walks. Inside, there are plenty of locals and the old bars on the right of the front entrance have varnished black oak 17th-c ship's timbers as beams and wall props, sporting and naval mementoes, wheelback chairs around wooden tables, and a big central fireplace; on the left is a comfortable no smoking dining area, and there's also a no smoking separate restaurant. Popular bar food at lunchtime includes filled baguettes (from £3.50), steak in ale pie or home-cooked ham and eggs (£6.95), locally made speciality sausages with onion gravy (£7.25), stuffed tomatoes with mushroom, parmesan and spinach risotto (£7.95), and thai crab cakes or chicken and asparagus salad (£8.95); also, home-made soup (£3.75), duck and orange pâté (£4.95), seafood mornay or medallions of pork with red cabbage, caramelised apple and calvados sauce (£9.95), roast haunch of venison steak with blueberry and orange sauce (£10.95), steaks (from £11.95), daily specials, and children's meals (£3.75); there can be a bit of a wait if they are busy. Well kept Cheriton Pots Ale, Greene King IPA and a couple of guests such as Greene King Ruddles County or Everards Tiger on handpump, and a decent wine list; cribbage, dominoes, and piped music. *(Recommended by Roger and Pauline Pearce, Ann and Colin Hunt, M W Turner, Charles and Pauline Stride, Michael and Robin Inskip, Val and Alan Green, Prof and Mrs Tony Palmer, Phyl and Jack Street, Alan and Paula McCully, Lynn Sharpless, Dennis Jenkin, W A Evershed, PR and S A White)*

Greene King ~ Tenants Clive Mansell and Alison Carter ~ Real ale ~ Bar food (all day summer Sat and Sun) ~ (01962) 777358 ~ Children welcome ~ Dogs allowed in bar ~ Open 11-3, 6-11; 11-11 Sat; 12-10.30 Sun; 11-3, 6-11 Sat in winter; closed winter Mon lunchtimes

PETERSFIELD SU7227 Map 2

Trooper

From B2070 in Petersfield follow Steep signposts past station, but keep on up past Steep, on old coach road; OS Sheet 186 map reference 726273

As we thought, the bedrooms in the extension behind this interesting pub are very nice indeed and readers have enjoyed staying here; we've given them a Stay Award this year. The charming and courteous licensee continues to offer a warm welcome to his many customers, most of whom have come to eat. There's an island bar, tall stools by a broad edge facing big windows that look across to rolling downland fields, blond wheelback and kitchen chairs and a mix of tripod tables on the bare boarded or red tiled floor, little Persian knick-knacks here and there, quite a few ogival mirrors, big baskets of dried flowers, lit candles all around, fresh flowers, logs burning in the stone fireplace, and good piped music; newspapers and magazines to read. From a sensibly short menu, the very good, popular food includes soup (£3.95), grilled halloumi with a tomato, basil and black olive dressing (£4.95), a warm salad of smoked pigeon, mango and kumquats and toasted pine nuts (£5.95), king prawns and scallops tossed in white wine, chilli and lime and served on toasted brioche (£6.95), apricot, minted couscous and pine nut filo parcel served on a carrot and orange purée (£9.95), free range chicken breast filled with a wild mushroom, leek, garlic and thyme stuffing with a mushroom and thyme cream sauce (£10.95), hoisin glazed breast of duck on vegetable noodles (£11.95), cod fillet and king prawns with tomato and dill cream sauce (£12.95), and Aberdeen Angus steaks (from £12.95); there may be quite a wait at peak times, and you must book to be sure of a table. The raftered restaurant is most attractive. Well kept Ringwood Best and a beer named for the pub, Trooper Ghost, and a couple of guests such as Ballards Nyewood Gold and Hop Back Crop Circle on handpump, and decent house wines. There are lots of picnic-sets on an upper lawn and more on the partly covered sunken terrace which has french windows to the dining area. The horse rail in the car park ('horses only before 8pm') does get used. *(Recommended by Simon Collett-Jones, John and Tania Wood, Roger and Pauline Pearce, Patrick Hancock, Steve McCathie, Wendy Arnold, Ann and Colin Hunt, Lynn Sharpless, Phyl and Jack Street, Charles and Pauline Stride, George and Brenda Jones, Ian Phillips)*

Free house ~ Licensee Hassan Matini ~ Real ale ~ Bar food ~ Restaurant ~ (01730) 827293 ~ Children welcome ~ Dogs allowed in bar ~ Open 11-2.30, 6.30-11; 12-3, 7-10.30 Sun ~ Bedrooms: £55B/£75B

White Horse ★

Priors Dean – but don't follow Priors Dean signposts: simplest route is from Petersfield, leaving centre on A272 towards Winchester, take right turn at roundabout after level crossing, towards Steep, and keep on for 4 miles or so, up on to the downs, passing another pub on your right (and not turning off into Steep there); at last, at crossroads signposted East Tisted/Privett, turn right towards East Tisted, then almost at once turn right on to second gravel track (the first just goes into a field); there's no inn sign; alternatively, from A32 5 miles S of Alton, take road by bus lay-by signposted Steep, then, after 1¾ miles, turn off as above – though obviously left this time – at East Tisted/Privett crossroads; OS Sheet 197 coming from Petersfield (Sheet 186 is better the other way), map reference 715290; the Pub With No Name (as most of its regulars know it – there's no inn sign)

Sadly, as we went to press, this fine old farmhouse was up for sale and being run by a series of relief managers. We are keeping our fingers firmly crossed that this period of instability passes quickly and a permanent licensee is installed. It's been a great favourite of ours for 20 years, and the two charming and idiosyncratic parlour rooms (candlelit at night) have open fires, various old pictures, farm tools, drop-leaf tables, oak settles, rugs, stuffed antelope heads, a longcase clock, and a couple of fireside rocking-chairs, and so forth; there's an attractive no smoking dining room with a big open fire. There have been up to nine real ales on handpump and decent bar food has included soup, filled baked potatoes and sandwiches, as well as meals such as steak and kidney pie, a vegetarian choice, and so forth. Rustic seats (which include chunks of tree-trunk) and a terrace outside; as this is one of the highest spots in the county it can be quite breezy. If trying to find it for the first time, keep your eyes skinned – not for nothing is this known as the Pub With No Name – though there are now boards as you approach. *(Recommended by Lynn Sharpless, W A Evershed, Ann and Colin Hunt, the Didler, Helen Sandelands, Irene and Derek Flewin, JP, PP, Brian and Anna Marsden)*

Gales ~ Real ale ~ Bar food (not Sun evening) ~ Restaurant ~ (01420) 588387 ~ Children in restaurant ~ Open 11-2.30, 6-11; 12-3, 7-10.30 Sun

PILLEY SZ3298 Map 2

Fleur de Lys

Village signposted off A337 Brockenhurst—Lymington

Decorated inside and out over the past year, this ancient thatched place is the oldest pub in the New Forest and was established as an inn in 1096. The lounge bar has a handwritten list of landlords that goes back to 1498, heavy low beams, a collection of brass and copper ornaments, and a huge inglenook log fire; the main bar and family room are no smoking. Good, popular bar food includes sandwiches (from £3.30), home-made soup (£3.50), filled baguettes (from £4), home-made pâté (£4.95), ham and eggs (£6.50), pasta dishes (from £7.95), home-made steak and kidney pie (£8.50), vegetable tacos (£8.95), seafood dishes (from £9.50), steaks (£12.95), and puddings (from £4.50). Well kept Gales HSB, Ringwood Best, and a guest such as Marstons Pedigree on handpump, decent wines, and country wines;

friendly service. Piped music, fruit machine, cribbage, and dominoes. There are seats in the garden, a children's play area, and fine forest and heathland walks nearby. *(Recommended by Lynn Sharpless, Alan Finley, George Atkinson, Charles and Pauline Stride, Derek and Sylvia Stephenson)*

Whitbreads ~ Lease Neil Rogers ~ Real ale ~ Bar food ~ (01590) 672158 ~ Children in family room ~ Open 11-2.30, 6-11; 12-3, 7-10.30 Sun; closed evenings 25 and 26 Dec

ROMSEY SU3520 Map 2

Three Tuns

Middlebridge Street; car park off A27 bypass

An excellent town pub, this friendly old-world place has good value food such as asparagus soup (£3.25), grilled goats cheese (£4.25), chicken liver parfait (£4.95), salmon (£8.75), fried chicken on cheddar and chive mash (£9.25), slow-roasted lamb shoulder (£9.50), roast bass (£11.95) and 10oz rib-eye steak (£12.95), with well kept Flowers Original, Gales GB and HSB and Ringwood Best on handpump. There's a good mix of drinking and eating, with a buzz of conversation drowning the faint piped jazz. Standard pub tables and chairs are quite closely grouped on the turkey carpet (bigger tables on the left, where there are big aeroplane and train pictures on panelled walls), with some nice bow-window seats, a coal-effect gas fire, and a few black beams in a low shiny maroon ceiling; cheerful attentive staff. It may be best to book on Saturday. Some seats outside. *(Recommended by Mr and Mrs R W Allan, Derek Stafford)*

Enterprise ~ Lease Sarah Dormer ~ Real ale ~ Bar food (12-2, 7-9; not Sun evening) ~ (01794) 512639 ~ Children allowed at lunchtime only ~ Dogs welcome ~ Open 11-3, 5-11; 11-11 Fri and Sat; 12-10.30 Sun

ROTHERWICK SU7156 Map 2

Falcon

4 miles from M3 junction 5; follow Newnham signpost from exit roundabout, then Rotherwick signpost, then turn right at Mattingley, Heckfield signpost; village also signposted from B3349 N of Hook, then brown signs to pub

This quietly placed and relaxed country pub has a light and fresh open-plan layout, with quite a mixture of dining chairs around an informal variety of tables on its varnished floorboards, big bay windows with sunny window seats, and minimal decoration on its mainly pale mustard-coloured walls; flowers on the tables, and perhaps a big vase of lilies on the terracotta-coloured central bar counter, give colour. There is a rather more formal no smoking back dining area round to the right, and on the left an overstuffed sofa and a couple of ornate easy chairs by one log fire. Interesting food includes home-made soup (£2.95), unusual generous sandwiches (from £3; bacon, melted brie and cranberry £3.50; toasties from £3.25; filled baguettes from £4), welsh rarebit (£4; with poached eggs £4.50), filled baked potatoes (from £4.25), smoked salmon and scrambled eggs (£5.50), sausage and egg (£5.95), burgers (from £6.50), roasted vegetable lasagne or pork and leek sausages (£6.95), steak and mushroom pie (£7.50), steamed halibut steak with white wine, mushroom and prawn sauce (£10.25), half shoulder of lamb with a lightly minted jus (£10.95), steaks (from £11.50), and specials such as thai fish cakes with sweet chilli dip (£4.95), mixed grill (£11.95), fresh monkfish medallions with ginger and exotic fruits, topped with crispy bacon (£13.95), and beef wellington (£14.95). Well kept Brakspears PA, Hampshire Ironside Best and Kelham Island Easy Rider on handpump, good coffee, very friendly helpful service; piped local radio. Terraces front and back have sturdy tables and benches, and there are picnic-sets in a sizeable informal back garden with a pair of swings and pasture views, with good easy walks nearby. *(Recommended by Margaret Ross, Anthony Barnes, Mrs Hilarie Taylor)*

Unique Pub Co ~ Lease Andy Francis ~ Real ale ~ Bar food ~ Restaurant ~ (01256) 762586 ~ Children in restaurant only ~ Dogs allowed in bar ~ Open 11-2.30, 6-11; 11-11 Sat; 12-10.30 Sun; 11-2.30, 6-11 winter Sat, 12-3, 7-10.30 Sun in winter

SOUTHSEA SZ6498 Map 2

Wine Vaults

Albert Road, opposite Kings Theatre

A haven for real ale enthusiasts, this basic pub keeps up to 11 beers on handpump, and has a double happy hour on any night from Monday to Thursday between 5.30 and 7.30 when the beers are cheaper (in fact on Monday it's £1.25 all night). If you arrive before 5.30 and are coming to eat, you get a free drink. There might be well kept Courage Best, Fullers London Pride, Greene King Ruddles County, Hop Back GFB and Summer Lightning, Itchen Valley Fagins, Marstons Pedigree, Ringwood Fortyniner, and a beer named for the pub, Offyatrolli. The busy straightforward bar has wood-panelled walls, a wooden floor, and an easy-going, chatty feel; the raised back area is no smoking; pool, piped music, dominoes, chess, draughts, and a football table. Bar food is good value and served in decent sized helpings, with sandwiches (from £1.95; grilled ones £3.35; not Sunday), filled baked potatoes (from £3.55), salads like cajun chicken, greek or brie and avocado (from £5.75), mexican dishes such as vegetable burrito or various nachos (from £5.95), and puddings (£2.95); friendly staff. There are seats in the little garden, and a wooden gazebo. More reports please. *(Recommended by Ann and Colin Hunt, Howard James, W A Evershed, Ian Phillips)*

Free house ~ Licensees Mike Hughes and J Stevens ~ Real ale ~ Bar food (12-9.30; not 25 Dec, 1 Jan) ~ (023) 9286 4712 ~ Children in family room; but under 5s to leave before 7.30 ~ Dogs welcome ~ Open 12-11; 12-10.30 Sun; closed 1 Jan

SPARSHOLT SU4331 Map 2

Plough

Village signposted off A272 a little W of Winchester

Run by helpful, friendly licensees, this village pub is popular for its good, interesting food. It's all neatly kept, and the main bar has a bustling atmosphere, an interesting mix of wooden tables and chairs, with farm tools, scythes and pitchforks attached to the ceiling; two no smoking areas. From quite a choice, the bar food might include lunchtime sandwiches, baguettes such as prawn, tomato and chive mayonnaise (£5.75), mushroom, pepper and leek stroganoff, ground steak burgers with boulangère potatoes and pepper sauce, salmon and crab fishcake with chilli salsa or seafood in a basil, tomato and spring onion sauce on pasta (all £8.95), tossed salad with strips of beef fillet in an oriental dressing (£9.50), breast of chicken filled with mushrooms on a tomato and basil ragoût (£11.95), roasted pork tenderloin wrapped in smoked bacon with apricot and ginger sauce (£12.50), and monkfish tails with roasted vine tomatoes, shallots and balsamic dressing (£13.95). To be sure of a table you must book beforehand. Well kept Wadworths IPA, 6X, Farmers Glory, and a seasonal guest on handpump, and an extensive wine list. There's a children's play fort, and plenty of seats on the terrace and lawn. *(Recommended by Mrs Rita Cox, Phyl and Jack Street, Julian McCarthy, John and Joan Calvert, Lynn Sharpless, Mr and Mrs W D Borthwick, John Wheeler, Mr and Mrs Ayrton, Marjorie and David Lamb)*

Wadworths ~ Tenants R C and K J Crawford ~ Real ale ~ Bar food ~ (01962) 776353 ~ Children welcome but no small children after 7.30 Fri/Sat ~ Dogs welcome ~ Open 11-3, 6-11; 12-3, 6-10.30 Sun; closed 25 Dec

STEEP SU7425 Map 2

Harrow

Take Midhurst exit from Petersfield bypass, at exit roundabout first left towards Midhurst, then first turning on left opposite garage, and left again at Sheet church; follow over dual carriageway bridge to pub

Like its many loyal customers, we are delighted that this country local (run by the same family for over 70 years) continues to remain as unspoilt and unchanging as ever. The cosy public bar has hops and dried flowers hanging from the beams, built-in wall benches on the tiled floor, stripped pine wallboards, a good log fire in the big inglenook, and maybe wild flowers on the scrubbed deal tables (and on the tables outside); dominoes. Generous helpings of unfussy and enjoyable home-made bar food include sandwiches, home-made scotch eggs (£2.80), wonderful, generous soups such as ham, split pea and vegetable (£4), ham off the bone that is used in sandwiches (£4), ploughman's (£7.50), and salads (£10), home-made cottage pie, lasagne or quiches (£7), and puddings like delicious treacle tart or seasonal fruit pies (£3.50). Well kept Ballards Trotton Bitter, Cheriton Diggers Gold, Pots or Village Elder, and Ringwood Best tapped from casks behind the counter, and local wine; polite and friendly staff, even when under pressure. The big garden is left free-flowering so that goldfinches can collect thistle seeds from the grass. The Petersfield bypass doesn't intrude on this idyll, though you will need to follow the directions above to find it. No children inside. *(Recommended by the Didler, Stephen Kiley, Tracey and Stephen Groves, Lynn Sharpless, JP, PP, Michael and Ann Cole, Mary and Dennis Jones, Ian Phillips, Charles and Pauline Stride, Simon Fox, Simon Collett-Jones, Irene and Derek Flewin, W A Evershed)*

Free house ~ Licensee Ellen McCutcheon ~ Real ale ~ Bar food (limited Sun evenings (not during winter)) ~ No credit cards ~ (01730) 262685 ~ Dogs welcome ~ Open 12-2.30, 6-11; 11-3, 6-11 Sat; 12-3, 7-10.30 Sun; closed winter Sun evenings

STOCKBRIDGE SU3535 Map 2

Three Cups 🍷 🛏

High Street

This 15th-c pub looks enticing, with its little dormer windows in a very low tiled roof, and inside your hopes rise further – a settle and hall chair in a small quarry-tiled hallway, then an old-fashioned leather porter's chair by the telephone in an inner lobby. The low-beamed bar on the right amply justifies your growing hopes: quite narrow and very dimly lit (candles in bottles on all the tables at night), it has an engaging mix of furnishings on its turkey carpet, from high-backed settles to a button-back leather sofa, with a variety of mainly oak tables, and its dark red walls are packed with old engravings, fishing gear, one or two guns, and a fair bit of taxidermy. The atmosphere is thoroughly relaxed and easy-going, with daily papers, logs blazing in the woodburning stove, friendly staff, well kept Exe Valley Devon Glory, Fullers London Pride and Ringwood Best on handpump, and several decent wines by the glass. Interestingly cooked fresh bar food might include home-made soup (£3.25), filled baguettes (from £3.60), ham and eggs (£5.95), omelettes (from £5.50), moules frites or a roast of the day (£7.25), lasagne (£7.95), and daily specials such as grilled pigeon breast on lentils (£5.50), fresh crab salad with mango and passion fruit sauce (£6.50), wild mushroom tart (£6.95), rack of lamb with fresh thyme sauce or skate wing with caper sauce (£10.95), and chicken breast stuffed with fresh crab and a ginger sauce (£13.95). Piped music is not too loud, but noticeable. There is a no smoking restaurant on the left. *(Recommended by David Hammond)*

Free house ~ Licensees Paul and Lucy Foster ~ Real ale ~ Bar food (not winter Sun evenings) ~ Restaurant ~ (01264) 810527 ~ Children in eating area of bar and restaurant ~ Dogs allowed in bar ~ Open 12-2, 5-11; 12-2, 7-10.30 Sun ~ Bedrooms: £40(£50B)/£50(£60B)

TICHBORNE SU5630 Map 2

Tichborne Arms

Village signed off B3047

As the Wayfarers Walk and Itchen Way pass close to this neat thatched pub, and many fine walks lead off in all directions, there are quite a few thirsty walkers here during the day. The pictures and documents on the walls inside recall the bizarre Tichborne Case (a mystery man from Australia claimed fraudulently to be the heir to this estate). The comfortable square-panelled room on the right has wheelback chairs and settles (one very long), a log fire in the stone fireplace, and latticed windows. On the left, there's a larger, livelier, partly panelled room used for eating. Bar food includes sandwiches (from £3.75), chicken, tarragon and mushroom pie (£7.50), steak in ale pie (£7.95), confit of duck with red onion marmalade (£9.50), and crab salad (£10.50). Well kept Ringwood Best and Wadworths 6X, and a guest beer tapped from the cask, country wines, and farm cider; sensibly placed darts, shove-ha'penny, and piped music. There are picnic-sets outside in the big well kept garden, a new pétanque pitch, and two pub dogs. No children inside. *(Recommended by W A Evershed, Lynn Sharpless, Ian Phillips, the Didler, Dr and Mrs M E Wilson, Ann and Colin Hunt, Mick Simmons, Phyl and Jack Street, Ron Shelton, Prof and Mrs Tony Palmer)*

Free house ~ Licensees Keith and Janie Day ~ Real ale ~ Bar food (12-1.45, 6.30-9.45) ~ (01962) 733760 ~ Dogs welcome ~ Open 11.30-2.30, 6-11; 12-3, 7-10.30 Sun; closed evenings 25 and 26 Dec and evening 1 Jan

UPHAM SU5320 Map 2

Brushmakers Arms

Shoe Lane; village signposted from Winchester—Bishops Waltham downs road, and from B2177 (former A333)

Readers really enjoy their visits to this attractive old village pub, and there's always a friendly welcome and a crowd of chatty locals. The comfortable L-shaped bar is divided into two by a central brick chimney with a woodburning stove in the raised two-way fireplace, and there are comfortably cushioned wall settles and chairs, a variety of tables including some in country-style stripped wood, a few beams in the low ceiling, and quite a collection of ethnic-looking brushes; also, a small snug. Well kept Ringwood Best, Wells Bombardier, and a beer named for the pub on handpump, Addlestone's cider, and country wines. Generous helpings of popular, reliable bar food include lunchtime snacks such as sandwiches (£3.75; filled hot croissants £4.25), filled baked potatoes (£3.75), ploughman's (from £4.25), and ham and egg (£5.25), as well as liver and bacon casserole (£5.95), spinach and goats cheese cannelloni (£6.95), steak and kidney pie or partridge with bacon and mushroom (£7.95), salmon fillet with mustard and chive butter (£8.95), steaks (from £9.95), half leg of lamb in garlic and rosemary (£10.95), and home-made puddings (£3.50). Dominoes and sensibly placed darts. The big garden is well stocked with mature shrubs and trees, and there are picnic-sets on a sheltered back terrace among lots of tubs of flowers, with more on the tidy tree-sheltered lawn. Good walks nearby. *(Recommended by Jenny Cridland, Gordon Cooper, P R and S A White, Alan and Paula McCully, Ann and Colin Hunt, Lynn Sharpless, John and Joan Nash, Martin and Karen Wake, Prof and Mrs Tony Palmer, Val and Alan Green, Godfrey and Irene Joly)*

Free house ~ Licensee Tony Mottram ~ Real ale ~ Bar food ~ (01489) 860231 ~ Children welcome away from bar area ~ Dogs welcome ~ Open 11-3.30, 5.30(6 Sat)-11; 12-3.30, 7-10.30 Sun

WHERWELL SU3839 Map 2

Mayfly

Testcombe (i.e. not in Wherwell itself); A3057 SE of Andover, between B3420 turn-off and Leckford where road crosses River Test; OS Sheet 185 map reference 382390

Particularly in good weather, the position here is a real draw so it's best to arrive early to bag one of the tables on the new decking area beside the River Test and watch the ducks and maybe plump trout, with a drink. Inside, the spacious, beamed and carpeted bar has fishing pictures on the cream walls, straightforward pub furnishings, and two woodburning stoves, and there's a no smoking conservatory overlooking the water. Good bar food comes from a buffet-style servery: home-made quiche (£5), a choice of hot and cold meats (from £5.10), pies and chicken tandoori (from £7.95). Well kept Flowers Original, and Ringwood Best and Old Thumper on handpump, and country wines; piped music. More reports please. *(Recommended by Alec and Barbara Jones, D J and P M Taylor, Charlie Harris, Pat and Robert Watt, Mike and Sue Richardson, Jess and George Cowley, Betsy and Peter Little, Tim and Jan Dalton, Leigh and Gillian Mellor, Alan and Ros Furley, Mrs J Wilson, Norman and Sheila Davies)*

Whitbreads ~ Managers Barry and Julie Lane ~ Real ale ~ Bar food (11.30-9.30) ~

(01264) 860283 ~ Children welcome away from bar area ~ Dogs welcome ~ Open 10-11; 12-10.30 Sun

White Lion

B3420, in village itself

The multi-level beamed bar in this friendly pub has delft plates, sparkling brass, and fresh flowers, and well kept Adnams Best, Flowers Original, and Ringwood Best on handpump; the Village bar has an open fire, and there are two dining rooms – the lower one is no smoking. Good bar food includes home-made soup (£3.50), pâté (£4.20), ploughman's (from £5.20), ham and egg (£7), spinach and red pepper lasagne (£7.25), a pie of the day (£7.50), salmon fishcakes (£7.80), pork in honey and mustard sauce or lamb cooked with apricots in a spicy sauce (£8), steaks (from £10.75), and daily specials such as liver and bacon, smoked haddock and prawn bake or minted lamb casserole; Sunday roasts (worth booking for these). The friendly black labrador is called Sam; piped music. There are plenty of seats in the courtyard and on the terrace, and the barn has been newly thatched. It's worth strolling through the village, and there's a nice walk over the River Test and meadows to Chilbolton. More reports please. *(Recommended by Lynn Sharpless, R Halsey, Brian Root)*

Inn Partnership (Pubmaster) ~ Lease Adrian and Patsy Stent ~ Real ale ~ Bar food ~ Restaurant ~ (01264) 860317 ~ Well behaved children in restaurant ~ Dogs welcome ~ Folk 1st and 3rd Thurs of month ~ Open 10-2.30(3 Sat), 6(7 Mon/Tues)-11; 12-3, 7-10.30 Sun ~ Bedrooms: £32.50/£45

WHITSBURY SU1219 Map 2

Cartwheel

Follow Rockbourne sign off A354 SW of Salisbury, turning left just before Rockbourne itself; or head W off A338 at S end of Breamore, or in Upper Burgate – we got mildly lost trying to find it direct from Fordingbridge!

Plenty of customers – both locals and visitors – enjoy this cheerful, rather out-of-the-way local. It's opened up inside, with pitched high rafters in one part, lower beams elsewhere, antlers, military prints, country pictures, what looks like a steam-engine's jockey wheel as a divider, and simple but comfortable cloth-cushioned wall seats and other chairs. There's a snug little room by the door, with a couple of tables either side of the fire; a small side room has darts, pool, fruit machine, dominoes, cribbage, Jenga, Scrabble, TV, and piped music. Generous food includes good sandwiches, whitebait (£4.25), scrambled eggs and smoked salmon (£5.50), cajun chicken with home-made chips (£6.25), fresh grilled lemon sole (£7.25), and Tuesday home-cooked fish and chips which you can eat here or take away. Adnams Broadside, Ringwood Best, and guests such as Shepherd Neame Spitfire or Youngs Waggle Dance on handpump, in top condition, ciders, and a beer festival on the second weekend in August; efficient service. The garden, sheltered by a shrubby steep slope, has weekly summer barbecues and a particularly good play area that children really enjoy. It's good walking country. More reports please. *(Recommended by Mr and Mrs Thomas, Dr D E Granger, Peter and Audrey Dowsett)*

Free house ~ Licensee Patrick James Lewis ~ Real ale ~ Bar food (not winter Mon evening) ~ (01725) 518362 ~ Children welcome ~ Dogs welcome ~ Occasional music evenings ~ Open 11-2.30(3 Sat), 6-11; 12-3, 7-10.30 Sun

WINCHESTER SU4829 Map 2

Wykeham Arms ★

75 Kingsgate Street (Kingsgate Arch and College Street are now closed to traffic; there is access via Canon Street)

To be sure of a table in the bar of this rather civilised but friendly inn, you do have to arrive early as they don't take bookings here. A series of stylish bustling rooms radiating from the central bar has 19th-c oak desks retired from nearby Winchester College, a redundant pew from the same source, kitchen chairs and candlelit deal tables and big windows with swagged paisley curtains; all sorts of interesting collections are dotted around. A snug room at the back, known as the Watchmakers, is decorated with a set of Ronald Searle 'Winespeak' prints, a second one is panelled, and all of them have a log fire; the Nelson Bar is no smoking. Served by neatly uniformed staff, the good food at lunchtime includes smoked salmon sandwich (£3.65), toasted mozzarella, sun-blush tomato, pesto and black olives on foccacia (£4.95), and open steak sandwich (£6.25), as well as roasted mediterranean vegetable and feta galette with thyme, garlic and sweet pepper dressing (£5.25), fresh mussels or smoked chicken breast with a waldorf salad (£6.50), steaks (from £12.50), and daily specials such as cream of asparagus soup (£3.25), cottage pie (£5.95), and pork casserole (£6.25). In the evening, there might be coarse farmhouse terrine with black pudding (£4.95), thai spiced salmon fishcakes or wild mushroom faggotini with gazpacho sauce (£5.25), caramelised red onion and goats cheese tartlet with fresh pesto (£9.95), marinated red mullet fillets on roasted vegetable couscous, chargrilled asparagus and sun-dried tomato juice (£13.50), chicken breast on chorizo and mushroom risotto with roasted garlic sauce (£13.75), and roast rack of local lamb with parsnip and potato mash, roasted mediterranean vegetables and tomato and olive jus (£14.25); puddings like lemon cheesecake or crème brûlée (£4.50). There's a fine choice of 20 wines by the glass (including sweet wines), and quite a few brandies, armagnacs and liqueurs. Also, well kept Bass, Gales Bitter, Best, and HSB, and a guest such as Flowers IPA on handpump. There are tables on a covered back terrace, with more on a small but sheltered lawn. The lovely bedrooms in the pub are thoughtfully equipped, and the Saint George, a 16th-c annexe directly across the street (and overlooking Winchester College Chapel) has more bedrooms, a sitting room with open fire, a post office/general stores, and a Burgundian wine store; you can enjoy the good breakfasts either in your room there or at the pub. No children inside. *(Recommended by Ann and Colin Hunt, the Didler, Phyl and Jack Street, Patrick Hall, Lynn Sharpless, L A E James, Peter and Audrey Dowsett, John Evans, Ian Phillips, David and Nina Pugsley, Philip Vernon, Kim Maidment, Betsy and Peter Little, Jess and George Cowley, John and Annabel Hampshire, Mr and Mrs A H Young, P R and S A White, Phil and Sally Gorton, Peter Saville, Felicity Stephens, Dennis Jenkin, W A Evershed, Steve Whalley, Ian and Nita Cooper, Tracey and Stephen Groves, Alan and Paula McCully, David Peakaleakall, Keith Barker, G T Brewster, Di and Mike Gillam, Patrick Hancock; also in the* Good Hotel Guide*)*

Gales ~ Managers Peter and Kate Miller ~ Real ale ~ Bar food (12-2.30, 6.30-8.45; not Sun evening) ~ Restaurant ~ (01962) 853834 ~ Dogs allowed in bar ~ Open 11-11; 12-10.30 Sun; closed 25 Dec ~ Bedrooms: £50S/£97.50B

Lucky Dip

Besides the fully inspected pubs, you might like to try these Lucky Dips recommended to us and described by readers (if you do, please send us reports: www.goodguides.com).

Alresford [SU5832]

Bell [West St]: Relaxing Georgian coaching inn with extended bar, smallish dining room, well kept beers, friendly service, quickly served good value straightforward food inc children's helpings, log fire, daily papers; attractive back courtyard, comfortable bedrooms, open all day *(Hazel and Michael Duncombe, Geoff Palmer, John Oates)*

Cricketers [Jacklyns Lane]: Large pub with good value straightforward food inc bargain wkdy lunches (book ahead for Sun), well kept real ales, friendly service, pleasant cottagey eating area down steps; garden with good play area *(Phyl and Jack Street, Dr C S Shaw)*

☆ ***Globe*** [bottom of Broad St (B3046)]: Nicely furnished mixing comfort and individuality, big log fires each end, fresh flowers and candles, unusual pictures, interesting bar food (all day summer wknds) from sandwiches up, lots of wines by the glass, well kept Brakspears SB, Courage Directors, Fullers London Pride and Wadworths 6X; no smoking restaurant (children allowed) and tented Garden Room; lots of picnic-sets in garden looking over historic Alresford Pond, open all day Sun, and summer Sat *(John Evans, David Peakall, I D Greenfield, Lynn Sharpless, Julie and Bill Ryan, Ron Shelton, Ann and Colin Hunt, Martin and Karen Wake, LYM)*

☆ ***Horse & Groom*** [Broad St; town signed off A31 bypass]: Nicely reworked open-plan carpeted bar with beams and timbers, good bow window seats, enjoyable reasonably priced food inc good puddings, well kept ales such as Bass, Fullers London Pride and Wadworths 6X, good choice of wines by the glass, attentive service, extended back no smoking restaurant area; decent piped music; children welcome, open all day Fri/Sat *(Ann and Colin Hunt, Hazel and Michael Duncombe, LYM, Ron Shelton, Lynn Sharpless)*

Alton [SU7138]

☆ ***French Horn*** [The Butts; S of centre on old Basingstoke rd, by railway line]: Welcoming dining pub refurbished in attractive traditional style with inglenook fireplace in both linked rooms, decent generous food (busy with regular business lunchers), obliging prompt service, well kept ales inc Courage Best; skittle alley; bedrooms *(D J and P M Taylor, Ron Shelton)*

Andover [SU3645]

Foresters Arms [London St]: Small lounge with simple lunchtime food (not Sun), Greene King IPA and Ruddles Best, separate public bar with games area *(Tony Hobden)*

Arford [SU8336]

☆ ***Crown*** [off B3002 W of Hindhead]: Unpretentious low-beamed bar with log fire, steps up to homely eating area, well kept Adnams, Fullers London Pride, Greene King Abbot, and a local guest beer, welcoming service, enjoyable bar food from sandwiches up inc children's menu, no smoking restaurant; piped music; children welcome in eating areas, picnic-sets out in peaceful dell by a tiny stream across the road *(Lynn Sharpless, LYM)*

Ashmansworth [SU4157]

Plough: Friendly no-frills pub in attractive village, Hampshire's highest; two quarry-tiled rooms knocked together, well kept Archers Village, Best and Golden and a changing guest tapped from the cask, simple home-cooked food, good attentive service, log fire, no piped music; seats outside, good walks, handy for Highclere Castle *(Guy Vowles, the Didler)*

Battramsley [SZ3099]

Hobler [A337 S of Brockenhurst]: Cheery heavy-beamed pub with nice well used mix of furniture, lots of books and rustic bric-a-brac, well kept Flowers Original, Wadworths 6X and a guest such as Gales HSB, dozens of malt whiskies and country wines, traditional games, food from snacks up; piped music; spacious lawn with summer bar, very good play area and livestock paddock, good Forest walks; no children or mobile phones inside, jazz Tues, blues 2nd Thurs *(A D Marsh, David and Nina Pugsley, Prof and Mrs Tony Palmer, LYM)*

Beaulieu [SU3902]

Montagu Arms [almost opp Palace House]: Civilised hotel in attractive surroundings; separate less formal Montys bar/eaterie, open all day, with usual food inc children's helpings, Boddingtons, Ringwood and Whitbreads ales, good wines, lots of malt whiskies, sofas and easy chairs, basic décor; may be piped music; children welcome, picnic-sets out on front courtyard, comfortable bedrooms, good spot for walks *(LYM, Mr and Mrs Ayrton)*

Bentley [SU8044]

Bull [A31 Alton—Farnham dual carriageway, not in village itself]: Low beams, lots of local prints, newly upholstered seating around dark wood tables, wide and interesting food choice *(LYM, Martin and Karen Wake)*

Bighton [SU6134]

Three Horseshoes [off B3046 in Alresford just N of pond; or off A31 in Bishops Sutton]: Quiet old-fashioned village local with new licensees doing wider range of reasonably priced standard food, well kept Gales HSB and BBB and Palmers BB and Copper, decent choice of house wines, small log fire dining room, darts in bare-boards stripped-stone public bar, solid-fuel stove in huge fireplace; may be piped music; children welcome, good walks nearby; cl Mon winter lunchtime *(the Didler, W A Evershed, Lynn Sharpless)*

Bishop's Sutton [SU6031]

Ship [B3047, former A31 on Alton side of Alresford – now bypassed]: Attractive and relaxed, with welcoming new licensees doing decent standard food, Ringwood Best and Porter with a guest such as Barum Original, good choice of wines by the glass, good fire, attractive small back dining room; well behaved dogs and children welcome, tables in garden with a couple of thatched parasols, handy for Watercress Line, good walks; has been cl Mon lunchtime *(Lynn Sharpless, Ron Shelton, LYM, Phyl and Jack Street)*

Bishop's Waltham [SU5517]

Barleycorn [Lower Basingwell St]: Georgian, with pleasant mix of dark oak and cream, some panelling, welcoming staff, well kept Greene King ales inc Ruddles Best, log fire, games in public bar, separate dining room – good value simple home-made food inc two-for-one lunch bargains Mon to Weds, popular Sun lunch, children's dishes and good vegetarian choice; garden *(David and Elizabeth Briggs, Val and Alan Green, Ann and Colin Hunt)*

Braishfield [SU3725]

☆ ***Newport*** [Newport Lane]: Very basic two-bar local, unsmart and unspoilt – quite a 1950s time warp; popular with older people at lunchtime (younger people evenings) for simple huge cheap sandwiches and occasional bargain ploughman's, particularly well kept Gales HSB, Best and Butser, country wines, decent milky coffee, down-to-earth long-serving licensees; piped music, cribbage, wknd piano singsongs; good garden with geese, ducks and chickens *(Phil and Sally Gorton, Lynn Sharpless, the Didler)*

Brambridge [SU4721]

Dog & Crook [just off B3335 Twyford—Eastleigh]: Open-plan L-shaped village pub currently doing well, with good food from pub standards to some more unusual and restauranty dishes inc lovely puddings, quick warmly welcoming young staff, real ales, country wines; handy for Itchen Way walks *(Diana Brumfit)*

Bramshill [SU7461]

Hatch Gate [Heckfield Rd]: Doing well under hard-working and helpful new northern landlord, friendly atmosphere, decent food in bar and restaurant, well kept Bass, Fullers London Pride and Marstons Pedigree, good wines by the glass; big garden *(Dylan William)*

Bransgore [SZ1997]

☆ *Three Tuns* [Ringwood Rd, off A35 N of Christchurch]: Pretty 17th-c thatched pub, much restored inside with stripped brickwork and beamery, comfortable dining area popular with older people at lunchtime for wide range of above-average imaginative food from ciabattas up, friendly efficient service, well kept Greene King IPA, Ringwood Fortyniner and Timothy Taylors Landlord, good range of wines, tasteful olde-worlde bar, fresh flowers; dogs allowed, pleasant back garden with play area and open country views, large flower-decked front terrace; bedrooms *(John and Vivienne Rice, W W Burke, P L Jones)*

Breamore [SU1517]

Bat & Ball [Salisbury Rd]: Bustling village pub, newish licensees doing good value food, well kept real ales, two connecting bars, attractive restaurant; pleasant side garden, bedrooms, Avon fishing and walks, inc lovely ones up by church and stately Breamore House to Breamore Woods and maze *(Geoff Palmer)*

Brook [SU2713]

Bell: Really a hotel and restaurant (with thriving golf club), but does good interesting lunches in its neatly kept quiet bar, with prompt friendly uniformed staff, good choice of well kept ales inc Ringwood, and lovely inglenook log fire; plush restaurant, big garden, delightful village, comfortable bedrooms *(David M Cundy)*

Green Dragon [B3078 NW of Cadnam]: Big welcoming open-plan New Forest dining pub (dating from 15th c) with wide quickly served food choice, variety of areas with scrubbed pine tables or longer refectory tables, good range of well kept beers; big garden with good enclosed play area, picturesque spot *(J and B Cressey)*

Broughton [SU3032]

☆ *Tally Ho* [High St, opp church; signed off A30 Stockbridge—Salisbury]: Open-plan square bar, mainly with pews and mixed pub furniture on big terracotta tiles, but one quarter carpeted, with nice seating, a small coal fire, hunting prints, and local landscapes for sale, and another taken up by the servery; well kept fff Stupidly Happy and Ringwood Best and True Glory, good house wines in two glass sizes, friendly staff, another log fire, darts, good value fresh home cooking and good sandwiches, no piped music; children welcome, tables in charming secluded back garden, good walks; has been cl Tues *(Phyl and Jack Street, Mary Kirman and Tim Jefferson, Lynn Sharpless, Prof and Mrs Tony Palmer, BB, Bernie Adams, Geoffrey Kemp, Margaret Ross)*

Buriton [SU7320]

Master Robert [Petersfield Rd]: Cheerful service, well kept Flowers IPA and Fullers London Pride, popular food (not Mon lunchtime) in low-ceilinged dining area, public bar with pool etc; bedrooms, good view from car park *(W A Evershed, Cathy Robinson, Ed Coombe)*

Burley [SU2202]

☆ *White Buck* [Bisterne Close; ¾ mile E, OS Sheet 195 map ref 223028]: Huge well run bar in 19th-c mock-Tudor hotel in lovely New Forest setting, emphasis on wide choice of reasonably priced good generous food, Gales Butser, HSB and GB and Ringwood Best, decent wines and country wines, cheap soft drinks, good coffee, log fire, civilised banquettes, courteous efficient staff (but service may slow with the wknd crowds), thriving atmosphere, smart and attractive added end dining room (should book – but no bookings Sun lunchtime); may be quiet piped music, dogs welcome despite the carpets, hitching posts, pleasant front terrace and spacious lawn; good value well equipped bedrooms, superb walks towards Burley itself and over Mill Lawn *(Norman and Sheila Davies, BB, Derek and Sylvia Stephenson, A and B D Craig, John H Smith, W W Burke, John Arthur)*

Cadnam [SU3013]

Coach & Horses [Southampton Rd]: Popular for wide choice of good value food from baguettes and baked potatoes to more imaginative dishes, OAP discounts on food and drink, efficient cheerful service *(A D Marsh, Ray Horrocks)*

Compass [Winsor, off Totton-Cadnam road at Bartley crossroads; OS Sheet 195 map ref 317143]: Popular 16th-c bare-boards and beamed local off the beaten track, plain food from good bacon doorsteps to Mon curry and Tues British beef nights (most tables may be booked), real ales inc Gales and Ringwood, May and Aug bank hol beer festivals, friendly helpful landlady, log fires; side garden with decorative arbour, Irish band Thurs, open all day *(Geoff Pidoux, Phyl and Jack Street, Dave Hills)*

☆ *Sir John Barleycorn* [Old Romsey Rd; by M27, junction 1]: Picturesque low-slung newly rethatched pub, attractive medieval core on left with dim lighting, low beams and timbers, more of a chain-pub feel in extension on right, big helpings of good value food, helpful efficient service, well kept ales such as Ringwood Fortyniner, reasonably priced wines, two log fires, no smoking restaurant end; can be very busy; suntrap benches in front, eye-catching flowers *(Phyl and Jack Street, LYM, A D Marsh)*

White Hart [½ mile from M27 junction 1]: Big rambling food-oriented pub, well kept Flowers Original, Greene King Old Speckled Hen, Ringwood Best and Whitbreads Best, pleasant efficient service, simple furnishings and no smoking section; piped music; children in eating area, garden tables *(Dr and Mrs A K Clarke, Phyl and Jack Street, LYM)*

Chandlers Ford [SU4320]

Monks Brook [Hursley Rd]: Welcoming late Victorian pub with wide range of real ales and comfortable lounge *(Dr and Mrs A K Clarke)*

Chilbolton [SU3939]

☆ *Abbots Mitre* [off A3051 S of Andover]: Wide choice of good generous food inc very good value OAP special in side lounge and attractive restaurant with small log fire, well kept ales such as Boddingtons, Flowers Original, Greene King Abbot and Old Speckled Hen and Ringwood, quick smartly dressed staff, separate front public bar and games room; a bit dark, but friendly, busy and roomy; garden with pleasant covered terrace, baskets and tubs of flowers, play area; open all day Sun, attractive village, River Test and other walks *(Michael and Robin Inskip, Phyl and Jack Street)*

Chilworth [SU4118]

Clump [A27 Romsey Rd]: Busy extended largely no smoking restaurant rather than pub, several rooms off central bar inc area with sofas and easy chairs, nice fireplaces, bookshelves, spacious conservatory; wide choice of enjoyable food, well kept Boddingtons, Fullers London Pride and Gales HSB, good choice of wines; unobtrusive piped music; open all day, large garden *(Emma Kingdon, Phyl and Jack Street, B and K Hypher, Jim Bush)*

Clanfield [SD7117]

Hogs Lodge [Gravel Hill]: Large well furnished and well run pub, cosy corners, good generous food in bar and restaurant, well kept Gales ales; big garden with nice views *(Ann and Colin Hunt, Keith and Suzie Stevens)*

Clanville [SU3149]

Red Lion: Updated 16th-c pub with enterprising food in bar, long conservatory and Victorian-style added evening bistro (not Sun-Tues; also Sun lunch), no smoking areas, well kept real ales such as Heritage Stonehenge, friendly service *(Darren Le Poidevin)*

Crondall [SU7948]

☆ ***Hampshire Arms*** [village signed off A287 S of Fleet; Pankridge St]: Relaxed and very friendly unpretentious local, fresh food from two soup cauldrons and good value well filled sandwiches, home-baked baguettes and baked potatoes (not Sun) to good enterprising main dishes cooked to order, so may be a wait, wider evening choice; well kept Greene King IPA, Abbot and Ruddles County and Wadworths 6X, good house wines, enthusiastic young staff, cosy L-shaped bar with hops on beams, sturdy furnishings, huge fireplace and candles in bottles, small conservatory restaurant with fresh flowers and linen napkins, french windows to fenced garden with picnic-sets and floodlit boules pitch; dogs welcome *(Martin and Karen Wake, Ian Phillips, BB)*

Plume of Feathers [The Borough]: Cosy and attractive 15th-c village pub under new licensees, enjoyable food from baguettes and usual bar dishes to more adventurous menu in smarter restaurant end, beams and dark wood, prints on cream walls, open fire in big brick fireplace, Greene King ales, decent wines by the glass, generous food from hot filled baguettes and double-decker sandwiches up, log fire; no piped music, children welcome; two red telephone boxes in garden, picturesque village *(Martin and Karen Wake)*

Crookham [SU7852]

Black Horse [The Street]: Friendly beamed village local with decent straightforward lunchtime food (not Sun), well kept Courage Best, Fullers London Pride, Wadworths 6X and Charles Wells Bombardier; tables out in nice back and side areas with some amusements for children, pleasant Basingstoke Canal towpath walks *(Tony Hobden)*

☆ ***George & Lobster*** [Crondall Rd]: Spaciously refurbished open-plan food pub with wide and interesting choice of good eats inc seafood, funny french accents and hats for bar food part, welcoming young licensees, very good wine choice, Courage Best and Directors, pleasant conservatory restaurant popular lunchtime with business people *(Ian Phillips, Martin and Karen Wake, Mr and Mrs J Brown)*

Curdridge [SU5314]

Cricketers [Curdridge Lane, off B3035 just under a mile NE of A334 junction]: Open-plan low-ceilinged Victorian village local with banquettes in lounge area, little-changed public part (can be smoky), rather smart dining area, friendly attentive licensees, wide choice of well presented generous food inc sandwiches and good value daily specials, Greene King Abbot and Old Speckled Hen; quiet piped music (live Thurs; tables on front lawn, two friendly dogs, pleasant footpaths *(Jenny Cridland, Gordon Cooper, Ron Shelton, Val and Alan Green)*

Dogmersfield [SU7852]

☆ ***Queens Head*** [village signed off A287 and B3016 W of Fleet]: Huge choice of attractively priced food from filled baguettes through lots of salads to restauranty main dishes, masses of menu boards and all tables set for eating in well divided dining bar, dark pink walls, some stripped brickwork, a couple of low beams, well kept Courage Best, Fullers London Pride and Youngs Special, good choice of wines esp New World, smart soft drinks, very swift friendly service; well reproduced piped pop music, booking advised evenings (two sittings); tree-shaded picnic-sets on front grass, pretty setting, cl Mon *(Andy and Yvonne Cunningham, BB, Ian Phillips)*

Droxford [SU6018]

Bakers Arms [High St]: Welcoming and roomy bar and dining areas, attractive old brick pillars, blazing log fire, food inc several Sun roasts (best to book), quick cheerful service, Badger Tanglefoot and Ringwood, unobtrusive piped music; conservatory, children welcome, small play area *(Peter and Audrey Dowsett)*

Hurdles [Station Rd, Brockbridge]: Dining pub with friendly new licensee doing decent food; Fullers London Pride and Charles Wells Bombardier, though little room for drinkers; nice tables outside *(Val and Alan Green)*

Dummer [SU5846]

Queen [½ mile from M3 junction 7; take Dummer slip road]: Very handy for motorway, with beams, lots of softly lit alcoves, log fire, Queen and steeplechase prints, food in bar and no smoking service-charge restaurant allowing children (they may keep your credit card), well kept Courage Best, Fullers London Pride and Greene King Old Speckled Hen; fruit machine, well reproduced piped music, no mobile phones; picnic-sets under cocktail parasols on terrace and in extended back garden, attractive village with ancient church *(KC, LYM, Geoffrey Kemp, B N F and M Parkin, Simon Collett-Jones)*

Dunbridge [SU3126]

Mill Arms [Barley Hill]: Friendly and cosily unpretentious open-plan bars with stripped pine beams, sofas, open fire, no smoking conservatory restaurant, decent blackboard food inc some interesting dishes, two ales brewed for the pub by Hampshire and Itchen Valley with a guest such as Stonehenge, late Sept beer festival, cafetière coffee, refurbished skittle alley; tables in pleasant two-level garden with wendy house, bedrooms *(Phyl and Jack Street, Tony Hobden, Margaret Ross)*

Dundridge [SU5718]

☆ ***Hampshire Bowman*** [off B3035 towards Droxford, Swanmore, then right at Bishops W signpost]: Friendly and cosy though not smart, with great atmosphere and mix of customers (children, dogs and walkers welcome, usually some classic cars or vintage motorcycles); well kept Archers Village and Golden and Ringwood Best and Fortyniner tapped from the cask, decent house wines, country wines, home-made food inc quite a few vegetarian dishes (and Sun bar nibbles), sensible prices, efficient staff, battered corner armchair for non-smokers, gentle lurcher/collie cross called Daisy; tables on spacious and attractive lawn, good downland walks *(Ann and Colin Hunt, W A Evershed, Val and Alan Green, LYM)*

East Boldre [SU3700]

☆ ***Turf Cutters Arms*** [Main Rd]: Relaxed and welcoming small dim-lit New Forest country local, lots of beams and pictures, elderly furnishings, two log fires, good freshly cooked food inc game, Flowers Original, Wadworths 6X and a guest such as Gales HSB, several dozen malt whiskies; friendly large black dog, tables in garden, some good heathland walks; three big old-fashioned bedrooms, simple but comfortable, good breakfast *(Phyl and Jack Street, Charles and Pauline Stride, Ben Stephenson)*

East End [SZ3696]

East End Arms [back road Lymington—Beaulieu, parallel to B3054]: Popular New Forest pub with pleasant atmosphere, well kept Ringwood ales tapped from the cask, good value home cooking, log fire, curious tree trunk in lounge bar, tables in small garden *(E S Funnell)*

East Meon [SU6822]

☆ ***George*** [Church St; signed off A272 W of Petersfield, and off A32 in West Meon]: Rambling and relaxing rustic pub with heavy beams and inglenooks, four log fires, cosy areas around central bar counter, deal tables and horse tack; well kept Badger Best and Tanglefoot, decent wines, country wines, wide choice of substantial enjoyable food, friendly licensees; children welcome, good outdoor seating arrangements, quiz night Sun; small but comfortable bedrooms (book well ahead), good breakfast; pretty village with fine church, good walks *(Ann and Colin Hunt, LYM, Mark Percy, Lesley Mayoh, Cathy Robinson, Ed Coombe, W A Evershed, Patrick Hancock, Brian and Anna Marsden)*

Easton [SU5132]

☆ ***Cricketers*** [off B3047]: Open-plan village local with well kept ales such as Otter, Ringwood Best, Timothy Taylors Landlord and Wessex Slip, wide choice of good value interesting piping hot food served promptly, friendly attentive traditional licensees, pleasant mix of pub furnishings, small bright restaurant, good wine range; darts and shove-ha'penny one end, jazz duo Weds *(Mr and Mrs R W Allan, Ron Shelton, Dr and Mrs A K Clarke, Lynn Sharpless)*

Emery Down [SU2808]

☆ ***New Forest*** [village signed off A35 just W of Lyndhurst]: Good position in one of the nicest parts of the Forest, with good walks nearby; attractive softly lit separate areas on varying levels, each with its own character, gently ageing furniture, hunting prints, two log fires, good imaginative generous food from filled baps up, well kept Greene King Abbot and two Ringwood beers, wide choice of realistically priced house wines, proper coffee, staff cope well with lively bustle; children allowed, small but pleasant three-level garden *(W W Burke, Mike and Sue Richardson, Dick and Madeleine Brown, LYM, Phyl and Jack Street)*

Emsworth [SU7406]

Coal Exchange [Ships Quay, South St]: Unspoilt but comfortable compact L-shaped Victorian local, low ceilings, lots of locals and yachtsmen, well kept Gales ales, cheerful service, good value lunchtime food inc good crab salad and popular Sun lunch (open all day then), real fire each end; tables outside, handy for Wayfarers Walk and Solent Walk *(Ann and Colin Hunt, Mr and Mrs T A Bryan, Val and Alan Green)*

Crown: Good range of ales, good food and friendly service in bar and restaurant, competitive prices, nice Sun lunchtime bar nibbles; bedrooms *(Ann and Colin Hunt)*

☆ ***Kings Arms*** [Havant Rd]: Comfortable and relaxing local popular for generous well priced interesting food cooked by landlady, fresh veg, good choice of wines, cheerful landlord, well kept Gales and a guest beer, good coffee, small restaurant area; pleasant garden behind *(Ann and Colin Hunt)*

Lord Raglan [Queen St]: Welcoming little Gales pub with nice atmosphere, good range of food esp fish, cheerful long-serving landlord, log fire, restaurant (must book summer wknds); live music Sun, children welcome if eating, pleasant sea-view garden behind *(Ann and Colin Hunt)*

Enborne [SU4264]

Craven Arms [W, towards Hamstead Marshall]: Recently refurbished, with some emphasis on enjoyable food, good choice of around five real ales; plenty of room in and out, cl Mon *(Sue and Jeff Evans)*

Everton [SZ2994]

☆ ***Crown*** [Old Christchurch Rd, 3 miles W of Lymington]: Good interesting food cooked to order (so may be a wait), smallish bookable no smoking dining room off relaxing and informal traditional main bar, log fire, lots of jugs and china, well kept Bass, Ringwood and Whitbreads-related ales, friendly attentive service; lively separate public bar with pool, darts, table football, good juke box and welcoming chatty locals; no dogs, picnic-sets on front terrace and back grass, some good walks *(Peter Adams, A D Marsh, Dr and Mrs A K Clarke, Phyl and Jack Street)*

Exton [SU6120]

Shoe [village signed from A32]: Smart façade and neat bright décor, attractive light oak-panelled room off bar, cheerful helpful service, popular food (not Sun night) in bar and cosy log-fire restaurant (may find all tables booked for Sun lunch – very popular with older people, with small helpings on request), well kept Wadworths; piped music; tables on lawn down to River Meon – pretty village, good walks *(Cathy Robinson, Ed Coombe, W A Evershed, Stephen and Jean Curtis)*

Fair Oak [SU4919]

Fox & Hounds [Winchester Rd (A3051)]: Busy, comfortable and attractive open-plan family dining pub with exposed brickwork, beam-and-plank ceilings, soft lighting; wide choice of good value food (all day wknds), good polite service, Courage Directors and Greene King Ruddles County, decent wines, no smoking conservatory; may be piped music; pretty hanging baskets, play area by car park, path to nearby Bishopstoke woods *(Phyl and Jack Street)*

Fareham [SU5806]

Cob & Pen [Wallington Shore Rd, not far from M27 junction 11]: Pleasant pine furnishings, flagstones and carpets, Hook Norton Best and Ringwood ales, good value straightforward food, nice separate games room; large garden *(Ann and Colin Hunt, Val and Alan Green)*

Lord Arthur Lee [West St]: Wetherspoons pub/diner named for the local 1900s MP who presented Chequers to the nation, attractively priced well kept beers, good value food *(Val and Alan Green)*

White Horse [North Wallington]: Smart friendly two-bar pub with Oakleaf ales (from Gosport), good fresh standard blackboard food, pleasant service *(Charles and Pauline Stride, Val and Alan Green)*

Farringdon [SU7035]

Royal Oak [Gosport Rd (A32 S of Alton), Lower Farringdon]: Pleasant open-plan roadside pub with good choice of straightforward generous food inc Sun roasts, quick friendly service, well kept real ales, log fire, pictures, brasses and some sturdier bric-a-brac such as smith's bellows; children welcome *(Betty Laker)*

Finchdean [SU7312]

George: Cheerful service with plenty of neat staff, decent food in lounge and smartened up public bar; good nearby walks *(Ann and Colin Hunt, W A Evershed, Jess and George Cowley)*

Fleet [SU80534]

Oatsheaf [Crookham Rd/Reading Rd]: 1920s corner pub refurbished as popular and comfortable local, clean, modern and largely no smoking, with good choice of low-priced snacks and meals, Bass, Greene King IPA and Worthington, no music or machines; large grounds, picnic-sets on lawns behind *(Ian Phillips)*

Fordingbridge [SU1414]

Ship [High St]: Strong well done nautical theme, welcoming staff, well kept real ales *(Dr and Mrs A K Clarke)*

Four Marks [SU6735]

Windmill [A31 Alton—Alresford]: Large main-road family dining pub, cosy feel, cheap plentiful food, quick pleasant service, carvery Sat evening and Sun lunch, OAP bargains Thurs, well kept ales, pleasant conservatory, separate locals' bar with skittle alley; adventure playground *(Phyl and Jack Street)*

Freefolk [SU4848]

Watership Down [Freefolk Priors, N of B3400 – sharp lane uphill at W end of village]: Fine choice of changing well kept ales from small breweries in genuine unaffected compact village pub, partly brick-floored, with functional furnishings, popular food from sandwiches to good value Sun roasts, no smoking conservatory; games area with plenty of old-fashioned slot machines and table football; piped music, Sun quiz night; nicely placed above grassy bank, huge attractive garden with play area and rabbit pen, pleasant walks and off-road cycling *(Dr and Mrs A K Clarke, T G Thomas, Mick Simmons)*

Frogham [SU1712]

☆ ***Foresters Arms*** [Abbotswell Rd]: Busy and well run extensively refurbished New Forest pub, flagstones and small woodburner, well kept Wadworths and guest ales, decent wines, reasonably priced enjoyable blackboard food from sandwiches to very popular Sun lunch, extended dining room; children welcome, pleasant garden and front verandah; small camp site adjacent, good walks *(John and Joan Calvert, LYM, J and B Cressey)*

Gosport [SZ5998]

☆ ***Alverbank House*** [Stokes Bay Rd, Alverstoke]: Pleasant lounge with half a dozen well kept interesting changing ales in immaculate hotel in woods at end of Walpole Park, over road from promenade; good choice of food with plenty for vegetarians, five well kept real ales such as Malton Ryedale, Ringwood and Vale Best, friendly well trained staff, piped music; nice big garden with Solent and Isle of Wight view and play area, bedrooms very well appointed *(Val and Alan Green)*

☆ ***Clarence*** [Mumby Rd (A32)]: Partly 18th-c, incorporating a former chapel from the Isle of Wight, heavy furnishings, old books, prints and other pictures, good-sized no smoking area; wide choice of food in bar and upstairs restaurant, guest beers and ones from their own microbrewery (viewed through glass panels in bar and minstrel's gallery), log and coal fires, relaxed atmosphere; dogs welcome, no games or piped music; medieval evenings, open all day *(Christina and Bob Buxey, Ann and Colin Hunt)*

Dolphin [Fort Rd, Alverstoke]: Comfortable family pub near sea, nautical décor, well kept beers inc Gales HSB, decent wines, reasonably priced popular food, quick friendly service, no piped music; big well laid out garden with huge play area, views to Isle of Wight *(Peter and Audrey Dowsett)*

Queens [Queens Rd]: Bare-boards pub whose landlady expertly keeps six or more changing strong ales with Badger Tanglefoot as a regular fixture, three areas off bar with coal fire in interesting carved fireplace; very quick service, perhaps huge filled rolls and other simple food; sensibly placed darts, family area with TV, no piped music, quiz night Thurs; bedrooms, open all day Sat *(Ann and Colin Hunt)*

Hamble [SU4806]

☆ ***Olde Whyte Harte*** [High St; 3 miles from M27 junction 8]: Cheerful low-beamed bar, lots of tables in well integrated flagstoned eating area, welcoming licensees and helpful pleasant staff, blazing inglenook log fire, imaginative well priced fresh food inc plenty of fish, well kept Gales Best, BBB and HSB, lots of country wines, decent coffee, yachting memorabilia; piped music may be loud and lively; children in eating area, some seats outside; handy for nature reserve *(LYM, Dr J Digby)*

Hambledon [SU6716]

☆ ***Bat & Ball*** [Broadhalfpenny Down; about 2 miles E towards Clanfield]: Extended dining pub opp seminal cricket pitch (matches most summer Sundays), plenty of cricket memorabilia, comfortable modern furnishings in three rooms and panelled restaurant, log fire; energetic landlord, well kept Gales ales, good interesting food from modestly priced snacks to fresh fish, lovely downs views *(W A Evershed, LYM, Tim Wellock)*

☆ ***Vine*** [West St]: Open-plan but traditional, with beams, panelling, old prints, china, ornaments, farm tools, high-backed settles, log fire – even a well in its dining area; chatty and smiley staff, well kept Cheriton Pots, Gales HSB and Charles Wells Bombardier, country wines, good range of generous fresh food, delightful dog; shove-ha'penny, darts; small informal back garden, pretty downland village with plenty of walks *(Val and Alan Green, P R and S A White)*

Havant [SU7106]

☆ ***Old House At Home*** [South St]: Much modernised low-beamed Tudor pub, nice rambling alcovey feel, two fireplaces in lounge, well kept Gales BBB, GB and HSB, welcoming licensees; piped music (live Sat – very popular with young people Fri/Sat night), back garden *(Ann and Colin Hunt, D P and J A Sweeney, Val and Alan Green, LYM)*

Parchment Makers [Park Road North]: Long Wetherspoons in former tax office, their usual food, up to 10 real ales, good service *(Ann and Colin Hunt)*

Robin Hood [Homewell]: Relaxing old pub with low ceilings in rambling open-plan bar, well kept Gales ales tapped from the cask, reasonably priced food, open fire; sensibly placed darts *(Ann and Colin Hunt)*

Wheelwrights Arms [Emsworth Rd]: Friendly relaxing traditional pub, four real ales, sensibly priced food, no smoking restaurant area; dogs and children welcome, bedrooms *(Anita Bushnell)*

Hazeley [SU7459]

Shoulder of Mutton [Hazeley Heath]: Warmly friendly old dining pub, lots of regular lunchers for consistently good choice of generous home-made food from ploughman's to good steaks (no snacks just meals on Sun, when many tables are booked), friendly helpful service, good fire in cosy lounge, no smoking area, well kept Courage ales; quiet piped music; attractive building, terrace and garden *(R Lake, Colin McKerrow)*

Herriard [SS6744]

Fur & Feathers [pub signed just off A339 Basingstoke—Alton]: New young licensees doing good value home-made food from filled rolls and baked potatoes up in open-plan pub with stripped pine tables and chairs on bare boards, Cheriton Pots, fff Moondance and Shepherd Neame Spitfire, log fire, lots of jockey cigarette cards; well lit pool table in carpeted area with big prints; picnic-sets out on front tarmac *(Jill Hurley, BB)*

Highclere [SU4359]

Red House [Andover Rd (A343)]: Friendly local with good value food inc children's, well kept real ales, relaxing lounge with pine furniture, bar with pool; tables out in front *(Mr and Mrs C Crichton)*

Hill Head [SU5402]

Osborne View [Hill Head Rd]: Roomy modern red plush clifftop pub with three stepped-back levels and picture windows for stunning views to the Isle of Wight, well kept Badger Best, Tanglefoot and ales from the Gribble at Oving, efficient service, nautical prints and memorabilia, no music, popular food inc children's and evening restaurant; open all day (busy wknds), garden and beach access, near Titchfield Haven bird reserve *(Jenny Cridland, Gordon Cooper, Michael and Robin Inskip, Val and Alan Green)*

Hook [SU7354]

☆ ***Crooked Billet*** [about a mile towards London]: Wide choice of good attractively presented food all day, swift pleasant service under good long-serving licensees, homely log fires, well kept Courage Best and Directors and two guest beers, good range of soft drinks; soft piped music; attractive garden by stream with trout and ducks; children welcome *(David Swann)*

Horndean [SU7013]

Ship & Bell [London Rd]: Comfortable and spacious pub/hotel adjoining Gales brewery, full range of their beers kept well, good range of wines, good standard food, quick friendly service, cheerfully relaxed bar with deep well, snug lounge with broad low steps up to dining room, interesting quotations and photographs; 14 bedrooms with own bathrooms, nice walk to Catherington church *(Phyl and Jack Street, Ann and Colin Hunt, Joan and Michel Hooper-Immins)*

Horsebridge [SU3430]

☆ ***John o' Gaunt*** [off A3057 Romsey—Andover,

just SW of Kings Somborne]: Retiring village pub very popular with walkers for good attractively priced food, well kept Itchen Valley Fagins, Palmers BB and Ringwood Best and Fortyniner, decent wines by the glass, friendly landlord, simple L-shaped bar, log fire, no piped music; pub black labrador, dogs welcome, picnic-sets out by mill on River Test, good walks *(Lynn Sharpless, Prof and Mrs Tony Palmer, Ron Shelton)*

Houghton [SU3432]

Boot [S of Stockbridge]: Quiet country pub with good interesting food in roomy and attractive dining bar on left, attentive service, pleasant garden running down to lovely stretch of River Test; good walks, and on Test Valley cycle way *(Norman and Sheila Davies)*

Hursley [SU4225]

Kings Head [A3090 Winchester—Romsey]: Substantial food pub with good value fresh food from temptingly filled baguettes to choice of steaks, no smoking dining area on left, well kept Fullers London Pride, decent wine; tables outside, skittle alley in cellar bar, attractive village apart from the traffic *(Phyl and Jack Street, J F M and M West, Lynn Sharpless)*

Ibsley [SU1409]

Old Beams [A338 Salisbury—Ringwood]: Busy big black and white thatched chain pub, large main room divided by panelling and canopied log-effect gas fire, lots of varnished wooden tables and country-kitchen chairs under aged oak beams, largely no smoking restaurant with own bar, no smoking buffet area and conservatory, Theakstons Best and XB, country wines; fruit machine and piped music; open all day (cl winter wkdy afternoons) *(the Didler, JP, PP, LYM, Phyl and Jack Street)*

Itchen Abbas [SU5332]

Trout [4 miles from M3 junction 9; B3047]: Smallish country pub with young and cheerful new licensees, unpretentious lounge with no smoking dining area, chatty public bar with traditional games, well kept Greene King IPA, Old Speckled Hen, Ruddles Best and County, decent wines; comfortable bedrooms, tables in sheltered pretty side garden, good river and downland walks nearby *(Lynn Sharpless, Phyl and Jack Street, LYM)*

Keyhaven [SZ3091]

☆ *Gun*: Busy yet cosy 17th-c pub looking over boatyard and sea to Isle of Wight, good choice of generous food using local produce; low beams, lots of nautical memorabilia, well kept beers such as Flowers, Greene King Old Speckled Hen, Marstons Pedigree and Ringwood True Glory, well over a hundred malt whiskies, bar billiards; children in back conservatory, garden with swings and fishpond *(Mayur Shah, Colin McKerrow, A D Marsh)*

Kingsclere [SU5258]

Crown [Newbury Rd]: Elegantly reworked former school, long comfortable partly panelled lounge with central log fire, good reasonably priced food, striking no smoking hammer-beam dining room (another allows smokers), well kept real ales, attentive service, games in simpler public bar; children in family room, nearby downs walks *(Dr and Mrs A K Clarke, Phyl and Jack Street, LYM)*

Langstone [SU7105]

☆ *Ship* [A3023]: Busy waterside 18th-c former grain store, smart and well cared for, plenty of tables out on quiet quay, lovely view across to Hayling Island from roomy dimly lit nautical bar with upper deck dining room, good no smoking areas, fast friendly helpful service, full Gales range kept well with a guest beer, good choice of wines by the generous glass, country wines, log fire, wide range of generous food inc fresh fish and platters for two, good no smoking areas; children's room, open all day, good coast walks *(Joan and Michel Hooper-Immins, Charles and Pauline Stride, W A Evershed, D P and J A Sweeney, Irene and Derek Flewin, A and B D Craig, Val and Alan Green, Tony Hobden, Geoff Pidoux, Tony and Wendy Hobden)*

Lee-on-the-Solent [SU5600]

☆ *Bun Penny* [Manor Way]: Carefully restored and extended, with low beams and flagstones, conservatory and restaurant, pleasant furnishings and bric-a-brac, two log fires (notices ask you to put on another log if you're cold), good choice of good food (and free peanuts), well kept Boddingtons, Flowers and Wadworths 6X, decent wines, daily papers, friendly efficient staff; garden, lots of flowers in summer *(Jenny Cridland, Gordon Cooper, Jess and George Cowley, Bryan McAlley, Val and Alan Green)*

Linwood [SU1910]

☆ *Red Shoot* [signed from A338 via Moyles Court, and from A31; go on up heath]: Nice New Forest setting, lots of space, attractive old tables, mixed chairs and rugs on bare boards, country pictures, large back dining area with generous good value food inc good sandwiches, interesting children's choice and OAP bargain, friendly atmosphere and staff, well kept Wadworths ales and Forest Gold or Toms Tipple brewed at the pub, Mar and Oct beer festivals; children, dogs and muddy boots welcome, some disabled access, open all day wknds and summer – very touristy then (by big campsite and caravan park) *(M Blatchly, G Coates, Uta and John Owlett, Rev John Hibberd)*

Liphook [SU8330]

Links Hotel [Portsmouth Rd]: Good range of beers and wines, enjoyable varied restaurant food esp crab and lobster, good atmosphere, friendly staff *(Miss C F Skelton)*

Liss [SU7826]

Jolly Drovers [London Rd, Hill Brow]: Straightforward pub notable for its very friendly service (good with disabled people); good choice of food inc good fish, real ales, garden *(Gloria Bax)*

Little London [SU6359]

Plough [Silchester Rd, off A340 N of Basingstoke]: Cosy unspoilt local with tiled floor, low beams, friendly landlord, limited food inc lots of good value baguettes, well kept Ringwood and interesting guest beers, log fire, darts, bar billiards; attractive garden, handy for

Pamber Forest and Calleva Roman remains *(J V Dadswell, Pat and Robert Watt, Mick Simmons)*

Locks Heath [SU5006]

☆ ***Jolly Farmer*** [2½ miles from M27 junction 9; A27 towards Bursledon, left into Locks Rd, at end T-junction right into Warsash Rd then left at hire shop into Fleet End Rd]: Emphasis on wide choice of food from filled baps to steaks and good value very popular Sun lunch in extensive series of softly lit rooms with nice old scrubbed tables and a forest of interesting bric-a-brac and prints, coal-effect gas fires, no smoking area, well kept Flowers Original, Gales HSB and Fullers London Pride, country wines, interesting landlord, neat friendly staff; piped music, service charge for parties of over 8; two sheltered terraces, one with a play area; bedrooms *(Charles and Pauline Stride, Roger and Pauline Pearce, Ann and Colin Hunt, LYM, Val and Alan Green)*

Longparish [SU4344]

Plough [B3048, off A303 just E of Andover]: Comfortable open-plan dining lounge divided by arches, pleasant atmosphere, very wide food choice from sandwiches with chips to steaks (service can slow right down), children's dishes, partly no smoking restaurant, well kept Boddingtons, Greene King Old Speckled Hen, Wadworths 6X and a guest such as Hampshire King Alfreds, country wines; piped music; children in eating areas, tables on terrace and in nice garden with pets corner, bedrooms *(Lynn Sharpless, Jess and George Cowley, Darren Le Poidevin, Ann and Colin Hunt, Mrs J Ekins-Daukes, Derek Allpass, Geoffrey Kemp, LYM, Geoff Palmer, David and Ruth Shillitoe, Chris Mawson, Gloria Bax, Jayne Capp)*

Lower Wield [SU6339]

☆ ***Yew Tree*** [off A339 NW of Alton, via Medstead or Bentworth]: Primarily a very good if pricy French restaurant, with good wines and friendly attentive service, but also has small central flagstoned bar used by locals and walkers, with real ales tapped from the cask and a good log fire; nice quiet spot by village cricket pitch, tables out on front terrace and in garden, attractive open walking country *(Michael Huberty, J Hale, Phyl and Jack Street, LYM, Louise English, Christopher and Elise Way)*

Lymington [SZ3294]

☆ ***Fishermans Rest*** [All Saints Rd, Woodside]: Wide choice of good interesting food inc very popular Sun lunch, reasonable prices, well kept Ringwood ales, decent wines, friendly staff, pleasant atmosphere, plenty of locals at bar; can get busy, wknd booking recommended *(A D Marsh, Steve Chambers, Mike and Sue Richardson, John and Joan Calvert, Mr and Mrs R Buckley)*

☆ ***Kings Head*** [Quay Hill]: 17th-c, timbers dividing unpretentiously upmarket bar into attractive cottagey areas, well kept Fullers London Pride, Gales HSB, Greene King Old Speckled Hen and Ringwood True Glory, welcoming staff, good food and atmosphere, comfortable settles, separate panelled back room with old-fashioned tables and dining chairs, tankards hanging from beams, open fire, local prints; can get very busy *(Sue and Mike Todd)*

Toll House [Southampton Rd (A337)]: Wide choice of good value food inc children's and Sun lunch, good friendly atmosphere, several real ales, pleasant efficient staff, oak beams; good-sized children's room, pleasant cottagey bedrooms *(A D Marsh, Phyl and Jack Street)*

Lyndhurst [SU2908]

Crown [High St]: Best Western hotel, cheerful log fire in cosy traditional panelled bar, stags' heads and antlers, obliging efficient staff, well kept Ringwood Best and Porter, good value well served food; bedrooms, fine Forest walks *(A D Marsh, Shirley Mackenzie, George Atkinson, Phyl and Jack Street, Dr and Mrs A K Clarke)*

Stag [High St]: Plush bar with well kept Greene King IPA and Abbot, limited bar lunches, smart Italian restaurant, good service *(Joan and Michel Hooper-Immins)*

Marchwood [SU3810]

☆ ***Pilgrim*** [Hythe Rd, off A326 at Twiggs Lane]: Attractive thatched pub with red plush banquettes in long L-shaped bar, wide choice of consistently good value food, welcoming service, well kept Bass and Courage, cosy fire, separate more expensive restaurant; can be crowded, handy for otter and owl park at Longdown; neat garden *(John Hart, Lynn Sharpless, LYM, E W and S M Wills)*

Mattingley [SU7357]

Leather Bottle [3 miles from M3 junction 5; in Hook, turn right-and-left on to B3349 Reading Road (former A32)]: Wisteria-covered tiled dining pub, well spaced tables in linked areas, black beams, flagstones and bare boards, good inglenook log fire, extension opening on to covered heated terrace, well kept Courage Best and Greene King Abbot with a guest beer, generous often good food; piped music; picnic-sets in two pretty garden areas, one pleasantly modern *(B and K Hypher, Karen and Graham Oddey, LYM, Ian Phillips)*

Meonstoke [SU6119]

Bucks Head [just off A32 N of Droxford; Bucks Head Hill]: Smallish 60s-style dining lounge with dark red banquettes and good log fire, well kept Greene King IPA and Ruddles County, decent wines, cheerful new young licensees, comfortable terracotta-coloured public bar with cosy fire (open all day Sun at least in spring and summer); pleasant walled garden, lovely village setting with ducks on pretty little River Meon, good walks, bedrooms *(Ann and Colin Hunt, Lynn Sharpless, W A Evershed)*

Milford-on-Sea [SZ2891]

White Horse [Keyhaven Rd]: Big friendly village inn with eight consistently well kept real ales, food very popular midweek with older people; sheltered garden; *(A and B D Craig)*

Minstead [SU2811]

☆ ***Trusty Servant*** [just off A31 nr M27 junction 1]: Three opened-up rooms inc sizeable restaurant area, ageing furniture and lots of character, wide choice of good generous food from huge baguettes with chips to imaginative main dishes, fresh fish and game, well kept changing ales such as Fullers London Pride, Ringwood Best and Wadworths 6X, annual beer festival, Thatcher's farm cider, decent house wines and country wines, very pleasant staff; may be piped music; open all day, tables in good-sized garden, simple bedrooms, good breakfast, pretty New Forest village with wandering ponies and easy walks *(Alan and Paula McCully, DWAJ, D P and J A Sweeney, Dr M and Mrs G S Crawford, BB, Mike and Sue Richardson, Dick and Madeleine Brown, Basil Minson)*

Monxton [SU3144]

Black Swan [High St]: Pretty extended pub among rose-covered thatched cottages, cosy lounge area with easy chairs and settee, two dining areas (one no smoking) off the main bar, wide range of good straightforward food from ample sandwiches or baked potatoes to steaks, well kept beers, decent wine, friendly licensees and good quick service; tables in courtyard and garden with play area, barbecue and slow-flowing stream *(Margaret Ross, John Braine-Hartnell, Phyl and Jack Street)*

Mortimer West End [SU6363]

Red Lion [Church Rd; Silchester turn off Mortimer—Aldermaston rd]: Country dining pub with good food from generous doorstep sandwiches up (they don't let you stray from the exact menu), well kept Badger and other ales, lots of beams, stripped masonry, timbers and panelling, good log fire, brisk service; quiet piped music; plenty of seats in pleasant garden with play area, and on small flower-filled front terrace, open all day, handy for Roman Silchester *(LYM, Pat and Robert Watt, J V Dadswell)*

Turners Arms [Fairfield Park, West End Rd, Mortimer Common]: Welcoming L-shaped open-plan Brakspears pub with their beers inc Mild, full range of decent generous bar food inc OAP special in no smoking dining area, prompt pleasant service, log fire; tables in garden *(June and Robin Savage, Tony and Wendy Hobden)*

Nether Wallop [SU2936]

☆ ***Five Bells*** [signed off B3084 W of Stockbridge]: Beamed village pub with long cushioned settles and good log fire, new young licensees doing enjoyable food, well kept Badger beers, traditional games in locals' bar, small restaurant, provision for children; seats outside, pretty thatched village *(LYM, Phyl and Jack Street)*

Newtown [SU4764]

Swan [A339 2 miles S of Newbury, by junction with old A34]: Attractive old-world flagstoned pub with friendly helpful staff, good interesting food, well kept Badger ales, well chosen wine list, old photographs; quite a quiet spot since the bypass *(Keith and Suzie Stevens, Stephen and Judy Parish)*

North Waltham [SU5645]

Fox [signed off A30 SW of Basingstoke; handy for M3 junction 7]: Comfortable village local in attractive spot, wide choice of food inc lots of seasonal game (landlord an ex-gamekeeper) in two bars and bright elongated dining area with log fire, well kept real ales, friendly well organised service; quiet piped music, darts, big-screen sports TV and juke box in public bar; children welcome, tables in garden, pleasant village *(Geoff Palmer, Phyl and Jack Street)*

Otterbourne [SU4623]

Old Forge [Main Rd]: Former restaurant pleasantly refurbished as Vintage Inn, well organised, with their usual decent food, good service, Bass and Worthington, good atmosphere *(Phyl and Jack Street)*

Over Wallop [SU2838]

White Hart: Pretty little thatched pub, warm, quiet and friendly, with Boddingtons, Flowers and Ringwood ales, decent food, open fire; tables on the lawn, good footpath network *(J R and J Moon, Phyl and Jack Street)*

Pamber End [SU6158]

Queens College Arms [Aldermaston Rd (A340)]: Large roadside pub with good value well presented food, well kept real ales, friendly staff, good atmosphere with a faintly elegant feel, roomy restaurant *(Dr and Mrs A K Clarke)*

Petersfield [SU7423]

☆ ***Good Intent*** [College St]: 16th-c core with low oak beams and well spaced good-sized pine tables, Fullers London Pride and other well kept ales, wide choice of decent food inc lots of unusual sausages, smart staff, cosy family area *(Phyl and Jack Street, W A Evershed, Patrick Hancock, Val and Alan Green)*

Portchester [SU6204]

Cormorant [next to Portchester Castle]: Big open-plan dining pub with solid 1930s feel, reasonably priced generous home-made food all day, well kept ales such as Fullers London Pride, Gales GB and HSB and Marstons Pedigree, cafetière coffee, children in raised dining area; tables on terrace with flower tubs, in pleasant close, views over Portsmouth harbour; plenty of parking *(Pete Yearsley, Val and Alan Green)*

Portsmouth [SU6500]

Connaught Arms [Guildford Rd/Penhale Rd]: Attractive and relaxing Tudor corner local with friendly long-serving licensees, good value straightforward food from lots of pasties to Sun roast, well kept changing ales such as Bass, Cheriton Pots and Fullers London Pride, sensibly placed darts; terrace *(Ann and Colin Hunt)*

Dolphin [High St, Old Portsmouth]: Spacious old timber-framed Hogshead with wide choice of food inc Sun roasts, half a dozen or more well kept ales, friendly staff, good log fire, cosy snug; video games; open all day Sat, children welcome in eating area, small terrace *(Ann and Colin Hunt, Keith and Suzie Stevens)*

Fountain [London Rd, North End]: Fairly large spick and span bar with family room off, nicely polished brass, interesting prints, mirrors each end, well kept Gales ales; seats outside *(Ann and Colin Hunt)*

George [Queen St, nr dockyard entrance]: Cosy and quiet one-room nautical pub with leather seats and panelling in front, more comfortably plush at back, well kept Wadworths 6X and Youngs, friendly staff, log fire, covered well and Nelson pictures, separate food bar; handy for dockyard and HMS *Victory (Ann and Colin Hunt, Jess and George Cowley, R T and J C Moggridge)*

Sallyport [High St, Old Portsmouth]: Comfortable spick-and-span hotel with relaxing beamed bar, leather chesterfields, soft lighting, lots of naval prints, well kept chilled Bass, Gales HSB, Greene King Abbot and Marstons Pedigree, enjoyable reasonably priced bar food esp fish, efficient friendly staff, decent coffee, upstairs restaurant; comfortable bedrooms *(Alan Thomas, Steve Whalley, Ann and Colin Hunt, Neil and Anita Christopher)*

☆ ***Still & West*** [Bath Sq, Old Portsmouth]: The star is for the position by the narrow harbour mouth, with big windows for vibrant views even to the Isle of Wight – but you pay for it; nautical décor, usual bar food, well kept Gales BB and HSB, upper partly no smoking restaurant; piped music may be intrusive; open all day, children welcome, lots of picnic-sets out on terrace *(LYM, Steve Whalley, W A Evershed, Mike and Jennifer Marsh, Ann and Colin Hunt, David and Carole Chapman, LM, Charlie Harris, Brenda and Rob Fincham, Ken Flawn)*

Surrey Arms [Surrey St]: Comfortable two-bar backstreet local popular lunchtime for good food, good choice of well kept beer; bedrooms *(Ann and Colin Hunt)*

Tap [London Rd, North End]: Simple open-plan pub with 10 or more changing well kept ales, bright and lively atmosphere, genuine service, straightforward wkdy bar food inc king-sized sandwiches *(Ann and Colin Hunt)*

Toby Carvery [Copnor Rd/Norway Rd, Hilsea]: Popular family dining pub specialising in generous daily carvery, busy on Sun (no booking); quick friendly service inc drinks at tables, real ale, decent value wine, tables in garden *(Peter and Audrey Dowsett)*

Wellington [High St, off Grand Parade, Old Portsmouth]: Comfortable open-plan pub with large Georgian bow window, near seafront and historic square tower, relaxed chatty atmosphere, good bar food esp fresh fish, well kept Wadworths 6X and a beer brewed for the pub, generous wine, friendly experienced licensees, courteous old-fashioned service *(Steve Whalley, Ann and Colin Hunt)*

Ringwood [SU1604]

Elm Tree [Hightown]: Attractive and roomy thatched pub converted from 300-year-old farm, well kept Ringwood Best, good value standard food, quietly efficient staff; may be piped pop music, big-screen sports TV; tables out under cocktail parasols *(R T and J C Moggridge)*

☆ ***Fish*** [off A31 W of town]: Several cosy areas, intriguing fishy decorations, bustling atmosphere, interesting choice of well presented reasonably priced food, well kept Boddingtons, Brakspears, Flowers and Fullers, good service, coffee and tea, log fire, no smoking eating area allowing children, no dogs; piped music may intrude; tables on riverside lawn (traffic noise) with play area and budgerigar aviary, open all day *(T R and B C Jenkins, LYM, Peter Neate, Geoffrey Hart)*

Rockbourne [SU1118]

☆ ***Rose & Thistle*** [signed off B3078 Fordingbridge—Cranborne]: Attractive thatched 16th-c pub with good fresh home-made food (best to book Sun lunch), well kept real ales, good range of wines, pleasant service, civilised bar with antique settles, old engravings and good coal fire, traditional games, log fires in front restaurant with no smoking area; may be piped classical music; children welcome, tables by thatched dovecot in neat front garden, charming tranquil spot in lovely village, good walks *(LYM, L M Parsons)*

Rockford [SU1608]

☆ ***Alice Lisle***: Family-friendly modernised open-plan pub attractively placed on green by New Forest (can get very busy), emphasis on big conservatory-style family eating area with generous helpings of good food inc sandwiches, some interesting dishes and sensible children's menu; well kept Gales and guest beers, country wines, welcoming attentive staff, baby-changing facilities; garden overlooking lake with peacock and other birds, ponies wander nearby, children's play area, summer entertainer and face-painter, separate adults-only garden; handy for Moyles Court *(A D Moss, K S Mossman, I R Fourmy, Mrs M Hughes, BB, Mr and Mrs J F Copping)*

Romsey [SU3521]

Abbey Hotel [Church St]: Comfortable plush and mahogany bar with enterprising food choice from sandwiches and baked potatoes to rabbit pie and guinea fowl, welcoming efficient service, well kept Courage Best and Directors, dining area with Victorian photographs; bedrooms, opp Abbey *(John Beeken, Ron Shelton)*

☆ ***Dukes Head*** [A3057 out towards Stockbridge]: Attractive 16th-c dining pub festooned with flowering baskets in summer, picturesque series of small linked rooms each with its own quite distinct and interesting décor, well kept Courage Best, Fullers London Pride and Theakstons Old Peculier, decent house wines, good coffee, rewarding choice of popular well presented food from unusual fresh sandwiches up, big log fire; may be quiet piped music; picnic-sets out in front, nicer tables on sheltered back terrace, attractive back garden *(Michael and Marion Buchanan, R T and J C Moggridge, Phyl and Jack Street, Gordon Prince, BB, Ann and Colin Hunt, Jestyn Phillips)*

Old House At Home [Love Lane]: Attractive 16th-c thatched pub with old-fashioned décor, good home-made food, well kept Gales and guest beers *(A and B D Craig)*

Tudor Rose [Cornmarket]: Single bar in old building, good value basic hot meals, Courage ales, friendly staff; side courtyard *(A and B D Craig)*

Rotherwick [SU7156]

Coach & Horses [signed from B3349 N of

Hook; also quite handy for M3 junction 5]: Individual furnishings and roaring fire in two small beamed front rooms, decent food from lunchtime sandwiches to steaks with some interesting dishes, no smoking eating areas, inner parquet-floored serving area with several Badger ales and a couple of Gribble guests, daily papers, relaxed atmosphere, may be voluble parrots; tables in back garden, pretty flower tubs and baskets *(Susan and Nigel Wilson, Charles Moncreiffe, Anthony Barnes, Gordon Stevenson, LYM)*

Rowlands Castle [SU7310]

☆ ***Castle Inn*** [Finchdean Rd]: Cheerful two-bar Edwardian village local with buoyant atmosphere, flagstones and rugs, enormous dim-lit bar with central log fire, cabinets of local handmade modern glass, wide choice of good value popular food from sandwiches up, well kept Gales Butser, GB, HSB and Winter Brew, friendly helpful staff, pleasant dining room; children and dogs welcome, good provision for disabled, picnic-sets in big garden, pleasant village, good walks *(Ann and Colin Hunt, Jess and George Cowley, Phyl and Jack Street, Ian Phillips, W A Evershed)*

Robin Hood [The Green]: Reopened after major refurbishment (still same friendly landlord, dog and cat), with extended upmarket dining area, comfortably modern bar, enjoyable food inc plenty of fish, three well kept ales; piped modern jazz; pretty village *(Ann and Colin Hunt)*

Selborne [SU7433]

☆ ***Selborne Arms*** [High St]: Hop-festooned village local with well kept Courage Best and Directors and Ringwood Best, enjoyable fresh food with good mix of pub standards and more inventive or sophisticated snacks and main dishes, dining room off unpretentious bar with old photographs, fresh flowers, log fire in fine inglenook, twinkly landlord, cheerful polite service even when very busy; tables in garden with terrace and good play area, right by walks up Hanger, and handy for Gilbert White museum *(Margaret Ross)*

Shedfield [SU5512]

Wheatsheaf [A334 Wickham—Botley]: Busy and friendly little family-run local with small dining area, half a dozen well kept ales tapped from the cask such as Itchen Valley, Mansfield and Ringwood Fortyniner, good value substantial lunchtime food, decent wine, impromptu piano sessions in public bar; garden, handy for Wickham Vineyard *(Val and Alan Green, Lynn Sharpless)*

Sherfield on Loddon [SU6858]

☆ ***White Hart*** [Reading Rd]: Pleasant atmosphere, well kept ales inc Courage and Hogs Back TEA, wide choice of reasonably priced generous fresh food, huge inglenook fireplace, good choice of wines, quick friendly service, interesting coaching-era relics; tables outside, handy for The Vyne *(LYM, Geoff Palmer)*

Sopley [SZ1597]

Woolpack [B3347 N of Christchurch]: Pretty thatched pub with rambling candlelit open-plan low-beamed bar, rustic furniture, woodburner and little black kitchen range, friendly service, enjoyable food from sandwiches and ploughman's to steaks and Sun roasts, well kept Flowers Original, Ringwood Best and Wadworths 6X, no smoking conservatory; piped music; open all day, children in eating areas, attractive garden, picnic-sets under weeping willows, stream with ducks and footbridges *(T J and J D Fitzgerald, LYM, Mrs A Trier, Ian Phillips, Colin McKerrow)*

Southampton [SU42132]

Avenue [Padwell Rd]: Friendly local with simple but surprisingly imaginative food, Fullers London Pride, Itchen Valley Wykehams Glory and Wadworths 6X, pavement tables and garden; parking residents only *(Val and Alan Green)*

Bosuns Locker [Castle Sq]: Social and clubby pub, bar food, Ringwood True Glory *(Val and Alan Green)*

Cowherds [The Common (off A33)]: Low-beamed Vintage Inn, welcoming atmosphere, cosy alcoves and tables in nice little bay windows, lots of Victorian photographs, carpets on polished boards, log fires, good unfussy food inc fresh fish, well kept Bass and Tetleys, good wine choice, cheery caring service; very busy with young people Sun; pleasant spot on common, tables outside with tie-ups and water for dogs (50p deposit on glasses taken outside) *(Neil Rose, Mr and Mrs Gordon Turner, Peter and Anne-Marie O'Malley)*

Duke of Wellington [Bugle St (or walk along city wall from Bar Gate)]: Ancient timber-framed building on 13th-c foundations, bare boards, log fire, friendly relaxed atmosphere, well kept reasonably priced ales such as Bass, Ringwood Best and JcB and Wadworths IPA, good choice of wines by the glass, decent home-made bar food, no smoking back dining room; front bar can get smoky; very handy for Tudor House Museum *(Val and Alan Green, Bruce Bird)*

Giddy Bridge [London Rd]: Pleasant Wetherspoons, partly divided and not too big, upstairs area with balcony terrace, good staff, well kept ales such as local Itchen Valley Wykehams Glory, sensibly priced food *(Val and Alan Green)*

Standing Order [High St]: Good Wetherspoons with relaxed intimate feel, cosy corners (strange and interesting collection of books in one), civilised atmosphere, reasonably priced food inc popular bargain Sun lunch, well kept beers inc interesting guests, helpful efficient young staff, no smoking area *(Val and Alan Green)*

Southsea [SZ6499]

Eldon Arms [Eldon St/Norfolk St]: Roomy rambling bar with old pictures and advertisements, attractive mirrors, lots of bric-a-brac and bookcases; changing well kept ales such as Bass, Brakspears, Theakstons Old Peculier and Youngs, lunchtime food (not Sat) inc carvery and cold buffet; sensibly placed darts, pool, fruit machine; tables in back garden *(Val and Alan Green, Ann and Colin Hunt)*

Hole in the Wall [Gt Southsea St]: Small and cosy, in old part, with John Smiths and several guest beers, well priced doubles bar, enjoyable well presented food, good friendly staff *(Garry and Karen Fairclough)*

Sirloin of Beef [Highland Rd, Eastney]: Good frequently changing choice of well kept ales, helpful friendly staff *(Gary Crabbe)*

Southwick [SU6208]

Golden Lion [High St; just off B2177 on Portsdown Hill]: Picturesque estate village setting for two-bar local popular for good value homely food inc Sun lunch; well kept Gales, also distinctive Suthwyk ales, brewed by local farm using its own barley which they malt themselves, friendly staff, antique pine, pleasant restaurant; where Eisenhower and Montgomery came before D-Day, scenic walks *(Val and Alan Green)*

Stockbridge [SU3535]

☆ *Greyhound* [High St]: Recently reopened substantial inn, log fires each end of bow-windowed bar, old trestle tables and simple seating on woodstrip floor, dark beams and joists with low-voltage spotlights, lots of good black and white photographs, very civilised atmosphere, well kept ales inc Courage Directors, Greene King IPA and Wadworths 6X, decent wines, short lunchtime food choice inc very generous sandwiches, friendly and courteous young staff (South African licensees), attractive dining area; tables in garden behind, children and dogs allowed, bedrooms and fly fishing *(Derek Harvey-Piper, BB)*

☆ *Grosvenor* [High St]: Quietly luxurious atmosphere and quick cheery service in pleasantly restrained and comfortable old country-town hotel's refurbished bar, decent food inc limited snacks such as good unusual sandwiches and toasties, well kept Greene King IPA, Abbot and Old Speckled Hen, several wines by the glass, country prints and log fire; piped music; big attractive garden behind, good value bedrooms *(Mrs E A Macdonald, Ian Phillips, BB, Geoffrey Kemp)*

Vine [High St]: Popular pub/restaurant with enjoyable reasonably priced food inc half helpings for children, helpful landlord/chef, old beams and woodwork, stripped bricks and purple wallpaper, delft shelf of china and pewter, bright floral curtains, Boddingtons, Brakspears and Flowers Original, good wine list, unobtrusive piped music; open all day, tables in nice big garden, wknd barbecues, comfortable bedrooms *(LYM, C Whittington)*

☆ *White Hart* [High St; A272/A3057 roundabout]: Good value food from soup and sandwiches to Sun lunch in roomy and welcoming divided bar, oak pews and other seats, attractive décor with antique prints, full range of Gales ales kept well, decent wines, country wines, cheerful service; children allowed in comfortable beamed restaurant with blazing log fire, tables in garden, bedrooms *(Colin and Janet Roe, Phyl and Jack Street, David and Ruth Shillitoe, Geoff Palmer, LYM)*

Stroud [SU7223]

Seven Stars [A272 Petersfield—Winchester]: Flint and brick, with good choice of food from good sandwiches to some exotic dishes served quickly and cheerfully in roomy and orderly open-plan bar around island servery with well kept Badger beers, large restaurant extension, bar billiards and darts; tables outside, comfortable bedrooms with own bathrooms, good if strenuous walking *(Ken Buck)*

Swanmore [SU5816]

Hunters [Hillgrove]: Much-extended family dining pub, excellent for children, with big plain family room, wide choice of freshly made straightforward food inc lots of fish specials, and winding garden with secluded tables and several good play areas for different age groups, plenty under cover and even one for babies; also plush bar with lots of boxer pictures, bank notes, carpentry and farm tools, Charles Wells Bombardier tapped from the cask and Gales HSB on handpump, good house wine, country wines; very busy wknds *(Val and Alan Green, David and Carole Chapman)*

New Inn [Chapel Rd]: Friendly village pub with attentive licensees, Greene King ales, straightforward home cooking; games, darts, cricket team *(Val and Alan Green)*

Rising Sun [Hill Pound; off B2177 S of Bishops Waltham]: Comfortable tile-hung pub redecorated by new licensees, low beams, scrubbed pine, good log fires, well kept Adnams, Greene King Old Speckled Hen and Marstons Pedigree, interesting if not cheap food from sandwiches up (booking advised wknd), good reasonably priced wines, quick friendly service, well separated extended dining area; pleasant garden with play area and perhaps summer bouncy castle, handy for Kings Way long distance path – best to head W *(Val and Alan Green)*

Swanwick [SU5109]

Elm Tree [handy for M27 junction 9]: Neat and comfortable, with two bars and dining room off, several real ales, wide range of home-made food; quiet piped music; children welcome, tables in garden, handy for Hampshire Wildlife Reserve *(Val and Alan Green)*

Sway [SZ2898]

Hare & Hounds [Durns Town, just off B3055 SW of Brockenhurst]: Bright and airy comfortable New Forest family dining pub, lots of children, good value food, well kept ales inc Ringwood and Wessex, friendly efficient staff; may ask to keep credit card at bar; picnic-sets and play frame in sizeable neatly kept garden, open all day Sat *(Geoff Palmer, LYM)*

Tangley [SU3252]

☆ *Cricketers Arms* [towards the Chutes]: Tucked away in unspoilt countryside, character small front bar with tiled floor, massive inglenook, roaring log fire, bar billiards and friendly labrador called Pots, bistroish back flagstoned extension with a one-table alcove off, some good cricketing prints, attractively priced food from fresh baguettes to imaginative main dishes, well kept Bass and Cheriton Pots tapped from the cask, hard-working landlord; tables on neat terrace *(Darren Le Poidevin, J A Cheverton, Bernie Adams, LYM, I A Herdman)*

☆ *Fox* [crossroads S of village, towards Andover]:

Cosy but lively little beamed and timbered pub with generous good value imaginative food inc fresh fish, generous veg and fine range of puddings, well kept Courage and guest ales, good choice of wines, two big log fires, newish licensees, prompt helpful service, two pleasant no smoking family dining rooms *(Phyl and Jack Street)*

Timsbury [SU3325]

☆ ***Bear & Ragged Staff*** [A3057 towards Stockbridge; pub marked on OS Sheet 185 map ref 334254]: Busy newly refurbished beamed country dining pub, wide choice of food all day, quick welcoming service, several well kept ales, lots of wines by the glass, country wines; children in eating area, garden tables, good play area, handy for Mottisfont *(Anthony Evers, J P Humphery, LYM)*

Malthouse [A3057 N of village]: Spacious pub with wide choice of decent blackboard food (best to book wknds), real ales such as Gales, Ringwood and Wadworths, courteous service; good back garden with terrace, pretty water feature, barbecue house and play area *(Phyl and Jack Street)*

Titchfield [SU5406]

Fishermans Rest [Mill Lane, off A27 at Titchfield Abbey]: Busy Whitbreads family pub/restaurant included for its riverside position opp Titchfield Abbey, tables out behind overlooking water; hearty food all day in eating area with close-set tables and no smoking family area, good choice of well kept ales inc Gales HSB, Flowers and Wadworths 6X, cheerful if not always speedy service, two log fires, daily papers, fishing memorabilia *(Ann and Colin Hunt, Peter and Audrey Dowsett, LYM)*

Queens Head [High St; off A27 nr Fareham]: Ancient pub with good value food esp fish cooked by landlord, changing well kept ales such as Greene King and Hop Back, sparkling glasses, cosy and friendly 1930s-feel bar with old local pictures, window seats and central brick fireplace, attractive restaurant, a couple of cats; bedrooms, pleasant conservation village near nature reserve and walks to coast *(Charles and Pauline Stride, E S Funnell)*

Titchfield Mill [A27, junction with Mill Lane]: Large popular Vintage Inn catering well for families in converted watermill, olde-worlde room off main bar, smarter dining room, upstairs gallery, stripped beams and interesting old machinery, well kept Bass and Worthington, freshly squeezed orange juice, neat attentive and friendly staff; piped music; open all day, sunny terrace by mill stream with two waterwheels *(Phyl and Jack Street, Charles and Pauline Stride)*

Totton [SU3612]

☆ ***Anchor*** [Eling Quay]: Much renovated pub in lovely setting with tables out overlooking quayside green, yachts and church across water; well kept Bass, Worthington and a guest such as Tetleys, very wide range of good value usual food from sandwiches and baked potatoes to sizzling steaks, friendly service, children welcome; open all day, handy for NT Tidal Mill *(Ian Phillips, Stephen Savill, Phyl and Jack Street)*

Turgis Green [SU6959]

☆ ***Jekyll & Hyde*** [A33 Reading—Basingstoke]: Bustling rambling pub with nice mix of furniture, black beams and flagstones, some interesting prints particularly in back room, welcoming prompt service, well kept Badger Best and IPA and Wadworths 6X, stepped-up dining area with varied food from sandwiches up all day inc breakfast, children's helpings; lots of picnic-sets in good sheltered garden (some traffic noise), play area and various games; lavatories for the disabled *(KC, LYM)*

Twyford [SU4724]

Phoenix [High St]: Cheerful open-plan local with lots of prints, bric-a-brac and big end inglenook log fire, wide choice of sensibly priced generous food from sandwiches to steaks, friendly enthusiastic landlord, well kept Greene King with a guest such as Black Sheep, decent wines, back room with skittle alley, children allowed at one end lunchtime; quiet piped music; garden *(Val and Alan Green, Ann and Colin Hunt, Lynn Sharpless)*

Upton [SU3555]

☆ ***Crown*** [N of Hurstbourne Tarrant]: Linked rooms with pine tables and chairs, a pleasant modicum of sporting prints, horse tack and so forth, good log fires, enjoyable fresh food inc interesting evening dishes, good service under friendly newish licensees, well kept real ales, good coffee, happy bustling atmosphere; may be piped music in public bar; conservatory, small garden and terrace *(Margaret Ross, BB)*

Upton Grey [SU6948]

☆ ***Hoddington Arms*** [signed off B3349 S of Hook; Bidden Rd]: Homely unpretentious local with consistently good value, interesting and generous food inc good puddings, well kept Adnams and Greene King Old Speckled Hen and Ruddles Best, good house wines, courteous attentive service, open-plan bar, dining rooms (one no smoking, children allowed) each end with similar unpretentious furnishings but fuller food choice, minimal decoration; small games room with darts and bar billiards, may be piped music; neat garden with terrace and good-sized play area, quiet village *(KC, BB, Mrs T Howell, Guy Consterdine)*

Vernham Dean [SU3456]

☆ ***George***: Rambling open-plan beamed and timbered pub under new ownership; exposed brick and flint, inglenook log fire, good blackboard food, well kept Greene King IPA, Abbot and Ruddles County, decent wines, roomy no smoking eating area (children allowed); darts, shove-ha'penny, dominoes and cribbage; picnic-sets in pretty garden behind, lovely thatched village, fine walks *(Ian Phillips, Phyl and Jack Street, the Didler, LYM, Joan and Dudley Payne, JP, PP)*

Waltham Chase [SU5616]

Chase [B2177]: Comfortable seating like smart lounge, second room with nicely extended no smoking eating area, real ales such as Greene King IPA and Old Speckled Hen and Wadworths 6X, experienced landlord, generous reasonably priced food from baguettes up; jazz nights *(Val and Alan Green, Ann and Colin Hunt, Keith and Jill Cowell)*

Well [SU7646]

☆ ***Chequers*** [off A287 via Crondall, or A31 via Froyle and Lower Froyle]: Low beams and panelling, cosy alcoves, pews and brocaded stools, 18th-c country prints and sepia photographs, roaring log fire, wide-ranging bar food from lots of baguettes to steak, seafood and Sun roasts, well kept Badger Best, Tanglefoot and Gribble Fursty Ferret, decent wines, restaurant; children welcome, open all day wknds, picnic-sets in back garden, attractive vine-covered front arbour, nice spot *(Mr and Mrs R Walton, Ian Phillips, LYM, Martin and Karen Wake)*

West End [SU4714]

Southampton Arms [Moorgreen Rd, off B3035]: Thriving local, quite big, with Flowers and Ringwood ales, reasonably priced food, friendly efficient service, comfortable and cosy bar and attractive conservatory restaurant *(Phyl and Jack Street)*

West Meon [SU6424]

☆ ***Thomas Lord*** [High St]: Attractive and well run village pub with good value generous food, well kept Ringwood Best and Wadworths 6X, good selection of wines, collection of cricket club ties in spacious lounge, separate dining area, fresh flowers; crayons and paper for children, soft piped music; tables in garden *(W A Evershed, Simon Collett-Jones)*

West Wellow [SU2919]

Rockingham Arms [off A36 Romsey—Ower at roundabout, signed Canada]: Beamed 19th-c pub down Forest-edge dead end, good choice of reasonably priced food, well kept Ringwood Best, Porter and Fortyniner and up to three frequently changing guest beers, good sensibly priced wine list, friendly atmosphere, open fire, comfortable and attractive back restaurant, games in public bar; children welcome, very good play area in garden opening on to pretty heathland with roaming horses *(Ann and Colin Hunt, Phyl and Jack Street, Mrs Thomas)*

Weyhill [SU3146]

Weyhill Fair [A342, signed off A303 bypass]: Popular local with six well kept sensibly priced ales inc good varied guests, wide choice of daily-changing enjoyable food, spacious solidly furnished lounge with easy chairs around woodburner, old advertisements, smaller family room, no smoking area; children welcome, occasional live music, handy for Hawk Conservancy *(A and B D Craig, Darren Le Poidevin, Phyl and Jack Street, Bernie Adams, BB)*

Whitchurch [SU4648]

☆ ***Red House*** [London St]: Family-friendly lounge with step up to no smoking dining room, 14th-c beams and fireplaces (one an inglenook with ancient flagstones in front), generous home-made food from home-baked rolls to good hot dishes inc interesting vegetarian ones, well kept Cheriton Pots and a guest such as Archers Golden, decent house wines, friendly service, separate public bar on left; attractive terrace with play area *(Val and Alan Green, LYM, Phyl and Jack Street, Bryan and Betty Southwell, Lynn Sharpless)*

Wickham [SU5711]

Greens [formerly Inn on the Square]: Upmarket feel, with smart dining pub on upper level, real ales such as Bass, Fullers London Pride and Mauldons Suffolk Pride, lower restaurant *(Val and Alan Green)*

Kings Head [The Square]: Pretty two-bar pub with no smoking restaurant up some steps, good log fire, wide choice of decent sensibly priced food, Gales ales, good coffee, friendly service; tables out on square and in back garden with play area, attractive village *(Val and Alan Green)*

☆ ***Roebuck*** [Kingsmead; A32 towards Droxford]: Well appointed, with two dining rooms (one no smoking), wide range of food inc some less usual things, Fullers London Pride and Gales Butser, good helpful service, lots of prints and plates, library of books, even a white grand piano; conservatory *(Charles and Pauline Stride, Carol and Dono Leaman, A D Marsh)*

Winchester [SU4829]

Albion [Stockbridge Rd/Andover Rd]: Small L-shaped pub brightly renovated with wood and wrought iron, all-organic lunchtime menu, attractive prices, well kept Black Sheep, Butcombe and Youngs Special, good atmosphere; open all day, nearby parking difficult *(Val and Alan Green)*

Bell [St Cross Rd]: Well kept Greene King ales inc Ruddles, decent fresh food, welcoming service, separate plain public bar; big garden, handy for St Cross Hospital – nice water-meadows walk from centre *(Val and Alan Green)*

Black Boy [Wharf Hill]: Beamed L-shaped bar with interesting bric-a-brac and memorabilia, enjoyable food, well kept beer and decent wines, welcoming staff, unusual games in separate part; dogs welcome, attractive secluded terrace with barbecues *(LYM, John and Annabel Hampshire)*

Crown & Anchor [Broadway (E end)]: Comfortable pub opp Guildhall, old pine furniture, three areas, popular food, Greene King Abbot and Wadworths IPA and 6X *(Val and Alan Green)*

Eclipse [The Square, between High St and cathedral]: Picturesque but decidedly unpretentious and well worn local, massive 14th-c beams and timbers, oak settles, well kept Flowers Original, Fullers London Pride, Hampshire King Alfred and Ringwood Old Thumper, decent choice of wines by the glass, well done generous lunchtime bar food; antique lavatories, no dogs, children in back area (no smoking lunchtime – front part can get smoky), seats outside, very handy for cathedral *(Dennis Jenkin, Mr and Mrs A H Young, Val and Alan Green, LYM, Lynn Sharpless)*

Jolly Farmer [Andover Rd]: Neatly kept Laurel (ex-Whitbreads) pub with decent standard menu, Boddingtons, Hook Norton Old Hooky, Ringwood Best and Wadworths 6X *(Val and Alan Green)*

Queen [Kingsgate Rd]: Roomy pub in attractive

setting opp College cricket ground, wide choice of reasonably priced mainstream food from baguettes and baked potatoes to huge meals inc popular Sun lunch, children's dishes, well kept Greene King ales, decent wines, friendly hard-working licensees, dark dado, cricketing and other prints, bric-a-brac on window sills, grandfather clock, central fireplace, darts in public bar; disabled facilities, open all day Fri-Sun, tables on front terrace and in large attractive garden *(the Didler, Lynn Sharpless, M Etherington)*

Roebuck [A272 past station]: Smart Victorianised sitting-room style with striking wallpaper, very friendly service, Greene King IPA, Abbot and Ruddles, good value generous food, attractive conservatory restaurant, tables out on terrace; piped music; disabled access, car park – rare in this city *(Val and Alan Green)*

☆ ***Royal Oak*** [Royal Oak Passage, off upper end of pedestrian part of High St opp St Thomas St]: Cheerful main area doubling as coffee bar, little rooms off (some raised), beams and bare boards, scrubbed tables, no smoking areas, good value quick food with ciabatta and roast veg leanings, real ales such as Caledonian Deuchars IPA and Hook Norton Old Hooky; piped music and several fruit machines; the cellar bar (not always open) has massive 12th-c beams and a Saxon wall which gives it some claim to be the country's oldest drinking spot *(the Didler, Val and Alan Green, David Peakall, Alan and Paula McCully, LYM)*

White Swan [Hyde St]: Red, cream and dark brown, with friendly bustle, Greene King Ruddles, sensibly priced food inc good vegetarian choice; can be rather smoky *(Val and Alan Green)*

☆ ***Willow Tree*** [Durngate Terr]: Warmly welcoming local notable for its unusually good food inc interesting dishes; well kept Greene King beers, good wines; attractive riverside setting *(Phil and Sally Gorton)*

Wolverton [SU5558]

George & Dragon [Towns End; just N of A339 Newbury—Basingstoke]: Comfortable rambling open-plan pub, beams and standing timbers, log fires, wide range of beers, decent wines, large menu, helpful service; no children in bar; pleasant large garden, skittle alley *(J V Dadswell)*

Woodgreen [SU1717]

☆ ***Horse & Groom*** [off A338 N of Fordingbridge]: Nice Forest setting, linked beamed rooms around servery, nature photographs, log fire in pretty Victorian fireplace, comfortable eating area; has had well kept Badger ales with a guest such as Ringwood and good choice of good value home-cooked food, but changed hands again summer 2002 – reports on new regime please; picnic-sets on front terrace and in spreading back garden *(LYM)*

Real ale to us means beer which has matured naturally in its cask – not pressurised or filtered. We name all real ales stocked. We usually name ales preserved under a light blanket of carbon dioxide too, though purists – pointing out that this stops the natural yeasts developing – would disagree (most people, including us, can't tell the difference!)

Herefordshire

Four good new entries here this year present quite a mosaic of contrasts: the unpretentious Victory in Hereford (great value, brewing its own interesting beers, and amusingly done up like a fighting ship of the 1800s), the picturesque old Moon at Mordiford (nice all round, well placed for walks), the Eagle in Ross-on-Wye (unusual mix of easy-going town pub with smart food place) and the Verzons at Trumpet (imaginative food in a stylish but very welcoming dining pub – likely to become quite a favourite). This county does very well indeed for top-notch pub food, with several other dining pubs currently on great form: the Roebuck at Brimfield (imaginative if pricy; civilised service and a nice place to stay in), the striking timbered Feathers in Ledbury (good meals in a dining bar that's got plenty of local atmosphere, good bedrooms too), the Lough Pool at Sellack (gaining a Food Award this year, for Stephen Bull's nice food, in an appealing atmosphere and surroundings), the Stagg at Titley (very popular for its imaginative use of good local ingredients, in its two dining rooms and the bar), and the Three Crowns at Ullingswick (very good food, in a simple unaffected country atmosphere). From this hot competition, the Lough Pool at Sellack carries off the title of Herefordshire Dining Pub of the Year. In all these pubs, readers particularly pick out the friendliness of the staff, and notably friendly licensees seem to be a special Herefordshire feature. Other welcoming pubs here on fine form include the beautifully placed stone-built Bulls Head at Craswall, the ancient New Inn in Pembridge, the old-fashioned Stockton Cross Inn at Stockton Cross, the bustling Moody Cow at Upton Bishop, and the Butchers Arms at Woolhope (a fine all-rounder, in a nice spot). In the Lucky Dip at the end of the chapter, current front-runners are the Englands Gate at Bodenham, Crown in Colwall, Green Man at Fownhope, Angel at Kingsland, Sun at Leintwardine, Saracens Head at Symonds Yat and Rhydspence at Whitney-on-Wye. Drinks prices in the area are well below the national average. The beers brewed at the Victory in Hereford are a particular bargain, and Wye Valley beers (also brewed in Hereford – see the Lucky Dip entry for the Barrels there) often turn out cheap. Other local beers to look out for, gaining a price edge from the 14p cut in duty, include Dunn Plowman and Woodhampton. And of course the classic local drink is farm cider.

AYMESTREY SO4265 Map 6

Riverside Inn

A4110; N off A44 at Mortimer's Cross, W of Leominster

This idyllically placed black and white timbered inn changed hands early in 2002, but the chef has stayed and although the atmosphere has changed a bit we're still getting good reports. The rambling beamed bar has several cosy areas and a good laid-back atmosphere (walkers and their dogs are just as welcome as diners – there's a big restaurant area). The décor is drawn from a pleasant mix of periods and styles, with fine antique oak tables and chairs, stripped pine country kitchen tables, fresh flowers, hops strung from a ceiling waggon-wheel, horse tack, and nice pictures.

There are warm log fires in winter, while in summer big overflowing flower pots frame the entrances; shove-ha'penny, cribbage, dominoes and piped music. At the back are picnic-sets by a flowing river, and rustic tables and benches up above in a steep tree-sheltered garden, as well as a beautifully sheltered former bowling green. Well kept ales on handpump could include Black Sheep Bitter and Wye Valley Butty Bach and Dorothy Goodbodys Golden Ale; local farm cider in summer, and decent house wines. The landlord likes to talk to his customers and service is good. The ambitious (not cheap) daily changing menu might include soup (£3.75) and filled baguettes (from £3.25), Cornish crab tartlet (£6.50), vegetable risotto and wild mushrooms (£9.50), duck breast with a sweetcorn galette and fruit sauce (£13.95), and a few lunchtime daily specials such as beef lasagne or mushroom stroganoff (£6.20), beef bourguignon (£6.70), and fried chicken with peppercorn and meat jus (£7.50); home-made puddings such as fresh lemon tart (from £4.25), and a local cheese platter (£5.50). Residents are offered fly-fishing (they have fishing rights on a mile of the River Lugg), and a free taxi service to the start of the Mortimer Trail. It does get busy at weekends, so booking would be wise. *(Recommended by Rev Michael Vockins, Pamela and Merlyn Horswell, Mr and Mrs A Swainson, Nigel Bowles, Katherine Ellis, R M Corlett)*

Free house ~ Licensees Richard and Liz Gresko ~ Real ale ~ Bar food ~ Restaurant ~ (01568) 708440 ~ Children welcome ~ Dogs welcome ~ Open 11-11; 12-10.30 Sun; 11-3, 6-11; 12-3, 7-10.30 Sun in winter; closed 25 Dec ~ Bedrooms: £90S(£90B)/£65B

BRIMFIELD SO5368 Map 4

Roebuck Inn

Village signposted just off A49 Shrewsbury—Leominster

Worth a detour and ideal for a special occasion, this smart country dining pub impresses with its imaginative home-made food. Where possible they use local produce, and now have five fresh fish deliveries a week. The innovative (though not cheap) menu includes soup (£3.50), seared scallops with carrot and cardamom purée (£6.50), steak and mushroom suet pudding or fish pie (£8.95), roast monkfish wrapped in parma ham with peppers and basil (£15.50), and fillet steak stuffed with stilton and wrapped in bacon with a madeira sauce (£15.95). The daily specials, equally tempting, might include steamed mussels with cider and apple broth (£4.95), venison, root vegetable casserole with port, bay and juniper sauce (£15.95) or Cornish turbot with mussel, saffron and vermouth sauce (£16.95); puddings such as plum and almond pie and a good cheese board (£5). They have an interesting reasonably priced wine list, a carefully chosen range of spirits and well kept Tetleys and Woods Parish and a guest such as Wadworths 6X on handpump. Each of the three rambling bars has a different but equally civilised atmosphere. The quiet old-fashioned snug is where you might find locals drinking and playing dominoes, cribbage, table skittles or shove-ha'penny by an impressive inglenook fireplace. Light oak panelling in the 15th-c main bar makes for a quietly relaxed atmosphere, and the Brimfield Bar with a big bay window and open fire is light and airy. The brightly decorated cane-furnished airy dining room is no smoking. The staff are courteous and welcoming. There are seats out on the enclosed terrace. This is a really enjoyable place to stay at, with good breakfasts. *(Recommended by W H and E Thomas, David and Helen Wilkins, Ralph and Gloria Maybourn, FS, Dr W J M Gissane, Mike and Wena Stevenson, Mike and Lynn Robinson, Richard Cole, Gene and Kitty Rankin, Mr and Mrs A H Young, Karen Eliot, John Kane, Pamela and Merlyn Horswell, Rodney and Norma Stubington)*

Free house ~ Licensees David and Sue Willson-Lloyd ~ Real ale ~ Bar food ~ Restaurant ~ (01584) 711230 ~ Children in eating area of bar ~ Dogs allowed in bar and bedrooms ~ Open 11.30-2.30, 6.30-11; 12-3, 7-10.30 Sun ~ Bedrooms: £45B/£70S(£70B)

If we know a pub does sandwiches we always say so – if they're not mentioned, you'll have to assume you can't get one.

CAREY SO5631 Map 4

Cottage of Content

Village signposted from good road through Hoarwithy

They sell some interesting flavours of locally made ice cream at this very pretty out-of-the-way medieval country cottage. You can choose from damson and sloe gin, gooseberry and elderflower, quince or pineapple (from £3.45). It's in a charming position, with a little lane winding past by a stream, and picnic-sets on the flower-filled front terrace. Inside, the rooms have a pleasant mix of country furnishings – stripped pine, country kitchen chairs, long pews by one big table, and a mix of other old-fashioned tables on flagstones and bare boards, and there are plenty of beams and prints; cribbage and dominoes. As well as the bar menu which includes soup (£2.50), tiger prawns in garlic butter (£4.50), gammon (£5.95), and scampi and chips (£7.25), there are changing blackboards with dishes such as mushroom lasagne (£5.95), fish pie (£7.95), and duck leg confit (£9.50), with puddings such as treacle tart and summer pudding (£2.95). Well kept Hook Norton Best on handpump, around 40 wines by the bottle, 40 malt whiskies and farm cider. A couple of picnic-sets on a back terrace look up a steep expanse of lawn. We're looking forward to hearing more about the new regime from readers. *(Recommended by Barry Collett, the Didler)*

Free house ~ Licensee John Clift ~ Real ale ~ Bar food (not Mon) ~ Restaurant ~ (01432) 840242 ~ Children in eating area of bar ~ Dogs allowed in bar ~ Open 11-11; 12-3, 7-10.30 Sun; closed Mon except bank hols

CRASWALL SO2736 Map 6

Bulls Head

Hay-on-Wye—Llanfihangel Crucorney road along Golden Valley, via Longtown; OS Sheet 161 map reference 278360

Genuinely welcoming, this remote stone-built pub is the kind of place where the helpful landlord will happily make you a packed lunch to take on your walk, and the chef brings your meal to the table with a smile. Dating back some 200 years, the unpretentious bar is like a Welsh farmhouse kitchen, with many original features: low beams, flagstones, antique settles and elderly chairs, logs burning in an old cast-iron stove, sentimental 19th-c engravings that have clearly never seen the inside of an antiques shop. Tapped from the cask and served through a hatch, Wye Valley Butty Bach and a guest beer (usually from a small brewer) are kept well; table skittles, cribbage and dominoes. The well prepared inventive food is served in the partly no smoking dining area. Make sure you come hungry, as the helpings are huge. Besides chunks of home-baked bread (they call them huffers) with all sorts of generous fillings from smoked bacon and stilton to locally made sausages or steak (£4.25-£8.95), they do dishes such as beef, gammon, bacon and ale pie, fried pigeon breast on haggis with game gravy, grilled aubergines or Hereford hotpot (£7.95), grilled monkfish with fennel and lemon (£9.95), and a very good rib-eye steak (11.95); with puddings such as strawberry pavlova and sticky toffee pudding (£3.50). There are tables outside, with a play area and room for camping. In a peaceful spot between the Golden Valley and the Black Mountains, this is a good area for walking. *(Recommended by Gwyneth and Salvo Spadaro-Dutturi, JP, PP, the Didler, Darren and Jane Staniforth, Chris and Maggie Kent, Jayne and Peter Capp)*

Free house ~ Licensee Paul Chicken ~ Real ale ~ Bar food ~ (01981) 510616 ~ Dogs welcome ~ Open 11-11 Mon-Sat; 11-5 Sun; closed Sun evening, all Mon and Tues ~ Bedrooms: £30(£40B)/£45(£50B)

DORSTONE SO3141 Map 6

Pandy

Pub signed off B4348 E of Hay-on-Wye

Said to be Herefordshire's oldest, this lovely half-timbered pub is surrounded by pretty countryside. It was built in 1185 by Richard de Brico to house workers constructing a chapel of atonement for his part in the murder of Thomas à Becket. The South African licensees are very hospitable, and it's an exceptionally friendly place; even Oscar the parrot will probably chat to you. You can try the landlady's South African dishes such as tomato bredie (a casserole of lamb, tomatoes and potatoes) and delicious bobotie (£7.55), alongside more indigenous soup (£2.95), sandwiches (from £2.95, filled baguettes from £3.50), mussels in white wine and cream sauce (£4.95), lamb and apricot casserole or pork stir fry (£7.95), salmon fillet poached in white wine (£8.50), and Herefordshire rump steak (£10.95), with some tasty vegetarian choices such as broccoli and cream cheese bake (£5.35) and four-bean chilli (£7.65); good puddings such as sherry trifle (£3.25). The neatly kept homely main room (on the right as you go in), has heavy beams in the ochre ceiling, stout timbers, upright chairs on its broad worn flagstones and in its various alcoves, and a vast open fireplace with logs; a side extension has been kept more or less in character; no smoking area. They've well kept Wye Valley Butty Bach and Dorothy Goodbodys and perhaps a guest such as Tetleys on handpump, lots of malt whiskies, farm cider and chilled fruit juices; darts, quoits and piped music. The hairy persian tom is Tootsie, and they've recently gained a ginger tom called Peanuts. There are picnic-sets and a play area in the neat side garden. *(Recommended by Sue Demont, Tim Barrow, Martin Jones, Cathy Robinson, Ed Coombe, Jim Abbott, Peter Meister, Muriel and Peter Gleave, Geoff Pidoux, Alan and Paula McCully, David and Elizabeth Briggs, Pam and David Bailey)*

Free house ~ Licensees Paul and Marja Gardner ~ Real ale ~ Bar food ~ Restaurant ~ No credit cards ~ (01981) 550273 ~ Well behaved children welcome ~ Open 12-3, 6-11 Tues-Fri; 12-11 Sat; 12-3, 6.30-10.30 Sun; closed Mon lunchtime except bank hols in summer, all day Mon in winter

HEREFORD SO5139 Map 6

Victory £

St Owen Street, opposite fire station

This combines the down-to-earth character of a proper drinking man's town pub with most unusual décor and an interesting collection of real ales. The front bar counter is like a miniature ship of the line, with cannon poking out of its top, and down a companionway the long back room is well decked out as the inside of a man o' war: dark wood, rigging and netting everywhere, long benches along sides that curve towards a front fo'c'sle, stanchions and ropes forming an upper crow's nest, appropriate lamps. The pub brews its own interesting ales such as Spinning Dog Chase Your Tail (you may even see Cassie the spinning dog herself in action, as we did on our inspection visit, apparently sparked off then by the telephone ringing – an extraordinary sight), Top Dog, Mutleys Dark, Flannerys Celtic Gold and Oatmeal Stout, with a guest such as SP Sporting Ales Double Top on handpump, and three farm ciders such as Bulmer's, Cheddar Valley and Thatcher's. Very reasonably priced straightforward bar food includes sandwiches (from £1.50), chilli con carne or chicken curry (£4), ploughman's or fish of the day (£4.50,) and 8oz steak (£4.95), with specials such as faggots, mash and peas (£4.50). Service is friendly and informal (they'll show you around the brewery if they're not busy). There's a pool table at the back; also a juke box, darts, fruit machine, TV, skittle alley, cribbage and dominoes. There are some tables out behind the pub. *(Recommended by Mike Pugh, Richard Lewis, Dr and Mrs M E Wilson)*

Own brew ~ Licensees James Kenyon and Rebecca Brookes ~ Real ale ~ Bar food (12-7; 12-5 Sun) ~ Restaurant (Sun only) ~ Children welcome ~ Dogs welcome ~ Live music Sun lunchtime, quiz Tues and 1st Thurs in month ~ Open 11-11; 12-10.30 Sun

LEDBURY SO7138 Map 4

Feathers

High Street, Ledbury, A417

The rather civilised Fuggles bar of this elegantly striking Tudor timbered inn is home to a congenial mix of drinkers and diners. You'll find cheerful locals gathered at one end of the room or at stools by the long bar counter, uninhibited by those enjoying the good food and fine wines at the brasserie tables behind them. There are beams and timbers, hop bines, some country antiques, 19th-c caricatures and fancy fowl prints on the stripped brick chimneybreast (lovely winter fire), and fresh flowers on the tables – some very snug and cosy, in side bays. In summer, abundant pots and hanging baskets adorn the sheltered back terrace. They serve well kept Bass, Fullers London Pride and Worthingtons and a guest such as Timothy Taylors Landlord on handpump; various malt whiskies, and farm cider. The nicely varied imaginative menu is not cheap, but is good value considering its restaurant quality. Dishes could include home-made soup (£3.95), baguette with gruyère and smoked bacon (£4.50), chargrilled vegetable terrine (£4.95), Cornish crab, spring onion and ginger tartlet (£5.25), couscous with roasted vegetables, chick peas and fresh herbs (£8.50), roast turbot fillet with red wine, thyme and wild mushroom (£15.25), grilled duck breast with glazed apple and calvados (£15.95), and tempting puddings such as dark chocolate and mint pot with crushed raspberries, or poached pear in a ginger basket with mocha sauce (£4.50). The chef will try to accommodate any special requests; service is good. They do excellent afternoon teas in the more formal quiet lounge by the reception area, which has comfortable high-sided armchairs and sofas in front of a big log fire, and newspapers to read. There is quite an emphasis on the hotel side of this operation, with its attractive timbered bedrooms, an indoor swimming pool and leisure spa. *(Recommended by David and Ruth Hollands, John Whitehead, Denys Gueroult, Mike and Mary Carter, Patricia Beebe, J M and P M Carver, Derek Carless, Jenny and Dave Hughes, David and Catherine Whiting, Mrs M Mills, Mrs T A Bizat, Duncan Cloud, Michael Dandy)*

Free house ~ Licensee David Elliston ~ Real ale ~ Bar food ~ Restaurant ~ (01531) 635266 ~ Children welcome ~ Dogs allowed in bedrooms ~ Open 11-11; 12-10.30 Sun ~ Bedrooms: £71.50B/£95B

LUGWARDINE SO5541 Map 4

Crown & Anchor 🍷

Cotts Lane; just off A438 E of Hereford

As well as lots of varieties of lovely fresh sandwiches (from £2.50), this attractive black and white timbered inn has at least half a dozen interesting vegetarian dishes each day. You might find aduki bean bake, mushroom, butterbean and basil stew, and mixed bean goulash (all £6.50), alongside a few equally interesting blackboard specials such as caerphilly cheese and walnut pâté (£4), and creamed white beans, potato pancake and roast peppers (£7). Meat and fish eaters have a good choice too, with smoked ham salad (£7), roast salmon with dill sauce (£8), and fried Herefordshire sirloin steak (£12), along with specials such as ham and leek hotpot (£7), baked bass with lemon and parsley butter (£9), and roast rack of lamb with blackberry and port sauce (£12); puddings (£3.75). A friendly relaxed atmosphere permeates the several smallish and charming rooms. There might be a few locals in the bar, which is furnished with an interesting mix of pieces, and has a big log fire. They've got decent wines, including a clutch of usefully priced bin ends; Butcombe, Worthington Best and a guest such as Marstons Pedigree on handpump are well kept, and there are lots of malt whiskies. The main eating area is no smoking. In summer the pretty garden is filled with honeysuckle. The pub is surrounded by newish housing, but in ancient times the Lugg flats round here – some of the oldest Lammas meadows in England – were farmed in strips by local farm tenants, and meetings with the lord of the manor were held in the pub. *(Recommended by Christopher and Jo Barton, MJVK, Denys Gueroult, Ian Phillips, Darly Graton, Graeme Gulibert, Jenny and Dave Hughes, Mike and Mary Carter, R M Corlett)*

Enterprise ~ Lease Nick and Julie Squire ~ Real ale ~ Bar food (till 10) ~ Restaurant ~ (01432) 851303 ~ Children welcome ~ Live jazz first Weds evening of month ~ Open 12-12; 12-10.30 Sun; closed 25 Dec

> If we know a pub has an outdoor play area for children, we mention it.

MORDIFORD SO5737 Map 4

Moon

B4224 SE of Hereford

Of great age, this picturesque timbered pub has hop bines strung along the black beams of its comfortable green-carpeted lounge, and a roaring log fire in a two-way fireplace dividing it from a dining extension. Enjoyable blackboard food runs from sandwiches (from £1.95, baguettes from £2.10) up, and might include mussels done with leeks, cream and cider, trout with lemon and parsley butter or spinach and ricotta cannelloni (£6.25), chicken done in various ways (£6.75), tagliatelle with smoked haddock, prawns and mushrooms (£7.25), steaks (from £8.20) and butterfly prawns, mussels and tiger prawns in white wine and garlic (£10.95), with puddings such as crumble and sticky toffee pudding (from £2.75); their Sunday lunches are locally very popular, so may be fully booked (£7 for two courses, three for £8). Pleasantly relaxed yet attentive service, well kept Marstons Pedigree, Tetleys and Wadworths 6X on handpump, local farm ciders, reasonably priced wines; there may be piped Classic FM. The back public bar, also comfortably carpeted, has rough low beams, darts, table skittles, shove-ha'penny and a juke box. There is a neat compact back lawn; this is a good spot for walkers, by a tributary of the River Wye, and on the Three Choirs Way. *(Recommended by Mike and Mary Carter, Martin Jennings, Guy Vowles, Keith Allen)*

Enterprise ~ Licensee Mr Hawkridge ~ Real ale ~ Bar food (not Sun evening) ~ Restaurant ~ 01432 870236 ~ Children in eating area of bar and restaurant ~ Dogs allowed in bar ~ Open 12-3.30, 6.30-11; 12-11(10.30 Sun) Sat

MUCH MARCLE SO6633 Map 4

Slip Tavern

Off A449 SW of Ledbury; take Woolhope turning at village stores, then right at pub sign

Recently taken over by friendly new licensees, this country pub has splendidly colourful gardens overlooking the cider orchards that stretch out behind. The cosy chatty bar is still popular with older people at lunchtime, with a more villagey local atmosphere in the evening. There are ladderback and wheelback upholstered chairs around black tables, and little country prints on neat cream walls. They plan to increase the decent wine list, and they've Hook Norton and a guest on handpump; piped music. Bar food includes sandwiches (from £2.95), home-made soup (£2.35), filled baked potatoes (from £3.85), ploughman's (£4.95), fish and chips (£6.95), spinach and mushroom lasagne (£6.45) and sirloin steak (£9.95), and specials include popular home-made steak and ale or chicken and mushroom pie (£6.95); puddings such as treacle sponge (£2.95). Some of their dishes are available in smaller portions. They've recently done up the restaurant which is in an attractively planted conservatory. Outside is a well separated play area. In spring and autumn they celebrate Apple Days here with lots of apple and cider dishes (Weston's Cider Farm, open weekdays and Saturday mornings, is close by). More reports please on the new regime. *(Recommended by Lucien, A and B D Craig, Edward Hughes, Chris Flynn, Wendy Jones, Patricia Beebe, Dr and Mrs Jackson, Kitt Gruseon)*

Free house ~ Licensees Ian Taylor and Julia Lusher ~ Real ale ~ Bar food (11.30-2.30, 6.30-9.30; 12-2.30, 7-9.30 Sun) ~ Restaurant ~ (01531) 660246 ~ Open 11.30-2.30, 6.30-11; 12-2.30, 7-10.30 Sun

ORLETON SO4967 Map 6

Boot

Just off B4362 W of Woofferton

Readers appreciate the way that this pleasantly relaxed 16th-c partly black and white timbered pub manages to preserve 'a proper pub atmosphere' while also serving good food. Cheerily popular with locals, the traditional-feeling bar has a mix of dining and cushioned carver chairs around a few old tables on the red tiles, one very high-backed settle, hops over the counter, and a warming fire in the big fireplace, with horsebrasses along its bressumer beam. The lounge bar is up a couple of steps, and has green plush banquettes right the way around the walls, mullioned windows, an exposed section of wattle and daub, and standing timbers and heavy wall beams. There's a small and pretty no smoking restaurant on the left. The garden, with brick barbecue, has seats on its lawn, some under a huge ash tree. Formerly a brewer at Hobsons, the landlord stocks well kept Hobsons Best and Town Crier and a local guest on handpump, and there's local cider. Along with daily specials such as home-made steak, ale and mushroom pie (£6.95), oriental prawn parcels with garlic mayonnaise (£7.25), and salmon steak with giant prawns (£8.95), the enjoyable, reasonably priced bar food includes sandwiches (from £2.50), soup (£2.50), creamy stilton mushrooms (£3.75), smoked fish platter (£4.95), poached salmon with a dill and mustard cream sauce (£7.25), chicken stuffed with stilton and wrapped in bacon with sherry sauce (£7.95), and steaks (from £9.75); puddings (from £3.50). There's a fenced-in children's play area with little tables and chairs, and a wooden wendy house and swing. More reports please. *(Recommended by Paul and Margaret Baker, Pamela and Merlyn Horswell, Doreen and Haydn Maddock, John and Christine Lowe, Mike and Lynn Robinson, P and J Shapley)*

Free house ~ Licensee Duncan Brooks ~ Real ale ~ Bar food ~ Restaurant ~ (01568) 780228 ~ Children welcome ~ Dogs allowed in bar ~ Open 12-2.30, 6-11(7-10.30 Sun)

PEMBRIDGE SO3958 Map 6

New Inn

Market Square (A44)

It's a pretty safe bet that any pub called 'New Inn' is actually very old indeed, and this one, beautifully set in the centre of an attractive black and white mini-town, is no exception. Its three simple but comfortable little beamed rooms ooze antiquity, with their oak peg-latch doors and elderly traditional furnishings including a fine antique curved-back settle on the worn flagstones; the log fire is the substantial sort that people needed long before central heating was reinvented. One room has sofas, pine furniture and books; the welcoming homely lounge is no smoking; darts, shove-ha'penny, and quoits. Well kept Black Sheep and Fullers London Pride and perhaps a couple of guests such as Adnams Broadside or Dunn Plowman Kingdom on handpump. As well as sandwiches (from £2.75) and ploughman's (from £3.95), the good bar food includes chicken and walnut lasagne (£6.50), beef casserole with horseradish dumplings (£6.75), and pork steak in mustard, wine and cream or mussel and smoked haddock chowder (£8.50); the same menu runs through the restaurant and bar. The staff are friendly. Tables out on the cobblestones between the pub and the former wool market overlook the church, which has an unusual 14th-c detached bell tower beside it. *(Recommended by Maurice and Gill McMahon, R M Corlett)*

Free house ~ Licensee Jane Melvin ~ Real ale ~ Bar food ~ Restaurant ~ (01544) 388427 ~ Children in eating area of bar till 8.30 ~ Dogs allowed in bedrooms ~ Open 11-3, 6-11; 12-3, 7-10.30 Sun; closed 1st week in Feb ~ Bedrooms: £20/£40

ROSS-ON-WYE SO6024 Map 4

Eagle 🍷

Broad Street

On the right, this is a fairly typical town pub, with upholstered pews in booths, turkey carpeting (except in the central flagstoned serving area), darts (which they take seriously here), a well lit pool table and audible fruit machine at the back, and some really entertaining period cigarette cards; also piped pop music, TV, dominoes and cribbage. On the left is a more stylish dining area, with black bentwood chairs around modern tables on bare boards, cream or deep blue walls, steps up to a carpeted section with an open kitchen, spiral stairs to an upper gallery, and a whole wall of wine bottles. Handily served all day, the food is interesting (you can choose from the bar or the restaurant menu), running from fill-your-own sandwiches (from

£2.50) to roast pheasant in bacon with chestnuts (£8.95); other dishes could be mussel, leek and chive soup (£2.95), baked goats cheese with peppers and olives (£3.50), steak and kidney pie, lamb and mint casserole or cod in beer batter (£5.50), baked ham hock with parsley and mustard (£7.95), haunch of venison with redcurrants and juniper (£8.95), and roast bass with vanilla and baby spinach (£10.95). Pleasant service from nicely uniformed waitresses, good wine, Hook Norton Best on handpump. *(Recommended by Jean-Claude Ohms)*

Enterprise ~ Lease James Arbourne ~ Real ale ~ Bar food (all day) ~ Restaurant ~ (01989) 562652 ~ Children in eating area of bar and restaurant ~ Dogs allowed in bar and bedrooms ~ Open 8.30-11(10.30 Sun) ~ Bedrooms: £19/£55B

SELLACK SO5627 Map 4

Lough Pool ★ 🍴 🍷

Back road Hoarwithy—Ross-on-Wye

Herefordshire Dining Pub of the Year

This year has seen a strong flow of enthusiastic reports about the very good food and pleasant atmosphere at this lovely old black and white timbered country cottage. The beamed central room has kitchen chairs and cushioned window seats around wooden tables on the mainly flagstoned floor, sporting prints and bunches of dried flowers, and a log fire at each end. Other rooms lead off, gently brightened up with attractive individual furnishings and nice touches like the dresser of patterned plates. The interesting well balanced menu, which changes every day, is available in the chatty bar as well as the restaurant. Using fresh local, and where possible organic, produce, delicious food might typically include cheese, white onion and thyme soup (£4), haggis fritters with beetroot relish (£4.75), mixed Spanish charcuterie (£4.95), venison and pork sausages with sweet and sour red cabbage or butternut squash risotto (£9), chargrilled lambs liver and bacon with crispy onion rings (£9.50), roast pigeon with lemon and thyme pearl barley (£12), and fried bass with fresh pea pancake and herb oil (£12.50), with puddings such as pecan tart and lime and chocolate cheesecake (£4.75); the restaurant is no smoking. Alongside well kept John Smiths and Wye Valley Bitter and Butty Bach, you'll find two guest beers such as Greene King Ruddles County and Theakstons XB on handpump; they've a good range of malt whiskies, local farm ciders and a well chosen reasonably priced wine list; good value coffee too. Service is good. There are plenty of picnic-sets on the neat front lawn, and pretty hanging baskets. The landlord hopes to add a few bedrooms in 2003. *(Recommended by GSB, Pat and Roger Fereday, Bernard Stradling, Mike and Mary Carter, Mr and Mrs A Swainson, Peter and Audrey Dowsett, Christopher and Jo Barton, Alec and Barbara Jones, Lynn Sharpless, Joyce and Maurice Cottrell, Jill McLaren)*

Free house ~ Licensee Stephen Bull ~ Real ale ~ Bar food ~ Restaurant ~ (01989) 730236 ~ Children in eating area of bar and restaurant ~ Open 11.30-3, 6.30-11; 12-2, 7-10.30 Sun; closed 25 Dec and 26 Dec evenings

ST OWEN'S CROSS SO5425 Map 4

New Inn

Junction A4137 and B4521, W of Ross-on-Wye

The big enclosed garden at this unspoilt black and white timbered coaching inn is lovely and sunny in summer. Inside, both the lounge bar (with a buoyant local atmosphere) and the no smoking restaurant have huge inglenook fireplaces, intriguing nooks and crannies, settles, old pews, beams, and timbers. The generous good value bar food includes soup (£3.25), sandwiches (from £3.25), chicken liver pâté (£4.75), ploughman's (£4.75), lasagne or sausage and mash (£4.95), and mushroom and asparagus pancake (£7.95), with around 10 regularly changing specials such as spicy vegetable and nut roast with port and cranberry sauce (£7.95), fried pork with orange and tarragon sauce (£9.25), venison in red wine and brandy sauce (£9.45), and poached local salmon with lime, mango and ginger (£9.95), with puddings such as apple pie (£3.50); friendly and pleasant service. They have well kept Bass, Tetleys and Wadworths 6X alongside a couple of guests such as Brains

Rev James Original and Shepherd Neame Spitfire on handpump, and a fair choice of malt whiskies; darts, shove-ha'penny, cribbage, dominoes, trivia and piped music. The big doberman is called Tia Maria. There are colourful hanging baskets at the front, and fine views stretch over rolling countryside to the distant Black Mountains. *(Recommended by R T and J C Moggridge, Gordon Prince, Tom Evans, R G Price, Mrs B M Smith, Pam and David Bailey)*

Free house ~ Licensee Nigel Donovan ~ Real ale ~ Bar food ~ Restaurant ~ (01989) 730274 ~ Children in eating area of bar and restaurant ~ Dogs welcome ~ Open 12-2.30(3 Sat), 6-11; 12-4, 7-10.30 Sun ~ Bedrooms: /£70S(£80B)

STOCKTON CROSS SO5161 Map 4

Stockton Cross Inn

Kimbolton; A4112, off A49 just N of Leominster

Readers really enjoy this beautifully kept little black and white timbered pub, with its old-fashioned local atmosphere and enjoyable food. A comfortably snug area at the top end of the long heavily beamed bar has a handsome antique settle facing an old black kitchen range, and old leather chairs and brocaded stools by the huge log fire in the broad stone fireplace. There's a woodburning stove at the far end too, with heavy cast-iron-framed tables and sturdy dining chairs; up a step, a small no smoking side area has more tables. Old-time prints, a couple of épées on one beam and lots of copper and brass complete the picture. Service is friendly and accommodating. Cooked by the landlady, good bar food includes soup (£3.50), portuguese sardines (£4.50), pancake filled with smoked chicken, bacon and mushrooms in a cream sauce (£5.25), lentil, pepper and sweetcorn bake with an almond and cheese crumb topping (£8.50), roast guinea fowl in a rich madeira sauce (£11.95), Torbay lemon sole (£12.95), and pork tenderloin filled with spinach wrapped in smoked bacon with white wine and cream sauce (£12.25), with a few simpler specials such as ham, egg and chips or stilton and mushroom fusilli with garlic bread (£6.75), and home-made steak and kidney pie (£7.25); tasty puddings might include jam roly-poly and fresh fruit pavlova (£3.95). The well kept real ales on handpump could be Batemans XXXB, Wye Valley Butty Bach and an occasional guest such as Flowers Best. You may need to book to be sure of a table. There are tables out in the pretty garden; it may have a fine summer show of sweet peas. *(Recommended by Nigel Bowles, Katherine Ellis, Denys Gueroult, John Saville, Ian Phillips, Mike and Mary Carter, Hazel and Michael Duncombe, Pamela and Merlyn Horswell, Mike and Lynn Robinson)*

Free house ~ Licensee R Wood ~ Real ale ~ Bar food ~ (01568) 612509 ~ Children over 6 allowed ~ Open 12-3, 7-11; closed Mon evening

TITLEY SO3360 Map 6

Stagg

B4355 N of Kington

In lovely countryside, this fairly simple-looking old place puts its main focus decidedly on the beautifully prepared food. The landlord/chef uses local suppliers wherever possible, and you can be sure of good, fresh often organic ingredients. The pubbier blackboard menu (not available Saturday evening or Sunday lunchtime) has at least 10 choices which, besides filled baguettes (from £3.20), could include steak sandwich (£6.90), crispy duck leg with cider sauce, liver and onions with mashed potato or moules marinière (£7.50), and smoked haddock with mustard mash (£7.90). On the more elaborate restaurant menu (which can also be eaten in the bar) you might find mussel tart or lamb sweetbread wrapped in parma ham with madeira sauce (£4.90), bass with braised fennel and coriander (£13.90), saddle of venison with port sauce (£14.50), and beef fillet with red wine sauce and caramelised shallots (£14.90). They do a variety of tasty puddings such as white chocolate and lemon cheesecake or crème caramel with rhubarb syrup (£3.90), and their good cheese board has up to a dozen mainly local types. They've put new chairs in the two dining rooms, one quite big, the other intimate; you'll need to book to be sure of a table.

An expanding wine list (which includes around 10 good wines by the glass) is nicely topped up with additional bin ends. They serve a couple of well kept real ales on handpump from brewers such as Bass, Brains and Hobsons, and keep a fine collection of malt whiskies, local farm cider and apple juice; you may also be able to try their home-made sloe or damson gin. Staff are friendly and enthusiastic. The bar, though comfortable and hospitable, is not large, and the atmosphere is civilised rather than lively. They've recently made improvements in the garden. *(Recommended by RJH, Tony Hall, Melanie Jackson, Alan and Paula McCully, John Kane, Alec and Barbara Jones, Nigel Bowles, Katherine Ellis, Tom Halsall, Mr and Mrs A H Young, Bob and Maggie Atherton, E M and H P N Steinitz, Chris Flynn, Wendy Jones, Joyce and Maurice Cottrell, Jean and Richard Phillips, W H and E Thomas, Gerry and Rosemary Dobson, Maurice and Gill McMahon, Stuart Turner)*

Free house ~ Licensees Steve and Nicola Reynolds ~ Real ale ~ Bar food (till 10 Mon-Sat) ~ Restaurant ~ (01544) 230221 ~ Children welcome ~ Dogs allowed in bar and bedrooms ~ Open 12-3, 6.30-11(7-10.30 Sun); closed Mon (except bank hols then closed Tues), May Day bank hol, 26 Dec, 1 Jan and 1st two wks in Nov ~ Bedrooms: £40S(£40B)/£60S(£60B)

TRUMPET SO6639 Map 4

Verzons 🍷

A438 W of Ledbury, just E of junction with A417/A4172

This 1790 roadside country hotel has been charmingly reworked to give an inviting and civilised bar, with appealing fresh food in attractive dining rooms opening off it. The main bar area, quite brightly lit, has well kept Hook Norton Best and Wye Valley Butty Bach on handpump, good house wines and espresso coffee, served by cheerful young staff from its end counter. This part has a big oriental rug on quarry tiles, a nice mix of country pub furniture including a couple of armchairs, little posies of flowers on its heavy sealed tables, and a woodburning stove in a big brick fireplace. A carpeted front section, with hop bines around its log fireplace, has a nice high-backed settle draped with a rug and lots of scatter cushions as well as other seats; with no piped music, the atmosphere is relaxed and chatty. The dining area off to the right is a series of small snug carpeted rooms. The big blackboard might include soup (£3.95), sandwiches (from £2.95), fresh asparagus and seared oak smoked salmon with tarragon butter sauce (£5.25), seafood salad with lemon and fennel chutney (£5.50), egg pasta with asparagus and mushrooms in a creamy tapenade sauce (£8.95), thai fish kebabs with warm sesame noodle salad (£9.95), chicken breast stuffed with camembert in a tomato and basil sauce (£10.75), and fillet steak medallions with sweet potato rösti and spiced shallot and red wine sauce (£14.95), with puddings such as apple and blackcurrant crumble tart with rum and raisin ice cream or strawberry iced parfait with ginger shortbread (£4.25); they do a roast on Sunday (£7.95). Tables out in extensive neatly kept gardens have broad views to the Malvern Hills. We have not yet heard from readers who have stayed overnight here since the 2001 make-over, but would expect this to be a thoroughly nice place to stay in. *(Recommended by J H C Peters)*

Free house ~ Licensee David Barnett-Roberts ~ Real ale ~ Bar food ~ Restaurant ~ (01531) 670381 ~ Children in eating area of bar and restaurant ~ Open 10.30-11.30(10.30 Sun) ~ Bedrooms: £55S(£55B)/£78S(£78B)

ULLINGSWICK SO5949 Map 4

Three Crowns 🍴 🍷

Village off A465 S of Bromyard (and just S of Stoke Lacy) and signposted off A417 N of A465 roundabout – keep straight on through village and past turn-off to church; pub at Bleak Acre, towards Little Cowarne

This place has a nice balance between imaginative food of a very high quality, and a welcoming atmosphere – you'll still see local farmers in the homely bar. The charmingly traditional interior has hops strung along the low beams of its smallish bar, a couple of traditional settles besides more usual seats, a mix of big old wooden tables with small round ornamental cast-iron-framed ones, open fires and one or two gently sophisticated touches such as candles on tables, and proper napkins; half the pub is no smoking. Using mostly local and organic products, the seasonally changing menu is quite short. It could include well presented dishes such as celeriac and apple soup with morels or crab cake with noodle salad and tomato jam (£5.25), grilled skate with crème fraîche, mustard and green vegetables, saffron risotto with wild mushrooms, roast mallard with morels and rösti, and grilled pork chops with charcutière sauce (£13), with puddings such as chocolate brownie with chocolate ice cream and pears or rhubarb and saffron brûlée (£4); local cheeses (£4). They have up to 10 wines by the glass, along with well kept Hobsons Best and a stronger guest ale from a small local brewer such as Wye Valley on handpump, and local farm ciders. There are good summer views from tables out on the attractively planted lawn. More reports please. *(Recommended by Sir Nigel Foulkes, Peter Burton, Mrs Ursula Hofheinz, Mike and Lynn Robinson, Rodney and Norma Stubington, Jenny and Dave Hughes, Roger White, David Edwards, Steve Furlong, Patricia Beebe, Denys Gueroult, Theocsbrian)*

Free house ~ Licensee Brent Castle ~ Real ale ~ Bar food (12-3, 7-9.30) ~ Restaurant ~ (01432) 820279 ~ Well behaved children welcome ~ Open 12-3, 6-11; 12-2, 7-10.30 Sun; closed Mon

UPTON BISHOP SO6527 Map 4

Moody Cow

2 miles from M50 junction 3 westbound (or junction 4 eastbound), via B4221; continue on B4221 to rejoin at next junction

In a sleepy village, this cheerful pub is popular for an enjoyable lunch. Several separate snug areas angle in an L around the bar counter, and there's a pleasant medley of stripped country furniture, stripped floorboards and stonework, a few cow ornaments and naïve cow paintings, and a lovely big log fire. On the far right is a biggish no smoking rustic and candlelit restaurant, with hop-draped rafters, and a fireside area with armchairs and sofas. The far left has a second smaller dining area, just five or six tables with rush seats, green-stained woodwork, shelves of country china; piped music. The staff are efficient and friendly, and there's a pleasantly relaxed and informal atmosphere. From a changing menu, the freshly cooked well presented food might include soup (£2.95), generous open ciabatta sandwiches (from £3.95), warm red onion tartlet with goats cheese (£4.95), king prawn salad (£5.95), battered cod and chips (£6.95), mixed mushrooms pie with thyme and crème fraîche (£8.95), chicken jalfrezi (£9.95), and pork medallions with Grand Marnier (£10.95), with specials such as duck leg confit (£3.95), pork loin with apple and cider sauce (£9.95), and cajun spiced ling (£10.50); puddings might be sticky toffee pudding or chocolate torte (£3.75). They serve well kept Hook Norton and Worthington Best on handpump, with a guest such as Wye Valley Butty Bach. *(Recommended by Guy Vowles, Jenny and Dave Hughes, Theocsbrian, Chris Flynn, Wendy Jones, R Davies, Sandra Wright, Mike and Mary Carter, LM, Ian Jones)*

Free house ~ Licensee James Lloyd ~ Real ale ~ Bar food ~ Restaurant ~ (01989) 780470 ~ Children in eating area of bar and restaurant ~ Dogs allowed in bar ~ Open 12-2.30, 6.30-11; 12-3, 7-10.30 Sun

WALTERSTONE SO3425 Map 6

Carpenters Arms

Village signposted off A465 E of Abergavenny, beside Old Pandy Inn; follow village signs, and keep eyes skinned for sign to pub, off to right, by lane-side barn

On the edge of the Black Mountains, this charming little stone cottage is the best sort of unspoilt country tavern, with a chatty, welcoming landlady (it's been in the same family for years) and a delightful old interior. The genuinely traditional rooms have ancient settles against stripped stone walls, some pieces of carpet on broad polished flagstones, a roaring log fire in a gleaming black range (complete with pot-iron, hot-water tap, bread oven and salt cupboard), pewter mugs hanging from beams, and the slow tick of a clock. The snug main dining room has mahogany tables and oak corner cupboards, with a big vase of flowers on the dresser. Another little dining area has old oak tables and church pews on flagstones. The reasonably priced home-made food might include sandwiches (from £2), soup (£3), farmhouse pâté (£4.25), prawn cocktail (£3.50), ploughman's (£4), scampi or plaice (£6), vegetarian lasagne, lamb korma or beef and Guinness pie (£6.50), chicken supreme with brandy and mushroom sauce (£8.50), pepper fillet steak (£12), and puddings (£3.50). They've well kept Wadsworths 6X and perhaps one of their seasonal ales such as Summer Sault tapped from the cask; farm cider. The outside lavatories are cold but in character. *(Recommended by R T and J C Moggridge, Ivor and Shirley Thomas)*

Free house ~ Licensee Vera Watkins ~ Real ale ~ Bar food ~ Restaurant ~ No credit cards ~ (01873) 890353 ~ Children welcome ~ Open 12-11; 12-3, 7-10.30 Sun; closed 25 Dec

WELLINGTON SO4948 Map 6

Wellington

Village signposted off A49 N of Hereford; pub at far end

This red brick Victorian roadside pub has been appealingly reworked and brightened up inside. It has big high-backed dark wooden settles, a brick fireplace with a log fire in winter and fresh flowers in summer, and bric-a-brac such as elderly or antique cricket bats, other sporting equipment and farm and garden tools around the red-painted walls; there is stripped brickwork in the former stables, which is now a pleasant candlelit eating area. Hop bines decorate the bar, which has five well kept ales such as Bass, Hancocks HB, Hobsons, and a couple of guests from local breweries such as Wye Valley on handpump, dutch Oranjeboom lager and farm cider; the public bar side has cribbage, darts, board games and a piano. Tasty food could include filled baguettes (from £3), scampi and chips (£4.50), home-made faggots (£7.50), fried chicken with bacon and leeks or rack of lamb (£8.95), and duck breast (£9.50). The restaurant is no smoking. Service is friendly; there may be quiet classical piped music. There are tables out in the garden behind, and an outside skittle alley. More reports please. *(Recommended by Jestyn Phillips, Anne Morris)*

Free house ~ Licensee Chris Powis ~ Real ale ~ Bar food (12-2(not Mon), 6-10) ~ Restaurant ~ (01432) 830367 ~ Children in eating area of bar and restaurant ~ Dogs allowed in bar ~ Open 12-2.30(3 Sat), 6-11; 12.30-3.30, 7-10.30 Sun; closed Mon lunchtime

WEOBLEY SO4052 Map 6

Salutation

Village signposted from A4112 SW of Leominster; and from A44 NW of Hereford (there's also a good back road direct from Hereford – straight out past S side of racecourse)

Said to be one of the oldest buildings in this quaint little medieval village, this heavily beamed inn is a very nice place to stay in, with pleasant well equipped bedrooms and good breakfasts. The two areas of the comfortable lounge – separated by a few steps and standing timbers – have a relaxed, pubby feel, brocaded modern winged settles and smaller seats, a couple of big cut-away cask seats, wildlife decorations, a hop bine over the bar counter, and logs burning in a big stone fireplace; more standing timbers separate it from the neat no smoking restaurant area, and there's a separate smaller parquet-floored public bar with sensibly placed darts, juke box, and a fruit machine; dominoes and cribbage, and TV. Friendly, obliging staff serve well kept Hook Norton Best, Fullers London Pride and Wye Valley Butty Bach on handpump; there's an extensive wine list with mainly new world wines, and around 20 malt whiskies. Tasty bar food includes soup (£4.10), fried mushrooms (£4.50), lunchtime filled baguettes including warm chicken and red onion (from £5.10), lunchtime ploughman's (£5.25), steak and stout pie or roasted mediterranean vegetables (£7.25), salmon and coriander fishcakes or supreme of pheasant with mushrooms, red onions and thyme (£7.95), and lamb shank (£8.50), with puddings such as lemon tart with raspberry coulis or bread and butter pudding (£4.25); three-course Sunday lunch (£14). There are tables and chairs with parasols on a sheltered back terrace. This quiet village is surrounded by lovely lush countryside. *(Recommended by Denys Gueroult, Chris Flynn, Wendy Jones, Duncan Cloud, Gerry and Rosemary Dobson, Brian Root, W H and E Thomas, Mr and Mrs W D Borthwick, Miss G Irving, R Styles, Mike and Wena Stevenson, Ann and Max Cross, Jim Abbott, Chris Bartlett, the Didler, Mr and Mrs A P Lawrence, Mike and Lynn Robinson, Maurice and Gill McMahon, Alec and Barbara Jones, Tony Hall, Melanie Jackson, R M Corlett)*

Free house ~ Licensee Dr Mike Tai ~ Real ale ~ Bar food ~ Restaurant ~ (01544) 318443 ~ Children in eating area of bar and family room ~ Open 11-11; 12-10.30 Sun; closed 25 Dec (apart from 11-1) ~ Bedrooms: £47S(£50B)/£78S(£75B)

WINFORTON SO2947 Map 6

Sun

A438 14 miles W of Hereford

There's a good play area and an 18-hole crazy golf course in the garden of this neatly kept little dining pub. Inside are two beamed areas on either side of the central servery, with an individual assortment of comfortable country-kitchen chairs, high-backed settles and good solid wooden tables, heavy-horse harness, brasses and old farm tools on the mainly stripped stone walls, and two woodburning stoves; no smoking area. They make their own bread, smoke their own meats, and do a good range of home-made chutneys (you can buy these by the jar to take home). As well as a tasty ploughman's (about 10 different cheeses to choose from), bar food could include lunchtime sandwiches (from £2.85) and snacks such as cod and chips or lasagne (£5.99), and thai chicken curry (£6.99), as well as regularly changing dishes such as smoked bavaria ham and three-cheese bake (£4.25), moroccan mint, chick pea and pepper casserole (£7.20), trout fried with leek and bacon (£8.99), and oxtail braised in cider with garden herbs (£9.75); puddings such as banoffi crumble tart (£4.05). They keep several malt whiskies and local cider, and there may be Shepherd Neame Spitfire and Hook Norton on handpump; sensibly placed darts, cribbage, dominoes, piped music. Readers tell us that the bedrooms are very nice.
(Recommended by Jennie and Jim Wingate, W W Burke, Alan and Paula McCully, R M Corlett)

Free house ~ Licensees Brian and Wendy Hibbard ~ Real ale ~ Bar food ~ Restaurant ~ No credit cards ~ (01544) 327677 ~ Children in eating area of bar and restaurant ~ Open 11.30-11; 12-10.30 Sun; closed Tues ~ Bedrooms: £35B/£55B

WOOLHOPE SO6136 Map 4

Butchers Arms

Signposted from B4224 in Fownhope; carry straight on past Woolhope village

Once they've found it, readers can't wait to return to this tucked-away 14th-c country pub. The relaxed atmosphere generated by the friendly licensees, cheery staff and cosy interior is enhanced by generous freshly prepared food. One of the spacious and welcoming bars has very low beams decorated with hops, old-fashioned well worn built-in seats with brocaded cushions, captain's chairs and stools around small tables, and a brick fireplace filled with dried flowers. Broadly similar though with fewer beams, the other bar has a large built-in settle and another log fire; there are often fresh flowers. Sliding french windows lead out to a little terrace with teak furniture, a few parasols and cheerful flowering tubs; there's also a tiny willow-lined brook. Their three very well kept beers on handpump might be Hook Norton Best and Old Hooky and a guest such as Shepherd Neame Spitfire, and they stock local farm ciders, quite a few malt whiskies, and decent wines; they do good coffees too. Enjoyable bar food includes sandwiches (from £2.95), soup (£3.50), whitebait (£4.95), ploughman's (from £4.95), mushroom biriani (£6.50), venison sausages and mash, beef curry or gammon steak (£7.95), and there are daily specials such as fish pie (£9.95), and bass with lemon and parsley, pork loin with apple, cream and brandy sauce and pheasant breast with wild berry sauce (£10.95); huge puddings such as butterscotch tart or bread and butter pudding (from £3.50); the restaurant is no smoking. Just outside the village in a quietly relaxing spot, the pub is surrounded by really lovely countryside – to enjoy some of the best of it, turn left as you come out and take the tiny left-hand road at the end of the car park; this turns into a track and then into a path, and the view from the top of the hill is quite something. *(Recommended by Martin Jennings, Alan and Paula McCully, Barry Collett, June and Mike Coleman, Lucien, Mr and Mrs A P Lawrence, Jenny and Dave Hughes, Derek Carless, Ian Jones, Greg Lacey, Chris and Maggie Kent, John Bowdler, Lynn Sharpless, Bernard Stradling, CathDonne)*

Free house ~ Licensees Sian and Mark Vallely ~ Real ale ~ Bar food (till 10 Fri and Sat) ~ Restaurant ~ (01432) 860281 ~ Children welcome ~ Open 11.30-3, 6.30-11; 12-3, 7-10.30 Sun ~ Bedrooms: £30/£39

Crown 🍷

In village centre

In summer this friendly and well run old pub, popular for its comprehensive choice of food, is festooned with flowers. The neatly kept lounge bar has plush button-back built-in wall banquettes and dark wood tables and chairs. There's also an open fire, a timbered divider strung with hop bines, good wildlife photographs and little country pictures on the cream walls, and lots of attention to details such as flowers on tables. Heavy oak posts support a thick stone wall partly dividing off the no smoking dining area; darts, shove-ha'penny, table skittles, quoits and occasional piped music. The Wye Valley Bitter here is very good value, and the two other well kept real ales on handpump are Smiles Best and a guest such as Timothy Taylors Landlord; they've a decent wine list, and farm cider. Nicely presented dishes could include home-made soup (£3.25), home-made potted stilton with mushrooms (£4.35), bacon and cheese crumpet (£4.55), grilled trout with almonds or smoked haddock kedgeree (£8.75), steak, stout and mushroom or rabbit pie, lamb and cranberry casserole or chicken and asparagus lasagne (£7.70), and around a dozen vegetarian dishes such as chestnut, onion and apple pie with cumberland sauce, nut moussaka with feta cheese topping, and courgette, mushroom and spinach lasagne (£7.50). A large variety of puddings could include black cherry pancakes or treacle tart with custard (£3.50), and they have a children's menu (from £3.45). There are picnic-sets on the neat front lawn. More reports please. *(Recommended by anon)*

Free house ~ Licensees Neil and Sally Gordon ~ Real ale ~ Bar food (till 10) ~ Restaurant ~ (01432) 860468 ~ Well behaved children in eating area of bar and restaurant till 8pm ~ Open 12-2.30, 6.30(7 winter)-11; 12-3, 6(6.30 winter)-11 Sat; 12-3, 6.30(7 winter)-10.30 Sun; closed 25 Dec

Lucky Dip

Besides the fully inspected pubs, you might like to try these Lucky Dips recommended to us and described by readers (if you do, please send us reports: www.goodguides.com).

Bodenham [SO5454]

☆ ***Englands Gate*** [just off A417 at Bodenham turn-off, about 6 miles S of Leominster]: Attractive black and white 16th-c coaching inn, recently refurbished, with big log fires, flowers on scrubbed tables, well kept ales inc Marstons Pedigree and Woods Shropshire Lad, Stowford Press cider, good wine choice, good food from bar favourites to adventurous dishes, huge mixed grill and Sun roast, reasonable prices; picturesque garden, open all day *(Alan and Paula McCully, Greta and Christopher Wells, Derek Carless)*

Bredenbury [SO6056]

☆ ***Barneby Arms*** [A44 Bromyard—Leominster]: Substantial hotel popular for wide range of generous well served food in clean bright busy bar with ceiling joists, horse tack, lots of old woodworking tools; well kept Banks's and Marstons Pedigree, friendly staff, popular carvery restaurant; children welcome, big garden, bedrooms *(Richard Gibbs)*

Bromyard [SO6554]

Bay Horse [High St]: Black and white 16th-c pub with well kept Fullers London Pride, Marstons Pedigree and Wye Valley Hereford, good choice of wines by the glass, enjoyable lunchtime bar food inc good hot baguettes, restaurant; tables on back terrace *(Alan and Paula McCully)*

Bromyard Downs [SO6755]

Royal Oak [just NE of Bromyard, signed off A44]: Beautifully placed 18th-c black and white pub with wide views, L-shaped flagstoned bar with carved oak beams and open fires, dining room with huge bay window, wide range of home-made food, Hook Norton, friendly staff; extensive colourful front terraces and gardens, good walks *(Alan and Paula McCully)*

Colwall [SO7342]

☆ ***Crown*** [Walwyn Rd]: Welcoming and carefully refurbished, carpeted bar with step up to parquet-floor area with log fire, nice prints and lighting, good honest food from sandwiches and ploughman's to popular Sun lunch, some classier dishes, friendly efficient service, well kept Bass, Timothy Taylors Landlord and Tetleys, decent wines, daily papers *(Mike and Mary Clark, Nick Bentley, BB)*

Ewyas Harold [SO3828]

Temple Bar: Very friendly, engaging landlord, well kept Bass and Hobsons, enjoyable food in public bar, lounge or small neat dining room *(Ron and Mary Nicholson)*

Fownhope [SO5734]

☆ ***Green Man***: Striking 15th-c black and white inn with big log fire, wall settles, window seats and armchairs in one beamed bar, standing timbers dividing another, popular well priced food from sandwiches to steak inc children's and Sun carvery (no smoking main restaurant is plainer), friendly efficient service, well kept Courage Directors, Hook Norton Best, Marstons Pedigree, John Smiths and Sam Smiths OB, Weston's farm ciders, attractive prices; children welcome, quiet garden with play area; comfortably refurbished bedrooms, good breakfast, back fitness centre *(J Hale, Barry Smith, MJVK, LYM)*

Fromes Hill [SO6747]

Majors Arms: Country pub with spectacular view from garden tables (great place for children if you keep them under control); enjoyable food esp steaks, real ales; comfortable bedrooms *(Richard Williams)*

Goodrich [SO5719]

Hostelrie: Village pub upgraded to small hotel with unusual turreted gothic extension, cosy softly lit carpeted bar and lounge, beams and stripped stone, generous helpings of bar food inc imaginative dishes, pleasant friendly service, pretty dining room; attractive garden, bedrooms, near Goodrich Castle and Wye Valley Walk *(John Brightley)*

Hereford [SO5139]

Barrels [St Owen St]: Plain and cheery two-bar local brewing its own good Wye Valley Hereford and Dorothy Goodbodys ales at attractive prices (esp 5-7 happy hour), barrel-built counter also serving guest beers such as Buffys Norwich Terrier, farm ciders from Bulmer's, Stowford Press and Weston's, friendly staff, no food, side pool room with games, juke box and TV sports, lots of modern stained glass; piped blues and rock, live music at beer festival end Aug; picnic-sets out on cobbles by brewery, open all day *(Mike Pugh, Richard Lewis, the Didler, BB)*

Bay Horse [Kings Acre Rd]: Dining pub with four well kept ales such as Bass and Cotleigh, large two-level main room, smaller side room, attractive upmarket décor, fresh flowers, good interesting food on colourful plates from enjoyable sandwiches up, quick friendly service, well chosen wines; pleasant piped music throughout *(Dr and Mrs M E Wilson)*

Gilbies [St Peters Cl]: Good relaxed bar and bistro, enjoyable food inc platters to share, several continental beers on tap and lots of bottled beers as well as Bitter and cider, good choice of wines *(Joyce and Maurice Cottrell)*

Green Dragon [Broad St]: Pleasant bars in long-established cathedral city hotel; good value bargain breaks *(Jestyn Phillips, MDN)*

Stagecoach [West St]: 16th-c black and white building, comfortable welcoming lounge with dark oak panelling and well kept Wye Valley ale, decent wines, tea and coffee, reasonable prices, good food from snacks up using local produce, upstairs restaurant *(Gill Waller, Tony Morriss, Dr and Mrs M E Wilson)*

Kingsland [SO4461]

☆ ***Angel***: Open-plan beamed and timbered dining pub with very wide range of nicely prepared food, often inventive, from filled baguettes to wild duck and braised pheasant, Weds OAP bargain lunch, well kept Ansells and Greene King Abbot, decent wines, sensible prices, prompt friendly service, comfortable beamed bar with big hot stove, neatly set restaurant extension on left; may be unobtrusive piped pop music, music night Fri; picnic-sets on front grass *(BB, Doreen and Haydn Maddock)*

Kington [SO3057]

☆ ***Olde Tavern*** [Victoria Rd, just off A44 opp B4355 – follow sign to Town Centre, Hospital, Cattle Mkt; pub on right opp Elizabeth Rd, no inn sign but Estd 1767 notice]: Wonderful time-warp old place, small plain parlour and public bar, dark brown woodwork, big windows, old settles and other antique furniture, china, pewter and curios; truly welcoming locals and long-serving landlady, well kept Ansells, gas fire, no music, machines or food; children welcome, though not a family pub; cl wkdy lunchtimes, outside gents' *(JP, PP, Pete Baker, BB, Norma and Keith Bloomfield, Edward Jago, the Didler, RWC)*

Ledbury [SO7138]

Ring of Bells [New St]: Good pub food, well kept beer *(Jenny and Dave Hughes)*

☆ ***Talbot*** [New St]: Relaxed local atmosphere in 16th-c inn's black-beamed bar rambling around island servery, antique hunting prints, plush wall banquettes or more traditional seats, log fire in big stone fireplace, new licensees doing enjoyable food from baguettes to full meals, well kept ales inc a local one, good house wines, quick friendly service, smart no smoking black-panelled dining roomt, tales of a friendly poltergeist; fruit machine, piped music; decent bedrooms sharing bath *(Dr and Mrs Jackson, Abi Benson, BB, Jenny and Dave Hughes)*

Leintwardine [SO4174]

☆ ***Sun*** [Rosemary Lane, just off A4113]: Unspoilt gem, three bare benches by coal fire in red-tiled front parlour off hallway, venerable landlady brings you well kept Woods tapped from the cask in her kitchen (and may honour you with the small settee and a couple of chairs by the gas fire in her sitting room); no food exc pickled eggs and crisps *(Pete Baker, RWC, BB,*

Brian and Halina Howes, Martin Grosberg)

Leominster [SO4958]

Black Horse [South St]: Big well run bustling bar with comfortably rustic furniture, snug lounge and eating area (no food Sun); well kept real ales inc one brewed for the pub by Dunn Plowman, enjoyable straightforward food inc good sandwiches, traditional games *(MLR, BB)*

☆ ***Talbot*** [West St]: Comfortable old coaching inn in charming town, standing timbers and heavy beams with hop bines, antique carved settles, fine log fires with 18th-c oak-panelled chimneybreasts, sporting prints; decent home-made bar food inc good complex toasties and children's dishes, wider choice in popular restaurant, well kept Greene King Ruddles, nice range of wines, good coffee, long-serving staff; piped music; good bedrooms and housekeeping *(LYM, Nick Holding, Alan and Paula McCully, Mrs T A Bizat, Hazel and Michael Duncombe)*

Little Cowarne [SO6051]

☆ ***Three Horseshoes*** [off A465 S of Bromyard, towards Ullingswick]: Wide choice of good home cooking in quarry-tiled bar and spacious restaurant extension (lunchtime carvery) with no smoking conservatory, well kept ales inc Greene King Old Speckled Hen and Wye Valley, decent wines, log fire, mix of solid tables and chairs, friendly obliging licensees, disabled access; juke box, pool, darts and fruit machine; lovely country views from terrace and charming simple garden, quite unspoilt village; comfortable bedrooms *(Mr and Mrs J Williams, Alan and Paula McCully, Sir Nigel Foulkes)*

Lyonshall [SO3355]

☆ ***Royal George*** [A480 S]: Unpretentious beamed and timbered village inn, clean and friendly, with good fresh food nicely served inc some lunchtime bargains, unusual dishes and Sun lunch, well kept Adnams with a guest such as Youngs Special, six good value wines by the glass, log and coal fire in small lounge bar, two pleasant partly no smoking dining areas off central servery, lots of clay pipes, old photographs and *Royal George* ship prints; comfortable bedrooms, picnic-sets on back terrace and in two-part flower-filled garden with swings *(BB, Norma and Keith Bloomfield)*

Mathon [SO7345]

Cliffe Arms [signed off B4220; or reached off A4103 via Cradley]: Pretty black and white heavy-beamed village pub, small slate-floored bar, dining area with woodburner, cushioned pews and nice dining chairs, Adnams, Hobsons and Tetleys, good generous food (not Mon; not winter Sun evening) inc adventurous dishes and Weds/Thurs evening bargains, simple public bar with well lit pool, games, TV and juke box; children welcome, tables in sizeable streamside garden below Malvern Hills, cl Mon lunchtime *(Derek Carless, Denys Gueroult, Dave Braisted)*

Much Marcle [SO6634]

Royal Oak [off A449 Ross-on-Wye—Ledbury]: Superb rural spot with magnificent views, pleasant lounge with stools around small round tables and open fire, wide range of bar food from sandwiches up inc good vegetarian choice, Courage Directors, John Smiths and Weston's very local cider, large back dining area, bar with pool table; pleasant garden *(Paul and Sue Merrick)*

Newtown [SO6144]

Newtown Inn [A4103 Hereford—Worcester, junction with A417]: Well renovated by experienced current landlord, good reasonably priced innovative food, friendly service and atmosphere, sensibly priced wines *(Anthony Bradshaw)*

Norton Canon [SO3748]

Three Horseshoes [A480 Yazor—Eccles Green]: Simple two-bar country pub brewing its own good Shoes ales, inc fearsomely strong Farrier; log fire and old sofas in one room, vintage juke box in the other, lunchtime food; one of the only two pubs we know of with an indoor shooting gallery; children welcome, tables in orchard – lovely orchard country near Davies Meadows wildflower reserve; cl Mon-Weds lunchtime *(Jonathan Smith)*

Pencombe [SO5952]

Wheelwright Arms: Cosy beamed 17th-c pub with welcoming licensees, dog and locals, log fire, bargain straightforward food (not Mon evening), Sat steak night, well kept Adnams Broadside, good local wine by the glass; pretty village nestling in hills; cl Mon lunchtime *(Alan and Paula McCully)*

Ross-on-Wye [SO6024]

Crown & Sceptre [Market Pl]: Nice bustling atmosphere in open-plan pub, Archers, Greene King, Shepherd Neame and guests, Easter beer festival, lunchtime meals, coal fire; very busy wknds; tables outside, open all day *(the Didler, JP, PP)*

Hope & Anchor [Riverside; coming from A40 W side, 1st left after bridge (Rope Walk)]: Big-windowed family extension looking out on gardens leading down to river, plenty of tables out here (and summer ice-cream bar and barbecues), thorough-going boating theme in cheery main bar, upstairs parlour bar and Victorian-style dining room, cosy touches and good housekeeping, generous good value food inc sandwiches and good choice for children, well kept Banks's and Marstons Pedigree, farm cider, good house wine, attractive prices; open all day, can be crowded wknds *(LYM, Keith Allen, David and Ruth Hollands)*

Mail Rooms [Gloucester Rd]: Light and airy new Wetherspoons, open and modern, with civilised atmosphere and pleasant terrace; open all day *(Mike and Mary Carter)*

Ruckhall [SO4539]

Ancient Camp [off A465 W of Hereford]: Beautifully placed out-of-the-way comfortable country inn firmly run by new owners, not really a pub any more; entirely no smoking, good baguettes and a few hot dishes lunchtimes, at least in season (set-time evening meals for residents), local farm cider, may have a real ale, prompt pleasant service; no children, in winter has been cl Mon-Thurs and Sun evening *(R T and J C Moggridge, Michael Lamm, R M Corlett, LYM)*

Stiffords Bridge [SO7348]
☆ ***Red Lion*** [A4103 W of Gt Malvern]: Roomy and busy main-road country local with good cheery atmosphere, log fire, sensible mix of table sizes, good food from rewarding sandwiches to lots of interesting home-made specials, fresh veg, sensible prices, well kept Banks's, Hobsons Best and Marstons Pedigree, local farm cider, pleasant service; tables on trellised terrace, bedrooms *(Mr and Mrs G Montrose, BB)*

Symonds Yat [SO5615]
☆ ***Saracens Head*** [Symonds Yat E, by ferry, ie over on the Gloucs bank]: Riverside beauty spot next to 60p ferry, busy down-to-earth flagstoned bar popular with canoeists, mountain bikers and hikers, cheerful efficient staff, good range of well presented nourishing food from good value sandwiches up, well kept Theakstons Best, XB and Old Peculier and Wye Valley, three farm ciders, pine tables, settles and window seats; cosy carpeted restaurant, games bar with pool, piped jazz and blues, SkyTV, lots of picnic-sets out on waterside terraces, live music Thurs; summer boat trips, nice good value bedrooms – good place to stay out of season *(Dave and Meg Richards, Keith Allen, Clare and Paul Howes, Ian Phillips, BB, Abi Benson)*

Tillington [SO4645]
Bell: Good family-friendly local, good range of reasonably priced food from nice baguettes to generous home-made hot dishes, several real ales such as Spinning Dog Top Dog, Timothy Taylors Landlord and Wye Valley Butty Bach, comfortable banquettes in lounge extension, warm welcome; good big garden with play area *(Gerry and Rosemary Dobson)*

Trumpet [SO6639]
☆ ***Trumpet Inn***: Black and white timbered pub dating from 15th c, friendly and good value, with interesting horse-racing memorabilia, beams and stripped brickwork, sandwiches and good choice of enjoyable home-made food largely from local farms and own garden, children's dishes, well kept Castle Eden, Flowers IPA and guest beers, their own perry, nice house wines, good service; no children Fri or Sat evenings; tables in big garden behind, camp site with hard standings *(A B Bamford, Paul and Sue Merrick)*

Upper Colwall [SO7643]
Chase [Chase Rd, off B4218 Malvern—Colwall, 1st left after hilltop on bend going W]: Great views from attractive garden and refined and comfortable lounge of genteel and friendly two-bar pub on Malvern Hills, well kept real ales inc Wye Valley Dorothy Goodbodys seasonal ones, limited choice of enjoyable lunchtime bar food inc good filled rolls; cl Tues *(Bruce M Drew, Dr and Mrs Jackson)*

Walford [SO5820]
☆ ***Mill Race*** [B4234 Ross—Lydney]: Nice mix of furnishings and some fine old features in partly flagstoned open-plan bar with high-raftered no smoking end and some stripped stone, good value food from sandwiches and filled baked potatoes to enterprising hot dishes, well kept Bass and quite a few malt whiskies, good wine choice, restaurant through Norman arch; unobtrusive piped pop music; garden and play area *(BB, Barry Smith, Andy Sinden, Louise Harrington)*

Weston-under-Penyard [SO6323]
☆ ***Weston Cross Inn***: Very pretty outside, with views of picturesque village from tables on front lawn, more tables and play area behind; good home-made food from basic bar snacks and ploughman's to wide choice of fine local meat and fresh fish, friendly service, simple beamed bar with Boddingtons and Tetleys, Weston's cider, two back dining rooms; pool and TV; walkers welcome *(Martin Jennings, BB, Paula Cuthbert)*

Whitney-on-Wye [SO2747]
☆ ***Rhydspence*** [A438 Hereford—Brecon]: Well run very picturesque ancient black and white country inn right on Welsh border, with attractive old-fashioned furnishings, heavy beams and timbers in rambling spick-and-span rooms, good interesting food using local produce, pretty dining room, well kept Robinsons Best, Dunkerton's farm cider, good wine choice, log fire; tables in attractive garden with fine views over Wye valley, comfortable bedrooms *(Hazel and Michael Duncombe, Denys Gueroult, LYM, Cliff Blakemore, Anne and Leuan Williams, Rodney and Norma Stubington, Pam and David Bailey)*

Wigmore [SO4169]
Compasses [Ford St]: Walker-friendly village inn with welcoming landlord, well kept changing ales such as Wadworths IPA and 6X and Woods, generous blackboard home cooking, old-fashioned bars; four bedrooms *(Pete Yearsley)*

Olde Oak: Olde-worlde front bar, elegant candlelit back lounge, well kept local Woodhampton Jack Snipe, good value food inc steaks (no sandwiches), pleasant service; tables in garden behind *(R T and J C Moggridge)*

Yarpole [SO4664]
Bell [just off B4361 N of Leominster]: Neat and tidy picturesquely timbered ancient pub, extended into former cider mill; comfortably smart, with brass and bric-a-brac, well kept Greene King Old Speckled Hen, good bar food, more ambitious menu in country dining area; tables in sunny flower-filled garden, very handy for Croft Castle *(Dr D E Granger)*

Post Office address codings confusingly give the impression that some pubs are in Herefordshire when they're really in Gloucestershire or even Wales (which is where we list them).

Hertfordshire

The two new main entries here both have good food: the Alford Arms tucked away near National Trust woodland in Frithsden (appealing décor, inventive cooking), and the bright and cheerful Fox & Hounds at Hunsdon (inventive dishes here too, and a nice garden). Both will be firmly in the running for a Food Award, and the Alford Arms at Frithsden, already praised by readers for many enjoyable meals out, gains the title of Hertfordshire Dining Pub of the Year. Other pubs on good form here have been the pleasantly old-fashioned Three Tuns in pretty Ashwell, the chatty White Horse in Hertford (very good beer, good value food), the Lytton Arms in Knebworth (another top place for beer, attractive layout), the Holly Bush at Potters Crouch (beautifully kept country pub, a relaxing motorway break), the rambling old Boot at Sarratt, the Rose & Crown in St Albans (good speciality sandwiches, nice pub) and the George & Dragon at Watton-at-Stone (civilised dining pub with imaginative food). In the Lucky Dip section at the end of the chapter, the Waggoners at Ayot Green, Bell at Benington and Crown & Sceptre near Hemel Hempstead are all noteworthy. Drinks prices in the county are generally now at or above the £2 mark, and a little above the national average. The two cheapest main entries we found were the Gibraltar Castle at Batford and White Horse in Hertford (both Fullers pubs). The main Hertfordshire brewery has been McMullens (as we go to press there is talk of a possible sale). Other smaller local beers worth looking out for include Tring and Green Tye.

ALDBURY SP9612 Map 4

Greyhound

Stocks Road; village signposted from A4251 Tring—Berkhamsted, or reached directly from roundabout at E end of A41 Tring bypass

The handsome Georgian-fronted pub is especially stunning in autumn when the blazing leaves of its virginia creeper provide a brilliant counterpoint to the backdrop of bronzing Chiltern beechwoods (part of the National Trust owned Ashridge Estate). Tables outside face a picturesque village green complete with stocks and lively duckpond. It's also well worth a winter visit, when the lovely warm fire and subtle lighting make it really cosy inside. There's a buoyant and thriving atmosphere, and service is smiling and efficient even when under pressure. There are some signs of the pre-Georgian original building – around the copper-hooded inglenook, for example; plenty of tables in the two rooms ramble off each side of the drinks and food serving areas. Badger Dorset Best, IPA, Tanglefoot and a Badger seasonal guest are kept well on handpump, and there's a weekday early evening happy hour (5-7pm). Generous bar food includes sandwiches (from £4.75), filled baked potatoes (£5.25), ham and eggs (£5.75), scrambled egg, chorizo and crispy black pudding or ploughman's (from £5.95), vegetable and bean chimichangas (£7.50), home-made steak and ale pie (£7.95), battered haddock seafood platter (£8.50), and a handful of daily specials such as tortelloni with mushroom sauce (£7.50) or rump steak with stilton sauce (£14.95). No smoking conservatory, piped music and fruit machine. There are plenty of good walks nearby (plastic bags are kept near the entrance for muddy boots), for instance, around the monument to the canal mogul, the 3rd Duke of Bridgewater, up on the escarpment, and for the less energetic, the toll road through the Ashridge

Estate is very attractive. *(Recommended by M A and C R Starling, Mike and Heather Watson, David and Ruth Shillitoe, Tracey and Stephen Groves, Ian and Joan Blackwell, Catherine and Richard Preston, Brian Root, Peter and Giff Bennett, Howard Dell, Len Banister)*

Badger ~ Manager Richard Coletta ~ Real ale ~ Bar food (12-2.30(3.30 Sun)-10; not Sun evening) ~ Restaurant ~ (01442) 851228 ~ Children welcome ~ Dogs allowed in bar ~ Open 11-11; 12-10.30 Sun ~ Bedrooms: £60B/£75B

Valiant Trooper

Trooper Road (towards Aldbury Common); off B4506 N of Berkhamsted

According to legend the Duke of Wellington once met his officers at this partly pink-painted and tiled pub to discuss tactics: its traditional atmosphere and antique cavalry prints do well in conjuring up those days. The first room is beamed and tiled in red and black, and has built-in wall benches, a pew and small dining chairs around the attractive country tables, and a woodburning stove in the inglenook fireplace. In the middle bar, which has a wooden floor, there's some exposed brickwork and spindleback chairs – and signs warning you to 'mind the step'. The far room has nice country kitchen chairs around individually chosen tables, and a brick fireplace. Bar food includes ciabatta sandwiches or filled baked potatoes (£3.50), ploughman's (from £4) and daily specials such as garlic mushrooms (£3.50), moules marinière (£4.50), roast vegetable lasagne (£7), steak and kidney pie (£7.50), duck with Pernod sauce (£9), and roast bass with garlic prawns (£10), with puddings such as sticky toffee pudding or white chocolate and raspberry torte (£3). The lounge bar is no smoking at lunchtime; pleasant obliging service. Well kept Fullers London Pride and Morrells Oxford Blue on handpump, with a couple of guests from brewers such as Adnams and Bass. Shove-ha'penny, dominoes, cribbage, bridge on Monday nights. The enclosed garden has a play house for children. *(Recommended by Darren Le Poidevin, Brian Root, Colin McKerrow, D J and P M Taylor, V F Sullivan, Ian Phillips)*

Free house ~ Licensee Tim O'Gorman ~ Real ale ~ Bar food (12-2(2.30 Sun), 6.30-9.15 Tues-Sat, not Sun/Mon evening) ~ Restaurant ~ (01442) 851203 ~ Children in eating area of bar, restaurant and family room till 8.30 ~ Dogs welcome ~ Open 11.30-11; 12-10.30 Sun

ARDELEY TL3027 Map 5

Jolly Waggoner

Village signposted off B1037 NE of Stevenage

Emphasis is on the good imaginative food at this pleasant, cream-washed dining inn, which is peacefully set in a pretty tucked-away village. Where possible using fresh local produce, the bar menu includes sandwiches (from £2.85), soup (£4.50), ploughman's (£6), and a very popular omelette Arnold Bennett (£7.50), as well as changing specials such as tomato and mozzarella salad (£4.50), vegetable and pasta bake (£6.50), fresh crab (£8.75), steak and kidney pie (£9), chicken in wine, garlic and cream or penne with tuna, tomato and parmesan sauce (£11), calves liver with sage and butter or roquefort cheese and horseradish (£12), and puddings such as chocolate truffle torte, pineapple crème brûlée or lemon tart (£4.25); booking is essential for their Sunday lunch, and there's a £1 surcharge for credit cards where the bill is under £10. The comfortable bar, with a window overlooking the garden, has a relaxed and civilised atmosphere, with open woodwork and beams, and a blazing fire in winter. Decorated with modern prints, the restaurant has been extended into the cottage next door. Well kept Greene King IPA tapped from the cask and Abbot on handpump, a decent range of wines and freshly squeezed orange juice in summer; there may be piped music. There's a pleasant garden and terrace; Cromer Windmill is nearby. *(Recommended by Jill McLaren, Catherine and Richard Preston, Ian Phillips, B, M and P Kendall)*

Greene King ~ Tenant Darren Perkins ~ Real ale ~ Bar food (12-2, 6.30-9.30, not Sun evening or Mon exc bank hol lunchtime) ~ Restaurant ~ (01438) 861350 ~ Children over seven in eating area of bar and restaurant ~ Open 12-2.30(3 Sat), 6.30-11; 12-3, 7-10.30 Sun; closed Mon except bank hols, then cl Tues

ASHWELL TL2639 Map 5

Three Tuns

High Street

You'll find this flower-decked 18th-c hotel in a pretty village that nestles in the lee of what in this part of the world passes for quite a hill, with far-reaching views from the top. It has a pleasantly old-fashioned pubby atmosphere, and is very popular with groups of hikers on summer weekends. There's an air of Victorian opulence in the cosy lounge with its relaxing chairs, big family tables, lots of pictures, stuffed pheasants and fish, and antiques. The simpler more modern public bar has pool, darts, dominoes, a fruit machine, SkyTV, and Greene King IPA, Abbot and Ruddles on handpump, and there's a good choice of wines; piped light classical music. Food is home-made, and the shortish very fairly priced bar menu includes soup (£3.95), chicken liver pâté (£4.50), devilled whitebait (£4.95), vegetable curry (£6.95), breaded scampi (£7.45), steak and kidney pie (£8.75), and a handful of daily specials such as pork in cider sauce (£8.95) or grilled scotch salmon fillet with herb butter (£10.45); no smoking dining room. The substantial shaded garden has boules, and picnic-sets under apple trees. One of the six bedrooms has a four-poster bed, and another its own dressing room; we look forward to hearing from readers who have stayed here. *(Recommended by Dr Paull Khan, David and Ruth Shillitoe, Ian Phillips, John and Christine Lowe, Gordon Neighbour, Joy and Colin Rorke)*

Greene King ~ Tenants Claire and Darrell Stanley ~ Real ale ~ Bar food (12-2.30, 6.30-9.30; 12-9.30 Sat/Sun) ~ Restaurant ~ (01462) 742107 ~ Children in eating area of bar and restaurant ~ Dogs allowed in bar ~ Open 11-11; 12-10.30 Sun ~ Bedrooms: £39(£59B)/£49(£59B)

AYOT ST LAWRENCE TL1916 Map 5

Brocket Arms

B651 N of St Albans for about 6 miles; village signposted on right after Wheathampstead and Mid Herts golf course; or B653 NE of Luton, then right on to B651

There's loads of pubby atmosphere at this peacefully set white-painted and tiled 14th-c brick free house, which is reputedly haunted by a monk from the local abbey who was tried and hanged here during the Reformation. It's particularly popular at the weekends, when you therefore might want to get here early. Two simple and very traditional low-ceilinged rooms have sturdy oak beams, a roaring fire in a big inglenook fireplace, old-fashioned furnishings and magazines to read. As well as a dozen or so wines by the glass, five or six real ales include Adnams Broadside, Batemans XXXB, Greene King IPA and Abbot and a guest or two such as Wadworths 6X or Tring Rebellion; darts, dominoes, cribbage and piped classical music. Lunchtime bar food includes sandwiches (from £2.50), soup (£3.50), macaroni cheese (£5), home-made curries and chilli con carne (from £5), venison and duck sausages (£5.50), and game pie (£6.50), with home-made puddings (from £3.50), and evening specials such as roast pheasant with redcurrant and port sauce (£13.50); there's an extended menu in the no smoking evening restaurant. The extensive south-facing suntrap walled garden is lovely in summer, with an outside bar and a children's play area. Just over the road are the romantic remains of a medieval church (a late 18th-c local squire decided it spoilt his view and started knocking it down, until a furious Bishop of Lincoln called a halt), and the pub is close to the house where George Bernard Shaw lived for over 45 years. *(Recommended by Susan and Nigel Wilson, Giles Francis, Ian Phillips)*

Free house ~ Licensee Toby Wingfield Digby ~ Real ale ~ Bar food (12-2.30, 7.30-9.30) ~ Restaurant ~ (01438) 820250 ~ Children welcome ~ Dogs welcome ~ Open 11-11; 12-11 Sun ~ Bedrooms: £70B/£80B

Please let us know what you think of a pub's bedrooms. No stamp needed: The Good Pub Guide, FREEPOST TN1569, Wadhurst, E Sussex TN5 7BR.

BATFORD TL1415 Map 5

Gibraltar Castle

Lower Luton Road; B653, S of B652 junction

This well run roadside pub has an interesting collection of militaria, particularly at the end on the right as you go in, which has something of the feel of a hunting lodge; here the low beams found elsewhere give way to soaring rafters, and glass cases show off pristinely kept uniforms, bullets, medals and rifles. There's plenty to look at in the rest of the long carpeted bar, with its nice old fireplace, comfortably cushioned wall benches, and a couple of snugly intimate window alcoves, one with a fine old clock. They serve well kept Fullers Chiswick, ESB, London Pride and a seasonal brew on handpump, a good range of malt whiskies, well made Irish coffee, and a thoughtful choice of wines by the glass; piped music, fruit machine. Tasty bar food might include club sandwiches or soup (from £3.50), smoked salmon stuffed with prawns and seafood sauce (£5.95), potato or grilled haloumi cheese, salad, olives and pitta bread with greek dips or steak and kidney pie (£8.95), beef stroganoff or fisherman's pie (£8.95), 10oz sirloin (£12.95), and puddings such as sticky toffee (£3.95); booking is recommended for their very popular good value Sunday roast (£8.95). There are tables and chairs on a new, safely enclosed back terrace, a few tables in front by the road, and pretty hanging baskets and tubs dotted around. *(Recommended by Norma and Keith Bloomfield, Ian Phillips)*

Fullers ~ Tenant Derek Phelan ~ Real ale ~ Bar food (12-2.30, 6-9, not Sun evening) ~ (01582) 460005 ~ Children welcome ~ Dogs welcome ~ Jam session Tues evening ~ Open 11-3, 5-11; 11-11 Sat; 12-10.30 Sun

COTTERED TL3129 Map 5

Bull

A507 W of Buntingford

The airy relaxing low-beamed front lounge at this old tree-surrounded inn is attractively laid out and well looked after, with polished antiques on a stripped wood floor, and a good fire. A second bar has darts, a fruit machine, shove-ha'penny, cribbage and dominoes; unobtrusive piped music. They have well kept Greene King IPA and Abbot on handpump, and decent wines. Thoughtfully presented bar food includes sandwiches (from £2.65), burgers (from £5.75), ploughman's (£5.95), steak, Guinness and stilton pie (£8), chicken in a cream, wine and garlic sauce (£11), and salmon fillet with cheese and mushroom sauce (£11.50); £1 surcharge for credit card bills under £10; friendly and obliging service. The pub faces a row of pretty thatched cottages, and there are benches and tables in the attractive big garden. *(Recommended by Mr and Mrs D Barlow, Peter and Joan Elbra, Ian Phillips)*

Greene King ~ Tenant Darren Perkins ~ Real ale ~ Bar food (12-2, 6.30(7 Sun)-9; not Tues evening) ~ Restaurant ~ (01763) 281243 ~ Well behaved children over 7 in eating area of bar and restaurant ~ Open 12-2.30(3 Sat), 6.30-11; 12-3, 7-10.30 Sun

FRITHSDEN TL0110 Map 5

Alford Arms

From Berkhamsted take unmarked road towards Potten End, pass Potten End turn on right, then take next left towards Ashridge College

Hertfordshire Dining Pub of the Year

Fashionably refurbished by thoughtful new licensees, this secluded country pub is an elegantly casual place for a good meal out. The airy interior has simple prints on pale cream walls, with areas picked out in blocks of Victorian green or picture gallery red, and an appealing mix of good furniture from Georgian chairs to old commodes stands on bare boards and patterned quarry tiles. It's all pulled together by luxurious richly patterned curtains. Imaginative changing bar food might include rustic bread with roast garlic and balsamic olive oil (£3), creamy asparagus soup (£3.50), dressed crab on rocket with lemon vinaigrette (£6.75), thai chicken sausages with mash and coriander gravy (£9.25), gnocchi with blue cheese, spinach, pine nuts and cream (£9), grilled red mullet fillet on couscous with red pepper sauce (£11), pork escalope on mash with apple and horseradish sauce and black pudding (£11.50), roast cod on wilted spinach with chorizo and new potatoes (£12), and bacon-wrapped pigeon breast on rösti with quince jus (£12.50); extra vegetables (from £2), and puddings such as warm bakewell tart, baked fig bread and butter pudding or roast plums with marsala and mascarpone (from £4.25); good sweet wines. It does get very busy so you may need to book. Well kept Flowers Original, Marstons Pedigree, Tetleys and Wadworths 6X on handpump; piped jazz. *(Recommended by Mike and Jennifer Marsh, John and Joyce Snell, BKA, M Fynes-Clinton)*

Enterprise ~ Lease Becky Salisbury ~ Real ale ~ Bar food (12-2.30(3 Sun, bank hols), 7-10) ~ Restaurant ~ (01442) 864480 ~ Children welcome ~ Dogs allowed in bar ~ Open 11-11; 12-10.30 Sun

HERTFORD TL3212 Map 5

White Horse £

Castle Street

Not to worry if you can't make it here for their May or September beer festivals, as this friendly, unpretentious town-centre pub generally has up to 10 perfectly kept brews all year. Especially impressive considering it's a tied house, the choice can be different every day, but you can expect to find beers from brewers such as Aviemore, Black Dog and fff, alongside the Adnams and Fullers London Pride, Chiswick and ESB; they also keep around 20 country wines. Very good value bar food includes filled baguettes (from £3.25), as well as hot dishes such as mushroom stroganoff (£3.50), curries and steak and kidney pie (£4.50), and thai fishcakes (£4.75). On Sunday they do a two-course lunch for £6, three courses for £7.50. Parts of the building are 14th c, and you can still see Tudor brickwork in the three quietly cosy no smoking rooms upstairs. Downstairs, the two main rooms are small and homely. The one on the left is more basic, with a bit of brewery memorabilia, bare boards, and a few rather well worn tables, stools and chairs; an open fire separates it from the more comfortable right-hand bar, which has a cosily tatty armchair, some old local photographs, beams and timbers, and a red-tiled floor. Service can be quite chatty, and though it's quite a locals' pub, visitors are made to feel welcome; shove-ha'penny, cribbage, dominoes. The pub faces the castle, and there's a bench on the street outside. *(Recommended by Pat and Tony Martin, Ian Phillips, R T and J C Moggridge, LM)*

Fullers ~ Tenant Nigel Crofts ~ Real ale ~ Bar food (lunchtime only) ~ (01992) 501950 ~ Children in family room ~ Dogs allowed in bar ~ Open 12-2.30, 5.30-11; 12-11(10.30 Sun) Fri/ Sat

HUNSDON TL4114 Map 5

Fox & Hounds

High Street; B180 N of Stanstead Abbotts

Beautifully modernised over the last couple of years, this rather foody village pub has a delightfully bright and sunny feel, thanks in part to a well placed little skylight, but mostly down to the cream and gold décor. The knocked-through partly carpeted bar has a few beams and standing timbers, as well as good tables and chairs, green plush cushions, tall windows with fold-back shutters, fresh flowers on the bar, careful spotlighting, and a couple of brick fireplaces; one end of the room has a more formal eating area. The doors leading to the lavatories are rather unusual: done out like mock library shelves. All home-made (including the bread), the sensibly-sized range of food might include soup (£3.95), unusual open sandwiches such as pear, blue cheese and watercress (£5.25), and very good changing dishes such as eggs benedict, pork and apple sausages, and fresh scallops with olive salsa and crispy fried aubergines (most main courses around the £10 mark); good puddings. Well paced service from smart, friendly staff. The restaurant and part of the bar are no smoking. Well kept Fullers London Pride and Greene King IPA, and a well chosen wine list, with 10 by the glass. Plenty of space and tables in the garden, which has regular summer barbecues. As we went to press they were planning to open earlier on Sundays for brunch. The only gripe we had on our inspection visit was the volume of the piped pop music: rather loud for anyone but the most diehard Westlife fan. *(Recommended by David and Pauline Loom)*

Sterling Pub Company ~ Licensees Tarquin and Sebastian Grist ~ Real ale ~ Bar food (not Sun evening) ~ Restaurant ~ (01279) 842369 ~ Dogs welcome ~ Open 12-3, 6-11; 12-10.30 Sun

KNEBWORTH TL2320 Map 5

Lytton Arms

Park Lane, Old Knebworth, 3 miles from A1(M) junction 7; A602 towards Stevenage, 2nd roundabout right on B197 towards Knebworth, then right into Old Knebworth Lane; at village T-junction, right towards Codicote

A sign outside this Victorian gabled brick pub boasts of a year-long beer festival, and, aside from their spring and autumn festivals, it's barely an exaggeration. Up to a dozen changing real ales well kept on handpump might include ones from brewers such as Adnams, Bass, Black Sheep, Fullers and Woodfordes. They also have Staropramen beer from Prague on draught, and up to 30 Belgian bottled beers. If you're not so keen on beer, they've 50 malt whiskies, country wines, around four farm ciders, hot chocolate and herb teas, and in winter they serve hot glühwein by the log fire (where they also roast chestnuts). Several solidly furnished simple big-windowed rooms, some panelled and each with a slightly different décor (railway memorabilia here, old Knebworth estate photographs there), amble around the big central servery, ending in a no smoking conservatory with orderly pale tables on its shiny brown tiles. Simple but well cooked bar food includes soup (£2.95), sandwiches (from £3), filled ciabatta (from £4.40), ploughman's (£5.75), spinach and ricotta cannelloni (£6.35), battered cod (£6.75), steak in Bass (£7.25), a couple of daily specials such as chicken breast wrapped in bacon with wild mushroom sauce (£7.25), and puddings such as strawberry and Amaretto meringue (£3.75); friendly, welcoming service. There are picnic-sets and a giant chessboard on a terrace in front, and the back garden has a play area; dominoes and shove-ha'penny. Sadly, Steve Nye, who has been landlord here for the last 14 years, was leaving as we went to press, but there's every reason to hope that the pub will continue along the same lines. *(Recommended by B, M and P Kendall, Mr and Mrs M Dalby, Richard Lewis, BKA, Ian Phillips, Pat and Tony Martin, Derek and Sylvia Stephenson)*

Free house ~ Real ale ~ Bar food ~ (01438) 812312 ~ Children welcome ~ Dogs allowed in bar ~ Open 11-3, 5-11; 11-11 Sat; 12-10.30 Sun; closed 25 Dec evening

LITTLE HADHAM TL4322 Map 5

Nags Head £

Hadham Ford; just S of A120 W of Bishops Stortford, towards Much Hadham

You can be sure of a good value meal at this sociable 16th-c country dining pub. Very reasonably priced dishes run from soup (£1.95), through sandwiches (from £2.50), ploughman's (£4.25), vegetable lasagne (£5.25), lambs liver and bacon (£5.95), and salmon cutlet with parsley sauce (£7.50), to daily specials such as beef madras (£4.15), and a good choice of fresh fish which might include fried skate, rock, cod or haddock (£8.95), and lobster mayonnaise (£16.95); three-course Sunday lunch (£10.45). The linked heavily black-beamed rooms feel cosy, and there are old local photographs, guns and copper pans in the small bar on the right, which has three well kept Greene King beers tapped from the cask, decent house wines, and freshly squeezed orange juice. The atmosphere is warm and relaxing, and staff are friendly and efficient. The no smoking restaurant is down a couple of steps (it's best to book for their good Sunday lunch). There are tables in a pleasant garden area, and Hopleys nursery specialising in unusual hardy perennials is just down the road; darts, fruit machine, TV. *(Recommended by B N F and M Parkin, A S and M E Marriott)*

Greene King ~ Tenant Kevin Robinson ~ Real ale ~ Bar food (12-2, 6(7 Sun)-9(9.30

Fri/Sat)) ~ Restaurant ~ (01279) 771555 ~ Children in eating area of bar and restaurant ~ Open 11-3, 6-11; 12-3, 7-10.30 Sun

PERRY GREEN TL4317 Map 5

Hoops

Village signposted off B1004 Widford—Much Hadham

This pleasant white-painted, tiled-roof house dates from around the 1650s. The bar has exposed brick walls, standing timbers, and plenty of tables squeezed in, several in a cosy no smoking dining area tucked behind an usual copper-hooded fireplace. Two or three well kept changing real ales are usually Fullers London Pride, Greene King IPA or local Green Tye Wheelbarrow; piped music. Bar food ranges from sandwiches (from £3.50) and soup (£3.50), through steak and mushroom pie (£6.95), seafood tagliatelle (£8.50) and chilli chicken (£8.95) to prawn stir fry (£10.15); traditional Sunday lunch (from £7.65). The restaurant is no smoking, and at busy times booking is recommended. Well established rose bushes line the path between the tables in front, and there are climbers, hanging baskets and a small, fenced-off pond. The Henry Moore Foundation is opposite; there are guided tours in summer, by appointment only on (01279) 843333. *(Recommended by Ruth and Paul Lawrence, Kevin Thorpe)*

Free house ~ Licensee Michael O'Connor ~ Real ale ~ Bar food (12-2, 7-9.30; 12.15-8 Sun) ~ Restaurant ~ (01279) 843568 ~ Children in eating area of bar and restaurant ~ Occasional live music ~ Open 12-3, 6.30-11; 12-10.30 Sun

POTTERS CROUCH TL1105 Map 5

Holly Bush ■

2¼ miles from M25 junction 21A: A405 towards St Albans, then first left, then after a mile turn left (ie away from Chiswell Green), then at T-junction turn right into Blunts Lane; can also be reached fairly quickly, with a good map, from M1 exits 6 and 8 (and even M10)

Handy for three motorways, this beautifully kept country pub is a good place to break your journey, read the papers and relax in delightful surroundings. The meticulously furnished bar has an elegantly timeless feel, and it's not the kind of place where you'll find fruit machines or piped music. Everything is spotless, and shows unusually dedicated attention to detail. Thoughtfully positioned fixtures create the illusion that there are lots of different rooms – some of which you might expect to find in a smart country house. In the evenings, neatly placed candles cast shadows over the mix of darkly gleaming varnished tables, all of which have fresh flowers, and china plates as ashtrays. There are quite a few antique dressers, several with plates on, a number of comfortably cushioned settles, the odd plant, a fox's mask, some antlers, a fine old clock, carefully lit prints and pictures, and on the left as you go in a big fireplace. The long, stepped bar counter has particularly well kept Fullers Chiswick, ESB, London Pride and the Fullers seasonal beer on handpump, and the sort of reassuringly old-fashioned till you hardly ever see in this hi-tech age. Service is calm and efficient even when they're busy. Straightforward bar food is served lunchtimes only (not Sunday), from a menu that includes sandwiches (from £2.40, toasted from £2.80), burgers (from £3.80), filled baked potatoes (from £4.30), ploughman's (from £5.10), and chilli con carne (£5.60). Behind the pretty wisteria-covered white cottagey building, the fenced-off garden has a nice lawn, handsome trees, and sturdy picnic-sets – a very pleasant place to sit in summer. Though the pub seems to stand alone on a quiet little road, it's only a few minutes from the centre of St Albans, and is very handy for the Gardens of the Rose. *(Recommended by B, M and P Kendall, Brian Root, Mike Ridgway, Sarah Miles, Stephen, Julie and Hayley Brown, Peter and Giff Bennett, John and Joyce Snell, Howard Dell, John Saville, BKA, Ian Phillips, Tracey and Stephen Groves)*

Fullers ~ Tenant R S Taylor ~ Real ale ~ Bar food (lunchtime only, not Sun) ~ (01727) 851792 ~ Open 11.30-2.30, 6-11; 12-2.30, 7-10.30 Sun

REED TL3636 Map 5

Cabinet

High Street; village signposted from A10

We are keeping our fingers crossed for this appealing 16th-c weatherboarded dining pub, which was changing hands just as we went to press. Although the emphasis is to a certain extent on the civilised no smoking restaurant (with its more elaborate menu), in the evening locals do still gather in the cosy, friendly public bar, with its comfortable seating by the inglenook fireplace; piped music, darts, shove-ha'penny, dominoes, cribbage. The adjoining snug has a collection of board games, added to make it more appealing to families with children. Good seasonally changing bar food might include soup (from £3.50), cumberland sausage and eggs (£4.65), ciabatta with mozzarella, tomato and red pepper (£5.25), chilli (£5.95), pancake with leeks, potato and parnsip and cheddar sauce (£5.95), chargrilled chicken with herb and citrus butter (£7.85), and rib-eye steak (from £8.50); puddings (from £3.95); children's menu (£4.45). Well kept Adnams, Greene King Abbot and IPA and a guest from a brewer such as Nethergate or Cottage on handpump. The pub has sizeable gardens. *(Recommended by Conor McGaughey, Catherine and Richard Preston, B, M and P Kendall, Ian Phillips, J H Bell, Keith and Janet Morris, M R D Foot, Ian Arthur)*

Free house ~ Licensee Justin Scarborough-Taylor ~ Real ale ~ Bar food (12-2.15, 7-9.15; 12-9 bank hols) ~ Restaurant ~ (01763) 848366 ~ Well behaved children in restaurant ~ Open 12-3, 6-11(10.30 Sun)

SARRATT TQ0499 Map 5

Boot

The Green

There's an authentic unspoilt and genuinely friendly feel to this attractive tiled house, which is prettily set facing the village green with an old-fashioned black wrought-iron bench and picnic-sets under a pair of pollarded century-old lime trees. Comfortable cushioned benches are arranged along the part-panelled walls in cosy rambling rooms, with carpet or dark flooring tiles, and a fine early 18th-c inglenook fireplace with a good winter log fire. Served at lunchtime only, bar food includes soup (£3.50), filling sandwiches (from £3.65), battered fish (£6.95), steak, kidney and Guinness pie or navarin of lamb (£7.65), and prawn or crayfish salad (£8.45); it's best to book for their very popular Sunday lunch, or if you want to eat from the more elaborate bistro-style restaurant menu (Wednesday to Saturday evenings). Well kept Greene King IPA, Abbot and Ruddles County and a guest such as Fullers London Pride on handpump; sensibly segregated darts, cribbage, fruit machine, space game and piped music. There are more seats on a pretty, sheltered lawn with roses, fruit trees and a weeping willow; children's play area. *(Recommended by Stan Edwards, W F Martin, John Hillman, Ian Phillips, Jarrod Hopkinson, Wendy Ryles, Mrs W Mabilat, Tracey and Stephen Groves)*

Free house ~ Licensee Richard Jones ~ Real ale ~ Bar food (lunchtime only) ~ Restaurant ~ No credit cards ~ 01923 262247 ~ Children in eating area of bar and restaurant ~ Open 11.30-3, 5.30-11; 12-10.30 Sun

Cock

Church End: a very pretty approach is via North Hill, a lane N off A404, just under a mile W of A405

In a pretty country setting opposite the village church, the latched door of this cosy cream-painted 17th-c country pub opens into a carpeted snug with a vaulted ceiling, original bread oven, and a cluster of bar stools. Through an archway, the partly oak-panelled cream-walled lounge has a lovely log fire in an inglenook, pretty Liberty-style curtains, pink plush chairs at dark oak tables, and lots of interesting artefacts and pictures of cocks; piped music, and well kept Badger Best, IPA, K&B and Tanglefoot. Friendly staff serve bar food including sandwiches or baked potatoes (from £4.75), ploughman's (from £5.25 – perhaps not the best choice for hearty appetites), and generous hot dishes such as sausages and mash or vegetable lasagne (£7.95), lamb shank (£10.95), and a handful of daily specials such as chicken and seafood paella (£9.75), and poached salmon salad (£10.25). The no smoking restaurant is in a nicely converted barn. At the front, picnic-sets look out across a quiet lane towards the churchyard, the terrace at the back gives open country views, and a pretty, sheltered lawn has tables under parasols, with a children's play area. *(Recommended by Peter Saville, BKA, Ian Phillips, Gerald Wilkinson, Jim Bush, David and Ruth Shillitoe)*

Badger ~ Manager Ken Jones ~ Real ale ~ Bar food (12-2.15(2.30 Sun), 6-9.30; not Sun evening) ~ Restaurant ~ (01923) 282908 ~ Children welcome ~ Dogs allowed in bar ~ Open 11-3, 5.30-11; 11-11 Sat; 12-10.30 Sun

ST ALBANS TL1507 Map 5

Rose & Crown

St Michaels Street; from town centre follow George Street towards the Abbey, right just before Abbey into Fishpool Street, pub is near Kingsbury Watermill

The welcoming American landlord's impressive collection of sporting memorabilia, from tickets and photographs through to rugby balls and golf clubs, covers the unevenly timbered walls of this cosy 400-year-old town pub. The traditional beamed public bars also have old-fashioned wall benches, chintzy curtains and cushions, black cauldrons in a deep fireplace (big fires in winter), and dominoes, cribbage and darts (which are sensibly set to one side). Well kept Adnams, Courage Directors, Tetleys and a guest such as Black Sheep or Timothy Taylors Landlord on handpump; a dozen or so malt whiskies, fruit wines. Served with potato salad, crisps and pickled cucumber on a granary or white loaf, the speciality sandwiches here are great. Choose from varieties such as ham, peanuts, american cheese, tomato and mayonnaise (£4.95), roast beef, onion, salami, swiss cheese and mustard (£5.50), or turkey, salami, swiss cheese, lettuce, tomato and mayonnaise double-decker toasted sandwich (£5.50), as well as from more traditional varieties (from £2). A few other dishes include soup (£2.95), vegetable stroganoff or moussaka (£6.50). There's a no smoking area at lunchtime. There are lots of tables and benches along the side, and at the back in a pretty ivy-hung yard with shrubs and roses, flower beds and attractive hanging baskets – a haven from the bustle up in the town. The walk from the town centre down Fishpool Street is pretty. *(Recommended by R J Davies, Pat and Tony Martin, Ian Phillips, the Didler, Tracey and Stephen Groves, BKA)*

Pubmaster ~ Tenant Neil Dekker ~ Real ale ~ Bar food (lunchtime only, not Sun) ~ (01727) 851903 ~ Children in family room ~ Dogs welcome ~ Acoustic session Mon evening, Irish folk Thurs evening ~ Open 11.30-3, 5.30(6 Sat)-11; 12-3, 7-10.30 Sun

WATTON-AT-STONE TL3019 Map 5

George & Dragon ★ 🍴 🍷

Village signposted off A602 about 5 miles S of Stevenage, on B1001; High Street

The atmosphere at this civilised country dining pub is gently sophisticated, with kitchen elbow-chairs around attractive old tables, dark blue cloth-upholstered seats in the bay windows, an interesting mix of antique and modern prints on the partly timbered ochre walls, and a big inglenook fireplace. A quieter room off the main bar has spindleback chairs and wall settles cushioned to match the green floral curtains, and old photographs of the village above its panelled dado. Proper napkins, antiques and daily newspapers add to the smart feel. Good, beautifully presented bar food includes dishes such as avocado filled with tuna, spring onion and ginger (£4.45), fried mushrooms with port and stilton sauce on toasted brioche (£4.75), steak, mushroom and ale pie (£7.25), filo pastry parcel filled with spinach, Quorn and ricotta on a tomato and herb sauce (£8.85), fried calves liver with sage and madeira (£11.75), and monkfish tail wrapped in prosciutto on roasted niçoise vegetables (£12.25); friendly professional service. As well as a good wine list they have well kept Greene King Abbot and IPA and a guest such as Wadworths 6X on handpump, and several malt whiskies; fruit machine, and boules in the pretty extended shrub-screened garden. The pub is quite handy for Benington Lordship Gardens. *(Recommended by Ian Phillips, Gordon Tong, David and Pauline Loom, Bob and Maggie Atherton, Pat and Tony Martin, BKA, Peter Saville, Tina and David Woods-Taylor, Peter and Marilyn Budden, David and Ruth Shillitoe, Boyd Catling, Enid and Henry Stephens)*

Greene King ~ Tenants Peter and Jessica Tatlow ~ Real ale ~ Bar food (12-2, 7-10, not Sun evening) ~ Restaurant ~ (01920) 830285 ~ Children in the restaurant till 8.30 ~ Open 11-3, 6-11; 11-11 Sat; 12-4, 7-10.30 Sun

Lucky Dip

Besides the fully inspected pubs, you might like to try these Lucky Dips recommended to us and described by readers (if you do, please send us reports: www.goodguides.com).

Amwell [TL1613]

☆ ***Elephant & Castle*** [signed SW from Wheathampstead]: Secluded and spacious floodlit grass garden behind low-beamed ancient pub with relaxed and welcoming local feel, great inglenook log fire, panelling, stripped brickwork, immensely deep covered well shaft in bar; good value hearty bar food (not Sun), well kept Marstons, friendly locals, good service; restaurant, children in eating area, *(LYM, Gordon Neighbour, Jill McLaren)*

Ashwell [TL2639]

☆ ***Bushel & Strike*** [off A507 just E of A1(M) junction 10, N of Baldock, via Newnham; Mill St opp church, via Gardiners Lane (car park down Swan Lane)]: Neat front dining bar with fresh flowers, hunting and coaching prints, local colour photographs, cheery prompt service, wide choice of food from nice sandwiches up, no smoking restaurant with 'conservatory' murals, sofas in back area, well kept Everards Tiger, Gales HSB and Greene King Old Speckled Hen, freshly squeezed fruit juice, hot toddies, mulled wine and half a dozen wines by the glass; tables on lawn and small terrace, maybe summer barbecues *(Norma and Keith Bloomfield, LYM, Ruth and Paul Lawrence)*

Rose & Crown [High St]: Comfortable open-plan local with good bar food esp popular Tues fish night, 16th-c beams, lovely log fire, no smoking candlelit restaurant, well kept Greene King IPA and Abbot; darts and machines at plainer public end of L-shaped bar; tables in big pretty country garden *(Jenny and Dave Hughes, Joy and Colin Rorke, Ian and Nita Cooper)*

Ayot Green [TL2213]

☆ ***Waggoners*** [off B197 S of Welwyn]: Recently reworked friendly pub, three cosy areas, mugs and tankards hanging from low ceiling, comfortable seating, nicely furnished eating area with proper napkins, good enterprising food inc three-course meals, efficient knowledgeable service, changing real ales; quiet suntrap back garden with play area, wooded walks nearby *(David and Pauline Loom)*

Benington [TL3023]

☆ ***Bell*** [Town Lane; just past Post Office, towards Stevenage]: Generous food from sandwiches to good main dishes, good service, well kept Greene King IPA, Abbot and Old Speckled Hen and a guest such as Batemans in cheery partly 15th-c pub in very pretty village; hops with fairy lights hanging from low beams, sloping walls, flowers and candles on tables, unusual faded stag-hunt mural over big inglenook fireplace with woodburner, mix of old furnishings, aircraft memorabilia and enamel advertising signs, separate dining room; no children in bars, piped music, weekly folk night; big pleasant garden with country views, handy for Benington Lordship *(Dave and Sue Thorneycroft, Gordon Neighbour, Martin Bishop, BB)*

Berkhamsted [SP9807]

☆ ***Old Mill*** [A4251, Hemel end]: Huge efficient Chef & Brewer, well restored, with cosy and attractive rambling rooms inc no smoking, well cared for furnishings, dark wood tables with candles, grandfather clock, two good fires; very wide blackboard choice of generous food from familiar to sophisticated, usually something available all day; well kept ales such as Marstons Pedigree, a dozen or so wines by the glass or half bottle, friendly staff; may be piped jazz, fruit machines; tables outside, some overlooking unspectacular stretch of Grand Union Canal *(Richard Crabtree, BB)*

Boxmoor [TL0406]

Fishery: Big-windowed roomy open-plan bar comfortably reworked as an Ember Inn, open fire, decently priced mainstream food in eating area with fine view of canal and brightly painted barges, three real ales, lots of wines by the glass; tables out by water *(LYM, John Branston)*

Bramfield [TL2915]

Grandiston Arms: Softly lit low-ceilinged pub with enjoyable food, very agreeable service, comfortable seats, log fire, Greene King real ales; plenty of space in attractive garden with huge carp in pond, peaceful setting, charming village *(Ellen Weld, David London)*

Bricket Wood [TL1502]

Moor Mill [off Smug Oak Lane – turn at Gate pub]: Attractive 18th-c restored watermill, central working wheel, beams, brick walls and flagstones, two floors, oak tables and comfortable chairs, with picnic-sets in big waterside garden with play area; now an Out & Out chain eating pub, open all day *(LYM)*

Broxbourne [TL3607]

Bull [High Rd]: Much enlarged local popular for lunch, helpful friendly staff, McMullens

Country Best and AK Mild; picnic-sets out on terrace *(Ian Phillips)*

Bushey [TQ1395]

Swan [Park Rd; turning off A411]: Homely atmosphere in rare surviving example of unspoilt single-room backstreet terraced pub, reminiscent of 1920s *(Pete Baker, LYM)*

Chandlers Cross [TQ0698]

Clarendon Arms [Redhall Lane]: Friendly traditional pub in attractive country setting, handy for woodland and canal walks, with well kept ales inc Fullers London Pride, wide choice of wines by the glass, consistently good value food esp Sun lunch and barbecues, attentive staff; live band Thurs, quiz nights; pleasant verandah, lots of tables and cocktail parasols *(Hans and Thelma Liesner)*

Chapmore End [TL3216]

Woodman [off B158 Hertford—Wadesmill]: Small two-bar village local by pond with well kept Greene King IPA and Abbot tapped from the cask, usual lunchtime food (not Sun) from sandwiches up, bare boards, simple furnishings; annual music festival; big back garden, small front one, pets corner and play area *(Ian Arthur)*

Charlton [TL1728]

Windmill: Pleasant streamside setting in small village, beams and blazing log stove, enjoyable food, well kept beers inc Adnams Broadside and Charles Wells Black Adder and Eagle, cheerful service, piped music; garden with ducks and weeping willow *(B, M and P Kendall)*

Chipperfield [TL0302]

Boot [Tower Hill, towards Bovingdon]: Neatly kept pub under new licensees, enjoyable blackboard food from sandwiches and burgers to pheasant, well kept Adnams, open fires and warm atmosphere *(Peter Walters)*

Royal Oak [The Street]: Friendly relaxed atmosphere and well kept beer in two small neatly kept bars, Youngs Special and guest beers, limited choice of enjoyable fresh lunchtime food, log fire, vintage car photographs; may be soft piped music *(Stan Edwards)*

☆ ***Two Brewers*** [The Common]: Attractive country hotel with roomy linked areas in bow-windowed bar, two log fires, dark décor; good if not cheap food all day from sandwiches up, real ales, but no bar stools or bar-propping; provision for children, comfortable bedrooms *(LYM, Robert F Smith, Andrew Scarr)*

Chorleywood [TQ0295]

☆ ***Black Horse*** [Dog Kennel Lane, the Common]: Very welcoming to families, walkers and even dogs (basket of dog biscuits on mantelpiece), nice seating under low dark beams in attractively divided traditional room with thick carpet, two massive log fires, good choice of well prepared food (not Mon) from sandwiches to good value Sun lunches (worth booking these), well kept Adnams, Flowers Original, Theakstons Best and Wadworths 6X, friendly landlord, no music; family area, separate bar with SkyTV; pretty setting, picnic-sets overlooking common *(Darren Le Poidevin, Ian Phillips, Stan Edwards)*

Rose & Crown [Common Rd, not far from M25 junction 18]: Compact cosy pub in cottage terrace, pretty setting facing common, well kept beer, old-fashioned atmosphere, friendly and homely; good freshly made food in small dining room *(M S Catling)*

Stag [Long Lane/Heronsgate Rd – handy for M25 junction 17]: Smart attractive open-plan pub in good walking area, well kept Courage Directors, Fullers London Pride and McMullens, friendly attentive staff, no smoking dining conservatory; quiet piped music, busy wknds, machines tucked around corner; tables on back lawn, play area *(Tracey and Stephen Groves)*

Colney Heath [TL2007]

Plough [just off back rd N, between A414 St Albans—Hatfield and A1057]: Popular pleasantly refurbished 18th-c low-beamed pub, warm and cosy at front with good log fire and small dining area, good value food (lunchtime Mon-Sat, and Fri/Sat evening), well kept Greene King Abbot, Fullers London Pride and Tetleys, friendly efficient service; less atmosphere in conservatory extension; small garden overlooking fields *(BG, RG, Monica Cockburn, Mike Jefferies)*

Epping Green [TL2906]

☆ ***Beehive*** [back rd Cuffley—Little Berkhamsted]: Cosy and popular local, comfortable beamed dining area on left, huge choice of good value generous fresh food esp fish, friendly staff, Greene King ales with a guest such as Adnams; garden seats overlooking fields *(GLD, Tina and David Woods-Taylor, Lucien)*

Flaunden [TL0100]

☆ ***Bricklayers Arms*** [village signed off A41; from village centre follow Boxmoor, Bovingdon road and turn right at Belsize, Watford signpost]: Cottagey country pub, low beams, log fire, timbered stub walls, attractive décor, several well kept ales such as Brakspears PA, Fullers London Pride and Ringwood Old Thumper, decent wines, food from normal or doorstep sandwiches to restaurant dishes, friendly obliging service, children in eating areas; nice old-fashioned garden, nearby walks *(M J Brooks, Patrick Renouf, BKA, Tracey and Stephen Groves, Jarrod Hopkinson, Wendy Ryles, LYM, Derek and Sylvia Stephenson, Chris Smith, Jill McLaren)*

Gravesend [TL4325]

Catherine Wheel [off A120 at Little Hadham]: Partly early 15th-c, with thatch, low beams and inglenook, friendly new licensees, good choice of freshly prepared food (so may be a wait), reasonable prices, two real ales, no smoking end room; picnic-sets in big garden, attractive hanging baskets *(CMW, JJW)*

Great Amwell [TL3612]

Waggon & Horses [Pepper Hill]: Roomy dining areas with enjoyable food from straightforward bar lunches to more elaborate evening meals, well stocked bar; children welcome, big garden with bottom play area *(Joy and Colin Rorke)*

Great Munden [TL3523]

☆ ***Plough*** [SW, towards Dane End]: Unique full-size working Compton theatre organ (from Gaumont, Finchley) in comfortable and lofty lounge extension built specially to house it; decent nicely presented food (Sun lunch with organ recital is worth booking), well kept Greene King IPA and Abbot, friendly landlord, pleasant staff, good facilities for the disabled; nearby walks *(LYM, Gordon Neighbour)*

Great Offley [TL1427]

☆ *Green Man* [signed off A505 Luton—Hitchin; High St]: Roomy, comfortable and attractive Chef & Brewer family dining pub open all day, with wonderful country view from large flagstoned conservatory and picnic-sets on pleasant back terrace and garden; roaring winter fires, their usual very wide food choice, good service, Courage Directors and Theakstons Old Peculier; unobtrusive piped classical music, very busy wknds; front play area, striking inn-sign *(LYM, Ian Phillips)*

Green Tye [TL4418]

Prince of Wales: Unpretentious and chatty traditional two-bar village local brewing its own Green Tye ales such as Snowdrop and IPA, one guest beer, friendly landlord, good value simple lunchtime food, coal fire; tables in garden *(Ian Arthur, Kevin Thorpe)*

Harpenden [TL1413]

☆ *Carpenters Arms* [Cravells Rd]: Cosy and welcoming, with chatty landlord, friendly efficient staff, cheap generous uncomplicated home cooking from good doorstep sandwiches up, well kept Greene King Ruddles with a guest beer such as Archers or Tring, open fire, lovingly collected car memorabilia inc models and overseas number-plates, special issue bottled beers; neat well planned terrace garden *(MP)*

Cross Keys [High St]: Likeable pub with Fullers London Pride, lovely flagstones; garden *(anon)*

Harpenden Arms [High St]: Lively old-fashioned pub divided by original chimneybreasts, with comfortable lounge, light and airy restaurant end with thai dishes (not wknd evenings), well kept Fullers ales *(anon)*

Rose & Crown [Southdown Rd]: Back to proper name after a Mexican-oriented spell, enjoyable food inc omelettes and home-made pizzas, well kept Fullers London Pride, friendly efficient service, woody interior; attractive conservatory, garden beyond *(MP)*

Hemel Hempstead [TL0411]

☆ *Crown & Sceptre* [leaving on A4146, right at Flamstead/Markyate sign opp Red Lion]: Classic country pub, cheerful and friendly cosy communicating rooms, some oak panelling, antique settles among more usual seating, enjoyable food from wide range of sandwiches and baguettes up, well kept Greene King IPA and Abbot and a guest such as Jennings, log fires; darts and dominoes, children and dogs welcome; back garden with chickens, ducks and scarecrow, heated front picnic-sets, good walks; open all day summer wknds *(LYM, Ian Phillips)*

Hertford [TL3213]

Baroosh [Fore St]: Stylish modern café/bar in former bank, good conversion by McMullens the local brewery, their real ales, very good wine choice, friendly attentive young staff, good modern food *(Pat and Tony Martin)*

☆ *Old Barge* [The Folly]: Nicely placed canalside pub, long and low, main bar and tables outside overlooking water, good service even when hectic, friendly helpful young staff, lots of barge pictures etc, well kept real ales, reasonably priced usual food from sandwiches, baguettes and baked potatoes up; fruit and games machines; open all day *(LYM, Pat and Tony Martin)*

Hexton [TL1230]

☆ *Raven* [signed off B655]: Large recently refurbished 1920s family dining pub, four neat areas inc long tidy public bar (open fire, pool one end), extensive no smoking areas, plenty of dining tables, oil paintings (some for sale); wide range of good value food from baguettes and baked potatoes up, two children's menus, well kept ales inc Fullers London Pride and Greene King IPA and Old Speckled Hen, friendly efficient service; children welcome, big garden with heated terrace, barbecue, well segregated play area *(Margaret and Roy Randle, Phil and Heidi Cook, Penny Miles)*

High Wych [TL4614]

Rising Sun: Cosy unspoilt local, serving hatch to carpeted lounge with coal or log fire, central area with Courage Best and good guest beers tapped from casks behind the counter, friendly landlord and locals, bare-boards games room (children allowed) with darts and woodburner; no food, no mobile phones or pagers, no music; tables in small garden *(Kevin Thorpe, JP, PP, the Didler, Pete Baker)*

Hinxworth [TL2340]

☆ *Three Horseshoes* [High St; just off A1(M)]: Well run thatched, beamed and timbered 18th-c dining pub with good value food (not Sun evening, Mon) inc children's dishes, pews in extended red plush bar, steps up to no smoking high-ceilinged dining area, well kept Greene King IPA, Abbot and Ruddles, decent wines, friendly attentive staff, woodburner in big brick inglenook, soft lighting; piped music may obtrude; children welcome, good big garden with play area *(Anthony Barnes, George Atkinson, Ian Phillips, BB)*

Ickleford [TL1831]

Plume of Feathers [Upper Green]: Good mixed choice of enjoyable fresh food from sandwiches to delicious salmon in pub with two good landladies; nice spot overlooking green *(Mrs Ann Adams)*

Kimpton [TL1718]

White Horse [High St]: Pleasantly extended around low-roofed half-timbered core, warm welcome, decent food inc seafood and fresh fish, real ales such as Bass, Courage Directors, McMullens Original AK and Gladstone *(Jestyn Phillips)*

Lemsford [TL2112]

Crooked Chimney [Cromer Hyde Lane (B653 towards Wheathampstead)]: Big comfortable open-plan Vintage Inn dining pub with good if not cheap food inc children's helpings; central feature fireplace and two further log fires, enjoyable food, well kept Bass and Tetleys, friendly helpful staff; pleasant garden by fields, play area *(B N F and M Parkin, Stephen, Julie and Hayley Brown, LYM)*

Ley Green [TL1624]

Plough [Plough Lane]: Simple unspoilt country local with little-used cottagey second room, well kept Greene King ales, no music; lovely big informal garden with tables on verandah and benches under tall trees, country views, perhaps a cockerel begging for crisps *(Conor McGaughey)*

Nuthampstead [TL4034]

☆ *Woodman* [off B1368 S of Barkway]: Tucked-away thatched and weatherboarded village local, welcoming and well run, with plenty of character, well kept Adnams and Greene King beers, 17th-c beams and timbers, generous home cooking (not Sun evening) for bar and small restaurant extension, efficient friendly service, fresh flowers, sofa and other comfortable furnishings, nice inglenook log fire and another fire opposite, pool; interesting USAF memorabilia (nearby World War II airfield), inc a memorial outside; benches outside overlooking tranquil lane; comfortable bedrooms, open all day Sat *(BB, R T and J C Moggridge)*

Redbourn [TL1011]

Hollybush [Church End]: Quaint white-fronted old pub in pretty spot near medieval church; cosy old-fashioned lounge with big brick open fire, black beams, heavy wooden doors, bigger public bar with built-in settles, cask tables, good straightforward home-made food, well kept changing ales inc Adnams, courteous service; pool, machines; tables in sunny garden (some M1 noise) *(MP)*

Rickmansworth [TQ0694]

Coach & Horses [High St]: Partly 16th-c, locally popular for good food inc ambitious dishes; tastefully furnished eating area, friendly service, cosy back bar, log fire, lots of farm tools *(Tracey and Stephen Groves)*

Rushden [TL3031]

Moon & Stars [Mill End; off A507 about a mile W of Cottered]: Unspoilt cottagey beamed country pub with neatly kept no smoking lounge bar, inglenook log fire, well kept Greene King ales, good value food (small dining room, worth booking); pleasant garden, peaceful country setting *(Joy and Colin Rorke, LYM)*

Sawbridgeworth [TL4814]

Gate [London Rd (A1184)]: 18th-c pub with good range of quickly changing well kept ales in lined glasses, bank hol beer festivals with live music, cheap fresh lunchtime food, roomy and relaxed front bar, back bar with pool and games; close to railway station *(JP, PP, the Didler)*

Spellbrook [TL4817]

Three Horseshoes: Spacious Chef & Brewer dining pub largely extended from thatched and very low-beamed core, Badger IPA, Courage Best and Greene King Old Speckled Hen, decent choice of wines by the glass, wide food choice from sandwiches to swordfish steak; bridge from streamside car park *(Ian Phillips, Miss Elaine Pugh)*

St Albans [TL1307]

Blue Anchor [Fishpool St]: Welcoming newish landlord, popular dining lounge with good value bar food (not Sun evening) from sandwiches up, well kept McMullens ales inc Mild, attractive prices, small locals' bar on left, daily papers, sensibly placed darts, real fire; sizeable garden, handy for Roman remains *(Pam Adsley)*

Cross Keys [Chequer St]: Popular L-shaped Wetherspoons, their usual menu, eight real ales, good wine choice, friendly helpful staff, nice furnishings and décor; open all day *(Richard Lewis)*

Farmers Boy [London Rd]: Bustling bay-windowed pub with back brewery producing Verulam IPA, Farmers Joy and a monthly special such as Ginger Tom, also their own lager and 10 continental bottled beers, lots of old prints on smoke-effect walls, imposing clock, real fire, back open kitchen serving straightforward food from sandwiches and baked potatoes up all day, helpful staff, two large friendly dogs; SkyTV; open all day, plenty of suntrap tables out behind *(Richard Lewis, Tracey and Stephen Groves, the Didler)*

Farriers Arms [Lower Dagnall St]: Plain but welcoming little local in no-frills old part, well kept McMullens Country, AK Mild and Gladstone, bar food wkdys; customers' bicycles seem chained to all the lampposts in the area *(the Didler, JP, PP)*

☆ *Fighting Cocks* [Abbey Mill Lane; through abbey gateway – you can drive down]: Odd-shaped former abbey gatehouse, much modernised inside but still showing the sunken area which was a Stuart cockpit, some low and heavy beams, inglenook fires, and pleasant nooks, corners and window alcoves, a dozen well kept interesting ales, food too – nice lunchtime atmosphere, can be very busy evenings; may be piped music; children welcome (good family room), attractive public park beyond garden, open all day *(the Didler, Meg and Colin Hamilton, Kevin Blake, Mr and Mrs M Dalby, Tracey and Stephen Groves, LYM)*

☆ *Garibaldi* [Albert St; left turn down Holywell Hill past White Hart – car park left at end]: Relaxed Fullers local with well kept Chiswick, London Pride and ESB and a guest such as Adnams, good low-priced wholesome lunchtime food (not Mon), good house wines, cheerful staff; may be piped music; children welcome, open all day *(the Didler, Tracey and Stephen Groves, MP, LYM)*

Lower Red Lion [Fishpool St]: Relaxing and convivial two-bar local, good chatty atmosphere, interesting changing range of well kept beers, May Day and Aug bank hol beer festivals, home-made food, log fire, red plush seats and carpet; open all day Sat, tables in good-sized back garden, pleasant bedrooms *(Tracey and Stephen Groves, the Didler)*

☆ *Plough* [Tyttenhanger Green; off A414 E]: Spacious and friendly village pub, polite prompt service even when packed, lovely longcase clock, good log fire, well kept Greene King and other ales, good value food, fine collection of old beer bottles, other bric-a-brac, pleasant young staff; conservatory, big garden with play area *(LYM, Gordon Neighbour, the Didler, Ian and Joan Blackwell)*

☆ ***Six Bells*** [St Michael St]: Well kept timbered and low-beamed food pub on site of a Roman bath house, well kept ales inc Adnams, cheerful helpful service even when bustling with locals, big helpings of good value freshly cooked food in quieter panelled eating area; children welcome, family room, occasional barbecues in small back garden, open all day Fri-Sun, handy for Roman Verulam Museum *(R T and J C Moggridge, LYM, Rita Scarratt)*

Stevenage [TL2324]

Chequers [High St]: Open-plan high-ceilinged Greene King pub, comfortable U-shaped bar, friendly staff, good value standard lunchtime bar food (not Sun) from sandwiches up inc Thurs night fish and chip bargains and early evening specials, Rugby football memorabilia; busy wkdys, juke box; plans to extend well kept sunny courtyard *(Gordon Tong, R W E Farr)*

Therfield [TL3336]

☆ ***Fox & Duck*** [The Green; off A505 Baldock—Royston]: Newly refurbished beamed village pub, attractive décor and enjoyable food inc adventurous dishes and seasonal game, well kept ales such as Greene King IPA and Ruddles and Theakstons, decent wines, courteous staff; good children's garden with play equipment *(Susan and Nigel Wilson, Len Banister)*

Tring [SP9211]

☆ ***Robin Hood*** [Brook St]: Neat well run olde-worlde pub popular for good food esp fresh fish such as strawberry grouper, marlin or eels (wide choice, but they don't buy much of each, so the blackboard may change as you watch); small drinking area with half a dozen well kept Fullers and guest ales, comfortable settles, lots of dark wood, nice conservatory *(John Branston, MP, Ken Richards)*

Rose & Crown [High St]: Roomy comfortable hotel lounge popular for bar lunches from sandwiches up; ornate fireplace, Wadworths 6X and local Tring Crown Glory, decent coffee, pleasant staff; bedrooms *(Mike and Heather Watson)*

Water End [TL0410]

Red Lion [A4146]: Good Chef & Brewer much extended from 18th-c core, their usual food from sandwiches and baked potatoes up, real ales such as Courage Directors and Marstons Pedigree, lots of wines by the glass *(Ian Phillips)*

Wellpond Green [TL4122]

Nags Head: Enjoyable fresh food in bar and no smoking restaurant (popular wknds), welcoming licensees; spotless newly decorated bedrooms *(John and Mary Jones)*

Westmill [TL3626]

Sword in Hand [village signed off A10 S of Buntingford]: 14th-c colour-washed pub in pretty village, well kept Greene King IPA and a guest such as Everards Tiger or Youngs, beams, pine tables and bare boards or tiles, log fires, fire service memorabilia, food in bar and partly no smoking dining room; children welcome till 8, tables on attractive terrace and in side garden, play area inc football, cl Sun evening and Mon *(LYM, Rosanna Ribolzi, Ian Phillips)*

Whitwell [TL1821]

☆ ***Maidens Head*** [High St (B651)]: First-class landlord and friendly staff in clean McMullens local with good value food esp gammon, well kept ales tapped from the cask, good coffee, interesting key-ring collection; seats in safe children's garden *(anon)*

Wilstone [SP9014]

Half Moon [Tring Rd, off B489]: Low-roofed village pub, part carpeted and part polished tiles, big focal log fire, wide choice of good value freshly made food from sandwiches and baked potatoes up, changing real ales, welcoming Scottish landlord, low beams, old local pictures and lots of brasses; handy for Grand Union Canal walks *(Jean and David Darby)*

Post Office address codings confusingly give the impression that some pubs are in Hertfordshire, when they're really in Bedfordshire or Cambridgeshire (which is where we list them).

Isle of Wight

No new main entries here this year, but quite a few changes in the pecking order of the island's top pubs. Those which currently stand out are the Crab & Lobster perched above the sea at Bembridge (lovely position, and great seafood earning it a Food Award this year), the cheerful Red Lion at Freshwater (imaginative food, attentive service, nice new garden, and excellent choice of wines by the glass – an award for this now), the hospitable and civilised Seaview Hotel in Seaview (good food and wine, a pleasant place to stay in, and a charming pubby back bar), the New Inn at Shalfleet (transformed over the last couple of years, a top-notch place now, with excellent seafood), the Crown at Shorwell (an attractive all-rounder, lovely inland setting), and the Spyglass in Ventnor (lots of character, good position, good value). The New Inn at Shalfleet – for the second year running – carries off the top title of Isle of Wight Dining Pub of the Year. The Lucky Dip section at the end of the chapter, swollen this year by more than a dozen newcomers, is interesting too; three places to note particularly are the Buddle at Niton, Chine near Shanklin and Bugle in Yarmouth. Drinks prices on the island are a little above the national average (the Blacksmiths Arms near Carisbrooke had the best prices we found for beer – an interesting choice too, in this nice pub). It's possible that the 14p duty cut for small breweries will now make the island's own local beers more worth looking out for – Goddards, Ventnor and (see the Lucky Dip entry for the St Lawrence Inn) Yates.

ARRETON SZ5486 Map 2

White Lion

A3056 Newport—Sandown

The pleasant beamed lounge bar at this cosy village pub has shining brass and horse tack on the partly panelled walls, cushioned wheelback chairs on the red carpet, and Badger Best and a guest such as Flowers Best kept well on handpump. It's popular, especially in summer, for good value straightforward food. Besides sandwiches and baguettes (from £3.25) and baked potatoes (from £3.95), mostly home-made dishes include wild rice and spinach bake (£5), lasagne or chilli con carne (£5.95), steak and kidney pie (£5.95), battered scampi (£6.95), and steaks (from £6.95), as well as specials such as gorgonzola and walnut pasta with green pesto sauce (£6.25), pork escalope in cream, paprika and pepper sauce (£7.45), venison steak with port and forest fruit sauce (£10.25), and enjoyable puddings with lots of cream or custard; no smoking restaurant and family room. There may be piped music, and the public bar has cribbage, dominoes, darts, fruit machine and TV. You can sit out in front by the tubs of flowers, and the pleasant garden has a small play area. *(Recommended by JDM, KM, Alan Skull, Pete Yearsley)*

Whitbreads ~ Lease Chris and Kate Cole ~ Real ale ~ Bar food (12-9) ~ Restaurant ~ (01983) 528479 ~ Children in family room ~ Dogs allowed in bar ~ Open 11-11; 12-10.30 Sun

If we know a pub does summer barbecues, we say so.

BEMBRIDGE SZ6587 Map 2

Crab & Lobster

Foreland Fields Road, off Howgate Road (which is off B3395)

Doing very well indeed at the moment, this clifftop pub is tucked away on a coastal bluff, an easy walk from the beach, and has great sea views from its terrace, garden and window seats. There's more room inside than you'd expect from the frontage, which is prettily bedecked with flower baskets in summer. The attractively decorated interior has a civilised, almost parlourish style, with lots of yachting memorabilia and old local photographs. They serve a very good choice of eight or nine changing fresh local seafood specials every day, from sardines in garlic butter and lemon (£3.95), through moules marinière (from £5.95), tasty home-made crab cakes (£7.25), grilled plaice topped with olives, garlic and basil (£7.50), and bass with garlic butter and lemon (£10.50), to whole lobster (£29.95). Other very well prepared food includes sandwiches (from £3.75), baked potatoes (from £3.95), ploughman's (£4.95), lasagne (£5.95), pork steaks with mozzarella and rosemary (£8.25), fillet steak (£10.50), and puddings such as spotted dick (£2.95); children's meals (£3.25); the restaurant is no smoking. Well kept Flowers Original, Greene King IPA and Goddards Fuggle-Dee-Dum on handpump, decent house wines, country wines from the barrel, good coffee; piped music (even in the lavatories) and darts. It does get very popular, so best to get there early or late at lunchtime. There are good views from their bedrooms – we look forward to hearing from readers who've tried them. *(Recommended by Terry Mizen, Phil and Heidi Cook, Pete Yearsley, E S Funnell, Ken Flawn, Jan and Alan Summers)*

Whitbreads ~ Lease Richard, Adrian and Pauline Allan ~ Real ale ~ Bar food (12-2.30, 6-9.30) ~ Restaurant ~ (01983) 872244 ~ Children welcome ~ Dogs welcome ~ Open 11-3, 5.30-11; 11-11 Sat; 12-10.30 Sun ~ Bedrooms: £30B/£60B

BONCHURCH SZ5778 Map 2

Bonchurch Inn

Bonchurch Shute; from A3055 E of Ventnor turn down to Old Bonchurch opposite Leconfield Hotel

Cut into the side of the hill, the various buildings of this old stone pub (once the stables for a nearby manor house) are spread around a central courtyard, giving it a slightly continental feel. The furniture-packed Victorian bar, good for a leisurely drink, conjures up images of salvaged shipwrecks, with its floor of narrow-planked ship's decking, and seats like the ones that old-fashioned steamers used to have. There's a separate entrance to the very simple no smoking family room (a bit cut off from the congenial atmosphere of the public bar). As well as Courage Directors tapped from the cask, there are Italian wines by the glass, a few bottled French wines, darts, bar billiards, shove-ha'penny, dominoes and cribbage. The welcoming landlord is Italian, and the menu includes several Italian dishes such as lasagne, seafood risotto, spaghetti bolognese or cannelloni (from £6), as well as sandwiches (from £2.80, toasted 30p extra), soup (£4), ploughman's (from £6), battered squid (£7), chicken cordon bleu (£7.50), and sirloin steak (£8.50); for puddings they have ice creams and sorbets (£3). They open the restaurant across the courtyard only for bookings in the evenings; the pub owns a holiday flat for up to six people. *(Recommended by J A Cheverton, Graham and Lynn Mason, Pete Yearsley)*

Free house ~ Licensees Ulisse and Gillian Besozzi ~ Real ale ~ Bar food ~ Restaurant ~ (01983) 852611 ~ Children in separate family room ~ Dogs allowed in bar and bedrooms ~ Open 11-3, 6.30-11; 12-3, 7-10.30 Sun; closed 25 Dec ~ Bedrooms: /£70B

CARISBROOKE SZ4687 Map 2

Blacksmiths Arms

Park Cross, Calbourne Road; B3401 1½ miles W – and pub signed off Tennyson Trail

This pretty blue and white painted roadside pub has a slightly old-fashioned feel in the neatly kept front bars, with their scrubbed tables on flagstone floors (table football in one). It's set on a quiet hillside (and signposted off the Tennyson Trail), with good views over the Solent from the simply built and furnished dining extension, and from tables in the smallish back garden, which has a play area with a bouncy castle. The cheerful Bavarian landlord serves an interesting range of hearty food from his homeland such as frikadellen (mini burgers, £5.75), various schnitzels (from £8.45) and rinderrouladen (beef stuffed with German mustard, olives, bacon and onions, £8.95) which all come with German-style potatoes and sauerkraut. More traditional English dishes include sandwiches (from £2.95), ploughman's (from £5.45), chicken and leek or steak and kidney pudding (£6.95), swordfish with lemon and herb butter (£7.95) and ice creams (from £2.95); helpful polite service. As well as four changing real ales such as Fullers London Pride, Goddards, Ventnor Golden and a guest such as Brakspears on handpump, every few months German draught and bottled beers and wines are delivered direct from Munich. *(Recommended by J A Cheverton, Mike and Maggie Betton, Pete Yearsley, Derek and Sylvia Stephenson)*

Free house ~ Licensees Edgar and Donna Nieghorn ~ Real ale ~ Bar food (12-3, 6-10) ~ No credit cards ~ (01983) 529263 ~ Children in restaurant ~ Dogs allowed in bar ~ Folk night Tues ~ Open 11-11; 11-3, 6-11 Mon-Fri winter

CHALE SZ4877 Map 2

Clarendon (Wight Mouse)

In village, on B3399; also access road directly off A3055

This extremely popular, rambling family pub has plenty to keep children occupied. The spacious back garden has a toddlers' play area, swings, slides, bouncy castle, a junior adventure challenge, tricycles, a pets corner, and sometimes even Punch and Judy shows, and there's an indoor play area for under-12s (admission £1). Less energetic parents can sit and appreciate the lovely views out towards the Needles and Tennyson Downs, where the poet was inspired to write *Idylls of the King*. The original core of the pub is surprisingly traditional, with musical instruments, guns, pistols and so forth hanging over an open log fire. One end opens through sliding doors into a pool room with dark old pews, large antique tables, video game, juke box, darts, dominoes, fruit machine and pinball. At the other end is a woody extension with more musical instruments, lots of china mice around a corner fireplace, decorative plates and other bric-a-brac, and even oars from old lifeboats hanging from its high pitched ceiling; piped music. Well kept real ales on handpump include Badger Best, IPA, K&B and Tanglefoot, Gribble Fursty Ferret and Ventnor Gold. Bar food includes soup (£2.40), sandwiches (from £2.50, baguettes from £3), filled baked potatoes (from £2.50), ploughman's (from £4.25), home-made steak and kidney pie (£6.95), chicken fried with garlic and herbs (£7.95) and 8oz sirloin steak (£10.25), with daily specials such as barbecued spare ribs (£6.95) and bass (£7.95), and puddings such as cheesecake (from £2.75). Cheerful and efficient service; no smoking dining area. The bedrooms, some in adjoining former farm buildings, include three two-bedroom family suites. *(Recommended by Graham and Lynn Mason, Mrs Thomas, Phil and Heidi Cook, Dr and Mrs A K Clarke)*

Badger ~ Managers Roger and Christine Burston ~ Real ale ~ Bar food (12-10) ~ (01983) 730431 ~ Children welcome ~ Dogs allowed in bar ~ Various live entertainment ~ Open 11-12; 12-10.30 Sun ~ Bedrooms: £39B/£78B

> If we know a pub has a no smoking area, we say so.

COWES SZ5092 Map 2

Folly

Folly Lane – which is signposted off A3021 just S of Whippingham

The splendid estuary setting is the main attraction of this old maritime pub, with big windows in the bar and seats on a waterside terrace looking out on to boats on the river; it gets understandably busy in summer. Its seafaring connections go back a long way – the original building is based around a sea-going barge beached here in the early 1700s, and the roof evidently still includes part of that barge's deck. The nautically themed opened-out bar has a wind speed indicator, barometer and chronometer among the railway bric-a-brac, farm tools, old pictures and brass lights on its old timbered walls; there are venerable wooden chairs and refectory-type tables, and shelves of old books and plates. Breakfast is served first thing, and then straightforward bar food includes soup (£2.50), sandwiches (from £2.85), garlic mushrooms (£3.35), steak and kidney pie (£6.25), 8oz sirloin steak (£10.95), and daily specials such as spinach and ricotta cannelloni (£5.95), red thai vegetable curry (£6.25), crewpot (stew) of the day with crusty bread (£6.30), caribbean beef or cottage pie (£6.50), and tuna steak with tomato concasse (£9.95). Flowers IPA and Original Goddards on handpump; no smoking area, pool, fruit machine, TV and piped music. There's a bouncy castle in the landscaped garden in summer. Watch out for the sleeping policemen along the lane if you're driving. If you're coming along the river, they have moorings, a water taxi, long-term parking, and showers, and they even keep an eye on weather forecasts and warnings. *(Recommended by Joyce and Geoff Robson, Pete Yearsley, Mrs Rita Cox, Mike and Sue Richardson)*

Whitbreads ~ Manager Chris Ford ~ Real ale ~ Bar food (breakfast 9-11, 12-9(9.30 wknds)) ~ Restaurant ~ (01983) 297171 ~ Children welcome ~ Dogs welcome ~ Live entertainment Sat evenings and Fri in summer ~ Open 9-11; 12-10.30 Sun

FRESHWATER SZ3487 Map 2

Red Lion 🍴 🍷

Church Place; from A3055 at E end of village by Freshwater Garage mini-roundabout follow Yarmouth signpost, then take first real right turn signed to Parish Church

The food at this quietly tucked-away pub is so popular that if you want to eat here it's a good idea to book ahead. As well as a couple of lunchtime snacks such as baguettes (from £4.25) and fish and chips (from £6.25), very well prepared imaginative daily specials are listed on a big blackboard behind the bar, and might include fish pie (£7.50), steak and mushroom pudding (£7.95), freshly caught fish such as halibut with watercress soup (£9.50), crab salad (£11.50), rack of lamb with lemon and garlic mint sauce (£13.95), and fillet steak with merlot sauce (£15.50). Service is thoughtful and warmly attentive, and there's a cheery bustling atmosphere in the comfortably furnished open-plan bar, which has open fires, low grey sofas and sturdy country-kitchen style furnishings on mainly flagstoned floors, with bare boards at one end, and lots of local pictures and photographs and china platters on the walls. Well kept Flowers Original, Fullers London Pride, Goddards Special and Shepherd Neame Spitfire on handpump, and the good choice of wines includes 16 by the glass. Fines on mobile phone users go to charity (they also collect a lot for the RNLI); there's a fruit machine. There are tables on a carefully tended grass and gravel area at the back (some under cover), behind which is the kitchen's herb garden, and a couple of picnic-sets in a quiet square at the front, by the church; nearby are good walks, especially around the River Yar. *(Recommended by Dr and Mrs P Truelove, Mike and Sue Richardson, Miss J F Reay, David and Kay Ross, June and Malcolm Farmer, E S Funnell, MDN, Tony and Wendy Hobden, Ken Flawn, Paul Humphreys, Jan and Alan Summers, D P and J A Sweeney, Darly Graton, Graeme Gulibert, Derek and Sylvia Stephenson)*

Whitbreads ~ Lease Michael Mence ~ Real ale ~ Bar food (12-2, 6.30-9) ~ (01983) 754925 ~ Children over 10 ~ Dogs welcome ~ Open 11.30-3, 5.30-11; 11-4, 6-11 Sat; 12-3, 7-10.30 Sun

ROOKLEY SZ5183 Map 2

Chequers

Niton Road; signposted S of village

Families will enjoy this former customs and excise house, which has a toboggan run and bouncy castle in the large play area outside, and a Lego table and colouring competitions in the large no smoking family room. There are inland views of rolling downland from the comfortable carpeted lounge bar, with its cottagey ornaments and in winter a good log fire. The flagstoned public bar beyond has a good lively local character (it's popular with young farmers); sensibly placed darts, fruit machine, TV, and perhaps piped music. There's also a mother and baby room. Courage Best and Directors, Gales HSB, Greene King Old Speckled Hen and John Smiths on handpump. Bar food includes sandwiches (from £2.20), soup (£2.50), baked potatoes (from £4.25), deep-fried brie with redcurrant jelly or moules marinière (£4.25), ploughman's (from £4.50), vegetable lasagne (£5.95), chicken curry (£6.25), rack of lamb (£7.95), roast duckling (£8.65), steaks (from £9.75), and puddings (from £2.95). *(Recommended by Pete Yearsley)*

Free house ~ Licensees R G and S L Holmes ~ Real ale ~ Bar food (12-9) ~ (01983) 840314 ~ Children welcome ~ Dogs allowed in bar ~ Open 11-11; 12-10.30 Sun

SEAVIEW SZ6291 Map 2

Seaview Hotel

High Street; off B3330 Ryde—Bembridge

Charming hospitality and warm service are the hallmarks of this comfortably bustling little hotel, with its various rooms ranging from pubby to smart dining. The relaxingly civilised airy bay-windowed bar at the front has an impressive array of naval and merchant ship photographs, as well as Spy nautical cartoons for *Vanity Fair*, original receipts for Cunard's shipyard payments for the *Queen Mary* and *Queen Elizabeth*, and a line of close-set tables down each side on the turkey carpet. There's a more informal down to earth atmosphere in the simpler nautical back bar, with traditional wooden furnishings on bare boards, lots of seafaring paraphernalia around its softly lit ochre walls, and a log fire. They keep Greene King Old Speckled Hen and Goddards on handpump, and have quite a few malt whiskies and a good wine list (the landlord used to be a director of Corney & Barrow, the wine merchants); darts, cribbage, dominoes, shove-ha'penny and piped music. Using local ingredients wherever possible, good well presented and generously served bar food includes soup (£2.95), smoked haddock and prawn chowder (£4.95), a hot crab ramekin that's been a favourite here for years (£5.50), marinated squid with roasted mediterranean vegetable salad (£5.95), scampi and chips (£6.95), seafood pasta (£8.95), entrecote steak (£9.95), a couple of daily specials such as grilled bass (£9.95), and a handful of puddings such as steamed chocolate or treacle sponge and cream (£3.95); the smart formal restaurant is no smoking. Tables on the little terraces on either side of the path to the front door look down to the sea and along the coast, and some of the attractive bedrooms also have a sea view. *(Recommended by MDN, JDM, KM, Geoffrey Kemp, J A Snell, E S Funnell, Tony and Wendy Hobden, Derek and Sylvia Stephenson)*

Free house ~ Licensee N W T Hayward ~ Real ale ~ Bar food ~ Restaurant ~ (01983) 612711 ~ Children in restaurant (no under-5s after 7.30pm) and eating area of bar ~ Dogs allowed in bar and bedrooms ~ Open 11-2.30, 6-11; 12-2.30, 7-10.30 Sun; closed three days at Christmas ~ Bedrooms: £55S(£65B)/£70S(£95B)

All *Guide* inspections are anonymous. Anyone claiming to be a *Good Pub Guide* inspector is a fraud, and should be reported to us with name and description.

SHALFLEET SZ4189 Map 2

New Inn

A3054 Newport—Yarmouth

Isle of Wight Dining Pub of the Year

The fish quay is just a short walk from this welcoming former fishermen's pub, an island byword for its crab or lobster salad (from £11.95) and seafood platter (£45 for two). It also has a great choice of up to 16 fresh fish dishes a day, such as grilled sardines with garlic and black pepper butter (£3.95), moules marinière (£5.95/£8.95), haddock cooked in basil, red onion and tomato (£11.95), and bass in lemon (£13.95). A little crab shack in the garden sells potted shrimps, dressed crab and local lobster, which you can snack on at the pub or take away. Other dishes include smoked venison with green fig chutney (£4.95), steak and ale pie (£7.95), and chicken breast with honey and cream (£8.95), alongside a short menu with sandwiches (from £2.95), filled baguettes (from £3.75), and ploughman's (from £5.25). You will need to book, and there may be double sittings in summer. The partly panelled flagstoned public bar has yachting photographs and pictures, a boarded ceiling, scrubbed deal tables, windsor chairs, and a roaring log fire in the big stone hearth, and the carpeted beamed lounge bar has more windsor chairs, boating pictures, and a coal fire. The snug and a new gallery area (with slate floors, bric a brac and windsor chairs at scrubbed pine tables) are no smoking. Well kept Bass, Flowers Original, Marstons Pedigree, Ventnor Golden and possibly a guest such as Badger Tanglefoot on handpump, and around 60 wines; piped music. *(Recommended by Jan and Alan Summers, Geoffrey Kemp, MDN,*

Dr and Mrs P Truelove, Michael and Robin Inskip, Joyce and Geoff Robson, Mike and Maggie Betton, Ian and Gail Isted)

Whitbreads ~ Lease Mr Bullock and Mr MacDonald ~ Real ale ~ Bar food (12-2.30, 6-9.30) ~ Restaurant ~ (01983) 531314 ~ Children welcome ~ Dogs allowed in bar ~ Open 12-3, 6-11(10.30 Sun)

SHORWELL SZ4582 Map 2

Crown

B3323 SW of Newport

Despite its rural setting this friendly old place can get very busy, so it is worth booking. In summer the lovely, peaceful tree-sheltered garden does pull in the crowds; picnic-sets and white garden chairs and tables overlook a little stream that broadens out into a wider trout-filled pool with prettily planted banks. A decent children's play area blends in comfortably, and the pub has a truly welcoming attitude towards children. The four rooms that wander around its central bar have a friendly traditional atmosphere, and the staff are pleasant. The cosy beamed two-room lounge has blue and white china in an attractive carved dresser, old country prints on the stripped stone walls, other individual furnishings, and a winter log fire with a fancy tilework surround. Black pews form bays around tables in a stripped-stone room off to the left, with another log fire; several areas are no smoking. The good range of tasty bar food includes sandwiches (from £2.75), soup (£2.95), lasagne or fisherman's pie (£6.95), and daily specials such as beef in stout (£7.95) and seafood platter (£11.50), with puddings (from £2.75) and children's meals. Well kept Boddingtons, Flowers Original and Wadworths 6X, with a guest such as Badger Tanglefoot on handpump; piped music, darts and TV. *(Recommended by Dr and Mrs P Truelove, D P and J A Sweeney, Prof H G Allen, Michael and Robin Inskip, Jan and Alan Summers, Lynn Sharpless, Terry Mizen, David and Kay Ross)*

Whitbreads ~ Lease Mike Grace ~ Real ale ~ Bar food (12-2.30, 6-9.30(9 in winter)) ~ (01983) 740293 ~ Children in eating area of bar and family room ~ Dogs welcome ~ Open 10.30-11; 12-10.30 Sun; 10.30-3, 6-11 winter

VENTNOR SZ5677 Map 2

Spyglass

Esplanade, SW end; road down very steep and twisty, and parking nearby can be difficult – best to use the pay-and-display (free in winter) about 100 yards up the road

Readers enjoy the great setting and atmosphere, and the good value food at this enviably placed seaside pub. If it's too wet to appreciate the view from seats on the terrace perched above the sea wall, there's plenty to look at inside. Among the really interesting jumble of mainly seafaring memorabilia are wrecked rudders, ships' wheels, old local advertisements, rope makers' tools, stuffed seagulls, an Admiral Benbow barometer and an old brass telescope. The bustling mainly quarry-tiled interior is snug and pubby, and the atmosphere is buoyant; fruit machine, piped music. Generous helpings of good, very fairly priced bar food are promptly served and include sandwiches (from £2.95, baguettes from £3.95), filled baked potatoes (from £4.75), whitebait or calamari (£5.25), ploughman's, vegetable moussaka or lasagne (£5.95), tuna steak (£6.95), fisherman's pie (£7.50), seafood platter (£17.50), a couple of daily specials such as steak and ale pie (£6.95), and seafood casserole (£8.75). They usually have well kept Badger Best and Tanglefoot, Ventnor Golden and possibly a guest on handpump. They don't mind muddy boots; no smoking area. On special occasions such as a lifeboat support week, there may be half a dozen or more guest ales tapped from the cask. *(Recommended by Darly Graton, Graeme Gulibert, Prof H G Allen, Michael and Marion Buchanan, Keith Fairbrother, Dr and Mrs P Truelove, Pete Yearsley, Jan and Alan Summers)*

Free house ~ Licensees Neil and Stephanie Gibbs ~ Real ale ~ Bar food (12-9.30 (9 Sun); 12-2.15, 7-9.30 winter wkdays) ~ (01983) 855338 ~ Children in eating area of bar and family room ~ Dogs welcome ~ Live entertainment most nights ~ Open 10.30-11; 12-10.30 Sun ~ Bedrooms: /£50B

Lucky Dip

Besides the fully inspected pubs, you might like to try these Lucky Dips recommended to us and described by readers (if you do, please send us reports: www.goodguides.com).

Fighting Cocks [Hale Common, just S]: Friendly, with limited choice of enjoyable food *(John Saville)*

Cowes [SZ4995]

Anchor [High St/Shooters Hill]: Decent sensibly priced pub food from baguettes up inc some interesting specials, well kept ales such as Badger Tanglefoot, Fullers London Pride and Goddards Fuggle-Dee-Dum, quick friendly service *(E S Funnell, Derek and Sylvia Stephenson)*

☆ ***Duke of York*** [Mill Hill Rd]: Enjoyable pub/restaurant, wide choice of well cooked food inc lots of fish (lobster with 24 hours' notice), friendly helpful staff, lots of nautical artefacts; comfortable bedrooms, heart-warming breakfast *(Ken Flawn)*

Globe [The Parade]: Lots of seafood from good tuna baguettes up, well kept Fullers London Pride, spotless housekeeping; tables out overlooking Solent *(Dr and Mrs P Truelove)*

Vectis [High St]: Good little unspoilt flagstoned pub near harbour, best at the front, with tables outside; welcoming attentive service, lively local atmosphere, well kept Bass and island ales; nearby parking difficult *(Veronica Brown)*

Downend [SZ5387]

Hare & Hounds [A3056]: Big thatched family dining pub with helpful new licensees, decent food from good sandwiches up, well kept real ales, lots of beams and stripped brickwork, cosy alcoves in original part, more room in airy barn-type extension; open all day, wide views from pleasantly cool terrace, nice spot by Robin Hill Country Park, which is a great place for children *(E S Funnell, LYM, Dr and Mrs P Truelove)*

Fishbourne [SZ5592]

Fishbourne Inn [from Portsmouth car ferry turn left into Fishbourne Lane no through road]: Hospitable and spacious, with comfortable wall settles, good choice of food from ploughman's to grills and local seafood, friendly staff, good range of real ales *(D and S Price)*

Godshill [SZ5381]

Griffin [High St]: Family pub in honeypot village, big helpings of well presented standard food, cheerful service, well kept Greene King Old Speckled Hen and local St Lawrence Underhill; good garden with play area and maze *(Pete Yearsley)*

Hulverstone [SZ3984]

☆ ***Sun*** [B3399]: Picture-book thatched pub with smart tables under cocktail parasols in charming flower-filled garden, even village stocks; friendly staff, well kept real ales, imaginative menu, stripped brickwork; may be piped music; peaceful setting, sea views *(Mrs Thomas)*

Niton [SZ5075]

☆ ***Buddle*** [St Catherines Rd, Undercliff; off A3055 just S of village, towards St Catherines Point]: Extended former smugglers' haunt, heavy black beams, big flagstones, broad stone fireplace, no smoking areas, decent straightforward food inc seafood, griddle dishes and Sun lunches, family dining room/games annexe, up to half a dozen real ales, friendly staff and dogs; views from well cared for sloping garden and terraces, good walks; open all day, some live jazz *(Brian Root, Tony and Wendy Hobden, LYM, Michael and Robin Inskip, Pete Yearsley, Carol and Dono Leaman)*

☆ ***White Lion*** [off A3055]: Well kept local Yates and varied straightforward food done well in clean, roomy and comfortable pub with good no smoking section, children's dishes and Sun lunches, welcoming landlord, polite service, good atmosphere; children welcome, nice setting *(John Oates)*

Sandown [SZ5983]

Ocean Deck [Esplanade]: New place with wide choice of generous tasty food from plenty of sandwiches and snacks to seafood from their own boat, Badger and Goddards real ales *(E S Funnell)*

Shanklin [SZ5881]

☆ ***Chine*** [Chine Hill]: Great clifftop setting, warm, welcoming and tastefully refurbished, with flagstones, beams, good food (can be a wait; not Sun evening or Mon), welcoming service, well kept local Goddards and a changing guest beer; some live music, bright family conservatory and small terrace overlooking beach and chine (which is illuminated at dusk) *(JDM, KM, D P and J A Sweeney)*

St Lawrence [SZ5376]

St Lawrence Inn [Undercliffe Drive/Steephill Rd (A3055)]: Two well kept and attractively priced Yates beers brewed in adjacent building, interesting menu inc good meat dishes, big split-level room (former stables) with much wood; piped music may be obtrusive *(Jeanne and Paul Silvestri, Pete Yearsley)*

Ventnor [SZ5677]

☆ ***Volunteer*** [Victoria St]: Small old-fashioned local with interesting customers and involved landlord, six well kept ales such as Badger, Ringwood, Ventnor Wight Spirit and Yates, reasonable prices, coal fire, darts, the local game of rings, no machines or juke box, no food; no children, open all day, quiz nights *(Darly Graton, Graeme Gulibert, Hywel Bevan)*

Whitwell [SZ5277]

☆ ***White Horse*** [High St]: Ancient well furnished beamed bar with small eating area and two large no smoking family dining areas off, wide range of food inc good Sun lunch, big helpings, full range of Gales ales kept well, cheerful quick service, country décor, horsebrasses, log fire; tables out on lawn *(Prof H G Allen, June and Malcolm Farmer, Jeanne and Paul Silvestri)*

Wroxall [SZ5479]

Four Seasons [Clarence Rd]: Modern pub with enjoyable food, beamery and timber-effect walls in comfortable carpeted bar, no smoking restaurant *(Joan and Brian Pickering)*

Yarmouth [SZ3589]

☆ ***Bugle*** [The Square]: Old inn with low-ceilinged panelled lounge, lively rather basic bar with nautical memorabilia and counter like galleon stern, enjoyable food from good soup and sandwiches to bass with scallops, quick cheerful service, well kept Whitbreads-related ales, decent house wines, restaurant, games room with pool, children very welcome; piped music, little or no nearby parking; sizeable garden, summer barbecues, bedrooms *(Dr and Mrs A K Clarke, JDM, KM, Michael and Robin Inskip, E S Funnell, LYM, Ken Flawn, Mrs Thomas, Derek and Sylvia Stephenson)*

Kings Head [Quay St]: Cosy low-ceilinged traditional pub opp car ferry, rather dark and quaint, with well kept ales, good food till quite late evening inc well prepared local fish, plush seats, friendly staff, open fires, children's eating area, unobtrusive piped music; can get crowded, public car park some way off; bedrooms *(Michael and Robin Inskip, Dr and Mrs A K Clarke, E S Funnell)*

☆ ***Wheatsheaf*** [Bridge Rd, nr ferry]: Well kept Goddards Fuggle-Dee-Dum, Greene King Old Speckled Hen and Wadworths 6X, cheerful staff, public bar with juke box and winter pool, wide choice of generous quick food all day inc fresh fish, plenty of room inc no smoking glazed extension; children welcome in most parts, open all day, tables on back terrace *(Miss J F Reay, LYM, Dr and Mrs A K Clarke, Derek and Sylvia Stephenson)*

'Children welcome' means the pub says it lets children inside without any special restriction. If it allows them in, but to restricted areas such as an eating area or family room, we specify this. Places with separate restaurants usually let children use them, hotels usually let them into public areas such as lounges. Some pubs impose an evening time limit – let us know if you find this.

Kent

Several Kent pubs are really shining this year: the Gate Inn at Boyden Gate (very well run, with good beer and wine, honest home cooking using local produce, and in a lovely spot), the friendly Green Man at Hodsoll Street (very enjoyable food), the ancient George & Dragon at Ightham (good food here too – earning it a Food Award this year), the Harrow on Ightham Common (an excellent country dining pub), the Hare at Langton Green (a nice all-rounder), the 16th-c George at Newnham (enjoyable food, nice layout with lots to look at), the ancient Shipwrights Arms surrounded by the salt marshes near Oare (good beer, cheap food, plenty of character), the striking Dering Arms at Pluckley (the landlord's love of seafood shows in the cooking), the cosy Rose & Crown tucked away in the woods near Selling (this fine all-rounder gains a Star now), the Chequers at Smarden (sensitively smartened up, good all round and a nice place to stay in), the Sportsman in Seasalter (a newcomer to the Guide*, and a surprise to find such a good bistro-style place here, with tempting food and yet a bar well used by locals), the staunchly unmodernised old Red Lion at Snargate (good beer and local cider), the very welcoming Red Lion at Stodmarsh (another new main entry, interesting food and fascinating décor), and the Pepper Box at Ulcombe (a charming country pub in a lovely spot). The strides it is making with its imaginative cooking earn the Harrow on Ightham Common the title of Kent Dining Pub of the Year. The Lucky Dip section at the end of the chapter has had a substantial influx of promising new entries this year: 72 pubs, just over half its total. This new blood is very encouraging for our inspection prospects over the next few months, and we'd be especially grateful for readers' views on which of the Kent Lucky Dips most deserve consideration for possible inspection. Ones that we would pick out particularly so far include the Woolpack in Chilham, Ship at Conyer Quay, Fountain at Cowden, Green Cross near Goudhurst, Plough at Ivy Hatch (restaurant rather than pub really, but good), Alma at Painters Forstal, Rose & Crown at Pluckley, Snail at Stone Street, Tiger at Stowting and White Lion in Tenterden – but all the entries with stars look to be of main entry quality in their different ways. Drinks prices here are higher than the national average: a pint of beer in Kent typically costs about 10p over the odds. Apart from the Swan in West Peckham (brewing its own interesting beers), the two cheapest main entries were both selling the local Goachers. The main local brewer is Shepherd Neame, often good value too (and their Mulberry Inns are establishing a good record for reliable food and decent wines). Larkins stands out among other local brewers, small enough to benefit from the new 14p duty concession. Others to look for here include Flagship (see Harbourmasters House, Chatham, in the Lucky Dip), Hopdaemon, Swale and Old Kent.*

Pubs with particularly interesting histories, or in unusually interesting buildings, are listed at the back of the book.

BIDDENDEN TQ8538 Map 3

Three Chimneys

A262, a mile W of village

Not far from Sissinghurst gardens, this pretty ochre-coloured country pub is a civilised restauranty place, with helpful staff and imaginative food. Well presented, but not cheap, dishes can be eaten in the bar or restaurant (though they'll serve you ploughman's in the garden): they could include soup (from £3.25), baked mushrooms with caramelised red onions and grilled goats cheese (£5.50), smoked salmon with roast new potatoes and cream cheese (£6.95), sautéed lambs liver with bacon, port and red onion (£9.95), roasted red pepper with grilled goats cheese and a cheese-laden risotto cake in tomato sauce (£10.95), rib-eye steak (£14.95), fried bass with roasted sweet potato, coconut and coriander chowder (£15.95), and fried monkfish and mussels in a white wine and shallot cream sauce (£17.95); puddings such as sticky toffee pudding or dark chocolate and Baileys torte with home-made toffee and praline ice cream (from £3.95). French windows in the civilised candlelit bare board restaurant open on to the garden, which has picnic-sets (some nice and shady on a hot day), and a smart terrace area has tables and outdoor heaters. Inside, the pub has a rambling, low oak-beamed series of small, very traditional rooms with plain wooden furniture and old settles on flagstones and coir matting, some harness and sporting prints on the stripped brick walls, and good log fires. The simple public bar has darts, dominoes and cribbage. As well as a good wine list, local Biddenden cider and several malt whiskies, they have well kept Adnams Best, Shepherd Neame Bitter and Spitfire and a seasonal beer tapped straight from the cask. *(Recommended by Peter Meister, Darly Graton, Graeme Gulibert, Colin and Janet Roe, John Eggleston, K J Diamond, the Didler, Louise English, Kevin Thorpe, Pat and Tony Martin, JP, PP, John Evans, Mr and Mrs A P Lawrence, Alan Cowell, Stephen and Jean Curtis)*

Free house ~ Licensee Craig Smith ~ Real ale ~ Bar food ~ Restaurant ~ (01580) 291472 ~ Dogs allowed in bar ~ Open 11.30-2.45, 6-11; 12-3, 7-10.30 Sun; closed 25 Dec and evening 31 Dec

BOUGH BEECH TQ4846 Map 3

Wheatsheaf

B2027, S of reservoir

Readers enjoy visiting this friendly and bustling pub, which is thought to have begun life as a hunting lodge belonging to Henry V. The neat central bar and the long front bar (with an attractive old settle carved with wheatsheaves, shove-ha'penny, dominoes, and board games) have unusually high ceilings with lofty oak timbers, a screen of standing timbers and a revealed king post. Divided from the central bar by two more rows of standing timbers – one formerly an outside wall to the building – is the snug, and another bar. Other similarly aged features include a piece of 1607 graffiti, 'Foxy Galumpy', thought to have been a whimsical local squire. There are quite a few horns and heads, as well as a sword from Fiji, crocodiles, stuffed birds, swordfish spears, and the only matapee in the south of England on the walls and above the massive stone fireplaces. The pleasant, helpful staff and sociable landlady work hard to make visitors feel welcome, and there's a nice mix of customers. Thoughtful touches include piles of smart magazines to read, tasty nibbles, chestnuts to roast and mulled wine in winter, summer pimms, and a range of local fruit juices. A good wine list includes local wines (they do nice big glasses), and several malt whiskies; they also serve well kept Fullers London Pride, Greene King Old Speckled Hen, Harveys and Shepherd Neame Bitter on handpump, along with a guest such as Charles Wells Bombardier. Besides lunchtime snacks such as minced beef and onion pie and ploughman's (£5.95), a large choice of bar food from an ambitious menu could include soup (£4.50), duck and orange pâté or grilled goats cheese ciabatta with pesto and caramelised red onion (£5.95), vegetarian sausages and mash (£7.95), poached smoked haddock with mash, spinach and citrus cream sauce (£9.95), lamb chops in red wine and tarragon sauce with mash (£10.95) and crispy duck with mash and plum sauce (£14.95), with nice puddings such as chocolate truffle torte or toffee and apple pie (£4.25); you may have to wait when they are busy. There's a rustic cottage, plenty of seats, and flowerbeds and fruit trees in the sheltered side and back gardens; shrubs help divide it into various areas, so it doesn't feel too crowded even when it's full. *(Recommended by Mr and Mrs D D Collins, Tony Brace, Linda and Jim Webb, Martin and Karen Wake, Debbie and Neil Hayter, John Robertson, Pat and Tony Martin, Jim Bush)*

Whitbreads ~ Lease Elizabeth Currie ~ Real ale ~ Bar food (12-10) ~ (01732) 700254 ~ Children in part of bar ~ Dogs welcome ~ Folk and country Weds 8.30 ~ Open 11-11; 12-10.30 Sun

BOYDEN GATE TR2265 Map 3

Gate Inn ★ 🍷 ☕

Off A299 Herne Bay—Ramsgate – follow Chislet, Upstreet signpost opposite Roman Gallery; Chislet also signposted off A28 Canterbury—Margate at Upstreet – after turning right into Chislet main street keep right on to Boyden; the pub gives its address as Marshside, though Boyden Gate seems more usual on maps

On fine summer evenings, it's so relaxing to sit at the picnic-table sets on the sheltered side lawn of this fine old-fashioned pub, the air filled with the contented quacking of a multitude of ducks and geese, coots and moorhens out on the marshes (they sell food inside – 10p a bag). Mr Smith was quite a new boy at the Gate when we first knew it, but he's run it for 27 years now, and his cheerful and sociable personality is an important part of the bustling pubby atmosphere; as well as being a proper local, it's a favourite with many visitors from afar. The winter inglenook log fire serves both quarry-tiled rooms, and there are flowery-cushioned pews around tables of considerable character, hop bines hanging from the beam and attractively etched windows. Where possible they use organically grown local produce to prepare their tasty straightforward bar meals, which include a good choice of sandwiches (from £2.50, filled baguettes from £4), burgers (from £2.75), home-made soup (£2.95), lots of filled baked potatoes (from £3.75), quite a few different ploughman's (£4.95), gammon and egg, home-made vegetable flan or grilled steak (£5.50), and various spicy hotpots (£5.75). The eating area is no smoking at lunchtime. Well kept Shepherd Neame Bitter and Spitfire and a seasonal ale are tapped from the cask; they've also interesting bottled beers, a fine range of 17 wines by the glass, and country wines. Shove-ha'penny, dominoes and cribbage, and bat and trap. *(Recommended by David and Betty Gittins, Kevin Thorpe, Steve Rudge, Tracey Griffiths, Andrea Rampley, Ian Phillips)*

Shepherd Neame ~ Tenant Christopher Smith ~ Real ale ~ Bar food (not Mon/Tues evening in winter) ~ No credit cards ~ (01227) 860498 ~ Well behaved children welcome ~ Dogs welcome ~ Open 11-2.30, 6-11; 12-4, 7-10.30 Sun

BROOKLAND TQ9724 Map 3

Woolpack £

On A259 from Rye, as you approach Brookland, take the first right turn where the main road bends left, just after the expanse of Walland Marsh; OS Sheet 189 map reference 977244

Especially inviting on a gloomy day when you'll find a roaring log fire, this crooked early 15th-c cottage was once the beacon keeper's house. Along with all the smuggling connections that you'd expect, there's still plenty of old-fashioned character and atmosphere here. The ancient entrance lobby has an uneven brick floor and black-painted pine-panelled walls, and on the right, the simple but homely softly lit main bar has basic cushioned plank seats in the massive inglenook fireplace, a painted wood-effect bar counter hung with lots of water jugs, and some ships' timbers that may date from the 12th c in the low-beamed ceiling. On the quarry-tiled floor is a long elm table with shove-ha'penny carved into one end, other old and newer wall benches, chairs at mixed tables, and photographs of the locals (and perhaps their award-winning sheep) on the walls. To the left of the lobby is a sparsely furnished little room, and an open-plan games room with central hearth, modern bar counter, and young locals playing darts or pool; dominoes, cribbage, shove-ha'penny, fruit machine, piped music and pub cat. Friendly staff serve well kept Shepherd Neame Bitter and Spitfire by handpump. Especially good value, the enjoyable straightforward bar food includes sandwiches (from £1.95), soup (£2.50), baked potatoes (from £3.95), ploughman's (£4.25), pint of prawns, vegetable curry or home-made steak pie (£4.95), pork chops or salmon (£5.95), and sirloin steak (£9.95), with daily specials such as cauliflower cheese, liver and bacon or whole grilled plaice (all £4.50); readers say the Sunday roast (£4.50) is a steal. *(Recommended by Lynn Sharpless, David and Rhian Peters, Jan and Alan Summers, John and Lynn Busenbark, Gill and Tony Morriss, Pamela and Merlyn Horswell)*

Shepherd Neame ~ Tenants John and Pat Palmer ~ Real ale ~ Bar food ~ (01797) 344321 ~ Children in family room ~ Dogs welcome ~ Open 11-3, 6-11; 12-3, 7-10.30 Sun

CHIDDINGSTONE TQ4944 Map 3

Castle Inn 🍷

Village signposted from B2027 Tonbridge—Edenbridge

It's worth a walk around the National Trust village to look at the picturesque cluster of unspoilt Tudor houses, and the countryside around here is pleasant too. A handsome, carefully modernised beamed bar has well made settles forming booths around the tables, cushioned sturdy wall benches, an attractive mullioned window seat in one small alcove, and latticed windows (a couple of areas are no smoking); darts, shove-ha'penny, dominoes and cribbage. There are tables in front facing the church, and more in the pretty secluded vine-hung garden. Served till 6, the straightforward bar snack menu might include open sandwiches (from £4.15, filled baguettes from £5.25), filled baked potatoes (from £4.55), chicken curry, chilli con carne or three-cheese tortellini (£5.75), and puddings such as toffee cheesecake (from £3.15); in the evening they do more elaborate (though not cheap) dishes such as wild rabbit and mushroom terrine wrapped in smoked venison (£6.45), seared duck breast with thyme jus or roast pepper and rosemary gnocchi with creamed basil sauce (£8.45), with puddings such as tiramisu (from £3.15); three courses for £14.20. You may have to wait when they're busy; they've a decent children's menu, and children's facilities (bottle warmers and so forth). There's an impressive wine list, well kept Harveys Best, Larkins Traditional (it's brewed in the village, and in winter they have Porter too), along with a guest such as Fullers London Pride on handpump; a good range of malt whiskies. Records show there was a building called Waterslip House here in 1420, and this rambling old place's stone foundations probably go back as far as that – so it could be where Anne Boleyn found shelter when she was stranded in a terrible blizzard on her way to nearby Hever. *(Recommended by Anthony Longden, Eve Samsow, Neil Rose, Michael and Ann Cole, James Nunns, Tina and David Woods-Taylor, Patricia Beebe, Pat and Robert Watt)*

Free house ~ Licensee Nigel Lucas ~ Real ale ~ Bar food (11-9.30) ~ Restaurant ~ (01892) 870247 ~ Children welcome (not in public bar) ~ Dogs welcome ~ Open 11-11; 12-10.30 Sun

DARGATE TR0761 Map 3

Dove 🍴

Village signposted from A299

The interesting restaurant-style food at this tucked-away pub is made using fresh seasonal local ingredients. As well as lunchtime dishes such as croque monsieur (£4.75), grilled sardines with olive oil and garlic (£5), caramelised pork with vegetable stir-fry (£6.50), and prawns with pickled ginger and herbs (£6.99), the menu could include glazed goats cheese with tomato and red onion salad (£4.99), braised lamb shank (£14.75), local free range chicken breast with pickled herbs and ginger (£14.99), and grilled swordfish (£15.50); you really have to book. The sheltered garden has roses, lilacs, peonies and many other flowers, picnic-table sets under pear trees, a dovecote with white doves, a rockery and pool, and a swing. The charmingly unspoilt rambling rooms have photographs of the pub and its licensees throughout the past century on the walls, a good winter log fire, and plenty of seats on the bare boards; piped music. Well kept Shepherd Neame on handpump. A bridlepath leads up from the pub (along the quaintly-named Plumpudding Lane) into Blean Wood. More reports please. *(Recommended by Mr and Mrs Thomas, Richard Siebert, Sean and Sharon Pines, Norman Fox, Kevin Thorpe, Barry and Patricia Wooding, David and Betty Gittins)*

Shepherd Neame ~ Tenants Nigel and Bridget Morris ~ Real ale ~ Bar food (not Sun and Tues evenings or all day Mon) ~ (01227) 751360 ~ Children in eating area of bar ~ Dogs allowed in bar ~ Open 11.30-3, 6-11.30; 12-3, 7-11 Sun; closed Mon except bank hols

DEAL TR3752 Map 3

Kings Head

Beach Street, just off A258 seafront roundabout

Handily open all day, this handsome three-storey Georgian inn is just across the road from the promenade and the sea. Picnic-sets out on a broad front paved terrace are prized in summer, when the pub is festooned with pretty hanging baskets and window boxes. You'll find a nice mix of locals and visitors in the four comfortable bar rooms which work their way round a central servery. The walls, partly stripped masonry, are decorated with marine architectural drawings, maritime and local pictures and charts, and other material underlining connections with the Royal and Merchant navies, and another area has an interesting collection of cricket memorabilia. There are a couple of flame-effect gas fires; quiet piped music and TV. They serve well kept Fullers London Pride, Shepherd Neame Bitter and Spitfire, and a guest such as Courage Best on handpump. Straightforward bar food includes sandwiches (from £2.25), omelettes (from £4), filled baked potatoes (from £4.25), ploughman's, broccoli cream cheese bake or chilli con carne (£4.95), and sirloin steak (£9.50) with daily specials on a blackboard; two-course Sunday lunch (£7.95). Beware that traffic wardens here are vigilant; there's pay-and-display parking nearby. *(Recommended by JMC, Kevin Thorpe, Michael Tack, David Gregory, Jan and Alan Summers, P Goodson, B J Harding)*

Courage (S & N) ~ Lease Graham Stiles and Shirley Russell ~ Real ale ~ Bar food (11.30-3, 6-9.30) ~ (01304) 368194 ~ Children in eating area of bar ~ Dogs welcome ~ Open 10-11; 12-10.30 Sun ~ Bedrooms: £40B/£56B

FORDCOMBE TQ5240 Map 3

Chafford Arms

B2188, off A264 W of Langton Green

Bar food prices at this tile-hung old pub haven't changed since last year. Enjoyable dishes (with a decent choice of seafood) could include sandwiches (from £2.65), home-made soup (£2.95), smoked salmon pâté (£4.65), ploughman's (£4.95), creamy vegetable and cheese kiev (£5.45), moules marinière (£5.95), grilled trout or gammon steak (£7.95), steaks (from £9.45), and skate wing or dressed crab and prawn salad (£9.95). The pub is quite a sight in summer when it's festooned with flowers against a backdrop of cascading creepers and carefully tended shrubs and perennials. Most of the flowers are in front but there's a pleasant sheltered lawn behind with an attractive shrubbery and arbours (unfortunately the record-breaking wych elm has now been pollarded, in an attempt to save it). Inside, there's plenty of room between neat tables and comfortable seats on a turkey carpet, and an uncluttered décor. Full of sporting memorabilia and trophies, the quite separate public bar often gets much busier towards the close of the evening as the dining side winds down; darts, shove-ha'penny, cribbage, dominoes, TV, and fruit machine. Service is friendly and the atmosphere relaxed; they welcome walkers. Well kept Fullers London Pride and Larkins on handpump, local farm cider, and decent house wines. Just up the steepish lane is an archetypal village cricket green. *(Recommended by Colin Draper, Peter and Patricia Burton, Roger and Pauline Pearce, Richard Gibbs, Ken Arthur)*

Laurel (Enterprise) ~ Lease Barrie Leppard ~ Real ale ~ Bar food (not Sun and Mon evening) ~ Restaurant ~ (01892) 740267 ~ Children welcome ~ Dogs welcome ~ Jazz 3rd Sun evening of month ~ Open 11.45-3, 6.30-11; 11-11 Sat; 12-4, 7-10.30 Sun

GROOMBRIDGE TQ5337 Map 3

Crown

B2110

This quaint Elizabethan inn is picturesquely set at the end of a row of pretty cottages overlooking the steep village green, and there are picnic-sets in front on a sunny old brick terrace. Inside, the well worn-in beamed rooms are snug, with locals gathered around the long copper-topped serving bar, and a jumble of bric-a-brac including old teapots, pewter tankards, and antique bottles. The walls, mostly rough yellowing plaster with some squared panelling and timbering, are decorated with small topographical, game and sporting prints, and a circular large-scale map with the pub at its centre. Large logs burn in the big brick inglenook in winter. The no smoking end room (normally for eaters) has fairly close-spaced tables with a variety of good solid chairs, and a log-effect gas fire in a big fireplace. Tasty bar food includes soup (£2.50), lunchtime ploughman's or baked potatoes (£5.20), avocado prawn salad (£5.40), home-made steak and mushroom pie (£7.90), stuffed chicken breast with creamy mushroom sauce (£8.50), roast lamb rump with honey and rosemary sauce (£9.80), and blackboard specials. They've Greene King Abbot, Harveys and Larkins on handpump, and local farm cider; shove-ha'penny, dominoes, cribbage and Scrabble. Service is efficient, though with a newish team it will no doubt take a little while for the pub to regain its easy urbanity. Across the road a public footpath beside the small chapel leads across a field to Groombridge Place Gardens. *(Recommended by Andrea Rampley, Peter Meister, Derek Thomas, Quentin and Carol Williamson)*

Free house ~ Licensee Peter Kilshaw ~ Real ale ~ Bar food (12-3, 7-9; not Sun evening) ~ Restaurant ~ (01892) 864742 ~ Children welcome ~ Dogs allowed in bar ~ Open 11-3, 6-11; 11-11 Sat; 12-10.30 Sun; 11-3, 6-11 Sat and Sun in winter ~ Bedrooms: £35/£40

HAWKHURST TQ7630 Map 3

Queens

Rye Road (A268 E)

This handsome wisteria-covered Georgian-faced building was first recorded as an inn in the 16th c, and the civilised interior has been sensitively opened up and appealingly decorated in keeping with its age. Light filters in through creeper tendrils that threaten to cover the old sash windows of the more pubby area at the front, which is pleasantly chatty, with locals on stools along the extensive counter, and a big brick inglenook fireplace; piped pop, fruit machine, pool. The mood becomes more like that of a wine bar further in: terracotta, sand or pea-green colour washes give an airy feel despite the heavy low beams, and there's a nice mix of old pine tables on bare boards. At night it's pleasantly candlelit. Cooked by the Italian chef, a good choice of bar food includes soup (£3.95), filled baguettes (from £4.95), ploughman's (£5.50), mussels in white wine and garlic or sausages and mash (£6.95), home-made spinach and ricotta cannelloni (£7.95), steak and ale pie or battered cod and chips (£9.95), fried duck breast with red wine, bacon and thyme sauce or baked monkfish medallions with herb and butter sauce (£13.95), and puddings such as fruit cheesecake (from £4.50). A couple of

daily specials might include pork medallions with spring onion mash and cider and brandy sauce (£11.95); there's an eat as much as you like Italian buffet on Thursdays, and they have a popular Sunday carvery (£8.99). Well kept Harveys Sussex Best and Fullers London Pride on handpump. More reports please.
(Recommended by Colin and Janet Roe, Jason Caulkin)

Enterprise ~ Lease Janelle Tresidder ~ Real ale ~ Bar food (12-9.30; 12-10.30 Fri/Sat) ~ Restaurant ~ (01580) 753577 ~ Children in eating area of bar ~ Jazz 1st Fri in month ~ Open 11-11; 12-12(10.30 Sun) Sat ~ Bedrooms: £45S(£45B)/£65S(£65B)

HODSOLL STREET TQ6263 Map 3

Green Man

Hodsoll Street and pub signposted off A227 S of Meopham; turn right in village

Readers are full of praise for the friendly licensees at this village pub. There's a welcoming and relaxing atmosphere in the big airy carpeted rooms which work their way round a hop-draped central bar; they've recently redecorated inside (and repainted the outside). Neat tables are spaced tidily around the walls, with interesting old local photographs and antique plates, and a log fire at one end. Skilfully cooked by one of the licensees, good bar food includes a light lunchtime menu with sandwiches (from £2.95), filled baked potatoes (from £3.95), ploughman's (£4.50), wild boar sausages or ham and egg (£5.95), and specials such as home-made lasagne or fisherman's pie (£6.95), as well as other enjoyable dishes such as home-made soup (£2.25), garlic prawns (£5.90), three-cheese pasta (£7.95), lamb shank with red wine jus, smoked haddock with bombay potatoes and poached eggs or roast duck with red onion marmalade and plum sauce (all £9.95); puddings include home-made rhubarb crumble or coconut sponge (£3.50). On Sunday (when the menu is slightly more limited and you may have to wait if they are busy) they do a choice of delicious roasts (from £5.95), and Wednesday is fish night. Well kept Flowers, Fullers London Pride, Youngs Bitter and a guest such as Gales HSB on handpump, and they've a decent wine list; piped music. On a well tended lawn, there are picnic-sets, an aviary and a goat, and pretty hanging baskets and flowering tubs; look out for morris dancers who practise here regularly. The nearby North Downs have plenty of walks.
(Recommended by S Collins, Tina and David Woods-Taylor, B, M and P Kendall, Annette Tress, Gary Smith, Andrew Scarr, Dr and Mrs R A Newbury , Jan and Alan Summers, Pat and Tony Martin)

Enterprise ~ Lease John, Jean and David Haywood ~ Real ale ~ Bar food ~ (01732) 823575 ~ Children welcome ~ Dogs allowed in bar ~ Open 11-2.30, 6-11; 11-11 Fri and Sat; 12-10.30 Sun

ICKHAM TR2257 Map 3

Duke William 🍷

Village signposted off A257 E of Canterbury

In a picturesque village, this welcoming and comfortable pub has been run by the same friendly and accommodating licensees for more than 20 years. They serve an incredible choice of enjoyable home-made food with plenty of fish dishes. You might typically find sandwiches (from £2, filled baguettes from £4.25), home-made soup (£3.50), avocado and crab salad (£5.25), about a dozen different pasta dishes (from £5.45), ploughman's (from £5.50), quite a few pizzas (from £5.95), steak and kidney pie (£6.95), chicken with asparagus and mushroom (£8.75), mixed mushroom stroganoff (£9.25), prawn curry or chargrilled tuna with parmentière potatoes (£9.95), peppered steak (£14.95), and dover sole (£22); puddings from a trolley (£3.50). It's bigger than its little street front exterior suggests. The open-plan carpeted bar extends either side of the serving counter; there's a pleasant lived-in feel in the front part, helped by the gas lighting and big inglenook, longcase clock and all the brasses, copper and other bric-a-brac. There's more formal seating behind, with a rather smart air-conditioned restaurant area and then a well shaded no smoking Victorian-style conservatory which overlooks the attractive neatly kept garden and fields beyond. Well kept beers are Adnams, Fullers London Pride, Shepherd Neame and a guest such as Charles Wells Bombardier on handpump, as well as 15 wines by the glass and freshly squeezed orange juice; darts, pool, shove-ha'penny, dominoes, fruit machine and juke box. More reports please. *(Recommended by Peter Scillitoe, Kevin Thorpe)*

Free house ~ Licensees Mr and Mrs A R McNeill ~ Real ale ~ Bar food (11-2, 6-10; not Sun or Mon evenings) ~ Restaurant ~ (01227) 721308 ~ Children in restaurant and conservatory ~ Dogs allowed in bar ~ Open 11-3, 6-11; 12-4, 7-10.30 Sun; closed Mon lunchtime (except bank hols)

IDEN GREEN TQ8031 Map 3

Woodcock

Iden Green is signposted off A268 E of Hawkhurst and B2086 at W edge of Benenden; in village at crossroads by bus shelter follow Standen Street signpost, then fork left at pub signpost – beware that there is an entirely different Iden Green just 10 miles away near Goudhurst

This unaffected little country pub is bustling and friendly, with a cheerful local atmosphere and a welcoming landlord. The small flagstoned bar is snugly comfortable, with stripped brick walls and very low ceilings bearing down heavily on a couple of big standing timbers; it has a comfortable sofa and armchairs by a warming woodburning stove, and chunky big old pine tables tucked snugly into little nooks; darts, shove-ha'penny, fruit machine, and piped local radio. Four well kept real ales on handpump could be Greene King IPA and Abbot, Harveys and a guest such as Rother Valley Level Best. Served in generous helpings, hearty bar food includes pâté (£3.50), whitebait (£3.95), filled baguettes (from £4), smoked salmon or ham, egg and chips (£5.50), scampi or steak and kidney pie (£7.95), and specials such as dover sole (£10.95), duck breast (£11.95), and rack of lamb with chilli, ginger and honey sauce (£12.95), with puddings such as treacle sponge or lemon meringue (£3.50); it can get very busy at weekends, so you may need to book. The partly panelled dining area opens on to a verandah, and there are seats in the pretty side garden. The car park is across the road. More reports please. *(Recommended by Tina and David Woods-Taylor, Colin and Janet Roe, Grahame Brooks, Kevin Thorpe)*

Greene King ~ Lease Frank Simmons ~ Real ale ~ Bar food ~ Restaurant ~ (01580) 240009 ~ Children welcome ~ Dogs welcome ~ Open 11-11; 12-10.30 Sun

IGHTHAM TQ5956 Map 3

George & Dragon

The Street; A227 S of Borough Green

Pleasing readers with its enjoyable food and relaxed friendly atmosphere, this well run wonky black and white timbered pub was built in 1515 for the Earl of Stafford. You can eat the well presented and reasonably priced food anywhere in the pub. Aside from open sandwiches which they serve till 6.30 (between 3 and 6.30 these are the only thing you can have), the very short menu could include lunchtime crumpets with red leicester, tabasco, cayenne and cream (£4), ploughman's or beef and onion patty melt with swiss cheese (£4.50), and more elaborate seasonally changing evening dishes such as clam chowder or goats cheese and artichoke pizza (£4), red wine and sausage pasta, poached chicken or fish of the day (£9), and steamed steak and suet pudding (£9.50), with daily specials such as rack of lamb (£11.50) and beef wellington (£13), and puddings such as home-made strawberry shortcake (£3.50); two-course Sunday lunch (£10). There may be a wait when they are busy; part of the restaurant is no smoking. The long main bar has a stripped wooden floor, a circular table with a mix of wooden dining chairs by the fireplace (another fireplace at the other end has a woodburning stove), plenty of high bar stools, leather sofas, and a good sociable atmosphere. The Duke of Northumberland was imprisoned in this room after the Gunpowder Plot was discovered. A very nice little end room is cottagey but simple, with a pretty view through a sash window to the heart of this tiny village, and has heavy black beams, some big jugs in a corner display cupboard, and a brick fireplace; piped music. Friendly and helpful young staff serve well kept Shepherd Neame Bitter and Spitfire and seasonal ales on handpump, decent wines, and a good choice of fruit juices. There are seats out on the back terrace. *(Recommended by Eve Samsow, Mike Pugh, Sarah Davis, Rod Lambert, Thomas Neate, Kevin Flack, Mary Ellen Cummings, Sean and Sharon Pines, Derek Thomas)*

Shepherd Neame ~ Managers Charles Edgeter and Carole Slingo ~ Real ale ~ Bar food (12-9.30; 12-3 Sun) ~ Restaurant ~ (01732) 882440 ~ Children in family area and restaurant ~ Dogs allowed in bar ~ Open 11-11; 12-10.30 Sun

IGHTHAM COMMON TQ5755 Map 3

Harrow

Signposted off A25 just W of Ightham; pub sign may be hard to spot

Kent Dining Pub of the Year

This civilised country pub is greatly enjoyed by readers for its consistently excellent food. Well presented imaginative dishes might include tuscan bean soup (£4.95), duck liver pâté with pistachios (£5.95), sun-dried tomato and courgette tart with garlic mayonnaise and new potatoes (£7.95), salmon and chive fishcakes with citrus sauce (£8.95), roast lamb shank with garlic mash and onion gravy (£9.95), cajun blackened salmon with red onion salsa (£10.95), and smoked haddock with welsh rarebit (£11.95); readers have a particular weakness for the delicious home-made puddings, which could include lemon torte or bread and butter pudding (£3.95). The staff are charming and courteous, and the atmosphere is smartly relaxed. The decent sensibly priced wine list has plenty of good wines by the glass, and well kept ales include Greene King IPA, Abbot and a guest from a local brewery on handpump. Assorted country furniture stands on nice old brick flooring or black and white squared vinyl in two simply but attractively decorated rooms, both warmed by log fires in winter. The straightforward traditional public bar is painted a cheerful sunny yellow above its dark green dado, and there is appealing attention to detail – daily papers, fresh flowers, candles on the tables. A lush grapevine grows around the delightful little antiquated conservatory which leads off an elegant dining room laid with white cloths; piped music; tables and chairs on a pretty little pergola-enclosed back terrace. Ightham Mote is nearby. *(Recommended by Andrea Rampley, David Twitchett, David R Crafts, Pat and Tony Martin, Di and Mike Gillam, B, M and P Kendall, Michael Martin, Chris Reeve, Mary Ellen Cummings, Bob and Margaret Holder, Derek Thomas, Guy Vowles, JP, PP, Bob White, Richard Gibbs, Oliver and Sue Rowell)*

Free house ~ Licensees John Elton and Claire Butler ~ Real ale ~ Bar food (12-2, 6-9.30; not Mon or evening Sun) ~ Restaurant ~ (01732) 885912 ~ Children in family area ~ Open 12-3, 6-11; 12-3 Sun; closed Sun evening and Mon

LANGTON GREEN TQ5538 Map 3

Hare

A264 W of Tunbridge Wells

Big windows and high ceilings in the knocked-through rooms give this civilised Edwardian roadside pub a pleasant feeling of space. There are dark-painted dados below light walls, oak furniture and turkey carpets on stained wooden floors, old romantic pastels, and plenty of bric-a-brac (including a huge collection of chamber-pots). Old books, pictures and two big mahogany mirror-backed display cabinets crowd the walls of a big chatty room at the back, which has lots of large tables (one big enough for at least a dozen) on a light brown carpet. From here french windows open on to a sheltered terrace with picnic-sets looking out on to a tree-ringed green. Service is very pleasant and efficient, and the atmosphere is pubby and sociable. Most people are here for the generous well presented food; if you want to eat in the evening it's a good idea to book. Aside from tasty sandwiches (from £4.25), a good selection of interesting dishes could include home-made soup (£3.75), moules marinière (£4.95), oriental duck spring rolls with sweet chilli sauce (£5.50), salmon and smoked haddock fishcakes (£6.95), chicken and mushroom lasagne or roast beef rib with yorkshire pudding, gravy and roast potatoes (£8.95), stilton, celery and walnut tart with cranberry and port sauce, game pie or roast monkfish wrapped in parma ham with coconut rice (£10.95), and 8oz fillet steak with stilton sauce (£15.95); puddings such as chocolate brownie with whipped ream and toasted almond (from £3.95). They've well kept Greene King IPA and Abbot, and a couple of guests such as Brains SA or Everards Tiger on handpump, lots of wines by the glass, and over 40 malt whiskies; piped pop music in the front bar area, shove-ha'penny, cribbage and dominoes. *(Recommended by Derek Thomas, Mrs Thomas, R T and J C Moggridge, Ian Phillips, Tony and Katie Lewis)*

Brunning & Price ~ Tenant Brian Whiting ~ Real ale ~ Bar food (12-9.30(9 Sun); not 25 Dec) ~ Restaurant ~ (01892) 862419 ~ Well behaved children in restaurant till 7pm ~ Dogs allowed in bar ~ Open 11-11; 12-10.30 Sun

NEWNHAM TQ9557 Map 3

George

44 The Street; village signposted from A2 just W of Ospringe, outside Faversham

Below the slopes of sheep pastures, the spacious sheltered garden of this 16th-c dining pub has picnic-sets and a fine cobnut tree. Inside, there's lots to look at in the atmospheric spreading rooms: dressers with teapots, prettily upholstered mahogany settles, dining chairs and leather carving chairs around candlelit tables, table lamps and gas-type ceiling chandeliers, and rugs on the waxed floorboards; hop bines hang from the beams and there are open fires, fresh flowers and quite a few pictures. Good nicely presented food includes lunchtime sandwiches or baguettes (from £2.25), baked potatoes (from £3.95) and ploughman's (from £4.95), along with dishes such as home-made soup (£3.50), king prawns fried in garlic butter (£5.75), thai-style steak salad (£5.95), steak and mushroom pie or vegetable stir fry (£7.95), and chicken balti (£9.25), with specials such as fried cajun swordfish with tomato salsa or fried pork with cider, bacon and mustard cream sauce (£10.95), and honey-glazed half shoulder of lamb with garlic and coriander sauce (£11.95), with home-made puddings such as cheesecake and spotted dick (from £3); good vegetables. They've a dozen wines by the glass, well kept Shepherd Neame Bitter, Spitfire, Bishops Finger and seasonal beers on handpump, and good coffee; piped music. Service is friendly and attentive. There are pleasant nearby walks. *(Recommended by Mr and Mrs Thomas, Peter Scillitoe, Jan and Alan Summers, J D M Rushworth)*

Shepherd Neame ~ Tenant Marc Perkins ~ Real ale ~ Bar food ~ Restaurant ~ (01795) 890237 ~ Children welcome ~ Dogs allowed in bar ~ Open 11-3, 6.30-11; 11-4, 6.30-11 Sun; closed evening 25 Dec

OARE TR0163 Map 3

Shipwrights Arms

S shore of Oare Creek, E of village; coming from Faversham on the Oare road, turn right into Ham Road opposite Davington School; or off A2 on B2045, go into Oare village, then turn right towards Faversham, and then left into Ham Road opposite Davington School; OS Sheet 178 map reference 016635

The three unspoilt little bars in this unchanging 17th-c inn are dark and cosy, and separated by standing timbers and wood part-partitions or narrow door arches. There's a medley of seats from tapestry cushioned stools and chairs to black wood-panelled built-in settles forming little booths, pewter tankards over the bar counter, boating jumble and pictures, flags or boating pennants on the ceilings, several brick fireplaces, and a good woodburning stove. They serve only Kent-brewed beers; tapped from the cask, these might include Goachers Gold Star, Mild and Shipwrecked and Hopdaemon Dominator and Skrimshanker; usually strong local farm cider too. Good value straightforward bar food includes sandwiches (from £2.75), filled baked potatoes (from £3.50), ploughman's (from £4.50), home-baked ham and egg (£4.95), chilli con carne or mushroom stroganoff (£6.25), and puddings such as treacle sponge (from £2.75); part of the eating area is no smoking; piped music, cribbage, shove-ha'penny and dominoes. Parking can be difficult at busy times. An interesting approach is a walk from the village through the tangle of boatyard; or you can moor a boat in the creek which runs just below the Saxon Shore Way, which is up a bank from the front and back gardens of the pub. The surrounding salt marshes are designated a Site of Special Scientific Interest, and delight birdwatchers. *(Recommended by Kevin Flack, the Didler, Kevin Thorpe, Richard Gibbs, JP, PP, Peter Scillitoe, Richard Siebert)*

Free house ~ Licensees Derek and Ruth Cole ~ Real ale ~ Bar food (not Mon/Tues) ~ No credit cards ~ (01795) 590088 ~ Children in family room ~ Dogs welcome ~ Open 11-3, 7-11; 11-11 Sat; 12-10.30 Sun; closed a week for refurbishments in Oct

PENSHURST TQ5243 Map 3

Bottle House (food award)

Coldharbour Lane, Smarts Hill; leaving Penshurst SW on B2188 turn right at Smarts Hill signpost, then bear right towards Chiddingstone and Cowden; keep straight on

You're forgiven if you have trouble choosing from the extensive regularly changing menu at this friendly tiled 15th-c pub. Just a few of the interesting and enjoyable dishes might be home-made soup (£3.75), honey and mustard vegetable tartlet with tomato chutney or thai spiced fishcake with chilli jam (£4.95), local sausages with garlic mash and onion gravy (£7.95), spicy chicken fajitas or locally smoked chicken with dauphinoise potatoes, goats cheese and rosemary sauce (£10.95), duck breast with bitter orange sauce (£13.95), and a wide choice of fish such as roast skate wing with lemon butter and capers (£11.95) and bass fillets with crayfish sauce (£13.95); all their puddings and ice creams are home-made, and might include date and ginger pudding with toffee sauce (£4.50); two-course children's menu (£4.95). The neatly kept low-beamed front bar has a well worn brick floor that extends to behind the polished copper-topped bar counter; big windows look on to a terrace with climbing plants and hanging baskets around picnic-sets under cocktail parasols, and beyond to views of quiet fields and oak trees. The unpretentious main red-carpeted bar has massive hop-covered supporting beams, two large stone pillars with a small brick fireplace (with a stuffed turtle to one side), and old paintings and photographs on mainly plastered walls; quite a collection of china pot lids, with more in the no smoking low-ceilinged dining room. Several cosy little areas lead off the main bar – all can be booked for private parties; one room is covered in sporting pictures right up to the ceiling, and another has pictures of dogs. Served by friendly helpful staff, Harveys Best and Larkins are kept well on handpump, and they have local wine; unobtrusive piped music. There are good surrounding walks. *(Recommended by R and S Bentley, Mr and Mrs S Oxenbury, Tina and David Woods-Taylor, Jeff Cameron, Carl and Jackie Cranmer, Chris Reeve)*

Free house ~ Licensees Gordon and Val Meer ~ Real ale ~ Bar food ~ Restaurant ~ (01892) 870306 ~ Children welcome ~ Dogs allowed in bar ~ Open 11-2.30, 6-11; 11-11 Sat; 12-10.30 Sun; closed 25 Dec

Spotted Dog

Smarts Hill; going S from village centre on B2188, fork right up hill at telephone box: in just under ½ mile the pub is on your left

From the tiered terrace behind this quaint old tiled pub (once again under a new licensee), stunning views stretch over 20 miles of lush countryside. There are also seats on the front terrace under a large umbrella, and there's an outside heater. The low-ceilinged, heavily beamed and timbered bar is neatly kept, with some antique settles as well as wheelback chairs on its rugs and tiles, a cosy log fire in a fine brick inglenook fireplace, and attractive moulded panelling in one alcove. Bar food includes soup (£3.95), baguettes (£5.50), pâté (£5.25), smoked salmon salad (£7.25), cumberland sausage and mash (£7.95), steak and kidney pie (£8.25), chicken with white wine, tarragon and garlic (£10.50), and sirloin steak (£11.95), with specials such as bass with lime butter (£8.95), and puddings such as banoffi pie (£3.75); the restaurant is no smoking. Well kept Larkins Best and Traditional and Harveys Best on handpump; piped music. More reports please. *(Recommended by Jeff Cameron, Mrs J H S Lang, John Robertson, Derek Thomas, Ian Wilson, Patricia Beebe, A E Brace)*

Free house ~ Licensee Diane Miller ~ Real ale ~ Bar food (12-2.30(3.30 Sat/Sun in summer), 6-9) ~ Restaurant ~ (01892) 870253 ~ Children welcome ~ Dogs welcome ~ Open 11-3, 6-11 (11-11 Thurs-Sat in summer); 12-3, 6-10.30(12-10.30 in summer) Sun

PLUCKLEY TQ9243 Map 3

Dering Arms 🍴 🍷

Pluckley Station, which is signposted from B2077

With massive blocks of grey stone, dutch gables outlined against the sky and heavy iron-studded oak doors, this striking old building was originally built as a hunting lodge on the Dering estate. The licensee/chef loves seafood, so it's not surprising that there's such an enjoyable range of well cooked interesting (though not cheap) fresh fish dishes, and everything here (even down to the marmalade) is home-made. You might find fried soft herring roes with crispy smoked bacon or grilled smoked mackerel with creamy cheese sauce (£4.45), tuna steak fried with lemon and garlic or grilled skate wing (£12.95), alongside specials such as monkfish with bacon, orange and cream sauce or whole crab salad (£13.95). A few tasty non-fishy dishes might include sautéed chicken livers with brandy and cream sauce (£4.45), pie of the day (£7.95), and duck confit with bubble and squeak potato cake and mushroom sauce (£12.95), with specials such as leg of lamb with peppers, olives, saffron and couscous (£12.95); puddings might include chocolate fudge cake with warm walnut sauce (£4.50). The stylishly plain high-ceilinged main bar has a variety of good solid wooden furniture on stone floors, and a roaring log fire in the great fireplace; dominoes, cribbage and shove-ha'penny. A smaller panelled back bar with wood floors has similar dark wood furnishings with some more comfortable chairs, and a lot of classic car pictures. They've a very good extensive wine list, well kept Dering Ale (made for the pub by Goachers), home-made lemonade, local cider and quite a few malt whiskies; friendly and accommodating service. The big simple bedrooms have old ad hoc furnishings. *(Recommended by Ken Arthur, Robert Coomber, Lynn Sharpless, Patricia Beebe, Kevin Thorpe, Peter Meister, Louise English, Alan and Gill Bull, John and Lynn Busenbark, Sarah Davis, Rod Lambert, Michael Doswell, Guy Consterdine, Oliver and Sue Rowell)*

Free house ~ Licensee James Buss ~ Real ale ~ Bar food ~ Restaurant ~ (01233) 840371 ~ Children in eating area of bar, family room and restaurant ~ Dogs allowed in bar and bedrooms ~ Open 11.30-3, 6-11; 12-3, 7-10.30 Sun; closed 26/27 December ~ Bedrooms: £30/£40

SANDGATE TR2035 Map 3

Clarendon

Head W out of Sandgate on main road to Hythe; about 100m after you emerge on to the seafront, park on the road across from a telephone box on the right; just back from the telephone box is an uphill track.

This small and simple local, with a good proper landlord, is only 10 minutes from the Eurotunnel. Halfway up a steep lane from the sea, it has pretty summer hanging baskets and window boxes, and a few benches at the front have views of the water. The big-windowed lounge on the left also gives a view of the sea (and even, in the right conditions, the coast of France). It has a few pictures of the pub and a full display of the 1950s and 1970s Whitbreads inn sign miniatures, as well as some period advertising. Popular with locals, the straightforward pubby right-hand bar has a chatty atmosphere, and lots of old photographs of the pub and of Sandgate; both bars have coal fires in winter. Well kept Shepherd Neame Bitter, Spitfire and Bishops Finger and seasonal ales on handpump from a rather nice Victorian mahogany bar with a mirrored gantry, as well as 16 wines by the glass, 19 malts, and home-made sloe gin; shove-ha'penny, cribbage, dominoes, chess, backgammon, and draughts. Straightforward food includes sandwiches or baguettes (from £2.10), soup (£2.95), ploughman's (from £4.15), ham and eggs (£5.15), scampi and chips (£5.45) and mussels (£6.35); the dining room is no smoking. They may close early if it's quiet. *(Recommended by David and Betty Gittins, Kevin Thorpe, Ian Phillips, John and Joan Calvert, Mike and Wendy Proctor, Peter Meister, Miss A G Drake)*

Shepherd Neame ~ Tenants Keith and Shirley Barber ~ Real ale ~ Bar food (till 8.30; not Sun evening) ~ No credit cards ~ (01303) 248684 ~ Well behaved children in dining area ~ Dogs allowed in bar ~ Folk alternate Thurs ~ Open 12-3, 6-11; 12-5 Sun; closed Sun evening

SEASALTER TR0864 Map 3

Sportsman

Faversham Road; A299 off M2, left onto B2040, then right

It was a surprise to find this popular dining pub in such an unlikely spot, just over the sea wall from the sea. The three connected rooms have an airy, open-plan feel, and the big buttery cream-painted main bar has pale and dark wooden wheelbacks and basket-weave dining chairs around a mix of pine tables on the stripped wood floor, large modern photographs above the pine dado, big chrome ceiling fans, and a relaxed but chatty bistro-type atmosphere. High chrome and red plush bar stools (favoured by the cheerful locals who crowd in towards the end of the evening to enjoy a drink), perhaps piped jazz, and a friendly landlord and helpful staff; the two rooms leading off at either end are similarly furnished. Good interesting food changes with the seasons, but might include asparagus soup with a soft boiled egg (£4.95), smoked eel with soda bread and horseradish (£6.95), an antipasti platter for two (£10.95), crispy duck with smoked chilli salsa and sour cream (£10.95), seared thornback ray with balsamic vinaigrette (£11.95), roast rump of lamb with chanterelles (£12.95), steamed wild bass fillet with a tartare of mussels (£15.95), and puddings such as tarte tatin, rhubarb sorbet with burnt cream or coffee parfait with earl grey granita (£4.95). Well kept Shepherd Neame Master Brew, a seasonal ale, and perhaps Spitfire, and a well chosen wine list; a couple of areas are no smoking. *(Recommended by Bruce Jamieson, Chris Parsons)*

Shepherd Neame ~ Tenant Phil Harris ~ Real ale ~ Bar food (no food Sun evening or Mon) ~ (01227) 273370 ~ Children in two areas ~ Dogs allowed in bar ~ Open 12-3, 6-11; 12-10.30 Sun

SELLING TR0456 Map 3

Rose & Crown ★

Signposted from exit roundabout of M2 junction 7: keep right on through village and follow Perry Wood signposts; or from A252 just W of junction with A28 at Chilham follow Shottenden signpost, then right turn signposted Selling, then right signposted Perry Wood

You can be sure of a warm welcome from the friendly and attentive licensees at this really well liked 16th-c pub. Winter is particularly cosy and snug, with a blazing log fire and memorable Christmas decorations. Around the central servery there are pretty fresh flowers by each of the sturdy corner timbers, hop bines strung from the beams, and an interesting variety of corn-dolly work – there's more of this in a wall cabinet in one cosy side alcove, and much more again down steps in the comfortably cottagey restaurant. Apart from a couple of old-fashioned housekeeper's chairs by the huge fireplace (filled in summer with an enjoyably colourful mass of silk flowers interlaced with more corn dollies and so

forth), the seats are very comfortably cushioned. The terrace has outdoor heaters, so in fine weather you can sit out contentedly all evening; the cottagey back garden, with lots of picnic-sets, is charmingly planted with climbers, ramblers and colourful cottage plants, and there's a fairy-lit apple tree. The flowering tubs and hanging baskets in front are pretty too, and there's a neatly kept children's play area, bat and trap, and a small aviary. Enjoyable popular bar food comes in generous helpings, and includes home-made soup (£3), spinach and feta cheese filo parcel (£3.75), filled rolls (from £4), ploughman's (£4.95), hearty steak and kidney pie (£6), cod and smoked haddock mornay (£7.90) and chicken tikka masala (£7.95), with daily specials such as beef stroganoff or sweet and sour chicken (£8); on show in a cold cabinet down steps in a small family room are lots of puddings such as apple bakewell and pecan and maple pie with local honey ice cream and Italian white chocolate (£3). They have a children's menu (from £2.95), and do roasts on Sundays (£7); service is informal and obliging. Well kept Adnams, Goachers Mild and Harveys Best, on handpump, with a guest from brewers such as Humpty Dumpty and Old Kent, local cider, a good range of malts and decent wines in good measures; cribbage, shove-ha'penny, dominoes and piped music; the local TVR club meets here on the first Sunday lunchtime of the month. The pub is surrounded by natural woodland – good walking.
(Recommended by Kevin Thorpe, Adam Clegg, Basil Wynbergen, Theocsbrian, Mr and Mrs Thomas, Patricia and Norman Pollard, Norman Fox, Peter Scillitoe, Colin and Sandra Tann, David and Betty Gittins, Mike Gorton, D J Roseveare)

Free house ~ Licensees Richard and Jocelyn Prebble ~ Real ale ~ Bar food (not Sun or Mon evenings) ~ Restaurant ~ (01227) 752214 ~ Children in restaurant and family room ~ Dogs allowed in bar ~ Open 11-3, 6.30-11; 12-3, 7-10.30 Sun; closed evenings 25/26 Dec

SMARDEN TQ8842 Map 3

Chequers

Off A20 in Charing, via Pluckley; or off A274 at Standen just under a mile N of its junction with A262; The Street

This 14th-c inn has been so sensitively refurbished by its hard-working and friendly licensees that although it's been smartened up quite a bit, not much character has been lost. The cosy and comfortable bar has a pleasantly relaxed atmosphere and plenty of chatty locals, and there are elegant reproduction tables and chairs in the dining area. A walkway in the attractive landscaped garden leads to a pond with fish and waterfowl, and there's an arbour with climbing plants; the terrace has nice green metal tables and chairs on the york stone. Using fresh local produce, good bar food (not served on Saturday evening – only restaurant meals then) includes home-made soup (£3.25), filled baguettes with chips (from £4.50), ploughman's (£4.95), ham and egg or sausage and mash (£6.95), and battered cod or home-made chicken curry (£7.95); or you can choose from the restaurant menu, which could include tempura prawns with sweet chilli dip or meat platter (£4.95), delicous home-made steak and kidney pie with shortcrust pastry (£8.50), lamb cutlets with minted gravy (£12.95), and monkfish thermidor (£13.50); home-made puddings such as hot chocolate fudge cake or cheesecake (£3.95). The no smoking restaurant has lots of beams, an enormous fireplace, and a flagstone floor. Friendly helpful staff serve well kept Bass and Harveys Best and a couple of guests such as Old Kent Fine Edge or Rother Valley Level Best on handpump, they've several malt whiskies, and a decent wine list; piped music. The charming bedrooms (one is a four-poster) have their own bathrooms, and they do huge breakfasts here. This is an attractive village. *(Recommended by Colin and Janet Roe, Charlie Harris, Nick Smith, Tina and David Woods-Taylor)*

Free house ~ Licensee Lisa Bullock ~ Bar food ~ Restaurant ~ (01233) 770217 ~ Children in eating area of bar and restaurant ~ Dogs allowed in bar ~ Open 11-3, 6-11; 11-11(10.30 Sun) Sat ~ Bedrooms: £40S(£40B)/£70S(£70B)

SNARGATE TQ9928 Map 3

Red Lion ★

B2080 Appledore—Brenzett

It's worth a special trip to visit this amazingly unspoilt village local. The father-in-law of the current landlady bought it in 1911 and declared that nothing should be done to it – the last time it was modernised was in 1890. The three perfectly simple little rooms, now lovingly kept by his friendly daughter-in-law and granddaughter, still have their original cream tongue and groove wall panelling, a couple of heavy beams in a sagging ceiling, and dark pine Victorian farmhouse chairs on bare boards; outdoor lavatories, of course. One charming little room, with a frosted glass wall through to the bar and a sash window looking out to a cottage garden, has only two dark pine pews beside two long tables, a couple more farmhouse chairs and a nice old piano stacked with books. Cheerful groups of regulars catch up on local news and play toad in the hole. As well as Double Vision cider from nearby Staplehurst, and country wines, they serve Goachers Light and up to three well kept real ales from small brewers such as Black Sheep, Hop Back, and Hopdaemon tapped straight from casks on a low rack behind an unusual shop-like marble-topped counter (little marks it as a bar other than a few glasses on two small shelves, some crisps and half a dozen spirits bottles). Although they don't serve food, you're welcome to bring your own. Darts, shove-ha'penny, cribbage, dominoes, nine men's morris and table skittles. *(Recommended by Mike Gorton, Andrea Rampley, the Didler, Peter Scillitoe, Professor and Mrs J Fletcher, JP, PP, Kevin Thorpe)*

Free house ~ Licensee Mrs Jemison ~ Real ale ~ No credit cards ~ (01797) 344648 ~ Children in family room ~ Dogs allowed in bar ~ Open 12-3, 7-11(10.30 Sun)

STAPLEHURST TQ7847 Map 3

Lord Raglan

About 1½ miles from town centre towards Maidstone, turn right off A229 into Chart Hill Road opposite Cross at Hand Garage; OS Sheet 188 map reference 785472

Whether you're here for a well kept pint or the enjoyable home-made food, this unpretentious and simple yet quite civilised cosy country inn is somewhere you'll want to linger. Everywhere you look its low beams are crammed with hops, and the mixed collection of comfortably worn dark wood furniture on quite well used dark brown carpet tiles and nice old parquet flooring is mostly 1930s; don't miss the rather battered life-size effigy of Lord Raglan (a general in the Crimean War) propped in a chair in the corner. The interior is quite compact, with a narrow bar – you walk in almost on top of the counter and chatting locals – widening slightly at one end to a small area with a big log fire in winter. In the other direction it works its way round to an intimate area at the back, with lots of wine bottles lined up on a low shelf. Small french windows lead out to an enticing little high-hedged terraced area with white plastic tables and chairs; there are wooden picnic-sets in the side orchard. Nicely presented on willow pattern plates, the hearty bar food is served generously. Blackboard menus behind the bar include a few pubby staples such as sandwiches (from £2.50), filled baguettes (from £4.50), ploughman's, chilli con carne and rice or sausage, egg and chips (£5.50), as well as more elaborate dishes such as marinated anchovies with apple and potato salad (£5.25), smoked venison and pickled quince (£5.50), beef and red wine casserole with mashed potatoes (£7.95), pork fillet with apple and cider sauce (£8.95), swordfish steak with lime butter, guinea fowl breast and red wine sauce or stir-fried beef fillet with peppers (£9.95), and puddings such as banoffi pie and chocolate and coffee cheesecake (£3.50); children's menu (£3.50). Their well kept real ales are Goachers Light and Harveys Best, with a guest such as Exmoor Fox, and there's a good wine list. No piped music or games machines here, just nice little conversational nooks; wheelchair access is reasonable. *(Recommended by Louise English, Peter Meister, Colin and Janet Roe, Ian Phillips)*

Free house ~ Licensees Andrew and Annie Hutchison ~ Real ale ~ Bar food (12-2.30, 7-10) ~ (01622) 843747 ~ Children welcome ~ Dogs welcome ~ Open 12-3, 6-11; closed Sun

STODMARSH TR2160 Map 3

Red Lion

High Sreet; off A257 just E of Canterbury

This little pub was a delightful culmination to our Kent inspection trips this year. Several idiosyncratic rooms wrapping themselves around the big island bar are full of character and interest. There are hops all over the place, wine bottles (some empty and some full) crammed along mantelpieces and along one side of the bar, all manner of paintings and pictures, copper kettles and old cooking implements, well used cookery books, big stone bottles and milk churns, trugs and baskets, old tennis racquets and straw hats, a collection of brass instruments in one area with sheet music all over the walls, and some jazz records; a couple of little stall areas have hop sacks draped over the partitioning. There are green-painted, cushioned mate's chairs around a happy mix of nice pine tables, lit candles in unusual metal candleholders, fresh flowers on every table and big arrangements on the bars, and high bar stools on which a cheery group of locals sat chatting to the particularly friendly landlord. The atmosphere is convivial and very relaxed, and large cats sit snoozily by the big log fire (lit on a dreary early July evening). Piped jazz, and bat and trap. Well kept Greene King IPA and a seasonal guest, a good wine list with several by the glass, excellent summer pimms and winter mulled wine, and cider. Good bar food using local produce might include filled baguettes with steak, avocado and bacon, and so forth (£4.95), crab with basil mayonnaise (£6.25), pigeon breast and partridge fillet with chutney (£6.50), a mixed platter of meat, fish and cheese (£6.25), fruity chicken korma (£11.25), sunblush pasta carbonara with oyster and wood mushrooms or Bantry Bay mussels with sweet chilli, parsley and wine (£11.25), poached wild salmon wrapped in horseradish leaves and fresh fennel (£12.95), local lamb stuffed with rosemary and garlic (£13.95), and puddings such as banoffi pie or bread and butter pudding with Tia Maria (£3.50); they sell eggs and chutneys. There are picnic-sets under umbrellas in the back garden, pretty flowerbeds, and perhaps some chickens. We have not yet heard from any readers who have stayed in this peaceful spot. *(Recommended by Allan and Toni Jones, Tony and Katie Lewis)*

Free house ~ Licensee Robert Whigham ~ Real ale ~ Bar food ~ (01227) 721339 ~ Well behaved children welcome ~ Dogs welcome ~ Regular live jazz ~ Open 10.30-11; 11-10.30 Sun ~ Bedrooms: /£45

TUNBRIDGE WELLS TQ5639 Map 3

Beacon 🍷

Tea Garden Lane; leaving Tunbridge Wells westwards on A264, this is the left turn off on Rusthall Common after Nevill Park

You'll usually find a good mix of customers at this airy Victorian pub, chatting at the sweeping bar counter with its ranks of shiny bottles, and on the comfortable sofas by the fine old wood fireplace. The dining area and spreading bar run freely into each other, with stripped panelling, lovely wood floors, ornately built wall units and glowing lamps giving a solidly comfortable feel. When it's warm enough though, the best place to sit is out on the pergola-covered wooden deck behind the pub, which has good hillside views. As well as lunchtime tortilla wraps (from £6.25) and baked potatoes (from £5) with interesting fillings such as teriyaki chicken and pineapple, enjoyable bar food includes soup (£4.25), smoked goose, quails egg, parmesan and anchovy salad (£6.75), steak and kidney pie or spinach and ricotta tortellini with tomato, olive and dill sauce (£7.50), duck confit with bubble and squeak and red wine jus (£10.50), and roast cod with shallot, tomato and chive velouté topped with crispy fried noodles (£14). Well kept Brakspears Special, Harveys Best and Timothy Taylors Landlord on handpump kept under light blanket pressure, and nine wines by the glass; shove-ha'penny, cribbage, dominoes, and in the summer volley ball, boules and (very rare for a pub these days) even rounders. More reports please. *(Recommended by Mr and Mrs S Oxenbury, Ian Phillips, Sarah Davis, Rod Lambert, Colin and Janet Roe, B J Harding, Peter Meister, Comus and Sarah Elliott)*

Free house ~ Licensee John Cullen ~ Real ale ~ Bar food (12(10 Sun for breakfast)-2.30, 6.30-9.30) ~ Restaurant ~ (01892) 524252 ~ Children in eating area of bar and restaurant ~ Dogs allowed in bar ~ Folk club 2nd and 4th Mon of month ~ Open 11-11; 12-10.30 Sun

Mount Edgcumbe Hotel

The Common

This handsome tile-hung and weatherboarded hotel stands on top of one of the several large rocky outcrops on the common. As you enter the small cosy bar, which has lots of exposed brick and old photographs of the town on the walls, there's a mini waterfall feature on the right, with a few tables (candlelit at night) in an unusual grotto-like snug built into the rock. In the evenings subdued wall lighting and the chatty buzz of customers make for a welcoming atmosphere; there may be piped music. An attractive small two-room restaurant has views out over the common, and tables out on a pleasant side terrace have a similar outlook, reaching over the grass to the town beyond. As well as tasty lunchtime filled baguettes (from £4.95, not Sunday), the fairly short bar menu might include ploughman's (£4.50), moules frites (£5.50), tagliatelle with salmon (£6.95), toulouse sausages and mash in rich onion gravy or crispy hot duck salad with hoi sin sauce (£7.95); you must book for Saturday evening. They've an extensive wine list, well kept Harveys Best on handpump, fresh orange juice and good coffee; service is cheerful. More reports please. *(Recommended by James Galbraith)*

Free house ~ Licensee Iain Arthur ~ Real ale ~ Bar food (12-2.30, 7-9.30; 12.30-6 Sun) ~ Restaurant ~ (01892) 526823 ~ Children welcome ~ Dogs allowed in bar ~ Open 11.30-11; 12-11(10.30 Sun) Sat ~ Bedrooms: £60S/£80S(£80B)

Sankeys

Mount Ephraim (A26 just N of junction with A267)

A cross between pub and wine bar, this lively bustling place is a favourite for *Good Pub Guide* office treats; it's down stairs below a seafood restaurant, and offers the same appealing menu. Skilfully cooked fresh dishes could include Morecambe Bay potted shrimps (£5.75), Scottish queen scallops grilled with garlic and breadcrumbs (£6.50), fish pie or battered cod (£8.50), fried bass with spring onion and soy ginger (£13.50), and giant spider crab (£15), also half a roast duck with port and orange sauce (£12.50), and fillet steak (£15), with puddings such as raspberry cheesecake (£3.95); they do lunchtime baguettes and daily specials such as pasta. You need to book or get there early for a table in the bar, and the restaurant is no smoking; service is friendly and efficient. The dimly lit bar has pews around closely spaced sturdy old pine tables, and old mirrors, prints, enamel advertising signs, antique beer engines and other bric-a-brac (most of which has been salvaged from local pub closures); french windows lead to a suntrap terrace with teak tables and chairs under cocktail parasols. Although most people take advantage of the very good wine list, they've well kept Harveys Best, Larkins and an occasional guest such as Timothy Taylors Landlord on handpump, and a selection of European bottled beers; also quite a choice of unusual teas. More reports please. *(Recommended by Jeff Cameron, Chris and Anna Rowley)*

Free house ~ Licensee Guy Sankey ~ Real ale ~ Bar food ~ Restaurant ~ (01892) 511422 ~ Children in eating area of bar ~ Dogs allowed in bar ~ Open 12-12 (11 Sun); closed 25 and 26 Dec

ULCOMBE TQ8550 Map 3

Pepper Box

Fairbourne Heath; signposted from A20 in Harrietsham, or follow Ulcombe signpost from A20, then turn left at crossroads with sign to pub

Nicely placed on high ground above the Weald, this cosy and traditional country inn is a pleasant, friendly place to visit. The homely bar has standing timbers and low beams hung with hops, copper kettles and pans on window sills, some very low-seated windsor chairs and wing armchairs, and two armchairs and a sofa by the splendid inglenook fireplace with its lovely log fire. A side area is more functionally furnished for eating, and there's a very snug little no smoking dining room; piped music. Very well kept Shepherd Neame Bitter, Spitfire and a seasonal guest tapped from the cask, and country wines. Served by good friendly staff, the enjoyable bar menu includes home-made soup (£3.50), sandwiches (from £3.50), ploughman's (from £5), local sausages and onion gravy (£6.50), braised beef and onions (£7), and daily specials such as avocado and bacon salad (£6), shepherd's pie (£6.50), and scampi and chips (£7.50), with puddings such as pecan pie (£3.50). You can also eat in the bar from the more elaborate restaurant menu, which includes dishes such as sizzling singapore beef or grilled tuna steak with lime and tomato sauce (£9.80). Views from the terrace stretch over a great plateau of rolling arable farmland, and if you're in the garden, with its small pond, shrubs and flowerbeds, you may be lucky enough to catch a glimpse of deer; the tabby tom is called Fred, and there are two more cats and a collie called Rosie. *(Recommended by Jan and Alan Summers, Colin and Janet Roe, Sarah Davis, Rod Lambert, Comus and Sarah Elliott, Peter Scillitoe)*

Shepherd Neame ~ Tenants Geoff and Sarah Pemble ~ Real ale ~ Bar food (12-2, 7-9.45; not Sun or Mon evenings) ~ Restaurant ~ (01622) 842558 ~ Dogs allowed in bar ~ Open 11-3, 6.30-11; 12-3 Sun; closed Sun evening

WEST PECKHAM TQ6452 Map 3

Swan on the Green

Off B2016, second turning left heading N from A26 (Swanton Road)

They've got their own microbrewery at this little tucked-away country pub, and a choice of around five of their well kept real ales might include Ginger Swan, Parliament, Swan Mild, Trumpeter and Whooper Pale. There's an emphasis on the enjoyable enterprising bar food which, from a daily changing menu, might include lunchtime dishes such as baguettes (£3.95), ploughman's (£5.50), home-made stilton beefburgers or thai spicy beef and asparagus salad (£7.50), and wild boar and apple sausages with mustard mash and onion gravy (£8), with evening dishes such as coriander and spring onion rösti with mozzarella and red pepper salsa (£5.50), pork fillet stuffed with chorizo cooked in tarragon oil (£9.25), and bass fillets with lemon butter and horseradish cream cheese (£11.25); they may add an 'optional' 10% surcharge to the bill. Inside, it's light, airy, and open-plan, with rush-seated dining chairs and cushioned church settles around an attractive mix of refectory and other pale oak tables on the wood strip floor, lovely big bunches of flowers (one placed in the knocked-through brick fireplace), hops and beams, some modern paintings at one end, black and white photographs of locals at the other end, and good aztec-patterned curtains. There's a nice mix of locals and visitors; piped music. There are picnic-sets under parasols in front of the building, and more on the charming cricket green opposite; they take a £10 deposit if you want to eat outside, and will lend you a picnic rug; the nearby church is partly Saxon. *(Recommended by Bob and Margaret Holder, Simon and Sally Small, Robin Drummond, Alan Cowell, Kevin Thorpe, Chris and Anna Rowley, Ken Arthur)*

Own brew ~ Licensee Gordon Milligan ~ Real ale ~ Bar food (not Mon evening) ~ Restaurant ~ (01622) 812271 ~ Children in eating area of bar ~ Dogs allowed in bar ~ Live jazz/blues a couple of Sun evenings in month ~ Open 11-3(4 Sat), 6-11(9 Mon); 12-4, 7-10.30 Sun

Lucky Dip

Besides the fully inspected pubs, you might like to try these Lucky Dips recommended to us and described by readers (if you do, please send us reports: www.goodguides.com).

Appledore [TQ9529]
Black Lion [The Street]: Unpretentious village pub, cosy and warm, with huge range of good value generous food all day esp local fish, partitioned eating area, friendly staff, three or four changing real ales; tables out by attractive village street *(Richard Fendick, CJ)*

Ashford [TQ0671]
County [High St]: Spreading open-plan Wetherspoons, pleasant booths, book-lined walls and historical displays, cheerful staff, very reasonably priced food, well kept beers *(Klaus and Elizabeth Leist)*

Aylesford [TQ7358]
☆ ***Little Gem*** [High St]: 12th-c pub, Kent's smallest, cosy and quaint unassuming survivor, with tiny front door, lots of atmosphere, ancient beams and masonry, interesting upper gallery; Fullers London Pride, Harveys Best and Charles Wells Bombardier, farm ciders, bar lunch and evening snacks, flame-effect fire; children welcome, SkyTV *(Kevin Thorpe, LYM)*

Barfrestone [TR2650]
☆ ***Yew Tree*** [off A256 N of Dover; or off A2 at Barham]: Country local tucked away behind huge yew tree, reopened under hospitable newish landlady, good unpretentious lunches Sat and Sun, chatty atmosphere, log fire, mix of old pine furniture on bare boards, cosy little dining room with another open fire, several well kept real ales, farm cider, good value wines; the church has wonderful Norman carvings *(LYM, I J and S A Bufton)*

Bethersden [TQ9239]
Bull [A28 E]: Refurbished pub opp village cricket ground, decent food from sandwiches and baked potatoes up, Shepherd Neame ales, open-style restaurant *(Colin and Janet Roe)*

Bishopsbourne [TR1852]
Mermaid [signed off A2]: Traditional welcoming unpretentious country local in same family for many years, simple food (not Sun) inc good filled rolls, well kept Shepherd Neame beers, small coal fire and darts in back public bar, no music or machines; lovely unspoilt Kentish village *(Kevin Thorpe)*

Bodsham [TR1045]
☆ ***Timber Batts***: 17th-c hilltop pub in lovely country, beams and big inglenook, good fresh plentiful food (all day wknds; Weds is fish day), good service, real ales such as Fullers London Pride and Charles Wells Naked Gold, annual beer festival, small public bar with pool; children welcome, Sun jazz; large garden with valley views *(Kevin Thorpe)*

Botolphs Bridge [TR1233]
Botolphs Bridge Inn [W of Hythe]: Handsome Edwardian local with airy and chatty open-plan bar, small dining room one end (children allowed here), big helpings of enjoyable home-made food with real chips, quick pleasant service, real ales such as Greene King IPA and Old Speckled Hen; games area, occasional barbecues in small garden *(Grahame Brooks)*

Boughton [TR0559]
Queens Head [The Street]: Neatly kept village pub named in 1703 for Queen Anne, Shepherd Neame real ales, pleasant service, table of magazines, good value food in civilised dining room; open all day Fri/Sat *(E G Parish)*

Boughton Aluph [TR0247]
☆ ***Flying Horse*** [Boughton Lees, just off A251 N of Ashford]: Interesting old pub with beams, shiny black panelling, stone-arched windows, two ancient glass-covered wells, big inglenook log fire, well kept Courage Best, Fullers London Pride and Greene King, good wines, traditional games, food (maybe not Mon, limited Tues) from sandwiches up; piped music; open all day, children in back dining area, tables in spacious rose-filled garden, barbecues and bat and trap *(Lynn Sharpless, LYM, Colin and Janet Roe)*

Boughton Monchelsea [TQ7848]
Red House [take Chart rd (Forge Lane) off A229 at Cross-at-Hand, then after 1¾ miles left into Hermitage Lane]: Well kept changing ales such as Hampshire, Oakham and Charles Wells Bombardier, Liefmanns Kriek on tap, continental bottled beers with their dedicated glasses, simple food, friendly staff, separate bar with pool and big-screen sports TV, children's area with games; small campsite *(Peter Meister)*

Boughton Street [TR0559]
☆ ***White Horse*** [nr M2 junction 7; The Street]: Carefully restored dark-beamed bars and timbered dining room, well prepared food all day inc early breakfast and good value carvery Thurs-Sat, well kept Shepherd Neame beers, decent wines, good tea and coffee, pleasant atmosphere; children welcome, tables in garden, bedrooms (not cheap; back ones quieter) *(Colin and Sandra Tann, LYM)*

Boxley [TQ7758]
Kings Arms [1¾ miles from M20 junction 7; opp church]: Cosy locally popular country dining pub, largely 16th/17th-c, low beams, red chesterfields by huge fireplace, well kept Adnams, Fullers London Pride and Gales HSB, good choice of sensibly priced straightforward food (all day Sun) from sandwiches and ploughman's up; may be piped music, quiet dogs allowed; good play area, open all day, pretty village, pleasant walks *(Gordon Neighbour, Ian Phillips)*

Brasted [TQ4654]
White Hart [High St (A25)]: Roomy Vintage Inn newly refurbished, several snug areas taking their mood from the original Battle of Britain bar (with signatures and mementoes of Biggin Hill fighter pilots), beams and log fires, well kept Bass and Tetleys, good choice of wine and fresh orange juice; children welcome, big neatly kept garden with well spaced tables and play area; bedrooms, pretty village with several antiques shops *(LM, LYM, Christopher Maxse)*

Bridge [TR1854]
Plough & Harrow [High St]: Particularly well kept Shepherd Neame in small 17th-c two-bar local, coal fire in lounge, lots of sporting prints on brick walls, good wine choice, darts and games in public bar; open all day Sat *(Kevin Thorpe, Roger Mardon)*
Broadstairs [TR3967]
Neptunes Hall [Harbour St]: Friendly early 19th-c two-bar local with Shepherd Neame beers, attractive bow windows and old bar, carpeted back lounge with open fire, lunchtime snacks; no juke box or piped music though occasional live folk (daily during Aug folk festival) or piped music, friendly staff and locals; enclosed terrace, open all day *(Kevin Thorpe)*
Canterbury [TR1556]
Bat & Ball [Old Dover Rd]: Handy for cricket ground, homely and traditional L-shaped bar with well kept ales such as Adnams, Shepherd Neame and Wolf, enjoyable food *(Tracey and Stephen Groves)*
Canterbury Tales [The Friars, just off main St Peters St pedestrian area]: Popular airy pub/bistro with well kept Greene King IPA, Fullers London Pride, Shepherd Neame and two guest beers, decent food in bar and upstairs bistro, theatrical memorabilia (quick service if you're going to a play or concert), cheerful young staff; may be piped jazz, busier with young people evening; live music nights, open all day *(Kevin Thorpe, John and Lynn Busenbark)*
Millers Arms [St Radigunds St]: Welcoming pub prettily set in quiet street near river and handy for Marlow Theatre, recently pleasantly refurbished by Shepherd Neame, several rooms, their beers well kept, good wine choice; decent bedrooms *(David and Betty Gittins)*
Old Gate [New Dover Rd]: Reliable Vintage Inn, several distinct areas, stripped brick and beams, open fires, bookshelves, old prints, dried flowers, old wooden table and chairs, reasonably priced food all day, fine wine choice, Bass, well trained staff, no music; bedrooms *(Kevin Thorpe)*
☆ *Olde Beverlie* [St Stephens Green; A290 from centre, then right at Tyler Hill/Univ sign]: Built in 1570 with adjoining almshouses, open-plan rooms with beams, wattle and daub walls, flagstones, old prints, brasses, jugs etc, enjoyable food (not Sun evening) from good value interesting sandwiches up, Shepherd Neame ales and good wine choice, good mix of customers, small restaurant; piped music; nicely restored walled courtyard garden with bat and trap *(Kevin Thorpe, David and Betty Gittins)*
Pilgrims [The Friars]: Partly 18th-c hotel handy for theatre, busy bar with well kept real ales, well presented food, quick accommodating staff; bedrooms *(Tony and Lyn Cassidy)*
Simple Simons [Church Lane, St Radigunds]: Step down into basic pub in 14th-c building, great beams, broad floorboards and flagstones, two woodburners, dim-lit upstairs banqueting hall, up to six well kept ales inc Bass, impressive pump clip collection, simple lunchtime food inc good value sandwiches, more studenty evening; good piped classical music in the daytime, live blues Tues, jazz Thurs; tables in courtyard, open all day *(Kevin Thorpe)*
Chartham Hatch [TR1056]
☆ *Chapter Arms* [New Town St]: Sizeable pub overlooking orchards with nice teak and some furniture in the garden and lots of flowering tubs, pots and baskets; heavily hop-hung ceiling with brass instruments and twinkling lights tucked between them, wheelbacks and cushioned wall seats, flowers and candles on tables on patterned carpet, quiet piped music, and Harveys Best, and Shepherd Neame Master Brew and Goldings on handpump; decent wine; restaurant through doorway decorated in lilac, green and silver; live 60s music last Tues of month; friendly service *(John and Elizabeth Thomason, Kath Libbert, BB)*
Chatham [TQ7569]
☆ *Harbourmasters House* [Historic Dockyard]: Right in the dockyard World Heritage Site, handsome little two-room building overlooking Medway, refurbished and run by nearby Flagship Brewery, their beers, sandwiches and rolls, old prints and naval items, no music; seats out by river wall; open to public 11-6 (members only later) *(Kevin Thorpe, Richard Gibbs)*
Chiddingstone Causeway [TQ5247]
Greyhound [Charcott, off back rd to Weald]: Clean and comfortable traditional local in quiet hamlet, very friendly and unpretentious, with enjoyable home cooking (not Tues, and all done fresh so can take a while) inc nice crisp veg, well kept Adnams, Flowers IPA and Harveys, good coffee, Sun bar and table nibbles; barbecue and tables out in front *(Tina and David Woods-Taylor, Angela Gibson, LM)*
Little Brown Jug [B2027]: Under new management and recently completely refurbished, spacious and comfortable, prompt welcoming service, generous sandwiches and reasonably priced blackboard meals, three guest beers; attractive garden with play area, bedrooms *(Alan M Pring, John Branston)*
Chilham [TR0753]
☆ *Woolpack* [off A28/A252; The Street]: Charming unfussy décor, pews, sofa, little armchairs, good inglenook log fires, good value food from soup and sandwiches up, cheerful welcoming service, well kept Shepherd Neame ales; children allowed in restaurant, bedrooms, delightful village *(John Sewell, LYM, Gloria Bax)*
Chillenden [TR2653]
☆ *Griffins Head*: Good-sized helpings of consistently appealing food in attractive beamed, timbered and flagstoned 14th-c pub with three comfortable rooms, Shepherd Neame real ales, good choice of house wines, big log fire, local regulars; small children not welcome; pleasant garden surrounded by wild roses, Sun barbecues, attractive countryside *(R J Davies, S Keens, Peter and Patricia Burton)*
Chipstead [TQ4956]
Bricklayers Arms [Chevening Rd]: Attractive old local overlooking lake and green, heavily beamed bar with open fire and fine racehorse

painting, larger back restaurant, good choice of appetising food (not Sun evening), full range of Harveys beers tapped from casks behind long counter, good atmosphere *(Gloria Bax)*

Conyer Quay [TQ9664]

☆ ***Ship***: Rambling collection of cosily nautical little rooms in cheery unspoilt creekside pub, good straightforward bar snacks (not wknds), friendly service, well kept Adnams and other beers, tea, coffee and hot chocolate, decent wines, upstairs rooms reworked as restaurant with popular evening meals and good value Sun lunch; open all day, tables out facing waterfront – road can flood at spring tides *(LYM, Glenn and Louise Hamilton, Eddie Edwards)*

Cowden [TQ4640]

☆ ***Fountain*** [High St; village usually signed off A264 and B2026]: Small unpretentious country local in pretty village with sensibly short choice of unusually good interesting food, well kept Harveys, Larkins and guests, decent wines, friendly licensees, darts, woodburner in small beamed back dining room; walkers and dogs welcome, annual flower show *(Ken Arthur, Robin Drummond, Derek Thomas, BB)*

☆ ***Queens Arms*** [Cowden Pound; junction B2026 with Markbeech rd]: Unspoilt and warmly welcoming two-room country pub like something from the 1930s, with splendid landlady, well kept Brakspears, darts; may be cl wkdy lunchtimes *(Pete Baker, RWC, Kevin Thorpe, the Didler)*

Crockham Hill [TQ4450]

Royal Oak: Well kept village pub with wide choice of enjoyable food from sensibly priced baguettes up, well kept Shepherd Neame Spitfire, good atmosphere; handy for walks *(G T Brewster)*

Crouch [TQ6155]

Chequers [Basted Lane]: Clean and bright, with limited choice of enjoyable food at reasonable prices, friendly newish licensees, efficient service, popular restaurant; nice sunny terrace *(Ken Arthur)*

Dartford [TQ5473]

Malt Shovel [Darenth Rd]: Quiet and welcoming old pub, unspoilt public bar and plush lounge with separate dining room, three well kept Youngs ales, good choice of food, old cameras hanging from ceiling *(Quentin and Carol Williamson)*

Denton [TR2147]

Jackdaw [A260 Canterbury—Folkestone]: Imposing brick and flint pub with comfortable open-plan bar decorated in cream and book-room red with RAF photographs and books, five real ales such as Cameron, Shepherd Neame Spitfire and Charles Wells Bombardier, good friendly staff, large back restaurant; quiet piped music; children welcome, tables in pleasant garden, handy for nearby Battle of Britain museum at Hawkinge, open all day *(Kevin Thorpe)*

Detling [TQ7958]

Cock Horse [The Street]: Pretty tiled and weatherboarded village local, enjoyable food in bars and back restaurant, real ales, friendly service; tables in yard behind *(Richard Gibbs)*

Dover [TR3141]

New Mogul [Chapel Pl, off York St South roundabout]: Constantly changing well kept ales tapped from the cask, lunchtime snacks inc good sandwiches, open-plan lounge with wicker furniture, small harbour-view public bar area, pool and pub games (no music or machines); tables outside, open all day *(Kevin Thorpe)*

Dunks Green [TQ6152]

☆ ***Kentish Rifleman***: Cosy early 16th-c two-bar local (the big stone-arched vaulted cellar may even be Roman); wide choice of good freshly cooked food inc traditional puddings, welcoming service, well kept ales such as Harveys and Charles Wells Bombardier, decent wine, plenty of character, no machines; dogs welcome; plenty of seats in unusually well designed garden behind *(LM, Carl and Jackie Cranmer)*

Eastling [TQ9656]

☆ ***Carpenters Arms*** [off A251 S of M2 junction 6, via Painters Forstal; The Street]: Pretty, cosy and cottagey 14th-c oak-beamed pub with big fireplaces front and back, welcoming staff, decent food (not Sun evening) inc good generous Sun lunch, well kept Shepherd Neame beers; children allowed in restaurant, some seats outside, small but well equipped bedrooms in separate building, huge breakfast *(LYM, Jan and Alan Summers)*

Edenbridge [TQ4446]

☆ ***Olde Crown*** [High St]: Pleasant Tudor pub with good choice of food in bar and restaurant, four real ales, tables out on side terrace, six bedrooms with own bathrooms, handy for Chartwell etc; one of the last pubs to have kept its 'gallows' inn-sign stretching right across the road *(Alan M Pring, LYM)*

Egerton [TQ8946]

Queens Arms [Forstal Rd]: 200-year-old village local, simple menu, friendly staff, seven real ales such as Fullers London Pride, three from Goachers, Charles Wells Bombardier and one brewed for the pub by Rother Valley; piped music; garden, open all day summer *(Kevin Thorpe)*

Elham [TR1743]

Rose & Crown [High St]: Small cosy inn, partly 16th-c, quiet and unpretentious, with comfortable sofa by stove, pub cat and dogs, well kept ales, food that's worth the price, evening restaurant; tables in garden, bedrooms *(Robert Coomber)*

Eynsford [TQ5365]

☆ ***Malt Shovel*** [Station Rd]: Neatly kept spacious old-fashioned dining pub, child-friendly and handy for castles and Roman villa, dark panelling, good choice of good value generous freshly cooked food – proper pies and curries, venison and fish and seafood (lobster tank) all praised; well kept ales inc Fullers, good choice of wine by the glass, quick helpful service, nice atmosphere; car park across busy road *(Kevin Flack, Simon and Gillian Wales, Pat and Tony Martin)*

Faversham [TR0161]

Albion [Front Brents]: The gifted French

chef/landlord has now left, but this is still an attractively light and airy waterside refuge, with solid pine furnishings and nautical decorations on its pale green walls; more traditional food now, from sandwiches up, Shepherd Neame ales such as Spitfire and Late Red from the nearby brewery, friendly efficient service; children welcome in restaurant area, disabled lavatories, picnic-sets out on riverside walkway, open all day summer *(LYM)*

Anchor [Abbey St]: Smallish friendly two-bar local in attractive old street near quay and station, several well kept Shepherd Neame ales, good quiet relaxed atmosphere, bare boards, open fires, settles and part-panelling, low-priced food all day, candlelit tiled eating area; piped radio; music nights, a couple of picnic-sets outside, open all day *(the Didler, Kevin Thorpe)*

Bull [Tanners St]: Friendly local with bat and trap in garden *(Kevin Flack)*

Elephant [The Mall]: Picturesque flower-decked terrace town pub now with two well kept Flagship ales, three guests inc a Mild, local farm cider, simple lunchtime food and Sun roasts, thoughtful staff, unpretentiously attractive furnishings on stripped boards, central fireplace, no smoking dining room; piped music, darts; suntrap terrace with summer barbecues, open all day *(the Didler, Kevin Thorpe)*

Sun [West St]: Roomy and rambling old-world 15th-c weatherboarded town pub with good unpretentious atmosphere in small low-ceilinged rooms, good value low-priced lunchtime food, well kept Shepherd Neame beers inc seasonal one from nearby brewery, good service; piped music; open all day, tables in pleasant back courtyard, interesting street *(Tony and Wendy Hobden, the Didler)*

Fordwich [TR1859]

☆ ***Fordwich Arms*** [off A28 in Sturry]: Civilised and handsome pub, clean and well cared for, with food from sandwiches and baked potatoes up, well kept real ales, open fire in attractive fireplace, dining room; spacious terrace and garden by River Stour, ancient town hall opp worth visiting *(Ruth and Paul Lawrence, LYM)*

Gillingham [TQ7768]

Frog & Toad [Burnt Oak Terr]: Busy and welcoming backstreet local revamped and renamed by ex local radio journalist, three or four well kept real ales, fine choice of mainly Belgian bottled beers, occasional beer festivals, perhaps free midweek snacks; pool, darts, no juke box or machines *(Peter Scillitoe)*

Goathurst Common [TQ4952]

Woodman: Large mainly no smoking Chef & Brewer, decent food and wine, Courage Directors and guest beers, well meaning young staff; delightful walking country *(Tina and David Woods-Taylor)*

Goudhurst [TQ7337]

Chequer Tree [A262 E]: Roomy comfortable main bar, enjoyable nicely presented food inc interesting dishes, well kept Harveys ales, friendly service, conservatory *(Jan and Alan Summers)*

☆ ***Green Cross*** [Station Rd (A262 W)]: Good interesting food, particularly fish and seafood, well kept Greene King IPA and Old Speckled Hen, Harveys and a guest such as Larkins, good wines, roomy and attractive back restaurant with good napkins, tablecloths etc, contrasting simple bar with open fire, informal service; bedrooms light and airy, good value; very handy for Finchcocks *(Mrs Barbara Wheatley, BB, Uta and John Owlett, Derek Thomas, Tina and David Woods-Taylor)*

Gravesend [TQ6474]

New Falcon [West St]: Handsome and well kept Georgian house by Tilbury ferry pier, cheap beer and food inc big bargain baguettes, historic river photographs; tables in garden, river view *(Charles Gysin)*

Groombridge [TQ5337]

Junction Inn [Station Rd, off B2110]: Village pub refurbished by new owners in airy yet friendly up-to-date style, good food inc interesting dishes, well kept Harveys, Fullers London Pride and Gales HSB, good wines; pleasant garden with boules *(Lachlan Milligan)*

Hadlow [TQ6252]

☆ ***Artichoke*** [Hamptons, 4 miles SE of Plaxtol; OS Sheet 188 map ref 627524]: Dating from 13th c, with ancient low beams, high-backed wooden settles, some unusual wrought-iron glass-topped tables, huge welcoming inglenook log fire, gleaming brass, country pictures and bric-a-brac, friendly capable service, good helpings of popular food inc good home-made pies, no smoking restaurant, well kept Adnams, Fullers London Pride, Greene King Abbot and Youngs Special, good range of spirits; children in eating area, seats outside inc pews in canopied front arbour, quiet rural setting; may keep credit card if you're running a tab; cl Sun evening, Mon *(J Hale, Sue Demont, Tim Barrow, BB, Martin Jennings, Mike Horler)*

Halstead [TQ4861]

Cock [Shoreham Lane]: Neatly kept open-plan linked rooms, well kept Fullers London Pride and Marstons Pedigree, welcoming staff, usual food from sandwiches, good ploughman's and baked potatoes to freshly prepared main dishes inc some interesting specials, log fire *(LM)*

Hawkenbury [TQ8045]

Hawkenbury Inn [Hawkenbury Rd]: Recently refurbished with plain wood furnishings on bare boards, welcoming atmosphere, half a dozen well kept ales inc local ones, good food at sensible prices; tables in garden *(Jan and Alan Summers)*

Hawkhurst [TQ7531]

Wellington Arms [Gills Green, just off A229 N]: Pretty tucked-away country pub dating from 16th c, varied enjoyable lunchtime food from sandwiches up, reasonable prices, five well kept ales inc Harveys, two farm ciders, restaurant *(Ken Arthur)*

Heaverham [TQ5758]

Chequers [Watery Lane]: Cottagey old pub with friendly locals' bar, enjoyable food from interesting baguettes up in attractive main bar, particularly well kept Shepherd Neame, popular Sun lunch, attached beamed restaurant; pleasant tables outside *(Lynn Sharpless, Gwyn Jones)*

Herne Bay [TR1768]
Rose [Mortimer St]: Spick and span small traditional pub with simple but good freshly made food (not Sun evening), reasonably priced well kept Shepherd Neame; can get crowded and smoky wknds *(David and Betty Gittins)*
Hernhill [TR0660]
☆ ***Red Lion*** [off A299 via Dargate, or A2 via Boughton Street and Staplestreet]: Pretty Tudor inn by church and attractive village green, densely beamed and flagstoned, log fires, pine tables, no smoking upstairs restaurant, enjoyable food, well kept Fullers London Pride and Shepherd Neame with a guest such as Marstons Pedigree, decent house wines, attentive staff; children welcome, garden with boules and good play area, bedrooms *(LYM, Brian Skelcher, Mr and Mrs Thomas)*
Hollingbourne [TQ8455]
Dirty Habit [B2163, off A20]: Dim-lit ancient pub under new regime, lots of different old kitchen and dining tables and chairs, nooks, crannies and uneven floors, well kept if not cheap ales, decent house wines, bar food, flame-effect gas fire in big fireplace; games area, piped music may be loud, no dogs; peaceful spot on North Downs Way *(LYM)*
Windmill [B2163, off A20]: Comfortable and welcoming, with various different levels and alcoves around central servery, enjoyable food inc good sandwiches, well kept real ales, quick service even when packed; sunny garden with play area *(Peter and Giff Bennett)*
Ide Hill [TQ4851]
Cock [off B2042 SW of Sevenoaks]: Pretty village-green pub with well kept Greene King, good value straightforward food (not Sun evening) from sandwiches and ploughman's up, fine log fire, bar billiards; piped music, no children; some seats out in front, handy for Chartwell and nearby walks – so gets busy *(LYM, DJH)*
Ightham Common [TQ5955]
Old House [Redwell, S of village; OS Sheet 188 map ref 591559]: Unspoilt and chatty two-room country local with no inn sign, bare bricks and beams, huge log fireplace filling one wall, basic furniture, four or five changing ales from all over, old cash register and small TV in side room; no food, music or machines, cl wkdy lunchtimes, opens 7 (later Tues) *(JP, PP, the Didler, Kevin Thorpe)*
Ivy Hatch [TQ5854]
☆ ***Plough*** [off A227 N of Tonbridge]: Restaurant rather than pub, often fully booked, with wide choice of consistently good food, fastidious French cooking, good neat thoughtful staff, impressive range of reasonably priced wines (and well kept Greene King IPA), attractive candlelit surroundings – upmarket in a friendly informal style, and priced to match; delightful conservatory and garden *(Christopher and Elise Way, Mary Ellen Cummings, LYM, Derek Thomas, Di and Mike Gillam)*
Kemsing [TQ5659]
Rising Sun [Cotmans Ash Lane]: Attractive old country pub like something out of one of H E Bates's lighter works, interesting range of generous bar food at alluring prices from good snacks up, several guest beers inc ones from small breweries, darts, children's room; informal garden with play things *(John and Elspeth Howell)*
Kingston [TR2051]
☆ ***Black Robin*** [valley rd, off A2 Canterbury—Dover at Barham sign]: Good range of well presented food in friendly old pub with Fullers London Pride and Greene King IPA, good wine choice, cheerful staff, wooden floors and wall benches, stripped brick, candles on chunky old pine tables, old prints and paintings for sale, flowers, low lighting; may be piped music; tables in large garden; cl Sun evenings and Mon until Easter *(Kevin Thorpe)*
Kippings Cross [TQ6439]
Blue Boys [A21 just S of Pembury bypass]: Welcoming and properly pubby, with well organised good bar food, bargain 9-pint beer jugs, good service; reasonably priced bedrooms, open all day (from 7 for breakfast) *(E G Parish)*
Knockholt [TQ4658]
Crown [Main Rd]: Attractive and cheerful, old-fashioned and unpretentious, with dark ochre décor, colourful house plants, good value food inc sandwiches and sensibly priced home-made hot dishes, well kept Adnams Bitter and Broadside, friendly service, second bar good for walkers; picnic-sets on lawn *(LM)*
Lamberhurst [TQ6735]
☆ ***Brown Trout*** [B2169, off A21 nr entrance to Scotney Castle]: Popular dining pub specialising in briskly served fish, lots of steaks too, sauce and vinegar bottles on tables in biggish extension off small beamed bar, well kept Fullers London Pride and Harveys, fair choice of decent wines, friendly staff, good log fire, children in eating areas; can be very busy wknds; picnic-sets in large safe garden with play area, pretty window boxes and flower tubs in summer, open all day Sun and summer *(B J Harding, Jeff Cameron, Ian Phillips, Roy and Margaret Jones, BB)*
Chequers [A21]: Refurbished (after 2000 floods) with low limed beams and standing timbers in fresh light open-plan main bar, parquet or flagstone floor, big leather sofa on turkey rug, nice mix of sturdy tables and dining chairs, big inglenook log fire, Shepherd Neame real ales, good house wines, daily papers, ambitious food, similar public bar; piped jazz or pop; some picnic-sets in small back garden *(BB, Colin and Janet Roe)*
Elephants Head [Hook Green; B2169 towards T Wells]: Ancient rambling timber-framed country pub, well kept ales inc Harveys Best and Old, friendly staff, wide food choice, heavy beams, brick or oak flooring, big inglenook log fire, plush-cushioned pews etc; darts and fruit machine in small side area, may be quiet piped music; picnic-sets in big back garden with terrace and impressive play area (peaceful view), and by front green; near Bayham Abbey and Owl House, popular with families wknds, quiz nights etc *(Ian Phillips, Peter Meister, LYM)*
Linton [TQ7550]
☆ ***Bull*** [A229 S of Maidstone]: Nice old carpeted

bar with some carved settles and fine fireplace, oddly contrasting bare-boards room with café-style chrome and wood furniture, well kept Shepherd Neame Bitter and Spitfire, enjoyable food (not Sun evening) from baguettes and sandwiches to steak and popular Sun roast; children welcome, lovely views from informal side garden, back terrace, open all day wknds *(Sally Anne and Peter Goodale, Ian Phillips, Sarah Davis, Rod Lambert, LYM)*

Littlebourne [TR2057]

☆ ***King William IV*** [High St]: Welcoming new licensees doing good fresh food from well filled sandwiches to imaginative meals inc fish collected daily from landlord's fishing family, fair choice of wines by the glass, spotless roomy straightforward bar with restaurant area; handy for Howletts Zoo *(anon)*

Loose [TQ7552]

Chequers [Old Loose Hill]: Attractive neatly kept riverside pub, popular under new management for good freshly made lunches; quick friendly service, well kept Badger K&B, Fullers London Pride and Harveys, nice atmosphere *(Comus and Sarah Elliott)*

Lower Rainham [TQ8167]

Three Mariners: Friendly and neatly kept nautical-theme pub handy for Thames mudflat walks in Riverside Country Park, real ales such as Courage Best, Fullers London Pride and Charles Wells Bombardier, reasonably priced food *(Ian Phillips)*

Lynsted [TQ9460]

Black Lion: 16th-c pub extended in keeping with original core, settles and old tables, plenty of old advertisements and something of a 1950s/60s feel, freshly made straightforward food, four real ales inc Goachers Mild and Crown Imperial Stout, Pawley's farm cider; well behaved children welcome, garden with play area *(Peter Scillitoe)*

Maidstone [TQ7656]

Pilot [Upper Stone St (A229)]: Busy old roadside inn, home-made bar food (not Sun), well kept Harveys Bitter, Mild and seasonal ales, whisky-water jugs hanging from ceiling, darts and pool; tables outside, boules *(the Didler, Sarah Davis, Rod Lambert)*

Rifle Volunteers [Wyatt St/Church St]: Unspoilt quiet coaching inn with good attractively priced home-made food, local Goachers Light, Mild and seasonal ales, no machines; tables outside *(the Didler)*

Martin [TR3347]

Old Lantern [The Street]: Good atmosphere in neatly kept bar with dining tables, hops on ceiling and candle holders, friendly helpful landlord, well kept Shepherd Neame, decent wines; sizeable play area and wendy house in sprawling pretty gardens, beautiful setting *(Gloria Bax)*

Matfield [TQ6642]

Standings Cross [Maidstone Rd]: Welcoming local with several Shepherd Neame beers, beams and panelling, leaded windows, scrubbed tables and darts in small front bar; cosy inglenook fireplace in attractive old back restaurant with good range of good value home-made food inc Sun lunch, pleasant helpful service; walkers and dogs welcome *(Ken Arthur)*

Newnham [TQ9557]

☆ ***Tapster*** [Parsonage Farm, Seed Rd]: Sympathetic pastiche of old building, candles and flowers on old tables in long bare-boards bistro/bar with big pots of ferns and huge end log fire, quiet atmosphere, well kept Goachers Gold Star, Orkney Dark Island, Timothy Taylors Landlord and changing guest beers, good if not cheap fresh food, friendly staff; dogs and children welcome, picnic-sets in big garden, open all day summer and wknds *(Kevin Thorpe, R E Davidson, RWC)*

Otford [TQ5359]

☆ ***Bull*** [High St]: Attractively laid out 15th-c Chef & Brewer, their usual huge food choice all day, decent wines, several quietly spacious rooms, log fires in two enormous fireplaces, friendly staff; nice garden *(Tina and David Woods-Taylor, Kevin Flack, Ken Arthur)*

Painters Forstal [TQ9958]

☆ ***Alma*** [signed off A2 at Ospringe]: Homely and attractive weatherboarded village local, busy but neat and tidy, with good steak and kidney pudding and other good value home cooking using local ingredients, well kept Shepherd Neame inc winter Porter, decent wines, cheerful helpful informal service, comfortable large-ish dining lounge, small bare-boards public bar; may be piped classical music; picnic-sets on lawn *(Glenn and Louise Hamilton, Barry and Verina Jones, Bob and Val Collman, J D M Rushworth, Tony Baldwin)*

Penshurst [TQ5243]

☆ ***Rock*** [Chiddingstone Hoath; OS Sheet 188 map ref 497431]: Charmingly old-fashioned pub, farmers and dogs in two spartan little beamed rooms, stripped brick and timbers, wonky brick floors, woodburner in inglenook, well kept Larkins from the nearby brewery, good blackboard food choice (not Sun evening), friendly staff, ring the bull (with a real bull's head); children welcome, no mobile phones; front terrace, back garden, beautiful countryside nearby, cl Mon *(Lachlan Milligan, Kevin Thorpe)*

Pett Bottom [TR1652]

☆ ***Duck*** [off B2068 S of Canterbury, via Lower Hardres]: Long crisply refurbished bare-boards room with pine panelling and wine racks, good blackboard choice of usual bar food from sandwiches and baked potatoes up, well kept Greene King IPA and Abbot with a guest beer, decent wines, welcoming attentive service, two log fires, restaurant; piped music; children and dogs welcome, tables in sizeable pretty garden, attractive spot, open all day at least in summer, new bedrooms *(F J Robinson, LYM, Kevin Thorpe, M Matson)*

Petteridge [TQ6640]

Hopbine: Friendly village local, tidied up without being spoilt, enjoyable generous food, well kept Badger ales inc K&B, darts; good-sized side garden *(Peter Meister)*

Plaxtol [TQ6054]

☆ ***Golding Hop*** [Sheet Hill (½ mile S of Ightham,

between A25 and A227)]: Secluded country pub, good for families in summer with suntrap streamside lawn; small and simple inside, with well kept changing ales on handpump or tapped from the cask, local farm ciders (sometimes even their own), limited basic bar food (not Mon evening), woodburner; portable TV for big sports events, bar billiards, game machine; well fenced play area *(JP, PP, LYM, Pat and Tony Martin, the Didler, Hugh Roberts)*

Pluckley [TQ9245]

Black Horse [The Street]: Attractive old house with open-plan bar, roomy back dining area, hops on beams, vast inglenook, cheery atmosphere, wide food choice from baguettes up (just roasts on Sun), well kept ales inc Fullers London Pride; piped music may be loud, big-screen TV, fruit machine, children allowed if eating; picnic-sets in spacious informal garden by tall sycamores, good walks, open all day Fri-Sun *(Patricia Beebe, Di and Mike Gillam, Catherine and Richard Preston, BB, JP, PP, Gerry and Rosemary Dobson)*

☆ ***Rose & Crown*** [Mundy Bois – spelled Monday Boys on some maps]: Welcoming quietly set pub very popular for good generous meals inc imaginative dishes and homely puddings in nicely furnished and cosy candlelit dining room, smallish saloon bar, good bar snacks esp notable baguettes, interesting sensibly priced wines and country wines, well kept Hook Norton Best and Shepherd Neame, farm cider, plenty of malt whiskies, helpful service; may be piped classical music, separate public bar with pool and TV, dogs welcome; garden with play area *(Kevin Thorpe, Michael Doswell, Colin and Janet Roe, I S Johnson, Tony and Katie Lewis)*

Ramsgate [TR3865]

Artillery Arms [West Cliff Rd]: Chatty open-plan corner local with Charles Wells Bombardier, Greene King Abbot and adventurous changing guest ales such as local Gadds No 3, two farm ciders, doorstep sandwiches, straightforward two-level bar with artillery prints, cannons and recently restored stained-glass windows dating from Napoleonic wars; juke box can be intrusive, fruit machine; children and dogs welcome, quiz nights, open all day *(Kevin Thorpe, Ian Phillips)*

Ramsgate Royal Harbour Brewhouse & Bakery [Harbour Parade]: Belgian-style café-bar brewing two beers of their own (you can look round the brewery), also six Belgian imports on tap, over 100 in bottles, and Biddenden farm ciders; table service, bread and cakes baked all day, simple snacks and ploughman's too, open from 9 for tea and coffee (from 10 for alcohol); piped music; children welcome, tables out under cocktail parasols *(Kevin Thorpe)*

Ringlestone [TQ8755]

☆ ***Ringlestone*** [Ringlestone Rd, signed Doddington off B2163 NE of Hollingbourne]: Former monks' hospice, an inn by 1615, pleasantly furnished to match the appealing antiquity of its worn brick floor and stripped masonry, with a large and very attractive garden; plenty of well kept real ales, country wines and cider, children and well behaved dogs welcome, bedrooms, open all day wknds; can be very busy in summer (inc coach parties), piped pop music not really suiting it, and food now pricy for what you get; more reports please *(LYM)*

Sandgate [TR2035]

Ship [High St]: Old-fashioned two-room local with well kept ales such as Greene King IPA, Harveys Best, Timothy Taylors Landlord and Theakstons Old Peculier tapped from the cask, farm cider, decent fairly priced wine, good value plain plentiful food, good service; not smart but warm and friendly, barrel seats and tables, lots of nautical prints and posters, sea views from seats out behind; piped radio, occasional live music *(Colin and Janet Roe, Kevin Thorpe, BB)*

Sandwich [TR3358]

Admiral Owen [Strand St/High St]: Fine heavily beamed 15th-c inn opp ancient Stour toll bridge, friendly helpful staff, log fires, Greene King ales and home-made food from good sandwiches up; medieval banquets, live music; open all day *(B Hurford, Kevin Thorpe)*

Kings Arms [Strand St]: Unpretentious pub with striking Elizabethan carving inside and out, welcoming service, wide choice of enjoyable food in bar and restaurant (where children allowed), well kept Shepherd Neame; traditional games and pool in public bar *(Bob and Margaret Holder, LYM)*

Red Cow [Moat Sole; 100 yds from Guildhall, towards Woodnesborough]: Carefully refurbished open-plan pub with separate dining room, old beams and pictures, five changing ales such as Boddingtons, Fullers London Pride, and Greene King Abbot and Old Speckled Hen, good value food, good atmosphere, friendly staff, lovely log fire, old local pictures; soft piped music; guide dogs only, picnic-tables outside with garden bar and hanging baskets *(Kevin Thorpe)*

Selling [TR0356]

☆ ***White Lion*** [off A251 S of Faversham (or exit roundabout, M2 junction 7); The Street]: 17th-c pub with friendly helpful staff, wide choice of popular food, well kept Shepherd Neame Bitter and Spitfire, decent wines, comfortable bar with two big log fires (one with a spit), pews on stripped boards, unusual semicircular bar counter, back restaurant; children welcome; rustic picnic-sets in attractive garden, colourful hanging baskets *(LYM, Tony and Katie Lewis)*

Shipbourne [TQ5952]

Chaser [Stumble Hill]: Attractive colonial-style hotel in lovely spot by village church and green, looks like settling down under new tenants; small cheerful public bar, second bar with stripped pine tables laid for eating (traditional pub food), friendly service, Greene King beers, log fires; tables outside, separate entrance to hotel with high-vaulted restaurant, comfortable bedrooms *(Derek Thomas, Peter Meister, Hugh Roberts)*

Shoreham [TQ5161]

Kings Arms [Church St]: Pretty and popular, with pleasant service, decent usual food from good value ploughman's to roast of the day, some bookable tables, plates and brasses; picnic-sets outside, quaint unspoilt village on River Darent, good walks *(Alan M Pring)*

Two Brewers [High St]: Busy unpretentious local with good choice of substantial value food, friendly efficient staff, wide choice of beers and ciders; good for walkers, but no dogs *(Ken Arthur)*

Smarden [TQ8743]

☆ ***Bell*** [from Smarden follow lane between church and Chequers, then left at T-junction; or from A274 take unsignposted turn E a mile N of B2077 to Smarden]: Pretty rose-covered 17th-c inn with striking chimneys, dim-lit snug low-beamed little rooms, ancient brick and flagstones or quarry tiles, pews and the like, warm inglenooks; no smoking room, end games area; simple bar food, wide choice of real ales, local cider, country wines, winter mulled wine; very pleasant mature garden, simple bedrooms *(the Didler, Peter Meister, JP, PP, Colin and Janet Roe, LYM)*

Southfleet [TQ6270]

Manor Farm Barn [New Barn Rd]: Shepherd Neame pub with enjoyable food in bar and pricier restaurant, real ale *(Thomas Neate)*

St Margaret's at Cliffe [TR3544]

Smugglers [High St]: Friendly staff in tiny bar, good cooking with a hispanic bias inc good value baguettes, attractive dining room and conservatory; tables in garden *(John and Elspeth Howell)*

St Margaret's Bay [TR3844]

Coastguard: Tremendous views to France from cheery and lively modernised seaside pub, food inc good fish and chips and more ambitious dishes; children and dogs welcome, lots of tables on balcony with pretty hanging baskets and other plants, below NT cliff and near Pines Garden; more reports on new regime please *(LYM, Oliver and Sue Rowell)*

St Mary in the Marsh [TR0627]

Star [opp church]: Relaxed and remote down-to-earth pub, Tudor but very much modernised; friendly family service, two well kept Shepherd Neame beers, good choice of decent food, pool, darts and quiz teams; tables in nice garden, good value attractive beamed bedrooms with Romney Marsh views *(the Didler, John Happel)*

St Nicholas at Wade [TR2666]

Bell [just off A299]: Current licensees doing well in olde-worlde 16th-c pub, four beamed rooms, well kept Greene King ales, reasonably priced food from baguettes to good Sun lunch in bar and restaurant, friendly staff, open fires *(David and Betty Gittins)*

Staplehurst [TQ7647]

Stilebridge [Staplehurst Rd]: Impressively refurbished under new licensees, large bar/dining area with smaller dining area off and separate barn-style restaurant, enjoyable food, Greene King Abbot and Old Speckled Hen, good wine choice, good friendly service *(Robert Swanborough)*

Stone in Oxney [TQ9427]

Crown [off B2082 Iden—Tenterden]: New licensees in country pub with pews and big inglenook fireplace in homely bar, bay-windowed carpeted lounge, well kept Shepherd Neame and guest beers, food from baguettes up; piped music; children welcome, open all day wknds *(LYM)*

Stone Street [TQ5754]

☆ ***Padwell Arms*** [off A25 E of Sevenoaks, on Seal—Plaxtol by-road; OS Sheet 188 map ref 573546]: Small relaxed country local with long tables on colourful front terrace overlooking orchards, more in nice back garden, plenty of shade, good choice of genuinely home-cooked food using local produce (may stop promptly at 1.45pm), sensible prices, quick friendly service, particularly well kept Badger, Hook Norton Old Hooky and lots of changing guest beers, two local farm ciders, good coffee, open fires; dogs welcome, occasional live music and other events inc barbecues; good walks *(Gloria Bax, the Didler, Pat and Tony Martin)*

☆ ***Snail***: Well run dining pub, wide choice of reasonably priced food from ploughman's up, well kept Harveys, ad lib coffee, friendly staff, pleasant brasserie layout with some stripped stone, good atmosphere in bar part; attractive rambling garden *(Colin and Janet Roe, LYM, Derek Thomas, Oliver and Sue Rowell)*

Stowting [TR1242]

☆ ***Tiger*** [off B2068 N of M20 junction 11]: Partly 17th-c country pub with consistently good food using fresh local produce, attractive unpretentious furniture, candles on tables, rugs on bare boards, good log fire, entertaining landlord, good staff and friendly atmosphere, well kept Everards Tiger, Fullers London Pride, Theakstons Best and Old Peculier and guest beers, well behaved children allowed; tables outside with occasional barbecues, good jazz Mon (cl Mon lunchtime) *(LYM, P Abbott, Professor and Mrs J Fletcher)*

Tenterden [TQ8833]

☆ ***Eight Bells*** [High St]: Old inn doing well under current management, emphasis on good value food from imaginative starters and specials to three fixed-price menus, young helpful and patient staff, restful traditional long bar, central courtyard glazed in as further no smoking eating area; easy wheelchair access, good value old-world beamed bedrooms, tasty breakfast *(I S Johnson, John Happel, David and Elizabeth Briggs)*

☆ ***White Lion*** [High St]: Tidily restored 16th-c inn, beams and timbers, open fires, books and fishing memorabilia, good service, wide choice of generous popular food inc huge fish and chips, Bass and changing ales such as Shepherd Neame Spitfire and Wadworths 6X, good choice of sensibly priced wines, smart back panelled restaurant; dogs welcome, wknd nights the bar can get crowded with young people; 15 comfortable bedrooms, tables on terrace overlooking street, open all day *(Kevin Thorpe, Kevin Blake, Nigel B Thompson, E G Parish, K J Diamond, John Beeken)*

William Caxton [West Cross; top of High St]: Cosy and friendly 15th-c oak-beamed local, big inglenook log fire, wide choice of enjoyable food made by licensees in two-room bar or pleasant restaurant, Shepherd Neame beers inc seasonal; children welcome, tables in attractive front area, open all day, bedrooms *(Colin and Janet Roe, the Didler)*

Woolpack [High St]: Striking-looking unpretentious 15th-c inn with pleasant staff, several oak-beamed rooms inc family dining room, inglenook log fires, good generous home-cooked food, well kept Boddingtons and Harveys, decent coffee, plenty of locals; open all day; comfortable bedrooms *(Colin and Janet Roe, Klaus and Elizabeth Leist)*

Thurnham [TQ8057]

Black Horse [not far from M20 junction 7; off A249 at Detling]: Reworked as popular restauranty dining pub, huge choice inc lunchtime snack meals, friendly atmosphere, small bar where dogs but not children allowed; live music Weds or Fri; nice views, near Pilgrims Way *(Nigel B Thompson, Carl and Jackie Cranmer)*

Toys Hill [TQ4751]

Fox & Hounds [off A25 in Brasted, via Brasted Chart and The Chart]: Mrs Pelling, who made this country pub with its lovely garden such an enjoyable old-fashioned retreat (and a very popular main entry), has alas retired, and it's all change now – out with the charmingly domestic old furnishings and even the darts, and in with more of a modernised food-oriented operation (some oaf has even nicked the classic old wooden till); may turn out to be good, but will certainly be different *(LYM)*

Tunbridge Wells [TQ5839]

Opera House [Mount Pleasant Rd]: Large Wetherspoons pub impressively restored to its glorious 1900s opera-house layout (had been a bingo hall later), with original circle and stalls, stage lighting and ornate ceiling; Courage Directors, Theakstons Best and good range of guest beers, usual cheap Wetherspoons food, no smoking area, no piped music, silenced fruit machines, trivia; no children, can get crowded wknd evenings *(Pat and Tony Martin, Kevin Blake)*

☆ ***Royal Wells*** [Mount Ephraim]: Well lit, friendly and civilised hotel bar with comfortable settees and padded dining chairs, cosy corners, views over T Wells, three well kept Shepherd Neame beers, good value brasserie with enterprising lunchtime menu and some tables on terrace, friendly efficient staff; bar can get smoky, occasional live music; bedrooms *(Peter Meister, BB)*

Under River [TQ5551]

White Rock [SE of Sevenoaks, off B245]: Welcoming village pub with friendly mix of customers, small comfortable bar with hop-hung beams and back extension, well kept Fullers London Pride, Greene King K&B and Harveys, no piped music, dining area; children welcome, picnic-sets on back lawn, handy for Greensand Way (walkers asked to use side door) *(John and Elspeth Howell, Derek Thomas)*

Upnor [TQ7570]

Kings Arms [High St]: Inexpensive pub food, nice staff and service and well kept beer in old pub in delightful riverside village near Upnor Castle; good walks *(Bev Brown)*

Upstreet [TR2363]

☆ ***Grove Ferry*** [off A28 towards Preston]: Open-plan refurbishment with modern pictures on warm pastel walls, comfortable chairs and table with papers and magazines in front of central bar, bare-boards dining area behind with candles on tables, big fireplace, french windows to heated deck overlooking river; enjoyable food all day, four Shepherd Neame ales, good wines by the glass, pleasant uniformed staff; quiet piped music; handy for Stodmarsh national nature reserve *(John Beeken, Kevin Thorpe)*

Warehorne [TQ9832]

Woolpack [off B2067 nr Hamstreet]: Big neatly kept heavy-beamed 16th-c dining pub with very wide choice of good value food in rambling bar and big restaurant, popular carvery Weds evening (booking essential), elaborate puddings, well kept Greene King ales, decent wines, friendly staff, huge inglenook, plain games room; picnic-sets out overlooking quiet lane and meadow with lovely big beech trees, lots of flower tubs and little fountain *(I D Greenfield, BB)*

Wateringbury [TQ6953]

Wateringbury [Tonbridge Rd]: Large Chef & Brewer with warm and welcoming pubby feel, their usual food, polite and helpful young staff, Courage beers, huge log fires, daily papers, no smoking area; children welcome and well catered for, small back garden *(Tina and David Woods-Taylor, Peter and Margaret Lodge)*

West Malling [TQ6857]

Swan [Swan St]: Trendy décor inc flat-screen soundless videos and TV link to kitchen in action – good interesting food cooked with real care, cheerful helpful service *(Wendy Arnold)*

Westerham [TQ4454]

Grasshopper [The Green]: Old village pub with three linked bar areas, good log fire in back one, lots of bric-a-brac and Royal pictures, delft shelf of vinyl records, friendly efficient staff, attractive range of food until 6 from good value sandwiches to blackboard specials in bar and no smoking upstairs restaurant, well kept Courage Best and Harveys Best; children welcome, busy at lunchtime, open all day *(Tina and David Woods-Taylor, Hazel and Michael Duncombe, LM)*

Whitstable [TR1064]

Long Reach [Thanet Way]: Beefeater with wide range of reasonably priced food (can be a wait), children welcome, good décor and service *(Patricia and Norman Pollard, Keith and Chris O'Neill)*

Old Neptune [Marine Terr]: Seafront pub, busy, friendly and relaxed, real ales inc Greene King Old Speckled Hen, enjoyable food; dogs and children welcome, tables out on beach *(Kevin Flack)*

Pearsons [Sea Wall]: What people go for is the plain fresh fish and seafood in the cheerful little upstairs restaurant (with oblique sea view); bar (no view) has nautical décor, decent wines, Whitbreads-related ales, and a huge lobster tank in its lower flagstoned part, but also piped pop music with video screens; children welcome in eating areas, open all day wknds, just above shingle beach *(Kevin Flack, LYM, Keith and Chris O'Neill)*

Royal Naval Reserve [High St]: Friendly, comfortable and cosy, much roomier than it looks from outside, with well kept Shepherd Neame, good fresh local fish, spotless and attractive upstairs dining room *(Di and Mike Gillam, David and Betty Gittins)*

Wickhambreaux [TR2258]

Rose [The Green]: Dating from 14th c, across green from church and watermill; three small rooms, stripped brick, beams and panelling, log fire in big fireplace, good home-cooked food inc quickly served Sun roasts, Greene King IPA and Youngs Special; children welcome, garden with summer barbecues, hanging baskets *(Kevin Thorpe)*

Willesborough Street [TR0341]

Blacksmiths Arms [The Street]: Consistently good value generous food, friendly staff, well kept beer and wine *(Mr and Mrs D A Cox)*

Wormshill [TQ8757]

Blacksmiths Arms [handy for M20 junction 8]: Comfortably old-fashioned and relaxed renovation of isolated low-beamed country cottage, now home to Swale Brewery with four of their beers tapped from the cask; small cosy rooms, tiled or wood floors, log fire, friendly staff, good freshly made food from baguettes to Sun roasts with nice blackboard choice, no smoking beamed dining rooms; children allowed after 7 if eating, open all day wknds, cl Mon and lunchtime Tues-Thurs; large pretty garden with country views *(Kevin Thorpe)*

Wye [TR0546]

☆ ***New Flying Horse*** [Upper Bridge St]: Friendly and comfortably modernised 17th-c beamed inn, pleasantly light, with two or three rooms, wide choice of interesting fresh bar food, helpful service, well kept Shepherd Neame ales, inglenook log fires, bric-a-brac inc carousel horse; attractive good-sized garden with boules, pleasant bedrooms, good breakfast *(Jan and Alan Summers, David Kidd)*

If a service charge is mentioned prominently on a menu or accommodation terms, you must pay it if service was satisfactory. If service is really bad you are legally entitled to refuse to pay some or all of the service charge as compensation for not getting the service you might reasonably have expected.

Lancashire (with Greater Manchester and Merseyside)

New entries here this year include one in the north Wirral (this area, within the Merseyside boundary, falls into our groupings for this chapter, although it's traditionally thought of as part of Cheshire). This is the Fox & Hounds in Barnston, an attractive all-rounder, earning a Beer Award on the drinks side. The other two, farther north, are the Bay Horse at Bay Horse (good food gaining it our Food Award straight off, and a handy diversion from the M6) and the chatty Lunesdale Arms up at Tunstall (nice food here too, and an interesting up-to-date refurbishment). Other pubs currently well worth special note are the cheerfully traditional Black Dog at Belmont (new landlord settling in well), the relaxing Cartford at Little Eccleston (unusually for a place with some emphasis on food it brews its own beers), the striking Baltic Fleet in Liverpool (now brewing on site, too), the Derby Arms at Longridge (good food, earning an Award this year, and thriving friendly atmosphere – run by the same family for generations), the Britons Protection in Manchester (a favourite city pub, great value, and a fine collection of malt whiskies) and the Lass o' Gowrie and Marble Arch there (both good for beers), the Red Lion in Mawdesley (top-notch food in this friendly traditional village pub), the Station Buffet in Stalybridge (a classic place for good interesting beers), the distinctive old Church Inn tucked away in the moors at Uppermill (nice all round, and brewing its own good beers), and the interesting and most enjoyable Inn at Whitewell (really good all round – a great favourite). Last year we broke precedent by naming a new main entry here as the area's top dining pub. This year, it is again a new entry that carries off the title: the Bay Horse at Bay Horse is Lancashire Dining Pub of the Year. Throughout the county, there are plenty of food bargains to be had: this area is great for low-priced generous food. This is also the best part of England for classic town pubs – several separate rooms, late Victorian or Edwardian décor, a welcoming and inclusive chatty atmosphere. Taking all types of pub together, ones showing particularly well these days in the Lucky Dip section at the end of the chapter are the Moorcock at Blacko, Plough at Eaves near Broughton, Lord Raglan up above Bury, Sun at Chipping, Farmers Arms at Eccleston, Stags Head at Goosnargh, Greave Dunning in Greasby, Hest Bank Hotel at Hest Bank, Ship at Lathom, Doctor Duncan in Liverpool, White Hart at Lydgate, Mr Thomas Chop House and Peveril of the Peak in Manchester, Royal Oak at Riley Green, and restauranty Spread Eagle at Sawley. Besides having good value food, this part of the world is very pocket-friendly on the drinks side, with beer prices typically at least 20p a pint lower than the national average. The beer brewed at the Church Inn at Uppermill, barely more than £1 a pint, is an absolute steal, and the beer brewed at the Baltic Fleet in Liverpool is also a bargain. Among local brewers, Holts stands out for its exceptionally low prices. The big regional brewers, also competing fairly intensively on price, are Thwaites and Robinsons. A host of smaller local beers are well worth looking out for, including Cains, Moorhouses, Lees, Hydes, Phoenix, Bank Top and Porter. Manchester is home to the national beer brand Boddingtons (owned by Interbrew of Belgium).

BARNSTON SJ2783 Map 7

Fox & Hounds

3 miles from M53 junction 3: A552 towards Woodchurch, then left on A551

Besides well kept Marstons Pedigree, Theakstons Best and Old Peculier and Websters Yorkshire, they have a couple of guest beers such as Brains SA and Jennings Cumberland on handpump here, and over 50 whiskies; darts, TV and dominoes. Enjoyable lunchtime bar food includes soup (£2.45), sandwiches (from £2.75), filled baked potatoes (from £3.50), quiche (£4.75), ploughman's (£5.25) and changing specials such as home-made lasagne (£4.95), chicken wellington (£5.95), dressed crab (£6.25), and lamb shank (£6.50); puddings such as lemon meringue and profiteroles (from £2.50). Sunday lunch is very popular, and service is efficient and well groomed. The main part of the roomy bay-windowed lounge bar has red plush button-back built-in banquettes and plush-cushioned captain's chairs around the solid tables on its green turkey carpet, and plenty of old local prints on its cream walls below a delft shelf of china, with a collection of police and other headgear. Tucked away opposite the serving counter is a charming old quarry-tiled corner with an antique kitchen range, copper kettles, built-in pine kitchen cupboards, and lots of earthenware or enamelled food bins. With its own entrance at the other end of the pub, a small quarry-tiled locals' bar is worth a peek for its highly traditional layout – not to mention a collection of hundreds of metal ashtrays on its delft shelf; beside it is a snug where children are allowed. There are some picnic-sets under cocktail parasols out in the yard behind, below a dairy farm, and in summer the garden is served by an outside bar. *(Recommended by Maurice and Gill McMahon)*

Free house ~ Licensee Ralph Leech ~ Real ale ~ Bar food (lunchtime) ~ Restaurant ~ (0151) 6487685 ~ Children in family area ~ Open 11-11; 12-11 Sun

BAY HORSE SD4952 Map 7

Bay Horse

1¼ miles from M6 junction 33: A6 southwards, then off on left

Lancashire Dining Pub of the Year

Down its quiet road, this upmarket dining pub is the first place that people in the area recommend for good food – it has plenty of local trade, and is a popular refuge for Lancaster University people. Comfortable and quiet, with beams throughout, it has a warm and cosy atmosphere in its attractively decorated red-walled bar, with a good log fire, cushioned wall banquettes in bays, a friendly cat, gentle lighting including table lamps on window sills, and well kept Boddingtons with two or three guest beers such as Lancaster Bomber and Wadworths 6X on handpump, as well as lots of fruit wines and decent fairly priced wine list. There are usually fresh flowers on the counter, and may be piped music (anything from pop to classical) or perhaps cricket or racing on TV. The main emphasis though is on the food, with a series of small no smoking dining areas rambling around – the feel of a civilised country restaurant, with a gentle purple décor, another log fire, candle-flame-effect lights and nice tables, including one or two good-sized ones having an intimate corner to themselves. With a good blackboard choice including some unusual sandwiches, starters or light dishes include soup (£2.95), smoked duck breast with carrot remoulade or baked goats cheese and prosciutto salad (£5.45), potted local shrimps (£5.75) and seared scallop and smoked salmon salad (£7.95); main dishes run from roast aubergine, couscous and goats cheese (£9.25) through braised lamb shank with a beer and thyme sauce, slow-cooked local duck with an elderberry and honey sauce or seared salmon with pak choi (£11.95) to fillet steak with a wild mushroom and madeira sauce (£15.95). When there's something really showy on the specials board (lobster and asparagus terrine with real caviar and champagne jelly, roast suckling pig with a peach, honey and mustard sauce), go for it. Besides good puddings (£4.50) such as chocolate marquise or pear poached in red wine, they have a British cheeseboard (£4.95) and good teas and coffee. Service is helpful and attentive. There are tables out in the garden behind (peaceful, though the railway is not far off). *(Recommended by Malcolm Taylor, Margaret Dickinson, R L Gorick, Karen Eliot)*

Mitchells ~ Tenant Craig Wilkinson ~ Real ale ~ Bar food (not Mon or evening Sun) ~ Restaurant ~ (01524) 791204 ~ Open 12-2, 6.30-11; 12-4, 8-10.30 Sun; closed Mon

BELMONT SD6716 Map 7

Black Dog

A675

Built in 1750 as a working farm and converted to an inn in 1825, this friendly and cosy pub is doing well under its new landlord. Two long benches on the sheltered sunny side of the pub give delightful views of the moors above the nearby trees and houses, while inside it's lovely and inviting, especially if you're tucked away in one of the various snug alcoves, one of which used to house the village court. The original cheery and traditional small rooms are packed with antiques and bric-a-brac, from railwaymen's lamps, bedpans and chamber-pots to landscape paintings. There are also service bells for the sturdy built-in curved seats, rush-seated mahogany chairs, and coal fires. An airy extension lounge with a picture window has more modern furnishings; pool, fruit machine and piped music. They serve very good value Holts Bitter and Mild well kept on handpump. Enjoyable well presented bar food includes sandwiches (from £3, baguettes from £3.40), very good ploughman's (from £4.40), steak and kidney pie, liver and onions or moussaka (£5.50), lamb steak or cumberland sausage (£5.95), peppered steak (£7.50), and puddings (£2); they don't take bookings, so get there early for a table as it does tend to fill up quickly. A small orchestra plays Viennese music on New Year's Day at lunchtime, and performs on several evenings throughout the year. A track leads from the village up Winter Hill and (from the lane to Rivington) on to Anglezarke Moor, and there are paths from the dam of the nearby Belmont Reservoir; the bedrooms are homely and reasonably priced. *(Recommended by Derek and Sylvia Stephenson, P Abbott, Michael and Marion Buchanan, Jim Abbott, Steve Whalley, Bob Broadhurst, Ann and Max Cross, Andy and Jill Kassube, Gordon Tong, Dr Paull Khan, Andy, Julie and Stuart Hawkins, MLR, John Robertson, Mike and Linda Hudson, Peter Heaton)*

Holts ~ Tenant Heino Chrobok ~ Real ale ~ Bar food (12-2, 6-8(not Mon or Tues evening); 12-3, 6.30-8 Sun) ~ (01204) 811218 ~ Children away from main bar ~ Open 12-11(10.30 Sun); closed 25 Dec evening ~ Bedrooms: £32.50S/£42.50S

BISPHAM GREEN SD4914 Map 7

Eagle & Child

Maltkiln Lane (Parbold—Croston road, off B5246)

The good range of well kept beers at this striking red brick pub includes Moorhouses Black Cat and Thwaites, with four or five changing guest ales from brewers such as Blackpool, Hanby, Hart, Jennings and Phoenix. They've also got changing farm cider, decent wines, some country wines and about 25 malt whiskies; piped music. The largely open-plan bar, well divided by stubs of walls, is appealingly simple and civilised. Attractively understated old furnishings include a mix of small oak chairs around tables in corners, an oak coffer, several handsomely carved antique oak settles (the finest apparently made partly from a 16th-c wedding bed-head), and old hunting prints and engravings. There's coir matting in the no smoking snug, and oriental rugs on flagstones in front of the fine old stone fireplaces. The newish chef is doing good home-made bar food, which might include soup and sandwiches (from £3.50), tomato and goats cheese tart (£4.50), sausages and mash, fish and chips with mushy peas or steak and ale pie (£7.50, £8 in the evening) with more elaborate specials such as green vegetable risotto with parmesan and parsley oil (£4), grilled sardines with couscous and tomato dressing (£4.50), grilled salmon, rösti and baby leeks with smoked salmon butter (£10), lamb with rissole potatoes and marinated aubergines (£12), and loin of veal saltimbocca (£13). The pub holds a popular beer festival in May, with live music in the evenings; look out for Harry the dog. You can watch players competing on the neat bowling green outside, and the pub can provide bowls for anyone who wants to try the crowns, which fool even the most experienced bowlers. A nice wild garden has crested newts and nesting moorhens. *(Recommended by Mr and Mrs S Mason, Ray and Winifred Halliday, John Holroyd, Revd D Glover, Jim Abbott, John Fazakerley, Brian Kneale, Pat and Roger Fereday, Derek and Sylvia Stephenson, Paul Boot)*

Free house ~ Licensee John Mansfield ~ Real ale ~ Bar food (12-2, 6-8.30(9 Fri, Sat); 12-8.30 Sun) ~ Restaurant ~ (01257) 462297 ~ Children away from main bar ~ Dogs allowed in bar ~ Open 12-3, 5.30-11; 12-10.30 Sun; closed evening 25 Dec

BLACKSTONE EDGE SD9716 Map 7

White House £

A58 Ripponden—Littleborough, just W of B6138

Spectacularly set on the Pennine Way 400 metres (1,300 ft) above sea level, even in summer this imposing 17th-c building may greet you with swirling mists and wild moorland winds, but take heart – it's lovely and cosy inside. There's a cheery atmosphere in the bustling main bar, which has a turkey carpet in front of a blazing coal fire, and a large-scale map of the area (windswept walkers hardly know whether to head for the map or the fire first). The snug Pennine Room opens off here, with brightly coloured antimacassars on its small soft settees; there's also a dining extension. A spacious room on the left has comfortable seating, and a big horseshoe window has impressive views over the moors. The enjoyably unpretentious bar food, served in huge helpings (prices haven't changed since last year), includes good soup (£2), sandwiches (from £3), cumberland sausage with egg, steak and kidney pie or vegetable quiche (£4.75), roast chicken breast (£5), chilli con carne, beef curry or lasagne (£5.50), steaks (from £7.50), puddings such as home-made apple pie and sticky toffee pudding (from £2), and daily specials. Service is prompt and friendly. Well kept real ales on handpump include Black Sheep Special, Theakstons Best and one or two guests such as Exmoor Gold and Moorhouses Pendle Witches Brew, also farm cider and malt whiskies; fruit machine. Muddy boots can be left in the porch. *(Recommended by Graham and Lynn Mason, Jo and Iain MacGregor, Bob Broadhurst, Michael and Marion Buchanan, Paul Fairbrother, Helen Morris, Andy Gosling, Derek and Sylvia Stephenson)*

Free house ~ Licensee Neville Marney ~ Real ale ~ Bar food ~ (01706) 378456 ~ Children welcome ~ Open 12-3, 6.30-11; 12-11 Sun

CHIPPING SD6243 Map 7

Dog & Partridge 🍷

Hesketh Lane; crossroads Chipping—Longridge with Inglewhite—Clitheroe

This neatly kept dining pub is in attractive countryside between Longridge and Wolf Fell. Served by friendly and well trained staff, the enjoyable lunchtime bar food (not Sun) includes tasty soup (£2.50), duck and orange pâté (£4.30), sandwiches (from £4.50), home-made steak and kidney pie or roast chicken with stuffing (£7.80), roast duckling with apple sauce and stuffing (£11), and grilled sirloin steak with mushrooms (£12.50), as well as around four vegetarian dishes

such as broccoli and stilton pancakes or leek and mushroom crumble (£7.80), and perhaps a few specials such as hot potted shrimps (£4.30), and grilled plaice (£9); puddings could be home-made fruit pie and raspberry shortcake (£3.40). Although parts date back to 1515, the pub has been much modernised and extended since, with the eating space now spreading over into a nearby stable. The comfortable main lounge has small armchairs around fairly close-set low wood-effect tables on a blue patterned carpet, brown-painted beams, a good winter log fire, and multi-coloured lanterns. As well as more than 40 wines, they have well kept Tetleys Bitter and Mild with a weekly changing guest such as Black Sheep Bitter on handpump, and a good range of malt whiskies. Smart casual dress is preferred in the restaurant – open evenings and Sunday lunchtime; dining areas are no smoking, and you may need to book. More reports please.
(Recommended by Margaret Dickinson, Norma and Noel Thomas, Steve Whalley)

Free house ~ Licensee Peter Barr ~ Real ale ~ Bar food (12-1.45 Mon-Sat) ~ Restaurant (7-9 Mon-Sat; 11.45-8.30 Sun) ~ (01995) 61201 ~ Children welcome ~ Open 11.45-3, 6.45-11; 11.45-10.30 Sun

CONDER GREEN SD4556 Map 7

Stork

3 miles from M6 junction 33: A6 towards Lancaster, first left, then fork left; just off A588

In a fine spot where the River Conder joins the Lune estuary, tables outside this rambling white-painted ancient inn look out over the bleak marshes. Inside though, there's a friendly bustling atmosphere and on cold days you'll find a good fire. One of the lived-in panelled rooms has a list of licensees going back to 1660; darts, pool, fruit machine, video game, juke box, dominoes and piped music (can be obtrusive at times). The well kept real ales could include Boddingtons, Marstons Pedigree, Timothy Taylors Landlord and perhaps a guest such as Barnsley IPA on handpump; good coffee. The generous bar food is popular, and could include soup (£2.50), sandwiches (from £2.25), home-made game pâté (£2.95), smoked duck breast or tasty hot potted shrimps (£3.25), steak pie (£5.50), bass with lemon, white wine and cream sauce or beef stroganoff (£6.95), lamb cutlets (£7.25), and daily specials such as sweet and sour pork or roasted pepper filled with vegetables and rice with parsley sauce (£6.25), baked lemon sole with herb butter (£8.95), and fillet steak filled with stilton in red wine sauce (£12.95), with puddings such as chocolate fudge cake (£2.50); there may be quite a wait when busy. A good break from Lancaster and the M6, the pub is handy for the Lune estuary path, and bustling Glasson Dock is just a mile away.
(Recommended by Margaret Dickinson, Roger and Jenny Huggins, Dr Paull Khan, David and Ruth Hollands, Helen Flaherty, Pat and Tony Martin, Steve Whalley, Robin Lord)

Free house ~ Licensee Tony Cragg ~ Real ale ~ Bar food (all day Sun) ~ Restaurant ~ (01524) 751234 ~ Children welcome ~ Dogs allowed in bar and bedrooms ~ Open 11-11; 12-10.30 Sun; closed 25 Dec ~ Bedrooms: £27S/£44S

DOWNHAM SD7844 Map 7

Assheton Arms

From A59 NE of Clitheroe turn off into Chatburn (signposted); in Chatburn follow Downham signpost

A massive stone fireplace helps divide the separate areas of the rambling beamed bar at this pleasant dining pub. Cosiest in winter, it has olive plush-cushioned winged settles around attractive grainy oak tables, some cushioned window seats, and two grenadier busts on the mantelpiece; part of the bar is no smoking. A fairly wide choice of swiftly served bar food includes home-made ham and vegetable broth (£2.95), sandwiches (from £3.75, not Saturday evening or Sunday lunchtime), ploughman's (£4.50), stilton pâté (£4.50), courgettes with tomato, garlic, pesto and mozzarella (£6.75), steak and kidney pie (£6.95), venison, bacon and cranberry casserole or chicken kiev (£7.95), and poached halibut in a creamy cheese sauce (£9.95); puddings and children's meals (£3.50). They serve

Boddingtons under light blanket pressure; decent wines by the glass or bottle; piped music. The pub is delightfully set in a sloping stone-built village, and window seats and picnic-sets outside look across to a church. It takes its name from the family of Lord Clitheroe, who bought the village in 1558 and have preserved it in a traditional style ever since. *(Recommended by Pierre and Pat Richterich, Bob Broadhurst, Norma and Noel Thomas, Keith Berrett, Greta and Christopher Wells)*

Whitbreads ~ Lease David Busby ~ Real ale ~ Bar food (12-2, 7-10) ~ (01200) 441227 ~ Children welcome ~ Dogs allowed in bar ~ Open 12-3, 7-11(10.30 Sun)

ENTWISTLE SD7217 Map 7

Strawbury Duck 🛏

Overshores Road, by station; village signposted down narrow lane from Blackburn Road N of Edgworth; or take Batridge Road off B6391 N of Chapeltown and take pretty ¾ mile walk from park at Entwistle reservoir; OS Sheet 109 map reference 726177

Tucked well away in a sheltered fold of the moors, this traditional beamed and flagstoned country pub is home to a relaxed mix of walkers, birdwatchers and locals. The cosy dimly lit L-shaped bar has Victorian pictures on its partly timbered, partly rough-stone walls, a variety of seats, stools, little settees and pews, a mounted gun, and one table made from an old church organ bellows. Their six well kept real ales on handpump are Black Sheep, Boddingtons, Moorhouses Pendle Witches Brew and Timothy Taylors Landlord, and a couple of guest beers; pool, fruit machine, TV and piped music. Handily served most of the day, bar food includes soup (£1.95), sandwiches (from £2.45), baked potatoes (from £2.95), crisp fried whitebait (£3.25), mushroom stroganoff (£5.99), steak and mushroom pie (£6.25), poached salmon fillet (£6.95), and steaks (from £9.25), with puddings such as strawberry cheesecake (from £2.65); they also do specials and children's dishes. Tables outside are perched high above a railway cutting, and a train ride from Blackburn or Bolton takes you along a little railway and through this cutting to a station next door. It's a popular base for Pennine walks (leave muddy boots in the porch). *(Recommended by Andy and Jill Kassube, Steve Whalley, Michael and Marion Buchanan, Revd D Glover)*

Free house ~ Licensee Lisa McEwan ~ Real ale ~ Bar food (12-9.30; 12-8 Sun) ~ (01204) 852013 ~ Children welcome ~ Open 12-11; 12-10.30 Sun ~ Bedrooms: £29.50S(£29.50B)/£39.50S(£39.50B)

GOOSNARGH SD5839 Map 7

Horns 🍷 🛏

Pub signed from village, about 2 miles towards Chipping below Beacon Fell

Prettily set in the foothills of the Pennines, this civilised hotel is a nice place to come for a meal. Flower displays add colour to the neatly kept snug rooms, all of which have log fires in winter. Beyond the lobby, the pleasant front bar opens into attractively decorated middle rooms; the dining rooms are no smoking. The atmosphere is relaxing, and the young staff are very welcoming and helpful; piped music. The emphasis here is on the enjoyable homely food which includes soup (£2.95), good well presented sandwiches (from £3.25), ploughman's (£4.95), steak and kidney pie (£7.50), roast local pheasant or grilled gammon and egg (£7.95), and sirloin steak with mushrooms (£10.50), with daily specials such as vegetable bake (£7.75), roast of the day (£7.95), and baked hake (£8.50), all nicely served with freshly cooked, piping hot chips; home-made puddings could include fruit pies or delicious sticky toffee pudding (£3.95). There's an extensive wine list with quite a few by the glass, and a fine choice of malt whiskies. They do good breakfasts. *(Recommended by R L Gorick, Margaret Dickinson, Lynette and Stuart Shore, Charles and Pauline Stride, Dave and Chris Watts, Gerald Wilkinson, Neville Kenyon)*

Free house ~ Licensee Mark Woods ~ Bar food (not Mon lunchtime) ~ Restaurant ~ (01772) 865230 ~ Children in eating area of bar and restaurant ~ Open 11.30-3, 6-11; 11-11 Sat; 12-3, 6-11 Sun; closed Mon lunchtime ~ Bedrooms: £55B/£75B

LITTLE ECCLESTON SD4139 Map 7

Cartford

Cartford Lane, off A586 Garstang—Blackpool, by toll bridge

Unusually for somewhere that is so popular for food, this welcoming pub is particularly strong on beer, with up to seven very well kept real ales on handpump. These include a couple from Hart (their own good microbrewery behind the pub, with brewery tours by arrangement), Boddingtons, Fullers London Pride and up to four changing ales from interesting brewers such as Moorhouses, Phoenix and Rooster; also decent house wines and several malt whiskies. The attractive rambling interior has oak beams, dried flowers, a lovely log fire and an unusual layout on three different levels, with pleasantly uncoordinated cosy seating areas. Two levels are largely set for dining (the upstairs part is no smoking). Service is friendly and obliging, and the atmosphere is nicely relaxed. Reasonably priced enjoyable food includes soup (£2.05), sandwiches (from £2.75), evening pizzas (from £4.40, you can take them away), home-made steak and mushroom pie (£4.95), lemon sole (£5.90), curries (from £6.35), and 10oz sirloin steak (£8.95); the blackboard adds specials such as cod and prawn crumble (£5.95), peppered pork steak or lamb dijonnaise (£6.95), and changing puddings (from £2.50). They've pool, darts, dominoes, fruit machine, TV and piped music; very popular with older lunchers on weekdays, it draws a livelier crowd on weekend evenings. It's peacefully placed by a toll bridge over the River Wyre (tidal here), and they have fishing rights along 1½ miles; there are tables out in a garden (not by the water), with a play area. *(Recommended by MLR, Abi Benson, Dr Paull Khan, Andy and Jill Kassube, Robert and Catherine Dunster)*

Own brew ~ Licensees Andrew Mellodew and Val Williams ~ Real ale ~ Bar food (12-9 Sun) ~ Restaurant ~ (01995) 670166 ~ Children welcome ~ Dogs welcome ~ Open 12-3, 6.30(7 Mon-Thurs in winter)-11; 12-10.30 Sun ~ Bedrooms: £36.95B/£48.95B

LIVERPOOL SJ4395 Map 7

Baltic Fleet

Wapping

The friendly landlord of this prominent Victorian pub, just across the water from the Albert Dock, has recently bought the little local Passageway Brewery and now brews his own Wapping beers in the cellar. Alongside well kept reasonably priced Wapping Bitter, Baltic Extra and Summer Ale, Cains Dark Mild and Traditional, they also have a couple of guests on handpump, served through a sparkler. With more entrances (eight) than any other pub in Liverpool, it's a unique triangular building with nice big arched windows and a bright green, burgundy and white painted exterior. An abundance of interior woodwork and stout mahogany board floors add to its nautical feel, as do the interesting old Mersey shipping prints. There's also a good mix of old school furniture and dark wood tables; piped music. At lunchtime they just do soup and sandwiches made with various types of bread (from £2.95), while in the evening reasonably priced tasty dishes from a fairly short menu might include breaded cod goujons with lemon and garlic mayonnaise (£2.95), pork sausages with creamy mash in onion gravy (£5.95), steak and ale pudding (£6.95), and seared tuna marinated in citrus juices, balsamic vinegar and olive oil with salsa (£7.95); their Sunday roast (£6.95) is very popular, so booking is a good idea. The small back room is no smoking. *(Recommended by the Didler, David Field, Arby)*

Own brew ~ Licensees Simon Holt and Julie Broome ~ Real ale ~ Bar food (12-2.30, 6-8.30(not Mon); 12.3, 6-9 Fri/Sat; 12-4 Sun) ~ Restaurant ~ (0151) 709 3116 ~ Children in restaurant ~ Open 11-11; 12-10.30 Sun; closed 25 and 26 Dec, 31 Dec evening and 1 Jan

If we know a pub does summer barbecues, we say so.

Philharmonic Dining Rooms ★

36 Hope Street; corner of Hardman Street

This late Victorian gin palace is worth a visit for its stunning opulence, from its smart marble façade to the elegant original fittings. The heart of the building is a mosaic-faced serving counter, from which heavily carved and polished mahogany partitions radiate under the intricate plasterwork high ceiling. The echoing main hall is decorated with stained glass including contemporary portraits of Boer War heroes such as Baden-Powell and Lord Roberts, rich panelling, a huge mosaic floor, and copper panels of musicians in an alcove above the fireplace. More stained glass in one of the little lounges declares 'Music is the universal language of mankind', and backs this up with illustrations of musical instruments; there are two plushly comfortable sitting rooms. The famous gents' (ladies are allowed a look if they ask first) are original 1890s Rouge Royale by Twyfords: all red marble and glinting mosaics. Throughout the pub there's a nice blend of customers (though no children), with theatre-goers, students, locals and tourists making up the contented bustle. Real ales on handpump could include well kept Bass, Cains Traditional, Fullers London Pride and Tetleys, and a couple of guests such as Cains Formidable and Timothy Taylors Landlord; chess tables, fruit machine, TV and piped music; the grand lounge is now a smart restaurant. Straightforward lunchtime bar food from a short menu includes soup (£2.25), sandwiches (from £3.50, hot sandwiches from £3.95), ploughman's or cauliflower cheese (£5.25), steak pie or fish and chips (£5.50) and cajun chicken (£5.75); puddings (£2.25). *(Recommended by Patrick Hancock, John A Barker, the Didler, David Field, George Little, JP, PP)*

Six Continents ~ Manager Marie-Louise Wong ~ Real ale ~ Bar food (lunchtime Mon-Sat) ~ Restaurant ~ (0151) 707 2837 ~ Open 12-11; 5-10.30 Sun; closed 25 Dec and 1 Jan

LONGRIDGE SD6039 Map 7

Derby Arms 🍴 🍷

Chipping Road, Thornley; 1½ miles N of Longridge on back road to Chipping

You get the feeling that lots of thought and real enjoyment go into running this very welcoming old stone-built country pub. It's been in the same family for over a century (the current licensee's great-grandmother was married from here in 1898), and the staff are friendly and well trained. They make good use of fresh local ingredients, and the food here is beautifully presented and delicious. The menu could include sandwiches (from £2.95), soup (£2.95), leek and mushroom crumble (£6.95), tasty steak and kidney pudding (£8.25), steaks (from £9.25), roast lamb shank with redcurrant gravy (£10.95), and puddings such as hot chocolate fudge cake (£3.50). The changing specials include a good choice of fish dishes such as grilled squid (£5.50), lobster pancakes (£5.75), monkfish fried in crisp beer batter (£13.50) or baby halibut poached with cider and mussels in shallot butter sauce (£14.95), as well as dishes such as chicken and sun-dried tomato spring rolls with sweet chilli sauce (£4.50), and fried veal with creamy dijon and mushroom sauce (£10.95); potatoes and vegetables come in separate dishes. There's something of a hunting and fishing theme in the main bar, with old photographs commemorating notable catches, some nicely mounted bait above the comfortable red plush seats, and a stuffed pheasant that seems to be flying in through the wall. To the right is a smaller room with sporting trophies and mementoes, and a regimental tie collection, while off to the left are a couple of no smoking dining areas. Along with a good range of wines including several half-bottles and a dozen or so by the glass (they're particularly strong on South African), they serve well kept Marstons Pedigree and Theakstons on handpump. The gents' has dozens of riddles on the wall; you can buy a sheet of them in the bar (the money goes to charity). A few tables out in front, and another two behind the car park, enjoy fine views across to the Forest of Bowland. *(Recommended by Margaret Dickinson, R L Gorick, Norma and Noel Thomas, Jean and Douglas Troup, Steve Whalley, Deborah Bamber)*

Inn Partnership (Pubmaster) ~ Lease Mrs G M Walme ~ Real ale ~ Bar food (all day Sun) ~ Restaurant ~ (01772) 782623 ~ Children in eating area of bar and restaurant ~ Open 12-2.15, 6.30-9.30; 12-2.15, 6-10 Sat; 12-9.15 Sun

LYTHAM SD3627 Map 7

Taps £

A584 S of Blackpool; Henry Street – in centre, one street in from West Beach

Well kept beers, friendly staff, and a lively atmosphere make this alehouse a popular place to spend an afternoon. A view-in cellar lets you admire the choice of around eight real ales on offer, and alongside Boddingtons, the weekly changing guests on handpump might include Batemans XXXB, Fullers London Pride, Taps (brewed for the pub by Titanic), Titanic Stout, Wadworths 6X and Wychwood Three Lions; there are seat belts on the bar and headrests in the gents' to help keep you out of harm's way if you have one too many. They also usually serve some country wines and a farm cider. The Victorian-style bare-boarded bar has a really sociable unassuming feel, with plenty of stained-glass decoration in the windows, depictions of fish and gulls reflecting the pub's proximity to the beach, captain's chairs in bays around the sides, open fires, and a coal-effect gas fire between two built-in bookcases at one end. There's also an expanding collection of rugby memorabilia with old photographs and portraits of rugby stars on the walls; shove-ha'penny, dominoes and a fruit machine. The straightforward home-made bar food is very good value (prices haven't gone up since last year) and includes sandwiches (from £1.50, hot roast beef £3.25), soup (£1.65), filled baked potatoes (from £1.95), curry (£3.50), and lasagne (£3.95). Although there are no meals on Sunday, their free platters of food then get a big thumbs-up from readers, with tasty snacks such as black pudding, chicken wings or minted lamb. There are a few seats outside. Parking is difficult near the pub so it's probably best to park at the West Beach car park on the seafront (free on Sunday), and walk. *(Recommended by Andy, Julie and Stuart Hawkins, Steve Whalley, J F M and M West, Dr and Mrs A K Clarke)*

Laurel Pub Company ~ Manager Ian Rigg ~ Real ale ~ Bar food (lunchtime only, not Sun) ~ (01253) 736226 ~ Children in eating area of bar ~ Open 11-11; 12-10.30 Sun

MANCHESTER SJ7796 Map 7

Britons Protection 🍷 £

Great Bridgewater Street, corner of Lower Mosley Street

More spacious than it appears from the outside, this deservedly popular city drinker's pub gets nothing but praise from readers. It's a really well run place, and the licensees, who have been here for years themselves, employ a proper career barman; service is friendly and accommodating, and there's a sociable welcoming atmosphere. The rather plush little front bar has a fine chequered tile floor, some glossy brown and russet wall tiles, solid woodwork and elaborate plastering. A tiled passage lined with battle murals leads to two inner lounges, one served by hatch, with attractive brass and etched glass wall lamps, a mirror above the coal-effect gas fire in the simple Art Nouveau fireplace, and again good solidly comfortable furnishings. As something of a tribute to Manchester's notorious climate, the massive bar counter has a pair of heating pipes as its footrail. As well as 175 malt whiskies, and an interesting range of spirits, they serve very well kept Jennings, Robinsons and Tetleys and a regularly changing guest on handpump; they also have good wines. Generous helpings of reasonably priced tasty bar food include home-made soup (£1.85), sandwiches (from £2), ploughman's (£3.75), ham and egg (£4.25), leek and mushroom crumble (£4.75), unusual pies such as wild boar, turkey, hare and pigeon in red wine and brandy sauce (£4.95), and home-made daily specials (from £3.95); piped music. Although it's busy at lunchtime, it's usually quiet and relaxed in the evenings. There are tables out on the terrace behind, and it's handy for the GMEX centre and Bridgewater Hall (and well known to many orchestral players). *(Recommended by*

Doug Christian, Brian and Anna Marsden, Beryl Hearman, Kevin Blake, John Hulme, GLD, P Abbott, the Didler, B, M and P Kendall, Patrick Hancock, Nick Holding, Stephen, Julie and Hayley Brown, Ken Richards, JES)

Punch ~ Lease Peter Barnett ~ Real ale ~ Bar food (11-2.30 only) ~ Restaurant ~ (0161) 236 5895 ~ Children in family area ~ Open 11-11; 12-10.30 Sun; closed 25 Dec

Dukes 92 £

Castle Street, below the bottom end of Deansgate

You can choose from an excellent range of over three dozen cheeses and several pâtés – some quite unusual – at this tastefully converted cavernous former stables. It's in a great setting near locks and railway arches in the rejuvenated heart of old industrial Manchester, with tables out by the canal basin which opens into the bottom lock of the Rochdale Canal. Inside, black wrought-iron work contrasts boldly with whitewashed bare plaster walls, the handsome bar is marble-topped, and an elegant spiral staircase leads to an upper room and balcony (which they were extending and refurbishing in a modern style when we went to press). Down in the main room the fine mix of furnishings is mainly rather Edwardian in mood, with one particularly massive table, elegantly comfortable chaises-longues and deep armchairs. As well as cheese and pâté with a generous helping of granary bread (£4), good value bar food includes soup (£2.50), baked potatoes (from £2.50), sandwiches (from £3.75, toasties from £2.75), tagliatelle and roasted vegetables or ham and leek pasta bake (£4.50), salmon and cod fishcakes, cajun chicken or moussaka (£5.50), mezze (£7.95), and oriental platter (£8.95). They serve well kept Boddingtons and a guest on handpump, with the Belgian wheat beer Hoegaarden on tap; decent wines and a wide choice of malt whiskies; piped jazz. There's a function room theatre, with temporary exhibitions of local artwork, and on bank holiday weekends the forecourt may host jazz and children's theatre. *(Recommended by Andrew York, P Abbott, Stephen, Julie and Hayley Brown)*

Free house ~ Licensee James Ramsbottom ~ Real ale ~ Bar food (12-3, 5-8.30 Mon-Thurs; 12-6 Fri-Sun) ~ Restaurant ~ (0161) 839 8646 ~ Children welcome ~ Dogs welcome ~ Live bands outside in summer ~ Open 11.30-11(12 Fri/Sat); 12-10.30 Sun

Lass o' Gowrie £

36 Charles Street; off Oxford Street at BBC

Behind its richly tiled arched brown façade, the simple big-windowed long bar of this lively traditional Victorian pub has gas lighting, bare floorboards, lots of stripped brickwork, and hop pockets draped from the ceiling. At weekends during term time, it's full of cheery university students, with the pavement outside pressed into service for extra room; piped pop music adds to the youthful buzz. At quieter times during the day, the music might be switched off to suit an older crowd of chatty locals. Although it might take some while to get served at busy periods, the staff are friendly and cheerfully obliging. Seats around a sort of glass cage give a view of the brewing process in the cellar microbrewery where they produce their Lass o' Gowrie Lass Ale, and alongside Black Sheep, Boddingtons and Greene King Old Speckled Hen, they've six other well kept beers on handpump from brewers such as Caledonian, Durham, Phoenix, Goose Eye, Moorhouses and Picks, changing weekly; they also have a changing farm cider. The straightforward bar food, which is very good value, includes sandwiches and baked potatoes (from £2.25), and daily specials such as sausages and mash (£3.65), steak and ale pie (£4.25) and vegetable lasagne (£4.65). The snug is no smoking; they've a fruit machine and satellite TV. More reports please. *(Recommended by Patrick Hancock, Andy, Julie and Stuart Hawkins, Richard Lewis, Ian Phillips)*

Own brew ~ Licensee Jamie Bell ~ Real ale ~ Bar food (11-6(3 Sat); 12-3 Sun) ~ (0161) 273 6932 ~ Children in family snug ~ Open 11-11; 12-10.30 Sun; closed 25 Dec

Marble Arch £

73 Rochdale Road (A664), Ancoats; corner of Gould Street, just E of Victoria Station

Given the unremarkable façade, the beautifully preserved interior of this Victorian city ale house comes as a nice surprise. There's a magnificently restored lightly barrel-vaulted high ceiling, and extensive marble and tiling – the frieze advertising various spirits, and the chimney breast above the carved wooden mantelpiece, particularly stand out. The pub is furnished with leather sofas, cushioned settles and deep armchairs, and all the walls are stripped back to the glazed brick; bar billiards, fruit machine, pinball and a juke box. The sloping mosaic floor in the bar can be a bit disconcerting after a few pints of their well kept own brew unfined organic (and vegan) real ales. From windows at the back of the pub you can look out over the brewery (tours by arrangement) where they produce the distinctive hoppy Cloudy Marble, Manchester Bitter, N/4, Old Lag, Uncut Amber and the seasonal brew – and their Marble Ginger Ale has been finding favour. From all round the country, their guest ales could include Ballards Best, Titanic White Star and Woodfordes Wherry, and they have a good choice of bottled beers, including some Belgian Trappist ones. Generous sandwiches have interesting fillings such as hot chicken with peanut and ginger sauce or roasted leek and wild mushroom with mint and garlic (£2.80), while other very reasonably priced bar food includes soup (£2), burgers (£3.25), and a few daily specials such as spicy mediterranean bake with fried potatoes and coriander, hungarian goulash, pork and pepper stir fry with ginger and lemon sauce or cod creole (£4). The Laurel and Hardy Preservation Society meet here on the third Wednesday of the month and show old films. There's a little garden.

(Recommended by the Didler, JP, PP, Richard Lewis, Peter F Marshall)

Own brew ~ Licensee Christine Baldwin ~ Real ale ~ Bar food (11.30-3, 5-8; 11.30-6 Fri; 12-2 Sat; not Sun) ~ No credit cards ~ (0161) 832 5914 ~ Open 11.30-11; 12-(10.30 Sun)11 Sat

MAWDESLEY SD4914 Map 7

Red Lion

Heading N on B5246 from Parbold, turn right into Maltkiln Lane at Bispham Green signpost, then keep on, bearing right after 1½ miles into Mawdesley High Street, and thence into New Street

Highly recommended for its food, this busily traditional village local uses high quality ingredients and beautiful presentation to put real flair into even ordinary-sounding dishes. Served in the brightly painted conservatory, the food could include mussels with tomato, onion and white wine (£4.50), duck leg confit with spring onion mash and red wine jus (£5), caramelised onion tartlets with sultanas and pine nuts (£9.50), baked bass with fennel, tarragon and Pernod sauce (£10.50), roast rack of lamb with apricot and madeira sauce (£12), peppered fillet steak medallions in brandy jus (£13.50), and irresistible puddings such as chocolate soufflé with mascarpone and black cherry sauce or lemon meringue pie with mango coulis (£4). Lunchtimes from Wednesday to Saturday they also do bar snacks such as home-made soup (£2.50) and sandwiches (from £3.50), and you can choose two courses from their good value set menu for £9. It's a good idea to book at the weekend. The colourful décor in the dining room is quite a surprise after the far more conventional bar, which has wooden tables, a brick bar counter, standing timbers, a few plants, a nice old clock, and a good sociable atmosphere; a separate public bar has a TV and fruit machine. The amiable landlord does his best to make everyone feel at home, and the staff are friendly and attentive (the landlady first worked here as a barmaid 30 years ago). Well kept Black Sheep, Theakstons Best and Websters, and several well chosen wines by the glass; piped music. There are tables in a courtyard behind, and more in front – surrounded by hanging baskets and flowering tubs. Notice that the two big lions standing guard by the main door are white, rather than red.

(Recommended by Michael Doswell, Paul Boot, Norma and Noel Thomas, Mike and Linda Hudson, Revd D Glover, Nick Holding)

Enterprise ~ Tenants Stella Thompson and Edward Newton ~ Real ale ~ Bar food (not Mon and Tues; Sun 12-8) ~ Restaurant ~ (01704) 822208/822999 ~ Children in eating area of bar and restaurant ~ Dogs allowed in bar ~ Jazz Sun of bank hols ~ Open 12-11(10.30 Sun)

MELLOR SJ9888 Map 7

Oddfellows Arms

Heading out of Marple on the A626 towards Glossop, Mellor is the next road after the B6102, signposted off on the right at Marple Bridge; keep on for nearly 2 miles up Longhurst Lane and into Moor End Road

Although you'll be made to feel welcome if you're just after a drink, most people come to this civilised old country pub for the enjoyable food. Alongside specials such as smoked cod poached in white wine with a light prawn sauce (£8.25), mediterranean meat balls (£8.75) and Goan monkfish fried in a mild curry sauce (£11.45), generous interesting dishes from lots of different countries could include soup (£2.20), sandwiches (from £3.50, hot ones from £3.95), button mushrooms in stilton with cream (£4.45), mussel chowder (£4.65), chicken balti (£6.95), mushroom and pepper goulash (£7.95), thai tiger prawns in oyster sauce (£9.45), moroccan lamb casserole (£9.95), lamb cutlets with mint and mango marinade (£10.45), and steaks (from £10.95), with puddings such as rhubarb and ginger torte (£3.45). Some meals are available in smaller helpings for children; they do a three-course Sunday lunch (£10.95). The pleasant low-ceilinged flagstoned bar has nice open fires and a cosy, chatty atmosphere; no piped music or games. Well kept Adnams Best, Flowers IPA, Marstons Pedigree and a weekly changing guest such as Charles Wells Bombardier on handpump, served with or without a sparkler; friendly service. There's a small no smoking restaurant upstairs, and a few tables out by the road. When the pub's busy parking can be difficult. *(Recommended by Revd D Glover, Mike and Linda Hudson, P Abbott, Brian and Anna Marsden, John Hulme, Hilary Forrest)*

Free house ~ Licensee Robert Cloughley ~ Real ale ~ Bar food (not Sun evening or Mon) ~ Restaurant ~ (0161) 449 7826 ~ Children in eating area of bar and restaurant ~ Dogs allowed in bar ~ Open 12-3, 5.30-11(7-10.30 Sun); closed Mon

NEWTON SD6950 Map 7

Parkers Arms

B6478 7 miles N of Clitheroe

The menagerie of pets at this pretty cream and green painted pub includes pygmy goats, rabbits, guinea pigs, hens, pheasants, parrots, two playful black labradors and a turkey. In a bowl of tree-sheltered pastures between Waddington Fell and Beatrix Fell, the setting is charming, especially in summer when you can enjoy lovely unspoilt views down over the River Hodder and its valley from the big front garden. A comfortable well run place with a cheerful atmosphere and welcoming staff, the pub has red plush button-back banquettes, a mix of new chairs and tables, stuffed animals, prints and an open fire. Beyond an arch is a similar area with sensibly placed darts, a log fire, cribbage, dominoes, fruit machine, TV and discreet piped music. Well kept Boddingtons, Flowers IPA and perhaps a guest such as Black Sheep on handpump, with a good range of malt whiskies and around 55 wines (nine by the glass). The generous nicely cooked bar food could include black pudding with creamy mustard sauce or prawn cocktail (£3.75), leek, ham and chicken crumble or ploughman's (£6.50), gammon and egg or pancake stuffed with vegetables with a three-cheese sauce (£6.75), kleftiko or leg of lamb with honey and mint gravy (£9.50), seafood pancake (£7.75), 10oz sirloin (£11.50), daily specials such as chilli and garlic crayfish tails (£4.95), vegetable and nut pie (£6.45), cajun chicken (£7.95), and trout with walnut and almond sauce (£10.50). They also do a children's menu (from £3.50); the restaurant is no smoking. *(Recommended by Mrs P J Carrol, Melanie Lawrenson, Margaret Dickinson, Norma and Noel Thomas,*

Jim Abbott, Mrs P J Carroll, Sue and Bob Ward, Steve Whalley, M W Turner)

Enterprise ~ Lease Barbara Clayton ~ Real ale ~ Bar food (12-9 summer; 12-2.30, 6-9; 12-9 wknds in winter) ~ Restaurant ~ (01200) 446236 ~ Children in eating area of bar and restaurant till 9pm ~ Open 11-11; 12-10.30 Sun; 11-2.30, 5.30-11 Mon-Fri in winter ~ Bedrooms: £38S/£50S

RABY SJ3180 Map 7

Wheatsheaf

From A540 heading S from Heswall, turn left into Upper Raby Road, village in about a mile; The Green, Rabymere Road

The nicely rambling rooms in this timbered and whitewashed country cottage are simply furnished, with an old wall clock and homely black kitchen shelves in the cosy central bar (it can get smoky), and a nice snug formed by antique settles built in around its fine old fireplace. A second, more spacious room has upholstered wall seats around the tables, small hunting prints on the cream walls, and a smaller coal fire. It's a popular place, attracting a good mix of customers. Good straightforward lunchtime bar food includes soup (£2.50), sandwiches including good rare beef and a very good range of toasties (from £2.55), ploughman's (£4.75), omelettes (£5.50), chicken breast with garlic and herbs (£5.95), steak and ale pie (£6), mixed grill (£6.40), and braised knuckle of lamb or poached salmon (£6.95), with daily specials such as pasta of the day (£4.15), and roast of the day (£5.95). Booking is a good idea, and expect to wait when it's busy. The spacious restaurant (with more elaborate evening menu) is in a converted cowshed that leads into a larger no smoking conservatory; piped music is played in these areas only. The good range of eight real ales on handpump include Cains, Greene King Old Speckled Hen, Tetleys, Theakstons Best, Old Peculier and XB, Thwaites Best and three or four weekly guests such as Dent Aviator, fff Stairway to Heaven and Weetwood Old Dog, and a good choice of malt whiskies. There are picnic-sets on the patio and in the pleasant garden behind, with more seats out front. In the quietly picturesque village the pub is known just as the Thatch. *(Recommended by E G Parish, Michael and Marion Buchanan, John Watson, Olive and Ray Hebson, Dr and Mrs R A Newbury , MLR)*

Free house ~ Licensee Wes Charlesworth ~ Real ale ~ Bar food (lunchtime only) ~ Restaurant (evenings 6-9.30, Tues-Sat; not Sun and Mon) ~ (0151) 336 3416 ~ Children in eating area of bar, conservatory and restaurant ~ Dogs allowed in bar ~ Open 11.30-11; 12-10.30 Sun

RIBCHESTER SD6435 Map 7

White Bull

Church Street; turn off B6245 at sharp corner by Black Bull

The Tuscan pillars that support the entrance porch to this early 18th-c stone dining pub have stood here or nearby for nearly 2,000 years. Inside, the spacious and attractively refurbished main bar has comfortable old settles, Victorian advertisements and various prints, and a stuffed fox in two halves that looks as if it's jumping through the wall. Most areas are set out for eating during the day, and in summer you can also eat out in the garden behind; the dining area is no smoking. The good reasonably priced bar food is popular, and the straightforward menu includes soup (£1.90), sandwiches (from £3), home-made chicken liver pâté (£3.50), ploughman's or half a roast chicken (£5.50), home-made steak and kidney pie or crispy battered haddock (£5.55), grilled lamb chops (£6.95), various steaks with a choice of toppings (from £7.95), and weekly changing specials such as roast salmon, tarragon and asparagus pancake (£3.25), chicken supreme glazed with madeira and sherry sauce (£7.50), and lemon sole filled with prawn and crabmeat with watercress sauce (£7.95); puddings include home-made cheesecake and sticky toffee pudding (£2.75). Well kept Boddingtons and Timothy Taylors Landlord and a guest such as Three Bs Tacklers Tipple on handpump; also several wines, and a good range of malt whiskies. Even when it's busy service is friendly and efficient; darts, TV, pool, juke box, and dominoes in the games room; piped music. The pub is in an interesting Roman village by the River Ribble; there are the remains of a Roman bath house scattered behind the pub, and a small Roman museum nearby. *(Recommended by Robert and Margaret Whelband, Dr Paull Khan, Norma and Noel Thomas, MLR)*

Whitbreads ~ Lease Neil Sandiford ~ Real ale ~ Bar food (11.30-2, 6.30-9; 12-8 Sun; not Mon evening) ~ Restaurant ~ (01254) 878303 ~ Children in eating area of bar and restaurant ~ Open 11.30-3, 6.30-11; 12-10.30 Sun ~ Bedrooms: £30.50S/£41S (£46B)

STALYBRIDGE SJ9698 Map 7

Station Buffet £

Five of the eight handpumps at this classic Victorian platform bar serve an impressive range of up to 20 guest ales a week, and such is their reputation for showcasing new real ales that they are continually being approached by interesting microbreweries to stock their latest brews. You'll also find well kept Boddingtons, Flowers IPA and Wadworths 6X, and they have farm cider, and Belgian and other foreign bottled beers. Not smart but comfortably nostalgic, the bar has a welcoming fire below an etched-glass mirror, newspapers and magazines to read, and old photographs of the station in its heyday and other railway memorabilia; there's a little conservatory. An extension along the platform leads into what was the ladies' waiting room and part of the station-master's quarters, with original ornate ceilings and a dining/function room with Victorian-style wallpaper; dominoes, cribbage, draughts. On a sunny day you can sit out on the platform. As well as good coffee and tea made freshly by the pot, they do cheap old-fashioned snacks such as black peas (50p) and sandwiches (from £1.50), and three or four daily specials such as home-made pie with peas (£1.50), bacon casserole (£2.20), and all day breakfast (£2.25). They hold good beer festivals in early May and late November. *(Recommended by Bernie Adams, JP, PP, Andrew York, Pete Yearsley, the Didler, John Hulme, Tim Butterworth, Nick Holding)*

Free house ~ Licensees John Hesketh and Sylvia Wood ~ Real ale ~ Bar food (all day) ~ Restaurant ~ (0161) 303 0007 ~ Children welcome ~ Dogs welcome ~ Folk music Sat evenings, quiz Mon night ~ Open 11-11; 12-10.30 Sun; closed 25 Dec

TUNSTALL SD6173 Map 7

Lunesdale Arms 🍷

A683 S of Kirkby Lonsdale

Shades of blue and yellow in much of this civilised and brightly opened-up dining pub: on yellow walls the big unframed oil paintings (some for sale) are often of bluebells, some of the pews and armchairs have blue and/or yellow upholstery, and the blinds for most of the big windows are also blue and yellow. Bare boards and lively acoustics add to a cheerful bustling atmosphere. On one side of the central bar part, a white-walled area (where the pictures are framed) has a good mix of stripped and sealed solid dining tables, and sofas around a lower table with daily papers, by a woodburning stove which has a couple of orchids on the stone mantelpiece. At the other end, an airy games section has pool, table football and TV, and a snugger little flagstoned back part has another woodburning stove. Food is undoubtedly the main focus here. With good home-baked bread, and using meat from local farms only, and a lot of local organic produce, it might include soup (£3), spring onion and gruyère cheese tartlet (£3.95), hummus and roasted vegetable open sandwich (£4), moussaka (£5/£7), steak and kidney pie (£8.50), roast cod with slow-roasted tomatoes, green beans and sauté potatoes (£9), and pork stuffed with parmesan, basil and sunblush tomatoes wrapped in parma ham (£9.50); puddings such as home-made sticky toffee pudding and lemon and lime tart (£3.75). They do small helpings for children. Service is helpful and friendly, and besides well kept real ales such as Black Sheep and Jennings Cumberland on handpump they have a good range of sensibly priced wines by the glass (in a choice of sizes), and good cafetière coffee. Piped music may sometimes obtrude (though there was none on our lunchtime inspection visit). This pretty Lune Valley village has a church with Brontë associations. *(Recommended by John and Sylvia Harrop, Malcolm Taylor, Dr K Roger Wood)*

Free house ~ Licensee Emma Gillibrand ~ Bar food ~ Restaurant ~ (01524) 274203 ~ Children welcome ~ Open 11-3, 6-11; 12-3, 6-10.30 Sun; closed Mon exc bank hols

UPPERMILL SD9905 Map 7

Church Inn

From the main street (A607), look out for the sign for Saddleworth Church, and turn off up this steep narrow lane – keep on up!

Managing to be smart and comfortable without losing any of its genuine local character, this ancient pub stands alone by an isolated church on a steep moorland slope. The big unspoilt L-shaped main bar has high beams and some stripped stone; one window at the end of the bar counter looks down over the valley, and there's also a valley view from the quieter no smoking dining room. The comfortable furnishings include settles and pews as well as a good individual mix of chairs, and there are lots of attractive prints, staffordshire and other china on a high delft shelf, jugs, brasses and so forth; TV and occasional unobtrusive piped music. The horse-collar on the wall is worn by the winner of their annual gurning (or face-pulling) championship (part of the lively Rush Cart Festival, usually held over the August bank holiday), and handbells here are the church bellringers' practice set. They brew their own good value Saddleworth ales here, including Saddleworth More, More Gold, Ayrtons, Bert Corner, Hopsmacker, Pete's Dragon and Shaftbender, along with seasonal ales. They also keep a couple of Scottish Courage guest beers on handpump, a good choice of wines, several malt whiskies and a farm cider. Children and dogs are given an especially warm welcome (if the dogs dare to brave an ever-increasing army of rescued cats). The decent range of reasonably priced bar food includes soup (£1.65), pâté (£2.95), sandwiches (from £3.25), steak and ale pie (£5.25), mixed grill (£11.50) and daily specials such as minted lamb shank (£6.25), and poached salmon (£6.25); puddings such as chocolate fudge cake and jam roly-poly (£2.25). Outside seats on a small terrace look up towards the moors, with more out in a garden – and anything from rabbits, ducks and geese to horses and a couple of peacocks; look out for the head brewer and his fellow morris dancers practising their moves in the garden. *(Recommended by Revd D Glover, JP, PP, the Didler, Bob Broadhurst)*

Own brew ~ Licensee Julian Taylor ~ Real ale ~ Bar food (12-2.30, 5.30-9; 12-9 Sat/Sun) ~ Restaurant ~ (01457) 872415 ~ Children welcome ~ Dogs allowed in bar ~ Open 12-11; 12-10.30 Sun

WHARLES SD4435 Map 7

Eagle & Child

Church Road; from B5269 W of Broughton turn left into Higham Side Road at HMS Inskip sign

Though you'de never guess from the outside, this unchanging thatched ale house is filled with an amazing collection of antique furniture, put together by the chatty landlord. The most interesting bit is in the L-shaped bar, where a beamed area round the corner past the counter has a magnificent, elaborately carved Jacobean settle which originally came from Aston Hall in Birmingham, and carries the motto *exaltavit humiles*. There's also a carved oak chimneypiece, and a couple of fine longcase clocks, one from Chester, and another with a nicely painted face and an almost silent movement from Manchester. The plain cream walls are hung with modern advertising mirrors and some older mirrors, and there are a few exotic knives, carpentry tools and so forth on the plastered structural beams. Even when it's not particularly cold, there should be a good fire burning in the intricate cast-iron stove, and the atmosphere is welcoming and relaxed. Beers change all the time but could include Boddingtons, Mansfield and

Robinsons Best on handpump. They've darts in a sensible side area, pool, fruit machine and a TV; look out for the two sociable cats. Outside are a couple of picnic-sets. Please note the limited opening hours; more reports please. *(Recommended by Ian and Nita Cooper, Kevin Blake, Andy and Jill Kassube)*

Free house ~ Licensee Brian Tatham ~ Real ale ~ No credit cards ~ (01772) 690312 ~ Open 7-11; 12-4, 7-10.30 Sun

WHITEWELL SD6546 Map 7

Inn at Whitewell ★★

Most easily reached by B6246 from Whalley; road through Dunsop Bridge from B6478 is also good

'Wonderful', 'a joy to visit' and 'a superb find' are typical of what readers have said recently about this superbly run hotel, deep in the Forest of Bowland and surrounded by wooded rolling hills set off against higher moors. The most dramatic way to approach it is probably from Abbeystead. It's impressively furnished: the old-fashioned pubby bar has antique settles, oak gateleg tables, sonorous clocks, old cricketing and sporting prints, roaring log fires (the lounge has a very attractive stone fireplace), and heavy curtains on sturdy wooden rails; one area has a selection of newspapers, dominoes, local maps and guide books, there's a piano for anyone who wants to play, and even an art gallery. Although it gets very busy (and booking is a good idea), it's spacious inside and out, so the atmosphere usually remains tranquil and relaxing; the staff are courteous and friendly. Very good bar food could include soup (£3.20), open sandwiches (from £3.90), apple and lancashire cheese tart with mustard dressing (£4.80), poached salmon salad with quail eggs and asparagus (£5.50), grilled kipper or ploughman's (£6.50), fish and chips (£8), fish pie (£8.40), and fried pork medallions with potato galette, apple and sultana compote and mustard sauce (£12); home-made puddings and ice cream (from £3.50) and farmhouse cheeses (from £3.50). You can get coffee and cream teas all day, they sell jars of home-made jam, and if you're staying they'll do you a picnic hamper. Their good wine list contains around 180 wines (including a highly recommended claret), and they've well kept Boddingtons and Marstons Pedigree on handpump. Down a corridor with strange objects like a stuffed fox disappearing into the wall is the pleasant suntrap garden, with wonderful views down to the valley. We highly recommend the excellent, spacious bedrooms; they've nice bathrooms, CD players, and some even have their own peat fires in winter. The hotel owns several miles of trout, salmon and sea trout fishing on the Hodder, and with notice they'll arrange shooting. *(Recommended by Peter and Giff Bennett, R L Gorick, Nigel Woolliscroft, Comus and Sarah Elliott, Steve Whalley, Norman Stansfield, Paul Humphreys, Revd D Glover, Anthony Longden, Robert and Catherine Dunster, Mrs P J Carroll, Sue and Bob Ward, Sally Anne and Peter Goodale; also in the* Good Hotel Guide*)*

Free house ~ Licensee Richard Bowman ~ Real ale ~ Bar food (12-2, 7.30-9.30) ~ Restaurant ~ (01200) 448222 ~ Children welcome ~ Dogs welcome ~ Open 11-3, 6-11; 12-2, 7-11 Sun ~ Bedrooms: £78B/£108B

YEALAND CONYERS SD5074 Map 7

New Inn

3 miles from M6 junction 35; village signposted off A6

Handy for the M6, this friendly 17th-c ivy-covered village pub is a good place to break a journey. The simply furnished little beamed bar on the left has a cosy village atmosphere, with its log fire in the big stone fireplace, and cribbage and dominoes. On the right, two communicating no smoking cottagey dining rooms have dark blue furniture, shiny beams and an attractive kitchen range. They've well kept Hartleys XB and Robinsons seasonal beer on handpump, around 30 malt whiskies, winter mulled wine and home-made lemonade in summer; piped music. Readers particularly recommend the soup (£2.60) and sandwiches (from £3.45), while other enjoyable dishes could include filled baked potatoes (from

£3.85), cumberland sausage (£7.65), stuffed mushrooms (£7.95), beef in beer or salmon fillet (£8.25), pies such as venison, beef and mushroom or chicken breast stuffed with bacon and stilton (£8.95), and specials such as stuffed roasted peppers with cheese and brandy cream sauce (£8.25), plaice with prawn and crab mousse or venison and black pudding casserole with red wine, shallots and mushrooms (£10.95), fillet steak (£13.50), and puddings such as sticky toffee pudding (from £3.65); the same menu runs through the no smoking restaurant and bar. Service is friendly and efficient. A sheltered lawn at the side has picnic-sets among roses and flowering shrubs. *(Recommended by Richard Greaves, John Watson, Revd D Glover, Eric Locker, Mike Tucker, MLR, Lorraine and Fred Gill, R T and J C Moggridge, Michael Doswell)*

Robinsons ~ Tenants Bill Tully and Charlotte Pinder ~ Real ale ~ Bar food (11.30 (12 Sun)-9.30) ~ Restaurant ~ (01524) 732938 ~ Children welcome ~ Dogs allowed in bar ~ Open 11.30-11; 12-10.30 Sun

Lucky Dip

Besides the fully inspected pubs, you might like to try these Lucky Dips recommended to us and described by readers (if you do, please send us reports: www.goodguides.com).

Affetside [SD7513]
Pack Horse [Watling St]: Attractive neatly kept moorland local on Roman road, well kept Hydes ale, big helpings of lunchtime bar food, snug pool room, restaurant; good walking country *(P Abbott, Norma and Noel Thomas)*
Altham [SD7732]
Walton Arms [Burnley Rd (A678)]: Attractive pub with wide range of food inc early evening bargains, well kept Jennings, good service *(Andy and Jill Kassube)*
Altrincham [SJ7688]
Carpenters Arms [Old Market Pl]: Friendly family-run local, cosy bar with side rooms, Marstons Pedigree and Theakstons XB, old photographs of former local pubs, wide choice of enjoyable food, upstairs bistro *(Robert Lester)*
Unicorn [Halebarns; nr M56 junction 6, via A538]: Former hotel recently reopened as Wetherspoons pub with split-level basement and ground-floor bar, Boddingtons, Courage Directors and Theakstons, good value food, friendly service; open all day *(Robert Lester)*
Anderton [SD6112]
Millstone [Bolton Rd (A673)]: Wide-ranging imaginative choice of good food, lots of wines by the glass *(O Richardson)*
Arkholme [SD5872]
Bay Horse [B6254 Carnforth—Kirkby Lonsdale]: Attractive neatly kept old country local, lovely inglenook, good pictures of long-lost London pubs, popular food inc good value sandwiches, well kept Bass, Boddingtons and Wadworths 6X; own bowling green, charming valley handy for Lune Valley walks *(Margaret Dickinson)*
Redwell: Pleasant 17th-c country inn with popular food all day from sandwiches, baked potatoes and enterprising hot baguettes to steaks and other chargrills, Fri fish night, children's dishes, well kept ales such as Coniston Bluebird; bedrooms *(Andy and Jill Kassube)*
Bacup [SD8623]
Queens [Yorkshire St]: Unspoilt, with back main bar, homely front room on left with coal fire, darts, cards, dominoes and shove-ha'penny, friendly efficient service, well kept John Smiths, pool on right *(Pete Baker)*
Bebington [SJ3385]
Travellers Rest [B5151, Higher Bebington]: Friendly semi-rural corner local with up to eight well kept ales inc some from small breweries, enjoyable reasonably priced bar lunches from sandwiches to mixed grill (orders stop 1.45), beams, brasses etc, no smoking room, efficient staff; no children *(MLR)*
Birkenhead [SJ3289]
Crown [Conway St]: Interestingly tiled alehouse with up to a dozen changing ales inc Cains and Jennings, Weston's farm cider, good basic food, low prices, several rooms; open all day, cl Sun lunchtime *(the Didler)*
Dispensary [Chester St]: Well kept Cains ales, good value lunchtime food, handsome glass ceiling; handy for ferry *(the Didler)*
Stork [Price St]: Early 19th-c, carefully done up without being spoilt; Threlfalls tiled façade, four rooms around island bar, polished original floor, old dock and ferry photographs, several well kept real ales, wkdy lunches; open all day (not Sun) *(MLR, the Didler)*
Blacko [SD8541]
☆ ***Moorcock*** [A682 towards Gisburn (and in fact over the Yorkshire border)]: Beautifully placed moorland dining pub, roomy and comfortable, with big picture windows for breathtaking views, tables set close for the huge range of popular and often enterprising food inc lamb from their own flock, excellent beef and some German dishes, very friendly helpful staff, decent wine, Thwaites Bitter and Mild under top pressure; tables in hillside garden with various animals, open all day for food Sun, children and dogs welcome, bedrooms *(John Watson, Steve Whalley, Norma and Noel Thomas, Patrick Hancock, LYM)*
Blackpool [SD3136]
Ramsden Arms [Talbot Rd, opp Blackpool

North station]: Large pub done up attractively with masses of mainly beer-related bric-a-brac and pictures, friendly helpful staff, no smoking area, well kept cheap house beer, also Boddingtons, Jennings, Tetleys and guest ales, over 40 whiskies; CD juke box, games; good value bedrooms *(Patrick Hancock)*

Stanley Beer Engine [Church St]: Alehouse-theme pub with good range of changing beers, photographs of Blackpool FC from Stanley Matthews era; live band nights, handy for Winter Gardens *(Patrick Hancock)*

Wheatsheaf [Talbot Rd, opp Blackpool North station]: Friendly traditional pub with well kept beers from nearby Blackpool brewery, lots of 60s pop music memorabilia *(Patrick Hancock)*

Bolton [SD7109]

Howcroft [Pool St]: Friendly backstreet local serving as tap for local Bank Top ales, also guest beers and Addlestone's cider; well preserved period interior, lots of small screened-off rooms around central servery with fine glass and woodwork, cosy snug with coal fire, good value lunches in lounge, plenty of games inc pinball, darts, bar billiards; bowling green, occasional live music, open all day *(the Didler)*

Spinning Mule [Nelson Sq]: Typical Wetherspoons, usual good choice of real ales and new world wines, decent coffee, reasonably priced food all day; very busy with young people Sat night *(Andy and Jill Kassube, Gordon Tong)*

Bolton by Bowland [SD7849]

Coach & Horses [Main St]: Untouristy traditional décor and good atmosphere under friendly newish licensees, good fresh food using local produce from sandwiches up, well kept Black Sheep and Boddingtons, log fires, separate dining room, darts and pool; big comfortable bedrooms with own bathrooms, good breakfast, lovely streamside village with interesting church *(Mr and Mrs I W Clough)*

Broughton [SD4838]

☆ ***Plough at Eaves*** [A6 N through Broughton, 1st left about a mile after traffic lights, then bear left after another 1½ miles]: Two very low-beamed carpeted bars, friendly, homely and good value, with consistently enjoyable home-made food, well kept Thwaites ales, lots of malt whiskies, plenty of old-fashioned charm; darts, pool and other games, piped music; tables outside, well equipped play area *(LYM, John and Elspeth Howell, Jackie and Martin Smith, Margaret Dickinson)*

Bury [SD8012]

Garsdale [Woodhill Rd]: Welcoming, with enjoyable generous fresh food, reasonable prices, good choice of wines by the glass, pleasant surroundings *(anon)*

☆ ***Lord Raglan*** [off A56 N under a mile E of M66 junction 1; Mount Pleasant, Nangreaves, down cobbled track]: Welcoming friendly ivy-covered cottage row in lonely moorside location, with great views, brewing its own good Leydens Raglan Sleeve and Nanny Flyer; carefully made food from sandwiches to good meals using fresh ingredients inc a monthly diners' club, pleasant young staff, good wines and interesting foreign bottled beers, lots of bric-a-brac in traditional front bar, big open fire in cosy back room, plainer blond-panelled dining room (where children allowed; crudités as you wait to go in) *(Gordon Tong, P Abbott, LYM, John and Sylvia Harrop)*

Carnforth [SD4970]

County Hotel [Lancaster Rd (A6)]: Neatly kept comfortable hotel, well used by locals, reliable traditional food from good sandwiches to full meals, restaurant off bar not too formal; bedrooms *(Ray and Winifred Halliday)*

Caton [SD5364]

Ship [Lancaster Rd]: Cosy little open-plan pub, immaculately kept with interesting range of nautical bric-a-brac, good fire in charming antique fireplace, good choice of reasonably priced food from sandwiches to generous fresh fish and Sun lunch, no smoking dining room, well kept Thwaites ales, efficient friendly staff, magazines; nostalgic piped music, can be busy wknds; tables in garden, handy for Lune Valley and Forest of Bowland *(Margaret Dickinson)*

Catterall [SD5042]

Pickerings Park [B6430]: Hotel with pleasant public bar, enjoyable bar food such as bargain rump steak, up to five real ales such as Charles Wells Eagle; good bedrooms *(Andy and Jill Kassube)*

Cheadle Hulme [SJ8785]

Church Inn [Ravenoak Rd (A5149 SE)]: Genuinely old inn, clean and friendly, good range of well kept Robinsons ales and of good slightly unusual food lunchtime and early wkdy evenings, ordered from small hatch and served by pleasant waitresses *(Stephen, Julie and Hayley Brown)*

Chipping [SD6243]

☆ ***Sun*** [Windy St]: Charming stone-built country local with three small snug panelled rooms, good value food, well kept Black Sheep, Boddingtons, Smiles Best, Theakstons Mild and Timothy Taylors Landlord (an underground stream cools the cellar), quick friendly service, open fire, papers and magazines, interesting local photographs and ironstone china, games room with pool and darts; very busy wknds, tables in courtyard, attractive village *(Margaret Dickinson, Steve Whalley)*

Churchtown [SD4843]

Horns [A586 just W of A6]: Sizeable roadside pub with good choice of enjoyable food from sandwiches and light lunches to steaks, well kept real ales inc Castle Eden; tables in large garden *(anon)*

☆ ***Punch Bowl*** [Church St, off A586 Garstang—St Michaels-on-Wyre]: Good choice of good food in busy and attractive mock-Tudor beamed pub/restaurant with three small quaint bar rooms, panelling, stained glass, lots of stuffed animals, dining rooms; friendly staff, well kept Tetleys, good fires, disabled facilities; lovely village *(anon)*

Clayton-le-Moors [SD7430]

Albion [Whalley Rd (A680)]: Canalside alehouse with at least six keenly priced local Porter ales, food too now inc good pasta and vegetarian ranges *(Andy and Jill Kassube)*

Colne [SD9242]
Hare & Hounds [Skipton Old Rd, Black Lane Ends – NE, towards Lothersdale]: Newish landlord doing wide choice of food all day inc some unusual dishes, relaxed unhurried atmosphere, Timothy Taylors ales *(Alison Keys)*
Cowan Bridge [SD6277]
☆ ***Whoop Hall*** [off A65 towards Kirkby Lonsdale]: Spacious, airy and comfortable linked areas with wide choice of interesting quick food all day from 8am from popular buttery, well kept Boddingtons and Theakstons Best and XB, decent wines, pleasant restaurant, friendly service; children welcome, tables in garden well off road with play area, well appointed bedrooms *(Alan Wilcock, Christine Davidson, LYM)*
Crank [SJ5099]
Red Cat: Friendly pub/restaurant with good if not cheap food, freshly cooked and generous (lamb pot-roast particularly praised), in front lounge and nicely decorated dining room – must book *(Rupert Nichols, Diana Stone)*
Croston [SD4818]
☆ ***Black Horse*** [A581 Chorley—Southport]: Friendly Victorian village local with well kept changing ales such as Black Sheep, Cains Bitter and Dark Mild, Moorhouses Premier, John Smiths and Timothy Taylors Best, beer festivals Apr and Oct, hearty low-priced food inc bargain wkdy lunches, popular Sun roast (all afternoon) and children's and OAP meals, big no smoking back dining area; pub games inc pool, piped music, SkyTV, Thurs quiz night; children in eating areas, picnic-sets outside, good solid play area, crown bowls green and boules pitch, open all day *(R Mathews, George Little, Jim Abbott, Steve Whalley, Mr and Mrs M Cooper, Kevin Thorpe, LYM, David Field)*
Wheatsheaf [Town Rd]: Convivial and chatty, nice décor, hops and fresh flowers, 19th-c Croston photographs, stripped boards and quarry tiles, alcoves, generous interesting food all day inc home-baked bread and lunchtime and early evening bargains, well kept weekly changing beers such as Flowers and Timothy Taylors Landlord, no smoking area, pleasant unobtrusive piped music *(Brian Kneale, Margaret Dickinson)*
Darwen [SD7222]
☆ ***Old Rosins*** [Pickup Bank, Hoddlesden, off B6232 Haslingden—Belthorn opp Grey Mare]: Isolated open-plan moorland inn with comfortable banquettes and good log fire, mugs and jugs hanging from beams, picture-window views from no smoking end, reasonably priced usual food all day from sandwiches to steaks, good cheerful service, well kept Jennings Bitter, No 1, Cumberland and Sneck Lifter, plenty of malt whiskies; fruit machine, piped music; children welcome, picnic-sets on big crazy-paved terrace, bedrooms with own bathrooms, open all day *(Pat and Tony Martin, Andy and Jill Kassube, Steve Whalley, Bob Broadhurst, LYM)*
Denshaw [SD9711]
☆ ***Rams Head*** [2 miles from M62 junction 2; A672 towards Oldham, pub N of village]: Cosy and comfortable moorland farm/pub with several small rooms mainly for diners (good meals, altogether more sophisticated than you'd expect from location), with well kept Theakstons, Timothy Taylors and perhaps a guest beer, reasonably priced wines, bric-a-brac on beams and panelling, log fires, traditional settles; children welcome, unobtrusive piped music; on special days eg Mothering Sunday dining room may be fully booked with no bar snacks served, but otherwise popular with walkers – lovely scenery, good walking *(Mrs P J Carroll)*
Dobcross [SD9906]
Swan [The Square]: Low beams, flagstones, three areas (one no smoking) off central bar, several real ales such as Moorhouses and Phoenix, enjoyable sensibly priced food inc children's, friendly staff; tables outside, attractive village below moors *(Richard and Ruth Dean, Bill Sykes)*
Dunham Town [SJ7288]
☆ ***Vine*** [Barns Lane, Dunham Massey]: Friendly and old-fashioned small-roomed local handy for the park, beamery and brass-topped tables, well kept Sam Smiths, enjoyable food from soup and sandwiches up inc some interesting dishes, hard-working helpful staff; darts, quiet piped music, dogs welcome; plenty of tables in garden *(Pete Yearsley, John Watson)*
Eccles [SJ7798]
Grapes [Liverpool Rd, Peel Green; A57 ½ mile from M63 junction 2]: Edwardian local with superb glass and tiling, lots of mahogany, brilliant staircase, cheap Holts Bitter and Mild, fairly quiet roomy lounge and smoke room, pool room, vault with Manchester darts (can get quite loud and smoky), drinking corridor; open all day *(the Didler, Pete Baker)*
Lamb [Regent St (A57)]: Gorgeous untouched and handsomely preserved Edwardian hotel, now a three-room local – an object-lesson for pub architects – with splendid etched windows, fine woodwork and furnishings, extravagantly tiled stairway, admirable trophies in display case; cheap well kept Holts Bitter and Mild, cheap lunchtime sandwiches, full-size snooker table in original billiards room; popular with older people *(GLD, JES, the Didler, Nick Holding)*
Queens Arms [Green Lane (B5231), Patricroft]: Said to have been the world's first railway pub; basic bar, comfortable lounge, delightful snug, Boddingtons and guest beer, many photographs of old Eccles (inc the original Eccles cake shop); tables outside, open all day wknds, cl wkdy lunchtimes *(Bernie Adams)*
Royal Oak [Barton Lane]: Large unspoilt Edwardian pub on busy corner, several rooms, handsome tilework, cheap Holts Bitter and Mild *(the Didler, Nick Holding)*
Stanley Arms [Eliza Ann St/Liverpool Rd (A57), Patricroft]: Busy mid-Victorian corner local with cheap Holts Bitter and Mild, lunchtime sandwiches, popular front bar, hatch serving two back rooms, drinking corridor *(the Didler)*

White Lion [Liverpool Rd, Patricroft, a mile from M63 junction 2]: Welcoming unchanging Edwardian local, clean, tidy and popular with older people, with games in lively traditional public bar, tiled side drinking corridor with separate smoke room (wknd pianist) and quiet lounge off, great value Holts Bitter and Mild *(Pete Baker, the Didler)*

Eccleston [SD5117]

☆ ***Farmers Arms*** [Towngate (B5250, off A581 Chorley—Southport)]: Big cheery low-beamed pub/restaurant, wide choice of consistently good generous food all day, wkdy bargains and some unusual twists to familiar themes; modernised but keeping character – black cottagey furniture, brocaded wall seats, quotations on stencilled walls, plates, pastoral prints, clocks and brasses; well kept Boddingtons, Tetleys and a guest such as Timothy Taylors Landlord, friendly helpful service, darts, interesting choice of piped music; parking can be tight when busy; good value bedrooms some with own bathroom, open all day *(Margaret Dickinson, Derek Stafford, Alan Bowker, J A Hooker, Richard Smerdon)*

Edgworth [SD7316]

Black Bull [Bolton Rd, Turton]: Three-room pub with well kept changing ales such as Lees, Moorhouses Pendle Witches Brew, Tetleys, Charles Wells Bombardier and Woodfordes Wherry, good service of good value food from sandwiches, baguettes and good home-made soup to hearty main dishes (all day wknds), open fire, very friendly landlord, light and airy new hill-view restaurant area, lovely summer floral displays; live music Thurs, Tues quiz night, moorside village, good walks *(Michael and Marion Buchanan, P Abbott, Norma and Noel Thomas)*

Euxton [SD5319]

Plough [Runshaw Moor; a mile from A49/B5252 junction]: Charming country dining pub with good atmosphere, enjoyable food inc upmarket dishes, well kept real ales, sympathetic extension, black beams, partitions and so forth; big sheltered back lawn with tables and small play area *(anon)*

Fence [SD8337]

Bay Horse [Wheatley Lane Rd, Higham]: Small and friendly, with well kept Marstons Pedigree, Theakstons and Charles Wells Bombardier, efficient service, good restaurant *(Norman Stansfield, Alan J Morton, Norma and Noel Thomas)*

☆ ***Forest*** [B6248 Brierfield rd, off A6068]: Civilised dining pub with Pennine views, big open fire, soft lighting, plush banquettes in open-plan bar, oak-panelled dining room, lots of paintings, vases, plates and books, partly no smoking conservatory, wide choice of food (all day Sun) inc some small helpings for children, real ales such as Greene King Old Speckled Hen and Ruddles, Marstons Pedigree and Theakstons Best, good choice of wines, friendly helpful service; unobtrusive piped music; children welcome, open all day *(Norman Stansfield, LYM, Louise English, I D Greenfield, Steve Whalley)*

Fleetwood [SD3247]

North Euston [Esplanade, nr tram terminus]: Big comfortably refurbished bar in architecturally interesting Victorian hotel overlooking seafront, long railway connections (was LMS terminal, with ferry to Scotland); decent lunchtime food esp in nice back Mediterranean Bar, wide range of well kept mainstream real ales, consistently good service, no smoking family area (till 7), seats outside; comfortable bedrooms, open all day *(Margaret Dickinson, Richard and Margaret Peers)*

Garstang [SD4944]

Bradbeer Bar [Garstang Country Hotel & Golf Club; B6430 S]: Relaxed and spacious bar overlooking golfing greens, helpful well trained staff, huge woodburner, very good value imaginative food; tables outside, bedrooms *(Margaret Dickinson)*

☆ ***Royal Oak*** [Market Pl]: Typical small-town inn in same family for nearly 50 years, cosy yet roomy and comfortably refurbished, with attractive panelling, several eating areas inc charming snug, generous consistently above-average food (all day Sun) inc imaginatively presented specials, small helpings for children or OAPs, pleasant staff, Robinsons real ales, good value coffee; main bar can be smoky; restaurant, disabled access, comfortable bedrooms, open all day Sun *(Margaret Dickinson, Malcolm Taylor)*

☆ ***Th'Owd Tithebarn*** [off Church St]: Rustically converted barn with big flagstoned terrace overlooking Lancaster Canal, thorough-going Victorian country life theme with antique kitchen range, masses of farm tools, stuffed animals and birds, flagstones and high rafters, even waitresses in period costume and a 9-metre (30-ft) central refectory table; simple food all day from filled baguettes up, Flowers IPA and Tetleys, lots of country wines; piped music, can get very busy; children in dining room, open all day summer *(Kevin Blake, LYM)*

Goosnargh [SD5537]

Bushells Arms [4 miles from M6 junction 32; turn right off A6 in Broughton, then left to Goosnargh in Whittingham]: Spotless straightforwardly refurbished pub with well kept Timothy Taylors Landlord and big dining area *(Christine and Neil Townend, Roger and Jenny Huggins, LYM, Pat and Tony Martin)*

☆ ***Grapes*** [Church Lane]: Welcoming local with well kept changing ales inc some rare brews, massive helpings of northern food (not Mon evening) from sandwiches to good Sun roast, friendly helpful landlord, two low-beamed areas separated by big coal fire, lots of brass around this, collection of whisky-water jugs and old telephones, separate games room with darts and pool; tables outside, bowling green, open all day Thurs-Sun *(Mike Pugh, Steve Whalley, R L Gorick)*

☆ ***Stags Head*** [B5269]: Recently well refurbished in a style reminiscent of a good Vintage Inn (it's actually an S&N franchise, though), with lots of separate mainly old-world areas rambling around a central servery, plenty of nice features (even proper old-fashioned radiators), good value freshly made food inc imaginative dishes, friendly well trained staff, Flowers IPA, popular restaurant (may be fully booked); well reproduced contemporary chart music, live music Fri *(Margaret Dickinson, R L Gorick, BB, Mike and Linda Hudson)*

Greasby [SJ2587]

☆ ***Greave Dunning*** [Greasby Rd (off B5139)]: Extended pub doing well after refurbishment and reopening, homely flagstoned bar with quiet alcoves, lofty main lounge with upper gallery, comfortable seating inc a sofa, enjoyable well presented food inc light dishes, polite helpful staff, well kept Fullers London Pride and Stones, decent wines *(E G Parish, Philip Hastain, Dawn Baddeley, LYM)*

Great Mitton [SD7138]

☆ ***Aspinall Arms*** [B6246 NW of Whalley]: Dual bar, popular and welcoming, with red plush wall banquettes, comfortable chairs, settees and bar stools, old-world prints, well kept changing ales such as Greene King IPA and Abbot, Skinners Spriggan, Timothy Taylors Landlord and Wyre Piddle Piddle in the Wind, enjoyable food from good cold or hot sandwiches up, coal fire, papers, books and magazines to read, no music or machines; children welcome away from bar; nice surroundings, picnic-sets on flagstoned terrace and in big informal garden just above River Ribble, bedrooms, usefully opens earlier than most pubs around here *(Mr and Mrs J G Smith, BB, KC)*

Hambleton [SD3741]

Shard Bridge [off A588 towards Poulton, next to toll bridge]: Attractive whitewashed pub on Wyre estuary by former toll bridge; small smartly refurbished lounge with restaurant tables beyond, wide choice of reasonably priced freshly cooked waitress-served food from soup and ploughman's up, well kept Marstons Pedigree; nice outdoor tables overlooking water *(Margaret Dickinson)*

Hest Bank [SD4666]

☆ ***Hest Bank Hotel*** [Hest Bank Lane; off A6 just N of Lancaster]: Picturesque and welcoming three-bar coaching inn, good for families, with wide range of good freshly made generous food all day from sandwiches through fresh local fish and potted shrimps to busy all-day Sun carvery, also children's dishes, bargain set menus and special food nights, well kept ales such as Boddingtons, Robinsons Best, Timothy Taylors Landlord and a monthly changing guest beer, decent wines, friendly efficient service, idiosyncratic cartoons of licensees, separate restaurant area, lively history, Weds quiz night; plenty of garden tables by Lancaster canal, attractive setting close to Morecambe Bay *(Margaret Dickinson, Denise Dowd, BB)*

Hindley Green [SD6204]

Spinners Arms [Castle Hill Rd]: Recently tastefully refurbished, with good value food, small cosy restaurant; piped music, CCTV inside and out *(anon)*

Holden [SD7749]

☆ ***Copy Nook*** [the one up by Bolton by Bowland]: Spick-and-span roomy and well renovated roadside pub increasingly popular for wide choice of good food, particularly beef, lamb and fish, well kept beer, decent wines, efficient obliging staff, friendly atmosphere; six bedrooms *(Geoffrey and Brenda Wilson)*

Hoylake [SJ2189]

Plasterers Arms [Back Seaview]: Small whitewashed backstreet pub with sensibly priced real ales such as Cains, Greene King Abbot and an interesting guest beer, filled rolls, narrow lounge, hatch-served back snug; happy hour 5-7 *(MLR)*

Irby [SJ2586]

☆ ***Irby Mill*** [Irby Mill Hill, off Greasby rd]: Two low-beamed largely flagstoned rooms, one largely set for eating, well cooked straightforward bargain food all day (no sandwiches), full Jennings range and several changing guest beers kept well, decent house wines, comfortable pub furniture, coal-effect gas fire, local atmosphere, interesting old photographs and history of the former mill; can get very busy; a few tables outside *(MLR, Tony Tollitt, BB)*

Lancaster [SD4761]

Brown Cow [Penny St]: Long narrow unpretentious bar, generous bargain home-cooked food in simple back dining area, Thwaites real ale, friendly staff *(MLR)*

Lathom [SD4511]

☆ ***Ship*** [Parbold Rd after Ring o' Bells heading into Burscough; off A5209]: Big well run pub tucked below embankment at junction of Leeds & Liverpool and Rufford Branch canals, several separate rooms with décor varying from interestingly cluttered canal memorabilia through naval pictures and crests to hunting prints, beams, lots of copper and brass, cheap popular food from good lunchtime sandwiches up (small helpings of some dishes available), prompt friendly service even when busy, up to nine well kept changing ales, often interesting; games room with pool; open all day Fri-Sun *(MLR, BB, Nick Holding)*

Lea Town [SD4832]

Saddle [Sidgreaves Lane, N towards Woodplumpton]: Neatly refurbished country pub with enthusiastic new licensees, wide choice of enjoyable home-made food cooked to order from sandwiches up inc children's, nice dining area, Thwaites real ales, sensibly priced wines, good service; tables outside, pleasant play area, bedrooms *(Margaret Dickinson)*

Leyland [SD5422]

Midge Hall [Midge Hall Lane]: Very popular for good value straightforward food from sandwiches and baked potatoes up, obliging friendly staff, Tetleys; children welcome, some live music, seats outside *(Margaret Dickinson)*

Rose & Crown [Ulnes Walton (A581 S)]: Friendly little roadside pub with good range of beers inc Batemans XXX, Burtonwood and Wychwood Hobgoblin, tasty good value food lunchtime and early evening inc OAP specials; disabled access, garden tables *(Margaret Dickinson)*

Liverpool [SJ4395]

Cains Brewery Tap [Stanhope St]: Splendidly

restored Victorian architecture with nicely understated décor, wooden floors, plush raised side snug, lots of old prints and breweriana, handsome bar, flame-effect gas fire, newspapers; cosy relaxing atmosphere, friendly efficient staff, good well priced food, four well kept attractively priced Cains ales with four guest beers from other small breweries; popular brewery tour ending here with buffet and singing; sports TV, open all day *(the Didler, JP, PP)*

Carnarvon Castle [Tarleton St]: Neat and welcoming city-centre pub next to main shopping area; long and narrow, with one main bar and back lounge, cabinet of Dinky toys, well kept Bass, Cains Bitter and Mild, lunchtime bar snacks; open all day, cl Sun *(the Didler, Dr and Mrs A K Clarke, John A Barker)*

Cracke [Rice St]: Attractively basic, bare boards, walls covered with posters for local events and pictures of local buildings, unusual Beatles diorama in largest room, juke box and TV, very cheap lunchtime food and Thurs curry night, well kept Cains, Marstons Pedigree and guest beers; popular mainly with young people; open all day, sizeable garden *(MLR, JP, PP, the Didler, Mr and Mrs S Mason, Patrick Hancock)*

☆ ***Dispensary*** [Renshaw St]: Small pub with well kept Cains ales and three or four interesting guest beers, decent wkdy food 12-7, friendly staff, lots of polished wood and glass inc marvellous etched windows, bare boards, comfortable raised back bar, Victorian medicine bottles and instruments; open all day *(the Didler, George Little, John A Barker, Rev John Hibberd, David Field)*

☆ ***Doctor Duncan*** [St Johns Lane]: Well run classic Victorian tiled pub with full Cains range and guest ales kept well, Belgian and German beers on tap, enjoyable reasonably priced food till 7, friendly staff, no smoking family room; open all day *(the Didler, Peter F Marshall, David Field)*

Excelsior [Dale St]: Good value Porterhouse food 11-6 (and breakfast from 9), Cains Bitter and Mild and guest beers; open all day, cl Sun *(the Didler)*

Globe [Cases St]: Welcoming crowded bustle in well appointed traditional local, pleasant staff, well kept Cains Bitter and Dark Mild and Tetleys, good port, lunchtime filled baps, tiny sloping-floor back lounge, lots of prints of old Liverpool; open all day *(JP, PP, John A Barker, the Didler, Peter F Marshall, MLR)*

Grapes [Mathew St]: Lively and friendly, with well kept Cains and Tetleys, good value lunchtime bar food, open-plan but pleasantly well worn cottagey décor (flagstones, old range, wall settles, no two chairs the same, gas-effect lamps); open all day, can get crowded Fri/Sat, cl Sun *(David Field, the Didler, Patrick Hancock, John A Barker, JP, PP)*

Head of Steam [Lime St]: Well restored old railway buildings with lots of character and railway memorabilia; well kept real ales *(David Field)*

Lion [Moorfields, off Tithebarn St]: Splendidly preserved ornate Victorian alehouse, etched glass and serving hatches in central bar, two small lounges off, unusual wallpaper, big mirrors, panelling and tilework, fine domed structure behind, well kept Lees, Timothy Taylor and Walkers, cheap lunchtime food; open all day *(the Didler)*

Midland [Ranelagh St]: Attractive and neatly kept Victorian pub with original décor, ornate lounge, long corner bar, nice etched glass and mirrors, Tetleys *(John A Barker, the Didler)*

Peter Kavanaghs [Egerton St, off Catherine St]: Well kept Cains, Greene King Abbot and guest beers in side-street local with plenty of character; open all day *(the Didler)*

Poste House [Cumberland St]: Small comfortable backstreet local with room upstairs, well kept Cains Bitter and Mild, good wkdy lunches, friendly licensees *(the Didler)*

Prince Arthur [Rice Lane]: Unspoilt Victorian alehouse, busy and friendly, well kept Walkers *(the Didler, JP, PP)*

Roscoe Head [Roscoe St]: Three tiny unspoilt rooms, friendly, quiet and civilised, with outstandingly well kept Jennings, good value wkdy lunches, huge and growing tie collection; open all day *(David Field, the Didler, Patrick Hancock)*

Ship & Mitre [Dale St]: Friendly gaslit local with very wide changing choice of well kept unusual beers served in over-sized lined glasses, good cheap basic lunches, pool, occasional beer festivals; popular with university people, open all day *(MLR, the Didler, Patrick Hancock)*

Swan [Wood St]: Well kept Marstons Pedigree and Owd Rodger, Phoenix Wobbly Bob, guest beers and farm cider in backstreet bare-boards pub with loud 1970s rock juke box, Mon live music, good value home-cooked lunches and Fri curry night, Sun brunch, friendly staff; open all day *(Patrick Hancock)*

Vernon Arms [Dale St]: Tap for Liverpool Brewery with six of their beers in top condition, pleasant service, good value meals till 7; open all day, cl Sun *(the Didler)*

Vines [Lime St]: Big traditional pub, comfortable and friendly, with mosaic tilework, high-ceilinged room on right with stained glass; may not always have real ale, can get very busy *(the Didler, JP, PP)*

White Star [Rainford Gdns, off Matthew St]: Traditional basic local with well kept changing ales such as Cains, lots of woodwork, magnificent Bass mirror in back room, prints, White Star shipping line memorabilia, friendly service; SkyTV; open all day *(the Didler, Patrick Hancock)*

Lydgate [SD9704]

☆ ***White Hart*** [Stockport Rd]: 200-year-old stone-built inn overlooking Saddleworth Moor, recently well refurbished keeping beams and traditional character, main bar and one side room now a largely no smoking brasserie with wide choice of good food from chicken and pesto sandwiches or home-made sausages up, two other rooms for drinkers (Boddingtons, Flowers, Lees, Websters and one or two guest beers, good wine and malt whisky range), modern-style back restaurant; 12 nice bedrooms, pretty village *(Andrew Crawford, Edward Leetham)*

Lydiate [SD3604]

Scotch Piper [Southport Rd]: Medieval white-painted thatched pub with heavy black beams, flagstones and thick stone walls, Burtonwood Bitter and Top Hat, coal fire in front room, darts in middle room off corridor, carpeted back room, no food, music or machines; picnic-sets in large garden with aviary, hens, donkey and abundant flower baskets, open all day wknds *(Kevin Thorpe, the Didler)*

Lytham [SD3627]

County [Church Rd]: Well kept Boddingtons in spaciously refurbished pub with strong sporting influence; good value bedrooms *(Dr and Mrs A K Clarke)*

Fairhaven [Marine Drive]: Neatly kept extended modern pub with decent food from sandwiches and baguettes up, Boddingtons, Marstons Pedigree and Theakstons, obliging staff *(Margaret Dickinson)*

Ship & Royal [Clifton St]: Welcoming nautical-theme pub with well kept real ales, separate pool room; handy for shopping centre *(Dr and Mrs A K Clarke)*

Manchester [SJ8284]

☆ ***Ape & Apple*** [John Dalton St]: Uncharacteristically smart and open-plan Holts pub with their great value beer kept well and monthly guest beer festival, bargain hearty bar food, comfortable seats in bare-boards bar with nice lighting and lots of old prints and posters, armchairs in upstairs lounge; TV area, games machines; good mix on busy wknd evenings (unusually for city centre, over-25s won't feel out of place), quieter lunchtime or midweek; unusual brick cube garden, bedrooms, open all day *(the Didler, Dr and Mrs A K Clarke, Richard Lewis, Stephen, Julie and Hayley Brown)*

Bar Centro [Tib St]: Continental-style two-floor café-bar, pale woodwork, well kept Hydes and a couple of local guest beers such as Boggart Clough Tip St Tipple and Phoenix Moonshine, several continental draught beers, wide choice of creole and other food, daily papers, friendly helpful staff, local paintings for sale, frequent live music and DJs; open all day (till 1am Thurs-Sat) *(Richard Lewis, the Didler)*

Bar Fringe [Swan St]: Friendly continental café-style bare-boards bar specialising in beers from the low countries, also well kept changing ales such as Bank Top Gold Digger, Boggart Clough Jacks Nasty Face and Hydes Jekylls Gold, farm cider, friendly staff, food till 7, daily papers, cartoons, prints and bank notes, polished motorcycle hung above door; good music; tables out behind, open all day *(Richard Lewis, the Didler)*

☆ ***Beer House*** [Angel St, off Rochdale Rd]: Lively basic open-plan pub with prodigious array of handpumps for fine range of changing well kept ales, mainly unusual, also farm ciders and perry, several Belgian beers on tap, good range of bottled foreign beers and country wines; bare boards, friendly landlady, old local prints, robust cheap bar food lunchtime and Thurs/Fri evening inc Mon bargain lunch; darts, good CD juke box (may be loud), games machine, more comfortable upstairs bar with bar billiards, table footer and SkyTV, ceilidh band Tues; tables out in small area behind, open all day *(Richard Lewis, Peter F Marshall, Doug Christian, the Didler, JP, PP, SLC)*

Castle [Oldham St, about 200 yards from Piccadilly, on right]: Unspoilt traditional front bar, small snug, full Robinsons range kept well from fine bank of handpumps, games in well worn back room, nice tilework outside; no food, children allowed till 7, blues Thurs, open all day (Sun afternoon closure) *(the Didler, Patrick Hancock, Richard Lewis)*

Circus [Portland St]: Great atmosphere in two tiny rooms, back one panelled with leatherette banquettes, very well kept Tetleys from minute corridor bar, friendly landlord, celebrity photographs, no music or machines; often looks closed but normally open all day wkdys (you have to knock) *(JP, PP, the Didler, Patrick Hancock, Stephen, Julie and Hayley Brown)*

City Arms [Kennedy St, off St Peters Sq]: Five well kept changing beers such as Cains, Caledonian, Fullers and Youngs, Belgian bottled beers, occasional beer festivals, popular bar lunches inc sandwiches and baked potatoes, quiet evenings; coal fires, bare boards, prints and panelling, wheelchair access but steps down to back lounge; good piped music, TV, games machine; open all day (cl Sat lunchtime, Sun) *(Richard Lewis, the Didler, Pete Yearsley, John Hulme)*

Coach & Horses [Old Bury Rd, Whitefield; A665 nr Besses o' the Barn Station]: Coaching inn built around 1830, little changed and keeping several separate rooms, very popular and friendly, with well kept Holts, table service, darts, cards; open all day *(the Didler)*

Crescent [The Crescent (A6), Salford – opp Salford Univ]: Three 18th-c houses converted into beer house in 19th, unusual layout and homely unsmart décor, chatty buzzing local atmosphere, interesting guest ales, good value food, friendly staff, pool room, juke box; popular with students and university staff, open all day *(the Didler)*

Eagle [Collier St, off Greengate, Salford]: Old-fashioned backstreet local, absolutely no frills, well kept Holts Bitter and Mild at old-fashioned prices, bar servery to tap and passage with two smoke rooms), old Salford pictures, very friendly manager, cheap filled rolls; open all day *(the Didler)*

Eagle & Child [Higher Lane, Whitefield]: Black and white pub set back from road, with Holts Bitter and Mild; open all day *(the Didler)*

Egerton Arms [Gore St, Salford; A6 by station]: Several rooms, chandeliers, Art Nouveau lamps, excellent value Holts Bitter and Mild, also Boddingtons and Marstons; open all day *(the Didler)*

Grey Horse [Portland St, nr Piccadilly]: Cosy traditional Hydes local, welcoming and busy, with timbering, pictures and plates, well kept

Bitter and Mild, some unusual malt whiskies, popular lunchtime food; no juke box or machines, open all day *(John Hulme, Patrick Hancock, the Didler)*

Hare & Hounds [Shudehill, behind Arndale]: Long narrow bar linking front snug and comfortable back lounge (with TV), notable tilework, panelling and stained glass, well kept Holts, Lees and Tetleys, sandwiches, friendly staff; games and machine, piano singalongs, upstairs Fri folk club; open all day *(Pete Baker, the Didler, Richard Lewis)*

Hat & Feathers [Mason St]: Big side lounge with stage for music nights, bar with darts, pool, games and TV, small back snug, well kept Cains Dark Mild, Holts, Timothy Taylors Landlord and wknd guest beers, friendly staff, old Manchester prints; open all day, cl Tues *(Richard Lewis)*

Hogshead [High St]: Popular ale house, brick and bare boards, barrel tables, interesting prints and breweriana, good choice of very well kept beers inc bottled imports, lots of drinking areas, pool, juke box, games machines, friendly staff, decent food, daily papers; open all day *(Richard Lewis)*

☆ ***Jacksons Wharf*** [Slate Wharf, Castlefield; across bridge from Barca]: Masses of carved oak in amazing cathedral-like interior, pulpits on upper level, lovely views over canal quay, good range of beers and food *(Kevin Blake, Doug Christian)*

Jolly Angler [Ducie St]: Unpretentious backstreet local, long a favourite; small and friendly, with well kept Hydes Bitter and Strong, coal fire, darts, pool and TV; informal folk singing Mon *(the Didler, Pete Baker, BB, Patrick Hancock)*

Kings Arms [Bloom St, Salford]: Big busy old local, not smart and in a decayed area, but friendly, with 10 or more well kept ales; small snug with a deep corridor and pinball machines; open all day, handy for Central station *(the Didler)*

Kro Bar [Oxford Rd, opp University faculty buildings]: Danish-theme bar with Scandinavian snacks and full meals, Boddingtons, Marstons Pedigree, Timothy Taylors Landlord and Theakstons Special and XB, pleasant atmosphere, mainly counter-seating with high stools; picnic-sets under cocktail parasols on front terrace *(Ian Phillips)*

Metropolitan [Lapwing Lane, Didsbury]: Huge welcoming dining pub, refurbished but with an unspoilt airy feel; good value generous food inc popular Sun lunch, real ales such as Timothy Taylors Landlord and Charles Wells Bombardier, open fires, separate areas, gabled roof; busy wknds; tables out on heated decking, outside summer bar *(Arby)*

Monroes [London Rd]: A shrine to Marilyn, beautifully framed photographs all over walls and ceiling, well kept reasonably priced Boddingtons and Flowers IPA, friendly staff, 70s décor; bedrooms *(W D Christian, Dr and Mrs A K Clarke)*

Moon Under Water [Deansgate]: Britain's biggest pub, Wetherspoons cinema conversion with entertainer stills, very long, two no smoking areas; half a dozen well kept ales inc bargain pints from very long bar counter, bustling atmosphere (very busy evenings, when upper gallery with two more bars open), friendly efficient staff, popular food all day inc deals for two, opens 10.30 for coffee *(Richard Lewis, Andy, Julie and Stuart Hawkins, Steve Whalley)*

Mother Macs [formerly the Wellington]: Comfortably solid little backstreet local, welcoming to strangers, with tall etched glass windows, old local photographs and grim history, cheap wkdy bar food inc huge baps and generous cheap hot dishes, well kept Boddingtons; piped music, TV; open all day (12-3 Sun) *(Stephen, Julie and Hayley Brown)*

☆ ***Mr Thomas Chop House*** [Cross St]: Long bustling Victorian city pub, bare boards, panelling and original gas lamp fittings in front bar with stools at wall and window shelves, back eating area with crisp tilework, interesting period features inc wrought-iron gates, good very popular lunchtime food with innovative touches, proper waiters and waitresses, efficient and friendly, well kept Boddingtons, Timothy Taylors Landlord and guests such as Archers Gold and Smiles Best, decent wines, no smoking area; open all day exc Sun *(the Didler, P Abbott, GLD, JP, PP, Steve Whalley, Stephen, Julie and Hayley Brown)*

Old Garratt [Princess St]: Alehouse décor with bare boards and smoke-effect walls, well kept Theakstons Best and XB, bar food, friendly staff; juke box, big-screen TV and games machine; tables out in front, open all day *(Richard Lewis)*

Old Monkey [Portland St]: Traditional Holts pub, built 1993 but you'd never guess from the etched glass and mosaic tiling; interesting memorabilia, warm hospitality, well kept cheap Bitter and Dark Mild, low-priced food, upstairs lounge, wide mix of customers *(the Didler, Dr and Mrs A K Clarke, Stephen, Julie and Hayley Brown)*

Old Wellington [Cathedral Gates, off Exchange Sq]: Tudor pub moved from Old Shambles Sq during Arndale rebuild, original flagstones, panelling and 16th-c gnarled oak beams and timbers, new bar fittings; open-plan downstairs with small bar and appetising snacks in food area, partly no smoking restaurant on two floors above, well kept Bass, afternoon tea; trendy piped music; lots of tables out overlooking new Exchange Sq *(BB, P Abbott, John Wooll, SLC, Stephen, Julie and Hayley Brown)*

Olde Nelson [Chapel St, Salford (A6 opp cathedral)]: Lots of brewery and whisky mirrors in drinking corridor linking front sliding-door snug and back lounge – more mirrors and brass here; Boddingtons, darts, dominoes, cards; live entertainment Sat *(Pete Baker, the Didler)*

Oxnoble [Liverpool Rd]: Tempting food, well kept ales inc Timothy Taylors Landlord; bedrooms *(Stephen, Julie and Hayley Brown)*

☆ ***Peveril of the Peak*** [Gt Bridgewater St]: Three

very welcoming traditional rooms around central servery, lots of mahogany, mirrors and stained or frosted glass, splendidly lurid Art Nouveau green external tilework; busy lunchtime but friendly and homely evenings, with cheap basic lunchtime food (not Sun), family service, log fire, well kept Boddingtons, Tetleys and Websters, sturdy furnishings on bare boards, interesting pictures, pub games inc pool, table football, juke box; seats outside, children welcome, cl wknd lunchtimes *(the Didler, Patrick Hancock, John Hulme, Doug Christian, JP, PP, P Abbott, LYM, Stephen, Julie and Hayley Brown)*

Plough [Hyde Rd (A57), Gorton]: Superb tiling, windows and gantry in basic local with TV and wooden benches in large public bar, two quieter back lounges, small pool room, Robinsons on electric pump – handpumps kept for emergencies *(the Didler)*

Pot of Beer [New Mount St]: Small refurbished pub with bare boards, stripped bricks and panelling, four well kept interesting changing beers (some tapped from casks projecting from temperature-controlled chamber), Thatcher's farm cider, good value generous Polish wkdy lunchtime food (and beers), friendly licensees; music nights, open all day, cl Sun *(Richard Lewis, the Didler)*

☆ ***Queens*** [Honey St, Cheetham; off Red Bank, nr Victoria Station]: Well preserved Empress Brewery tiled façade, well kept Phoenix Bantam, Timothy Taylors Landlord and several guest beers from small breweries, Belgian imports, Weston's farm cider, simple enjoyable food all day, coal fire, bar billiards, backgammon, chess, good juke box; children welcome, quiz night Tues; unexpected views of Manchester across the Irk Valley and its railway lines from large back garden with good play area, worth penetrating the surrounding viaducts, scrapyards and industrial premises; open all day *(the Didler)*

☆ ***Rain Bar*** [Gt Bridgewater St]: High-standard umbrella works conversion, lots of woodwork and flagstones, full range of Lees beers kept well, decent wines, good value food from 9am breakfast, warmly friendly service, daily papers, great canal views, large upstairs bar too; no under-21s, good canalside terrace, open all day *(the Didler, Chrissie Pickering, Stephen, Julie and Hayley Brown)*

Rising Sun [Queen St, off Deansgate]: 18th-c, recently refurbished but keeping character, with Greene King and guest ales, good choice of low-priced food, old pictures, pleasant atmosphere *(Doug Christian)*

☆ ***Royal Oak*** [Wilmslow Rd, Didsbury]: Refurbished suburban pub well worth knowing for its vast array of cheeses (all day wkdys, not wknds); well kept Banks's Mild and Original and Marstons Bitter and Pedigree, guest beers, friendly service; tables outside, open all day *(Mike and Linda Hudson, LYM)*

Salisbury Ale House [Wakefield St]: Traditional pub stripped out as bare brick and flagstone alehouse, with friendly staff, well kept ales such as Courage Directors, Goffs Jouster and Shepherd Neame; popular with young people, can be busy and noisy, with loud piped rock; open all day *(Richard Lewis)*

Sams Chop House [Back Pool Fold, Chapel Walks]: Sister pub to Mr Thomas Chop House, with identical good value food, proper waitresses and waiters *(GLD)*

Sawyers Arms [Deansgate]: Handsome crimson-tiled façade, good range of real ales *(Dr and Mrs A K Clarke)*

☆ ***Sinclairs*** [2 Cathedral Gates, off Exchange Sq]: Largely 18th-c low-beamed and timbered pub reopened after being dismantled, moved a short distance, and re-erected brick by brick, as part of the city centre reconstruction; cheap food, bargain Sam Smiths, friendly service, great atmosphere, upstairs bar with snugs and Jacobean fireplace; tables out by ultra-modern Exchange Sq *(LYM, JP, PP, the Didler)*

Sir Ralph Abercrombie [Bootle St, off Deansgate]: Edwardian pub with cheap popular food, well kept Boddingtons, Flowers Original and Marstons Pedigree in panelled drinking areas, welcoming service; tables on small terrace *(Dr and Mrs A K Clarke, Stephen, Julie and Hayley Brown)*

Smithfield [Swan St]: Open-plan family-run local with several unusual well kept changing beers, monthly beer festivals, enjoyable bargain food from sandwiches up from open kitchen servery, TV in back lounge area, daily papers, friendly licensees; pool on front dais, games machine, juke box; open all day, bedrooms in nearby building *(Richard Lewis, the Didler, BB)*

Thirsty Scholar [New Wakefield St, under arches of Oxford Rd Station bridge]: Bare boards, cask tables, lots of prints, newspapers, good juke box, sound basic lunchtime food with good choice of filled rolls, friendly staff, well kept ales such as Marstons Pedigree and Timothy Taylors Landlord, perhaps Get Brewing GB Lager on tap; something of a nightclub bar feel (and in fact has nightclub attic upstairs), games machine, piped music; tables outside, open all day (lunchtime only, Sat) *(Richard Lewis)*

Union [Liverpool St, Salford]: Down-to-earth local in industrial area, excellent value Holts Bitter and Mild and home-cooked food, impressive bar; open all day, Sun afternoon closure *(the Didler)*

Waldorf [Gore St]: Modernised but still quietly old-fashioned, with soft lighting, bare boards and brickwork, alcove areas off central bar, well kept Boddingtons and other real ales, busy friendly staff, wide food choice; games machines, music nights *(Dr and Mrs A K Clarke)*

Wetherspoons [Piccadilly]: Large busy pub (upstairs bar can be quieter), good range of well kept beers, decent wines, friendly efficient service, sensibly priced food all day, pleasant open-plan décor with old Manchester prints, bookshelves and no smoking areas; open all day *(Richard Lewis)*

White House [122 Gt Ancoats St]: Friendly local with big lounge and vault with pool table,

well kept cheap Holts and guest beers *(the Didler)*
White Lion [Liverpool Rd, Castlefield]: Busy but friendly Victorian pub, tables for eating up one side of three-sided bar, home-made food all day till 10 inc good curries, separate steak and sausage menus and children's helpings, several changing ales, decent house wine, good tea, friendly service, real fire, lots of prints and Man Utd pictures, shelves of bottles and jugs; sports TV, disco Fri; children welcome, tables out among excavated foundations of Roman city overlooking fort gate, handy for Museum of Science and Industry and Royal Exchange Theatre, open all day *(the Didler, Richard Lewis)*

Mellor Brook [SD6431]
Feildens Arms [Whalley Rd]: Three linked bar areas done up in terracotta and ochre, pine and flagstones, books, old signs and pictures, quick friendly service, good choice of wines by the glass, Boddingtons, good reasonably priced food, swish popular restaurant *(Steve Whalley, Keith Barker)*

Moreton [SJ2588]
Saughall [Saughall Rd, off A553 Hoylake Rd]: Large open-plan family dining pub with usual food, well kept Thwaites real ales, separate non-food bar with wide-screen TV, friendly staff; tables outside *(MLR)*

Mossley [SD97602]
Church Inn [Stockport Rd (B6175)]: Well kept John Smiths, friendly staff, good food inc good value Sun lunch and tempting puddings trolley; bedrooms *(Rev John Hibberd)*

Nether Burrow [SD6175]
Highwayman [A683 S of Kirkby Lonsdale]: 17th-c inn with three well kept real ales, good value home-made food from sandwiches up, some small helpings available, friendly staff, comfortable banquettes and highwayman theme in civilised bar with coal fire, pleasant restaurant; french windows to big terrace and lovely gardens with play area, pretty Lune Valley countryside *(MLR)*

Oldham [SD9606]
☆ ***Roebuck*** [Roebuck Low, Strinesdale, off A62 NE]: Welcoming unpretentious moorland pub, a local byword for wide choice of good value generous food (often booked up even midweek); well kept Wadworths 6X, decent wines, helpful staff, log fire in front lounge, central bar, back dining room, great hillside views day and night *(E D Fraser)*

Parbold [SD4911]
Wayfarer [A5209/Alder Lane]: Civilised pub doing well under newish management, enjoyable food, good service and atmosphere *(Mike Ernest, Brian Kneale)*

Prescot [SJ4692]
Clock Face [Derby St]: Former mansion house with well kept cheap Thwaites beer from long bar counter, enjoyable lunchtime food, comfortable seating in several areas; open all day summer *(Dave Hawkins)*

Preston [SD5330]
Black Horse [Friargate]: Thriving friendly untouched pub in pedestrian street, full Robinsons ale range kept well, inexpensive lunchtime food, unusual ornate curved and mosaic-tiled Victorian main bar, panelling, stained glass, mosaic floor and two quiet cosy enclosed snugs off, upstairs 1920s-style bar; pictures of old town, lots of artefacts, good juke box; no children, open all day *(Pete Baker, the Didler, Jonty MacRae-Campbell)*

☆ ***Fleece*** [39 Liverpool Rd, Penwortham Hill]: Well presented good value pubby food inc imaginative dishes, real ales, good service, happy atmosphere, comfortable no smoking area; large garden with play area *(Norman Revell, Margaret Dickinson)*

Rainford [SD4700]
Golden Lion [Church Rd (B5203)]: Nice village pub with good food inc Sun lunch, well kept beer *(Ian and Sandra Thornton)*

Ramsbottom [SD7715]
Hare & Hounds [Bolton Rd W, Holcombe Brook]: Four well kept changing guest beers a week, welcoming service, reasonably priced usual food, occasional beer festivals; plenty going on, from pool and sports TVs to loud pop music some nights – heady mix from youngsters to OAPs *(P Abbott)*
Shoulder of Mutton [Lumb Carr Rd (B6214), Holcombe]: Popular traditional country pub with warm atmosphere, appealing good value food, well kept guest beers, nice variety of old tables, attractive lounge, separate dining room; worth booking wknds and busy even midweek, good walking area *(Jim Abbott, Michael and Marion Buchanan, P Abbott)*

Rawtenstall [SD8022]
Old Cobblers [New Hall Hey Rd]: Comfortable well furnished family dining pub purpose-built from local stone, with lots of antique advertisements for fashion shoes, pre-Raphaelite prints; wide choice of well priced food from fresh sandwiches up, well kept John Smiths and Theakstons, upstairs play area; near East Lancs steam railway *(Doug Christian)*

Riley Green [SD6225]
☆ ***Royal Oak*** [A675/A6061]: Cosy low-beamed three-room former coaching inn near canal, well kept Thwaites Bitter and Mild and a seasonal beer from long back bar, friendly efficient service, ancient stripped stone, open fires, seats from high-backed settles to red plush armchairs, lots of nooks and crannies, turkey carpet, soft lighting, impressive woodwork, fresh flowers, interesting model steam engines and plenty of bric-a-brac, two dining rooms; can be packed Fri night and wknds; short walk from Leeds & Liverpool Canal, footpath to Hoghton Tower, open all day Sun *(Catherine and Martin Snelling, Margaret Dickinson, Norma and Noel Thomas, Steve Whalley, BB)*

Rimington [SD8045]
☆ ***Black Bull*** [off A59 NW of Clitheroe]: Spotless popular dining pub with good food (not Sun evening) from sandwiches with real chips to fresh fish, unusual specials and Aberdeen Angus steaks, tasteful dining area (bar tables may be booked too), flower arrangements and other nice touches, very friendly good service, comfortable furniture, real fire, lots of wildlife

paintings; interesting railway museum behind, inc impressive model trains; well kept Theakstons, well chosen piped music; cl Mon exc bank hols *(JES)*

Sawley [SD7746]

☆ ***Spread Eagle***: Quiet upmarket 16th-c pub/restaurant, splendid food inc good value wkdy set lunches and bargain early suppers, very imaginative puddings, occasional themed evenings and dinner dances; comfortably sophisticated feel in light and airy lounge bar with well kept Tetleys, several dozen malt whiskies, well chosen wines inc good value bin ends, friendly efficient service, good coal fire, comfortable green banquettes, lots of small round tables, growing collection of prints and paintings; food orders taken here for restauranty eating areas, inc soothing no smoking back dining room with big picture windows overlooking a pretty stretch of the River Ribble; may be piped music; watch out for ducks on the road, close to ruined abbey; cl Sun evening, Mon *(Norman Stansfield, BB, Steve Whalley)*

Slyne [SD4765]

Slyne Lodge [Main Rd]: Clean well run hotel, very popular, well kept Jennings ales, caring helpful staff, good food in imaginative mediterranean-style dining room, open fire, welcoming bar, conservatory; terrace tables, bedrooms with own bathrooms *(Margaret Dickinson)*

Southport [SD3317]

Bold [Lord St]: Big Victorian inn with spacious lounge bar leading to front terrace, well kept Boddingtons and Flowers IPA from long counter, decent wines, bargain food all day, friendly competent service, no smoking dining room on left; comfortable bedrooms *(Steve Whalley)*

St Anne's [SD3229]

Victoria [Church Rd]: Good range of well kept real ales in large and civilised lofty-roomed local's lounge bar, public bar with full-size snooker table, friendly helpful staff, food inc pizzas; originally designed by Mr Boddington the brewer as his own local *(Dr and Mrs A K Clarke)*

Standish [SD5708]

Boars Head [A49/A5106 (Wigan Rd)]: Heavy low beams, log fires, cosy bays of curved wall seats, high wooden stools, sofa, two quieter rooms off; very friendly helpful staff, well kept Burtonwood and guest beers, occasional home-made wines, bargain simple tasty food, well chosen piped music; tables in flower-filled garden, bowling green, open all day Sat *(Brian Kneale, R T and J C Moggridge)*

Stansfield Moor [SD9227]

☆ ***Sportsmans Arms*** [Kebcote; old packhorse rd Burnley—Hebden Bridge – actually just over the W Yorks border]: Remote old moorland farm building, a pub since 1920, comfortable mix of old and new furnishings, beams, some dark panelling, stone-mullioned windows, country bric-a-brac, enjoyable food (esp steaks and inventive wknd dishes) freshly cooked by landlord using local supplies, well kept ales such as Black Sheep, Daleside and Thwaites, plenty of malt whiskies, decent wines, log fires; separate room with darts, pool, games machine; walkers and dogs welcome; open all day wknds, cl wkdy lunchtimes *(David Bowyer, LYM)*

Stockport [SJ8889]

Alexandra [Northgate Rd]: Large backstreet pub with listed interior, reputedly haunted; Robinsons beers, pool room *(the Didler)*

Arden Arms [Millgate St, behind Asda]: Traditional and welcoming, with several room areas inc old-fashioned snug through servery, 1920s décor, fine old vault, brighter lounge area, great collection of working grandfather clocks, also Dinky toys; good value limited lunchtime bar food, well kept Robinsons *(the Didler, Pete Baker)*

Armoury [Shaw Heath]: Small unspoilt locals' bar, comfortable lounge, Robinsons Best and Hatters Mild, maybe Old Tom from a cask on the bar, lunchtime family room upstairs; open all day *(the Didler)*

Blossoms [Buxton Rd (A6)]: Busy traditional main-road local, very friendly, with well kept Robinsons Best and Hatters Mild, perhaps Old Tom tapped from the cask, superb back room; open all day wknds *(the Didler, Bernie Adams, Stephen, Julie and Hayley Brown)*

Crown [Heaton Lane, Heaton Norris]: Well run town local under arch of vast viaduct, partly open-plan with three cosy lounge areas (one no smoking) off gaslit bar, stylish décor, wide range of well kept ales from 10 handpumps (Bank Top is a regular), farm cider, good value lunchtime bar food, pool, darts, TV; some live music; seats outside, open all day Sat *(the Didler)*

Florist [Shaw Heath]: Refurbished local keeping several separate rooms, Robinsons Best and Hatters Mild *(the Didler)*

Nursery [Green Lane, Heaton Norris; off A6]: 1930s pub tucked down cobbled lane in pleasant setting with bowling green behind, several rooms inc handsomely panelled lounge, good food inc very popular set Sun lunch (children welcome if eating), friendly efficient service, Hydes Bitter and Mild on electric pump, seasonal ale on handpump *(the Didler, R Davies)*

Queens Head [Little Underbank (can be reached by steps from St Petersgate)]: Long narrow late Victorian pub with delightful separate snug and back dining area; good friendly bustle, reasonable bar food, well kept Sam Smiths, daily papers, rare brass cordials fountain and old spirit lamps, old posters and adverts; no smoking area, some live jazz, open all day; famous narrow gents' *(the Didler, Bernie Adams, Stephen, Julie and Hayley Brown)*

☆ ***Red Bull*** [Middle Hillgate]: Beamed and flagstoned local, very friendly and well run, with very well kept Robinsons Best and Best Mild from nearby brewery, good value home-cooked bar lunches (not Sun), substantial settles and seats, open fires, impressive bar with lots of pictures, brassware and traditional island servery; quiet at lunchtime, can get crowded evening, open all day (Sun afternoon closure) *(the Didler, LYM)*

Swan With Two Necks [Princes St]: Traditional panelled local, comfortable bar, back lounge and drinking corridor, skylight ceiling, Robinsons Mild and Bitter; handy for shops *(the Didler)*

Swinton [SD7602]

Morning Star [Manchester Rd, Wardley (A6)]: Busy Holts local, well kept ales, good value basic food wkdy lunchtime, lively games-oriented bar, usually some Sat entertainment in lounge *(Pete Baker)*

Thurstaston [SJ2484]

Cottage Loaf [A540]: Comfortable and friendly, with well kept Cains and Marstons Pedigree, enjoyable food inc starters and light dishes, professional service *(Rita and Keith Pollard)*

Treales [SD4432]

Derby Arms: Good food in refurbished bar areas and sizeable restaurant, attractive prices, well kept Boddingtons, Jennings and Theakstons, decent wines by the glass *(A G Park, J F M and M West)*

Tyldesley [SD6802]

Mort Arms [Elliott St]: Two-room pub popular with older locals, mahogany bar, etched glass and panels, comfortable lounge, very reasonably priced Holts Bitter and Mild, friendly landlord, crowds huddled around TV for Sat horseracing; open all day *(the Didler)*

Waddington [SD7243]

☆ ***Lower Buck*** [Edisford Rd]: Traditional moorland local with well kept Black Sheep, Moorhouses Black Cat, Pride of Pendle and Premier, Rudgate Maelstrom and Timothy Taylors Landlord, popular basic home cooking inc evening meals, friendly licensees, real fires, hatch-service lobby, front bar with built-in dresser, plain back room; pretty village *(J A Boucher, Norma and Noel Thomas, BB, Alyson and Andrew Jackson)*

Wallasey [SJ3191]

Brighton Hotel [Brighton St, Seacombe]: Handsome building in fine setting opp gothic Town Hall, Mersey views; consistently well kept real ales, reasonable prices *(Dave Hawkins)*

Farmers Arms [Wallasey Village]: Small L-shaped front bar with TV and fruit machine, small side snug, bigger back lounge mainly for food (usual dishes from sandwiches up wkdy lunchtimes only), reasonable prices, well kept real ales inc Cains and a guest *(MLR)*

West Kirby [SJ2186]

Hilbre Court [Banks Rd]: Reopened after extensive reworking, comfortable furnishings in spacious open-plan bar inc grandfather chairs, Bass, Tetleys and an interesting Mild, food inc good fresh sandwiches, homely atmosphere, good young staff, seats out on balcony; wheelchair access, underground parking *(E G Parish)*

White Lion [A540 Chester rd]: Small 17th-c sandstone pub under new landlord, interesting beamed interior divided into several small areas on different levels, enjoyable bar lunches inc some unusual snacks, Courage Directors, John Smiths, Theakstons and a guest beer, friendly staff, coal stove; attractive secluded back garden *(MLR)*

Wheelton [SD6021]

☆ ***Dressers Arms*** [just off A674 Chorley—Blackburn; Briers Brow]: Good choice of beers inc ones brewed at the pub and good value home-made food in attractive tucked-away converted cottage row with good atmosphere; restaurant, children welcome *(Andy and Jill Kassube)*

Wigan [SD5805]

Swan & Railway [Wallgate, opp Wigan NW Station]: Appealing traditional local that reverberates with passing trains, several rooms, high ceilings, mosaic tiling of swan and railway train, lovely swan stained-glass window, welcoming service, cheap basic lunchtime food (not wknds), Banks's and related ales, friendly staff, dominoes, TV; bedrooms *(Pete Baker, Nick Holding)*

Winmarleigh [SD4749]

Patten Arms [B5272 N of Garstang]: Isolated beamed pub with well kept Tetleys, enjoyable food (not Mon exc bank hols) from good baguettes to Sun lunch, cosy bar and larger room with pool; side bowling green *(Andy, Julie and Stuart Hawkins)*

Wiswell [SD7437]

☆ ***Freemasons Arms*** [Vicarage Fold; just NE of Whalley]: Cosy, friendly and spotless tucked-away Victorian pub with small bar and overflow upstairs dining room, friendly efficient service, several well kept real ales inc Black Sheep, lots of malt whiskies, and excellent meals cooked by the landlady (must book restaurant Fri/Sat evening); lovely village below Pendle Hill; cl Mon/Tues evening *(John Kane)*

Wrea Green [SD3931]

☆ ***Grapes*** [Station Rd]: Busy but roomy open-plan Chef & Brewer with unusually imaginative food, pleasant clean dining area, well kept Boddingtons, Marstons Pedigree and Theakstons, good choice of wines by the glass, good service, open fire; tables out overlooking village green, picturesque church *(Maurice and Gill McMahon, M S Catling)*

Wrightington Bar [SD5313]

Mulberry Tree: Stylish restauranty pub, good food and service *(Mr and Mrs C J Frodsham, Paul Boot)*

Wycoller [SD9339]

Herders [Laneshawbridge—Haworth rd, overlooking village]: Farm pub high in the Pennines, simple hearty home cooking, welcoming licensees and locals *(Mrs P J Carroll)*

Post Office address codings confusingly give the impression that some pubs are in Lancashire when they're really in Yorkshire (which is where we list them).

Leicestershire and Rutland

Just one new main entry here this year: the friendly and attractively updated Red Lion in Great Bowden, a nice all-rounder. Other pubs here on top form are the Exeter Arms at Barrowden (this friendly and pubby place earns its Food Award this year – a nice place to stay, and it brews its own good Blencowe beers), the Blue Bell at Belmesthorpe (thriving atmosphere, nice food and garden), the Nags Head in Castle Donington (a charming dining pub), the civilised and relaxed Olive Branch at Clipsham (new to the Guide *last year – a great success, gaining its Food Award this time), the Bell at East Langton (a firm favourite, gaining a Star this year for its all-round quality – including Langton beer brewed on the premises), the Old White Hart at Lyddington (a good civilised dining pub), the bustling Black Bull in Market Overton (good all round, under its cheerful hands-on landlord), the Nevill Arms at Medbourne (a Star this year, for this all-round favourite – good food, drink and bedrooms), the friendly Grainstore in Oakham (the beers brewed on the premises are the thing here), the New Inn at Peggs Green (a lovely little old-fashioned country tavern), and the friendly and relaxing Kings Arms at Wing (which gains a Place to Stay Award this year). Against stiff competition, particularly from the Exeter Arms at Barrowden and Nags Head in Castle Donington, the Olive Branch at Clipsham wins the top accolade of Leicestershire and Rutland Dining Pub of the Year. Keen contenders in the Lucky Dip section at the end of the chapter are the Wheatsheaf at Greetham, unspoilt Fox & Goose at Illston on the Hill, Cow & Plough in Oadby (restricted opening), Chandlers Arms at Shearsby, Jackson Stops at Stretton, Griffin at Swithland, Bulls Head at Tur Langton and Wheatsheaf at Woodhouse Eaves. The area's drinks prices are usefully a little lower than the national average. The Swan in the Rushes in Loughborough, and the Old Brewery in Somerby (with Parish beers brewed just behind), had real bargains on the drinks side. Besides Grainstore, Parish, Langton and Blencowe, it's worth looking out for local beers from Hoskins & Oldfield and Brewsters. Ruddles, formerly famous as a Rutland brew, is a Greene King beer, from down in Suffolk. Everards of Leicester is the main regional brewer.*

BARROWDEN SK9400 Map 4

Exeter Arms

Main Street, just off A47 Uppingham—Peterborough

In an old free-standing barn behind this tranquil 17th-c coaching inn, they brew their own Blencowe beers. Served from handpumps, these might include Beach Boys, Bevin Boys, Farmer Boys, Young Boys, and perhaps seasonal brews such as Choir Boys, Lover Boys and Fruity Boys on handpump, as well as a guest such as Greene King IPA. Painted a cheery yellow, the simple long open-plan bar stretches away either side of a long central counter; the atmosphere is friendly and pubby. It's quite straightforwardly furnished with wheelback chairs at tables at either end of the bar, on bare boards or blue patterned carpet. The blackboard menu changes every day, and freshly prepared generous dishes might include soup and a sandwich (£3.50), smoked fish platter, home-made duck liver pâté and fruit coulis or garlic mushrooms (all £4), with main courses such as liver and onions (£7.50), sweet and sour pork stir fry (£8), local trout with Pernod and mushroom sauce (£8.50), rack of lamb with redcurrant and wine sauce (£9), duck breast with strawberry and plum sauce (£9.50), and sea bream (£10.50); home-made puddings such as strawberry pavlova or fruit crumbles (£3.50). It's well placed in a pretty tucked-away Rutland stone village, and picnic-sets on a narrow terrace in front overlook the pretty village green and ducks on the pond, with broader views stretching away beyond; there are more well spaced picnic-sets in a big informal grassy garden at the back; boules and horseshoe pitching. *(Recommended by Stephen, Julie and Hayley Brown, Barry Collett, Norma and Keith Bloomfield, A C and E Johnson, Richard Lewis, Bob and Maggie Atherton, DC, David Field, Jim Farmer, Mike and Sue Loseby, JWAC, Derek and Sylvia Stephenson, Susan and John Douglas)*

Own brew ~ Licensees Pete and Elizabeth Blencowe ~ Real ale ~ Bar food (not Sun evening or Mon) ~ Restaurant ~ (01572) 747247 ~ Children and dogs welcome away from the bar ~ Blues band alternate Sun evenings, folk club alternate Mon evenings ~ Open 12-2(3 Sat/Sun), 6-11(7-10.30 Sun); closed Mon lunchtime ~ Bedrooms: £30S/£55S

BELMESTHORPE TF0410 Map 8

Blue Bell

Village signposted off A16 just E of Stamford

With mulled wine in winter and sangria in summer, not to mention well kept Badger IPA, Bass, Greene King Old Speckled Hen and Ruddles County on handpump and a good choice of wines by the glass, this is a pleasant place for a drink – though the main draw for most of our readers is in fact the enjoyable food. Originally three cottages that have been knocked through into one, this is a lovely old building on two levels: so you peer down into the bar counter, and a slope winds down round the counter to another area with the same cottagey furniture they've used throughout. The atmosphere is very homely, particularly in the first little beamed cottagey room, which has brocaded wing armchairs and a sofa around a low coffee table, gleaming brass platters, an open fire in a huge stone inglenook – which is open through to the games room – and lots of fresh flowers. As well as good value sandwiches (£2.25), soup (£3.25), fried mushrooms with stilton sauce (£3.45), ploughman's (£5.45), tasty tagliatelle with fresh tuna or lasagne (£5.75), and grilled gammon with egg (£6.25), they've more elaborate, seasonally changing dishes such as leek, smoked bacon and swiss cheese tartlet with tomato fondue (£4.35), chicken and tarragon sausage (£4.75), couscous with spiced aubergine and red pepper coulis (£9.75), and roast quail with glazed vegetables and mushroom sauce (£10.75); specials such as smoked haddock and tomato hotpot (£10.95), and beef stroganoff (£11.75). The pub has darts and pool (the landlord plays in both teams, while the landlady prefers cribbage and dominoes); keep an eye out for Rufus the black labrador who steals crisps from behind the bar. *(Recommended by Phil and Jane Hodson, Bob and Maggie Atherton, Rona Murdoch)*

Free house ~ Licensees Susan Bailey and Andrew Cunningham ~ Real ale ~ Bar food (not Sun evenings except in Dec) ~ Restaurant ~ (01780) 763859 ~ Children in eating area of bar and restaurant till 9.30pm ~ Open 12-2.30, 6(5 Sat)-11; 12-10.30 Sun

CASTLE DONINGTON SK4427 Map 7

Nags Head Ⓣ 🍷

Hill Top; A453, S end

If you want to enjoy the well prepared and presented food at this civilised low-beamed dining pub, you'll have to book a table. The little bar area as you enter is

the simplest part, with quarry tiles, dark green dado and dark tables and wheelback chairs. A step takes you up into a small intimate dining room with simple pressed and punctured iron wall lamps and nice signed French prints on fresh cream walls, three chunky old pine candlelit tables on seagrass, and a little turkey rug in front of a pretty Art Deco slate fireplace. The other end of the bar takes you into a second much bigger and similarly decorated yellow-washed dining area, its well spaced tables giving it a more elegantly informal feel, and from here through an opening to the kitchen you can watch the chefs at work. You order at the bar and are then shown to your table by the waitress when your food is ready. Changing daily, the menu includes sandwiches (from £3.95 lunchtime and early evening) and starters or snacks such as soup and baguette (£3.95), tomato and mozzarella with pesto (£4.95), and bacon and poached egg salad with garlic croutons (£6.95), along with main courses such as leek and potato bake with cheese sauce (£10.50), lamb rump with mustard mash (£12.95), swordfish steak with crème fraîche and lime (£13.95), and sliced beef fillet with cajun spices and tzatziki dressing (£15.95); puddings could be treacle oat tart or chocolate rum torte (from £3.95). Well kept Banks's Mild, Marstons Pedigree and Mansfield on handpump, around 35 malt whiskies and quite a few wines by the glass; they've pétanque outside. It's handy for Donnington Race Track.
(Recommended by A C and E Johnson, the Didler, Theo, Anne and Jane Gaskin, George and Brenda Jones, Chris and Jo Nicholls, Wendy and Bob Needham, Ian and Jane Irving, JP, PP, Peter and Jean Hoare, Paul Hopton, Gillian and Peter Moore, J F Stackhouse)

Marstons (W & D) ~ Tenant Ian Davison ~ Real ale ~ Bar food (not Sun) ~ Restaurant ~ (01332) 850652 ~ Open 11.30-2.30, 5.30-11; 12-3, 7-10.30 Sun; closed 27/28 Dec and 1/2 Jan

CLIPSHAM SK9616 Map 8

Olive Branch

Take B668/Stretton exit off A1 N of Stamford; Clipsham signposted E from exit roundabout

Leicestershire and Rutland Dining Pub of the Year

We've recently had lots of very happy reports from readers about this well run stone-built country pub. The emphasis is on the good imaginative food, and it's worth booking or arriving early for a table, especially at lunchtime when they do a good value two-course meal (£9.50, not Sunday when they do three courses for £14.50). Skilfully cooked using lots of fresh local produce, the menu changes every day, and typically includes soup (£3.75), sandwiches (from £4.50), pea and mint risotto (£4.75), thai-style salmon with lime and coriander mayonnaise (£5.50), lincolnshire sausages and sauerkraut with herb mash (£8.25), honey-glazed ham hock with poached egg and bubble and squeak (£9.95), monkfish with red thai curry and jasmine rice (£13.50), and grilled john dory with saffron potatoes in orange and fennel sauce (£14.50), with puddings such as frozen raspberries with hot white chocolate sauce or pistachio tart with chocolate ice cream (£4.95); a nice touch is the board of home-baked bread they bring for you to slice yourself, and the cheeseboard is very tempting. A good blackboard choice of wines includes interesting bin ends, old clarets and unusual sherries; they've well kept Grainstore Olive Oil with a guest such as Timothy Taylors Landlord on handpump, freshly squeezed fruit juices and good coffee. There are dark joists and beams in the various smallish attractive rambling room areas, a log fire in the stone inglenook fireplace (they use old menus to light it), and an interesting mix of pictures, some by local artists, country furniture and books (many bought at antique fairs by one of the partners – ask if you see something you like, as much is for sale). The friendly young staff are efficient and helpful, and the atmosphere is relaxed and civilised. Two of the dining rooms are no smoking; there may be unobtrusive piped music. Lovely in summer, there are picnic-sets out on a heated terrace, with more on the neat lawn sheltered in the L of its two low buildings.
(Recommended by JWAC, Bob and Maggie Atherton, RB, Mike and Sue Loseby, Chris and Susie Cammack, Barry Collett, James Muir, Mrs V Middlebrook, Alan and Gill Bull, Bernie Adams, Sally Anne and Peter Goodale, Mrs Kay Dewsbury, D F Clarke)

Free house ~ Licensees Sean Hope, Ben Jones and Marcus Welford ~ Real ale ~ Bar food (12-2(3 Sun), 7-9.30, not Sun evening) ~ Restaurant ~ (01780) 410355 ~ Children in restaurant ~ Dogs allowed in bar ~ Open 12-3, 6-11; 12-11 Sat; 12-5 Sun; 12-3, 6-11 Sat winter; closed Sun evening

COTTESMORE SK9013 Map 7

Sun 🍷

B668 NE of Oakham

This year, when the weather relents, you can eat outside on the new terrace behind this 17th-c thatched and stone-built village pub. Its emphasis is on good value food, which might include soup (£2.75), baked sardines with lemon and garlic butter (£3.25), baguettes (£3.95), mushroom tagliatelle (£6.95), seared salmon fillet (£7.50), and sirloin steak (£12.95), with specials such as smoked haddock and salmon fishcakes with parsley sauce (£6.50) or lamb shank with port and redcurrant jus (£7.50); puddings such as hot chocolate sponge pudding (£3.25). As there aren't many tables in the rooms off the bar, it pays to get there early in winter, or even book. Along with stripped pine furnishings, there's a winter log fire in the stone inglenook, and pictures on the newly painted olive and terracotta walls; piped music, and boules outside. Besides Adnams and Everards Tiger they have a guest beer such as Marstons Pedigree on handpump, and also decent wines. *(Recommended by Paul and Sue Merrick, Barry Collett, Peter and Patricia Burton, Mike and Sue Loseby, Anthony Barnes)*

Everards ~ Tenant David Johnson ~ Real ale ~ Bar food (not Sun evening or Mon) ~ Restaurant ~ (01572) 812321 ~ Children in eating area of bar ~ Dogs allowed in bar ~ Open 11.30-2.30, 6.30-11; 12-3, 7-10.30 Sun; closed 25 Dec

EAST LANGTON SP7292 Map 4

Bell ★ 🍺 🛏

The Langtons signposted from A6 N of Market Harborough; East Langton signposted from B6047

With its very friendly obliging staff, enjoyable food and home brew beers, this creeper-covered pub is doing so well at the moment that this year it earns a star. Lovely and cosy in winter, the long stripped-stone beamed bar has a good log fire and plain wooden tables, while in summer the garden is a pleasant place to sit. Their well kept Caudle ales, produced in a converted outbuilding, include Caudle Bitter and Bowler Strong Ale, which are served alongside Greene King Abbot and IPA on handpump, with a couple of guests such as Bass and Marstons Pedigree tapped straight from the cask (there's a £1 discount on a four-pint pitcher). The interesting home-made bar food changes regularly, and besides lunchtime sandwiches (from £2.75) could include soup (£3.15), mushroom provençale (£4.50), tortilla chicken wraps (£4.75), Quorn and lentil casserole (£8.95), particularly tasty sausages (£9.25), caribbean chicken with coconut and lime sauce (£10.25), beef bourguignon (£10.75), and puddings (£3.50); readers recommend the Sunday carvery and weekday OAP lunches – booking is advised at busy times. The green-hued dining room is no smoking. They do good breakfasts, and the attractive village is in peaceful countryside. *(Recommended by Bernie Adams, Joan and Michel Hooper-Immins, M Robinson, Wendy and Bob Needham, Philip Atkins, Eric Locker, Phil and Jane Hodson, Rona Murdoch, David Field, Comus and Sarah Elliott, R T and J C Moggridge, Anthony Barnes, Duncan Cloud, Mike and Sue Loseby, Steve Whalley, Jim Farmer, A C and E Johnson, Dorsan Baker, Gerry Hollington, Angus Lyon, O K Smyth, Derek and Sylvia Stephenson, Mrs P Sarson, Gerry and Rosemary Dobson)*

Own brew ~ Licensee Alastair Chapman ~ Real ale ~ Bar food (till 10 wknds) ~ Restaurant ~ (01858) 545278 ~ Children welcome till 8.30pm ~ Dogs welcome ~ Open 11.30-2.30, 7(6.30 Sat)-11; 12-3, 7-10.30 Sun; closed 25 Dec ~ Bedrooms: £39.50S(£39.50B)/£55S(£55B)

EMPINGHAM SK9408 Map 4

White Horse

Main Street; A606 Stamford—Oakham

There's a nicely relaxed dining atmosphere at this attractive and bustling old inn, and handily it's open all day. The open-plan carpeted lounge bar has a big log fire below an unusual free-standing chimney-funnel, and lots of fresh flowers; outside are some rustic tables among urns of flowers. Served by pleasant and efficient staff, tasty bar food might be soup (£2.95), filled baguettes (from £3.95), smoked salmon and cod terrine (£5.25), dolcelatte, roasted tomato and chive tart (£5.75), ploughman's or lasagne (£7.65), fishcakes (£8.45), beef and Guinness pie (£8.95), pork steak with three-cheese sauce (£9.25), and sirloin steak (£13.95), with daily specials such as home-made curried vegetable pancakes (£7.95), and lemon sole with white wine and prawn marinière (£9.55), and puddings (£3.95); they also do morning coffee and afternoon tea. The restaurant and the Orange Room are no smoking. They've well kept Courage Directors, Grainstore Triple B, Greene King Ruddles County and Marstons Pedigree on handpump, and up to 10 wines by the glass; TV, fruit machine and piped music. Bedrooms are in a converted stable block, and in case any of their residents get lucky with the fishing rod on nearby Rutland Water, they offer freezing facilities. *(Recommended by Eric Locker, Mrs Sally Kingsbury, C J Cox, A Monro, Barry Collett, Keith and Di Newsome, Phil and Jane Hodson, Rona Murdoch)*

Courage (S & N) ~ Lease Roger Bourne ~ Real ale ~ Bar food ~ Restaurant ~ (01780) 460221 ~ Children in eating area of bar and restaurant till 8pm ~ Dogs allowed in bedrooms ~ Open 10-11; 10-10.30 Sun ~ Bedrooms: £50S(£50B)/£65S(£65B)

EXTON SK9211 Map 7

Fox & Hounds

Signposted off A606 Stamford—Oakham

Only a couple of miles away from Rutland Water, this handsome former coaching inn is a useful stop for walkers on the Viking Way. Civilised and comfortable, the high-ceilinged lounge bar has some dark red plush easy chairs as well as wheelback seats around lots of dark tables, maps and hunting and military prints on the walls, brass and copper ornaments, and a winter log fire in a large stone fireplace; piped music. The quite separate public bar has a more pubby atmosphere; darts, pool, cribbage and dominoes. Attentive staff serve up to three well kept real ales on handpump, which might be Brewsters Hophead, Greene King IPA and Sam Smiths OB. In generous helpings, nicely prepared bar food includes sandwiches (from £2.75), soup (£3), lasagne or lamb chops with mint and apple sauce (£8.25), liver, bacon and onions or seafood pasta (£7.75), plaice and prawns or steak and kidney pie (£8.25), honey-roasted local trout (£9.50), daily specials such as lamb curry, lincolnshire sausages or oxtail casserole (£6.50), and puddings (£3.75); the dining room is no smoking. On the pleasant well kept back lawn, seats among large rose beds look out over paddocks, and the tranquil village green with its tall trees out in front is most attractive. *(Recommended by Dr Paull Khan, Jim Farmer, John Saville, Angus Lyon, Eric Locker, Norma and Keith Bloomfield, Phil and Jane Hodson, F J Robinson, Gordon Neighbour, C J Cox, A Monro, J Hale, Mike and Sue Loseby, Barry Collett, Mr and Mrs J Brown, Carol and Dono Leaman)*

Free house ~ Licensees David and Jennifer Hillier ~ Real ale ~ Bar food ~ Restaurant ~ No credit cards ~ (01572) 812403 ~ Children in eating area of bar and restaurant ~ Dogs allowed in bar and bedrooms ~ Open 11-3, 6.30-11; 12-3, 7-10.30 Sun ~ Bedrooms: £24/£38

There are report forms at the back of the book.

GREAT BOWDEN SP7488 Map 4

Red Lion

Village signposted off A6 just N of Market Harborough; Main Street

Attractively reworked by the friendly and enthusiastic newish licensees (who previously lived nearby), this strikes a comfortable chord with the four dark red leather button-back chesterfields in the lounge bar on the left. Other seats around well spaced tables on the polished boards are more orthodox, except perhaps for the group of ultra-tall seats around one unusually lofty table; the walls too are dark red, and have old-fashioned prints (some of them genuinely old) and a huge mirror. Even the gents' has attractive prints (we haven't seen the ladies'). The central bar counter, perhaps with a big vase of lilies, has well kept Greene King IPA and Charles Wells Bombardier on handpump, and occasionally a guest such as Adnams, with a beer festival around the first summer bank holiday; there is an open fire (and a TV). On the right is a simply furnished turkey-carpeted dining area. Changing weekly and cooked fresh to order, a short choice of food might include soup (£3.95), breaded plaice and chips or penne pasta with spicy tomato and red pepper sauce (£5.25), chilli con carne (£5.95), and steak and Guinness pie (£6.25), as well as specials such as home-made lasagne or curry (£6.25), and puddings (from £3.75); they also do lunchtime baguettes (£4.50) and ploughman's (£4.95). Wednesday is curry night, they hold barbecues on Sunday lunchtimes in summer, and have regular wine tasting evenings. Service is prompt and pleasant. There are tables out in a recently well planted green garden behind; look out for their friendly dog. *(Recommended by Stephen, Julie and Hayley Brown, Rona Murdoch, Wendy and Bob Needham, Duncan Cloud)*

Pubmaster tenancy~ Licensees Mandy and Richard Kitson ~ Real ale ~ Bar food (till 10 Fri/Sat, not Sun evening or winter Mon) ~ 01858 463106 ~ Children in restaurant ~ Live bands on bank hol Sun ~ Open 12-2.30, 5.30-11; 12-11 Sat; 12.10.30 Sun

GUMLEY SP6790 Map 4

Bell

Off A6 Market Harborough—Kibworth, via Foxton; or off A5199 via Laughton; Main Street

Readers strongly recommend the good value two-course OAP lunches at this neatly kept and cheerful village pub (£3.95). Other tasty bar food includes sandwiches (from £2.25), soup (£2.50), beef casserole (£6.95), chicken cooked in Southern Comfort (£10.95), strips of steak with port and mushroom sauce (£11.95), and home-made puddings such as bread and butter pudding or trifle (£2.75); the no smoking dining room fills up quickly at lunchtime, so get there early if you want to eat. Pleasant attentive staff serve well kept Everards Tiger and Beacon and Greene King IPA with guests from brewers such as Batemans and Cottage on handpump. There are lots of cricketing prints and cartoons, and a miniature bat collection in the lobby. The almost L-shaped bar on the right, with typical pub furnishings, has lots of hunting prints on its cream walls, game bird plates above the bar, china jugs and mugs and horsebrasses on some of its black beams and joists, more china on a delft shelf, and ornaments on the window sills, with perhaps a big flower arrangement in the corner; there may be quiet piped music (but no mobile phones). The pretty terrace garden behind is not for children or dogs. More reports please. *(Recommended by Jim Farmer, George Atkinson, David Field, John March, Gerry and Rosemary Dobson, Eric Locker, Tim Wellock)*

Free house ~ Licensee David Quelch ~ Real ale ~ Bar food ~ (0116) 2792476 ~ Children over 5, and not in garden ~ Open 11-3, 6-11; 12-5 Sun; closed Sun evening, 25 and 26 Dec evenings

Post Office address codings confusingly give the impression that some pubs are in Leicestershire, when they're really in Cambridgeshire (which is where we list them).

HALLATON SP7896 Map 4

Bewicke Arms

On good fast back road across open rolling countryside between Uppingham and Kibworth; village signposted from B6047 in Tur Langton and from B664 SW of Uppingham

This ancient thatched inn has an interesting collection of memorabilia, and some very old photographs of the ancient game of bottle kicking and hare pie tossing and its associated parades and celebrations which take place outside the pub every Easter Monday. Depending on Hallaton's victory or defeat in the last competition, the display will include either the bottles themselves, or a dummy bottle. It's neatly kept, with a couple of old-fashioned settles, a wall bench, some big pine-topped tables on the original old oak legs, and log fires. Well kept beers on handpump might be Flowers IPA, Grainstore Cooking and Langton Caudle; there's darts, shove-ha'penny and piped music. Bar food includes soup (£3.50), sandwiches (£3.50-£3.95), smoked mackerel with horseradish sauce (£4.75), gammon and egg or scampi and chips (£7.95) and chargrilled rump steak (£9.55); typical specials are black pudding salad with bacon and strawberries (£4.85), mussels in cream and white wine (£6.95) and spinach soufflé with buttered leeks and soft cheese or sausage with mustard mash and onion marmalade (£7.95). The pub is prettily set on the edge of the village green, and across the courtyard a converted stable houses a tearoom, with a big terrace overlooking an animal paddock and lake. *(Recommended by Patrick Hancock, Norma and Keith Bloomfield, Eric Locker, David Field, Jim Farmer, Barry Collett, Wendy and Bob Needham)*

Hunter Inns ~ Licensee Gail Spiers ~ Real ale ~ Bar food (not Sun evening) ~ (01858) 555217 ~ Children in eating area of bar and restaurant ~ Open 12-3, 6-11; 12-10.30 Sun

KEGWORTH SK4826 Map 7

Cap & Stocking ★

A mile or so from M1 junction 24: follow A6 towards Loughborough; in village, turn left at chemists' down one-way Dragwall opposite High Street, then left and left again, into Borough Street

The star is for the atmosphere: the three rooms of this town local (handy for the M1) are an appealing throwback to another age, with the brown paint and etched glass in the right-hand room making it seem little changed since the 1940s. The two determinedly simple but cosy front rooms both have their own coal fire and an easy-going feel, and furnishings include big cases of stuffed birds and locally caught fish, fabric-covered wall benches and heavy cast-iron-framed tables, and a cast-iron range; cribbage, dominoes, trivia and piped music. The back room has french windows to the pretty garden, where there may be floodlit boules and barbecues in summer. They still serve Bass from an enamelled jug, and you'll find well kept Hancocks HB and a guest such as Fullers London Pride on handpump. Straightforward bar food includes filled rolls (from £1.60), soup (£2.15), burgers (from £2.70), ploughman's and pizzas (from £5), hungarian goulash (£6.25), and daily specials such as welsh rarebit (£2.10), and pork in brandy (£6.50). *(Recommended by Martin and Jane Bailey, the Didler, Simon Collett-Jones, Bernie Adams, B, M and P Kendall, JP, PP, Pete Baker, Adam and Joan Bunting, L Davenport, Gillian and Peter Moore, Mandy and Simon King, Patrick Hancock, Shaun Pinchbeck, David Carr, John Robertson, Mr and Mrs J McRobert, Keith Allen, D L Parkhurst, M W Turner)*

Punch ~ Tenants Graham and Mary Walsh ~ Real ale ~ Bar food (11.30-2.15, 6.30-8.45; 12-2.45, 7-8.45 Sun) ~ No credit cards ~ (01509) 674814 ~ Children welcome ~ Dogs welcome ~ Open 11.30-2.30(3 Sat), 6.30-11; 12-3, 7-10.30 Sun; closed 25 Dec evening

Places with gardens or terraces usually let children sit there – we note in the text the very few exceptions that don't.

LOUGHBOROUGH SK5319 Map 7

Swan in the Rushes ★ £

The Rushes (A6)

There's a fine choice of drinks at this basic but rather civilised bare-boards pub, especially if you like real ale. Alongside Archers Golden, Castle Rock Gold and Tetleys, some of their six changing guests might be Adnams Regatta, Burton Bridge Porter, Hop Back Summer Lightning and Oakham JHB; they've also got a good range of bottled beers from all over the world, over 30 malt whiskies, nine flavoured Polish vodkas, changing farm cider, perry, fruit wines and (as in all Tynemill pubs) very good value soft drinks. There's a nice variety of customers and a relaxed chatty atmosphere in the several neatly kept and simply furnished room areas, each with its own style. For the most comfortable seats, head to the left-hand bay-windowed bar (which has an open fire) or the snug no smoking back family room. The straightforward bar food is reasonably priced and includes filled baguettes (from £1.80), filled baked potatoes (from £2.25), a choice of ploughman's (£4.50), chilli con carne (from £3.75), and enjoyable home-made specials such as sweet and sour chicken or roast vegetable pasta (£5.25), minted lamb chops (£5.50), and chicken breast wrapped in bacon (£5.95). Even when it gets really crowded, service is friendly and efficient. Daily newspapers, cribbage, dominoes and juke box; the function room doubles as a skittle alley. The bedrooms, newly refurbished, gain a Place to Stay award this year, and they do generous breakfasts. There are tables in an outside drinking area; usefully situated not far from the bustle of the town centre, the pub is not far from the M1. *(Recommended by Pete Baker, Gillian and Peter Moore, the Didler, JP, PP, A C and E Johnson, David Carr, Rona Murdoch)*

Tynemill ~ Manager Ian Bogie ~ Real ale ~ Bar food (12-2.30, 6-8.30; not Sat/Sun evenings) ~ No credit cards ~ (01509) 217014 ~ Children welcome in eating area of bar till 8pm unless staying ~ Dogs allowed in bar ~ Acoustic Club first, second and third Thurs in month, folk alternate Suns ~ Open 11-11; 12-10.30 Sun ~ Bedrooms: £25(£35S)/£50(£70S)

LYDDINGTON SP8797 Map 4

Old White Hart

Village signposted off A6003 N of Corby

The pretty walled garden at this old country inn is a pleasant place for a civilised drink, though you'll probably feel you're missing out if you don't try the very good food here too. An original 17th-c window in the passage to the cosy bar is a discreet reminder that the pub was once part of the Burghley Estate. The softly lit low-ceilinged bar has just three close-set tables in front of its roaring log fire, with heavy bowed beams and lots of nice dried flower arrangements. The bar opens into an attractive restaurant, and on the other side is another tiled-floor room with some stripped stone, cushioned wall seats and mate's chairs, and a woodburning stove; this second part is no smoking. Service is helpful and courteous. The menu changes according to the season, but might include home-made soups (£3.25), goats cheese and red pepper tartlet (£4.50), lunchtime filled baguettes or ciabattas (£4.95), crispy duck leg with spring onion and cucumber on swiss chard (£5.95), home-made chicken and tarragon pie (£9.50), rack of lamb with a herb crust and roast gravy (£11.95), and sirloin steak (£13.95), with lots of daily specials such as wild mushroom risotto with truffle oil and parmesan (£9.25), Grimsby haddock (£10.50), and bass with sauté potatoes and sauce vierge (£10.95); puddings such as rhubarb and raspberry crème brûlée and warm chocolate nut brownie with caramel ice cream (from £4.50). Well kept Greene King IPA, Abbot and a guest such as Timothy Taylors Landlord on handpump; piped music, shove-ha'penny, cribbage and dominoes. The pub has no fewer than 12 floodlit boules pitches, and if you sit outside on Thursday evening you'll probably hear the church bell-ringers. In a picturesque village with good nearby walks, the pub is handy for Bede House. *(Recommended by Barry Collett, David and*

Helen Wilkins, Mike and Sue Loseby, Duncan Cloud, John A Barker, Eric Locker, A C and E Johnson, Rona Murdoch, Les and Barbara Owen, Revd A Nunnerley, Jim Farmer, Bob and Maggie Atherton)

Free house ~ Licensee Stuart East ~ Real ale ~ Bar food (12-2(2.30 Sun), 6.30-9, not Sun evening) ~ Restaurant ~ (01572) 821703 ~ Well behaved children welcome ~ Open 12-3, 6.30-11(7-10.30 Sun) ~ Bedrooms: £45B/£65B

MARKET OVERTON SK8816 Map 7

Black Bull

Village signposted off B668 in Cottesmore

A popular choice with locals and visitors alike, this friendly old thatched stone-built pub is a cheerful place, with a jolly landlord and helpful staff. There's a good variety of well cooked reasonably priced dishes on the bar menu, and if they have the ingredients they will be happy to accommodate any special requests. You might find filled ciabattas (from £3.75), baked avocado with creamy stilton sauce or duck pancakes with spring onion and plum sauce (£3.95), popular lambs liver and bacon with caramelised onion (£7.95), chicken breast stuffed with brie and asparagus wrapped in bacon with a creamy tomato sauce (£9.95), bass with salmon and prawn mousse and dill, asparagus and lemon sauce or half a roast duck with redcurrant sauce (£12.95), and fillet steak with stilton sauce (£14.95); good daily specials (some of them are on a blackboard, ask the landlord for others) include interesting fish dishes such as roast zander (a freshwater fish) with potato, salmon and prawns with lemon and dill sauce (£9.95), and turbot fillet with scallop mousse wrapped in parma ham with prawn sauce (£12.95); home-made puddings such as tangy lemon cheesecake or crème brûlée (£3.25). The low black-beamed bar has an appealing bustling atmosphere, with raspberry mousse walls, red plush stools and cushioned spindleback chairs at dark wood pub tables, and flowers on the sills of its little curtained windows. The main dining room has a no smoking area. They serve well kept Greene King IPA, Hook Norton Best, Theakstons Black Bull and Charles Wells Bombardier on handpump; piped music, darts, fruit machine, cribbage and dominoes. *(Recommended by Anthony Barnes, RB, Barry Collett, Eric Locker, Stephen and Jean Curtis, Phil and Jane Hodson, June and Malcolm Farmer, Patrick Hancock, Rodney and Norma Stubington)*

Free house ~ Licensees John and Val Owen ~ Real ale ~ Bar food ~ Restaurant ~ (01572) 767677 ~ Children welcome ~ Open 11-2.30, 6-11; 12-3, 7-10.30 Sun; closed 25 Dec ~ Bedrooms: £30S/£45S

MEDBOURNE SP7993 Map 4

Nevill Arms ★

B664 Market Harborough—Uppingham

Readers enjoy eating, drinking and staying at this village pub very much, and the friendly owners do a good job of making everyone feel at home. With handsome stonework and imposing latticed mullioned windows, it's an attractive place, charmingly set in the middle of a peaceful quaint village; you reach it by a footbridge over the little duck-filled River Welland. There's a buoyant atmosphere in the inviting main bar, which has two winter log fires in stone fireplaces at either end, chairs and small wall settles around its tables, and a lofty, dark-joisted ceiling; piped music. Much needed at busy times, a spacious back room by the former coachyard has pews around more tables, and some toys to amuse children. In summer most people prefer to eat at the tables out on the grass by the dovecote. Five real ales tapped straight from the cask include Adnams, Fullers London Pride and Greene King Abbot, with two changing guests such as Brakspears and Langton Caudle on handpump, and about two dozen country wines. Readers enjoy the home-made food which, from a short but good value menu, includes sandwiches (from £2), paninni with hot fillings such as mozzarella and chargrilled peppers or chicken and smoky bacon (£3.95), and blackboard specials such as lamb with apricots, pork with cream and mustard and chicken with bacon and asparagus (all £5.75). A wide choice of games includes darts, shove-ha'penny, cribbage, dominoes, table skittles, and other board games and table football on request. The comfortable well appointed rooms are in two neighbouring cottages, and they do delicious breakfasts in the sunny conservatory. The cat is called Truffles, and there's Cleo the great dane and her son Bertie. The church over the bridge is worth a visit. *(Recommended by Angus Lyon, J and C J Dean, David Field, Norma and Keith Bloomfield, Duncan Cloud, Mrs B M Spurr, Joan and Michel Hooper-Immins, George Atkinson, Eric Locker, Jim Farmer, Mrs M Smith, Sue Holland, Dave Webster, Mike and Sue Loseby, JP, PP, Mrs K J Betts, R Pring, Wendy and Bob Needham, Richard Gibbs, R T and J C Moggridge, Mrs Phoebe A Kemp)*

Free house ~ Licensees Nicholas and Elaine Hall ~ Real ale ~ Bar food (not 25 Dec) ~ (01858) 565288 ~ Children welcome ~ Dogs allowed in bar ~ Open 12-2.30(3 Sat), 6-11; 12-3, 7-10.30 Sun; closed 25 Dec evening and 31 Dec ~ Bedrooms: £45B/£55B

NEWTON BURGOLAND SK3708 Map 4

Belper Arms

Village signposted off B4116 S of Ashby or B586 W of Ibstock

As we went to press this roadside pub was on the market, so some of the details we give may change – perhaps even including the masses to look at inside, from a suit of old chain mail, a collection of pewter teapots and some good antique furniture. But the story of the pub ghost – Five to Four Fred – will surely still be there, framed on the wall. It's quite a big place, knocked through, with ancient features – heavy beams, changing floor levels and separate areas with varying floor and wall materials – all reflecting the various stages in its development (they help give it a cosy intimate feel). Parts are said to date back to the 13th c, and much of the exposed brickwork certainly looks at least three or four hundred years old. A big freestanding central chimney has a fire one side and a range on the other, with chatty groups of captain's chairs. Adnams and Marstons Pedigree on handpump, along with a guest or two, and 10 wines by the glass; pleasant piped music. Freshly prepared bar food includes soup (£2.95), sandwiches (from £3.75), garlic mushrooms or coronation chicken salad (£3.75), steak and ale pie (£7.25), butterfly pork steak (£7.75), and sirloin steak (£9.95), with specials such as salmon fillet or cod and chips (£8.95), and puddings (from £2.75); three-course Sunday lunch (£10.25). Up a step on one side of the bar, the big square restaurant is no smoking. A rambling garden has boules, cricket nets and children's play area, and works its way round the pub to white tables and chairs on a terrace, and a steam-engine-shaped barbecue; campsite. More reports please. *(Recommended by the Didler, Gillian and Peter Moore, Anthony Barnes, Kevin Blake, JP, PP, Duncan Cloud, Ian and Jane Irving)*

Free house ~ Licensee Angela Morris ~ Real ale ~ Bar food ~ Restaurant ~ (01530) 270530 ~ Children in eating area of bar and restaurant ~ Dogs allowed in bar ~ Open 12-3, 6-11; 12-11 Sat; 12-10.30 Sun

OAKHAM SK8508 Map 4

Grainstore

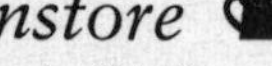

Station Road, off A606

This three-storey Victorian grain warehouse has been converted into a traditional tower brewhouse, with raw materials starting on the upper floor and the finished beer coming out on the bottom floor. As soon as you arrive you get the feel of a working brewery, and you can see the vats of beer through glass doors in the functional open-plan bar. The interior is very simple, with wide well worn bare floorboards, bare ceiling boards above massive joists (and noises of the workings above) which are supported by red metal pillars, a long brick-built bar counter with cast-iron bar stools, tall cask tables and simple elm chairs. The friendly staff will give you samples and, depending on which end of the bar you choose, you can have your beer with or without a head. Their fine beers (Grainstore Cooking, Steamin' Billy, Triple B, Ten Fifty and Mild) are served traditionally at the left end of the bar counter, and through swan necks with sparklers on the right. You can tour the brewery by arrangement, and they do take-aways. In summer they open huge glass doors on to a terrace stacked with barrels, and with picnic-sets; sporting events on TV, fruit machine, bar billiards, darts, giant Jenga and bottle-walking. They serve very good value lunchtime filled baguettes; disabled access. Loading trucks used to pass right through the building, and for those wanting to taste the beers too comprehensively to come by car it's strategically positioned right by the station. *(Recommended by Barry Collett, Bernie Adams, June and Malcolm Farmer, the Didler, Mike and Sue Loseby, Norma and Keith Bloomfield, Stephen, Julie and Hayley Brown, Ian and Eileen Johnson, Rona Murdoch, A C and E Johnson, JP, PP)*

Own brew ~ Licensee A H Davis ~ Real ale ~ No credit cards ~ (01572) 770065 ~ Dogs allowed in bar ~ Blues, jazz or folk first Sun of month ~ Open 11-2.30, 5-11; 11-11 Fri/Sat; 12-10.30 Sun

OLD DALBY SK6723 Map 7

Crown

By school in village centre turn into Longcliff Hill

Outside this smart tucked-away creeper-covered former farmhouse, there's cast-iron furniture and rustic tables and chairs on the terrace, hanging baskets and urns of flowers; steps lead down through the sheltered sloping lawn where you can practise your boules with the pub's two teams. The three or four intimate little rooms have black beams, one or two antique oak settles, a mix of carvers and wheelback chairs, hunting and other rustic prints, open fires, and darts and cribbage; the snug is no smoking. Made wherever possible from fresh local produce, the fairly short choice of well prepared (though not cheap) dishes is cooked to order. Changing every three months, the interesting menu could include lunchtime (not Sun) sandwiches (£3.95) and filled ciabattas (from £6.95), as well as soup (£3.95), sausage and mash or wild mushrooms with creamy garlic sauce and puff pastry (£6.95), steamed steak and ale pudding, spicy chicken pasta or goats cheese tartlet with tomato and courgette (£8.95), lamb shank or chicken supreme with orange and cream sauce (£10.95), fillet steak (£11.95), and fried duck breast with home-cooked ham and ox tongue (£14.95); puddings such as summer pudding or hot apple lattice (£4.50). The dining room has a pleasantly relaxed bistro feel. They've Theakstons Black Bull and Hook Norton with a guest such as Springhead Roaring Meg either on handpump or tapped straight from the cask, and two dozen or more malt whiskies; darts, cribbage. *(Recommended by Mike and Sue Loseby, the Didler, Gillian and Peter Moore, Brian Skelcher, David and Helen Wilkins, Simon Chell, Eric Locker, David Carr, JP, PP, A J Bowen)*

Free house ~ Licensee Lynn Busby ~ Real ale ~ Bar food (not Sun evening or Mon lunchtime) ~ Restaurant ~ (01664) 823134 ~ Open 12-3, 6-11(7-10.30 Sun); 12-2.30, 6.30-11(7.30-10.30 Sun) in winter; closed Mon lunchtime

PEGGS GREEN SK4117 Map 7

New Inn £

Signposted off A512 Ashby—Shepshed at roundabout, then Newbold sign down Zion Hill

The cheery Irish licensees like to think of this quirky village pub (now in the second generation of the same family) as an extension of their home. An incredible collection of old bric-a-brac covers almost every inch of the walls and ceilings of the two cosy tiled front rooms. The little room on the left, a bit like a kitchen parlour, has china on the mantelpiece above a warm coal fire, lots of prints and photographs and little collections of this and that, three old cast-iron tables, wooden stools and a small stripped kitchen table. The room to the right has quite nice stripped panelling, and masses of the sort of bric-a-brac you can spend ages trawling through. The little back lounge, with a stripped wooden floor, has a really interesting and quite touching display of old local photographs including some colliery ones. There's a nice welcoming and relaxed local atmosphere, perhaps with a cluster of regulars gathered round the old-fashioned booth bar. Aside from filled cobs which are served all day (from £1.20), the short very good value menu could include home-made sausage and champ or faggots and peas (£2.95), and corned beef hash or smoked haddock (£3.50); children's meals (£1.95); note the limited food serving times. Well kept Bass and Marstons Pedigree on handpump; piped music, dominoes, board games and various special events throughout the year. *(Recommended by the Didler, JP, PP, Bernie Adams, George and Brenda Jones, R T and J C Moggridge, Kevin Blake)*

Enterprise ~ Lease Maria Christina Kell ~ Real ale ~ Bar food (12-2; 6-8 Mon; not Tues-Sat evenings; not Sun) ~ No credit cards ~ (01530) 222293 ~ Well behaved children welcome ~ Dogs allowed in bar ~ Open 12-2.30, 5.30-11; 12-3, 6.30-11 (7-10.30 Sun) Sat

SIBSON SK3500 Map 4

Cock

A444 N of Nuneaton

Some parts of this incredibly attractive thatched and timbered black and white pub date back as far as the 13th c, and proof of its age can still be seen in the unusually low doorways, ancient wall timbers, heavy black beams and genuine latticed windows of the neatly kept interior. A room on the right has comfortable seats around cast-iron tables, and more seats built in to what was once an immense fireplace (fabled as a highwayman's hideaway, of course). The room on the left has country kitchen chairs around wooden tables, and there's a no smoking dining area. Well kept Bass and a guest such as Wadworths 6X on handpump; fruit machine and piped music. Generously served reasonably priced tasty bar food includes home-made soup (£2.20), sandwiches (from £2.70), sautéed garlic mushrooms (£3), steak and kidney pie, battered cod, lasagne or ham and egg (£7.95), steaks (from £10.50), and daily specials such as delicious mushroom stroganoff (£8.75), pigeon casserole or mackerel fillet (£8.95) and poached scampi (£9.50); on Sunday lunchtime the only food is a three-course roast lunch (£10.50). The restaurant was converted from a former stable block. A little garden (there used to be a cock pit here) and courtyard area has tables, summer hanging baskets and a flower-filled dray cart in front. They have a caravan field (certified with the Caravan Club); the pub is handy for Bosworth battlefield. *(Recommended by Geoffrey and Penny Hughes, JP, PP, Ian and Joan Blackwell, Christopher and Jo Barton, Susan and John Douglas, Tony Walker, Mike Horler)*

Punch ~ Lease Graham Lindsay ~ Real ale ~ Bar food (11.30-2, 6.30-9.45) ~ Restaurant ~ (01827) 880357 ~ Children in eating area of bar and restaurant ~ Open 11.30-2.30, 6.30(6 Sat)-11; 12-3, 7-10.30 Sun; closed 25 and 26 Dec evenings

SOMERBY SK7710 Map 4

Old Brewery £

Off A606 Oakham—Melton Mowbray, via Cold Overton, or Leesthorpe and Pickwell; can also be reached direct from Oakham via Knossington; High Street

Brewed by the former landlord, Barrie Parish, interesting good value real ales here include Baz's Bonce Blower, Poachers Ale and Special which are well kept on handpump, alongside a guest such as Black Sheep; groups can still book tours of the little brewery in the former stables. The comfortable L-shaped main bar has red plush stools and banquettes and plush-cushioned captain's chairs, a sofa in one corner, and a good log fire in the big stone fireplace; another bar has bays of button-back red seating. The straightforward, reasonably priced bar menu includes soup (£2), sandwiches (from £2.95), garlic mushrooms (£3.75), ploughman's or home-made vegetable curry (£4.95), breaded plaice (£5.25), broccoli and cream cheese bake or home-made steak and Parish ale pie (£5.95); they do a bargain three-course lunch (£5.95, not Monday). The dining area and part of the restaurant are no smoking. Fruit machine, TV and piped music; they hold a beer festival in May. A fenced-off area by the car park has white plastic tables and a climbing frame, and in summer they have a children's bouncy castle.

(Recommended by O K Smyth, JP, PP, Richard Lewis, Barry Collett, Bernie Adams, CMW, JJW, Phil and Jane Hodson, Jim Farmer, Rona Murdoch)

Own brew ~ Licensees Wendy and Mick Farmer ~ Real ale ~ Bar food (not Mon lunch except bank hols) ~ Restaurant ~ (01664) 454777 ~ Well behaved children till 9pm ~ Dogs allowed in bar ~ Live bands Sat evening ~ Open 12-2.30, 6.30-11; 12-10.30 Sun

Stilton Cheese

High Street; off A606 Oakham—Melton Mowbray, via Cold Overton, or Leesthorpe and Pickwell; can also be reached direct from Oakham via Knossington

A good place to relax, this comfortable and welcoming 16th-c pub has a thriving atmosphere; it's busy here even on a midweek lunchtime in winter, and the feeling of a good many people enjoying themselves is thoroughly restorative. The hop-strung beamed bar/lounge has lots of country prints on its stripped stone walls, a collection of copper pots, a stuffed badger and plenty of restful seats; shove-ha'penny, cribbage, dominoes, board games and piped music. Well kept local Grainstore Ten Fifty, Marstons Pedigree, Tetleys and two changing guests such as Orkney Dark Island and Timothy Taylors Landlord on handpump, a good choice of wines, and about two dozen malt whiskies; good friendly service. Reasonably priced well cooked food (there are three chefs in the family) might include sandwiches (from £2.15), soup (£2.35), mushrooms in garlic and herb butter (£3.50), ploughman's (£4.50), home-made lasagne or local sausages and mash (£5.50), scampi or chilli con carne (£5.75), and tasty specials such as home-made chicken, ham and mushroom pie (£6.25), salmon and mascarpone roulade (£3.95), jumbo prawns in garlic and tarragon butter (£4.25), sliced duck breast with ginger and orange sauce (£6.95), and Rutland trout with honey and almonds (£7.95), with tempting puddings such as almond tart and bread and butter pudding (£2.95); the restaurant is no smoking. The patio area has wooden seating and outdoor heaters. More reports please. *(Recommended by Joan and Michel Hooper-Immins, RB, Rona Murdoch, Jim Farmer, John Brightley)*

Free house ~ Licensees Carol and Jeff Evans ~ Real ale ~ Bar food (12-2, 6-9) ~ Restaurant ~ (01664) 454394 ~ Children in eating area of bar and restaurant ~ Open 12-3, 6-11(7-10.30 Sun)

STRETTON SK9416 Map 8

Ram Jam Inn

Just off A1: heading N, look out for warning signs some 8 miles N of Stamford, turning off at big inn sign through service station close to B668; heading S, take B668 Oakham turn-off, inn well signed on left ¼ mile from roundabout

Good for a few minutes' refreshing break from the A1 or a comfortable overnight stop, a quick snack or a full meal – well worth its place in the *Guide*, as although it's not exactly a pub it comes closer than almost anywhere else to being the true modern equivalent of a coaching inn. As you go in, the first part of the big stylish open-plan bar/dining area has terracotta-coloured walls decorated in one place with a spread of old bread boards, big ceramic tiles on the floor, bentwood chairs and café tables, and sofas in a cosy panelled alcove with daily papers and a standard lamp. The bar on the left here has Fullers London Pride and John Smiths on handpump, good house wines, freshly squeezed orange juice and fresh-ground coffee. This area spreads on back to a no smoking oak-boarded part with old prints and maps, more of the bentwood chairs, dining chairs, and (by a woodburning stove) another sofa and some wicker armchairs. On the right is a more formal dining layout, also no smoking, with well spaced solid tables and attractive Mediterranean photoprints by Georges Meris. Opposite the bar an open kitchen does interesting if not cheap food, which is handily served almost all day. Enjoyable dishes could include soup (£3.50), duck terrine (£5.75), open prawn sandwich (£6.95), steak burger or ricotta and spinach pasta (£7.95), and chargrilled lamb cutlets with mediterranean vegetables and mint pesto dressing

(£8.75), with specials such as steamed cod with mashed potato, spinach and lemon butter sauce or thai-style fishcakes (£8.95), while puddings could be jam sponge or chocolate and orange mousse (from £3.95); good children's dishes (£3.95). The bread is baked on the premises and comes with proper butter, and they also do cream teas (£3.95). Swift service from the friendly staff; there may be faint piped music. *(Recommended by Mike and Heather Watson, John Coatsworth, B, M and P Kendall, P Abbott, Francis Johnston, Peter and Patricia Burton)*

Free house ~ Licensees Mike Littlemore and Mrs Margaret Cox ~ Real ale ~ Bar food (12-9.30) ~ Restaurant ~ (01780) 410776 ~ Children in eating area of bar and restaurant ~ Open 11(12 Sun)-11; closed 25 Dec ~ Bedrooms: £57B/£76B

THORPE LANGTON SP7492 Map 4

Bakers Arms

Village signposted off B6047 N of Market Harborough

Tucked away in a little village, this thatched pub is very much a place to go for a relaxing meal rather than just a drink. Stylishly simple old-fashioned furnishings in the knocked-through cottagey beamed interior include stripped pine tables and oriental rugs on bare boards, and nice black and white photographs; service is friendly and helpful. The popular attractively presented meals might include home-made pâté with spiced apple chutney (£4.25), home-made fishcakes with creamed leeks (£4.75), cod filled with crab meat with crushed potatoes (£10.75), fried calves liver with rösti and wild mushrooms (£11.50), and roast lamb shank with roast vegetables and couscous (£12.95); puddings such as apple and sultana tarte tatin with calvados cream or warm chocolate fudge cake with pecan nut sauce (£3.75); booking is advisable, and it's worth checking their opening times below carefully. They've an extensive wine list with around five by the glass (and winter mulled wine), and well kept Tetleys on handpump; no games or piped music. The garden has picnic-sets. *(Recommended by David Field, Eric Locker, Wendy and Bob Needham, Mike and Sue Loseby, Duncan Cloud)*

Free house ~ Licensee Kate Hubbard ~ Real ale ~ Bar food (12-2.15 Sat/Sun only; 6.30-9.30; not Sun evening, Mon) ~ Restaurant ~ (01858) 545201 ~ Children over 12 ~ Pianist Fri evening ~ Open 6.30-11; 12-2.15, 6.30-11 Sat; 12-2.15 Sun; closed Mon, lunchtime Tues-Fri, Sun evening

UPPER HAMBLETON SK9007 Map 4

Finches Arms

Village signposted from A606 on E edge of Oakham

There are delightful views over the expanse of Rutland Water from the suntrap hillside terrace of this stone-built dining pub. Besides home-made soup (£2.95) and filled ciabattas (from £4.95), the enjoyable menu changes frequently and could include grilled sardines with red wine and shallot dressing (£4.25), asparagus with spring onion butter sauce (£4.50), cod fillet with creamed leeks and bacon (£9.75), fried rump steak with roasted mediterranean vegetables (£10.95), and herb-crusted rack of lamb with braised red cabbage (£11.95); puddings such as lemon and lime tart. Both the bar and modern no smoking restaurant (good views from here too) have stylish cane furniture on wooden floors. They serve well kept Grainstore Cooking and Triple B along with a guest such as Timothy Taylors Landlord on hand or electric pump; piped music. There are good walks around the reservoir; what used to be Lower Hambleton is now under the waters. *(Recommended by Stephen, Julie and Hayley Brown, Mike and Sue Loseby, Anthony Barnes, Roger and Maureen Kenning, David Peakall, Keith and Di Newsome, Rona Murdoch, Peter H Stallard, David Field)*

Free house ~ Licensees Celia and Colin Crawford ~ Real ale ~ Bar food ~ Restaurant ~ (01572) 756575 ~ Children in eating area of bar and restaurant ~ Open 11-11; 12-10.30 Sun ~ Bedrooms: £55S(£55B)/£65S(£65B)

WING SK8903 Map 4

Kings Arms

Village signposted off A6003 S of Oakham; Top Street

The charming bar of this friendly and relaxing early 17th-c inn has a traditional feel, with beams, some stripped stone and a flagstone floor, captain's chairs around pine and darker wood tables, old local photographs and a collection of tankards and old-fashioned whisky measuring pots. Two large log fires, one in a copper-canopied central hearth, make it very cosy in winter, and service is very friendly and courteous. Home-made food in huge helpings from a regularly changing menu could include soup (£3.90), filled baguettes (from £4.50), ploughman's (£6.90), fish stew or steak and kidney pie (£7.90), haddock in beer batter with chunky chips and mushy peas (£8.50), and specials such as chicken supreme wrapped in bacon with stilton sauce (£9.50), and roast bass with wild rocket and citrus dressing (£11.50). They serve four well kept real ales which could include Batemans, Grainstore Cooking and Oakham JHB on handpump. In the snug are fishing rods and tackle; piped music. The restaurant (and bedrooms) are no smoking. Outside are colourful hanging baskets in summer, and the sunny yew-sheltered garden has seats, swings and slides. Just up the road is a medieval turf maze. *(Recommended by Norma and Keith Bloomfield, Duncan Cloud, Mrs E Rae, Dr Phil Putwain, JP, PP, Barry Collett, Jim Farmer, Mike and Sue Loseby, Eric Locker, Stephen, Julie and Hayley Brown, Wendy and Bob Needham, Tracey and Stephen Groves, Susan and John Douglas)*

Free house ~ Licensees Neil and Karen Hornsby ~ Real ale ~ Bar food ~ Restaurant ~ (01572) 737634 ~ Children welcome ~ Open 12-2.30, 6-11; 12-11(12-3, 6-11 winter) Sat; 12-10.30 Sun; closed Mon lunch all year and Sun evening in winter ~ Bedrooms: £50S(£50B)/£60S(£60B)

Lucky Dip

Besides the fully inspected pubs, you might like to try these Lucky Dips recommended to us and described by readers (if you do, please send us reports: www.goodguides.com).

Ashby-de-la-Zouch [SK3516]
Thirsty Millers [Mill Lane Mews]: Brightly cheerful old cottage pub with tales of tunnels to castle, no smoking dining area with big helpings of fresh food using local produce, plenty of salads and lighter food, well kept real ales, good generous house wines, friendly landlord, good service, civilised atmosphere *(Charmaigne Taylor, Mr and Mrs P Eastwood, D and M T Ayres-Regan, Bernie Adams)*
Bagworth [SK4408]
Maynard Arms [Station Rd]: Village pub with enjoyable restaurant food, Marstons Pedigree, new indoor play area; piped music *(Rod Weston, Barbara Barber)*
Barnsdale [SK9008]
☆ *Barnsdale Lodge* [just off A606 Oakham—Stamford]: Extensive conservatory dining bar with good choice of generous attractively presented food, charming décor, comfortable sitting-roomish coffee lounge, cream teas, friendly attentive staff, Courage Directors, Greene King Old Speckled Hen and Ruddles, Marstons Pedigree and local guest beers; prices on the high side; bedrooms comfortable and attractive, with good breakfast, adjacent antiques centre and handy for Barnsdale Gardens *(Peter H Stallard, BB, O K Smyth, Gerry and Rosemary Dobson)*
Barrow upon Soar [SK5717]
Navigation [off South St (B5328)]: Extended split-level pub based on former barge-horse stabling, attractive and comfortable, with lovely canal view from small back terrace with moorings; good value freshly made food (may be limited winter) inc interestingly filled baguettes and Sun roast, unusual bar top made from old pennies, central open fire, friendly staff, family room; several well kept ales such as Marstons Pedigree and Tetleys, good prices, daily papers, old local photographs, darts, skittle alley; piped music, SkyTV, games machine; open all day *(CMW, JJW, Bernie Adams, Tony and Wendy Hobden)*
Belton [SK4420]
Queens Head [off A512/A453 between junctions 23 and 24, M1; Long St]: Former coaching inn with two pleasant bars and large dining room, tempting and imaginative blackboard food, welcoming efficient service, well kept Bass, good wines; bedrooms, attractive village *(John and Sylvia Harrop)*
Billesdon [SK7102]
Queens Head [Church St]: Beamed and partly thatched local under new licensees, wide range of enjoyable home-made food, well kept Everards and a guest beer, decent wines, comfortable lounge bar with warm log fire,

unspoilt public bar, small conservatory eating area and upstairs restaurant; children welcome, pretty stone village *(Duncan Cloud)*

Blaby [SP5697]

Bakers Arms [quite handy for M1 junction 21; The Green]: Tucked-away 15th-c newly thatched pub with lots of low beams, nooks and crannies in linked rooms, recently refurbished by new licensees, wide choice of reasonably priced home-made food from sandwiches and baguettes up, efficient friendly local staff, real ales; tables in big newly landscaped garden *(Mr and Mrs R W Monk, Ron Johnson)*

Botcheston [SK4805]

Greyhound [Main St, off B5380 E of Desford]: Traditional village pub with welcoming service, good freshly made food inc bargain lunches, children's food, evening specials and Sun carvery, well kept beer, small restaurant *(Bernie Adams)*

Burbage [SP4492]

Chequers [Lutterworth Rd]: Open-plan village pub with well kept Charles Wells Eagle and Bombardier, home-made food Tues-Sat lunchtimes, pool room, dominoes; excellent family garden, lots of pet animals and even a pony behind; open all day, three twin bedrooms *(Bernie Adams)*

Burrough on the Hill [SK7510]

Stag & Hounds [Main St, off B6047 S of Melton Mowbray]: Bustling local feel with some concentration on good value food; well kept Bass or Tetleys and Greene King IPA, friendly service, open fires, dining room; children allowed, garden with play area *(LYM, Jim Farmer)*

Catthorpe [SP5578]

Cherry Tree [Main St, just off A5 S of M1/M6/A14 interchange]: Attractive country local with good value food (may be filled rolls only, wknds), well kept Bass, Hook Norton Best and an interesting guest beer, quick service, dark panelling, lots of plates and pictures, may be elderly dog sprawled by woodburner; hood skittles, may be piped radio; cl wkdy lunchtimes *(Bernie Adams)*

Church Langton [SP7293]

Langton Arms [B6047 about 3 miles N of Market Harborough; just off A6]: Extended village pub with wide choice of good value nicely presented food, good mix of customers, good service even when busy, well kept Marstons Pedigree and fortnightly guest beers; piped music; garden with play area *(V Green)*

Earl Shilton [SP4697]

Branagans [A47]: Good home-made food from sandwiches up inc OAP bargains and entertaining children's menu, well kept Bass, Marstons Pedigree and guest beers (OAP happy prices at times), good friendly service, two comfortable lounges, one with TV and celebrity photographs, another no smoking and music-free; bare-boards public bar with singer photographs, darts, machines and TVs; open all day, disabled access *(Bernie Adams)*

Enderby [SP5399]

Plough [Mill Hill]: Cosy and spacious inside, separate no smoking eating area, home-made food inc late breakfasts and always a vegetarian dish (they do their best to suit special wishes), good range of puddings, Marstons real ales, decent house wines *(anon)*

Fleckney [SP6493]

Golden Shield [Main St]: Popular two-course bargain lunches Weds-Sat, good beer range inc Greene King Abbot, successful Indian restaurant Sun-Tues evenings inc take-aways *(P Tailyour)*

Foxton [SP6989]

Bridge 61 [Foxton Locks, off A6 3m NW of Market Harborough (park by bridge 60/62 and walk)]: In good setting at foot of long flight of canal locks, spartan flagstones and pine furniture, quickly served food, lots of canalia and boating relics, Everards and a guest ale, games and family room; gift and provision shop next door; hope it won't be affected by British Waterways redevelopment plans *(Dave Braisted, Bernie Adams)*

Shoulder of Mutton [Main St, off A6 N of Market Harborough]: Cheerful service, lots of pine tables and chairs, well kept Marstons Pedigree and Tetleys, wide choice of reasonably priced food (not Mon in winter) from sandwiches to sizzler steaks and Sun lunch, big woodburner, well behaved children welcome in no smoking dining area; piped music, no dogs (exc guide dogs); picnic-sets on big front lawn, new licensees now doing bedrooms *(Ian and Nita Cooper)*

Glaston [SK8900]

Monckton Arms [A47 Leicester—Peterborough, E of Uppingham]: Attractive stone inn with three-room bar, big woodburner in inglenook, well kept Courage Directors, Marstons Pedigree and Charles Wells Bombardier, wide range of decent food; piped music; picnic-sets on sheltered terrace by sizeable modern extension, children welcome *(LYM, R Pring, Jim Farmer)*

Glooston [SP7595]

☆ ***Old Barn*** [off B6047 in Tur Langton]: Decent generous home-made food in extensively restored 16th-c village pub with beams, stripped kitchen tables, country chairs and log fire, cheery young licensees, changing ales such as Batemans XB, Cains Dr Duncans and Elgoods Pageant, no smoking dining area (well behaved children allowed); tables out in front, bedrooms with compact shower cabinets, good breakfast, cl Mon lunchtime *(Jim Farmer, Patrick Hancock, LYM)*

Greetham [SK9214]

Plough [B668 Stretton—Cottesmore]: Tied to Grainstore of Oakham, with their beers inc a Mild and a seasonal beer kept well, interesting home-made food (baguettes sold by the inch), friendly helpful licensees and staff, coal-effect gas fire dividing cosy lounge from eating area, lots of prints and really exhilarating variety of pub games; games machine, tables out behind (with quoits), open all day Fri-Sun *(Richard Lewis, Bernie Adams)*

☆ ***Wheatsheaf*** [B668 Stretton—Cottesmore]: Comfortable and welcoming L-shaped communicating rooms, country prints and plates on dining room walls, odd pivoted clock, roaring woodburner, wide choice of good value generous food served till 11 from baguettes through bargain specials to lots of chargrills, well kept Boddingtons and Tetleys, polite, attentive and speedy service, pool and other games in end room; piped music; wheelchair access, picnic-sets out in front and in tidy garden by back car park beside little kingfisher stream (running under pub, it keeps the cellar cool); bedrooms in annexe *(Michael and Jenny Back, Mr and Mrs J Brown, BB)*

Hathern [SK5021]

Anchor [Loughborough Rd (A6)]: Long comfortable open-plan bar with real ale such as Mansfield or Marstons Pedigree, tea or coffee, fair choice of good value lunchtime food freshly made (so may be a wait), log-effect gas fire; darts, games machine, piped pop, live music Fri/Sat, quiz Sun; picnic-sets in garden with play area, open all day *(CMW, JJW)*

Three Crowns [Wide Lane, just off A6]: Busy three-room village local with real fires, Bass, M&B Mild and guest beers, inc Wicked Hathern ales from local microbrewery; skittle alley, nice garden *(the Didler)*

Heath End [SK3621]

☆ *Saracens Head* [Heath End Lane; follow Calke Abbey coach signs from main rd]: Basic unspoiled two-room farm pub by Staunton Harold Reservoir visitor centre, handy for Calke Abbey; well kept Bass served by jug from the cask, great value filled rolls and toasties, helpful and friendly long-serving licensees, cosy coal fires in lounge and tiled-floor bar with scrubbed tables; picnic-sets on nice grass area, popular with walkers and cyclists *(Bernie Adams, the Didler, JP, PP)*

Hose [SK7329]

Black Horse [Bolton Lane]: Friendly little two-room local, part of Tynemill group, with four or five well kept real ales and attractively priced soft drinks, good value food inc interesting dishes, quarry tiles, darts, open fire, amicable landlord *(the Didler, Darly Graton, Graeme Gulibert, Phil and Jane Hodson, JP, PP)*

☆ *Rose & Crown* [Bolton Lane]: Unpretentious Vale of Belvoir pub with four or five well kept and well priced real ales from far and wide, very friendly attentive service, pub games, generous nicely priced standard food (not Sun evening) from baguettes to Sun lunch, no smoking areas in lounge and dining room (children allowed), pub games; piped music; tables on fairy-lit back terrace, fenced family area; cl lunchtimes Mon-Weds *(JP, PP, the Didler, A C and E Johnson, LYM)*

Hoton [SK5722]

☆ *Packe Arms* [A60]: Welcoming and tidy village pub with old front part, spacious and comfortable back bar, good well priced food from substantial sandwiches up, well kept beers, personable staff *(BB, Sandra and Dave Chadwick)*

Hungarton [SK6907]

☆ *Black Boy* [Main St]: Refurbished by new young licensees, landlord doing wide choice of good home-made food (wknd booking advised) *(S J Robinson)*

Illston on the Hill [SP7099]

☆ *Fox & Goose* [Main St, off B6047 Mkt Harboro—Melton]: Welcoming and idiosyncratic unspoilt chatty two-bar local, plain but comfortable and convivial, with interesting pictures and assorted oddments, well kept Everards Beacon, Tiger, Original and a guest beer such as Archers Golden, table lamps, good coal fire; no food, but bedrooms sometimes available *(Eric Locker, LYM, Des and Jen Clarke, Rona Murdoch)*

Kegworth [SK4826]

Britannia [London Rd]: Good value food inc bargain Sun lunch 12-9 *(the Didler, Mrs P Withers)*

Red Lion [a mile from M1 junction 24, via A6 towards Loughborough; High St]: Very traditional brightly lit village local with four plainish rooms around small servery, well kept Adnams, Banks's Original and several guest beers, limited choice of good wholesome food, good prices; assorted furniture, coal and flame-effect fires, delft shelf of beer bottles, daily papers, darts and cards; picnic-sets in small back yard, garden with play area, open all day *(the Didler, JP, PP, BB, Pete Baker)*

☆ *Station Hotel* [Station Rd towards West Leake, actually just over the Notts border (and its postal address is in Derbyshire!)]: Busy well refurbished pub with bare brick and woodwork, coal fires, two rooms off small bar area, well kept Bass, Courage Directors, Worthington and guest beers, upstairs restaurant with good home cooking; big back lawn, play area; simple good bedrooms, sharing bathroom *(Tony and Wendy Hobden, the Didler, JP, PP)*

Keyham [SK6706]

Dog & Gun [Main St]: Pleasant bar very popular wkdy lunchtimes (food inc good sandwiches with voluminous sandwich garnish), well kept Everards and Marstons Pedigree, helpful staff *(Eric Locker)*

Kibworth Beauchamp [SP6893]

☆ *Coach & Horses* [A6 S of Leicester]: Congenial turkey-carpeted local with welcoming and unobtrusively helpful staff, good home-made food, heartening log fire in huge end inglenook, relaxed atmosphere, good range of well kept beers such as Ansells and Bass, decent wines, china and pewter mugs on beams, cosy candlelit restaurant *(Eric Locker, Duncan Cloud, Jim Farmer, BB)*

Kibworth Harcourt [SP6894]

☆ *Horseshoes* [Main St]: Now restaurant rather than pub, with two-course prix fixe meals (lots of attention to detail, full separate vegetarian menu), though it still has well kept Everards real ales; proficient service, comfortable and spacious plush seating, armchairs in conservatory; piped music, children welcome; tables on attractive back terrace, cl wkdy lunchtimes *(Duncan Cloud, LYM, Rona Murdoch)*

Knipton [SK8231]

Red House [signed off A607 Grantham—Melton Mowbray]: Handsome refurbished Georgian hunting lodge, generous interesting food, well kept Marstons, John Smiths and a guest beer, good friendly landlord, hunting prints in busy lounge with open fire, sizeable restaurant with attractive conservatory, traditional games in public end; open all day, terrace with ornamental pool, lovely views over pretty village near Belvoir Castle, comfortable bedrooms *(LYM, Bernie Adams)*

Langham [SK8411]

Noel Arms [Bridge St]: Beams, flagstones and lots of pictures in long pleasant low-ceilinged bar/dining area, generous good value standard food, well kept Greene King Abbot, Mansfield and Marstons Pedigree, friendly service, central log fire; can get smoky, piped music, well behaved dogs allowed; good tables on front terrace *(Jim Farmer, George Atkinson, LYM)*

Leicester [SK5804]

Ale Wagon [Rutland St/Charles St]: The first pub tied to Hoskins & Oldfields, with up to eight of that small brewery's good interesting ales from Mild to fruit beers, also a couple of guest beers and Weston's perry; good knowledgeable service, basic two-room 1930s interior; open all day, handy for station *(the Didler, Joan and Michel Hooper-Immins)*

Gateway [The Gateway]: Tynemill conversion of old hosiery factory (ladies' underwear on show), bare boards except in no smoking area, five interesting changing ales (one at bargain price), well priced soft drinks, good range of sandwiches and hot dishes till 8 (6 Sun) inc good vegetarian/vegan range, friendly knowledgeable service; piped music, TV; quiz Sun, open all day *(Rona Murdoch, the Didler, Claire Dunn, Rod Weston)*

Globe [Silver St]: Carefully reworked to keep an old-fashioned feel, lots of woodwork in rooms off central bar, charming more peaceful upstairs dining room, wrought-iron gas lamps, good service, Everards real ales, usual food cooked to order; children allowed in some parts *(the Didler, Rona Murdoch, LYM, Peter H Stallard)*

Hat & Beaver [Highcross St]: Basic two-room local handy for Shires shopping centre, good well filled rolls, Hardys & Hansons Best, Best Mild and Classic; TV *(the Didler)*

Hogshead [Market St]: Long thin Whitbreads alehouse, bare boards and flagstones, panelling, old local photographs, up to 10 changing real ales, bottled beers, lots of country wines, no smoking area, friendly young staff, daily papers; all day food, open all day *(Gerry and Rosemary Dobson, the Didler, Joan and Michel Hooper-Immins, Richard Lewis)*

Marquis of Wellington [London Rd]: Splendid gold and black Edwardian exterior, horsey and old Leicester prints on high panelling, bare boards, soft lighting, well kept Everards ales inc seasonal from long marble counter, reasonably priced usual food, good friendly service, flame-effect gas fire, big windows; piped music, big-screen TV, fruit machine, can get noisy and smoky; open all day, disabled access and facilities, colourful heated back courtyard with murals and attractive plants *(Richard Lewis, Esther and John Sprinkle)*

Swan & Rushes [Oxford St/Infirmary Sq]: Good choice of real ales inc Oakham JHB and four changing guest beers, several imported beers on tap and many dozens in bottle, farm cider, beer festivals, enjoyable food; open all day *(the Didler)*

Talbot [Thurcaston Rd]: Roomy open-plan pub, Ansells Bitter and Mild and Marstons Pedigree, basic good value lunchtime food (not Sun) *(Tony and Wendy Hobden)*

Vaults [Wellington St]: Very basic concrete-floored cellar bar with interesting quickly changing microbrews, some tapped from the cask by knowledgeable landlord – a great place for beers; friendly staff, filled rolls, Sunday cheeses, low ceiling with iron pillars (can get smoky), tall settles forming booths, stripped brick walls with old signs rather reminiscent of a railway station; may be entrance fee for Sun live bands; open all day Fri-Sun, cl Mon-Thurs lunchtime *(the Didler)*

Little Bowden [SP7386]

☆ ***Cherry Tree*** [Church Walk; edge of Market Harborough, nr Sainsburys]: Attractive low-beamed thatched and timbered pub under go-ahead new management, two sitting rooms, lots of prints, well kept Everards Beacon, Tiger and Old Original, friendly staff, good value food (not Sun evening) from filled baked potatoes up, no smoking dining room on left, Royal Naval Assoc room and games room; children welcome, garden with picnic-sets and play area, open from noon, all day Sat/Sun, near 12th-c church *(P Tailyour)*

Littlethorpe [SP5497]

Plough [not far from M1 junction 21; Station Rd, off B4114]: Friendly partly thatched 16th-c local, local pictures, landlady's tapestries and china in beamed lounge (a couple of bedlingtons may hog the fire – other dogs welcome), smoke room with darts, copper tabletops and kettles, well kept Everards ales and a guest beer, usual food (not Sun evening, must book Sun lunch) inc fish and chip suppers some nights, early-evening bargains; piped music quieter in dining room; children welcome, picnic-sets outside *(MLR, CMW, JJW)*

Loughborough [SK5319]

Albion [canal bank, about ¼ mile from Loughborough Wharf]: Down-to-earth little old canalside local with emphasis on well kept Mansfield Bitter and Riding Dark Mild, Sam Smiths OB and guest beers; friendly owners, cheap straightforward home-made food, coal fire; children welcome, occasional barbecues, budgerigar aviary in pleasant big courtyard *(the Didler, Christopher Hartley)*

Tap & Mallet [Nottingham Rd]: Fairly plain pub distinguished by five or six changing microbrews, farm cider, occasional beer festivals; back garden, open all day Sat/Sun *(the Didler, JP, PP)*

Lount [SK3819]

Ferrers Arms [A453 NE of Ashby de la Zouch]: Attractive pub with good value food; friendly efficient service, beers inc Marstons Pedigree, good choice of wines *(Ian and Jane Irving)*

Lubenham [SP7087]

Coach & Horses [Main St]: Village local with welcoming licensees, landlord doing good value food, well kept Everards and guest ales, coal fire, pictures and jugs etc in quiet lounge bar *(Max)*

Lyddington [SP8797]

Marquess of Exeter [Main St]: Comfortable series of well furnished decorous rooms, wing armchairs by big inglenook log fire, black beams, neat staff, well kept real ales, good coffee, two eating areas facing bar, restaurant (children allowed);, good bedrooms *(Joy and Colin Rorke, LYM)*

Market Harborough [SP7388]

☆ *Three Swans* [High St]: Comfortable and handsome coaching inn renovated as conference hotel, with beams and old local prints in plush and peaceful panelled front bar, comfortable no smoking back dining lounge and fine conservatory (also no smoking) in more modern part, wide range of food from well priced sandwiches up, decent wines, well kept Courage Directors and changing guest beers such as Everards, good coffee, friendly helpful staff, more formal upstairs restaurant; piped music; attractive suntrap courtyard, good new bedrooms in extension *(George Atkinson, Joan and Michel Hooper-Immins, Jim Farmer, Gerry and Rosemary Dobson, Barry Smith, Ian and Joan Blackwell, Angus Lyon)*

Melton Mowbray [SK7519]

Anne of Cleves [Burton St, by St Mary's Church]: Basic-feel pub with stripped tables, Tudor beams and stonework, cheery staff, separate snug for smokers, well kept Everards Tiger and Old Original, popular usual food in long no smoking bar with small end dining room; may be piped music, no under-7s *(Angus Lyon, Paul and Sue Merrick)*

Mountsorrel [SK5714]

☆ *Swan* [Loughborough Rd, off A6]: Old flagstones, red banquettes, short choice of good food cooked to order (so can be quite a wait), recently refurbished simple small side dining area, well kept Greene King Ruddles, Theakstons Old Peculier and a changing guest beer, wide choice of bottled beers and of good wines by the glass, log fires, good landlady; can get smoky, outside lavatories; small walled back garden leading down to canalised River Soar, bedrooms *(Ian and Eileen Johnson, A C and E Johnson, Jim Farmer)*

Waterside [Sileby Rd]: Comfortable modern split-level lounge and dining area overlooking busy lock on the Soar, four well kept Everards ales, good range of bar food from filled baps to Sun roast (to order, so may be a wait); piped music, games machine; children welcome, disabled access and facilities, picnic-sets outside *(Tony and Wendy Hobden, CMW, JJW)*

Muston [SK8237]

Muston Gap [Church Lane; just off A52 W of Grantham]: Family-oriented Brewers Fayre well refurbished (after a fire), original part now lounge (with its serving bar cl when quiet), main part a comfortable, light and airy extension, with wide choice of reliable reasonably priced family food – at busy times you get a pager to tell you when it's ready; well kept Flowers IPA, decent wines, good disabled facilities; tables outside with play area *(Richard Lewis)*

Newbold Verdon [SK4402]

☆ *Windmill* [Brascote, via B582 (off A447 Hinckley—Coalville)]: Country pub based on former mill house, cobbled back way into airy open-plan two-part bar with small snug and upper no smoking restaurant, good food choice (not Sun evening) from baguettes through good value main dishes to Sun roasts, relaxed friendly service, lots of local pictures, darts; children welcome, games machines; open all day wknds, roomy garden with pretty hanging baskets *(Bernie Adams, Stan and Dot Garner)*

Oadby [SK6200]

☆ *Cow & Plough* [Stoughton Farm, Gartree Rd]: In former farm park and still on a working farm (which makes silage), with Grainstore Steaming Billy, Hoskins & Oldfields HOB and two changing guest beers in top condition, also bottled beers and wines by the glass, Weston's cider and country wines, quick service, three friendly relaxed rooms filled with brewing memorabilia, interesting enamel signs, old church pews; occasional jazz Mon; nice seats outside, cl 10pm, cl wkdy lunchtimes *(Phil and Jane Hodson, Jim Farmer, the Didler, Rona Murdoch, Richard Lewis, JP, PP, Ian and Eileen Johnson)*

Oakham [SK8508]

Horseshoe [Braunston Rd]: 1960s pub with attractive open-plan lounge bar, smaller lounge leading to restaurant, Everards and guest beers, generous bar food, welcoming staff; some picnic-sets out in front, garden behind *(Barry Collett)*

Normanton Park [off A606 E, S of Rutland Water nr Empingham]: Refreshingly informal waterside hotel's Sailing Bar with good choice of food, well kept Greene King Old Speckled Hen and Ruddles and Tetleys; bedrooms, fine views, Rutland Water walks straight from extensive gardens *(BB, Peter H Stallard)*

Wheatsheaf [Northgate]: Neat down-to-earth three-room 17th-c local near church, full Everards range, good basic lunchtime pub food, friendly attentive service, open fire; pleasant back garden *(Norma and Keith Bloomfield, Barry Collett)*

Queniborough [SK6412]

Horse & Groom [School Lane]: Wide choice of good value food from baguettes to cheap traditional and more exotic dishes, very popular two-for-one bargains, well kept Greene King Old Speckled Hen and Tetleys; pool in small back public bar *(Mr and Mrs R W Monk, Howard and Margaret Buchanan)*

Redmile [SK7935]

Peacock [off A52 W of Grantham; at crossroads follow sign for Belvoir Castle, Harlby, and Melton]: Attractive though not cheap stone dining pub with beams, open fires, pews, stripped country tables and chairs, the odd sofa and easy chair, some stripped golden stone, old prints, chintzy curtains, spacious conservatory-style area; well kept Boddingtons, Flowers IPA, Timothy Taylors Landlord and

Whitbreads, no smoking area, dominoes; piped music; tables outside, peaceful setting near Belvoir Castle, good bedrooms *(Simon Chell, Roger and Maureen Kenning, LYM)*

Windmill [off A52 Grantham—Nottingham; Main St]: Comfortable lounge and dining room, well kept Boddingtons and Wadworths 6X, good house wines, enjoyable good value home-made food from baguettes to steaks inc all the usual favourites and children's dishes *(Mrs P J Pearce, W and P J Elderkin)*

Saddington [SP6591]

Queens Head [S of Leicester between A5199 (ex A50) and A6]: Dining pub popular for bargain OAP wkdy lunches, wide choice of other promptly served blackboard food (not Sun evening) from baguettes up, well kept Adnams, Everards Beacon and Tiger and a guest beer, decent wines, polite service, daily papers, lots of knick-knacks and plastic plants, dining conservatory; no under-5s; country views from tables in long sloping garden *(Gerry and Rosemary Dobson, LYM)*

Seaton [SP9098]

George & Dragon [Church Lane, off B672 Caldecott—S Luffenham]: Two bars, one now for dining with pine furniture and generous attractively priced food cooked to order, well kept Greene King IPA, Marstons Pedigree and Theakstons Best, helpful friendly prompt service, nice atmosphere; juke box, pool; tables outside, unspoilt village, good views of famous viaduct *(Rona Murdoch, Norma and Keith Bloomfield, Jim Farmer)*

Sharnford [SP4891]

Countryman [Leicester Rd]: 18th-c beamed and timbered village local with world-wide range of good value food inc OAP bargains in new dining extension, three real ales, darts; children allowed, garden may have bouncy castle, handy for Fosse Meadows nature park, open all day wknds *(Bernie Adams)*

Shawell [SP5480]

White Swan [Main St; village signed down declassified rd (ex A427) off A5/A426 roundabout – turn right in village; not far from M6 junction 1]: Attractive 17th-c beamed and panelled pub, open fire, good range of food from baguettes through some unusual specialities to good Sun lunch, well kept Greene King IPA, Abbot and Ruddles County, good house wines, service chatty and helpful even when busy, no smoking restaurant (best to book at wknds); tables out in front, bedrooms, cl lunchtime exc Sun *(Rona Murdoch, Gerry and Rosemary Dobson)*

Shearsby [SP6290]

☆ ***Chandlers Arms*** [Fenny Lane, off A50 Leicester—Northampton]: Comfortable and friendly village pub with brocaded wall seats, wheelback chairs, flowers on tables, house plants, swagged curtains, candlemaker pictures, Marstons Bitter and Pedigree, no smoking bar on left, interesting food choice (not Sun evening), plenty of locals; may be piped music; tables in secluded raised garden *(Jim Farmer, Mr and Mrs R W Monk, P Tailyour, BB, Bernie Adams)*

Sileby [SK6015]

☆ ***White Swan*** [Swan St]: Bright, cheerful and relaxed, with imaginative attractively priced home-made food (not Sun evening or Mon lunchtime) from snacks up inc wkdy bargains, well kept Marstons Pedigree, nice house wines, good friendly service, comfortable and welcoming dining lounge, small tasteful book-lined restaurant (booking needed) *(K D J Slowe, Bridget Smith, Jim Farmer)*

Smeeton Westerby [SP6792]

Kings Head [Main St]: Small neatly kept village pub with well kept Ansells, Ind Coope Burton and Tetleys, good value limited-choice lunchtime food, more extensive evening menu; cl Mon lunchtime *(David Stone)*

South Croxton [SK6810]

Golden Fleece [Main St]: Large, clean and friendly, with enjoyable good value fresh food from good baguettes to popular Sun lunch, proper bar with some sofas, dark corners and attractive separate restaurant, good service, well kept ales such as Bass, M&B Mild, Marstons Pedigree and Timothy Taylors Landlord, good house wine, log fire; big TV; lovely area *(Jim Farmer)*

Stretton [SK9415]

☆ ***Jackson Stops*** [Rookery Lane]: Thatched dining pub doing well under current newish ownership, very good interesting upmarket food at reasonable prices, decent wines, well kept real ale, log fire, old farm tools, friendly efficient staff, cosy separate locals' bar on left kept for drinkers; local for three-nation fighter squadron at RAF Cottesmore, with lots of relevant memorabilia *(Mrs C Sleight, LYM, RB)*

Sutton Cheney [SK4100]

☆ ***Hercules*** [off A447 3 miles S of Market Bosworth]: Attractive old local with darts and dominoes in cheerfully comfortable long bar, frequently changing well kept guest ales and two brewed for the pub, good choice of home-made bar lunches (not Mon), evening restaurant (not Mon; also Sun lunch), friendly staff (landlord was a Wolves footballer), open fire; piped music; Sun quiz night, children welcome, cl Mon lunchtime *(LYM, Bernie Adams)*

Swithland [SK5413]

☆ ***Griffin*** [Main St; between A6 and B5330, between Loughborough and Leicester]: Good value local, with well kept Everards, enjoyable straightforward food from sandwiches up (not Sun-Tues evenings), friendly staff, pleasant décor in two cosy arch-linked rooms with old-fashioned woodburners; hallway has memorabilia about footballer landlord Alan Birchinell, back skittle alley; gardens by stream, nice setting *(Pete Baker, LYM, Wendy and Bob Needham)*

Thornton [SK4607]

Bricklayers Arms [S of M1 junction 22; Main St]: Traditional old village local with roaring fire and old photographs in beamed bar, Everards Tiger, Beacon and Mild and Greene King Old Speckled Hen, friendly landlord and good staff, good value food, cosy restaurant; piped radio, quiz nights; large back garden with play area, handy for reservoir walks *(Bernie Adams)*

Thringstone [SK4217]

George & Dragon [Ashby Rd]: Recently refurbished, efficient and friendly, with varied bistro food *(Mrs G Williams)*

Tilton on the Hill [SK7405]

Rose & Crown [B6047]: Friendly old place with genuine pub atmosphere, enjoyable and reasonably priced freshly made food, well kept Bass and Boddingtons, good coffee; unobtrusive piped traditional jazz; garden with boules *(Jim Farmer)*

Tur Langton [SP7194]

☆ ***Bulls Head*** [B6047 N of Market Harborough]: Beamed village pub with old-world prints, table skittles and darts in appealing L-shaped tiled-floor public bar, pleasantly plain little lounge with a homely dining end, and picnic-sets in garden; had been headed for the main entries in this edition on the strength of its good value fresh home cooking, well kept ales such as Flowers IPA and Timothy Taylors Landlord, decent wines and friendly helpful service, but after our inspection changed hands in summer 2002 – news please *(Arthur Baker, Melv Tebbett, Eric Locker, David Field, Jim Farmer, Rona Murdoch, LYM)*

Twyford [SK7210]

Saddle [Main St; off B6047 E of Leicester]: Friendly family-run local with comfortable L-shaped knocked-through bar, well kept Mansfield and John Smiths, open fire, reasonably priced usual food, charming little beamed dining area; pool, piped music and TV in games end *(Rona Murdoch, Bernie Adams)*

Ullesthorpe [SP5087]

Chequers [Main St]: Big country inn popular with lunchtime businessmen, beamed and flagstoned bar and most of lounge areas with emphasis on very wide choice of reasonably priced food from large servery (pay as you order), Banks's Original, Marstons Pedigree and a guest beer, no smoking areas; may be faint piped music; children welcome, family room and play area, comfortable bedrooms *(Roger and Jenny Huggins)*

Uppingham [SP8699]

Falcon [High St East/Market Sq]: Civilised town-centre hotel with plenty of character in oak-panelled bar and comfortable lounge, light and airy, with skylights and big windows over market square, pleasant light lunches inc sandwiches and rolls, afternoon teas, cheerful willing staff, well kept Courage Directors, good coffee, nice open fire, serious dailies and fashionable magazines; bedrooms, back car park (can get full) *(P Tailyour, Norma and Keith Bloomfield, George Atkinson, Sheila and Robert Robinson)*

Vaults [Market Pl]: Attractive pub next to church with some tables out overlooking picturesque square, well kept Marstons ales, popular reasonably priced fresh food, comfortable banquettes; piped music; bedrooms *(Barry Collett)*

Walton on the Wolds [SK5919]

Anchor [Loughborough Rd]: Long rambling open-plan beamed pub popular lunchtime with businessmen for good straightforward food (not Sun eve, Mon); friendly and unpretentious local evening atmosphere, two well kept real ales, no smoking end, daily papers; quiet piped 50s music, darts, no credit cards; tables outside, nice village *(CMW, JJW, Norma and Keith Bloomfield)*

Welham [SP7692]

☆ ***Old Red Lion*** [off B664 Market Harborough—Uppingham; Main St]: Popular dining pub (part of small local chain) with several beamed rooms and attractive if rather dark barrel-vaulted back area, limited choice of low-priced good food inc good steaks, Courage Best and Directors, decent wines, efficient hard-working staff, no smoking areas, lovely fire; piped music *(Stephen, Julie and Hayley Brown)*

Whetstone [SP5597]

Bulls Head [Victoria Rd]: Doing well under friendly new landlady, two bars and cosy no smoking area (used for Sun lunches), pleasant décor, Everards and a guest beer; pub games and juke box, entertainment Fri, fortnightly quiz, garden with play area and barbecue *(Bernie Adams)*

Whitwell [SK9208]

☆ ***Noel Arms*** [Main Rd]: Wide choice of good sensibly priced food (till 10) from good value ploughman's and bacon baguette to fish and delicious puddings, in spaciously extended light pine restaurant and smart carpeted bar with lower side room, well kept Courage and Marstons Pedigree, table drinks service; piped music, can get busy; children welcome, suntrap tables outside with play area and occasional barbecues, handy for Rutland Water, bedrooms *(Peter H Stallard, C J Cox, A Monro, LYM)*

Wing [SK8903]

Cuckoo [Top St]: Smart and friendly thatched open-plan pub, good value generous food (not Tues) inc authentic curries, well kept Bass, Marstons Pedigree and interesting guest beers, nice log fires, midsummer beer festival, cuckoo clock, darts and pool at one end, dining area with small fishtank the other; children and dogs welcome, wknd live music, plenty of tables in tidy garden *(JP, PP, Stephen, Julie and Hayley Brown, Norma and Keith Bloomfield, Bernie Adams)*

Woodhouse Eaves [SK5214]

☆ ***Pear Tree*** [Church Hill; main street, off B591 W of Quorndon]: Attractive upper flagstoned food area with pitched roof and pews forming booths, open kitchen doing wide choice of food (not Sun night) from sandwiches to grills, helpful welcoming staff; hunting prints in simply furnished lower pub part with conservatory, log fire, Bass, Greene King IPA and Marstons Pedigree, good choice of malt whiskies, decent wines; may be piped radio; children welcome, two large friendly dogs, open all day bank hol wknds, picnic-sets and summer bar with barbecue area outside, good nearby walks *(David and Helen Wilkins, Brian and Genie Smart, Roger and Maureen Kenning, A C and E Johnson, JP, PP, Michael and Jenny Back, LYM, Keith Routley, George Atkinson)*

☆ *Wheatsheaf* [Brand Hill; beyond Main St, off B591 S of Loughborough]: Plush and busy open-plan beamed country pub with light and airy upstairs dining area, smart customers, good interesting home-cooked food from sandwiches to chargrills and other upmarket dishes, changing ales such as Greene King Abbot, Hook Norton Best, Timothy Taylors Landlord and Tetleys, good house wines, friendly landlord, attentive helpful service, log fire, motor-racing memorabilia; floodlit tables outside, dogs welcome but no motor-cyclists or children *(Margaret Jack, JP, PP, Doug Christian, A C and E Johnson, the Didler, LYM, George Atkinson)*

Wymeswold [SK6023]

Three Crowns [45 Far St]: Snug village pub with welcoming chatty atmosphere, good value basic lunchtime food, well kept Adnams, Marstons, Tetleys and usually a local guest beer, pleasant character furnishings in beamed bar and split-level lounge, a couple of dogs *(Derek and Sylvia Stephenson, Ian and Eileen Johnson, the Didler, A C and E Johnson)*

Wymondham [SK8518]

Berkeley Arms [Main St]: Welcoming and attractive old stone building, two cosy bars comfortably done up, enjoyable freshly made straightforward food from crusty bread sandwiches up, nice prices, good choice of beers such as Adnams, Marstons Pedigree and Tetleys, good coffee; restaurant *(John and Anne Latham, Steven and Sally Knight, Anthony Barnes)*

Real ale may be served from handpumps, electric pumps (not just the on-off switches used for keg beer) or – common in Scotland – tall taps called founts (pronounced 'fonts') where a separate pump pushes the beer up under air pressure. The landlord can adjust the force of the flow – a tight spigot gives the good creamy head that Yorkshire lads like.

Lincolnshire

The pubs that are doing best here this year span an extraordinary range of different characteristics: the Welby Arms at Allington and the Tally Ho at Aswarby are both friendly all-rounders, with nice food and good bedrooms; the simple Cider Centre at Brandy Wharf is an exhilarating one-off with its enthusiastic devotion to cider; and the magnificent old George of Stamford is another one-off, but right at the other end of the scale – every modern comfort, but loads of atmosphere. With good interesting food too, and excellent wines, the George of Stamford gains the title of Lincolnshire Dining Pub of the Year. Two places to pick out particularly in the Lucky Dip section at the end of the chapter are the Bell at Halton Holegate and Vine in Skegness. Drinks prices in the county are closely in line with the national average. Among the main entries, the Victoria in Lincoln (a nice pub, in the good East Midlands Tynemill group) had the cheapest beer. Bathams is the area's classic brewer. Other local beers to look out for, from smaller newer brewers, include Oldershaws and Newby Wyke (see Lucky Dip entry for Willoughby Arms, Little Bytham).

ALLINGTON SK8540 Map 7

Welby Arms

The Green; off A1 N of Grantham, or A52 W of Grantham

This well run, friendly village local, in a quiet village in pleasant countryside, makes a handy respite from the A1. The atmosphere is traditional and welcoming, and the landlord clearly enjoys chatting to his customers. Cheerful obliging waitresses serve really good home-cooked food (with good, crunchy chips), which might include soup (£2.95), filled baguettes and ploughman's (from £3.75, lunchtime only), garlic mushrooms (£3.95), fried brie wedges (£4.25), battered haddock Tues-Fri (£7.45), fish pie (£8.95), and brie and bacon chicken (£9.45), and puddings such as cherry cheesecake and boozy tiramisu (£2.95). Booking is advisable, especially at weekends. The civilised back no smoking dining lounge (where they prefer you to eat) looks out on to tables in a sheltered walled courtyard with pretty hanging baskets in summer. The large bar area, divided by a stone archway, has black beams and joists, log fires (one in an attractive arched brick fireplace), red velvet curtains and comfortable burgundy button-back wall banquettes and stools. Half a dozen ales include Bass, Fullers London Pride, John Smiths, Timothy Taylors Landlord and a couple of guests such as Phoenix Wobbly Bob, kept well but served through a sparkler; they have decent wines, and a good range of country wines; piped music, cribbage and dominoes. There are picnic-sets on the front lawn, and more tables in a back courtyard formed by the restaurant extension and the comfortable new bedrooms beyond. *(Recommended by Michael and Jenny Back, Mr and Mrs W D Borthwick, Peter and Patricia Burton, Peter F Marshall, JP, PP, Brian Clapham, Stephen and Jean Curtis, Kevin Thorpe, the Didler, Tony Gayfer, Barry Collett, Michael Hicks, J R Ringrose, Margaret and Roy Randle, Peter and Jean Hoare)*

Free house ~ Licensees Bob and Josie Dyer ~ Real ale ~ Bar food (12-2, 6-9.30(6-9 Sun)) ~ Restaurant ~ (01400) 281361 ~ Children in eating area of bar ~ Open 12-2.30(3 Sat), 6-11; 12-3, 6-10.30 Sun ~ Bedrooms: £48S/£60S

ASWARBY TF0639 Map 8

Tally Ho 🍷 🛏

A15 S of Sleaford (but N of village turn-off)

With the exterior still looking like an estate property, this handsome, civilised place was built as a farm manager's house in the 17th c, and became an inn about 150 years ago. The comfortably worn-in bar is more or less divided in two by an entrance lobby stacked full with logs, giving the feel of two chatty little rooms, each with its own stripped stone fireplace, candles on a nice mix of chunky old pine tables and small round cast-iron-framed tables, big country prints on cream walls, and big windows; daily papers, piped music. Real ales on handpump, appreciated by thirsty locals standing around the counter, include well kept Bass, Batemans XB and a guest such as Marstons Pedigree, and they have good house wines. The generous bar food includes soup (£2.85), lincolnshire sausage (£4.95), ploughman's or filled french bread (£4.95), and blackboard specials such as four-cheese tartlet or smoked mackerel pâté (£3.85), mediterranean vegetable lasagne (£6.25), lambs liver and bacon in red wine gravy, salmon and spinach fishcakes or beef and ale pie (£6.95), chicken pieces in pepper and orange sauce (£7.15), and rump steak (£10.50); carefully home-made puddings might include lemon crumble and blackberry sponge (£2.85). It's worth booking if you want to eat in the attractive no smoking pine-furnished restaurant. There are tables out behind, among the fruit trees. The bedrooms are in a neatly converted back block, formerly the dairy and a barn. Over the road, the pretty estate church, glimpsed through the stately oaks of the park, is worth a visit. *(Recommended by Mrs Caryn Paladina , Richard Cole, Bill and Sheila McLardy, R & M Tait)*

Free house ~ Licensees Christine and Peter Robertson ~ Real ale ~ Bar food (12-2.30, 6.30-10) ~ Restaurant ~ (01529) 455205 ~ Children in eating area of bar and restaurant ~ Dogs welcome ~ Open 12-3, 6-11(7-10.30 Sun) ~ Bedrooms: £35B/£50B

BARNOLDBY LE BECK TA2303 Map 8

Ship 🍷

Village signposted off A18 Louth—Grimsby

It's worth making a short trip out of the way to this genteel little pub, to see its amazing collection of Edwardian and Victorian bric-a-brac. Heavy dark-ringed drapes and net curtains swathe the windows, throwing an opaque light on the beautifully laid out nostalgic collection of half-remembered things like stand-up telephones, violins, a horn gramophone, bowler and top hats, old racquets, crops and hockey sticks, a lace dress, stuffed birds and animals, and grandmotherly plants in ornate china bowls. Comfortable dark green plush wall benches have lots of pretty propped-up cushions, and there are heavily stuffed green plush Victorian-looking chairs on a green fleur de lys carpet. Only the piped music is slightly incongruous. Many of the tables are booked for dining. Good bar food could include mushrooms with cream and garlic sauce (£3.45), scotch salmon and prawns (£4.95), beef madras or vegetarian lasagne (£6.95), halibut steak with herb and garlic butter (£9.95), lamb steak with port sauce (£10.95), and daily specials (with lots of good fresh fish from Grimsby) such as vegetable stir fry or stilton and mushroom crêpe (£6.95), lemon sole with salmon and prawns in a cheese sauce, fresh dressed crab or lamb steak with port sauce (£10.95), and puddings such as chocolate and brandy fudge cake or white chocolate crème brûlée (£2.95). Well kept Batemans XB and Black Sheep on handpump, and an extensive wine list with plenty by the glass. There are a few picnic-sets under pink cocktail umbrellas outside at the back, next to big hanging baskets suspended from stands. *(Recommended by R Mathews)*

Inn Business ~ Tenant Michele West ~ Real ale ~ Bar food (12-2, 7-9.30) ~ Restaurant ~ (01472) 822308 ~ Children in eating area of bar and restaurant ~ Open 11.30-3, 5.30-11; 11.30-11 Sat; 12-10.30 Sun

BRANDY WHARF TF0197 Map 8

Cider Centre

B1205 SE of Scunthorpe (off A15 about 16 miles N of Lincoln)

Built in the 18th c to serve the needs of canal-building navvies and then the bargemen, this canalside inn now offers much more than just a drink and a bite. It's now one of only a handful of cider taverns left in England, and stocks a huge range, with up to 15 on draught, eight tapped from casks, and the rest kept in stacks of fascinating bottles and small plastic or earthenware kegs on shelves behind the bar (they also keep country wines and mead). The friendly knowledgeable landlord is more than happy to talk about cider, and may even open up his small museum to show you his collection of different cider bottles and jugs from around the country. The down-to-earth main bar has wheelback chairs and brown plush wall banquettes, cheery customer photographs, and a good little coal fire. The dim-lit lounge bar has all sorts of cider memorabilia and humorous sidelights on cider-making and drinking – look out for the foot of 'Cyril the Plumber' poking down through the ceiling. Generous good value bar food includes sandwiches (£2.20, £2.60 toasted), burgers (from £3.20), ploughman's (from £3.60), pork and cider sausages (from £3.60), broccoli and cream cheese bake (£5.80), and chicken curry or chilli con carne (£5.90) with wonderful real chips. The whole place is no smoking; piped British folk music. A simple glazed verandah looks on to the river, where there are moorings and a slipway. Children are not allowed inside, but there's plenty to do along the water banks and in the four acres of orchard (pick-your-own fruit when available) and meadows, which have tables and chairs; caravan site; quite a few appropriate special events. *(Recommended by Marlene and Jim Godfrey, JP, PP, David and Ruth Shillitoe, Mike and Lynn Robinson, WAH, the Didler, Bernie Adams, Patrick Hancock, Christopher Turner)*

Free house ~ Licensee Ian N Horsley ~ Bar food (not Tues lunchtime, not winter Mon) ~ No credit cards ~ (01652) 678364 ~ Open 12-3, 7-11; 12-4(3 winter), 7-10.30 Sun; closed Mon Nov-Easter

CASTLE BYTHAM SK9818 Map 8

Castle Inn

Village signposted off A1 Stamford—Grantham, or off B1176 N of Stamford; High Street

You can't help but be cheered by the thriving village atmosphere and amiably welcoming service (everyone's 'dearie', 'sweetie', 'my darling') at this happy place. The bar, cosily lit with table lamps and soft wall lights, has some small dark brown plush button-back banquettes and a mix of other seats, lots of brass and copper toasting forks, tongs, candlesticks, jugs and pots gleaming around the log fire, horsebrasses on the black beams and joists, and a few farm tools, antlers and heavy horse tack on the stripped stone walls. Bow windows look down over the village (which is attractive) to rolling countryside beyond. Robust home cooking is a high point. The menu includes soup (£2.95), sandwiches (from £3.25), hot smoked mackerel with horseradish sauce (£3.95), crispy thai-style prawns (£4.25), chicken curry or steak and kidney pie with suet crust (£6.25), ham and mushroom tagliatelle (£6.50), grilled lamb cutlets (£7.50), salmon in asparagus and lobster sauce (£8.25), and puddings (£3.50). Main dishes come with six or seven carefully cooked vegetables – their sauté potatoes are particularly good. Well kept real ales such as Adnams, Oakham JHB and Shepherd Neame Bishops Finger on handpump; efficient cheerful service even on very busy nights; pop music. A back dining area on the left, with regency striped pink wallpaper and a collection of china and other pigs, is no smoking, and their Christmas decorations can be rather special. There are metal tables on a little back terrace, and they have CCTV for parked cars. *(Recommended by Michael and Jenny Back, Ray and Winifred Halliday, Beryl and Bill Farmer)*

Free house ~ Licensees Gary and Jill Ward ~ Real ale ~ Bar food ~ Restaurant ~ (01780) 410504 ~ Children in restaurant ~ Open 12-2, 6.30-11(10.30 Sun); closed Mon

CONINGSBY TF2458 Map 8

Lea Gate Inn

Leagate Road (B1192 southwards, off A153 E)

This friendly 16th-c inn stood by one of the perilous tracks through the marshes before the fens were drained, and outside the door you can still see the small iron gantry that used to hold a lamp to guide travellers safely through the mist. Inside is pleasant and friendly, with three separate cosy and softly lit areas linked together around the corner bar counter. It's attractively furnished with a variety of tables and chairs, including antique oak settles with hunting-print cushions, and two great high-backed settles making a snug around the biggest of the fireplaces. Another fireplace has an interesting cast-iron fireplate depicting the Last Supper; heavy black beams support ochre boards, and one cabinet holds a collection of ancient bottles. Promptly served good value bar food includes soup (£2.30), nicely presented lunchtime sandwiches (from £2.60), garlic mushrooms (£2.95), lunchtime ploughman's (£4.95), lincolnshire sausages or spinach lasagne (£6.95), smoked chicken breast (£7.95), lemon sole filled with scallop and shrimp mousse with a lime, wine and olive sauce (£8.25), and steaks (from £9.95), with specials such as game pie (£7.95), and crab salad (£8.50). Well kept Marstons Pedigree, Theakstons XB and possibly a guest such as Adnams on handpump; piped jazz or pop music, fruit machine. There are tables out in an appealing garden, with an enclosed play area. Bedrooms are in a newish block. *(Recommended by Bill and Sheila McLardy, the Didler, Dr John Lunn, Peter J Royle, JP, PP, Michael and Marion Buchanan, Michael and Jenny Back)*

Free house ~ Licensee Mark Dennison ~ Real ale ~ Bar food ~ Restaurant ~ (01526) 342370 ~ Children welcome ~ Open 11.30-2.30, 6.30(6 Sat)-11; 12-3, 6-10.30 Sun ~ Bedrooms: £49.50B/£65B

DYKE TF1022 Map 8

Wishing Well

Village signposted off A15 N of Bourne; Main Street

Yes, there really is a wishing well at the end of the long, rambling front bar in this bustling big black and white village inn – as well as lots of heavy beams, dark stone, brasswork, candlelight, and a cavern of an open fireplace. The carpeted lounge area has a chesterfield settee, green plush button-back low settles and wheelback chairs around individual wooden tables. Smaller and plainer, the quite separate public bar has sensibly placed darts, pool, fruit machine, video game and piped music. Well kept Everards Tiger and Greene King Abbot are served alongside three regularly changing guests such as Brakespears, Fullers London Pride and Smiles on handpump. The popular, good value bar food is the main draw. It includes soup (£2.50), sandwiches (from £2.80), starters such as prawn cocktail and chicken wings (from £4), home-made lasagne or steak and ale pie (£6.50), breaded scampi (£6.95), and steaks (from £7.95), with puddings such as apple pie or carrot cake (from £2.50); no smoking restaurant. There's a small conservatory, and the garden has tables and a play area. *(Recommended by John Curtis, Peter H Stallard, JP, PP, Richard Lewis)*

Free house ~ Licensee Theresa Gallagher ~ Real ale ~ Bar food (11.30-2, 6.30-9; 12-2, 7-9 Sun) ~ Restaurant ~ (01778) 422970 ~ Children welcome ~ Open 11-3, 6-12 (7-10.30 Sun) ~ Bedrooms: £35B/£65B

GEDNEY DYKE TF4125 Map 8

Chequers

Village signposted off A17 Holbeach—Kings Lynn

The main draw at this friendly Fenland pub (which is a few feet below sea level) is the good imaginative food, and particularly their speciality, the really fresh fish and seafood specials such as seared monkfish with herb crumb and coriander relish, bass fillet with beurre blanc, and Cromer crab salad. Other fairly priced and attractively presented food includes sandwiches (from £2.75), home-made soup (£3.50), warm potato and black pudding salad (£4.95), pigeon breast with leek and potato purée in cider sauce (£8.95), haunch of local venison (£11.50), 6oz fillet of lincoln red beef (£11.95), and good home-made puddings (£3.50); roast Sunday lunch. Well kept Adnams Bitter and Greene King Abbot on handpump, decent wine list with about 10 by the glass, and elderflower pressé. The fairly simple interior is spotlessly kept, with an open fire in the bar, a rather old-fashioned restaurant area at one end and, overlooking a garden with picnic-sets, a no smoking dining conservatory; piped music. *(Recommended by Dr G E Martin, June and Ken Brooks, June and Malcolm Farmer, O K Smyth, R C Wiles, Tony Middis, W M Paton, Peter and Jean Hoare, Roger Everett, Val and Alan Green, Mrs Thomas, JP, PP)*

Free house ~ Licensees Simon and Linda Rattray ~ Real ale ~ Bar food ~ Restaurant ~ (01406) 362666 ~ Children welcome ~ Open 12-2, 7-11(10.30 Sun); closed Mon winter

GRANTHAM SK9135 Map 7

Beehive £

Castlegate; from main street turn down Finkin Street opposite St Peter's Place

It's the great atmosphere and cheerfully down-to-earth landlady that earn an entry for this popular unpretentious pub. Its other claim to fame is its remarkable pub sign – a hive full of living bees, mounted in a lime tree. It's been here since at least 1830, and probably a hundred years before that, making this one of the oldest populations of bees in the world. The comfortably straightforward L-shaped bar is partly divided by a wall and fireplace (coal fire), and has a bustling, friendly atmosphere, tables on bare boards, and plenty of comfortable seating. Two well kept real ales on handpump come from the local Newby Wyke brewery. Good value bar food includes sandwiches (from £1.75), burgers (from £2), filled baked potatoes (£2.50), scampi or gammon and egg (£4.75), and 8oz rump steak (£5.50). A back room has a fruit machine, juke box, pool,TV, piped music; there's a large garden. *(Recommended by Derek and Sylvia Stephenson, JP, PP, the Didler, Phil and Jane Hodson, Rona Murdoch)*

Free house ~ Licensee Tina Hayward ~ Real ale ~ Bar food (12-2(3 Sun), 6.30-9.30; not Mon, Fri-Sun evenings) ~ Restaurant ~ (01476) 404554 ~ Children welcome ~ Dogs welcome ~ Open 12-11; 12-10.30 Sun

GRIMSTHORPE TF0422 Map 8

Black Horse

A151 W of Bourne

Readers enjoy the beautifully presented bar food (of a standard and style rare for this part of the world) at this handsome grey stone coaching inn. Changing dishes (not cheap) might include soup of the day (£3.25), baked sardines with garlic butter (£4.25), poached black pudding with mustard or fried haloumi with lime and caper dressing (£4.35), sausage and mash or fish and chips (£8.95), braised lamb shank (£10.95), fried bass on citrus-zested vegetables (£12.75), and glazed duck breast with rösti, red cabbage and red wine jus (£12.85). A cosy window seat and a nice round oak table stand on oak flooring just as you go in. The narrowish room then stretches away past the oak-timbered bar counter with a row of stools running down one side, and a row of tables, some of which are quite intimate in their own little booths, down the opposite wall. A warming coal fire in a stripped stone fireplace, lamps, fresh flowers and patterned wallpaper give it all a homely feel. They serve well kept Black Horse Bitter and Grimsthorpe Castle (both brewed for the pub by Oldershaws), and have decent wines. Some tables may have notices reserving them for parties of four or six; piped music. *(Recommended by Peter Burton, Robin and Diana Rumsam, Walter and Susan Rinaldi-Butcher, Peter and Anne-Marie O'Malley, John and Daphne Lock Necrews, Tony Gayfer)*

Free house ~ Licensees Brian and Elaine Rey ~ Real ale ~ Bar food (12-1.45,

7-9.30(8.30 Sun)) ~ Restaurant ~ (01778) 591247 ~ Children welcome ~ Open 11.30-2.30, 6.30(6 Sat)-11; 12-3, 7-10.30 Sun ~ Bedrooms: £45B/£69B

LINCOLN SK9771 Map 8

Victoria £

Union Road

It's well worth the short walk up a steep back street behind the castle to this quaint, tucked-away early Victorian local. This is a proper alehouse with no pretensions and a chatty, buoyant atmosphere – typical of the pubs in this excellent small group. The simply furnished little tiled front lounge has a coal fire and pictures of Queen Victoria. It attracts a good mix of ages and is always bustling, especially at lunchtime and later on in the evening. The good range of well kept real ales includes Batemans XB, Castle Rock Union Gold and Timothy Taylors Landlord, with up to five guests from brewers such as Black Sheep, Holts and Oldershaws, as well as foreign draught and bottled beers, around 20 country wines, a farm cider on tap and cheap soft drinks. Limited but good value lunchtime food includes filled cobs (from £1.30, huge bacon ones £2.75), toasted sandwiches (£1.95), all-day breakfast and basic home-made hot dishes such as beef stew, sausage and mash, chilli con carne or curry (£3.75), ploughman's (£3.75); Sunday roast (£5). You can sit in the small conservatory or out in the gravelled side garden, which has good views of the castle. They hold beer festivals in the third week in June and the first week in December. *(Recommended by JP, PP, Barbara Wensworth, Patrick Hancock, the Didler, Mike and Lynn Robinson, Richard Lewis, Stephen, Julie and Hayley Brown, Chris and Elaine Lyon, Nick and Pam Hancock, Di and Mike Gillam)*

Tynemill ~ Manager Neil Renshaw ~ Real ale ~ Bar food (12-2.30, 11-2.30 Sat, 12-2 Sun) ~ Restaurant ~ (01522) 536048 ~ Children in restaurant ~ Jazz or folk first Sun of month ~ Open 11-11; 12-10.30 Sun

Wig & Mitre ★ 🍷

30-32 Steep Hill; just below cathedral

The pre-war opening hours (8am-12pm), and the fact that you can get refreshments at almost any hour of the day, are two truly old-fashioned things about this popular place between the castle and the cathedral. It's unlikely though that you'd have found such imaginative (though by no means cheap) food and a caviar menu back in those days. The building itself dates from the 14th c, and has plenty of period features. There's a real buzz in the simpler beamed downstairs bar, which has exposed stone walls, pews and Gothic furniture on oak floorboards, and comfortable sofas in a carpeted back area. Upstairs, the civilised dining room is light and airy, with views of the castle walls and cathedral, shelves of old books, and an open fire. It's decorated with antique prints and more modern caricatures of lawyers and clerics, with plenty of newspapers and periodicals lying about. This is the sort of place where you can pop in for anything from a coffee up. There's a full breakfast menu (English breakfast £7.50), and various other menus which between them might include wild mushroom and madeira soup (£5), cheese soufflé with baby ratatouille (£6.95), baked goats cheese with roasted red peppers and rocket salad (£6), salmon and herb fishcakes with spinach on a lemon and herb butter sauce (£9.50), spiced lamb braised with tomatoes with saffron and lemon couscous and minted crème fraîche (£10.95), steak on horseradish and potato rösti with béarnaise sauce (£17), daily specials, puddings such as rhubarb crème brûlée with lemon shortbread (£4.50), and a cheeseboard (£4.95). Besides well kept Greene King Ruddles Best and County on handpump, they have an excellent selection of over 95 wines, many of them available by the glass, and lots of liqueurs and spirits; they serve freshly squeezed orange juice, and have proper espresso machines. *(Recommended by Lucien, Mike and Lynn Robinson, Patrick Hancock, Dr and Mrs*

M E Wilson, Stephen, Julie and Hayley Brown, Irene and Ray Atkin, Steve Chambers, Mike and Heather Watson, June and Ken Brooks, Anthony Barnes, Torrens Lyster, Patricia Beebe, JP, PP)

Free house ~ Licensees Valerie Hope and Toby Hope ~ Real ale ~ Bar food (8am-11pm) ~ Restaurant ~ (01522) 535190 ~ Children welcome ~ Dogs allowed in bar ~ Open 8am-12pm

NEWTON TF0436 Map 8

Red Lion

Signposted from A52 E of Grantham; pub itself also discreetly signed off A52

The carvery roasts (from £7.95) at this welcoming old pub are so popular that they are now running them on Friday and Saturday evenings as well as Sunday lunchtime. The impressive daily help-yourself cold buffet (from £10.50) is also a real draw. Other good value bar food, aside from a good range of very tasty steaks (from £9.95), could include courgette bake topped with herb, cheese and breadcrumb crust (£5.95), battered haddock (£7.50), steak and ale pie (£7.95), gammon, salmon or trout (£8.95), and specials such as chicken curry or chilli con carne (£6.95), and swordfish steak with lemongrass and coriander sauce (£7.95), with up to 10 puddings. It's comfortable and civilised here, with old-fashioned seating, partly stripped stone walls with old tools and stuffed creatures. The dining room is no smoking. Well kept Batemans XB and a guest such as Fullers London Pride on handpump, friendly service; fruit machine, and perhaps piped music. The pub runs two squash courts which can be used by non-members. A neat, sheltered back garden has some seats on the grass and on the terrace, and there's a good play area. The nearby countryside has pleasant walks; according to local tradition, this village is the highest point between Grantham and the Urals. *(Recommended by John Curtis, JP, PP, Natalie and Alan Strange)*

Free house ~ Licensee Mr Blessett ~ Real ale ~ Bar food ~ Restaurant ~ (01529) 497256 ~ Children in restaurant ~ Open 12-3, 6-11; 12-4, 7-10.30 Sun

SOUTH WITHAM SK9219 Map 8

Blue Cow

Village signposted just off A1 Stamford—Grantham (with brown sign for pub)

You enter this old stone-walled country pub past an endearing little water feature on floodlit steps which go down to the cellar. The two bars inside are served by a central counter. One dark-beamed room has nice hardwood Indonesian tables, bentwood chairs, wickerwork and panelling, and prettily curtained windows. The second has shiny flagstones and dark blue flowery carpet, big black standing timbers and beams and partly stripped stone walls. One of the main attractions here is the product of their on-site microbrewery: Thirlwells Best and Cuddy, kept well on handpump. Families go for the good value food, from sandwiches which are served all day, through a good choice of bar food including soup (£3.50), cheese and garlic stuffed mushrooms (£3.95), malaysian chicken satay (£4.50), ploughman's (£5.75), pie of the day (£6.95), battered Grimsby haddock (£7.30), vegetable pancake (£7.40), sweet and sour pork (£8.85) and rump steak topped with crispy bacon and stilton sauce (£11.75); no smoking restaurant; piped music; darts, TV, cribbage, table skittles and dominoes. There are tables out on a pleasant terrace by the garden. We still haven't heard from anyone who has stayed here, but they will even stable your horse overnight. *(Recommended by the Didler, Derek and Sylvia Stephenson, Mr and Mrs M Doherty, Rona Murdoch, Kevin Thorpe, JP, PP, Stephen, Julie and Hayley Brown, Phil and Jane Hodson, David and Ruth Hollands, Joan and Michel Hooper-Immins)*

Own brew ~ Licensees Dick and Julia Thirlwell ~ Real ale ~ Bar food (12-2.30, 6-9.30) ~ Restaurant ~ (01572) 768432 ~ Children in eating area of bar, restaurant and family room ~ Dogs allowed in bar and bedrooms ~ Open 12-11 ~ Bedrooms: £40S/£45S

STAMFORD TF0207 Map 8

Daniel Lambert

St Leonards Street

Daniel Lambert, a 19th-c prison warden, weighed more than 330 kg (52 stone) when he died suddenly during an overnight stop in Stamford. He's buried in St Martin's churchyard, and you can see items of his clothing in the Stamford Museum in Broad Street: a lot to see, as he measured nearly 3 metres – to be exact, 9 ft 4 in – round the body. There's a big picture of Lambert and other bits and pieces about him in the simply decorated and unpretentious smallish bar, which has maroon plush stools and chairs on a green carpet, and a winter log fire. They have well kept Adnams, Courage Directors, Tetleys and Timothy Taylors Landlord with a guest such as Woodfordes Great Eastern on handpump, as well as eight wines by the glass. Bar food includes sandwiches (from £2.75), soup (£2.95), hot filled baguettes (from £3.50), stilton and Guinness pâté (£4.75), burgers (from £4.50), battered haddock or stilton and vegetable crumble (£6.95), lime and chilli chicken (£7.50), mussels (£8.50), steaks (from £10.95), a couple of daily specials, and puddings such as banoffi pie or jam roly-poly (from £3.50). They do only a roast on Sunday (two-course £10.95); no smoking restaurant; fruit machine, cribbage, dominoes and piped music. The tidy, thoughtfully planted little terraced back garden has aluminium tables and chairs, and, with its subtle lighting, looks nice at night. *(Recommended by MLR, the Didler, Beryl and Bill Farmer, Lorraine and Fred Gill)*

Free house ~ Licensees Chris and Carol Welsh ~ Real ale ~ Bar food (not Sun/Mon evenings) ~ Restaurant ~ (01780) 755991 ~ Children in the bar till 9.30 ~ Dogs allowed in bar ~ Open 11.30-3, 6-11; 11-11 Sat; 12-3, 7-10.30 Sun

George of Stamford ★

71 High Street, St Martins

Lincolnshire Dining Pub of the Year

Built in 1597 for Lord Burghley (with visible parts of a much older Norman pilgrims' hospice, and a crypt under the cocktail bar that may be 1,000 years old), this attractive old coaching inn has kept its considerable character, while adding a good deal of modern style and comfort. Seats in its smart yet relaxed rooms range through leather, cane and antique wicker to soft settees and easy chairs, while the central lounge has sturdy timbers, broad flagstones, heavy beams, and massive stonework. If you look hard enough, a ghostly face is supposed to appear in the wooden panelling of the London Room (used by folk headed that way in coaching days – the other front room making up the surprisingly pubby bar is the York Room). Snacks here include soup (from £4.45), filled ciabattas (from £4.95), chicken liver pâté with hot bread (£5.95), sausage and mash (£6.95), and a pudding of the day (£3.95). Our Food Award however is for the informal Garden Lounge restaurant, which has well spaced furniture on herringbone glazed bricks around a central tropical grove. It serves not cheap but very good food with a continental tilt (one of the licensees, here ever since we've known the inn, is Italian). As well as several pasta dishes such as herb linguini with spring vegetables in a cream sauce (£9.95) and half a lobster with spaghetti (£14.95), the menu includes gruyère fritters with quince jelly (£5.95), moules marinière (£6.95), chargrilled lambs liver (£10.75), dressed crab (£11.95), an attractively set out cold buffet (£12.95), seafood platter (£18.95), and puddings (£4.95). Well kept Adnams Broadside, Fullers London Pride and Greene King Ruddles Best on handpump, but best of all are the wines, many of which are Italian and good value, with about 18 by the glass; there's also freshly squeezed orange juice, and good coffees. The staff are friendly and very professional, with waiter drinks service in the charming cobbled courtyard at the back – lovely in summer, with comfortable chairs and tables among attractive plant tubs and colourful hanging baskets on the ancient stone buildings; there's also a neatly maintained walled garden, with a sunken lawn where croquet is often played. *(Recommended by J F M and M West, Michael Sargent, H Paulinski, Lorraine and Fred Gill, Paul Hopton, Steve Chambers, Mike and Sue Loseby, John Saville, R C Wiles, Gordon Neighbour, S F Parrinder, the Didler, John and Enid Morris, A J Bowen; also in the* Good Hotel Guide*)*

Free house ~ Licensees Chris Pitman and Ivo Vannocci ~ Real ale ~ Bar food (11-11) ~ Restaurant ~ (01780) 750750 ~ Children welcome ~ Dogs allowed in bar and bedrooms ~ Open 11-11; 12-11 Sun ~ Bedrooms: £78B/£105B

SURFLEET TF2528 Map 8

Mermaid

Just off A16 N of Spalding, at bridge

We're hoping there won't be too many changes at this genuinely old-fashioned dining pub (it was on the market as we went to press). Much of it looks unchanged since the 70s, but it's still absolutely pristine and fresh-looking inside. A small central glass-backed bar counter (complete with original Babycham décor) serves two high-ceilinged rooms, which have huge netted sash windows, green patterned carpets, beige Anaglypta dado, brass platters, navigation lanterns and horse tack on cream textured walls, and a mixture of banquettes and stools. Two steps down, the restaurant is decorated in a similar style. You may need to book for the big helpings of enjoyable food, which come on very hot plates. The menu, little changed for many years, includes soup (£2.25), garlic mushrooms (£2.95), cottage pie, liver and bacon or seafood platter (£6.25), steaks (from £9.50), and a couple of daily specials such as minted lamb casserole (£6.25) or rack of lamb (£8.75), with puddings such as cheesecake (£2.50); on Sunday they do a three-course lunch (£8.95). The service is friendly and helpful, and this is the sort of place where you can feel comfortable lingering. Well kept Adnams Broadside and John Smiths on handpump, with a couple of guests such as Batemans XXX and Hook Norton Old Hooky. The pretty garden has seats for a hundred, and a children's play area is safely walled from the River Glen which runs beside the pub. *(Recommended by Michael and Jenny Back, Beryl and Bill Farmer)*

Free house ~ Licensee C D Wilcox ~ Real ale ~ Bar food (11.30-2, 6.30-9.30; 12-2, 7-9 Sun) ~ Restaurant ~ (01775) 680275 ~ Children over 5 in restaurant ~ Open 11.30-3, 6.30-11; 12-3, 7-10.30 Sun; closed 26 Dec, 1 Jan

WOODHALL SPA TF1963 Map 8

Abbey Lodge

Tattersall Road (B1192 Woodhall Spa—Coningsby)

This unchanging family-run roadside inn has a good bustling atmosphere in its discreetly decorated bar, with Victorian and older furnishings. Pictures show its World War II connections with RAF Coningsby – Squadron 617 which was based at the former airfield opposite still holds reunion dinners here. They serve well kept Bass, Worthington and a guest such as Greene King IPA on handpump; friendly atmosphere and staff. The straightforward bar food includes soup (£2.75), pâté with cumberland sauce (£4.25), deep-fried crispy vegetables (£4.95), ploughman's (£5.50), lamb lasagne (£5.50), poached cod with prawns (£7.50), and steaks (from £9.75), as well as specials such as chilli con carne (£6.50) and beef in beer (£7.95), with quite a few puddings such as marshmallow and butterscotch sundae or jam sponge (£2.95). Piped Radio 1 may make its presence felt, and they don't open on Sundays. *(Recommended by JP, PP, John Branston, Bill and Sheila McLardy)*

Free house ~ Licensee Annette Inglis ~ Real ale ~ Bar food (12-2, 7-9(9.30 Weds/Thurs; 6.30-10 Sat); not Sun) ~ Restaurant ~ (01526) 352538 ~ Children over 10 in restaurant ~ Open 11-2.30, 6.30(6 Sat)-11; closed Sun

Pubs brewing their own beers are listed at the back of the book.

Lucky Dip

Besides the fully inspected pubs, you might like to try these Lucky Dips recommended to us and described by readers (if you do, please send us reports: www.goodguides.com).

Barkston [SK9341]
Stag [Church St]: Beamed pub with good home-made food inc imaginative dishes and flexible children's food in left-hand dining bar with mixed tables and chairs, friendly helpful staff, well kept Everards Tiger and Beacon and a guest beer, good wine choice, pool, darts and TV in second bar, small back conservatory; picnic-sets out in front and in big back garden, pleasant village *(Richard Lewis, Bill and Sheila McLardy)*
Billingborough [TF1134]
Fortescue Arms [High St]: Cosy traditional atmosphere in attractive beamed former coaching inn, big log fire, country bygones, good value generous well prepared food esp home-made pies and good veg, bar dining area and restaurant, well kept Ansells, Bass, Ind Coope Burton and a guest beer, decent wines, friendly attentive staff; tables under apple trees in big back garden, attractive village *(John Curtis, Bill and Sheila McLardy)*
Boston [TF3244]
Carpenters Arms [Witham St]: Lively traditional bare-boards local, well kept Bass, Batemans Mild and XB and guest beers, enterprising home-cooked lunchtime food inc good cheap rolls; bedrooms reasonably priced *(the Didler, JP, PP)*
Coach & Horses [Main Ridge]: Friendly traditional one-bar pub with well kept Batemans XB and good coal fire; handy for football ground *(the Didler)*
Eagle [West St, towards station]: Basic cheery local with well kept Batemans, Castle Rock, Timothy Taylors Landlord and three guest beers at low prices, cheap soft drinks too, good value food, children in eating area lunchtime; Mon folk club, live music Sat, open all day Sat *(BB, the Didler, JP, PP)*
Ropers Arms [Horncastle Rd]: Batemans corner local in nice spot by river and windmill, quiet and unassuming – gets lively for big-screen TV football Sun; some live entertainment; open 2-11, all day wknds and summer *(the Didler, JP, PP)*
Brigg [SE9907]
Lord Nelson [Market Pl]: Tastefully renovated, plenty of room with big leather chairs, sofas etc, interesting real ales, café/bar with good hot food counter inc some interesting dishes; bedrooms *(Alison Keys)*
Cleethorpes [TA3008]
No 2 Refreshment Room [Station Approach]: Tiny basic 60s-throwback bar almost on platform, Mansfield Mild, John Smiths Magnet and usually a good guest beer from a small brewery, no food; open all day *(the Didler, JP, PP)*
☆ *Willys* [Highcliff Rd; south promenade]: Open-plan bistro-style seafront pub with café tables, tiled floor and painted brick walls; brews its own good beers, also well kept Batemans and guest beers and good value basic lunchtime home cooking; friendly staff, quiet juke box, panoramic Humber views; popular beer festival Nov, open all day *(the Didler, JP, PP)*
Corby Glen [TF0024]
Coachman [A151, between A1 and Bourne]: Former Woodhouse Inn, renamed and reworked under new owners, with wide choice of blackboard food from sandwiches, baguettes and baked potatoes through curries and so forth to specials such as jugged hare, Greene King Abbot and John Smiths, scrubbed pine tables and open fire *(LYM)*
Dunston [TF0663]
Red Lion [Middle St; ½ mile off B1188 SE of Lincoln]: Pleasant tucked-away village pub, big beamed lounge and restaurant, good home cooking inc plenty of blackboard dishes and very good puddings, good choice of well kept beers, good house wines *(Mr and Mrs J Brown)*
East Kirkby [TF3362]
☆ *Red Lion* [Fen Rd]: Lots of chiming clocks, jugs, breweriana and interesting old tools (some for sale behind), well kept Bass, Worthington and a guest beer, good value standard food, friendly staff, open fire, family room, traditional games; wheelchair access, tables outside (and more machinery), camping; handy for Air Museum *(the Didler, Dave Braisted, JP, PP)*
Frampton [TF3239]
Moores Arms [signed off A16 S of Boston; Church End]: Small beamed rooms, bigger no smoking back family room and conservatory extension, well kept Bass, good traditional food inc choice of Sun roasts, accommodating landlord, woodburning stove; big-screen TV; perhaps the prettiest Fenland village *(Sally Anne and Peter Goodale)*
Frognall [TF1610]
☆ *Goat* [Spalding Rd (B1525, off A16 NE of Mkt Deeping)]: Friendly pub with low beams and stripped stone, particularly well kept changing ales such as Benskins, Clarks Classic Blonde, Elgoods North Brink Porter and Robinsons Robin, enjoyable food inc children's, log fires, two dining rooms (one no smoking) where children welcome, helpful landlord; may be piped music; good wheelchair access, big garden with terrace and play equipment, separate area for under-5s – also a hop garden *(Michael and Jenny Back, Richard Lewis)*
Gainsborough [SK8189]
Eight Jolly Brewers [Ship Court, Silver St]: Bustling unpretentious pub with beams, bare bricks and brewery posters, up to eight well kept well priced changing ales and one brewed for them by Highwood, quieter bar upstairs, simple lunchtime food (not Sun), friendly staff and locals; folk club, open all day Fri-Sun *(JP, PP, the Didler)*
Grantham [SK9135]
Angel & Royal [High St]: Hotel in line for

major restoration (scaffolding up and one bar closed spring 2002) but has huge potential – remarkable worn 13th-c carved stone façade, medieval oriel window seat in upstairs bar on left, massive inglenook in high-beamed main bar opp; well kept Greene King IPA and Abbot, decent bar food, quick friendly service; open all day Fri/Sat, bedrooms in comfortable back extension *(JP, PP, LYM, the Didler, Richard Lewis)*

Blue Bull [Westgate]: Two-bar local with four well kept ales such as Adnams, Newby Wyke White Squall, Oldershaws High Dyke and John Smiths, Oldershaws, partly no smoking back dining room with good value food (not Sun or Mon evenings), darts, pool and juke box in side room; tables out behind, handy for station *(the Didler, Richard Lewis)*

☆ ***Blue Pig*** [Vine St]: Two-bar Tudor pub, low beams, panelling, stripped stone and flagstones, lots of cosy nooks and corners, friendly bustle, helpful staff, well kept Castle Eden, Flowers Original and changing guests such as Robinsons Hartleys XB and York Yorkshire Terrier, good simple lunchtime food, open fire, daily papers, lots of prints and bric-a-brac; piped music, games machine; tables out behind, open all day *(the Didler, Richard Lewis, Tony and Wendy Hobden, Rona Murdoch, JP, PP)*

Chequers [Market Pl]: Friendly open-plan local popular for its well kept ales such as Marstons Pedigree, Phoenix St Georges, Oldershaws Old Boy and Rudgate Thors Best; beer-related magazines, juke box, games machine *(Richard Lewis)*

Muddle Go Nowhere [main Nottingham rd, nr A1/A52]: Large comfortable Tom Cobleigh family pub, lots of beams, woodwork and bare brick, country décor with range fireplaces, no smoking area, their usual generous food inc Sun roasts, well kept Courage Directors, John Smiths Magnet and Theakstons, quick helpful service even when busy; outside and inside play areas inc new play barn, baby changing and disabled facilities, Mon quiz night, open all day *(R C Vincent, Richard Lewis)*

Nobody Inn [Watergate]: Friendly bare-boards open-plan local with five well kept changing ales inc cheap Sam Smiths OB and two or three from local Newby Wyke and Oldershaws; back games room with pool, table footer, good juke box, SkyTV; open all day *(the Didler, Richard Lewis, M W Turner)*

Tollemache [St Peters Hill/Catherine Rd]: Roomy and popular L-shaped Wetherspoons, unusual in being good for families yet having a proper pub atmosphere; interesting choice of well kept ales, good generous food choice inc generous children's bargains, efficient friendly service, usual high-standard décor with big lower-level family no smoking area, leather settee and armchairs by open fire, old books, local pictures and Co-op memorabilia; attractive big terrace with fountain and play area, open all day, handy for Belton House *(Richard Lewis)*

Grimsby [TA2609]

Lincoln Castle [Fishermans Wharf; follow Heritage Centre signs, behind Sainsburys]: Former Humber paddle-steamer converted to friendly bar and lower deck restaurant, good value food inc Sun carvery, well kept ales such as Bass and Theakstons, engines preserved and on view, cabinet showing ship's history, seats out on upper deck; games machine, piped music; handy for National Fishing Heritage Centre *(Ted Gaytor)*

Halton Holegate [TF4165]

☆ ***Bell*** [B1195 E of Spilsby]: Unchanging pretty village local, simple but comfortable and consistently friendly, with wide choice of decent generous home-made food inc Sun lunches and outstanding fish and chips, tempting prices, well kept Batemans XB, Tetleys and Highwood Bomber County, Lancaster bomber pictures, pub games; the pub dog's called Samson; children in back eating area (with tropical fish tank) and restaurant *(the Didler, Michael and Jenny Back, LYM, JP, PP, Derek and Sylvia Stephenson)*

Haxey [SK7799]

Kings Arms [Low St]: Cosy and friendly village local, real fires, good choice of ales such as Caledonian Deuchars IPA, John Smiths, Tetleys and other changing beers, enthusiastic licensees, lounge bars, conservatory with pool table; quiz, entertainment and theme nights; children welcome, garden with play area *(Andrew Crawford)*

Heckington [TF1444]

Nags Head [off A17 Sleaford—Boston; High St]: Well worn in two-room 17th-c village pub with huge inglenook fireplace, wall banquettes, well kept Bass, Tetleys and perhaps a guest beer, generous home-made food from sandwiches up, no smoking upstairs dining room; darts, pool, shove-ha'penny, fruit machine, juke box, TV and piped music; children welcome, open all day, Sun quiz night, fortnightly live entertainment, picnic-sets and play area in garden (beyond dogs' yard), bedrooms *(Dr Paull Khan, B N F and M Parkin, LYM)*

Holbeach [TF3524]

Lion [Spalding Rd]: Bargain home-made food served piping hot, well kept Greene King Old Speckled Hen, Marstons Pedigree and Tetleys, cheerful helpful service, big coal and log fire, massive beams in neat no smoking end restaurant area; juke box, fruit machines *(Michael and Jenny Back)*

Irnham [TF0226]

Griffin [Bulby Rd]: Small old stone-built village pub noted for three well kept changing guest beers, with up to three dozen in early July beer festival (lots of room for tents and caravans); big log fire in lounge, back snug, restaurant, friendly staff; nice village setting *(Richard Lewis)*

Kirkby la Thorpe [TF0945]

Queens Head [Boston Rd, backing on to A17]: Comfortably plush, with good choice of good home-made food from well filled sandwiches and baguettes to fresh fish, interesting changing specials, enjoyable puddings and home-baked bread, good service and atmosphere, well kept Marstons, decent house wine, small cosy no smoking restaurant; easy disabled access *(Keith Patching)*

Kirkby on Bain [TF2462]

Ebrington Arms [Main St]: Generous good value food inc cheap Sun lunch, five or more well kept changing ales from small breweries far and wide, prompt welcoming service, daily papers, low 16th-c beams, two open fires, nicely set out dining areas each side, copper-topped tables, wall banquettes, jet fighter and racing car pictures; games area with darts, restaurant, may be piped music; beer festivals Easter and Aug bank hols, wheelchair access, tables out in front, swings on side lawn, camp site behind, open all day *(the Didler, Richard Lewis)*

Leadenham [SK9552]

☆ *George* [High St; A17 Newark—Sleaford]: Enjoyable sensibly priced food from sandwiches to steaks in unassuming bar, good welcoming service, well kept real ales, good choice of wines by the glass, massive range of whiskies, restaurant; side games room, may be piped music; good value bedrooms, good breakfast *(LYM, Michael Hicks, DC, Anthony Barnes)*

Lincoln [SK9871]

Adam & Eve [Lindum Rd (towards Wragby)]: Civilised pub, one of the oldest here, opp gate to cathedral close; good value food, well kept John Smiths and Theakstons, friendly cheerful staff; boules, tree-shaded play area *(Mr and Mrs G Baker)*

Cornhill Vaults [Exchange Arcade]: Vaulted underground pub with cheap well kept Sam Smiths, freshly made bar lunches inc unusual sandwiches, pool table in separate area, friendly service; juke box after 3, live music evenings *(the Didler, JP, PP)*

Golden Eagle [High St]: Cheerfully busy basic two-bar town pub, wide choice of well kept and very attractively priced changing ales such as Batemans, Everards, Fullers and Timothy Taylors, good choice of country wines, cheap soft drinks, good value lunchtime food; open all day Fri/Sat *(JP, PP, the Didler)*

☆ *Jolly Brewer* [Broadgate]: Busy Art Deco real ale pub with some items of special interest, real fire, thriving atmosphere and enthusiastic owners, well kept Bass, Theakstons XB and four guests, good well priced lunches inc Sun roasts; games machines and juke box, can be crowded wknd evenings; tables in good outside area, open all day *(the Didler, JP, PP)*

Magna Carta [Exchequer Gate]: Upstairs restaurant with cathedral and castle view, further seating downstairs, wide variety of food (not Fri-Sun evenings) inc children's, breakfast and afternoon teas, Banks's, Mansfield and Marstons New Fangled and Pedigree, low prices, friendly staff, comfortable carpeted layout, lots of balustrading; piped music, games machine; open all day *(Richard Lewis, P and D Carpenter)*

Morning Star [Greetwellgate]: Unpretentious well scrubbed local handy for cathedral, friendly atmosphere, good value lunches esp Fri specials, well kept reasonably priced Bass, Greene King Ruddles Best and a guest beer, coal fire, aircraft paintings, nice outside area; piano night Sat, open all day exc Sun *(the Didler, Patrick Hancock, JP, PP)*

☆ *Queen in the West* [Moor St; off A57 nr racecourse]: Well kept changing ales such as Bass, Marstons Pedigree, Theakstons XB and Old Peculier and reasonably priced simple bar lunches in busy and welcoming old backstreet pub below cathedral; military prints and miniatures in well decorated lounge, interesting sporting prints in public bar with TV, darts, games; open all day Fri/Sat *(the Didler, JP, PP)*

Royal William IV [Brayford Wharf N]: Attractive riverside pub with bric-a-brac in comfortable L-shaped lounge, good beer choice inc guests, bargain food; very handy for new cinema complex *(Kevin Blake)*

Sippers [Melville St, opp bus station]: Popular two-bar lunchtime pub with good food (not wknd evenings), Courage Directors, Greene King Old Speckled Hen, Marstons Pedigree and guest beers, very friendly licensees; quieter evenings, cl Sun lunchtime *(the Didler, JP, PP)*

Strugglers [Westgate]: Small refurbished local with well kept Bass, Marstons Pedigree and a guest such as Fullers London Pride, coal-effect fire in small back snug; no under-18s, can be smoky; open all day Fri-Sun *(the Didler, Alison Keys)*

Tap & Spile [Hungate]: Five or so well kept interesting changing ales, farm cider and country wines from central bar, small choice of food, framed beer mats, prints and breweriana, bare boards and brickwork, stone floors, friendly atmosphere; open all day *(Richard Lewis)*

Little Bytham [TF0118]

☆ *Willoughby Arms* [Station Rd, S of village]: Good generous straightforward food, well kept Batemans XB, several guest beers and (brewed in rebuilt back outbuilding) Newby Wyke ales, also frequent folk and beer festivals; good food choice from sandwiches to venison inc children's helpings (fish and chips Mon, inc takeaways), friendly staff, big log fire and lots of prints in beamed stripped stone lounge, side dining room, games room with TV; good piped music, live music in cellar bar wknds; children welcome, pleasant terrace and back garden overlooking fields, open all day wknds *(Richard Lewis, Kevin Thorpe)*

Long Bennington [SK9135]

☆ *Reindeer* [just off A1 N of Grantham]: Welcoming old inn, buoyant atmosphere, chatty staff, good choice of generous reasonably priced home-cooked food in bar and more formal dining lounge, cheaper small helpings, well kept Scottish Courage ales, good wines *(Mr and Mrs P Rich)*

Louth [TF3387]

Kings Head [Mercer Row]: Large unpretentious bar, well kept beer, good range of good value bar food inc roasts and traditional puddings *(the Didler, JP, PP)*

☆ *Masons Arms* [Cornmarket]: Light and airy, with plush seats, big sunny bay window, good mix of different-sized tables, panelled back bar, friendly landlord and family, well kept full

Batemans range, Marstons Pedigree and guest beers, farm cider, decent coffee, good home-made food from big hot sandwiches up, good upstairs dining room (remarkable Art Deco former masonic lodge meeting room); piped radio; good bedrooms, open all day exc Sun *(David and Ruth Hollands, the Didler, A J Jones, JP, PP, BB)*

Olde Whyte Swanne [Eastgate]: Popular and friendly, ancient low beams, comfortable front bar with open fire, decent soup, Bass and guest beers *(JP, PP, the Didler)*

Wheatsheaf [Westgate]: Cheerful well kept early 17th-c inn, real fires in all three bars, Bass, Boddingtons and Flowers, decent lunchtime food; can be crowded; tables outside, open all day Sat and summer Sun *(the Didler)*

Woolpack [Riverhead Rd]: 18th-c wool merchant's house popular for good home cooking (not Sun or Mon evenings) and Batemans ales inc a Mild, Marstons Pedigree and guest ales; bar, lounge, snug, two real fires; cl Mon lunchtime, open all day Sat *(Mike and Lynn Robinson, the Didler)*

Nettleham [SK9975]

Brown Cow [A46 N of Lincoln]: Spotless civilised lounge bar with good value generous basic food inc two-course bargain lunch and popular Sun lunch, helpful friendly staff; dogs welcome; pleasant village *(Mr and Mrs G Baker)*

North Kelsey [TA0401]

Butchers Arms [Middle St; off B1434 S of Brigg]: Busy village local, opened up but not too modern, low ceilings, flagstones, bare boards, dim lighting, with five well kept Highwood beers (brewed by owner on his farm), good value cold lunches, enthusiastic cheerful service, woodburner; pub games, no juke box, tables outside, opens 4 wkdys, open all day wknds *(the Didler, JP, PP)*

Norton Disney [SK8859]

☆ ***St Vincent Arms*** [Main St, off A46 Newark—Lincoln]: Attractive and welcoming village pub with well kept Batemans XXXB or Marstons Pedigree, guest beers sometimes, open fire, good cheap generous plain food from sandwiches up inc beautifully cooked veg, pleasant landlord, appropriately decorated family room (Walt Disney's ancestors came from here) and adults' dining room; tables and big adventure playground out behind *(the Didler, JP, PP)*

Rippingale [TF0927]

Bull [just off A15 Bourne—Sleaford; High St]: Fresh and spotless, with welcoming American landlady, attentive service, good varied reasonably priced food using local produce in bar and nice restaurant, wide range of well kept ales, good wine selection, no smoking areas, no piped music; tables in garden with big play area *(Gordon B Thornton)*

Scamblesby [TF2778]

Green Man [just off A153 Horncastle—Louth]: Restored to its original name, and something like its original condition; good range of beers such as Fullers London Pride and Highwood Tom Wood Harvest, inexpensive food *(Derek and Sylvia Stephenson)*

Skegness [TF5660]

☆ ***Vine*** [Vine Rd, off Drummond Rd, Seacroft]: Unspoilt extended hotel based on late 18th-c country house, calm and comfortable well run bar overlooking drive and own bowling green, imposing antique seats and grandfather clock in turkey-carpeted hall, juke box in inner oak-panelled room; well kept Batemans XB, Mild and XXB, good value food using local produce in bar and restaurant, friendly staff, welcoming fire; tables on big back sheltered lawn with swings, good reasonably priced bedrooms, peaceful suburban setting not far from beach and birdwatching *(JP, PP, BB, the Didler, Derek and Sylvia Stephenson)*

Skendleby [TF4369]

☆ ***Blacksmiths Arms*** [off A158 about 10 miles NW of Skegness]: Some concentration on good imaginative generous food in big busy back restaurant extension, very generous one-price main courses, also old-fashioned two-room bar, cosy and quaint, with view of cellar, deep 17th-c well, well kept Batemans XB and XXXB tapped from the cask, friendly staff, open fire *(JP, PP, the Didler, Val and Alan Green)*

South Ormsby [TF3775]

☆ ***Massingbird Arms*** [off A16 S of Louth]: Homely refurbished 17th-c pub, very helpful and obliging landlord, well kept John Smiths Magnet and a guest beer, interesting freshly cooked food all day, tea and coffee, Sun lunch, restaurant Thurs-Sun evenings; good value bedrooms, open all day *(the Didler, JP, PP, Martin Dormer)*

South Thoresby [TF4077]

☆ ***Vine*** [about a mile off A16 N of Ulceby Cross]: Large two-room village inn with small pub part – tiny passageway servery, steps up to three-table lounge, wide choice of good food inc Aberdeen Angus steaks in nicely panelled no smoking dining room, well kept Batemans XB and a guest beer, first-class choice of malt whiskies, good value wines, separate pool room; bedrooms, tables in pleasant big garden *(JP, PP, the Didler)*

Stamford [TF0207]

Green Man [Scotgate (A606/B1081)]: Bare boards or flagstones, stripped brickwork, up to eight well kept changing ales, open fire, welcoming regulars, lunchtime food (not Sun), pub games, SkyTV in small back room; big beer festivals with live music Easter and late summer; unusual alley to nicely planted back terrace with picnic-sets, bedrooms *(the Didler, Richard Houghton, Richard Lewis)*

Lord Burghley [Broad St]: Busy old pub with several rooms, stripped stone, good atmosphere and service, well kept Bass, Fullers London Pride and Greene King IPA, farm cider, food (not Sun evening) inc good steak and kidney pie and steamed puddings; pleasant small walled garden, open all day *(the Didler)*

Periwig [Red Lion Sq/All Saints Pl]: Gallery above narrow split-level bar, well kept Courage Directors, Oakham JHB, John Smiths and Theakstons XB, well filled good value baguettes, baked potatoes, ploughman's and salads (not Sun), chequered tablecloths in bistro-style eating area; unobtrusive piped music; open all day *(the Didler)*

Swineshead Bridge [TF2142]

Barge [A17, nr A1121 junction]: Welcoming lunch stop esp for their bargain fresh fish; relaxing uncrowded front room, good friendly service, lots of interesting knick-knacks and old beer bottles, pool table in public bar; quiet garden with swing *(Gerald Wilkinson)*

Tealby [TF1590]

☆ ***Kings Head*** [Kingsway, off B1203 towards bottom of village]: Mossy-thatched and beamed pub in quiet Wolds village famous for its cottage gardens; generous food inc sandwiches and meaty home-made pies (very popular lunchtime with older people), Fri-Sun fish nights, well kept Bass, Stones and Worthington, farm cider, pleasant service; restaurant, wheelchair access, picnic-sets in attractive garden, handy for Viking Way walk *(Martin Dormer, the Didler, BB)*

Tetford [TF3374]

White Hart [East Rd, off A158 E of Horncastle]: Early 16th-c pub with interesting layout, old-fashioned settles, slabby elm tables and red tiled floor in pleasant quiet inglenook bar, no smoking snug, basic games room, well kept real ales, lots of whiskies, usual food; seats and swings on sheltered back lawn, simple bedrooms *(the Didler, JP, PP, LYM)*

Welbourn [SK9654]

Joiners Arms [High St]: Interesting choice of enjoyable food, real ale, friendly staff *(Mrs Sheila MacPhail)*

Welton Hill [SK9872]

Farmers Arms [A46 Lincoln—Market Rasen]: Well run independent pub with hearty helpings of good freshly made food *(M Clark, Patrick Hancock)*

West Deeping [TF1009]

Red Lion [King St]: Long low-beamed partly stripped stone bar with plenty of tables, very popular lunchtime for wide choice of generous food from appetising cheap hot snacks up; helpful prompt cheerful service, well kept ales such as Fullers London Pride, John Smiths, Tetleys and Timothy Taylors Landlord, good coffee, roaring coal fires each end, brassware and pictures; big pool room, open all day, tables in back garden with attractive play area *(Michael and Jenny Back)*

Willoughby [TF4771]

Willoughby Arms [Church Lane]: Wide choice of freshly made competitively priced food, good individual service; quiet village *(R J Malkin)*

Woolsthorpe [SK8435]

☆ ***Chequers*** [Main St; the one nr Belvoir, signed off A52 Grantham—Nottingham]: Attractively refurbished and extended village pub in sight of Belvoir Castle, with good freshly made food in bar and restaurant inc interesting lunches and local game, well kept ale, friendly service, warmly local winter atmosphere (roaring fires, dominoes), lots of events esp Fri in big entertainments area, own cricket ground; tables outside, boules; bedrooms *(June and Malcolm Farmer, BB)*

Please keep sending us reports. We rely on readers for news of new discoveries, and particularly for news of changes – however slight – at the fully described pubs. No stamp needed: The Good Pub Guide, FREEPOST TN1569, Wadhurst, E Sussex TN5 7BR or send your report through our web site: www.goodguides.com

Norfolk

A number of Norfolk pubs are currently on particularly good form: the White Horse looking over the tidal marshes at Brancaster Staithe (good food and bedrooms, friendly young staff), the Hoste Arms in Burnham Market (refitting and expansion was not entirely without its minor troubles, but all seems to have worked out splendidly in the end), the Ratcatchers at Cawston (a thriving dining pub with friendly hard-working licensees), the individualistic Saracens Head at Wolterton near Erpingham (good food, three more bedrooms), the cheerful Adam & Eve in Norwich (the city's most ancient pub) and the Fat Cat there (incredible beer range), the Rose & Crown in Snettisham (a good all-rounder), the Lifeboat at Thornham (like many places on this north coast, at its best out of high season), the Red Lion at Upper Sheringham (enjoyable food in this simple little cottage – they tend to keep the tables for diners so you may have to sit out if all you want's a drink), the proudly old-fashioned Three Horseshoes at Warham (a favourite for many), the Crown in Wells-next-the-Sea (boldly refurbished by new owners, lovely food in its new brasserie bar as well as the smart restaurant), and the welcoming and unassuming Fishermans Return at Winterton-on-Sea (very nice long-serving licensees giving good value). We'd add to these three new entries: the cheerful Three Swallows at Cley next the Sea (lovely garden), the Crown at Colkirk (newish licensees doing enjoyable food) and the stylishly reworked Victoria at Holkham. For a special meal out, several of these pubs have noteworthy food; the pub that earns the title of Norfolk Dining Pub of the Year is the Ratcatchers at Cawston. The Lucky Dip section at the end of the chapter shows up several particularly promising pubs: the Chequers at Binham, Hare & Hounds at Hempstead, Blue Bell at Hunworth, Scole Inn, Crown at Stanhoe, Chequers at Thompson, Wheatsheaf at West Beckham, Bell at Wiveton and Green Dragon in Wymondham. Norfolk drinks prices are rather above the national average, with the Fat Cat in Norwich and Darbys at Swanton Morley having considerably cheaper beer than most other main entries. Local beers to look out for, with the possibility of low prices backed by the new cut in beer duty for small brewers, include Woodfordes, Wolf, Iceni, Chalk Hill, Broadlands and Reepham.

BAWBURGH TG1508 Map 5

Kings Head

Pub signposted down Harts Lane off B1108, which leads off A47 just W of Norwich

Opposite a small green, this cosy old pub has four sunny yellow linked rooms with low beams, some standing timbers, a warming log fire in a large knocked-through canopied fireplace, a woodburner in the attractive inglenook in the end room, and comfortable upholstered seats and banquettes. Quite a choice of ambitious bar food might include lunchtime sandwiches (from £3.75), spicy thai chicken broth, stilton cheesecake with pickled pears and lemon and mustard dressing or warm smoked chicken with couscous, orange scented hummus and roast pepper coulis (£4.95), braised beef and wild mushrooms with a cheese muffin (£7.50), steak and kidney pudding (£7.95), halloumi cheese with red

pesto, vine tomatoes, fresh spinach, roasted pine nuts and balsamic vinegar and basil oil (£9.95), organic breast of chicken with roast asparagus and cherry tomatoes and a lemon cream sauce (£11.50), lamb rump with ratatouille, spinach, rösti and saffron aïoli or organic salmon with crayfish potatoes, crab and basil sauce and roast red peppers (£12.95), and puddings like passion fruit, mango and cardamom orange soup with shortbread biscuit and mascarpone cream or chocolate and Amaretto torte with lime anglaise (£4.50); the restaurant is no smoking. Well kept Adnams Bitter, Woodfordes Wherry and a guest such as Nethergate Hares Breadth on handpump and quite a few wines by the glass; fruit machine. There are rustic tables and benches on the gravel outside and a garden with outdoor heaters on the terrace and herbaceous plants. More reports please.
(Recommended by Kelly Lewis, Pete Beasley, Stephen, Julie and Hayley Brown)

Free house ~ Licensee Anton Wimmer ~ Real ale ~ Bar food (12-2(2.30 Sun), 6.30-9.30; not evenings 25 or 26 Dec) ~ Restaurant ~ (01603) 744977 ~ Children in eating area of bar and restaurant ~ Solo musician every 2nd Mon ~ Open 11-11; 12-10.30 Sun; closed 25 Dec evening

BLAKENEY TG0243 Map 8

Kings Arms

West Gate Street

Bustling and friendly (and run by the same licensees for 27 years now), this unchanging 18th-c pub has a good mix of chatty locals and visitors. The three simply furnished, knocked-through pubby rooms have low ceilings, some interesting photographs of the licensees' theatrical careers, other pictures including work by local artists, and what can only be the smallest cartoon gallery in England in a former telephone kiosk. Look out for the brass plaque on the wall that indicates a flood level mark; two small rooms are no smoking – as is the airy garden room; darts, table skittles, shove-ha'penny, cribbage and dominoes. Well kept Adnams, Greene King Old Speckled Hen, Marstons Pedigree, Websters Yorkshire, and a couple of guests such as Adnams and Woodfordes Wherry on handpump. Enjoyable, reasonably priced bar food includes sandwiches (from £1.75; toasties from £2.10; club from £2.25), soup (£2.75), ploughman's (from £4.95), local summer crab (£5.50), cream cheese and broccoli bake (£5.95), local winter mussels (£6.50), cod or haddock (£6.95), evening salads (from £7.25), steaks (from £9.95), and children's meals (£3.25); good breakfasts. The large garden has lots of tables and chairs and a separate, well equipped children's area.
(Recommended by MDN, Di and Mike Gillam, Patrick Hancock, Nigel Woolliscroft, Patricia Beebe, Paul and Ursula Randall, Klaus and Elizabeth Leist, Keith and Chris O'Neill, Val and Alan Green, John Robertson, Jim Abbott, B N F and M Parkin, Kevin Thorpe)

Free house ~ Licensees John Howard and Marjorie Davies ~ Real ale ~ Bar food (12-9.30(9 Sun)) ~ (01263) 740341 ~ Children welcome ~ Dogs welcome ~ Open 11-11(10.30 Sun); closed evening 25 Dec ~ Bedrooms: /£60S

White Horse

Off A149 W of Sheringham; High Street

Although this little hotel does get busy in high season, there's always a good leavening of local people. The chatty long main bar is predominantly green with a Venetian red ceiling, and restrained but attractive décor – including framed watercolours by a local artist. Well kept Adnams Best and Broadside, Bass, and Woodefords on handpump, a wide choice of reasonably priced wines, and home-made elderflower cordial in summer; cribbage. Bar food includes sandwiches or filled ciabattas (lunchtime, from £3.50), home-made soup (£3.25), deep-fried whitebait (£4.25), roquefort, spinach and onion tartlet (£6.95), steak in ale pie (£7.50), sirloin steak (£11.95), home-made puddings (£3.25), and children's meals (from £3.95). The no smoking conservatory restaurant is attractive. Tables out in a suntrap courtyard and pleasant paved garden. More reports please.
(Recommended by Peter and Pat Frogley, Eric Locker, Basil Minson, Pamela Goodwyn,

A D Cross, Minda and Stanley Alexander, Val and Alan Green, Brian Haywood, David Field)

Free house ~ Licensees Dan Goff and Simon Scillitoe ~ Real ale ~ Bar food (12-2, 6-9) ~ Restaurant ~ (01263) 740574 ~ Children in family room ~ Open 11-3, 6-11; 12-3, 6-10.30 Sun; closed 2 wks in Jan ~ Bedrooms: £40B/£90B

BRANCASTER STAITHE TF7743 Map 8

Jolly Sailors

Main Road (A149)

This is prime birdwatching territory and the pub is set on the edge of thousands of acres of National Trust dunes and salt flats. It's unpretentious and simply furnished with three small rooms, a log fire, and a good mix of seats. Bar food includes sandwiches (from £2.70; fresh crab £4.25), hot sausage and onion baguette (£3.95), goats cheese and spinach tartlet (£3.95), garlic king prawns (£5.50), sausage and mash with onion gravy (£6.95), mussels provençale (£8.50), Brancaster baked crab salad or lamb shank (£8.95), swordfish steak (£9.50), grilled bass (£9.95), rib-eye steak topped with garlic prawns (£11.95), and home-made puddings (£3.25); the attractive restaurant is no smoking. Well kept Adnams Bitter, Woodfordes Wherry, a beer named for the pub, and a guest from Iceni, Nethergate or Wolfe on handpump, and decent wines; piped music, fruit machine, cribbage and TV. There are sheltered tables in the nice garden with a terrace, enclosed play area. *(Recommended by Nigel Woolliscroft, John Beeken, Mike and Sue Loseby, Mike and Wendy Proctor, M J A Switzer, Pat and Clive Sherriff, David and Rhian Peters, Di and Mike Gillam, Derek Carless, Ian Arthur, Tracey and Stephen Groves, J H Bell)*

Free house ~ Licensees Darren Humphrey and George Humphrey ~ Real ale ~ Bar food (all day in summer) ~ Restaurant ~ (01485) 210314 ~ Children in eating area of bar and restaurant ~ Dogs allowed in bar ~ Open 11-11; 12-10.30 Sun; 11-3, 6-11 weekdays in winter

White Horse

A149 E of Hunstanton

From the airy conservatory, restaurant and sun deck here, you get lovely views of the Norfolk Coastal Path, tidal marsh and Scolt Head Island beyond. It's all open-plan in style, and there are big windows, solid stripped tables with country chairs and pews on the mainly stripped wood floors, and cream walls packed with interesting local black and white photographs. Stools line a handsome counter manned by friendly young staff, and there's a particularly easy-going relaxed atmosphere. All dining areas are no smoking. Well kept Adnams Bitter and Broadside, Greene King IPA, and a guest such as Woodfordes Wherry or Wychwood Hobgoblin on handpump, 20 malt whiskies and about a dozen wines by the glass from an extensive and thoughtful wine list; piped music, bar billiards, and TV. The menu changes twice a day and is extremely good. At lunchtime, there might be home-made soup (from £2.50), caesar salad or ploughman's (£4.95), salmon and crab fishcakes, marinated beetroot salad and crème fraîche (£5.10; main course £8.95), dressed local crab (£5.25; main course £8.25), seafood risotto (£5.75; main course £9.25), roast loin of pork with apple sauce and red wine gravy or marinated mediterranean vegetables with pesto and pasta (£8.50), chargrilled rump steak (£11.75), and lemon sole with orange and saffron fennel (£12.95), with evening choices such as carpaccio of beef with lemon, garlic and thyme dressing (£5.95), baked fillet of black bream, pickled Vietnamese coleslaw (£5.75), rib-eye steak with potato and gruyère pie and pepper sauce (£12.95), seared loin of tuna with puy lentil dahl and lime crème fraîche (£13.95), and fillet of bass with chorizo sausage risotto (£14.20). Very well designed bedrooms most with fine views and some with their own terrace. *(Recommended by John Wooll, Mike and Sue Loseby, Mrs Pamela Westley, Tracey and Stephen Groves, Pamela Goodwyn, Eric Locker, John Beeken, O K Smyth, Paul and Ursula Randall, M J A Switzer, J P Marland, Angela and Andrew Webster, Neil and Angela Huxter, Mr and Mrs B Golding, Brenda Crossley)*

Free house ~ Licensees Cliff Nye and Kevin Nobes ~ Real ale ~ Bar food (lunchtime only) ~ Restaurant ~ (01485) 210262 ~ Children welcome ~ Dogs allowed in bar ~ Open 12-11(10.30 Sun) ~ Bedrooms: £68B/£96B

BURNHAM MARKET TF8342 Map 8

Hoste Arms

The Green (B1155)

There have been some changes to this civilised and smart 17th-c hotel over the past year. The main bar has been renovated, there's a big new awning covering a sizeable eating area in the garden, more bedrooms and a business centre have been added, and you can now enjoy full restaurant service in the walled garden. The friendly, welcoming atmosphere remains – as does the good mix of customers: gentry, farmers, fishermen and shoppers. The panelled bar on the right has a series of watercolours showing scenes from local walks, there's a bow-windowed bar on the left, a nice sitting room, a little art gallery in the staircase area, and massive log fires. Well kept Greene King IPA, Woodfordes Wherry and Nelson's Revenge, and a guest like Adnams Regatta on handpump, a good wine list with plenty of big names including champagne by the glass, a decent choice of malt whiskies, and freshly squeezed orange juice. Good food includes soup (£3.75), lunchtime sandwiches (from £4.75), chicken liver parfait with orange spicer tea jelly (£5.25), chargrilled tuna niçoise (£5.25; main course £8.95), sweet and sour beef strips, noodles and pak choi or dressed Cromer crab salad (£5.95; main course £9.75), half a dozen local oysters (£7.25), wild mushrooms, greens, parmesan and pasta (£8.50), burger, crispy bacon, cheddar and chips (£8.75), chicken biryani (£9.95), seafood casserole with oriental vegetables and a coconut and lime bisque (£10.75), cornfed chicken with brioche dumplings (£11.25), and puddings such as passion fruit crème brûlée, raspberry and honeycomb parfait or light chocolate mousse cake (£4.50). *(Recommended by Nigel Woolliscroft, R J Walden, Messrs Louden and Bishop, Gillian and Peter Moore, J Hale, David Heath, Enid and Henry Stephens, M J A Switzer, David and Anne Culley, Peter Rozee, Ian Phillips, Pat and Roger Fereday, Gordon Stevenson, A D Cross, John Davis, Patricia Beebe, DF, NMF, J Strain, Michael and Ann Cole, Nick Lawless, Tracey and Stephen Groves, Shirley Mackenzie, Roy Bromell, Gerry and Rosemary Dobson)*

Free house ~ Licensees Paul and Jean Whittome and Christopher Bensley ~ Real ale ~ Bar food ~ Restaurant ~ (01328) 738777 ~ Children in restaurant ~ Dogs welcome ~ Open 11-11; 12-10.30 Sun ~ Bedrooms: £71S/£96B

BURNHAM THORPE TF8541 Map 8

Lord Nelson

Village signposted from B1155 and B1355, near Burnham Market

The celebrated sailor was born in this sleepy village, so it's no surprise to find lots of pictures and memorabilia of him lining the walls here, and they have an unusual rum concoction called Nelson's Blood. Although there have been some refurbishments this year, the characterful little bar still has well waxed antique settles on the worn red flooring tiles and smoke ovens in the original fireplace, and an eating room has flagstones, an open fire, and more pictures of Nelson; there are two no smoking rooms. Well kept Greene King IPA or Abbot or Woodfordes Wherry tapped from the cask in a back stillroom and brought to you by the very friendly staff. Good bar food includes home-made cauliflower soup with herb oil (£3.25), filled baguettes (from £4), star anise duck confit, sweet honey couscous and caramelised lime (£4.75), seared scallops with crushed potatoes and melted onions (£7.10), tagliatelle, butter beans and spring onion with gorgonzola cream (£7.50), whole plaice in polenta crust with garlic butter (£8.25), mackerel with pea purée and chive cream (£8.50), braised lamb shank with tomato cassoulet (£9.50), rib-eye steak (£11.95), and puddings like toffee and banana pudding with warm toffee sauce or chocolate brownies with chocolate chip ice cream (£3.10); friendly staff, and shove-ha'penny and dominoes. There's a good sized play area in the very big garden. *(Recommended by DF, NMF, the Didler, John Wooll, Anthony Barnes, Ian Phillips, Sue and Geoff Price, Nigel Woolliscroft, Rosemary and Jeremy Jessel, Neville Kenyon, Barry Collett, Tracey and Stephen Groves, Phil and Sally Gorton, Guy Vowles, Mike and Shelley Woodroffe, M J A Switzer, Mike and Wendy Proctor, David and Rhian Peters)*

Greene King ~ Lease Lucy Tagg ~ Real ale ~ Bar food (12-2.30, 6.30-9) ~ Restaurant ~ (01328) 738241 ~ Children in eating area of bar ~ Dogs allowed in bar ~ Open 11-3, 6-11; 12-3, 7-10.30 Sun

CAWSTON TG1422 Map 8

Ratcatchers

Eastgate, S of village – on B1149 from Norwich turn left towards Haveringland at crossroads ½ mile before the B1145 Cawston turn

Norfolk Dining Pub of the Year

This is a thriving dining pub run by hard-working and friendly licensees. The cosy L-shaped beamed bar has an open fire, nice old chairs and a fine mix of walnut, beech, elm and oak tables; there's a quieter and cosier candlelit dining room on the right, and a conservatory. Several no smoking areas. Very good bar food includes plenty of imaginative daily specials, with starters (£3.45-£4.95) such as home-made local mussel soup with crunchy garlic crouton, scallops poached in white wine, served with a breadcrumb and fresh sage crust, Lenwade pike, salmon and prawn wrapped in a herb pancake and served in a Noilly Prat sauce or Cromer crab baked with cheese, English mustard and cream and served with their own pickled samphire, with main courses (£7.95-£14.95) like braised local rabbit with herbs and vegetables and topped with a pastry lid, sautéed monkfish flamed in vodka with pink peppercorns and cream, rack of spring local lamb on sautéed mushrooms or local guinea fowl, pot roasted in a rich burgundy sauce with suet and herb dumplings and vegetables. Also, lunchtime sandwiches (not Sunday), mushrooms with cambozola cheese and smoked bacon cooked in a pot and topped with a puff pastry lid (£4.95), ploughman's or sausage and mash with an onion and red wine gravy (£6.25), omelettes (from £7.50), vegetable stroganoff (£8.25), steak and kidney pie (£8.55), chicken stir fry (£9.50), steaks (from £10.95; special sauces £2.95 extra), puddings like raspberry crème brûlée, dark and white chocolate torte or toffee apple crumble (£3.75), and children's dishes (£4.85). Well kept Adnams Bitter, Greene King IPA and a guest such as Mauldons Pickwick on handpump, a good wine list with half a dozen by the glass, and 25 malt whiskies; dominoes, cribbage, and piped music. There are tables on the terrace by special outside heaters for dining in cooler weather. *(Recommended by Anthony Barnes, Di and Mike Gillam, W W Burke, Neville Kenyon, Roy Bromell, Philip and Susan Philcox, Jim Mansfield, Roger and Maureen Kenning, John Beeken, Messrs Louden and Bishop, Sally Anne and Peter Goodale, Ian Phillips)*

Free house ~ Licensees Peter and Denise McCarter ~ Real ale ~ Bar food (12-2, 6-10) ~ Restaurant ~ (01603) 871430 ~ Children welcome ~ Open 11.45-3, 6(6.30 Sun)-11; closed 26 Dec

CLEY NEXT THE SEA TG0443 Map 8

Three Swallows

Off A149 E of Blakeney; in village, turn into Holt Road and head for church at Newgate Green

This cheery take-us-as-you-find-us village local, handy for the salt marshes, is a favourite with birdwatchers. The unpretentious carpeted bar on the right has a mix of pubby furnishings including long green leatherette benches around high leathered tables, a good log fire in the small fireplace at one end, and team photographs and pictures of local old boys above its dark dado; they have various board games. You can get well kept Adnams and Greene King IPA and Abbot from a counter richly carved with fantastical figures and faces, with a handsome carved mirror backing, and a couple of steps lead up to a small family eating

area. There's a second log fire in the informal no smoking stripped pine restaurant on the left. Good value generous quickly served home-made food includes sandwiches (from £2.50; good crab), home-made soup (£2.95), filled baked potatoes (from £4.50), ploughman's (from £4.95), home-made lasagne (£6.75), large haddock (£6.95), steaks (from £10.25), daily specials such as seasonal local crab and mussels, vegetarian quiche (£6.75) or cajun chicken (£6.95), and children's meals (£3.95). They have decent wines, and service is prompt; there may be wandering tabby cats. The big garden is a plus. Below the very handsome flint church tower, it has picnic-sets on two grass terraces, and is prettily planted with flowering shrubs. There is a prominent water feature with a surprisingly grandiose fountain, and keeping children entertained are a wooden climbing frame, a budgerigar aviary and a goat pen; they have popular summer barbecues. The bedrooms are simple and comfortable, with a good breakfast.
(Recommended by Peter and Pat Frogley, Barry Collett, Shaun and Diane, S Watkin, P Taylor, David Lovegrove, Kevin Macey)

Pubmaster ~ Tenants Jean and James Walker ~ Real ale ~ Bar food (12-2, 6-9; all day weekends) ~ (01263) 740526 ~ Children in restaurant and family room ~ Dogs welcome ~ Open 11-11; 12-10.30 Sun ~ Bedrooms: £35B/£49B

COLKIRK TF9126 Map 8
Crown

Village signposted off B1146 S of Fakenham; and off A1065

Doing well under its new licensees, this red brick local is in an attractive and peacefully prosperous village. The public bar and small lounge both have open fires, solid straightforward country furniture, and rugs and flooring tiles; the no smoking dining room leading off is pleasantly informal. Well kept Greene King IPA, Abbot, Mild, and Ruddles County on handpump. Good bar food includes home-made soup (£2.95), lunchtime baguettes (from £3.45), smoked mackerel and almond pâté (£3.75), roast vegetable and goats cheese bake (£7.25), chicken fillet with blue cheese sauce (£8.50), grills (from £8.50), and daily specials such as fruity pork curry, steak and kidney pie, fresh crab salad or roast duck breast with cumberland sauce (all £8.50), with puddings such as lemon and lime cheesecake or dutch apple tart (£3.25), and popular Sunday roast. Darts, fruit machine, cribbage and dominoes. There's a garden and suntrap terrace with picnic-sets.
(Recommended by Mike and Karen England, Barry Collett, R Cross, Ian Phillips, Jim Mansfield, G R Smith, Malcolm and Hilary Leeves, Messrs Louden and Bishop)

Greene King ~ Tenant Roger Savell ~ Real ale ~ Bar food (12-1.45(2 Sun), 6.30-9.30(9 Sun)) ~ Restaurant ~ (01328) 862172 ~ Children welcome ~ Dogs allowed in bar ~ Open 11-2.30, 6-11; 12-3, 7-10.30 Sun

ERPINGHAM TG1732 Map 8
Saracens Head

At Wolterton – not shown on many maps; Erpingham signed off A140 N of Aylsham, keep on through Calthorpe, then where road bends right take the straight-ahead turn-off signposted Wolterton

The demand for bedrooms in this gently civilised place is so high, that the licensee is to open up three more. The two-room bar is simple and stylish with high ceilings, terracotta walls, and red and white striped curtains at its tall windows – all lending a feeling of space, though it's not actually large. There's a mix of seats from built-in leather wall settles to wicker fireside chairs as well as log fires and flowers, and the windows look out onto a charming old-fashioned gravel stableyard with picnic-sets. There's a pretty little five-table parlour on the right in cheerful nursery colours, and another big log fire. Well kept Adnams Bitter and Woodfordes Wherry or Blickling on handpump, an interesting wine list, and decent malt whiskies. It's almost essential to book for the imaginative bar food, served in a relaxed and informal atmosphere, which might include starters and snacks (from £4.50) such as local mussels with cider and cream, crispy fried aubergine with garlic mayonnaise, home-made game pâté, red onion and goats cheese tart or deep-fried brie with apricot sauce, main courses (from £9.25) like baked avocado with sweet pear and mozzarella, scallops with bacon and white wine, roast local pheasant with calvados and cream, roast leg of lamb with red and white beans, and baked Cromer crab with mushrooms and sherry, and puddings such as chocolate pot with orange jus, treacle tart or mulled wine and red fruit pudding (£3.50); remarkably good value two-course weekday lunch (£5.50), and enjoyable breakfasts. The Shed next door (run by Mr Dawson-Smith's daughter Rachel) is a workshop and showcase for furniture and interior pieces. *(Recommended by R M Corlett, John Wooll, Bob Arnett, Judy Wayman, David Field, Denys Gueroult, Irene and Ray Atkin, Minda and Stanley Alexander, Kevin Thorpe, Neil Powell, David Twitchett, B N F and M Parkin, S Watkin, P Taylor, Roger and Maureen Kenning, Anthony Barnes)*

Free house ~ Licensee Robert Dawson-Smith ~ Real ale ~ Bar food ~ Restaurant ~ (01263) 768909 ~ Well behaved children in eating area of bar and restaurant ~ Dogs allowed in bedrooms ~ Open 11.30-3, 6-11; 12-3, 7-10.30 Sun; closed 25 Dec ~ Bedrooms: £45B/£65B

HOLKHAM TF8943 Map 8

Victoria

A149 near Holkham Hall

Lots of effort and thought have gone into transforming this stylish place over the last 18 months or so, and the results have quickly paid off: it was recently included in a list of the 32 coolest hotels in the world. Beautifully and individually decorated throughout, it's smart, vibrant and fiercely popular; though there's enough space to stop it being crowded, you'll need to book to bag a table in the bustling dining room. On our Saturday night visit the atmosphere was delightfully inviting, particularly in the main bar, an engagingly cosmopolitan room with an eclectic mix of furnishings and décor: sprawling sofas arranged around a big, low table with chunky candles, flowers and even fruit, colourful wall-hangings, a nice fireplace, and quality light wooden tables. The dining room has the same elegantly funky feel, with polished wooden floors, plenty of contemporary art, and piped jazz. A couple of smaller areas open off (one like a tiny, intimate conservatory), and at the other end of the hall, towards the entrance, there's a simpler public bar with TV. Well regarded by readers, the good, unfussy food might include soups such as roast butternut with greek yoghurt (£4.50), lunchtime sandwiches or fish and chips (£6.75), evening dishes like spicy thai fishcakes (£9.50), tandoori pheasant with spicy plum chutney (£11.95), and pan-fried lemon sole (£15.25), and puddings like chocolate cake brûlée or deep-fried Bounty (£4.95); they do a two-course children's menu (£4.95). There's often an emphasis on game or seafood. The main dining room is no smoking. Well kept beers such as Adnams, Badger Tanglefoot, Fullers London Pride, Morlands Old Speckled Hen and Woodfordes Wherry on handpump, and a good range of wines, with plenty by the glass and several half bottles; friendly service from hard-working young staff. Outside has been appealingly landscaped, with tables on the terrace and lawn, and a children's play area. The bedrooms are all different, some done in a colonial style, others with a more Victorian theme. The hotel was built in 1838 for Thomas Coke (best known for the revolutionary farming techniques he introduced at nearby Holkham Hall), and named in honour of the new Queen who'd recently created him Earl of Leicester; it's still owned by his family. *(Recommended by MDN, John Wooll, Ian Arthur, Minda and Stanley Alexander, David and Anne Culley, Simon Menzies, Tessa Rose; also in the* Good Hotel Guide*)*

Free house ~ Licensee Charles Ockendon ~ Real ale ~ Bar food (12-2.30, 7-9.30) ~ Restaurant ~ (01328) 711008 ~ Children welcome ~ Dogs allowed in bar ~ Open 11-11; 12-10.30 Sun ~ Bedrooms: £70B/£125S(£170B)

We say if we know a pub has piped music.

HORSEY TG4522 Map 8

Nelson Head

Signposted off B1159 (in series of S-bends) N of Great Yarmouth

The name of the licensee hasn't changed, but the people running this pub are in fact new – the local butcher and his family – who offer a friendly welcome to all. The two homely unpretentious little rooms are furnished with straightforward but comfortable seats (including four tractor-seat bar stools), bits of shiny bric-a-brac, small local pictures for sale, a good fire and geraniums on the window sill, with Woodfordes Wherry, Great Eastern, and (of course) Nelsons Revenge on handpump; cribbage, dominoes and piped music. Bar food includes filled baguettes, soup (£2.95), devilled whitebait (£3.95), ploughman's (£4.95), home-made cheese and potato bake (£5.50), home-made burgers (from £5.75), ham and egg (£5.95), home-made cottage pie or chilli (£6.95), home-made steak and kidney pie (£7.50), steaks (from £9.25), and children's meals (from £3.95); the restaurant is no smoking. The garden has picnic-sets and an outside marquee. Horsey Windmill and the beach are just down the road and it's the nearest pub to Horsey Mere so there's a good mix of customers from ramblers to birdwatchers and yachtsmen. The pub sign is often hidden by trees in summer. More reports please. *(Recommended by Ian Phillips, Lawrence Bacon, Jean Scott)*

Free house ~ Licensee Reg C Parsons ~ Real ale ~ Bar food ~ No credit cards ~ (01493) 393378 ~ Children in eating area of bar and restaurant ~ Dogs allowed in bar ~ Open 11-2.30, 6-11; 12-3, 7-10.30 Sun

ITTERINGHAM TG1430 Map 8

Walpole Arms

Village signposted off B1354 NW of Aylsham

The two-acre garden behind this red brick dining pub has been newly landscaped this year and there are lots of seats and a bigger car park; the restaurant has been attractively refurbished, too. The biggish open-plan bar has a good bustling friendly atmosphere, little windows, stripped brick walls, exposed beams, and a mix of dining tables. You probably won't hear the faint piped music over the sound of contented chat. Good, popular bar food (they tell us prices have not changed since last year) includes cauliflower and leek cheese (£4.50), pork pie or chicken waldorf on toasted ciabatta (£4.75) and ham and eggs (£6), and a more inventive contemporary menu might have roast asparagus on watercress with a soft egg and smoked trout or potato pancake with sweet pickled herrings and cucumber yoghurt (£5.25), sausage, bubble and squeak (£7.25), saltimbocca (£9.25), roast cod with noodles, bok choi and crab broth (£9.50), rib-eye steak and béarnaise sauce (£11), and puddings such as a greek tart with yoghurt, lemon curd, honey and sunflower seeds, apricot, banana and strawberry crumble or tarte tatin of peaches with ice cream, almonds and raspberry sauce (£4.50). Well kept Adnams Bitter and Broadside, and Woodfordes Wherry and a beer brewed for the pub by them on handpump, and a well chosen wine list. *(Recommended by Peter and Jean Hoare, Philip and Susan Philcox, A D Cross, Stephen, Julie and Hayley Brown, Roger and Maureen Kenning, Di and Mike Gillam, Anthony Barnes)*

Free house ~ Licensee Keith Reeves ~ Real ale ~ Bar food ~ Restaurant ~ (01263) 587258 ~ Children in eating area of bar and restaurant ~ Open 12-3, 6-11; 12-3, 7-10.30 Sun

LARLING TL9889 Map 5

Angel

A11 S of Attleborough

The present licensee's great-grandfather used to stable the horses and host the coach travellers here, and they still have the original visitor's books with guests from 1897 to 1909. The comfortable 1930s-style lounge on the right has cushioned wheelback chairs, a nice long cushioned and panelled corner settle, some good solid tables for eating off and some lower ones, squared panelling, a collection of whisky-water jugs on the delft shelf over the big brick fireplace which houses a big woodburner, a couple of copper kettles, and some hunting prints; there are two dining rooms (one of which is no smoking). Reliable bar food includes soup (£2.50), lots of sandwiches and toasties (from £2.50; the bacon and banana is popular), crispy whitebait or home-made pâté (£3.95), creamy mushroom pot (£4.25), welsh rarebit (£4.50), omelettes (from £4.95), ploughman's (£5.75), home-made burgers (from £5.95), ham and egg, chicken korma or spinach and ricotta cannelloni (£6.95), fisherman's crumble (£7.95), steaks (from £10.95), daily specials such as home-made steak and kidney pie or fresh cod in beer batter (£7.25), and lamb steak with redcurrant and port sauce or chicken with honey and mustard (£7.95), home-made puddings (£2.95), and children's meals (£3.25). Well kept Adnams Best and guests from brewers like Grainstore, Iceni, and Wolf on handpump, and over 100 malt whiskies. The quarry-tiled black-beamed public bar has a good local atmosphere, with darts, dominoes, cribbage, juke box and fruit machine; piped music. A neat grass area behind the car park has picnic-sets around a big fairy-lit apple tree, and a safely fenced play area. Peter Beale's old-fashioned rose nursery is nearby. *(Recommended by Anthony Barnes, John Robertson, Laura and Stuart Ballantyne, G Coates, Peter and Barbara Ayre, James Morton, Ian Phillips, Mike and Karen England, Tony W Dickinson, Dave Braisted, J F M and M West, Stephen, Julie and Hayley Brown)*

Free house ~ Licensee Andrew Stammers ~ Real ale ~ Bar food (12-2, 6.30-9.30(10 Fri and Sat)) ~ Restaurant ~ (01953) 717963 ~ Children welcome ~ Karaoke last Thurs of month ~ Open 10-11; 12-10.30 Sun ~ Bedrooms: £30B/£50B

LETHERINGSETT TG0538 Map 8

Kings Head

A148 just W of Holt

Run with energy and enthusiasm, this busy pub has good live music events on most weekends throughout the year, and lots for families to do. There's a play castle, a living willow tunnel, toys, bikes and games, and a children's menu with a better choice than usual. The carpeted bar has metal-legged tables, a couple of armchairs and log fires, with various interesting prints, pictures and other items, including a signed poem by John Betjeman, on the walls. There's also a small plush lounge, and a separate games room with darts, pool, shove-ha'penny, dominoes, cribbage, fruit machines, and piped music. Reasonably priced bar food includes soup (£2.95), sandwiches, baps or baguettes (from £2.95), home-made liver pâté (£4.10), filled baked potatoes (from £4.45), salads and ploughman's (from £5.95), home-made steak and kidney pie or home-cooked ham and egg (£6.55), home-made vegetarian lasagne (£6.65), steaks (from £10.80), and puddings like home-made profiteroles or apple pie (£2.95). Well kept Greene King Abbot and IPA, and a couple of guests such as Wolf in Sheeps Clothing or Woodfordes Ketts Rebellion on handpump, local apple juice, and good service. The spacious lawn has plenty of tables, and is quite attractive on a sunny day. The pub is in a very pleasant setting, in grounds well back from the road, opposite a church with an unusual round tower, and not far from an interesting working water mill. More reports please. *(Recommended by Tony W Dickinson, Sue and Mike Todd, R C Vincent)*

Free house ~ Licensees David and Pamela Watts ~ Real ale ~ Bar food (11-10; 12-10 Sun) ~ Restaurant ~ (01263) 712 691 ~ Children welcome ~ Dogs welcome ~ Live music Sat evening Sept-June, Sun afternoons June-Sept ~ Open 11-11; 12-10.30 Sun

MUNDFORD TL8093 Map 5

Crown £

Village signposted off A1065 Thetford—Swaffham; Crown Street

On the quiet village square, this attractive 17th-c former posting inn is handy for nearby Thetford Forest. The beamed lounge bar has a friendly bustle, a huge open fireplace in a flint wall, captain's chairs around highly polished tables, and interesting local advertisements and other memorabilia. If the pub is full, a spiral iron staircase with Vanity Fair cartoons beside it leads up to the club room, an elegant restaurant and the garden. There are more heavy beams in the separate red-tiled locals' bar on the left, which has cast-iron-framed tables, another smaller brick fireplace with a copper hood, sensibly placed darts, cribbage, dominoes, fruit machine, TV, juke box, and a screened-off pool table. Well kept Courage Best and Directors, Theakstons, Woodfordes Wherry and a couple of guests from Iceni and Nethergate on handpump, and around 50 malt whiskies. Helpful staff serve popular bar snacks such as sandwiches (from £2.75), filled baguettes from (£4.65), home-made soup (£3.25), burgers (from £3.95), local herby sausage (£5.75), honey fried chicken (£6.25), local trout (£6.95), fillet of cod in tomato and mustard seed batter (£7.25), and daily specials such as roast pepper and tomato tagliatelle (£5.50), poached skate wing with green onion and cheddar cream (£8.75), and T-bone with brandy and cracked peppercorn cream (£12.95); children's helpings of most meals. *(Recommended by Michael and Ann Cole, Charles Gysin, Stephen, Julie and Hayley Brown, Ian Phillips, Bill and Sheila McLardy, Mike and Karen England, Anthony Barnes, Dr Paull Khan, Nigel Hopkins, Keith and Janet Morris, Darly Graton, Graeme Gulibert)*

Free house ~ Licensee Barry Walker ~ Real ale ~ Bar food (12-3, 7-10) ~ Restaurant ~ (01842) 878233 ~ Children welcome ~ Dogs welcome ~ Open 11-11; 12-10.30 Sun ~ Bedrooms: £35B/£55B

NORWICH TG2308 Map 5

Adam & Eve 🍷 £

Bishopgate; follow Palace Street from Tombland, N of cathedral

The first records of this ancient alehouse were in 1249 when it was being used by workmen building the cathedral, and there's even a Saxon well beneath the lower bar floor. The striking dutch gables were added in the 14th and 15th c. The little old-fashioned bars quickly fill at lunchtime with a good mix of customers, and there are antique high-backed settles (one handsomely carved), cushioned benches built into partly panelled walls, and tiled or parquet floors; the snug room is no smoking at lunchtime. Enjoyable, good value bar food includes sandwiches or granary baps (from £2.55), soup (£2.95; good cheese and ale soup £3.85), ploughman's (£4.75), spinach and feta goujons with honey and ginger dip, ham and egg, chilli or chicken curry (£4.95), daily specials such as halloumi and mediterranean vegetables chargrilled and served in foccacia bread (£4.55), sticky chicken wings (£4.95), and sesame and ginger breaded prawns with soy dip (£5.25). Well kept Adnams Bitter, Greene King IPA, Wells Bombardier and Theakstons Old Peculier, and a guest such as Adnams Broadside on handpump, over 50 malt whiskies, about a dozen decent wines by the glass, Addlestone's cider and freshly squeezed orange juice. There are wooden picnic-sets in front of the pub and very pretty summer tubs and hanging baskets. *(Recommended by A S and M E Marriott, Tina and David Woods-Taylor, Jim Abbott, Patricia Beebe, Charles and Pauline Stride, Steve Chambers, the Didler, Michael Tack, MJVK, Pat and Clive Sherriff, Su and Bob Child, Tim and Ann Newell, W W Burke, Anthony Barnes)*

Unique Pub Co ~ Lease Rita McCluskey ~ Real ale ~ Bar food (12-7;12-2.30 Sun) ~ (01603) 667423 ~ Children in snug until 7 ~ Open 11-11; 12-10.30 Sun; closed 25, 26 Dec, 1 Jan

Fat Cat 🍺

West End Street

It's an extraordinary feat to keep so many real ales in top condition, but Mr Keatley manages to serve up to 26 at any one time. About half are on handpump, while the rest are tapped from the cask in a still room behind the bar – big windows reveal all: Adnams Bitter, Bartrams Gooseberry Goosegrog, Caledonian 80/-, Durham White Bishop, Fullers ESB and an organic one, Honeydew, Greene King Abbot and Ruddles County, Hop Back Summer Lightning, Kelham Island

Pale Rider, North Yorkshire Flying Herbert, Oakham Bishops Farewell, Orkney Dark Island, and RCH Old Slug Porter, Timothy Taylors Landlord, Tipperary Carlo Red Ale and Dwan Black Pearl Stout, and Woodfordes Norfolk Nog. They also keep four draught Belgian beers (two of them fruit), draught lagers from Germany and the Czech Republic, up to 15 bottled Belgian beers, 15 country wines, and local Norfolk cider. Open all day, this is a classic town pub, with a good mix of customers and a lively bustling atmosphere at some times of the day, and tranquil lulls in the middle of the afternoon. The no-nonsense furnishings include plain scrubbed pine tables and simple solid seats, lots of brewery memorabilia, bric-a-brac and stained glass. Bar food consists of a dozen or so rolls at lunchtime (60p; not Sunday). There are tables outside. *(Recommended by Tim and Ann Newell, Kit Ballantyne, Su and Bob Child, Keith and Suzie Stevens, the Didler, David Twitchett, Tracey and Stephen Groves, Ian Phillips)*

Free house ~ Licensee Colin Keatley ~ Real ale ~ No credit cards ~ (01603) 624364 ~ Open 12(11 Sat)-11; 12-10.30 Sun

REEDHAM TG4101 Map 5

Ferry Inn

B1140 Beccles—Acle; the ferry here holds only two cars but goes back and forth continuously till 10pm, taking only a minute or so to cross – fare £2.80, 25p foot passengers

The ideal way to approach this splendidly placed Broads pub is by boat, either on the interesting working chain ferry (see above) or on a holiday hire boat – if you eat in the pub, they give you free mooring and showers; there are plenty of well spaced tables on the terrace overlooking the water. Inside, the long front bar has big picture windows, comfortable banquettes and some robust rustic tables carved from slabs of tree-trunk; the secluded back bar has antique rifles, copper and brass, and a fine log fire. Decent food includes home-made soup (£2.65), sandwiches and filled baguettes (from £3.10), half rack of pork ribs (£3.95), home-made lasagne (£6.25), a roast of the day (£6.35), home-made steak in ale pie (£6.50), and daily specials such as local filled mushrooms in a cream, brandy and peppercorn sauce (£6.35), and Cromer crab salad, lamb hotpot or chicken tikka masala (£6.95). The restaurant and family room are no smoking. Well kept Adnams Bitter and Broadside and Woodfordes Wherry and a guest such as St Peter's Mild on handpump, quite a few malt whiskies, country wines, and good cheerful staff; piped music. The Archers own the caravan touring park next door. More reports please. *(Recommended by Anthony Barnes, Miss J Durbridge, W Shakeshaft)*

Free house ~ Licensee David Archer ~ Real ale ~ Bar food (all day Sun) ~ Restaurant ~ (01493) 700429 ~ Children in restaurant ~ Dogs allowed in bar ~ Live music twice weekly in summer ~ Open 11-3, 6.30-11; 12-10.30 Sun

REEPHAM TG0922 Map 8

Old Brewery House

Market Square; B1145 W of Aylsham

Set back from the market square, this Georgian hotel has a big high-ceilinged bar with a good pubby atmosphere, a nice mix of oldish pub tables, lots of farming and fishing bric-a-brac and old enamel advertisements on its pale ochre walls, a piano and a dark green dado. A step down from this main seating area takes you to a tiled-floor serving part with well kept Adnams, Greene King Abbot, local Reepham, and a guest such as Greene King Ruddles County on handpump, and several malt whiskies. There's also a red-carpeted lounge leading off, with dark panelling and sturdy brocaded armchairs; piped music and fruit machine. Bar food includes lunchtime sandwiches (from £2.95; not Sunday), filled baked potatoes (from £3.25), and ploughman's (£4.95), soup or devilled whitebait (£2.95), sausage and mash (£5.25), spinach and ricotta plait with a wild mushroom sauce or chicken korma (£5.95), thai prawn salad or beef in ale pie (£6.95), daily specials, and children's meals (£2.95). The dining room and conservatory are no smoking. There are picnic-sets on the front terrace and gardens at the back with a pond and fountain. *(Recommended by Ian Phillips, Brian Haywood, Su and Bob Child, the Didler)*

Free house ~ Licensee David Peters ~ Real ale ~ Bar food ~ Restaurant ~ (01603) 870881 ~ Children welcome ~ Dogs allowed in bar and bedrooms ~ Open 11-11; 12-10.30 Sun ~ Bedrooms: £47.50B/£75B

RINGSTEAD TF7040 Map 8

Gin Trap

Village signposted off A149 near Hunstanton; OS Sheet 132 map reference 707403

Full of interest, this carefully run village local has lots of gin traps ingeniously converted to electric candle-effect wall lights, carpenters' tools, cartwheels, and bottles hanging from the beams in the lower part of the well kept chatty bar, toasting forks above the woodburning stove, and captain's chairs and cast-iron-framed tables on the green-and-white patterned carpet. A small no smoking dining room has over 100 chamber-pots suspended from the ceiling, and high-backed pine settles; you can book a table in here. Well kept Adnams Best, Greene King Abbot, Woodfordes Norfolk Nog and Nelson's Revenge, and Gin Trap Bitter brewed by Woodfordes for the pub, and a guest on handpump. Decent bar food includes lunchtime sandwiches (£2.75) and ploughman's (from £3.75), as well as lasagne (£6), steak and kidney pie (£6.25), tomato and basil pasta (£6.50), scampi (£6.75), steaks (from £9.75), daily fish specials such as cod, plaice or salmon (from around £6), and home-made puddings like Jamaican bread and butter pudding and fruit crumbles (£3.25). A handsome spreading chestnut tree shelters the car park, and the back garden has seats on the grass or small paved area and pretty flowering tubs. The pub is close to the Peddar's Way; hikers and walkers are welcome, but not their muddy boots. There's an art gallery next door, and self-catering accommodation. *(Recommended by John Beeken, Chris Mawson, Michael Tack, Ian Phillips, O K Smyth, M J A Switzer, Keith and Chris O'Neill, M Joyner, Paul and Margaret Baker, Tracey and Stephen Groves)*

Free house ~ Licensees Brian and Margaret Harmes ~ Real ale ~ Bar food ~ Restaurant ~ No credit cards ~ (01485) 525264 ~ Children in eating area of bar and restaurant ~ Open 11.30-2.30, 6.30-11; 12-2.30, 6.30-10.30 Sun

SNETTISHAM TF6834 Map 8

Rose & Crown

Village signposted from A149 King's Lynn—Hunstanton just N of Sandringham; coming in on the B1440 from the roundabout just N of village, take first left turn into Old Church Road

A new kitchen has been built here to cope with the demand for the imaginative, popular food. Using fresh local produce and changing at least twice a week, the menu at lunchtime might include cider and onion soup (£3.95), ham hock, asparagus and pistachio terrine with home-made piccalilli (£4.95), sandwiches or tortilla wraps (from £4.95; oak smoked salmon, asparagus and lavender crème fraîche £5.25), sweet pimento and goats cheese pie, avocado purée and sweetcorn relish (£5.25), fillet of smoked haddock, bubble and squeak, blue cheese sauce and a poached egg (£8.95), lambs liver and bacon with tomato and basil jus (£9.25), and wok fried beef, hokien noodles, black beans, and plum sauce (£9.50), with evening choices such as tiger prawns, soba noodles, cucumber and sticky orange (£5.75), seared king scallops, chilli sea salt, crab apple jelly and scallop biscuit (£7.50), grilled fillets of red mullet, chilli and papaya salsa, caper berry, sweet potato and ruby chard (£10.95), and crisp confit of duck, bubble and squeak cake, fig and date molasses (£11.50), and puddings like caramelised banana bavarois, star anise and vanilla, pineapple carpaccio with champagne granita or warm sticky toffee pudding with toffee sauce (£4.50). The interior has been very thoughtfully put together, with several separate areas each with its own character: an old-fashioned beamed front bar with black settles on its tiled floor, and a great log fire; another big log fire in a back bar with the landlord's sporting trophies and old sports equipment; a no smoking bar with a colourful but soothing décor (this room is favoured by people eating); and another warmly decorated room, nice for families, with painted settles and big old tables. Some lovely old pews and other interesting furniture sit on the wooden floor of the dining room, and there are shelves with old bottles and books, and old prints and watercolours. The restaurant is no smoking. Well kept Adnams Bitter and Broadside, Fullers London Pride, Greene King IPA and maybe a guest such as Greene King Old Speckled Hen on handpump, quite a few wines by the glass and local organic fruit juices. The colourful enclosed garden has picnic-sets among herbaceous borders and flowering shrubs, and two spectacular willow trees; also a great wooden fort, swings, a playhouse and chipmunks. The bedrooms are most attractive. *(Recommended by John and Sylvia Harrop, Mike and Wena Stevenson, Pat and Roger Fereday, David Eberlin, JMC, Eric Locker, J M and P M Carver, John Wooll, Ian Phillips, Pippa Brown, Nick Lawless, J F M and M West, M Borthwick, David and Rhian Peters, David and Anne Culley, David and Helen Wilkins, Jim Cowan, Jane Scarrow, Mrs Thomas, Tracey and Stephen Groves, DF, NMF, Mike Ridgway, Sarah Miles)*

Free house ~ Licensee Anthony Goodrich ~ Real ale ~ Bar food (12-2(till 2.30 wknds), 7-9(9.30 Fri, Sat)) ~ Restaurant ~ (01485) 541382 ~ Children in eating area of bar and in family room ~ Dogs welcome ~ Open 11-11; 12-10.30 Sun ~ Bedrooms: £60B/£90B

STIFFKEY TF9743 Map 8

Red Lion

A149 Wells—Blakeney

Perhaps at its best when the holiday crowds have gone, this traditional roadside place has a proper pubby atmosphere. The oldest parts of the simple bars have a few beams, aged flooring tiles or bare floorboards, big open fires, a mix of pews, small settles and a couple of stripped high-backed settles, a nice old long deal table among quite a few others, and oil-type or lantern wall lamps. Well kept Greene King Abbot, Woodfordes Wherry and a guest beer on handpump, plus Adnams wines, and Stowford Press cider; dominoes, cribbage, and board games. Good value bar food might include excellent local whitebait, sandwiches (from £3.25), home-made soup (£3.95), a cheese board (£4.50), goats cheese salad (£4.95), steak and kidney pie, leek and sour cream quiche or pork and leek sausages (£7.95), and lots of fish like cod, plaice, occasional sea trout, butterfish, bass, lemon sole and local Wells crab (from £7.95); nice puddings and popular Sunday roast. The back restaurant leads into a no smoking conservatory. There are wooden seats and tables out on a back gravel terrace, with more on grass further up beyond, and a pretty stream with ducks and swans across the road; some pleasant walks from this unspoilt village. *(Recommended by Martin Jennings, Brian Haywood, M J A Switzer, Brian and Halina Howes, Judy Wayman, Bob Arnett, Nigel Woolliscroft, the Didler, Sue Demont, Tim Barrow, Su and Bob Child, Kevin Macey, John Wooll, Peter and Pat Frogley, Barry Collett, Peter Meister, Chris and Anna Rowley)*

Free house ~ Licensee Matthew Rees ~ Real ale ~ Bar food ~ (01328) 830552 ~ Children in eating area of bar ~ Dogs welcome ~ Open 12-3, 6(7 in winter)-11

STOW BARDOLPH TF6205 Map 5

Hare Arms 🍷

Just off A10 N of Downham Market

By the time this book is published, the large garden behind this creeper-covered pub will have been landscaped and there will be plenty of seats; picnic-sets in the pretty front garden, too. Inside, it's neatly kept with a timelessly traditional village atmosphere that Mr and Mrs McManus have been preserving for 25 years. The welcoming bar is decorated with old advertising signs and fresh flowers, with plenty of tables around its central servery, and a good log fire; maybe two friendly ginger cats and a sort of tabby. This bar opens into a spacious heated and well planted no smoking conservatory. Bar food includes lunchtime sandwiches (from £2.50), filled baked potatoes (from £4.50), and ploughman's (from £6.75), as well as home-made soup (£3.25), home-made curry or mushroom stroganoff (£7.25), home-made lasagne (£7.95), steaks (from £11.25), daily specials such as ricotta cheese and spinach cannelloni bake or chicken breast stuffed with brie and coated with a spicy red pepper sauce (£7.95), and lemon sole fillets topped with basil and lemon butter or tuna steak with a prawn, chilli and coriander dip (£8.95), and children's menu (from £3.50). Well kept Greene King IPA, Abbot and Old Speckled Hen, and a guest such as Bass or Batemans XXXB on handpump, a decent range of wines, and quite a few malt whiskies; maybe cockles and whelks on the bar counter; fruit machine. *(Recommended by Judy Pearson, John Wooll, R C Wiles, J F M and M West, Anthony Barnes, Ian Phillips, Tracey and Stephen Groves, Michael and Ann Cole)*

Greene King ~ Tenants David and Trish McManus ~ Real ale ~ Bar food (12-2, 7-10) ~ Restaurant ~ (01366) 382229 ~ Children in conservatory and family room ~ Open 11-2.30, 6-11; 12-2.30, 7-10.30 Sun; closed 25 and 26 Dec

SWANTON MORLEY TG0117 Map 8

Darbys

B1147 NE of Dereham

One couple are happy to regularly drive over 80 miles to come to this well run creeper-covered brick pub. It's a careful conversion of two derelict farm cottages, and has a friendly, bustling atmosphere, a long bare-boarded country style bar with a comfortable lived in feel, lots of gin-traps and farming memorabilia, a good log fire (with the original bread oven alongside), tractor seats with folded sacks lining the long, attractive serving counter, and fresh flowers on the big stripped pine tables; maybe papers to read. A step up through a little doorway by the fireplace takes you through to the no smoking dining room. The children's room (also no smoking) has a toy box and a glassed-over well, floodlit from inside. Enjoyable bar food includes filled baguettes and baked potatoes (from £3.75), barbecue spare ribs (£4.50), prawn and pasta fruit salsa (£4.95), curries (from £6.75), mushroom and blue cheese pasta (£7.50), chicken and cashew nuts in oyster sauce (£8.75), cajun tuna steak (£9.45), steak and mushroom pudding (£9.85), steaks (from £11.65), and children's menu (from £3.75). Around eight well kept real ales include Adnams Best and Broadside, Badger Tanglefoot, Greene King IPA, Woodfordes Wherry and guests such as Brakspears Special, Fullers London Pride, and Marstons Pedigree on handpump. Maybe a labrador and border collie; piped music. The garden has a really good play area. The bedrooms are in carefully converted farm buildings a few minutes away (they usually run a free (pre-booked) taxi service to and from the pub for residents), and there's plenty to do if you're staying as the family also own the adjoining 720-acre estate, and can arrange clay pigeon shooting, golf, fishing, nature trails, and craft instruction. *(Recommended by Michael and Jenny Back, Ian Pendlebury, David Field, MDN)*

Free house ~ Licensees John Carrick and Louise Battle ~ Real ale ~ Bar food (12-2.15, 6.30-9.15; 12-9.45 Sat and Sun; not 25 Dec) ~ (01362) 637647 ~ Children in family room ~ Dogs allowed in bar ~ Open 11.30-3, 6-11; 11.30-11 Sat; 12-10.30 Sun ~ Bedrooms: £25S/£38S

THORNHAM TF7343 Map 8

Lifeboat

Turn off A149 by Kings Head, then take first left turn

When the summer crowds have gone, you can appreciate the genuine character of this rambling old white-painted stone pub much more. The main Smugglers bar is atmospherically lit with antique paraffin lamps suspended amongst an array of traps and yokes from its great oak beamed ceiling, and is cosily furnished with low settles, window seats, pews, and carved oak tables on the rugs on the tiled floor; there are also masses of guns, swords, black metal mattocks, reed-slashers and other antique farm tools. A couple of little rooms lead off here, and all in all there are five open fires. No games machines or piped music, though they still play the ancient game of 'pennies', which was outlawed in the late 1700s, and dominoes. Very well prepared bar food includes home-made soup (£3.75), grilled sardines (£4.75; main course £7.50), whitebait (£5.25; main course £8.25), filled baguettes (from £4.95), ploughman's (from £5.95), spicy five bean chilli or burger (£7.95), Cromer crab salad or liver and bacon on chive mash with rich red wine jus (£8.25), fish in beer batter and chips (£8.75), daily specials like smoked duck, toasted pecans and cranberry salad (£4.95), wok fried beef fillet with hoisin sauce and crispy noodles (£11.25), whole Brancaster lobster (£18), home-made puddings such as fresh fruit crumble or sticky toffee pudding (£3.65), and children's dishes (from £3.50). Well kept Adnams, Bass, Greene King IPA and Abbot, Woodfordes Wherry, and a guest such as Youngs on handpump and several malt whiskies. Up some steps from the bustling verdant conservatory is a sunny terrace with picnic-sets, and further back is a children's playground with fort and slide. The pub faces half a mile of coastal sea flats, most of the bedrooms have sea views (this is a nice and very popular place to stay), and there are lots of lovely surrounding walks. *(Recommended by Keith Fairbrother, the Didler, Charlie Harris, David Twitchett, Gillian and Peter Moore, David Eberlin, Peter Rozee, Mike and Shelley Woodroffe, O K Smyth, John Robertson, Ian Phillips, Mike and Sue Loseby, Sue and John Harwood, John Wooll, Mrs Thomas, Nick Lawless, Mike and Wendy Proctor, June and Malcolm Farmer, Nigel Woolliscroft, Mr and Mrs J Curtis; also in the* Good Hotel Guide*)*

Free house ~ Licensee Charles Coker ~ Real ale ~ Bar food (12-2.30, 6-9.30) ~ Restaurant ~ (01485) 512236 ~ Children welcome ~ Dogs welcome ~ Open 11-11; 12-10.30 Sun ~ Bedrooms: £55B/£80B

TITCHWELL TF7543 Map 8

Titchwell Manor

A149 E of Hunstanton

Reopened after a careful refurbishment, this comfortable hotel is now up and running again. It is in a wonderful spot surrounded by wild marshes, unspoilt beaches and gently rolling countryside, and enjoyed by a good mix of bird-watchers (the RSPB reserve is opposite), golfers (there's a championship course only moments away), sailors, hikers, and families. You can enjoy a pint of well kept Greene King IPA on handpump in the bar or large lounge with its roaring fire or even on the terrace and lawn in the walled garden. The airy restaurant, with cushioned wicker chairs on the wood-strip floor, is no smoking. Enjoyable food includes sandwiches, cream of haddock and potato soup (£4), crispy whitebait or local duckling pâté with home-made chutney (£5.50), crayfish cocktail, baby red mullet fillets with caper berries and cherry tomato salad or Brancaster crab (£5.50; main course £8.50), sausage with bubble and squeak and onion gravy (£8.50), chargrilled steaks (from £14.50), and daily specials such as Brancaster oysters (£1 each), Brancaster mussels (£5.50), fillet of bass with olive tapenade (£12.50), and fillet of turbot with samphire and a light seafood and white wine sauce (£18.50). The pretty bedrooms overlook the marshes to the sea. More reports please. *(Recommended by M J A Switzer, Peter and Pat Frogley)*

Free house ~ Licensees Ian and Margaret Snaith ~ Real ale ~ Bar food ~ Restaurant ~ (01485) 210221 ~ Children welcome ~ Dogs welcome ~ Open 12-2, 6-11(10 Sun) ~ Bedrooms: £50B/£70B

TIVETSHALL ST MARY TM1686 Map 5

Old Ram

A140 15 miles S of Norwich, outside village

With food being served all day from 7.30am, this much extended dining pub is a very handy place to know about. The spacious country styled main room has lots of stripped beams and standing timbers, antique craftsmen's tools on the ceiling, a huge log fire in the brick hearth, a turkey rug on rosy brick flooring, and a longcase clock. It's ringed by smaller side areas, and one no smoking dining room has striking navy walls and ceiling, swagged curtains and an open woodburning stove; this leads to a second comfortable, no smoking dining room and gallery. Unobtrusive fruit machine, TV, cribbage, dominoes, and piped music. Bar food includes soup (£3.50; with a sandwich £5.95), tomato and goats cheese tartlet on a marmalade sauce (£4.95), king prawns in garlic butter (£5.95), chargrilled burgers (from £6.95), sausage and mash (£7.95), steak and mushroom pie (£8.95), mushrooms en croûte with tomato and sage sauce (£8.95), chicken curry (£8.95), grilled skate (£10.95), fillet of bass with red pepper and lime sauce (£13.95), steaks (from £13.95), and puddings such as lemon tart and crème brûlée (£3.95). They also offer an Over Sixty Club menu with two courses at £6.95. Well kept Adnams, Bass, Woodfordes Wherry and a couple of guests such as Fullers London Pride and Hancocks on handpump, around two dozen wines by the glass, carafe or bottle, freshly squeezed juices and milkshakes. The sheltered flower-filled terrace is very civilised with outdoor heaters and big green parasols. More reports please. *(Recommended by Ian and Nita Cooper, Steve Chambers, J F M and M West)*

Free house ~ Licensee John Trafford ~ Real ale ~ Bar food (all day) ~ Restaurant ~ (01379) 676794 ~ Children in eating area and in restaurant; under 7s must leave by 8pm ~ Open 11-11; 12-10.30 Sun; closed 25, 26 Dec ~ Bedrooms: £51.95B/£70B

UPPER SHERINGHAM TG1441 Map 8

Red Lion

B1157; village signposted off A148 Cromer—Holt, and the A149 just W of Sheringham

Most people do come to this simple little flint cottage to eat and as the tables in the main bar are allocated to those dining, you might have to sit outside if all you want is a drink and the restaurant is very busy (which it is most Sundays and weekends during the holiday season). The two modest but charming little bars have stripped high-backed settles and country-kitchen chairs on the red tiles or bare boards, terracotta painted walls, a big woodburning stove, and newspapers to read; the red-walled snug is no smoking. It's best to book a table if you want to enjoy the good bar food which might include home-made soup (£3.50), home-made pâté (£4), stilton-stuffed mushrooms (£4), sweet and sour chicken (£6.50), lasagne (£6.95), vegetable curry, lambs liver in port and orange gravy (£6.75), thai red chicken curry (£7.25), steak and kidney pie (£7.50), and fresh fish such as plaice, sole, cod, haddock, halibut, trout, and salmon with various sauces (from £8.50); well liked breakfasts. Well kept Greene King IPA, and Woodfordes Wherry and Great Eastern on handpump, with over 30 malt whiskies and decent wines; dominoes and card games. *(Recommended by Roger and Maureen Kenning, David and Julie Glover, John Davis, S Watkin, P Taylor, Peter and Pat Frogley, Jim Abbott, Michael Porter, Lord Sandhurst, Neville Kenyon, Mr and Mrs W M Thomas, Anthony Gill)*

Free house ~ Licensee Sue Prew ~ Real ale ~ Bar food (12-2, 6.30-9) ~ Restaurant ~ No credit cards ~ (01263) 825408 ~ Children in eating area of bar but no young children in candlelit bar in evening ~ Dogs welcome ~ Open 11.30-3, 6.30-11 (all day during school hols); 12-4, 7-10.30 Sun ~ Bedrooms: £25/£45

WARHAM TF9441 Map 8

Three Horseshoes

Warham All Saints; village signposted from A149 Wells-next-the-Sea—Blakeney, and from B1105 S of Wells

There's a genuinely pubby atmosphere in the three rooms of this old-fashioned and traditional country pub, and although parts of the building date back to the 1720s, the simple interior with its gas lighting looks little changed since the 1920s. There are stripped deal or mahogany tables (one marked for shove-ha'penny) on a stone floor, red leatherette settles built around the partly panelled walls of the public bar, royalist photographs, and open fires in Victorian fireplaces; an antique American Mills one-arm bandit is still in working order (it takes 5p pieces; there's a 1960s one that takes 1p pieces), there's a big longcase clock with a clear piping strike, and a twister on the ceiling to point out who gets the next round. Popular bar food includes lunchtime rolls and sandwiches (not at weekends), filled baked potatoes (from £3.60), cheese-baked mushrooms (£4.90), and ploughman's (from £5.90), as well as potted cheese (£3.90), mixed liver and pork terrine (£4.20), vegetable and cheese bake (£6.20), steak and kidney pudding (£7.50), local game pie (£8.70), and puddings; half helpings for children. As they don't take bookings, you must get here early to be sure of a seat. Well kept Greene King IPA, Woodfordes Wherry, and a weekly guest such as Leatherbritches Goldings or Woodfordes Great Eastern on handpump or tapped from the cask, good home-made lemonade, country wines, and local summer cider. The dining room is no smoking. Darts, cribbage, shove-ha'penny, and dominoes, and one of the outbuildings houses a wind-up gramophone museum – opened on request. There are rustic tables out on the side grass. *(Recommended by John Beeken, John Wooll, Philip and Susan Philcox, Paul and Ursula Randall, Tracey and Stephen Groves, Barry Collett, Anthony Longden, Brian Haywood, Simon Chell, Mike and Wendy Proctor, Peter Meister, Phil and Sally Gorton, Angela and Andrew Webster, Messrs Louden and Bishop, Kevin Thorpe, Mike and Shelley Woodroffe, the Didler, Su and Bob Child, Patrick and Ann Healy, Pam and David Bailey)*

Free house ~ Licensee Iain Salmon ~ Real ale ~ Bar food (12-1.45, 6-8.30; not 25 or 26 Dec) ~ No credit cards ~ (01328) 710547 ~ Children welcome in family room ~ Dogs welcome ~ Open 11.30-2.30, 6-11; 12-3, 6-10.30 Sun ~ Bedrooms: £22/£48(£52S)

WELLS-NEXT-THE-SEA TF9143 Map 8

Crown

The Buttlands

The owners of the well known Rococo restaurant (which was previously in King's Lynn) have taken over this 16th-c coaching inn and have completely refurbished it. The various rooms are boldly decorated in olive green, mustard, and red with stylish modern furnishings on the stripped wooden or tiled floors, and there are paintings by Mrs Anderson on the walls. The bedrooms are now light, airy and simply furnished, and there's a comfortable residents' sitting room. The main restaurant is open in the evenings and on Sunday lunchtime, but the more informal Jewel brasserie is open every day for lunch and in the evening. Of course most customers come to enjoy the exceptional food but they do keep Adnams Bitter and Broadside, and a guest from Marstons, Wolf or Theakstons on handpump, there's a good wine list, and service is welcoming. Using the freshest ingredients, the first class bar food includes fish soup with cheese croûtes and rouille (£3.95), fresh tagliatelle with wild mushrooms (£4.95; main course £6.95), chicken liver parfait with toasted brioche and onion marmalade (£5.25), sesame goats cheese salad with roasted peppers and a lime, chilli and ginger dressing (£5.25; main course £7.25), crab cakes with two sauces (£5.95; main course £8.25), burger with cheese, crisp smoked bacon and red onion rings with sweet chillis or spinach, roasted vegetables and feta cheese moussaka (£6.95), sausage and sage mash with shallot gravy (£7.50), smoked haddock risotto with parmesan crisp and green sauce (£7.95), crisp duck confit with braised cabbage and bacon (£9.50), whole baked bass with basil butter sauce (£12.95), and puddings such as caramelised banana crème brûlée, sticky toffee pudding with toffee sauce or chocolate marquise with two fruit sauces (£4.75); all main courses are available in child helpings at a reduced cost. The conservatory and dining rooms are no smoking. There are seats on the terrace. More reports please. *(Recommended by Peter and Anne Hollindale, Mike and Shelley Woodroffe, John Wooll, Keith and Chris O'Neill, O K Smyth, Denys Gueroult, Cathy Robinson, Ed Coombe, Guy Vowles, Patrick Hancock, Charles Gysin, John Robertson, Jim Cowan, Jane Scarrow, Brian Root, John and Sylvia Harrop, Tony Middis)*

Free house ~ Licensee Nick Anderson ~ Real ale ~ Bar food (12-2, 6-9(10 weekends))

~ Restaurant ~ (01328) 710209 ~ Children welcome ~ Dogs allowed in bar ~ Open 11-11; 12-10.30 Sun ~ Bedrooms: £85B/£110B

WINTERTON-ON-SEA TG4919 Map 8

Fishermans Return

From B1159 turn into village at church on bend, then turn right into The Lane

Come rain or shine, this brick and flint inn is a popular place. It's been run by the same hospitable licensees for the last 27 years, and on a miserable winter's night there will be a friendly welcome and a warm fire lit in the grate, and in fine weather you can sit at the attractive wrought-iron and wooden benches on a pretty front terrace with nice views or in the sheltered garden; there's a lovely sandy beach nearby. The cosily attractive white-painted no smoking lounge bar has vases of fresh flowers, neat brass-studded red leatherette seats and a log fire. The panelled public bar has low ceilings and a glossily varnished nautical air; the family room and dining room are no smoking. Well liked bar food includes toasties (from £2.25), cottage pie (£4.50), king prawns in ginger and garlic or ploughman's (£4.75), popular fish pie (£5.50), battered cod (£6.75), meaty or vegetable burgers or omelettes (from £6.75), steak (£10.50), and puddings such as lemon and lime cheesecake, sticky toffee pudding or apricot and apple crumble. Well kept Adnams Fisherman, Woodfordes Wherry and Norfolk Nog, and two guests like Adnams Regatta or Burton Bridge Bitter on handpump, decent wines, around 30 malt whiskies, and farm cider; darts, piped music, dominoes, cribbage, pool, fruit machine, and juke box. The newly refurbished and characterful bedrooms, up the steep curving stairs, have low doors and uneven floors. *(Recommended by Dave Braisted, Shaun and Diane, Roger Everett, MJVK, Mike and Sue Loseby, Mike and Wendy Proctor, Tony W Dickinson, Mike and Shelley Woodroffe, Ian Phillips, Carol Horne, JDM, KM)*

Free house ~ Licensees John and Kate Findlay ~ Real ale ~ Bar food ~ (01493) 393305 ~ Children in family room ~ Dogs welcome ~ Open 11-2.30, 6.30-11; 11-11 Sat; 12.10.30 Sun ~ Bedrooms: £45B/£70B

WOODBASTWICK TG3315 Map 8

Fur & Feather

Off B1140 E of Norwich

Friendly new licensees have taken over this converted thatched cottage and have redecorated the restaurant to make it much more cosy. The style and atmosphere here are not what you'd expect of a brewery tap (Woodfordes brewery is next door) as it's set out more like a dining pub – but you are virtually guaranteed a really good pint, and they keep all eight of their beers on at the same time. Changing with the seasons, the enjoyable bar food includes soup (£2.95), sandwiches or filled baguettes (from £2.95), whitebait or crispy crumbed chicken with sweet and sour sauce (£4.25), filled baked potatoes (from £4.25), creamy button mushrooms on thick granary toast (£4.75), ratatouille pasta, lasagne or home-baked ham and eggs (£7.50), home-made steak and kidney pudding (£8.50), steaks (from £10.75), daily specials, and puddings like chocolate sponge or baked alaska with warm forest fruits (£3.50); fried fish on Fridays, a roast on Sundays, and children's menu (£3.50). The restaurant and part of the bar are no smoking; piped music. There are tables out in the very pleasant garden, and the pub forms part of a very attractive estate village. *(Recommended by the Didler, Nick Lawless, Pat and Clive Sherriff, Jonathan and Gillian Shread, Tony W Dickinson, Stephen, Julie and Hayley Brown, David and Julie Glover, Mike and Wendy Proctor, Klaus and Elizabeth Leist, Ian Phillips)*

Woodfordes ~ Tenants Tim and Penny Ridley ~ Real ale ~ Bar food (12-2, 6-9; all day Sun) ~ Restaurant ~ (01603) 720003 ~ Children in restaurant ~ Open 11.30-3, 6-11; all day during summer school hols; 12-10.30 Sun

Lucky Dip

Besides the fully inspected pubs, you might like to try these Lucky Dips recommended to us and described by readers (if you do, please send us reports: www.goodguides.com).

Banningham [TG2129]
Crown [Colby Rd]: Interesting building which now includes a post office, nice choice of good food, consistently friendly welcome, well kept beer, decent wines *(Ken and Barbara Turner, Roger and Maureen Kenning)*

Beachamwell [TF7505]
☆ *Great Danes Head* [off A1122 Swaffham—Downham Market]: Cosy and friendly genuine village pub, with good varied food using local produce inc game and good steaks, helpful licensees, Greene King Abbot and Marstons Pedigree, good house red; children and dogs welcome, small separate public bar with dominoes and pool, no smoking restaurant; by green of tiny village *(Sally Anne and Peter Goodale)*

Billingford [TM1673]
Horseshoes [A143]: Friendly local near windmill, well kept beer inc Tindalls Best from Bungay, good generous bargain food in quaint and homely smallish no smoking restaurant, quick friendly service; pool *(David Oakley)*

Binham [TF9839]
☆ *Chequers* [B1388 SW of Blakeney]: Long low-beamed bar with coal or log fires each end, one in inglenook, sturdy plush seats, well kept Adnams Best, Greene King IPA and Abbot, Nethergate Monks Habit and Woodfordes Wherry, decent house wines, landlord cooks enterprisingly using local produce, very popular Sun lunch, good rolls and sandwiches, small no smoking dining area, prompt cheerful service, good coal fires each end, some nice old local prints, no piped music (but may be sports TV); picnic-sets out in front and on grass behind, open all day, two bedrooms, interesting village with huge priory church *(John Wooll, John Beeken, Kevin Thorpe, Shaun and Diane, BB, Barry Collett, ML, Graham and Jill Wood)*

Blakeney [TG0244]
Blakeney Hotel [The Quay]: Well run hotel nicely set near bird marshes, good food, well kept Adnams, attentive pleasant staff, good atmosphere, games room; bedrooms very comfortable, swimming pool, well set up for family breaks *(MDN)*

☆ *Manor* [The Quay]: Attractive hotel in own grounds with civilised, comfortable and peaceful bar, popular esp with older people for good enterprising waitress-served bar food, not expensive, from well filled crab sandwiches to attractive puddings; well kept Adnams Best and Broadside, decent house wines, friendly helpful staff, conservatory, good restaurant; sunny tables in walled garden with ancient mulberry and room for children to run around, good bedrooms; opp wildfowl reserve and sea inlet *(Stephen Watson, Paul and Ursula Randall, John Beeken, BB, Kevin Macey, Keith and Chris O'Neill, Tony Middis)*

Blickling [TG1728]
☆ *Buckinghamshire Arms* [B1354 NW of Aylsham]: Handsome Jacobean inn by gates to Blickling Hall (NT), neat pews around stripped pine tables in lounge, banquettes in small front snug, enjoyable undemanding food from baguettes and baked potatoes up, well kept Adnams Best and Broadside and Woodfordes Wherry, local cider, good range of wines; well behaved children in restaurant, lots of tables out on big lawn with summer food servery, perhaps all-day opening in summer if busy, bedrooms (two nights minimum stay at wknds) *(M Borthwick, John Wooll, J H Bell, LYM)*

Brancaster [TF7743]
Ship [A149]: Comfortable and relaxing old country inn with good value food, good choice of well kept beers, big coal fires, obliging staff, extended dining room, attractive local paintings; four comfortable bedrooms, good breakfast, restored garden *(anon)*

Brisley [TF9521]
Bell [B1145]: Newish licensees doing well in 16th-c local in good spot on edge of sheep-grazed common (England's biggest), olde-worlde long beamed bar with some stripped brick, well kept ales such as Wolf Festival and Woodfordes Wherry, good service, wide choice of popular food inc local fresh fish and children's dishes, log fire, separate restaurant; tables out on green; children and dogs welcome; bedrooms *(Ian Phillips, Chris Rogers)*

Briston [TG0633]
☆ *John H Stracey* [B1354, Aylsham end of village]: Cheerful well run country dining pub, wide choice of reasonably priced quickly served food inc fresh fish Tues and other good value speciality nights, decent house wines, real ales, comfortable seats, log fire, long-serving landlord, friendly obliging staff, dog and cat; popular pleasant restaurant, a few tables in small well kept garden; good value bedrooms with good breakfast – nice for people who like being part of family *(John Wooll, Mr Biggs)*

Burgh St Peter [TM4693]
Waveney [Waveney River Centre, Staithe Rd]: Spotless pub with nice lunches (children welcome) and Greene King Abbot, swift friendly service; in large leisure centre with swimming pool, among boatyards *(Quentin and Carol Williamson)*

Burnham Market [TF8342]
☆ *Lord Nelson* [Creake Rd]: Hard-working licensees doing good food in pleasantly laid out pub; tables outside, attractive new bedrooms with own bathrooms *(LYM, A D Cross)*

Caister-on-Sea [TG5211]
Ship [Victoria St, off Tan Lane]: Busy welcoming local notable for its riot of magnificent hanging baskets and spectacular flower tubs and other less likely containers on front terrace and small back garden; modern furnishings, spacious family room (with pool table closed off at lunch), well kept Greene King IPA and Old Speckled Hen, decent house wines, heaps of good value cheap

satisfying food inc fresh local fish, coal fire; nostalgic piped pop music, darts, euchre, big screen TV and games machines in side areas, no dogs; not far from long sandy beach *(Tony W Dickinson, Mr and Mrs A Medlar, BB)*

Castle Acre [TF8115]

Ostrich [Stocks Green]: Ungentrified pub prettily placed overlooking the tree-lined green, individual mix of utilitarian furnishings and fittings with some ancient beams, masonry and huge inglenook fireplace, well kept Greene King ales, cheerful staff, cheap food inc plenty of vegetarian, dominoes, cribbage; piped music, fruit machine, family room (but children run pretty free); jazz 2nd and 3rd Weds of month, folk last Weds; picnic-sets in sheltered informal garden with doves and aviary, attractive village with castle and monastery remains *(LYM, John Saul)*

Castle Rising [TF6624]

Black Horse: Comfortable dining pub by church and almshouses in pleasant unspoilt village, good furnishings inc sofas, decent food inc wkdy set lunches in L-shaped bar and back dining room, real ales inc Woodfordes Wherry, good choice of wines by the glass, helpful manager; children welcome, no dogs, pleasant tables out under cocktail parasols, play area *(John Wooll)*

Cockley Cley [TF7904]

☆ ***Twenty Churchwardens*** [off A1065 S of Swaffham]: Cheerful no-frills village pub in converted former school, small, clean and welcoming, with three linked beamed rooms, well kept Adnams and Elgoods, Weston's farm ciders, good coffee, courteous landlord, chatty barmaid, helpful bustling waitresses, limited but good bar food inc bargain home-made pies, darts alcove *(Brian Horner, Brenda Arthur, Anthony Barnes)*

Coltishall [TG2719]

☆ ***Kings Head*** [Wroxham Rd (B1354)]: Refurbished dining pub close to river majoring on good choice of good imaginative food esp fish, also bargains, children's meals and pretty puddings, well kept Adnams and local Broadlands Harvest, decent wines, quick cheerful service, no smoking area, open fire, lots of fishing nets and several stuffed fish inc a 50lb pike (personable chef/landlord competes in international fishing contests); piped music; reasonably priced bedrooms, decent breakfast, moorings nearby *(BB, Alan M Pring, D Roberts, Mr and Mrs R Bromley)*

Denver Sluice [TF6101]

☆ ***Jenyns Arms*** [signed via B1507 off A1122 Downham Market bypass]: Extensive well laid out roadhouse-style pub in fine spot by spectacular hydraulic sluices controlling Great Ouse, tables out by water, generous usual food (not Sun evening) from good sandwiches to roasts and tempting puddings, friendly, helpful and efficient staff, real ales such as Greene King IPA and Old Speckled Hen and M&B Mild; children welcome, big light and airy games area with pool, piped music; bedrooms *(BB, Judy Pearson, Gerry and Rosemary Dobson)*

Deopham [TG0400]

Victoria [Church Rd]: Buoyant atmosphere, friendly licensees, wide choice of well cooked food at sensible prices, well kept real ales; compact bedrooms and bathrooms *(Bill and Sheila McLardy)*

Docking [TF7637]

Pilgrims Reach [High St]: Emphasis on imaginative food in quiet restaurant, starters from that menu available as imaginative bar food in warm and comfortable small bar (can be busy), well kept Adnams Bitter and Broadside and their good wines, friendly chef/landlord, children's room; tables on attractive sheltered back terrace *(O K Smyth, Chris Rogers)*

Railway Inn [Station Rd]: Wide choice of enjoyable home-made food from doorstep sandwiches up, quick friendly service, well kept real ales inc local microbrews, lounge bar and compact restaurant, fresh flowers, some rail posters (station closed 50 years ago), smaller chummy public bar with pool in annexe; usually open all day *(John Wooll, Chris Rogers, Mark and Amanda Sheard, Mike and Wendy Proctor)*

East Barsham [TF9133]

White Horse [B1105 3 miles N of Fakenham]: Attractively done extended pub, big log fire in long main bar, good range of well kept ales inc Greene King, decent wine, good coffee, efficient service, reasonably priced meals (rather than snacks, no sandwiches) inc children's, OAP lunches and steak nights, two small attractive dining rooms; piped music, darts; children welcome, bedrooms – a pleasant quiet place to stay *(R C Vincent)*

Fakenham [TF9229]

Wensum Lodge [Bridge St]: Large bar in extensive modern hotel built around mill conversion, two beamed restaurant areas (one no smoking), generous food from sandwiches to some interesting hot dishes and good puddings, bustling service, Greene King IPA and Woodfordes Wherry, conservatory, restaurant; tables outside with riverside lawn, comfortable bedrooms *(Anthony Barnes, LYM, Susan and Nigel Wilson)*

Framingham Pigot [TG2803]

Gull [A146 SE of Norwich]: Cosy country pub with welcoming helpful staff, log fires, stone floors, enjoyable food esp fish, Adnams, Greene King and Nethergate *(David Cosham)*

Garboldisham [TM0081]

☆ ***Fox*** [A1066 Thetford—Diss, junction with B1111]: Rambling old pub with attractive beamed décor, old pews and massive woodburner, enjoyable food inc unusual variations on usual dishes in relaxing bar and no smoking restaurant), well kept Greene King IPA and Shepherd Neame Spitfire, friendly staff *(David Oakley, LYM, Paul and Sue Merrick)*

Gayton [TF7219]

☆ ***Crown*** [B1145/B1153]: Attractive flower-decked pub, well kept and quietly comfortable, with some unusual old features; friendly relaxed atmosphere, wkdy lunchtime salad buffet and interesting evening meals, well kept Greene King IPA, XX Mild and Abbot, limited but good wine choice, pleasant staff, games room; tables in sheltered garden *(DC, Judy Wayman, Bob Arnett, David and Rhian Peters, LYM)*

Geldeston [TM3991]

☆ ***Locks*** [off A143/A146 NW of Beccles; off Station

Rd S of village, obscurely signed down long rough track]: Remote drinking pub alone at the navigable head of the River Waveney, virtually unchanged in several decades, ancient candlelit core with brick walls, tile floor, big log fire, well worn assorted chairs and tables, Woodfordes ales tapped from casks, friendly informal service; big extension for summer crowds and wknd music nights, summer evening barbecues, meadow camping; may be cl winter wkdys *(LYM, the Didler)*

Great Bircham [TF7632]

Kings Head [B1155, S end of village (called and signed Bircham locally)]: Unassuming lounge bar (two room areas), mix of high and low tables suiting both diners and drinkers, log fires, some good Italian food specialities and lots of seafood, no smoking dining area, well kept Adnams, Bass and Greene King IPA, malt whiskies, good Italian wines; big side lawn with picnic-sets and play things, attractive village with Houghton Hall and striking windmill nearby, good value bedrooms *(LYM, Mr Biggs, John Wooll)*

Great Cressingham [TF8401]

☆ ***Windmill*** [Water End, off A1065 Swaffham—Brandon]: Roomy family pub with three beamed bars, partitioned nooks and crannies, huge log fireplace, good value ample popular food, friendly prompt service, well kept Adnams Best and Broadside, Bass, Greene King IPA and a beer brewed for them by Bass, decent well priced wines, lots of prints, posters and farm tools, stripped brick and tiled floors, conservatory; piped music, games room with pool, SkyTV, live music; dogs allowed, comfortable bedrooms, well kept big garden *(Charles Gysin, Kevin Thorpe)*

Great Ellingham [TM0197]

☆ ***Crown*** [pub signed off B1077, which is off A11 SW of Norwich]: Open-plan bar recently refurbished and well divided into quiet alcoves, comfortable plush and other seats, soft lighting, relaxed atmosphere, enjoyable food inc good fresh fish and seafood and bargain lunches (the three small attractive dining rooms do get booked), well kept Adnams, Greene King IPA and Woodfordes Wherry, good friendly service; tables in garden, no dogs *(Paul and Sue Merrick, BB)*

Great Yarmouth [TG5206]

Red Herring [Havelock Rd]: Welcoming relaxing backstreet pub, nice Victorian décor, at least six well kept changing ales, farm ciders, good value food inc wide choice of good local sausages, fresh eggs for sale, rock collection, books to read *(the Didler)*

Gunton Station [TG2535]

Suffield Arms [off A149 Cromer—N Walsham; Station Rd]: Decent pubby food in bar and new restaurant extension, pleasant local atmosphere, welcoming landlord, well kept Greene King; garden tables *(David Twitchett)*

Harpley [TF7825]

Rose & Crown [off A148 Fakenham—Kings Lynn; Nethergate St]: Modest good value home cooking inc fresh veg, unusual vegetarian dishes, lots of good puddings and children's meals in small comfortable lounge and dining room, nice range of well kept real ales, decent wine, efficient service, open fire; high chairs provided; good tables in attractive garden with play equipment, quietly attractive village *(John Wooll, P J and R D Greaves, R C Vincent, Tom Gondris)*

Hempstead [TG1137]

☆ ***Hare & Hounds*** [towards Baconsthorpe]: Cottagey country pub recently reopened after refurbishment by warmly welcoming new landlord, two beamed rooms with log fire in one broad fireplace, well kept Greene King IPA and Abbot and a changing guest beer, enjoyable meals and snacks; picnic-sets and play area on side grass by pond and rockery *(P J and R D Greaves, Mr and Mrs P Thompson, LYM)*

Heydon [TG1127]

Earle Arms [off B1149]: Largely unchanged two-room pub in delightfully unspoilt village, nice old-fashioned décor and furnishings inc a grandfather clock, cupboards with interesting bric-a-brac, attractive prints, good log fires; usual food (not Sun/Mon evenings), well kept Adnams, Woodfordes Wherry and a guest beer, decent wines; piped music; children welcome, picnic-sets in small prettily cottagey back garden *(Su and Bob Child, John Wooll, LYM)*

Holt [TG0738]

☆ ***Feathers*** [Market Pl]: Bustling town hotel with locals' bar comfortably extended around original panelled area with open fire, busy on Sat market day, attractive entrance/reception area with antiques, helpful service from friendly staff, good value promptly served generous food, well kept Greene King IPA and Abbot, decent wines; piped music, can get smoky; decent roomy bedrooms *(June and Perry Dann, Blaise Vyner, B N F and M Parkin, BB, Peter H Stallard, Chris Mawson)*

Honingham [TG1011]

☆ ***Olde Buck*** [just off A47]: Ancient pub with four beamed rooms, some emphasis on wide choice of good food inc huge sandwiches and lunchtime bargains; helpful attentive service, well kept Greene King IPA and Flowers IPA *(Mrs J A Trotter, Jestyn Phillips)*

Horstead [TG2619]

Recruiting Sergeant [B1150 just S of Coltishall]: Spacious pleasantly refurbished village pub, enjoyable good value meals and snacks, welcoming obliging service, real ales, big open fire, brasses and muskets *(Alan M Pring, T and A Wyatt)*

Hunworth [TG0635]

☆ ***Blue Bell*** [aka Hunny Bell; signed off B roads S of Holt]: Modest country pub with some settees in comfortable L-shaped bar, wide choice of good value well presented food from soup and sandwiches to crab salad and steak, well kept ales such as Adnams and Woodfordes Wherry tapped from the cask, cheerful landlord, no smoking flagstoned dining room; children welcome, pleasant garden with summer bar service and play area *(Jim Mansfield, LYM, Judy Wayman, Bob Arnett, Brian Haywood)*

Kelling [TG0942]

Pheasant [A149 Sheringham—Blakeney]: Beautifully placed small hotel with moderately priced lunchtime and evening bar meals inc interesting specials in large comfortable lounge, Adnams ales; picnic-sets on small sheltered lawn, bedrooms *(Paul and Ursula Randall)*

King's Lynn [TF6019]

Freebridge Farm [Clenchwarton Rd, West Lynn]: Chain family dining pub with good helpful food choice, quick smart service, well equipped indoor and outdoor play areas; bedrooms in adjoining Travel Inn *(R C Vincent, Julie Vincent)*

London Porterhouse [London Rd]: Small, friendly and lively local with good mix of customers and well kept Greene King IPA and Abbot tapped from the cask; open all day Fri-Sun *(the Didler)*

Little Plumstead [TG3112]

Brick Kilns [B1140]: Friendly recently refurbished family pub, good value home-made food, fresh fish from Lowestoft; small garden *(Paul Weeks)*

Longham [TF9315]

White Horse [Wendling Rd]: Wide choice of good value home-made food inc good generous Sun lunch and well kept ales such as Woodfordes Wherry tapped from the cask in friendly traditional village pub; pleasant garden *(Jim Mansfield)*

North Walsham [TG2931]

Blue Bell [B1150 a mile NE]: Good drinks choice and big helpings of good value GM-free home cooking from hearty sandwiches and baguettes up in modern pub, smiling service, well behaved children allowed in back dining area; back lawn with good play area and wendy house, *(Alan M Pring)*

Northwold [TL7596]

Crown [off A134]: Quarry-tiled bar with wolf-whistling parakeet and woodburner, decent food in dining area beyond fireplace, small games room with pool; lovely old church opp *(Ian Phillips)*

Norwich [TG2512]

Blue Boar [Wroxham Rd, Sprowston]: Nicely refurbished, with good service, usual food, large clean good value bedrooms *(Stephen, Julie and Hayley Brown)*

Coach & Horses [Thorpe Rd]: Light and airy tap for Chalk Hill brewery, with their own Bitter, Flint Knappers Mild, CHB, Dreadnought and Old Tackle, also guests such as Boddingtons and Timothy Taylors, friendly service, wide choice of reasonably priced food 12-9 (8 Sun), also breakfast with limitless coffee; bare-boards L-shaped bar with open fire, lots of dark wood, posters and prints, pleasant back dining area; disabled access possible (not to lavatories), picnic-sets out in front *(the Didler, G Coates)*

Eagle [Newmarket Rd]: Attractively reworked under new management, welcoming layout, wide choice of food inc some non-standard dishes; pleasant garden *(Anthony Barnes)*

Gardeners Arms [Timber Hill]: Small attractive rooms converted from some of the last original shops and houses in old part of town, neatly themed inc convincing kitchen, more room in glassed-over former yard, relaxed friendly staff, real ales inc Murderer (recalling pub's former name), good value food inc sandwiches from breakfast on (not Mon evening), lots of bric-a-brac, no smoking and air-conditioned areas; families welcome, though more of a young people's pub evenings *(Shaun and Diane)*

☆ *Ribs of Beef* [Wensum St, S side of Fye Bridge]: Warm and welcoming high-ceilinged old pub, well kept ales such as Adnams, Boddingtons, Fullers London Pride and Woodfordes Wherry, farm cider, decent wine; deep leather settees and small tables upstairs, attractive smaller downstairs room with river view and some local river paintings, generous cheap reliable food (till 5 Sat/Sun), quick friendly service, long-serving licensees; can be studenty evenings, but without deafening music *(John Wooll)*

Rose [Rupert St/Trinity St]: Pleasant surprisingly spacious main bar, some Irish touches but not overdone, real ales such as Chalk Hill CHB, Fullers London Pride and Greene King Abbot, good choice of wines by the glass, dining area with plentiful freshly cooked food inc interesting variations on standard menu; tables outside *(Anthony Barnes, Su and Bob Child)*

Steam Packet [Crown Rd, behind Anglia TV]: Popular and friendly two-bar Adnams pub, no smoking at lunchtime, good pork pies, open all day; great for music *(the Didler)*

Take Five [St Andrews St, next to Cinema City]: Not a pub (in the evenings you can get in only through Cinema City for which it serves as the cafeteria), but very pleasant relaxed atmosphere, with well kept Woodfordes Wherry and a guest beer, two farm ciders, organic wines, consistently good value food, changing local art, some no smoking tables; piped classical music; tables in nice old courtyard *(Peter and Pat Frogley)*

Wig & Pen [St Martins Palace Plain]: Good range of real ales and staff who take a genuine interest in partly modernised old beamed bar opp cathedral close, lawyer and judge prints, roaring stove with horsebrasses on overmantel, prompt generous bar food, good value wine, good atmosphere; piped music *(Richard and Karen Holt)*

Old Buckenham [TM0691]

☆ *Gamekeeper* [The Green]: Pretty 16th-c pub with good atmosphere and blazing log fire in cosy friendly bar, good seasonal food here and in larger dining room, well kept ales such as Adnams, local Wolf and one brewed for the pub, good wine list, no machines *(Melissa Adams)*

Old Hunstanton [TF6842]

Ancient Mariner [part of L'Estrange Arms Hotel, Golf Course Rd]: Large bar, relaxed and cheerful, well done up with lots of dark wood, bare bricks and flagstones, several little areas inc upstairs gallery, pleasant furnishings, four well kept ales inc Adnams and Broadside and Bass, unusually good wines by the glass, friendly service, open fires, papers and magazines; hotel has good restaurant and nice bedrooms, long sea-view garden down to dunes, play area *(John Wooll, Peter Rozee, M J A Switzer, David and Rhian Peters)*

Lodge [A149]: Comfortable main-road pub with good choice of quickly served food in bar or (at higher price) restaurant, real ales inc Greene King IPA and Abbot, friendly staff, plenty of seats; good bedrooms *(Gordon Neighbour)*

Pulham Market [TM1986]

Crown [Harleston Rd]: Beautiful low thatched white pub by church overlooking green, heavy beams, unusual mix of pictures, very welcoming landlady, plentiful good value food, well kept beer, good service even when very busy *(David Twitchett, Keith Berrett)*

Reedham [TG4101]

Railway Tavern [just off B1140 Beccles—Acle]: Character two-bar village local in imposing Victorian building, well kept Adnams, Batemans, Everards ales, over 80 malt whiskies, Apr and Sept beer festivals, usual food (all day in summer); small dining room, piped music, games and TV in public bar; children welcome, pretty gravelled courtyard and garden behind, bedrooms, open all day Fri-Sun and summer *(Bob Arnett, Judy Wayman, LYM)*

Roydon [TM0980]

White Hart [A1066 just W of Diss]: Roomy and attractive partly 15th-c pub, good choice of enjoyable generous food at sensible prices, attentive landlord, old-fashioned atmosphere, brasses on beams, Greene King ales, restaurant *(Gordon Neighbour, Chris Richards, Emily Fletcher)*

Rushall [TM1982]

Half Moon [The Street]: Spotless extended 16th-c coaching inn popular for generous and competitively priced straightforward food inc lots of fish and big puddings, in bar or back dining room; Adnams, Woodfordes and other real ales, dolls and bric-a-brac for sale, pleasant service; bedrooms in adjacent chalets *(Alan M Pring)*

Salthouse [TG0743]

Dun Cow [A149 Blakeney—Sheringham]: Extensively refurbished well run airy bar overlooking salt marshes, decent usual food all day from sandwiches and baked potatoes to fresh crab salad and steak, friendly service, well kept Adnams, Greene King and other ales, open fires, stripped beams and cob walls in big barn-like bar; piped radio, blues nights; children welcome (games in family room), big attractive walled garden with sheltered courtyard, figs and apples, separate family garden with play area, good walks and birdwatching nearby (may have sightings blackboard); bedrooms *(S Watkin, P Taylor, Kevin Macey, BB, Eric Locker, Rodney and Norma Stubington)*

Scole [TM1579]

☆ ***Scole Inn*** [off A140 bypass just N of A143; Ipswich Rd]: Stately old coaching inn of outstanding architectural interest, with a real sense of history, antique settles, old oak chairs and tables, two impressive inglenook log fires, old prints and collectables and other old-fashioned features in lounge and bare-boards public bar used by locals; decent bar food from baguettes to steak, more elaborate menu in large no smoking restaurant, well kept Greene King IPA and XX Mild; cribbage, dominoes; children and dogs welcome, open all day, comfortable bedrooms in former stable block *(P G Plumridge, Mike and Wendy Proctor, LYM, Ian Phillips, Steve Chambers, Pat and Clive Sherriff, Eddie Edwards)*

Sculthorpe [TF8930]

Horse & Groom [The Street]: Unpretentious country local with good value generous home cooking *(Chris Rogers)*

☆ ***Sculthorpe Mill*** [inn signed off A148 W of Fakenham, opp village]: Sympathetically converted 18th-c mill, dim-lit beamed bar with several rooms, open fire, real ales such as Greene King, decent house wines, enjoyable food from sandwiches up, helpful prompt service; children in eating areas, spacious streamside garden, open all day wknds and summer, comfortable bedrooms, good breakfast *(Sue and Geoff Price, LYM, Michael Porter)*

Sea Palling [TG4226]

Hall Inn: Roomy and pleasant old bar, fairly unspoilt, with low-beamed dining area off, Adnams and Sam Smiths, decent food, friendly efficient service; picnic-sets on front lawn, 10 mins from beach *(Mike and Wendy Proctor, John Wooll)*

Sheringham [TG1543]

Lobster [High St]: Almost on seafront, clean and tidy, seafaring décor in small comfortable lounge bar with old sewing-machine treadle tables, welcoming service, good cheap food inc crab, lobster and fish specials, also children's things, well kept Adnams, Bass, Greene King Abbot and Marstons Pedigree, warm fire; no piped music, dogs on leads allowed, enclosed courtyard and garden *(C Galloway)*

Robin Hood [Station Rd]: Busy central pub, open-plan bar with dining area, smaller side room, Adnams, Bass and Greene King, good value generous food, efficient service; children very welcome, tables outside *(Jim Abbott, John Wooll)*

Smallburgh [TG3324]

Crown: 15th-c thatched and beamed village inn with friendly landlord, reliable fresh country cooking from immaculate kitchen in bar and small popular dining room, well kept Adnams, Greene King Abbot and a guest beer; tables outside, bedrooms *(N I Wright, Marguerite Pointer)*

South Wootton [TF6422]

Farmers Arms [part of Knights Hill Hotel, Grimston Rd (off A148/A149)]: Olde-worlde conversion of barn and stables, wide choice of good value food all day in bar and restaurant, real ales inc a guest beer, good wines, abundant coffee, friendly prompt service; children welcome, open all day; comfortable motel bedrooms (Best Western), health club *(R C Vincent, John Wooll)*

Spooner Row [TM0997]

Three Boars [just off A11 SW of Wymondham]: Pleasant village local with good restaurant *(RB)*

Stanhoe [TF8036]

☆ ***Crown*** [B1155 towards Burnham Mkt]: Cosy and friendly Elgoods local, popular for short choice of good value home cooking inc excellent game (food may stop early on quiet evenings), well kept Elgoods Cambridge, decent wine and coffee, convivial ex-RAF landlord and wife, small bright traditional bar with interesting nooks and corners, central log fire, one beam studded with hundreds of coins; well behaved children welcome, tables on side lawn, lots of fancy fowl (and chicks) outside; caravan site, self-catering cottage available *(John Wooll, BB, Tracey and Stephen Groves)*

Stoke Holy Cross [TG2302]

Wildebeest [Norwich Rd]: Dining pub with

emphasis on the good interesting bistro-style food but provision for drinkers too, good beer and wine by the glass, some unusual decorations inc African wooden masks *(J F M and M West)*

Thetford [TL8782]

Dolphin [Old Market St]: New licensees doing well in 17th-c pub, lots of old beams and brass, friendly local atmosphere, efficient service, well kept Black Sheep, Fullers London Pride and Greene King IPA, decent food; quiet piped music *(Mike and Karen England)*

Thompson [TL9296]

☆ ***Chequers*** [Griston Rd, off A1075 S of Watton]: Long, low and picturesque 15th-c thatched dining pub with good interesting food inc local game and lots of fresh fish in series of olde-worlde quaint rooms, Adnams, Fullers London Pride, local Wolf and occasional guest beers, good modestly priced wine list, friendly service and atmosphere, low beams, inglenooks, some stripped brickwork, antique tools and traps; games machines; tables outside, good newish bedroom block *(R Cross, LYM, Kelly Lewis, Pete Beasley, Mike and Karen England)*

Thornham [TF7343]

☆ ***Kings Head*** [Church St/High St (A149)]: Pretty old pub with lots of hanging baskets, roomy low-beamed bars with banquettes in well lit bays, Greene King IPA and Abbot, Marstons Pedigree and Tetleys, good food inc local fish, unpretentious no smoking dining room, friendly Northern landlord and helpful staff, open fire; dogs allowed; well spaced tables on back lawn with barbecues, three homely and comfortable bedrooms (one now with own bath), pleasant walks *(G J Hill, Nick Lawless, JMC, Pippa Brown)*

Tibenham [TM1389]

Greyhound [The Street]: Friendly old local, welcoming landlord, comfortable well kept bars with standing timbers, well kept Adnams, Greene King IPA and Youngs, public bar with TV, darts, juke box, fruit machine; may be open all day wknds; play area behind *(BB)*

Titchwell [TF7543]

Briarfields [Main Rd]: Good substantial bar food esp seafood inc local mussels, well kept Adnams, moderately priced house wines and friendly service in hotel's pleasantly refurbished back bar and lounge; terrace overlooking salt marshes, telescope and bird-sightings book; bedrooms comfortable and well appointed – a nice place to stay *(Gordon Neighbour, O K Smyth)*

Walsingham [TF9336]

☆ ***Bull*** [Common Place/Shire Hall Plain]: Comfortable and friendly straightforward pub in centre of pilgrimage village, walls covered with clerical visiting cards, welcoming landlord, well kept Adnams and Greene King, generous fresh home cooking; attractive flowery terrace on busy village square *(Chris Rogers, W A Evershed)*

West Beckham [TG1339]

☆ ***Wheatsheaf*** [off A148 Holt—Cromer; Church Rd]: Gently renovated separate beamed areas, roaring log fire in one part, a smaller coal one in another, comfortable chairs and banquettes, usually good generous food (not Sun evening; may be a wait) from sandwiches up, two no smoking dining rooms, well kept Bass and several Woodfordes ales, good wine choice, local country wines, enormous black cat; darts, bar billiards, shove-ha'penny, dominoes, piped music; children welcome, partly terraced front garden with restored gipsy caravan *(Derek R A Field, Jim Abbott, Philip and Susan Philcox, S Watkin, P Taylor, LYM)*

West Runton [TG1842]

Village Inn [Water Lane]: Large pub worth knowing for its comfortable restaurant; also plain side bar, and big pizzeria-style back dining room open all day from breakfast on; large garden area with separate snack counter *(Jim Abbott)*

West Walton [TF4713]

☆ ***King of Hearts*** [N of Wisbech; School Rd]: Comfortably refurbished beamed dining pub with wide choice of good genuine food inc OAP lunch in smartly furnished bar and restaurant, good hot buffet (as much as you want), friendly very helpful service copes well even with big parties and special diet needs, full Elgoods range and a guest beer, lots of decorative china and brassware, no smoking area; holds key for lovely next-door church; tables in raised garden *(Michael and Jenny Back, John Beeken)*

Weston Longville [TG1115]

Parson Woodforde [signed off A1067 Norwich—Bawdswell in Morton]: Clean and spacious beamed pub with well kept Adnams Extra, Wolf Golden Jackal and Woodfordes Wherry, lots of alcoves, two huge fireplaces, willing welcoming service, big restaurant; tables on terrace, flower-filled back garden *(Anthony Barnes, Norma and Keith Bloomfield)*

Wiveton [TG0342]

☆ ***Bell*** [Blakeney Rd]: Big welcoming open-plan dining pub with Danish landlord cooking wide choice of interesting food for bar and restaurant inc some Danish dishes and special nights, Adnams Bitter and Broadside and Bass, good wines, efficient helpful service even under pressure, no music or machines; carpeted no smoking conservatory, picnic-sets on lawn and small garden behind *(Kevin Macey, BB, John Wooll, Paul and Ursula Randall, Peter and Pat Frogley, Charles Gysin)*

Wymondham [TG1101]

☆ ***Green Dragon*** [Church St]: Very picturesque heavily timbered jettied 14th-c inn, bulky beams, log fire (Tudor mantelpiece), well kept Adnams and Greene King, friendly relaxed service, welcoming locals, good food from sandwiches to attractively priced main dishes, small back bar, bigger no smoking turkey-carpeted dining area, some interesting pictures; children and dogs welcome; modest bedrooms, near glorious 12th-c abbey church *(the Didler, M S Catling, BB)*

> Post Office address codings confusingly give the impression that some pubs are in Norfolk when they're really in Suffolk (which is where we list them).

Northamptonshire

Two new entries here this year are the unassuming and welcoming George at Kilsby, and the Old Sun at Nether Heyford, full of interesting things to look at. And back among the main entries after a break of a few years is the attractive Olde Coach House at Ashby St Ledgers, on good form all round these days. Other pubs doing particularly well here are the Windmill at Badby (good all round), the cheerful Red Lion at Crick (bargain food), and the civilised Falcon at Fotheringhay (very good inventive food, and gaining a Place to Stay Award this year). It is a clear indication of its quality that this is the fourth year on the trot that the Falcon at Fotheringhay carries off the title of Northamptonshire Dining Pub of the Year. New people in the charming Star at Sulgrave now allow children in the dining room: a useful change, given the attraction of the costumed events at nearby Sulgrave Manor. And on the family front it's worth knowing that the Mill just outside Oundle is now completely no smoking at weekends. In the Lucky Dip section at the end of the chapter, pubs doing notably well currently are the Queens Head at Bulwick, Eastcote Arms at Eastcote, White Hart at Grafton Regis, Fox & Hounds at Great Brington, Dusty Fox at Harlestone, Red Lion at Hellidon, Griffins Head at Mears Ashby, Red Lion at Sibbertoft, Boat at Stoke Bruerne, Kings Head at Wadenhoe and Narrow Boat at Weedon. Drinks prices are generally close to the national average here; among the main entries, the White Swan at Woodnewton, which also had bargain food, had much the cheapest beer. A local beer worth looking out for is Frog Island, from Northampton – especially as the new 14p duty cut for small breweries should let it undercut bigger brewers' prices.

ASHBY ST LEDGERS SP5768 Map

Olde Coach House

4 miles from M1 junction 18; A5 S to Kilsby, then A361 S towards Daventry; village also signed off A5 N of Weedon; Main Street

This handsome creeper-covered stone inn was originally a farmhouse, and converted into a pub when Lutyens restyled this interesting village and the estate farm workers lost their former watering-hole. There's a cheerfully traditional feel in its several comfortable, rambling little rooms, which have high-backed winged settles on polished black and red tiles, old kitchen tables, harnesses on a few standing timbers, hunting pictures (often of the Pytchley, meeting outside), Thelwell prints, and a big winter log fire. A front room has a TV and piped music. A fine drinks selection includes well kept Everards Old Original, Flowers Original, Fullers London Pride on handpump, and a couple of guests usually from small breweries, such as Timothy Taylors Landlord and local Frog Island, with lots more during their spring beer festival; also over a dozen wines by the generous glass, and an unusual choice of non-alcoholic drinks; bar food includes hot beef roll (£5.95), cold cut pies (from £6.95), burger topped with bacon, cheese and mushrooms (£7.95), lamb and mint casserole (£8.95), and sometimes game or woodpigeon. No smoking in the restaurant or part of the bar. There are tables out among fruit trees and under a fairy-lit arbour (with occasional summer barbecues), and an activity centre for children; disabled entrance, and baby-changing facilities. They have a very full diary of events throughout the year, with anything from Indian food festivals to fireworks displays and bank holiday pig roasts. The nearby church is well worth a look. *(Recommended by E J and M W Corrin, G Coates, Patrick Hancock, Robert and Catherine Dunster, Susan and John Douglas, Mandy and Simon King)*

Traditional Freehouses ~ Managers Pete and Christine Ballinger ~ Real ale ~ Bar food (12-2, 6-9) ~ Restaurant ~ No credit cards ~ (01788) 890349 ~ Children welcome ~ Open 12-11(10.30 Sun); 12-2.30, 6-11 winter ~ Bedrooms: £51B/£65B

BADBY SP5559 Map 4

Windmill

Village signposted off A361 Daventry—Banbury

The licensees take a genuine hands-on interest in seeing that their customers really enjoy themselves in this unchanging old thatched inn. The atmosphere is relaxed and civilised in the two chatty beamed and flagstoned bars, with their cricketing and rugby pictures, simple country furnishings in good solid wood, and an unusual white woodburning stove in an enormous white-tiled inglenook fireplace. There's also a cosy and comfortable lounge. The pub is not that big and can get busy, so it may be worth booking. Good generous bar food from a well balanced menu is served promptly by good-natured efficient staff, and might include sweet potato and coriander soup (£2.75), potato skins with yoghurt and mint dip (£3.75), grilled goats cheese on garlic bread with basil and tomato (£4.95), nut roast with cranberry and chilli sauce or steak and kidney pie (£7.95), venison burgers with creamy peppercorn sauce (£8.75), fresh crab salad (£9.75), wild boar steak with whisky and mushroom sauce (£11.95), brill topped with crab and prawn sauce (£12.50), and puddings (from £3.50). The snug and the more modern-feeling and brightly lit carpeted restaurant are no smoking. Well kept Bass, Boddingtons, Flowers Original and Wadworths 6X on handpump, and good fairly priced wines by the bottle; dominoes, quiet piped music. The bedrooms are in an unobtrusive modern extension, well tucked away at the back. There are a few seats out in front by the green; this is a pretty village, with lots of nearby woodland walks. *(Recommended by Robin and Sheila Pitt, George Atkinson, Di and Mike Gillam, Dr T E Hothersall, Paul Humphreys, Anthony Barnes, Sheila and Gerry McGrady, John Kane, Bob Arnett, Judy Wayman, Dennis John Boddington, P Tailyour, Karen and Graham Oddey, John Bramley, RM Corlett, Mr and Mrs S J Spademan, Martin and Penny Fletcher)*

Free house ~ Licensees John Freestone and Carol Sutton ~ Real ale ~ Bar food ~ Restaurant ~ (01327) 702363 ~ Children in eating area of bar, family room and restaurant ~ Dogs allowed in bar and bedrooms ~ Open 11.30-3(4 Sat), 5.30-11; 11.30-4, 7-11 Sun ~ Bedrooms: £55S/£69B

CHACOMBE SP4943 Map 4

George & Dragon

2½ miles from M40 junction 11: A361 towards Daventry, then village signposted on right; Silver Street

The relaxed atmosphere and pretty village setting make this attractive inn a peaceful respite from the nearby M40; and they do sandwiches right through the afternoon. The neat, spacious bar has comfortable seats, beams, flagstones, and logs burning in a massive fireplace, and Theakstons XB and Best and possibly a guest on handpump; fruit wines. The wide range of food from a fortnightly changing blackboard is not cheap; well prepared dishes might include baked potatoes (from £3.40), sandwiches (from £3.65, filled baguettes from £4.95), black pudding salad (£4.95), mussels in garlic cream (£5.75), aubergine and mushroom curry or baked stuffed peppers (£7.95), faggot and sausage casserole (£8.50), fillet steak (£14.95), and good fish dishes such as monkfish and salmon kebabs, poached cod with tomato, onion and basil sauce or fried shark steak (£10.95), with puddings such as tangy lemon mousse and coffee and Tia Maria panna cotta in a brandy snap (£3.45); no smoking area in restaurant. Darts, dominoes and piped music. *(Recommended by Howard and Margaret Buchanan, Stuart Turner, B H and J I Andrews, Karen Eliot, Bob and Maggie Atherton, Tom Evans, Martin and Karen Wake, Charles Moncreiffe, W W Burke, Martin and Penny Fletcher, Comus and Sarah Elliott, J M Pitts, M A and C R Starling, Jenny and Brian Seller, John Robertson, Jim Bush)*

Free house ~ Licensee Ray Bennett ~ Real ale ~ Bar food (12-9.30) ~ Restaurant ~ (01295) 711500 ~ Children welcome ~ Dogs allowed in bar ~ Open 12-11(10.30 Sun) ~ Bedrooms: £42.50B/£60B

CHAPEL BRAMPTON SP7266 Map 4

Brampton Halt

Pitsford Road; off A5199 (was A50) N of Northampton

Built originally as a station master's house, this pretty red brick Victorian inn stands alone by the little Northampton & Lamport Railway, and has pleasant meadow views. A visit here makes part of a good day out for the family, as there are train rides at weekends with additional bank holiday and Santa specials, and the Nene Valley Way – a 14-mile walk and cycle-way – runs along an adjacent converted old track through attractive countryside. It's a friendly, relaxed place, with Victorian-style floral wallpaper throughout, matching swagged curtains, and sturdily comfortable furniture. One low-ceilinged area has a woodburning stove and wash drawings of steam trains, and by the bar counter, a high-raftered dining area has old farm tools. Windows at the back overlook the garden and fenced-off rolling stock. Straightforward bar food includes sandwiches (from £2.95), ploughman's (£4.95), ham and eggs or various burgers such as chicken, beef or spicy bean (£5.95), bacon and stilton salad or scampi (£5.95), and sirloin steak (£8.95); puddings (£2.95). Well kept Adnams, Everards Old Original and Tiger, Fullers London Pride and a guest such as Greene King IPA on handpump; decent wines; friendly service; trivia, perhaps piped music. They may stay open all day at weekends when the weather's fine. There are a few tables in a small sun lounge. *(Recommended by Bernie Adams, Michael Tack, Ian Phillips, Gerry and Rosemary Dobson, Rona Murdoch, Dave Braisted, J Attwood)*

Free house ~ Licensees Roger and Caroline Thom ~ Real ale ~ Bar food ~ Restaurant ~ (01604) 842676 ~ Well behaved children welcome ~ Open 12-2.30(4 Sat), 5.30-11; 12-4, 7-10.30 Sun

CLIPSTON SP7181 Map 4

Bulls Head

B4036 S of Market Harborough

The enthusiastic landlord at this ancient village inn keeps an amazing choice of over 550 whiskies. He also serves well kept Bass, Greene King IPA and Old Speckled Hen, Marstons Pedigree and possibly a guest such as Everards Tiger from handpump, and half a dozen wines by the glass. The hundreds of coins that gleam from the low black beams are part of a tradition started by US airmen based nearby during World War II – they used to leave their money wedged in the cracks of the ancient woodwork, ready for their return and their next round. The carpeted bar is divided into three cosily dim areas leading down from the servery, with comfortable seats, sturdy small settles and stools upholstered in red plush, a grandmother clock, some harness and tools, and a log fire. There's a dining area in the room at the back with oak settles, high-backed chairs and a grandfather clock keeping time; the walls are hung with china meat platters. Bar food includes home-made soup (£2.95), sandwiches and baked potatoes (from £3.25), breaded mushrooms (£3.95), battered haddock (£4.95), vegetable stir fry, home-made pies or generous gammon (£6.95), daily specials such as shellfish broth (£4.95), lemon sole with Pernod and dill butter (£9.50) or roast duckling with orange and ginger glaze (£9.95), and puddings (£2.95). One of the bars and the restaurant are no smoking; table skittles, darts, TV, fruit machine, dominoes, piped music and newspapers. Slightly saucy pin-ups decorate the gents', and the ladies' has an eye-opener of a picture too. Outside, a terrace has tables under cocktail parasols. *(Recommended by E J and M W Corrin, Rona Murdoch, George Atkinson, Graham and Lynn Mason, Phil and Jane Hodson, John Bramley, Sally Anne and Peter Goodale, Mike and Sue Loseby, Sir Clive Rose, Grahame McNulty, Brian and Anna Marsden, Duncan Cloud, Dr D J and Mrs S C Walker, Bernie Adams)*

Free house ~ Licensees George, Sue and Jo Price ~ Real ale ~ Bar food (12-2, 6-9.30 (9 Mon, 7-9 Sun)) ~ Restaurant ~ (01858) 525268 ~ Children in eating area of bar and restaurant till 9.30 ~ Dogs allowed in bar ~ Open 11.30-3, 5.30-11; 12-3, 7-10.30 Sun; closed Mon lunchtime ~ Bedrooms: £29.50S/£45S

CRICK SP5872 Map 4

Red Lion £

1 mile from M1 junction 18; A428

You can't help but be impressed by the good value generous food, served by friendly staff in a relaxed and welcoming atmosphere, at this old thatched stone-built pub. The real bargains are to be had at lunchtime, when the menu includes sandwiches (from £1.30), ploughman's (from £2.90), and straightforward hearty main courses such as chicken and mushroom pie, leek and smoky bacon bake, plaice or vegetable pancake rolls (all £4.10); in the evening they do a wider range of dishes, including wild mushroom lasagne (£6.50), stuffed salmon fillet (£7.25), roast duck (£11), and steaks (from £10), as well as puddings such as lemon meringue pie (from £2.20); Sunday roast (£4.25). The snug low-ceilinged bar has lots of comfortable seating and a tiny log stove in a big inglenook. Four well kept changing beers on handpump might be Greene King Old Speckled Hen, Marstons Pedigree, Theakstons Best and Websters Yorkshire. There are a few picnic-sets under cocktail parasols on grass by the car park, and in summer you can eat on the terrace in the old coachyard, which is sheltered by a Perspex roof; lots of pretty hanging baskets. *(Recommended by Steve Riches, Karen Eliot, Mandy and Simon King, V Green, Darly Graton, Graeme Gulibert, Basil Minson, Wendy and Bob Needham, Roger and Pauline Pearce, Sheila Rowell, Geoffrey Johns, R T and J C Moggridge, George Atkinson, Roger and Jenny Huggins, Kevin Blake, Humphry and Angela Crum Ewing, Mr and Mrs J McRobert)*

Wellington ~ Lease Tom and Paul Marks ~ Real ale ~ Bar food (till 9.30 Sat, not Sun evening) ~ (01788) 822342 ~ No children under 14 in evenings ~ Dogs welcome ~ Open 11-2.30, 6.15-11; 12-3, 7-10.30 Sun

EAST HADDON SP6668 Map 4

Red Lion

High Street; village signposted off A428 (turn right in village) and off A50 N of Northampton

Good meals and comfortable bedrooms are the most important aspects at this elegantly substantial golden stone hotel. Popular (though not cheap) bar food from a daily changing menu might include soups (£3.50), sandwiches (£4), wild mushroom potato cake, breaded pork escalope with sweet and sour sauce (£9), grilled plaice (£10), pie of the day (£11), half a roast duckling with bitter orange sauce, spring lamb cutlets with black pudding and minted gravy or beef strips in brandy with peppercorn sauce (£12), and puddings such as crème brûlée, bread and butter pudding and gateaux from the trolley (£4). The pretty no smoking restaurant overlooking the garden has a more elaborate menu; good breakfasts. This is one of our smarter entries, and the neat lounge bar has some attractive antique furniture, including panelled oak settles, library chairs and a mix of oak, mahogany and cast-iron-framed tables. Little kegs, pewter, brass pots, swords and so forth are hung sparingly on a couple of beams, and there's attractive white-painted panelling with recessed china cabinets and old prints. They serve very well kept real ales such as Adnams Broadside and Charles Wells Bombardier on handpump, and decent wines; piped music. The walled side garden is a pleasant place to enjoy coffee after a meal, with lilac, fruit trees, roses and neat flower beds; it leads back to the bigger lawn, which has well spaced picnic-sets. A small side terrace has more tables under cocktail parasols, and a big copper beech shades the gravel car park. *(Recommended by Stuart Turner, R M Corlett, Tony Lauf, Maysie Thompson, Martin and Penny Fletcher, Sarah Markham, Gerry and Rosemary Dobson)*

Charles Wells ~ Lease Ian Kennedy ~ Real ale ~ Bar food (12-2, 7-9.30, not Sun evening) ~ Restaurant ~ (01604) 770223 ~ Children in eating area of bar at lunchtime and in restaurant ~ Open 11-2.30, 6-11; 12-2.30, 7-10.30 Sun ~ Bedrooms: £60S/£75S

FARTHINGSTONE SP6155 Map 4

Kings Arms

Off A5 SE of Daventry; village signposted from Litchborough on former B4525 (now declassified)

They've taken a very traditional country pub approach at this handsome gargoyled 18th-c stone inn, where British cheeses are the speciality – indeed it's the only food they serve. Listed on a board, they come on a platter (from £5.50), in a filled baguette (£2.80), or as a ploughman's (£4.95), and you can also buy them to take away. They may serve soup in the winter. The small and timeless flagstoned bar has a huge log fire, comfortably homely sofas and armchairs near the entrance, whisky-water jugs hanging from oak beams, and lots of pictures and decorative plates on the walls. A games room at the far end has darts, dominoes, cribbage, table skittles and board games. Hook Norton is kept well on handpump, alongside three guests such as Adnams, Jennings and Timothy Taylors; they have decent wines and fruit wines, and sell local crafts, and wines and olive oil. The terrace is a tranquil spot, with its plant-filled painted tractor tyres, and lots of pots with more plants and herbs; the outside gents' has an interesting newspaper-influenced décor. The village is picturesque, with good walks nearby (including the Knightley Way). Do check the limited opening and food serving times below before you head out to visit this pub. *(Recommended by Pete Baker, Tom Evans, George Atkinson)*

Free house ~ Licensees Paul and Denise Egerton ~ Real ale ~ Bar food (Sat and Sun lunchtime only) ~ No credit cards ~ (01327) 361604 ~ Children welcome ~ Dogs welcome ~ Open 7-11; 12-3, 7-11 Sat; 12-3, 9-11 Sun; closed Mon and Weds, also lunchtime Mon-Fri

FOTHERINGHAY TL0593 Map 5

Falcon ★

Village signposted off A605 on Peterborough side of Oundle

Northamptonshire Dining Pub of the Year

Tremendous attention to detail is the hallmark of this very civilised dining pub, which makes a good place to come for a special occasion – it's understandably popular, so it's a good idea to book. Service is genuinely welcoming: you'll be made to feel just as special if you're here for only a sandwich as people coming for a full three-course meal. The neatly kept bar has cushioned slatback armchairs and bucket chairs, good winter log fires in a stone fireplace, fresh flower arrangements, and a hum of quiet conversation. The pretty conservatory restaurant is usually busy with diners, and if the weather's nice the attractively planted garden is a particularly enjoyable place to eat. The dining room and conservatory are no smoking; locals gather in the much smaller tap bar, which has darts. A very good range of drinks includes well kept Adnams and Greene King IPA, alongside a couple of guests from brewers such as Nethergate and Potton on handpump, good wines with about 15, as well as a champagne, by the glass, organic cordials and fresh orange juice. Very well presented, inventive food from the seasonally changing bar menu might include starters such as pea and mint soup with parma ham and crème fraîche (£4.75), chicken liver pâté with toasted brioche, red onion and apple chutney (£4.75), main courses such as warm salad of roasted vegetables with falafel, sweet garlic and olive salsa (£9.75), lightly curried pork fillet with fruit and nut rice and poppadoms (£12.75), calves liver with olive oil mash, bacon, spinach and red wine shallot sauce (£13.75), and puddings (they do a good list of sweet wines by the glass) such as soft fruit and mascarpone trifle (£4.75), and sticky toffee pudding with rum and raisin ice cream and caramel sauce (£5.50). They also do open sandwiches, and readers like their set lunches, which are good value considering the standard of cooking (two courses £11, three £14.75) and might include slightly simpler dishes such as cream of cauliflower soup, herb roasted chicken and poached pears in red wine with crème fraîche. The vast church behind is worth a visit, and the ruins of Fotheringhay Castle, where Mary Queen of Scots was executed, are not far away. *(Recommended by Martin and Penny Fletcher, Marion Turner, Philip and Susan Philcox, Steve Chambers, Terry Mizen, Mike and Sue Loseby, Roger and Maureen Kenning, Maysie Thompson, Eric Locker, R C Wiles, B, M and P Kendall, Lorraine and Fred Gill, David and Mary Webb, Derek and Sylvia Stephenson, Howard and Margaret Buchanan, Michael Sargent, Oliver and Sue Rowell)*

Free house ~ Licensees Ray Smikle and John Hoskins ~ Real ale ~ Bar food (12-2.15, 6.30-9.30) ~ Restaurant ~ (01832) 226241 ~ Children welcome ~ Dogs allowed in bar ~ Open 12-3, 6-11; 12-2, 7-10.30 Sun

GREAT OXENDON SP7383 Map 4

George

A508 S of Market Harborough

The cosy and convivial interior of this popular dining pub is a warming surprise, given its rather gaunt-looking exterior (it's set high on a bank over the main road). A great deal of care has gone into the furnishings and décor, from the welcoming lobby with its overstuffed chairs, former inn-sign, and lavatories entertainingly decked out with rather stylish naughty pictures, through the attractive prints and engravings in the two opened-together rooms of the main beamed bar, to the Portmeirion plates, and the turkey-carpeted no smoking conservatory overlooking the shrub-sheltered garden. There's a comfortable mix of chairs with the odd cushioned pew, and a thriving atmosphere boosted by good staff who clearly enjoy their work. They put quite an emphasis on the food, which is very popular with older lunchers (you might want to book), and includes soup (£3.35), filled rolls (from £4.45), ploughman's (£5.50), beef and Guinness pie or grilled haddock (£8.25), salmon and asparagus in filo with mornay sauce (£8.95), and honey-roast lamb shank (£9.65). Well kept Adnams, Shepherd Neame Spitfire and possibly a guest such as Bass on handpump, around 10 wines by the glass, daily papers on sticks, a big log fire (with a nice club fender); there may be piped easy-listening classical music. *(Recommended by Jeff and Wendy Williams, I C Millar, Gerry and Rosemary Dobson, Mr and Mrs D J Nash, Mrs J Purry, Bernie Adams, Anthony Barnes)*

Free house ~ Licensee Allan Wiseman ~ Real ale ~ Bar food (12-2, 7-10) ~ Restaurant ~ (01858) 465205 ~ Children welcome ~ Dogs allowed in bedrooms ~ Open 12-2, 6.30-11; closed bank hol and Sun evenings ~ Bedrooms: /£55.50B

HARRINGWORTH SP9298 Map 4

White Swan

Seaton Road; village SE of Uppingham, signposted from A6003, A47 and A43

The blocked-in traces of its carriage-entry arch hint at the past of this imposing limestone Tudor inn, with its big gable and stone window lintels. It's in a pretty village famous for its magnificent 82-arch railway viaduct. There's plenty of exposed stone inside, a pleasantly calming localish atmosphere, and a friendly welcome. The neatly kept central bar area has good solid tables, a hand-crafted oak counter with a mirror base and an attractive swan carving, an open fire, pictures relating to the World War II airfield at nearby Spanhoe among a collection of old village photographs (in which many of the present buildings are still recognisable), and well kept Greene King IPA and Abbot and Marstons

Pedigree on handpump; darts and piped music. The roomy and welcoming lounge/eating area has comfortable settles, while a quieter no smoking dining room has a collection of old jugs, craft tools, dried flower arrangements and locally painted watercolours. Good varied bar food includes sandwiches (from £2.50), cream of broccoli and stilton soup (£3.25), hot baguettes (from £3), home-made chicken liver pâté or grilled goats cheese with sun-dried tomatoes and black olives (£3.95), asparagus, mushroom and brie pancakes or grilled chicken stuffed with onion and mushrooms and topped with stilton, (£7.95), venison sausages, bubble and squeak and onion gravy (£7.95), braised lamb knuckle with rosemary, orange and redcurrant sauce (£8.95), and steaks (from £9.95), with puddings such as strawberry jam sponge pudding and hot chocolate brownies (£3.25); good Sunday lunch. There are tables out on a little terrace, and Rockingham race track is four miles from here. *(Recommended by Lorraine and Fred Gill, Norma and Keith Bloomfield, Angus Lyon, Mike and Sue Loseby, Joan and Michel Hooper-Immins)*

Free house ~ Licensees Stephen and Lara Hobbs ~ Real ale ~ Bar food ~ Restaurant ~ (01572) 747543 ~ Children in eating area of bar and restaurant ~ Open 11.30-2.30, 6.30-11; 12-3, 7-10.30 Sun ~ Bedrooms: £40S/£55S

KILSBY SP5671 Map 4

George

2½ miles from M1 junction 18: A428 towards Daventry, left on to A5 – look out for pub off on right at roundabout

Under its hard-working and welcoming landlady, this substantial pub is a friendly and relaxing refuge from the motorway. Interestingly, it was rebuilt 150 years ago using the same source of bricks as the Kilsby Tunnel. A high-ceilinged bar on the right, with plush banquettes, dark panelling, a coal-effect gas stove and a big bay window, opens on the left into a cheerful and attractive dining area with solidly comfortable furnishings. Enjoyable home-made food includes sandwiches (£1.95), soup (£2.80), filled baguettes (from £3.25), ploughman's (£4.50), battered cod (£5.50), steak and kidney pudding (£6.30), meat or vegetable lasagne (£6.50), evening steaks (from £7.50), and puddings such as chocolate fudge cake or home-made bread and butter pudding (£2.50). It's worth booking for the good Sunday lunch. Well kept Adnams, Greene King IPA, Abbot and Old Speckled Hen and a guest such as Belhaven Fruity Partridge on handpump, a splendid range of malt whiskies in generous measures, and decent wines in big glasses. A long brightly decorated back public bar has darts, a good pool table, fruit machine and a huge TV; there may be piped music; no dogs. There are wood and metal picnic-sets out in the back garden, by the car park. We have not yet heard from any readers who have stayed overnight here, but expect that you would be well looked after. *(Recommended by George Atkinson, Ted George)*

Punch ~ Lease Maggie Chandler ~ Real ale ~ Bar food (12-2.30, 6.30-9) ~ Restaurant ~ (01788) 822229 ~ Children in restaurant ~ Dogs allowed in bar ~ Live music first Sat in month ~ Open 11.30-3, 5.30(6 Sat)-11; 12-10.30 Sun ~ Bedrooms: £25/£40

NETHER HEYFORD SP6558 Map 4

Old Sun

1¾ miles from M1 junction 16: village signposted left off A45 westbound – Middle Street

The several small linked rooms of this mainly 18th-c family-run golden stone pub are packed with all sorts of decorative bric-a-brac, especially gleaming brassware (one fireplace is a veritable grotto of large brass animals), but lots more too, such as colourful relief plates, 1930s cigarette cards, railway memorabilia and advertising signs, World War II posters, rope fancywork – really worth a good look around. There are beams and low ceilings (one painted with a fine sunburst), partly glazed dividing panels, steps between some areas, rugs on parquet, red tiles or flagstones, a big inglenook log fire – and up on the left a room with full-sized hood skittles (and a veteran fruit machine). Furnishings are mostly properly pubby, with the odd easy chair. Good value home-made bar food includes soup (£2.25), sandwiches with salad and crisps (£2.75), pasties (£3.75), steak pie (£7.25), battered cod (£7.50) and ricotta cannelloni with spinach and goats cheese (£7.85), with good vegetables; they do more restauranty dishes at weekends and in the evenings. Well kept Banks's, Greene King Ruddles Best, Marstons Pedigree and a guest such as Hook Norton Best on handpump from the two serving bars; very welcoming chatty service; there may be piped music, or SkyTV. Picnic-sets out on a fairy-lit front terrace are fenced off by a line of blue-painted grain kibblers and other antiquated hand-operated farm machines, some with plants in their hoppers. *(Recommended by CMW, JJW, Gerry and Rosemary Dobson, George Atkinson)*

Free house ~ Licensees Geoffrey and James Allen ~ Real ale ~ Bar food (not Sun/Mon evenings) ~ Restaurant ~ (01327) 340164 ~ Children in restaurant ~ Open 12-3 (4 Sat), 6-11; 12-4, 7-10.30 Sun

OUNDLE TL0487 Map 5

Mill

Barnwell Road out of town; or follow Barnwell Country Park signs off A605 bypass

There are records of a mill on this site by the River Nene well before the Doomsday Book (which mentions it too), and the waterwheel of the present building, which dates partly from the early 17th c, did not stop turning till 1930. It's now been well restored, and you can watch the stream race below the building through a big glass panel by the entrance. A ground-floor bar (open in the evening and weekends only) has red leatherette button-back built-in wall banquettes against its stripped-stone walls. They serve bar food in the upstairs Trattoria, which has stalls around tables with more banquettes in bays, stripped masonry and beams, another mill race feature, and small windows which look down over the lower millpond and the river. There's a no smoking area during the week, and at weekends it's no smoking throughout the building; piped music. As well as quite a few tex-mex dishes such as hickory ribs (£8.95) and fajitas (from £11.95), the wide range of bar food might include soup (£2.95), filled baguettes and baked potatoes (from £3), crab and prawn fishcakes (£8.95), and steaks (from £9.95), with daily specials such as sweet and sour vegetables (£6.95), thai green curry (£8.95), and pesto salmon (£9.95). Puddings might include crumble and cheesecake (£3.50); they do a lot of liqueur coffees. Three changing beers might be from brewers such as Courage, Elgoods, or Nethergate. There are picnic-sets under cocktail parasols on a bricked area in front, and on a grassy area at the side. More reports please. *(Recommended by Michael Tack)*

Free house ~ Licensees Neil Stewart and Peter Bossard ~ Real ale ~ Bar food (12-2, 6.30-9(9.30 Sat)) ~ Restaurant ~ (01832) 272621 ~ Children in eating area of bar and restaurant ~ Open 12-3, 6.30-11(10.30 Sun); closed Christmas

Ship

West Street

This companionable bustling local gains its entry on the strength of its relaxed atmosphere and friendly smiling service. The heavily beamed lounge bar is made up of three rooms that lead off the central corridor, one of them no smoking. Up by the street there's a mix of leather and other seats, with sturdy tables and a log fire in a stone inglenook, and down one end a panelled snug (also generally smoke-free) has button-back leather seats built in around it. The wood-floored public side has darts, dominoes, fruit machine and juke box. Changing beers might include well kept Adnams, Bass, Hop Back Summer Lightning, Oakham JHB and Shepherd Neame on handpump, as well as a good range of malt whiskies (and cocktail specials on Weds, Fri and Sat evenings). Straightforward reasonably priced bar food from a changing blackboard menu might include soup (£3), sandwiches (from £3), chicken liver pâté (£4), ham and egg (£4.50), steak and ale pie (£5.50), and lunchtime specials such as barnsley lamb chop or home-made seafood pie (£5.25); puddings might include raspberry meringue or home-made fruit crumble (£2.50). The wooden tables and chairs out on the series of small sheltered terraces are lit at night. Several of the clean and comfortable bedrooms are in a recent extension. *(Recommended by Rona Murdoch)*

Free house ~ Licensees Andrew and Robert Langridge ~ Real ale ~ Bar food (12-3, 7-9) ~ Restaurant ~ (01832) 273918 ~ Children in eating area of bar and restaurant till 9pm ~ Dogs welcome ~ Jazz last Sun in month, DJs Fri, Sat ~ Open 11-11; 12-10.30 Sun ~ Bedrooms: £25(£30S)(£50B)/£40(£50S)(£60B)

SULGRAVE SP5545 Map 4

Star

E of Banbury, signposted off B4525; Manor Road

New licensees have made subtle improvements (new crockery and so forth) in this creeper-covered stone-built inn, but its hospitable farmhouse interior remains largely unchanged. And children are now allowed into the no smoking back restaurant. Furnishings are mainly small pews, cushioned window seats and wall benches, kitchen chairs and cast-iron-framed tables, with polished flagstones in an area by the big inglenook fireplace, and red carpet elsewhere. Look out for the stuffed backside of a fox, seeming to leap into the wall; or you can browse memorable framed newspaper front pages, recording events such as Kennedy's assassination and the death of Churchill; alley skittles, cribbage, dominoes. Bar food might include tuscan bean soup (£3.50), mozzarella, tomato and pesto bruschetta (£4.75), penne with gorgonzola, walnuts and peas (£4.95/£8.95), field mushroom and spinach lasagne (£8.25), smoked haddock fishcakes (£8.75), grilled rump steak with red wine sauce, mushroom and tarragon butter (£9.95), and puddings such as lemon tart, chocolate and pear fondant and baked egg custard (£3.95). Well kept Hook Norton Best, Haymaker, Old Hooky and a monthly changing guest beer such as Fullers London Pride on handpump. Tables outside are in a pleasant spot under a vine-covered trellis. The pub is on the village road to George Washington's ancestral home (and is handy for Silverstone). *(Recommended by J D M Rushworth, R T and J C Moggridge, Patrick Hancock, Martin and Penny Fletcher, Susan and John Douglas, Jack Clarfelt, Gwyneth and Salvo Spadaro-Dutturi, Comus and Sarah Elliott, Mike and Sue Loseby, Rona Murdoch, Joy and Colin Rorke)*

Hook Norton ~ Tenants Jamie and Charlotte King ~ Real ale ~ Bar food (12-2, 6.30-9; 12.30-3 Sun; not Sun evening, Mon) ~ Restaurant ~ (01295) 760389 ~ Children in restaurant ~ Open 11-2.30(3 Sat), 6-11; 12-5 Sun; closed 25 Dec ~ Bedrooms: £40S/£60S

WOODNEWTON TL0394 Map 5

White Swan £

Main Street; back roads N of Oundle, easily reached from A1/A47 (via Nassington) and A605 (via Fotheringhay)

The unremarkable frontage of this friendly country pub hides a surprisingly capacious interior, where the main focus is on the dining area – pleasantly simple, decorated with a few otter pictures. The other end has a woodburner and space for drinkers, with well kept Adnams, Bass, Batemans, Otter Bright and a guest such as Charles Wells Bombardier on handpump, and perhaps local radio. It's worth going for lunch one day between Tuesday and Saturday, or in the evening between Tuesday and Thursday, during which times you can eat from their good value no bookings menu. Starters, which include soup, pâte and thai-style fishcake are all £3, main courses including battered cod, roasted vegetable lasagne or sirloin steak are £5.50, and puddings such as profiteroles with chocolate sauce or chocolate pie are £2.50. Other dishes might include mushroom stroganoff (£7.99), steak and ale pie (£8.99), and scampi in a creamy sauce (£11.99). The restaurant is no smoking, and service is cheerfully unruffled. There are tables and a boules pitch on the back lawn (league matches Tuesday evenings). *(Recommended by George Atkinson, David and Mary Webb)*

Free house ~ Licensees Susan and David Hydon ~ Real ale ~ Bar food (12-1.45(2.30 Sun), 7(6 Fri)-9) ~ Restaurant ~ (01780) 470381 ~ Children in restaurant ~ Open 12-2, 7(6 Fri)-11; 12-2.30, 6.30-11 Sat; 12-3.30 Sun; closed Sun evening, Mon

Lucky Dip

Besides the fully inspected pubs, you might like to try these Lucky Dips recommended to us and described by readers (if you do, please send us reports: www.goodguides.com).

Ashton [TL0588]

Chequered Skipper [the one NE of Oundle, signed from A427/A605 island]: Handsome thatched pub on chestnut-tree green of elegant estate village, light and airy open-plan layout with tables left and right, interesting changing real ales, reasonably priced food (not Mon) from baked potatoes and ciabattas to restauranty main courses, young friendly staff *(David and Brenda Tew, Michael and Jenny Back, Oliver and Sue Rowell)*

Aynho [SP5133]

☆ ***Cartwright Arms*** [Croughton Rd]: Small busy stone-built country inn, accent on good home-made food in nicely modernised beamed lounge and bar, well kept Hook Norton Best and Theakstons XB, helpful friendly staff, reasonably priced restaurant; a few tables in pretty corner of former coachyard, comfortable attractive bedrooms, nice village *(George Atkinson, Dr and Mrs A K Clarke, BB)*

☆ ***Great Western Arms*** [B4031 W, towards Deddington]: Unpretentious welcoming creeper-covered pub by what used to be station on main Oxford—Banbury rail line, good generous cheap food in roomy informal dining areas, clubby lounge with log fire, well kept Hook Norton Bitter and Mild, pleasant staff, interesting GWR memorabilia inc lots of steam locomotive photographs; small games area with darts and bar billiards, children's room; enclosed garden by Oxford Canal with moorings, flower-decked back courtyard *(Pete Baker)*

Badby [SP5559]

☆ ***Maltsters Arms*** [The Green]: Stone-built pub with light wood furniture in long beamed room, roaring fire each end, good reasonably priced food inc unusual dishes (several blackboards), well kept ales inc interesting guest beers, friendly attentive service; soft piped music, darts, hood skittles, fruit machine, TV; garden with terrace and new seats, well placed for walks on nearby Knightley Way; bedrooms *(CMW, JJW, George Atkinson)*

Barby [SP5470]

Arnold Arms: Recently refurbished and extended, with pleasant atmosphere, friendly licensees, landlord enthusiastic about his well kept ales such as Adnams Broadside, Tetleys, Thwaites Thoroughbred and Charles Wells Bombardier, good wine choice, reasonably priced traditional food from sandwiches to steaks, mixed grills and good old-fashioned puddings, no smoking area, games room with pool; garden with barbecues *(Andrew Crawford)*

Barnwell [TL0484]

☆ ***Montagu Arms*** [off A605 S of Oundle, then fork right at Thurning, Hemington sign]: Attractive unspoilt stone-built pub in pleasant streamside village, two bars with low beams, flagstones or tile and brick floors, not smart but warm, cosy and welcoming; well kept Adnams Bitter and Broadside and Flowers IPA and Original, good choice of interesting food running up to swordfish, hearty helpings, good puddings, log fire, neat back dining room; games room off yard, big garden with good well equipped play area, barbecue and camping; open all day wknd, comfortable bedrooms in separate block *(BB, Oliver and Sue Rowell)*

Blisworth [SP7253]

Royal Oak [off M1 junction 15, off A508; Chapel Lane/High St]: 17th-c thatched and beamed open-plan pub, carpeted no smoking dining areas off tiled bar, enjoyable home-made usual food from sandwiches up (also take-aways), well kept Adnams Broadside, Flowers, Hook Norton, Charles Wells Bombardier and a guest beer, hospitable licensees; darts, pool and skittles, may be piped music; garden with play area, near Grand Union canal, open all day Fri-Sun *(Kevin Thorpe)*

Boughton [SP7565]

Whyte-Melville [off A508 N of Northampton; Church St]: Pleasantly renovated, with reasonably priced food from good open sandwiches up, three or four real ales such as EverardsTiger and Greene King IPA, bare boards and carpeting, coal fire, beams, lots of brasses and Victorian pictures, friendly attentive service, piped music; spacious, but can get very busy lunchtime *(George Atkinson)*

Brackley [SP5836]

Manor [Manor Rd]: Well staffed tucked-away local, changing ale such as Greene King Ruddles County or Marstons Pedigree, pool, juke box *(Areola May)*

Brafield-on-the-Green [SP8258]

Red Lion [A428 5 miles from Northampton towards Bedford]: Largely stone-built village pub, comfortable banquettes and matching chairs in large extended bar and room off, no smoking dining room, good reasonably priced food choice, two real ales, good soft drinks choice, prompt attentive service; pool, games machine, TV or piped music *(CMW, JJW)*

Brixworth [SP7470]

Coach & Horses [Harborough Rd, just off A508 N of Northampton]: Welcoming old stone-built inn near Pitsford reservoir, good helpful staff, generous food from wide choice of good sandwiches to fresh fish and popular Sun lunches, well kept ales such as Adnams, Black Sheep and Marstons Pedigree, decent house wine, friendly helpful service, beams and lots of pictures, small no smoking restaurant; piped music; attractive village with famous Saxon church *(Gordon Neighbour, George Atkinson, Gerry and Rosemary Dobson)*

Buckby Wharf [SP6066]

☆ ***New Inn*** [A5 N of Weedon]: Simple welcoming pub with tables out on pleasant terrace by busy Grand Union Canal lock, friendly licensees, new furniture in several rooms radiating from central servery, inc small dining room with nice fire; good range of decent sensibly priced food, Greene King IPA and Old Speckled Hen and Marstons Pedigree *(LYM, George Atkinson)*

Bugbrooke [SP6757]

Wharf Inn [The Wharf; off A5 S of Weedon]: Spotless pub in super spot by canal, current landlord putting emphasis on big water-view restaurant, pleasant raised informal eating area and lounge bar too, lots of stripped brickwork, good choice of generous food from good value baguettes up, five well kept ales inc Frog Island, speedy friendly service; weekly quiz nights and monthly jazz; plenty of tables on waterside lawn *(George Atkinson, Ted George, Gerry and Rosemary Dobson)*

Bulwick [SP9694]

☆ ***Queens Head*** [just off A43 Kettering—Duddington]: Very friendly new licensees, shortish changing choice of good interesting fresh food from sandwiches and unusual starters or snacks to popular Sun roasts and imaginative puddings in neat and unpretentious partly beamed bar, small fire each end, well kept ales such as Adnams, Fullers London Pride, Greene King, Hancocks HB and Marstons Pedigree; live folk music Mon, when menu may be limited; nice garden, attractive village, interesting church, red kites may be seen from Southwick road *(Anthony Barnes, BB, JWAC, Lorraine and Fred Gill)*

Burton Latimer [SP9075]

Olde Victoria [Bakehouse Lane]: Spacious mix of genuine and contrived old-world inc ornate gas lamps and lots of china, with nice atmosphere, well kept Greene King Abbot, good friendly staff, enjoyable food from sandwiches and baked potatoes up, comfortable raised back restaurant area; quiet piped music; garden and terrace with picnic-sets under cocktail parasols *(Stephen, Julie and Hayley Brown)*

Castle Ashby [SP8659]

☆ ***Falcon***: Stone walls and hop-hung dark beams in 16th-c cellar bar down tricky steps from smart hotel in attractive preserved village, limited choice of enjoyable bar food inc imaginative sandwiches, welcoming landlord, real ale, open fire; restaurant overlooking pretty garden, nicely decorated bedrooms, good breakfast *(Colin and Janet Roe)*

Chapel Brampton [SP7366]

Spencer Arms [Northampton Rd]: Very big beamed chain family dining pub, good value straightforward food, welcoming staff, Tetleys; piped music *(Stephen, Julie and Hayley Brown)*

Collyweston [SK9902]

Collyweston Slater [A43]: Stone-built stepped former cottage row, enjoyable reasonably priced freshly made food from ploughman's to Sun lunch and curry night, three real ales, good house wines and choice of soft drinks, slate-mining memorabilia, comfortable restaurant; games room with pool, darts, machine and TV, quiz night; children welcome, picnic-sets outside, four good bedrooms (double-glazed – traffic all night) with own bathrooms *(Mrs Jane Basso, CMW, JJW)*

Daventry [Sp5762]

Coach & Horses [Warwick St]: Former coaching inn, lovely hanging baskets in old coach entry to garden with picnic-sets and play area, four real ales, lunchtime food; pool, quiet piped music *(CMW, JJW)*

Plume of Feathers [Market Sq/New St]: Lots of brick, brasses and woodwork giving countrified feel, banknotes on low ceiling over bar, big real fire, three real ales, friendly landlord, reasonably priced lunchtime food, good cheap coffee; quiet piped music, pool, games machine, TV *(CMW, JJW)*

Eastcote [SP6753]

☆ ***Eastcote Arms*** [village signed from A5 3 miles N of Towcester]: Friendly and unpretentious village pub, traditional furnishings and cottagey décor, well kept ales such as Adnams, Bass, Friary Meux Best, Fullers London Pride and Greene King IPA, decent wines and malt whiskies, honest food, no smoking restaurant (Fri/Sat night, good Sun lunch), two flame-effect gas fires, often a barn owl around at lunchtime, new hood skittles in small back bar; unobtrusive piped music; picnic-sets and other tables out behind with roses, geraniums and so forth around the neat lawn, peaceful village *(Susan and John Douglas, George Atkinson, Gerry and Rosemary Dobson, Peter Batty, LYM, Colin Mason)*

Easton on the Hill [TF0104]

Exeter Arms [Stamford Rd]: Comfortable and attractive country pub/restaurant, clean and well kept, with some emphasis on fish; John Smiths and Theakstons, lots of wines, friendly service, live music Thurs (mainly jazz) *(Peter J Holmes)*

Evenley [SP5834]

☆ ***Red Lion*** [The Green]: Small beamed local very popular lunchtime for enjoyable food from good sandwiches to plenty of grills, fish and vegetarian, also Sun lunches, Banks's, Marstons Pedigree and a guest such as Morrells Varsity, decent coffee and choice of wines, friendly attentive service, inglenook, some flagstones, cricketing books and other memorabilia; piped music; opp attractive village cricket green, tables out on lawn *(George Atkinson, Marjorie and David Lamb)*

Eydon [SP5450]

☆ ***Royal Oak*** [Lime Ave; village signed off A361 Daventry—Banbury, and from B4525]: Old-fashioned extended late 17th-c local, several rooms with stripped stone and assorted old furnishings on polished flagstones, thriving informal atmosphere, enjoyable food (not Sun evening or Mon), Hook Norton Best, Theakstons Black Bull and Timothy Taylors Landlord, friendly young staff, daily papers; darts, hood skittles and TV; children welcome, tables out in partly covered back courtyard, picnic-sets in front *(Lucy Pellerin, LYM, Michael Jones, George Atkinson, CMW, JJW, Richard Joyce)*

Gayton [SP7054]

Queen Victoria [High St]: Spotless smartly refurbished village pub, several areas off central bar, light panelling, beams, lots of pictures, books and woodburner, decent food from baguettes up, Theakstons Best, good wine choice; may be piped music *(LYM, Gerry and Rosemary Dobson, George Atkinson)*

Grafton Regis [SP7546]

☆ ***White Hart*** [A508 S of Northampton]: Thatched pub in thatched village, several linked rooms, good home-made bar food (not Sun evening) inc several good soups, also bookings-only restaurant with open fire – very popular for flamboyant chef's good reasonably priced imaginative cooking; well kept Greene King IPA, Abbot and Ruddles County, lots of decent wines by the glass, friendly hard-working helpful staff, pensive african grey parrot; piped music; good-sized garden (food not served there); cl Mon exc bank hols *(Dr Alan Sutton, George Atkinson, BB)*

Great Addington [SP1159]

Hare & Hounds [Main St]: Small friendly L-shaped pub with cheerful landlord, good value interesting lunches (worth booking), very friendly staff, Charles Wells Eagle and Bombardier with a guest such as Wychwood *(David and Mary Webb, George Atkinson)*

Great Billing [SP8162]

Elwes Arms [High St]: Thatched stone-built 16th-c village pub, two bars, wide choice of good value food inc tempting Sun lunch, three well kept real ales; darts, machines, TVs, may be piped music, Thurs and Sun quiz nights, no dogs; children welcome, wheelchair access to top level, garden with play area *(CMW, JJW)*

Great Brington [SP6664]

☆ ***Fox & Hounds/Althorp Coaching Inn*** [off A428 NW of Northampton, nr Althorp Hall]: Attractive thatched stone-built pub with fine log fires in quaint low-beamed flagstoned bar with lots of bric-a-brac, Greene King IPA and Abbot and several interesting guest beers, decent wines, bar food (not Mon-Weds or Sun evening) from pricy baguettes to good Sun lunch, friendly service, small restaurant with no smoking area; games room down steps, piped music (live Tues/Weds); children welcome, open all day wknds and summer, tables in attractive courtyard and side garden with play area, nice setting *(George Atkinson, Peter and Giff Bennett, LYM, Martin and Penny Fletcher, Gerry and Rosemary Dobson, Robert and Catherine Dunster)*

Great Houghton [SP7958]

White Hart [off A428 Northampton—Bedford; High St]: Attractive and pleasantly unpretentious thatched pub, enjoyable freshly cooked food, friendly helpful staff *(Anthony Barnes)*

Greens Norton [SP6649]

Butchers Arms [High St]: Large comfortably refurbished lounge, four well kept changing ales, some emphasis on wide choice of good value food, service attentive if not quick; separate bar (can be rather smoky), games room with darts, pool, machines and TV, piped pop music; disabled access, picnic-sets out in front, pretty village near Grafton Way walks *(Edward Leetham, CMW, JJW)*

Hackleton [SP8055]

White Hart [B526 SE of Northampton]: Comfortable welcoming 18th-c country pub with dining area down corridor, stripped stone, beamery and brickwork, illuminated well, brasses and artefacts, soft lighting, fresh flowers, good value generous fresh food inc local produce, well kept Fullers London Pride and Greene King IPA and Ruddles, split-level flagstoned bar with flame-effect fire, pool and hood skittles; quiz Sun; children welcome, garden with picnic-sets and goal posts, open all day *(CMW, JJW, Mr Biggs)*

Hardingstone [SP7657]

Sun [High St]: Busy open-plan pub with real ales such as Courage Directors, Theakstons and Youngers, wide food choice, some 18th-c beams and stripped stone; piped music, games machine, TV, no dogs; children welcome, barn bar/function room, tables on attractive back terrace with play area *(CMW, JJW)*

Harlestone [SP7064]

☆ ***Dusty Fox*** [A428, Lower Harlestone]: Nicely redone Vintage Inn, relaxed atmosphere, small front bar and lounge, pleasant furnishings, hops on beams, local photographs, mainly no smoking dining area and conservatory-style barn; enjoyable food all day from separate servery, some nouvelle-ish dishes, Bass and Tetleys, decent wines, friendly speedy highly attentive service, two log fires, no piped music; children welcome, some tables outside, open all day *(Dr Alan Sutton, CMW, JJW, George Atkinson, Tim and Ann Newell)*

Harrington [SP7779]

Tollemache Arms [High St; off A508 S of Mkt Harboro]: Pretty thatched Tudor pub in quiet stone-built village, compact red-ceilinged bar with log fire and cask seats, wide food choice from sandwiches and baguettes up, pleasant partly stripped stone eating area with books and bric-a-brac, well kept ales such as Badger Tanglefoot, Ridleys Rumpus and Charles Wells Eagle and Bombardier, cheap house wines, friendly if not speedy service, candlelit restaurant; piped pop music may obtrude; children welcome, small back garden with country views, clean and attractive bedrooms *(George Atkinson, BB)*

Hartwell [SP7850]

Rose & Crown [off A508 or B526 S of Northampton]: Popular early 18th-c pub with pleasant views, two or three real ales, good choice of other drinks, real fires, daily papers, reasonably priced food, no smoking dining area, games room with pool; quiet piped music,

Please use this card to tell us which pubs *you* think should or should not be included in the next edition of *The Good Pub Guide*. Just fill it in and return it to us – no stamp or envelope needed. Don't forget you can also use the report forms at the end of the *Guide*, or report through our web site: www.goodguides.com

ALISDAIR AIRD

In returning this form I confirm my agreement that the information I provide may be used by The Random House Group Ltd, its assignees and/or licensees in any media or medium whatsoever.

YOUR NAME AND ADDRESS (BLOCK CAPITALS PLEASE)

☐ *Please tick this box if you would like extra report forms*

REPORT ON *(pub's name)*

Pub's address

☐ **YES MAIN ENTRY** ☐ **YES *Lucky Dip*** ☐ **NO don't include**

Please tick one of these boxes to show your verdict, and give reasons and descriptive comments, prices etc

☐ Deserves FOOD award ☐ Deserves PLACE-TO-STAY award

REPORT ON *(pub's name)*

Pub's address

☐ **YES MAIN ENTRY** ☐ **YES *Lucky Dip*** ☐ **NO don't include**

Please tick one of these boxes to show your verdict, and give reasons and descriptive comments, prices etc

☐ Deserves FOOD award ☐ Deserves PLACE-TO-STAY award

The Good Pub Guide

2

The Good Pub Guide
FREEPOST TN1569
WADHURST
E. SUSSEX
TN5 7BR

games machine *(CMW, JJW)*

Hellidon [SP5158]

☆ ***Red Lion*** [Stockwell Lane, off A425 W of Daventry]: Good popular Tues/Weds OAP lunch in small wisteria-covered inn, clean, cosy and comfortable, wide choice of other good value food too inc some interesting dishes, softly lit no smoking stripped stone dining area with lots of hunting prints, well kept Greene King IPA, Hook Norton Best and Worthington BB, two farm ciders, very helpful cheerful staff, comfortable lounge, friendly retriever by woodburner in bar; piped music, games room with hood skittles and TV; picnic-sets in front, beautiful setting by green of unspoilt village, good bedrooms, windmill vineyard and pleasant walks nearby *(CMW, JJW, George Atkinson, P Tailyour, J J and B Dix)*

Holcot [SP7969]

White Swan [Main St; nr Pitsford Water, N of Northampton]: Attractive partly thatched two-bar village local with hospitable series of rooms, well kept Hook Norton and other ales from thatched servery, good fair-priced food (not Sun-Weds evenings) from baked pots up inc good value Sun lunch, cheery service, games room with darts, skittles and pool; open all day Sun and summer, children welcome *(Brian Root)*

Kettering [SP8777]

Piper [Windmill Ave]: Theakstons and guest beers (three or four a week), always well kept; quite handy for Wicksteed Park *(Rob Walker)*

Kings Sutton [SP4936]

Butchers Arms [Whittall St]: Well kept village pub with buoyant local atmosphere, full range of well kept Hook Norton ales, decent reasonably priced food; in neat sandstone village easily spotted by spire *(Giles Francis)*

White Horse [The Square]: Attentive new licensees doing good food in neat surroundings; well kept Wadworths 6X *(Anne P Heaton)*

Kislingbury [SP6959]

Old Red Lion [High St, off A45 W of Northampton]: New owners doing wide choice of enjoyable fresh food inc game and fresh fish, well kept Bass and Greene King IPA, good choice of other drinks, friendly service, bar, lounge/restaurant (lower part no smoking) and games room; piped music; picnic-sets on terrace with swings and slide *(R M Corlett, Ted George, David Robinson)*

Little Harrowden [SP8671]

☆ ***Lamb*** [Orlingbury Rd/Kings Lane – off A509 or A43 S of Kettering]: Neatly kept 17th-c pub, cosy three-level lounge with log fire, brasses on beams, intimate no smoking dining area, hard-working jovial landlord, modest choice of good fresh food (not Sun evening) inc Sun lunch and OAP discount Tues and Thurs lunchtime, well kept Charles Wells Eagle and Bombardier and a guest beer, decent coffee: quiet piped music, small public bar, games room with darts and hood skittles, theme and quiz nights; children welcome, small terrace and garden, delightful village *(David and Mary Webb)*

Loddington [SP8178]

Hare [Main St]: Renamed and thoroughly refurbished, with emphasis on wide choice of enjoyable food in two eating areas, one no smoking; small bar with well kept Adnams, Greene King IPA and Fullers London Pride or Youngs Special, decent house wines *(Stephen, Julie and Hayley Brown, Gerry and Rosemary Dobson)*

Lowick [SP9780]

☆ ***Snooty Fox*** [signed off A6116 Corby—Raunds]: Attractive and interesting two-room lounge with handsome 16th-c beams, log fire in huge stone fireplace, neat dining tables, enjoyable food from well filled baguettes up, Greene King IPA and Abbot and a guest such as Hook Norton Best or Ridleys IPA, helpful service, restaurant; piped music, live Fri, service can sometimes slow; disabled access, floodlit picnic-sets out on front lawn *(Michael and Jenny Back, LYM)*

Maidwell [SP7477]

☆ ***Stags Head*** [A508 Northampton—Market Harborough]: Attractively refurbished as light and airy dining pub by attentive new owners, four sections (two no smoking), enjoyable fresh food, good friendly service, nice pubby atmosphere in small comfortable beamed front bar with log fire and well kept Fullers London Pride, Greene King and Hook Norton Best; tables on back lawn with paddock beyond, bedrooms *(Stephen, Julie and Hayley Brown, P Tailyour, George Atkinson)*

Mears Ashby [SP8466]

☆ ***Griffins Head*** [Wilby Rd]: Pleasantly refurbished country pub very popular for substantial OAP bargain wkdy lunches, also bargain midweek suppers and other enjoyable food from sandwiches to good value Sun roasts; smart front lounge, small dining room with no smoking area, cosy back locals' bar, attractive views and hunting prints, huge fireplace, friendly courteous service, well kept ales such as Everards Beacon, Frog Island Head in the Clouds and Greene King IPA; games room with darts, skittles and machine, piped music; children welcome, seats out in small garden, on edge of attractive thatched village *(Mary Morris, Eric Locker, George Atkinson)*

Milton Malsor [SP7355]

☆ ***Greyhound*** [2¼ miles from M1 junction 15, via A508]: Big busy but friendly Chef & Brewer, well refurbished in olde-worlde mode, lots of secluded areas, 15th-c beams, old pictures and china, pewter-filled dresser, candlelit pine tables, good log fire, well kept John Smiths, Theakstons Best and Old Peculier, good range of wines, wide choice of food all day from filled rolls up; piped music; open all day, well behaved seated children welcome, spreading front lawn with duck/fish pond *(George Atkinson, Pamela and Merlyn Horswell, Mrs G R Sharman, LYM, Stephen, Julie and Hayley Brown)*

Nassington [TL0696]

☆ ***Black Horse*** [Fotheringhay Rd – 2½ miles S of A1/A47 interchange W of Peterborough]: Civilised 17th-c beamed and panelled dining pub in nice village, splendid big stone fireplace, panelling, easy chairs and small settees in two rooms linked by bar servery, well kept real ales, good varied wine list, very attentive quick service; attractive garden, open all day summer wknds *(Peter H Stallard, LYM, Rona Murdoch)*

Northampton [SP7761]

Abington Park [Wellingborough Rd]: Large open-plan Victorian pub, several bars and restaurant, cheap lunchtime bar food, real ales, helpful staff, family room; piped music, games machines; picnic-sets outside, handy for cricket ground *(Dr and Mrs A K Clarke)*

Bold Dragoon [High St, Weston Favell; off A4500 Wellingborough Rd]: Wide range of well kept reasonably priced beers, enjoyable food, no smoking conservatory restaurant; terrace and garden *(Gerry and Rosemary Dobson)*

☆ ***Britannia*** [3¾ miles from M1 junction 15; Old Bedford Rd (off A428)]: Rambling refurbished Chef & Brewer with massive beams, mix of flagstones and carpet, attractive 18th-c kitchen, three or four real ales, wide choice of decent food all day from baguettes up, polite attentive young staff, no smoking area, conservatory; may be piped jazz or light classics, Tues quiz night; picnic-sets by River Nene, open all day *(Dr Alan Sutton, LYM, CMW, JJW)*

Fox & Hounds [Harborough Rd, Kingsthorpe (A508)]: Spacious pub recently smartened up, popular for wide range of all-day food (bargains 2-6), raised no smoking area *(George Atkinson)*

Malt Shovel [Bridge St (approach rd from M1 junction 15); best parking in Morrisons opp back entrance]: Long pine and brick bar opp Carlsberg Brewery, well kept Banks's, Frog Island Natterjack, Fullers London Pride, Tetleys and several interesting changing guests inc a Mild, Rich's farm cider, Belgian bottled beers, about 50 malt whiskies, country wines, occasional beer festivals, daily papers, good value home-made usual food from hot baguettes up lunchtime and early evening (not Sun, can take a while), breweriana, open fire, darts, live music Weds; piped music and/or mobile phones may be obtrusive, can get smoky; picnic-sets on small back terrace *(CMW, JJW, Bruce Bird, Stephen, Julie and Hayley Brown)*

Moon on the Square [The Parade, Market Pl]: Popular Wetherspoons, with some café-style furnishings, masses of books, around nine real ales from long bar, good value prompt food all day inc bargains, good coffee, efficient staff patient with old folk, steps up to partly no smoking back conservatory (and stairs up to lavatories); no music, open all day *(Ted George)*

Old House at Home [Wellingborough Rd]: Nicely kept and welcoming, with well kept real ales and interesting brickwork *(Dr and Mrs A K Clarke)*

Wig & Pen [St Giles St]: L-shaped pub under new licensees, big chandelier and panelling, plain cheap lunchtime pub food, four well kept ales, real fire; piped music, TV, machines, entertainment most nights – popular with young people; two sets of steps up to tables in attractive heated back courtyard, open all day *(Ted George, CMW, JJW)*

Orlingbury [SP8572]

Queens Arms [signed off A43 Northampton—Kettering, A509 Wellingborough—Kettering; Isham Rd]: Stone-built pub with super choice of changing well kept ales in sensibly varying strengths, large comfortable airy lounge with banquettes, stools and side no smoking area, wide choice of good fresh food in bar and evening restaurant, good atmosphere; may be piped music; nice garden with play area, open all day wknds *(Gerry and Rosemary Dobson, Peter D B Harding)*

Oundle [TL04887]

Angel [St Osyths Lane]: Clean and friendly, with bargain food; very busy Thurs market day *(David and Mary Webb)*

Rose & Crown [Market Pl]: Mansfield real ales, armchairs, sofas and lots of pictures in friendly stripped-stone beamed front bar, good imaginative food in back conservatory, fine view of superb church from suntrap back terrace *(George Atkinson, Guy Vowles)*

Ravensthorpe [SP6670]

Chequers [Chequers Lane]: Spotless refurbished beamed pub with wide range of good value bar food, well kept Greene King IPA, Jennings, Thwaites and a guest beer, good service, mainly no smoking restaurant (not Sun night or Mon/Tues – best to book wknds); TV, fruit machine, piped music, monthly quiz night; open all day Sat, quiet garden with terrace and play area *(Gerry and Rosemary Dobson)*

Rothwell [SP8181]

Rowell Charter [Sun Hill (A6)]: Ancient pub with two open fires, friendly service, unusual range of up to eight consistently well kept beers, wide choice of home-made food *(Stephen, Julie and Hayley Brown)*

Rushden [SP9566]

Station Bar: Not a pub, but part of station HQ of Rushden Historical Transport Society (non-members can sign in), restored in 1940s/60s style, with real ales such as Archers Velvet, Fullers London Pride, Moor Withy Cutter, RCH Pitchfork, Oakham Helterskelter and Wye Valley Brew 69 and Dorothy Goodbodys Stout, enamelled advertisements, one bar stool (home of station cat); authentic waiting room with piano, also museum and summer trains *(P Abbott)*

Rushton [SP8482]

Thornhill Arms [Station Rd]: Pleasantly refurbished rambling dining pub prettily set opp attractive village's cricket green, wide choice of good value food from sandwiches up inc OAP bargain lunch in several neatly laid out dining areas (one no smoking) inc smart high-beamed back restaurant, welcoming helpful service, well kept Courage Directors and Greene King, relaxed comfortable atmosphere, open fire; bedrooms *(Graham and Lynn Mason, DC, W W Burke, Pat and Derek Roughton)*

Sibbertoft [SP6782]

☆ ***Red Lion*** [Welland Rise, off A4303 or A508 SW of Market Harborough]: Cosy and civilised recently extended dining pub, lounge tables set for generous food with good veg selection, well kept ales such as Adnams Best, Everards Tiger and Greene King Old Speckled Hen, decent wines, welcoming landlord, good service, magazines, comfortably cushioned wall seats, some dark panelling, attractive no smoking beamed dining room, covered tables outside; cl Mon/Tues lunchtimes, two self-contained holiday flats *(Gerry and Rosemary Dobson, George Atkinson, P Tailyour)*

Stoke Bruerne [SP7450]

☆ *Boat* [3½ miles from M1 junction 15 – A508 towards Stony Stratford then signed on right; Bridge Rd]: Busy pub in nice spot by beautifully restored lock opp British Waterways Museum and shop; cheerful landlord and friendly staff, nice little character flagstoned bar by canal though main focus is modernised central-pillared back lounge without the views (children allowed in this bit), tables by towpath; well kept ales such as Adnams, Banks's, Marstons Pedigree and a guest such as Mansfield Mild or Thwaites; hood skittles; bar snacks, OAP wkdy bargain lunches, no smoking restaurant and all-day tearooms, pub open all day summer Sats, canal boat trips *(G W A Pearce, Norma and Keith Bloomfield, George Atkinson, Ian Phillips, Roger and Debbie Stamp, V Green, Kevin Thorpe, LYM)*

Thorpe Mandeville [SP5344]

Three Conies [off B4525 E of Banbury]: Stone-built 17th-c dining pub under friendly newish tenants, bar food from baguettes to good fish, flagstoned bar, cheerful modern colours and décor celebrating Englishness from King Arthur on, well kept Hook Norton beers; children welcome, tables on terrace and spacious back lawn *(Anne P Heaton, LYM, Comus and Sarah Elliott, Ted George)*

Towcester [SP6654]

Peggottys [Fosters Booth (A5 3m N)]: Bar/restaurant rather than pub, but has changing well kept ales such as Batemans XB and Everards Beacon, wide range of good value food from sandwiches to full meals inc popular Sun lunch, genial landlord, welcoming service, light and airy flagstoned room with settees and armchairs as well as table seating, also no smoking restaurant and snug *(George Atkinson, Gerry and Rosemary Dobson)*

Saracens Head [Watling St W]: Substantially modernised coaching inn with interesting *Pickwick Papers* connections, high windows in thick walls and reworked cavernous fireplace in comfortable carpeted partly no smoking L-shaped lounge and dining area, Greene King IPA or Old Speckled Hen, neat efficient staff, bar food from baked potatoes up; Victorian dining room in hotel part across courtyard, gents' down steep steps; children given their head, well equipped bedrooms *(LYM, Gerry and Rosemary Dobson, George Atkinson, Christopher Hayle)*

Wadenhoe [TL0083]

☆ *Kings Head* [Church Street; village signposted (in small print) off A605 S of Oundle]: Beautifully placed two-bar 17th-c country pub with picnic-sets on sun terrace and among trees on big stretch of grass by River Nene, pretty village; solid pine furniture, enjoyable food, well kept Adnams Bitter and Broadside and Badger IPA, good selection of books, no smoking areas, beamed dining room, games room with skittles; children in eating areas, has been cl Mon lunchtime *(Michael Tack, Patricia Beebe, Eric Locker, J Hale, Sir Clive Rose, LYM, John Saul)*

Walgrave [SP8072]

Royal Oak [Zion Hill, off A43 Northampton—Kettering]: Old ironstone building with well kept Adnams, Youngs and a couple of interesting guest beers, wide choice of food (not Sun evening) inc wkdy OAP lunches and some interesting dishes, friendly attentive landlord, bar and dining lounge split into smaller areas, no smoking area, good coffee; may be piped music; children welcome, tables outside, play area *(CMW, JJW, George Atkinson)*

Weedon [SP63259]

Crossroads [3 miles from M1 junction 16; A45 towards Daventry; High St, on A5 junction]: Plush and spacious, now a Premier Lodge hotel, enjoyable sensibly priced food in well divided beamed bar and dining area, friendly service, real ales such as Timothy Taylors Landlord; piped jazz or classical music; attractive gardens down to river, comfortable bedroom block *(George Atkinson, LYM)*

Globe [High St; junction A5/A45]: Attractive, tidy and roomy hotel with with well cooked fresh food in good-sized helpings, friendly obliging staff, well kept changing beers, log fire, restaurant – open for coffee from breakfast on; picnic-sets outside, bedrooms *(George Atkinson)*

☆ *Narrow Boat* [Stowe Hill (A5 S)]: Very popular in summer for spacious terrace and big garden overlooking canal, barbecues; plain décor with canal prints, low bar tables, high-raftered back restaurant extension with canal views, two no smoking rooms, enjoyable food from ciabatta sandwiches to popular good value Sun lunch and tempting puddings, friendly helpful service, well kept Charles Wells and occasional guest ales, open fire; fruit machine, skittles, quiet piped music; bedrooms in back motel extension, narrowboat hire next door *(LYM, George Atkinson, Roger and Pauline Pearce, Mary Morris, Gerry and Rosemary Dobson)*

Plume of Feathers [Bridge St/West St, Weedon Bec, off A5/A45]: Beams, stripped brickwork, pine furniture, candles and old books, very reasonably priced food cooked to order (not Sun evening), largely no smoking dining area, attentive service, three well kept real ales inc Greene King IPA and Charles Wells Eagle; quiz night, piped music (some live), TV, pool, hood skittles and games machines; children welcome, picnic-sets and play area in garden, canal and walks nearby *(CMW, JJW, Wendy and Bob Needham)*

Welton [SP5866]

☆ *White Horse* [High St; off A361/B4036 N of Daventry]: Friendly two-bar beamed village pub, cosy dining areas inc one no smoking, go-ahead young landlord doing choice of good value food, changing well kept ales such as one from Frog Island, Greene King Old Speckled Hen and Theakstons Black Bull, decent house wines, attentive service, big open fire, public bar with woodburner, darts, table skittles and pool room; attractively lit garden with play area, terrace and barbecue *(Peter Phillips)*

Weston [SP5846]

Crown [the one N of Brackley; Helmdon Rd]: Spacious no-frills 17th-c stone-built ex-farmhouse, log fires, beams and flagstones, welcoming family service, four well kept ales, good coffee, promptly served home-made food (not Sun evening), unusual long room (former skittle alley) with cubicle seating; pool room, darts alcove; bedrooms, handy for NT Canons Ashby and Sulgrave, cl Mon lunchtime and winter Sun evening *(Christopher Hayle)*

Whittlebury [SP6943]

Fox & Hounds [High St]: Cosy and friendly front bar area with real fires, back dining room with open kitchen, good value fresh food from lean rare beef baguettes up, real ales; children welcome, play area *(Mr and Mrs B J P Edwards)*

Wicken [SP7439]

Old White Lion [Deanshanger Rd]: Mix of carpets and bare boards, some ancient beams, some board ceilings, hat collection, plates, posters and lots of photographs, friendly newish licensees doing very wide choice of decent food from baguettes to bargain hot dishes, Courage Directors and Greene King Old Speckled Hen, front restaurant, back conservatory/games room; children welcome, picnic-sets in garden *(George Atkinson)*

Yardley Hastings [SP8656]

Red Lion [High St, just off A428 Bedford—Northampton]: Pretty thatched stone-built local under welcoming newish licensees, good value food (not Sun/Mon evenings) cooked by Italian landlord, well kept Charles Wells Eagle and Bombardier with a guest such as Adnams Broadside, decent wines, good coffee and range of soft drinks, friendly efficient service, cosy lounge with lots of pictures, interesting brass and copper; piped music, no dogs or credit cards; tables in garden *(CMW, JJW, George Atkinson, Marina Pearce)*

'Children welcome' means the pub says it lets children inside without any special restriction. If it allows them in, but to restricted areas such as an eating area or family room, we specify this. Some pubs may impose an evening time limit.

Northumbria (County Durham, Northumberland and Tyneside)

Under friendly new licensees and doing good food that looks to be heading for a Food Award, the Fox & Hounds at Cotherstone makes a welcome return to these pages, after an absence of some years. Four entirely new main entries are the Victoria in Durham (delightfully unspoilt Victoriana, good beers and whiskeys), the restauranty Fox & Hounds in Newfield (a nice place for a good meal out, in an area where that must count as particularly good news), the unpretentious Ship at Newton-by-the-Sea (superb setting, good newish landlady), and the Anglers Arms at Weldon Bridge (quite a substantial hotel, with a very welcoming and attractive bar, and nice food and drink). Other pubs doing particularly well here are the welcoming old-fashioned Rat at Anick (a good all-rounder), the airy and civilised County in Aycliffe village (very good food), the Manor House Inn at Carterway Heads (gaining its Food Award and Place to Stay Award this year), the Dipton Mill Inn at Diptonmill near Hexham (an attractive country pub with good value food and good Hexhamshire beer – there's a connection to the brewery), the Queens Head at Great Whittington (good all round), the civilised and relaxed Morritt Arms at Greta Bridge (quite a favourite, with a lovely bar and charming bedrooms), the Cook & Barker Arms at Newton-on-the-Moor (very popular for imaginative food, and keeps a nice pubby bar), the friendly and well run Rose & Crown at Romaldkirk (another favourite, good imaginative food, nice bedrooms), the Seven Stars in Shincliffe (buoyant local atmosphere even when it's full of diners), and the friendly and homely Pheasant up at Stannersburn near Kielder Water (another well run all-rounder). The Rose & Crown at Romaldkirk, on fine form, gains the title of Northumbria Dining Pub of the Year. The Lucky Dip section at the end of the chapter has some rich pickings this year, with over 130 entries (57 of them new). Ones to note particularly are the Barrels in Berwick-upon-Tweed, Black Bull in Corbridge, Jolly Fisherman at Craster (a favourite for its crab sandwiches and soup, but just squeezed out of the main entries this year by all those newcomers), Dun Cow in Durham, Tankerville Arms at Eglingham, Northumberland Arms at Felton, General Havelock at Haydon Bridge, High Force Hotel, Carts Bog Inn at Langley on Tyne (missing its place in the main entries this year only through a lack of reports from readers), Apple at Lucker, Bridge Hotel, Cluny and Cooperage in Newcastle, Badger at Ponteland and Ridley Arms at

Stannington. Drinks prices in the area are lower than the national average, and there are quite a few local beers well worth looking out for, such as Castle Eden, Mordue, Durham, Northumberland, Hadrian & Border, Big Lamp (see Lucky Dip entry for the Keelman, at Newburn), Wylam, Darwin and Hexhamshire.

ALLENDALE NY8355 Map 10

Kings Head £

Market Place (B6295)

In the rambling square of a very attractive small town, this welcoming former coaching inn dates from the early 18th c. Cosy inside, it's recently been redecorated, with lemon walls, navy curtains and a tartan carpet; the spacious bar/lounge has a lovely warming log fire and some interesting bric-a-brac. Hearty reasonably priced bar food could include soup (£1.60), sandwiches (from £1.75), fish and chips or beef and ale pie (£4.95), lasagne or venison sausage (£5.95), and half a roast duck with cherry sauce (£9.50), with blackboard specials such as cumberland sausage with onion sauce (£4.95), and grilled tuna steak (£5.95); puddings (£2.25). Their half a dozen real ales on handpump could include Jennings Bitter, Cockerhoop, Cumberland and Sneck Lifter along with a couple of monthly changing guests such as Timothy Taylors Landlord and Charles Wells Bombardier, all kept well in a temperature-controlled cellar; around 60 malt whiskies. Darts, dominoes, and piped pop music. It's popular with locals, and gets particularly busy on market days. There are good walks in the area, and the road through the valley is a fine scenic drive. *(Recommended by Patrick Hancock, Jack and Heather Coyle, Michael Doswell)*

Jennings ~ Tenants Tracy Thompson and Lenny Slater ~ Real ale ~ Bar food (12-2.30, 6-9) ~ Restaurant ~ (01434) 683681 ~ Children welcome ~ Folk/blues most Fri or Sat evenings ~ Open 11-11; 12-10.30 Sun; closed 25 Dec evening ~ Bedrooms: £24B/£45B

ALLENHEADS NY8545 Map 10

Allenheads Inn £

Just off B6295

You certainly won't run out of things to look at in this cheerfully run, welcoming pub. All available space on the walls, ceilings, and bar is covered by thousands of collectibles, and in the loosely themed rooms you can find stuffed animals, mangles, old radios, typewriters, long-silenced musical instruments, an engine-room telegraph, brass and copper bygones, a plastic lobster, a four-foot wooden chicken, brooms, birdcages and even shoes – the list is endless, and it's all well cared for. The games room (with darts, pool, cribbage, dominoes and an antique juke box) has perhaps the most effervescent collection, and the car club discs and number plates on the panelling echo the efforts by members of a classic car club to try to persuade their vehicles to wend their way up here. Tables outside are flanked by more hardware – the sort of machinery that wouldn't fit inside. The Forces room and the dining room are no smoking. Reasonably priced straightforwardly pubby food in hearty helpings includes sandwiches (from £1.65), vegetarian chilli or curry (£4.50), cod (£5), lasagne (£5.25), steak or chicken pie (£5.50), and puddings such as home-made rice pudding (from £2.50). They usually have well kept Greene King Abbot Ale and Yates Bitter along with a couple of guest beers such as Black Sheep and Timothy Taylors Landlord on handpump; decent coffee, real fire, piped music. They do good breakfasts. The pub is on the Sustrans C2C cycle route; it is particularly peaceful here in winter. *(Recommended by Michael Doswell, Kevin Thorpe, G D Marsh, Christopher J Darwent, Mike and Lynn Robinson, Brian Root)*

Free house ~ Licensee Stephen Wardle ~ Real ale ~ Bar food ~ Restaurant ~ (01434) 685200 ~ Children allowed away from main bar ~ Open 12-4, 7-11; 12-11 Fri/Sat; 12-10.30 Sun; closed 25 Dec ~ Bedrooms: £26.50B/£46B

ANICK NY9665 Map 10

Rat

Village signposted NE of A69/A695 Hexham junction

Warm, cosy and softly lit, this pleasantly unspoilt pub has a coal fire blazing in a blacked kitchen range, and lots to look at: antique floral chamber-pots hanging from the beams, china and glassware, maps and posters, framed sets of cigarette cards, and quite a lot of Laurel and Hardy memorabilia, from figurines to a signed photograph. Furnishings keep up the relaxed traditional mood, with brocaded chairs around old-fashioned pub tables. Besides the two small eating areas, a conservatory gives lovely views of the North Tyne valley, shared by the tables out on the terrace and in a charming garden, with dovecote, statues and even flowers sprouting unexpectedly from boots. The enjoyable straightforward home-made bar food is generously served and reasonably priced. It could include dishes such as soup (£2.20), hot sandwiches (from £3.50), ploughman's (£3.95), mince and dumplings (£5.80), beef and ale pie (£5.95), chicken in Pernod sauce (£6.50), scampi and good chips (£6.95), and mussels (£7.50), with blackboard specials such as fried tuna in tomato, garlic and basil sauce (£8.95) or half roast duck in Cointreau and orange sauce (£12.50); puddings such as apple and raspberry crumblecake. Served by the attentive and friendly landlady or helpful staff, well kept ales on handpump could be Greene King Old Speckled Hen and Ruddles County, John Smiths and a couple of guests such as Mordue Radgie Gadgie and Theakstons Black Bull; piped music, daily papers and magazines. *(Recommended by Dr Graham Thorpe, Mike and Lynn Robinson, John Foord, Michael Doswell, Jack and Heather Coyle, Andy and Jill Kassube, Pat and Stewart Gordon)*

Free house ~ Licensees Joan and Donald D'Adamo ~ Real ale ~ Bar food (not Sun evening in winter) ~ (01434) 602814 ~ Children welcome away from main bar ~ Open 11-3, 6-11; 12-3, 7-10.30 Sun

AYCLIFFE NZ2722 Map 10

County

The Green, Aycliffe village; just off A1(M) junction 59, by A167

Don't mistake this white pub, with its name emblazoned on the walls in big fancy script, for a roadside local – the high quality cooking brings diners here from far and wide. Skilfully cooked by the young chef/landlord using mostly local produce, the sensibly limited choice of reasonably priced bar food is served at lunchtime and in the early evening (until the bistro opens at 7pm). It might include soup (£3.75), open sandwiches (from £4.50), smoked salmon and scrambled egg muffin (£4.95), mushroom stroganoff (£6.95), cajun chicken (£7.50), pork and beer sausages with black pudding, mashed potato and onion gravy (£7.95), and chinese crispy beef with stir-fried green peppers, mushrooms and noodles in oyster sauce (£9.45). It's best to book for the evening bistro menu, which is more elaborate, including dishes such as crayfish tails with tarragon and lemon mayonnaise (£6.50), chargrilled tuna with spiced couscous and basil dressing (£13.45), roast lamb chump with a herb crust, chargrilled vegetables, gremolata mash and rosemary gravy (£13.95), and delicious puddings such as chocolate torte with Grand Marnier crème anglaise and chocolate and orange crème brûlée (£4.50). They also do specials such as king prawns fried in garlic and lemon juice (£6.95), and cajun spiced blue marlin (£11.50); everything is cooked fresh, so there might be a bit of a wait. Furnishings in the extended bar and bistro are fresh and modern, definitely geared to grown-up dining, and the minimalist décor gives a light and airy feel; the atmosphere is friendly and civilised. Four well kept real ales on handpump include Charles Wells Bombardier, John Smiths Magnet and a couple of guests from brewers such as

Northumberland and Greene King, and a good choice of wines by the glass; there may be piped music. Good swift service from the friendly young staff. The green opposite is pretty. *(Recommended by Jenny and Dave Hughes, Pat and Tony Martin, M Borthwick, Keith Mould)*

Scottish Courage ~ Tenant Andrew Brown ~ Real ale ~ Bar food (12-2, 6-9.30; 12-3 Sun) ~ Restaurant ~ (01325) 312273 ~ Children welcome ~ Open 12-3, 5.30(6.30 Sat)-11; 12-3 Sun; closed Sun evening, 25 and 31 Dec

BELFORD NU1134 Map 10

Blue Bell

Village signed off A1 S of Berwick; Market Place

This substantial and attractive old coaching inn is a pleasant place to take a break from the busy A1. The comfortable lounge bar has upholstered seats on the turkey carpet, coaching prints on the walls and a warming log fire, and the handsome counter was taken from the Theatre Royal in Newcastle; piped music, darts, pool, hood skittles, dominoes, juke box, TV and fruit machine. There's an extensive wine list, around 20 malt whiskies, and John Smiths on handpump; service is attentive and welcoming. A decent selection of tasty bar food includes sandwiches (from £2.75), garlic king prawns with lemon mayonnaise (£4.25), tomato, feta and basil omelette (£4.45), steak and kidney pie (£6.85), lambs liver with fried onions and bacon in red wine gravy (£6.95), and vegetable fajitas, siamese chicken with ginger and coconut or poached scottish salmon with black pepper and paprika (£7.95), with puddings (£3.75); children's meals (from £3.75). The garden restaurant is no smoking; there's a large garden. *(Recommended by Peter and Patricia Burton, Dr Paull Khan, David Carr, KN-R, Dr R G J Telfer, Michael Doswell, Mrs Jane Orbell)*

Free house ~ Licensee Paul Shirley ~ Real ale ~ Bar food ~ Restaurant ~ (01668) 213543 ~ Children welcome ~ Dogs allowed in bedrooms ~ Open 11-2.30, 6.30-12 (1 Sat); 11-2.30, 7-12 Sun ~ Bedrooms: £44B/£82S(£82B)

BLANCHLAND NY9750 Map 10

Lord Crewe Arms

B6306 S of Hexham

This fine old inn was originally part of the 13th-c guest-house of a Premonstratensian monastery, and you can eat in the attractive walled garden which was formerly the cloisters (before it became home for several distinguished families after the dissolution in 1536). Its tremendous age is evident everywhere. The narrow bar is housed in an unusual stone barrel-vaulted crypt, its curving walls being up to eight feet thick in some places. Plush stools are lined up along the bar counter and next to a narrow counter down the opposite wall, and there are two built-in wood banquettes at one end. They've Castle Eden on handpump, and darts and dominoes. Upstairs, the Derwent Room has low beams, old settles, and sepia photographs on its walls, and the Hilyard Room has an massive 13th-c fireplace once used as a hiding place by the Jacobite Tom Forster (part of the family who had owned the building before it was sold to the formidable Lord Crewe, Bishop of Durham). Bar food includes soup (£2.30), filled rolls (from £3.35), ploughman's (from £4.80), brie and broccoli pastry bake (£7.25), and sirloin steak (£10.75), with specials such as tagliatelle with cream, parma ham, mushrooms and cheese (£4.75), chicken breast stuffed with pâté and madeira sauce (£6.25), puddings (£3.50). The pub is in the heart of a lovely old stone village, which is separated from the rest of the world by several miles of moors, rabbits and sheep. *(Recommended by Anthony Longden, J Hale, Andy and Jill Kassube, Kevin Thorpe, Hazel and Michael Duncombe, Greta and Christopher Wells, Tracey and Stephen Groves)*

Free house ~ Licensees A Todd, Peter Gingell and Ian Press, Lindsey Sands ~ Real ale ~ Bar food ~ Restaurant ~ (01434) 675251 ~ Children welcome ~ Dogs welcome ~ Open 11-11.30; 12-10.30 Sun ~ Bedrooms: £80B/£110B

CARTERWAY HEADS NZ0552 Map 10

Manor House Inn

A68 just N of B6278, near Derwent Reservoir

Winning lots of praise from readers these days, this popular slate-roofed stone house serves good food all day on weekends and bank holidays. An enticing well prepared menu (with especially tasty sauces) includes good ham and lentil soup (£3.50), chicken liver pâté with onion marmalade (£3.95/£6.95), king prawns in lemon and dill butter (£4.95/£9.95), local smoked kippers (£4.30/£7.70), mediterranean vegetables with goats cheese en croûte (£7.50), lamb with blueberry, port and rosemary (£11), duck breast with black cherry, honey and ginger (£11.50), and beef fillet with claret and juniper berries (£14.95), with specials such as local stuffed trout (£8.95); puddings include raspberry and vanilla panna cotta and honey and ginger sponge (£3.50), and they do local cheese and biscuits (£3.95). Part of the restaurant (which has a large collection of jugs) is no smoking; welcoming service by helpful young staff. The locals' bar has an original boarded ceiling, pine tables, chairs and stools, old oak pews, and a mahogany counter. There's a woodburning stove in the comfortable lounge bar. Picture windows give fine views over moorland pastures. Well kept Charles Wells Bombardier, Courage Directors, Theakstons Best, and a guest from a local brewer such as Durham or Mordue on handpump (they do non-alcoholic beers too), farm cider, around 70 malt whiskies, and decent wines with about eight by the glass; darts, dominoes, TV and piped music (only in the bar). There are rustic tables out on a small side terrace and lawn. They do good breakfasts.
(Recommended by John and Sylvia Harrop, Peter and Patricia Burton, Andy and Jill Kassube, Michael Doswell, J F M and M West, Jack and Heather Coyle, John Oddey, John Poulter, Stephen, Julie and Hayley Brown, Graham Clarke)

Free house ~ Licensees Moira and Chris Brown ~ Real ale ~ Bar food (all day Fri-Sun and bank hols) ~ Restaurant ~ (01207) 255268 ~ Well behaved children welcome ~ Dogs allowed in bar and bedrooms ~ Open 11-11; 12-10.30 Sun; closed 25 Dec evening ~ Bedrooms: £33B/£55B

CHATTON NU0628 Map 10

Percy Arms

B6348 E of Wooller

This partly creeper-covered stone-built inn has an attractively lit and neatly kept bar with horse bits and brasses on beams, maps and country pictures on the walls, upholstered wooden wall seats, and cushioned farmhouse chairs and stools. Through a stone arch is a similar room with a woodburning stove. The public bar has darts, pool, dominoes, fruit machine, video game, a juke box and a TV. They keep Theakstons on electric pump, and they've around 30 malt whiskies; the piped music is fairly unobtrusive. The panelled dining room with its pretty plates on a delft shelf is attractive. Served by cheerful and efficient staff, straightforward bar food in large helpings includes soup (£2.45), lunchtime filled baguettes or baked potatoes (from £3.75), mushroom and pepper risotto (£5.95), steak and kidney pie or battered haddock (£6.95), chicken steamed with white wine in lime and tarragon sauce (£7.95), and fried duck breast with plum and hoi sin sauce (£9.95), with puddings such as sherry trifle (£3.25); children's meals (£3.25). There are picnic-sets on the small front lawn above the village road. Residents have the use of 12 miles of private fishing, where there may be salmon, sea trout or stocked rainbow trout. *(Recommended by Jack and Heather Coyle, Hans and Thelma Liesner, Jo and Iain MacGregor, Michael Doswell, Ann and Max Cross, Dr R G J Telfer, Dr Paull Khan, Joy and Peter Heatherley, Darly Graton, Graeme Gulibert, Mrs J Booth)*

Free house ~ Licensee Paul Trett ~ Bar food (12-2.30, 6-9.30) ~ Restaurant ~ (01668) 215244 ~ Children in family area and restaurant ~ Dogs allowed in bar ~ Open 11-3, 6-11; 12-3, 7-10.30 Sun ~ Bedrooms: £30S(£30B)/£60S(£60B)

COTHERSTONE NZ0119 Map 10

Fox & Hounds

B6277 – incidentally a good quiet route to Scotland, through interesting scenery

A cheerful bustling place, this simple 200-year-old country inn is in a pretty spot overlooking the village green. After what might be called rather a mixed spell, it now has good generous bar food, freshly prepared by the new landlady using lots of local ingredients including beef and lamb. Served in the L-shaped lounge, well presented dishes could include lunchtime ploughman's (£5.40), battered Whitby cod and tasty chips or crêpe filled with chicken, mushroom and tarragon (£5.95), with evening dishes such as fried scallops with lemon and parsley butter (£5), aubergine and cashew nut loaf with cucumber and mint salsa (£7.30), baked cod provençale (£9.50), roast duckling breast with apricot and orange sauce (£10.80), and baked rack of lamb with cranberry, port and orange (£11.90), while tempting puddings could be rich fruit cake served with Cotherstone cheese or fresh fruit fondue with hot chocolate sauce (£3.50); both of the dining rooms are no smoking. The beamed bar has a peaceful atmosphere and a good winter log fire, various alcoves and recesses, with comfortable furnishings such as thickly cushioned wall seats, and local photographs and country pictures on the walls. Black Sheep Best and Greene King Ruddles County on handpump, perhaps with a guest such as Hambleton, kept under light blanket pressure; the landlord is welcoming. Look out for the unusual lavatory attendant – an african grey parrot called Reva. There are good nearby walks, and the pub is fairly handy for the Otter Trust North Pennine Reserve. *(Recommended by Mrs Phoebe A Kemp, Michael Doswell, Phil Heys)*

Free house ~ Licensees Nichola and Ian Swinburn ~ Real ale ~ Bar food ~ Restaurant ~ (01833) 650241 ~ Children in restaurant ~ Open 12-2.30, 6.45-11(10.30 Sun); closed 25-26 Dec ~ Bedrooms: £40B/£60B

DIPTONMILL NY9261 Map 10

Dipton Mill Inn £

Just S of Hexham; off B6306 at Slaley, Blanchland and Dye House, Whitley Chapel signposts (and HGV route sign); not to be confused with the Dipton in Durham

Tucked away in a little hamlet by steep hills in a peaceful wooded valley, this little two-roomed pub is not easy to find, but it's worth making the effort if you like real ale. The chatty landlord is a brewer in the family-owned Hexhamshire Brewery, and so there's a good choice of their well kept beers: Hexhamshire Shire Bitter, Devils Water, Devils Elbow and Whapweasel are served on handpump, alongside a guest such as Hambleton Stallion; also two dozen malt whiskies, and Weston's Old Rosie cider. In summer, it's nice to head for the seats on the sunken crazy-paved terrace by the restored mill stream, or in the attractively planted garden with its aviary. Inside, the snug little bar is very relaxed and friendly, with dark ply panelling, red furnishings (and a new dark red carpet) and open fires. Freshly prepared by the landlady, the food is generous and good value, and might include well presented dishes such as soup (£1.75), sandwiches (from £1.60), ploughman's from a very good choice of 11 cheeses (from £4), and salads (£4.50), with specials such as ratatouille with couscous (£4.50), tomato, bean and vegetable casserole (£5.25), steak and kidney pie or haddock baked with tomato and basil (£5.40), and chicken breast in sherry sauce (£6.25); puddings such as syrup sponge and custard or chocolate cake (from £1.60). The recently redecorated back games room has darts, bar billiards, shove-ha'penny and dominoes. There are plenty of easy-walking footpaths nearby. *(Recommended by John Foord, Patrick Hancock, Mike and Lynn Robinson, J G Thorpe, Kevin Thorpe, JWAC, Tracey and Stephen Groves)*

Own brew ~ Licensee Geoff Brooker ~ Real ale ~ Bar food (12-2.30, 6.30(7.30 Sun)-8.30) ~ (01434) 606577 ~ Children welcome till 9pm ~ Open 12-2.30, 6-11; 12-4, 7-10.30 Sun; closed 25 Dec

DUNSTAN NU2520 Map 10

Cottage 🍷

Village signposted off B1339 Alnmouth—Embleton

Handily serving sandwiches and snacks all day, this large dining pub is in a quiet village not far from the sea, by an outstanding stretch of the Northumberland coast. The extensive low-beamed carpeted bar area is quite handsomely laid out, with stools, small chairs and wall banquettes around dimpled copper tables, some panelling and stripped brickwork, soft lighting, and quite a bit of bric-a-brac, including a fine model sailing ship on the mantelpiece of the substantial brick fireplace; piped music. Tasty bar food in large helpings might include sandwiches (from £3.45), soup (£2.45), smoked chicken breast with watercress and orange salad (£5.45), ramekin of pigeon pie (£5.75), chicken and leek crumble or fried lambs liver with white pudding and sausages (£6.95), aubergine bake, Craster crab cakes or steak and leek pie (£7.95), and sautéed pheasant breast with redcurrant jus (£10.95), with puddings such as tropical cheesecake (from £2.95); children's meals (£2.95). There's a good choice of reasonably priced wines, and they've well kept real ales from Belhaven and Wylam, and a changing guest such as John Smiths. The neatly dressed young staff are friendly and efficient, and the pub attracts a nice mix of locals and visitors (though it can be very quiet midweek out of season). You can eat in the bar, or in a pleasant well planted no smoking conservatory with café furnishings on its tiled floor; there's also a comfortable beamed medieval-theme restaurant. A games area has pool, darts, dominoes, a fruit machine and TV. Outside are white plastic tables and chairs on a flowery terrace by the conservatory, with some tables in a sheltered arbour; these look out on quite a stretch of lawn, and there's a children's adventure play area. The modern bedrooms overlook the garden. *(Recommended by Brian Root, Roy and Lindsey Fentiman, J A Hooker, Dr Paull Khan, M S Catling)*

Free house ~ Licensee Zoe Finlay ~ Real ale ~ Bar food (all day) ~ Restaurant ~ (01665) 576658 ~ Children welcome ~ Folk bands most Fri or Sats ~ Open 11 (12 Sun)-11 ~ Bedrooms: £35B/£63B

DURHAM NZ2742 Map 10

Victoria 🍷

Hallgarth Street (A177, near Dunelm House)

This down-to-earth cosy local is a treasure-house of Victoriana for all who like their pubs truly unspoilt. Built in the closing years of Queen Victoria's reign, it celebrates her life with lots of period prints and engravings, and staffordshire figurines of her and the Prince Consort. The layout too takes one straight back to 1899: three work-a-day rooms off a central bar, with mahogany, etched and cut glass and mirrors, colourful William Morris wallpaper over a high panelled dado, some maroon plush seats in little booths, some worn leatherette wall seats, long narrow leather-topped drinkers' tables, handsome iron and tile fireplaces for the coal fires, a piano – and some photographs and articles showing a very proper pride in the pub. Well kept local Darwins Ghost, Marstons Pedigree, McEwans 80/- and Theakstons Best alongside a frequently changing guest such as Mordue Workie Ticket on handpump, good cheap house wines, around 40 malts and a remarkable collection of 30 Irish whiskeys. In one room they've dominoes, a veteran space invaders game, a Trivial Pursuit machine and a TV; at lunchtime they do toasties (from £1). The pub is run with considerable individuality and has been in the same family for 27 years. The bedrooms are simple but pleasant and good value, and you get a hearty breakfast in the upstairs dining room. *(Recommended by the Didler, Eric Larkham, A Reeves, Pete Baker, Tracey and Stephen Groves, Oliver Drerup)*

Free house ~ Licensee Michael Webster ~ (0191) 386 5269 ~ Children welcome ~ Dogs welcome ~ Open 11.30-3, 6-11; 12.30-3, 7-10.30 Sun ~ Bedrooms: £40S(£40B)/£54S(£54B)

GREAT WHITTINGTON NZ0171 Map 10

Queens Head

Village signposted off A68 and B6018 just N of Corbridge

Well run by a friendly landlord, this simple but civilised stone inn is in an attractive and very neatly kept stonebuilt village surrounded by partly wooded countryside. The food is good, and aside from tasty lunchtime sandwiches (from £3.50), the bistro menu (which you can eat in the bar) could include home-made ravioli filled with seafood mousse and glazed with cheese sauce or smoked chicken, orange and hazelnut salad with mustard dressing (£5.95), honey-roast gammon with caramelised apples and rich madeira sauce or vegetable strudel with black bean and ginger sauce (£9.95), rack of lamb on rösti with garlic and rosemary jus (£13.95), and roast duck breast with bacon, pecan and mustard seed glaze with noodles (£14.95), with a few daily specials such as pot-roasted pheasant with mushroom, bacon and onion jus (£13.50), and puddings such as nougat ice cream on fruit coulis or sticky toffee pudding (£3.50); they do a reasonably priced two-course lunch (£8.95, not Sunday – when they do three courses for £13.95). The two comfortably furnished and neatly decorated beamed rooms have some handsome carved oak settles among other more modern furnishings, old prints and a collection of keys, and log fires; the one nearest the bar counter has a mural over its fireplace. The restaurant is no smoking. Very well kept Black Sheep Best, Hambleton Bitter and Queens Head (brewed for them by Hambleton) on handpump, 30 malt whiskies, and decent wines; perhaps unobtrusive piped music. There are six picnic-sets on the small front lawn. *(Recommended by Mike and Lynn Robinson, Peter and Patricia Burton, Michael Doswell, Colin McKerrow, RJH)*

Free house ~ Licensee Ian Scott ~ Real ale ~ Bar food (not Mon) ~ Restaurant ~ (01434) 672267 ~ Well behaved children in eating area of bar ~ Open 12-2.30, 6-11; 12-3, 7-10.30 Sun; closed Mon except bank hols

GRETA BRIDGE NZ0813 Map 10

Morritt Arms

Hotel signposted off A66 W of Scotch Corner

This civilised and characterful country inn is a lovely and comfortable place to stay, but even if you want just an enjoyable meal or a relaxing drink it's well worth stopping here too. The charming pubby bar is named after Charles Dickens, who stayed here in 1838 on his way to start his research for *Nicholas Nickleby*, and a jolly larger-than-life Dickensian mural runs round its walls. It was painted in 1946 by J V Gilroy (more famous for his old Guinness advertisements, six of which are displayed on the walls here too). There are also big windsor armchairs and sturdy plush-seated oak settles clustered around traditional cast-iron-framed tables, and big windows that look out on the extensive lawn. Flowers brighten up the rooms, and there are nice open fires; piped music. Well kept Black Sheep, Theakstons and Timothy Taylors Landlord on handpump along with a guest, quite a few malt whiskies, and a very extensive wine list with about two dozen by the glass; obliging professional staff. There's a proper old shove-ha'penny board, with raisable brass rails to check the lie of the coins, pool, cribbage and dominoes. Freshly prepared well presented bar food includes filled baguettes (from £2.95; there's a good coronation chicken one £3.75), soup (£3.50), steak and mushroom pie or fish and chips (£6.50), scampi or tasty ploughman's (£6.95), and braised lamb shank (£7.95). There's a more elaborate menu in the adjacent no smoking bistro, which has wood floors and wrought iron, and is densely hung with paintings and prints by local artists (which you can buy). There are some picnic-sets in the attractively laid out and fairly large garden, teak tables in a pretty side area looking along to the graceful old bridge by the stately gates to Rokeby Park, and swings, slide and rope ladder at the far end. *(Recommended by R L Gorick, Dr Paull Khan, Pat and Tony Martin, JHBS, Susan and John Douglas, Mr and Mrs J E C Tasker, Greta and Christopher Wells, Derek and*

Sylvia Stephenson, Jack and Heather Coyle, Peter Burton, Peter and Ruth Burnstone)

Free house ~ Licensees Peter Phillips and Barbara Johnson ~ Real ale ~ Bar food (12-3, 6-9) ~ Restaurant ~ (01833) 627232 ~ Children welcome ~ Dogs allowed in bar and bedrooms ~ Open 11-11; 12-10.30 Sun ~ Bedrooms: £59.50B/£83.50B

HALTWHISTLE NY7166 Map 10

Milecastle Inn

Military Road; B6318 NE – OS Sheet 86 map reference 715660

This 17th-c pub could hardly be more handy for visiting Hadrian's Wall so, although it's remotely set, it can get very busy – and it pays to get here early. The snug little rooms of the beamed bar are decorated mainly with brasses, horsey and local landscape prints and attractive dried flowers, and have two winter log fires; at lunchtime the small comfortable restaurant is used as an overflow. Two changing well kept real ales on handpump might include Northumberland Castles and Tetleys; they have a fair collection of malt whiskies, and a good wine list. Walkers are welcome (but no rucksacks allowed); no games or music. Bar food includes tasty lunchtime sandwiches (£3), ploughman's (£5.25), soup (£2.50), vegetable spring rolls (£3.75), vegetable curry (£5.75), breaded plaice (£6.25), and steak and kidney pie (£7.25), and daily specials such as shepherd's pie with cheese and leeks (£6.50), and smoked fish pie (£7.25). The tables and benches out in a pleasantly sheltered walled garden with a dovecote are popular in summer; there's a large car park nearby. *(Recommended by Paul Thompson, Anna Blackburn, Jenny and Dave Hughes, Michael Doswell, Andy and Jill Kassube, Mike and Wendy Proctor)*

Free house ~ Licensees Ralph and Margaret Payne ~ Real ale ~ Bar food ~ Restaurant ~ (01434) 321372/320682 ~ Children over 5 allowed if eating ~ Open 12-3, 6.30-11

HEDLEY ON THE HILL NZ0859 Map 10

Feathers (🍴)

Village signposted from New Ridley, which is signposted from B6309 N of Consett; OS Sheet 88 map reference 078592

Although the emphasis at this attractive old stone pub is on the home-made food, there's still a good pubby atmosphere in the three well kept turkey-carpeted traditional bars, with beams, open fires, stripped stonework, solid brown leatherette settles and old black and white photographs of local places and country folk working the land. They've well kept Boddingtons, Mordue Workie Ticket and two guest beers from brewers such as Big Lamp and Wylam on handpump; also decent wines, and around 30 malt whiskies. Darts, shove-ha'penny, table skittles, cribbage, and dominoes. The fairly short but interesting menu usually changes twice a week. Besides around five good vegetarian dishes such as curried carrot, parsnip and apple soup (£2.15), tortilla filled with spiced sweet potato and puy lentils or leek, mushroom, parsnip and almond croustade (£6.75), you might find chilli minced steak pancake (£6.75), smoked haddock and spinach pasta bake (£7.50), and morrocan lamb casserole with chickpeas, spices and apricots (£7.75); tempting puddings such as treacle tart and plum crumble with custard. Around Easter they hold a mini beer festival with over two dozen real ales, which ends with a barrel race on Easter Monday. From picnic-sets in front you can watch the world drift by. *(Recommended by Norman Stansfield, Mike and Lynn Robinson, Gwyneth and Salvo Spadaro-Dutturi, Patrick Hancock, Andy and Jill Kassube, RJH, Michael Doswell, Jenny and Dave Hughes, Peter Burton, C A Hall)*

Free house ~ Licensee Marina Atkinson ~ Real ale ~ Bar food (not wkdy lunchtimes or Mon except bank hols) ~ No credit cards ~ (01661) 843607 ~ Children in eating area of bar and family room till 9pm ~ Dogs welcome ~ Open 6-11; 12-3, 6-11 Sat; 12-3, 7-10.30 Sun; closed wkdy lunchtimes except bank hols and 25 Dec

We say if we know a pub allows dogs.

NEW YORK NZ3370 Map 10

Shiremoor Farm ★

Middle Engine Lane/Norham Road; from A19 going N from Tyne Tunnel, right into A1058 then next left signposted New York, then left at end of speed limit (pub signed); or at W end of New York A191 bypass turn S into Norham Road, then first right (pub signed)

There's a busy chatty atmosphere and a good mix of customers at this smartly relaxed dining pub, a splendid conversion of former derelict farm buildings. The wide blackboard choice of very good bar food is served all day, and could include hearty sandwiches (£1.95), fried filo parcels with goats cheese (£3.95), smoked chicken and waldorf salad (£5.95), steak pie or Mordue beer sausages (£5.95), scampi (£6.95), fried chicken supreme (£7.95), rack of lamb with rosemary and redcurrant sauce (£8.95), and chargrilled tuna steak (£9.95), with puddings such as banana and chocolate pudding with a brandy truffle or marbled chocolate cheesecake (from £2.95). The spacious interior is furnished with a charming mix of interesting and comfortable furniture, a big kelim on the broad flagstones, warmly colourful farmhouse paintwork on the bar counter and several other tables, conical rafters of the former gin-gan, a few farm tools, and good rustic pictures such as mid-West prints, big crisp black and white photographs of country people and modern Greek bull sketches. Gentle lighting in several well divided spacious areas cleverly picks up the surface modelling of the pale stone and beam ends. Well kept Mordue Workie Ticket, Timothy Taylors Landlord, Theakstons Best and a guest such as Batemans XXXB; decent wines by the glass. The no smoking granary extension is pleasant for families, and good electric heaters mean that the covered terrace is popular even in late autumn and early spring. *(Recommended by Michael Butler, David Carr, Mike and Lynn Robinson, Brian Taylor)*

Free house ~ Licensee C W Kerridge ~ Real ale ~ Bar food (12-10) ~ (0191) 257 6302 ~ Children welcome away from main bar ~ Open 11-11; 12-10.30 Sun

NEWCASTLE UPON TYNE NZ2563 Map 10

Crown Posada 🍺

The Side; off Dean Street, between and below the two high central bridges (A6125 and A6127)

If you're in Newcastle, you shouldn't miss this marvellously unspoilt place: it's the second oldest and one of the most architecturally interesting pubs in the city. The building is not the only attraction here, though; even when it's busy, you'll get a warm welcome from the friendly barmen, and the atmosphere is nice and chatty. From half a dozen handpumps, they serve superbly kept continually changing real ales from brewers such as Bass, Durham, Jennings and Mordue. A golden crown adds grandeur to an already imposing carved stone façade – as do the magnificent Pre-Raphaelite stained-glass windows. Inside has lots of architectural charm, such as an elaborate coffered ceiling, stained glass in the counter screens, a line of gilt mirrors each with a tulip lamp on a curly brass mount matching the great ceiling candelabra, and Victorian flowered wallpaper above the brown dado; below this are fat heating pipes – a popular footrest when the east wind brings the rain off the North Sea. It's a very long and narrow room making quite a bottleneck by the serving counter, and beyond that, a long soft green built-in leather wall seat is flanked by narrow tables. They don't do food, but at lunchtime you can get a sandwich with a packet of crisps for £1. There's a fruit machine, and an old record player in a wooden cabinet provides mellow background music when the place is quiet. Best to visit during the week when regulars sit reading the papers in the front snug; at the weekend it's usually packed. It's only a few minutes stroll to the castle. *(Recommended by John W Allen, Kevin Thorpe, Tracey and Stephen Groves, Peter and Patricia Burton, the Didler, David Carr, Mike and Lynn Robinson, Pete Baker, Eric Larkham, Stephen, Julie and Hayley Brown, Val Stevenson, Rob Holmes)*

Free house ~ Licensee Malcolm MacPherson ~ Real ale ~ No credit cards ~

(0191) 232 1269 ~ Well behaved children over 12 allowed ~ Dogs welcome ~ Open 11(12 Sat)-11; 7-10.30 Sun; closed Sun lunchtime

NEWFIELD NZ2033 Map 10

Fox & Hounds 🍷

Turn off A688 at 'Willington, Newfield' signpost, or off A690 in Willington, into aptly named Long Lane; Newfield signposted off this, then turn left at Queens Head into Stonebank Terrace

Decidedly a restaurant rather than a pub, this still keeps a pub layout with its serving bar in the single main room, and they do welcome you if all you want is a drink – there's a cosy carpeted ante-room with a three-piece suite in brown velour by an old cream-coloured kitchen stove in a high stone fireplace (good fires in winter). The appealing attractively priced food, though, is the reason for coming. It might include lunchtime baguettes (£3.50), scrambled eggs with smoked salmon and chorizo sausage or pasta with cannellini beans, roast aubergine and red pesto sauce (£4.95), and ground beef with red thai curry (£5.50), with more elaborate evening dishes such as smoked salmon with black pepper, lemon and olive oil (£4.95), tagine of pumpkin, squash, sweet potato and figs (£8.50), halibut steak with lime, dill, prawns and red onion butter (£11.50), and venison steak with orange, cranberry and red wine sauce (£13.50). The comfortable and gently lit no smoking main area has a polished wood-strip floor, with candles and flowers on the neatly laid tables all around its sides, big brass platters on its dark pink timbered walls, and mugs, tankards and whisky-water jugs hanging from beams skeined with fairy-lights. Big windows look down over steeply rolling countryside. The house wines are good; they do aim to keep a real ale on handpump, but may not always have one on; service is friendly and thoughtful. Saturday night gets fully booked well ahead. *(Recommended by Tony Hall, Melanie Jackson, Angela Smurthwaite)*

Free house ~ Licensee William Thompson ~ Bar food (not Mon) ~ (01388) 662787 ~ Open 12-3, 7-11; 12-3 (7-10.30 in summer) Sun; cl Sun evening in winter; closed Mon

NEWTON-BY-THE-SEA NU2424 Map 10

Ship

Village signposted off B1339 N of Alnwick; Low Newton – paid parking 200 metres up road on right, just before village (none in village)

Tucked into the top corner of a National Trust courtyard of low white-painted stone cottages, this simple refuge looks down over the sloping grassy square to the broad beach, and off-shore rocks packed with seabirds and often visited by seals. It's easy to see why the landlady, who never thought she'd want to run a pub, fell in love with the place; she's been here over three years now, and let's hope she stays for many more. The plainly furnished bare-boards bar on the right has nautical charts on its dark pink walls, beams and hop bines. In winter (when it's very quiet here) they have only one or two real ales, but in the summer they usually have Black Sheep, Hadrian & Border Farne Island and Northumberland Original well kept on handpump, with a guest such as Durham Prince Bishop; decent wines, an espresso machine (colourful coffee cups, good hot chocolate), and good soft drinks; daily papers too. Enjoyable lunchtime snacks include local crab sandwiches (£2.95), warm ciabattas with enterprising fillings (around £3.75), fishcakes and salad (£3.75), crab-filled stotties (£4.75), and ploughman's with local cheddar cheese (£5.50). You must book for the appealing evening meals: using fresh local produce, the short daily-changing menu could include toasted goats cheese with tomato and basil (£3.50), vegetarian pasta with tomato and basil sauce (£4.95), grilled haddock (£7.75), and venison steak with red wine and peppercorn sauce and stir-fried vegetables (£8.75); organic ice creams (£1.50). Service is welcoming and efficient, though queues can build on hot days; there may be piped music. Another simple room on the left has some bright modern pictures on stripped stone walls, and a woodburning stove in its stone fireplace. There are some tables out under cocktail parasols in the corner, among pots of flowers, and picnic-sets out on the grass. *(Recommended by Darly Graton, Graeme Gulibert, Michael Doswell, Ruth and Paul Lawrence, Geoffrey and Penny Hughes, Mike and Lynn Robinson, John Foord, Comus and Sarah Elliott, David Cooke)*

Free House ~ Licensee Christine Forsyth ~ Bar food (12-2, 7-8(not Tues-Thurs evenings in winter; not Sun or Mon evenings) ~ (01665) 576262 ~ Children welcome ~ Dogs welcome ~ Open 11-11; 12-3, 9(7 Fri)-11 winter wkdays, 11-4, 6.30-11 winter Sat, 12-4, 8-10.30 Sun in winter; closed Mon Nov-Feb

NEWTON-ON-THE-MOOR NU1605 Map 10

Cook & Barker Arms

Village signposted from A1 Alnwick—Felton

An inviting choice of imaginative food makes this bustling stone inn a popular place for dinner. Although the food is the main focus, there's still a good pubby atmosphere in the relaxing and unfussy long beamed bar, which has stripped, partly panelled walls, brocade-seated settles around oak-topped tables, brasses, a highly polished oak servery, and a coal fire at one end with a coal-effect gas fire at the other. A no smoking eating area has tables, chairs, an old settle, scrubbed pine furniture, and french windows leading on to the terrace; the top bar area is no smoking, too. Generous changing bar food might include sandwiches (from £2.75), broccoli and stilton soup (£3.50), warm pigeon salad (£4.95), smoked salmon and black pepper (£5), mushroom, broccoli and cauliflower bake (£5.95), salmon spring rolls with soy sauce (£6.50), duck confit (£7.95), braised lamb shank (£8.95), and puddings such as summer pudding (£3.95); they do a good value two-course lunch (£10, not Sunday), and their home-made bread is delicious. Well kept rotating ales on handpump include Black Sheep, Northumberland Secret Kingdom and Theakstons with a guest such as Northumberland Castles; they have local bottled beer, quite a few malt whiskies, an extensive wine list, and over 20 wines by the glass. *(Recommended by Adam and Joan Bunting, Dr R G J Telfer, Joy and Peter Heatherley, Stephen and Jean Curtis, Mike and Wendy Proctor, Karen and Graham Oddey, Jack and Heather Coyle, Jim Bush, Robin and Joyce Peachey, Paul and Annette Hallett)*

Free house ~ Licensee Phil Farmer ~ Real ale ~ Bar food (12-2, 6-9, not evenings 25 Dec or 1 Jan) ~ Restaurant ~ (01665) 575234 ~ Children welcome ~ Open 11-3, 6-11; 12-3, 6-10.30 Sun ~ Bedrooms: £39.95S(£39.95B)/£75S(£75B)

RENNINGTON NU2119 Map 10

Masons Arms

Stamford Cott; B1340 NE of Alnwick

A handy place to know about if you want to explore the nearby Northumbrian coast, this comfortable pub (now under new licensees) has comfortable, spotlessly clean bedrooms in an adjacent stable block, and they do good breakfasts too. There's a relaxed atmosphere in the thoughtfully modernised beamed lounge bar, which has wheelback and mate's chairs around solid wooden tables on the patterned carpet, plush bar stools, and lots of brass, pictures and photographs on the walls. The dining rooms (one is no smoking) have pine panelling and wrought-iron wall lights. Reasonably priced tasty bar food includes lunchtime sandwiches (from £2.75), home-made soup (£2.50), mushrooms in stilton sauce (£3.95), home-made Craster kipper pâté (£4.15), Italian sausage with basil and tomato sauce or spicy lentil lasagne (£6.75), game casserole (£7.25) and steaks (from £12.45), with daily specials such as scampi (£6.50) or pork, lemon and ginger casserole (£6.95), and puddings such as chocolate fudge gateau (from £2.95); their good value Sunday lunch is understandably popular (£5.50). Two weekly changing real ales on handpump might be Hadrian & Border and John Smiths; shove-ha'penny, dominoes, darts and piped music. Service is helpful and courteous. There are sturdy rustic tables on the little front terrace, surrounded by lavender. Only children over five are allowed to stay overnight; they have a kennel for dogs. *(Recommended by Graham and Ann Smith, Joy and Peter Heatherley, David Cooke, Comus and Sarah Elliott, D S Jackson, W K Wood, Lynette and Stuart Shore, Mrs Jane Orbell)*

Free house ~ Licensees Paul and Carol Forster ~ Real ale ~ Bar food ~ (01665) 577275 ~ Well behaved children welcome ~ Open 12-2.30, 6.30-11(10.30 Sun) ~ Bedrooms: £39(£39S)/£55S(£55B)

ROMALDKIRK NY9922 Map 10

Rose & Crown ★

Just off B6277

Northumbria Dining Pub of the Year

'Outstanding in every respect' writes one reader about this very well run 18th-c coaching inn, while others mention the 'exceptionally good food', 'first-class accommodation' and – frequently – the top-notch friendly service. The imaginative bar menu changes every week (it's very popular, so you will need to book), and as well as lunchtime baps, delicious food might include home-made soup (£3.25), kipper pâté with lime and caper dressing and potato salad (£5.50), creamed scrambled eggs with smoked salmon (£5.95), fried pork sausages and black pudding with mustard mash and onion gravy or red onion and tomato risotto with goats cheese (£6.75), fried pigeon breast with bubble and squeak, onion confit and juniper sauce (£10.50), roast scottish salmon with sweet and sour aubergine and red wine jus or baked smoked haddock with mild spiced potatoes and a poached egg (£10.95), and specials such as goats cheese soufflé (£4.50), and roast belly pork with sweet and sour pork (£9.75); puddings such as dark chocolate torte or walnut and syrup tart (£3.25). They make their own marmalades, jams, chutneys and bread. The cosy beamed traditional bar has old-fashioned seats facing the warming log fire, a Jacobean oak settle, lots of brass and copper, a grandfather clock, and gin-traps, old farm tools, and black and white pictures of Romaldkirk on the walls. It has well kept Black Sheep and Theakstons Best on handpump. The smart bistro-style Crown Room (bar food is served in here) has recently been redecorated, and now has large cartoons of french waiters on the dark red walls, a new grey carpet and smart new high-back chairs. The farm tools have been moved out to the hall, which has wine maps and other interesting prints, along with a photograph of the Hale Bopp comet over Romaldkirk church (taken by a customer). There's also a no smoking oak-panelled restaurant. Tables outside look out over the village green, still with its original stocks and water pump. The top-floor rooms are particularly well equipped. The village is close to the superb Bowes Museum and the High Force waterfall, and has an interesting old church. *(Recommended by Graham Banks, Peter and Wynne Davies, S J Heaton, Robin and Joyce Peachey, Susan and John Douglas, Hans and Thelma Liesner, Kevin Thorpe, David Kidd, Sue and Geoff Price, Comus and Sarah Elliott, Robert Barnes, Mrs Phoebe A Kemp, Greta and Christopher Wells, Chloe and Robert Gartery, Stephen P Edwards, Geoff and Tricia Alderman, Alan and Mandy Maynard, Dr R G J Telfer, David and Heather Stephenson, R L Gorick; also in the* Good Hotel Guide*)*

Free house ~ Licensees Christopher and Alison Davy ~ Real ale ~ Bar food (12-1.30, 6.30-9.30) ~ Restaurant ~ (01833) 650213 ~ Children welcome, must be over 6 in restaurant ~ Dogs allowed in bar and bedrooms ~ Open 11-3, 5.30-11; 12-3, 7-10.30 Sun; closed 24-26 Dec ~ Bedrooms: £65B/£90B

SEAHOUSES NU2232 Map 10

Olde Ship ★

Just off B1340, towards harbour

The treasure-trove of genuine seafaring memorabilia at this nice stone harbour hotel makes it a very rewarding place for a drink, and the exceptionally friendly and cheerful staff are an added bonus. The entire bar is a tribute to the sea and seafarers – even the floor is scrubbed ship's decking. An anemometer takes wind speed readings from the top of the chimney. Besides lots of other shiny brass fittings, ship's instruments and equipment, and a knotted anchor made by local fishermen, there are sea pictures and model ships, including fine ones of the North Sunderland lifeboat, and Seahouses' lifeboat the *Grace Darling*. There's also a model of the *Forfarshire* (the paddle steamer that Grace Darling went to rescue in 1838 – they've got the story, so you can find out more), and even the ship's nameboard. They're continually adding nautical curios (and you'll now find even more fishing memorabilia outside). The bar is gently lit by stained-glass sea picture windows, and it has an open fire in winter; dominoes and piped music. One clear window looks out across the harbour to the Farne Islands, and as dusk falls you can watch the Longstones lighthouse shine across the fading evening sky; the low-beamed Cabin Room is no smoking. A good choice of real ales on handpump includes Bass, Courage Directors, Greene King Old Speckled Hen, Theakstons Best and possibly a guest such as John Smiths, and over two dozen malt whiskies; they serve tasty lunchtime sandwiches as well as other bar food (they may finish serving food earlier in the evening if it's quiet). The pub is not really suitable for children though, along with walkers, they are welcome on the battlemented side terrace, which with a sun lounge looks out on the harbour; putting and quoits. You can book boat trips to the Farne Islands Bird Sanctuary at the harbour, and there are bracing coastal walks, particularly to Bamburgh, Grace Darling's birthplace. *(Recommended by Comus and Sarah Elliott, the Didler, Filip Lemmens, Daphne and Peter Ross, J V Dadswell, D J Hulse, Brian Root, Keith and Janet Morris, Mike and Lynn Robinson, S Watkin, P Taylor, David Carr, Dr R G J Telfer, Ruth and Paul Lawrence, KN-R)*

Free house ~ Licensees Alan and Jean Glen ~ Real ale ~ Bar food (not 25 Dec) ~ Restaurant ~ (01665) 720200 ~ Children allowed in family room ~ Open 11-11; 12-10.30 Sun ~ Bedrooms: £41B/£82B

SHINCLIFFE NZ2941 Map 10

Seven Stars

High Street North; A177 a mile or so S of Durham

Although this early 18th-c village inn attracts lots of diners with its very good food, it manages to keep a nice local atmosphere. The comfortable and welcoming interior is civilised but still largely unspoilt: the lounge bar has a coal fire in its handsome Victorian fireplace, with a pair of big staffordshire dogs on the mantelpiece below a big mirror, old brewery advertisements, copper kettles hanging from the beams, and cushioned wall banquettes and stools around cast-iron-framed tables. Friendly staff serve well kept Theakstons and a couple of guests such as Marstons Pedigree and Charles Wells Bombardier from handpump, and they've 25 malt whiskies; chess, draughts, dominoes and piped music. The romantic candlelit dining room and half the lounge are no smoking. From a changing menu, interesting dishes might include home-made soup (£3.50), sandwiches (from £3.50), seafood chowder (£4.50), mexican chicken on a tortilla with guacamole, salsa and sour cream (£5.50), excellent steak and ale pie (£7.50), roast chicken breast wrapped in parma ham topped with brie with herb mash and a tomato fondue (£11.50), and monkfish medallions on herb mash with saffron sauce, mussels and spinach (£12.50), with specials such as lemon sole stuffed with crayfish with creamy mash and chive butter (£11), and mouth-watering puddings such as white chocolate and blueberry brûlée (£3.50); you have to pay extra for vegetables. Parking can be a problem but it's just ten minutes or so drive from central Durham, with fairly frequent buses passing the door. There are pretty window boxes, creepers, and seats out at the end of the attractive village street. *(Recommended by Jenny and Dave Hughes, Darly Graton, Graeme Gulibert, Peter Burton, Keith Mould, R M Corlett, R T and J C Moggridge, Bob and Valerie Mawson, Michael Doswell, Peter and Patricia Burton, M Borthwick, Pat and John Morris)*

Mortal Man Inns ~ Managers Louise Swinburne and Feargus Ryan ~ Real ale ~ Bar food (12-2.30, 6-9.30; 12-2.30, 6-9 Sun) ~ Restaurant ~ (0191) 384 8454 ~ Children welcome ~ Dogs allowed in bar ~ Open 11-11; 12-10.30 Sun ~ Bedrooms: £40S/£55S

STANNERSBURN NY7286 Map 10

Pheasant

Kielder Water road signposted off B6320 in Bellingham

You'll get a particularly warm welcome at this homely old village pub, in a peaceful valley with quiet forests all around. Up on blackboards, the enjoyable home-made bar food could include lunchtime sandwiches (from £2.80) and ploughman's (£5.50), garlic chicken breast salad (£6.75), and game and mushroom pie or roast lamb with redcurrant jus (£6.95), as well as a few more elaborate evening dishes such as grilled salmon with herb mayonnaise or fried marinated chicken with honey-roast peppers (£9.25), and duck confit (£11.95), with puddings such as home-made sticky toffee pudding or lemon and lime cheesecake (£3.35); prices for the same dishes go up a bit in the evenings; they do a roast Sunday lunch (£6.95), and if you're staying the breakfasts are good. The traditionally comfortable lounge is partly stripped stone and partly panelled, and a separate public bar, similar but simpler, opens into a games room with darts, pool, and dominoes; piped music. There's a good mix of visitors and locals in the evening (when the small no smoking dining room can get crowded), and the landlord and staff are particularly friendly. Well kept Black Sheep, Timothy Taylors Landlord and Theakstons on handpump, around 36 malt whiskies, and a decent reasonably priced wine list. There are picnic-sets in a streamside garden, with a pony paddock behind; Kielder Water is just up the road. *(Recommended by Ron and Mary Nicholson, John Poulter, Michael Doswell, David and Heather Stephenson, Kate and Byron Davies, GSB)*

Free house ~ Licensees Walter and Robin Kershaw ~ Real ale ~ Bar food ~ Restaurant ~ (01434) 240382 ~ Children welcome away from main bar till 9.30 ~ Dogs allowed in bedrooms ~ Open 11-3, 6-11; 12-3, 7-10.30 Sun; closed Mon and Tues Nov-Mar, 25 and 26 Dec ~ Bedrooms: £40S/£65S

THROPTON NU0302 Map 10

Three Wheat Heads

B6341

In the heart of Coquetdale, this stone-built 17th-c village hotel has an attractive garden with lovely views towards the Simonside Hills, and a play area and dovecote. The carpeted bar on the right and the pleasant and roomy dining area have good fires, which you might find lit even when it's not that cold (there's a fine tall stone fireplace), wheelback chairs around neat rows of dark tables, more heavily cushioned brocaded seats, comfortable bar stools with backrests, and an elaborate longcase clock; darts and dominoes, and piped music. The pub is popular with older customers, and the emphasis is enjoyably on the food, which might include home-made soup (£2.50 – go for cream of onion if it's on), sandwiches (from £2.50), breaded crab claws (£4.50), fresh battered cod (£5.95/£8.95), pork stroganoff or home-made steak and mushroom pie (£7.25), chicken breast stuffed with roquefort cheese and pepper sauce or wild mushroom and brandy parcel (£8.95), and sirloin steak (£10.50); puddings (£2.95), and children's meals (from £3.50). The no smoking restaurant, recently renovated, is becoming quite a local haunt. Staff are friendly and efficient, and the Marstons Pedigree and Theakstons on handpump are kept well. *(Recommended by David and Heather Stephenson, Comus and Sarah Elliott, Kevin Thorpe, KN-R, Barry Collett, Keith Mould)*

Pubmaster ~ Lease Danny Scullion ~ Real ale ~ Bar food (12-2, 6-9; 12-9 Sat/Sun) ~ Restaurant ~ (01669) 620262 ~ Children welcome ~ Dogs allowed in bar and bedrooms ~ Open 11-3, 6-11; 11-11 Sat; 11-10.30 Sun ~ Bedrooms: £39B/£59S(£59B)

Pubs staying open all afternoon at least one day a week are listed at the back of the book.

WARENFORD NU1429 Map 10

Warenford Lodge

Off A1 3 or 4 miles S of Belford

It's worth tracking down the interesting local cheese platter (£4.85) at this slightly quirky stone house. Often using local ingredients and served by friendly staff, other well presented home-made dishes could include stottie sandwiches (£2.50), soup with turkestan bread (£2.80), wild mushroom risotto (£4.25), leek and sour cream flan (£5.70), fish chowder (£7.90), thai green curry with monkfish and prawns (£9.50), and a couple of daily specials such as home-made cannelloni with smoked ham and beef (£6.50), and baked salmon with a garlic crumb crust (£7.20), with puddings such as steamed marmalade pudding (£3); children's meals (from £2.50). Quite simple 60s décor makes the partly stripped stone bar look less old than in fact it is. It has cushioned wooden seats around pine tables, and a warm fire in the big stone fireplace; steps lead up to an extension with comfortable dining tables and chairs, and a big woodburning stove. They serve a decent selection of wines and malt whiskies, a good choice of teas, and keg John Smiths. You'll need to keep your eyes open to find the pub as there's no sign outside, and check their limited opening times before you set out. More reports please. *(Recommended by Hans and Thelma Liesner)*

Free house ~ Licensees Ray and Marion Matthewman ~ Bar food (12-1.30(not wkdys), 7-9.30; not Mon or winter Tues) ~ Restaurant ~ (01668) 213453 ~ Children in eating area of bar and restaurant ~ Open 7-11; 12-2.30, 7-11 Sat and Sun; closed Mon and winter Tues

WELDON BRIDGE NZ1399 Map 10

Anglers Arms

B6344, just off A397; village signposted with Rothbury off A1 N of Morpeth

This substantial hotel (with a mile of fishing on the nearby River Coquet) has a relaxed and welcoming atmosphere in its comfortable traditional lounge bar, with all ages from small children to octogenarians chatting happily over their food. This includes lunchtime sandwiches (from £3.95; a generous mixed platter for two, served with chips, is £9.95), soup (£2.75), prawn and smoked salmon cocktail (£5.45), battered cod and chips or steak and ale pie (£7.25), grilled rainbow trout with lemon butter stuffed with prawns (£7.75), and lamb cutlets with root mash and rosemary sauce or grilled gammon steak (£8.45), with specials such as lemon and pepper chicken (£8.95), and beef wellington (£11.95); their school puddings such treacle sponge with custard and apple pie (£3.95) are excellent. The nicely lit turkey-carpeted bar is in two parts, cream walls on the right, oak panelling and some shiny black beams hung with copper pans on the left, with a grandfather clock and sofa by the coal fire, staffordshire cats and other antique ornaments on its mantelpiece, old fishing and other country prints, some in heavy gilt frames, a profusion of other fishing memorabilia, and some taxidermy. Some of the tables are lower than you'd expect for eating, but their chairs have short legs to match – different, and rather engaging. They have well kept Bass, alongside two changing guests such as Marstons Pedigree and Timothy Taylors Landlord on handpump, decent wines and an espresso machine; pleasant uniformed service; there may be almost imperceptible piped music. The side restaurant is in a former railway dining car: more formal but light and airy, with crisp white linen and pink carpet. There are tables in an attractive garden with a good play area. We have not yet heard from readers who have stayed overnight, but would expect the thumbs-up. *(Recommended by Keith Mould, Paul and Sue Merrick, Dr Ben Green, the Very Rev Stephen Platten)*

Free house ~ Licensee John Young ~ Bar food (12-2, 6-9.30) ~ Restaurant ~ (01665) 570271 ~ Children welcome ~ Open 11-3, 6-11; 12-3, 7-10.30 Sun ~ Bedrooms: £35S/£55S

Lucky Dip

Besides the fully inspected pubs, you might like to try these Lucky Dips recommended to us and described by readers (if you do, please send us reports: www.goodguides.com).

Allendale [NY8355]
Allendale Inn [B6295]: Friendly two-room local, real fire in kitchen range, good value food inc plenty of game and children's dishes in bars and upstairs restaurant, Tetleys; pool in public bar, may be piped pop music when the young people are in *(Mike and Lynn Robinson)*
Alnmouth [NU2511]
☆ ***Saddle*** [Northumberland St (B1338)]: Unpretentious but hospitable stone-built hotel rambling through several areas inc spacious dining area, wide choice of generous pubby food inc particularly good cheeseboard, well kept real ales such as Greene King Old Speckled Hen and Theakstons Best, games room with ping pong as well as pool etc, no smoking restaurant; unobtrusive piped music; children welcome, open all day Sat, tables outside, comfortable bedrooms, attractive beaches, good coastal walks *(Richard and Karen Holt, Jack and Heather Coyle, LYM)*
Bamburgh [NU1835]
Lord Crewe Arms [Front St]: Small hotel prettily set in charming coastal village dominated by Norman castle; back hotel bar with log fire, more modern side bar with hunting murals (children and dogs allowed here), Bass and Stones under light blanket pressure, decent basic food inc lunchtime sandwiches and much fried food, no smoking restaurant (not always open); shame about the piped music; short walk from splendid sandy beach, bedrooms comfortable if creaky, good breakfast esp kippers; winter opening may be restricted *(LYM, Barry Collett, Mike and Lynn Robinson, David Carr)*
Barnard Castle [NZ0516]
☆ ***Old Well*** [The Bank]: Tudor coaching inn with big helpings of good food from sandwiches and baked potatoes through good fish and chips to gourmet evenings, in two bars and three pleasant dining areas (well behaved children allowed in the no smoking one), welcoming helpful staff, well kept Courage Directors, Greene King Ruddles Best and Theakstons Best, decent wines; terrace over town walls, big comfortable bedrooms – a good base for Bowes Museum *(Paul A Moore, Jack and Heather Coyle, David and Kay Ross)*
Beamish [NZ2055]
Black Horse [Red Row (off Beamishburn Rd NW, nr A6076); OS Sheet 88 map ref 205541]: Small and peaceful old pub out in the countryside, real fire, good ales, no music, food or space games; outside lavatories *(Dennis Nisbet)*
Bedlington [NZ2681]
Northumberland Arms [Front St E]: Well kept real ales inc a guest such as Shepherd Neame, welcoming staff and customers *(John W Allen)*
Belford [NU1033]
Black Swan [village signed off A1 S of Berwick; Market Pl]: Busy welcoming beamed local with three clean and comfortable olde-worlde bars (one at the back quieter), quick polite service, friendly landlord with an eye for detail, well kept Jennings, good plain home cooking in bar and dining room inc good value three-course lunch, open fire; bedrooms *(Stephen Ashby)*
Bellingham [NY8383]
Riverdale Hall: Biggish Victorian hotel on River North Tyne, in same family for 25 years; two smart bars, well kept Jennings, interesting bar food here, overlooking swimming pool or cricket field, or out on the lawn, long-serving welcoming staff, Asian touches to restaurant menu, good wine list; bedrooms, lots of facilities, salmon fishing *(Guy Vowles)*
Belsay [NZ1079]
☆ ***Highlander*** [A696]: Well run spacious country dining pub with good range of food from well prepared lunchtime sandwiches up in extensively refurbished side bar and open-plan dining area, nice plain wood tables, plenty of nooks and corners for character, reasonable prices, welcoming helpful service, well kept Scottish Courage ales, good log fires, unobtrusive piped music, separate locals' bar; open all day *(Joy and Peter Heatherley, J A Hooker)*
Berwick-upon-Tweed [NT9952]
☆ ***Barrels*** [Bridge St]: Convivial pub, homely feel despite bistro style, with thorough-going nautical décor in bar, car memorabilia, Beatles pictures and interesting pine furniture inc old school desks in lounge, attractive prices, well kept Boddingtons, Marstons Pedigree and guests such as Hambleton Stud and Hanby Premium and Rainbow Chaser, lunchtime filled rolls, imaginative evening food (perhaps not Mon) inc tapas, munchies, snacks and main dishes, friendly accommodating staff; varying live music downstairs, good juke box; open all day *(Ruth and Paul Lawrence, Comus and Sarah Elliott, Keith and Janet Morris, Mike and Lynn Robinson, P Abbott, Steve Williams)*
Leaping Salmon [Golden Sq]: Popular Wetherspoons, decent food, good range of very competitively priced beers, very good service *(R M Corlett)*
Birtley [NZ2756]
Millhouse [Blackfell; handy for A1 southbound, just S of Angel, off A1231 Sunderland/Washington slip rd]: Popular extended dining pub with reliable food all day inc lunch and early-supper bargains, some special nights, olde-barn décor, alcoved eating areas, Theakstons Best and XB, no smoking restaurant *(Jenny and Dave Hughes)*
Moulders Arms [Peareth Terr]: Busy pleasantly refurbished local by church in old part of village, good substantial plain cooking (till 10 evenings) inc children's, well kept changing ales such as Camerons, quick service; garden *(Jenny and Dave Hughes)*
Bolam [NZ1922]

Countryman: Four or five well kept ales, full food choice, friendly staff, attractive décor inc local Millennium tapestry *(Ewan Marshall)*

Bowes [NY9913]

☆ ***Ancient Unicorn***: Substantial stone inn with some 17th-c parts and interesting *Nicholas Nickleby* connection; spacious and comfortable open-plan bar, sparing decoration, good honest generous food from sandwiches to steak, two real ales, new coffee shop; good-sized clean bedrooms in converted stables block around big cobbled courtyard *(LYM, Guy Vowles)*

Carlbury [NZ2115]

Carlbury Arms [just off A67 just E of Piercebridge]: Busy dining pub locally popular for good choice of reasonably priced food (may take a while), well kept John Smiths Magnet or Theakstons *(Keith Mould, Francis Johnston)*

Chester-le-Street [NZ2751]

Butchers Arms [Middle Chare]: Warm and friendly partly carpeted open-plan local, pictures on pink walls, lots of china, Camerons Strongarm, Marstons Pedigree and a guest such as Wadworths Gooses Revenge; pool, juke box or piped music *(Kevin Thorpe)*

Chester Moor Inn [Chester Moor, A167 just S]: Wide range of cheerfully served good value food, well kept beer, pleasant surroundings *(Jenny and Dave Hughes)*

Church Mouse [A167 S, Chester Moor]: Enjoyable food inc come new dishes, good drinks choice *(Jenny and Dave Hughes)*

Consett [NZ1151]

Grey Horse [Sherburn Terr]: Two-bar beamed 19th-c pub brewing its own Derwent Rose beers in former back stables, inc Paddy named for the pub dog, and Red Dust, Steel Town and The Works recalling the former steel works here; also guests such as Camerons Strongarm and Daleside Monkey Wrench, lots of malt whiskies, occasional beer festivals, very friendly licensees, cheap bar lunches inc toasties, baguettes and all-day breakfast, good range of customers, pool; pavement tables, open all day *(Eric Larkham, Andy and Jill Kassube, Kevin Thorpe)*

Corbridge [NY9964]

☆ ***Angel*** [Newcastle Rd]: Small 17th-c hotel with new owners emphasising fresh imaginative food in bar and (not cheap) carefully refurbished restaurant, attentive happy staff, well kept real ale, decent wines, good coffees, panelled lounge and locals' back bar; bedrooms *(John Foord, LYM, Graham and Lynn Mason)*

☆ ***Black Bull*** [Middle St]: Roomy unpretentious pub, old-fashioned and low-ceilinged, with comfortable mix of seating inc traditional settles in stone-floored bar, good value generous fresh food inc popular all-day Sun lunches, well kept Black Sheep, Boddingtons, Castle Eden and Flowers Original, good attractively priced wine choice, friendly attentive staff, roaring fire, large no smoking restaurant; good atmosphere even on crowded Fri/Sat night, open all day *(Mike and Lynn Robinson, John Foord, Liz and John Soden)*

Dyvels [Station Rd]: Unassuming, informal and relaxing pub under new management, five or six well kept real ales, wide choice of reasonably priced usual food from toasties up; tables in pleasant area outside, open all day, decent bedrooms *(John Foord)*

Errington Arms [about 3 miles N, at junction A68/B6318]: Recently re-opened as family-run dining pub, stylishly done with some stripped stone and some panelling, bare boards and quarry tiles, good mix of candlelit tables, well prepared lunchtime food, wider more adventurous evening menu inc good vegetarian choice, three real ales, good coffee; quiet piped music *(Michael Doswell)*

☆ ***Wheatsheaf*** [Watling St/St Helens St]: Big refurbished stone-built village hotel, very popular (esp with older lunchers) for wide choice of generously served tasty food from good sandwiches through exemplary fish and chips to seasonal game, pleasantly decorated dining lounge and big warm conservatory restaurant with distant hill views, well kept Theakstons and guest beers, good choice of wines and malt whiskies, good service; pub games, piped music, some picnic-sets outside; bedrooms *(Jack and Heather Coyle, Michael Doswell, LYM, Hilary Forrest)*

Craster [NU2620]

☆ ***Jolly Fisherman*** [off B1339, NE of Alnwick]: Simple well worn in local, a favourite for its crab sandwiches, crab soup and picture-window harbour and sea views, with well kept Caledonian Deuchars IPA and Tetleys, and other basic snacks; dogs welcome, games area with pool and juke box; picnic-sets on grass behind, lovely clifftop walk to Dunstanburgh Castle. *(the Didler, Joy and Peter Heatherley, David Carr, Barry Collett, Adam and Joan Bunting, W K Wood, Robin and Joyce Peachey, Mr and Mrs Richard Osborne, Mike and Wendy Proctor, Des and Jen Clarke, Michael Doswell, LYM)*

Crawcrook [NZ1363]

Rising Sun [Bank Top]: Well refurbished, with huge choice of hearty popular food in dining area and conservatory, well kept and priced Boddingtons, Castle Eden, Mordue Workie Ticket and two or three guest beers from long bar, cheerful staff, steps up to lounge, separate pool room; neatly kept garden, open all day *(John Foord)*

Darlington [NZ2814]

Quaker Coffee House [Mechanics Yard, High Row (narrow passage by Binns)]: Small, narrow and cheerful, with cellar-bar feel from dim lighting and bare bricks, well kept changing unusual beers such as Fyfe Fyre and High Force as well as Quaker Ghost brewed for the pub, friendly staff, daily papers and magazines, upstairs daytime restaurant with good choice of food and wines; lively band nights Mon, Weds and Thurs, open all day (not Sun lunchtime) *(Andrew York, Richard Lewis)*

Durham [NZ2743]

Cathedrals [Court Lane]: Huge high-ceilinged functional bar very visibly brewing its own Bitter, Bobbys Best, Irish Stout, lager, a seasonal beer such as Priory Summer Ale, and a bottle-conditioned beer, also farm cider and cheap cocktails, generous and enjoyable usual food from sandwiches up from corner kitchen servery; well reproduced piped music; separate next-door café and deli, and light and airy upper bistro and restaurant; open all day *(Richard Lewis, BB)*

Colpitts [Colpitts Terr/Hawthorn Terr]: Basic and friendly, with particularly cheap Sam Smiths, sandwiches, open fires, pool in one room, TV and machines; perhaps the country's smallest beer garden in yard *(the Didler, Eric Larkham)*

Court Inn [Court Lane]: Good generous home-made food all day (not Sun) from sandwiches to steaks and late-evening bargains in unpretentious traditional town pub's extensive stripped brick eating area, real ales such as Durham Magus and Priors Gold, no mobile phones; bustling in term-time with students and teachers, piped pop music; seats outside, open all day *(C A Hall, BB, Eric Larkham, Andy and Jill Kassube, Pete Baker)*

Duke of Wellington [A167 S of Nevilles Cross]: Busy but spacious Victorian-style pub reopened after refurbishment, wide range of hearty good value generous food all day, well kept Bass, Worthington and a guest beer, efficient friendly service, pleasant separate restaurant *(John Watson)*

☆ ***Dun Cow*** [Old Elvet]: Unsmart but very welcoming traditional town pub in pretty 16th-c black and white timbered cottage, tiny chatty front bar with wall benches (unusual sliding door gives it a homely parlour feel), corridor linking it to long narrow back lounge with machines etc (this can be packed with students), real ales inc particularly well kept Castle Eden, cheap soup and sandwiches etc, friendly staff; piped music; children welcome, open all day Mon-Sat, Sun too in summer *(the Didler, Tracey and Stephen Groves, LYM, Pete Baker, Eric Larkham, Richard Lewis)*

Hogshead [Saddler St]: Closest to castle and cathedral, usual bare-boards style, jolly atmosphere, half a dozen or so real ales, good range of reasonably priced food from sandwiches up; piped music *(Andy and Jill Kassube)*

Old Elm Tree [Crossgate]: Big busy pub with three linked rooms on steep hill opp castle; unpretentious but warm welcoming atmosphere, prompt cheerful service, open fires, Adnams, Bass, Camerons, Tetleys and a guest beer, farm cider, seats outside; TV, machines, juke box; good value bedrooms *(the Didler)*

Shakespeare [Saddler St]: Unchanging pub with signed actor photographs in busy basic front bar, charming panelled snug and another back room with simple cheap bar snacks, lots of malt whiskies, well kept McEwans 80/- with guest beers such as Theakstons Best and Charles Wells Banana Bread, pub and board games; children welcome, open all day – convenient for castle, cathedral and river *(Pete Baker, LYM, Richard Lewis, the Didler)*

Swan & Three Cygnets [Elvet Bridge]: Comfortably refurbished Victorian pub in good bridge-end spot high above river, city views from big windows and picnic-sets out on terrace, bargain food from hot filled baguettes up, cheap well kept Sam Smiths OB; open all day *(Andy and Jill Kassube, BB)*

Ebchester [NZ1055]

☆ ***Derwent Walk*** [Ebchester Hill (B6309 outside)]: Friendly pub by the Gateshead—Consett walk for which it's named, walkers welcome, fine Derwent Valley views from conservatory, enterprising choice of good generous home-made food inc interestingly filled cobblers, full Jennings range kept well and a guest such as Adnams, good wine range, good log fire *(James Brown, Andy and Jill Kassube)*

Egglescliffe [NZ4213]

☆ ***Blue Bell*** [Yarm Rd (A67)]: Open-plan John Barras pub with good choice of cheap food all day in spacious and comfortable big-windowed bar, four real ales, good value wines by the glass, friendly service, tables out on deck by goat-cropped grass sloping down to the River Tees with fine view of the great 1849 railway viaduct (and boat trips to Stockton); children's room, no dogs *(LYM, JHBS)*

Eggleston [NY9924]

Moorcock [Hill Top]: Pleasantly unpretentious and congenial, with enjoyable fresh reasonably priced food inc local lamb, log fire in lounge, games room with darts, pool and TV, small dining room; dogs welcome, tables out on front terrace, Teesdale views from comfortable bedrooms, good walks *(Keith Mould)*

Eglingham [NU1019]

☆ ***Tankerville Arms*** [B6346 Alnwick—Wooler]: Pleasant long stone village pub with good food using local ingredients from sandwiches to interesting main dishes and Sun roasts (best to book esp Tues), early evening bargains Mon-Thurs, well kept Black Sheep, Courage Directors and two Mordue beers, friendly obliging service, decent choice of wines, malt whiskies and of teas and coffees; black joists, some stripped stone, plush banquettes, captain's chairs and turkey carpet, coal fires each end, snug no smoking lounge; dominoes, piped music; children welcome, garden tables *(Jenny and Peter Lowater, C A Hall, Darly Graton, Graeme Gulibert, Michael Doswell, Joy and Peter Heatherley, Jack and Heather Coyle, LYM, Mrs Jane Orbell)*

Ellingham [NU1625]

☆ ***Pack Horse*** [signed off A1 N of Alnwick]: Friendly local bar hung with jugs, Black Sheep, very quick service, some emphasis on freshly prepared food from sandwiches to steaks and mixed grill, spacious dining room, pool room; bedrooms *(Mr and Mrs Richard Osborne)*

Etal [NT9339]

Black Bull [off B6354 SW of Berwick]: Pretty white-painted cottage, the only thatched pub in Northumberland, spacious unpetentious open-plan lounge bar with glossily varnished beams, well kept Stones and Tetleys, 30 malt whiskies, farm cider, quick service; children in eating area, games room with darts, dominoes, pool, TV, juke box and piped music; open all day Sat, a few picnic-sets out in front; nice spot near castle ruins and light railway *(Brian and Lynn*

Young, Mike and Lynn Robinson, Michael Doswell, LYM, Angus Lyon)

Felton [NU1800]

☆ ***Northumberland Arms*** [village signed off A1 N of Morpeth]: New regime doing good interesting food all day, from bargain Tues lunch to local game specials, also children's dishes; roomy and comfortable open-plan bar with beams, stripped stone and good coal fires, nice mix of furnishings inc big blue settees, elegant small end restaurant; pleasant atmosphere, friendly caring service, well kept Bass and Black Sheep Best, good coffee and wines; well reproduced piped music, esp in conservatory pool room, monthly live music 1st Weds; five bedrooms, steps down to bench by River Coquet, open all day *(Michael Doswell, BB)*

Gateshead [NZ2657]

Angel View [Low Eighton; A167, just off A1]: Named for exceptional view of Angel of the North nearby; sympathetically refurbished hotel, several small attractively furnished areas, good value bar food from sandwiches to steaks, helpful friendly staff, restaurant; bedrooms *(Mike and Lynn Robinson)*

Ship [Eighton Banks, quite handy for A1(M)]: Extended open-plan pub popular at lunchtime for good blackboard food choice inc unusually good side salads, Sun lunch, large pleasantly decorated no smoking dining room, model ships and marine artefacts, well kept real ale; south-facing garden with play area, great moor views *(Jack and Heather Coyle)*

Waggon [Galloping Green Rd, Eighton Banks]: Extended and refurbished local, good value generous straightforward food (can be ordered ahead) from sandwiches and baked potatoes to Sun lunch, comfortable airy eating areas inc conservatory (now no smoking) overlooking old Bowes Railway, well kept beers, friendly prompt service *(M Borthwick)*

Wetherspoons [The Galleria, Metrocentre]: One of the few Wetherspoons catering for children; good value food from sandwiches up, good range of real ales such as Batemans, reasonably priced wines *(Mike and Lynn Robinson)*

Greenhaugh [NY7987]

Holly Bush [8 miles SW of Otterburn]: Quaint beamed stone-built pub with good value home-made food and well kept Jennings Cumberland, Theakstons Best and Wylam Tankard, pink-washed walls, Victorian kitchen range and mixed furnishings, simple dining room; may be discreet piped classical music; nice spot near Kielder Water *(Michael Doswell)*

Haltwhistle [NY7064]

Black Bull [just off Market Sq, behind Indian restaurant]: Half a dozen particularly well kept changing ales such as Jennings and Northumberland, inc ones brewed at the pub, beams, stripped stone, two real fires, darts and quiz night; no music or food, cl Mon-Weds lunchtimes *(Andy and Jill Kassube, Eric Larkham)*

Manor House Hotel [Main St]: Small friendly hotel with Jennings Cumberland, restaurant, lovely views over churchyard and Tyne from garden tables; bedrooms *(Eric Larkham)*

☆ ***Wallace Arms*** [Rowfoot, Featherstone Park]: Lively atmosphere in unpretentious linked rooms of rambling former farmhouse, beams, dark woodwork, some stripped stone, good log fire; new landlord doing generous simple food from sandwiches to bargain Sun lunch, well kept Batemans XB and Charles Wells Bombardier, three dozen malt whiskies, games room with another fire; children in eating areas and family room, fairly good disabled access, picnic-sets with lovely fell views, play area and quoits, walks on South Tyne Trail, open all day wknds *(Guy Vowles, LYM)*

Hamsterley [NZ1131]

Cross Keys [nr Witton-le-Wear]: Generous helpings of good value waitress-served food, wide choice inc takeaways, John Smiths real ale; good walking in nearby Hamsterley Forest *(Tony Gayfer)*

Hartlepool [NZ5032]

Causeway [Stockton Rd, Stranton]: Victorian pub with panelled bar, two carpeted snugs, Banks's Bitter and Original and Camerons Bitter and Strongarm, enjoyable food, low prices; live folk and jazz two or three nights a week, open all day *(JHBS)*

Harbour of Refuge [Bedford St/York Pl, The Headland]: Comfortable two-bar pub and restaurant overlooking harbour entrance, panoramic coastal views and interesting local port photographs, local fish as well as traditional lunchtime pub food, all cheap, coal fire; keg beers; open all day Fri/Sat *(JHBS)*

King Johns [South Rd]: Wetherspoons with photographs and diagrams giving a good introduction to local history – trams, ships, the German bombardment; enjoyable food, bargain wine *(JHBS)*

Hawthorn [NZ4145]

Stapylton Arms: Enjoyable food from sandwiches to steaks in carpeted bar with lots of old local photographs, Nimmos XXXX and a guest beer, chatty ex-miner landlord; dogs on leads allowed, may be open on busy wknds, nice wooded walk to sea (joins new Durham Coastal Path) *(JHBS)*

Haydon Bridge [NY8364]

☆ ***General Havelock*** [A69]: Civilised and individually furnished dining pub with good food inc imaginative dishes and fresh local ingredients prepared in open-view kitchen, well kept changing beers such as Black Sheep Best and Big Lamp Prince Bishop, good wines by the glass, welcoming service, open fires, smart Tyne-view stripped stone restaurant; children welcome, tables on terrace *(J G Thorpe, John Oddey, LYM)*

Heddon-on-the-Wall [NZ1366]

Swan: Spacious well run open-plan stone-built pub, beamed area with farm tools and bric-a-brac, comfortable corners eslewhere with built-in banquettes, good value popular food with separate sandwich menu, welcoming efficient staff, John Smiths and Theakstons; picnic-sets in large informal garden with Tyne Valley views *(Mike and Lynn Robinson)*

Hexham [NY9364]

Forum [Market Pl]: Popular Wetherspoons in former cinema, good choice of food from sandwiches and wraps to Aberdeen Angus pie, usual good range of real ales; children allowed for meals *(Andy and Jill Kassube)*
Tap & Spile [Battle Hill/Eastgate]: Congenial open-plan bare-boards pub with half a dozen quickly changing well kept ales from central bar (they've notched up over 1,000 now), country wines, good filling low-priced food from hot filled stotties up, open fire, welcoming expert service; children welcome, no dogs, regular live music, open all day *(John Foord, Andy and Jill Kassube, Hazel and Michael Duncombe, Patrick Hancock)*
High Coniscliffe [NZ2215]
Spotted Dog [A67, W of A1]: Friendly and expansive pub, well kept ales such as Black Sheep and Hook Norton Old Hooky, interesting menu with good vegetarian options; unobtrusive piped music, front pool table *(Andrew York)*
High Force [NY8728]
☆ ***High Force Hotel*** [B6277 about 4 miles NW of Middleton-in-Teesdale]: Beautifully placed high-moors hotel, named for England's highest waterfall nearby and doubling as mountain rescue post, with interestingly basic décor to suit; brews its own good value hoppy Teesdale Bitter, Cauldron Snout and Forest, also Theakstons and good choice of bar food (and of malt whiskies), helpful service, friendly atmosphere; quiz night Fri, usually open all day summer (when it can get busy) but may be cl quiet lunchtimes out of season; children very welcome, comfortable bedrooms, pleasant garden *(LYM, Kevin Thorpe, Liz and John Soden)*
Holy Island [NU1241]
Crown & Anchor: Comfortable and welcoming straightforward four-room pub with emphasis on enjoyable quickly served food though bar much used by locals, good décor inc interesting rope fancy-work *(Peter Lewis, R E and E C M Pick)*
☆ ***Ship*** [Marygate; causeway passable only at low tide, check times (01289) 330733]: Nicely set summer pub, spotless bar with eating area off, beamery, wooden furniture, bare boards, panelling, maritime/fishing memorabilia and pictures; good value straightforward food (may be a wait even for sandwiches) esp local crab and fish, well kept real ales in summer such as Hadrian & Border Blessed, Holy Island and Sacred Kingdom, good choice of whiskies, cheerful service; no dogs, even in garden; three comfortable Victorian-décor bedrooms, may close for a while Jan/Feb *(Mike and Di Saxby, Rosemary and Tom Hall, Keith and Janet Morris, Neil and Anita Christopher)*
Horsley [NZ0966]
Lion & Lamb [B6528, just off A69 Newcastle—Hexham]: Plentiful reasonably priced food (not Sun evening) from sandwiches to daily roast, Mon steak night, bargains for two Tues/Weds, well kept changing ales such as Castle Eden, Durham Magus, Fullers London Pride and Shepherd Neame Spitfire, cafetière coffee, good service, two main rooms, small smart restaurant, stripped stone, flagstones, panelling, untreated tables and chairs; Tyne views from attractive garden with roomy terrace and particularly good adventure play area, open all day *(John Foord, Mike and Lynn Robinson, Andy and Jill Kassube)*
Houghton Gate [NZ2950]
Smiths Arms [Castle Dene; off A183 Chester-le-Street—Sunderland via A1052 then Forge Lane]: Small bar with old black kitchen range, old photographs and three real ales with a guest most weeks, comfortable lounge with two log or coal fires, games room with another, tasteful upstairs restaurant (Weds-Sat evenings) with good interesting food, lunchtime bar food; cl Mon-Thurs lunchtime *(Mike and Lynn Robinson, Jenny and Dave Hughes)*
Houghton-Le-Spring [NZ3450]
Chilton Moor Country Pub [Chilton Moor]: Good value generous changing food inc good fresh fish and popular Sun lunch; keg beer *(Jenny and Dave Hughes)*
Kenton Bankfoot [NZ2068]
☆ ***Twin Farms*** [Main Road]: Sir John Fitzgerald pub in elegant period rustic style, recycled stone, timbers etc, several areas, nooks and crannies off central bar, decent food from good value sandwiches through unusual snacks to interesting main dishes and meals in well run restaurant, well kept ales inc local ones such as Darwin and Mordue, well chosen wines, real fire, courteous efficient service, families welcome; piped music, machines; disabled facilities, open all day *(Michael Doswell, Andy and Jill Kassube, Robin Hilton, GSB, Jenny and Dave Hughes)*
Lamesley [NZ2557]
Ravensworth Arms [minor rd S of Gateshead western bypass, A1, Team Valley junction]: Large good value stone-built dining pub, good fish specials; children welcome, play area and picnic-table sets outside, open all day *(Jenny and Dave Hughes)*
Langley on Tyne [NY8160]
☆ ***Carts Bog Inn*** [A686 S, junction B6305]: Isolated rambling black-beamed moorside pub, big central log fire, some stripped stone and flagstones, good freshly made food from sandwiches up inc local lamb, good friendly service, well kept Jennings Cumberland, Yates and guest beers from small northern breweries, lots of malt whiskies, side games lounge; children in eating areas, garden tables with high views, quoits *(LYM, Peter and Anne-Marie O'Malley)*
Longbenton [NZ2768]
Benton Ale House [Front St]: Comfortably refurbished, with decent choice of real ales (lined glasses), good cheap simple lunchtime food (not Sat) from hot and cold sandwiches up, friendly staff, TV alcove, back room with pool, juke box and machines; good disabled facilities, open all day *(Mike and Lynn Robinson)*
Lucker [NU1631]
☆ ***Apple*** [village (and pub) signed off A1 N of Morpeth]: Surprisingly good food cooked by

youngish landlord, from inventively filled baguettes and enterprising light lunches to creative evening meals and good Sun lunch, with thoughtful children's dishes or half-price small helpings, in refurbished village pub (doubles as post office); stripped stone, bare boards or carpet, solid pub furnishings, woodburner, keg beers but well priced wines and good coffee, friendly landlady, pleasantly fresh and airy décor in roomy side restaurant extension (must book for this); piped radio; cl Mon lunchtime *(C J Cox, A Monro, BB, Michael Doswell)*

Matfen [NZ0372]

Black Bull [off B6318 NE of Corbridge]: Well placed by green of attractive out-of-the-way 18th-c estate village, tables out on terrace; the part of the pub containing the original attractive dining room has now been hived off as a private house, and it may take time for the refurbished remainder to regain its former appeal (it was a popular main entry); usual food, perhaps a real ale such as Theakstons Black Bull, a good few malt whiskies, log fires; games area, no dogs; has been open all day wknds *(LYM)*

Meldon [NZ1185]

Dyke Neuk Inn: Nicely decorated roadside pub with good varied menu from lunchtime sandwiches up, choice of roasts for Sun lunch; large gardens *(Mike and Lynn Robinson)*

Mickley [NZ0761]

Blue Bell [Mount Pleasant, off A695 Prudhoe—Stocksfield]: Cosy little pub with rural feel (though on edge of built-up area), good range of real ales, friendly staff, popular food cooked to order – may have to book wknds *(John Oddey)*

Middlestone [NZ2531]

Ship [Low Rd]: Buoyant comfortable atmosphere, welcoming licensees and locals, good fire, four well kept real ales (they do beer festivals and lots of other events), good choice of food inc Sun lunch; piped music; good carol singing 25 Dec *(anon)*

Morpeth [NZ1986]

☆ ***Tap & Spile*** [Manchester St]: Consistently welcoming cosy and easy-going two-room pub, good choice of well kept real ales, farm cider and country wines, limited choice of good value food lunchtime and early evening (not Tues) made by excellent landlady, fair prices, stripped pine furniture, interesting old photographs, quieter back lounge with coal-effect gas fire; folk music Sun afternoons, Mon quiz night, sports TV in front bar, board games, dominoes, cards, darts, fruit machine, unobtrusive piped music; children welcome, open all day Fri-Sun *(John W Allen)*

Netherton [NT9807]

Star [off B6341 at Thropton, or A697 via Whittingham]: Unspoilt local in superb remote countryside, spartan but clean, many original features, well kept Castle Eden tapped from the cask and served in small entrance lobby, large high-ceilinged room, welcoming landlady and regulars; no food, music or children; open evenings and Sun lunch *(RWC, Kevin Thorpe, the Didler)*

Newburn [NZ1665]

☆ ***Keelman*** [Grange Rd, by Tyne Riverside Country Park]: Shares attractive granite-built former 19th-c pumping station with good Big Lamp Brewery (which you can visit), their full range at attractive prices; high ceiling, lofty windows, wooden gallery, no smoking area, obliging staff; straightforward food (not Sun evening), fruit machine, piped music; open all day, very popular with families in summer, lots of picnic-sets outside, bedrooms in new block, handy for walks *(Kevin Thorpe, John Foord, Mike and Lynn Robinson, John Oddey, Andy and Jill Kassube)*

Newcastle upon Tyne [NZ2266]

Bodega [Westgate Rd]: Edwardian drinking hall worth a look for the well restored colourful walls and ceiling with two magnificent original stained-glass domes (has been a mosque), boards, tiles and a handsome rug, cosy alcove banquettes; well kept Durham Magus and Prince Bishop, Mordue Geordie Pride (sold here as No 9) and Timothy Taylors Ram Tam tapped from the cask, lunchtime food; juke box or piped music (can be obtrusive), machines, TV, Tues quiz night, busy evenings (and if Newcastle Utd at home or on TV); open all day, next to Tyne Theatre *(Mike and Lynn Robinson, the Didler, Eric Larkham, Michael Doswell)*

☆ ***Bridge Hotel*** [Castle Sq, next to high level bridge]: Big cheerily rough-and-ready high-ceilinged room divided into several areas leaving plenty of space by the bar with replica slatted snob screens, six particularly well kept changing ales such as Black Sheep, Jennings and Mordue Workie Ticket, decent lunchtime food, magnificent fireplace, great views of river and bridges from back windows; sports TV, piped music, fruit machines, very long-standing Mon folk club upstairs; tables on flagstoned back terrace overlooking section of old town wall, open all day *(John Oddey, Mike and Lynn Robinson, Eric Larkham, the Didler, John W Allen, David Carr, LYM, John Foord)*

Centurion [Central Station, Neville St]: Glorious high-ceilinged Victorian décor with tilework and columns in former 1st-class waiting room well restored as comfortable bar/brasserie, interesting menu; keg beers *(Tracey and Stephen Groves)*

Centurion [Central Station, Neville St]: Recently rediscovered former 1st-class waiting room well restored as bar/brasserie, magnificent Victorian tilework and columns, good interesting menu *(Mike and Lynn Robinson)*

Chillingham [Chillingham Rd, Heaton]: Two big rooms, fine panelling and furnishings, well kept Black Sheep, Mordue Workie Ticket, Theakstons and guest beers, occasional beer festivals, good cheap food lunchtime and (not wknd) early evening; piped music or juke box in bar with TV and pool room with two tables and darts; children in quieter lounge (Weds quiz night), open all day *(Mike and Lynn Robinson, Eric Larkham)*

☆ ***Cluny*** [Lime St (no inn sign; entrance opp Ship Inn at top of cobbled way down to Ouseburn, by Byker city farm)]: Impressive trendy bar/café in well refurbished 1870s whisky warehouse, striking setting below Metro bridge; friendly bohemian cavern feel, reasonably priced food all day (all home-made so may be a wait), well kept ales such as Durham Magus and Prince Bishop, Hexhamshire Whipweasel and Shepherd Neame Bishops Finger, exotic beers too, cheerful staff, daily papers and local art magazines, interesting back gallery with paintings, sculptures and craft works by artists with studios in same complex; piped music, live comedy and music Thurs; open all day (cl Mon afternoon) *(Tracey and Stephen Groves, GSB, Andrew York, Mike and Lynn Robinson, Eric Larkham, John Foord)*

☆ ***Cooperage*** [The Close, Quayside]: One of city's most ancient buildings, great atmosphere in stripped stone bar and cosy beamed lounge, good waterfront setting; fine choice of well kept real ales (good prices Mon, Thurs and till 9 Fri/Sat), hearty fresh sensibly priced lunchtime food, disabled facilities; pool, juke box, quiz night Tues, cl Sun, upstairs night club Mon (student night) and Thurs-Sat *(the Didler, LYM, Chris Doyle, David Carr, Eric Larkham, Stephen, Julie and Hayley Brown)*

Duke of Wellington [High Bridge West, between Grey St and Bigg Mkt]: Small L-shaped Victorian-style pub with many dozens of pictures commemorating the Iron Duke and Waterloo, well kept Ind Coope Burton, Marstons Pedigree, Tetleys and up to four guest beers, occasional beer festivals, hot and cold lunchtime sandwiches and baked potatoes (not Sun); shame about the loud music, TV and flashing machines, very busy match days; open all day (cl Sun afternoon) *(John W Allen, Eric Larkham)*

Fighting Cocks [Albion Row]: Basic friendly if mildly eccentric pub tied to local Four Rivers with their beers kept well, farm cider, hot and cold sandwiches, good bridge views, keen staff, free juke box, games machines; Thurs quiz night, occasional live music; couple of steps down to bar, open all day (cl Sun afternoon) *(Mike and Lynn Robinson)*

Fitzgeralds [Grey St]: Handsomely refurbished Victorian pub in elegant street on fringe of Bigg Market, lots of levels and alcoves (two short sets of steps between entrance, main area and lavatories), discreet lighting, red mahogany and polished brass, Black Sheep, Mordue Workie Ticket and two guest beers, wide range of good value lunchtime food (not Sun) inc freshly baked baguettes; can get very busy, piped music, machines; cl Sun am *(Eric Larkham, Michael Doswell)*

Free Trade [St Lawrence Rd, off Walker Rd (A186)]: Chattily friendly atmosphere in artfully basic split-level pub with big windows for grandstand river and bridge views, well kept Hadrian, Marstons Pedigree and Mordue Workie Ticket, good wkdy early lunchtime sandwiches, real fire, original Formica tables; cricket radio, eclectic free CD juke box, quiz Weds, steps down to back room and lavatories (high-standard gents' graffiti); tables out on terrace a bit like a Buddhist pebble garden (or sit on grass overlooking Tyne), open all day *(Tracey and Stephen Groves, Eric Larkham, Mike and Lynn Robinson, Kevin Thorpe)*

Lonsdale [Lonsdale Terr, W Jesmond]: Large comfortable open-plan pub in student area, cheap food all day, Courage Directors, Theakstons Best and guest beers, efficient service; piped music, big-screen sports TV *(Michael Doswell)*

Newcastle Arms [St Andrews St]: Open-plan pub on fringe of chinatown, well kept Black Sheep, Fullers London Pride and one or two guest beers, occasional mini beer festivals, friendly staff, decent food till 6 inc sandwiches, interesting old local photographs; piped music, big-screen sports TV, can get very busy esp on match days; open all day (cl Sun afternoon) *(Mike and Lynn Robinson, Eric Larkham)*

Opera House [Westgate Rd]: Small Dylans Bar, with separate street entrance but hidden in cellar bowels of beautiful Victorian theatre, has whitewashed brick and pine panelling, lots of theatre photographs, well reproduced Dylan and Beatles music, welcoming staff and regulars, well kept Timothy Taylors Landlord; separate Bistro Bar (no street entrance) has food *(John W Allen, Eric Larkham)*

Pitcher & Piano [Quayside]: Stylish and roomy modern bar in revitalised riverside area opp new Millennium bridge, great views of Tyne and other bridges, good if not cheap range of lunchtime food and of beer *(Michael Doswell)*

Ship [Stepney Bank]: Traditional local beside Byker city farm, little changed in 30 years; particularly well kept Boddingtons and Castle Eden Bitter and Nimmos XXXX, unusual toasted sandwiches (normally all day), very friendly locals, pool and juke box in lounge, darts and TV in bar; seats outside and picnic-sets on green opp, open all day *(Mike and Lynn Robinson, John W Allen, Eric Larkham)*

Tilleys [Westgate Rd]: Large old-fashioned well worn in bar next to Tyne Theatre and near performing arts college, so interesting mix of customers; scores of classic film stills, good lunchtime soup, ploughman's with up to 16 cheeses and six pâtés, full Jennings beer range kept well, keen friendly manager and staff; big TV, juke box, machines, pool table in the small mirrored snug, can get very busy with students and can be smoky; open all day (not Sun lunchtime unless Newcastle playing at home) *(Eric Larkham, Michael Doswell, Mike and Lynn Robinson)*

Tyne [Maling St]: Single-room pub at confluence of Ouseburn and Tyne, plastered with band posters and prints; Black Sheep, Durham Magus and two Mordue ales, exotic hot or cold sandwiches all day, free interestingly stocked CD juke box; fruit machine, sports TV, live music Sat afternoon, Weds/Sun evening, lavatories up stairs, can get very busy; usefully placed at end of quayside walk, fairy-lit garden (loudspeakers out here too) under an arch of Glasshouse Bridge, barbecues Sun lunch, early Fri evening; open all day *(Mike and Lynn Robinson, Kevin Thorpe,*

Eric Larkham, GSB, Dave Braisted)

North Bitchburn [NZ1732]

☆ ***Red Lion***: 17th-c beams, log fires, welcoming staff, good food inc good value hot meat sandwiches, well kept beers inc interesting guests, thriving atmosphere *(Keith Mould)*

North Hylton [NZ3557]

☆ ***Shipwrights*** [Ferryboat Lane; N bank of River Wear almost under the A19 bridge]: Welcoming pubby feel in bar and eating area of small riverside hotel, great log fire, chamber-pots and copper pans hanging from beams, extraordinary choice of enjoyable food running to ostrich and crocodile, mainstream things too, huge helpings, good friendly service; cosy bedrooms *(Bernie Adams)*

North Shields [NZ3470]

☆ ***Magnesia Bank*** [Camden St]: Big well run refurbished Victorian pub overlooking Tyne, well kept Durham, Mordue and guest beers in lined glasses, vast choice of cheerful home-made lunchtime food, friendly staff, open fire; quiet piped pop music, TV, machines; children welcome, tables outside, open all day, live music Thurs and Sun often featuring members of Lindisfarne *(Mike and Lynn Robinson)*

☆ ***Wooden Doll*** [Hudson St]: The high view of the fish quay and outer harbour is the big draw at this Jennings pub – get there early for a table in the largely no smoking glass-fronted extension; their full beer range kept well, enjoyable food inc fresh fish priced by size, helpful welcoming service, informal mix of furnishings in bare-boards bar, lots of paintings by local artists for sale; disabled facilities, children welcome till 8, some live music, open all day Sat *(Michael Doswell, Mike and Lynn Robinson, Eric Larkham, LYM, John Oddey)*

Piercebridge [NZ2115]

George [B6275 just S of village, over bridge]: Attractively placed rambling old inn, more hotel than pub now; usual bar food, pleasant riverside dining room and garden, provision for children; bedrooms, open all day *(John Poulter, LYM, Michael Doswell)*

Ponteland [NZ1871]

☆ ***Badger*** [Street Houses; A696 SE]: Well done Vintage Inn (unexpectedly sharing approach with main road garden centre), relaxing rooms and alcoves, old furnishings and olde-worlde décor, flagstones, carpet or bare wood, timbered ceilings, stripped stone, brick and timbering, real fires, Bass and Tetleys, good choice of wines by the glass and good hot drinks, generous reasonably priced food all day inc imaginative good value light dishes and interesting lunchtime sandwiches (most people here to eat – can get busy Sun lunchtime), pleasant attentive uniformed staff; quiet piped music; open all day, swallows may nest in porch *(GSB, John Foord, Karen and Graham Oddey, Keith Mould, M Borthwick, Jenny and Dave Hughes, BB)*

Rennington [NU2118]

Horseshoes: Neat flagstoned pub, comfortable and friendly, with good helpings of enjoyable honest food freshly cooked by cheerful landlady, well kept Bass and Courage Directors, good service, simple bar with lots of horsebrasses, compact restaurant with blue and white china; children welcome, tables outside, attractive quiet village near coast *(Stephen Auster, Michael Doswell)*

Riding Mill [NZ0161]

☆ ***Wellington*** [A695 just W of A68 roundabout]: Good 17th-c Chef & Brewer, carefully refurbished in tune with its age, beams, two big log fires and mix of tables and chairs, some upholstered, some not; very wide good value blackboard food choice from ciabatta sandwiches to nice puddings, Courage Directors and Theakstons Bitter and Black Bull, good shortish wine choice, friendly welcome and service; piped classical music, can get busy; disabled access, children welcome, play area and picnic-sets outside, pretty village with nearby walks and river *(Stephen, Julie and Hayley Brown, Andy and Jill Kassube, Michael Doswell)*

Rochester [NY8497]

Redesdale Arms [A68 3 miles W of Otterburn]: Comfortably pubby, with interesting prints and hunting photographs in prettily rebuilt terracotta-pink room, welcoming staff, well kept beer, good traditional food choice inc local organic lamb, one or two Scottish dishes and Sun carvery; good bedrooms *(Michael Doswell, Peter and Anne-Marie O'Malley)*

Romaldkirk [NY9922]

☆ ***Kirk***: Cosy and very friendly family-run local (landlord/chef is a schoolteacher), wide choice of interesting changing good value food (not Mon-Weds), well kept Castle Eden and a guest such as Black Sheep, good coffee and log fire, 18th-c stonework, paintings for sale; darts, piped popular classics; picnic-sets out by green of attractive moorland village, doubles as post office *(V Green, Kevin Thorpe)*

Rothbury [NU0602]

☆ ***Newcastle Hotel***: Small solid Victorian hotel in imposing spot at end of green, comfortably refurbished lounge with separate dining area, second bar, friendly service and entertaining locals (can be quite noisy wknd afternoons, when piped music may be loud), good plentiful carefully prepared food inc substantial Sun lunch, cheap high teas 3.30-5.30 Apr-Oct, toasties only winter Sun pm, real ales such as Blackawton Exhibition and Greene King Old Speckled Hen, no smoking upstairs dining room; good value comfortable bedrooms, open all day, handy for Cragside (NT) *(Keith and Janet Morris, Paul and Sue Merrick)*

Seaton Carew [NZ5230]

Charters [Staincliffe Hotel, The Cliff]: Nautical bric-a-brac, cheap doubles, decent wine choice (keg beers), full-size snooker table, evening food from sausages and mash up, sea view to Boulby Cliffs; quiz night Thurs, open all day wknds, bedrooms *(JHBS)*

Slaley [NY9757]

Rose & Crown: Early 18th-c pub with good home-made food from sandwiches to restaurant meals inc good value roast, well kept ales such as Black Sheep, Theakstons and Charles Well Bombardier, good choice of malt whiskies, chatty landlady and welcoming service, comfortable dark-beamed lounge hung with lots of mugs and jugs, public bar with darts, fruit machine, juke box; tables in small neat garden, quiet village with views behind, bedrooms attractive and well equipped *(Michael Doswell, Andy and Jill Kassube, Jack and Heather Coyle, Eric Larkham)*

☆ ***Travellers Rest*** [B6306 S of Hexham]: Large open-plan country pub, beams, flagstones and polished wood floors, comfortable high-backed settles forming discrete areas; enjoyable food (not Sun evening) from well filled baguettes and simple hot dishes (12-5) to more elaborate mealtime dishes in bar and pretty dining room, good children's menu, five well kept ales such as Black Sheep, Mordue and Wylam Gold Tankard, decent wines; tables outside with well equipped adventure play area behind, three bedrooms, open all day *(Eric Larkham, Andy and Jill Kassube, Michael Doswell)*

South Shields [NZ3766]

Alum Ale House [Ferry St (B1344)]: Unpretentious and relaxed 18th-c pub handy for ferry, big bars with real fire in old inglenook range, pictures and newspaper cuttings, well kept Banks's, Camerons, Marstons and a beer brewed for them by Durham, beer festivals with all sorts of rarities, good value basic lunchtime bar food inc good cheap filled stotties; piped music, machines, some live music; children welcome, open all day *(Mike and Lynn Robinson, Dave Braisted, Eric Larkham)*

Stamfordham [NZ0772]

Bay Horse [off B6309]: Cheery and comfortable long beamed bar with harness on walls, wide range of good value standard food, well kept ales such as Castle Eden and Marstons Pedigree, good coffee, friendly hard-working licensees; at end of green in attractive village *(John Oddey)*

Stanley [NZ1953]

Harperley Hotel [Harperley Country Park, 1½ miles W]: Good home cooking inc bargain three-course restaurant lunch and evening carvery, well kept Courage Directors and Jennings or Greene King; extensive grounds, good walks *(Mike and Lynn Robinson, M Borthwick)*

Stannington [NZ2279]

☆ ***Ridley Arms*** [just off A1 S of Morpeth]: Big dining pub, pleasantly and comfortably refurbished and extended in cosily relaxed rustic style, with good sensibly priced food served generously all day in several areas off main bar, popular family Sun lunch, friendly efficient staff, four well kept ales such as Batemans, Black Sheep, Caledonian Deuchars IPA and Timothy Taylors Landlord, quiet lounge, restaurant; children very welcome *(David and Heather Stephenson, John Oddey, LYM, M Borthwick, John Foord)*

Stockton-on-Tees [NZ4217]

☆ ***Masham*** [southern outskirts]: Four small rooms, each with its own character, from black and gold flock wallpaper to panelling, with showy chandeliers; well kept Black Sheep Special, good cheap baps, sandwiches and straightforward meals (not Sat evening or Sun), keen dominoes players, occasional live music; garden with aviary and play area backing on to paddock *(Pete Baker)*

Sun [Knowles St]: Friendly town local specialising in particularly well kept Bass, well served at tempting price; folk night Mon, open all day *(the Didler)*

Summerhouse [NZ2019]

Raby Hunt [B6279 7 miles NW of Darlington]: Well appointed old inn with burgundy upholstered seats, old wooden settle, antique prints with local connections, stuffed lady amherst pheasants; well kept Marstons, good reasonably priced imaginative food, friendly staff; dogs welcome, tables in back yard and in front *(Keith Mould)*

Tanfield Lea [NZ1855]

Peacock: Friendly pub with short choice of mainly home-cooked food inc good salads, welcoming staff and regulars *(Mike and Lynn Robinson)*

Thorpe Thewles [NZ4023]

Hamilton Russell Arms [Bank Terr (A177 Stockton—Sedgefield)]: Wide choice of enjoyable food from snacks to good fish range, well kept Charles Wells Bombardier, decent wines by the glass *(Eileen Wilkinson)*

Tynemouth [NZ3668]

Tynemouth Lodge [Tynemouth Rd (A193), ½ mile W of Tynemouth Metro station]: Genuine-feeling little Victorian-style pub (actually older), very popular for particularly well kept Bass, Belhaven 80/-, Caledonian Deuchars IPA, occasional guest beers and farm ciders, decent wines, cheap lunchtime filled rolls, coal fire; quiet on wkdy afternoons, can be packed and smoky evenings, and is very decidedly a local; no dogs or children; open all day, tables in back garden *(David Bell, Eric Larkham, LYM, Adrian Don)*

Wall [NY9269]

☆ ***Hadrian*** [Hexham—Bellingham/Rothbury Rd]: Two-room beamed lounge with wide choice of generous food inc speciality pies, well kept Jennings Cumberland and Worthington, good house wine, interesting reconstructions of Romano-British life, woodburner, quick pleasant service, no smoking bar and airy dining room; children welcome, unobtrusive piped music, games in public bar; neat garden, roomy comfortable bedrooms – back ones quieter, with good views *(Brian Root, Michael Doswell, Jack and Heather Coyle, BB)*

Warden [NY9267]

Boatside [½ mile N of A69]: Extended dining pub with pretty country-style interior redecorated in light warm colours, interesting bric-a-brac and World War II memorabilia, restaurant and smaller dining room, good range of bar food using fresh ingredients, friendly attentive service, Courage Directors and Theakstons; small neat enclosed garden, arractive spot by Tyne bridge *(Michael Doswell, Jack and Heather Coyle)*

Warkworth [NU2506]

Hermitage [Castle St]: Rambling local with interesting quaint décor, old range for heating, well kept Jennings and John Smiths, good value generous food from sandwiches to fresh local fish, quick service, dry-humoured landlord and staff, dining area and small plush upstairs restaurant; TV or piped music may obtrude; bedrooms, tables out in front, attractive setting *(Keith and Janet Morris, BB, Stephen and Jean Curtis, Eric Locker, Des and Jen Clarke)*

Masons Arms [Dial Pl]: Welcoming and comfortable thriving local, quick friendly service, good generous food inc good fish choice and bargain lunch, well kept Scottish Courage ales, good coffee, local pictures; dogs allowed, attractive back flagstoned courtyard *(Des and Jen Clarke, Jack and Heather Coyle)*

West Boldon [NZ3460]

Red Lion [Redcar Terrace]: Good very varied menu, big helpings, helpful staff *(Margaret and Brian Sanderson)*

West Moor [NZ2770]

George Stephenson [Great Lime Rd; northern outskirts of Newcastle]: Nicely refurbished, with friendly staff, good choice of interesting changing northern ales such as Durham, Northumberland and Wylam, frequent bargains; good busy live music nights Weds, Thurs and Sat, Mon quiz night, open all day *(Ian Cook, Mike and Lynn Robinson)*

West Sleekburn [NZ2985]

Foresters Arms: Welcoming, with good value generous usual lunchtime food esp gammon, well kept Stones and Worthington *(John W Allen)*

Whittonstall [NZ0757]

Anchor [B6309 N of Consett]: Spotless stone-built beamed dining pub with comfortable banquettes in L-shaped lounge, dining area with high-raftered pitched roof, attractive rag-rolling above pine dado, interesting old north-east photographs and facsimile posters, huge choice of generous food from good sandwich and baguette range through unusual hot dishes to popular Sun lunch, well kept Courage Directors and Theakstons, good coffee; piped music; nice countryside *(Michael Doswell, Andy and Jill Kassube, John Oddey)*

Wooler [NT9928]

Tankerville Arms [A697 N]: Pleasant hotel bar in tastefully modernised old building, good choice of local meat and fish (small helpings on request), Hadrian & Border Farne Island and other ales such as Greene King Old Speckled Hen and Tetleys, very helpful service, smart restaurant (may have local folk music Sun lunchtime); pleasant setting, nice garden, bedrooms *(Jack and Heather Coyle, Darly Graton, Graeme Gulibert, Stephen and Jean Curtis)*

Wylam [NZ1265]

Boathouse [Station Rd; across Tyne from village]: Warm and comfortable two-room pub with up to nine real ales inc several from the local Wylam Brewery, good choice of malt whiskies, succulent generous lunchtime sandwiches, early evening pizzas, kebabs, curries etc, Sun lunch, roaring coal fire; children welcome, Sat afternoon impromptu folk/blues sessions, open all day *(Andy and Jill Kassube, John Foord, Eric Larkham)*

Nottinghamshire

Nottinghamshire scores highly for pub value, with drinks prices well below the national average, and plenty of bargain food. In this pocket-friendly vein, pubs currently doing particularly well here are the Victoria in Beeston (interesting food and lots of real ales), the friendly Nelson & Railway just by Hardys & Hansons brewery in Kimberley, the canalside Fellows Morton & Clayton brewing its own very cheap beers in Nottingham, the intriguing Olde Trip to Jerusalem burrowed into the sandstone rock below Nottingham castle, and the cheerful Three Horse Shoes up in Walkeringham – a remarkable sight in summer, with the thousands of flowering plants they raise each year. Two more upmarket dining pubs are rewarding for a special meal out: the Caunton Beck at Caunton, and the Martins Arms at Colston Bassett. Both (particularly the Martins Arms) are expensive, but both serve such good interesting food in such pleasant surroundings that this year readers – always quick to condemn a bad price/quality balance – give unqualified approval. In a close finish, the Caunton Beck at Caunton takes the title of Nottinghamshire Dining Pub of the Year; it has the extra merit of serving food all day, from breakfast-time till late. Two new entries here make a nice contrast with each other: the relaxing rambling beamed Full Moon at Morton (good attractively priced food), and the extraordinary Pit & Pendulum in Nottingham (a thoroughly well done weird theme bar). The Lucky Dip section at the end of the chapter also has some interesting prospects, most notably the Horse & Plough at Bingham, Beehive at Maplebeck, Market Hotel in Retford and Stratford Haven in West Bridgford. Throughout the area, it's worth looking out for Tynemill pubs: reliably good unpretentious value. As we have said, drinks prices here are relatively low. Besides Hardys & Hansons, and the former main regional brewer Mansfield (which is now part of the same combine as Banks's and Marstons), the county has quite a few good value small brewers to look out for, including Castle Rock, Springhead, Mallard, Broadstone, and three brewers associated with pubs included in the Lucky Dip section – Dover Beck (Black Horse at Caythorpe), Alcazar (Fox & Crown in Nottingham) and Nottingham (Plough there).

BEESTON SK5338 Map 7

Victoria

Dovecote Lane, backing on to railway station

A good all-rounder, with interesting enjoyable food and an impressive choice of drinks. Around half of the daily changing blackboard menu is vegetarian, and alongside sandwiches (from £1.50), good value dishes could include chilli vegetable burritos (£5.95), halloumi and red pepper kebabs (£6.50), and lentil and roast vegetable moussaka (£6.95), as well as lincolnshire sausages and mash (£5.95), caribbean-style red snapper (£8.50), and sautéed guinea fowl with wild mushrooms and pastis or lamb souvlakia (£8.95); home-made puddings such as Irish whiskey trifle or apple and cinnamon crumble (from £2.95). They serve around 12 real ales, including Batemans XB, Caledonian IPA, Castle Rock

Hemlock and Rylands Gold and Everards Tiger, alongside changing guests such as Dark Star Cascade, Hop Back Thunderstorn, Oakham JHB, Ossett Silver King and Whim Hartington IPA; they've also farm ciders, over 100 malt whiskies, 20 Irish whiskeys, and a dozen wines by the glass. An unpretentious place, the pub has been converted from an almost derelict railway hotel, and the lounge and bar back on to the railway station; a covered area outside with heaters has picnic-sets overlooking the station platform where trains pass a few feet below. The three downstairs rooms in their original long narrow layout have simple solid traditional furnishings, very unfussy décor, stained-glass windows, stripped woodwork and floorboards (woodblock in some rooms), newspapers to read, and a chatty atmosphere; dominoes, cribbage, piped music. *(Recommended by Keith Allen, Revd D Glover, Kevin Blake, MP, Darly Graton, Graeme Gulibert, JP, PP, Peter and Jean Hoare, David Eberlin, the Didler, Shaun Pinchbeck, James and Laura Newton, Blaise Vyner, Stephen Buckley, Mike and Wena Stevenson, Mandy and Simon King, Andrew Crawford)*

Free house ~ Licensee Neil Kelso ~ Real ale ~ Bar food (12-8.45; 12-7.45 Sun) ~ (0115) 925 4049 ~ Dogs allowed in bar ~ Live music Sun night ~ Open 11-11; 12-10.30 Sun

CAUNTON SK7460 Map 7

Caunton Beck

Main Street; village signposted off A616 Newark—Ollerton

Nottinghamshire Dining Pub of the Year

With lots of flowers and plants in summer, the terrace of this civilised, pleasantly set dining pub is a nice place to sit when the weather is fine. Readers really enjoy the good well presented (though not cheap) food here, which is served all day. As well as delicious sandwiches (from £4.95) and a hearty English breakfast (£6.50), the monthly changing menu might include thai spiced fishcakes with ginger and lime mayonnaise or tiger prawn tempura with chilli spiced plum sauce (£5.95), roast lamb shoulder with ratatouille vegetables and rosemary jus or battered cod goujons with home-made chunky chips (£9.95), and fried steak with lyonnaise potatoes (£13.50), with changing daily specials such as chicken liver parfait with fig and grape chutney or warm goats cheese salad with orange and beetroot (£4.95), oriental marinated duck breast with wilted bok choy (£12.95), and seared bass with hollandaise (£13.95); puddings could be dark chocolate truffle with cherries or white chocolate and raspberry crème brûlée (£4.50). They also do daily specials and two- and three-course set meals (£9/£12, not Friday and Saturday nor lunchtime Sunday). Good house wines include a choice of half bottles, and they've well kept Greene King Ruddles Best and County on handpump, and a guest such as Charles Wells Bombardier; freshly squeezed orange juice too. Service is pleasant and attentive; daily papers and magazines, no music. Almost new, but not new-looking, this spacious pub was reconstructed, using original timbers and reclaimed oak, around the skeleton of the old Hole Arms. Scrubbed pine tables and country-kitchen chairs, low beams and rag-finished paintwork help create a relaxed atmosphere. *(Recommended by Neville Kenyon, Kevin Thorpe, Mr and Mrs J Glover, Roger and Maureen Kenning, Derek and Sylvia Stephenson, Blaise Vyner,*

B, M and P Kendall, Ray and Winifred Halliday, David and Helen Wilkins, Michael Doswell, Dr G E Martin, David and Ruth Hollands,John Brightley, Tim and Sue Halstead, Darly Graton, Graeme Gulibert, Joy and Peter Heatherley, Margaret and Roy Randle, Bob Arnett, Judy Wayman)

Free house ~ Licensees Paul Vidic and Julie Allwood ~ Real ale ~ Bar food (8am-10.30pm) ~ Restaurant ~ (01636) 636793 ~ Children welcome ~ Dogs allowed in bar ~ Open 8am-12 midnight

Planning a day in the country? We list pubs in really attractive scenery at the back of the book.

COLSTON BASSETT SK7033 Map 7

Martins Arms

Village signposted off A46 E of Nottingham; School Lane, near market cross in village centre

Although they are quite happy to serve you just a drink at this smart country dining pub, it is very restauranty at heart. The food is imaginative and good (but certainly not cheap), and using high quality ingredients dishes could include soup (£4.50), sandwiches (from £4.50, speciality ones such as chargrilled chicken with chorizo and pepper mayonnaise from £7.50), poached quails egg with truffle and chive salad, smoked haddock with welsh rarebit and wilted spinach or rabbit and goats cheese croquette (£9), delicious ploughman's (£9.50), halibut poached in red wine with creamed celeriac, pancetta and savoy cabbage or quail and foie gras ravioli with leeks, red wine and madeira (£17.50), and lamb fillets with wild mushroom polenta (£18), with tempting puddings such as chocolate fondant with bitter chocolate ice cream and white chocolate sauce or roasted pears (£5.50); they also have English cheeses (£7). The elegant restaurant is smartly decorated with period fabrics and colourings. Antique furnishings, hunting prints and warm log fires in the Jacobean fireplaces give an upmarket air to the comfortable bar, and there's a proper snug; staff are neatly uniformed and well trained. Around eight well kept real ales on handpump could include Bass, Batemans XB, Black Sheep, Greene King IPA, Marstons Pedigree and Woodfordes Wherry; they've a good range of malt whiskies and cognacs, and an interesting wine list; cribbage and dominoes. There are tables out in the sizeable attractive lawned garden, which backs on to estate parkland, but you might be asked to leave your credit card behind the bar if you want to eat outside; in summer you can play croquet. They've converted the pub stables into an antiques shop; readers recommend Colston Bassett Dairy just outside the village, which sells its own stilton cheese. *(Recommended by Derek and Sylvia Stephenson, Ian Phillips, R Naish, the Didler, Roger A Bellingham, Hugh Roberts, Phil and Jane Hodson, Roger and Maureen Kenning, Philip Atkins, JP, PP, A C and E Johnson, Doug Christian)*

Free house ~ Licensees Lynne Strafford Bryan and Salvatore Inguanta ~ Real ale ~ Bar food (12-2, 6-10; not Sun evenings) ~ Restaurant ~ (01949) 81361 ~ Children in restaurant and family room ~ Open 12-3, 6-11; 12-3, 7-10.30 Sun; closed 25 Dec evening

ELKESLEY SK6975 Map 7

Robin Hood

High Street; village well signposted just off A1 Newark—Blyth

They do good coffees at this friendly village local – a handy place to know about if you need a break from the A1. Readers like the tasty well presented changing bar food, which might include sandwiches (from £2.50), delicious bacon and brie baguettes (£4.50), moules marinière (£5), smoked haddock fishcakes with steamed spinach and mustard cream sauce, ploughman's or ham, egg and chips with mushy peas (£5.50), roast vegetable lasagne (£7.50), roast lamb rump with pesto mash and rosemary and garlic gravy (£11.50), and blackboard specials such as stir-fried chicken and peppers with chilli sauce (£8) and grilled plaice with spring onion and garlic dressing (£8.50); puddings (£4). The warm and welcoming roomy carpeted dining room and lounge area are both decorated in a traditional style; darts, TV, fruit machines, and unobtrusive piped music. The friendly and efficient staff serve Boddingtons, Flowers IPA and Marstons Pedigree on handpump. The garden (which is moderately well screened from the A1) has picnic-sets and a play area. *(Recommended by D L Parkhurst, Tony Gayfer, John and Sylvia Harrop, Mr and Mrs J Glover, Mr and Mrs J E C Tasker, Peter Walker, Irene and Ray Atkin, Mrs P J Pearce, Hazel and Michael Duncombe, Peter Wrobbel, Rita and Keith Pollard)*

Enterprise ~ Lease Alan Draper ~ Real ale ~ Bar food (not Sun evening) ~ Restaurant ~ (01777) 838259 ~ Children welcome ~ Dogs allowed in bar ~ Open 12-3, 6-11 (7-10.30 Sun)

KIMBERLEY SK5044 Map 7

Nelson & Railway £

1¾ miles from M1 junction 26; at exit roundabout take A610 towards Ripley, then signposted Kimberley, pub in Station Road

Well worth the short diversion from the M1, this two-roomed Victorian pub is a cheery, bustling place. The friendly beamed bar and lounge have a mix of Edwardian-looking furniture, with interesting brewery prints and railway signs on the walls (the pub's name comes from a shortening of its original title the Lord Nelson Railway Hotel, in the days when it stood yards away from two competing stations). The Hardys & Hansons brewery is directly opposite, and they've well kept Kimberley Best and Classic and a seasonal ale on handpump. The staff are friendly and hardworking, and it's popular locally; darts, alley and table skittles, dominoes, chess, cribbage, Scrabble, fruit machine and juke box. Readers enjoy the good value straightforward bar food, which includes soup (£1.50), sandwiches (from £1.40; hot rolls from £1.70), garlic chicken goujons (£2.90), cottage pie (£3.30), ploughman's (£4.70), steak and ale pie or mushroom stroganoff (£4.90), breaded scampi or chicken tikka masala (£5.40), blackboard specials such as Mexican avocado (£3.90), shark (£4.95), and puddings (£1.90); the dining room is no smoking at meal times. They also do a good Sunday lunch (£4.50), and children's meals (£1.65). There are tables and swings out in a good-sized cottagey garden. *(Recommended by Pete Baker, Roger and Maureen Kenning, Peter F Marshall, Bernie Adams, the Didler, Derek and Sylvia Stephenson, JP, PP, Richard Lewis, Andy Gosling, Mr and Mrs J McRobert, David Carr, Shaun Pinchbeck, Karen Eliot, Dr and Mrs A K Clarke)*

Hardys & Hansons ~ Tenant Harry Burton ~ Real ale ~ Bar food (12-2.30, 5.30-9; 12-6 Sun) ~ (0115) 938 2177 ~ Children in eating area of bar ~ Dogs allowed in bar ~ Open 11.30-11; 12-10.30 Sun ~ Bedrooms: £24S(£24B)/£39S(£39B)

LAXTON SK7267 Map 7

Dovecote

Signposted off A6075 E of Ollerton

Close to the A1, this popular red brick house is an enjoyable place to stop for something to eat. The central room has brocaded button-back built-in corner seats, stools and chairs, and a coal-effect gas fire, and it opens through a small bay (the former entrance) into another similar room. Around the other side, another simple room with some entertaining Lawson Wood 1930s tourist cartoons leads through to a pool room with darts, TV, fruit machine, pool, dominoes and piped music; no smoking area. Served by very friendly and helpful staff, large helpings of reasonably priced bar food include home-made soup (£2.85), sandwiches (from £3.25), mushroom stroganoff or steak and kidney pie (£6.20), and sweet and sour battered chicken (£6.99), with specials such as fresh cod with good chips or lambs liver (£6.99), and pork loin (£7.50); puddings such as cheesecake (£2.85), and a range of ice creams (from £3.25); part of the dining area is no smoking. Mansfield Bitter and two weekly changing guests such as Everards Beacon and Hardys & Hansons Guzzling Goose. There are wooden tables and chairs on a small front terrace by a sloping garden, which has a disused white dovecote and a children's play area. As well as the two bedrooms, they have a site for six caravans with lavatories and showers. Laxton is one of the few places in the country still farmed using the traditional open field system, and the pub stands next to three huge medieval open fields. Every year in the third week of June the grass is auctioned for haymaking, and anyone who lives in the parish is entitled to a bid – and a drink. You can find out more at the visitor centre behind the pub. *(Recommended by Nick and Pam Hancock, Kevin Thorpe, JWAC, JP, PP, Keith and Chris O'Neill, Marcus Byron, Patrick Hancock)*

Free house ~ Licensees Stephen and Betty Shepherd ~ Real ale ~ Bar food ~ (01777) 871586 ~ Children away from bar ~ Dogs allowed in bar ~ Open 11.30-3, 6.30-11.30; 12-3, 7-11 Sun ~ Bedrooms: £30B/£45B

MORTON SK7251 Map 7

Full Moon

Pub and village signposted off Bleasby—Fiskerton back road, SE of Southwell

This rambling beamed pub is a pleasantly relaxed spot for a good value lunch – especially if you qualify for the £5.25 two-course OAP bargain. The main part has pink plush seats and cushioned black settles around a variety of pub tables, with wheelback chairs in the side dining area, and a couple of fireplaces; fresh flowers and the very long run of Christmas plates on the walls give a spot of colour. The enjoyable food could include soup (£2.25), sandwiches (from £2.95), home-made pâté with cumberland sausage (£3.85), smoked salmon with scrambled egg (£5.50), leek and mushroom samosas (£7.25), grilled salmon with basil mayonnaise or braised lamb knuckle with mint sauce (£8.75), and steaks (from £9.95); puddings such as blackberry and apple pie or treacle sponge pudding (£3.75). Well kept Caythorpe Dover Beck and Charles Wells Bombardier alongside a couple of guests such as Archers Best and Theakstons Old Peculier on handpump, friendly service; there may be piped music. There are picnic-sets out on a peaceful back terrace, with a sizeable garden, and some sturdy play equipment. This out-of-the-way hamlet is not far from the River Trent; look out for the two sociable pub cats. *(Recommended by Dr B and Mrs P B Baker, JP, PP, the Didler, CMW, JJW)*

Free house ~ Licensees Clive and Kim Wisdom ~ Real ale ~ Bar food (12-2; 6.30-9.30(10 Fri/Sat); 12-2.30, 7-9.30 Sun) ~ Restaurant ~ (01636) 830251 ~ Children welcome ~ Open 11-3, 6-11(10.30 Sun); closed 26 Dec evening and 1 Jan

NOTTINGHAM SK5640 Map 7

Fellows Morton & Clayton £

Canal Street (part of inner ring road)

Just a short walk away from Nottingham station, this carefully converted old canal building pub is especially worth visiting if you like real ale. From a big window in the quarry-tiled glassed-in area at the back of the pub you can see the little brewery where they brew their own Samuel Fellows and Post Haste; around five other well kept real ales could include Oakham JHB, Mallard Best and Timothy Taylors Landlord on handpump. There's a really buzzy atmosphere in the softly lit bar which has dark red plush seats built into alcoves, wooden tables, more seats up two or three steps in a side gallery, and bric-a-brac on the shelf just below the glossy dark green high ceiling; a sympathetic extension provides extra seating. Piped pop music, fruit machine, big TV, and daily newspapers on a rack; service is prompt and friendly. The reasonably priced bar food is popular: it includes home-made soup (£1.95), filled baguettes (from £4.95), chicken and pasta bake, steak and kidney pie and 5oz rump steak (£5.95), battered haddock (£5.95), and a couple of daily specials such as roast beef (£4.25), and tortellini with creamy spinach sauce (£4.95), with puddings such as crêpes suzette, cheesecake and profiteroles (£2.95-£4.95); the no smoking restaurant does a bargain two-course lunch (£4.95). At lunchtime it's popular with local workers, while in the evenings you'll find a younger set, when it can get smoky. The large terrace has views of the canal from good seats and tables. *(Recommended by JP, PP, Patrick Hancock, SLC, David Carr, the Didler, Richard Lewis)*

Own brew ~ Licensees Les Howard and Keely Willans ~ Real ale ~ Bar food (11.30-10; 12-6 Sun) ~ Restaurant ~ (0115) 950 6795 ~ Children in restaurant ~ Open 11-11(12.30 Fri/Sat); 12-10.30 Sun

Lincolnshire Poacher £

Mansfield Road; up hill from Victoria Centre

Food prices at this homely, popular town pub haven't changed since last year, and they now do tapas too (£1.50-£3.95). Most people, however, come for the well kept real ale. Twelve handpumps serve around eight changing guest ales from brewers such as Caledonian, their linked local Castle Rock brewery, Grainstore Oakham and Whim, alongside Batemans XB and XXXB, Castle Rock Poachers Gold and Oakham JHB; also good ciders, around 85 malt whiskies and 10 Irish ones, and good value soft drinks. Apart from sandwiches (from £1.50, served all day), tasty reasonably priced daily specials might include lincolnshire sausages and mash or home-made steak and kidney pie (£5.25), grilled tuna steak (£5.50), lasagne (£4.95), and goats cheese ravioli (£4.75); no chips. The traditional big wood-floored front bar has wall settles and plain wooden tables, and is decorated with breweriana; it opens on to a plain but lively room on the left, from where a corridor takes you down to the chatty panelled back snug, with newspapers to read; cribbage, dominoes, cards, backgammon, piped music; no smoking area at lunchtime. In the evenings, when it's popular with a younger crowd, it can get very busy. A conservatory overlooks tables on a large terrace behind. *(Recommended by Comus and Sarah Elliott, David Carr, Patrick Hancock, Tony and Wendy Hobden, the Didler, Rona Murdoch, JP, PP, Derek and Sylvia Stephenson, Roger and Jenny Huggins, Doug Christian)*

Tynemill ~ Manager David Whittaker ~ Real ale ~ Bar food (12-7.30; 12-4 Fri-Sun) ~ (0115) 9411584 ~ Dogs allowed in bar ~ Open 11-11; 12-10.30 Sun

Olde Trip to Jerusalem ★ £

Brewhouse Yard; from inner ring road follow The North, A6005 Long Eaton signpost until you are in Castle Boulevard, then almost at once turn right into Castle Road; pub is up on the left

A fascinating pub this, built into caverns burrowing into the sandstone rock below the castle; the panelled walls of the unique upstairs bar (thought to have served as cellarage for an early medieval brewhouse which stood here) soar narrowly into a dark cleft above. Also mainly carved from the rock, the downstairs bar has leatherette-cushioned settles built into the dark panelling, tables on flagstones, and more low-ceilinged rock alcoves; there's also a no smoking parlour/snug, and two more caves open to visitors. Service is prompt and friendly, and the pub attracts a good mix of people, with tourists, locals and students all adding to the chatty atmosphere. They keep their real ales in top condition, and you'll find Hardys & Hansons Kimberley Best, Best Mild, Classic, a beer brewed for the pub, and their Cellarman's Cask (brewed every two months or so) alongside Marstons Pedigree on handpump. Attractively priced straightforward bar food includes soup (£1.20), sandwiches (from £1.99), burgers (from £2.29), sausage and mash (£3.99), giant filled yorkshire pudding, liver and onions, steak and ale pie and cod and chips (£4.99), scampi (£5.29), and rump steak (£5.99), with puddings (from £1.99). They've ring the bull (and a fruit machine), and there are some seats outside. The name of the pub is a reference to the 12th-c crusaders who used to meet on this site on the way to the Holy Land. *(Recommended by David Carr, R T and J C Moggridge, Rona Murdoch, Patrick Hancock, the Didler, Keith and Janet Morris, Kevin Blake, James Nunns, JP, PP, John W Allen, Peter F Marshall, SLC, Keith Allen, Richard Lewis, Stephen Buckley)*

Hardys & Hansons ~ Manager Claire Underdown ~ Real ale ~ Bar food (11(12 Sun)-6; not 25 Dec) ~ (0115) 9473171 ~ Children in family area ~ Open 11-11; 12-10.30 Sun

Pit & Pendulum

Victoria Street

This is worth seeing for its well done gothic horror film décor, with really entertaining attention to detail: it's dark and dramatic, lit by heavy chandeliers and (electronically) flaring torches, with flashes of colour from an overhead tangle of Frankenstein-laboratory glass tubing and wiring. Dark seating runs from gothick thrones to spooky red-padded side booths with a heavy bat's-wing hint, tables are inset with ancient documents and arcane jewellery – and even cups and saucers have a spider's web design (the coffee is good). There is plenty of ghoulish carving and creeping ivy, and when we went an old black and white *Dracula* film was showing in silence above the bar counter – where a tortuous web of piping replaced the usual beer taps. Good wheelchair ramps add cleverly to the design, with their curves and heavy black balusters, and the disabled lavatory is through a false bookcase. Down stairs (and that is indeed a shackled skeleton looming through the distorted glass) there's more of the same, with more clearly separated areas, and some more conventional seating. On our visit the only false note was a Spice Girl disc playing, but the piped music is very well reproduced. Friendly staff; usual bar food; fruit machine. *(Recommended by Kevin Blake)*

Scottish Courage ~ Licensee Ian Povey ~ Bar food (11-10.30; 12-9 Sun) ~ (0115) 9506383 ~ Open 11-11; 12-10.30 Sun

Vat & Fiddle £

Queens Bridge Road, alongside Sheriffs Way (nr multi-storey car park)

It's not surprising that this plain brick pub keeps its five Castle Rock beers in such good condition – it's right next to the brewery. Alongside the mostly quite full-bodied real ales, which often include a Stout, they serve an equal number of guests from brewers such as Caledonian, Oakham and Whim on handpump; occasional beer festivals. They also have around 70 malt whiskies, farm cider, continental bottled beers and Polish vodkas; good value soft drinks, too. The simple bar has quite a strong 1930s feel with cream and navy walls and ceiling, varnished pine tables and bentwood stools and chairs on parquet and terrazzo flooring, plain blue curtains, and some brewery memorabilia; there are magazines and newspapers to read, and occasional TV and piped music. The atmosphere is chatty and relaxed. Aside from a decent choice of rolls which are served all day (from £1.50), the very short (and reasonably priced) straightforward menu includes soup (£2.25), vegetarian sausage and mash (£3.25), chilli (£3.50), Hemlock sausage and mash (£3.95), and beef in ale (£4.95). There are picnic-sets on a front terrace by the road, and more on a back terrace; the train and bus stations are both a short walk away. *(Recommended by SLC, Richard Lewis, C J Fletcher, JP, PP, the Didler, David Carr)*

Tynemill ~ Managers Julian Grocock and N Trafford ~ Real ale ~ Bar food (12-3, 6-8, not Sun evening) ~ (0115) 985 0611 ~ Dogs allowed in bar ~ Open 11-11; 12-10.30 Sun

Via Fossa

Canal Street (on corner of inner ring road)

This surreally romantic interpretation of a medieval castle is interesting to wander around, with big winding staircases, dark red passages, organ pipes and ecclesiastical woodwork in a chapel, a massive clock that seems to be tumbling off the wall, iron chandeliers, Royal portraits in oils, roaring fires in stone fireplaces, intricately carved panelling – and then some decadent 90s twists such as zebra print upholstery on asymmetrical furniture against sea-green walls. Exploring the various galleries and balconies of this huge converted warehouse, you get the feeling that you are looking up or down on to different sections and rooms on a film set. A wall of french windows opens on to a big tiered terrace next to the canal, and there are more smart wood tables out on a heavily planted first-floor terrace with the same view; both of these are very popular in the summer. The enjoyable bar food includes soup (£3.50), filled toasted baguettes (from £4.25), steak and red onion tortilla wrap (£4.75), moules marinière (£5.75), fish and chips or sausages and mash (£6.25), and red thai chicken curry or indonesian vegetable curry (£6.95), with puddings such as hot chocolate pudding (from £3.95); there may be a wait when they're busy. The well reproduced piped pop has more presence than just background music, and the monastic-style antiqued lavatories have rows of butler's sinks for hand-washing. John Smiths is served at the six counters dotted around; they've decent wines and daily papers. *(Recommended by David Carr, Kevin Blake, the Didler, Keith and Suzie Stevens, JP, PP)*

Scottish Courage ~ Manager Alan Townend ~ Real ale ~ Bar food (11-10.30; 12-10 Sun) ~ Restaurant ~ (0115) 947 3904 ~ DJs Fri and Sat ~ Open 11-11(12 Thurs-Sat); 12-10.30 Sun; closed 25 Dec

WALKERINGHAM SK7792 Map 7

Three Horse Shoes

High Street; just off A161, off A631 W of Gainsborough

Summer's the best time to visit this friendly village pub, when the licensees' spectacular hanging baskets and flower displays transform the frontage into a blaze of colour. The 9,000 plants they use make a charmingly vivid contrast to the slight austerity of the simple old-fashioned décor inside. But this isn't just a feast for the eyes: served by cheerfully welcoming staff, a good choice of enjoyable food could include sandwiches (from £1.25), home-made soup (£1.95), fried mushrooms stuffed with garlic cheese or home-made pâté (£3.25), home-made steak pie or mushroom, cheese, leek and nut pie (£6.25), gammon and pineapple (£6.50), sirloin steak (£8.95), and – a favourite with readers – beef medallions in a brandy and stilton sauce (£9.95); puddings such as sticky toffee pudding (£2.25). You'll find well kept Bass, Stones, Worthington Best and a guest beer such as Adnams Broadside on handpump. Darts, dominoes, fruit machine, video game, and piped music. Outside there are seats among the flowers, and a japanese-style millennium garden up by the top car park. *(Recommended by JP, PP, Walter and Susan Rinaldi-Butcher, WAH, Mike and Sue Loseby, CMW, JJW, Derek and Sylvia Stephenson)*

Free house ~ Licensee John Turner ~ Real ale ~ Bar food (not Sun evening) ~ Restaurant ~ (01427) 890959 ~ Children welcome ~ Open 11.30-3, 7-11; 12-3.30, 7-10 Sun

Lucky Dip

Besides the fully inspected pubs, you might like to try these Lucky Dips recommended to us and described by readers (if you do, please send us reports: www.goodguides.com).

Annesley Woodhouse [SK4953]
General Havelock [Skegby Rd]: Good choice of home-made food inc traditional Sun lunch and special menus, good welcoming atmosphere, friendly landlord and staff, quiz nights *(Joanne Whitmore)*

Awsworth [SK4844]
Gate [Main St, via A6096 off A610 Nuthall—Eastwood bypass]: Friendly old traditional local with Hardys & Hansons Best and Mild, coal fire in lounge, small pool room; near site of once-famous railway viaduct – photographs in passage *(JP, PP, the Didler)*

Bagthorpe [SK4751]
Dixies Arms [2 miles from M1 junction 27; A608 towards Eastwood, then first right on to B600 via Sandhill Rd, then first left into School Rd; Lower Bagthorpe]: Well kept real ales in quaint 18th-c beamed and tiled-floor local, entrance bar with tiny snug next to bar, small part-panelled parlour with fine fireplace, longer narrow room with toby jugs and darts, friendly landlord and labrador; unobtrusive fruit machine, rarely used juke box; jazz or folk Sat, quiz night Sun, big garden with wknd barbecues, play area and football pitch, own pigeon, gun and morris dancing clubs; open 2-11, all day wknds *(JP, PP, the Didler)*

Beeston [SK5236]
Hop Pole [High Rd, Chilwell]: Welcoming local with well kept ales such as Bass, Ind Coope Burton, Marstons Pedigree and two or three guests, limited evening food, comfortable new seating in lounge, bare-boards stripped-brick back bar with pool and small TV; good juke box not too loud, games machine; children and dogs welcome, tables outside *(TF, Julie James)*

Besthorpe [SK8264]
Lord Nelson [Main Rd]: Tastefully refurbished keeping old character, flagstones, old wooden furniture, very attentive helpful staff, wide choice of good reasonably priced fresh home-made food, good range of well kept beers inc Timothy Taylors Landlord *(Graham and Elizabeth Hargreaves)*

Bingham [SK7039]
☆ ***Horse & Plough*** [A52]: Low beams, flagstones and stripped brick, prints and old brewery memorabilia, comfortable open-plan seating inc pews, good value generous lunchtime baguettes, melts, baked potatoes and three or four hot dishes, well kept Courage Directors, Charles Wells Bombardier and guest beers such as Everards Beacon, Gales Trafalgar, Greene King

Old Speckled Hen and Ringwood Best, good wine choice, popular upstairs grill room (Tues-Sat, and Sun lunch) with polished boards, hand-painted murals and open kitchen; piped music, corner TV; open all day *(Hugh Roberts, the Didler, BB)*

Bleasby [SK7149]

Waggon & Horses [Gypsy Lane]: Comfortable banquettes in carpeted lounge, open fire in character bar, Banks's and Marstons Pedigree, reasonably priced fresh lunchtime food from snacks up, Fri fish and chips night, chatty landlord; piped music; back lobby with play area and comfortable chairs to watch over it, tables outside, small camping area behind *(the Didler)*

Blidworth [SK5954]

Fox & Hounds [Calverton Rd, Blidworth Bottoms]: Unpretentious comfort in two-part lounge and partly no smoking back dining room, enjoyable bargain food (not Sun evening, may be a wait when busy), attractively priced Hardys & Hansons real ales; piped music; children and dogs allowed, tables outside, bedrooms, riding school nearby *(Michael and Jenny Back)*

Blyth [SK6287]

Angel [Bawtry Rd]: Cheerful much-modernised coaching inn with partly no smoking lounge/dining area, nice coal fire, assorted furniture, full range of Hardys & Hansons ales kept well, usual food inc good value Sun lunch (rare around here so get there early – they don't take bookings), good friendly service; piped music, smaller public bar and pool room; children welcome, garden with play area, simple bedrooms *(CMW, JJW, LYM, Derek and Sylvia Stephenson)*

Brinsley [SK4649]

Yew Tree [Cordy Lane]: Large well appointed pub with friendly helpful staff, lots of copper and brass and coal fire in attractive lounge, wide-ranging nicely presented food, well kept Hardys & Hansons ales, restaurant *(Kevin Blake)*

Burton Joyce [SK6443]

☆ *Wheatsheaf* [A612 E of Nottingham]: Well refurbished Chef & Brewer, several softly lit and fairly individually furnished rooms around a central bar, antiques and grandfather clock, lots of wine bottles scattered around; very wide choice of decent food, well kept Courage Directors and Theakstons Best and XB, log and coal fires; piped music; good garden areas, good disabled access and facilities *(BB, Kevin Blake)*

Car Colston [SK7242]

Royal Oak [The Green, off Tenman Lane (off A46 not far from A6097 junction)]: Largeish 18th-c pub opp one of England's biggest village greens, woodburner in main room, unusual vaulted brick ceiling in second room, good choice of reasonably priced food inc children's and popular Sun lunch, well kept Mansfield and Marstons Pedigree, decent coffee, good soft drinks choice, fresh flowers and pot plants; piped music; picnic-sets on roomy back lawn, open all day Sun, cl Mon lunchtime *(Andrew Crawford, CMW, JJW)*

Caythorpe [SK6845]

Black Horse [Main St, off A6097 NE of Nottingham]: 300-year-old country local, recently extended but unspoilt and uncluttered, run by same family for many years; microbrewery producing its own good Dover Beck ales, guests such as Bass and Black Sheep, enjoyable food (not Sun) inc imaginative sandwiches, good fresh fish Weds-Fri, Mon curry night, small bar, larger tap room across yard, real fire; opp pottery, handy for Trent walks *(the Didler, CMW, JJW, Norma and Keith Bloomfield)*

Clarborough [SK7383]

Gate [Smeath Lane]: Welcoming open-plan pub in attractive spot by Chesterfield Canal, good value food esp fish and chips, all freshly cooked (so can be a wait if busy), Adnams, Mansfield and Stones, good choice of other drinks, open fire, no smoking area, restaurant overlooking waterside garden; piped music; moorings available *(CMW, JJW, Mike and Sue Loseby)*

Cossall [SK4843]

Gardeners [Awsworth Lane (A6096, Cossall Marsh)]: Open-plan local with cheap well kept Hardys & Hansons Bitter, Mild and seasonal beers, good value lunchtime food, end games area with pool and sports TV *(the Didler)*

Cotgrave [SK6435]

Rose & Crown [Main Rd, off A46 SE of Nottingham]: Comfortably refurbished, with good value food all day inc more elaborate evening dishes, Boddingtons and guest beers such as Burton Bridge Golden Delicious *(Norma and Keith Bloomfield, Sally Bates)*

Drakeholes [SK7090]

White Swan [off A631 Bawtry—Gainsborough]: Several spacious carpeted rooms, lots of pictures, civilised plush lounge bar, partly no smoking, attractively airy brasserie-style restaurant with good range of light dishes from sandwiches up all day, extensive lunchtime carvery, friendly efficient staff, two real ales, good wine choice; piped music; children in eating area, neat landscaped gardens with pretty view above Chesterfield Canal, open all day, quiet bedrooms, good breakfast *(LYM, David and Ruth Hollands)*

Dunham [SK8174]

Bridge Inn [Main St]: Near toll bridge, well kept ales such as Black Sheep, Cropton and local Broadstone Retford, enjoyable blackboard food, friendly landlord and locals, L-shaped beamed room with lots of bric-a-brac, prints and posters, good log fire, small no smoking dining room; piped music, large TV; well behaved children welcome, wheelchair access, a few tables outside, open all day Sun *(Kevin Thorpe, Richard Lewis, the Didler, Kevin Blake)*

White Swan [A57 Retford—Lincoln; Main St]: Pleasant local with two comfortable lounge areas, wide choice of usual food (breakfast too), well kept Bass, Mansfield and Tom Woods ales at attractive prices, decent wines, friendly staff; large grass area, caravan site, sizeable fishing pond *(Richard Lewis, Kevin Thorpe)*

East Markham [SK7373]

Crown [High St (off A57)]: New landlord doing good food, friendly atmosphere, good service *(Geoff and Angela Jaques)*

Eastwood [SK4846]

Foresters Arms [Main St, Newthorpe]: Proper two-room village inn, clean and cosy, with Hardys & Hansons on electric pump, relaxing lounge, TV and old local photographs in bar, darts, dominoes and skittles, piano sing-along wknds; nice garden, occasional barbecues *(the Didler, JP, PP)*

Elton [SK7638]

Manor Arms [A52]: Ivy-clad beamed pub with nice furnishings, bric-a-brac and pictures, good choice of generous food, welcoming service, well kept Mansfield Riding and Marston Pedigree, real fire, back dining area *(Richard Lewis)*

Everton [SK6991]

Blacksmiths Arms [Church St]: L-shaped bar with no smoking dining area down step, four or five real ales, food inc bargain family Sun lunches, friendly chatty service, pool in games room; quiet piped music, dogs welcome; smallish garden with play area, open all day wknds *(CMW, JJW)*

Farnsfield [SK6456]

Plough [E end]: Attractive L-shaped beamed lounge, lunchtime and early evening food, well kept Mansfield beers, good fireplace, bar with TV and video games *(anon)*

Halam [SK6754]

Waggon & Horses [Turnpike]: Welcoming and attractive old dining pub with enjoyable food inc interesting dishes, well kept Flowers, pleasant staff, friendly local regulars *(Colin Fisher)*

Kimberley [SK5044]

Stag [Nottingham Rd]: Friendly 16th-c local run by devoted landlady, low beams, dark panelling and settles, well kept changing ales such as Boddingtons and Marstons Pedigree; attractive back garden with play area, cl wkdy lunchtime (opens 5; 2 Sat, 12 Sun) *(the Didler, JP, PP)*

Kirkby in Ashfield [SK5056]

Countryman [Park Lane (B6018 S)]: Lively traditional atmosphere in upgraded former miners' local, attractive bas relief murals of shooting scenes in cottagey beamed lounge bar, decorative plates and mining memorabilia, well kept Bass, Theakstons and usually two guests, beer festivals, good value generous bar food (not Sun, Mon evening), public bar with pool; popular with walkers, play area, good live folk, rock and blues Fri; open all day *(Kevin Blake, the Didler)*

Duke of Wellington [Church St]: Plush beamed lounge with lots of pictures, pool and TV in pleasant bar, friendly staff, well kept Mansfield beers, good cheap food; tables outside *(Kevin Blake)*

Lambley [SK6245]

Robin Hood & Little John [Main St]: Welcoming old-fashioned village local, two beamed bars off central servery with well kept Banks's, Mansfield and Marstons Pedigree, roaring log fires, food inc hearty lunchtime sandwiches and Sun lunch, darts, dominoes, cards and table skittles in heavy-beamed public bar, heavyweight pub dog called Eadie; piped music; popular with walkers *(CMW, JJW, Brian and Halina Howes)*

☆ *Woodlark* [Church St]: Well preserved and interestingly laid out two-room pub, careful extension into next house giving extra lounge/dining area, good value lunches and more ambitious evening meals (not Sun evening or Mon), cheerful welcome, three well kept ales, wide range of pub games inc pool room, table skittles and skittle alley; children in annexe *(BB, CMW, JJW)*

Lowdham [SK6746]

Magna Charta [Southwell Rd]: Attractive Hardys & Hansons pub with good range of enjoyable food inc interesting dishes, plenty of tables, lots of busy young staff; special children's lavatory, garden *(Andy and Jill Kassube)*

Old Ship [nr A612/A6097; Main St]: Friendly traditional beamed country pub with above-average imaginative blackboard food in extended split-level lounge/bar, attractive dining area with big round tables, well kept ales such as Marstons Pedigree and John Smiths, occasional guest beers, friendly service, open fire, lots of pictures, plates, copper and brass, separate public bar; quiz nights, pleasant walks nearby *(W M Paton, Kevin Blake)*

Worlds End [Plough Lane]: Small and friendly old beamed village pub with log fire at one end of long room, dining area the other, fresh flowers, some original features, very reasonably priced straightforward food using local produce (may be a wait), small-helping OAP lunches, well kept Marstons; piped music, smoking allowed throughout; good window boxes, picnic-sets in garden *(CMW, JJW, Rona Murdoch)*

Mansfield [SK5362]

Pheasant [Chesterfield Road S]: Lots of panelling, with plush seats, copper, brass and pictures, well kept Banks's and Mansfield, cheap snacks, friendly service; handy for leisure centre *(Kevin Blake)*

Railway Inn [Station St; best approached by viaduct from nr market pl]: Friendly traditional pub with divided main bar and separate room, bargain lunches, well kept attractively priced Batemans XB *(Pete Baker)*

Maplebeck [SK7160]

☆ *Beehive* [signed down pretty country lanes from A616 Newark—Ollerton and from A617 Newark—Mansfield]: Cosy and unspoiled beamed country tavern in nice spot, excellent landlady, tiny front bar, slightly bigger side room, traditional furnishings, open fire, free antique juke box, well kept local Maypole and Rudgate ales, log fires, good cheese or ham rolls, tables on small terrace with flower tubs and grassy bank running down to little stream, play area with swings, barbecues; may be cl wkdy winter lunchtimes, very busy wknds and bank hols *(LYM, Brian and Halina Howes, the Didler, Anna, Dr B and Mrs P B Baker, Bernie Adams, JP, PP)*

Newark [SK7953]
Castle & Falcon [London Rd]: Former coaching inn with local atmosphere, John Smiths and guest beers, two bars and family area; darts and pool teams, evening opening 7 *(the Didler)*
Fox & Crown [Appleton Gate]: Bare-boards but comfortable Tynemill pub, nooks and corners inc no smoking back family areas, stone or wood floors, big brewery mirrors and other breweriana, well kept changing real ales, Inch's cider, dozens of malt whiskies, continental draught and bottled beers, flavoured vodkas, good choice of wines, freshly made food from sandwiches up, friendly efficient staff; good wheelchair access, occasional live music, open all day *(the Didler, Richard Lewis, Ian Phillips, David Carr)*
☆ *Mail Coach* [London Rd, nr Beaumond Cross]: Friendly open-plan Georgian local, pleasant décor in three candlelit separate areas, lots of pictures, big fire, well kept Boddingtons, Flowers IPA and interesting guest beers, enjoyable home-made lunchtime food inc some unusual dishes, pleasant staff; pub games, jazz, blues or folk wknds; tables outside *(Kevin Blake, the Didler)*
Navigation Waterfront [Mill Gate]: Converted warehouse rising out of canalised River Trent, bare bricks and flagstones, iron pillars, well kept Everards Tiger, friendly staff, good atmosphere, lunchtime food; live music twice a week *(David Carr)*
Wing [Bridge St, just off Market Pl]: Tucked-away character tavern down paved area beside magnificent church, well kept Theakstons Best, XB and Old Peculier, two small plain rooms, one with games; tables outside *(the Didler)*
Woolpack [Stodman St, off Castlegate]: Ancient pub with three small rooms, good home cooking (inc breakfast from 9am), John Smiths and guest beers; back terrace, skittle alley *(the Didler)*

Newstead [SK5252]
Station Hotel [Station Rd]: Busy basic red-brick village local opp station on Robin Hood rail line, bargain well kept Barnsley Bitter and Old Tom Mild, old railway photographs; no food Sun (nor rail service then) *(the Didler, JP, PP)*

Normanton on Soar [SK5123]
Plough [village signed from A6006]: Pleasantly refurbished, consistently enjoyable food *(Matthew Glynn)*

Normanton on the Wolds [SK6232]
Plough [off A606 5m S of Nottingham]: Unspoiled local with wide choice of home-made food in small dining room, friendly service, well kept Bass, John Smiths Magnet and Theakstons; large garden, attractive village *(Neil and Jenny Dury)*

Nottingham [SK5640]
☆ *Bell* [Angel Row, off Market Sq]: Bustling friendly low-beamed 15th-c pub, small timbered and panelled front bars, carefully extended back bar, ancient stairs to attractive calmer raftered room with nice window seats used as lunchtime family restaurant for good value simple well presented lunchtime food, simpler snacks downstairs, full range of Hardys & Hansons ales kept well in extraordinarily deep sandstone cellar, good value wines; trad jazz Sun lunchtime, Mon and Tues evenings; open all day, cl Sun afternoon *(Derek and Sylvia Stephenson, Rona Murdoch, Patrick Hancock, JP, PP, the Didler, LYM, Richard Lewis)*
Bunkers Hill [Hockley, next to Ice Stadium]: Former bank with effective and unusual green décor, high beams, comfortable traditional feel, Bass and Greene King Old Speckled Hen with perhaps a guest such as Oakham JHB, bar food; TV, games machines, live music upstairs, quiz Sun, well behaved children welcome, open all day *(Graham Palmer)*
Canal House [Canal St]: Big alehouse conversion of wharf building by Tynemill, bridge over indoors canal spur complete with narrowboat, lots of bare brick and varnished wood, huge joists on studded steel beams, long bar with Castle Rock Hemlock, Timothy Taylors Landlord and changing ales such as Black Sheep Special, Fullers London Pride and Springhead Gardeners Tap, good choice of house wines (two glass sizes), lots of standing room; good upstairs restaurant and second bar, masses of solid tables out on attractive waterside terrace; piped music (live Sun), student nights, open all day *(the Didler, Richard Greenwood, Richard Lewis, BB)*
Company [Castle Wharf, Canal St]: New canalside Wetherspoons, open-plan café/bar layout, usual wide range of well kept ales and sensible food; picnic-sets outside *(Richard Greenwood, Richard Lewis)*
Coopers Arms [Porchester Rd, Thornywood]: Solid Victorian local with three unspoilt rooms, real ales inc Theakstons XB; small family room in skittle alley; cl Weds lunchtime *(JP, PP, the Didler)*
Elwes Arms [Oakdale Rd, Carlton]: Comfortable, with huge range of home-cooked food, good beer range, nice garden *(Richard Greenwood)*
Falcon [Canning Circus/Alfreton Rd]: Traditional intimate unspoilt two-room corner local, Adnams, Boddingtons and Tetleys, daily papers, good upstairs restaurant *(the Didler, JP, PP)*
Forest [Mansfield Rd]: Tynemill pub different from most of theirs, varied rather mediterranean food inc dishes with pick-list of ingredients, well kept Castle Rock Hemlock, Greene King Abbot, Woodfordes Wherry and a guest such as Batemans XB, low prices for soft drinks too, two smallish rooms knocked together, prints and beer posters on tiled and panelled walls *(Rona Murdoch, Roger and Jenny Huggins, Derek and Sylvia Stephenson, Darly Graton, Graeme Gulibert)*
Fox & Crown [Church St/Lincoln St, Old Basford]: Open-plan local refurbished in bright pine, back microbrewery producing its own Alcazar Vixens Vice, Brush Bitter, New Dawn and Maple Magic winter ale, brewery tours Sat, perhaps a guest from another pub brewery; wide choice of pizzas and other dishes inc

sandwiches, helpful staff and Canadian landlord; good piped music, games machines, Tues quiz night, big-screen sports TV; disabled access possible (lavatories difficult), tables out behind, open all day *(the Didler, G Coates, JP, PP)*

Framptons [Mount St/St James Terr]: Small interesting pub with three well kept attractively priced changing ales inc one from Nottingham Brewing, enjoyable cheap food *(the Didler)*

Frog & Onion [Noel St, Hyson Green]: Lively and friendly alehouse-style local with particularly well kept Marstons Pedigree and Theakstons; busy Thurs quiz night and Fri band night *(Andrew Crawford)*

Globe [London Rd]: Former Greyhound, reopened under new regime with real ales such as Mallard, Nottingham, Oakham JHB and three changing guests, farm cider, good food all day; handy for Trent Bridge *(the Didler)*

Hogshead [Pelham St]: Wide range of real ales and imported beers, good value food, pleasant staff, two very large open bars *(Doug Christian)*

Horse & Groom [Radford Rd, New Basford]: Popular and well run partly open-plan local next to former Shipstones brewery, with their name over door and other memorabilia; nice snug, several changing well kept ales, good value fresh food from sandwiches up, daily papers; jazz, folk, blues or skiffle nights Fri in converted back stables; open all day *(the Didler, JP, PP, David Atkinson, Darly Graton, Graeme Gulibert)*

☆ ***Limelight*** [Wellington Circus, nr Playhouse]: Extended convivial Tynemill bar and restaurant attached to Playhouse theatre, well kept Adnams, Batemans XB, Courage Directors, Marstons Pedigree, Theakstons XB and guests inc a Mild, reasonably priced food from rolls to full meals (not Sun lunchtime), pleasant efficient staff, theatre pictures, maybe live celebrities (also good mix of customers inc nearby lawyers), occasional modern jazz, attractive continental-style outside seating area; open all day, live blues and jazz *(Patrick Hancock, the Didler, JP, PP, Derek and Sylvia Stephenson, Kevin Blake, A C and E Johnson)*

Lion [Lower Mosley St, New Basford]: Well run open-plan bare bricks and boards pub with up to 10 well kept ales inc local Mallard from one of city's deepest cellars (glass viewing panel – and can be visited at quiet times), farm cider, wide choice of good wholesome food inc doorstep sandwiches, sensible prices, log fire, daily papers, live folk, jazz and blues Fri-Sun; summer barbecues, open all day *(the Didler, JP, PP, David Atkinson)*

News House [Canal St]: Reopened April 2002 as Tynemill pub, one of its two rooms filled with local newspaper front pages spanning years of events and personalities, eight real ales inc bargain Castle Rock, Belgian and Czech imports on tap, lots of flavoured vodkas, enjoyable fresh food inc Sun lunch, mix of bare boards and carpet *(the Didler)*

☆ ***Plough*** [St Peters St, Radford]: Unspoilt two-room backstreet local now the home of new Nottingham Brewing Co, producing interesting beers to 19th-c local standards inc a Mild and Oatmeal Stout, also well kept guest beers, good bargain food inc popular Sun lunch (live jazz then), two coal fires *(the Didler)*

Royal Children [Castle Gate]: Open-plan, busy but relaxed, three basic but comfortable areas with bare boards, lots of panelling, old pictures, converted gas lamps, brass water fountains on bar, well kept ales such as Fullers London Pride, Hook Norton Old Hooky, Mansfield Cask and Home, Marstons Pedigree and Theakstons XB, snacks all day and lunchtime meals, friendly staff *(Richard Lewis)*

☆ ***Salutation*** [Hounds Gate/Maid Marion Way]: Up to a dozen or more well kept changing ales and lots of bottled beers, ancient lower back part with beams, flagstones and well worn cosy corners inc two small quiet rooms and a no smoking area, plusher modern front lounge, helpful staff, speedily served enjoyable plain food till 7; piped music, games machine, can get busy – but a haven in the centre, increasingly dominated by designer bars *(BB, Des and Jen Clarke, JP, PP, Derek and Sylvia Stephenson, Patrick Hancock, Richard Lewis)*

Stick & Pitcher [University Boulevard, Dunkirk]: New Tynemill pub next to city tennis courts and overlooking Highfields hockey club; comfortable upstairs bar with highly polished woodwork, three Castle Rock ales and two guests, enjoyable food, sports TV; open all day *(the Didler)*

Travellers Rest [B684, Mapperley Plains]: Long friendly Chef & Brewer with snug alcoves, candlelit tables, feature curtains, lots of decorative plates and bottles, coal fire, well kept Theakstons and changing guest beer, good wine choice, wide range of good value food all day (not after 2 Sun/Mon) from filled baguettes to interesting main dishes, popular lunchtime no smoking area, friendly welcoming staff, back family building with adjacent play area; pleasant lawn with country views, open all day *(Kevin Blake)*

Nuthall [SK5144]

Three Ponds [Kimberley Rd (B600, away from city), off A610 nr M1 junction 26]: Friendly and tastefully refurbished family dining pub, mainly no smoking, with wide range of good value food till 8 inc OAP and off-peak bargains, Sun roast, Hardys & Hansons Best, Best Mild and Classic, good coffee, good staff; piped music and games machines; children in family room, big back garden with play area, open all day *(CMW, JJW)*

Orston [SK7741]

Durham Ox [Church St]: Welcoming country local opp church, well kept Marstons Pedigree, John Smiths, Theakstons and a guest beer, wine fresh from sensible small bottles, good value beef, ham and other rolls (no hot food); comfortable split-level open-plan bar with interesting RAF/USAF memorabilia, collection of whisky bottles; tables outside (may be hitching rail for ferrets as well as for horses) *(JP, PP, Phil and Jane Hodson, the Didler, Bernie Adams)*

Radcliffe on Trent [SK6439]

Black Lion [A52]: Friendly bar, big comfortable lounge, good choice of food from beef cobs to full meals, three or four well kept changing ales; big garden and play area, Oct charity steam fair *(the Didler)*

Ranby [SK6580]

Chequers [Old Blyth Rd, just off A1 by A620 Worksop—E Retford]: Nice building in lovely setting by Chesterfield Canal, delightful waterside terrace, some mooring, wknd boat trips; two or three well kept beers, cheerful service, several attractive and comfortable areas off bar inc dining room with farm tools and bric-a-brac, games area with darts, pool and machines; children very welcome, open all day, food all day wknds; handy for A1 *(Peter and Anne Hollindale, JHBS)*

Ravenshead [SK5554]

Hutt [A60 Nottingham—Mansfield]: Recently refurbished Chef & Brewer, character softly lit rooms, alcoves and intimate areas, very wide choice of enjoyable food inc unusual dishes, well kept Courage Directors, Theakstons XB and an occasional guest beer; open all day *(Richard Greenwood, Kevin Blake)*

Retford [SK7080]

☆ ***Market Hotel*** [off West Carr Rd, Ordsall; follow Leisure Centre signs from A620, then just after industrial estate sign keep eyes skinned for pub sign on left]: Owned by same family for over 40 years, with particularly good choice of changing well kept ales (up to 40 in autumn beer festival), comfortable plush banquettes, generous good value straightforward food (not Sun evening) from sandwiches and rolls through hefty fresh haddock to popular Sun carvery lunch, friendly helpful service; very busy Fri/Sat night, jazz 3rd Sun in month, open all day Sat *(Richard Lewis, JP, PP, LYM, Mike and Sue Loseby)*

Selston [SK4553]

Horse & Jockey [just off M1 junction 27]: Three carefully refurbished main rooms on three levels, cosy snug off lower bar area, beams, flagstones and coal fire in cast-iron range, Bass, Greene King Abbot, Timothy Taylors Landlord and other ales on handpump or in jugs direct from the cellar, decent lunchtime food (not wknds), bar billiards in top room; open all day Sat *(the Didler, JP, PP)*

South Leverton [SK7881]

Plough [Town St]: Tiny pub doubling as morning post office, little changed under new owners; basic trestle tables and benches, real fire, Greene King Ruddles Best and a guest beer, traditional games, tables outside; open 2-11 (all day Sat, 12-4, 7-10.30 Sun) *(JP, PP, Mike and Sue Loseby, the Didler)*

Southwell [SK6953]

Bramley Apple [Church St (A612)]: Now owned by Springhead with several of their beers and guests kept well, enjoyable food with some concentration on this evenings, good service *(BB, the Didler)*

Old Coaching House [Church St]: Beams and old-world nooks around central bar, up to six changing well kept ales, roaring coal fires, bar billiards, shove-ha'penny and other traditional games; tables on terrace, may be cl wkdy lunchtimes, open all day wknds *(JP, PP, the Didler)*

Stoke Bardolph [SK6441]

Ferry Boat [off A612 in Burton Joyce; Riverside]: Large family dining pub in lovely spot overlooking River Trent, waterside picnic-sets, sheep, ducks, geese and swans opposite, several comfortable largely no smoking areas, lots of wood, copper, brass and ornaments, good choice of good value food inc wkdy lunchtime loyalty discounts for OAPs, two real ales, fair choice of wines, attentive service, daily papers (inc framed sheets in gents'); fruit machine, quiet piped music, Tues quiz night; open all day *(Kevin Blake, CMW, JJW)*

Sutton in Ashfield [SK5059]

King & Miller [Kings Mill Rd E]: Comfortable and relaxed family pub, play areas inside and out, alcove tables, huge range of low-priced enjoyable food, warm welcome, decent wines, Hardys & Hansons beers *(Andy and Jill Kassube, Peter and Audrey Dowsett)*

Snipe [A38 bypass, towards Mansfield]: Roomy, convivial and well furnished family pub, good choice of reasonably priced food inc OAP discounts some days, quick service, Mansfield ales, good coffee; unobtrusive piped music; play areas inside and out *(Peter and Audrey Dowsett)*

Staff of Life [West End/Church Hill]: Neat and comfortable local with wide choice of reasonably priced food, well kept beer, quick service; quiet piped music *(Peter and Audrey Dowsett)*

Travellers Rest [Huthwaite Rd]: Friendly panelled local with pictures, shelves of bric-a-brac, attractive fireplace, well kept Mansfield beers, good value lunchtime food, darts, pool and TV in separate bar *(Kevin Blake)*

Thurgarton [SK6949]

☆ ***Red Lion*** [Southwell Rd (A612)]: Bright and cheery 16th-c inn, recently extended in front, with good unusual freshly cooked food (all day Sat, Sun and bank hols) inc fresh fish in roomy split-level beamed bars and restaurant, well kept Mansfield and Marstons Pedigree, flame-effect fire, unobtrusive fruit machine; children welcome, well spaced tables and dogs on leads in attractive big garden, comfortable bedrooms *(Richard Greenwood, Kevin Blake, W and P J Elderkin)*

Underwood [SK4751]

Red Lion [Church Lane; off B600, nr M1 junction 27]: Character 17th-c split-level beamed village pub, spacious open-plan bar with open fire, some cushioned settles, pictures and plates on dressers, good value family food inc OAP lunches, well kept Marstons Pedigree and an interesting local guest beer, good friendly service, penny arcade machine, no piped music; children welcome, picnic-sets and large adventure playground in big garden with terrace, attractive setting; open all day Fri-Sun *(Kevin Blake, Derek and Sylvia Stephenson, the Didler)*

Upton [SK7354]

French Horn [A612]: New management in

neatly comfortable open-plan bar with wall banquettes and glossy tables, well kept Charles Wells Bombardier, some emphasis on wide choice of generous food (all day Sun) inc some interesting dishes as well as lunchtime sandwiches, baguettes and baked potatoes; piped music; children welcome, picnic-sets in big sloping back paddock, open all day *(LYM, Darly Graton, Graeme Gulibert)*

Watnall Chaworth [SK5046]

☆ ***Queens Head*** [3 miles from M1 junction 26: A610 towards Nottingham, left on B600, then keep right; Main Rd]: Cosy and tastefully extended three-room old pub with wide range of good value food, well kept Theakstons XB, Old Peculier and guest beers, efficient friendly service; intimate snug, dining area, beams and stripped pine, coal fires; fruit machine, piped music; picnic-sets in spacious and attractive back garden with big play area, open all day Fri/Sat *(the Didler, JP, PP)*

Wellow [SK6766]

☆ ***Olde Red Lion*** [Eakring Rd, just off A616 E of Ollerton]: Low-beamed and panelled 16th-c pub by green with towering maypole, good value fresh food from sandwiches to bargain Sun roasts, three well kept changing beers, quick friendly service, no smoking restaurant and dining area, no piped music; children welcome, picnic-sets outside *(LYM, Eric Locker, CMW, JJW)*

West Bridgford [SK5838]

Southbank [Trent Bridge]: Under same ownership as Fellows Morton & Clayton (see Nottingham main entries); bright and airy refurbishment extended into former insurance offices, polished wood floors, local Mallard, Timothy Taylors Landlord and a guest beer, good food choice; handy for cricket ground and Nottingham Forest FC *(the Didler)*

☆ ***Stratford Haven*** [Stratford Rd, Trent Bridge]: Busy and chatty Tynemill pub, bare-boards front bar, well kept changing ales such as Batemans XB, Burton Bridge Golden Delicious, Caledonian Deuchars IPA, Castle Rock Bitter and Stratford Gold, Exmoor Gold, Hook Norton Old Hooky, Marstons Pedigree, Moorhouses Black Cat and Woodhouses Wonderful, farm ciders, good choice of whiskies and wines, relaxed local atmosphere in airy and skylit carpeted yellow-walled back part, good value home cooking, daily papers, tables outside; can get crowded and smoky; handy for cricket ground and Nottingham Forest FC; open all day *(Patrick Renouf, the Didler, A C and E Johnson, Des and Jen Clarke, JP, PP, Derek and Sylvia Stephenson, BB)*

West Leake [SK5226]

☆ ***Star*** [Melton Lane, off A6006]: Comfortable oak-panelled dining lounge with good central log fire (enjoyed by Cracker the ginger tom), pewter mugs, china, pictures and attractive table lamps, traditional beamed and quarry-tiled country bar on left with wall settles, plenty of character and traditional games, good value home-made food inc cheap steaks, well kept Bass and two or three changing guest beers, good choice of malt whiskies, good coffee, welcoming licensees and friendly helpful service, no piped music or machines; children in eating area, picnic-sets on front terrace (quiet spot) and in garden with play area *(the Didler, CMW, JJW, LYM, Richard and Jean Green, JP, PP, Michael and Jenny Back)*

Widmerpool [SK6429]

Pullman [1st left off A606 coming towards Nottingham from A46 junction; Kinoulton Lane]: Popular family dining pub in well converted and extended station building, generous Sun carvery, good vegetarian dishes, real ale *(Darly Graton, Graeme Gulibert)*

Wilford [SK5637]

Ferry [off B679 S of Nottingham]: Split-level Chef & Brewer with low beams and bare boards, candlelit tables, bays of comfortable banquettes, chesterfield by one of the open fires, pictures, two snugs, restaurant with pitched roof and imposing fireplace, good choice of food, well kept Theakstons; piped pop music; tidy back terrace, pleasant garden with play area, view over River Trent to Nottingham Castle *(Kevin Blake)*

Woodborough [SK6247]

Four Bells [off A6097; Main St]: Two-bar pub with Mansfield and Charles Wells Bombardier, good soft drinks choice, good value food inc bargains; darts, piped music, games machines, quiz night, no dogs; small garden with play area *(CMW, JJW)*

Worksop [SK5879]

Mallard [Station, Carlton Rd]: Friendly local feel in idiosyncratic station building handy for Mr Straw's House (NT), and noted for its quickly changing beers from small breweries and wide range of foreign bottled beers; coal fire, traditional games; wheelchair access, seats outside, parking in station pay-and-display, open all day (Sun afternoon closure) *(JP, PP, Tony Hobden, R T and J C Moggridge)*

People don't usually tip bar staff (different in a really smart hotel, say). If you want to thank a barman – dealing with a really large party say, or special friendliness – offer him a drink. Common expressions are: 'And what's yours?' or 'And won't you have something for yourself?'

Oxfordshire

welcoming licensees really make this attractive country local), the smart and friendly Lamb at Buckland (good food), the civilised old Lamb in Burford (an all-round favourite), the good value Horse & Groom at Caulcott (a proper village pub), the Chequers in Chipping Norton (great for drinkers, good food too), the Fox & Hounds on Christmas Common (lively landlady doing good food in this rejigged pub, back in the Guide *after a gap of some years – and quite different from the simple tavern we knew then), the largely no smoking Merrymouth at Fifield (good food, warm welcome), the Gate Hangs High near Hook Norton (new landlord's cooking earns him a Food Award), the friendly Sun in Hook Norton (a fine all-rounder), the Five Horseshoes at Maidensgrove (nice food, new landlord settling in well), the evocative Turf Tavern tucked into a medieval Oxford enclave, the Royal Oak at Ramsden (good beer and atmosphere, good food using largely organic produce), the cosy and unspoilt old Bishop Blaize at Sibford Gower (this new entry has a lovely garden and views), and the Masons Arms at Swerford (yet another new entry – and more great views – with cooking that's in the running for a Food Award). Pride of place on the food front this year goes to the Lamb in Burford, Oxfordshire Dining Pub of the Year. There are rich pickings in the Lucky Dip section at the end of the chapter, with around 160 entries this year – over 60 of them new. We'd particularly pick out the Tite at Chadlington, foody Bull in Charlbury, Crown at Church Enstone, Barley Mow at Clifton Hampden, Bear & Ragged Staff at Cumnor, Bell at Ducklington, Five Alls at Filkins, Trout at Godstow, King William IV at Hailey, Rose & Crown in Oxford, Crown at Pishill, Moody Cow at Sibford Gower, Red Lion at Steeple Aston (a favourite), restauranty Crooked Billet at Stoke Row, Fish at Sutton Courtenay, Swan at Swinbrook, Crown at Sydenham and Killingworth Castle at Wootton. Drinks in Oxfordshire pubs tend to be more expensive than the national average. The local Hook Norton beers are generally attractively priced. Brakspears has been the county's other main brewer. And it is likely that the smaller brewer Wychwood (now owned by Refresh, which markets several other beer brands) will become more widely known.*

BANBURY SP4540 Map 4

Reindeer £

47 Parsons Street, off Market Place

A fine old town pub full of atmosphere and character, and run by friendly, chatty licensees. The long front room has heavy 16th-c beams, very broad polished oak floorboards scattered with rugs, a magnificent carved overmantel for one of the roaring log fires, and traditional solid furnishings; there's a second log fire. Ask them to show you the Globe Room – an attractively proportioned room, where Cromwell held court before the Battle of Edgehill, with original wonderfully carved 17th-c panelling. Arrive early for their very popular straightforward lunchtime bar food: soup (£2.10), doorstep or hot sandwiches (from £2.20), home-made stilton and port or chicken liver pâté (£2.95), all-day breakfast (£3.10), filled baked potatoes (from £3.20), pasta topped with spicy tomato and basil sauce (£3.30), ploughman's (from £3.50), omelettes (from £3.60), shepherd's pie (£3.80), home-made salmon fishcakes (£3.95), and chicken and mushroom pie (£4.85); they now do evening meals on Tuesday, Wednesday and Thursday which might include jumbo prawns in filo pastry (£5.95), three sausages and fried eggs (£5.75), chicken in wild mushroom sauce (£6.25), salmon and broccoli pasta bake (£6.50), steak and kidney pudding (£6.75), and puddings such as red plum and cinnamon pudding or sticky toffee sponge (£2.95). Well kept Hook Norton Best, Old, and Mild, and a couple of guests on handpump, country wines, winter mulled wine, 30 Irish whiskies, and even snuffs and clay pipes for the more adventurous; shove-ha'penny, cribbage, dominoes and piped music. A smaller back room up steps is no smoking at lunchtime. The little back courtyard has picnic-sets under parasols, aunt sally, and pretty flowering baskets; no under-21s (but see below). *(Recommended by Geoff Pidoux, P M Hewitt, Steve Whalley, Leigh and Gillian Mellor, Ted George, Derek and Sylvia Stephenson, George Atkinson, CMW, JJW, the Didler, Ian and Nita Cooper, Bruce Bird)*

Hook Norton ~ Tenants John and Hazel Milligan ~ Real ale ~ Bar food (11-2 all week (not Sun); 6-9 Tues-Thurs) ~ (01295) 264031 ~ Children in Globe Room lunchtime only if eating ~ Dogs welcome ~ Open 11-11; closed Sun, bank hol Mon

BARNARD GATE SP4010 Map 4

Boot

Village signposted off A40 E of Witney

There are more than 100 items of celebrity footwear at this stone-tiled dining pub from Jeremy Irons to Douglas Hurd, and Graham Hill to Jeremy Clarkson. Stout standing timbers and stub walls with latticed glass break up the main area, there's a huge log fire, and nice solid country tables and chairs on bare boards. Good food includes lunchtime filled ciabattas and baguettes (from £6.95), home-made soup (£3.25), mediterranean vegetables with goats cheese (£4.95), king prawns with garlic mayonnaise (£5.95; main course £9.95), tortellini with tomato sauce (£9.95), steak in Guinness pie, lamb shank or chicken in white wine and mushroom sauce (£10.95), and puddings such as sticky toffee or chocolate pudding (£4.25); part of the restaurant is no smoking. Well kept Hook Norton Best and Wadworths 6X on handpump, and decent wines. The tables out in front are out of earshot of the nearby road. *(Recommended by Geoff Pidoux, D and M T Ayres-Regan, Philip and Ann Board, J G E Bell)*

Traditional Freehouses ~ Manager Frazier Williams ~ Real ale ~ Bar food (12-2.30, 7-9.30; 12-9.30 Sat, 12-9 Sun) ~ Restaurant ~ (01865) 881231 ~ Children in eating area of bar and restaurant ~ Open 11-3; 11-11 Sat; 12-10.30 Sun

BLEWBURY SU5385 Map 2

Blewbury Inn 🍷

London Road (A417)

Most people come to this small downland dining pub to enjoy the imaginative food cooked by the French landlord: cornish mussel soup with chervil and fennel (£4.10), grilled bagel with parma ham, brie de meaux, apple and cider chutney, and mixed leaves (£4.70), and chicken liver pâté with crunchy bean and apple salad, roast red peppers, pumpkin oil dressing and grilled brioche or artichoke and smoked salmon risotto on rocket and walnuts with a basil dressing (£5.20); there are also two-course (£18.50) and three-course (£23.50) options. The bar on the left has an attractive wood-effect floor, a tremendous mix of simple furnishings from a blue director's chair to a big box settle, and French art and period advertising posters on the dusky red walls, with a good log fire. They have good house wines, as well as well kept Fullers London Pride and Hook Norton

Best on handpump. The carpeted dining room has wheelback chairs around pub tables, and just one or two carefully chosen plates and pictures on its stencilled cream walls above a green dado. More reports please. *(Recommended by Doreen and Haydn Maddock, Mike and Heather Watson, Jane Buekett)*

Free house ~ Licensees Franck and Kally Peigne ~ Real ale ~ Bar food (not Fri, Sat or Sun evenings, not Mon) ~ Restaurant ~ (01235) 850496 ~ Children welcome ~ Dogs allowed in bar ~ Open 12-3, 6-11; 12-3 Sun; closed Sun evening, all day Mon

BROADWELL SP2504 Map 4

Five Bells

Village signposted off A361 N of Lechlade, and off B4020 S of Carterton

Run by friendly, helpful and chatty licensees, this attractive country pub is popular with both locals and visitors. The spotlessly kept and well furnished series of rooms has two big, warming log fires, a pleasant mix of flagstones and carpeting, low beams, antique pistols, and plates and rural pictures on the walls. The sizeable dining room to the right of the lounge and the small conservatory (both no smoking), overlook the spacious flower-filled garden – where they play aunt sally, and grow some of the vegetables used in the kitchen. Well liked, reasonably priced bar food includes sandwiches (from £1.75), soup (£2.95), and dishes such as stilton mushrooms (£3.95), ham, egg and chips (£5.25), fish and chips (£5.95), salmon and prawn gratin or chicken breast in wine and mushrooms (£6.50), popular bird pie (£6.75), almond roast or gammon and pineapple (£6.95), steaks (from £9.95), and puddings such as ginger pudding (from £2.95); best to book for Sunday lunch. Well kept Bass with a guest beer such as Archers Village on handpump, and decent house wine. The public bar has darts, shove-ha'penny, and dominoes. Wheelchair access. The friendly brown labrador is called Toby. *(Recommended by Marjorie and David Lamb, Des and Jen Clarke, Rev Michael Vockins, KN-R, Phil and Jane Hodson, Sue and Jeff Evans, Dick and Madeleine Brown, Mr and Mrs D Lines)*

Free house ~ Licensees Trevor and Ann Cooper ~ Real ale ~ Bar food (12-1.45, 7-9; not Sun evening, not Mon) ~ Restaurant ~ (01367) 860076 ~ Well behaved children if eating in dining rooms only; not Sat evening ~ Dogs allowed in bar ~ Open 11.30-2.30, 7-11; 12-3, 7-10.30 Sun; closed Mon except bank hols ~ Bedrooms: /£55S

BUCKLAND SU3497 Map 4

Lamb

Village signposted off A420 NE of Faringdon

Most people come to this rather smart and friendly 18th-c stone village pub to enjoy the very good food. Of restaurant quality (with prices to match) there might at lunchtime be sandwiches (from £3.50), sautéed herring roes or home-made soup (£3.95), welsh rarebit or mushroom pot (£4.95), grilled Cornish mackerel with mustard sauce (£5.95), ploughman's (£6.25), omelettes (from £6.25), scrambled eggs with smoked salmon and prawns (£7.25), and black pudding or tagliatelle carbonara (£8.95), with evening dishes such as rabbit and guinea fowl terrine (£4.95), duck rillettes (£5.95), hot turbot mousse with shellfish sauce (£8.95), monkfish and prawn ragoût (£14.95), breast of chicken with oriental spices (£14.95), dover sole (£17.95), best end of English lamb (£18.25), and roast saddle of venison (£18.95), and puddings like sticky date and toffee pudding, dark chocolate mousse or summer pudding with clotted cream (from £3.50); three-course Sunday lunch £21.95. The restaurant is no smoking. Opening off a hallway, and divided in two by dark painted timbers, the neatly civilised little bar has plush blue furnishings, potted plants around the windows, and a few carefully chosen sheep and lamb pictures and models around the cream-painted walls. On a piano are newspapers to read, and examples of their own chutneys and jams. Hook Norton Best and a guest such as Adnams Broadside or Wadworths 6X on handpump, a dozen or so wines by the glass, and carefully mixed pimms or bucks fizz; very obliging service; piped music. There are a couple of white plastic tables on a terrace, and a good few wooden picnic-sets in the very pleasant tree-shaded garden; good walks nearby. *(Recommended by R M Gibson, Sue Demont, Tim Barrow, Ian Phillips)*

Free house ~ Licensees Paul and Peta Barnard ~ Real ale ~ Bar food (not Sun evening, Mon or 25 Dec) ~ Restaurant ~ (01367) 870484 ~ Children welcome ~ Open 11-3, 6-11; 12-4 Sun; closed Sun evening, Mon, 25 Dec ~ Bedrooms: £47.50B/£59.50B

BURFORD SP2512 Map 4

Lamb ★★

Sheep Street; A40 W of Oxford

Oxfordshire Dining Pub of the Year

The unchanging character and atmosphere in this civilised 500-year-old stone inn appeals very much to many of our readers. The roomy beamed main lounge is charmingly traditional, with distinguished old seats including a chintzy high winged settle, ancient cushioned wooden armchairs, and seats built into its stone-mullioned windows, bunches of flowers on polished oak and elm tables, oriental rugs on the wide flagstones and polished oak floorboards, and a winter log fire under its fine mantelpiece. Also, a writing desk and grandfather clock, and eye-catching pictures, shelves of plates and other antique decorations. The public bar has high-backed settles and old chairs on flagstones in front of its fire. It's best to get there early if you want a table in the bar where enjoyable daily changing bar food includes sandwiches or filled baguettes (from £4; fresh Cornish crab with dill and lime crème fraîche £6), cream of broccoli and blue cheese soup (£4.25), terrine of brill, bass and bream with lime mayonnaise (£5.95), ploughman's (£6.75), grilled sardine fillets with garlic and thyme butter (£7.50), warm asparagus and brie tart with rocket pesto (£7.95), fresh herb pancake filled with ham and leeks in mustard and cheese sauce (£8.25), calves liver casserole with pancetta and mushrooms, crispy duck leg confit with red onion sauce or grilled fillet of pink bream with saffron creamed spinach (£10.50), and puddings such as steamed chocolate pudding with orange compote and chocolate sauce, pear and cinnamon tart with berry compote and fromage blanc or iced banana parfait (£4.25); on Sundays there are proper roasts (three courses £20) but no bar meals. They stick quite rigidly to food service times; the peaceful formal restaurant is no smoking. Well kept Hook Norton Best, Wadworths 6X and a guest such as Badger IPA are dispensed from an antique handpump beer engine in a glassed-in cubicle (you'll be given the choice between straight glass or handle when you order); good wines. A pretty terrace leads down to small neatly-kept lawns surrounded by flowers, flowering shrubs and small trees, and the garden itself is a real suntrap enclosed as it is by the warm stone of the surrounding buildings. *(Recommended by David Rule, Lynn Sharpless, Chris Richards, K H Frostick, Nigel Williamson, C A Hall, Paul Humphreys, Philip and Ann Board, Steve Whalley, Ian Phillips, Nigel Woolliscroft, Denis and Dorothy Evans, B A Littlewood, R Huggins, D Irving, E McCall, T McLean, Simon and Laura Habbishow, Roger Braithwaite, Geoff Pidoux, the Didler, R Michael Richards, Esther and John Sprinkle, Angela Cerfontyn, Patrick Hancock, John and Enid Morris, Gordon Stevenson, Robin and Joyce Peachey, Angus Lyon, Mr and Mrs J McRobert, John Bramley, Ben and Sheila Walker, Felicity Stephens; also in the* Good Hotel Guide*)*

Free house ~ Licensee Richard de Wolf ~ Real ale ~ Bar food (lunchtime only; not Sun) ~ Restaurant (evenings; Sun lunch) ~ (01993) 823155 ~ Children welcome ~ Open 11-2.30, 6-11; 12-2.30, 7-10.30 Sun; closed 25 and 26 Dec ~ Bedrooms: £70B/£120S(£130B)

Mermaid

High Street

Some parts of this bustling pub date back to the 14th c, and the handsome Tudor-style frontage juts out onto the broad pavement of this famously picturesque sloping Cotswold street. Inside, there's a cottagey feel, with mullioned bay windows and an attractive long and narrow bar with beams, polished flagstones, brocaded seats in bays around the single row of tables down one side, and pretty dried flowers. The inner end, with a figurehead over the fireplace and toby jugs hanging from the beams, is panelled, the rest has stripped stonework; there's an airy dining room and a no smoking upstairs restaurant. Well liked bar food at lunchtime (which you order from a desk and computer opposite the bar) might include filled baguettes (from £3.95; hot sausage and onion £5.65), ploughman's (£5.50), roasted vegetables in a yorkshire pudding (£6.95), a daily roast (from £7.50), and fresh fish and chips or sausages wrapped in bacon in a red wine onion gravy (£7.95), with evening dishes such as baked field mushrooms filled with pâté topped with goats cheese and tomatoes (£5.25), crispy duck pancakes with hoisin sauce (£5.95), braised ham hock with cider and apple sauce (£8.50), chicken curry (£8.95), marinated red snapper fillet with a spicy lime butter (£13.95), steaks (from £13.95), and roast breast of pheasant on chestnut mashed potatoes with an old port and cranberry sauce (£13.95). Well kept Greene King IPA and Old Speckled Hen on handpump; fruit machine and piped music. There are picnic-sets under cocktail parasols outside. *(Recommended by Peter Sutton, Steve Whalley, Cathy Robinson, Ed Coombe, Geoff Pidoux, Martin Jones, D George, John Saville, Geoffrey and Penny Hughes, Phil and Jane Hodson, Patrick Hancock)*

Greene King ~ Lease John and Lynda Titcombe ~ Real ale ~ Bar food (12-2.30, 6-9.30, 11-11 Sat and Sun) ~ Restaurant ~ (01993) 822193 ~ Children over 5 years in restaurant ~ Open 11-11; 12-10.30 Sun; closed 25 Dec

CAULCOTT SP5024 Map 4

Horse & Groom

Lower Heyford Road (B4030)

The hard-working licensees have built this creeper-covered and partly thatched cottage into a local magnet without turning it into a restaurant or spoiling its village pub atmosphere. An L-shaped red-carpeted room angles around the servery, with plush-cushioned settles, chairs and stools around a few dark tables at the low-ceilinged bar end, a polo cap collection, framed racehorse cigarette cards, and a blazing fire in the big inglenook with masses of pump clips under its long bressumer beam; shove-ha'penny, cribbage and dominoes. The far end, up a shallow step, is set for dining (and is no smoking), with lots of decorative jugs hanging on black joists, and some decorative plates. There are some lovely watercolours and original drawings dotted around including a charming one of Harvey the west highland terrier who greets everyone on arrival; there's also a nice old poster of the auction of the pub in 1899. The food majors on a wide variety of O'Hagan speciality sausages (£6.75), and also includes sandwiches, home-made soup (£3.20), home-made cauliflower cheese or chilli (£6.75), daily specials such as avocado topped with crab and grilled cheese or buffalo mozzarella wrapped in parma ham and fried (£4.95), mixed crab and prawn pancakes topped with grilled cheese (£8.95), fresh tuna steak (£9.50), pork tenderloin with cider and apple sauce or rack of lamb with cranberry and sherry sauce (£9.75), steaks (from £9.75), and puddings (£3.50). Well kept Hook Norton Best on handpump, with quickly changing interesting guest beers such as Bank Top Flat Cap, Black Sheep, Dwan Irish Gold from Tipperary, and Isle of Skye Black Cuillin; decent house wines. There is a small side sun lounge, with picnic-sets under cocktail parasols on a neat side lawn. *(Recommended by David Campbell, Vicki McLean, George Atkinson, W W Burke, D C T and E A Frewer, Stuart Turner, John Branston, Susan and John Douglas, Ian Phillips)*

Free house ~ Licensees Chris and Celestine Roche ~ Real ale ~ Bar food ~ Restaurant ~ (01869) 343257 ~ Children in eating area of bar and restaurant ~ Open 11-3, 6-11; 12-3, 7-10.30 Sun; closed evenings 25 Dec, 1 Jan

The symbol shows pubs which keep their beer unusually well or have a particularly good range.

CHALGROVE SU6396 Map 4

Red Lion

High Street (B480 Watlington—Stadhampton)

The partly thatched main street of this village is pretty, and the pub is opposite the village cross. The décor has a smartly contemporary twist – all the walls are painted a crisp white which contrasts strikingly with the simple dark furnishings, the windows have neatly chequered green curtains and fresh flowers, and there's an old woodburner and a log fire. Across from the fireplace is a painting of the landlady's aunt, and there are a few carefully collected prints and period cartoons. There's quite an emphasis on the food, and changing menus might include lunchtime sandwiches, filled ciabatta rolls or filled baguettes (from £3.50; club sandwich with chips £6.50), as well as soup (£3.25), smooth chicken liver pâté with home-made bread and cumberland sauce (£3.95), crab cakes with red onion tartare sauce (£4.50), caesar salad (£4.95; main course £9.95), sausages with spicy red cabbage (£6.25), duo of beans and tomato cassoulet with a cheese crumble topping (£7.95), braised shank of lamb with slow-baked cherry tomato chutney and rich port jus (£9.45), beer battered cod (£9.95), rump steak (£13.50), and puddings such as steamed treacle pudding or chocolate tart (from £3.75); popular Sunday lunch, and they serve small helpings for children at reduced prices. Well kept Adnams, and Fullers London Pride and one of their seasonal ales on handpump, and a decent wine list. The back dining room (sometimes used for functions) is no smoking; piped music, shove-ha'penny and darts in the tiled public bar. They play aunt sally in the good big garden behind, which has a pergola and play equipment. There are some notable medieval wall paintings in the church. *(Recommended by Dick and Madeleine Brown, R J Chenery, Susan and John Douglas)*

Free house ~ Licensees Jonathan and Maggi Hewitt ~ Real ale ~ Bar food (not Sun evening; restricted menu Mon and Tues) ~ Restaurant ~ (01865) 890627 ~ Well behaved children in eating area of bar and restaurant ~ Dogs allowed in bar ~ Open 12-3, 6-11; 12-3, 7-10.30 Sun; closed a few days between 25 Dec and 1 Jan

CHECKENDON SU6684 Map 2

Black Horse

Village signposted off A4074 Reading—Wallingford; coming from that direction, go straight through village towards Stoke Row, then turn left (the second turn left after the village church); OS Sheet 175 map reference 666841

Those who like their pubs basic and tucked away in fine walking country will not be disappointed with this traditional country local, run for many decades by the same family. There's a refreshingly relaxed atmosphere in the back still room, where well kept Brakspears and a few local guests such as West Berkshire Good Old Boy or Mr Chubbs are tapped from the cask. The room with the bar counter has some tent pegs ranged above the fireplace, a reminder that they used to be made here; a homely side room has some splendidly unfashionable 1950s-look armchairs, and there's another room beyond that. They keep pickled eggs and usually do fresh filled rolls (from £1.60). There are seats out on a verandah and in the garden. *(Recommended by Pete Baker, the Didler, LM, Paul Vickers)*

Free house ~ Licensees Margaret and Martin Morgan ~ Real ale ~ No credit cards ~ (01491) 680418 ~ Children allowed but must be well behaved ~ Open 12-2(2.30 Sat/Sun), 7-11(10.30 Sun); closed evening 25 Dec

CHIPPING NORTON SP3127 Map 4

Chequers ■

Goddards Lane

'A treasure of a pub' is how one group of seasoned pub-goers describes this unpretentious place. It has three softly lit beamed rooms which are nicely old-fashioned – no frills, but clean and comfortable, with plenty of character – with log fires and low ochre ceilings, friendly efficient service, and a lively evening atmosphere. Besides very well kept Fullers Chiswick, London Pride, ESB and seasonal brews on handpump (unusual to have the full Fullers range around here), they have good house wines and espresso and cappuccino coffee; cribbage, dominoes, shove-ha'penny, and board games. Good bar food at lunchtime includes home-made soup, sandwiches (from £2.45), home-made vegetable spring rolls (£3.75), ploughman's (£4.95), home-cooked honey and cider roast ham with salad or egg (£6.50), thai mixed bean curry (£6.75), and chicken breast and cashew nut stir fry (£7.95), with evening dishes such as chicken liver pâté with home-made tomato chutney (£4.25), thai fishcakes with a sweet and sour dipping sauce (£5.25), salmon fillet with cajun spices with lemon and lime mayonnaise (£7.95), roasted half shoulder of lamb with mint gravy (£8.95), and chargrilled rib-eye steak (£9.50); daily specials, too. The no smoking restaurant at the back (quiet piped music) was converted from an old barn adjacent to the courtyard. It's very handy for the town's Victorian theatre. *(Recommended by Richard Greaves, M Benjamin, Geoff Pidoux, R Huggins, D Irving, E McCall, T McLean, Michael Jones, Chris Richards, Robert Gomme, Stephen, Julie and Hayley Brown, Val and Alan Green, George Atkinson, Stuart Turner, Mrs N W Neill, Di and Mike Gillam, PL Haigh, Mary and Dan Robinson, Derek Harvey-Piper, KN-R, Chris Glasson)*

Fullers ~ Tenants Josh and Kay Reid ~ Real ale ~ Bar food (12-2.30, 6-9; 12-5 Sun, not Sun evening) ~ Restaurant ~ (01608) 644717 ~ Children in restaurant ~ Open 11-11; 12-10.30 Sun

CHRISTMAS COMMON SU7193 Map 4

Fox & Hounds

Village signposted from B480 at junction with B481; or follow Fox & Hounds Hill Road from B4009 in Watlington

Although a barn extension has been added here to house a new restaurant, open-plan kitchen, a couple of bars and inside lavatories, many customers feel that much of the charm has been kept. The original bars remain largely unchanged, and the cosy beamed one on the left is plainly furnished with just a few tables and wooden wall benches or bow-window seats, a little carpet down on the red-and-black flooring tiles, two sturdy logs to sit on in the big inglenook – which has a fire burning even in summer – and a framed Ordnance Survey walker's map on one cream wall. The room on the right is popular with locals and pretty much for drinking only, though you may also see the cats and a friendly alsatian. Bar food at lunchtime includes soup (£4), doorstep sandwiches (from £4), ploughman's (£6), and half a roast ham hock caramelised with brown sugar and thyme (£6.50), as well as wild mushroom risotto (£5.50; main course £9.50), home-smoked duck breast (£6; main course £12), leek and bean cassoulet (£9), pork loin with bubble and squeak (£11), a pie of the week (£12), baked monkfish (£13), and Sunday roasts (from £8.50); they also sell free range eggs and honey. The restaurant is no smoking. Well kept Brakspears Bitter, Special, Mild, and seasonal ales tapped from the cask in a back still room, good coffee; dominoes, cribbage, and card games. The picnic-sets are being slowly replaced by rustic benches and tables. This is lovely Chilterns countryside and the pub has been a favourite spot for local walkers to end up in, especially during the bluebell season. More reports on the changes, please. *(Recommended by Mayur Shah, Andrew French, the Didler)*

Brakspears ~ Tenant Judith Bishop ~ Bar food (12-2.30, 7-10; not Sun evening) ~ Restaurant ~ (01491) 612599 ~ Children in family room lunchtime only ~ Dogs allowed in bar ~ Open 11.30-3, 6-11; 11.30-11 Sat; 12-10.30 Sun; closed evening 25 and 26 Dec

You are allowed 20 minutes after 'time, please' to finish your drink – half-an-hour if you bought it in conjunction with a meal.

CLIFTON SP4831 Map 4

Duke of Cumberlands Head

B4031 Deddington—Aynho

Although the emphasis here is on the good food, drinkers are not neglected and there's a good choice of wines, well kept Adnams Southwold, Black Sheep, and Hook Norton Best on handpump and more than 30 malt whiskies. Most of the tables are in the spacious if rather reserved lounge with a lovely log fireplace, and there are more in the cosy yellow-painted no smoking restaurant. Enjoyable bar food includes lunchtime sandwiches (not weekends), soup such as french onion (£3.50), deep fried camembert with cranberry dip or chicken liver pâté (£4.50), deep fried fillet of haddock (£5 or £8), pork normandy, mediterranean lamb casserole, wild mushroom stroganoff or beef curry (all £6 or £9), tuna steak niçoise (£10), breast of duck with pineapple and ginger (£12), steaks (from £13), and puddings such as summer pudding, cherry and almond tart or sticky toffee pudding (£3.50); two-course Sunday lunch £13, and decent breakfasts. There are tables out in the garden and the pub is only a short walk from the canal. *(Recommended by Miles and Deborah Protter, Susan and John Douglas, Anthony Barnes, Gerald Wilkinson, Paul Craddock, Martin and Penny Fletcher, Sir Nigel Foulkes, John Bowdler, George Little, Michael Hasslacher, David Green, Robert Coates, Stuart Turner)*

Free house ~ Licensee Nick Huntington ~ Real ale ~ Bar food (not Sun evening) ~ Restaurant (not Mon and Tues evening) ~ (01869) 338534 ~ Children welcome ~ Dogs welcome ~ Open 12-2.30(3 Sat), 6.30-10.30(11 Sat); 12-3 Sun; closed Sun evening ~ Bedrooms: £35S(£45B)/£50S(£70B)

CUDDESDON SP5903 Map 4

Bat & Ball

S of Wheatley; if coming from M40 junction 7 via Great Milton, turn towards Little Milton past church, then look out for signpost; in village centre

Cricket fans will be fascinated by this pub as every inch of wall-space is covered with cricketing programmes, photographs, porcelain models in well lit cases, score books, cigarette cards, pads, gloves and hats, and signed bats, bails and balls. The L-shaped bar has beams and low ceilings, comfortable furnishings, a partly flagstoned floor, and well kept Banks's LBW, Marstons Pedigree and a changing guest on handpump as well as a decent wine list; cribbage, dominoes and piped music. Served by obliging staff, well liked bar food includes soup (£3.95), hot sanwiches, filled paninni and baguettes, and fajitas (from £4.95; goats cheese, spinach and tomato paninni £4.95; hoisin chicken sandwich £8.95), deep fried whitebait (£5.25), spaghetti with smoked salmon and cream (£5.95), trio of sausages with mash or a pie of the day (£8.95), steak and kidney pudding (£9.95), smoked salmon and prawn fishcakes (£10.95), braised half shoulder of lamb (£12.95), and puddings such as lemon and stem ginger brûlée, white chocolate cheesecake or crumble of the day (from £3.95). The restaurant is no smoking; in the evenings most of the tables are laid out for eating. A very pleasant terrace at the back has seats, aunt sally, and good views over the Oxfordshire plain. *(Recommended by Mr and Mrs Richard Osborne, Paul Craddock, Jim Bush, Steve and Liz Tilley, Mayur Shah, Ron Harris, Geoff Pidoux, J V Dadswell)*

Banks's (W & D) ~ Tenant Tony Viney ~ Real ale ~ Bar food (12-2.45, 6.30-9.45) ~ Restaurant ~ (01865) 874379 ~ Well behaved children welcome ~ Dogs allowed in bar ~ Open 11-11; 12-10.30 Sun ~ Bedrooms: £49S/£60S

CUXHAM SU6695 Map 2

Half Moon

4 miles from M40 junction 6; S on B4009, then right on to B480 at Watlington

Sadly this thatched country pub had a bad chimney fire earlier this year which destroyed the whole of the upstairs floor. They are aiming to be open again by Christmas 2002 with everything much as it had been before. It's a smashing little pub and you can buy local eggs, honey and chutney, and the three comfortable low-beamed bar areas each have an open fire, with rather country cottage-style furnishings, and books and prints. The landlord also does the cooking which has included sandwiches, potato pancake with smoked trout and pickled beetroot or home-made soup, baked salmon with panzanella salad and wilted pea vine or grilled calves liver with smoked bacon and cheddar pancake, and steaks, with puddings such as vanilla and greek yoghurt cheesecake with baked peach. Well kept Brakspears Bitter and Special and maybe one of their seasonal ales on handpump; piped music. There are seats sheltered by an oak tree on the back lawn, pretty roses, clematis and honeysuckle, and a climbing frame. Across the road, a stream runs through the quiet village. More reports please. *(Recommended by Rob Webster, Paul Vickers)*

Brakspears ~ Tenant Kieron Daniels ~ Real ale ~ Bar food (12-2.30, 6.30-9.30) ~ Restaurant ~ (01491) 614110 ~ Children welcome ~ Open 11.30-2.30(12-3 Sat), 5.30-11; 12-10.30 Sun

EXLADE STREET SU6582 Map 2

Highwayman

Signposted just off A4074 Reading—Wallingford

Set in magnificent wooded countryside, this rambling inn is mainly 17th-c, but with some parts dating back another 300 years or so. The two beamed rooms of the bar have quite an unusual layout, with an interesting variety of seats around old tables and even recessed into a central sunken inglenook; an airy no smoking conservatory dining room has more seats (mainly for eating) and overlooks the garden. Under the new licensees, bar food includes soup (£4.50), lunchtime filled baguettes (from £5.95), omelettes (from £6.75), ploughman's or wild boar, apple and leek sausages with onion gravy (£6.95), fried fish and chips (£7.75), wild mushroom risotto (£8.50), thai spiced chicken (£9.95), and blade of beef (£10.95); two-course Sunday roast lunch £15.95. Well kept Fullers London Pride and IPA, and Wadworths 6X on handpump, several malt whiskies, decent wines (by the large and small glass as well as bottle), freshly squeezed orange juice, and champagne and kirs; piped music. The attractive garden has tables and fine views. *(Recommended by Paul Vickers, Simon Chell, Nick Holmes, the Didler, JP, PP, Mrs E A Macdonald, Phyl and Jack Street, Bob and Margaret Holder, LM, Nigel Williamson, Dr M Mills)*

Mercury Taverns ~ Licensee Michel Rosso ~ Real ale ~ Bar food (12-2.30, 7-9.30) ~ Restaurant ~ (01491) 682020 ~ Children welcome ~ Dogs allowed in bar ~ Open 12-3, 6-11; 12-3, 7-10.30 Sun ~ Bedrooms: £60S/£70S

FIFIELD SP2318 Map 4

Merrymouth

A424 Burford—Stow

It's so easy to speed past this friendly, family-run, 13th-c stone inn that they have put up a sign saying 'you have missed a treat' – which would be quite true. It has a civilised but warmly welcoming atmosphere in the simple but comfortably furnished L-shaped bar, with nice bay-window seats, flagstones, horsebrasses and antique bottles hanging from low beams, some walls stripped back to the old masonry, and an open fire in winter; backgammon and piped classical music. Popular, enjoyable bar food might include home-made soup (£3.25), tipsy mushrooms (£4.25), black pudding with apple, mustard and cream sauce (£4.50), lunchtime filled baguettes and platters (£4.95), cold baked ham (£6.50), chicken with bacon, mushrooms, cream and cheese (£7.95), shank of lamb (£8.75), pork tenderloin with mango chutney sauce (£9.50), steaks (from £9.95), vegetarian dishes, interesting daily specials, fresh fish, and home-made puddings (£3.75). Well kept Hook Norton Best and Wychwood Hobgoblin on handpump, and decent wines; except for five tables in the bar, the pub is no smoking. There are tables on a terrace and in the back garden (there may be a little noise from fast traffic on the road). The bedrooms are well cared for and quaint. The Domesday Book mentions an inn on this site and its name comes from the Murimuth family, who once owned the village in which it is set. *(Recommended by Mrs N W Neill, Martin Jennings, Colin McKerrow, Susan and John Douglas, Bernard Stradling, B A Dale, KN-R, Robert Gomme, Paul and Penny Rampton)*

Free house ~ Licensees Andrew and Timothy Flaherty ~ Real ale ~ Bar food ~ Restaurant ~ (01993) 831652 ~ Well behaved children in restaurant and family rooom ~ Dogs allowed in bedrooms ~ Open 12-3, 6-10.30(11 Sat); 12-3, 7-10 Sun; closed Sun evening in winter ~ Bedrooms: £45S/£65B

FYFIELD SU4298 Map 4

White Hart

In village, off A420 8 miles SW of Oxford

Under the new licensee, this interesting pub is shortly to be redecorated outside, and the gardens have already been smartened up. It was originally built for Sir John Golafre in about 1450 to house priests who would pray for his soul for ever; the atmosphere may be less pious these days, but it's still impressive. The bustling main room is a grand (and draughty) hall with soaring eaves, huge stone-flanked window embrasures and an attractive carpeted upper gallery. The cosy low-ceilinged side bar has an inglenook fireplace with a huge black urn hanging over the grate, and a framed history of the pub on the wall, and makes a pleasant contrast. The restaurant and gallery are no smoking. Under the new chefs, food at lunchtime includes sandwiches (from £4.75; steak sandwich with caramelised onion and fries £7.50; blackened swordfish with mango mayonnaise and fries (£8), and a quiche of the day (£6), as well as soup (£3.95), mixed seafood salad (£6.95), steak and mushroom in ale pie or pasta with grilled vegetables in a tomato cream sauce (£8.50), seared escalope of salmon in orange butter sauce (£11), and braised shank of lamb with rosemary jus and leek and potato gratin (£12.95), and daily specials such as escalope of turkey with cranberry jus (£8), cumberland sausage with onion gravy (£8.50), fresh local trout with port and almond cream sauce (£8.95), and liver and bacon (£10.95). Well kept Hook Norton Best, Fullers London Pride, Theakstons Old Peculier, and Wadworths IPA and 6X on handpump; darts and piped music. It's well worth wandering out through the heavy wooden door to the rambling, sheltered back lawn, which has a children's playground. *(Recommended by Geoff Pidoux, JCW, Ian Phillips, Kevin Blake, Susan and John Douglas, T G Thomas, Stephen, Julie and Hayley Brown, MP, Ian Jones)*

Free house ~ Licensee Ian Mintrim ~ Real ale ~ Bar food (till 10pm) ~ Restaurant ~ (01865) 390585 ~ Children in eating area of bar and restaurant ~ Dogs allowed in bar ~ Open 11.30-3, 6-11; 11.30-11 Sat; 12-10.30 Sun; closed 25 and evening 26 Dec

GREAT TEW SP3929 Map 4

Falkland Arms

Off B4022 about 5 miles E of Chipping Norton; The Green

This lovely inn is set in a charming village of untouched golden-stone thatched cottages. The partly panelled bar has high-backed settles and a diversity of stools around plain stripped tables on flagstones and bare boards, one, two and three-handled mugs hanging from the beam-and-board ceiling, dim converted oil lamps, shutters for the stone-mullioned latticed windows, and a fine inglenook fireplace with a blazing fire in winter. The bar counter is decorated with tobacco jars and different varieties of snuff which you can buy; darts, cribbage, and dominoes. Well kept Wadworths IPA, 6X and JCB, and four guests on handpump, 60 malt whiskies, quite a few country wines, and farm cider. Lunchtime bar food (they tell us prices have not risen this year) includes soup (£2.95), filled baguettes (from £3.50), ploughman's (£5.95), steak and kidney pie, bangers and mash or a vegetarian dish (from £6.50), with more sophisticated evening restaurant meals (booking necessary); home-made puddings include sharp lemon tart with orange sorbet and sticky toffee pudding (£4.25). The dining room is no smoking. You have to go out into the lane and then back in again to use the lavatories. There are tables outside in front of the pub, with picnic-sets under umbrellas in the garden behind – where there's a dovecote; they hold an annual summer beer festival. Small good value bedrooms (no under 14s). *(Recommended by Martin Jennings, Barry Collett, K H Frostick, C A Hall, Robert Coates, Kevin Blake, Chris Glasson, Jenny and Chris Wilson, Geoff Pidoux, JP, PP, the Didler, Mrs Mary Walters, Giles Francis, Martin and Karen Wake, Paul Boot)*

Wadworths ~ Managers Paul Barlow-Heal and S J Courage ~ Real ale ~ Bar food (lunchtime; not Sun evening) ~ Restaurant ~ (01608) 683653 ~ Children in restaurant lunchtimes only ~ Dogs allowed in bar ~ Live folk Sun night ~ Open 11.30-2.30, 6-11; 11.30-11 Sat; 12-10.30 Sun; 11.30-2.30(3 Sat), 6-11 in winter; 12-3, 7-10.30 Sun in winter ~ Bedrooms: £40S/£65S(£80B)

HENLEY SU7882 Map 4

Anchor

Friday Street; coming in over bridge, first left towards A4155 then next right

Homely and friendly, this old-fashioned local is a refreshing contrast to the gloss and style of the rich little town. Informally run by a friendly and obliging landlady, it has a well worn-in mix of elderly traditional pub furnishings in its two main rooms, with throw rugs, scatter cushions, chintz curtains, some venerable wall boarding and dim lighting adding to the cottagey feel. The beams in the dark ochre ceiling are thickly hung with chamber-pots, steins, whisky-water jugs, copperware and so forth, and there are interesting pictures: mainly local river photographs in the left room, a mix of antique sporting, ship and comical prints on the right, which has a piano and TV. Generous bar food includes an impressive choice of sandwiches (from £3), baked potatoes (from £4.50) and baguettes (from £5) as well as mains (from £6.50) such as steak and ale pie, stroganoff, seafood mornay, rack of ribs and thai or indian curry. Well kept Brakspears PA and SB on handpump, and a good range of malt whiskies and of wines by the glass. A simply furnished back dining room has lots of rowing photographs, and a cage with a chatty cockatiel; behind is a charming informal terrace surrounded by lush vegetation and hanging vines. The friendly chocolate labrador is called Rüger. More reports please. *(Recommended by the Didler, Ian Phillips, Simon Collett-Jones, JP, PP)*

Brakspears ~ Tenant G A Ion-Savage ~ Bar food (not winter Sun evening) ~ (01491) 574753 ~ Well behaved children in restaurant until 8.30 ~ Dogs allowed in bar ~ Open 11-11; 12-10.30 Sun; closed 25 Dec

HIGHMOOR SU6984 Map 2

Rising Sun

Witheridge Hill, signposted off B481; OS Sheet 175 map reference 697841

Most customers come to this pretty black and white building to eat and you may find it difficult to get a table for just a drink. There are seats around a few simple tables in a smallish carpeted area on the right, by the bar, with some bar stools too, and a big log-effect stove in a big brick inglenook fireplace. The main area spreading back from here has shiny bare boards and a swathe of red carpeting, with well spaced tables, attractive pictures on cream or dark salmon walls, and a side bit with a leather settee, low games table and shove-ha'penny, liar dice, chess and so forth. Bar food might include peppers stuffed with a medley of vegetables (£7.25), baked onion tart (£8.25), coq au vin or calves liver and bacon (£8.45), medallions of pork or ricotta cheese and spinach cannelloni (£8.75), and fresh cod or haddock (from £8.75). Well kept Brakspears PA and SB on handpump, good pleasant service. There are picnic-sets on a fairy-lit terrace and on grass among trees; it's a nice quiet spot, by a rough sloping green. More reports please. *(Recommended by Bob and Margaret Holder)*

Brakspears ~ Licensees Bill and Beryl Farrell ~ Real ale ~ Bar food (12-2.30, 7-9.30; 12-2.30, 6.30-9.15 Sun) ~ Restaurant ~ (01491) 641455 ~ Children welcome ~ Dogs allowed in bar ~ Open 11-3, 6-11; 12-3, 6.30-10.30 Sun

HOOK NORTON SP3533 Map 4

Gate Hangs High

Banbury Road; a mile N of village towards Sibford, at Banbury—Rollright crossroads

New licensees have taken over this tucked-away country pub, and readers have been quick to voice their enthusiasm for the food – including several, like us, following them from their previous much smaller pub, the White Swan at Wigginton. The bar has joists in the long, low ceiling, a brick bar counter, stools and assorted chairs on the carpet, baby oil lamps on each table, a gleaming copper hood over the hearth in the inglenook fireplace, and hops over the bar counter. Well kept Hook Norton Best and Old Hooky on handpump, a good wine list, and a range of malt whiskies; piped music. Good, popular food includes pork crackling and apple sauce (£2.50), sandwiches (from £3.50; the hot beef one is recommended), smoked mackerel mousse (£4.50), pork fillet with mushrooms, sherry and cream (£11.95), swordfish steak and horseradish sauce (£12.95), and home-made puddings. You'll need to book for Saturday evening and Sunday lunch. In summer, there are flowering tubs and wall baskets around the picnic-sets in front of the pub and the broad back lawn is a nice place for a drink, with holly and apple trees, and fine views. Five miles south-west of the pub are the Bronze Age Rollright Stones – said to be a king and his army who were turned to stone by a witch. *(Recommended by M Benjamin, Stuart Turner, Mike and Mary Carter, Marjorie and David Lamb, John Robertson, Geoff Pidoux, Martin Jennings, Eric George, Ted George, John Mason, Sir Nigel Foulkes, Malcolm Taylor)*

Hook Norton ~ Tenant Stephen Coots-Williams ~ Real ale ~ Bar food (12-2.15, 6-10) ~ Restaurant ~ (01608) 737387 ~ Children welcome ~ Dogs allowed in bar ~ Open 12-3, 6-11; 12-4, 7-11 Sun

Pear Tree

Village signposted off A361 SW of Banbury

The main attraction here, not surprisingly, is the beer as this little pub is barely 100 yards away from the Hook Norton brewery, and has the full range of their ales on handpump including very well kept Hook Norton Best, Old Hooky, Generation, Mild, and seasonal ales; country wines. The chatty knocked together bar area has country-kitchen furniture on the nicely timbered floor, some long tables, a well stocked magazine rack, and a welcoming log fire; dominoes, and Jenga. Bar food from a short menu includes sandwiches, soup (£2.95), filled baked potatoes (from £4.50), ploughman's (from £5.50), home-cooked ham and eggs (£6.50), beef in ale or fish pie (£6.75), and puddings such as lemon meringue pie (£2.95). They play aunt sally and there's an outdoor chess set in the attractive, sizeable garden which has plenty of seats. It does get busy at weekends. *(Recommended by Mike Gorton, Geoff Pidoux, the Didler, Martin and Penny Fletcher, Dick and Madeleine Brown, GSB, Steve Whalley, Chris Glasson, JHBS, Derek and Sylvia Stephenson, C A Hall, Barry Collett, K H Frostick, Robert Gomme, Mike and Wena Stevenson)*

Hook Norton ~ Tenant J Sivyer ~ Real ale ~ Bar food (not Sun evening) ~ (01608) 737482 ~ Children in eating area of bar until 9 ~ Dogs allowed in bar ~ Open 11.30-2.30(4 Sat), 6-11; 12-4, 7-10.30 Sun ~ Bedrooms: £35S/£50S

Sun

High Street

They've cleverly found a balance between pub and restaurant in this bustling place, and there's even a table reserved for domino players. The flagstoned front bar has a buoyant and laid-back local atmosphere, a huge log fire, hop-strung beams, and well kept Hook Norton Best, Mild, Generation and Old Hooky on handpump; good value wines including nine by the glass, and friendly, cheerful service. Behind the central servery, a cosy carpeted room with comfortable banquettes and other seats leads into the attractive no smoking green-walled restaurant. Tasty bar food includes home-made soup (£2.95), very good filled baguettes (from £3.25; sun-dried tomato ciabatta topped with roasted peppers, tomatoes, olives and mozzarella £5.45), mussels in white wine and cream (£3.95), smoked haddock topped with Hooky rarebit (£4.25), ploughman's (£5.50), beef pie (£6.95), chicken in a mild curry sauce (£7.95), fillet of pork with apricot jus (£10.95), fillet of bass with petit ratatouille and roasted tomato oil (£12.75), and roast best end of lamb with rosemary and mint jus (£14.95). Tables out on a back terrace with more on the street in front which gives a continental feel on summer evenings; good wheelchair access and disabled facilities. *(Recommended by Simon Collett-Jones, Sir Nigel Foulkes, John Bowdler, Dick and Madeleine Brown, Richard Greaves, Steve Whalley, Pete Baker, Geoff Pidoux, Chris Glasson, Roger Braithwaite, K H Frostick)*

Hook Norton ~ Tenants Richard and Jane Hancock ~ Bar food ~ Restaurant ~ (01608) 737570 ~ Children in eating area of bar and restaurant ~ Dogs allowed in bar ~ Open 11.30-3, 6-11; 12-3.30, 7-10.30 Sun ~ Bedrooms: £35B/£50B

LEWKNOR SU7198 Map 4

Olde Leathern Bottel

Under a mile from M40 junction 6; just off B4009 towards Watlington

Very handy for the M40, this busy country pub is in a charming village, and has an attractive sizeable garden with a children's play area. The two bar rooms have heavy beams in the low ceilings, rustic furnishings, open fires, and an understated décor of old beer taps and the like. The no smoking family room is separated only by standing timbers, so you won't feel segregated from the rest of the pub. Bar food includes lunchtime filled baguettes or ploughman's (from £4.95), ham and eggs or all-day breakfast (£5.95), and daily specials. Well kept Brakspears Bitter, Special, winter Old, and a monthly guest on handpump, and all their wines are sold by the glass; dominoes and piped music. *(Recommended by Stuart Turner, Andy Gosling, B, M and P Kendall, Patrick Hancock, MLR, Brian Skelcher)*

Brakspears ~ Tenant Mr L S Gordon ~ Real ale ~ Bar food (12-2, 7-9.30; 12-2, 6-10 Fri/Sat) ~ (01844) 351482 ~ Children in restaurant and family room ~ Dogs welcome ~ Open 11-2.30(3 Sat), 6-11; 11-3, 7-10.30 Sun

MAIDENSGROVE SU7288 Map 2

Five Horseshoes

W of village, which is signposted from B480 and B481; OS Sheet 175 map reference 711890

From each of the three areas outside this friendly 17th-c brick pub, there are lovely views over the wooded Chiltern Valley – you may be lucky enough to see a red kite. They hold summer barbecues and have interesting dishes such as capsicum pepper filled with dijon mustard and wild mushroom risotto parcelled in foil (£7.45), tuna steak marinated in lime, lemon grass and ginger (£9.95), swordfish, salmon and king prawn skewers with lemon (£11.25), and half shoulder of spring lamb (£12.95). The rambling main bar is furnished with mostly modern wheelback chairs around stripped wooden tables (though there are some attractive older seats and a big baluster-leg table), and there's a proper log fire in winter; the low ceiling in the main area is covered in bank notes from all over the world, mainly donated by customers, and the airy dining conservatory is decorated with shoe artefacts. Good, interesting food includes soup (£4.25), home-made chicken liver pâté with onion relish (£4.75), wild mushroom and smoked cheddar tartlet with a sweet pepper coulis (£5.75), thai-style crab salad with fried tiger prawns (£6.75), lambs liver with bacon, onions and mushrooms on mustard mash with rich creamy gravy (£7.95), coconut scented vegetable curry with tempura battered aubergine (£8.45), chargrilled steaks (from £9.45), and fillet of bass wrapped in bacon with stir-fried vegetables and oriental oyster sauce (£12.95). Well kept Brakspears PA, SB and seasonal ales on handpump, and 15 wines by the glass, including champagne; piped music. *(Recommended by Joan Thorpe, Brian Root, Desmond Hall, Jayne and Peter Capp, T R and B C Jenkins, Michael Porter, Paul Hopton, Derek Thomas, John and Barbara Main, Andrew Barker, Claire Jenkins, M Borthwick)*

Brakspears ~ Tenants Mr and Mrs Hills ~ Real ale ~ Bar food ~ Restaurant ~ (01491) 641282 ~ Children in restaurant ~ Dogs allowed in bar ~ Open 11-3, 6-11; maybe all day in good weather; 12-4, 7-10.30 Sun

MURCOTT SP5815 Map 4

Nut Tree 🍷

Off B4027 NE of Oxford, via Islip and Charlton-on-Otmoor

This neatly thatched pub dates back to the War of the Roses and later was a favourite with Roundhead soldiers when Cromwell had his headquarters at nearby Boarstall. The civilised beamed lounge has a long polished bar with pictures all round, and a winter log fire, and the small back conservatory-style restaurant is no smoking. There is still a quiet part for those wanting only a drink, but much space is given over to diners. Bar food includes soup such as hot or cold leek and potato (from £3.95), chicken liver parfait with onion marmalade and cumberland sauce (£4.95; main course £8.50), home-made fishcakes on avocado salsa (£4.95; main course £9.95), open sandwiches (ciabatta, bloomer and baguettes; from £4.95), hand-made sun-dried tomato and parma ham sausages with mash and onion gravy (£8.95), breast of chicken with a lemongrass sauce (£10.95), shank of lamb (£12.95), and puddings such as crème brûlée or chocolate and caramelised hazelnut délice (£4.50). Well kept Hook Norton Best and Timothy Taylors Landlord, and a guest from Batemans or West Berkshire Brewery on handpump, a fair number of malt whiskies, and a decent range of wines with several by the glass; piped music. On a wall in front of the pub is an unusual collection of gargoyles, each loosely modelled on one of the local characters. There are usually ducks on the front pond, pretty hanging baskets and tubs in summer, and peacocks; aunt sally in the well kept garden. No children inside. More reports please. *(Recommended by Mrs M Reid)*

Free house ~ Licensees Mr Sparks and Mr Wood ~ Real ale ~ Bar food (12-2, 6-9.30; not Mon) ~ Restaurant ~ (01865) 331253 ~ Dogs allowed in bar ~ Open 12-3, 6-11; 12-4.30 Sun; closed Sun evening

OXFORD SP5203 Map 4

Isis Tavern

Off Donnington Bridge Road (between A4144 Abingdon Road and A4158 Iffley Road); park in Meadow Lane, walk over bridge, then turn left and walk 300 yds along towpath); no car access

Summer weekends are particularly busy for this waterside pub with many customers arriving by boat. It's handy for pretty Iffley Lock (and Iffley church) and is beside a water-meadow nature reserve with plenty of geese, ducks, swans and coots. Around the central bar servery is a pleasantly informal medley of furnishings on the turkey carpet, including a couple of little settees by a log fire, but the mood is set by the forest of mainly nautical bric-a-brac hanging from the high ceiling – anything from nets and buoys to full-size boats. A similar mass of stuff covers the walls, among it some fine old photographs of racing yachts and one or two attractive model boats. Vying for attention are big menu boards, which under the new licensee might list soup (£2.95), filled soft rolls with chips (from £4.25), ploughman's or sausage and mash (£4.50), popular cajun chicken (£5.20), vegetarian lasagne (£5.50), steak in ale pie (£6.50), steaks (from £7.50), and puddings (from £2.50). As we went to press Greene King were in the process of buying the pub, but they had well kept Morrells Oxford and Oxford Blue on handpump and a changing guest; friendly service; daily papers; sensibly placed well lit darts and bar billiards in one corner, shove-ha'penny, chess, dominoes, cribbage, maybe piped pop music and TV. There are picnic-sets out on a terrace and in the garden, which has a massive yew tree among other trees and shrubs, and outdoor heaters; swings, slide, aunt sally by arrangement, even a traditional bowling alley. *(Recommended by R M Gibson, LM, Tim and Ann Newell)*

Greene King ~ Manager Roger Nicol ~ Real ale ~ Bar food (11.30-9; 12-8 Sun) ~ Restaurant ~ (01865) 247006 ~ Children in eating area of bar until 8.30pm ~ Open 11.30-11; 12-10.30 Sun; they may open shorter hours in winter if the weather is poor, so best to phone first

Kings Arms £

40 Holywell Street

Although this 16th-c pub is nearly always busy with a good mix of students, dons and tourists, staff manage to remain obliging and friendly and there's a good relaxed atmosphere. There's a big rather bare main room, with a no smoking coffee room just inside the Parks Road entrance, and several cosy and comfortably worn-in side and back rooms, each with a different character and customers. An extra back room has a sofa and more tables and there's a tiny room behind that. They still keep a dictionary for the crossword buffs in the Dons Bar, with its elderly furnishings and tiled floor, mix of old prints and photographs of customers, and sympathetic lighting; daily newspapers, fruit machine, video game and cribbage. Well kept Youngs Bitter, Special and one of their seasonal ales with guests such as Smiles Best and Wadworths 6X on handpump, a fine choice of wines with over 15 by the glass, and up to 20 malt whiskies. The menu was being changed as we went to press, but had included home-made soup, filled baked potatoes, filled baguettes, good quiche, meat pies and help-yourself salads, and hot dishes such as burgers, spaghetti bolognese, three bean chilli, beef pie, and steaks. On Sundays they open at 10.30 for breakfast and coffee. *(Recommended by Dick and Madeleine Brown, Rona Murdoch, Margaret and Roy Randle, Derek and Sylvia Stephenson, Dr and Mrs M E Wilson, Mr and Mrs G Owens, the Didler, I D Greenfield, Kevin Blake, M Joyner, R Huggins, D Irving, E McCall, T McLean)*

Youngs ~ Manager David Kyffin ~ Real ale ~ Bar food (11.30-9.30) ~ (01865) 242369 ~ Children in eating area of bar and family room till 8pm ~ Open 10.30-11; 10.30-10.30 Sun

Turf Tavern

Tavern Bath Place; via St Helen's Passage, between Holywell Street and New College Lane

Cut off from the modern bustle of the city by the high stone walls of some of its oldest buildings, including part of the ancient city wall, this pretty place is usually overflowing with quite a mix of customers. The little dark-beamed and low-ceilinged rooms have an infectious lively atmosphere and a fine range of up to 11 well kept ales on handpump: Adnams Jubilee, Badger Tanglefoot, Cains Sundowner, Coach House Dick Turpin, Exmoor Fox, Nethergate Wild Goose, Orkney Dark Island, Robinsons Young Tom, Shepherd Neame Early Bird, Titanic Rule Britannia, and Woodfordes Great Eastern. They also stock Hoegaarden Belgian beer and Weston's Old Rosie cider, and offer winter mulled wine; quiz machine. The cellar is open to the public and they are happy to show people around. Straightforward bar food (they tell us prices have not changed since last year) is served by friendly young staff and includes baguettes (from £2.90), filled baked potatoes (from £3), sausage and mash (£4.25), lasagne (£4.75), fish and chips (£4.95), steak and ale pie (£5.35), and blackened cajun chicken (£5.15); the top food area is no smoking. On long summer evenings it's especially nice to sit out at the tables in the three attractive walled-in flagstoned or gravelled courtyards (one has its own bar); in winter, they have coal braziers and sell chestnuts and marshmallows, and there are canopies with lights and heaters. Very popular with students in the evening, so you may have problems finding a seat. *(Recommended by Philip and Ann Board, David Peakall, Catherine Pitt, T R and B C Jenkins, the Didler, R Huggins, D Irving, E McCall, T McLean, Eric Locker, Mr and Mrs J McRobert, Dr and Mrs M E Wilson, David and Carole Chapman, Rona Murdoch, Kevin Blake, Geoff Pidoux, Nigel Woolliscroft, Dick and Madeleine Brown, Andrew Barker, Claire Jenkins, Stephanie Smith, Gareth Price, Jim and Maggie Cowell, Paul Hopton, Howard Dell)*

Laurel (Enterprise) ~ Manager Darren Kent ~ Real ale ~ Bar food (12-7.30) ~ (01865) 243235 ~ Dogs welcome ~ Open 11-11; 12-10.30 Sun

RAMSDEN SP3515 Map 4

Royal Oak

Village signposted off B4022 Witney—Charlbury

Very well run by a friendly licensee, this unpretentious village inn continues to earn warm praise from readers. There's a good pubby atmosphere and a nice mix of customers, and the basic furnishings are comfortable, with fresh flowers, bookcases with old and new copies of *Country Life* and, when the weather gets cold, a cheerful log fire. Using fresh seasonal produce from local suppliers (and organic when possible), the good, popular bar food might include lunchtime ploughman's (£4.95), club sandwich (£5.50), smoked Scotch salmon and scrambled egg (£5.95), and pork and sage sausage with onion gravy (£6.95), as well as home-made soup (£3.25), Scottish haddock cooked with whisky and cream topped with cheese (£4.95; main course £9.50), home-made burgers (from £7.25), a pie of the week (£6.95), stilton, leek and mushroom puff (£8.95), mediterranean-style lamb casserole (£10.95), and daily specials like popular moules marinière or skewered monkfish, chargrilled fresh Evesham asparagus (£5.75), vegetable lasagne (£8.50), organic coq au vin (£9.50), and confit of duck with puy green lentils (£11.50). On Thursday evenings they offer a steak, fries and salad, a home-made pudding and a glass of house wine for £12.95; roast Sunday lunch. The dining room is no smoking. Well kept real ales on handpump include Arkells 2B, Hook Norton Best, and Youngs Bitter with a guest such as Badger Tanglefoot or West Berkshire Good Old Boy, and they serve 20 wines by the glass. There are tables and chairs out in front and on the terrace behind the restaurant (which has new folding back doors this year giving easy access to the outside seating area). The cosy bedrooms are in separate cottages. *(Recommended by Richard Greaves, Dick and Madeleine Brown, Rainer Zimmer, Simon Reynolds, George Cowie, Suzanne Baylis, P W E Sheldon, Les and Barbara Owen, Ronald Harry, Christine Harmer-Brown, Angus Lyon, Tony Duley, Geoff Pidoux, Stuart Turner, Peter Dolan)*

Free house ~ Licensee Jon Oldham ~ Real ale ~ Bar food (12-1.45, 7-9.45) ~ Restaurant ~ (01993) 868213 ~ Children in eating area of bar and restaurant; no under 5s Sat evening (unless arranged beforehand) ~ Dogs allowed in bar ~ Open 11.30-3, 6.30-11; 12-3, 7-10.30 Sun; closed 25 and 26 Dec and evening 1 Jan ~ Bedrooms: £35S/£50S

ROKE SU6293 Map 2

Home Sweet Home

Village signposted off B4009 Benson—Watlington

There's a pleasant, relaxed atmosphere in the two smallish bar rooms of this traditional, rather smart pub. Also, a lovely big log fire, heavy stripped beams, leather armed chairs on the bare boards, a great high-backed settle with a hefty slab of a rustic table in front of it, and a few horsey or game pictures such as a nice Thorburn print of snipe on the stone walls. On the right, a carpeted room with low settees and armchairs and an attractive corner glass cupboard leads through to the restaurant. A wide choice of good, popular bar food includes sandwiches, toasties, and club sandwiches, lots of ploughman's (from £4.50), filled baked potatoes (from £5), and daily specials such as warm smoked salmon and watercress tart (£7.50), fresh salmon fishcakes with parsley sauce, steak and kidney pudding or pasta with crayfish tails (£7.95), calves liver and crispy bacon

(£8.50), and chicken breast filled with parma ham and smoked cheese (£8.95). Well kept Brakspears on handpump, and a good choice of malt whiskies; welcoming, efficient staff. The low-walled front garden is ideal for eating on a sunny day; there are lots of flowers around the tables out by the well.

(Recommended by Iain and Joan Baillie, Mrs E A Macdonald, Nick Holmes, Mayur Shah, Marjorie and David Lamb, C A Hall)

Free house ~ Licensees Jill Madle, Peter & Irene Mountford ~ Real ale ~ Bar food (not Sun evening) ~ Restaurant ~ (01491) 838249 ~ Well behaved children in eating area of bar and in restaurant ~ Dogs allowed in bar ~ Open 11(12 Sun)-3, 6-11; closed Sun evening

SHENINGTON SP3742 Map 4

Bell

Village signposted from A422 W of Banbury

This is a tranquil and picturesque village and the 300-year-old pub is part of a row of golden Hornton stone cottages. The heavy-beamed and carpeted lounge has cushioned wall and window seats, vases of flowers on the tables, horsebrasses and an old document on the cream walls, and a relaxed atmosphere; the wall in the flagstoned area on the left is stripped to stone and decorated with heavy-horse harness, and the right side opens into a little pine-panelled room (popular with locals) with decorated plates; cribbage, dominoes, coal fire. Well kept Hook Norton Best on handpump. Cooked by the landlady, good wholesome food from a short menu might include sandwiches (from £2.50), kipper pâté (£3.50), prawn and salmon quiche or home-cooked ham salad (£6.75), macaroni bake with tomatoes and mushrooms or lasagne (£6.95), chicken wrapped in bacon with stilton sauce (£7.50), salmon in watercress sauce or lamb and mint casserole (£7.95), popular foil-baked trout with fresh herbs (£8.95), and duck with port and black cherries (£9.95), and puddings such as rhubarb crumble or sticky toffee pudding (£2.95). Tables at the front look across to the green, and there are seats in the small attractive back garden. The west highland terrier is called Lucy, the labrador, Daisy, and the great dane, Oliver. Good surrounding walks.

(Recommended by Sir Nigel Foulkes, John Kane, K H Frostick, Geoffrey and Penny Hughes, Martin Jones, John Bramley)

Free house ~ Licensee Jennifer Dixon ~ Real ale ~ Bar food (not Mon lunchtime) ~ Restaurant ~ (01295) 670274 ~ Children in eating area of bar and restaurant ~ Dogs welcome ~ Open 12-2.30(3 Sat), 7-11; 12-3.30, 7-10.30 Sun; closed Mon lunchtime (except bank hols) ~ Bedrooms: £25/£50S

SHIPTON-UNDER-WYCHWOOD SP2717 Map 4

Shaven Crown

There's quite a history to this imposing building. In the 14th c it was a hospice for the monastery of Bruern, and Elizabeth I is said to have used parts of it as a hunting lodge. There's a magnificent double-collar braced hall roof, lofty beams and a sweeping double stairway down the stone wall, and the beamed bar has a relief of the 1146 Battle of Evesham, as well as seats forming little stalls around the tables and upholstered benches built into the walls. From a long menu, bar food includes soup (£3.50), sandwiches or filled baguettes (from £3.50), mixed game terrine (£4.50), deep-fried whitebait (£5), ploughman's (£7.50), pasta with tomato, olives, capers, basil and mozzarella (£7.95), steak and mushroom pie, salmon and crab fishcakes or chicken curry (£8.50), lamb shank (£8.95), duck breast with blackcurrant coulis or sirloin steak (£9.95), and puddings such as treacle tart, rich chocolate mousse or sticky toffee pudding (£3.50); children's dishes (£4.50), Sunday lunch, and good breakfasts; service is friendly and efficient. The restaurant is no smoking. Well kept Hook Norton Best, and a couple of guests such as Fullers London Pride and Wells Bombardier on handpump, and several wines by the glass; shove-ha'penny, dominoes and cribbage. The courtyard is a tranquil place to sit on a sunny day, and is pleasantly lit up at night when gas heaters allow you to soak up the atmosphere without shivering; the pub has its own bowling green. *(Recommended by Ian Phillips, JMC, Bob and Valerie Mawson, Marjorie and David Lamb)*

Free house ~ Licensees Robert and Jane Burpitt ~ Real ale ~ Bar food (12-2, 5.30-9.30) ~ Restaurant ~ (01993) 830330 ~ Children welcome away from main bar ~ Dogs welcome ~ Open 11.30-2.30, 5-11; 12-3, 7-10.30 Sun ~ Bedrooms: £55B/£85S(£95B)

SIBFORD GOWER SP3537 Map 4

Bishop Blaize

Village signposted just off B4035 W of Banbury; Burdrop

The garden at this welcoming stone-built local is magnificent, with a splendid view down over the sheep-strewn hillside and across the surrounding fields, on a clear day stretching into Gloucestershire and Warwickshire. It's attractively planted, and there are plenty of seats out here (perhaps more than inside), as well as swings in the corner. On our Saturday visit, the car park was already starting to fill before the doors had opened – it's clearly very popular, and not just because of the view: the unspoilt feel of the 17th-c bar, and the especially attentive thoughtful service, are both draws too. The landlord in particular is genuinely friendly and helpful, and works hard to ensure everyone is happy. The heavily beamed partly tiled bar has big windows overlooking the garden, some panelling, cosy and comfortable country furnishings, a few framed cartoons, and leaflets advertising local concerts and events. There's an unusual curved wooden counter, opposite which is a very snug inglenook, once used for wakes, but now squeezing in a couple of tiny tables and chairs by an ancient stove. Down a step is a small area with a fruit machine. Blackboards list the well liked home-made food, typically including soup (£2.75), filled baked potatoes (£4.25), thai vegetable schnitzel (£4.65), their speciality pies such as steak and kidney or chicken and mushroom (£6.75), and changing specials; children's menu. Well kept Hook Norton and a couple of beers from the local Vale brewery on handpump; soft piped music. Morris dancers occasionally visit in summer. There are quite a few steps down from the car park; it's a flatter entrance from the front. Good walks nearby. Originally known as the Old Inn, it's thought to have been renamed after the patron saint of wool combers early in the 19th c. *(Recommended by Lisa Tallis, Giles Francis, Ted George)*

Free house ~ Licensees Sam and Sheila Merchant ~ Real ale ~ Bar food (not winter Sun-Tues evening) ~ (01295) 780323 ~ Children welcome away from bar ~ Open 12-2.30, 6-11; 12-3, 7-10.30 Sun

STANTON ST JOHN SP5709 Map 4

Star

Pub signposted off B4027; village is signposted off A40 heading E of Oxford (heading W, you have to go to the Oxford ring-road roundabout and take unclassified road signposted to Stanton St John, Forest Hill etc); bear right at church in village centre

Interestingly arranged over two levels, this pleasant old pub has an attractive extension on a level with the car park. There are old-fashioned dining chairs, an interesting mix of dark oak and elm tables, rugs on flagstones, pairs of bookshelves on each side of an attractive inglenook fireplace, shelves of good pewter, terracotta-coloured walls with a portrait in oils, and a stuffed ermine; down a flight of stairs are little low-beamed rooms – one has ancient brick flooring tiles and the other quite close-set tables. Served by helpful staff, the well liked bar food includes sandwiches (£2.40), soup (£2.40, soup and sandwich £4.25), filled baked potatoes (from £2.95), ploughman's (from £3.95), chicken liver pâté (£3.95), deep-fried whitebait (£4.95), vegetarian cannelloni or steak in Guinness pie (£6.95), venison pie or seafood pasta (£7.50), gammon and pineapple (£8.50), whole bass baked in ginger, lime and coriander (£8.95), and puddings (£3.25). Well kept Wadworths IPA and 6X and one of their other ales on handpump, and country wines. The family room is no smoking; piped music, darts, shove-ha'penny, cribbage and dominoes. The walled garden has seats among the rockeries and children's play equipment. *(Recommended by Ian Phillips, Marjorie and David Lamb, Paul Hopton, Geoff Pidoux, Canon and Mrs Michael Bourdeaux, Kevin Blake, K H Frostick, Susan and John Douglas)*

Wadworths ~ Tenant Michael Urwin ~ Real ale ~ Bar food (not Sun evening) ~ (01865) 351277 ~ Children welcome ~ Dogs welcome ~ Open 11-2.30, 6.30-11; 12-2.30, 7-10.30 Sun

Talk House 🍷 🛏

Wheatley Road (B4027 just outside village)

There's a pleasant atmosphere in the various capacious rooms inside this peacefully set 17th-c pub: lots of oak beams, flagstoned and tiled floors, stripped original stonework, simple but solid rustic furnishings, and attractive pictures and other individual and often light-hearted decorations. While most of the tables are set for dining, there's enough room for those just wanting a sociable drink, and there's a new drinkers' area with comfortable leather sofas around the fireplace. Well kept Greene King Old Speckled Hen, Hook Norton Best and a guest such as Fullers London Pride on handpump, good house wines, and several malt whiskies; piped music. Enjoyable bar food includes home-made soup (£3.95), home-made crab and fishcakes with red chilli sauce (£5.50), smooth chicken liver and armagnac pâté (£5.75), baked field mushroom stuffed with ratatouille and cream cheese topping (£5.95), steak and kidney in ale pie (£9.95), warm duck and bacon salad with plum sauce (£10.95), roast loin of pork with a honey and wholegrain mustard crust (£11.95), chargrilled sirloin steak or calves liver and bacon with brandy cream sauce (£12.95), and thai king prawn stir fry (£13.95); they add a 10% service charge to tables of more than six people. There are tables in the sheltered courtyard. More reports please. *(Recommended by Geoff Pidoux, Tim and Ann Newell, Martin Jennings, Darly Graton, Graeme Gulibert)*

Traditional Freehouses ~ Manager Anne-Marie Carlisle-Kitz ~ Real ale ~ Bar food (12-9 Sun) ~ Restaurant ~ (01865) 351648 ~ Children welcome ~ Open 11-11; 12-10.30 Sun; 10-3, 5.30-11 winter ~ Bedrooms: £40B/£60B

SWALCLIFFE SP3737 Map 4

Stags Head

Bakers Lane, just off B4035

The welcoming licensees of this charmingly picturesque, old thatched village pub have opened up a letting bedroom with its own kitchenette this year, the lavatories in the inn have been updated, and a new reclaimed oak floor has been laid. There's a big woodburner at the end of the low-beamed bar and next to it a standard lamp, and high-backed wooden pews and cushioned seats beside the stone walls. Lots of little jugs hang from the ceiling, and the 'head' of a Master of Foxhounds rather than the fox. A lighter room has lots more tables, and a tiled fireplace, along with newspapers to read, plenty of books, and lists of various local events and activities; there are candles on all the tables in the evening, and it's all very snug and welcoming. As well as lunchtime baguettes (from £4.95), enjoyable bar food might include avocado and bacon salad or oriental crab cakes with sweet chilli dip (£4.50), cheddar, leek and spring onion pasta (£7.95), spinach, goats cheese and bacon pasta bake (£8.95), salmon fillet with a lemon and pesto cream sauce or thai green chicken curry with chilli bread (£9.50), pork tenderloin with a cider, herb and camembert sauce (£9.95), lamb fillet with melting garlic and rosemary butter (£10.95), steaks (from £10.95), and puddings such as white chocolate, rhubarb and ginger tart or lemon drizzle pudding (£3.75); the top bar area is no smoking. Well kept Brakspears, Hook Norton Best, and a guest from breweries such as Archers, Batemans or Wychwood; good changing wine list, with six by the glass, port by the glass, half pint or pint, and a generous, well made bloody mary. They have two dogs and a cat. Piped easy listening music, darts, shove-ha'penny, cribbage, a dominoes team, and two quiz teams. Tables in front of the building look down over a peaceful, steeply winding little lane opposite the church. Behind is a series of neatly terraced gardens with palm trees, a small fountain, several tables under a pergola, and a sensibly segregated play area. There should be more ducks and chickens arriving soon. More reports please. *(Recommended by George Atkinson, John Kane, Mrs Mary Walters, Martin Jones)*

Free house ~ Licensees Ian and Julia Kingsford ~ Real ale ~ Bar food (12-2.15, 7-9.30; not Sun evening or Mon) ~ Restaurant ~ (01295) 780232 ~ Children in eating area of bar and restaurant ~ Dogs welcome ~ Open 11.30-2.30(3 Sat), 6.30-11; 12-4 Sun; closed Sun evening and all day Mon ~ Bedrooms: £35S/£60S

SWERFORD SP3731 Map 4

Masons Arms

A361 Banbury—Chipping Norton

New licensees took over this smartly refurbished dining pub not long before our summer inspection, and the steady stream of happy customers while we were there confirms that they've already established an enviable reputation for their cooking. The bar has been brightly modernised in a neatly contemporary way: light wooden floors with rugs, a carefully illuminated stone fireplace, thoughtful spotlighting, and comfortable blue armchairs around big round tables in light wood. Doors open on to a small terrace with a couple of stylish tables, while steps lead down into a plank-walled room with chunky tables and a couple of big mirrors. There's a big pile of newspapers. Round the other side of the bar is a roomy dining room, with great views by day, candlelight at night, and a relaxed civilised feel. The monthly changing menu includes dishes such as roast rack of lamb with roasted red peppers, grilled mustard polenta, and spinach and rosemary jus or cornfed chicken breast on shallot tarte tatin with spinach and buttered mushrooms (£11), and whole roast bass stuffed with lemongrass, lime leaves and thyme (£13); there's also a short bar menu with sandwiches such as red onion and cheddar ciabatta or BLT (£4.95). Well kept Hook Norton Best, and a decent wine list (mostly by the bottle rather than the glass). The staff are efficient and hard-working; when not serving customers they're constantly keeping everywhere spotless. Behind is a neat square lawn with picnic-sets, and the views over the Oxfordshire countryside are very relaxing, especially if there's a good sunset (though this north-facing ridge can be breezy). *(Recommended by David Campbell, Vicki McLean, Ted George)*

Free house ~ Licensee Jeanette Hill-Wickham ~ Real ale ~ Bar food ~ Restaurant ~ (01608) 683212 ~ Children welcome away from bar ~ Dogs allowed in bar ~ Open 12-3(4 Sat, Sun), 6-11(10.30 Sun)

TADPOLE BRIDGE SP3300 Map 4

Trout 🍷

Back road Bampton—Buckland, 4 miles NE of Faringdon

Though many customers come to this peacefully set Thames-side pub to enjoy the very good food, walkers and those arriving by boat often just drop in for a drink. The cheerful, bustling atmosphere is helped along by the friendly staff who also serve the interesting and varied meals: home-made soup, caesar salad (£4.50; main course £9), chicken liver parfait with a poached pear and cinnamon and pear dressing (£4.95), home-smoked duck breast with pickled apple and an apple and blackberry cumberland sauce (£5.95), seared scallops on a noodle cake with sweet chilli sauce (£6.95; main course £13.90), cumberland sausage (£7.95), roasted vegetable lasagne (£8.75), chargrilled pork steak with greek salad (£8.95), chargrilled Aberdeen Angus steak with café de paris butter (£13.95), roast loin of lamb with ratatouille couscous and black olive sauce or roast supreme of guinea fowl with wild mushroom duxelle served with a savoury vanilla risotto (£14.95), and puddings; the restaurant is no smoking. The small L-shaped original bar has plenty of seats on flagstones, well kept Archers Village, Youngs Bitter, and a guest or two from Hook Norton or West Berkshire Brewery, and home-made sloe gin, cherry plum brandy and elderflower cordial; a comprehensive, interesting wine list, and they will happily open any of their wines (under £25) and only charge you for the amount you drink; 18 by the glass plus half a dozen sweet ones. Darts, dominoes, cribbage, backgammon, and piped music. The well kept garden is pretty in summer with small fruit trees, attractive hanging baskets, and flower troughs; you can fish on a two-mile stretch of the river (the pub sells day tickets). *(Recommended by Peter and Audrey Dowsett, P R and S A White, Mary Rayner, R M Gibson, David Humphreys, Herbert and Susan Verity, Harold Copeman, Paul Craddock, Bob and Margaret Holder, Alan Wilson)*

Free house ~ Licensee Christopher J Green ~ Real ale ~ Bar food (not Sun except over bank hol) ~ Restaurant ~ (01367) 870382 ~ Children welcome ~ Dogs welcome ~ Open 11.30-3, 6-11; 12-3, 7-10.30 Sun; closed Sun evening in winter, Christmas and New Year and 1st week in Feb ~ Bedrooms: £55B/£80B

THAME SP7005 Map 4

Swan

Upper High Street

There's a bustling, friendly atmosphere in this civilised 16th-c hotel, and an interesting mix of furnishings. Though nothing seems to match, it all blends together perfectly. The tables in the main bar are either chests, trunks or a butcher's block, and there's an assortment of well worn armchairs and comfortable old sofas, several grouped together around the stone fireplace. Brightly painted tiles cover the bar counter and the wall behind, and there are beams, timbers, faded rugs, old-fashioned saucy seaside postcards and a handsome clock. Cushioned sofas meander along a passageway, then down a step is an odd but cosy low-ceilinged room with paintings of erstwhile locals on the walls. Well kept Brakspears, Hook Norton and a guest such as Timothy Taylors Landlord on handpump, and quite a few wines by the glass. Bar food such as sandwiches (£2.95) or filled baguettes (£4.25), plus cream of watercress soup (£3.95), cottage pie or pork and leek sausages with onion gravy (£5.95), smoked duck and chorizo sausages or gammon and egg (£6.95), chargrilled chicken in barbecue sauce with stir fry vegetables (£7.25), and chargrilled T-bone steak (£7.95). The upstairs restaurant still has its medieval ceiling. Piped classical music, newspapers to read, good cappuccino, dominoes, cribbage, chess, and backgammon. There are a few tables at the back, in a small shopping arcade. It can get very busy in the evening and parking is quite tricky on market days – the Farmers' Market is held on Tuesdays. *(Recommended by Tim and Ann Newell, M Joyner, Ian Phillips, Susan and John Douglas)*

Free house ~ Licensee Sue Turnbull ~ Real ale ~ Bar food (12-2.30, 7-9) ~ Restaurant ~ (01844) 261211 ~ Children in eating area of bar and restaurant ~ Dogs allowed in bar and bedrooms ~ Open 11-11; 12-10.30 Sun; closed 25 and 26 Dec ~ Bedrooms: £50B/£90B

WOODSTOCK SP4416 Map 4

Feathers

Market Street

Of course this is a formal Cotswold stone hotel but we continue to include it in this book because it has a relaxed, unstuffy atmosphere, and customers really like the old-fashioned Courtyard Bar at the back. With oils and watercolours on its walls, stuffed fish and birds (don't miss the live parrot, too), and a central open fire, it opens on to the beautiful sunny courtyard with a small water feature, and attractive tables and chairs among geraniums and trees. Well presented food from a short bar menu might include moroccan lamb casserole (£4.95; main course £9.95), bruschetta of mozzarella with tomato and onion confit (£5.45; main course £7.45), brochette of tiger prawns with rocket and pepper (£5.95; main course £7.95), mediterranean fish soup (£6.95), salmon fishcakes with braised fennel and lemon beurre blanc (£6.95; main course £10.95), mackerel kebab with piccalilli (£8.45), confit of free range chicken with red onion marmalade (£10.45), and puddings such as sticky toffee pudding or crème brûlée (£5.95); the restaurant is no smoking. Well kept (if pricy) John Smiths on electric pump, decent house wine, a good choice of malt whiskies, summer home-made lemonade and pimms, freshly squeezed orange juice and afternoon teas; excellent service; piped music. Get there early for a table. *(Recommended by John and Enid Morris, Derek Thomas, John Bowdler, Patricia Beebe, Andrew Barker, Claire Jenkins, Robin and Joyce Peachey)*

Free house ~ Licensees Messrs Pendril, Bate and Shelton ~ Real ale ~ Bar food (12.30-2.30, 6.30-9; not Sat evening) ~ Restaurant ~ (01993) 812291 ~ Children welcome ~ Dogs allowed in bedrooms ~ Open 10.30-11(10.30 Sun); closed to non-residents evening 25 Dec ~ Bedrooms: /£135B

WOOTTON SP4419 Map 4

Kings Head

Chapel Hill (which is near the church and marked by a wooden triangle in the road covering the old well); off B4027 N of Woodstock

The spacious and formal no smoking restaurant is pretty much the focal point of this attractive 17th-c Cotswold stone house, although you can choose to eat in the bar or garden instead. The food is good (though not cheap) and all home-made – they even make their own bread and ice cream: soup (£3.95), warm duck salad or smoked haddock tart (£4.95), muscovado and lime cured Scottish salmon (£5.50), braised duck legs with plum sauce (£8.95), fillet of pork with orange, port and juniper berry sauce (£10.95), butterfly fillet of gilt head bream stuffed with herbs and crab with a port and lemon sauce (£12.95), and puddings such as lemon and lime tart, délice of white chocolate or summer pudding (£4.95). Greene King Ruddles Best and Wadworths 6X on handpump, and a good wine list with up to seven by the small or friendly glass. The civilised and relaxing beamed no smoking lounge bar has a nice mix of old oak settles and chairs around wooden tables, comfortable armchairs and chintzy sofas, an open log fire, and old prints and ceramics on the pale pink walls. Although they are allowed in the no smoking restaurant, this is not really a place geared towards children; no children's meals. *(Recommended by Robin and Joyce Peachey, Sir Nigel Foulkes, Martin and Karen Wake, Geoff Pidoux, Miles and Deborah Protter)*

Free house ~ Licensees Tony and Amanda Fay ~ Real ale ~ Bar food (not Sun evening) ~ Restaurant ~ (01993) 811340 ~ Children over 12 and only if very well behaved ~ Open 12-2.30, 6.30-11; 12-11 Sat; 12-3 Sun; closed Sun evening ~ Bedrooms: £65B/£75B

Lucky Dip

Besides the fully inspected pubs, you might like to try these Lucky Dips recommended to us and described by readers (if you do, please send us reports: www.goodguides.com).

Abingdon [SU4996]
Old Anchor [St Helens Wharf]: Front bar looking across road to Thames, flagstoned back bar with shoulder-height serving hatch, roomy lounge, panelled dining room overlooking neat almshouse gardens; warm fire, some comfortable leather armchairs, wide food choice from good sandwiches to inviting blackboard, friendly service, good wine choice; piped music; plenty of tables outside, summer barbecues *(David H T Dimock)*

Adderbury [SP4635]
☆ ***Bell*** [High St; just off A4260, turn opp Red Lion]: Unpretentious largely unspoilt beamed village local with chiming grandfather clock, some panelling, relaxed atmosphere, generous good fresh food, well kept Hook Norton inc seasonal ales; homely front room with armchairs and sofa by huge log fire, sewing machines and standard lamp, smaller back music room with two pianos, old settles, and folk nights 1st and 3rd Mon of month; candlelit restaurant *(Geoff Pidoux, BB, Pete Baker)*

Plough [Aynho Rd]: Upgraded thatched pub with attractive furnishings and friendly cottagey atmosphere, popular for enjoyable food from wide choice of sandwiches and baguettes to good home-made hot dishes; helpful efficient staff, Charles Wells Bombardier, restaurant area *(Ian and Nita Cooper)*

☆ ***Red Lion*** [The Green; off A4260 S of Banbury]: Smartly civilised but welcoming, with big inglenook, panelling, high stripped beams and stonework, cosy no smoking back dining room up steps, good food, full Wadworths range kept well, several wines by the glass, daily papers, games area on left; piped music; children in eating area, tables out on well kept terrace, comfortable bedrooms, open all day summer *(M Joyner, LYM, Geoff Pidoux, D C T and E A Frewer)*

Alvescot [SP2704]

Plough [B4020 Carterton—Clanfield]: Friendly and attractive partly 17th-c beamed village pub popular at lunchtime for wide blackboard choice of good value food inc Sun lunch (must book), quick service, well kept Wadworths and a guest beer, decent wines, good coffee, lots of pictures, old maps and plates, log fire (but cool and pleasant on hot days), pleasant dining extension; end games bar with bar billiards and big-screen TV; colourful hanging baskets *(Peter and Audrey Dowsett, Des and Jen Clarke, Marjorie and David Lamb, Nigel and Anna Boden, R M Gibson)*

Appleton [SP4401]

Thatched Tavern [Eaton Rd]: Attractive 16th-c pub (actually tiled now), very low beams, enjoyable food from sandwiches to Portuguese dishes and Sun roast, no smoking dining area with woodburner, well kept Brakspears, soft piped music, good atmosphere, convivial licensees; small garden *(Rose Weymouth)*

Ardington [SU4388]

Boars Head [signed off A417 Didcot—Wantage]: Low-beamed dining pub with deceptively simple country décor (it's smart and not cheap), two-room bar and plainer no smoking extension, well kept Arkells 3B, Brakspears and a guest beer, good wines; darts, shove-ha'penny, cribbage, dominoes, board games, TV and piped music; children welcome, cl Sun evening, peaceful attractive village *(J Hale, LYM, O Richardson, Peter B Brown)*

Ardley [SP5427]

Fox & Hounds [B430 (old A43), just SW of M40 junction 10]: Old stone pub with long opened-up low-beamed dining lounge, big fireplaces each end, lots of horsebrasses, pictures and old glassware, goldfish tank, flowers and candles on tables, straightforward generous food from ploughman's to steaks and Sun lunch, barbecue and curry nights, well kept Fullers London Pride and Greene King Old Speckled Hen, decent house wines, another open fire in cosy carpeted bar *(CMW, JJW, Neil and Anita Christopher)*

Ashbury [SU2685]

☆ ***Rose & Crown*** [B4507/B4000; High St]: Restful, roomy and comfortable open-plan beamed bar, part of old-fashioned hotel, with highly polished woodwork, traditional pictures, chesterfields, deep armchairs and pews, lovely view down pretty village street of thatched cottages, raised section with further oak tables and chairs, lots of wines, well kept Arkells 2B and 3B, nice range of other drinks, friendly helpful staff, sensibly priced usual food, charming restaurant, separate public bar with pool and juke box; tables out in front; 11 bedrooms, attractive village near Ridgeway *(CMW, JJW, Peter and Audrey Dowsett, Dick and Madeleine Brown, BB)*

Bablock Hythe [SP4304]

Ferryman [off B4449 S of Stanton Harcourt, W of Cumnor]: Wide choice of enjoyable inexpensive food inc Sun lunch in cheery and roomy big-windowed riverside eating area, welcoming and helpful landlord (who works a steel ferry-boat for walkers and cyclists), Greene King Ruddles County, comfortable seating, displays of old ferry equipment; terrace, moorings; open all day (and specialises in group events eg OAP teas with entertainment), cl Tues, well equipped bedrooms with river-view balconies *(Peter and Audrey Dowsett)*

Bampton [SP3103]

Elephant & Castle [Bridge St (A4095 W end)]: Homely and friendly feel with central fireplace dividing off part of bar, stripped stone, cosy and interesting mix of furniture inc fine sideboard, well kept and well priced real ales such as Adnams, Archers Village and Vale Wychert, darts, dominoes, cards *(Pete Baker, R Huggins, D Irving, E McCall, T McLean)*

Morris Clown [High St]: Folies Bergère-style murals in former coaching inn with well kept cheap Archers Village, Courage Best and a changing guest beer, may be farm cider, darts, bar billiards; garden with old mangle collection, morris dancing late spring bank hol, open all day wknds, cl wkday lunchtimes *(R M Gibson)*

Romany [Bridge St; off A4095 SW of Witney]: 17th-c local, partly stripped stone, with well kept cheap Archers and guest ales from ancient pre-Norman cellars, low-priced food from sandwiches to Sun lunch, TV and piped music in plain main bar, cosier side bar partitioned off from corridor, log fire, no smoking restaurant; darts, cribbage, dominoes, fruit machine; picnic-sets in big back garden with good play area and aunt sally *(Paul Hopton, LYM, Peg and Paul Cuskley, C A Hall, M Joyner, R M Gibson, Patrick Hancock)*

Banbury [SP4540]

Wine Vaults [Parsons St]: Gleaming bare boards and flagstones, cushioned wall seats and unusual lamps in two snugs past small bar on right, small eating area beyond, another room on left leading to comfortable front lounge, well kept Morrells Oxford Blue, handsome array of bottles, cheap wholesome pub food, smart staff, daily papers; popular with young people evenings and wknds, piped pop music, games machines; walled garden, open all day *(Ted George)*

Beckley [SP5611]

Abingdon Arms [signed off B4027; High St]: Handsome old pub with a variety of seating inc pews, bare boards, lots of beams and stripped stone, two real fires, well kept Brakspears sold metrically, enjoyable food from sandwiches up, friendly staff, separate dining room, board games; floodlit terrace, extensive pretty garden dropping away into orchard, good walks *(Geoff Pidoux, John Roots, Neil and Anita Christopher, LYM)*

Begbroke [SP4713]

Royal Sun [A44 Oxford—Woodstock]: Busy

much refurbished open-plan stripped-stone pub with emphasis on prompt good value food from baguettes to Sun roasts, well kept changing real ales, friendly staff; may be piped music; tables on terrace and in small streamside garden *(Geoff Pidoux)*

Benson [SU6191]

Crown [High St]: Good choice of good value food, pleasant bar, thriving atmosphere, good service; good value bedrooms *(Nick Holmes)*

Bicester [SP5722]

Acorn [Pingle Drive]: Busy Greene King pub with enjoyable food, well kept real ales inc Old Speckled Hen, speedy cheerful service *(Damian Dixon)*

Penny Black [Sheep St]: Large open-plan Wetherspoons conversion of former 1920s main post office, comfortable screened-off sections and raised area, popular with older people for cheap hot food such as slow-roasted lamb, well kept competitively priced ales inc three guests (bar service may slow at busy times), good cheap coffee, good choice of wines, books and newspapers *(D C T and E A Frewer, Charles Harvey)*

Binfield Heath [SU7478]

Bottle & Glass [off A4155 at Shiplake; between village and Harpsden]: Pretty thatched black and white timbered Tudor cottage, low beams and flagstones, fine fireplace, black squared panelling, three well kept Brakspears ales, blackboard bar food from sandwiches up, shove-ha'penny, dominoes; no children or dogs inside; big attractive garden with tables under little thatched roofs *(the Didler, LYM)*

Blewbury [SU5385]

☆ ***Red Lion*** [Nottingham Fee – narrow turning N from A417]: Beamed tiled-floor downland village pub, well kept Brakspears, friendly managers, enjoyable food from soup and sandwiches to duck and venison, big log fire, cribbage, dominoes, no piped music, restaurant (children allowed); tables in nice back garden, decent bedrooms, pretty surroundings *(Howard Dell, Michael Clough, LYM)*

Bloxham [SP4235]

Joiners Arms [off A361; Old Bridge Rd]: Welcoming chatty atmosphere in bar and restaurant, well kept real ales, enjoyable food, good choice of wines, good service, two fires *(BB, Mr and Mrs J Cooke, Chris Glasson)*

Bodicote [SP4537]

Plough [Goose Lane/High St; off A4260 S of Banbury]: Quaint and dark 14th-c pub with well kept Archers Best, Theakstons XB and Old Peculier and guest beers, country wines, wide choice of well cooked straightforward food, good friendly service; old beams, pictures and brasses, dining area *(the Didler)*

Britwell Salome [SU6793]

Goose [B4009 Watlington—Benson]: Emphasis on limited choice of good fresh home-made food in two small back dining rooms, reasonably priced wines, good coffee; sandwiches served in the bar *(Geoffrey Kemp)*

Brize Norton [SP3007]

Chequers [Station Rd]: Roomy open-plan pub with wide choice of proper pub food inc enjoyable and generous OAP lunches, friendly staff, real ales, pleasant atmosphere, RAF theme *(KN-R)*

Bucknell [SP5525]

Trigger Pond [handy for M40 junction 10; Bicester Rd]: Neat stone-built pub opp the pond, mainly eating area, with good value home cooking inc old-fashioned puddings (must book Sun lunch), nice atmosphere, well kept changing ales such as Charles Wells Bombardier; piped music; pleasant terrace and garden *(Mrs Marion Evans, D C T and E A Frewer, Marjorie and David Lamb)*

Burcot [SU5695]

Chequers [A415 Dorchester—Abingdon]: Attractive thatched pub with smartly comfortable spacious beamed lounge, well kept Brakspears and guest beers, charming service, open fire, no smoking dining tables up in art gallery; shove-ha'penny, cribbage, dominoes; children welcome, wheelchair access, tables out on floodlit terrace and on lawn among flowers and fruit trees *(LYM)*

Burford [SP2512]

☆ ***Bull*** [High St]: Handsome ancient building well reconstructed a decade ago, beams and panelling, chatty front bar on left, steps down to comfortable sofas and armchairs in middle room, back dining room, three big log fires, well kept Hook Norton, good choice of wines by the glass, food from sandwiches up; piped music; children welcome, open all day, tables out in front or back through old coach entry, comfortable bedrooms *(LYM, Ted George, Patrick Hancock, R Huggins, D Irving, E McCall, T McLean, Phil and Jane Hodson)*

☆ ***Royal Oak*** [Witney St]: Neat 17th-c local tucked away from summer crowds, two Wadworths beers, wide range of simple food, beams and stripped stone, great collection of beer mugs and steins, pine tables and chairs, antlers over log-effect gas fire, bar billiards, back dining room; tables out on terrace, sensibly priced bedrooms off garden behind *(Patrick Hancock, Peter and Audrey Dowsett, R Huggins, D Irving, E McCall, T McLean)*

Chadlington [SP3222]

☆ ***Tite*** [off A361 S of Chipping Norton, and B4437 W of Charlbury; Mill End, slightly out of village – at garage turn towards Churchill, then left at playground]: Civilised and welcoming food-oriented local with good if not cheap home-made food from sandwiches to lovely puddings, some unusual dishes, vine-covered back restaurant evenings and Sun lunchtime, well kept Brakspears, Charles Wells Bombardier and a changing Mild, good house wines, cheerful traditional landlord, friendly efficient service, big log fire in huge fireplace, settles, wooden chairs, prints, rack of guide books, daily papers, pink-painted walls; piped classical music, children welcome, cl Mon exc bank hols; superb garden full of shrubs, some quite unusual, with stream running under pub – path from car park winds through it; plenty of tables outside, good walks nearby *(Richard Greaves, BB, John and Janet Davey, Pat and Tony Martin)*

Chalgrove [SU6396]

Lamb [Mill Lane]: Generous food, cheerful staff, Greene King and Morrells ales; tables in garden by cricket green *(Marjorie and David Lamb)*

Charlbury [SP3519]

☆ ***Bull*** [Sheep St]: Very good bistro-style atmosphere and surroundings, interesting range of well presented good generous food from light dishes to delicious Aberdeen Angus Sun roast, restaurant on left, freshly furnished dining bar on right with armchairs and magazines, well kept Greene King IPA, good wines and coffee, friendly jolly staff; attractive sunny back terrace, bedrooms, cl Mon *(Mrs K I Burvill, BB, Caroline Shenton, Janet and Philip Shackle)*

Charlton-on-Otmoor [SP5615]

Crown [signed off B4027 in Islip; High St]: Quiet unassuming two-room local, good value straightforward lunchtime food inc wkdy OAP specials, well kept Morrells Oxford, welcoming service, games-oriented public bar; good folk night Thurs *(Pete Baker)*

Charney Bassett [SU3794]

Chequers: Bustling 18th-c two-room village-green local, spacious and rambling beamed interior with more space for dining room than bar, decent sensibly priced popular food from sandwiches up (may be snacks only, Sat lunchtime), well kept ales such as Archers Golden and Greene King IPA and Ruddles Best, cheerful licensees and good service, daily papers; pool, piped music; mall garden, children welcome, has been cl Mon *(Dick and Madeleine Brown, M Shepherd, Vanessa Clark, Kate Parry, Paul Bevan, Debbie and Neil Hayter, BB)*

Chinnor [SU7698]

☆ ***Sir Charles Napier*** [Spriggs Alley, up on the ridge above Chinnor]: More good smart upmarket restaurant than pub, but does have small, friendly and traditional bar with sofas, log fire and (at a price) Wadworths IPA or 6X as well as champagne on draught and good choice of other drinks; good piped music; charming crazy-paved back courtyard, croquet lawn and paddocks, Chilterns and red kite views; cl Sun evening and Mon *(Patricia Purbrick, William Dale, John and Glenys Wheeler, Bob and Maggie Atherton, LYM)*

Chipping Norton [SP3126]

Albion [Burford Rd]: Welcoming helpful service, food inc good sandwiches, well kept Hook Norton *(C A Hall)*

☆ ***Blue Boar*** [High St/Goddards Lane]: Spacious and cheerful stone-built pub divided by arches and pillars, wide choice of food inc OAP lunches and good generous Sun roasts (Sun evening too) from separate servery, Hook Norton and Marstons Pedigree, good value coffee, beamed back restaurant by long light and airy flagstoned dining conservatory; dogs welcome, juke box or piped music, fruit machines, TV, piano; open all day Sat *(George Atkinson)*

☆ ***Crown & Cushion*** [High St]: Attractive homely and laid-back bar at the back of handsome old-fashioned 16th-c hotel, beams, some stripped stone and flagstones, well kept ales inc Hook Norton Copper, bar food, log fire, flower-decked conservatory, tables in sheltered garden with suntrap terrace; children welcome, good bedrooms *(R Huggins, D Irving, E McCall, T McLean, LYM)*

Fox [Market Pl]: Softly lit lounge, clean, tidy and quiet, with lots of pictures, groups of seats, open fire, well kept Hook Norton ales, good coffee, simple inexpensive bar food (lunchtime can use upstairs dining room for it), welcoming landlord; children welcome, well equipped good value bedrooms *(Chris Glasson, LYM)*

White Hart [High St]: Pleasant bar in town centre hotel with nice fires in both sections of spacious high ceilinged lounge, lots of sofas and comfortable armchairs, friendly attentive staff, well kept beers inc Hook Norton Best in well stocked bar; bedrooms *(George Atkinson)*

Chislehampton [SU5998]

Coach & Horses [B480 Oxford—Watlington, opp B4015 to Abingdon]: Small comfortable two-bar beamed 16th-c pub, homely but civilised, with good choice of well prepared food in sizeable dining area (polished oak tables and wall banquettes), well kept ales inc Flowers and Hook Norton, big log fire, welcoming cheerful staff; piped music; well kept terraced gardens overlooking fields by River Thame, comfortable bedrooms in back courtyard *(Nick Parslow, George Atkinson)*

Cholsey [SU5886]

Red Lion: Friendly local with decent food inc fresh fish in nicely refurbished dining room; quiet wkdy lunchtimes, busy evenings and wknds *(Mr and Mrs Hugh Spottiswoode)*

Church Enstone [SP3724]

☆ ***Crown*** [Mill Lane; from A44 take B4030 turn off at Enstone]: Popular and attractive old pub with good fresh food cooked by licensees' son, good lunchtime baguettes, pleasant cottagey bar, good-sized light modern dining area and conservatory, log fire in brass-fitted stone fireplace, beams and stripped stone, real ales such as Hampshire King Alfred, Hook Norton Best and Wadworths 6X, decent wines by the glass, plenty of atmosphere; may be piped music; four spotless bedrooms *(Geoff Pidoux, Stuart Turner, Angus Lyon, Mrs C A Baggaley, Terry Mizen, LYM, Pam Adsley)*

Clanfield [SP2802]

Clanfield Tavern [A4095 S of Witney]: New regime in pretty, extended pub with series of small beamed, flagstoned and stripped-stone rooms, nice prints, attractive restaurant and no smoking conservatory, Brakspears and Greene King IPA and Ruddles County, big log fire, wide food choice; jazz nights, children welcome, picnic-sets under cocktail parasols in pleasant front garden *(Peter and Audrey Dowsett, LYM, Ian Phillips)*

Clifton Hampden [SU5495]

☆ ***Barley Mow*** [towards Long Wittenham, S of A415]: Interesting and attractively refurbished thatched Chef & Brewer, very low ancient beams, oak-panelled family room, inviting blackboard choice of food all day from sandwiches to good range of fish, real ales inc Courage Directors, efficient friendly service, log fire, restaurant; piped music; tables on pleasant terrace and in well tended waterside garden with doves and fancy fowls, short stroll from the Thames; bedrooms, open all day *(David Humphreys, David Dintock, Nick Holmes, LYM, I D Greenfield)*

☆ ***Plough*** [A415]: Thatched pub, unusual in being Turkish-run and entirely no smoking, with low beams, panelling and dim lighting, simple antique furniture on tiled floor, wide range of mainly restauranty food all day (but sandwiches too), well kept Courage Best and Directors and John Smiths, good wines, light and airy restaurant; open all day, children in eating areas, tables outside, bedrooms in converted building across courtyard *(Gill and Keith Croxton, Mayur Shah, Tom and Ruth Rees, C A Hall, LYM, Geoff Pidoux, the Didler)*

Coleshill [SU2393]

Radnor Arms [B4019 Faringdon—Highworth]: Attractive pub with huge forge chimney and lots of smith's tools in high-raftered bar, two coal-effect gas fires, two other cosy bars; Bass and Flowers tapped from the cask, lots of wines, good blackboard choice of reasonably priced food cooked to order, friendly quick service, no piped music; picnic-sets in small garden behind, charming preserved village (like the pub, owned by NT), lots of good walks *(CMW, JJW)*

Crawley [SP3412]

☆ ***Lamb*** [Steep Hill; just NW of Witney]: Comfortably extended 17th-c stone-built pub, several levels inc unspoilt old beamed bar, no smoking family area and restaurant, good value varied food, good house wines, well kept Fullers London Pride, Greene King IPA and Wadworths 6X, quick service, friendly young licensees, log fire in big fireplace, cricketing décor; may be quiet piped music; views from tables on terraced lawn behind, pretty village, good walks *(R M Gibson, Tim and Ann Newell, Mike and Mary Carter, Malcolm and Maralyn Hinxman)*

Cropredy [SP4646]

☆ ***Red Lion*** [off A423 N of Banbury]: Rambling old thatched stone-built pub charmingly placed opp pretty village's churchyard, low beams, inglenook log fire, high-backed settles, brass, plates and pictures; reasonably priced food from baguettes up (two rooms set for eating, children allowed in restaurant part), well kept changing ales such as Greene King Ruddles County, Hook Norton Best, Oakhill Yeoman 1767 and Wychwood Hobgoblin, games room; piped music, picnic-sets under cocktail parasols on back terrace by car park *(George Atkinson, LYM)*

Cumnor [SP4603]

☆ ***Bear & Ragged Staff*** [signed from A420; Appleton Rd]: Busy comfortably rambling dining pub with lots of kitsch bric-a-brac in romantically dim-lit small rooms, good choice of enjoyable food inc popular Sun roasts and enterprising vegetarian dishes, well kept ales such as Batemans XXXB, Fullers London Pride and Morrells Oxford Blue with a proper drinking area, efficient attentive staff, two big log fires, no smoking area; children in eating areas, open all day Sun in summer *(LYM, Malcolm and Jane MacDonald, David Humphreys, Jim Bush, Karen McInman, Dick and Madeleine Brown, Colin and Maureen Butterworth, Kevin Blake, Darren and Jane Staniforth, D C T and E A Frewer, Sue Demont, Tim Barrow)*

Vine [Abingdon Rd]: Restauranty modernised pub keeping same tried and tested style despite management changes, with wide choice of enjoyable food from good baguettes to Sun family lunches (must book these), service coping well with wknd bustle, extended back dining area, no smoking area in conservatory, three well kept guest ales, good wine range; picnic-sets in attractive back garden *(B and F A Hannam, Dick and Madeleine Brown)*

Curbridge [SP3208]

Lord Kitchener [Lew Rd (A4095 towards Bampton)]: Comfortably refurbished, with good value food in end dining area, old local photographs, big log fire, well kept real ales; may be piped music; garden with play area *(R M Gibson)*

Deddington [SP4631]

☆ ***Deddington Arms*** [off A4260 (B4031) Banbury—Oxford; Horse Fair]: Welcoming beamed and timbered hotel with mullioned windows, four well kept ales inc Wadworths 6X, good choice of wines by the glass, good log fire, friendly efficient young staff, rather modern décor with much ochre paintwork, sizeable eating area (allowing children) and ambitious restaurant; open all day, comfortable chalet bedrooms around courtyard, attractive village with lots of antiques shops *(Chris Glasson, LYM, Garry Lucas, Michael Sargent, Gordon Tong, Charles Moncreiffe)*

☆ ***Unicorn*** [Market Pl]: Busy and friendly 17th-c inn, nicely redecorated modernised bar, inglenook fireplace, very big helpings of usual food inc inexpensive set lunch in oak-beamed restaurant (but veg and sauces extra), three real ales, morning coffee, pleasant efficient service; cobbled courtyard leads to lovely walled back garden, with smartly matching tables, chairs and deckchairs; bedrooms *(George Little, Mr and Mrs Hugh Spottiswoode, BB, Geoff Pidoux, Pam Adsley)*

Dorchester [SU5794]

☆ ***George*** [just off A4074 Maidenhead—Oxford; High St]: Handsome timbered hotel with fine old furnishings in smart beamed bar, roaring log fire, enjoyable but pricy food from sandwiches to some interesting main dishes (just roast and sandwiches Sun lunchtime), well kept Brakspears and a guest beer, good wines; open all day, children in restaurant, bedrooms *(Sheila and Gerry Mc Grady, LYM, Ray and Jacki Davenport)*

Ducklington [SP3507]

☆ ***Bell*** [off A415, a mile SE of Witney; Standlake Rd]: Pretty thatched local with wide choice of reasonably priced home-made food (not Sun eve) inc particularly good value sandwiches, well kept Greene King Old Speckled Hen and Ruddles, good house wines, friendly service; big stripped stone and flagstoned bar with scrubbed tables, woodburner (and glass-covered well), old local photographs, farm tools, hatch-served public bar, roomy and attractive well laid out back restaurant (its beams festooned with bells); cards and dominoes, no piped music; folk night 1st Sun of month, regular events such as morris dancing or raft races; small garden behind with play area, colourful hanging baskets, nine bedrooms *(Peter and Audrey Dowsett, Lucien, BB, Pete Baker)*

Strickland Arms [off A415 SE of Witney; Witney Rd]: Welcoming and cosy local, smart bar half for dining, good value food, well kept Adnams and Wadworths, decent wine, small no smoking restaurant; small garden *(Geoff Pidoux)*

Duns Tew [SP4528]

White Horse [off A4260 N of Kidlington]: 16th-c beamed pub in attractive village, roomy bar and pretty dining extension, stripped bricks and stonework, rugs on flagstones, oak timbers and panelling, enormous inglenook, settles and homely stripped tables, daily papers, smaller quieter room, good service, enjoyable food, well kept beers inc Hook Norton Best and Wadworths 6X, decent wine list; disabled access, bedrooms in former stables *(Gary Wright, Christine and Neil Townend, LYM)*

East Hagbourne [SU5288]

Fleur de Lys [Main Rd]: Attractive black and white timbered pub with clean and tidy open-plan bar – half drinking place with cards and darts (lots of trophies in cabinet), half lounge with more emphasis on good value fresh food; well kept Greene King ales, good welcoming service, quite a few stuffed fish; ceilidhs 3rd Weds, tables in neat small garden behind *(Mrs E Bell, Pete Baker, J J and B Dix)*

East Hanney [SU4193]

Black Horse [Main St]: Comfortable and civilised, with chef/landlord doing good reasonably priced food, welcoming landlady *(anon)*

East Hendred [SU4588]

Eyston Arms [off A417 E of Wantage; High St]: Thriving atmosphere in proper basic local with Courage Best, Fullers London Pride, Wadworths 6X and guest beers such as West Berkshire Full Circle and Wychwood Fiddlers Elbow; sandwiches and baked potatoes – no restaurant *(Dick and Madeleine Brown)*

☆ ***Plough*** [off A417 E of Wantage; Orchard Lane]: Roomy beamed village pub with attractive and airy main bar, good value restaurant (booking advised for Sun lunch), interesting farming décor and wartime news, good range of enjoyable food, Greene King and other real ales, copes well with anything from small leisurely family parties to dozens of walkers; occasional folk nights; pleasant garden with good play area, attractive village *(Dick and Madeleine Brown, BB)*

☆ ***Wheatsheaf*** [signed off A417; Chapel Sq]: Attractive 16th-c black and white timbered village pub with high-backed settles in quarry-tiled inglenook bar, booth seating up steps, well kept ales such as Gales and Greene King, reasonably priced usual food from sandwiches up, dominoes, shove-ha'penny; piped music; open all day wknds, tables in colourful back garden *(LYM, Peter and Jean Hoare, David Humphreys, R Huggins, D Irving, E McCall, T McLean, Chris Glasson)*

Enstone [SP3724]

Harrow [A44 Chipping Norton—Woodstock]: Attractive family-friendly village pub, softly lit bar, brasses, pictures and lots of basket and cane work in spacious beamed back dining area, wide choice of straightforward enjoyable home-made food inc basket meals, Hook Norton and Morrells Oxford Blue; steps up from car park; seats in pretty back courtyard and on large lawn *(Angus Lyon, George Atkinson)*

Epwell [SP3540]

Chandlers Arms [Sibford Rd, off B4035]: Chatty and unspoilt two-roomed 16th-c local, friendly down-to-earth landlord, well kept Hook Norton ales inc Mild, several ciders, cheap cheerful food; pleasant quiet garden, in attractive out-of-the-way village near Macmillan Way long-distance path *(Guy Vowles, Giles Francis, John Brightley)*

Eynsham [SP4309]

Newlands [Newland St]: Cosily unpretentious beamed and flagstoned bar, generous enjoyable food, quick friendly service, real ales, decent wine, big inglenook log fire, stripped early 18th-c pine panelling, pretty restaurant on left; very busy and bustling wknds, may be piped music *(P W E Sheldon)*

Faringdon [SU2895]

Crown [Market Pl]: Civilised old inn, flagstones, beams, panelling, leaded lights, huge woodburner, two bars and tiny comfortable hidden-away snugs, popular well presented food, friendly young staff, well kept Greene King Ruddles, John Smiths and Theakstons, good coffee; children welcome, may be piped music; good big quiet bedrooms overlooking lovely cobbled summer courtyard *(Peter and Audrey Dowsett, LYM, Colin and Janet Roe)*

Filkins [SP2304]

☆ ***Five Alls*** [signed off A361 Lechlade—Burford]: Welcoming Cotswold stone pub, part of a small upmarket local group, with particularly friendly staff and locals in light and functional bar, comfortable and relaxing stripped-stone lounge (doubling as ante-room for bookable nicely furnished restaurant) with settees, armchairs and rugs on polished boards, good choice of well presented if not cheap food, well chosen house wines, well kept Hook Norton beers, good coffee, log fire, daily papers, lots of cartoons; unobtrusive piped music; plenty of tables on terrace and neat lawns, garden chess, attractive well-equipped bedrooms, nice village *(Ted George, Peter and Audrey Dowsett, R Huggins, D Irving, E McCall, T McLean, Sue and Jeff Evans, BB)*

Finstock [SP3616]

☆ ***Plough*** [just off B4022 N of Witney]: Rambling thatched and low-beamed village local, long well divided unpretentious bar with armchair by open woodburner in massive stone inglenook, entertaining pub dogs, real ales such as Adnams, Brakspears and Hook Norton, separate games area with bar billiards, food, often good, from generous sandwiches up, stripped-stone dining room; children in eating areas, dogs allowed in public bar; sizeable garden with old-fashioned roses and aunt sally, good walks, bedroom *(R M Gibson, Stuart Turner, Geoff Pidoux, R Naish, R T and J C Moggridge, Patricia Beebe, Lynn Sharpless, Simon and Laura Habbishow, LYM)*

Godstow [SP4809]

☆ ***Trout*** [off A34 Oxford bypass northbound, via Wytham, or A40/A44 roundabout via Wolvercote]: Creeper-covered medieval pub, recently nicely and extensively reworked as Vintage Inn, with old-fashioned furnishings in several linked rooms (all but one no smoking), log fires in three huge hearths, beams, carvings and shiny ancient flagstones, attractive pictures; decent food all day inc good lunchtime sandwiches, well kept Bass and Fullers London Pride, a good choice of wines by the glass, friendly quick service; can get packed, quiet piped music; charming in summer with lovely flagstoned heated terrace by a stream full of greedily plump perch, long restored footbridge to island (owned by pub), abbey ruins opp *(LYM, P R and S A White, Denzil Martin, Chris Glasson, Simon Pyle, Bill Sykes, R M Gibson, Ian Phillips, Geoff Pidoux, P and J Shapley, Andy Brown, Mrs M Shardlow, Sue Dyson)*

Goring [SU6080]

☆ ***Catherine Wheel*** [Station Rd]: Good value food inc lots of fish, well kept Brakspears BB, Mild, SB and Old, also Ted & Bens Organic, maybe taster samples, Stowford Press cider, decent wine, good informal atmosphere, very friendly landlord, staff and locals, two cosy bars, good log fire, restaurant; notable door to gents'; nice courtyard and garden, handy for Thames Path, attractive village *(Catherine Pitt, the Didler, Sue and Mike Todd)*

☆ ***John Barleycorn*** [Manor Rd]: Endearing and well run low-beamed cottagey local in pretty Thames village, prints in cosy little lounge bar, good choice of well priced generous home-made food in adjoining eating area, well kept Brakspears, pool in end room, friendly helpful service; bedrooms clean and simple *(the Didler)*

Hailey [SP3414]

☆ ***Bird in Hand*** [Whiteoak Green; B4022 Witney—Charlbury]: Greatly extended old beamed and timbered Cotswold pub, smart and spotless, doing well on the food side, with a good choice (just set meals on Sun), quick friendly service, well kept ales such as Adnams and Brakspears, subdued lighting (inc candles on tables), large open fire, stone walls, comfortable armchairs, cosy corners in attractive spreading restaurant, nice views; piped music; tables in garden, comfortable quietly set cottage-style bedrooms, huge car park *(George Atkinson, Richard Marjoram, Angus Lyon, Nigel and Sue Foster, BB)*

Lamb & Flag [B4022 a mile N of Witney; Middletown]: Charming pub with good interesting food prepared to order, friendly helpful staff, well kept Greene King beers inc Old Speckled Hen; good garden for children *(Marjorie and David Lamb, Deborah Gee)*

Hailey [SU6485]

☆ ***King William IV*** [the different Hailey nr Ipsden, off A4074 or A4130 SE of Wallingford]: Attractive 16th-c pub in charming peaceful countryside, some concentration on wide choice of good generous food, friendly landlord and helpful staff, thriving atmosphere, full Brakspears range kept well, beams, bare bricks and tiled floor, big log fire, well kept traditional furnishings and fittings, extended dining room; super views from tables on front terrace *(the Didler, J Hale, John and Glenys Wheeler, Wendy Arnold, Colin McKerrow, JP, PP, LYM)*

Headington [SP5407]

Butchers Arms [Wilberforce St; off London Rd by Oxford UFC, past housetop shark, then first left and first right]: Welcoming backstreet local with long narrow seating area, good value wkdy lunchtime food, well kept Fullers beers, lots of sports trophies and memorabilia, games corner with darts, bar billiards and sports TV; pleasant garden with barbecues *(Pete Baker)*

Henley [SU7882]

Old Bell [Bell St]: Well kept Brakspears PA, Old and Mild in homely and attractive heavily beamed front bar with wall-length window filled with pot plants, good food in back dining room *(the Didler)*

Three Tuns [Market Pl]: New licensees doing fresh home cooking in two spotless rooms opened together around old-fashioned central servery, heavy beams and panelling, well kept Brakspears, young friendly staff, coal-effect gas fire, lots of pub games; piped music; civilised cane furniture in pleasant awning-covered back courtyard *(Ian Phillips, the Didler, JP, PP, LYM, Rona Murdoch)*

Hethe [SP5929]

Whitmore Arms [Main St]: Open-plan pub with well kept Brakspears and Hook Norton, sensibly priced food inc interesting dishes, games area on right; lovely village *(Rona Murdoch)*

Highmoor [SU6984]

☆ ***Dog & Duck*** [B481 N of Reading, off A4130 Henley—Oxford]: Cosy and cottagey low-beamed country pub with chintzy curtains, floral cushions, lots of pictures; relaxing bar on left, dining room on right, log fire in each, smaller dining room behind, fine choice of good generous food inc good vegetarian dishes, hard-working young licensees, well kept Brakspears PA, SB and Old; tables in garden *(the Didler)*

Kidlington [SP4914]

Kings Arms [The Moors, off High St (not the Harvester out on the Bicester Rd)]: Welcoming unpretentious two-bar local with enjoyable wkdy lunchtime food from sandwiches to a few basic hot meals and good value daily roast, well kept Greene King IPA, Ind Coope Burton and a guest beer; occasional barbecues in courtyard *(Pete Baker)*

Kingston Lisle [SU3287]

Blowing Stone [signed off B4507 W of Wantage]: Popular pub/restaurant with brightly modernised bar, comfortable lounge, attractive dining conservatory, real ales such as Fullers London Pride, daily papers, log fire; children welcome, tables out in pretty garden with

goldfish pond, pretty bedrooms, handy for Uffington Castle hill fort and the Downs *(Peter and Audrey Dowsett, LYM, John Poulter)*
Launton [SP6022]
Bull [just E of Bicester]: Good range of beers inc Morrells, good service, enjoyable food esp steaks *(Denzil Martin)*
Little Bourton [SP4544]
Plough [Southam Rd]: Open-plan, with enjoyable generous food in restaurant end, Bass, Hook Norton and other local beers, friendly service *(Anthony and Elizabeth Barker)*
Little Coxwell [SU2893]
Eagle [just off A420 SW of Faringdon]: Reopened under friendly new local management, pleasantly refurbished airy bar with comfortable sofa and armchairs among other furnishings, well kept Archers and Bass, generous food inc good value Sun lunch in bar and new restaurant; 10 bedrooms with own bathrooms, charming thatched village *(Peter and Audrey Dowsett, Charlie Harman)*
Plough [A420 just SW of Faringdon]: Extended stone-built pub with friendly atmosphere, log fires, good blackboard choice of reasonably priced food, two well kept real ales, daily papers, back restaurant; pool, games machines, piped music; children allowed in conservatory with bowls; swings in big garden, no dogs *(CMW, JJW)*
Little Milton [SP6100]
☆ ***Lamb*** [3 miles from M40, junction 7: A329 Thame—Wallingford]: Pretty 17th-c thatched pub with beams, stripped stone, low windows, soft lighting, lots of tables for wide choice of food (all day Sun – very busy then) from sandwiches to good specials and steaks, well kept real ales; no piped music, children in eating area (good choice for them), peaceful and attractive garden with swings, pleasant countryside *(BB)*
Lower Heyford [SP4824]
Bell [Market Sq]: Uncluttered refurbished rooms around central beamed bar, enjoyable food inc some interesting dishes, well kept Adnams Broadside, Flowers IPA and Greene King Abbot; disabled access, charming creeper-clad building in small village square of thatched cottages, bedrooms, nearby canal walks *(Denzil Martin, Ian Phillips)*
Marsh Baldon [SU5699]
Seven Stars [the Baldons signed off A4074 N of Dorchester]: Good range of enjoyable generous food (no sandwiches; only barbecues some Sat lunchtimes) in big open beamed room, decent wines, good coffee, real ales such as Black Sheep or Greene King Ruddles; on attractive village green *(George Atkinson)*
Middle Assendon [SU7385]
☆ ***Rainbow*** [B480]: Good choice of unpretentious but tasty food cooked by landlady in pretty and cottagey country local with unspoilt low-beamed divided bar, welcoming landlord, well kept Brakspears; tables on front lawn, peaceful setting, may be red kites overhead *(Keith and Margaret Kettell, Mr and Mrs McKay)*
Middleton Stoney [SP5323]
Jersey Arms [Ardley Rd (B430/B4030)]: Small 19th-c stone-built Best Western hotel, low and rambling, with relaxing atmosphere in cosily upmarket traditional bar, beams and panelling, dark tables and chairs, good log fire in big fireplace, good range of interesting if not cheap home-made fresh food from well filled baguettes up, friendly owner and staff, efficient service, well kept Courage Best, good wine list and coffee, no smoking dining room, another for smokers; piped music, popular for business lunches, car park across road; tables in courtyard and garden, comfortable bedrooms *(George Atkinson, Dennis John Boddington, Barry and Anne Cooper)*
Milcombe [SP4034]
☆ ***Horse & Groom*** [off A361 SW of Banbury]: Bustling beamed and flagstoned village local doing well under friendly new Australian licensees, nice atmosphere with settee and pub parrot, good simple reasonably priced food, well kept Greene King IPA and Ruddles, separate coffee menu, inglenook woodburner; occasional live music; children welcome, lots of tables out in front, bedrooms (they can organise fishing) *(Mrs C Watson, Chris Glasson, BB)*
New Yatt [SP3713]
Saddlers Arms: Small welcoming pub with good choice of generous food inc fresh fish and OAP specials in bar or light and airy dining conservatory, prompt service, chatty licensee, occasional unusual beers; friendly dogs *(Marjorie and David Lamb)*
Newbridge [SP4001]
Maybush [A415 7 miles S of Witney]: Compact low-beamed dining pub in lovely Thameside setting, most tables booked (good range of food) and little room for drinkers, welcoming efficient service, well kept Greene King Abbot, no piped music; children welcome, moorings, pretty and neatly kept waterside garden with tables in verandah too *(Peter and Audrey Dowsett, LYM)*
☆ ***Rose Revived*** [A415 7 miles S of Witney]: Big open-plan dining pub well worth knowing for its lovely big lawn by the upper Thames, prettily lit at night (good overnight mooring free); huge range of usual fairly priced food all day inc Sun carvery, quick waitress service, helpful landlord, well kept Greene King ales, log fires; dogs allowed, piped music, games machines; children welcome, comfortable bedrooms with good breakfast *(LYM, Peter and Audrey Dowsett)*
Northmoor [SP4202]
Red Lion [B4449 SE of Stanton Harcourt]: Refurbished 15th-c stone-built village pub, good choice of enjoyable low-priced down-to-earth food inc good value Sun lunch, well kept real ales, friendly landlord and locals, heavily beamed bar and small dining room off, welcoming log fire; walkers welcome, no dogs; garden *(Geoff Pidoux, T R and B C Jenkins)*
Oxford [SP5106]
Crown [Cornmarket St]: Remaining part of former coaching inn with medieval origins, well kept Bass, good choice of usual food from toasted baps and baked potatoes up, pleasant service, long bare-boards bar; piped music may obtrude; tables out in courtyard *(Neil and Anita Christopher)*

☆ ***Eagle & Child*** [St Giles]: Busy pub with nice panelled front snugs, tasteful stripped-brick modern back extension with no smoking conservatory, well kept Greene King Abbot and Old Speckled Hen, Ind Coope Burton, Marstons Pedigree and Wadworths 6X, plentiful quickly served food, newspapers, events posters; tourists head for the tiny mid-bars full of actors' and Tolkien/C S Lewis memorabilia; piped music *(Chris Glasson, Paul Hopton, BB, R Huggins, D Irving, E McCall, T McLean)*

Grapes [George St]: Traditional pub, some original features, lots of theatrical posters and memorabilia, bar snacks, well kept Morrells *(Patrick Hancock, Kevin Blake)*

Harcourt Arms [Cranham Terr]: Friendly local with proper landlord and some character, pillars dividing it, good value snacks inc cheap sandwiches and baked potatoes, well kept Fullers ales, open fires, well reproduced piped jazz, good choice of board games *(Jonathan Ives, Pete Baker)*

Hobgoblin [St Aldates]: Small interesting pub with friendly welcome and good atmosphere, three well kept Wychwood ales and up to four guest beers such as Batemans XXXB; open all day, good value food till 6pm (may be a wait), wkdy student discount till 8, special beer price Tues *(Tim and Ann Newell, Catherine Pitt, Jonathan Smith, M Joyner, Paul Hopton)*

Lamb & Flag [St Giles/Banbury Rd]: Attractive old pub owned by nearby college, modern in front with big windows over street, more atmosphere in back rooms with exposed stonework and panelled ceilings, well kept real ales, good value well served food, cheerful service; can be packed with students *(Chris Glasson, R Huggins, D Irving, E McCall, T McLean)*

Marsh Harrier [Marsh Rd, Cowley]: Friendly Fullers pub with their beers kept well, enjoyable food inc wide choice of sandwiches and baguettes, daily papers *(Alain and Rose Foote)*

Old Ale House [Iffley Rd]: Good choice of well kept changing ales, decent food, friendly helpful staff, dim lighting, lots of barrels, breweriana and bric-a-brac, split levels, friendly efficient service *(Jenny and Chris Wilson, Kevin Blake)*

Old Tom [St Aldates]: Good straightforward town pub, small and attractive with mirrors giving it a sense of more space, well kept Morrells, decent usual lunchtime food, good friendly service; tables outside *(M Joyner)*

☆ ***Perch*** [narrow lane on right just before MFI, leaving city on A420]: Part-thatched pub in pleasant quiet setting with dozens of tables and summer bar in big garden hedged off from riverside meadow; big and busy, with low beams, flagstones, stripped stone, high-backed settles as well as more modern seats, good log fires, well kept ales such as Tetleys and Marstons Pedigree, decent wine, generous food servery (hot dishes may run out on busy Sun lunchtime), no smoking eating area (children allowed); machines, piped music; open all day in summer, good robust play area (and giant chess), barbecues, own landing stage and moorings, attractive waterside walks, pretty village *(LYM, R M Gibson, Susan and John Douglas)*

☆ ***Rose & Crown*** [North Parade Ave]: Lots of atmosphere, good well priced lunchtime home cooking inc Sun roasts and particularly well kept Adnams and Ind Coope Burton in friendly and unspoilt old local; decent wine, prompt service from enthusiastic and concerned bearded landlord and wife; reference books for crossword buffs, no piped music, machines or mobile phones, jazz piano Tues; traditional small rooms, pleasant back yard with little end eating room, also motorised awning and huge gas heater – children not allowed here or inside unless with friends of landlord *(Chris Glasson, R Huggins, D Irving, E McCall, T McLean, BB, Paul Hopton, Torrens Lyster, R E M Lawson)*

Three Goats Heads [Friars Entry, St Michaels St]: Steps up to charming little upper bar, clean and sparkling, with light panelling, ceiling plasterwork and booths of elegant bench seats, political prints and architectural drawings showing details of the work; relaxed downstairs bar (cl afternoons) with bare boards, TV, fruit machine and piped music – can be loud; well kept cheap Sam Smiths, good choice of quick generous food, friendly and helpful young barman *(Dr and Mrs M E Wilson, Margaret and Roy Randle)*

Pishill [SU7389]

☆ ***Crown*** [B480 Nettlebed—Watlington]: Lovely wisteria-covered ancient building with black beams and timbers, deep burgundy paintwork, log fires and candlelight, relaxed atmosphere, good home-cooked food (not Sun or Mon evenings) from filled baguettes to hearty but modern and imaginative dishes and popular Sun lunch, well kept Brakspears, Flowers Original and a guest beer, prompt friendly service even when full; children allowed Sun lunchtime in restaurant, pleasant bedroom in separate cottage, picnic-sets on attractive side lawn, pretty country setting – lots of walks *(Dr M W A Haward, JP, PP, LYM, Chris Richards, Susan and John Douglas, the Didler, David and Joan Mason)*

Play Hatch [SU7476]

Crown: Good choice of interesting and attractively presented food, good value if not particularly cheap, in spacious rambling olde-worlde 16th-c pub, very popular with families; two bars and several rooms inc barn extension restaurant and big no smoking conservatory, well kept Brakspears PA, SB and Old tapped from the cask, decent wines, good welcoming service; pleasant garden with play area *(J and B Cressey, James Edge, Joan Thorpe)*

Sandford-on-Thames [SP5301]

Kings Arms [Church Rd]: Delightful lockside spot on Thames with picnic-sets on waterside terrace, and plenty for children; usual food from decent baguettes up, well kept ales inc Courage, good choice of wines by the glass, cheery service; moorings *(Martin and Karen Wake)*

Shilton [SP2608]

☆ ***Rose & Crown*** [off B4020 S of Burford]: Mellow 17th-c low-beamed stone-built village local under new licensees, small beamed bar with tiled floor, woodburner and inglenook, some new furnishings in small dining area, good choice of reasonably priced food (should book for Sun roasts), well kept Greene King beers, quick friendly service; soft piped music, darts; tables in garden, nice setting opp pond in pretty village *(Dr and Mrs A K Clarke, Marjorie and David Lamb, Peter and Audrey Dowsett, G W A Pearce)*

Shiplake [SU7476]

☆ *Flowing Spring* [A4155 towards Play Hatch and Reading]: Well kept Fullers ales in three-room countrified pub, cosily renovated, with open fires and floor-to-ceiling windows overlooking the water meadows, reasonably priced food and friendly staff; no mobile phones, steps up from car park; tables out on deck, big attractive garden *(LYM, June and Robin Savage)*

Shiplake Row [SU7478]

White Hart [off A4155 W of Shiplake]: Relaxed and friendly, with three connecting rooms mainly set for good choice of food (just roasts Sun lunchtime), cheerful staff, well kept Brakspears, decent house wines, log fires; interestingly planted back garden, nice location, fine views, good walks *(Simon Collett-Jones, June and Robin Savage)*

Shipton-under-Wychwood [SP2717]

Lamb [off A361 to Burford]: Pleasantly furnished and formerly very popular civilised Greene King pub, with log fire, partly stripped old stone walls, no smoking restaurant allowing children, comfortable bedrooms, and garden tables, which has been open all day; being refurbished as we go to press, to reopen under a new tenant – news please *(LYM)*

Sibford Gower [SP3537]

☆ *Moody Cow* [signed off B4035 Banbury—Shipston on Stour; Temple Mill Rd]: Pretty and cottagey thatched and flagstoned dining pub, well run sister pub to the one at Upton Bishop in Herefs, similar good value if not cheap meals inc upmarket dishes throughout; comfortable open-plan low-beamed stripped-stone lounge, nice pictures, table made from glass-topped well, inglenook tap room, attractive partly no smoking restaurant, friendly efficient staff, well kept Banks's, Hook Norton and a guest ale, good coffee, good if pricy house wines, dominoes; children welcome; country views from big well planted garden, lovely manor house opp; has been cl Mon lunchtime *(Guy Vowles, John Kane, Mike and Mary Carter, K H Frostick, LYM)*

South Moreton [SU5588]

☆ *Crown* [off A4130 or A417 E of Didcot; High St]: Rambling old open-plan village pub with friendly new licensees, well kept Wadworths and guest beers, some tapped from the cask, decent coffee, wide range of good fresh home-made food from sandwiches up (OAP discounts), good service; piped music, Mon quiz night; children allowed, small garden *(Marjorie and David Lamb)*

South Stoke [SU5983]

☆ *Perch & Pike* [off B4009 2 miles N of Goring]: Relaxing brick and flint dining pub just a field away from the Thames, comfortable cottagey low-beamed bar with open fires and well kept Brakspears PA, SB, Old and a guest beer, enjoyable simple home-made bar food, also more elaborate menu with sizeable timbered restaurant extension where children allowed; may be piped music; tables out on terrace and flower-bordered lawn *(LYM, Derek Harvey-Piper)*

Sparsholt [SU3487]

Star [Watery Lane]: Comfortable old local, quiet and relaxed, horse-racing talk, short choice of enjoyable freshly made food, well kept beers inc a guest, daily papers, log fire, attractive pictures; may be subdued piped music; back garden, pretty village *(David Humphreys, Marjorie and David Lamb)*

Standlake [SP3902]

Bell [High St]: New landlord doing good choice of inexpensive food in tidy pub with well kept ales such as Brains and Greene King, plush back restaurant *(Peter and Audrey Dowsett)*

Steeple Aston [SP4725]

☆ *Red Lion* [off A4260 12 miles N of Oxford]: A treat of a surprise for us has been that Colin Mead, for many the epitome of the classic long-serving civilised landlord, postponed his 2001 retirement plans and stayed on at this charming pub – but for how long? Catch it while you can – good food from proper rare beef sandwiches up, well kept Hook Norton ales with a guest such as Gales, a great range of wines and of malt whiskies and brandies in the comfortable beamed and panelled bar, with an evening no smoking restaurant (children are allowed in this) and suntrap front terrace; and of course there are all those reference books for crossword fanatics *(JHBS, Pat and Robert Watt, Mrs Jean Clarke, Guy Vowles, Miles and Deborah Protter, LYM)*

Steventon [SU4691]

☆ *North Star* [Stocks Lane, The Causeway, central westward turn off B4017]: A favourite with people who like their pubs simple and old-fashioned, now bought by relatives of the former long-serving landlord, keeping it much as before with only gentle behind-the-scenes updating; tiled passage to plain main bar with built-in settles forming snug, steam-engine pictures and interesting brassware, open fire in parlourish lounge, simple dining room; Greene King ales tapped from casks in a side room, cheap wkdy lunchtime bar food from improved kitchen, cribbage; tables on side grass, front gateway through living yew tree *(Pete Baker, LYM)*

Stoke Lyne [SP5628]

☆ *Peyton Arms* [off B4100]: Largely unspoilt stone-built pub with new licensees doing some simple home-made lunchtime food as well as filled cobs, well kept Hook Norton beers (full range) tapped from casks behind small corner bar in sparsely decorated front snug, log fire, hops on beam, bigger refurbished room with darts, dominoes and cribbage, charity book store; well behaved children and dogs welcome, pleasant garden with aunt sally; cl Mon/Tues lunchtimes *(Rona Murdoch, Pete Baker,*

Wendy Muldoon, the Didler, JP, PP)
Stoke Row [SU6784]
Cherry Tree [off B481 at Highmoor]: Low-beamed village local which may be in line for gentrification but has been well liked for its simple parlour-like décor, well kept Brakspears BB, Mild and SB tapped from casks in back stillage room, well priced sandwiches and soup, log fire; families welcome in lounge and back games room (with pool), swings in good garden *(the Didler, JP, PP)*
☆ ***Crooked Billet*** [Nottwood Lane, off B491 N of Reading – OS Sheet 175 map ref 684844]: Rustic pub layout with heavy beams, flagstones, antique pubby furnishings and great inglenook log fire, but in practice a restaurant – good, with wide choice of well cooked interesting meals inc good value lunch, attentive welcoming service, well kept Brakspears tapped from the cask (no bar counter), decent wines, relaxed homely atmosphere – like a French country restaurant; children welcome, occasional live music, big garden by Chilterns beechwoods *(Chris Doyle, James Alcock, Stewart Tyler, LYM, D and M T Ayres-Regan, Mrs E A Macdonald, the Didler, JP, PP)*
☆ ***Grouse & Claret*** [Kingwood Common; a mile S of Stoke Row, signed Peppard and Reading, OS Sheet 175 map ref 692825]: Well run 18th-c dining pub with a wide range of good freshly made food from filled baguettes up inc imaginative specials and outstanding puddings, pleasant traditional interior with cosy nooks, drinkers made welcome by friendly helpful staff, Brakspears PA and Fullers London Pride, good wine choice; piped music; attractive terrace *(B H and J I Andrews, Sheila Keene, Darren and Jane Staniforth)*
Stoke Talmage [SU6899]
Red Lion [signed from A40 at Tetsworth]: Basic old-fashioned country local, very friendly and cheerful; sociable bare-boards public bar with well kept Hook Norton and lots of changing guest beers from small corner servery, chatty landlord, open fire, prints, posters, darts, shove-ha'penny and other games, carpeted modern lounge; tables under cocktail parasols in pleasant garden, cl lunchtime Mon-Thurs *(Torrens Lyster, Pete Baker, the Didler, JP, PP)*
Stonor [SU7388]
☆ ***Stonor Arms***: Elegant upmarket 18th-c village inn with comfortable flagstoned bar, sofas and armchairs, rowing and cricket memorabilia, log fires, good food from soup and sandwiches to sophisticated dishes at appropriate prices (canapés with drinks, petits fours with good coffee) in elegant restaurant and romantic conservatory dining room, welcoming young staff, well kept real ale, decent wines, daily papers and magazines, wonderful Christmas decorations; walled garden, good bedrooms *(J F M and M West, Susan and John Douglas)*
Stratton Audley [SP6026]
Red Lion [off A421 NE of Bicester; Church St]: Thatched village pub with stripped stone and low beams, big inglenook log fire, antique sale posters, old varnished wooden furniture, enjoyable food inc notable burgers and more restauranty dishes, real ales, quick friendly service; may be piped music; tables out by road and on terrace in small colourful garden, pretty village *(Denzil Martin)*
Sutton Courtenay [SU5094]
☆ ***Fish*** [Appleford Rd]: Attractive and well run dining pub with good fresh-cooked food with some emphasis on fish, starters that can double as interesting bar snacks, well kept real ale, good house wines, welcoming efficient staff, garden room and no smoking back dining area where children allowed; tables out on terrace *(T R and B C Jenkins, Dr W J M Gissane, C A Hall)*
George & Dragon [Church St]: Chatty 16th-c pub with attractive mix of furnishings, nice log fire, good choice of fair-priced home-made food from thick sandwiches up inc popular Sun lunch, well kept Greene King Old Speckled Hen and Ruddles, welcoming landlord, good range of decent wines, candles on tables, pewter mugs hanging from low beam; no dogs, restaurant, big back terrace overlooking graveyard where Orwell is buried – church worth a visit but may be locked *(David H T Dimock)*
Swinbrook [SP2811]
☆ ***Swan*** [back rd a mile N of A40, 2 miles E of Burford]: Softly lit little beamed and flagstoned 16th-c pub prettily set by a bridge over the Windrush, gently smartened up, with antique settles, sporting prints and woodburner in friendly flagstoned tap room and back bar (now mainly laid for dining); good attractively presented food (all day wknd) inc interesting specials, well kept Archers and Greene King ales, farm ciders, decent wines, cheery laid-back service, traditional games, magazines, no piped music; seats by the lane and in small pretty side garden; the nearby churchyard has the graves of the Mitford sisters *(Matthew Shackle, Martin and Karen Wake, LYM, Geoff Pidoux, R and S Bentley)*
Swinford [SP4308]
Talbot [B4044 just S of Eynsham]: Roomy beamed pub with very wide choice of good value generous fresh food inc interesting dishes, well kept Arkells, friendly prompt service, long bar with some stripped stone and naval memorabilia, log-effect gas fire, games room; tables in garden (some traffic noise), pleasant walk along lovely stretch of the Thames towpath *(Marjorie and David Lamb, Chris Glasson)*
Sydenham [SP7201]
☆ ***Crown*** [off B4445 Chinnor—Thame]: Relaxed low-beamed village local with welcoming and attentive new licensees, wholesome good value home cooking inc good Fri/Sat fresh fish, well kept Morrells Best and Varsity, and open fires in long narrow bar; may be quiet piped music, dominoes, darts, quiz and dress-up theme nights; children welcome, small garden with roses and climbing frame, views of lovely church, picturesque village *(Howard Dell, BB, Lesley Bass, John and Glenys Wheeler)*
Tackley [SP4720]
Gardeners Arms [Medcroft Rd, off A4260]: 17th-c village pub with wide choice of food

from sandwiches and baguettes up inc several chicken specials, efficient service even when busy, comfortable spick and span lounge bar with beams, brasses and coal-effect gas fire in inglenook, well kept ale inc an unusual guest, prints, brasses, old photographs and cigarette cards; separate public bar with darts, TV and fruit machine, piped music, bookable skittle alley; picnic-sets on sunny terrace, handy for Rousham House *(Marjorie and David Lamb)*

Thame [SP7005]

Bird Cage [Cornmarket]: Quaint black and white beamed and timbered pub refurbished in bistro style, three or four bare-boards rooms sharing flame-effect fire in central hearth, good menu (late-night diners' club Weds-Sat), well kept Brakspears, Charles Wells Bombardier and Youngs Special, espresso machine, friendly staff, daily papers; piped music *(Ian Phillips, LYM, Tim and Ann Newell)*

Old Trout [High St]: Attractive old pub with welcoming new tenants doing particularly good food inc good value set lunches and interesting dishes, pleasant unobtrusive service, good house wine and coffee *(Betty Hampton, B H and J I Andrews)*

Thrupp [SP4815]

☆ ***Boat*** [off A4260 just N of Kidlington]: Relaxing stone-built local in lovely surroundings by Oxford Canal, good value decent food from good baguettes up, quick attentive service, well kept Morrells, decent wine, coal fire, old canal pictures and artefacts, bare boards and stripped pine, no piped music; good folk nights 2nd and 4th Sun, occasional theatre; restaurant, nice garden behind with plenty of tables, some in shade *(Denzil Martin, M Joyner, Sue Demont, Tim Barrow, Geoff Pidoux, Pete Baker)*

Towersey [SP7304]

☆ ***Three Horseshoes*** [Chinnor Rd]: Unpretentious flagstoned country pub with good value food inc good baguette and vegetarian choice, old-fashioned furnishings in two low-beamed bars, good log fire, well kept Flowers IPA and Charles Wells Bombardier, small restaurant; piped music, darts; children allowed lunchtime, biggish garden with fruit trees and play area, handy for new Thame—Princes Risborough cycle path *(Tim and Ann Newell, LYM)*

Wallingford [SU6089]

George [High St]: Reliable old coaching inn with much done-up series of rooms and places to eat, four well kept ales and cosy seats by big fire in main bar, friendly regulars, spacious and attractive sycamore-shaded courtyard; bedrooms *(LYM, M Joyner)*

Wantage [SU4087]

☆ ***Royal Oak*** [Newbury St]: Very friendly and popular take-us-as-you-find-us two-bar local with lots of ship photographs and naval hatbands, particularly well kept ales such as Bass or Marstons Pedigree, Wadworths 6X and two beers brewed for the pub by West Berkshire, landlord who really knows his beers, lunches Fri-Sat; table football, darts, cribbage; has been cl Mon-Thurs lunchtimes, bedrooms *(BB, the Didler, JP, PP, Dick and Madeleine Brown)*

Shoulder of Mutton [Wallingford St]: Friendly and chatty local, old-fashioned and unchanging, coal fire and racing TV in bar, passage to two small snug back rooms, well kept Greene King Morlands Original, popular food; tables outside, bedrooms *(the Didler, JP, PP, Pete Baker)*

Warborough [SU6093]

Six Bells [The Green S; just E of A329, 4 miles N of Wallingford]: Low-ceilinged thatched pub facing cricket green, attractive country furnishings in interconnecting seating areas off bar, good interesting food, well kept Brakspears and a guest beer, decent wines, welcoming efficient service; big log fire, antique photographs and pictures; tables in back orchard *(LYM, Marjorie and David Lamb)*

Watlington [SU6994]

Carriers Arms [Hill Rd]: Good choice of cheap well cooked food in giant helpings from sandwiches through enormous bargain omelettes to full meals (free range eggs for sale too); genial landlord, well kept Brakspears, thriving local atmosphere, Chilterns view *(Dick and Madeleine Brown)*

☆ ***Chequers*** [3 miles from M40 junction 6, via B4009; Love Lane]: Attractive rambling bar with character seating and a few good antique oak tables, low beams and candles, well kept Brakspears PA, SB and a seasonal beer, nicely presented food from sandwiches through extremely hot chilli to steaks and popular Sun lunch, steps down to further eating area, vine-hung conservatory (children allowed here); picnic sets in very pretty garden, nice walks nearby; more reports please *(D and M T Ayres-Regan, LYM)*

West Hanney [SU4092]

☆ ***Plough*** [Church St]: Unspoilt and pretty thatched local with attractive timbered upper storey, original timbers and uneven low ceilings, homely and welcoming panelled lounge with good log fire in stone fireplace, genial Cornish landlord, straightforward reasonably priced food inc good value Sun lunch, Tetleys-related ales, interesting whiskies, darts in public bar; tables in back garden, children welcome *(Pete Yearsley)*

West Hendred [SU4489]

☆ ***Hare*** [A417, outside village]: Civilised and welcoming dining pub, very popular for generous good interesting food served till late evening, nice light lunch menu, efficient friendly staff, good choice of wines; pleasant garden *(Canon and Mrs Michael Bourdeaux, David Humphreys)*

Westcott Barton [SP4325]

Fox [Enstone Road; B4030 off A44 NW of Woodstock]: Spacious yet cosy stone-built village pub, low beams and flagstones, pews and high-backed settles, well kept Greene King Abbot, Hook Norton, John Smiths and guest beers, log fires, usual food from sandwiches to steaks, small no smoking restaurant (children allowed here); piped music, steps down to lavatories; open all day Thurs-Sun, pleasant garden with water feature, play area and peaceful view *(Dave Braisted, LYM)*

Weston-on-the-Green [SP5318]

Ben Jonson [B430 nr M40 junction 9]: New management again in thatched country pub, comfortable dark wood settles in welcoming if rather barn-like beamed lounge bar, reasonably priced food from filled baguettes up, good house wine, friendly service, discreet pool room; usually open all day, children welcome, big sheltered garden *(D C T and E A Frewer)*

Wigginton [SP3833]

White Swan [off A361 SW of Banbury]: Friendly new licensees doing enjoyable standard food in small simply but comfortably furnished country pub with well kept Hook Norton real ales and good inglenook log fire; quick service, children welcome, picnic-sets outside; the landlord whose cooking catapulted this pub into the main entries in the last edition has already moved on to the Gate Hangs High near Hook Norton *(Martin Jennings, C A Hall, David and Pam Wilcox, LYM)*

Witney [SP3509]

Angel [Market Sq]: Popular 17th-c town local, extended but unchanging, several well kept ales inc Hook Norton Old Hooky, wide choice of attractively priced food from good sandwiches up, homely surroundings and hot coal fire, quick friendly service even when packed; pool room, coffee bar; parking nearby can be difficult *(Sue and Mike Todd, Peter and Audrey Dowsett)*

☆ ***Three Horseshoes*** [Corn St, junction with Holloway Rd]: Attractive 16th-c stone-built pub with heavy beams, flagstones, log fires, simple comfortable well polished old furniture, separate dining room, friendly welcome, good carefully prepared home-made food from filled baguettes, ciabattas and other pubby lunchtime food to more imaginative restauranty dishes, well kept Greene King Abbot and Morlands Original and a guest beer, decent house wines *(George Cowie, LYM)*

Wolvercote [SP5009]

Plough [First Turn/Wolvercote Green]: Lots of comfortably well worn in pubby linked areas, warm and friendly, with armchairs and Victorian-style carpeted bays in main lounge, good varied reasonably priced food esp soups and fresh seafood in flagstoned ex-stables dining room and library (children allowed here), well kept Morrells, decent wines, traditional snug, woodburner; picnic-sets on front terrace looking over rough meadow to canal and woods *(BB, Peter and Audrey Dowsett)*

Woodstock [SP4416]

☆ ***Black Prince*** [A44 N]: Subtly lit timbered and stripped-stone 18th-c pub with old-fashioned furnishings, armour, swords, big fireplace, good value food from traditional to Tex-Mex in bar and dining room (worth booking Sun lunch), well kept Hook Norton, Theakstons Old Peculier and guest beers, fast friendly service, children allowed; Mon quiz night, occasional live music; tables out in attractive garden by small river, nearby right of way into Blenheim parkland *(Geoff Pidoux, David Campbell, Vicki McLean)*

Crown [High St]: Busy town pub with enjoyable food and pleasant conservatory; very popular with young people some evenings *(Geoff Pidoux)*

Kings Arms [Market St/Park Lane]: Good food and atmosphere in bistro-type bar, quick happy service, well kept beer; bedrooms *(Geoff Pidoux)*

Marlborough Arms [Oxford St (A44)]: Proper bar, comfortable and attractive lounge and dining area in Best Western hotel dating partly from 14th c, cheerful log fires, well kept Theakstons Best, reasonably priced food inc good value lunchtime specials, friendly attentive staff, conservatory restaurant; bedrooms *(George Atkinson)*

Star [Market Pl]: Big cheerful beamed town pub with decent food all day from good filled baguettes up (can take a time when busy), lunchtime salad bar and popular family Sunday lunches, well kept beers inc Wadworths 6X, bare boards, some stripped stone, daily papers, open fires; piped music, quiz machine, TV; bedrooms clean and spacious, good breakfast *(Geoff Pidoux, BB, Mr and Mrs J McRobert, Patricia Theodorou)*

Wootton [SP4320]

☆ ***Killingworth Castle*** [Glympton Rd; B4027 N of Woodstock]: Striking three-storey 17th-c coaching inn, good local atmosphere, well kept Greene King ales, decent house wines, friendly service, wide choice of generous food, long narrow main bar with pine furnishings, parquet floor, candles, lots of brasses and log fire with books above it, bar billiards, darts and shove ha'penny in smaller games end, pleasant garden; jazz 1st and 3rd Weds, folk 2nd and 4th, music some other nights too; bedrooms *(Geoff Pidoux, Pete Baker, BB)*

Yarnton [SP4812]

Turnpike [A44 N of Oxford]: Extensively rebuilt as comfortable food pub, wide good value choice, well kept Bass, good staff *(Geoff Pidoux)*

The Post Office makes it virtually impossible for people to come to grips with British geography, by using a system of post towns which are often across the county boundary from the places they serve. So the postal address of a pub often puts it in the wrong county. We use the correct county – the one the pub is actually in. Lots of pubs which the Post Office alleges are in Oxfordshire are actually in Berkshire, Buckinghamshire, Gloucestershire or Warwickshire.

Shropshire

We have two new entries here this year. One is the welcoming old Lion charmingly placed on the Severn at Hampton Loade, with good food and drink. The other, the Lime Kiln at Porth-y-waen, is almost in Wales; charmingly spruced up by friendly newish licensees, it does food that also looks to be heading for a Food Award. Other pubs doing particularly well these days are the Three Tuns in Bishop's Castle (despite shifting production of its beers from its own classic tower brewhouse to Hobsons), the unusual Cookhouse at Bromfield (contemporary surroundings and food, good drink), the Burlton Inn (a welcoming all-rounder), the Crown at Hopton Wafers (on top form, back under the landlord who originally made its name), the big lively Malthouse in Ironbridge, the George & Dragon in Much Wenlock (doing well all round under its newish landlord), the Hundred House at Norton (good for atmosphere, food, drink, and as a place to stay), the Armoury in Shrewsbury (civilised and welcoming, interesting drinks and food), and the Plough at Wistanstow (its proper country cooking earns it a Food Award this year – and it has a great landlord and lovely beer). The Hundred House at Norton, a charming place for a special meal (and growing a lot of its own herbs), is Shropshire Dining Pub of the Year. In the Lucky Dip section at the end of the chapter, current stars are the Sun in Clun, Sun at Corfton, Black Lion in Ellesmere, Bear at Hodnet, Church Inn in Ludlow and Three Fishes in Shrewsbury. Drinks tend to cost somewhat less in Shropshire pubs than they do in most places. We found the local Hobsons beer was often a bargain, as were the beers brewed at the Six Bells in Bishop's Castle, and other local beers to look out for include Woods (see the Plough at Wistanstow), Salopian, Hanby and Corvedale (see the Lucky Dip entry for the Sun at Corfton).

BISHOP'S CASTLE SO3289 Map 6

Castle Hotel

Market Square, just off B4385

Right at the top of town, this substantial early 18th-c stone coaching inn is neatly kept, with a relaxed, civilised atmosphere and a good mix of customers. The enjoyable bar food includes lunchtime sandwiches (from £2.80), crispy battered cod (£5.95), game pie or feta cheese and spinach parcels (£6.95), with evening dishes such as smoked fish pâté (£5.95), good cheese, leek and mushroom sausages (£7.95), salmon fillet poached in white wine or chicken breast in an apricot and cream sauce (£8.50), and 10oz rump steak with port and stilton sauce (£10.95), with home-made puddings such as chocolate squidgey cake and strawberry meringue (£3.50); at Sunday lunchtime they do roasts (£6.45). There is a no smoking dining room in the evening and at Sunday lunchtime. On the right as you go in, a clubby small beamed and panelled room is glazed off from the entrance, with old local prints and sturdy leather chairs on its muted carpet; on the left a bigger room has maroon plush wall seats and stools, big Victorian engravings, a coal fire and nice table-lamps; they have shove-ha'penny, dominoes and cribbage, and no piped music. Well kept Hobsons and local Six Bells Big Nevs on handpump, and around 40 malt whiskies. In summer the pub is

festooned with pretty hanging baskets, and there are a couple of picnic-sets by flowering tubs in front, with more in the reworked back garden, which has two terraces on either side of a large formal raised fish pond, pergolas and climbing plants, and stone walls; the views are very pretty. The spacious and comfortable bedrooms are attractively decorated, with antique furniture; good breakfasts.
(Recommended by the Didler, Derek and Sylvia Stephenson, Christopher and Jo Barton, G Coates, Tim Maddison, MDN)

Six Continents ~ Licensees David and Nicky Simpson ~ Real ale ~ Bar food (12-1.30, 6.30(7 Sun)-8.45) ~ (01588) 638403 ~ Children welcome ~ Open 12-2.30, 6.30 (7 Sun)-11 ~ Bedrooms: £37.50B/£65S(£65B)

Six Bells

Church Street

You can arrange tours of the brewery at this cheerful and unpretentious former coaching inn. Of the excellent beers brewed here (some of which are stocked by other pubs in the area), Big Nev's is most people's favourite, and you'll also find Marathon, Cloud Nine and a seasonal ale. The beers aren't the pub's only attraction, and although it's all fairly no-frills, there's an appealingly relaxed and welcoming atmosphere in the two simple chatty rooms. One bar is really quite small, with plenty of locals tucked around the fireplace or on benches around plain wooden tables; the second, bigger room has bare boards, another fireplace, and lots of board games (they have regular Scrabble nights). Bar food might include soup (£2.50), hearty sandwiches (from £2.50), fidget pie (£6), bangers, mash and onion gravy (£6.50), filo basket filled with ginger stir-fried vegetables (£7.50), medallions of lamb with tarragon, parsley and red wine sauce or grilled halibut with asparagus and cream sauce (£9), and good home-made puddings; they use organic suppliers wherever possible. The lounge is no smoking at meal times. They keep a wide range of country wines. More reports please.
(Recommended by the Didler, Pauline Davies, Derek and Sylvia Stephenson, Jane and Adrian Tierney-Jones)

Own brew ~ Licensees Neville and Colin Richards ~ Real ale ~ Bar food (not Sun evening or Mon) ~ No credit cards ~ (01588) 630144 ~ Children welcome ~ Folk last Fri in month and live music first Mon in month ~ Open 12-2.30, 5-11; 12-11 Sat; 12-10.30 Sun; closed Mon lunchtimes and winter Tues lunchtime

Three Tuns

Salop Street

Sadly Three Tuns real ale is no longer brewed in the four-storied Victorian brewhouse across the yard from this friendly thriving pub, but you can still look inside the unusual Grade I listed building, which now houses a little beer museum. Now brewed for them by Hobsons, and still using their flavoursome recipes, well kept Three Tuns XXX, Offa, Sexton and a seasonal ale (along with the odd guest beer such as Hobsons itself) are served on old-fashioned handpump. They also do bottled Clerics Cure, Little Tun and Bellringer; you can get carry-out kegs, and there are sales by the barrel or cases of Clerics Cure – phone for details. The no-frills beamed rooms are very simply furnished with low-backed settles and heavy walnut tables, chatty locals, and newspapers to read; cribbage, shove-ha'penny, dominoes, backgammon and cards. Served by sociable staff, the enjoyable (though not cheap) bar food includes fish soup (£4.50), filled baguettes (from £4.50), various home-made pâtés (£4.25), pork and ale sausages (£7.50), grilled goats cheese with onion marmalade (£8), well liked beef in ale (£9), daily fresh fish (around £9), and good organic steaks (£13.50), with puddings such as summer pudding (£4); they use locally grown vegetables. There's a small garden and terrace. An annual beer festival takes place in July, with morris dancers in the yard. Readers' young children have been warmly welcomed. The bedrooms are in outbuildings; they do a good breakfast.
(Recommended by Chris and Maggie Kent, the Didler, Margaret and Andrew Leach, MDN,

Barry Lane, Malcolm Taylor, Gene and Kitty Rankin, Pat and Tony Martin, Jane and Adrian Tierney-Jones, Christopher and Jo Barton, John Sandilands)

Free house ~ Licensee Jan Cross ~ Real ale ~ Bar food (not Mon lunch (except bank hols) or Sunday evening) ~ Restaurant ~ (01588) 638797 ~ Children in eating area of bar and restaurant ~ Occasional live music in function room ~ Open 12-3, 5-11; 12-10.30(11 Sat) Sun ~ Bedrooms: /£75B

BRIDGES SO3996 Map 6

Horseshoe

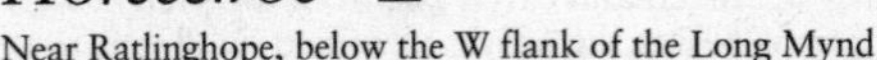

Near Ratlinghope, below the W flank of the Long Mynd

This old place, which owes much of its appeal to its picturesque setting among deserted hills in good walking country, is now handily open all day. The comfortable bar has interesting windows, a good log fire, well kept Adnams Bitter, Shepherd Neame Spitfire, Timothy Taylors Landlord and Worthington on handpump, as well as several malt whiskies, and farm and bottled cider; a small dining room leads off from here. The staff and locals are friendly; darts and piped music. Straightforward bar food includes soup (£2.50), sandwiches (from £1.90), ploughman's (£4.75), gammon, egg and pineapple, scampi or steak and kidney pie (£5.95), with specials such as mushroom stroganoff (£5.95), and puddings (from £2.10). Outside by the little River Onny, there are very pleasantly positioned tables; the pub is handy for walks on the Long Mynd and on the Stiperstones. *(Recommended by Dr Bob Bland, John and Diana Niblett, Keith Jacob, Nigel Woolliscroft, Tim Maddison, G Coates, Di and Mike Gillam)*

Free house ~ Licensee Colin Waring ~ Real ale ~ Bar food (12-3, 6-9; 12-9 Sat/Sun) ~ (01588) 650260 ~ Children welcome ~ Dogs welcome ~ Open 11-11; closed 25 Dec evening

BROMFIELD SO4877 Map 6

Cookhouse

A49 2 miles NW of Ludlow

This handsome brick house looks from the outside like an immaculately maintained Georgian home, so it's a real surprise to discover the astonishing conversion inside (one reader tells us he drove past many times without guessing what was inside). Everywhere has been brightly modernised in a smartly contemporary – almost minimalist – fashion; the only area that still has anything of a period feel is the back bar, itself something of a contrast after the rest of the place. During the day the focus is on the café-bar style dining room, rather like a funky canteen, with modern light wood tables, and a big open kitchen behind a stainless steel counter at one end. A door leads through into the bar, sparse but neat and welcoming, with round glass tables and metal chairs running down to a sleek, space-age bar counter with fresh flowers, newspapers and spotlights. Then it's down a step to the cosier, high-ceilinged back room, where traditional features like the huge brick fireplace, exposed stonework, and soaring beams and rafters are delightfully juxtaposed with wicker chairs, well worn sofas and new glass tables. Friendly staff serve well kept Hobsons Best and Town Crier on handpump, and the good wine list includes eight by the glass; there's also a good choice of coffees and teas. Some areas are no smoking; piped music. The well presented bar food is very good, and besides lunchtime dishes such as pizza, croque monsieur or delicious fish and chips (£5.95), could include soup (£3.95), various salads (from £4.95), fennel and mushroom risotto (£6.95), and slow-roasted lamb shank with butter beans, tomato and coriander or smoked haddock fishcakes with light tomato salsa (£7.95); Sunday roasts (£6.95). You can get two courses for £10.50, and they do children's helpings. An attractive secluded terrace has tables under cocktail parasols and a fish pond. The building was once home to Clive of India, and the pub used to be called the Clive Arms. More reports please. *(Recommended by John Whitehead, Guy Vowles, Christopher and Jo Barton, Gordon Tong)*

Free house ~ Licensee Paul Brooks ~ Real ale ~ Bar food (11-3, 6-10; all day Sat/Sun) ~ Restaurant ~ (01584) 856565 ~ Children in eating area of bar and restaurant ~ Dogs allowed in bar ~ Open 11-11; 12-10.30 Sun

BURLTON SJ4626 Map 6

Burlton Inn

A528 Shrewsbury—Ellesmere, near junction with B4397

Everything in the three fresh-feeling cottagey connecting rooms of this welcoming and popular inn seems meticulously arranged and cared for, from the pretty flower displays in the brick fireplace or beside the neatly curtained windows, to the piles of *Country Living* and interior design magazines left seemingly casually in the corner. There are a few sporting prints, spurs and brasses on the walls, and open fires in winter; dominoes and cribbage. Well liked bar food from an interesting menu could include home-made soup (£3.25), smoked mackerel pâté with ricotta and capers (£5.50), thai pork satay with peanut sauce (£5.75), steak, kidney and beer pie (£8.50), bacon chop grilled with honey with mustard and parsley butter (£8.95), pink trout fillets (£10.95), and moroccan lamb shank with sweet potato, garlic and tomato in a red wine sauce with mint couscous (£11.50), and they've a good choice of home-made puddings. Well kept Banks's and three continually changing guests such as Greene King Abbot, Wychwood Hobgoblin and Wye Valley Butty Bach on handpump. The licensees are very welcoming and helpful and the staff are friendly. There are tables on a small lawn behind, with more on a strip of grass beyond the car park, and smart wooden furniture on the pleasant terrace. The modern bedrooms are comfortable and well equipped, and they do good breakfasts; small dogs are welcome in the bar and bedrooms. *(Recommended by Janet and Peter Race, S Horsley, John and Caroline, Tim Lawrence, Mrs P J Carroll, John Sandilands, Mr and Mrs F Carroll, A J Bowen)*

Free house ~ Licensee Gerald Bean ~ Real ale ~ Bar food (12-2, 6.30-9.45(7-9.30 Sun); limited menu Mon lunchtime) ~ (01939) 270284 ~ Children in eating area of bar ~ Open 11-3, 6-11; 12-3.30, 7-10.30 Sun; closed bank hol Mon lunchtimes; evening 25/26 Dec and 31 Dec ~ Bedrooms: £45B/£70B

CARDINGTON SO5095 Map 4

Royal Oak

Village signposted off B4371 Church Stretton—Much Wenlock, pub behind church; also reached via narrow lanes from A49

Tables in the rose-filled front courtyard of this splendid old place (it's been licensed as a pub for longer than any other in Shropshire) have lovely views over hilly fields. Inside, there's plenty of character in the rambling, low-beamed bar with its roaring winter log fire, cauldron, black kettle and pewter jugs in its vast inglenook fireplace, old standing timbers of a knocked-through wall, and red and green tapestry seats solidly capped in elm; darts, dominoes and perhaps piped music. Hobsons, and a couple of guests such as Cottage Golden Arrow and Salopian Heaven Sent, are kept under light blanket pressure on handpump. As well as lunchtime snacks such as filled baguettes (from £3.25), filled baked potatoes (from £3.50) and ploughman's (from £4.50), reasonably priced bar food includes soup (£2.50), home-made pâté (£3), vegetable kiev (£7), lasagne or grilled trout with buttered almonds (£7.50), steak and onion pie (£8), and steaks (from £9.95), with puddings such as lemon sponge (from £2.65); children's meals (from £2.50). A comfortable no smoking dining area has exposed old beams and studwork. A mile or so away – from the track past Willstone (ask for directions at the pub) – you can walk up Caer Caradoc Hill, which looks over scenic countryside. More reports please. *(Recommended by David Field, Malcolm Taylor, Pete Yearsley, Patrick Hancock, Carolle Roberts, Dr Bob Bland, Kerry Law, Simon Smith)*

Free house ~ Licensee Michael Carter ~ Real ale ~ Bar food (not Sun evening or Mon) ~ Restaurant ~ (01694) 771266 ~ Children in restaurant and eating area of bar during meal times ~ Open 12-2, 7-11(10.30 Sun); closed Mon except bank hols

HAMPTON LOADE SO7586 Map 4

Lion

Off A442, 4½ miles S of Bridgnorth; look out for ducks on the pot-holed lane

For the last few years this charming 16th-c pub, tucked away in a delightful spot overlooking the River Severn, has been destined for the main entries, but we always hesitated to include it because of the real risk that declining winter trade would force it to close its doors. So great news this year is that the dedicated family who have had it since 1958 have now secured its future (mainly by selling the camp site nearby), and are confident that they will be able to continue for the foreseeable future. The two cosy and well worn in bar rooms and lounge are fairly plainly decorated, but have plenty of character and atmosphere, with stripped stone, and log fires likely to be roaring away even in late spring and early autumn. The busy landlord is friendly and helpful, with a word for everyone. He has well kept Ferrymans (brewed for the pub by a small local brewery) and Hook Norton Old Hooky on handpump, with a usually local guest beer such as Enville White or Worfield Shropshire Pride. The wine list is a good one, and they also have an interesting range of locally made country wines such as damson or birch bark wine (also used generously in the cooking, giving some unusual flavours). The regular bar menu includes sandwiches (from £2.60, not Saturday evenings), particularly good ploughman's with home-made pickles (from £4.40, go for the rare beef if it's on), battered cod (£5.50), mushroom and spinach lasagne (£6.20), chicken breast stuffed with asparagus and stilton or beef bourguignon (£8), and 8oz sirloin (£9.50); children's meals (from £2.70). It's the evening restaurant menu, and bar specials such as grilled gammon with mint and poached pear soaked in ginger (£7.50) or chunks of wild boar in rhubarb and redcurrant wine sauce (£8), that show the imaginative cooking at its best. They also do a generous winter Sunday lunch (£9). The linked dining rooms, stretched behind the smaller of the two bars, are comfortable and quite smart; you should book for restaurant meals. Quiet as the pub may be in winter, in summer it does get packed, especially when the Severn Valley Railway has its weekend steam spectaculars – there's a quaint ferry crossing to the station on the opposite bank. Lots of picnic-sets out on a big lawn make the most of this remote and rustic spot, and the day-ticket fishing is said to be good. *(Recommended by Nigel Woolliscroft, Steve Whalley, Gill and Tony Morriss, Dave Braisted, Hilary Forrest)*

Free house ~ Licensee Rob Whittle ~ Real ale ~ Bar food (12-2, 7-9.30(10 Fri/Sat); 12-3(2.30 winter), 7-9 Sun) ~ Restaurant ~ (01746) 780263 ~ Children welcome if eating lunchtime or booked evening ~ Dogs allowed in bar ~ Open 12-2.30, 7-11; 12-3.30(3 winter), 7-10.30 Sun; closed Mon except bank hols, 25 Dec and evening 26 Dec

HEATHTON SO8192 Map 4

Old Gate

Off B4176 W of Wombourn; heading W, fork left via Halfpenny Green

Even though it's out of the way, this welcoming pub gets plenty of customers. Lots of people come here for the freshly prepared, well presented food, which could include lunchtime baguettes (from £3.95, not Sunday), home-made soup (£4.25), steak and ale pie, ricotta cheese and herb pancakes or gammon and egg (£7.95), caribbean jerk chicken (£9.95), and steaks (£13.50), with specials such as baked tuna with soy sauce noodles (£12.95), and good home-made puddings such as triple chocolate terrine (£3.80); it's worth booking a table if you want to eat on Saturday evening. They do children's meals (£3.95), and readers with children have especially enjoyed eating here. It's a chatty sociable place: staff may greet you at the door, and the locals are friendly. The building dates from around 1600, and has a busily traditional feel; everything has a slight reddish tinge (the licensees tell us this reflects their passion for Manchester United football team), and plenty of tables are packed into the two small main rooms, along with plush seats, lots of bric-a-brac, two open fires, and the odd idiosyncratic touch like a model bird or balloons hanging from the ceiling. Well kept Enville, Greene King Abbot, Olde Swan Entire and perhaps a guest such as Timothy Taylors Landlord from the tiny bar counters; also draught cider, and they serve wines from the licensees' own vineyard in Burgundy. A small lawn behind has picnic-sets and play equipment, and is very colourful in summer; the outside of the pub is decorated with window boxes and hanging baskets. The golden retriever is called Cromwell. *(Recommended by Mike and Mary Carter, John and Gillian Scarisbrick, Ian S Morley, Joy and Peter Heatherley)*

Punch ~ Lease Jamie Atkins ~ Real ale ~ Bar food (Sun evening, Mon) ~ Restaurant ~ (01746) 710431 ~ Children welcome ~ Open 12-2.30, 6.30-11; 12-3, 7-10.30 Sun; closed Mon except for bank hols, 25 Dec

HOPTON WAFERS SO6476 Map 6

Crown ★

A4117 Kidderminster—Ludlow

This attractive creeper-covered inn is now back in the hands of the landlord who made it such a success to start with, some years ago – and it shows. A delight in summer, its lovely streamside garden has tubs of bright flowers and a duck pond, and there are pleasant terrace areas with tables under cocktail parasols. Inside, the emphasis is on the wide range of freshly prepared interesting food, and the frequently changing bar menu could include sandwiches (£3.50), soup (£3.25), fried whitebait and prawn cocktail (£4.25), duck and black cherry pie or roasted mediterranean vegetables with provençale sauce (£7.95), grilled chicken stuffed with Boursin wrapped in bacon (£8.95), and half a shoulder of lamb with mint and mango (£11.95); lots of blackboard specials include plenty of fresh fish such as sea bream fillets with warm spinach and sauce vierge (£10.95), and monkfish tails with bacon, red wine and garlic (£12.75); home-made puddings such as toffee and banana cream pie or poached spiced pears in red wine (£3.75); children's meals (from £3.95). The cosy cream-painted beamed bar has a large inglenook fireplace and purpose-built dark wood furniture, oil paintings, and fresh flowers. The restaurant, with another impressive inglenook and pretty table settings, is no smoking, and is closed on Sunday evening and all Monday; piped music and cribbage. Staff are friendly and efficient. Besides Banks's Bitter, well kept real ales could include Timothy Taylors Landlord and Woods Parish and Shropshire Lad on handpump; also 10 wines by the glass. *(Recommended by J Hale, Barry Smith, Dr T E Hothersall, Mike and Mary Carter, Hugh Bower, David and Helen Wilkins, Neil and Brenda Skidmore, Joe Green)*

Free house ~ Licensee Howard Hill-Lines ~ Real ale ~ Bar food ~ Restaurant ~ (01299) 270372 ~ Children must be well behaved and away from bar ~ Dogs allowed in bedrooms ~ Open 12-3, 6-11(10.30 Sun) ~ Bedrooms: £47.50B/£75B

IRONBRIDGE SJ6704 Map 6

Malthouse

The Wharfage (bottom road alongside Severn)

There's live music at this enjoyably bustling pub every night except Monday and Tuesday – mostly jazz, but also funk, latin and world music. It's a big barn of a place, very nicely decorated (the walls are covered with changing works by local artists), with a really laid-back feel despite the lively buzz. Spotlessly clean, the spacious bar is broken up by pine beams and concrete pillars, and has lots of scrubbed light wooden tables with candles; piped music. The bar food is enjoyable, and although the fresh fish is delivered from Brixham, most other ingredients are firmly local – the pork comes from the woods opposite. The menu typically includes home-made soup (£2.50), baked mushrooms with smoked cheese and garlic (£3.50), chicken and black pudding terrine (£3.75 – a favourite with readers), fried cheese and herb gnocchi with sun-dried tomato mayonnaise (£4.50), cajun chicken or spinach and cashew curry (£6.95), and lamb sausages with bubble and squeak and rosemary gravy or baked salmon in thai mussel sauce with noodles (£7.50), with puddings such as orange sponge pudding with hot fudge sauce (£3.50); children's menu, and good Sunday roasts. Though there may be a wait when it's busy, readers are very impressed with the friendly and obliging, hardworking staff, and the young licensees are enthusiastic. Well kept Boddingtons, Courage Directors and Flowers Original on electric pump, and a wide choice of wines, several by the glass. The atmosphere is quite different in the restaurant (most of which is no smoking), and the bedrooms are all individually decorated. There are a few tables in front. *(Recommended by John Whitehead, Mike and Linda Hudson, M Joyner, Dr Bob Bland, Tony Ounsworth, Sue and Geoff Price)*

Free house ~ Licensees Alex and Andrea Nicoll ~ Real ale ~ Bar food (12-2.30, 5.30-9) ~ Restaurant ~ (01952) 433712 ~ Children welcome ~ Dogs allowed in bar ~ Live music Weds-Sat evenings ~ Open 11-3, 5-11; 11-11 Sat; 12-10.30 Sun; closed 25 Dec ~ Bedrooms: £55B/£65B

LONGVILLE SO5393 Map 4

Longville Arms

B4371 Church Stretton—Much Wenlock

This relaxed and comfortable inn is surrounded by some really beautiful countryside. The two spacious bars have stripped beams and original stone, and the lounge bar on the left has dark plush wall banquettes and cushioned chairs, with some nice old tables. The room on the right has oak panelling, and a large no smoking dining room (with disabled access) overlooks the terrace. The shortish bar menu includes tasty dishes such as soup (£1.95), deep-fried whitebait with a yoghurt mint dip (£2.95), home-made pâté (£3.25), mushroom and mixed pepper tagliatelle or lasagne (£5.95), gammon steak (£7.95), and rump steak (£9.95) with regular specials such as steak and ale pie (£6.95), and cajun chicken (£7.50), and home-made puddings such as spotted dick (£2.50). Friendly staff serve well kept Courage Best or Directors, Charles Wells Bombardier, and a guest such as Flowers Original on handpump; also several malt and Irish whiskies; a games room has darts, pool, dominoes (no children in here), and there's piped music. In a terraced side garden are picnic-sets and a children's play area. *(Recommended by Ray and Winifred Halliday, TOH, DJH, David Field, Gene and Kitty Rankin, John Whitehead, Paul and Margaret Baker, Dr D Parker, Abi Benson)*

Free house ~ Licensees Chris and Wendy Davis ~ Real ale ~ Bar food (12-2.30, 7(6 Fri/Sat)-9.30) ~ Restaurant ~ (01694) 771206 ~ Children in eating area of bar and restaurant ~ Dogs welcome ~ Open 12-3, 7-12; 12-3, 6-12 Sat; 12-3, 6(7 in winter)10.30 Sun ~ Bedrooms: £30S/£48S

LUDLOW SO5175 Map 4

Unicorn (🍴)

Corve Street, off main road to Shrewsbury

Outside this busy 17th-c inn, tables shelter pleasantly among willow trees on the pretty little terrace right next to the modest River Corve. The enjoyable food is the main draw, and it's best to get here early if you want to eat. The menu could include home-made soup (£3.25), garlic mushrooms or bacon, ham and stilton terrine (£4.25), sausages with bubble and squeak (£6.50), mushroom stroganoff (£7.25), battered cod and chips or salmon, seafood and pasta bake (£7.50), braised oxtail with juniper and red wine and mustard mash (£10.50), and plaice goujons (£12.50), with good home-made puddings such as apple crumble (£3.50). The very welcoming and efficient staff cope well with the crowds, and the landlord is helpful. There's an appealing sociable buzz in the solidly beamed and partly panelled bar, with a mix of friendly locals and visitors, and a huge log fire in a big stone fireplace; the timbered candlelit restaurant is no smoking. Well kept Bass, Hancocks HB and a guest such as Timothy Taylors Landlord on handpump; cribbage and dominoes. This is a picturesque town. *(Recommended by Gene and Kitty Rankin, Joe Green, Dennis Jenkin, Nick Holding, Ann and Max Cross, P G Plumridge, Alan Thomas, Mr and Mrs R Wilson, Roland Curtis, Elaine Thompson, Ray and Jacki Davenport, Charles Moncreiffe, Mike and Mary Carter, David Twitchett, Karen and Graham Oddey, Mr and Mrs P Lally, Di and Mike Gillam, Stan and Hazel Allen, MLR)*

Free house ~ Licensees Alan and Elisabeth Ditchburn ~ Real ale ~ Bar food (12-2.15, 6(7 Sun)-9.15) ~ Restaurant ~ (01584) 873555 ~ Children welcome ~ Dogs welcome ~ Open 12-3, 6-11; 12-3.30, 6-(10.30 Sun)11 Sat; closed 25 Dec

MUCH WENLOCK SO6299 Map 4

George & Dragon

High Street

Your eyes will be kept busy at this unassuming town pub, as the cosily atmospheric rooms house an impressive collection of old brewery and cigarette advertisements, bottle labels and beer trays, and George-and-the-Dragon pictures, as well as around 500 jugs hanging from the beams. Furnishings such as antique settles are among more conventional seats, and there are a couple of attractive Victorian fireplaces (with coal-effect gas fires). At the back, the quieter snug old-fashioned rooms have black beams and timbering, little decorative plaster panels, tiled floors, a big mural as well as lots of smaller pictures (painted by local artists), and a little stove in an inglenook. The pub is popular with locals, and the pleasant atmosphere is helped along by the courteous landlord. The enjoyable bar food could include soup (£3.25), sandwiches (from £3.25), ploughman's (£4.25), leek and mushroom bake, thai curry or tasty local faggots and onion gravy (£5.95), salmon fillet (£7.95), and rack of lamb (£10.95), with puddings such as apple crumble (£2.95); they do a Sunday roast (£6.95). Four well kept continually changing real ales on handpump could include Adnams Broadside, Greene King Abbot and Old Speckled Hen and Hobsons Town Crier; also country wines, and cranberry, elderflower, and ginger pressé. *(Recommended by MLR, Pete Yearsley, Andy and Jill Kassube, O K Smyth, John Oates, John Whitehead, Gill and Tony Morriss, Denzil Martin, Di and Mike Gillam, David Field, Pat and Tony Martin, Nigel Woolliscroft, Dr Bob Bland)*

Punch ~ Licensee Milton Monk ~ Real ale ~ Bar food (12-2, 6-9; not Sun or Weds evenings) ~ Restaurant ~ (01952) 727312 ~ Well behaved children welcome away from bar ~ Open 12-11(10.30 Sun); 12-3, 6-11(10.30 Sun) winter

Talbot

High Street

At this comfortable 14th-c pub, a charming little coach entry leads off the High Street to green seats and tables in an attractive sheltered courtyard, and the entrance to the bar. Inside are several neatly kept areas with comfortable green plush button-back wall banquettes around tables, low ceilings, and two big log fires in inglenooks; the walls are decorated with prints of fish and brewery paraphernalia, and there are Art Deco-style lamps and gleaming brasses. In large helpings, tasty bar food includes soup (£2.95), sandwiches with nice fresh salad (from £4.25), omelettes (from £5.95), chicken supreme in mushroom sauce (£7.50), poached salmon with white wine and mushroom sauce (£8.45), and daily specials such as chilli (£6.95), and steak and ale or shropshire pie (pork, leeks, cider and cheese, £7.50); puddings (£3.75). They usually serve well kept Bass, and a guest from Enville or Woods on handpump, and they've several malt whiskies; quiet piped music. The landlady works hard to please her customers, and service is prompt and friendly. The pub was originally part of Wenlock Abbey. Readers tell us there's a cheap car park behind the pub. *(Recommended by John Saville, Tim Maddison, M Joyner, John Whitehead, Gill and Tony Morriss, Andrea and Guy Bradley)*

Free house ~ Licensees Mark and Maggie Tennant ~ Real ale ~ Bar food (12-2, 7-9.30(8.30 Sun)) ~ Restaurant ~ (01952) 727077 ~ Children welcome ~ Open 9.30-11(10.30 Sun); 9.30-3, 6(7 Sun)-11 winter; closed 25 Dec ~ Bedrooms: £35B/£70B

NORTON SJ7200 Map 4

Hundred House

A442 Telford—Bridgnorth

Shropshire Dining Pub of the Year

The outstanding cottagey gardens at this welcoming, well run pub are well worth a visit in themselves, with old-fashioned roses, trees, herbaceous plants, and a very big working herb garden that supplies the kitchen (you can buy bags of their herbs for £1, and the money goes to charity). Good well presented food is another great draw, and the well prepared menu could include home-made soup (£3.95), chicken liver pâté with brioche and chutney (£4.95), local pork sausages with onion gravy (£6.95), hot potato cakes with tempura onion rings, aïoli and mushroom sauce (£7.95), steak and kidney pie or chargrilled cajun chicken with sweet red pepper coulis, mint yoghurt and fennel salad (£8.95), and daily specials such as fish chowder (£3.95), whiting and clam casserole (£10.95), and grilled smoked gammon in mushroom sauce (£11.95); you must book for the restaurant (though you can eat from the restaurant menu in the bar). The neatly kept interior is pleasant and interesting too, prettied up with lots of dried and fresh flowers, herbs and hops, and divided into several separate areas, with old quarry tiles at either end and modern hexagonal ones in the main central high-beamed part. Steps lead up past a little balustrade to a partly panelled eating area, where the stripped brickwork looks older than elsewhere. Handsome fireplaces have log fires or working Coalbrookdale ranges (one has a great Jacobean arch with fine old black cooking pots), and around sewing-machine tables are a variety of interesting chairs and settles with some long colourful patchwork leather cushions; the main dining room is no smoking. Well kept Heritage Bitter (brewed for them by a small brewery: light and refreshing and not too bitter) along with a couple of guests such as Highate Mild and Saddlers Best on handpump, an extensive wine list with house wines by the carafe, half carafe, and big or small glass, farm cider and lots of malt whiskies. Service is very friendly, and readers tell us their young children have been treated really nicely. *(Recommended by David Field, John Sandilands, Peter and Patricia Burton, Mike and Wendy Proctor, Gill and Keith Croxton, Lynda and Trevor Smith, Mike and Mary Carter, Stephanie Smith, Leigh Hughes, Patrick Hancock, Mr and Mrs G Owens)*

Free house ~ Licensee the Phillips family ~ Real ale ~ Bar food (12-2.30, 6-9.30) ~ Restaurant ~ (01952) 730353 ~ Children welcome ~ Dogs allowed in bedrooms ~ Open 12-3, 5.30-11; 12-3.30, 7-10.30 Sun ~ Bedrooms: £69B/£99B

PORTH-Y-WAEN SJ2623 Map 6

Lime Kiln

A495, between village and junction with A483, S of Oswestry

Well opened up under newish licensees, this has some stripped joists and pine dado, a mix of neat small chairs and cushioned pews and settles around big scrubbed deal tables on quarry tiles, and warm coal fires. A bare-boards no smoking corner has a big photograph of the local lime quarry a century ago, and throughout there are attractive mainly local photographs on the apricot walls – with a big family photograph of the Beatles in their earliest days (who also featured, after Brian Ferry, in the quiet piped music on our inspection visit). Good inventive blackboard food (using lots of local produce) might include leek and potato soup (£2.25), baguettes (from £3.95), duck livers wrapped in bacon with hot and sour beetroot (£3.75), thai crab cakes with cucumber relish (£4.50), warm pigeon breast salad with black pudding and chorizo (£6.50), grilled bass on crispy noodles with roasted pepper dressing (£8.95), and fillet steak medallions with shallot and red wine jus (£12.95), with puddings such a sticky toffee pudding with butterscotch sauce (£3.75). There's a cheerful atmosphere, and the friendly staff are very helpful (for example, happily making up non-menu dishes for one reader's children). Fullers London Pride and Timothy Taylors Landlord on handpump, good value wines, coffee in nice big mugs (they have good cutlery, too). There are picnic-sets out in a side garden with a boules pitch and terraced lawn; the sociable dog is called Blue. *(Recommended by Margaret and Andrew Leach, Mrs Suzy Miller)*

Free house ~ Licensees Ian and Jane Whyte ~ Real ale ~ Bar food (12-2, 6-9; 12-3, 5.30-9 Sat; 12-4 Sun; not Mon or evening Sun) ~ Restaurant ~ (01691) 831550 ~ Children under 14 welcome in eating area of bar till 9pm ~ Open 12-3, 5.30-11; 12-11(10.30 Sun) Sat; closed Mon and a week in Jan

SHREWSBURY SJ4912 Map 6

Armoury

Victoria Quay, Victoria Avenue

The long bar counter at this former warehouse has an eye-catching range of drinks, with well kept Boddingtons, Wadworths 6X, Woods Shropshire Lad and up to five changing guest beers on handpump, a good choice of wines (with 15 by the glass), around 50 malt whiskies, a dozen different gins, lots of rums and vodkas, a variety of brandies, and some unusual liqueurs. Big arched windows overlooking the river light up the single airy room, which is packed with old prints, documents and other neatly framed ephemera, with glass cabinets showing off collections of explosives and shells as well as corks and bottle openers; two entire walls are covered with copiously filled bookshelves. A mix of good heavy wooden tables and chairs is interspersed with the occasional green-painted standing timber, and colonial fans whirr away on the ceiling; tables at one end are laid out for eating, with a grand stone fireplace at the other end. The interesting bar menu could include soup (£3.25), sandwiches (from £3.95), crispy fried beef with horseradish crème fraîche or mussel, garlic and coriander broth (4.25), macaroni cheese (£5.95), aubergine gratin with mozzarella and olives (£7.25), lamb tagine (£8.95), roasted pork chop with rhubarb, celeriac mash and mustard leeks (£9.45), and baked cod with smoked bacon mash and minted broad beans (£11.75); puddings such as chocolate fudge brownie (£4.50). It does get busy here in the evenings, particularly at weekends. The pub doesn't have its own parking but there is some metered parking up nearer the quarry. *(Recommended by I D Greenfield, Dr Bob Bland, Darly Graton, Graeme Gulibert, John Brightley, M Joyner, SLC, Tony Ounsworth)*

Brunning & Price ~ Manager Jill Mitchell ~ Real ale ~ Bar food (12-9.30(9 Sun); not evenings 26 Dec and 1 Jan) ~ (01743) 340525 ~ Children under 14 till 9pm ~ Open 12-11(10.30 Sun); closed 25 and 26 Dec

WENTNOR SO3893 Map 6

Crown

Village and pub signposted (not very clearly) off A489 a few miles NW of junction with A49

This has been an inn ever since it was built in 1640, and inside are beams, standing timbers, some nice big prints, a collection of china and cut glass, and a good log fire. Much of the main bar area is laid for eating, and one end has a snug area with pictures and two sofas. They serve well kept Hobsons Best, Greene King Old Speckled Hen, Salopian Shropshire Gold and Worthington Best on handpump, and they've decent wines and a good choice of malt whiskies; piped music, dominoes. Besides sandwiches (from £2.35) and soup (£2.40), bar food includes dishes such as grilled goats cheese (£3.95), smoked salmon and dill quiche (£5.50), curry or home-made west country pie (£6.50), chicken with garlic and herbs in a cream and white wine sauce (£6.95), and tarragon chicken or bass with tomato and basil salad (£8.95), with home-made puddings such as lemon cheesecake (£3.25); the cosy beamed restaurant is no smoking. On the neat back lawn, picnic-sets and old-fashioned teak garden seats give a fine view of the Long Mynd. *(Recommended by Barry and Verina Jones, Guy Vowles, Collin and Julie Taylor, Tim Maddison, John and Angela Main, Malcolm Taylor, Stan and Hazel Allen, DJH, MDN)*

Free house ~ Licensees Simon and Joanna Beadman ~ Real ale ~ Bar food ~ Restaurant ~ (01588) 650613 ~ Children in eating area of bar ~ Open 12-(5 Sat)3, 7-11; 12-4, 7-10.30 Sun ~ Bedrooms: £27S(£30B)/£53S

WHITCHURCH SJ5345 Map 7

Willey Moor Lock £

Actually just over the Cheshire border, the pub is signposted off A49 just under 2 miles N of Whitchurch

You have to cross a little footbridge over the Llangollen Canal and its rushing sidestream to get to this picturesquely placed pub. It used to be the lock-keeper's cottage, so there are good views of the colourful narrowboats that drift past. Neatly kept by the friendly landlady, the low-beamed rooms attract a pleasant mix of customers, with brick-based brocaded wall seats, stools and small chairs around dimpled copper and other tables, a large teapot collection, a decorative longcase clock, and two winter log fires. Alongside well kept Theakstons Best, there might be Abbeydale, John Smiths, Timothy Taylors Landlord and Weetwood Eastgate on handpump, with a choice of around 30 malt whiskies. Straightforward bar food includes sandwiches (from £2.25), filled baked potatoes (£3.20), vegetable curry (£5), home-made steak pie or boiled ham (£5.25), battered cod (£5.50), and gammon steak (£7.50), with puddings such as toffee apple crumble pie (from £1.75); children's meals (from £2). Fruit machine, dominoes, piped music, and several dogs and cats. There are tables under cocktail parasols on a terrace, and the garden has a large children's play area. More reports please. *(Recommended by Mike and Wena Stevenson, Rob Fowell)*

Free house ~ Licensee Elsie Gilkes ~ Real ale ~ Bar food (12-2, 6-9.30(9 Mon); 12-2 6(7 winter)-9 Sun) ~ (01948) 663274 ~ Children welcome away from bar ~ Open 12-2.30, 6-11; 12-3, 6-11(10.30 Sun) Sat; 12-2, 7-11(10.30 Sun) in winter; closed 25 Dec and evening 26 Dec

WISTANSTOW SO4385 Map 6

Plough

Village signposted off A49 and A489 N of Craven Arms

Seeing as tasty Woods beers are brewed right by the pub, you'd expect this place to appeal to drinkers, but readers have very good things to say about the food here too. The building is simply furnished (and spotlessly kept), with high rafters, cream walls and mahogany furniture on a russet turkey carpet, and oak tables and chairs and welsh dressers to give the modernised bar a more homely feel; service is warm and friendly. Woods Parish, Special, Shropshire Lad and seasonal ales are well kept on handpump; also Addlestone's and Weston's cider. The Hardings use local suppliers for their enjoyable English cooking which, from a nicely varied, seasonally changing menu, could include dishes such as fried black pudding with home-made chutney (£3.95), avocado and prawn salad (£4.90), ham, two eggs and chips (£6.85), leek, sausagemeat and bacon pie (£7.50), lamb steak with red wine and redcurrant sauce (£9.95), plaice fillets stuffed with crab meat with a creamy lemon sauce (£10.25), and duck breast with ginger and black cherry sauce (£10.75); puddings could include home-made meringues with clotted cream ice cream and tiramisu (from £3.30), and they do a good cheeseboard (£6.95); on Sundays, they only do two roasts, and a fish and vegetarian choice. You can buy bottles of Woods beer to take away, and they also sell home-made chutney and marmalade. The games area has darts, pool, juke box, and fruit machine and piped music. There are some tables under cocktail parasols outside. *(Recommended by Ruth and Andrew Crowder, TOH, John Whitehead, B, M and P Kendall)*

Own brew ~ Licensee Denis Harding ~ Real ale ~ Bar food (not Mon or evenings Sun) ~ Restaurant ~ (01588) 673251 ~ Children welcome ~ Dogs allowed in bar ~ Open 11.30-2.30, 6.30-11; 12-2.30, 7-10.30 Sun; closed Mon

Waterside pubs are listed at the back of the book.

Lucky Dip

Besides the fully inspected pubs, you might like to try these Lucky Dips recommended to us and described by readers (if you do, please send us reports: www.goodguides.com).

All Stretton [SO4595]

☆ ***Yew Tree*** [Shrewsbury Rd (B4370)]: Comfortable beamed bars and dining room, good value food inc interesting vegetarian choice, cheerful service, well kept Hobsons Best and Wye Valley Butty Bach, bookable dining room, lively public bar; children welcome, small village handy for Long Mynd, cl Tues *(TOH, Sarah and Peter Gooderham, C J Cox, A Monro)*

Ash [SJ5739]

White Lion: Two-room village local, beams and bare boards, well kept Bass, Worthington and a guest beer, simple food, friendly staff and regulars, blazing log fires *(MLR)*

Boningale [SJ8102]

Horns [A464 NW of Wolverhampton]: Three friendly bars with eight changing ales inc local brews such as Salopian, wide choice of wholesome nicely presented food inc midweek specials, sizzling steaks and good quickly served Sun lunch, panelled dining room; children welcome *(Andy and Jill Kassube)*

Bridgnorth [SO7293]

☆ ***Bear*** [Northgate (B4373)]: Pleasant new licensees in former coaching inn with well kept ales such as Fullers London Pride, Greene King IPA, Hop Back Crop Circle, Oakhill Yeoman Strong and Timothy Taylors Landlord, attractively priced straightforward lunchtime food (not Sun) from sandwiches up, decent wines by the glass, two unpretentious bars with wall banquettes and a mix of other furnishings, french windows to small sheltered lawn with picnic-sets; bedrooms *(LYM, MDN)*

☆ ***Punch Bowl*** [B4364 towards Ludlow]: Comfortable open-plan country pub, soft lighting, lots of interesting pictures on pink walls, good generous bar food from inventive starters and hot filled baguettes to good Sun carvery (best to book), friendly helpful service, well kept Bass, decent wines, good coffee, separate restaurant with own bar; piped music; pretty country views from picnic-sets on small side terrace, compact bedrooms *(BB, Mr and Mrs M Browning)*

☆ ***Railwaymans Arms*** [Severn Valley Station, Hollybush Rd (off A458 towards Stourbridge)]: Good interesting more or less local ales inc a Mild in converted waiting-room at Severn Valley steam railway terminus, bustling on summer days; coal fire, station nameplates, superb mirror over fireplace, tables out on platform; may be simple summer snacks, children welcome, wheelchair access; the train to Kidderminster (another bar there) has an all-day bar and bookable Sun lunches *(P and M Rudlin, the Didler, JP, PP, Nigel Woolliscroft, Gill and Tony Morriss, LYM)*

Broome [SO4081]

☆ ***Engine & Tender***: Homely bar with well kept Woods from Art Deco servery, railway memorabilia and other bric-a-brac, cosy corners with tables for eating, also quite extensive restaurant with interesting collection of pottery inc teapots and shelves of jugs, good straightforward food inc generous Sun roast, good value wines, cheerful unhurried service, forest of good-sized plants in conservatory, games room with pool and glassed-over well; caravan site with hook-up points and showers *(TOH, Pete Yearsley)*

Broseley [SJ6701]

☆ ***Pheasant*** [Church St]: Smartly done-up dining pub with good imaginative restauranty food, small friendly bar, two rooms with sturdy seats, big stripped tables on oak boards, large oil paintings, log fires, candles and gas lamps, real ales, good wines; two bedrooms, plans for more; cl Sun evening and Mon, perhaps other wkdy lunchtimes *(Sally Downes, Mr and Mrs P Lally, Mr and Mrs P Grant)*

Burwarton [SO6185]

Boyne Arms [B4364 Bridgnorth—Ludlow]: Imposing Georgian building, wide choice of generous good value home-made food, changing well kept ales such as Bass and local Hobsons and Woods, cheerfully unassuming local atmosphere, friendly helpful staff, public bar with pool; tables in large garden with good wooden adventure playground *(John Oates, Michael Mellers)*

Clun [SO3081]

☆ ***Sun*** [High St]: Tudor beams and timbers, some sturdy antique furnishings and interesting prints, enormous open fire in flagstoned public bar, friendly helpful staff and character landlord, good value generous food in larger carpeted lounge bar, well kept ales inc Banks's Bitter and Mild and Hobsons; children allowed in eating area, tables in sheltered well planted back garden with terrace; nice bedrooms, hearty breakfast, lovely village *(DC, Abi Benson, David and Helen Wilkins, David Field, BB, the Didler, MLR)*

☆ ***White Horse*** [Market Sq]: Well laid out and neatly kept beamed L-shaped bar with inglenook and woodburner, newish friendly and helpful landlord doing enjoyable reasonably priced food, well kept changing ales, farm cider, good coffee, books and pub games near front, pool table and games machine far end; children welcome, tables in front and small back garden; newly refurbished bedrooms *(John Brightley, MLR)*

Clunton [SO3381]

Crown: Cosy old village local with log fire, friendly staff and simple food inc Sun lunch (separate dining room) *(John Brightley)*

Coalbrookdale [SJ6704]

☆ ***Coalbrookdale Inn*** [Wellington Rd, opp Museum of Iron]: Long flight of steps up to handsome dark brick 18th-c pub, simple, cheerful and bustling tiled-floor bar with local pictures, six or seven well kept changing ales from square counter also serving rather smaller room set more for the huge platefuls of good value often imaginative food (not Sun) from sandwiches to steaks; good log fire, farm cider, country wines, good mix of people, piano, remarkable bottled beer collection, no piped music; dogs welcome, opens noon *(Phil and Heidi Cook, the Didler, BB, Dr Bob Bland)*

Coalport [SJ6903]

☆ ***Boat*** [Ferry Rd, Jackfield; nr Mawes Craft Centre]: Cosy 18th-c quarry-tiled bar, coal fire in lovely range, good food inc meat, game and cheeses and good value Sun lunch, well kept Banks's Bitter and Mild and Marstons Pedigree, Weston's farm cider, darts; summer barbecues on big tree-shaded lawn, in delightful part of Severn Gorge, footbridge making it handy for Coalport China Museum *(Dr Bob Bland, BB, the Didler, M Joyner)*

Brewery Inn [High St]: Good value generous food, friendly staff and locals; children welcome *(Abi Benson)*

Shakespeare [High St]: Simple friendly cream-washed timbered pub by pretty Severn gorge park, handy for china museum, with large quantities of good value quickly served home-made traditional and mexican food, well kept real ales inc local brews *(Gill and Tony Morriss, BB, Andy and Jill Kassube)*

Corfton [SO4985]

☆ ***Sun*** [B4368 Much Wenlock—Craven Arms]: Unpretentious country local with well kept Corvedale ales such as Normans Pride, Dark & Delicious, Junior, Secret Hop and Divine Inspiration from brewery behind (tours available), well kept guest ales, friendly chatty landlord, wide choice of good value blackboard food from generous baguettes to bargain Sun lunch, children's dishes, refurbished lounge with interesting prints, lively beamed bar, and dining room with no smoking area, beer bottle collection and covered well; tables on terrace and in good-sized garden with good play area; piped music; open all day, tourist information, particularly good disabled access throughout *(Pete Yearsley, BB, Michael and Jenny Back)*

Cressage [SJ5904]

Riverside [A458 NW]: Spacious pub under new ownership, lovely Severn views from big conservatory and garden tables, pleasant mix of furnishings inside, real ales such as Hobsons Town Crier, Salopian Golden Thread and one brewed for the pub, lunchtime baguettes and more expensive hot dishes; bedrooms, open all day wknds *(LYM)*

Edgerley [SJ3517]

☆ ***Royal Hill*** [off A5 following MoD Nesscliff Trg Camp signs, then Melverley signs]: Charmingly unspoilt 17th-c beamed country local, worn tiled corridor behind tall settles forming snug around coal fire, little parlour with settee, easy chair, rocking chair and TV, back bar with two well kept Salopian beers and Worthington, no food exc Sun rolls and (busy) Thurs night fish and chips; children welcome, long old-fashioned benches out in front, picnic-sets over lane on banks of River Severn, pleasant caravan/camp site, cl winter wkdy lunchtimes *(BB, Brian and Halina Howes, Kevin Thorpe)*

Ellesmere [SJ3934]

☆ ***Black Lion*** [Scotland St; back car park on A495]: Good value simple cheap substantial food all day inc bargains for children and OAPs, pleasantly relaxed and well run beamed bar off tiled entrance corridor, interesting décor and some nice unusual features, quiet and comfortable roomy dining room, cheery and enthusiastic young staff, well kept Marstons Bitter and Pedigree, restaurant; piped music; bedrooms, not far from canal wharf *(BB, Lynda Payton, Sam Samuells)*

Frodesley [SJ5101]

Swan [just off A49 S of Dorrington]: Restauranty pub with interesting varied bistro menu inc good Aberdeen Angus chargrills and Sun lunch, elegant dining room with two log fires, small bar; cl lunchtime Mon-Weds *(TOH)*

Hadnall [SJ5219]

New Inn [A49 6 miles N of Shrewsbury]: Enjoyable bar snacks inc toasties with home-baked bread, pleasant welcoming service, Bass, Fullers London Pride and Worthington *(J M Renshaw)*

Halfway House [SJ3411]

Seven Stars [A458 Shrewsbury—Welshpool]: Spotless and unspoilt, like a private house; very small bar with two high-backed settles by the gas fire, well kept cheap Burtonwood Best and Mild tapped from casks in the friendly owner's kitchen area, no food or music *(RWC, the Didler, JP, PP)*

Harley [SJ5901]

Plume of Feathers [A458 NW of Much Wenlock]: Spacious and popular beamed pub with big open fire, good range of reasonably priced well cooked food, well kept Scottish Courage and guest ales, good welcoming service even when busy, restaurant; darts, piped music (Sun evening live); tables outside, bedrooms with own baths, good walks *(K R Harris)*

Hodnet [SJ6128]

☆ ***Bear*** [Drayton Rd (A53)]: Relaxing refuge from the busy road, small beamed quarry-tiled bar with log fire and Courage Directors, Theakstons Best and Youngs Special, broad arch to rambling open-plan carpeted main area with blond seats and tables set for eating (good range of reasonably priced well presented food from sandwiches up, well filled puddings cabinet), snug end alcoves with heavy 16th-c beams and timbers, friendly helpful service; may be faint piped radio; open all day, children welcome (high chairs and child-size cutlery), six good value comfortable bedrooms, opp Hodnet Hall gardens and handy for Hawkstone Park *(BB, Louis and Jeanne Grein, Neil and Brenda Skidmore)*

Ironbridge [SJ6703]

Golden Ball [Newbridge Rd/Wesley Rd, off Madeley Hill]: Interesting partly Elizabethan local at the top of the town, with good atmosphere, helpful landlord and friendly staff, well kept mainstream and more local beers, good choice of competitively priced substantial food, real fire, quietish lunchtime, more lively evenings; children welcome, pleasant terraced walk down to river, comfortable bedrooms *(Gill and Tony Morriss, M Joyner, Martin Jennings)*

Meadow [Buildwas Rd]: Cheerful Severnside family dining pub done up with old-fashioned beamery, cigarette cards, tasteful prints and brasses; wide choice of good value generous fresh food inc imaginative specials in lounge and downstairs restaurant, smiling service, well kept Greene King Old Speckled Hen, decent wines; piped music; children very welcome, pretty waterside garden *(John Whitehead, Mrs J Small)*

Robin Hood [Waterloo St]: Popular and welcoming Severnside pub, five comfortable and attractive connecting rooms with various alcoves inc barrel-vaulted dining room, lots of gleaming brass and old clocks, well kept interesting changing ales, Stowford Press and Weston's Old Rosie ciders, friendly service, good value standard food from sandwiches to good Sun carvery; attractive seating area out in front, nice setting handy for museums, bedrooms, good breakfast *(Andy and Jill Kassube, Stephanie Smith, Leigh Hughes)*

Knockin [SJ3322]

Bradford Arms [B4396 NW of Shrewsbury]: Spotless modernised pub, helpful staff, well kept Marstons Bitter and Pedigree, reasonable food choice in bar and restaurant, good sensibly priced wine range, interesting RAF prints *(John A Barker)*

Knowle Sands [SO7191]

☆ ***Swan*** [off B4555 just S of Bridgnorth, nr Eardington]: Friendly and attractive dining pub, reasonably priced enjoyable restauranty food, prompt helpful service, good beer choice; comfortable bedrooms *(David Cosham, David Wilson)*

Leebotwood [SO4798]

☆ ***Pound*** [A49 Church Stretton—Shrewsbury]: Attractive, spotless and comfortable beamed and thatched 16th-c pub, good value blackboard food from sandwiches to fresh fish in bar and big recently refurbished no smoking restaurant, good local roasts for Sun carvery, well kept ales inc John Smiths, Marstons Pedigree and Woods Shropshire Lad, good wine list (occasional tastings), friendly efficient staff; tables in garden *(C H and B J Owen, TOH)*

Leintwardine [SO4175]

Jolly Frog [Toddings]: Distinctive yellow-green building with cosy rural atmosphere, mix of table sizes, enjoyably imaginative food esp fish, good wine list, sensible prices *(Christopher Woodward, Margaret and Andrew Leach)*

Little Stretton [SO4392]

☆ ***Green Dragon*** [village well signed off A49]: Well kept Tetleys, Wadworths 6X, Woods Shropshire Lad and quickly changing guest beers, reasonably priced food from good interesting baguettes up, cheap house wine, malt whiskies, helpful staff, children in eating area and restaurant; tables outside, handy for Cardingmill Valley (NT) and Long Mynd *(Margaret and Andrew Leach, DAV, LYM, Nigel Woolliscroft)*

Llanyblodwel [SJ2423]

☆ ***Horseshoe*** [signed off B4936, quite a long narrow lane]: Easy-going black and white timbered Tudor inn in lovely riverside spot, plenty of outside seats, a mile of fly-fishing; basic low-beamed front bar with old black range in inglenook fireplace, built-in settles, lots of brass and china, well worn in rooms rambling off, food (not Sun evening or Mon) from good value lunchtime sandwiches and baguettes up, oak-panelled dining room, Bass and Worthington and a range of malt whiskies; darts, pool, cribbage, dominoes, fruit machine, piped music, can be smoky; children in eating area, bedrooms, cl Mon lunchtime exc bank hols *(John Kane, LYM, M Joyner, Mrs Ursula Hofheinz, R Davies)*

Loppington [SJ4729]

Dickin Arms [B4397]: Warmly welcoming two-bar country local, dining room with good food inc inventive dishes and popular Sun lunch, good service, three real ales, open fire; babies and dogs welcome, play area outside, pretty village *(Lorna and Howard Lambert, Pamela and Merlyn Horswell)*

Ludlow [SO5174]

Blue Boar [Mill St]: Big rambling inn under new family, lots of linked areas (one no smoking), bright and airy at the front, darker further back, country bygones and boar memorabilia, food from lunchtime sandwiches, baguettes and baked potatoes up, Greene King IPA and Abbot, hard-working staff; big bedrooms, open all day *(Joe Green, Martin Grosberg)*

☆ ***Church Inn*** [Church St, behind Butter Cross]: Remarkably welcoming, nice décor with banquettes in cosy alcoves off central bar, pews and stripped stonework, good changing range of well kept ales such as Brains, Hook Norton, Weetwood Eastgate, Wye Valley and Youngs, cheerful atmosphere, helpful prompt service, good sandwiches and various hot dishes, no smoking restaurant; quiet piped music, car parking some way off; children welcome, open all day, comfortable bedrooms, good breakfast *(J M and P M Carver, P G Plumridge, Joe Green, Dave Braisted, LYM, P and D Carpenter, Mrs M M Westwood, Martin Grosberg)*

Feathers [Bull Ring]: Superb timbered building, striking inside too with Jacobean panelling and carving, fine period furnishings, pleasant service and nice bedrooms; unfortunately for a snack or drink you'll probably be diverted to a less distinguished side café-bar (good sandwiches and other decent bar food, Woods real ale); good parking, comfortable bedrooms, not cheap *(W W Burke, the Didler, Alan Thomas, LYM, Gene and Kitty Rankin)*

Queens [Lower Galdeford]: Long town bar with tables and banquettes, pine tables in rather smartly Mediterranean-feel dining area with decent food, friendly welcome, Greene King IPA *(Val and Alan Green)*

Wheatsheaf [Lower Broad St]: Traditional welcoming 17th-c beamed pub spectacularly built into medieval town gate, spotless housekeeping, generous usual food, good

service, well kept ales inc Woods Shropshire Lad, choice of farm cider, restaurant; attractive bedrooms, warm and comfortable *(Alan Thomas, W W Burke, P and D Carpenter)*
Marshbrook [SO4489]
Station Hotel [over level crossing by B4370/A49, S of Church Stretton]: Newly extended, quiet, relaxed and comfortable, with welcoming young licensees, prompt service, well kept Boddingtons, Flowers and Woods ales from high-gloss carved bar, food from warm baguettes and good choice of interesting light dishes up, sensible prices; unobtrusive piped music *(John Whitehead, TOH)*
Melverley [SJ3316]
Tontine [off B4393 W of Shrewsbury]: Old-fashioned small local with lots of books and bric-a-brac, Greene King Old Speckled Hen and Worthington, friendly staff, enjoyable home-made food inc good pies and puddings, dining conservatory, pool in separate bar; small garden *(John A Barker)*
Much Wenlock [SO6299]
Gaskell Arms [High St (A458)]: 17th-c beams, brasses, pubby décor and big brass-canopied log fire dividing the two rooms; good value food using local produce inc good Sun lunch in busy bars and civilised old-fashioned restaurant, friendly service, well kept Courage Directors and John Smiths, banknote collection; subdued piped music, fruit machine in lobby; bedrooms *(Pete Yearsley, John Whitehead, R M Corlett)*
Nesscliffe [SJ3819]
Old Three Pigeons [A5 Shrewsbury—Oswestry]: Dating from 16th c, with two quaint well worn in bar areas, brown sofas, mix of tables, log fires, brasses, log fires, dining room with wide range of food inc bargains for two, Moles real ale; juke box (not always switched on); children welcome, some tables outside, grounds with Russian tank and lots of other used military hardware, ducks and swans on lake, very well stocked bird garden; opp Kynaston Cave, good cliff walks *(John A Barker, LYM)*
Norbury [SO3692]
Sun [OS Sheet 137 map ref 363928]: Ancient welcoming place opp church in remote village; lovely simple building, open fire, low beams, steps and lots of gleaming brass, good basic bar food (not Mon) inc soup and sandwiches, pleasant restaurant with antique furniture and short but good menu, well kept beer, decent house wine; bedrooms, fine walks inc unusual route up to the Stiperstones *(John and Angela Main, Dr Bob Bland)*
Northwood [SJ4633]
Horse & Jockey: Low-beamed country pub with simple décor, friendly and helpful young licensees, Banks's Bitter and Original and Marstons Pedigree, wide choice of popular straightforward food inc OAP bargains, huge mixed grill (free if you finish it all) and good children's dishes in central lounge and plain dining area, nice fire, games room, lots of horse and jockey memorabilia; children and dogs welcome, play area *(Michael and Jenny Back, Sue and Bob Ward)*
Picklescott [SO4399]
☆ ***Bottle & Glass*** [off A49 N of Church Stretton]: Warmly welcoming unspoilt early 17th-c country local tucked away in delightful spot below N end of Long Mynd, pleasant quarry-tiled bar and lounge/restaurant, two log fires, good service, well kept Woods real ales, good value food esp home-made pies; quiet in winter, busy summer – wise to book for food then, esp Sun lunch; bedrooms *(DC, MDN)*
Ryton [SJ4803]
Fox [the one nr Dorrington, S of Shrewsbury]: Smart but relaxed hill-view country pub with very welcoming licensees doing good range of tasty home-made blackboard food, wider choice evenings; comfortable lounge bar and dining area, good range of ales inc Bass, no smoking restaurant *(Sarah and Peter Gooderham)*
Shifnal [SJ7407]
Oddfellows [Market Pl]: Bistro-style pub with wide range of interesting sensibly priced food in four linked rooms, three real ales inc Timothy Taylors, good wine choice, foreign lagers; tables outside *(Andy and Jill Kassube, M Joyner)*
White Hart [High St]: Good value friendly timbered 17th-c pub, quaint and old-fashioned, separate bar and lounge, comfortable but without frills, good range of interesting changing well kept ales such as Bathams and Enville, wide range of sandwiches, promptly served reasonably priced home-made hot dishes, welcoming staff; lively evenings *(Andy and Jill Kassube, Gill and Tony Morriss)*
Shrewsbury [SJ4912]
Albert [Smithfield Rd]: Two congenial linked rooms, well kept Banks's Bitter and Original and Marstons Pedigree, decent wines, good carvery – eat as much as you like *(Stephen, Julie and Hayley Brown, SLC, John A Barker)*
Boat House Inn [New St/Quarry Park; leaving centre via Welsh Bridge/A488 turn into Port Hill Rd]: Comfortably modernised Whitbreads Hogshead in lovely position by footbridge to Severn park, river views from long lounge bar, tables out on sheltered terrace and rose lawn; good range of well kept changing ales and of standard food, friendly helpful staff, bare boards, low ceilings, darts in smaller bar; children welcome, summer barbecues, popular with young people evening; open all day *(M Joyner, Dr Bob Bland, LYM)*
☆ ***Coach & Horses*** [Swan Hill/Cross Hill]: Welcoming unspoilt Victorian pub, panelled throughout, with main bar, cosy little side room and back dining room, good value food inc daily roasts and some unusual dishes, well kept Bass, Goodalls Gold (brewed for pub by Salopian) and a guest beer, relaxed atmosphere, prompt helpful service even when busy, interesting prints, wide mix of customers; pretty flower boxes outside *(the Didler, Pete Baker, JP, PP, David and Pam Wilcox)*
Cromwells [Dogpole]: Good affordable fresh food from baguettes to good game casserole, notable steak and kidney pie and inventive puddings in smallish dim-lit bar, warm, clean, cosy and friendly; well kept Woods, good house

wines, pleasant staff, attractive restaurant (same menu); well chosen piped music; raised garden and heated terrace behind, open all day Sat, nice bedrooms sharing bathrooms *(Dr Bob Bland, Margaret and Andrew Leach, John Whitehead)*
Dolphin [A49 ½ mile N of station]: Early Victorian pub now with its own Dolphin ales from back brewhouse, changing guest beers, foreign bottled beers and perhaps farm ciders, friendly staff, two small gas-lit rooms; cl lunchtime Mon-Sat but opens 3 Fri/Sat *(the Didler)*
Hop & Friar [St Julians Friars]: Large Victorian pub simply refurbished, cheap straightforward food, Banks's beers, pleasant vibrant atmosphere, old red telephone box, some cinema seats, high stools; small conservatory *(MLR)*
Loggerheads [Church St]: Small pub done out in old style, back panelled smoke room with scrubbed-top tables, high-backed settles and real fire, three other rooms with lots of prints, flagstones and bare boards, quaint linking corridors, friendly staff and locals, good choice of real ales inc local Salopian, darts, dominoes, food all day Mon-Sat till 6, poetry society *(the Didler, John Whitehead, JP, PP, MLR)*
Nags Head [Wyle Cop]: Small and welcoming, not smart but with plenty of atmosphere; Adnams Broadside, Ansells Mild, Bass, Batemans and Benskins *(John A Barker)*
Old Post Office [off Milk St almost opp Wheatsheaf, nr St Julians Craft Centre]: Long busy split-level town pub with plenty of bric-a-brac and brass, good atmosphere, good value food inc proper puddings from heated counter at far end, Banks's Bitter and Mild; piped music, full of young people Sat night; tables in courtyard *(Sue and Mike Todd)*
☆ ***Three Fishes*** [Fish St]: Extensively refurbished heavy-beamed timbered and flagstoned pub, popular esp with older people for its clean fresh atmosphere (no smoking throughout – no mobile phones either); well kept changing ales such as Adnams, Corvedale Normans Pride, Fullers London Pride, Salopian Minsterley and Timothy Taylors Landlord, good value wines, simple robust food, cheerful quick service, lots of interesting photographs, prints and bric-a-brac; open all day, cl Sun *(Sue and Mike Todd, M Joyner, Dr Bob Bland, LYM, the Didler, Janet and Peter Race, Derek and Sylvia Stephenson, Tony Ounsworth, Sue and Geoff Price)*
Upton Magna [SJ5512]
☆ ***Corbet Arms***: Big well decorated L-shaped lounge bar, armchairs by log fire, three well kept ales such as Marstons Pedigree, decent house wine, blackboards for wide range of good value freshly made food, helpful friendly service, darts in smaller public bar; great view to the Wrekin from tables in neatly kept garden, handy for Haughmond Hill walks and Attingham Park (NT), busy wknds *(Dave and Jill Head)*
Wellington [SJ6511]
Cock [Holyhead Rd]: Former coaching inn popular for its real ale bar, with six or seven well kept beers usually from small breweries and often changing from day to day, farm cider, good pork pies, large pine tables and big fireplace, also comfortable no smoking lounge; open all day Thurs-Sat, bedrooms *(Denzil Martin, James Windsor)*
Wenlock Edge [SO5796]
Wenlock Edge Inn [B4371 Much Wenlock—Church Stretton]: Charmingly placed country pub under new owners, pleasant two-room bar (dogs allowed) with open fire and inglenook woodburner, more modern no smoking dining extension with plans for small conservatory, food from baguettes up (not Mon in winter, and not the home baking and organic emphasis of the previous owners), well kept local Hobsons Best and Town Crier; children welcome in eating areas, tables out on terraces, cosy well appointed bedrooms (plans for more), lots of walks; cl Mon lunchtime in winter *(LYM)*
Whitchurch [SJ5441]
Horse & Jockey [Church St]: Three or four cosy and comfortable dining areas with good value carefully prepared food cooked by the landlord using local fresh produce, from interesting starters and light dishes up, Ind Coope Burton and Worthington *(MLR)*
Worfield [SO7595]
☆ ***Dog*** [off A454 W of Bridgnorth; Main St]: Recently refurbished country pub now very popular for its food, from good value baguettes to steaks and specials such as crab and lobster, well kept real ales, decent wines, log fire; beautiful unspoilt stone-built village *(Brian and Carole Polhill, Andy and Jill Kassube)*
Yorton [SJ5023]
Railway: Same family for over 60 years, friendly and chatty mother and daughter, unchanging atmosphere, simple cosy bar with coal fire, big comfortable lounge with fishing trophies, well kept Wadworths 6X, Woods Parish, Special and Shropshire Lad on handpump, a guest beer tapped from the cask, simple sandwiches if you ask, pub games – no piped music or machines *(Sue and Bob Ward, the Didler)*

If you have to cancel a reservation for a bedroom or restaurant, please telephone or write to warn them. A small place – and its customers – will suffer if you don't. And people who failed to cancel have been taken to court for breach of contract.

Somerset

In this county we include Bristol, as well as nearby Bath. It's an area that has a fine range of interesting pubs, often run by real individualists who know what they want to do and do it – instead of following the latest fashion, or someone else's idea of what might or might not be politically correct. There are plenty of thoroughly genuine country pubs, with equally genuinely friendly people – and a good deal of excellent food to be found, in nice surroundings. Several most enjoyable new entries made this year's Somerset inspection trips particularly memorable: the 16th-c Queens Arms in Bleadon (very good beers, nice food and atmosphere), the White Hart near Congresbury (a friendly country dining pub, good value), the Carew Arms at Crowcombe (warmly welcoming and unspoilt – quintessential Somerset), the Ring o' Roses at Holcombe (civilised country comfort, good modern food gaining them a Food Award straight off), the Pilgrims Rest at Lovington (quaint, cottagey and again very civilised, upmarket food winning another Food Award, and good beer from nearby Cottage), and the Windmill in Portishead (a distinctive family dining pub looking out over the Bristol Channel). Other main entries on top form this year are the rambling Old Green Tree in Bath and the unspoilt Star there (good beers and atmosphere in both), the homely Malt Shovel in Bradley Green (good all round), the Crown at Churchill (unspoilt, friendly and bustling, good home cooking and excellent beers), the Ring o' Bells at Compton Martin (nice all round, with enjoyable cheap food and a particular welcome for families), the civilised Horse & Groom at East Woodlands (quickly turns casual visitors into regulars), the exceptional unspoilt Tuckers Grave at Faulkland, the unpretentious old Rose & Crown at Huish Episcopi (great for farm ciders, in the appropriate atmosphere), the warmly welcoming Bird in Hand at North Curry (interesting food in a proper village pub), the Halfway House at Pitney (excellent beers, good value simple food, nice atmosphere), the cheerful Rose & Crown at Stoke St Gregory (nice food, pleasant place to stay), and the Blue Ball at Triscombe (nice staff, good food and wines, and an exemplary reworking of the old building). Against all this competition, it is a newcomer which carries off the title of Somerset Dining Pub of the Year – the Ring o' Roses at Holcombe. The Lucky Dip section at the end of the chapter has about 160 entries this year, more than 70 of them new. Ones to note particularly are the Ring o' Bells in Ashcott, Kings Head in Bristol, Gardeners Arms in Cheddar, Manor House at Ditcheat, Anchor at Exebridge, Ring o' Bells at Hinton Blewett, Stag at Hinton Charterhouse, Old Crown in Kelston, Hood Arms at Kilve, Kings Arms and Phelips Arms at Montacute, Fleur de Lys at Norton St Philip, Royal Oak at Over Stratton, Ship at Porlock Weir, Greyhound at Staple Fitzpaine, Masons Arms in Taunton, Cotley Inn at Wambrook, Fountain in Wells, Fox & Badger at Wellow, Slab House at West Horrington and Crossways at West Huntspill. And we agree with the reader who pointed out that there seem to be a great many nice pubs along or near the B3110 S of Bath. Drinks prices in the area are close to the national average, with quite a few bargains to be had if you look around. Local Butcombe beer often undercuts other bigger names, and other local brews to look out for include Smiles, Cotleigh, Exmoor, Cottage, RCH, Abbey, Bath, Clearwater and Moor.

APPLEY ST0621 Map 1

Globe

Hamlet signposted from the network of back roads between A361 and A38, W of B3187 and W of Milverton and Wellington; OS Sheet 181 map reference 072215

Enjoyed by readers, this 15th-c country pub has a simple beamed front room with benches and a built-in settle, bare wood tables on the brick floor, and pictures of magpies, and there's a further room with easy chairs and other more traditional ones, open fires, and a collection of model cars, Art Deco items and *Titanic* pictures; skittle alley. A stone-flagged entry corridor leads to a serving hatch from where Cotleigh Tawny and guests such as Palmers IPA or John Smiths are kept on handpump. Popular bar food includes sandwiches or rolls (from £1.75), home-made soup (£2.95), mushrooms in cream, garlic and horseradish (£4.25; £7.25 main course), smoked haddock and bacon chowder (£5.50; main course £8.50), a light cold egg pancake filled with prawns, celery and pineapple in marie rose sauce (£6.95), home-made steak and kidney in ale pie (£7.95), thai vegetable curry (£8.25), steaks (from £9.50), chicken breast stuffed with mozzarella and parma ham with a tomato, basil and cream sauce (£10.25), crispy duckling with madeira sauce (£11.95), daily specials like hungarian pork (£7.95), fresh whole lemon sole (£10.95), and rossini steak (£12.95), and puddings such as hot Toblerone crêpes with clotted cream (from £3.75); roast Sunday lunch (£6.25), and children's meals (from £3.95). The restaurant is no smoking. Seats, climbing frame and swings outside in the garden; the path opposite leads eventually to the River Tone. New disabled lavatories. *(Recommended by Martin Dormer, James Flory, P Duffield, Brian and Bett Cox, Paul and Annette Hallett, the Didler, S G N Bennett, Ian Phillips, Su and Bob Child, George R Ayres, Dr and Mrs M E Wilson)*

Free house ~ Licensees A W and E J Burt ~ Real ale ~ Bar food (till 10) ~ Restaurant ~ (01823) 672327 ~ Children welcome ~ Open 11-3, 6.30-11; 12-3, 7-10.30 Sun; closed Mon except bank hols

ASHILL ST3116 Map 1

Square & Compass

Windmill Hill; off A358 between Ilminster and Taunton; up Wood Torad for 1 mile behind Stewley Cross service station; OS Sheet 193 map reference 310166

Run by helpful, friendly licensees, this bustling and unassuming country pub remains popular with readers. The bar has simple comfortable furnishings, an open fire, and well kept Exmoor Ale and Gold and a guest from breweries such as Branscombe or Otter. Generous helpings of enjoyable bar food include home-made soup (£2.50), good sandwiches (from £2.95), filled baked potatoes (from £3.95), deep-fried brie (£4.50), ploughman's (£5.50), omelettes (£5.75), tuna pasta bake (£5.95), thai chicken curry or mushroom stroganoff (£6.50), seafood crêpes (£6.95), steaks (from £7.50), big farmhouse grill (£8.95); Sunday roast (£6.95), and children's menu (£2.95). Piped music; the cats are called Daisy and Lilly. There's a terrace outside and a garden with picnic-sets, sweeping views over the Blackdown Hills, and a children's play area. *(Recommended by Mr and Mrs Colin Roberts, S Palmer, Ian Phillips, Dr and Mrs M E Wilson)*

Free house ~ Licensees Chris, Janet and Beth Slow ~ Real ale ~ Bar food (not Tues lunchtime) ~ (01823) 480467 ~ Children welcome ~ Dogs welcome ~ Open 12-2.30, 6.30-11; 12-3, 7-10.30 Sun; closed Tues lunchtime

AXBRIDGE ST4255 Map 1

Lamb

The Square; off A371 Cheddar—Winscombe

The National Trust's medieval King John's Hunting Lodge is opposite, and this ancient inn is set in a notably attractive market square. The big rambling bar is full of heavy beams and timbers, cushioned wall seats and small settles, an open fire in one great stone fireplace, and a collection of tools and utensils including an unusual foot-operated grinder in another. Well kept Butcombe Bitter and Gold, and Wadworths 6X on handpump from a bar counter built largely of bottles, and local cider; shove-ha'penny, cribbage, dominoes, table skittles and skittle alley. Under the new licensee, enjoyable bar food includes home-made soup (£2.25), sandwiches (from £2.95), deep-fried brie with redcurrant jelly (£3.95), deep-fried whitebait (£3.95; large £4.95), filled baguettes or baked potatoes (from £3.95), home-cooked ham and eggs (£5.50), home-made vegetable lasagne (£5.60), home-made curry (£6.50), salmon fillets dusted with cheese and chives or home-made beef in ale pie (£6.95), steaks (from £7.95), and daily specials such as chicken and bacon carbonara (£6.95), fillet of pork with cream and grain mustard sauce (£7.25), and fresh crab salad (£7.95); on Wednesday evening they offer home-made pizzas. The dining room is no smoking. Though the sheltered back garden's not big, it's prettily planted with rock plants, shrubs and trees. More reports please. *(Recommended by KC, Alan and Paula McCully)*

Butcombe ~ Manager Alan Currie ~ Real ale ~ Bar food (12-2.30, 6.30-9(9.30 Fri and Sat); not Sun evenings) ~ (01934) 732253 ~ Children in eating area of bar and restaurant ~ Dogs allowed in bar ~ Open 11.30-3, 6-11; 11.30-11 Sat; 12-10.30 Sun ~ Bedrooms: £30B/£50B

BATCOMBE ST6838 Map 2

Three Horseshoes

Village signposted off A359 Bruton—Frome

New licensees have taken over this honey stone, slate-roofed pub but have no plans for any major changes. The longish narrow main room has a relaxed atmosphere, cream-painted beams and planks, attractive stencils and fruit and flower decorations, a few naïve cow and farm animal paintings on the lightly ragged dark pink walls, built-in cushioned window seats and stripy-cushioned solid chairs around a nice mix of old tables, a couple of clocking-in clocks, and a woodburning stove at one end with a big open fire at the other; there's a plain tiled room at the back on the left with more straightforward furniture. Good, interesting bar food might include home-made soup (£3.75), moules marinière or terrine of chicken livers with smoked pork and brandy (£4.95), tian of fresh cornish crab and prawns (£5.25), steak and Guinness pie (£8.95), aubergine filled with provençale vegetables and feta cheese (£9.95), chicken strips with tagliatelle and a mustard and mushroom cream (£10.50), calves liver, onion and bacon with red wine gravy, duck breast with wild berry jus or grilled fillet of salmon on roast mediterranean vegetables (£12.95), grilled fillet of beef with wild mushrooms (£15.95), and puddings such as white and dark chocolate cappuccino mousse, madeira, pineapple and treacle sponge or apple strudel (£4.25). The stripped stone dining room is pretty, and the conservatory is no smoking. Well kept Butcombe and Wadworths 6X on handpump, and decent wines by the glass. The back terrace has picnic-sets, with more on the grass, and a big well equipped play area. The pub is on a quiet village lane by the church which has a very striking tower. More reports please. *(Recommended by Terry Stewart, Mrs Katie Roberts, Mike and Sue Richardson, Michael Doswell, S G N Bennett, Ian Phillips, Pippa Rose)*

Free house ~ Licensees David and Liz Benson ~ Real ale ~ Bar food ~ Restaurant ~ (01749) 850359 ~ Children welcome ~ Dogs allowed in bar ~ Open 12-3, 6.30-11; 12-3, 7-10.30 Sun

BATH ST7464 Map 2

Old Green Tree

12 Green Street

By arriving when this bustling little pub opens you should be sure of getting a table. It's extremely popular as there are no noisy games machines or piped music to spoil the chatty, friendly atmosphere, and they keep up to seven real ales on handpump: Bath SPA, RCH Pitchfork, Stonehenge Benchmark, and four changing guests; also, several malt whiskies, a nice little wine list with helpful notes (and quite a few by the glass), winter hot toddies, a proper pimms, and good coffee. The three little oak-panelled and low wood-and-plaster ceilinged rooms include a comfortable lounge on the left as you go in, its walls decorated with wartime aircraft pictures in winter and local artists' work during spring and summer, and a no smoking back bar; the big skylight lightens things up attractively. Lunchtime bar food includes soup (£3.50), tasty salads or bangers and mash, and daily specials such as home-made pâté, authentic spicy dishes, coq au vin, Italian lamb, and vegetarian curry (all £5). Chess, backgammon, shut the box, Jenga. The gents', though good, are down steep steps. No children. *(Recommended by Catherine Pitt, Roger Wain-Heapy, Mike Pugh, Dr and Mrs A K Clarke, Roger and Jenny Huggins, Val and Alan Green, David Carr, the Didler, Derek and Sylvia Stephenson, Val Stevenson, Rob Holmes, Jack Taylor, Pete Baker, Simon and Amanda Southwell, M V Ward, Jonathan Smith, Alan J Morton, Susan and Nigel Wilson)*

Free house ~ Licensees Nick Luke and Tim Bethune ~ Real ale ~ Bar food (lunchtime) ~ No credit cards ~ (012250 448259 ~ Open 11-11; 12-10.30 Sun

Star

23 Vineyards; The Paragon (A4), junction with Guinea Lane

An unchanging favourite for its many customers, this old pub may have been modernised – but if so, it was at least 50 years ago. Four (well, more like three and a half) small linked rooms are served from a single bar, separated by sombre panelling with glass inserts, and furnished with traditional leatherette wall benches and the like – even one hard bench that the regulars call Death Row. The lighting's dim, and not rudely interrupted by too much daylight (most of the windows were blocked in years ago). With no machines or music, chat's the thing here – or perhaps cribbage if you dare take on the adept locals, on the green baize tables in one of the back rooms; dominoes and shove-ha'penny. Particularly well kept Bass is tapped from the cask, and they have Abbey Bellringer, Adnams Bitter, Black Sheep, Wadworths 6X, and Wells Bombardier on handpump; 23 malt whiskies. They just offer filled rolls (from £1.60; served throughout opening hours during the week), and Sunday lunchtime bar nibbles (quail eggs, chopped sausage, chicken wings and so forth). No children inside. *(Recommended by Pete Baker, Dr and Mrs A K Clarke, Catherine Pitt, the Didler, Jonathan Smith, Mike and Heather Watson, Roger Wain-Heapy, Mr and Mrs S Carter, David Carr)*

Punch ~ Managers Terry Langley and Julie Schofield ~ Real ale ~ Bar food (see text) ~ (01225) 425072 ~ Dogs welcome ~ Open 12-2.30, 5.30-11; 12-11 Sat; 12-10.30 Sun

BLAGDON ST5059 Map 2

New Inn

Park Lane/Church Street, off A368

The two interesting rooms in this old-fashioned pub have been redecorated this year giving a lighter and more friendly feel. There are ancient beams decorated with gleaming horsebrasses and a few tankards, some comfortable antique settles, mate's chairs and so forth, and big logs burning in both stone inglenook fireplaces; one area is no smoking. Good bar food includes soup (£2.75), filled rolls £2.95), ploughman's or ham and eggs (£5.95), vegetarian lasagne (£6.15), daily specials such as crab cakes (£5.75), vegetarian choices (from £6.15), and pork steak in a cider, cream and mustard sauce or pies such as beef in ale or game (£6.75), and Sunday roast; the main dining area is also no smoking. Well kept Butcombe and Wadworths IPA and 6X on handpump; piped music. From seats outside at the back you can look down over fields to the wood-fringed Blagdon Lake and to the low hills beyond. No children inside. *(Recommended by B and F A Hannam, Ken Flawn, Roger and Jenny Huggins, Michael Doswell, Ian and Rose Lock, M G Hart)*

Free house ~ Licensee Pat McCann ~ Real ale ~ Bar food (not Mon) ~ (01761) 462475 ~ Open 11-2.30, 7-11; 12-2.30, 7-10.30 Sun; closed Mon except bank hols

BLEADON ST3357 Map 1

Queens Arms

Village signposted just off A370 S of Weston; Celtic Way

Dating from the 16th c, this has been opened up with carefully divided separate areas that still let the comfortably chatty and convivial atmosphere run right through. Plenty of distinctive touches include the dark flagstones of the terracotta-walled main part, candles in bottles on sturdy tables flanked by winged settles, old hunting prints, a frieze of quaint sayings in Old English print, and above all the focal servery where well kept changing ales such as Badger Tanglefoot, Butcombe Bitter and Gold, Palmers Copper and 200 and Ringwood Old Thumper are tapped from a stack of casks behind the counter; they have Bulmer's farm cider too, and good coffee. Nicely cooked fresh honest food includes lunchtime sandwiches of filled baps (from £2), filled baked potatoes, ploughman's (£3.95), and ham and egg (£4.95), as well as soup or pork and chicken liver pâté (£2.95), moules marinière (£3.75), grilled oriental chicken salad (£6.95), broccoli and cheese bake (£7.25), fillet of lemon sole (£7.75), steaks (from £8.25), and daily specials such as pork valentin, lemon peppered chicken or cod with a citrus fruit glaze. Service is quick and friendly, and there is a big cylindrical solid fuel stove in the main bar, with another woodburning stove in the stripped-stone back tap bar. They have a quiz night on Sunday, and there are a few benches and picnic-sets out on the tarmac by the car park entrance.

(Recommended by P M Wilkins, J Coote, Hugh Roberts, Kate and Peter Bird, Comus and Sarah Elliott)

Free House ~ Licensees C and A Smith and M Sanders ~ Real ale ~ Bar food (not Sun evening) ~ Restaurant ~ (01934) 812080 ~ Children welcome ~ Dogs allowed in bar ~ Open 11.30-2.30, 5.30-11; 11.30-11 Sat; 12-10.30 Sun

BRADLEY GREEN ST2538 Map 1

Malt Shovel

Pub signposted from A39 W of Bridgwater, near Cannington; though Bradley Green is shown on road maps, if you're booking the postal address is Blackmoor Lane, Cannington, BRIDGWATER, Somerset TA5 2NE; note that there is another different Malt Shovel on this main road, 3 miles nearer Bridgwater

Readers enjoy their visits to this pleasant, friendly pub very much indeed – and it's deservedly popular with locals too. The homely, beamed main bar has window seats, some straightforward elm country chairs and sturdy modern winged high-backed settles around wooden tables, various boating photographs, and a black kettle standing on a giant fossil by the woodburning stove. There's also a little snug with white walls and black beams, a solid oak bar counter with a natural stone front, and red tiled floor. Well liked bar food includes lunchtime sandwiches and filled rolls (from £2.95), ploughman's (£4.50), and filled baked potatoes (from £4.50), home-made flans such as prawn and asparagus, cheese and broccoli or spinach and mushroom (from £5.50), all sorts of curries or spinach and mushroom, beef or seafood lasagne (all £6.50), home-made pies like steak and kidney, turkey and apricot or chicken and mushroom (from £6.50), fresh sea bream, bass, turbot, scallops, salmon or trout (from £7.50), steaks (from £9.50), and puddings such as popular chocolate fruit crunch or steamed puddings (around £2.65). The restaurant and family room are no smoking. Well kept Butcombe Bitter, Exmoor Fox, and two guests from Archers, Cotleigh, Cottage, Moor or RCH on handpump, farm cider, and a fair choice of malt whiskies, and wines by the glass; sizeable skittle alley, dominoes, cribbage, and piped music. The family room opens on to the garden, where there are picnic-sets, a fishpond, and an aviary. West of the pub, Blackmore Farm is a striking medieval building.

(Recommended by Maysie Thompson, Brian and Anna Marsden, Ian Phillips, V Green, Pamela Goodwyn, Duncan Cloud, H L Dennis, Leo and Barbara Lionet, Comus and Sarah Elliott)

Free house ~ Licensees R and F Beverley & P and S Monger ~ Real ale ~ Bar food ~ Restaurant ~ (01278) 653432 ~ Children in restaurant and family room ~ Dogs

allowed in bedrooms ~ Open 11-3, 6.30-11; 12-3, 7-10.30 Sun; evening opening 7 in winter; closed winter Sun evenings; 25 Dec ~ Bedrooms: £26.50B/£38B

CATCOTT ST3939 Map 1

Crown

Village signposted off A39 W of Street; at war memorial turn off northwards into Brook Lane and keep on

Not easy to find at the end of a maze of little roads, this is a tucked away treasure. To the left of the main door is a pubby little room with built-in brocade-cushioned settles, a church pew and red leatherette stools around just four rustic pine tables, a tall black-painted brick fireplace with dried flowers and a large cauldron, and working horse plaques; around the corner is a small alcove with a really big pine table on its stripped stone floor. Most of the pub is taken up with the roomy, more straightforward dining area with lots of wheelback chairs around tables, and paintings on silk of neighbouring views by a local artist on the cream walls – and it's obviously here that people come to enjoy the good, popular food: sandwiches or toasties (from £1.70), soup (£2.30), smoked fish in cream topped with melted cheese or deep fried whitebait (£3.65), ploughman's (from £4.25), filled baked potatoes (from £3.75), ham and egg (£5.60), almond and mushroom bake or home-made fish or steak and kidney pie (£5.95), steaks (from £9.55), puddings such as banoffi pie or sticky toffee pudding (£3.25), daily specials like cheese and port pâté (£2.95), mushrooms with bacon and cream (£3.85), breast of chicken filled with olive tapenade and a red pepper mousse with a fresh plum tomato and thyme sauce (£8.25), pork tenderloin stuffed with gorgonzola and tarragon with a white wine sauce (£8.45), tuna steak with port and cream (£8.95), lamb fillet with rosemary and garlic, wrapped in smoked bacon and served with a dijon mustard sauce (£10.45), and a thoughtful children's menu with proper food (from £1.70). Well kept Butcombe Bitter and Smiles Best, and a guest such as Badger Tanglefoot or Shepherd Neame Spitfire on handpump or tapped from the cask, and piped old-fashioned pop music; fruit machine and skittle alley. The original part of the pub is white-painted stone with black shutters and is pretty with window boxes and tubs. Out behind are picnic-sets and a play area for children with wooden equipment. *(Recommended by Mark Weber, Jenny and Chris Wilson, Comus and Sarah Elliott, George Atkinson)*

Free house ~ Licensees C R D Johnston and D Lee ~ Real ale ~ Bar food (11.30-2, 6(7 Sun)-10) ~ Restaurant ~ (01278) 722288 ~ Children welcome ~ Open 11.30-2.30, 6-11; 12-3, 7-10.30 Sun; closed 25 Dec

CHURCHILL ST4560 Map 1

Crown £

The Batch; in village, turn off A368 into Skinners Lane at Nelson Arms, then bear right

'Every time we come here we wonder why we haven't been back sooner,' one reader told us – and many other customers feel the same. It's an unspoilt little stone-built cottage with a hard-working but friendly landlord, a marvellous range of up to 10 real ales, proper home-cooking, and a good mix of customers. The small and local stone-floored and cross-beamed room on the right has a wooden window seat, an unusually sturdy settle, and built-in wall benches; the left-hand room has a slate floor, and some steps past the big log fire in a big stone fireplace lead to more sitting space. Tapped from the cask, the real ales might include Bass, Hop Back GFB, Palmers IPA, P G Steam, and six changing guests; country wines. Enjoyable bar food using fresh local produce includes good home-made soups like carrot and coriander or leek and potato (small £2.60, large £3.20), excellent rare beef sandwich (£2.70), ploughman's (£4.25), chilli cauliflower cheese or quiche (£4.25), various casseroles or summer salmon (£5.95), and puddings such as treacle pudding or spotted dick. They do get busy at weekends, especially in summer. There are garden tables on the front and a smallish back lawn, and hill views; the Mendip Morris Men come in summer. Good walks nearby. *(Recommended by Mike and Mary Carter, Brian Root, Tom Evans, Rob Webster, Catherine*

Pitt, Joy and Peter Heatherley, Alan and Paula McCully, Guy Vowles, Ian Phillips, the Didler, Jane and Graham Rooth, Jonathan Smith, Paul Hopton, Matthew Shackle)

Free house ~ Licensee Tim Rogers ~ Real ale ~ Bar food (lunchtime) ~ No credit cards ~ (01934) 852995 ~ Children in eating area of bar ~ Dogs welcome ~ Open 12-11

CLAPTON-IN-GORDANO ST4773 Map 1

Black Horse

4 miles from M5 junction 19; A369 towards Portishead, then B3124 towards Clevedon; in N Weston opp school turn left signposted Clapton, then in village take second right, maybe signed Clevedon, Clapton Wick

Tucked away down a country lane this pretty flower-decked white house has an exceptionally pretty little flagstoned front summer garden; there are some old rustic tables and benches, with more to one side of the car park and a secluded children's play area. Paths from the pub lead up Naish Hill or along to Cadbury Camp. Inside, the partly flagstoned and partly red-tiled main room has winged settles and built-in wall benches around narrow, dark wooden tables, window seats, a big log fire with stirrups and bits on the mantelbeam, and amusing cartoons and photographs of the pub. A window in an inner snug is still barred from the days when this room was the petty-sessions gaol; high-backed settles – one a marvellous carved and canopied creature, another with an Art Nouveau copper insert reading East, West, Hame's Best – lots of mugs hanging from its black beams, and plenty of little prints and photographs. There's also a simply furnished room just off the bar (where children can go), with high-backed corner settles and a gas fire; piped music. Straightforward bar food includes soup (£2.95), filled baguettes (from £3.40), and a few hot dishes like corned beef hash or chilli (from £4.75). Well kept Bass, Courage Best, Shepherd Neame Spitfire, Smiles Best, and Websters Green Label on handpump or tapped from the cask, and Thatcher's farm cider. *(Recommended by the Didler, Comus and Sarah Elliott, Tom Evans, June and Ken Brooks, A C and E Johnson, Kevin Blake, Colin and Janet Roe, Ian Phillips)*

Inntrepreneur ~ Tenant Nicholas Evans ~ Real ale ~ Bar food (not evenings, not Sun lunchtime) ~ No credit cards ~ (01275) 842105 ~ Children in family room ~ Dogs welcome ~ Live music Mon evening ~ Open 11-2.30, 5-11; 11-11 Fri and Sat; 12-3, 7-10.30 Sun

COMBE HAY ST7359 Map 2

Wheatsheaf

Village signposted from A367 or B3110 S of Bath

Perched on the side of a steep wooded valley, this popular country pub has pleasantly old-fashioned rooms with low ceilings, warm burgundy walls, brown-painted settles, pews and rustic tables, a very high-backed winged settle facing one big log fire, old sporting and other prints, and quite a few earthenware jugs. Well liked bar food includes filled baguettes (from £3.25), home-made soup (£3.95), ploughman's (from £5.25), smoked chicken and ham terrine or home-made lasagne (£6.50), home-made vegetarian nut roast with madeira sauce (£6.95), home-made steak and kidney pie (£8.50), venison or pork and wild mushroom sausages with an onion and cranberry sauce (£9.50), sautéed tiger prawns in garlic butter and dill (£11.95), steaks (from £11.95), and puddings (£3.95); the restaurant is no smoking. Well kept Courage Best and Greene King Old Speckled Hen tapped from the cask, several malt whiskies, and decent wines; shove-ha'penny, dominoes and cribbage. Outside, there are three dovecotes built into the walls, tables on a spacious terraced lawn overlooking the lovely valley, church, and ancient manor stables, and award-winning flowers; plenty of good nearby walks, too. *(Recommended by Roger Wain-Heapy, Dr and Mrs A K Clarke, Keith Stenner)*

Free house ~ Licensee Pete Wilkins ~ Real ale ~ Bar food (12-2, 6.15-9.30) ~ (01225) 833504 ~ Children in eating area of bar and restaurant ~ Dogs allowed in bar ~ Open 11-3, 6-11; 12-3, 7-10.30 Sun; closed 25 and 26 Dec and 1 Jan ~ Bedrooms: £50S/£75S

COMPTON MARTIN ST5457 Map 2

Ring o' Bells £

A368 Bath—Weston

There's a happy, bustling atmosphere and a good mix of customers in this attractively placed pub, and no matter how busy they are, the landlord and his staff remain friendly and helpful. The cosy, traditional front part of the bar has rugs on the flagstones and inglenook seats right by the log fire, and up a step is a spacious carpeted back part with largely stripped stone walls and pine tables. Popular, reasonably priced bar food includes sandwiches (from £1.50; toasties from £2.25; BLT in french bread £3.25), soup (£2.50), filled baked potatoes (from £3.50), stilton mushrooms (£3.75), ham and eggs (small £3.80, large £4.50), good omelettes (from £3.80; not Sundays), ploughman's (from £3.80), lasagne, mushroom, broccoli and almond tagliatelle or beef in ale (£5.50), generous mixed grill (£10.75), daily specials like various fresh fish dishes (from £5.50), home-made pies or curries (£5.95), somerset pork (£6.25), salmon en croûte (£6.75), and puddings (£2.50); best to get here early to be sure of a seat. On handpump or tapped from the cask, there might be Butcombe Bitter and Gold, Wadworths 6X and a weekly guest; malt whiskies. The public bar has darts, cribbage, dominoes, and shove-ha'penny; table skittles. The family room is no smoking, and has blackboards and chalks, a Brio track, and a rocking horse; they also have baby changing and nursing facilities, and the big garden has swings, a slide, and a climbing frame. Blagdon Lake and Chew Valley Lake are not far away, and the pub is overlooked by the Mendip Hills. *(Recommended by Keith Stenner, Tom Evans, David Carr, Comus and Sarah Elliott, Ian and Rose Lock)*

Free house ~ Licensee Roger Owen ~ Real ale ~ Bar food ~ Restaurant ~ (01761) 221284 ~ Children in family room ~ Dogs allowed in bar ~ Open 11.30-2.30(3 Sat), 6.30-11; 12-3, 7-10.30 Sun

CONGRESBURY ST4464 Map 1

White Hart

Wrington Road, which is off A370 Bristol—Weston just E of village – keep on

This companionable country dining pub has an L-shaped carpeted main bar with a few heavy black beams in the bowed ceiling of its longer leg, brown country-kitchen chairs around good-sized tables, and a big stone inglenook fireplace at each end, with woodburning stoves and lots of copper pans. The short leg of the L is more cottagey, with teddy bears and other bric-a-brac above yet another fireplace and on a delft shelf, lace and old-gold brocaded curtains, and brocaded wall seats. A roomy family Parlour Bar, open to the main bar, is similar in mood, though with lighter-coloured country-style furniture, some stripped stone and shiny black panelling, and big bright airy conservatory windows on one side. A wide choice of generous tasty home-made food includes home-made soup (£2.75), deep-fried cheese with cranberry sauce (£4.25), ham and eggs (£5.95), vegetarian dishes like cauliflower cheese or stilton, leek and walnut pie (£6-£7), home-made lasagne (£7.25), home-made steak and kidney pie (£7.50), chicken in stilton or tomato sauce (£8.95), Andalusian shoulder of lamb (£11.95), and puddings such as home-made fruit crumbles (£3.50); the bread is home-baked, and they do good Sunday roasts. Service is welcoming and efficient; well kept Badger Best, K&B and Tanglefoot on handpump; perhaps faint piped pop music. There are picnic-sets under an arbour on the terrace behind, and on grass out beyond; the hills you see are the Mendips. *(Recommended by Stan Edwards, M G Hart, Christopher and Mary Thomas, Kate and Peter Bird)*

Badger ~ Tenant Ken Taylor ~ Real ale ~ Bar food (12-2, 6-9) ~ (01934) 833303 ~ Children in conservatory ~ Dogs allowed in bar ~ Open 11-2.30, 6-11; 12-3, 7-10.30 Sun

CROWCOMBE ST1336 Map 1

Carew Arms

Village (and pub) signposted just off A358 Taunton—Minehead

An absolute delight for anyone who likes their pubs untouched by modern fads and thoroughly in tune with their surroundings, this 17th-c beamed village inn is unspoilt and original – and could hardly be more welcoming. The front bar has long benches and a couple of old long deal tables on its dark flagstones, a high-backed antique settle and a shiny old leather wing armchair by the woodburning stove in its huge brick inglenook fireplace, and a thoroughly non-PC collection of hunting trophies to remind you that this is the Quantocks. A back room behind the bar is a carpeted and gently updated version of the front one, with more seating in the skittle alley off it, and on the right is a neat little grey-carpeted dining room decorated with hunting prints and plates; dominoes. Lively conversation is lubricated by well kept Exmoor tapped from the cask and a guest beer such as Black Sheep on handpump – or likely by Lane's strong farm cider, or the whiskies. Good straightforward food using game from the local estate and carefully sourced meat from the local butcher includes excellent hearty soup such as leek and potato (£2.75), a good choice of filled baguettes (from £3.25), ploughman's (£4.75), good locally made sausages with onion gravy (£5.50), local ham and egg or home-made steak and kidney pie (£5.75), grilled plaice with parsley butter (£6.90), sirloin steak (£9.50), daily specials such as soft roes on buttered toast (£4.50), thai vegetable curry (£5.90), chicken breast in a wine, cream and mushroom sauce (£6.90), and smoked duck breast (£8.50), and puddings such as treacle tart or sticky toffee pudding (£2.75). Picnic-sets out on the back grass look over rolling wooded pasture, and the attractive village at the foot of the hills has a fine old church and church house; this is a good value place to stay, in a quiet spot. *(Recommended by Richard Gibbs, Alan and Paula McCully, Hugh Roberts, the Didler, R M Corlett, Richard and Jean Green)*

Free house ~ Licensees Simon Jones and Sheila Hartley-Dobbs ~ Real ale ~ Bar food (not Sun evening or Mon (except bank hols)) ~ Restaurant ~ No credit cards ~ (01984) 618631 ~ Children in lounge, restaurant and skittle alley ~ Dogs welcome ~ Annual folk festival during last weekend in Sept ~ Open 11.30-3.30, 6-11; 12-3.30, 7-10.30 Sun; closed winter Sun evening ~ Bedrooms: £22/£44

DOULTING ST6445 Map 2

Waggon & Horses

Doulting Beacon, 2 miles N of Doulting itself; eastwards turn off A37 on Mendip ridge N of Shepton Mallet, just S of A367 junction; the pub is also signed from the A37 at the Beacon Hill crossroads and from the A361 at the Doulting and Cranmore crossroads

One good reason to visit this attractive 18th-c inn is to enjoy some of the remarkable classical music and other musical events during the spring and autumn that take place in a big raftered upper gallery to one side of the building, and there can be few pubs where the piano is a carefully tuned Steinway grand (concert performances are available on request); there is always an exhibition of local artists' work, too. The rambling bar has studded red leatherette seats and other chairs, a homely mix of tables including antiques, and well kept Ushers Best and Founders and seasonal ales on handpump, a small, carefully chosen wine list, and cocktails. Two rooms are no smoking. Bar food includes sandwiches (from £2.90), filled baguettes (from £4.90), leek and mushroom bake (£6.90), ham and eggs (£7.50), paella (£8.90; must be ordered a couple of days in advance), ambitious daily specials, and puddings such as tarte tatin or steamed ginger and lemon pudding (£3.90). The big walled garden (with summer barbecues) is lovely: elderly tables and chairs stand on informal terracing, with picnic-sets out on the grass, and perennials and flowering shrubs intersperse themselves in a pretty and pleasantly informal way. There's a wildlife pond, and a climber for children. Off to one side is a rough paddock with a horse (horses are one passion of Mr Cardona, who comes from Colombia and who has bred an Olympic horse, Sir

Toby) and a goat called Dennis, and various fancy fowl, with pens further down holding many more in small breeding groups – there are some really quite remarkable birds among them, and the cluckings and crowings make a splendidly contented background to a sunny summer lunch. They often sell the eggs, too. More reports please. *(Recommended by MRSM, Mr and Mrs Thomas, Jacquie and Jim Jones, Guy Vowles, Michael and Ann Cole, Dr and Mrs J F Head, Ian Phillips, Richard Stancomb)*

InnSpired ~ Lease Francisco Cardona ~ Real ale ~ Bar food ~ Restaurant ~ (01749) 880302 ~ Children tolerated but must be well behaved and quiet ~ Dogs allowed in bar ~ Classical concerts and some jazz ~ Open 11.30-3, 6-11; 12-3, 7-11 Sun; closed 25 Dec

DOWLISH WAKE ST3713 Map 1

New Inn

Village signposted from Kingstone – which is signposted from old A303 on E side of Ilminster, and from A3037 just S of Ilminster; keep on past church – pub at far end of village

Bustling and friendly, this neat village pub has a dark beamed bar with old-fashioned furnishings that include a mixture of chairs, high-backed settles and attractive sturdy tables, and a woodburning stove in the stone inglenook fireplace. Enjoyable bar food includes tasty soup (£2.50), soft roes on toast (£2.95), sandwiches, filled baguettes or filled baked potatoes (from £2.95), pâté or stuffed mushrooms (£3.25), whitebait (£3.95), ploughman's (from £4.65), chilli (£5.50), mediterranean pasta bake (£5.95), duck à l'orange (£8.95), steaks (from £8.95), daily specials and puddings like home-made treacle tart or spotted dick (from £2.25). Well kept Bass, Butcombe Bitter, and Otter Ale with maybe a guest such as Fullers London Pride or Wadworths 6X on handpump, a decent choice of whiskies, and local cider. The cider comes from just down the road, and the thatched 16th-c stone cider mill is well worth a visit for its collection of wooden bygones and its liberal free tastings (you can buy the half-dozen different ciders in old-fashioned earthenware flagons as well as more modern containers; it's closed on Sunday afternoons). In a separate area they have darts, shove-ha'penny, bar billiards, table skittles as well as alley skittles. The family room looks out on the pleasant back garden which has flowerbeds and a children's climbing frame. There's a rustic bench, tubs of flowers and a sprawl of clematis in front. *(Recommended by Gaynor Gregory, Dennis Jenkin, Douglas Allen, Richard and Jean Green, P Duffield, H D Wharton, Mr and Mrs M Dalby, R T and J C Moggridge, Pat and Tony Martin, Alan and Paula McCully, MDN, Theo, Anne and Jane Gaskin, Susan and Nigel Wilson, Mike Gorton)*

Free house ~ Licensees Rebecca Gray and Alan Toms ~ Real ale ~ Bar food (not Sun evening) ~ Restaurant ~ (01460) 52413 ~ Children in family room and eating area of bar ~ Dogs welcome ~ Open 11-3, 6-11; 12-3, 7-10.30 Sun

EAST LYNG ST3328 Map 1

Rose & Crown

A361 about 4 miles W of Othery

In summer, you can relax with a drink on one of the many seats in the pretty back garden (largely hedged off from the car park) and enjoy the lovely rural views. Inside, the open-plan beamed lounge bar has a winter log fire (or a big embroidered fire screen) in a stone fireplace, a corner cabinet of glass, china and silver, a court cabinet, a bow window seat by an oak drop-leaf table, copies of *Country Life*, and impressive large dried flower arrangements. Well liked bar food includes sandwiches (from £2.10), soup (£2.60), ploughman's (from £4.10), ham and egg (£4.75), omelettes (from £5.25), steaks (£10), roast duckling with orange sauce (£12.25), puddings like home-made treacle tart or fruit crumble (£3), and daily specials such as vegetable curry, liver and bacon casserole or home-made chilli (£6.25); the dining room is no smoking. Well kept Butcombe

Bitter and Gold, and Palmers 200 on handpump; skittle alley and piped music. *(Recommended by Brian and Bett Cox, Ian and Rose Lock, Bob and Margaret Holder, Ian Phillips, Richard and Margaret Peers)*

Free house ~ Licensee Derek Mason ~ Real ale ~ Bar food (not 26 Dec) ~ Restaurant ~ (01823) 698235 ~ Children in restaurant ~ Open 11-2.30, 6.30-11; 12-3, 7-10.30 Sun ~ Bedrooms: £30S/£50S

EAST WOODLANDS ST7944 Map 2

Horse & Groom

Off A361/B3092 junction

This small civilised place set on the edge of the Longleat estate is a favourite with many of its customers – and it's particularly well liked for Sunday lunch, followed by a walk. The pleasant little bar on the left has stripped pine pews and settles on dark flagstones, well kept Branscombe Vale Bitter and Branoc, Wadworths 6X, and a guest such as Brakspears Bitter or Butcombe Gold on handpump, and an extensive wine list with several by the glass. The comfortable lounge has a relaxed atmosphere, an easy chair and settee around a coffee table, two small solid dining tables with chairs, and a big stone hearth with a woodburning stove. Well liked bar food includes home-made soup (£2.85), interestingly filled baguettes like sweet and sour pork, garlic basted chicken with cheese coleslaw or stir-fried beef with oriental vegetables (from £3.40), ploughman's (from £4.75), and daily specials such as pasta carbonara (£6.50), curried potatoes with smoked haddock and poached egg (£6.80), peking duck (£6.95), cajun chicken (£7), cromer crab salad (£8.50), and puddings such as banoffi mallow meringue tower, golden syrup sponge pudding with berries or apricot ambrosia (from £3.80). The restaurant is no smoking. Cribbage, shove-ha'penny, and dominoes. There are picnic-sets in the nice front garden by five severely pollarded limes and attractive troughs and mini wheelbarrows filled with flowers; more seats behind the big no smoking dining conservatory. *(Recommended by P Duffield, MRSM, the Didler, Jack Taylor, Richard Gibbs, Pat and Tony Martin)*

Free house ~ Licensees Rick Squire and Kathy Barrett ~ Real ale ~ Bar food (11.30-2, 6.30-9; not Sun evening or Mon) ~ Restaurant ~ (01373) 462802 ~ Children in lounge and restaurant ~ Dogs welcome ~ Open 11.30-2.30(3 Sat), 6.30-11; 12-3, 7-10.30 Sun; closed Mon lunchtime

EXFORD SS8538 Map 1

White Horse

B3224

You can be sure of a genuinely warm welcome from the cheerful barman in this sizeable creeper-covered inn – whether you are a local or a visitor. The more-or-less open-plan bar has windsor and other country kitchen chairs, a high-backed antique settle, scrubbed deal tables, hunting prints, photographs above the stripped pine dado, and a good winter log fire. Well kept Exmoor, Ale, Gold and Stag, and maybe a guest such as Marstons Pedigree on handpump, and over 100 malt whiskies. Enjoyable bar food (with prices unchanged for two years now) includes soup (£1.95), sandwiches (from £1.95; baguettes from £2.95), ploughman's (from £3.75), sausage, egg, beans, and chips (£4.55), cauliflower cheese (£5.45), home-made lasagne (£5.75), home-made steak and kidney pie (£5.95), daily specials such as game pie (with whatever the chef has, £5.95), gammon and pineapple (£6.25), half a roast chicken (£7.45), and whole lemon sole (£9.25), puddings like gooseberry pie or bread and butter pudding (£2.75), and popular Sunday carvery (£5.75); friendly service. The restaurant and eating area of the bar are no smoking; fruit machine, TV, cribbage, dominoes, and winter darts. This is a pretty village set beside the River Exe. *(Recommended by Lynda and Trevor Smith, Simon Chell, Peter and Audrey Dowsett, Richard Gibbs, Jane and Adrian Tierney-Jones)*

Free house ~ Licensees Peter and Linda Hendrie ~ Real ale ~ Bar food (11.30-2.30, 6-9.30) ~ Restaurant ~ (01643) 831229 ~ Children welcome ~ Dogs allowed in bar ~ Open 10-11; 12-10.30 Sun ~ Bedrooms: £35B/£70B

FAULKLAND ST7354 Map 2

Tuckers Grave ★ £

A366 E of village

This is an exceptional place with an atmosphere all of its own. It's a warmly friendly basic cider house where, luckily, nothing ever changes. It still claims the title of Smallest Pub in the *Guide*, and the flagstoned entry opens into a teeny unspoilt room with casks of well kept Bass and Butcombe Bitter on tap and Thatcher's Cheddar Valley cider in an alcove on the left. Two old cream-painted high-backed settles face each other across a single table on the right, and a side room has shove-ha'penny; dominoes. There's a skittle alley and tables and chairs on the back lawn, as well as winter fires and maybe newspapers to read. Food is limited to sandwiches and ploughman's at lunchtime. There's an attractive back garden. *(Recommended by John Poulter, Pete Baker, the Didler, CMW, JJW, R Huggins, D Irving, E McCall, T McLean, R T and J C Moggridge, David Carr, Paul Boot, Dr and Mrs M E Wilson)*

Free house ~ Licensees Ivan and Glenda Swift ~ Real ale ~ Bar food ~ No credit cards ~ (01373) 834230 ~ Children in family room ~ Open 11-3, 6-11; 12-3, 7-10.30 Sun; closed evenings 25 and 26 Dec

FRESHFORD ST7960 Map 2

Inn at Freshford

Village signposted off B3108 – OS Sheet 172 map reference 790600

The pretty garden here – looking across the road to the bridge by the River Frome – has seats for warm weather, and there are walks to the Kennet & Avon Canal. Inside is comfortably modernised, and the bar has plenty of atmosphere, interesting decorations, and a particularly friendly, helpful landlord. Well kept Bass, Courage Best, Marstons Pedigree, and Wadworths 6X on handpump, and reliable, tasty bar food that might include home-made soup (£3.25), sandwiches (from £3.65), ploughman's (from £5.75), good steak sandwich or spare ribs (£5.95), thai-style vegetable curry or steak in ale pie (£6.45), half a dozen fresh fish specials (from £8.95), and daily specials. The restaurant is no smoking. *(Recommended by R T and J C Moggridge, Susan and Nigel Wilson, Meg and Colin Hamilton, Dr and Mrs M E Wilson)*

Latona Leisure ~ Manager John Williams ~ Real ale ~ Bar food (12-2, 6-9) ~ Restaurant ~ (01225) 722250 ~ Children welcome ~ Dogs allowed in bar ~ Open 11-3, 6-11; 12-3, 7-10.30 Sun

GLASTONBURY ST5039 Map 2

Who'd A Thought It

Northload Street (off A39/B3151 roundabout)

Full of interest, this bustling place makes nice use of mellow reclaimed brick, relaid flagstones and pine panelling. The walls (and even the ceiling of the no smoking eating area) are profusely decorated with blue and white china, lots of photographs including aerial ones of old Glastonbury, and bygones from a shelf of earthenware flagons and another of old bottles to venerable enamel advertising signs; above an old-fashioned range are fly-fishing rods and a gun. There are several linked areas, friendly, light and airy, with black beams and joists, coal fires, and a mix of furnishings from built-in pews to stripped country tables and chairs; one room shows a well uncovered in the 1980s. Under the new licensees, bar food now includes lunchtime sandwiches and filled baguettes and ciabatta bread (from £2.95), home-made soup (£3.50), cauliflower cheese with garlic bread (£5.76), thai red chicken curry (£6.95), steak and mushroom in ale pie (£7.25), pork escalope in a creamy mushroom sauce (£7.95), fresh trout stuffed with lemon and herbs with a lemon butter sauce (£8.50), and puddings such as popular chocolate fudge cake or rhubarb crumble (£3.50). Well kept Palmers IPA, Gold and 2000 on handpump, good value wines, pleasant staff and daily papers. The lavatories are worth a look (the gents' has all you don't need to know, from what to do in a gas attack to a history of England from the Zulu Wars to World War II, the ladies' is more Beryl Cook). The outside of the pub is attractive. More reports please. *(Recommended by David Carr, David and Gilly Wilkins, Christopher Woodward, Brian and Anna Marsden, Liz and Jeremy Baker, Michael Hicks)*

Palmers ~ Tenants Roger and Irene Davis ~ Real ale ~ Bar food (12-2.30, 6-9.30) ~ Restaurant ~ (01458) 834460 ~ Children in the well room ~ Dogs welcome ~ Open 11-11; 12-10.30 Sun ~ Bedrooms: £40B/£58B

HOLCOMBE ST6649 Map 2

Ring o' Roses

Village signposted off A367 by War Memorial in Stratton-on-the-Fosse, S of Radstock

Somerset Dining Pub of the Year

Extensively modernised, this quietly placed open-plan country pub has a relaxed and comfortably civilised feel, helped by broad swathes of turkey carpet. There's some emphasis on the good-sized dining area on the left, nicely divided by balustrades and so forth, with blue and white plates and some modern prints on the walls. The handsome central bar faces attractively cushioned window seats, with a woodburning stove in a free-standing stone fireplace flanked by bookshelves. There are some orthodox cushioned captain's chairs around cast-iron-framed pub tables in this part, and behind is a gently lit parlourish area with sofas and cushioned chairs around low tables; there are more easy chairs in a pleasant panelled lounge on the right. Consistently good food using only local suppliers includes lunchtime sandwiches, seafood dishes of the day such as thai fishcakes (£4.95), seared scallops with cream and chives (£6.25), grilled plaice (£9.25), poached salmon (£9.50), grilled lemon sole or half a lobster (£11.95), and crab salad (£12.50), soup (£3.50), rich duck liver and port parfait with toasted walnut bread and peach marmalade (£4.50), savoury parcels of goats cheese and spinach deep fried and served with a sweet and sour plum dip (£5.25), roasted vegetables wrapped in savoury pancakes on a tomato and oregano coulis or roulade of chicken and broccoli mousse steamed and set on a red onion confit with a pepper coulis (£9.95), roasted loin of local pork with a calvados cream topped with a fanned poached pear scented with sage (£10.50), porterhouse steak (£12.95), seared fillet of lamb on cumin couscous and drizzled with coriander pesto (£13.50), and baked breast of duck filled with a roasted pistachio and date stuffing served on slices of caramelised oranges flamed in brandy (£12.95); Sunday lunch is popular (three courses £12.95), and they do afternoon teas. The restaurant is no smoking. Smiles Best and a seasonal beer such as April Fuel on handpump, a variety of local bottled ciders, quietly friendly and helpfully efficient service; daily papers; perhaps faint piped radio. There are peaceful farmland views from picnic-sets on a terrace and on the lawn around the side and back, with nice shrub plantings and a small rockery. They do a good breakfast and have a chocolate labrador puppy. *(Recommended by Susan and Nigel Wilson, Philip Crawford)*

Free House ~ Licensee Richard Rushton ~ Real ale ~ Bar food ~ Restaurant ~ (01761) 232478 ~ Children welcome ~ Dogs allowed in bar ~ Open 11-11; 12-10.30 Sun ~ Bedrooms: £65B/£75B

Most pubs in the *Guide* sell draught cider. We mention it specifically only if they have unusual farm-produced 'scrumpy' or specialise in it. Do please let us know about any uncommon draught cider you find in a pub.

HUISH EPISCOPI ST4326 Map 1

Rose & Crown

A372 E of Langport

Mrs Pittard's family have run this marvellous place for well over 130 years and its atmosphere and character remain as determinedly unpretentious and welcoming as ever. There's no bar as such – to get a drink (prices are very low), you just walk into the central flagstoned still room and choose from the casks of well kept Teignworthy Reel Ale and a couple of local guest beers such as Butcombe Bitter, Hop Back Summer Lightning or Timothy Taylors Landlord or several farm ciders (and local cider brandy). This servery is the only thoroughfare between the casual little front parlours with their unusual pointed-arch windows; genuinely friendly locals. Food is home-made, simple and cheap and uses local produce (and some home-grown fruit): generously filled sandwiches (from £1.80), broccoli and stilton or tomato and lentil soup (£2.60), good filled baked potatoes (from £3.20), ploughman's (£3.80), cottage pie (£5.75), spinach lasagne or creamy cauliflower cheese (£5.95), pork, apple and cider cobbler, spicy chicken and vegetable pie or steak in ale pie (all £6.25), and puddings like home-made apple pie or bread and butter pudding (£2.95); good helpful service. Shove-ha'penny, dominoes and cribbage, and a much more orthodox big back extension family room has pool, darts, fruit machine, and juke box; skittle alley and popular quiz nights. They hope to have a no smoking room soon. There are tables in a garden outside, and a second enclosed garden with a children's play area. The welsh collie is called Bonny. The local folk singers visit regularly, and on some summer weekends you might find the pub's cricket team playing out here (who always welcome a challenge); good nearby walks, and the site of the Battle of Langport (1645) is close by. *(Recommended by R T and J C Moggridge, Su and Bob Child, Ian and Joan Blackwell, the Didler, C J Mullan, Pete Baker, Richard Stancomb, Kevin Thorpe, OPUS)*

Free house ~ Licensee Mrs Eileen Pittard ~ Real ale ~ Bar food (12-2, 6-8; sandwiches throughout opening hours) ~ No credit cards ~ (01458) 250494 ~ Children welcome ~ Dogs welcome ~ Open 11.30-2.30, 5.30-11; 11.30-11 Fri and Sat; 12-10.30 Sun

KINGSDON ST5126 Map 2

Kingsdon Inn

At Podimore roundabout junction of A303, A372 and A37 take A372, then turn right on to B3151, right into village, and right again opposite post office

Bedrooms should have been opened here by the time this book is published, and there's a new no smoking dining area created in what was the old kitchen, and decorated in keeping with the rest of the pub. This is a pretty little thatched cottage, bustling and friendly with four charmingly decorated, low-ceilinged rooms, and on the right are some very nice old stripped pine tables with attractive cushioned farmhouse chairs, more seats in what was a small inglenook fireplace, a few low sagging beams, and an open woodburning stove with colourful dried and artificial fruits and flowers on the over-mantel; down three steps through balustrading to a light, airy room with cushions on stripped pine built-in wall seats, curtains matching the scatter cushions, more stripped pine tables, and a winter open fire. Another similarly decorated room has more tables and another fireplace. At lunchtime, good, reasonably priced food includes home-made soup (£3.20), deep-fried whitebait or ploughman's (£4.40), grilled goats cheese salad with walnut dressing (£4.80), and leek, stilton and walnut pie, lambs liver, bacon and onions, gammon steak with parsley sauce or chicken breast in a cider and cream sauce (all £5.90), with evening dishes such as kidneys in madeira sauce (£4.60), crab and prawn mornay (£4.80), king prawns with lime and ginger (£5.40), wild mushroom parcel with wild mushroom sauce (£7.80), wild rabbit in dijon mustard sauce (£9.50), grilled wild salmon with hollandaise (£10.90), half a roast duck in scrumpy sauce (£12.50), and fillet steak with a chilli and tomato sauce (£14.50); two dining areas are no smoking. Well kept Butcombe Bitter,

Cotleigh Barn Owl, Otter Bitter, and a guest from Cottage or Otter on handpump, decent wines, and 20 malt whiskies; piped music. Picnic-sets on the grass. The Lytes Cary (National Trust) or the Fleet Air Arm Museum are nearby. *(Recommended by P Duffield, Brian and Anna Marsden, B J Harding, Richard and Jean Green, Peter and Audrey Dowsett, Pat and Robert Watt, Ian Phillips, Stephen Brocklebank, JCW, Dr and Mrs M E Wilson, Martin and Karen Wake, Sheila and Phil Stubbs, Jack Taylor)*

Free house ~ Licensees Leslie and Anna-Marie Hood ~ Real ale ~ Bar food ~ Restaurant ~ (01935) 840543 ~ Well behaved children away from main bar; under 12s to leave by 8pm ~ Open 12-3, 6-11; 12-3, 7-10.30 Sun

LANGLEY MARSH ST0729 Map 1

Three Horseshoes

Village signposted off B3227 from Wiveliscombe

The barn at the back of this red sandstone country pub has now been converted to self-catering and they have also bought the cottage next door for letting. Both these can be used for bed and breakfast if they are not already booked up. This is a proper traditional local with all that goes with that – the landlady doing the cooking and the landlord looking after the beer. The back bar has low modern settles and polished wooden tables, dark red wallpaper, planes hanging from the ceiling, banknotes papering the wall behind the bar counter, a piano, and a local stone fireplace. Well kept Bass, Fullers London Pride, Otter Bitter, and Palmers IPA tapped from the cask, and farm cider. Genuinely home-made, good value food includes filled rolls (from £2.45), soup (£2.50), pizzas (from £4.50; can take away as well), chilli and chick pea hotpot (£4.95), lamb in Pernod (£7.25), good steak and kidney pie (£6.25), and daily specials such as courgette, mushroom and barley bake or cheese and leek pancakes (£5.20), lambs liver in milk, bacon and mushrooms (£5.25), pork tenderloin in ginger and sherry (£7.25), and cod fillet and prawns in white wine sauce (£7.95); no chips or fried food and most vegetables come from the garden. The no smoking dining area has antique settles and tables and benches, and the lively front room has sensibly placed shove-ha'penny, table skittles, darts, dominoes, and cribbage; separate skittle alley, and piped music. You can sit on rustic seats on the verandah or in the sloping back garden, with a fully equipped children's play area; in fine weather there are usually vintage cars outside. *(Recommended by the Didler, Brian Monaghan, Jan MacLaran, Julian Hosking, James Greenwood, Stephen, Julie and Hayley Brown, Tony and Maggie Bundey, Ian Phillips)*

Free house ~ Licensee John Hopkins ~ Real ale ~ Bar food (not winter Mon) ~ Restaurant ~ (01984) 623763 ~ Well behaved children away from bar area ~ Occasional folk music ~ Open 12-2.30, 7-11(10.30 Sun); closed winter Mon ~ Bedrooms: £30S/£60B

LOVINGTON ST5930 Map 2

Pilgrims Rest

B3153 Castle Cary—Keinton Mandeville

Cosy, chatty and relaxed, this quietly placed and civilised country bar/bistro mixes eating and drinking particularly well. There are a few bar stools (and a frieze of hundreds of match books) by a corner counter with nice wines by the glass and well kept Cottage Champflower on handpump, from the nearby brewery, and a cosy little maroon-walled inner area has sunny modern country and city prints, a couple of shelves of books and china, a cushioned pew, a couple of settees and an old leather easy chair by the big fireplace. With flagstones throughout, this runs into the compact heavy-beamed eating area, with candles on its american-cloth tables, heavy black beams and joists, and some stripped stone; piped music. The landlord cooks using all fresh ingredients including local meat and cheeses and daily fresh fish. The menu might include beer-battered mushrooms with garlic mayonnaise or local oak-smoked chicken with avocado guacamole (£5), tiger prawns in tempura batter with a soy and lime dipping sauce or crab cakes with tomato salsa (£6), mixed fish fillets grilled or deep fried with home-made caper mayonnaise or vegetable paella (£12), spinach tagliatelle with wild and cultivated mushrooms in creamy white wine and mascarpone sauce (£13), breast of chicken filled with creamy local goats cheese and sautéed with a light wine sauce flavoured with pesto and served on celeriac dijon mash (£14), calves liver and bacon (£16), and puddings such as rhubarb crème brûlée, sticky toffee pudding or tiramisu cheesecake (from £4); there is also a separate more formal carpeted no smoking dining room. The landlady's service is efficient and friendly, and a newspaper rack runs to the *Independent*. There are picnic-sets and old-fashioned benches on the side grass, and the car park exit has its own traffic lights. The labrador is called Sooty. *(Recommended by Anne Westcott, Mrs J Kent)*

Free house ~ Licensees Sally and Jools Mitchison ~ Real ale ~ Bar food ~ Restaurant ~ (01963) 240597 ~ Children welcome ~ Dogs allowed in bar ~ Open 12-2.30, 7-11; 12-2.30 Sun; closed Sun evening, Mon, Tues lunchtime

LUXBOROUGH SS9837 Map 1

Royal Oak ★

Kingsbridge; S of Dunster on minor roads into Brendon Hills – OS Sheet 181 map reference 983378

New licensees again for this country inn, ideally situated for exploring Exmoor. Apart from some bedroom improvements, nothing seems to have changed here, and there's always a friendly welcome and a thriving ambience. The atmospheric bar rooms have beams and inglenooks, good log fires, flagstones in the front public bar, a fishing theme in one room, and a real medley of furniture; two characterful dining rooms (one is no smoking). Well kept real ales such as Bass, Cotleigh Tawny, Palmers 200, and a beer named for the pub called Acorn on handpump, local farm cider, and country wines. Highly enjoyable bar food includes home-made soup (£3.25), filled baguettes (from £4.25), thai salmon and crab fishcakes with a tomato and coriander salsa (£6.95), chargrilled vegetables with lemon couscous and yellow pepper pesto or chargrilled breast of chicken on spring greens tossed with smoked bacon with a tomato and mustard seed dressing (£9.50), steaks (from £10.95), honey and soy glazed duck with stir-fried noodles and plum sauce (£10.25), charred fillet of halibut with a gentleman's relish butter (£12.75), and puddings (£3.25); really good breakfasts. Dominoes and cribbage – no machines or music. Tables outside, and lots of good surrounding walks. More reports please. *(Recommended by the Didler, Stephen, Julie and Hayley Brown, Lynn Sharpless, Lorna and Howard Lambert, the Ransley family, Julia and Richard Tredgett, Suzanne Stacey, Mike and Shelley Woodroffe, Geoff and Linda Dibble, Simon Chell, James Flory, Nigel Woolliscroft, Richard Gibbs, R M Corlett, Jane and Ross Pascoe, Mrs Katie Roberts, D A Price, Neil Rose, Robert Connor, Mrs K I Burvill, Julie Gilbert, Jenny Grimshaw, Andy Sinden, Louise Harrington, Neil and Anita Christopher, John Dwane, Peter and Audrey Dowsett, George Atkinson, Phil and Heidi Cook)*

Free house ~ Licensees James and Sian Waller and Sue Hinds ~ Real ale ~ Bar food ~ Restaurant ~ (01984) 640319 ~ Children in restaurant ~ Dogs allowed in bar ~ Folk every 2nd Fri evening ~ Open 11-2.30, 6-11; 12-2.30, 7-10.30 Sun ~ Bedrooms: £55B/£60(£75B)

MELLS ST7249 Map 2

Talbot

W of Frome; off A362 W of Buckland Dinham, or A361 via Nunney and Whatley

Most people come to this rather smart place to eat but they do have a couple of bars in which drinkers are welcomed, and at weekends there is a 15th-c tithe barn with a high beamed ceiling which is opened up: well kept Butcombe and Fullers London Pride tapped from the cask. Taken in the restaurant, the lunchtime food might include sandwiches, home-made soup (£3.95), ploughman's (£6.95), hot tomato and mozzarella tartlet (£7.50), ham and free range eggs (£7.65), and tagliatelle with smoked salmon or a curry of the day (£7.95), with evening dishes such as terrine of seasonal local game with citrus salad and home-made chutney (£5.50), mussels in wine, garlic and cream (£5.95; main course £10.95), fresh crab mousse wrapped in smoked salmon with avocado and tomato salsa (£6.95; main course £12.95), home-made pie of the day (£11.95), chargrilled steaks (from £11.95), and roast best end of lamb (£13.95); fresh Brixham fish, too. The licensee is friendly and helpful, and the attractive main room has stripped pews, mate's and wheelback chairs, fresh flowers and candles in bottles on the mix of tables, and sporting and riding pictures on the walls, which are partly stripped above a broad panelled dado, and partly rough terracotta-colour. A small corridor leads to a nice little room with an open fire; piped music, darts, TV, shove'ha'penny, cribbage and dominoes. Sunday roast, and nice breakfasts; good wines, and well chosen staff. There are seats in the cobbled courtyard and a vine-covered pergola. The village was purchased by the Horner family of the 'Little Jack Horner' nursery rhyme and the direct descendants still live in the manor house next door. The inn is surrounded by lovely countryside and good walks. *(Recommended by Jane and Graham Rooth, Kevin Flack, H E Wynter, Philip Pedley, Roger Wain-Heapy, Jack Taylor, Richard Stancomb, Susan and Nigel Wilson)*

Free house ~ Licensee Roger Stanley Elliott ~ Real ale ~ Bar food ~ Restaurant ~ (01373) 812254 ~ Children welcome ~ Dogs welcome ~ Open 12-2.30(3 Sat), 6.30-11; 12-3, 7-10.30 Sun; closed 25 Dec ~ Bedrooms: £55B/£75B

MONKSILVER ST0737 Map 1

Notley Arms ★ 🍴

B3188

In a lovely village, this bustling pub is popular for its enjoyable, reasonably priced food but it does tend to fill up quickly and as – in proper pub fashion – they don't take reservations, you do have to get there pretty promptly. The beamed and L-shaped bar has small settles and kitchen chairs around the plain country candlelit tables, original paintings on the black-timbered white walls, fresh flowers, a couple of woodburning stoves, and maybe a pair of cats. Good bar food includes sandwiches, home-made soup (£2.95), country-style pâté (£4.75), home-made tagliatelle with bacon, mushrooms and cream (£4.95), lasagne, basque-style chicken, aubergine tagine with dates and almonds served with couscous or bacon, leek and cider pudding (£5.95), pork braised with wild mushrooms, cream and sherry (£7.50), beef pie with bacon, mushrooms and red wine (£7.75), cod fillet with lemon and parsley butter or red mullet fillets mediterranean-style with orange and capers (£8.50), local sirloin steak (£8.95), and puddings such as treacle tart with clotted cream, lemon tart or fresh fruit crumble (from £2.85); winter Sunday lunch; good cheerful staff. Well kept Exmoor Ale, Smiles Best, and Wadworths 6X on handpump, farm cider, and country wines; cribbage, dominoes, chess, Scrabble, trivia, and alley skittles. Families are well looked after, with colouring books and toys in the bright no smoking little family room. There are more toys outside in the immaculate garden, running down to a swift clear stream. *(Recommended by Mr and Mrs J M Lefeaux, Rob Webster, Stephen, Julie and Hayley Brown, John Close, Peter and Audrey Dowsett, John Dwane, Pat and Tony Martin, M G Hart, David Biggins, the Didler, P Duffield, J Roy Smylie, Mr and Mrs Thomas, Mrs Katie Roberts)*

Inn Partnership (Pubmaster) ~ Lease Alistair and Sarah Cade ~ Real ale ~ Bar food (no food for 2 wks end Jan-beg Feb) ~ (01984) 656217 ~ Children in family room ~ Dogs allowed in bar ~ Open 11.30-2.30, 6.30-11; 12-2.30, 7-11(10.30 in winter) Sun; closed 25 Dec

NORTH CURRY ST3225 Map 1

Bird in Hand

Queens Square; off A378 (or A358) E of Taunton

This is very much a village pub with a warm welcome for its many customers – both locals and visitors. The busy but cosy main bar has pews, settles, benches, and old yew tables on the flagstones, and original beams and timbers; log fire in inglenook fireplace. Well liked bar food includes baked mushrooms stuffed with crab and prawns (£4.95), moules marinière (£5.25), baked aubergine, courgette and peppers in a pesto sauce on pasta (£7.25), venison steak in redcurrant, orange and port sauce, halibut in orange, Cointreau and dill sauce or rack of lamb with red wine and mint sauce (£13.95), and home-made puddings such as crème brûlée, sticky toffee pudding or dark and white chocolate mousse (£4.25); fresh fish from Brixham and Plymouth, and Sunday roast lunch. More formal dining is available in the separate no smoking restaurant area. Well kept Badger Tanglefoot, Butcombe Gold and Otter Ale on handpump, and Rich's farm cider; piped music and fruit machine. *(Recommended by Patrick Hancock, Mike and Sue Loseby, Mandy and Simon King, Ian Phillips, Christine and Neil Townend, J Davidson, Tony and Maggie Bundey, Alan and Paula McCully, Dr and Mrs J F Head, F A D Cripps, Andrew Barker, Claire Jenkins)*

Free house ~ Licensee James Mogg ~ Real ale ~ Bar food (not Mon) ~ Restaurant ~ (01823) 490248 ~ Children in restaurant ~ Dogs allowed in bar ~ Open 12-3(4 Sat), 6-11; 12-3, 7-10.30 Sun; closed Mon lunchtime (but may change)

NORTON ST PHILIP ST7755 Map 2

George ★ 🛏

A366

This remarkable old building has been a pub for over 700 years, and was originally built to house merchants buying wool and cloth from the rich sheep-farming Hinton Priory at the great August cloth market. The central Norton Room, which was the original bar, has really heavy beams, an oak panelled settle and solid dining chairs on the narrow strip wooden floor, a variety of 18th-c pictures, an open fire in the handsome stone fireplace, and a low wooden bar counter. Well kept Wadworths IPA, 6X, and a guest on handpump, decent wines with a good choice by the glass, and pleasant service. As you enter the building, there's a room on the right with high dark beams, squared dark half-panelling, a broad carved stone fireplace with an old iron fireback and pewter plates on the mantelpiece, a big mullioned window with leaded lights, and a round oak 17th-c table reputed to have been used by the Duke of Monmouth who stayed here before the Battle of Sedgemoor – after their defeat, his men were imprisoned in what is now the Monmouth Bar. The Charterhouse Bar is mostly used by those enjoying a drink before a meal: a wonderful pitched ceiling with trusses and timbering, heraldic shields and standards, jousting lances, and swords on the walls, a carved oak mirror above the fine old stone fireplace, high backed cushioned heraldic-fabric dining chairs on the big rug over the wood plank floor, an oak dresser with some peweter, and heavy brocaded curtains in mullioned windows. Lunchtime bar food includes sandwiches (from £2.95), home-made soup (£3.95), ploughman's (£4.95), game terrine with chutney or vegetable lasagne (£5.95), pork and leek sausage with onion gravy (£6.95), steak in ale pie (£7.95), chicken breast in stilton and asparagus sauce (£8.95), and fresh local trout topped with lemon butter (£9.45); in the evening, there might be honey-glazed wood pigeon (£5.45), mussels with garlic, wine and cream or fishcakes (£5.95), stuffed peppers (£8.45), steaks (from £11), duck breast on a wild berry sauce (£13.25), and medallions of pork tenderloin with a three peppercorn sauce (£14.95). The no smoking dining room – a restored barn with original oak ceiling beams, a pleasant if haphazard mix of early 19th-c portraits and hunting prints, and the same mix of vaguely old-looking furnishings, has a good relaxing, chatty atmosphere. The bedrooms are very atmospheric and comfortable – some reached by an external Norman stone stair-turret, and some across the cobbled and flagstoned courtyard and up into a fine half-timbered upper gallery (where there's a lovely 18th-c carved oak settle). A stroll over the meadow behind the pub (past the picnic-sets on the narrow grass pub garden) leads to an attractive churchyard around the medieval church whose bells struck Pepys (here on 12 June 1668) as 'mighty tuneable'. More reports please. *(Recommended by the Didler, R Huggins, D Irving, E McCall, T McLean, J and B Cressey, Richard Stancomb, Jane and Graham Rooth, Ann and Colin Hunt, Su and Bob Child, Joan and Brian Pickering, David Carr, George Atkinson, John Robertson, Paul Boot)*

Wadworths ~ Managers David and Tania Satchel ~ Real ale ~ Bar food ~ Restaurant ~ (01373) 834224 ~ Children in eating area of bar and restaurant ~ Dogs allowed in bar ~ Open 11-2.30, 5.30-11; 11-11 Sat; 12-3, 7-10.30 Sun ~ Bedrooms: /£80S(£90B)

PITNEY ST4428 Map 1

Halfway House

Just off B3153 W of Somerton

It's not surprising that this old-fashioned pub is popular. It's a friendly place with good value simple food, a fine range of up to 10 real ales, and a nice mix of customers. There's a bustling, chatty atmosphere in the three rooms which all have good log fires, and a homely feel underlined by a profusion of books, maps, and newspapers. As well as six regulars ales tapped from the cask such as Butcombe Bitter, Cotleigh Tawny, Hop Back Summer Lightning, and Teignworthy Reel Ale, there might be guests like Archers Golden, Hop Back Crop Circle, and RCH Pitchfork. They also have 20 or so bottled beers from Belgium and other countries, Wilkins's farm cider, and quite a few malt whiskies; dominoes, cards and chess. Good simple filling food includes sandwiches (from £2.50; the smoked salmon and the turkey with walnut seasoning are very tasty), soup (£2.95), filled baked potatoes (from £2.95), and a fine ploughman's with home-made pickle (from £4.50). In the evening they do about half a dozen home-made curries (from £7.95). There are tables outside. *(Recommended by Evelyn and Derek Walter, Andrea Rampley, Pat and Tony Martin, the Didler, R J Walden, Su and Bob Child, Richard Stancomb, Jane and Adrian Tierney-Jones, Richard Gibbs, Ian and Nita Cooper, OPUS)*

Free house ~ Licensees Julian and Judy Lichfield ~ Real ale ~ Bar food ~ (01458) 252513 ~ Well behaved children welcome ~ Dogs welcome ~ Open 11.30-3, 5.30-11; 12-3, 7-10.30 Sun

PORTISHEAD ST4777 Map 1

Windmill

3¾ miles from M5 junction 17; A369 into town, then follow 'Sea Front' sign off left and into Nore Road

Quite different from most of the pubs in this book, this big popular place started life as a golf club-house and reopened a couple of years ago as a three-level all-day family dining pub: to eat, you find a numbered table, present yourself at the order desk (by a slimline pudding show-cabinet), pay for your order, and return to the table with a tin (well, stainless steel) tray of cutlery, condiments and sauce packets. It works well: the good value generous food then comes quickly, and unexpectedly they have five quickly changing real ales on handpump, such as Bass, Butcombe Gold, Courage Best, Smiles Best and Wickwar Cotswold Way; Thatcher's cider. The food includes sandwiches (from £2.95), filled baked potatoes (from £3.75), spiced thai fishcakes with sweet chilli dressing (£3.95), ploughman's (£4.75), pasta with home-made tomato sauce (£6.25), home-made steak and kidney pie (£6.50), seared tuna steak with warm mediterranean salad (£7.95), steaks (from £9.95), and puddings (£3.25); there are dishes for smaller appetites (from £2.95) and early-bird offers. A big plus is the great view over the Bristol Channel to Newport and Cardiff (with the bridges on the right), from the wall of picture windows on the top and bottom floors – the bottom a simple easy-going no smoking family area, the top a shade more elegant with its turkey carpet, muted green and cream wallpaper and dark panelled dado. The middle floor, set back from here, is quieter and (with its black-painted ceiling boards) more softly lit. A third of the building is no smoking; piped music and fruit machine. Out on the seaward side are picnic-sets on three tiers of lantern-lit terrace, with flower plantings and a play area. *(Recommended by Tom Evans, Ian Phillips)*

Free house ~ Licensee J S Churchill ~ Real ale ~ Bar food (12-9.30 all week) ~ (01275) 843677 ~ Children in family area ~ Dogs allowed in bar ~ Open 11-11; 12-10.30 Sun

ROWBERROW ST4558 Map 1

Swan

Village signposted off A38 ¾ mile S of junction with A368

In good weather after enjoying one of the surrounding walks, you can have a drink at the picnic-sets by a pond in the attractive garden here; there's a tethering post for horses. Inside this spacious olde-worlde pub there are low beams, some stripped stone, warm red décor, comic hunting and political prints, an ancient longcase clock, and a good chatty atmosphere; huge log fires, darts, table skittles, and shove-ha'penny. Well liked bar food includes lunchtime sandwiches or filled baguettes (from £1.80), as well as soup (£2.30), stuffed mushrooms (£3.85), duck and orange pâté (£3.95), ploughman's (from £4.30), filled baked potatoes (from £4.75), ham and egg (£5.85), mushroom stroganoff (£5.95), salad niçoise, beef in ale pie or lamb casserole (£6.95), mediterranean-style chicken (£8.95), steaks (from £9.95), and daily specials. Well kept Bass, Butcombe Bitter and Gold, and a guest beer on handpump, and Thatcher's cider. No children inside. *(Recommended by Hugh Roberts, Ken Flawn, Bob and Margaret Holder, MRSM, Ian and Rose Lock, Ian Phillips, Comus and Sarah Elliott, Roger and Jenny Huggins, Colin and Janet Roe)*

Butcombe ~ Managers Elaine and Robert Flaxman ~ Real ale ~ Bar food ~ (01934) 852371 ~ Dogs welcome ~ Open 12-3, 6-11; 12-3, 7-10.30 Sun

RUDGE ST8251 Map 2

Full Moon

Off A36 Bath—Warminster

By the time the *Guide* is published, Mr and Mrs Gifford will have built four self-catering holiday cottages on land next to this unspoilt 17th-c inn, and an indoor swimming pool which all guests will be able to use. Inside the inn, the two rooms on the right have low white ceilings with a few black beams, a built-in settle by the bar, wheelbacks and slatback chairs around cast-iron-framed tables, a woodburning stove in an inglenook fireplace with riding boots on the mantelbeam, and original shutters by the cushioned window seats. The flagstoned tap room has old stripped pine tables, there's a small private no smoking dining room with polished furniture and a skittle alley, and a formal back no smoking restaurant that looks out over the pretty gardens (plenty of seats); shove-ha'penny, dominoes and cribbage. There's quite an emphasis on the food which at lunchtime and early evening might include soup (£3.50), open sandwiches (from £4.75; double decker toastie £5.95), fish in beer batter or curry (£5.95), lasagne (£6.25), and home-made fishcakes with fresh tomato and basil sauce or stilton and cauliflower bake (£6.95); more elaborate evening dishes such as goats cheese crostini with plum and apple chutney (£4.95), smoked salmon, spinach and cream cheese gateau (£5.95), spinach, feta cheese and mushroom pancakes with a rich cheese sauce (£9.50), goujons of chicken on saffron rice with lemon and cashew nuts or pork medallions with cider and caramelised apple (£11.50), lamb shank with a mint, redcurrant and wine sauce (£14.50), and king prawns and scallops on buttered tagliatelle (£15.95). Well kept Butcombe Bitter, Wadworths 6X, and a beer from Worthington named for the pub on handpump, local ciders, and several malt whiskies. *(Recommended by Peter D B Harding, Michael Hicks, Edmund Coan, Steve Whalley, Andrew Barker, Claire Jenkins, Gloria Bax, Dr and Mrs A K Clarke)*

Free house ~ Licensees Chris and Patrick Gifford ~ Real ale ~ Bar food (12-2.30, 6.30-9.30) ~ Restaurant ~ (01373) 830936 ~ Children welcome ~ Dogs allowed in bar ~ Open 12-11; 12-11 Sat; 12-10.30 Sun ~ Bedrooms: £45S/£65B

SHEPTON MONTAGUE ST6731 Map 2

Montague Inn

Village signposted just off A359 Bruton—Castle Cary

As we went to press new licensees had just taken over this country pub. The rooms are simply but tastefully furnished with stripped wooden tables, kitchen chairs and a log fire in the attractive inglenook fireplace, and there's a no smoking candlelit restaurant. Using fresh organic produce where possible, the interesting food might include winter soup, pâté with caramelised onions (£4), buffalo mozzarella and tomato salad or crispy mushrooms with garlic mayonnaise (£5), pork, tomato and basil sausages with mash and onion gravy (£6), filled ciabatta or ploughman's (from £6), popular avocado, bacon and new potato salad, steak and kidney pie or king prawns in garlic butter (£7), ravioli filled with cheese, olives and sun-dried tomatoes (£8), chicken stuffed with stilton wrapped with bacon on a wild mushroom sauce (£12), and puddings such as apple pie, sticky toffee pudding or raspberry meringue (£4). Well kept Bass and Greene King IPA with maybe a guest like Butcombe Bitter on handpump, local cider, and good coffee; shove-ha'penny, cribbage and dominoes. The pretty back garden and terrace have good views. More reports please. *(Recommended by Simon Collett-Jones, Richard and Jean Green, Robert Newton, Steve Dark, Paul A Moore, John Robertson, Kerry Milis, Mrs J H S Lang, M G Hart, OPUS)*

Free house ~ Licensees Julian and Linda Bear ~ Real ale ~ Bar food (not Mon) ~ Restaurant ~ (01749) 813213 ~ Children in restaurant and family room ~ Open 11-2.30, 6-11; 12-2.30, 7-10.30 Sun; closed Mon ~ Bedrooms: /£60S

SPARKFORD ST6026 Map 2

Sparkford Inn

High Street; just off A303 bypass W of Wincanton

Although this rambling old coaching inn can get very busy (the Fleet Air Arm Museum at Yeovilton and Haynes Motor Museum are both nearby), and they do take coach parties, you can usually find plenty of small areas to tuck yourself away in. The rather low-beamed, dimly lit rooms have good dining chairs around a nice mix of old tables in varying sizes, a colour scheme leaning towards plummy browns and dusky pinks, and plenty of worthwhile prints and other things to look at; some areas are no smoking, piped music. Well liked bar food includes sandwiches, nice ploughman's using local brie, home-made soup (£3.25), creamy garlic mushrooms (£4.45), filled baked potatoes (from £4.50), home-cooked ham and egg (£5.95), home-made chilli (£6.45), half rack of barbecued pork ribs (£7.95), steaks (from £9.75), and daily specials such as cottage pie (£5.45), carrot slice with cranberry sauce (£6.45), lasagne, smoked haddock and bacon au gratin or chicken and leek casserole (£6.95); lunchtime carvery, and maybe hog roasts. The restaurant is no smoking. Well kept Badger Tanglefoot, Butcombe Gold, and Otter Ale, and a guest like Butcombe Bitter on handpump. Tables outside, with a decent play area, and pretty tubs of flowers. *(Recommended by Ian Phillips, Guy Consterdine, M G Hart, Kevin Flack, John and Glenys Wheeler, Richard and Judy Winn, Christopher and Mary Thomas, Doreen and Haydn Maddock , Laura Wilson, Ian and Nita Cooper, Esther and John Sprinkle, Dr and Mrs R E S Tanner, Richard and Margaret Peers, Jayne Capp, Dr and Mrs M E Wilson, Alan and Paula McCully, OPUS)*

Free house ~ Licensee Paul Clayton ~ Real ale ~ Bar food ~ Restaurant ~ (01963) 440218 ~ Children welcome ~ Dogs allowed in bar ~ Live bands several times a year ~ Open 11-11; 12-10.30 Sun ~ Bedrooms: £35B/£49.50B

STANTON WICK ST6162 Map 2

Carpenters Arms

Village signposted off A368, just W of junction with A37 S of Bristol

Run by a friendly licensee, this long and low tile-roofed inn is set in peaceful countryside with pretty flowerbeds and picnic-sets on the front terrace, and maybe lots of lovely crimson geraniums. Inside, the Coopers Parlour is on the right and has one or two beams, seats around heavy tables with fresh flowers, and attractive curtains and plants in the windows; on the angle between here and the bar area there's a fat woodburning stove in an opened-through corner fireplace. The bar has wood-backed built-in wall seats and some red fabric-cushioned stools, stripped stone walls, and a big log fire. Diners are encouraged to step down into a snug inner room (lightened by mirrors in arched 'windows'), or to go round to the sturdy tables angling off on the right; most of these tables get booked at weekends. Good bar food includes devilled crispy whitebait with caper mayonnaise (£4.25), sandwiches (from £4.75; smoked chicken and bacon with mustard mayonnaise £5.25), chicken liver and pork pâté with apricots, herbs and brandy with red onion chutney (£4.95), interesting salads (from £4.95; main course from £8.45), stack of gratinated goats cheese, roasted peppers and rocket leaves drizzled with pesto dressing (£5.25; main course £9.25), stir fry of mediterranean vegetables and wild mushrooms finished with soy sauce and balsamic vinegar or pork, apple, sage and black pepper sausage on bubble and squeak with a rich red wine and onion gravy (£8.95), roast fillet of cod on green and red pepper salsa with olives, chilli and garlic (£9.95), medallions of pork tenderloin flambéed in sweet sherry with bacon batons, mushrooms and cream (£10.95), and chargrilled steaks (from £12.95), with popular daily specials, too. Well kept Bass, Butcombe Bitter, Courage Best, and Wadworths 6X on handpump, a decent wine list, and several malt whiskies; fruit machine and TV. More reports please. *(Recommended by June and Ken Brooks, Michael Doswell, Nigel and Sue Foster, Richard Kitson, Roy and Lindsey Fentiman, Ken Flawn)*

Buccaneer Holdings ~ Manager Simon Pledge ~ Real ale ~ Bar food ~ Restaurant ~ (01761) 490202 ~ Children in eating area of bar and restaurant ~ Dogs allowed in bar ~ Pianist Fri/Sat evenings ~ Open 11-11; 12-10.30 Sun ~ Bedrooms: £62B/£84.50B

STOGUMBER ST0937 Map 1

White Horse £

From A358 Taunton—Williton, village signposted on left at Crowcombe

At the top of the closely huddled village and facing the red stone church stands this whitewashed little local. The neatly kept long bar room has cushioned captain's chairs around heavy wooden tables, old village photographs with more recent ones for comparison, warm winter fires, and unobtrusive piped jazz and folk music. Straightforward bar food includes sandwiches, soup (£2.50), filled baked potatoes (from £3), ploughman's (£3.50), ham and egg (£3.75), omelettes (from £3.75), chicken curry (£5.50), steak and kidney pudding (£6.50), and steak (£9). Well kept Cotleigh Tawny and maybe Bath Gem or Exmoor Fox on handpump. There's a no smoking dining area, a games room with darts, fruit machine, cribbage, and dominoes, and skittle alley. The garden is quiet except for rooks and sheep in the surrounding low hills. The West Somerset Steam Railway is nearby and the restored railway halt is worth a visit. More reports please. *(Recommended by Gene and Kitty Rankin, Tom Evans, James Leasor, Pat and Derek Westcott, Ian Phillips, Joan and Michel Hooper-Immins, Roger and Jenny Huggins, Ron and Val Broom)*

Free house ~ Licensees Graham Roy, Edith Boada ~ Real ale ~ Bar food ~ (01984) 656277 ~ Children in eating area of bar and restaurant ~ Dogs welcome ~ Open 11.30-2.30, 6.30-11; 12-3, 7-10.30 Sun ~ Bedrooms: /£40B

STOKE ST GREGORY ST3527 Map 1

Rose & Crown

Woodhill; follow North Curry signpost off A378 by junction with A358 – keep on to Stoke, bearing right in centre, passing church and follow lane for ½ mile

One reader described this as 'one of the best country pubs we've been in for a long time' and many others voice the same opinion. It's been run for 23 years by the same hard-working licensees, remains a friendly place for an enjoyable meal or drink and is a popular place to stay. The bar is decorated in a cosy and pleasantly romanticised stable theme: dark wooden loose-box partitions for some of the interestingly angled nooks and alcoves, lots of brasses and bits on the low beams and joists, stripped stonework, and appropriate pictures including a highland pony carrying a stag; many of the wildlife paintings on the walls are the work of the landlady, and there's an 18th-c glass-covered well in one corner. Using fresh local produce, fresh fish from Brixham, and their own eggs, the enjoyable bar food at lunchtime might include home-made soup (£3.50), sandwiches (from £3.50), ploughman's (£4.25), deep-fried whitebait (£5.25), ham and eggs (£5), lambs liver and bacon, scrumpy chicken or gammon and pineapple (£7), grilled skate wings (£10.50), steaks (from £9), and puddings (£3); evening dishes are similar (but cost a bit more) with extras such as prawn stir fry (£7.50), and vegetarian dishes such as nut roast chasseur or vegetable stroganoff (from £7.50), and they also offer a three-course meal for £13.75 with more elaborate dishes. Plentiful breakfasts, and a good three-course Sunday lunch. The attractive dining room is no smoking. Well kept Black Sheep and Exmoor Ale and Gold on handpump, and a good wine list; unobtrusive piped classical music, fruit machine, and dominoes. Under cocktail parasols by an apple tree on the sheltered front terrace are some picnic-sets; summer barbecues and a pets corner for children. The pub is in an interesting Somerset Levels village with willow beds still supplying the two basket works. *(Recommended by Nigel Williamson, Ann and Max Cross, J Davidson, Ken Flawn, Theo, Anne and Jane Gaskin, KC, Brian and Bett Cox, Mike and Wena Stevenson, Tony Lunn, Dr and Mrs J F Head, Peter Burton, Ian Phillips, Mr and Mrs Thomas, Andy Sinden, Louise Harrington, John and June Hayward, Comus and Sarah Elliott, JCW, Steve Dark)*

Free house ~ Licensees Ron and Irene Browning ~ Real ale ~ Bar food ~ Restaurant ~ (01823) 490296 ~ Children welcome ~ Dogs allowed in bedrooms ~ Open 11-3, 7-11; 12-3, 7-10.30 Sun ~ Bedrooms: £27.50(£35B)/£40(£50B)

TRISCOMBE ST1535 Map 1

Blue Ball

Village signposted off A358 Crowcombe—Bagborough; turn off opposite sign to youth hostel; OS Sheet 181 map reference 155355

Now on the first floor of a lovely 15th-c thatched stone-built former coaching stables, this pub is peacefully located in a narrow lane beneath the Quantock Hills. The long, low building slopes gently down on three levels, each with its own fire, and is cleverly divided into seating by hand-cut beech partitions; all the work was carried out with old-fashioned craftsman's skills, and there is plenty of space. Well kept Cotleigh Tawny, Otter Ale and Head, and a guest such as Timothy Taylors Landlord or Youngs Special on handpump; there are 400 wines on the list and they will open any under £20 for just a glass; old cognacs and armagnacs, farm ciders, and home-made damson gin or elderflower pressé. At lunchtime, the very good, well presented bar food includes filled rolls (£4.95), specials such as panzanella with chorizo – raw vegetables in a balsamic dressing with crispy garlic and olive oil breadcrumbs (£5.50), cod in beer batter (£7.95), scallops with sweet chilli and crème fraîche (£7.95 or £13.95), lemon and thyme risotto (£8.95), and thai curries (£10.25); in the evenings, there might be mushroom and stilton soup (£3.95), chicken liver parfait with toasted brioche (£5.50), pasta with garlic and rosemary sauce (£7.95), whole grilled plaice with tartare sauce (£9.95), venison saddle with braised red cabbage and juniper (£13.50), and steaks (from £10.25), with puddings such as crème brûlée or Italian lemon tart (£3.95), and Sunday roast (£6.95); friendly, helpful staff. They have two tortoisehell cats, whippets, and a lurcher. The decking at the top of the woodside, terraced garden makes the most of the views. *(Recommended by Robin Fawcett, John and Joan Calvert, Brian and Bett Cox, Bob and Margaret Holder, John Saville, Nick and Lesley Warboys, Rob Webster, Richard and Margaret Peers, Mrs Katie Roberts, Ron and Val Broom, Gene and Kitty Rankin, Paul and Annette Hallett)*

Free house ~ Licensee Patrick Groves ~ Real ale ~ Bar food (12-1.45, 7-9) ~

Restaurant ~ No credit cards ~ (01984) 618242 ~ Well behaved children welcome ~ Dogs welcome ~ Open 12-2.30, 7-11; 12-3, 7-10.30 Sun

WELLS ST5545 Map 2

City Arms

High Street

To reach this former jail (but a pub since 1810), you walk through a cobbled courtyard with metal seats and tables, trees and flowers in pots, and an attractive side verandah. Inside, it's rather like a cellar bar with arched doorways and double baluster-shaped pillars, green-cushioned mate's chairs, a nice old black settle, a Regency-style settee and a couple of well worn, homely sofas, and a plush pink sturdy wall settle; up a step is a similar room with pictures and Wills Grand National cigarette cards on the walls, big tables and solid chairs, and beyond that, a separate bar with neat sturdy brocaded settles forming booths around tables; plenty of Victorian and Victorian-style engravings. One area and the fine open-beamed upstairs restaurant are no smoking while people are eating. Bar food includes sandwiches (from £2.25), vegetable soup (£2.95), chicken liver and cognac pâté (£3.75), sausage and mash with rich onion gravy (£4.95), ham and eggs (£5.50), Quorn and sweetcorn pie (£6.75), steak and kidney pie (£7.50), pork chops with apple and whisky sauce (£7.95), and Aberdeen Angus steaks (from £8.95). They keep six real ales on handpump: Greene King IPA, Abbot, and Ruddles County, and Palmers IPA, and guests from Adnams, Butcombe, Cotleigh, Hop Back, and Teighworthy, as well as farm ciders, 12 wines by the glass, and 25 malt whiskies; piped pop music, dominoes and cribbage. *(Recommended by Joan and Michel Hooper-Immins, JCW, Eric Locker, Comus and Sarah Elliott, Michael Hicks, Peter Meister, Derek and Sylvia Stephenson, Brian and Anna Marsden, Pat and Tony Martin, Lynn Sharpless, Gene and Kitty Rankin, B H and J I Andrews, Guy Consterdine)*

Free house ~ Licensees Jim Hardy and Paul Harrop ~ Real ale ~ Bar food (all day until 10(9 Sun) ~ Restaurant ~ (01749) 673916 ~ Children in eating area of bar and restaurant ~ Dogs welcome ~ Open 10-11; 12-10.30 Sun

WINSFORD SS9034 Map 1

Royal Oak 🍷 🛏

In Exmoor National Park, village signposted from A396 about 10 miles S of Dunster

This is a lovely thatched inn by the village cross, nicely placed beneath peaceful rolling fields and hills, with good nearby walks. The attractively furnished lounge bar has a cushioned big bay-window seat from which you can look across the road towards the village green and foot and packhorse bridges over the River Winn, tartan-cushioned bar stools by the panelled counter (above which hang horsebrasses and pewter tankards), armed and cushioned windsor chairs set around little wooden tables, and a gas-fired stove in the big stone hearth. Another similar bar offers more eating space with built-in wood-panelled seats creating booths, fresh flowers, and country prints; there are several pretty and comfortable lounges. Served by friendly staff, lunchtime bar snacks include home-made soup (£3.95), sandwiches (with salad and crisps, from £4.25), chicken liver parfait with red onion marmalade (£4.95), and ploughman's (from £5.95), with evening dishes such as baked pepper filled with nut flavoured couscous and served with fresh pesto sauce (£7.95), chargrilled chicken with smoked bacon and hickory sauce (£8.95), and rib-eye steak (£10.95), daily specials like confit of duck with raspberry and honey dressing (£5.50), home-made steak and kidney pudding (£9.95), and breast of guinea fowl filled with chicken and bacon mousse with spring onion risotto and thyme scented jus (£14.95), and home-made puddings such as rhubarb and apple crumble or chocolate truffle (£3.50). Well kept Brakspears Bitter and Butcombe Bitter and a guest from Cotleigh or Exmoor on handpump. *(Recommended by Mr and Mrs S Kerry Bedell, Jane and Adrian Tierney-Jones, David and Ruth Hollands, Bob and Margaret Holder, Diana Brumfit, Colin Fisher, Ron and Val Broom)*

Free house ~ Licensee Charles Steven ~ Real ale ~ Bar food ~ Restaurant ~ (01643) 851455 ~ Children in eating area of bar and restaurant ~ Dogs allowed in bar ~ Open 11-2.30, 7-11; 12-3, 7-11 Sun ~ Bedrooms: £79.50B/£135B

WITHYPOOL SS8435 Map 1

Royal Oak 🍷 🛏

Village signposted off B3233

Tucked down below some of the most attractive parts of Exmoor, this country local has wooden benches on the terrace, and just up the road, some grand views from Winsford Hill. The River Barle runs through the village itself, with pretty bridleways following it through a wooded combe further upstream. Inside, the beamed lounge bar has a fine raised log fireplace, comfortably cushioned wall seating and slat-backed chairs, and stags heads, stuffed fish, several fox masks, sporting prints and paintings and various copper and brass ornaments on its walls. The locals' bar (named after the barman Jake who has been here for over 25 years) has some old oak tables, and plenty of character. Well liked bar food includes sandwiches, soup (£3.50), smoked salmon terrine with citrus juice (£4.75), smoked chicken and mango salad with raspberry vinaigrette (£4.95), home-baked ham and free range eggs (£7.95), steak and Guinness pie (£8.50), chicken and bean cassoulet with fresh herbs and red wine (£8.85), seared fillet of salmon on creamed tagliatelle and sun-dried tomatoes (£8.95), braised shank of lamb with redcurrant and rosemary jus (£9.75), and daily specials such as red pepper and garlic terrine (£4), smoked haddock fishcake with spring onion and coriander mayonnaise (£5.50), dressed crab (£11.95), and baked black bream (£12.95). Well kept Exmoor Ale and Stag on handpump, quite a few malt whiskies, a decent wine list, and farm cider. It can get very busy (especially on Sunday lunchtimes), and is popular with the local hunting and shooting types; cribbage and dominoes; piped music in the restaurant only. *(Recommended by Bob and Margaret Holder, V Green, R M Corlett, Peter and Audrey Dowsett, Jane and Adrian Tierney-Jones)*

Free house ~ Licensee Gail Sloggett ~ Real ale ~ Bar food (12-2, 6.30-9.30) ~ (01643) 831506 ~ Children in bottom bar and restaurant ~ Open 11-2.30, 6-11; 12-2.30, 6-11 Sun ~ Bedrooms: £50B/£100B

WOOKEY ST5145 Map 2

Burcott

B3139 W of Wells

The window boxes and tubs in front of this neatly kept and friendly little roadside pub are pretty in summer, and the sizeable garden is well spread and has picnic-sets and plenty of small trees and shrubs; there's a paddock beyond. Inside, the two simply furnished small front bar rooms are connected but different in character. There's a square corner bar counter in the lounge, fresh flowers at either end of the mantelpiece above the tiny stone fireplace, Parker-Knollish brocaded chairs around a couple of tables, and high bar stools; the other bar has beams (some willow pattern plates on one), a solid settle by the window and a high-backed old pine settle by one wall, cushioned mate's chairs and fresh flowers on the mix of nice old pine tables, old-fashioned oil-type wall lamps, and a hunting horn on the bressumer above the fireplace. A little room on the right has darts, shove-ha'penny, cribbage and dominoes, neat built-in wall seats, and small framed advertisements for Schweppes, Coke, Jennings and Oakhill, and there's a roomy back restaurant with black joists, stripped stone walls and sea-green check tablecloths; piped music. Tasty bar food includes home-made soup (£2.95), sandwiches (from £3.45 for 1½ rounds), filled baked potatoes (from £3.45), deep-fried whitebait (£3.95), ploughman's (£4.95), ham and eggs (£5.75), vegetable and cashew nut bake (£5.95), home-made lasagne (£6.50), home-made steak in ale pie (£6.95), roasted duck breast flamed in whisky with a fresh orange marmalade sauce (£9.95), steaks (from £10), roasted salmon steak drizzled with

coriander, lime and chilli dressing (£10.45), and daily specials. Well kept Cotleigh Barn Owl, Sharps Doom Bar, and a guest such as Exmoor Gold or RCH Pitchfork on handpump, and several wines by the glass. More reports please.
(Recommended by Philip Bardswell, Su and Bob Child, Tom Evans)

Free house ~ Licensees Ian and Anne Stead ~ Real ale ~ Bar food (12-2, 6.30-9.30; not Sun or Mon evenings) ~ Restaurant ~ (01749) 673874 ~ Children in family room ~ Open 11.30-2.30(3 Sat), 6-11; 12-3, 7-10.30 Sun; closed 25 and 26 Dec, 1 Jan

Lucky Dip

Besides the fully inspected pubs, you might like to try these Lucky Dips recommended to us and described by readers (if you do, please send us reports: www.goodguides.com).

Ashcott [ST4336]
Ashcott Inn [A39 W of Glastonbury]: Stripped-stone beamed bar, mix of old-fashioned and newer furniture, woodburner in big inglenook, usual food from sandwiches up (all day in summer), partly no smoking restaurant, real ales such as Butcombe, Fullers London Pride and Otter, decent wines; quiet piped music; skittle alley, tables on terrace and in garden with adventure play areas, open all day summer *(Ian Phillips, LYM, Richard and Margaret Peers, Comus and Sarah Elliott)*

☆ ***Ring o' Bells*** [High St; follow Church and Village Hall signs off A39 W of Street]: Neatly kept comfortably modernised local, steps up and down making snug areas (at least for the able-bodied), well kept local Moor Merlins Magic and two interesting guest beers, Wilkins's farm cider, wide choice of good value wholesome home-made food from good sandwiches and rolls to unusual dishes and sturdy puddings, separate no smoking stripy pink dining room, decent wines, chatty landlord and helpful service, inglenook woodburner; piped pop music; skittle alley, fruit machines; attractively planted back garden with play area, camping *(Richard and Margaret Peers, Dr and Mrs J F Head, BB, Richard Fendick)*

Backwell [ST4969]
George [A370 N]: Popular main road dining pub with very wide choice of food, friendly young staff, three mainstream real ales; eclectic piped music; tables out behind *(Richard Fendick)*

George [Farleigh Rd; A370 W of Bristol]: Pleasantly modernised old coaching inn with soft lighting, well kept Ushers, well priced good food inc fresh fish in bar and separate restaurant, good choice of wines, good service; children welcome, pleasant terrace and garden with play area *(Roger Wain-Heapy)*

Bath [ST7564]
Ale House [York St]: City-centre local with well kept Fullers London Pride, more seating upstairs *(Susan and Nigel Wilson)*

Bell [Walcot St]: Lively and studenty musicians' pub, with up to nine well kept changing ales mainly from small breweries, hops hanging from dark ceiling, lots of pump clips and notices, good value baguettes (bargain sell-off end of evening), friendly efficient informal service; piped music, frequent live music *(Jonathan Smith, LM, Dr and Mrs A K Clarke)*

Boathouse [Newbridge Rd]: Large riverside pub near Kennet & Avon marina on outskirts, rugs on wooden floor, apple-theme and riverside decorations, good value food from filled ciabattas to steaks and restaurant dishes, efficient courteous service, decent house wine, Greene King IPA and Old Speckled Hen; wicker furniture and potted plants in conservatory on lower level, picnic-sets out in neat garden with labelled herbs and steps up to waterside balcony *(Ian Phillips)*

☆ ***Coeur de Lion*** [Northumberland Pl; off High St by W H Smith]: Tiny single-room pub (twelve's a crowd), not smart but perhaps Bath's prettiest, cosy and friendly, with well kept Bass and changing ales, log-effect gas fire, good mulled wine at Christmas, lunchtime filled rolls in summer; open all day, tables out in charming flower-filled flagstoned pedestrian alley *(LYM, Dr and Mrs A K Clarke, the Didler, SLC, Val and Alan Green)*

Devonshire Arms [Wellsway]: Well worn in local, very cheap good food *(Dr and Mrs A K Clarke)*

☆ ***George I*** [Mill Lane, Bathampton (off A36 towards Warminster or A4 towards Chippenham)]: Busy creeper-covered pub distinguished by its nice canalside position, attractive upstairs no smoking family dining room overlooking water, and tables on quiet waterside terrace, safe and spacious, with garden bar; wide choice of enjoyable if not cheap food inc baguettes and fish, good log fires, well kept Bass, Courage Directors and Wadworths 6X, service usually quick and friendly; can get crowded, esp wknds *(Meg and Colin Hamilton, Dr and Mrs A K Clarke, GSB, Neil and Anita Christopher, Peter and Audrey Dowsett)*

Grapes [Westgate St]: One long room, dark oak style, well kept Courage Best and Directors, friendly local bustle *(Dr and Mrs M E Wilson)*

Hop Pole [Albion Buildings, Upper Bristol Rd]: Tastefully reworked Bath Ales pub, their beers and a guest kept well, good value lunchtime food (not Mon) inc popular Sun lunches, traditional settles, no smoking area, no juke box or pool; skittle alley, garden with boules *(A Boss)*

Olde Farmhouse [Lansdown Rd]: Pleasant setting on hill overlooking Bath, well kept Abbey Bellringer (from neighbouring microbrewery), Butcombe and Wadworths, real fire, perhaps filled cobs, L-shaped parquet-floor bar with wall seats, panelling, stained-glass lamps and bar gantry, big jazz pictures; juke box, big-screen TV; jazz some evenings, open all day *(the Didler, SLC, G Coates)*

Pig & Fiddle [Saracen St]: Small busy pub tied to Ash Vine, with their full range kept well at sensible prices from island bar, maybe guests such as Abbey and Bath, friendly and attractive service, two big open fires, clocks set to different time zones, good value home-made food, upper restaurant area, takeaways too; very lively at night (lots of students), good if loud piped music; seats on big front terrace *(Dr and Mrs A K Clarke, Jonathan Smith, Catherine Pitt, Derek and Sylvia Stephenson, Dr and Mrs M E Wilson, SLC)*

Pulteney Arms [Daniel St/Sutton St]: Small, with well kept Bass, Smiles, Wadworths 6X and a guest tapped straight from the cask, good chip baps and other food, jugs and lots of rugby posters and Bath RFC memorabilia; unobtrusive piped music; pavement tables *(Pete Baker, Colin and Peggy Wilshire)*

Salamander [John St]: After a spell as a modern wine bar now a bare-boards pub tied to Bath Ales, full range of their beers and good food choice at attractive prices, no pool, juke box or machines *(Colin and Peggy Wilshire)*

Sam Weller [Upper Borough Walls]: Well kept Bass and Wadworths 6X, good food cooked to order inc all-day breakfast, no smoking area, friendly young staff, lively mix of customers *(Dr and Mrs A K Clarke)*

Beckington [ST8051]

Woolpack [off A36 Bath—Warminster]: Well refurbished old inn with big log fire and candlelit tables in flagstoned bar, attractive no smoking dining room and conservatory, well kept ales such as Batemans, Greene King Old Speckled Hen and Wadworths 6X, decent wines, helpful staff; children welcome, comfortable period bedrooms with own bathrooms (but avoid the attic), open all day *(LYM, Dr and Mrs M E Wilson, Philip Irons, Mr and Mrs A H Young)*

Bishops Lydeard [ST1828]

☆ ***Kingfisher*** [A358 towards Taunton]: Two neat communicating rooms, cottagey and relaxing, with quick cheerful service and concentration on food, from good beef sandwiches up; well kept local real ale, comfortably shaded tables outside *(LYM, Bob and Margaret Holder)*

☆ ***Lethbridge Arms*** [off A358 Taunton—Watchet; Gore Sq]: Large village pub doing well under current welcoming licensees, enjoyable food inc interesting dishes, well kept Cotleigh Tawny and Greene King Abbot, Thatcher's farm cider, well priced wines, red plush banquettes and stools in well divided open-plan black-beamed lounge bar, linked dining room with some stripped stone, turkey-carpeted public bar opening into big games area with two pool tables and fruit machines; tables in garden, comfortable bedrooms, two with own bathrooms *(BB, Pat and Derek Westcott)*

Blue Anchor [ST0243]

Smugglers [end of B3191, off A39 E of Minehead]: Mellow building in spectacular clifftop setting, well run split-level hotel bars inc a beamed and flagstoned cellar, friendly atmosphere and service, good range of food from sandwiches and baked potatoes to admirable duck, real ales inc Wadworths 6X, chatty and obliging licensees and pleasant staff, civilised restaurant, big trim sheltered garden; piped music; children welcome, comfortable pretty bedrooms, site for touring caravans *(Donald Godden, George Atkinson)*

Bridgwater [ST3037]

Cross Rifles [Bath Rd]: Very generous reasonably priced traditional food esp good steaks, friendly barman; pool, skittles, piped music, TV *(Ken Flawn)*

Bristol [ST5773]

Alma [Alma Vale Rd, Clifton]: Cheerful town pub well refurbished without losing character, real ales such as Greene King Abbot, Theakstons XB and Wadworths 6X, good plain cheap food, friendly service, no music; popular upstairs theatre Tues-Sat – best to book *(Simon and Amanda Southwell, Dr and Mrs M E Wilson)*

Bag o' Nails [St Georges Rd, Hotwells]: Small shop front for cosy but airy room, well worn benches and small tables along its length, bare boards, soft gas lighting, inglenook seat by gas fire, glazed portholes into cellar, old local pictures, well kept Bass, Burton Bridge, Wye Valley and three changing ales such as Adnams Oyster Stout, RCH East Street Cream and Smiles Best from long bar, lots of bottled beers, friendly interesting landlord, helpful staff, good soup and sandwiches; piped jazz, port and stilton nights 2nd and 4th Weds *(Brian and Halina Howes, Simon and Amanda Southwell, Paul Hopton, Jonathan Smith, Catherine Pitt, Mike Pugh, Ian and Nita Cooper)*

☆ ***Brewery Tap*** [Upper Maudlin St/Colston St]: Tap for Smiles brewery, small and busy – get there early for a seat; their beers kept well and sensibly priced, also unusual continental bottled ones, interesting unpretentious décor, good chatty atmosphere even when packed, log fire in no smoking room, food inc filled rolls, no piped music; open all day *(the Didler, Simon and Amanda Southwell, David Kilham, Paul Hopton, Jane and Graham Rooth, Matthew Shackle)*

Bridge [Passage St]: Neat tiny one-bar city pub near floating harbour, good friendly service, lots of film stills, well kept Bath and Courage Best, popular lunchtime snacks *(Jonathan Smith, the Didler, Paul Hopton)*

☆ ***Commercial Rooms*** [Corn St]: Vast Wetherspoons conversion of impressive former merchants' club, hall with lofty domed ceiling and snug cubicles along one side, gas lighting, comfortable quieter no smoking room with ornate balcony; wide changing choice of good real ales, food all day inc super granary bread sandwiches, reasonable prices; good location, very busy wknd evenings, side wheelchair access *(David Kilham, G Coates, Alan and Paula McCully, Brian and Halina Howes, Simon and Amanda Southwell, Tony and Wendy Hobden,*

Joyce and Maurice Cottrell, David Carr)
Cornubia [Temple St]: Old pub handy for station, good range of real ales, good value home-cooked food (not Sat); cl Sun *(the Didler)*
Cottage [Baltic Wharf, Cumberland Rd]: Converted customs house on southern bank of Floating Harbour, near Maritime Heritage Centre, with fine views of Georgian landmarks and Clifton suspension bridge from terrace; comfortable, roomy and civilised, with big helpings of home-made food all day, well kept Flowers IPA, Smiles Best and Wadworths 6X; may be piped music; open all day, access through sailing club or on foot along waterfront *(Colin and Peggy Wilshire, Ian and Nita Cooper)*
Highbury Vaults [St Michaels Hill, Cotham]: Nice series of small rooms with old-fashioned furniture and prints; now tied to Youngs, with their beers and guests inc Smiles, cheap bar food (not Sat/Sun evenings), bar billiards, dominoes, cribbage; attractive back terrace with heated arbour, open all day, busy with University students and teachers, children welcome *(Paul Hopton, Catherine Pitt, the Didler, LYM)*
Hope & Anchor [Jacobs Wells Rd, Clifton]: Take-us-as-you-find-us bare-boards 18th-c pub with lively studenty atmosphere, hop bines, large shared pine tables, well kept changing ales from small breweries, fast pleasant service, reliable substantial cheap food inc lots of sandwiches, interesting dishes and sumptuous ploughman's – very popular lunchtime; piped music may be loud, can get crowded and smoky late evening, gents' not the smartest; disabled access, summer evening barbecues on good back terrace with interesting niches, occasional live music *(David Kilham, Catherine Pitt, Jonathan Smith, Paul Hopton, Simon and Amanda Southwell, Debbie Wall, Jane and Graham Rooth, Matthew Shackle)*
☆ ***Kings Head*** [Victoria St]: Tiny narrow 17th-c pub, unspoilt and keeping original features, lots of polished brass and wood, charming cosy back snug, well kept Bass, Courage Best and Smiles (splendid mirrored bar back and interesting gas pressure gauge), friendly atmosphere, sandwiches and substantial snacks wkdy lunchtimes; pavement table, cl Sat lunchtime, open all day Weds-Fri *(the Didler, Di and Mike Gillam, Brian and Halina Howes, Pete Baker)*
Llandoger Trow [off King St/Welsh Back]: By docks, interesting as the last timber-framed building built here, and making the most of its picturesque past in very cosy collection of cleverly lit small alcoves and rooms with original fireplaces and carvings; reasonably priced simple bar food, draught sherries, eclectic array of liqueur coffees, friendly staff, good mix from students to tourists *(David and Kay Ross, Val Stevenson, Rob Holmes)*
Magic Box [A38 Cheltenham rd, nr Stokes Croft]: Large airy Wetherspoons cinema conversion, no smoking areas, real ales inc bargains; small terrace *(Matthew Shackle)*
Micawbers Ale House [St Michaels Hill]: Friendly two-bar pub with Butcombe, Smiles Best and Ushers Best, good service; quiet garden *(Matthew Shackle)*
Nova Scotia [Baltic Wharf, Cumberland Basin]: Unspoilt old pub on S side of Floating Harbour, views to Clifton and Avon Gorge, good changing range of real ales usually inc Bass, good value food inc filling baguettes, wooden seats, some nautical touches *(Sue Demont, Tim Barrow, Dr and Mrs A K Clarke)*
Old Fish Market [Baldwin St]: Imposing red and cream brick building converted to roomy and airy pub, good mural showing it in 1790s along one wall, lots of wood inc rather ornate counter, parquet floor, relaxed friendly atmosphere, good value lunchtime food from sandwiches through home-baked pies to Sun lunch, well kept Fullers London Pride, ESB and Jack Frost with guests such as Jennings Cumberland and Smiles Best, good coffee, daily papers; quiet piped music, sports TV *(Joyce and Maurice Cottrell, David and Kay Ross, Nick Elliott, Simon and Amanda Southwell)*
Prince of Wales [Gloucester Rd, Bishopston, opp Redland turn]: Warm and friendly local atmosphere, plush seats well divided (some nice stained glass), well kept Bath SPA, Butcombe and Courage Best, good value lunches from sandwiches and baked potatoes to a few cheap home-made hot dishes, pleasant staff; suntrap terrace *(Pete Baker)*
Shakespeare [Victoria St]: Neat and simple partly panelled 17th-c pub with well kept Bass, Courage Best and Directors and Wadworths 6X, friendly quick service, open fire, good atmosphere, quiet back lounge *(Dr and Mrs M E Wilson, BB)*
White Lion [Quay Head, Colston Ave]: Now taken over by Wickwar, three of their nice beers kept well, log fire; small, so get there early; garden with wrought-iron furniture *(Catherine Pitt)*

Burnham-on-Sea [ST3049]
Lighthouse [Highbridge Rd]: Good value food from cheap generous children's helpings to massive fish and chips in modern pub with Boddingtons and Fullers, garden with hatch for ice-cream sales etc *(Rev John Hibberd)*

Castle Cary [ST6333]
Brookhouse [N of centre]: Wide choice of good value bar food inc Tues steak night, Weds pasta, Fri fish and popular Sun roasts *(P Tailyour)*
☆ ***George*** [just off A371 Shepton Mallet—Wincanton; Market Pl]: Thatched coaching inn, quiet and civilised, with big inglenook in small front bar, inner no smoking lounge off main central reception area, decent food from sandwiches and filled baked potatoes up, well kept real ales, decent house wines, no smoking restaurant; children welcome, 16 bedrooms, open all day *(Dr and Mrs J F Head, James Woods, Neville and Anne Morley, LYM)*

Catcott [ST3939]
☆ ***King William*** [signed off A39 Street—Bridgwater]: Cottagey pub with spacious bar, traditional furnishings, Victorian fashion plates and other old prints, one or two rugs on the stone floors; big stone fireplaces, food inc good value Sun lunch, well kept Palmers Bridport,

IPA and 200, good range of malt whiskies; darts, cribbage, dominoes, piped music, big back extension with skittle alley and glass-topped well; children welcome *(R F Grieve, LYM)*

Cheddar [ST4653]

☆ ***Gardeners Arms*** [Silver St]: Friendly and old-fashioned 16th-c beamed pub with some emphasis on wide choice of enjoyable freshly made food from lunchtime sandwiches and baguettes to interesting main dishes, local beers inc Butcombe, good choice of reasonably priced wine, log fire in handsome fireplace, nice atmosphere, cosy bar with interesting old local photographs; children welcome, garden *(Gill and Keith Croxton, Christopher and Mary Thomas, Mr and Mrs D C Groves)*

Kings Head [Silver St]: Interesting 16th-c thatched pub, open fire, stripped stone, cosy lounge with woodburner, enjoyable food inc good puddings, well kept Bass, darts in public bar; picnic-sets in pleasant covered courtyard and on small lawn *(Alan and Paula McCully, Guy Consterdine)*

Chew Magna [ST5763]

Bear & Swan [South Parade]: Good interesting food at sensible prices, good choice of wines, attentive but unfussy friendly service, long bar with good choice of real ales, attractive redecoration strong on timber and local stone; book well ahead wknds *(Mr and Mrs Jeremy Watkins, Angus and Rosemary Campbell)*

☆ ***Pony & Trap*** [New Town; back rd to Bishop Sutton]: Small gently refurbished tucked-away pub under new landladies, comfortable layout, flagstones and antiques, relaxing atmosphere, well kept Butcombe and Ushers, good coffee, generous straightforward food, daily papers (ballpoint pens for crosswords), attentive service; quiet piped music, children's room, good views at the back; good walks, delightfully rural hillside setting near Chew Valley Lake *(Ian and Rose Lock, M G Hart, Keith Stenner, Michael Doswell, Dr and Mrs B D Smith)*

Chilcompton [ST6451]

Somerset Wagon [B3139; Broadway]: Cosy and friendly, with wide range of enjoyable food, well kept Wadworths IPA, 6X and other ales, pleasant areas off central bar, lots of settles, log fire, books, stuffed animals and militaria; small front garden *(Susan and Nigel Wilson)*

Churchill [ST4560]

Nelson Arms [Skinners Lane; A368, just off A38 SW of Bristol]: Roomy and attractively homely bar with lots of dining tables, small rustic dining room, cheap food inc bargain generous daily roasts, Ushers ales, several ciders; piped music, pool room; tables outside *(Bob and Margaret Holder)*

Clevedon [ST4071]

Regent [Hill Rd]: Simply furnished light and roomy bistro bar looking out on Victorian shopping street, generous light meals inc sandwiches and baked potatoes, refurbished lounge bar, well kept Badger Best, K&B and Tanglefoot, wide wine choice, downstairs restaurant; small pretty sunken garden with lilies and jasmine *(JCW, Alan and Paula McCully)*

Congresbury [ST4363]

Prince of Wales [A370 ½ mile from village]: Small, cosy and comfortable, with olde-worlde stripped brickwork, beamery and door frames, lots of brass and china, good sensible furniture, wide choice of good value generous food inc very popular bargain two-course lunch (or supper Mon-Thurs), good ice creams, low-priced real ales inc Oakhill, friendly professional service, separate dining room; tables in garden *(K R Harris, Tom Evans)*

Ship & Castle [High St (just off A370 from lights at W end of bypass)]: Hungry Horse budget dining pub with generous daily bargains and vast mixed grills, well kept Greene King IPA and Abbot, pleasant service, big family area inc no smoking room, oldish wooden furniture and couple of big settles; good play area *(Tom Evans)*

Corfe [ST2319]

☆ ***White Hart*** [B3170 S of Taunton]: Friendly licensees, son cooks good food worth waiting for, priced in snack or full meal size, also sandwiches, ploughman's and unusual home-made ice creams; lounge with small stools, attractive small no smoking dining room, good choice of real ales with guests such as Fullers London Pride; children welcome *(Bob and Margaret Holder, John Close)*

Coxley [ST5243]

Pound: Busy local, dark and cosy, good beer choice inc Butcombe and Palmers, enjoyable food with fresh veg, bar games and interesting bric-a-brac *(James Morrell)*

Cranmore [ST6643]

Strode Arms [off A361 Frome—Shepton Mallet]: Dining pub, largely no smoking, under new management; attractive country furnishings in linked rooms of former farmhouse; decent food at a price, well kept Wadworths real ales, good wines; piped music; children in restaurant, tables on front terrace and in back garden, handy for East Somerset Railway *(Angus Gorringe, Susan and Nigel Wilson, LYM)*

Cross [ST4155]

New Inn [A38 Bristol—Bridgwater, junction A371]: Pleasant and friendly, wholesome reasonably priced food, well kept Wadworths 6X, fine views; games room upstairs; parking opp can be rather awkward *(Alan and Paula McCully)*

White Hart [not far from A38]: Attractive and relaxing old two-bar pub, beams, pillars and big log fires, good choice of generous bar food, good service, nice wines *(Alan and Paula McCully)*

Ditcheat [ST6236]

☆ ***Manor House*** [signed off A37 and A371 S of Shepton Mallet]: Pretty village pub, enthusiastic young new licensees, decent reasonably priced bar food, well kept Butcombe tapped from the cask, interesting wines, open fires, unusual arched doorways linking big flagstoned bar to comfortably relaxed lounge and restaurant (should book for evening meals at busy times); children welcome, skittle alley, tables on back grass *(Jack Taylor, BB, Alan and Paula McCully, J G E Bell, Nick Mann)*

Doulting [ST6443]
☆ ***Poachers Pocket*** [Chelynch Rd, off A361]: Cheerful and popular modernised black-beamed local, log fire in stripped-stone end wall, lots of stripped pine, gundog pictures, welcoming efficient staff, good generous reasonably priced straightforward food from sandwiches up, well kept Butcombe, Oakhill Best, Wadworths 6X and a guest beer, local farm cider, pub games, children in eating area and large family room/skittle alley, friendly but well behaved cat and dog, back garden with country views *(Alan and Paula McCully, LYM)*

Dunster [SS9943]
Dunster Castle Hotel [High St]: Popular hotel bar with modern light oak furnishings, well kept Courage Best and Smiles, sensibly priced enjoyable food in eating area and dining room from good sandwiches to Sun lunch; bedrooms with own bathrooms, useful car park *(H O Dickinson, Chris and Anna Rowley, David Biggins, George Atkinson)*
☆ ***Luttrell Arms*** [High St; A396]: Hotel in interesting 15th-c timber-framed abbey building, old-fashioned back bar with high beams hung with bottles, clogs and horseshoes, stag's head and rifles on walls above old settles and more modern furniture, big log fires, well kept Bass and Exmoor Gold, interesting bar menu inc local fish, ancient glazed partition dividing off small galleried and flagstoned courtyard, upstairs access to quiet attractive garden with Civil War cannon emplacements and great views; comfortable bedrooms *(LYM, George Atkinson, Derek and Sylvia Stephenson, H O Dickinson)*

Easton-in-Gordano [ST5175]
Rudgleigh Inn [A369 a mile from M5 junction 19]: Modernised two-bar roadside pub with popular promptly served food, well kept Courage and Smiles, extension restaurant suiting families; open all day wkdys, big enclosed garden with willows, tamarisks, play area and cricket-field view *(J Osborn-Clarke, LYM)*

Evercreech [ST6538]
Bell [Bruton Rd (B3081)]: Stone-built pub with enjoyable home-made food from sandwiches and baguettes to thai and several fish dishes, Adnams and Butcombe, cafetière coffee, several recently pleasantly refurbished high-ceilinged linked rooms, watercolours above panelled dado, mix of solid furnishings, woodburner and log-effect gas fire; quiet piped music; tables in new garden, quiet village handy for Bath & West Showground *(Pat and Robert Watt, B and K Hypher)*

Exebridge [SS9224]
☆ ***Anchor*** [B3222 S of Dulverton; pub itself actually over the river, in Devon]: Well furnished, clean and comfortable rather hotelish pub in idyllic Exmoor-edge spot, nice big riverside garden with plenty of tables and play area; wide food choice from sandwiches up, well kept ales such as Exmoor and Wadworths 6X, local farm cider, above-average wines, friendly attentive staff, pleasant bar with woodburner, some attractive furnishings, oak panelling and pictures, neatly ranked dining room; children welcome, restaurant, smaller back games bar, skittle alley; open all day at least in summer, comfortable bedrooms, good breakfast, fishing rights *(Dr and Mrs M E Wilson, George Atkinson, LYM)*

Exford [SS8538]
☆ ***Crown*** [The Green (B3224)]: Civilised country hotel, one small bar mainly for drinkers, another for the generous food from good ploughman's to good imaginative main dishes, well kept ales such as Exmoor Fox and Gold and one brewed for the pub by Clearwater, good choice of wines by the glass, big log fire, friendly helpful service, hunting memorabilia and ancient firearms, close-set but comfortable tables, no piped music; a welcome for children, attractive streamside garden, good bedrooms *(Dick and Madeleine Brown, Jane and Adrian Tierney-Jones)*

Farleigh Hungerford [ST7957]
☆ ***Hungerford Arms*** [A366 Trowbridge—Norton St Philip]: Relaxed and friendly local atmosphere, well kept Bass, Courage Best, Otter and Wadworths 6X, maybe Thatcher's cider, sensibly priced food, pleasant staff, good solid furnishings inc snug alcoves, pink walls, stained glass and hunting prints, heavy dark beams, carved stone fireplaces, steps down to brighter comfortable no smoking family restaurant with nice country view inc Hungerford Castle ruins; darts, fruit machine; back terrace with same view, open all day wknds *(Dr and Mrs M E Wilson, LYM, Meg and Colin Hamilton, Mrs J H S Lang, Hugh Roberts, George Atkinson)*

Farmborough [ST6661]
New Inn [Bath Rd (A39)]: Roomy pub/restaurant with enjoyable traditional food, well kept real ale, good wine choice inc quarter-bottles, friendly staff *(Dr and Mrs A K Clarke, A B Clarke, Ken Flawn)*

Faulkland [ST7354]
Faulkland Inn: Very friendly, good food in bar or restaurant, well kept and priced Greene King Ruddles County, Thatcher's cider, pubby atmosphere with a welcome for families; small back garden, four good value bedrooms, pretty village *(N G A Chambers)*

Frome [ST7749]
☆ ***Farmers Arms*** [Spring Gardens, N towards Oldford]: Child-friendly little riverside pub with young chef doing good interesting food inc good fish choice, friendly landlord and welcoming staff, Butcombe ale, log fire, plenty of games; pretty raised garden, open all day *(Peter D B Harding, Meg and Colin Hamilton, Geoff and Brigid Smithers)*

Gurney Slade [ST6249]
George [A37 N of Shepton Mallet]: Doing well under newish owners, decent food inc baked potatoes and ploughman's, real ales inc Butcombe and Wadworths 6X *(M G Hart)*
Olde Mendip [A37 S, junction B3135; Little London]: Tastefully restored, island bar with partly stripped stonework, friendly attentive staff, food worth waiting for, daily papers, well kept ales inc Butcombe and Otter; good bedrooms *(Dave Braisted, Geoff Withers)*

Hallatrow [ST6357]

Old Station [A39 S of Bristol]: Worth a look for the forest of cluttered bric-a-brac, full of zany interest; usual bar food, real ales such as Bass and Butcombe, Italian dishes in no smoking railcar restaurant; piped music may be loud; children in eating areas, garden with well equipped play area, bedrooms *(Ian Phillips, LYM)*

Hambridge [ST3921]

Lamb & Lion [B3168 S of Curry Rivel]: Pleasant licensees, nice food from good menu, Butcombe and Courage ales *(John A Barker)*

Hatch Beauchamp [ST3020]

☆ ***Hatch Inn*** [old village rd, not bypass]: Cheerfully welcoming carpeted lounge bar, lots of copper and brass, attractive bow-window seats and log fire, well priced waitress-served food here and in dining area, well kept ales such as Bass, Courage Directors and Fullers London Pride, farm ciders, simple separate village bar with games, skittle alley across yard; good value bedrooms *(BB, Derek Harvey-Piper, F J Davis, Peter and Audrey Dowsett)*

Hinton Blewett [ST5957]

☆ ***Ring o' Bells*** [signed off A37 in Clutton]: Charming low-beamed stone-built country local opp village green, very friendly landlord, good value fresh home cooking (not Sun evening) from sandwiches to some interesting main dishes, huge helpings, well kept Abbey Bellringer, Wadworths 6X and guests such as Badger Best and Exmoor Fox, good cafetière coffee, log fire; children welcome, pleasant view from tables in sheltered front yard *(LYM, Michael Doswell)*

Hinton Charterhouse [ST7758]

Rose & Crown [B3110 about 4 miles S of Bath]: Roomy recently refurbished partly divided pub with well kept Bass, Butcombe and Smiles tapped from casks, wide choice of good value generous home-made food inc plenty of fish and vegetarian, nice panelling, ornate stone fireplace, rugby memorabilia, restaurant, skittle alley; open all day Sat *(BB, Dr and Mrs M E Wilson, Meg and Colin Hamilton, Dr and Mrs A K Clarke)*

☆ ***Stag*** [B3110 S of Bath; High St]: Attractively furnished ancient pub with good sensibly priced home-made food in snug and in nicely furnished and well thought out stripped-stone dining area, well kept ales such as Bass and Butcombe, smiling helpful service, log fire, provision for children, no piped music; tables outside, has been open all day *(Dr and Mrs M E Wilson, Meg and Colin Hamilton, Michael and Daphne Tighe, LYM)*

Hutton [ST3458]

Old Inn [Main Rd]: Several linked rooms off large central bar, friendly local evening bustle, efficient cheerful service even when busy, good value food, well kept Bass and Greene King IPA and Old Speckled Hen *(Brian Root)*

Kelston [ST7067]

☆ ***Old Crown*** [Bitton Rd; A431 W of Bath]: Four small friendly traditional rooms with hops on beams, carved settles and cask tables on polished flagstones, logs burning in ancient open range, two more coal-effect fires, well kept ales such as Bass, Butcombe, Smiles and Wadworths 6X tapped from the cask, Thatcher's cider, well priced wines, cheap wholesome bar food (not Sun or Mon evenings), small restaurant (not Sun), no machines or music; children in eating areas, open all day wknd, picnic-sets under apple trees in sunny sheltered back garden *(Ian and Rose Lock, Colin and Peggy Wilshire, LYM, Mr and Mrs Thomas, Mr and Mrs S Carter)*

Keynsham [ST6568]

Lock-Keeper [A4175]: Lovely spot by Avon with big garden, lock, marina and weir; well kept ales inc Smiles, wide range of decent food from baguettes and baked potatoes up, welcoming young staff, three nicely decorated yet unpretentious areas; boules *(JCW)*

Kilve [ST1442]

☆ ***Hood Arms*** [A39 E of Williton]: Woodburner in bar, cosy little plush lounge, enjoyable and attractive bar food cooked to order (no sandwiches), well kept ales such as RCH Pitchfork and Wadworths 6X, friendly attentive service, no smoking restaurant; skittle alley, tables on sheltered back terrace by garden, nice bedrooms – back are quietest *(David and Gilly Wilkins, Gene and Kitty Rankin, LYM)*

Langport [ST4226]

Kelways [towards Huish Episcopi]: Converted Victorian seed warehouse, spacious flagstoned main area divided by stable stalls, well kept ales tapped from the cask, good food in two upstairs restaurant areas *(Dr and Mrs A K Clarke)*

Leigh upon Mendip [ST6947]

☆ ***Bell*** [Leigh St]: Friendly L-shaped bar, new French chef doing good value food from baguettes to good main dishes (not cheap except for two-course lunches), efficient French waiters, Bass, Butcombe and Wadworths 6X; garden *(Jack Taylor, Alan Bowker)*

Litton [ST5954]

Kings Arms [B3114, NW of Chewton Mendip on A39 Bath—Wells]: Interesting partly 15th-c pub rambling more extensively than you'd have thought, low heavy beams, polished flagstones, nice old-fashioned settles, huge fireplace, large family room; some emphasis on food from sandwiches up, real ales such as Bass and Wadworths 6X; picnic-sets in neat streamside gardens with good play equipment *(Michael Doswell, LYM)*

Long Ashton [ST5570]

Angel [Long Ashton Rd]: Two-level lounge bar attractively hung with pewter tankards, well kept Courage Best and Smiles, comfortable seating and blazing log fire, local memorabilia inc old balloon prints, fresh flowers, front smoking room and two other rooms (children allowed there), imaginative well presented food from baked potatoes and baguettes up, friendly sophisticated service; tolerable piped music; tables in quiet courtyard *(P and D Carpenter, JCW, Simon and Amanda Southwell)*

Lower Langford [ST4660]

☆ ***Langford Inn*** [just off A368]: Spotless refurbished family dining pub, roomy and quietly attractive, with solid furnishings in alcoves, fresh flowers and bird prints, popular food inc bargain daily roasts (also smart private dining area), real ales such as Butcombe, Courage, Ruddles and Smiles, decent wines, country wines, accommodating staff, lots of toys in amazing children's room; piped music may obtrude; pretty courtyard, popular barbecues *(Brian Root)*

Marston Magna [ST5922]

Marston Inn [A359 just S]: Friendly well run village pub, good choice of real ales, good house wine, basic reasonably priced food and some interesting dishes, good cheerful service, old beams, attractive restaurant; good juke box in main bar, sometimes unobtrusive piped music; handy for Fleet Air Arm Museum at Yeovilton *(Andrew York)*

Midsomer Norton [ST6654]

White Hart [The Island]: Chatty Victorian local with several rooms, Bass and Butcombe tapped from the cask; open all day *(the Didler)*

Misterton [ST4508]

White Swan [Swan Hill/Middle St (A356)]: Spick and span small pub with good choice of bar and restaurant food cooked by landlady, well kept Butcombe and Greene King, no smoking rooms, framed tapestries, collection of old wireless sets; attractive garden behind, skittle alley *(John A Barker)*

Monkton Combe [ST7862]

Viaduct [A36/B3108]: Popular and welcoming straightforward pub, handy for canal boats *(Peter and Audrey Dowsett)*

Montacute [ST4916]

☆ ***Kings Arms*** [Bishopston]: Extended partly 16th-c hotel with pleasantly furnished stripped stone bars, blazing log fires, cheerful staff, enjoyable food from good two-round sandwiches up, Courage Directors and Greene King Old Speckled Hen, good house wines and coffee, no smoking restaurant; children welcome, pleasant garden, comfortable bedrooms *(James Nunns, Dennis Jenkin, Dr and Mrs J F Head, LYM, Sir Richard FitzHerbert, Shirley Mackenzie)*

☆ ***Phelips Arms*** [The Borough; off A3088 W of Yeovil]: Roomy and airy open-plan bar, good wide range of freshly cooked food inc sandwiches, big filled rolls and interesting specials, character landlord, friendly efficient service even when busy, well kept Palmers, farm cider, low prices, smart yet relaxed restaurant; skittle alley, tables in attractive garden – village would be delightful if the road were quieter; comfortable bedrooms, next to Montacute House *(E Bradford, R J Davies, E M Jones, Mrs Pam Mattinson, Miss E Forster)*

Nailsea [ST4670]

Blue Flame [West End]: Small traditional local with distinctive old-fashioned feel, several intriguing rooms, well kept ales such as Bass, Fullers London Pride and Smiles tapped from the cask, Thatcher's farm cider, filled rolls, cosy open fires, great mix of all ages; pub games, children's room, sizeable informal garden *(the Didler, Jonathan Smith, Paul Hopton, John and Felicity Ford, A C and E Johnson)*

Nether Stowey [ST2139]

☆ ***Cottage*** [Keenthorne, A39 E of village; not to be confused with Apple Tree Cottage]: Warm, friendly and roomy local with good low-priced food from baguettes up, Bass, Butcombe and Otter, Coombe's cider, comfortable music-free dining lounge with woodburner, aquarium, interesting pictures; games room (children allowed here); skittle alley, tables on terrace *(LYM, Ian Phillips)*

Rose & Crown [St Mary St]: Local bustle in former 16th-c posting inn, well kept Cotleigh, Cottage, Moor and guest beers, farm cider, enjoyable food, separate public bar, restaurant (not Mon/Tues); bedrooms, open all day *(the Didler)*

Newton St Loe [ST7064]

☆ ***Globe***: Roomy bar attractively split into smaller areas by dark wood partitions, pillars and timbers giving secluded feel, good atmosphere, friendly efficient service (can slow when very busy), enjoyable food all day, well kept beer, large no smoking area *(Roger Wain-Heapy, Dr and Mrs M E Wilson)*

North Perrott [ST4709]

☆ ***Manor Arms*** [A3066 W of Crewkerne; Middle St]: Attractive 16th-c pub on pretty village green, beams and mellow stripped stone, good value imaginative freshly made meals rather than snacks inc plenty of fish and fresh veg in clean and tidy bar and cosy restaurant, no smoking area, well kept Boddingtons, Butcombe and Smiles, good wine choice, good coffee, inglenook log fire; bedrooms (those in the inn may be warmer than the former stable block), pleasant garden with adventure play area *(John A Barker, Stephen S Goodchild, Mr and Mrs D Gould Smith)*

Norton Fitzwarren [ST1925]

Cross Keys [A358 roundabout]: Stone-built 19th-c pub extended as Chef & Brewer, friendly staff, enjoyable well prepared food, log fires, good wine list *(Ian Phillips)*

Norton St Philip [ST7755]

☆ ***Fleur de Lys*** [High St]: 13th-c stone cottages joined centuries ago, cosy rooms off warren of flagstoned passages, cosy unspoilt local atmosphere, friendly new landlord, Wadworths IPA and 6X, good choice of good value home-made food from baked potatoes up, huge fireplace; children very welcome, skittle alley *(Bob and Sue Hardy, the Didler, Colin and Peggy Wilshire, Meg and Colin Hamilton, Dr and Mrs M E Wilson, Dr and Mrs A K Clarke, Susan and Nigel Wilson)*

Nunney [ST7345]

George [Church St; signed off A361 Shepton Mallet—Frome]: Rambling much modernised open-plan bar with panelling and stripped stone, log fire, four well kept changing ales such as Exmoor and Timothy Taylors Landlord, good food choice (no sandwiches) in bar and restaurant, afternoon teas; piped music, pool; rare gallows inn-sign spanning road, in quaint village with stream and ruined castle; no dogs, children allowed in side room, bedrooms *(BB, Alan and Paula McCully)*

Oakhill [ST6347]

Oakhill Inn [A367 Shepton Mallet—Radstock]: Good atmosphere, well kept local Oakhill real ales, enjoyable honest food inc filled baguettes, pool *(Susan and Nigel Wilson)*

Over Stratton [ST4315]
☆ ***Royal Oak*** [off A303 via Ilminster turn at S Petherton roundabout]: Welcoming well run thatched family dining pub, attractive line of linked rooms, flagstones and thick stone walls, prettily stencilled beams, scrubbed and bleached kitchen tables, pews, settles etc, log fires and rustic décor; good choice of competitively priced enjoyable food, no smoking restaurant, well kept Badger ales, efficient friendly service; open all day Aug, tables outside with barbecues and good play areas for toddlers and older children inc an assault course with trampolines *(John A Barker, LYM, Guy Consterdine)*
Porlock [SS8846]
Castle Hotel [High St]: Lively and cheerful beamed bar, well kept real ales inc Exmoor, attractively priced usual food, no smoking restaurant; bedrooms *(George Atkinson)*
Ship [High St]: Picturesque thatched partly 13th-c pub with well kept Cotleigh Barn Owl, Courage Best and guest beers such as Clearwater Cavalier, low beams, flagstones and big inglenook log fires, small locals' front bar, back dining room, pub games and pool; children very welcome, sunny garden, nearby nature trail to Dunkery Beacon, bedrooms *(Richard Gibbs, Kate and Stuart Clow, LYM, Jane and Adrian Tierney-Jones, C J Fletcher)*
Porlock Weir [SS8547]
☆ ***Ship*** [separate from but run in tandem with neighbouring Anchor Hotel]: Prettily restored old inn in wonderful spot by peaceful harbour, with tables in terraced rose garden and good walks (but no views to speak of from bars); nets and chalked beams in busy Mariners Bar with friendly efficient staff, well kept ales such as Exmoor and Ushers, Taunton cider, huge log fire, usual food; piped music, dogs welcome, back family room; attractive bedrooms; little free parking, but pay & display opposite *(Lynda and Trevor Smith, John Saville, Roger and Jenny Huggins, Dave Irving, H O Dickinson, Peter and Audrey Dowsett, LYM, R M Corlett, George Atkinson)*
Portbury [ST4975]
Priory [Station Rd, ½ mile from A369 (just S of M5 junction 19)]: Spotless much extended Vintage Inn dining pub, several rooms with nice mix of solid furnishings in alcoves, good wide choice of enjoyable food inc some light dishes, well kept Bass, good range of house wines; piped music; bedrooms, open all day *(Tom Evans, S H Godsell, J Osborn-Clarke)*
Portishead [ST4777]
Phoenix [Victoria Sq, just off High St]: Thriving local open all day, small and cosy, well kept Marstons Pedigree, just crisps and such *(Tom Evans)*
Poacher [High St]: Popular with regular older lunchers for wide range of freshly cooked straightforward food with real veg, well kept changing ales such as Banks's and Smiles (still has a proper part for village beer-drinkers), friendly staff, no smoking restaurant area; cl Sun pm *(Tom Evans, K R Harris)*
Ship [the one on Down Rd (coast rd to Walton in Gordano)]: Quiet and relaxing, worth a sunset visit for the lovely Severn estuary views; good value usual food lunchtime, real ales inc Bass and Butcombe *(Tom Evans)*
Puriton [ST3141]
Puriton Inn [just off M5 junction 23; Puriton Hill]: Friendly character pub with enjoyable food, well kept beer, good pleasant service even when busy; large garden *(Geoff Pidoux)*
Rimpton [ST6021]
White Post Inn: Small pub straddling Dorset border, well kept Butcombe and Greene King IPA, choice of Swedish and more traditional pub food from good soups up, smaller helpings for children, jolly Swedish landlord, small dining area with pretty view over fields *(Joan and Michel Hooper-Immins)*
Rode [ST8053]
Bell [Frome Rd (A361)]: Comfortable, spotless and roomy, nicely balanced choice of good food, real ales such as Butcombe, Courage and John Smiths, quick and friendly well trained staff *(Ted George, Peter and Audrey Dowsett)*
Rodney Stoke [ST4850]
Rodney Stoke Inn [A361 Wells—Weston]: Cheery front bar with wall banquettes, plush stools and dimpled copper tables, well kept Bass and Butcombe, well lit pool table, flashing fruit machine and juke box or piped pop music, large nicely set back no smoking restaurant, good imaginative well presented and well priced food, good wine list, skittle alley; very busy holidays and wknds; picnic-sets out on roadside terrace, camp site *(Richard Fendick, Michael and Jeanne Shillington, BB, Ken Flawn)*
Ruishton [ST2626]
Blackbrook [just off M5 junction 25]: Busy chain dining pub with various kinds of generous decent food in several different roomy wooden-screened areas, quick helfpul service, Courage-related ales, beams; good-sized garden with play area *(Meg and Colin Hamilton)*
Rumwell [ST1923]
Rumwell Inn [A38 Taunton—Wellington, just past Stonegallows]: Good comfortable atmosphere, old beams, lots of tables in several areas, interesting choice of well presented good value food inc lots of fish and local meat and other produce, children's dishes, well kept changing ales such as Bass and Wadworths 6X, friendly efficient service, roaring log fire, restaurant (best to book), family room; tables outside, handy for Sheppy's Cider *(June and Robin Small)*
Somerton [ST4828]
☆ ***Globe*** [Market Pl]: Chatty and bustling old stone-built local with log fire, good interesting reasonably priced home-made bar food, attentive landlord and friendly staff, well kept ales inc Bass, Boddingtons and Butcombe, good choice of wine, two spacious bars, dining conservatory, back pool room; no music, skittle alley, tables in garden *(Ken Flawn, Graham and Elizabeth Hargreaves, Theo, Anne and Jane Gaskin, Dr and Mrs J F Head)*
Somerton Hotel [New St]: Reasonably priced food including light meals, quick friendly service, good choice of beers, comfortable seating *(Mrs T A Bizat)*

Unicorn [West St]: Good buoyant atmosphere, enjoyable sensibly priced food, friendly helpful staff *(Richard and Helene Lay)*

South Stoke [ST7461]

☆ ***Pack Horse*** [off B3110, S edge of Bath]: Intriguing medieval pub, a former priory (central passageway still a public right of way to the church); heavy beams, handsome inglenook log fire, antique settles, well kept Courage Best, Ushers Best and Wadworths 6X, farm cider, shove-ha'penny tables, very wide food choice; piped music, winter quiz nights; children welcome, tables in spacious back garden, boules, open all day wknds *(Liz and Jeremy Baker, M G Hart, R Huggins, D Irving, E McCall, T McLean, Richard Stancomb, MRSM, LYM)*

Staple Fitzpaine [ST2618]

☆ ***Greyhound*** [off A358 or B3170 S of Taunton]: Rambling country pub with usual countrified décor (olde-worlde pictures, farm tools and so forth) but genuinely antique layout, flagstones and inglenooks, pleasant mix of settles and chairs, log fires throughout; well kept changing ales such as Badger Tanglefoot, Exmoor, Fullers London Pride and Otter, occasional beer festivals, decent house wines, good freshly made food (high chairs available), cheerful prompt service; good bedrooms in modern extension *(Ashley Comer, Mr and Mrs Colin Roberts, Neil Kellett, Andrew Barbour, Brian and Bett Cox, LYM)*

Star [ST4358]

Star [A38 NE of Winscombe]: Reliable roadside pub with good honest food, well kept Bass, friendly service, good log fire in huge inglenook fireplace, nice mix of tables, big fish tank, enthusiastic Sun lunchtime raffle (bar nibbles then); country views from picnic-sets in field behind *(Alan and Paula McCully, Bob and Maggie Atherton)*

Stoke St Mary [ST2622]

Half Moon [from M5 junction 25 take A358 towards Ilminster, 1st right, right in Henlade]: Roomy much-modernised village pub, five neat open-plan main areas, food from sandwiches to steaks, one no smoking restaurant, pleasant staff, well kept real ales inc Wadworths 6X, quite a few malt whiskies; bar billiards, may be piped music; children welcome, picnic-sets in well tended garden *(Bob and Margaret Holder, LYM)*

Stoke sub Hamdon [ST4717]

Fleur de Lis [West St, off A303/A3088 W of Yeovil]: Welcoming golden stone inn dating from 14th c, spacious rambling part-flagstoned carpeted bar with large comfortable chairs and well spaced tables, uncomplicated food here and in simple dining room, well kept Courage Best and Directors and Hardy Country, local ciders, good solicitous service, log fires; can be busy wknds, piped radio may obtrude; skittle alley, garden, good value bedrooms with own bathrooms, charming village *(Joan and Michel Hooper-Immins, LYM)*

Prince of Wales [Ham Hill]: Ham Hill pub with superb views, new owner doing interesting blackboard choice of food closely involving local producers, several real ales, children well catered for; lots of walkers in summer *(June and Robin Small)*

Stratton-on-the-Fosse [ST6554]

White Post Inn [A367 S of Midsomer Norton, by B3139 roundabout]: Comfortable Victorian pub with several rooms, popular and friendly; four well kept ales inc Bass and Butcombe tapped from casks behind the bar, good value traditional food very popular lunchtime with businessmen and older people; varied live entertainment, open all day *(the Didler, Susan and Nigel Wilson)*

Street [ST4836]

Two Brewers [Leigh Rd]: Pleasantly refurbished and welcoming, with wide choice of well cooked reasonably priced food, well kept Courage Best and Directors and interesting guest beers; garden with play area; same good management as Two Brewers in Shaftesbury – see Dorset main entries *(anon)*

Tatworth [ST3206]

Olde Poppe: Very old, with some character, pleasant staff, well kept Branscombe Vale and Wadworths 6X, good value bar snacks, restaurant *(John A Barker)*

Taunton [ST2525]

☆ ***Hankridge Arms*** [Hankridge Way, Deane Gate (nr Sainsbury); very handy for M5 junction 25]: 16th-c former farm restored a few years ago as well appointed old-style dining pub in modern shopping complex, buoyant atmosphere and good service, good choice of reasonably priced generous enjoyable food from soup and sandwiches to some interesting dishes in bar and largely no smoking restaurant, Badger Best, K&B and Tanglefoot, big log fire; quiet piped music, can be hard for older people to get to when surrounding shops busy; plenty of tables outside *(Ian Phillips, Andy and Jill Kassube, Jonathon and Jane Still, Pamela and Merlyn Horswell)*

☆ ***Masons Arms*** [Magdalene St, opp St Mary's church]: Traditional town pub with old-fashioned genial landlord and atmosphere, good changing range of particularly well kept ales such as Bass, Exe Valley and Juwards, reasonably priced quick home-made food (not Sun but served late other evenings) from interesting soup to sizzling steaks and a good daily special, comfortably basic furnishings, pool table, no music; pin-ups in gents', good bedrooms *(Peter L Skinner, Andy and Jill Kassube, Mrs J James, Douglas Allen, Poppy Howard, Ian Phillips)*

Perkin Warbeck [East St]: Good cheerful Wetherspoons with interesting décor, efficient service even when busy, decent food, bargain coffee in big beakers; open all day *(Joyce and Maurice Cottrell)*

Shepherds Rest [Galmington Rd]: On outskirts, lively, attractive and welcoming, with good range of particularly well kept beers, pub games *(Dr and Mrs A K Clarke)*

☆ ***Vivary Arms*** [Middleway, Wilton; across Vivary Park from centre]: Quiet and pretty pub with good value distinctive freshly made food inc good soup and plenty of fish, in snug plush lounge and small dining room; prompt friendly service, relaxed atmosphere, well kept ales such as Smiles Best, John Smiths and Charles Wells Bombardier, decent wines, no music; bedrooms with own bathrooms in Georgian house next door, easy street parking *(Frank Willy, Ian Phillips)*

Thurloxton [ST2730]

☆ *Maypole* [A38 Taunton—Bridgwater]: Attractively refurbished beamed pub with several traditional areas, wide choice of generous fresh food using local produce from filled baps up, quick friendly obliging service, well kept real ales, biggish no smoking area, log fire; soft piped music, skittle alley; enclosed garden with play area, lovely flowers, peaceful village *(Bob and Margaret Holder, Dr and Mrs A K Clarke, June and Robin Small)*

Tintinhull [ST4919]

Lamb [Vicarage St]: Village pub with friendly helpful staff, good value straightforward food inc bargain lunches (must book for no smoking restaurant), well kept Courage Best, good choice of other drinks; may be piped local radio; nice garden, handy for Tintinhull Manor (NT) *(Theo, Anne and Jane Gaskin, Dr and Mrs M E Wilson)*

Trudoxhill [ST7443]

White Hart [off A361 SW of Frome]: Beams, stripped stone, friendly atmosphere, mainly table seating with a couple of easy chairs by one of the two log fires, enjoyable food inc good baguettes and off-peak bargains, real ales, Thatcher's farm cider, country wines; children in eating area, restaurant, no dogs, picnic-sets in flower-filled sheltered side garden *(the Didler, LYM, Hugh Roberts)*

Tytherington [ST7645]

Fox & Hounds: 17th-c, with roomy and tidy L-shaped stripped-stone bar, small no smoking dining area, generous interesting food (not Mon) inc all sorts of interesting curries (new licensees spent several years in the Far East), Sun roasts, well kept Bass, Butcombe and a guest beer tapped from the cask, farm ciders; tables outside, comfortable bedrooms with own bathrooms, good breakfast *(A L and L R Barnes, MRSM)*

Upton Noble [ST7139]

☆ *Lamb* [Church St; off A359 SW of Frome]: Small 17th-c stripped-stone village local with warmly welcoming efficient staff, well kept Butcombe, Flowers, Greene King Old Speckled Hen and Wadworths 6X, good home-made food, comfortable lounge bar, lovely view from no smoking restaurant; darts, pool etc in public bar, two dogs; big garden, cl Mon lunchtime, perhaps other wkdy lunchtimes *(Susan and Nigel Wilson, Michael and Rosalind Dymond)*

Vobster [ST7049]

Vobster Inn [Lower Vobster]: Spacious and comfortable old village pub, good food choice from sandwiches to fish specialities in open-plan bar and restaurant, friendly staff, well kept beers; tables on side lawn with boules, adventure playground behind *(H E Wynter)*

Wadeford [ST3110]

Haymaker: Good choice of interesting home-made food with fresh veg, plenty of vegetarian dishes, good helpings and reasonable prices, friendly atmosphere and pleasant décor, obliging hospitable service, real ales inc Timothy Taylors Landlord, nicely set out restaurant, separate games room; bedrooms *(D and S Price, D Pettet)*

Wambrook [ST2907]

☆ *Cotley Inn* [village signed off A30 W of Chard; don't follow the small signs to Cotley itself]: Stone-built pub in quiet spot with plenty of surrounding walks; smart but unpretentious, with simple flagstoned entrance bar opening on one side into small plush bar, two-room no smoking dining area (children allowed here), several open fires, good food, Otter and Wadworths 6X; pool, piped music, skittle alley; seats and play area in garden, good bedrooms *(Theo, Anne and Jane Gaskin, LYM, Bob and Margaret Holder)*

Wanstrow [ST7141]

Pub: Attractive interior, friendly newish owners, well kept beer, enjoyable food, charming little floral courtyard *(Peter Neate)*

Watchet [ST0743]

Bell [Market St]: Snug and unpretentious, good value simple food, pleasant newish licensees *(Peter Neate)*

Wellow [ST7358]

☆ *Fox & Badger* [signed off A367 SW of Bath]: Friendly bustle in flagstoned bar with snug alcoves, small winged settles, three log fires, flowers on the tables, well kept Badger, Bass, Butcombe and Wadworths 6X, Thatcher's farm cider, decent cheap bar food (try the ploughman's), good service, restaurant; games and piped music in cosy public bar, Tues is fly-tying night; children in eating areas, courtyard with barbecues, open all day Thurs/Fri *(Richard Stancomb, LYM, Dr and Mrs M E Wilson)*

Wells [ST5545]

Crown [Market Pl]: Old coaching inn with William Penn connection, partly no smoking bistro on right with good choice of reasonably priced food and friendly service, L-shaped public bar on left with magnificent fireplace behind counter, Tetleys, maybe Butcombe and Oakhill tapped from the cask, back espresso/wine bar starting with continental breakfast; can be very busy with young people; seats in back courtyard; bedrooms *(M J A Switzer, Anthony Barnes, Peter and Audrey Dowsett)*

☆ *Fountain* [St Thomas St]: Comfortable dining pub, good wholesome choice inc wkdy lunchtime bargains, fresh fish, crisp veg, interesting ice creams and puddings in unpretentious carpeted downstairs bar with roaring log fire, or popular upstairs restaurant (worth booking wknd, good Sun lunch); quick service, well kept Ushers Best, Founders and Puck, farm cider, good choice of wines with Spanish emphasis, good coffee; can get very full wknd lunchtimes, may be piped music; right by cathedral – popular with choir, and you may even be served by a Vicar Choral; children welcome *(Mr and Mrs Colin Roberts, David Biggins, Peter Meister, Ken Flawn, Michael Collier)*

West Horrington [ST5948]
☆ ***Slab House*** [B3139 Wells—Emborough, NE of village]: Pretty open-plan country dining pub, smallish partly flagstoned bar area with cosy corners, old engravings, lots of cottagey bric-a-brac and quite a clock collection, roaring log fire in big fireplace, extensive dining area, wide choice of good generous food from sandwiches to imaginative dishes, good quick service, nice relaxed atmosphere, well kept Flowers Original; discreet piped music; spotless lavatories, tables out on floodlit nicely planted sunken terrace and on big neat lawns, play area *(Richard Fendick, BB, Mrs J L Wyatt)*
West Huntspill [ST3044]
☆ ***Crossways*** [A38 (between M5 exits 22 and 23)]: Informal and well worn in, with variety of places to sit inc a family room, interesting decorations and log fires, well kept real ales, notable local farm cider, decent wines, enjoyable piping hot sensibly priced food, friendly staff, no piped music; skittle alley and pub games, picnic-sets among fruit trees in sizeable informal garden *(R J Walden, B J Harding, John and Elizabeth Cox, Geoff and Tricia Alderman, LYM, David Carr, Tom Evans, Tim and Sue Halstead)*
Weston-Super-Mare [ST3261]
Claremont Vaults [Birnbeck Rd; seafront, N end]: Large well used dining pub included for wonderful views down the beach or across the bay, Tetleys, decent wine, friendly obliging service; pool, quiet piped music *(Peter and Audrey Dowsett)*
Regency [Lower Church Rd]: Comfortable, spacious and civilised, with strong emphasis on well kept real ales, particularly local ones; good value lunchtime food inc well presented sandwiches and baguettes, pool room; seats out in front *(Dr and Mrs A K Clarke)*
☆ ***Woolpack*** [St Georges, just off M5, junction 21]: Olde-worlde 17th-c coaching inn with friendly relaxing atmosphere, good varied well priced food inc some sophisticated dishes and lots of fresh fish, pleasant window seats and library-theme area, well kept and attractively priced Oakhill with guests such as RCH PG Steam, good house wines, keen efficient service, small but attractive restaurant; skittle alley *(Comus and Sarah Elliott, Brian Root)*
Westonzoyland [ST3534]
Sedgemoor Inn [Main Rd]: Small comfortable pub, good atmosphere, decent food, pleasant friendly service, Bass, Flowers IPA, Marstons Pedigree and Oakhill Mendip Gold; Royalist base before Battle of Sedgemoor, with interesting memorabilia inc Monmouth's declaration of his illegitimacy *(John A Barker)*
Winscombe [ST4157]
Woodborough [Sandford Rd]: Extensively refurbished as dining pub, popular for good range of reasonably priced food; Bass, Butcombe and Courage *(anon)*
Winsley [ST7961]
Seven Stars [B3108 W of Bradford-on-Avon (pub just over Wilts border)]: Big stripped-stone open-plan restaurant pub with good food from well presented ploughman's up, snug alcoves, log-effect gas fires, Ushers ales (though not a place for a drop-in drink); picnic-sets out on terrace, attractive village *(MRSM, PB, JB)*
Witham Friary [ST7440]
Seymour Arms [signed from B3092 S of Frome]: Welcoming unspoilt local, two simple rooms off hatch-service corridor, one with darts, the other with central table skittles; well kept Ushers Best, Rich's local farm cider, cards and dominoes – no juke box or machines; attractive garden by former railway line *(the Didler, Pete Baker)*
Wiveliscombe [ST0827]
Bear [North St]: Home-cooked food, good range of well kept local beers (wknd brewery visits, beer festival with music and morris dancers), farm ciders, very attentive friendly landlord; play area, good value bedrooms *(the Didler)*
Wookey [ST5145]
☆ ***Ring o' Bells*** [High St]: Welcoming recently upgraded village local, well kept Butcombe and Smiles, enjoyable nicely served food from sandwiches up inc children's meals; may be piped pop music *(Tom Evans)*
Worth [ST5145]
Pheasant [B3139 Wells—Wedmore]: Cheerful and relaxed, with basic bar, attractively unpretentious dining area, speciality pastas and other Italian dishes as well as more conventional reasonably priced home-made pub food from baguettes up, well kept ales such as Woods Sum'Er That, decent house wines, smiling service; skittle alley, garden *(Tom Evans)*
Wraxall [ST4872]
Old Barn [just off Bristol Rd (B3128)]: Traditionally done barn conversion, attractive, welcoming and spotless, with scrubbed tables, school benches and dried flowers on beams, stripped boards and flagstones; wide choice of good home-made food, five well kept beers inc local brews tapped from the cask, friendly service; good for children, beautiful garden with good play area and barbecues (bring your own food or buy here) on pretty cobbled terrace, Sun quiz night *(the Didler, Alan and Paula McCully, Jonathan Smith)*
Wrington [ST4662]
Golden Lion [Broad St]: Two-bar village coaching inn with well kept Bass and Flowers IPA, plenty of regulars, simple lunchtime food, early evening rolls, pool room, occasional Sat piano sing-songs; small back courtyard with wknd barbecues, open all day Sat *(Alan and Paula McCully)*
Plough [2½ miles off A370 Bristol—Weston, from bottom of Rhodiate Hill]: Large friendly pub with open fire and lots of dark wood, good value well cooked bar food inc tapas, well kept Smiles and Youngs, interesting wine list, good atmosphere, small pleasant no smoking dining area; pretty front and side garden, open all day *(Alan and Paula McCully, Comus and Sarah Elliott)*

Staffordshire

Pub food here is very fairly priced, and drinks too tend to cost less than the national average – bargain prices particularly in the Yew Tree at Cauldon, a wonderful old place under its individualistic landlord. Burton Bridge beers turn up quite often in this county, and are good value (though the best place to try them is their home, the Burton Bridge Inn in Burton upon Trent). Other beers to look out for from small local brewers include Enville, Titanic, and Slaters (see Lucky Dip entry for the George in Eccleshall); and this is home territory for Marstons and Bass. On the food side, pubs currently in special favour with readers are the welcoming George in Alstonefield (down-to-earth home cooking, ordered from the kitchen door), the Holly Bush at Salt (local ingredients nicely cooked with some individuality, earning this lovely building its Food Award this year), the Greyhound at Warslow (good food and beer, and a very friendly landlord – comfortable bedrooms, too), and the Olde Royal Oak at Wetton (good value meals and snacks in this timeless country pub). A more restauranty pub than any of these is the Queens at Freehay near Cheadle (now handed on to the licensees' son). Of these, it is the Holly Bush at Salt which earns the title of Staffordshire Dining Pub of the Year. The Lucky Dip section at the end of the chapter has a promising influx of new blood this year – about half its entries are new to this edition. In this section, we'd particularly pick out the Moat House at Acton Trussell, Coopers Tavern in Burton upon Trent, Cat at Enville, Bluebell at Hardings Wood and Olde Dog & Partridge in Tutbury. It's worth noting that quite a few of the more interesting pubs here tend to be closed for some lunchtimes or evenings each week.

ALSTONEFIELD SK1355 Map 7

George

Village signposted from A515 Ashbourne—Buxton

Readers really enjoy the welcoming village atmosphere at this agreeably simple stone pub, which attracts all sorts, from locals to campers and hikers – though no dogs or muddy boots. It's in a peaceful farming hamlet, by the village green, and in fine weather it would be hard to beat sitting out on the stone seats beneath the inn-sign, watching the world go by. And if you really love it you can arrange with the landlord to camp on the croft. The unchanging straightforward low-beamed bar has pewter tankards hanging by the copper-topped bar counter, a collection of old Peak District photographs and pictures, and a warming coal fire in winter. The spacious no smoking family room has plenty of tables and wheelback chairs. Well kept Burtonwood Bitter and a guest such as Top Hat are on handpump, and there are darts and dominoes. Good value down-to-earth home-cooked food (which you order from the friendly staff at the kitchen door) includes sandwiches (£2.20), soup (£2.40), ploughman's (from £4.85), meat and potato pie (£5.95), quiche (£6.50), chicken breast, lasagne or breaded plaice (£6.75), and a couple of daily specials; home-made puddings such as apple bakewell or fudge and walnut pie (£2.60). The big sheltered stableyard behind the pub has picnic-sets by a pretty rockery. *(Recommended by Anthony Barnes, the Didler, Dr P S Fox, John and Christine Lowe, Catherine and Richard Preston, Eric Locker, Peter F Marshall, Roger*

Bridgeman, Kevin Thorpe, Rob Fowell, Mike and Wendy Proctor, I J Thurman, Nigel Woolliscroft, L Davenport, John Brightley)

Burtonwood ~ Tenants Richard and Sue Grandjean ~ Real ale ~ Bar food ~ (01335) 310205 ~ Children in family room ~ Open 11-3, 6-11; 11-11 Sat; 12-10.30 Sun; closed 25 Dec

Watts Russell Arms

Hopedale

This 18th-c shuttered stone house is outside the village, in a deep leafy valley. Close to Dovedale and the Manifold, it's inevitably popular with walkers, and on weekends gets very busy. The cheerful beamed bar has brocaded wall banquettes and wheelback chairs and carvers, an open fire below a copper hood, a collection of blue and white china jugs hanging from the ceiling, bric-a-brac around the roughcast walls, and an interesting bar counter made from copper-bound oak barrels; no smoking area. Straightforward bar food includes sandwiches (from £2.95), soup (£3.45), filled baked potatoes or baguettes (from £3.95), home-made chilli or breaded plaice (£6.35), ploughman's (£6.95), and daily specials such as rabbit stew (£6.95), moussaka (£7.45), and gowompki – spicy mince wrapped in a cabbage leaf with gravy (£8.25). Well kept Black Sheep, Timothy Taylors Landlord and Whim Hartington IPA on handpump, about a dozen malts, decent range of soft drinks; piped music. Outside there are picnic-sets under parasols on the sheltered tiered terrace, and in the garden. *(Recommended by Mike and Wendy Proctor, Rob Fowell, the Didler, Doug Christian)*

Free house ~ Licensee George Tunney ~ Real ale ~ Bar food (12-2.30, 7-9) ~ (01335) 310126 ~ Children welcome ~ Open 12-3, 7-11(10.30 Sun); closed Mon in winter

BURTON UPON TRENT SK2423 Map 7

Burton Bridge Inn £

Bridge Street (A50)

The interior of this straightforward, bustling brick local is a pleasantly basic reminder of how pubs used to be a century ago. What most people come for is indeed this atmosphere, just right for enjoying their Burton Bridge ales. These, brewed on the premises, might include Bitter, Festival, Golden Delicious, Gold and Medal Porter, very well kept on handpump alongside a guest such as Woodfordes Wherry; they also have around 25 whiskies and over a dozen country wines. The simple little front area leads into an adjacent bar, separated from a no smoking oak-panelled lounge by the serving counter. The bar has wooden pews, plain walls hung with notices, awards and brewery memorabilia, and the lounge has oak beams, a flame-effect fire and old oak tables and chairs. Good simple filling bar snacks include cobs (from £1.30, hot roast pork or beef £2.40), giant yorkshire puddings with fillings such as sausage, ratatouille or faggots and mash (from £2.20), filled baked potatoes (from £2.50), and ploughman's or tasty oatcakes filled with cheese (£3); the panelled upstairs dining room is open at lunchtime only. A blue-brick patio overlooks the brewery in the long old-fashioned yard at the back. *(Recommended by Theo, Anne and Jane Gaskin, the Didler, Rob Fowell, Pete Baker, C J Fletcher, Dr S J Shepherd, Kevin Douglas, D L Parkhurst, Tony Hobden)*

Own brew ~ Licensee Kevin McDonald ~ Real ale ~ Bar food (lunchtime only, not Sun) ~ No credit cards ~ (01283) 536596 ~ Children in eating area of bar ~ Dogs welcome ~ Open 11.30-2.30, 5-11; 12-2.30, 7-10.30 Sun; closed bank hol Mon lunchtime

Children – if the details at the end of an entry don't mention them, you should assume that the pub does not allow them inside.

BUTTERTON SK0756 Map 7

Black Lion

Village signposted from B5053

This unspoilt 18th-c stone-built inn is well placed for the Peak District, and if it's not the sort of day for enjoying the outdoors there are plenty of interesting things to look at in the neat rambling rooms. One welcoming bar has a low black beam-and-board ceiling, lots of brassware and china, a fine old settle curling around the walls, well polished mahogany tables, and a good log fire (when it's lit). Off to the left are red plush button-back banquettes, sewing-machine tables and Victorian prints, while an inner room has a fine old kitchen range. Bar food, under new licensees, might include winter soup (£2.50), creamy garlic mushrooms (£3.25), broccoli and brie rösti (£6), steak and ale pie, chicken curry or cod and prawn crumble (£6.50), and steaks (from £9), with puddings such as strawberry jam sponge (£2.75). Changing well kept real ales on handpump could be Charles Wells Bombardier, Everards Tiger, Marstons Pedigree and Theakstons Best; several malt whiskies. Darts, TV, dominoes, cribbage, and separate well lit pool room; piped music. Outside, picnic-table sets and rustic seats on a prettily planted terrace look up to the tall and elegant spire of the local church of this pretty conservation village. *(Recommended by Mike and Wendy Proctor, Kevin Blake, the Didler, John Nielsen)*

Free house ~ Licensees Bob and Carol Davies ~ Real ale ~ Bar food ~ Restaurant ~ (01538) 304232 ~ Children in eating area of bar and restaurant till 9 ~ Open 12-2(3 Sat), 7-11(10.30 Sun); closed Mon lunchtime ~ Bedrooms: £35B/£55B

CAULDON SK0749 Map 7

Yew Tree ★★ £

Village signposted from A523 and A52 about 8 miles W of Ashbourne

This old favourite hides its riches behind quite a plain exterior, tucked unpromisingly between enormous cement works and quarries, and almost hidden by a towering yew tree. Inside is an Aladdin's cave of treasure – a veritable museum's-worth of curiosities all lovingly collected by the lively landlord himself (his latest addition is a small 800BC Greek vase). The most impressive pieces are perhaps the working Polyphons and Symphonions – 19th-c developments of the musical box, often taller than a person, each with quite a repertoire of tunes and elaborate sound-effects; take plenty of 2p pieces to work them. But there are also two pairs of Queen Victoria's stockings, ancient guns and pistols, several penny-farthings, an old sit-and-stride boneshaker, a rocking horse, swordfish blades, and even a fine marquetry cabinet crammed with notable early Staffordshire pottery. Soggily sprung sofas mingle with 18th-c settles, plenty of little wooden tables and a four-person oak choir seat with carved heads which came from St Mary's church in Stafford; above the bar is an odd iron dog-carrier (don't ask how it works!). As well as all this there's an expanding choir of fine tuneful longcase clocks in the gallery just above the entrance, a collection of six pianolas (one of which is played most nights) with an excellent repertoire of piano rolls, a working vintage valve radio set, a crank-handle telephone, a sinuous medieval wind instrument made of leather, and a Jacobean four-poster which was once owned by Josiah Wedgwood and still has the original wig hook on the headboard. The very cheap, simple snacks include hot pork pies (70p), meat and potato pies, chicken and mushroom or steak pies (85p), hot big filled baps and sandwiches (from £1), quiche, smoked mackerel or ham salad (£3.40), and home-made puddings (£1-£1.50). Well kept beers – also very reasonably priced – include Bass, Burton Bridge and Titanic Mild on handpump or tapped from the cask, and there are some interesting malt whiskies such as overproof Glenfarclas; spirits prices are very low here, too. Piped music, darts, shove-ha'penny, table skittles (taken very seriously here), dominoes and cribbage. Dovedale and the Manifold Valley are not far away. *(Recommended by C J Fletcher, the Didler, Mike and Wendy Proctor, Ann and Colin Hunt, Tim Lawrence, Bernie Adams, Nigel Woolliscroft)*

Free house ~ Licensee Alan East ~ Real ale ~ Bar food (12-2.30(3 Sat, Sun); 6-9.15) ~ No credit cards ~ (01538) 308348 ~ Children in Polyphon room ~ Dogs welcome ~ Folk music first Tues in month ~ Open 10-3, 6-11; 12-3, 7-10.30 Sun

CHEADLE SK0342 Map 7

Queens at Freehay

A mile SE of Cheadle; take Rakeway Road off A522 (via Park Avenue or Mills Road), then after a mile turn into Counslow Road

The good food is the main draw here – it generates quite a thriving dining atmosphere. Dishes are mainly familiar, nothing too far out, but all cooked carefully with good flavours, and nicely presented. The menu might include lunchtime sandwiches (£3.25 up), hoisin duck in a tortilla wrap (£3.95) and ploughman's (£4.50), with other dishes such as soup (£2.95), local black pudding with crispy bacon and cheddar (£3.95), fried garlic tiger prawns (£4.95), mushroom stroganoff, beef and Guinness pie or fish and chips (£7.95), fisherman's bake, mini lamb on mint mash (£8.95), sirloin steak (£10.95), and blackboard specials such as rack of lamb on spinach mash with port, cranberry and orange sauce (£9.95), or local trout with lemon butter, almonds, peppers, leeks and ginger (£10.95), with puddings such as hot chocolate fudge cake and treacle and walnut tart (from £3.25). Its good reputation was built up by the previous licensees who have now handed over to their son, so more reports please. The comfortable lounge bar is attractively decorated with small country pictures, and pretty curtains with matching cushions. It opens through an arch into a light and airy dining area, with neatly spaced tables. Well kept Bass and Worthington on handpump; quick attentive service. *(Recommended by Mike and Wendy Proctor, John and Gillian Scarisbrick)*

Free house ~ Licensee Adrian Rock ~ Real ale ~ Bar food (12-2(2.30 Sun), 6(6.30 Sun)-9.30) ~ Restaurant ~ (01538) 722383 ~ Well behaved children welcome ~ Open 12-2.30, 6-11; 12-3.30, 6.30-10.30 Sun; closed 25 and 26 Dec, evening 31 Dec, 1 Jan

LONGDON SK0714 Map 7

Swan With Two Necks ■

Off A51 Lichfield—Rugeley; coming from Lichfield turn right into Brook Road

This pleasant pub is especially cosy on cold winter days, when its five hot coal fires are alight. The long quarry-tiled bar is divided into three room areas, with low beams (very low at one end), a restrained décor, and house plants in the windows; there is also a two-room carpeted restaurant. Bar food includes soup (£2), lunchtime sandwiches (from £2.30), sausage and egg or lunchtime ploughman's (£4.50), particularly good cod and chips (small £6.50, large £7.50), seafood platter or pies such as beef, ale and mushroom or chicken, ham and leek, beef stroganoff, venison steak or fresh salmon and asparagus (£6.50), and rack of spring lamb (£6.90); limited menu on Sunday evening. Four real ales on handpump might be from brewers such as Ansells, Fullers, Holdens and Youngs; decent wines and kir, friendly helpful service; piped music. The garden has picnic-sets and swings, and an outdoor summer servery. *(Recommended by Gill and Tony Morriss, Paul and Margaret Baker, Barry Smith, Roger Bridgeman, D C Abberley)*

Punch ~ Lease Jacques and Margaret Rogue ~ Real ale ~ Bar food ~ Restaurant ~ (01543) 490251 ~ Open 12-2.30(3 Sat, Sun), 7-11(10. 30 Sun)

ONECOTE SK0555 Map 7

Jervis Arms

B5053, off A523 Leek—Ashbourne

Families enjoy this cheerful 17th-c pub, which has a pets corner with pygmy goats, slides and swings, two family rooms (one is no smoking) with high chairs, and a mother and baby room. The irregularly shaped cosy main bar has white planks over shiny black beams, window seats, wheelback chairs, two or three unusually low plush chairs, beer pump clips and bottles, and a big stone fireplace. Interesting beers include well kept Bass and Whim Arbor Light alongside three guests from brewers such as Highwood, Sarah Hughes and Titanic on handpump; they've a fair range of malt whiskies. Bar food such as soup (£1.60), sandwiches (from £2), breaded lobster (£2.75), filled baked potatoes or ploughman's (from £4.95), steak and kidney pie (£5.25), and puddings (£2.50); children's menu (from £2.25); one of the dining rooms is no smoking; darts, dominoes, cribbage, fruit machine, piped music and occasional TV. A spacious converted barn behind the pub has self-catering accommodation. *(Recommended by Rob Fowell, Peter Dale)*

Free house ~ Licensee Pete Hill ~ Real ale ~ Bar food (12-2, 7-9; 12-9.30 Sun) ~ (01538) 304206 ~ Children in family room and garden ~ Open 12-3, 7(6 Sat)-11; 12-10.30 Sun

SALT SJ9527 Map 7

Holly Bush

Village signposted off A51 S of Stone (and A518 NE of Stafford)

Staffordshire Dining Pub of the Year

A picture-postcard pub, this lovely old white-painted flower-decked thatched house is very popular for its honestly priced home-made bar food – get there early if you want to eat, as it fills very quickly. They use a lot of fresh local produce, and besides lunchtime snacks such as sandwiches (from £1.95), breaded mushrooms or pâté (£3.50), steaks (from £6.25), poached plaice (£7.50), and steak and ale pie or greek lamb (£7.95), blackboards show interesting specials such as grilled black pudding with poached egg on spinach and nutmeg (£3.45), fresh scottish mussels steamed in cider with cream and onion sauce (£6.45), wild mushroom stroganoff (£6.50), cod with a herb and goats cheese crust (£8.95), and duck breast in green peppercorn and sherry sauce (£10.50); home-made puddings (from £2.75); Sunday roast (£5.50). The oldest part of the building dates back to the 14th c, and has a heavy beamed and planked ceiling (some of the beams are attractively carved), a salt cupboard built in by the coal fire, and other nice old-fashioned touches such as an antique pair of clothes brushes hanging by the door, attractive sporting prints and watercolours, and an ancient pair of riding boots on the mantelpiece. Several cosy areas spread off from the standing-room serving section, and there are comfortable settees as well as more orthodox seats. The room on the left is no smoking, and a modern back extension blends in well, with beams, stripped brickwork and a small coal fire. Well kept Bass, Boddingtons and Marstons Pedigree on handpump, friendly efficient service; darts, shove-ha'penny, cribbage, backgammon, Jenga; fruit machine, perhaps piped nostalgic pop music. The big back lawn has rustic picnic-sets and a busy dovecote; they may have traditional jazz and a hog roast in summer, and do a fireworks display on 5 November. *(Recommended by Peter and Patricia Burton, Brian and Anna Marsden, Gavin Wells, Andy Gosling, Brian Kneale, June and Mike Coleman, Keith John Ryan, Darly Graton, Graeme Gulibert, Maurice and Gill McMahon, Stan and Hazel Allen, Phil and Jane Hodson, Alan and Paula McCully, Dr and Mrs R A Newbury , Patrick Hancock, Jim Bush, R Davies, Joy and Peter Heatherley)*

Free house ~ Licensee Geoffrey Holland ~ Real ale ~ Bar food (12-2, 6-9.30; 12-9.30 Sat, Sun) ~ (01889) 508234 ~ Children welcome if eating ~ Open 12-3, 6-11; 12-11 Sat; 12-10.30 Sun

WARSLOW SK0858 Map 7

Greyhound

B5053 S of Buxton

'One of the friendliest pubs we've ever been to' is typical of what many enthusiastic readers say about this congenial slated stone-built pub. It also generates praise for its good choice of tasty unfussy food, well kept beer, and good value bedrooms. Straightforward but cosy and comfortable inside, the beamed bar has long cushioned antique oak settles (some quite elegant), houseplants in the windows, and cheerful fires; piped music, darts, pool and fruit machine. The generous home-made bar food includes soup (£2.75), thai fishcakes with lime and ginger dip (£4.75), moules marinière (£5), stuffed peppers, creamy chicken curry or battered Whitby cod (£7.25), and steak and mushroom pie or minted lamb casserole (£7.75). Well kept Black Sheep, Marstons Pedigree and Worthington on handpump. In the side garden there are picnic-sets under ash trees, with rustic seats out in front where window boxes blaze with colour in summer. The pub is surrounded by pretty countryside and is handy for the Manifold Valley, Dovedale and Alton Towers. The licensees also run the Devonshire Arms in Hartington. *(Recommended by Derek and Sylvia Stephenson, Mike and Wendy Proctor, Gareth and Toni Edwards, Nigel Woolliscroft, Bernard Stradling, Jo and Iain MacGregor, Stephen Jeal, Paul and Margaret Baker, Rob Fowell, Doug Christian)*

Free house ~ Licensees David and Dale Mullarkey ~ Real ale ~ Bar food ~ (01298) 84249 ~ Children in eating area of bar ~ Dogs allowed in bar ~ Live music Sat evenings ~ Open 12-2.30, 7-11; 12-3, 7-10.30 Sun; closed Mon and Tues lunchtime (except bank hols) ~ Bedrooms: £17.50/£35

WETTON SK1055 Map 7

Olde Royal Oak

Village signposted off Hulme End—Alstonefield road, between B5054 and A515

Described by one reader as 'everything you could ask for in a rural pub', this aged white-painted and shuttered stone-built village house is in lovely National Trust walking country, and has a welcomingly inclusive, timeless atmosphere. The relaxing bar serves over 40 whiskies, and has well kept Black Sheep, Greene King Ruddles County and Jennings Cumberland on handpump, as well as Anklecracker (an ale brewed especially for them to celebrate the official world toe-wrestling championship that takes place here in the first week of July). It has black beams – hung with golf clubs – supporting the white ceiling boards, small dining chairs around rustic tables, a piano surrounded by old sheet music covers, an oak corner cupboard, and a coal fire in the stone fireplace. It extends into a more modern-feeling area, which in turn leads to a carpeted sun lounge looking out on to the small garden; piped music, darts, cribbage and dominoes; the family room is no smoking. Generous, promptly served and reasonably priced bar food includes soup (£2.50), prawn cocktail (£4.25), ploughman's (£5.50), battered cod (£6.25), scampi (£6.50), mediterranean vegetable lasagne, or steak and Guinness pie (£6.95), and puddings such as ginger sponge pudding or cherry cheesecake (from £2.50); Sunday roast (£5.95). Behind the pub is a croft suitable for caravans and tents, and Wetton Mill and the Manifold Valley are nearby. *(Recommended by MLR, Mike and Wendy Proctor, Kevin Blake, Sue Holland, Dave Webster, the Didler, Nigel Woolliscroft, I J Thurman, Sue and Dave Harris, Tim and Jan Dalton, Eric Locker)*

Free house ~ Licensees Kath and Brian Rowbotham ~ Real ale ~ Bar food ~ (01335) 310287 ~ Folk music Sat evening ~ Open 12-3, 7-11(10.30 Sun); cl Weds in winter ~ Bedrooms: /£45S

Lucky Dip

Besides the fully inspected pubs, you might like to try these Lucky Dips recommended to us and described by readers (if you do, please send us reports: www.goodguides.com).

Abbots Bromley [SK0724]
Royal Oak [Bagot St]: Traditionally furnished old inn, usual main menu from sandwiches to steaks with imaginative blackboard dishes, generous helpings, well kept Mansfield, Marstons Pedigree and a guest beer, decent wine, efficient friendly service, open fire, comfortable and attractive dining lounge (worth booking) *(Geoff and Tricia Alderman, David Cosham)*

Acton Trussell [SJ9318]
☆ *Moat House* [signed from A449 just S of Stafford; handy for M6 junction 13]: Busy timbered canalside food place, partly dating from 1320, attractive grounds with picnic-sets overlooking Staffs & Worcs Canal; comfortable oak-beamed bar with big open fireplace and armchairs, nice décor, sophisticated bar food inc good fresh fish and produce from the family's

farm (only restaurant meals on Sun, and may stop serving rather early if too busy other lunchtimes), well kept Banks's Bitter and Original and Marstons Pedigree, good wine list, helpful efficient service, no smoking restaurant; fruit machine, piped music; children welcome, open all day wknds, bedrooms *(Roger Cass, Dr S J Shepherd, Maurice and Gill McMahon, Rob Fowell, Karen Eliot, Alan Thomas, Mike and Wendy Proctor, Graham and Lynn Mason, LYM, L Davenport, J Attwood)*

Alrewas [SK1714]

William IV [William IV Rd, off main st]: Warm and friendly, with real ales inc monthly guest beers, enjoyable food lunchtime and from early evening on (all day Fri-Sun), good specials changing weekly, two for one lunchtime bargains (not Sun) – separate raised bookable eating area; music nights, sports TV; tables in garden with aviary and chipmunks *(Paul McGonnell)*

Amington [SK2304]

Pretty Pigs [Shuttington Rd]: Welcoming old inn with well kept beers, wide choice of quickly served food inc popular carvery; piped music; tables outside *(Colin Gooch)*

Anslow [SK2024]

Burnt Gate [Hopley Rd]: Pleasant country pub, comfortable lounge with well kept Bass and Marstons Pedigree, good fresh home-made food in separate restaurant *(C J Fletcher)*

Balterley [SJ7450]

Broughton Arms [A531/B5500, Balterley Heath]: Well run family dining pub, clean and airy, with lots of prints, ornaments and central fire in bar, friendly staff, well kept Bass, Boddingtons, Greenalls and Marstons Pedigree; wide choice of generous home-made food inc children's dishes (all tables kept for dining on Sun – very busy then, with food all day), comfortable banquettes and no smoking section in dining balcony; back pergola facing open countryside *(E G Parish, Richard Lewis, Graham and Lynn Mason)*

Barton-under-Needwood [SK1818]

Shoulder of Mutton [Main St]: Attractive pub with pleasant staff, well kept Bass-related and changing guest beers, good range of bar meals and snacks *(Tony and Wendy Hobden)*

Bradley [SJ8717]

☆ ***Red Lion*** [Smithy Lane]: Friendly and spotless 16th-c village pub, well kept Bass and guest beers, good varied sensibly priced food inc good Sun lunch, decent wine choice, no smoking dining room *(Geoff Palmer)*

Bramshall [SK0534]

Robin Hood [Leigh Rd]: Popular good value dining pub (best to book wknds), three real ales inc Bass, friendly attentive service *(Kevin Upton)*

Burton upon Trent [SK2423]

Alfred [Derby St]: Tied to local small Burton Bridge brewery, their full range kept well from central bar serving two spartan rooms, good beer-oriented food too; pool in back, friendly landlord, lots of country wines; open all day Fri/Sat, cheap bedrooms *(the Didler, Tony and Wendy Hobden)*

☆ ***Coopers Tavern*** [Cross St]: Traditional counterless back tap room with notably well kept Bass, Hardys & Hansons Classic and Best and Marstons Pedigree straight from imposing row of casks, barrel tables, cheap nourishing lunchtime hot filled cobs, pie and chips etc (not Sun), homely front parlour with piano and coal fire, very friendly staff; tap room can get smoky; impromptu folk nights Tues *(Pete Baker, the Didler, LYM, C J Fletcher, Bernie Adams)*

Derby Inn [Derby Rd]: Unspoilt friendly local with cosy panelled lounge, great collection of railway memorabilia in long narrow bar, Marstons Pedigree, local veg, eggs and cheese for sale; sports TV, open all day Fri/Sat *(C J Fletcher, the Didler)*

Devonshire Arms [Station St]: Now tied to Burton Bridge, with a good range of their ales and of continental bottled beers, decent lunchtime food, lots of snug corners; open all day Fri/Sat *(the Didler)*

Roebuck [Station St]: Comfortable Victorian-style alehouse opp former Bass and Ind Coope breweries, Greene King Abbot, Ind Coope Burton, Marstons Pedigree, Tetleys and guest beers, enjoyable cheap food inc add-it-up dishes (you choose the ingredients), friendly staff, prints and artefacts; piped music; open all day wkdys, decent bedrooms *(the Didler)*

Thomas Sykes [Anglesey Rd]: In former stables and waggon shed of ex-Everards brewery (latterly Heritage Brewery Museum), two high-ceilinged rooms with stable fittings and breweriana, wood benches, cobbled floors, well kept Bass and Marstons Pedigree on handpump and guest beers tapped from the cask, fine pump clip collection, good cheap basic food; outside gents'; open all day Fri *(the Didler, C J Fletcher)*

Chorley [SK0711]

Malt Shovel [off A51 N of Lichfield via Farewell]: Friendly village local esp popular with older people, central partly stripped brick bar, comfortable lounge, proper bare-boards public bar with darts, dominoes and cards, well kept Ansells Bitter and Mild, Tetleys and a guest beer, real fires; organist 1st Sat of month *(Pete Baker)*

Codsall [SJ8603]

Codsall Station [Chapel Lane/Station Rd]: Pub in simply restored listed waiting room and ticket office (station still used by trains), good range of Holdens beers kept well inc one brewed for the pub, lots of railway memorabilia, reasonably priced home-made food inc baked potatoes and good sandwiches; open all day wknds *(Robert Garner, Keith Jacob, Gill and Tony Morriss)*

Consall [SK0049]

☆ ***Black Lion*** [Consall Forge, OS Sheet 118 map ref 000491; best approach from Nature Park, off A522, using car park ½ mile past Nature Centre]: Traditional country tavern tucked away in rustic old-fashioned canalside settlement, by steam railway, enjoyable food inc good fish choice and some interesting dishes, good coal fire, well kept Marstons Best and Pedigree, friendly landlady; piped music; children (but not muddy boots) welcome; busy wknds, good walking area *(LYM, Mike and Wendy Proctor)*

Coseley [SO9494]

Painters Arms [Avenue Rd]: Well kept Holdens inc Mild and special ales, good low-priced sandwiches and lunchtime meals *(D Crutchley)*

Dilhorne [SJ9743]
Red Lion [off A521 Cheadle—Blyth Bridge, opp turn to village at Boundary]: Cosy and attractive long traditional beamed bar with lots of brass and lamps, friendly staff, well kept Courage Directors and Marstons Pedigree, log fire, good value food from soup and inexpensive baguettes to huge steaks and bargain Sun lunch in small unpretentious country dining room, children's dishes; piped music; on ridge overlooking the wooded Cheadle Hills with plenty of country walks, handy for Foxfield Steam Railway *(Edward Leetham, Tim Wellock)*

Dovedale [SK1450]
☆ *Izaak Walton* [follow Ilam sign off A52, or Thorpe off A515, NW of Ashbourne]: Relaxing, informal and pleasantly individual low-beamed bar in sizeable hotel, walkers welcome, some distinctive antique oak settles and chairs, good log fire in massive central stone chimney; well kept real ales inc guests such as Grainstore Steaming Billy, decent wines by the glass, efficient courteous service, ample nicely presented food in bar and restaurant, morning coffee and afternoon tea; very tranquil spot – seats on two spacious well kept lawns by sheep pastures, superb views; bedrooms comfortable *(John Saul, LYM)*

Draycott in the Moors [SJ9840]
Draycott Arms [Cheadle Rd]: Friendly pub with particularly well kept real ales, good value food, dining room with new conservatory extension *(Kevin Upton)*

Eccleshall [SJ8329]
☆ *George* [A519/B5026]: The star is for the Slaters beers brewed by the licensees' son, Bitter, Original, Top Totty, Organ Grinder and Premium; also good wines by the glass in snug comfortably worn beamed bar with big inglenook and cosy alcoves, friendly service, food served all day wknds; may be piped music; children in eating areas, dogs welcome, open all day *(Christine and Neil Townend, Stan and Hazel Allen, Margaret Ross, LYM)*

Enville [SO8286]
☆ *Cat* [A458 W of Stourbridge]: Mainly 17th-c, with four friendly and relaxing areas rambling around central bar, cheerful fire, landlord helpful with the very wide choice of well kept ales inc local Enville, mulled wine, quickly served generous food from imaginative sandwiches to unusual specials, popular upstairs restaurant, games room; cl Sun, popular with walkers – on Staffordshire Way *(Gill and Tony Morriss, the Didler)*

Etruria [SJ8746]
Duke of Bridgewater [Rectory St/Etruria Vale Rd, Shelton]: Three-room pub with welcoming new licensees doing good value food, Bass *(Edward Leetham)*

Forton [SJ7521]
Swan [A519 Newport—Eccleshall]: Long main room opening into another big room that extends into conservatory, as does restaurant; four well kept real ales, good choice of attractively priced food in bar and carvery, consistently good welcoming service; handy for Shrops Union Canal walks *(Dave and Jill Head)*

Fradley [SK1414]
White Swan [Fradley Junction]: Perfect canalside location, very popular summer wknds; wide choice of quickly served food from sandwiches to Sun lunch, well kept Tetleys-related ales inc Mild, cheery traditional public bar, quieter plusher lounge and lower vaulted back bar (where children allowed), lots of malt whiskies, real fire, cribbage, dominoes; waterside tables, good canal walks *(LYM, Dave Braisted)*

Gailey [SJ8810]
Bell [A5 a mile S]: Former coaching inn with good real ale range inc Banks's Mild, pleasant service, plentiful reasonably priced food esp ham and eggs *(R A Watson)*

Great Wyrley [SK9907]
Star [Walsall Rd]: Good value generous food (not Sun evening), well kept beer, friendly staff, dining conservatory *(Sue Wheeler)*

Hanbury [SK1727]
Cock [Hanbury Hill]: Welcoming village pub with traditional public bar and quieter lounge, current licensees doing good food in bar (lunchtime) and attractive new restaurant (Sun lunchtime and evenings – not Sun/Mon), well kept Bass and Marstons Pedigree; lovely walks inc poignant one to the vast crater of the 1944 Fauld bomb dump explosion (which wrecked the pub and everything else in this area) *(Andrew Bullock)*

Hanley [SJ8747]
Coachmakers Arms [Lichfield St]: Unpretentious friendly town local, three small rooms and drinking corridor, well kept Bass and Worthington, well filled cobs, popular darts, cards and dominoes, skittles *(the Didler, Pete Baker)*

Golden Cup [Old Town Rd]: Friendly local with imposing Edwardian façade and bar fittings, Bass and Greene King Ruddles County; open all day (cl Sun afternoon), can be busy wknds, nice garden *(the Didler)*

Hardings Wood [SJ8354]
☆ *Bluebell*: Unpretentious traditional boaters' tavern between Macclesfield and Trent & Mersey canals, half a dozen or more real ales from small breweries, Belgian beers, farm cider, filled rolls, friendly landlord and customers, busy front bar, quieter back room; may be cl wkdy lunchtimes, very popular wknds *(Edward Leetham, Mike and Wendy Proctor, Nigel Woolliscroft, C J Fletcher)*

Hartshill [SJ8745]
Jolly Potters [Hartshill Rd (A52)]: Outstanding Bass in four-room local, gently smartened-up but largely unspoilt, with classic central bar, corridor to public bar (with TV) and three small homely lounges; very welcoming to strangers *(the Didler, Pete Baker)*

High Offley [SJ7725]
Anchor [off A519 Eccleshall—Newport; towards High Lea, by Shrops Union Canal, Bridge 42; Peggs Lane]: Basic canal pub in same family for over a century, two plain rooms behind partition, well kept Marstons Pedigree and Wadworths 6X tapped into jugs, Weston's farm ciders, may be lunchtime sandwiches; outbuilding with small shop and semi-open

lavatories, seats outside, caravan/campsite; cl Mon-Thurs winter *(Nigel Woolliscroft, Mike and Wena Stevenson, the Didler)*

Hulme End [SK1059]

☆ ***Manifold Valley Hotel*** [B5054 Warslow—Hartington]: Comfortable 18th-c country pub near river, spacious but snug lounge bar with open fire, four well kept real ales inc local Whim, wide choice of generous food from superb stilton sandwiches to Sun lunch, separate light and airy dining room; children and cyclists welcome; bedrooms in converted stone smithy off secluded back courtyard, disabled facilities *(BB, DC, Derek and Sylvia Stephenson)*

Kinver [SO8483]

Plough & Harrow [High St (village signed off A449 or A458 W of Stourbridge; aka the Steps]: Popular old split-level local, one of a handful tied to Black Country brewers Bathams, with their Best, Mild and XXX kept well, a welcome for strangers, good choice of ciders and malt whiskies, cheap plain bar food (filled rolls even Sun lunchtime), low prices, film star pictures; proper public bar with darts, dominoes etc, lounge with nostalgic juke box, SkyTV and fruit machine, folk nights 1st and 3rd Weds; children allowed in some parts, tables in back courtyard, open all day wknds *(Pete Baker, Gill and Tony Morriss)*

Lapley [SJ8713]

Vaughan Arms [Bickford Rd]: Popular village pub, well kept Banks's Bitter and Original, Marstons Pedigree and a guest such as Greene King Abbot, good reasonably priced home cooking, good wine choice, friendly landlord and dog *(Robert Garner)*

Leek [SJ9856]

☆ ***Den Engel*** [St Edward St]: Belgian-style bar in high-ceilinged former bank, over 40 beers from there, bottled and draught, three changing British real ales, upstairs restaurant with continental dishes inc Flemish beer-based specialities (Fri/Sat lunch, Thurs-Sat night, bar food Sun night); piped classical music, very busy Fri/Sat evening, cl Sun-Thurs lunchtime *(the Didler, Mike and Wendy Proctor, C J Fletcher)*

☆ ***Swan*** [St Edward St]: Comfortable and friendly old three-room pub with good cheap lunchtime food, pleasant helpful staff, no smoking lounge, well kept Bass and guest ales, occasional beer festivals, lots of malt whiskies, choice of coffees; downstairs wine bar; folk club, seats in courtyard *(C J Fletcher, Mike and Wendy Proctor, the Didler)*

☆ ***Three Horseshoes*** [A53 NNE, on Blackshaw Moor]: Friendly family-run inn with emphasis on reliable generous food inc good bar carvery with self-service veg, brasserie, and candlelit beamed restaurant – Sat dinner-dance; lots of nooks and crannies, open fire, no smoking area, good service, good range of real ales, sensible prices, children's area; bedrooms *(Lynette and Stuart Shore)*

☆ ***Wilkes Head*** [St Edward St]: Basic convivial three-room local dating from 18th c (still has back coaching stables), tied to Whim with their ales and interesting guest beers kept well; welcoming regulars and dogs, friendly landlord happy to chat, lunchtime rolls, home-made stilton for sale, good choice of whiskies, farm cider, pub games, gas fire; children allowed in one room (but not really a family pub), fair disabled access, tables outside, open all day *(Pete Baker, the Didler, C J Fletcher)*

Lichfield [SK0705]

Boat [Walsall Rd, Summerhill (A461 SW)]: Newly refurbished, good atmosphere, open kitchen with interesting menu, several real ales *(Peter Hobson)*

Queens Head [Queen St]: Marstons alehouse-theme pub with their own and well kept guest beers, bare boards and comfortable old wooden furniture, short but interesting range of well-cooked daily specials and self-choice counter of unusual cheeses with sour-dough bread or muffins, huge helpings (doggy bags provided) at very reasonable prices; friendly staff *(C J Butler, Gill and Tony Morriss, C J Fletcher)*

Long Compton [SJ8522]

☆ ***Yew Tree***: Attractive pub with 17th-c core, smart and friendly, interesting food range from varied bar dishes to good restaurant meals, well kept Greene King Abbot and Marstons Pedigree; comfortable bedrooms *(Paul and Margaret Baker)*

Longnor [SK0965]

☆ ***Olde Cheshire Cheese***: 14th-c building, a pub for 250 years, some emphasis on the two attractive dining rooms full of steam railway models and bric-a-brac with their own separate bar and cosy after-dinner lounge, wide choice of good attractively priced home-made food here and in traditionally furnished main bar, well kept Robinsons ales, friendly staff; hikers welcome, bedrooms *(Doug Christian)*

Marston [SJ8314]

Fox [a mile NW of Wheaton Aston]: Remote farm-type local with changing well kept ales such as Hook Norton Generation, Mitchells, Parish Premium and Charles Wells Bombardier, bar food, two coal fires, dark wood benches and chairs, traditional games in family room; tables outside, open wknds, and summer lunchtimes *(G Coates)*

Muckley Corner [SK0806]

Olde Corner House [A5/A461]: Good generous sensibly priced food in two restaurants (the smarter one is no smoking), well kept Marstons Pedigree and Wadworths 6X, wide choice of good value wines, friendly licensees and staff, pleasant décor; good value bedrooms *(Colin Fisher)*

Penkridge [SJ9214]

Boat [Penkridge Lock, Cannock Rd (B5012), by Staffs & Worcs Canal, Bridge 86]: Comfortably old-fashioned pub by canal (not very scenic here), pleasant layout, good value food (not Sun) inc sandwiches and vegetarian, real ales; piped music; picnic-sets out by car park *(DC)*

Bridge House [Stone House]: Family-run hotel and restaurant, small bar with well kept Courage Directors, emphasis on good value food, quick efficient service; open all day *(Geoff Palmer)*

Horse & Jockey [Market St]: Friendly licensees, good service, Banks's, Marstons Pedigree and two guests such as Adnams and Youngs, enjoyable food lunchtime and evening *(Robert Garner)*

☆ *Star* [Market Pl]: Open-plan but friendly, with lots of low black beams and button-back red plush, well kept cheap Banks's and guest ales, pleasant service; piped music, sports TV in bar; open all day, tables on terrace *(Colin Gooch, BB)*

Reaps Moor [SK0861]

Butchers Arms [off B5053 S of Longnor]: Isolated moorland pub, lots of atmosphere in several distinct areas, good value food inc Sun lunch, Marstons Pedigree and a guest beer; free camping for customers *(the Didler)*

Rocester [SK1039]

Red Lion [High St]: Well run, with attractive décor and fresh flowers, friendly staff, huge choice of generous food, Marstons Best and Pedigree at attractive prices; 1930s piped music *(FS, Brian and Genie Smart)*

Rolleston on Dove [SK2427]

Jinnie [Station Rd]: Comfortable and attractively set Banks's pub with friendly staff and customers, well kept Marstons Pedigree, good range of inexpensive food running up to steaks, quick service, coal-effect gas fires; picnic-sets on small lawn *(Peter and Audrey Dowsett)*

Spread Eagle [Church Rd]: Well run and friendly chain dining pub with well kept Bass, good value food all day inc fresh fish and popular Sun carvery, speedy attentive service; pleasant garden, nice village, *(M Borthwick, Dr S J Shepherd)*

Rushton Spencer [SJ9362]

Knott Inn: Large welcoming local opp former railway and station, decent fresh standard food, well kept local beer; on Staffordshire Way *(Guy Vowles)*

Stafford [SJ9223]

Hogshead [Earl St]: Large bare-boards conversion with high ceilings, no smoking area with big fans, good choice of well kept real ales and bottled beers from long back bar, Inch's cider, breweriana and bric-a-brac, friendly staff, good food choice; piped music, games machine; open all day *(Richard Lewis)*

Olde Rose & Crown [Market St]: Well kept and comfortable traditional town pub with equally traditional landlady, busy all day from 10.30, SkyTV sports, pool, fresh sandwiches; keg beers inc bargain Boddingtons, live entertainment wknds *(Andrew Crawford)*

Stafford Arms [Railway St; turn right at main entrance outside station, 100 yards down]: Unpretentious nautical-theme beamed real ale pub, interesting changing guest beers, farm cider, cheap simple food (all day wkdys, not Sun evening or Sat); pool, bar billiards, table skittles, juke box; bedrooms with own bathrooms, open all day exc Sun afternoon *(Richard Lewis)*

Stoke-on-Trent [SJ8744]

O'Learys [London Rd]: Good local atmosphere, good drink, good value food *(Kieran)*

Staff of Life [Hill St]: Character city local, welcoming even when packed, unchanging layout of three rooms and small drinking corridor, well kept Bass ales *(the Didler, Pete Baker)*

Tamworth [SK2004]

Moat House [Lichfield St]: Former manor house, beams, panelling and bare boards, well kept Banks's ales inc Marstons Pedigree, wide food choice from sandwiches to huge mixed grill; large garden and play area *(Colin Gooch)*

Tatenhill [SK2021]

☆ *Horseshoe* [off A38 W of Burton; Main St]: Civilised tiled-floor bar, cosy no smoking side snug with woodburner, two-level restaurant and back family area, good value food (all day Sat) from sandwiches to steaks inc children's, well kept Marstons ales, good wine range, quick polite service; pleasant garden, good play area *(LYM, M Borthwick, C J Fletcher)*

Teanford [SK0040]

☆ *Ship*: Small local with good choice of enjoyable freshly made food in modest lounge bar and pleasant separate dining room/bistro, welcoming efficient staff, range of well kept real ales *(John and Gillian Scarisbrick, Mike and Wendy Proctor, Keith John Ryan)*

Thorncliffe [SK0360]

Mermaid [2 miles NE at N edge of the Morridge; pub named on OS Sheet 119]: Isolated well run moorland pub with good bar food, friendly atmosphere, old well and mermaid pictures, panoramic views from restaurant (Fri/Sat night, good Sun lunch) *(Mike and Wendy Proctor)*

Tutbury [SK2028]

☆ *Olde Dog & Partridge* [High St; off A50 N of Burton]: Handsome and well managed Tudor timbered inn, largely given over to big and attractively laid out carvery with plenty of separate snug areas; early-eater and lunch bargains, impressive puddings range, friendly service, second small restaurant, well kept Marstons Pedigree and a guest beer, good wine choice; children welcome, comfortable bedrooms in separate block *(M Borthwick, LYM, John and Christine Lowe, Peter and Patricia Burton, Eric Locker, Dr S J Shepherd)*

Uttoxeter [SK0933]

Vaults [Market Pl]: Unpretentious three-room local with a real welcome for visitors, Bass, Marstons Pedigree and Worthington, no food (just crisps etc), large bottle collection; handy for station *(Joe Green, the Didler)*

Wall [SK0906]

Trooper [Watling St, off A5]: Big choice of good bar food inc lots of specials and children's dishes, quick friendly service *(Colin and Sandra Tann)*

Weston [SJ9727]

Saracens Head [Stafford Rd]: Wide range of enjoyable food inc huge Scotch steaks, particularly friendly staff, well kept Bass, Greene King Old Speckled Hen and Marstons Pedigree, large conservatory; unobtrusive piped music; not far from Trent & Mersey Canal *(Sam Samuells)*

Wrinehill [SJ7547]

Hand & Trumpet [A531 Newcastle—Nantwich]: Comfortable family-run pub, obliging young staff, real ales inc guest beers, well cooked good value food in spotless bar, popular grill room and restaurant, large back room for families; splendid garden with pond and ducks, bedrooms *(E G Parish)*

Suffolk

A pleasantly diverse clutch of new entries here consists of the Crown at Buxhall (imaginative cooking in an engaging 17th-c pub), the Fox & Goose at Fressingfield (even older, in a delightful spot, good food and atmosphere), the St Peters Brewery at South Elmham (not exactly a pub, but well worth a visit – if you can fit in with its restricted opening – for exceptional beers in a lovely building; good food too), the Maybush at Waldringfield (a busy riverside family pub, nice all round), and – back in these pages after a break of several years – the Harbour Inn in Southwold (its name says it all, really: just what you'd hope for). Other pubs on top-notch form here are the friendly and relaxed Queens Head at Bramfield (good cooking of carefully chosen largely organic food), the smart and civilised Cornwallis at Brome (very good food, nice to stay in), the cheerful unpretentious Oyster at Butley (a good all-rounder), the down-to-earth Victoria at Earl Soham (still has good Earl Soham beers, though they're no longer brewed at the pub), the happy and immaculately kept Crown at Great Glemham (good all round), the cosy and civilised Beehive at Horringer (gains a Food Award this year), the Kings Head at Laxfield (delightfully unspoilt), the Ship at Levington (new licensees and very early days, but looks extremely promising, especially on the food side), the friendly and distinctive Star at Lidgate (good all round), the Crown in Southwold (well reorganised this year, good food and exceptionally good drinks), the homely and nicely idiosyncratic Moon & Mushroom at Swilland (nice home cooking, good beer), the good-hearted Gardeners Arms at Tostock (good value food, good beer), and the beautifully restored De La Pole Arms at Wingfield (a fine all-rounder). Suffolk pubs often have particularly good local fish: always worth looking out for. And the county now has no fewer than 14 pubs with the Food Award – making it one of the very best parts of Britain for seriously good pub dining. With so much competition, the title of Suffolk Dining Pub of the Year is not easily won: this year it goes to the Cornwallis at Brome. The Lucky Dip section at the end of the chapter also includes a lot of fine pubs now (with 46 added to this edition). Ones to note particularly are the Cross Keys in Aldeburgh, White Hart at Blythburgh, Ferry Boat at Felixstowe Ferry, Old Chequers at Friston, Crown at Hartest, Swan at Hoxne, Bull in Long Melford, Bell at Middleton, Ramsholt Arms at Ramsholt, Duke of Marlborough at Somersham and Lord Nelson in Southwold. Drinks prices in the area are a touch above the national norm. The classic Suffolk beer is Adnams, always good value here (as are their wines). Greene King brews here too, on a bigger scale – it is becoming more of a national than a regional brewer now. Besides St Peters and Earl Soham, smaller local brewers to look out for include Nethergate, Mauldons, Tolly and Old Chimneys.

Post Office address codings confusingly give the impression that some pubs are in Suffolk when they're really in Norfolk or Cambridgeshire (which is where we list them).

BRAMFIELD TM4073 Map 5

Queens Head

The Street; A144 S of Halesworth

The licensee himself visits the local organic farms that supply much of the produce used at this popular old pub. He's confident that as much care and attention goes into the production of the ingredients as goes into the rather special end-result dishes. The delicious menu (dotted with the names of local farms) changes daily, and might include starters (served with organic bread and butter) such as thai chicken broth (£3.75), grilled chicken breast kebab marinated in coriander, garlic and ginger with sweet chilli sauce, or grilled dates wrapped in bacon on a mild mustard cream sauce (£4.95), and galia melon with carpaccio (£5.95), with main courses such as tagliatelle carbonara (£6.95), seafood crumble or steak and kidney pie (£7.95), filo parcel with spinach, tomatoes, pine nuts, goats cheese and olives (£9.95), pork steaks with peppers in sweet and sour dressing (£10.95), and grilled dover sole with herb butter (£13.95). Although much emphasis is placed on the food, plenty of drinking locals help to make for a relaxed, bustling atmosphere. The high-raftered lounge bar has scrubbed pine tables, a good log fire in its impressive fireplace, and a sprinkling of farm tools on the walls; a separate no smoking side bar has light wood furnishings (one side of the pub is no smoking). Good polite service (real linen napkins), well kept Adnams Bitter and Broadside, a good wine list, including lots of organic ones and half a dozen good wines by the glass, home-made elderflower cordial, and organic apple juices and cider. *(Recommended by Tracey and Stephen Groves, Pat and Roger Fereday, A J Bowen, Pat and Tony Martin, Bruce Jamieson, Pamela and Merlyn Horswell, A C and E Johnson, Comus and Sarah Elliott, P F Whight, Maurice and Gill McMahon, MJVK, June and Perry Dann, Neil Powell, Simon Watkins, Su and Bob Child, Sally Anne and Peter Goodale, David Field, Sir Clive Rose, Ann and Colin Hunt, Neil and Lorna Mclaughlan, David and Rhian Peters, Frederic Chadburn)*

Adnams ~ Tenants Mark and Amanda Corcoran ~ Real ale ~ Bar food (12-2, 6.30-10(7-9 Sun)) ~ (01986) 784214 ~ Children in eating area of bar ~ Dogs welcome ~ Open 11.45-2.30, 6.30-11; 12-3, 7-10.30 Sun; closed 26 Dec

BROME TM1376 Map 5

Cornwallis

Rectory Road; after turning off A140 S of Diss into B1077, take first left turn

Suffolk Dining Pub of the Year

This very civilised largely 19th-c country hotel is grandly approached down a tree-lined drive through its 20 acres of grounds, with magnificent topiary, wandering ducks and a very attractive water garden. The beamed and timbered 16th-c bar at the core has all the virtues that you'd want in a country pub. A step up from the tiled-floor serving area takes you through heavy timber uprights to a stylishly comfortable carpeted area, which is attractively furnished with a good mix of old and antique tables, some oak settles alongside cushioned library chairs, a glazed-over well, and a handsome woodburning stove. The imaginative choice of excellent bar food changes every two months, and might include balsamic shallot soup with lemon and blue cheese celery (£4.50), pea, smoked hock and parsley risotto or fine beans in a herb vinaigrette on grilled mozzarella ciabatta (£5.95), basil grilled vegetables on a goats cheese and rocket potato cake (£8.95), roast salmon fillet with spring greens, thyme, wild mushrooms and celeriac cream, or Italian herb sausages with garlic and gruyère bubble and squeak (£9.25), huge steak and kidney pudding (£10), roast sirloin with marinated tomatoes, watercress sauerkraut and truffle oil sauce (£14.25), and puddings such as melon soup with strawberries and lime jelly, chocolate or cherry trifle with tutti frutti cookie, or mint and lemon brûlée with peanut brittle (£4.25); warm friendly service from attentive young staff. They keep an extensive carefully chosen wine list with 20 by the glass, organic local juices, bottled beers and champagne, as well as Adnams, St Peters Best and a guest such as Adnams

Broadside on handpump. A nicely planted Victorian-style side conservatory has coffee-lounge cane furniture, and there's an elegant restaurant. *(Recommended by Ian Phillips, Mike and Wendy Proctor, MDN, David Twitchett, J F M and M West, Stephen, Julie and Hayley Brown)*

Free house ~ Licensees Jeffrey Ward and Richard Leslie ~ Real ale ~ Bar food ~ Restaurant ~ (01379) 870326 ~ Children welcome ~ Dogs allowed in bedrooms ~ Open 11-11(10.30 Sun) ~ Bedrooms: £84.50B/£105.50B

BUTLEY TM3651 Map 5

Oyster

B1084 E of Woodbridge

The same cheery family have run this little country pub for over 13 years, and its traditions seem rooted even further in the past – you may be charged for a beer in pre-decimal currency. There's a medley of stripped pine tables, stripped pews, high-backed settles and more orthodox seats on bare boards, a pair of good coal fires in fine Victorian fireplaces, and a twister dial hanging below one of the very heavy beams for deciding who'll buy the next round – the Adnams Bitter, Broadside and their seasonal beers on handpump are well kept. They tend to play the quiet piped music (Frank Sinatra and the like) only in the winter; darts and dominoes. Good, varied and reasonably priced bar food includes sandwiches (from £2.75), soup (£3.50), ploughman's (£4.95), vegetable lasagne, moussaka and broccoli pasta bake (£5.95), local ham in parsley sauce (£7.95), daily specials such as wild boar and pheasant pie or crab (£6.95), roast partridge (£7.95), half a lobster (£12.95), and puddings (£3.25). The back garden has picnic-sets and solid wooden tables and chairs, with budgerigars in three aviaries. *(Recommended by Ian Phillips, Sarah Davis, Rod Lambert, Pat and Tony Martin, Bob and Margaret Holder, JKW, Ann and Colin Hunt, Gill Pennington)*

Adnams ~ Tenant Mr Hanlon ~ Real ale ~ Bar food (not Sun evening) ~ (01394) 450790 ~ Children welcome ~ Dogs allowed in bar ~ Folk Sun evening ~ Open 11.30-3, 6-11; 11.30-11 Sat; 12-4, 7-10.30 Sun

BUXHALL TM0057 Map 5

Crown

Village signposted off B1115 W of Stowmarket; fork right by post office at Great Finborough, turn left at Buxhall village sign, then second right into Mill Road, then right at the T-junction

Doing very well these days (you will need to book), this welcoming 17th-c timber framed country pub offers a good choice of carefully cooked food, with the emphasis on fresh seasonal ingredients. As everything is individually prepared, they can usually match personal preferences. As well as lunchtime snacks such as sandwiches (from £3.95), nice little finger snacks such as marinated olives or hummus with ciabatta bread sticks (£2.95), whitebait (£6.95), fish pie (£7.50), chilli con carne (£7.95), and sausage and mash (£8.25), the monthly changing menu might include spicy sweet potato and spinach soup (£3.95), warm duck liver and orange salad (£4.75), Loch Fyne mussels grilled with pesto topping (£4.95), wild mushroom, garlic and parmesan risotto (£8.50), rack of lamb with cherry tomato and red onion ragoût with rosemary butter (£9.25), monkfish wellington with white wine, tomato and basil sauce (£12.50), fried pigeon breasts wrapped in parma ham with port and juniper berry sauce (£12.25), and puddings such as coffee and hazelnut cheesecake or lemon mousse with a dipped chocolate viennese biscuit (£3.95). Well kept Greene King IPA, Abbot, XX Dark Mild and a guest from a local brewer such as Adnams, Earl Soham or Woodfordes; quick friendly service. The intimate little bar on the left has an open fire in a big inglenook, a couple of small round tables on a tiled floor, and low hop-hung beams. Standing timbers separate it from another area with pews and candles, and flowers in summer on big stripped oak or pine tables, and there's a further light and airy room which they call the Mill Bar. A pretty enclosed garden has tables under parasols on a heated terrace, and a children's swing. *(Recommended by*

Derek R A Field, Roy McFruin, A F Scotford, Chris and Sarah Wishlade)

Greene King ~ Lease Trevor Golton ~ Real ale ~ Bar food ~ Restaurant ~ (01449) 736521 ~ Children in eating area of bar and restaurant ~ Dogs welcome ~ Open 12-3, 6.30-11; closed Sun evening

CAVENDISH TL8046 Map 5

Bull

High Street (A1092 Long Melford—Clare)

Run by a welcoming, genuinely helpful landlord with help from his friendly efficient staff, this attractive 16th-c pub has a lively bustling atmosphere. It's on the main street of an especially pretty village (and it's useful to know that it has a car park behind). A good mix of diners and locals gathers in the open-plan beamed interior, which has heavy standing timbers and fine fireplaces, as well as well kept Adnams Bitter, Broadside and a seasonal ale, and several wines by the glass. Besides sandwiches (from £1.95) and ploughman's (from £4.25), a very big choice of daily specials chalked up all round the pub on blackboards might include smoked salmon stuffed with prawns, or tiger prawns in filo with a dip (£5.95), various curries (from £7.95), baked lamb shank with Greek herbs, tortellini stuffed with prawns with a wine, cream and mascarpone sauce (£8.95), breaded veal escalope topped with ham and mozzarella with a tomato and oregano sauce (£10.95), a good mixed grill (£11.95), and steaks (from £12.95); fresh fish is delivered daily, and might include tasty grilled haddock or cod (£6.95), skate (£9.95), and Torbay sole (£11.95); good Sunday roast; home-made puddings like tiramisu, cheesecakes or crumbles (from £3.50). There may be piped music. There are tables in the garden, and they have summer barbecues. *(Recommended by Patrick Hancock, R F Ballinger, Nick Holmes, E J and M W Corrin, John Saville, Nicholas Collins, Ruth Kitching)*

Adnams ~ Tenant Gavin Crocker ~ Real ale ~ Bar food (12-2.30, 6-9) ~ Restaurant ~ (01787) 280245 ~ Children in eating area of bar and restaurant ~ Dogs allowed in bar ~ Open 11-3, 6-11; 12-10.30 Sun

CHELMONDISTON TM2038 Map 5

Butt & Oyster

Pin Mill – signposted from B1456 SE of Ipswich

You might end up chatting to one of the local barge residents at this staunchly simple old bargeman's pub, attractively set by the River Orwell. Failing that there's entertainment enough looking out through its bay windows to the lines of moored black sailing barges, ships coming down the river from Ipswich, and the woods beyond. The half-panelled timeless little smoke room is pleasantly worn and unfussy, with model sailing ships around the walls and high-backed and other old-fashioned settles on the tiled floor; ferocious beady-eyed fish made by a local artist gaze at you from the walls. Adnams Best and Broadside and Tolly Bitter, Original and Mild on handpump or tapped from the cask, and decent wines; shove-ha'penny, shut-the-box, cribbage and dominoes. The good value straightforward bar food is popular and space is limited, so you might need to get here early at the weekend. The menu includes soup (£3.25), lunchtime filled baguettes (£3.95), smoked mackerel pâté (£4.45), battered cod or haddock (£6.95), and lemon and dill chicken or beef and ale pie (£7.95), with puddings (£3.25). Most of the eight or so daily specials are likely to be fresh fish: Orkney herrings (£4.95), wild boar sausages (£7.45), moules marinière or Cromer crab (£7.95), pot-roasted partridge (£8.95), and half a lobster (£9.95); the restaurant is no smoking. Readers especially enjoy visits here during the annual Thames Barge Race (end June/beginning July). *(Recommended by George Atkinson, Richard Gibbs, Rona Murdoch, Pamela Goodwyn, Ian Phillips, Comus and Sarah Elliott, Peter Thomas, Mike and Mary Carter, Ann and Colin Hunt, Alan Thomas, the Didler, James Nunns)*

Pubmaster ~ Tenant Steve Lomas ~ Real ale ~ Restaurant ~ (01473) 780764 ~ Children in restaurant ~ Dogs allowed in bar ~ Open 11-11; 12-10.30 Sun

COTTON TM0467 Map 5

Trowel & Hammer

Mill Road; take B1113 N of Stowmarket, then turn right into Blacksmiths Lane just N of Bacton

Much emphasis is placed on the highly enjoyable food at this civilised wisteria-covered pub. The menu changes daily, but might include creamy onion and leek soup (£2.75), squid, goujons of plaice and whitebait with tartare sauce (£4.50), baked goats cheese in filo pastry with red onion marmalade (£4.55), spinach and ricotta pasta with tomato and cheese topping (£7.50), pork steak with stilton and walnut sauce (£7.95), baked bass with cranberry sauce (£8.50), grilled salmon fillet with dill and cucumber sauce (£8.95), and roast duck breast with wild cherry and orange sauce (£9.75). The spreading series of quiet rooms has fresh flowers, lots of beamery and timber baulks, a big log fire (as well as an ornate woodburning stove at the back), and plenty of wheelbacks and one or two older chairs and settles around a variety of tables. Well kept Adnams, Greene King IPA and Abbot, and a guest, probably from Mauldons or Nethergate, are on handpump or tapped from the cask, and they have an interesting wine list, and lots of unusual spirits; pool, fruit machine and piped music. A pretty back garden has lots of roses and hollyhocks, neat climbers on trellises, picnic-sets and a recently renovated swimming pool. *(Recommended by Mike and Mary Carter, Ian Phillips, J D M Rushworth, Paul and Margaret Baker, Mike and Wendy Proctor, Stephen P Edwards, Charles and Pauline Stride)*

Free house ~ Licensees Simon and Jonathan Piers-Hall ~ Real ale ~ Bar food ~ Restaurant ~ (01449) 781234 ~ Well behaved children in eating area of bar ~ Dogs allowed in bar ~ Open 12-3, 6-11; 12-11(10.30 Sun) Sat

DENNINGTON TM2867 Map 5

Queens Head

A1120

The arched rafters in the steeply roofed part of the bar of this picturesque Tudor pub, which is prettily set on the village green by the church, are reminiscent of a chapel, and indeed it was owned for centuries by a church charity. The main neatly kept L-shaped room, usually full of happy customers, has carefully stripped wall timbers and beams, a handsomely carved bressumer beam, and comfortable padded wall seats on the partly carpeted and partly tiled floor. Well kept Adnams Bitter and Mauldons Mole Trap on handpump are served from the brick bar counter by the helpful landlord and his staff, who are clearly keen to make sure you get a warm welcome; piped classical music. Reasonably priced bar food includes good sandwiches (from £2.20), soup (£2.95), fried whitebait or chicken liver and garlic pâté (£3.75), smoked salmon and prawn rolls (£4.25), ploughman's (£4.50), layered sausage pie (£6.50), cheesy baked cod (£6.95), lamb shank or steak and mushroom pie (£7.75), lemon sole stuffed with crab and seafood sauce (£6.75), and lots of puddings such as lemon and lime pie, banana and toffee pancake or chocolate terrine (£3). There are seats on a side lawn, attractively planted with flowers, and sheltered by some noble lime trees, and the pub backs on to Dennington Park, which has swings and so forth for children. *(Recommended by R J Walden, Sir Clive Rose, Michael Sargent, A J Bowen, June and Perry Dann, David and Rhian Peters, Charles and Pauline Stride, Terry Mizen, Ian Phillips, Mr and Mrs M Hayes)*

Free house ~ Licensees Ray and Myra Bumstead ~ Real ale ~ Bar food ~ Restaurant ~ No credit cards ~ (01728) 638241 ~ Children in family room, must be over 7 Sat evening ~ Open 12-2.30, 6.30-11; 12-3, 6.30-10.30 Sun

Pubs in outstandingly attractive surroundings are listed at the back of the book.

DUNWICH TM4770 Map 5

Ship £

St James Street

It's hard to imagine that centuries ago Dunwich was one of England's busiest ports – it's such a charming little place today. Since then fairly rapid coastal erosion has put most of the village under the sea, and there are those who claim that on still nights you can sometimes hear the old church bells tolling under the water. There's plenty to do around here, and this old brick pub makes a great break from your exploring. The Dunwich Museum almost next door is certainly worth a visit, the RSPB reserve at Minsmere is close by, and there are plenty of surrounding walks. The cosy main bar is traditionally furnished with benches, pews, captain's chairs and wooden tables on its tiled floor, a woodburning stove (left open in cold weather) and lots of sea prints and nautical memorabilia; fruit machine, dominoes and cribbage. The long-serving and very popular licensees retired in the spring of 2002, but early reports since then on the new regime are encouraging, and it seems that most of the friendly and helpful staff (as well as the chef) have stayed on – coping cheerfully with the crowds at busy lunchtimes and making everyone feel welcome, to produce a good bustling atmosphere. The handsomely panelled bar counter has well kept Adnams Bitter and Broadside and a changing beer from Mauldons on handpump. They serve simple fresh fish and home-made chips, with the fish bought straight from boats on the beach (£5.95 lunchtime, £7.95 in the evening). The lunchtime menu also includes home-made soup (£2), sausage and chips (£4.50), potato and onion bake or ploughman's (£5), and pork and bean stew (£5.50); in the evening there is stilton and walnut pâté (£4.95), sausages or ratatouille (£6.95), fried cod or plaice (£7.95), fish crumble (£8.95), and duck breast with orange sauce (£10.25). The restaurant is no smoking. A simple conservatory looks on to an attractive sunny back terrace, and the large garden is very pleasant, with its well spaced picnic-sets and enormous fig tree. *(Recommended by Sarah Davis, Rod Lambert, Comus and Sarah Elliott, June and Perry Dann)*

Free house ~ Licensee David Sheldrake ~ Real ale ~ Bar food (12-7, 7-9) ~ (01728) 648219 ~ Children in restaurant and family room ~ Dogs allowed in bar and bedrooms ~ Open 11-11; 12-10.30 Sun; closed 3-6 in winter ~ Bedrooms: £50S/£60S

EARL SOHAM TM2363 Map 5

Victoria £

A1120 Yoxford—Stowmarket

The interesting range of Earl Soham ales here used to be brewed at this charmingly unpretentious little village pub, but the previous licensees – who still do the brewing – have moved the brewery to bigger pemises just along the road: superbly kept Victoria Bitter, a Mild called Gannet, and a stronger ale called Albert are well kept on handpump. There's a friendly and easy-going local atmosphere in the bar, which is fairly basic, with stripped panelling, kitchen chairs and pews, plank-topped trestle sewing-machine tables and other simple scrubbed pine country tables with candles, tiled or board floors, an interesting range of pictures of Queen Victoria and her reign, a piano, and open fires; cribbage and dominoes. Good value home-made bar food includes sandwiches (from £2), soup (£2.75), ploughman's (from £4.25), tasty corned beef hash (£3.95), vegetarian pasta dishes (£4.25), meat or vegetable lasagne (£5.25), pork and pineapple or lamb curry (£5.75), feta and onion tart (£5.95), beef casserole or fish pie (£6.25), and a winter Sunday roast (£6.25). A raised back lawn has seats, and there are more out in front. The pub is quite close to a wild fritillary meadow at Framlingham, and a working windmill at Saxtead. *(Recommended by Pat and Tony Martin, Comus and Sarah Elliott, David and Rhian Peters, A C and E Johnson, Stuart and Valerie Ray, Barry Collett, Ian Phillips, J F M and M West, T G Thomas, Kevin Thorpe, Pam and David Bailey)*

Free house ~ Licensee Paul Hooper ~ Real ale ~ Bar food (12-2, 7-10) ~ No credit cards ~ (01728) 685758 ~ Children in eating area of bar ~ Dogs welcome ~ Open 11.30-3, 6-11; 12-3, 7-10.30 Sun

ERWARTON TM2134 Map 5

Queens Head

Village signposted off B1456 Ipswich—Shotley Gate; pub beyond the attractive church and the manor with its unusual gatehouse (like an upturned salt-cellar)

It's worth getting to this unassuming and relaxed 16th-c pub early to bag one of the window tables looking out over fields to the Stour estuary. The friendly bar has bowed black oak beams in its shiny low yellowing ceiling, comfortable furnishings, a cosy coal fire, and several sea paintings and photographs. The conservatory dining area, partly no smoking, is also very pleasant. Adnams Bitter and Broadside and Greene King IPA are well kept on handpump, and they have a decent wine list with several half bottles, and a wide choice of malt whiskies. Good value tasty bar food includes sandwiches, home-made soup (£2.95), ploughman's (£5.50), vegetable lasagne, home-made moussaka or beef and ale casserole (£7.50), chicken breast in Pernod and prawn sauce (£7.95), breaded prawns with lemon and cajun dip (£8.50), delicious steak and kidney pudding, fried pork loin with apple and mustard sauce (£7.95), steaks (from £9.50), and daily specials such as crab salad (£6.95), chestnut casserole, seafood stroganoff, or partridge casserole (£7.95), with puddings such as pecan pie or chocolate truffle torte (from £3.75). It can get busy at the weekends, when service might slow down a little. Darts, bar billiards, shove-ha'penny, cribbage, dominoes; there may be piped music. The gents' has quite a collection of navigational charts. There are picnic-sets under summer hanging baskets in front. *(Recommended by Colin and Dot Savill, Tom Gondris, David Field, Peter Thomas, George Atkinson, Ian Phillips, Pamela Goodwyn)*

Free house ~ Licensees Julia Crisp and G M Buckle ~ Real ale ~ Bar food ~ Restaurant ~ (01473) 787550 ~ Children in restaurant ~ Open 11-3, 6.30-11; 12-3, 7-10.30 Sun; closed 25 Dec

FRAMSDEN TM1959 Map 5

Dobermann 

The Street; pub signposted off B1077 just S of its junction with A1120 Stowmarket—Earl Soham

In summer a mass of flowers festoons this charmingly restored tucked-away thatched pub. It's a lively little place with a really good friendly welcome, lots of prints of dobermans and schnautzers and photographs of show rosettes won by the owner's dogs all over the white walls, and perhaps Puss Puss the cat. A central open fire separates the two spotlessly kept knocked-through areas which have pale stripped beams in the very low ceilings, a big comfortable sofa, a couple of chintz wing armchairs, and a mix of other chairs and plush-seated stools and winged settles around polished rustic tables. Enjoyable bar food in generous helpings includes sandwiches (from £2), soup (£3.25), ploughman's (from £5.25), cream and nut pasta (£5.50), battered haddock (£7.15), plaice stuffed with prawn sauce (£7.25), chicken and mushroom pie (£8.75), pork with creamy mushroom and pepper sauce (£8.95), and sirloin steak (from £11.75), with puddings such as banana split (£3.95). Well kept Adnams Bitter and Broadside, and a guest such as Mauldons Mole Trap on handpump; efficient service. Cribbage, dominoes; piped radio. They play boules in the little sheltered garden, where there are picnic-sets by trees and a fairy-lit trellis. *(Recommended by Alan Cowell, Michael Gray, George Atkinson, Marjorie and Bernard Parkin, Mr Norbury, Mrs Hughes, Peter Thomas, Mike Ridgway, Sarah Miles)*

Free house ~ Licensee Susan Frankland ~ Real ale ~ Bar food ~ No credit cards ~ (01473) 890461 ~ Open 12-3, 7-11(10.30 Sun); closed Mon except bank hols ~ Bedrooms: /£50S

FRESSINGFIELD TM2677 Map 5

Fox & Goose

B1116 N of Framlingham; Church Road

Perhaps more like an interesting old house than a typical pub, this restful place has been owned by the neighbouring church for countless generations, and at one time was the village guildhall. A new licensee took over almost as we inspected, and the pub was then closed for a month for restoration work. Don't expect too much to change: the delightfully timeless, peaceful feel is very much part of its charm. On sunny afternoons rays of light stream through the pretty latticed windows of the little bar, which, with its comfortably worn armchairs and only a few small tables, has the feel of a living room a century ago. There's a brick fireplace, high-backed settles, old prints, and a small corner bar with Adnams Broadside and St Peters Golden Ale tapped from the cask; tucked behind here too is a surprising range of brandies, whiskies and wines (including some from the local Oakhill Vineyard). The back windows look out over the churchyard. Another similarly furnished but slightly more formal room is for eating; part of this room is no smoking. Very good lunchtime bar food includes soup (£3.50), rib-eye steak sandwich (£5.95), and main courses such as loin of pork on a black pudding and sage risotto with blue cheese sauce (£7.50), while in the evening you might go for something grander such as king scallops on herb risotto with red wine vinaigrette (£7.50), chicken breast with pea and goats cheese potatoes and summer vegetable sauce (£11.50), lamb with almond rösti, apricots, fine beans and redcurrant sauce (£13.95), and trio of fish with buttered spinach, asparagus, pink shrimp and vanilla sauce (£14.50); they do Sunday lunches (two courses £12.50, three £15). All the food – including breads and ice cream – is made on the premises. No music or machines. In front of the building, which dates from the 16th c, are a couple of tables, some old stocks, and a small, safely fenced-off pond. Note the unusual opening times. *(Recommended by Comus and Sarah Elliott, Ray and Jacki Davenport, Neil Powell)*

Free house ~ Licensee Paul Yaxley ~ Real ale ~ Bar food (12-2; not evenings or Mon) ~ (01379) 586247 ~ Children welcome ~ Open 12-2.30, 7-10(11 Sat); closed Mon

GREAT GLEMHAM TM3361 Map 5

Crown

Between A12 Wickham Market—Saxmundham and B1119 Saxmundham—Framlingham

Readers heap unanimous praise on this beautifully kept free house, which is in a particularly pretty village. The simple airy interior is spotless. Past the sofas on rush matting in the big entrance hall, an open-plan beamed lounge has wooden pews and captain's chairs around stripped and waxed kitchen tables, local photographs and interesting paintings on cream walls, fresh flowers, and some brass ornaments; log fires in two big fireplaces. Well kept Greene King IPA and Old Speckled Hen are served from old brass handpumps by a cheery barman – there's a happy atmosphere here. Satisfying generously served food (it's worth booking) includes sandwiches (from £2.95), soup (£3.25), coarse pâté (£3.25), baked potatoes (from £4.25), ham and eggs (£5.25), ploughman's (£5.50) and daily specials such as whitebait (£4.25), butterfly prawns with lemon mayonnaise (£4.95), mushroom and spinach lasagne or beef rissoles (£7.95), steak and kidney pie or salmon steak with lime and chives (£7.95), and sirloin steak (£9.95); children's menu (£3.50). Dominoes and cribbage. A tidy, flower-fringed lawn, raised above the corner of the quiet village lane by a retaining wall, has some seats and tables under cocktail parasols; disabled access. *(Recommended by Comus and Sarah Elliott, D S Cottrell, J F M and M West, David Field, Peter Thomas, David and Rhian Peters, Ann and Colin Hunt, June and Perry Dann, Ian Phillips, Gill Pennington, MDN)*

Free house ~ Licensees Barry and Susie Coote ~ Real ale ~ Bar food ~ (01728) 663693 ~ Children welcome ~ Dogs welcome ~ Open 11.30-3, 6.30-11; 12-3, 7-10.30 Sun; closed Mon (except bank hols)

HORRINGER TL8261 Map 5

Beehive

A143

This civilised place is particularly popular as a dining pub, but you're just as welcome if you pop in for only a drink. They've refrained from pulling walls down to create the usual open-plan layout, so its rambling little rooms have a pleasantly cottagey feel. Despite some very low beams, good chalky wall colours keep it light and airy; there are carefully chosen dining and country kitchen chairs on coir or flagstones, one or two wall settles around solid tables, picture-lights over lots of 19th-c prints, and stripped panelling or brickwork. Food from the daily changing imaginative menu is very good, and might include cream of wild mushroom soup (£3.95), smoked fish pâté with capers and red onion with crostinis (£4.95), seared scottish king scallops with thai sauce (6.95), warm roast tomato and brie tart (£7.95), sautéed lambs kidneys with grain mustard and cream sauce or lasagne (£8.95), pork, ale and apple sausages and mash (£9.50), and fried cod fillet on saffron and chive risotto or chicken breast filled with garlic salami on pesto crushed potato (£10.95), and puddings such as warm apricot and frangipane tart or raspberry and vanilla roulade (£3.95); coffee and cookies (£1.95). Well kept Greene King IPA and a second changing Greene King beer on handpump, and decent changing wines with half a dozen by the glass. An attractively planted back terrace has picnic-sets and more seats on a raised lawn. Their dog Muffin is very good at making friends, although other dogs are not really welcome. *(Recommended by Pat and Tony Martin, Derek Thomas, David Twitchett, Mike and Mary Carter, David Kidd, Ian Phillips, D S Cottrell, R C and J M Clark, Hazel Morgan, Reg J Cox)*

Greene King ~ Tenants Gary and Dianne Kingshott ~ Real ale ~ Bar food (not Sun evening) ~ (01284) 735260 ~ Children welcome ~ Open 11.30-2.30, 7-11; 12-2.30, 7-10.30 Sun

HUNDON TL7348 Map 5

Plough

Brockley Green – nearly 2 miles SW of village, towards Kedington

Five acres of lovely landscaped gardens with fine views of the Stour valley surround this remotely set pub. A pleasant terrace has good wooden furniture under a wisteria-covered pergola, there are koi in an ornamental pool, and croquet and putting. Inside, the neatly kept knocked-through carpeted bar has plenty of old standing timbers, cushions on low side settles, pine kitchen chairs and sturdy low tables on the patterned carpet, and lots of horsebrasses on the beams. Bar food might include carrot and coriander soup (£2.95), greek salad (£4.95), smoked salmon with dill dressing (£5.95), wild mushroom quiche (£7.50), battered chicken fillet with sweet and sour dip (£8.50), pot-roasted minted lamb (£8.75), lamb shank in mint jus (£9.25), and steaks (from £10.75); Sunday roasts (£8.95). Seafood night is Friday, when they might have oriental crab cakes with herbed chilli sauce (£7.95), monkfish tails roasted in parma ham with lemon butter sauce (£9.50), and grilled dover sole with mixed herbs (£9.95). Well kept Greene King IPA, Woodfordes Wherry and a guest beer such as Shepherd Neame Spitfire on handpump; quite a few wines, and over 30 malt whiskies; piped music. Parts of the bar and restaurant are no smoking. There's a sheltered site behind for caravans, and in the pub the bedrooms (some recently refurbished) have good views. There are two friendly resident labradors. More reports please. *(Recommended by Richard Gibbs, MLR)*

Free house ~ Licensees David and Marion Rowlinson ~ Real ale ~ Bar food (till 9.30 Mon-Sat) ~ Restaurant ~ (01440) 786789 ~ Children welcome but no under-5s in bar Sat evenings ~ Dogs welcome ~ Open 11(12 winter)-2.30, 6-11; 12-3, 7-10.30 Sun ~ Bedrooms: £45S(£50B)/£65S(£75B)

ICKLINGHAM TL7872 Map 5

Red Lion

A1101 Mildenhall—Bury St Edmunds

Arrive at this civilised 16th-c thatched dining pub early (or book ahead) for a table in the best part – the beamed open-plan bar, which has a cavernous inglenook fireplace and is attractively furnished with a nice mixture of wooden chairs, big candlelit tables and turkey rugs on the polished wood floor. Another area behind a knocked-through fireplace has closely spaced dark wood pub tables on carpets. Emphasis is on the generously served enjoyable if not cheap bar food, which includes soup or pâté (£4.25), sausages and mash (£6.75), lambs liver and bacon (£7.95), pork chops with apple and cider sauce (£9.95), wild boar fillet steak with red onion and garlic butter (£15.95), and around a dozen fish dishes such as moules marinière (£7.95), grilled oysters with cream and parmesan (£8.95), and bass with chilli butter (£15.95). Well kept Greene King IPA and Abbot on handpump, lots of country wines and fruit pressés, and winter mulled wine. There are picnic-sets with colourful parasols on a lawn in front (the pub is well set back from the road), and more behind on a raised terrace facing the fields, with Cavenham Heath nature reserve beyond; giant outside Jenga; handy for West Stow Country Park and the Anglo-Saxon Village. *(Recommended by J F M and M West, Andrew Scarr, David Cosham, R M Harrold, Mrs A Scott, Mandy and Simon King, Ian Phillips)*

Excalibur ~ Lease Jonathan Gates and Ian Hubbert ~ Real ale ~ Bar food (12-2.30, 6-10; 12-2, 7.15-9.30 Sun) ~ Restaurant ~ (01638) 717802 ~ Children welcome ~ Open 12-2.30, 6-11(7.15-10.30 Sun); closed 25 Dec, 26 Dec/1 Jan evening

LAVENHAM TL9149 Map 5

Angel ★

Market Place

As well as being an excellent place to eat and stay in, this very friendly Tudor inn is still popular with locals popping in for just a drink and a chat. The long bar area, facing on to the charming former market square, is light and airy, with a buoyantly pubby atmosphere, plenty of polished dark tables, a big inglenook log fire under a heavy mantelbeam, and some attractive 16th-c ceiling plasterwork (even more elaborate pargeting in the residents' sitting room upstairs). Round towards the back on the right of the central servery is a further no smoking dining area with heavy stripped pine country furnishings. The very good food can be eaten in either the bar or the restaurant, and might include starters such as celeriac and sweet potato soup (£3.50), tomato and feta salad with basil (£5.25), tomato, brie and sage tart, sausages and mash or ploughman's (£5.95), steak and ale pie (£8.25), aubergine and mozzarella lasagne (£8.25), braised shank of lamb with redcurrant and rosemary (£9.75), mullet fillet with lemon and herb risotto (£9.50), fried venison fillet with blackberry and brandy sauce (£10.95), and puddings such as steamed syrup sponge or crème brûlée (£3.75). Well kept Adnams Bitter, Greene King IPA and Broadside and Nethergate Bitter on handpump, quite a few malt whiskies, and eight or so decent wines by the glass or part bottle (you get charged for what you drink). They have shelves of books, dominoes, and lots of board games; classical piped music. There are picnic-sets out in front overlooking the square, and tables under cocktail parasols in a sizeable sheltered back garden; it's worth asking if they've time to show you the interesting Tudor cellar. *(Recommended by the Didler, Sir Clive Rose, Dr and Mrs M E Wilson, Tina and David Woods-Taylor, Jeff and Wendy Williams, Charles Gysin, Peter Saville, Giles and Liz Ridout, Mr and Mrs M Hayes, MDN, Pamela Goodwyn, Patricia Beebe, David Kidd, Ian Phillips, Maysie Thompson, George Atkinson, Brian and Janet Ainscough, Fiona Wynn, Derek Thomas, David and Ruth Hollands, Pam and David Bailey, John Robertson, Virginia Greay)*

Free house ~ Licensees Roy Whitworth and John Barry ~ Real ale ~ Bar food (12-2.15, 6.45-9.15) ~ Restaurant ~ (01787) 247388 ~ Children welcome ~ Dogs allowed in bar ~ Classical piano Fri evenings ~ Open 11-11; 12-10.30 Sun; closed 25-26 Dec ~ Bedrooms: £50B/£75B

Swan ★

High Street

Many of Lavenham's buildings are famously attractive, and this hotel is one of them – and here, unlike most of the others, you can wander around inside. It actually incorporates several fine half-timbered buildings, including an Elizabethan house and the former Wool Hall. It's quite smart and does have all the trimmings of a well equipped hotel (and not a cheap one), but buried in its heart is a peaceful little tiled-floor bar with leather chairs, a set of handbells that were used by the local church bellringers for practice, and memorabilia of the days when this was the local for the US 48th Bomber Group in World War II. In the evening it's laid up with tablecloths for dining. From here armchairs and settees spread engagingly through a network of beamed and timbered alcoves and more open areas – such as the airy Garden Bar which overlooks the neat, sheltered courtyard garden. Well kept Adnams and Greene King IPA on handpump. A fairly short lunchtime bar menu includes soup (£3), terrine with red onion marmalade (£3.75), moules marinière (£4.50/£9), sausage and mash (£6.75), thai fishcakes with chilli dip (£8), fried chicken breast with penne and pesto cream sauce (£8.50), grilled sirloin topped with smoked cheese (£9.50), and puddings such as sticky toffee pudding with treacle cream, or banana split with profiteroles and chocolate sauce (£3.50); good morning coffee and afternoon tea. There is also a lavishly timbered no smoking restaurant with a minstrel's gallery. *(Recommended by David and Ruth Hollands, the Didler, Peter Saville, Brian and Janet Ainscough, Patricia Beebe, Maysie Thompson, Derek Thomas, George Atkinson, Fiona Wynn)*

Heritage Hotels ~ Manager Francis Guildea ~ Real ale ~ Bar food ~ Restaurant ~ (01787) 247477 ~ Children welcome ~ Open 11-3, 6.30-11; 12-2.30, 6.30-10.30 Sun ~ Bedrooms: £95B/£145B

LAXFIELD TM2972 Map 5

Kings Head ★

Behind church, off road toward Banyards Green

A great time to visit this superbly unspoilt thatched 15th-c house is Tuesday afternoon, when a bunch of musicians and singers get together for an improvisation session. There's a really friendly unspoilt atmosphere in its three charmingly old-fashioned rooms. For many, the best is the front room, which has a high-backed built-in settle on the tiled floor, and an open fire. Two other equally unspoilt rooms – the landlady calls them the card and tap rooms – have pews, old seats, scrubbed deal tables, and some interesting wall prints. There's no bar: the well kept Adnams Best, Broadside, and Regatta and a guest such as Fullers London Pride are tapped straight from the cask in a cellar. Tasty bar food is served in a separate dining area, and includes sandwiches (from £2.50), baked banana with stilton (£3.25), pork and leek sausages with mash and onion gravy (£5.50), baked aubergine and goats cheese parcel with red pepper dressing (£6.25), good steak in ale pie (£7.50), grilled plaice (£8), and puddings such as apple and rhubarb crumble or lemon and lime syllabub (£3.25). The old bowling green forms the major part of the garden, and is surrounded by benches and tables; there's an arbour covered by a grape and hop vine, and a small pavilion for cooler evenings. *(Recommended by A C and E Johnson, Mr and Mrs Thomas, Rev John Hibberd, Pete Baker, J Hale, Neil Powell, Mrs Kay Dewsbury, the Didler, J F M and M West, Pippa Brown, Kevin Thorpe, Tim Maddison, Richard Siebert, Patrick Hancock, Phil and Sally Gorton, Comus and Sarah Elliott, Pam and David Bailey, Mr and Mrs J Brown)*

Adnams ~ Tenants George and Maureen Coleman ~ Real ale ~ Bar food (not Mon evening) ~ Restaurant ~ No credit cards ~ (01986) 798395 ~ Children in restaurant ~ Dogs allowed in bar ~ Impromptu trad music 1-7 Tues ~ Open 12(11.30 Sat)-3, 6-11(7-10.30 Sun)

LEVINGTON TM2339 Map 5

Ship

Gun Hill; village signposted from A14, then follow Stratton Hall sign

Now fully restored after a bad fire to the thatch, this charming old pub prettily placed by a little lime-washed church is open again – under new licensees who did a lot to make the Angel at Stoke-by-Nayland such a favourite, and who look like repeating the process here. Lots of ship prints and photographs of sailing barges, a marine compass under the serving counter in the middle room, and a fishing net slung overhead don't let you forget that you're near the sea. As well as benches built into the walls, there are comfortably upholstered small settles, some of them grouped round tables as booths, and a big black round stove. The flagstoned dining room has more nautical bric-a-brac and beams taken from an old barn; two no smoking areas. Good sensibly priced bar food includes Italian breads with olives (£2.50), tomato and fennel soup (£2.95), melon and bruschetta ham (£5.95), meat platter and pickles (the hikers like this one), pork schnitzel, liver and bacon with madeira sauce (£6.95), individual joint of lamb with mint and honey glaze (£7.50), dressed crab (£8.75), lemon sole (£10.95), and puddings such as white chocolate and summer berry mousse, or pear and cinnamon strudel with vanilla sauce (£3.75). Main courses can be a couple of pounds dearer in the evening. Well kept Adnams Bitter and Broadside and Greene King IPA on handpump or tapped from the cask, and decent wines; dominoes. If you look carefully enough, there's a sea view from the picnic-sets in front. No children inside. *(Recommended by Ian Phillips, Peter Thomas, Giles and Liz Ridout, Charles and Pauline Stride, Mike and Mary Carter, MDN, Gill Pennington)*

Pubmaster ~ Tenants Stella and Mark Johnson ~ Real ale ~ Bar food (12-2(4 Sun), 6.30-9.30) ~ (01473) 659573 ~ Open 11.30-2.30, 6-11; 12-3.30 Sun; closed Sun evening

LIDGATE TL7257 Map 5

Star

B1063 SE of Newmarket

Readers really enjoy the delightful mix of traditional English and Mediterranean influences at this pretty little village pub. It's run by a charmingly friendly Spanish landlady, who is very much responsible for its lovely relaxed atmosphere and very good food. Its intimate main room has lots of pubby character, with handsomely moulded heavy beams, a good big log fire, candles in iron candelabra on good polished oak or stripped pine tables, bar billiards, dominoes, darts and ring the bull, and just some antique Catalan plates over the bar to give a hint of the Mediterranean. Besides a second similar room on the right, there's a cosy little dining room on the left. The easy-going atmosphere, and the changing bar menu with crisp and positive seasoning in some dishes, speak more openly of the south. There might be mediterranean fish soup or prawns in garlic, catalan salad or venison carpaccio (£5.90), spanish omelette, grilled cod or venison sausages, (£6.50), lambs kidneys in sherry, paella, lasagne or roast lamb in garlic and wine (£11.50), stuffed quail in honey or monkfish marinière (£12.50), parrillada – seafood stew (£14.50), and puddings such as strawberry cream tart or chocolate roulade (£4); two-course lunch £10.50. Greene King IPA, Abbot and Old Speckled Hen on handpump, and enjoyable house wines; perhaps unobtrusive background music. There are tables on the raised lawn in front, and in a pretty little rustic back garden. *(Recommended by C W Dix, Michael Sargent, Gordon Theaker, Wendy Dye, R C Wiles, Stephen P Edwards, B N F and M Parkin, David Field, Derek Thomas, Shirley Mackenzie)*

Greene King ~ Lease Maria Teresa Axon ~ Real ale ~ Bar food (12-2, 7-10; not Sun evening) ~ Restaurant ~ (01638) 500275 ~ Children welcome ~ Dogs allowed in bar ~ Open 11-3, 5(6 Sat)-11; 12-3, 7-11 Sun; closed 25 Dec, 1 Jan

ORFORD TM4250 Map 5

Jolly Sailor £

Quay Street

You'll feel welcome as soon as you open the door of this unspoilt old brick pub. It was built in the 17th c, mainly from wrecked ships' timbers, and once had a reputation as a smugglers' hangout. These days it makes a good base for walkers, fishermen and birdwatchers. The several snugly traditional rooms have lots of exposed brickwork, and are served from counters and hatches in an old-fashioned central cubicle. There's an unusual spiral staircase in the corner of the flagstoned main bar – which also has 13 brass door knockers and other brassware, local photographs, and a good solid fuel stove; a small room is popular with the dominoes and shove-ha'penny players, and has draughts, chess and cribbage. Cheerful friendly staff serve well kept Adnams Bitter and Broadside on handpump, and big helpings of good straightforward pubby food. This might include irresistible battered local cod, eel or flounder with chips, home-made steak pie or lasagne, home-cooked ham and egg, local seasonal pheasant, and daily roasts (all £5.25); the dining room is no smoking. There are lovely surrounding coastal walks and plenty of outside pursuits; several picnic-sets on grass at the back have views over the marshes. *(Recommended by Ann and Colin Hunt, Dr and Mrs M E Wilson, Barry Collett, David and Rhian Peters, Comus and Sarah Elliott, MDN, Peter Thomas, Mr and Mrs S Oxenbury, Graham Jones, June and Perry Dann, Kevin Thorpe, Peter D B Harding)*

Adnams ~ Tenant Philip Attwood ~ Real ale ~ Bar food (not Mon evening, nor Mon-Thurs evenings Nov-Easter) ~ No credit cards ~ (01394) 450243 ~ Dogs allowed in bar ~ Open 11.30-2.30, 7-11; 12-2.45, 7-10.30 Sun; closed evenings 25, 26 Dec ~ Bedrooms: /£40

RATTLESDEN TL9758 Map 5

Brewers Arms

Signposted on minor roads W of Stowmarket, off B1115 via Buxhall or off A45 via Woolpit

There's a warmly welcoming atmosphere in this solidly built 16th-c village local. The pleasantly simple beamed lounge bar on the left has book-lined walls, individually chosen pictures and bric-a-brac. It winds back through standing timbers to the main eating area, which is partly flint-walled, and has a magnificent old bread oven and new more comfortable seating. French windows open on to a garden edged with bourbon roses. As well as lunchtime sandwiches (from £3.75), a good range of bar food might include soup (£3.25), grilled beef mushrooms topped with wild mushroom risotto and stilton (£4.25), moules marinière (£4.75), fish crumble, steak and kidney or vegetable pie (£7.95), chicken in white wine, mushroom and tarragon sauce (£8.95), baked lemon sole (£14.95) and puddings such as sticky toffee pudding, orange and lime cheesecake or orange and Cointreau bread and butter pudding (£3.50). The restaurant is no smoking. Well kept Greene King Abbot, IPA and Old Speckled Hen are served by a friendly barmaid; fruit machine and piped music. *(Recommended by Mrs Kay Dewsbury, David Kidd, Charles and Pauline Stride, MDN, Mrs A Scott, Pat and Tony Martin, Stephen, Julie and Hayley Brown, Michael and Marion Buchanan, JMC)*

Greene King ~ Tenants Mr and Mrs Davies ~ Real ale ~ Bar food ~ Restaurant ~ (01449) 736377 ~ Children in eating area of bar and restaurant ~ Jazz Thursdays ~ Open 11.30-2.30, 6-11; 12-3, 7-10.30 Sun

REDE TL8055 Map 5

Plough ♀

Village signposted off A143 Bury St Edmunds—Haverhill

At the end of a quiet green, this quaint partly thatched pink-washed pub does get surprisingly busy, so you may need to book. Very enjoyable changing bar food might include herb bread topped with melted goats cheese and garlic, or paw paw filled with prawns and curried yoghurt dressing (£4.95), rabbit braised with spring onions or leek and hazelnut (£8.95), venison shank with wild mushrooms (£9.50), calves liver with baby onions on spring onion mash (£10), monkfish with shellfish sauce (£10.50), lemon sole with fish paste (£11.95), and puddings such as strawberry and clotted cream tart or chocolate gateau topped with profiteroles and chocolate sauce (£3.95); the restaurant is no smoking. The traditionally simple bar has copper measures and pewter tankards hanging from low black beams, decorative plates on a delft shelf and surrounding the solid fuel stove in its brick fireplace, and red plush button-back built-in wall banquettes. Adnams, Bass and Greene King Old Speckled Hen and Ruddles are served from electric pumps and kept under light blanket pressure; piped pop music. There are picnic-sets in front, and pheasants may strut across the lawn in the sheltered cottagey garden at the back. *(Recommended by JKW, Philip and Susan Philcox, Patricia Beebe, P F Whight, J Hale)*

Greene King ~ Tenant Brian Desborough ~ Real ale ~ Bar food (not Sun evening) ~ Restaurant ~ (01284) 789208 ~ Children (no babies) in restaurant ~ Open 11-3, 6.30-11; 12-3, 7-10.30 Sun

SNAPE TM3959 Map 5

Crown

B1069

The attractive interior of this popular unspoilt inn is furnished with striking horseshoe-shaped high-backed settles around a big brick inglenook with a woodburning stove, spindleback and country kitchen chairs, and nice old tables on some old brick flooring. An exposed panel shows how the ancient walls were constructed, and there are lots of beams in the various small side rooms. Food mixes tried and tested favourites with more ambitious dishes, and might include courgette, basil and tomato soup (£2.95), coarse game pâté or cromer crab risotto with saffron (£4.50), steak and kidney pudding or confit of honey-roast duck on red cabbage and apple with wild mushroom jus (£9.50), herb-crusted rack of lamb with red wine and mint gravy (£10.95), scallops with lemon and couscous and spiced cream sauce (£11.95), fillet steak (£12.95), and puddings such as sticky toffee pudding or crème brûlée (£3.75). The dining room is no smoking, and in the Festival they do a useful pre-concert short menu. Adnams Bitter, Broadside and a seasonal ale are well kept on handpump, and there's a good thoughtful wine list, with eight by the glass (including champagne). A pretty roadside garden has tables with cocktail parasols. The bedrooms, up steep stairs, are quaint, with beamed ceilings, sloping floors, and doorways that you may have to stoop through. *(Recommended by Pat and Roger Fereday, Peter and Pat Frogley, Anthony Barnes, MDN, Mrs D Hall, Tracey and Stephen Groves, Barry Collett, D J Hayman, R C Wiles, Phil and Heidi Cook, R M Corlett, Maurice and Gill McMahon, Mr and Mrs S Oxenbury, Mrs Fay Cori , Comus and Sarah Elliott, June and Malcolm Farmer, Sir Clive Rose, J F M and M West, E J and M W Corrin, M A and C R Starling, Neil Powell, Mrs Rosalie Croft)*

Adnams ~ Tenant Diane Maylott ~ Real ale ~ Bar food ~ Restaurant ~ (01728) 688324 ~ Open 12-3, 6-11(7-10.30 Sun); closed 25 Dec, 26 Dec evening ~ Bedrooms: £55B/£65B

Golden Key

Priory Lane

The cheerfully friendly Mr and Mrs Kissick-Jones are Adnams's longest-serving tenants, and have been at this civilised and beautifully kept inn for over 25 years. The low-beamed and stylish lounge has an old-fashioned settle curving around a couple of venerable stripped tables on the tiled floor, a winter open fire, and, at the other end, some stripped modern settles around heavy pine tables on a turkey carpet, and a solid fuel stove in the big fireplace. The cream walls are hung with pencil sketches of customers, a Henry Wilkinson spaniel and so forth; a brick-floored side room has sofas and more tables. Well kept Adnams, Broadside and Old Ale, as well as a decent wine list, and about a dozen malt whiskies. Unfussy but remarkably good home-cooking might include filled rolls (from £2.25), soup (£3.95), prawns in filo pastry with chilli dip (£4.75), mushrooms with stilton (£5.25), sausage, egg and onion pie or smoked haddock quiche (£6.95), vegetable lasagne, broccoli cheese and potato bake or steak, mushroom and Guinness pie (£7.95), honey-roast ham (£8.95), loin lamb chops (£9.95), and puddings such as hot lemon cake or sticky toffee pudding (£3.75); one dining room is no smoking, and there's good disabled access. There are plenty of white tables and chairs on a terrace at the front, near the small sheltered flower-filled garden. *(Recommended by Tracey and Stephen Groves, Stuart and Valerie Ray, D S Cottrell, Comus and Sarah Elliott, Neil Powell, Richard Siebert, MDN, Paul Bailey, Phil and Heidi Cook, Gill Pennington)*

Adnams ~ Tenants Max and Suzie Kissick-Jones ~ Real ale ~ Bar food (12-2.30, 6(7 Sun)-9.30) ~ Restaurant ~ (01728) 688510 ~ Children in restaurant ~ Dogs allowed in bar ~ Open 12-3, 6(7 Sun)-10.30(11Sat) ~ Bedrooms: /£70B

Plough & Sail

Snape Maltings Riverside Centre

The big enclosed flower-filled courtyard at this busy extended pub has teak tables and chairs out under parasols – nice to sit with a drink and a newspaper before enjoying a concert at the Snape Maltings concert hall alongside. There's a light and airy feel in its four different areas, which include the original part with its log fires, sofas and settles, the bar where the Adnams Bitter, Broadside and seasonal ales are well kept on handpump, and two restaurants, one with a mezzanine which is actually under the eaves and has a balcony overlooking the bustle. There's a nice mix of customers, and the atmosphere is relaxed and friendly. As well as lunchtime sandwiches (from £3.45), ploughman's (£5.50), crispy hoi sin duck in a tortilla wrap, lasagne or sausage and mash (£7.25), more elaborate food (from a not particularly cheap menu) might include starters such as soup (£3.75), warm chorizo salad with butter beans, red onion and tomato (£6.45), beef carpaccio with red onion and stilton salad (£6.50), and main courses such as roast ciabatta topped with tomatoes, leeks, black olives and brie (£8.95), fried calves liver with baby leeks and tarragon sauce (£10.25), baked cod filled with garlic and herb cream cheese and topped with pancetta (£12.45), grilled steak medallions with spring cabbage, shallots and red wine jus (£14.75), and puddings such as lime and kiwi cheesecake with kiwi coulis or steamed apple and ginger sponge with apple syrup sauce (£3.95). *(Recommended by Jeff and Wendy Williams, Pamela Goodwyn, Anthony Barnes, R C Wiles, Ann and Colin Hunt, T G Thomas, Tracey and Stephen Groves)*

Free house ~ Licensees G J C and G E Gooderham ~ Real ale ~ Bar food (12-2.30 (3 Sat, Sun), 7-9(9.30 Fri, Sat)) ~ Restaurant ~ (01728) 688413 ~ Dogs allowed in bar ~ Open 11-11; 12-10.30 Sun; 11-3, 5.30-11 Sat, 12-3, 7-10.30 Sun in winter

SOUTH ELMHAM TM3389 Map 5

St Peters Brewery

St Peter S Elmham; off B1062 SW of Bungay

This lovely medieval manor is open only three days a week, but it's the ideal place to sample the full range of the acclaimed St Peter's beers, best known for their distinctive green bottles – they've been brewed here since 1996. The hall itself dates back to the late 13th c, but was much extended in 1539 using materials from the recently dissolved Flixton Priory. Genuinely old tapestries and furnishings perhaps make enjoying a drink or a meal in the small main bar feel more like a trip to a historic home than a typical pub outing, but the atmosphere is civilised and welcoming, with candles and fresh flowers on the dark wooden tables, soft classical music, and comfortable seats – from cushioned pews and settles to a 17th-c French bishop's throne. St Peters Best and Strong are served on draught from a little hatch, while the rest of their brews are available by the bottle; also various teas, and coffee. It's best to book for the good waitress-served food, which usually includes a short choice of things like soup (£3.95), toasted open sandwiches (£3.95), venison sausages with honey and mustard mash (£9.95), and braised steak (£10.95), as well as menu dishes such as pork fillet with caramelised apples (£10.95) or tempura battered monkfish with warm herb salad and pesto (£12.95); three-course Sunday lunch (£15.95). There's a particularly dramatic high-ceilinged dining hall (no smoking in here), with elaborate woodwork, a big flagstoned floor, and an imposing chandelier, as well as a couple of other appealing old rooms reached up some steepish stairs: one is no smoking, while the other is a light, beamed room with comfortable armchairs and nice big rug. Outside, tables overlook the original moat. The beers are made using water from a 60-metre (200-ft) bore hole, in brewery buildings laid out around a courtyard; they do tours on the hour between 12 and 4pm. The gift shop has unusual new brews under development (a tasty ruby beer on our visit) *(Recommended by David Field, Dr D J and Mrs S C Walker, Comus and Sarah Elliott)*

Own brew ~ Licensee George Wortley ~ Real ale ~ (01986) 782322 ~ Children welcome ~ Open 11-11 Fri/Sat; 12-6 and bank hols Sun; closed Mon-Thurs

SOUTHWOLD TM5076 Map 5

Crown ★

High Street

As Adnams's flagship pub, this rather smart old hotel maintains expected high standards throughout its bars, restaurant and accommodation. A great improvement this year is the extension of the elegant beamed main bar into what was a dining area – this should reduce problems with getting a table. The relaxed atmosphere and décor remain unchanged: a stripped curved high-backed settle and other dark varnished settles, kitchen chairs and some bar stools, pretty flowers on the mix of kitchen pine tables, a carefully restored and rather fine carved wooden fireplace, and newspapers to read. The smaller back oak-panelled locals' bar has more of a traditional pubby atmosphere, red leatherette wall benches and a red carpet; shove-ha'penny, dominoes and cribbage. The no smoking restaurant (with tall red upholstered chairs) is in what was the little no smoking parlour on the left, and now feels more separate. Very popular changing bar food from a stylish menu includes butternut and parmesan soup (£3.20), six oysters with red wine and shallot reduction (£8.10), tapas (£8.50 for two), fresh fish in a watermelon curry with aubergine and yoghurt (£9.50), duck leg confit with grilled aubergine and crushed potatoes (£9.75), grilled lemon sole with roasted new potatoes and caper mayonnaise (£10.25), roast loin of lamb with creamy parmesan risotto (£10.95), and puddings such as banana cheesecake with lemon icing (£3.95), chocolate nut torte with berry compote and honey mascarpone (£4.10), with good cheeses (£4.25). As well as the full range of Adnams beers, which are perfectly kept on handpump, there's a splendid wine list, with a monthly changing choice of 20 interesting varieties by the glass or bottle, and quite a few malt whiskies. Tables out in a sunny sheltered corner are very pleasant. *(Recommended by Marlene and Jim Godfrey, J F M and M West, MJVK, Stephen P Edwards, John Wooll, Tracey and Stephen Groves, Howard James, Richard Pinnington, T R and B C Jenkins, Tim Maddison, Ian Phillips, the Didler, Richard Siebert, Mike and Sue Loseby, Comus and Sarah Elliott, Bob and Margaret Holder, John Davis, Mrs Fay Cori , Dr and Mrs A K Clarke, Neil and Lorna Mclaughlan, Tina and David Woods-Taylor, Pamela and Merlyn Horswell, G T Brewster, Patrick Hancock, David Peakall, Hilary McLean, Steve Chambers, R C Wiles, J D M Rushworth, Sir Clive Rose, David Kidd, Nigel Woolliscroft, Stanley and Sally Brooks, Pam and David Bailey)*

Adnams ~ Tenant Michael Bartholomew ~ Real ale ~ Bar food (12-2, 7-9.30) ~ Restaurant ~ (01502) 722275 ~ Children in eating area of bar ~ Dogs allowed in bar ~ Open 11-3, 6-11; 12-3, 6-10.30 Sun ~ Bedrooms: £75B/£92B

If you know a pub's ever open all day, please tell us.

Harbour Inn

Blackshore, by the boats; from A1095, turn right at the Kings Head, and keep on past the golf course and water tower

The very friendly landlord at this interesting old waterside place, which stands among the small black fishing huts, is a lifeboatman, so the nautical character here is pretty genuine. It was even more so in the old days, when the lifeboat station was next door and the lifeboat telephone, and needless to say quite often the lifeboat men, were housed in the pub. There's still very much the feel of a fisherman's pub in the tiny, low-beamed, tiled and panelled front bar with antique settles, and in the back bar which has a wind speed indicator, model ships, a lot of local ship and boat photographs, smoked dried fish hanging from a line on a beam, a lifeboat line launcher, and brass shellcases on the mantelpiece over a stove. This room has rustic stools and cushioned wooden benches built into its stripped panelling. Behind here, the dining area is no smoking. Good value food includes soup (£3.25), filled baguettes (from £4.60), ploughman's (£6.95), half a pint of prawns (£4.95, a pint £7.95), fish and chips, which you can have wrapped in paper Friday night and Saturday lunchtime, (£7.35), moules marinière (£7.85), fish pie (£7.95), and chilli con carne (£8.25). Three Adnams ales are well kept on handpump. The back garden, on former marshland, has lots of tables, and there are more in front facing the jumbly waterfront bustle. *(Recommended by Howard James, Richard Pinnington, MJVK, Simon Watkins, Barry Collett, Neil and Lorna Mclaughlan, Ann and Colin Hunt, Comus and Sarah Elliott, Bob and Margaret Holder)*

Adnams ~ Tenant Colin Fraser ~ Real ale ~ Bar food (12-2.30, 6-9) ~ (01502) 722381 ~ Children welcome away from bar ~ Dogs allowed in bar ~ Live rock, folk Fri, Sat ~ Open 11-11; 12-10.30 Sun

STOKE-BY-NAYLAND TL9836 Map 5

Angel

B1068 Sudbury—East Bergolt; also signposted via Nayland off A134 Colchester—Sudbury

You may have to book well ahead for a weekend table at this stylishly elegant place. Imaginative, attractively presented and generously served bar food from changing blackboards might include home-made soup (£2.95), griddled fresh sardines in oregano, deep-fried cambazola with cranberry sauce or steamed mussels in white wine and cream (£4.75), fresh dressed crab with home-made mayonnaise (£5.95), roast ballotine of duckling with a cassis sauce (£7.15), steak and kidney pudding (£7.25), chicken and king prawn brochette with yoghurt and mint dip (£9.75), grilled fresh skate wing (£9.95), brochette of scallops wrapped in bacon (£11.50), and honey-glazed roast rack of lamb (£11.75); home-made puddings such as dark chocolate gateau or raspberry bavarois (£3.90). The comfortable main bar area has handsome Elizabethan beams, some stripped brickwork and timbers, a mixture of furnishings including wing armchairs, mahogany dining chairs, and pale library chairs, local watercolours and older prints, attractive table lamps, and a huge log fire. Round the corner is a little tiled-floor stand-and-chat bar – with well kept Adnams Bitter, Greene King IPA and Abbot and a guest such as Adnams Broadside on handpump, and a thoughtful wine list. One no smoking room has a low sofa and wing armchairs around its woodburning stove, and Victorian paintings on the dark green walls. There are cast-iron seats and tables on a sheltered terrace. *(Recommended by Ian Phillips, Stephen Buckley, David Twitchett, Derek Stafford, Hazel Morgan, Pamela Goodwyn, Mary and Dennis Jones, J D M Rushworth, Sir Clive Rose, MDN, Sally Anne and Peter Goodale, Jeff and Wendy Williams, Anthony Longden, Rob Webster, John Prescott, John and Enid Morris, Mrs Jane Kingsbury, J F M and M West, Peter and Marilyn Budden, Gill Pennington)*

Horizon Inns ~ Manager Michael Everett ~ Real ale ~ Bar food ~ Restaurant ~ (01206) 263245 ~ Children over 8 in restaurant ~ Open 11-2.30, 6-11; 12-3, 6-10.30 Sun; closed 25, 26 Dec, 1 Jan ~ Bedrooms: £52.50B/£67.50B

SWILLAND TM1852 Map 5

Moon & Mushroom

Village signposted off B1078 Needham Market—Wickham Market, and off B1077

There's a delightfully idiosyncratic yet gentle feel to this cosy old place. It's run by cheerful, genuinely helpful people, including the very efficient local ladies who deal with the meals, and there's a good mix of chatty customers – all of which creates a bustling but relaxed atmosphere. They keep only independent East Anglian beers such as Buffys Hopleaf and Norwich Terrier, Nethergate Umbel, Wolf Bitter and Coyote and Woodfordes Norfolk Nog and Wherry, which are tapped straight from casks functionally racked up behind the long counter. They have about 10 decent wines by the glass, and 20 malt whiskies. The homely interior is mainly quarry-tiled, with a small coal fire in a brick fireplace, old tables (with lots of board games in the drawers) arranged in little booths made by pine pews, and cushioned stools along the bar. A really homely touch is the four hearty hotpots in the no smoking dark green and brown painted cottagey dining room through a small doorway from the bar. These are served to you from Le Creuset dishes on a warming counter and might include coq au vin, pork with peppers, minted lamb and pheasant au vin (all £6.55). You then help yourself to a choice of half a dozen or so tasty vegetables. Another couple of dishes might include a very good ploughman's (£4.25), halibut mornay and stilton and pasta bake (£5.95), with proper home-made puddings like raspberry and apple crumble, bread and butter pudding and toffee and ginger pudding with butterscotch sauce (£2.95). As it is still a real local, food service does end quite early. You approach the pub through an archway of grapevines and creepers, and a little terrace in front has flower containers, trellis and nice wooden furniture under parasols. *(Recommended by George Atkinson, J F M and M West, JKW, Pat and Tony Martin, D S Cottrell, Peter Thomas, David Field, Comus and Sarah Elliott, Roger Bridgeman, MDN, Mr and Mrs M Hayes, Pam and David Bailey)*

Free house ~ Licensees Clive and Adrienne Goodall ~ Real ale ~ Bar food (12-2, 6.30-8.15; not Sun, Mon) ~ (01473) 785320 ~ Dogs allowed in bar ~ Open 11-2.30, 6-11; 12-3, 7-10.30 Sun; closed Mon lunchtime except bank hols

THORINGTON STREET TM0035 Map 5

Rose

B1068 Higham—Stoke by Nayland

Frequent fresh fish deliveries to this friendly village pub mean that the fish and seafood are particularly tasty: battered cod (£6.25), whitebait (£8.95), grilled skate with black butter and capers (£11.95), and bass (£12.95). Other dishes might include sandwiches (from £2.20), home-made soup (£3.95), ploughman's (from £3.75), baked potatoes (from £4.95), chicken goujons (£7.25), steaks (from £8.95) and puddings such as pineapple upside-down cake, popular melt-in-the-mouth meringues filled with fruit and cream, and blackberry and apple pie (£3.25); carvery only on Sunday (£8.40). The very cheery landlady makes a nice mix of customers welcome, and keeps a good pubby village atmosphere going. The building is partly Tudor, and has been knocked through into a single longish partly divided room, with old beams, pine tables and chairs, and enough pictures, prints and brasses to soften the room without overdoing the décor. Among them are old photographs of the landlady's family, who were in the fishing trade. The top end of the restaurant is no smoking. Well kept Adnams, Greene King Abbot and IPA, Woodfordes Wherry, and a guest beer on handpump, and decent wines; dominoes, cribbage, cards, dice; there may be piped music. The fair-sized garden has picnic-sets and summer barbecues, and overlooks the Box valley. *(Recommended by Charles and Pauline Stride, Ian Phillips, Stephen Kiley, M A and C R Starling, Keith Fairbrother, MDN, J F M and M West)*

Free house ~ Licensee Kathy Jones ~ Real ale ~ Bar food ~ Restaurant ~ No credit cards ~ (01206) 337243 ~ Children welcome ~ Dogs allowed in bar ~ Open 12-3, 7-11(10.30 Sun); closed Mon

TOSTOCK TL9563 Map 5

Gardeners Arms

Village signposted from A14 (former A45) and A1088

The cheerful natures of the jovial landlord and his wife (and probably Badger the lurcher) help along the bustling villagey atmosphere at this reliably good and charmingly unspoilt pub. Lots of people are here for the enjoyable particularly good value bar food, which includes sandwiches (from £1.60), ploughman's (from £4.50), gammon and eggs (£6.75), and daily specials such as avocado and prawns (£4.25), fresh dressed crab (£4.75), smoked mackerel, cream cheese and tomato tart or mediterranean cakes on tomato and pesto sauce (£6.25), lamb chops with redcurrant sauce (£6.50), steak and kidney pie (£6.75), salmon salad niçoise (£7.25), and puddings such as treacle tart or tiramisu and strawberry trifle (£2.95); the dining area is no smoking. The cosily smart lounge bar has heavy low black beams and lots of carving chairs around decent-sized black tables, and a warming fire, and the lively tiled public bar has darts, pool, shove-ha'penny, dominoes, cribbage, juke box, and an unobtrusive fruit machine; regular quiz nights. Very well kept Greene King IPA and Abbot and a guest such as Charles Wells Bombardier on handpump. A pleasantly sheltered lawn has picnic-sets among roses and other flowers. *(Recommended by JKW, Derek R A Field, Mike and Mary Carter, Michael and Marion Buchanan, Joyce and Geoff Robson, Mrs Kay Dewsbury, Mr and Mrs M Hayes, Pippa Daniels, Mr and Mrs J Brown)*

Greene King ~ Tenant Reg Ransome ~ Real ale ~ Bar food (12-2, 7.15-9.30 (7-9 Sun) not Mon, Tues evening, Sun lunchtime) ~ Restaurant ~ (01359) 270460 ~ Children in restaurant ~ Dogs allowed in bar ~ Open 11.30-2.30, 7-11; 12-3, 7-10.30 Sun

WALBERSWICK TM4974 Map 5

Bell

Just off B1387

To put you in the right frame of mind for visiting this unpretentious old pub, and make the most of its lovely setting, it's worth taking the little ferry from Southwold, and then enjoying the short walk. This is a nice spot close to the beach, and the tables on the sizeable lawn here are sheltered from the worst of the winds by a well placed hedge. The charming interior has brick floors, well worn flagstones and oak beams that were here 400 years ago when the sleepy little village was a flourishing port. The rambling traditional bar has curved high-backed settles, tankards hanging from oars above the counter, and a woodburning stove in the big fireplace; a second bar has a very large open fire. Changing bar food in generous helpings (they call out your number when it's ready) might include carrot and coriander soup (£3), marinated herrings (£3.95), ploughman's (£5), battered cod, haddock or plaice (£5.95), lentil and potato pie (£6.95), thai green chicken curry (£7.20), and home-made puddings (£3.50). Well kept Adnams Bitter, Broadside and Regatta on handpump, darts, shove-ha'penny, cribbage, dominoes, and boules outside. There are two resident boxer dogs, and dogs are welcome. There may be piped music, and in summer it can get so busy that service slows. Most of the bedrooms look over the sea or river. *(Recommended by John Wooll, Comus and Sarah Elliott, David Peakall, Howard James, Richard Pinnington, Ian Phillips, RB, Mrs Fay Cori , David Field, Richard Siebert, MDN, Jack and Jemima Valiant, J F M and M West, Tracey and Stephen Groves, T G Thomas, Tim Maddison, the Didler, Mike and Sue Loseby, John Hulme, Su and Bob Child, Penny Miles, Rob Kelvey, Neil and Lorna Mclaughlan, A C and E Johnson, MJVK, David and Anne Culley, Ann and Colin Hunt, Pam and David Bailey, Mrs Rosalie Croft)*

Adnams ~ Tenant Sue Ireland Cutting ~ Real ale ~ Bar food ~ Restaurant ~ No credit cards ~ (01502) 723109 ~ Children in family room ~ Dogs allowed in bar and bedrooms ~ Open 11-3, 6-11(all day during school hols); 11-11 Sat; 12-10.30 Sun ~ Bedrooms: £60S/£70S(£90B)

WALDRINGFIELD TM2844 Map 5

Maybush

Off A12 S of Martlesham; The Quay, Cliff Road

Beautifully placed at the end of a narrow lane by the banks of the bird-haunted River Deben, this busy family pub boasts what seems like dozens of well arranged outside tables to soak up the view. On our spring visit the neighbouring sailing club was out in force, so there was plenty of boating action to enjoy from the verandah (along with a fresh, salty breeze). The spacious bar has quite a nautical theme, with lots of old lanterns, pistols and so forth, as well as aerial photographs, an original Twister board, and fresh flowers; though it's all been knocked through, it's divided into separate areas by fireplaces or steps. A glass case has an elaborate ship's model, and there are a few more in a lighter, high-ceilinged extension. A number of the dark wooden tables are set for eating, and though it can fill quickly at lunchtime (particularly in summer), service remains prompt, efficient and friendly. There's something of an emphasis on fish and seafood on the big blackboard menu. As well as lunchtime soup (£3.25), sandwiches and ploughman's (£4.45), this might include generously served cod and chips (from £6.45), steak and Guinness pie (£6.95), vegetable wellington (£7), good grilled bass with garlic butter and prawns (£9.95), and 18oz T-bone steak (£11.95); children's menu. Flowers IPA, Greene King IPA and a guest such as Adnams on handpump, and a good range of wines, with around nine or ten by the glass. Plenty of the locals bring their dogs. Fruit machine, pool, piped music. River cruises are available nearby. *(Recommended by Pamela Goodwyn, Mike and Mary Carter, Rev John Hibberd, J F M and M West, Howard James, Richard Pinnington)*

Pubmaster ~ Tenants Steve and Louise Lomas ~ Real ale ~ Bar food (12-2.30, 6.30-9.30; 12-9.30 Sat, Sun) ~ Restaurant ~ (01473) 736215 ~ Children in restaurant ~ Dogs allowed in bar ~ Open 11-11; 12-10.30 Sun

WESTLETON TM4469 Map 5

Crown 🍷 🛏

B1125 Blythburgh—Leiston

Readers enjoy unpretentious bar lunches in this extended coaching inn, such as open sandwiches made with home-baked bread (from £3.95), ploughman's (£5.95), and fish and chips, good local sausages and mash, or steak and kidney pie (£7.50), with a reasonably priced children's menu. There is a more ambitious evening and restaurant menu. The parlour room has a sanded wooden floor, a nice mix of old settles (one dated 1780), pews, old chairs, and old barrel tables, and a big log fire that roars away nicely on winter days. Henry James mentioned the red quarry-tiled floor in the main bar, which also has country chairs and attractive stripped tables, good local photographs and farm tools, and there's a carpeted no smoking dining conservatory. Well kept on handpump, the half a dozen or so real ales include Adnams, Greene King IPA and Abbot and three guests from local brewers such as St Peters and Tindalls; 90 malt whiskies, and a carefully chosen wine list. Dominoes, cribbage, shove-ha'penny, darts, bar skittles, bar quoits; piped music. The charmingly landscaped gardens have plenty of seats (the ones on the floodlit terrace are warmed by outside heaters), and a pets corner with pot bellied pigs, budgerigars and ducks; the stables are still used by horses. Good walks nearby. *(Recommended by Robert and Catherine Dunster, J F M and M West, Tracey and Stephen Groves, Mr and Mrs W D Borthwick, Roy and Lindsey Fentiman, Comus and Sarah Elliott, Richard Siebert, Sir Clive Rose, Neil Powell, Ian Phillips)*

Free house ~ Licensees Richard and Rosemary Price ~ Real ale ~ Bar food (12-2.15, 7-9.30) ~ Restaurant ~ (01728) 648777 ~ Dogs allowed in bar and bedrooms ~ Open 11-3, 6-11; 12-3, 7-10.30 Sun; closed 25 and 26 Dec ~ Bedrooms: £59.50B/£74.50B

Tipping is not normal for bar meals, and not usually expected.

WINGFIELD TM2277 Map 5

De La Pole Arms

Church Road; village signposted off B1118 N of Stradbroke

Like the other two pubs owned by St Peters, this tucked-away village inn has been beautifully restored. Deliberately simple yet stylish décor maximises the appeal of its timbered 16th-c interior. Dark wood tables on quarry-tiled floors, light timbers criss-crossing cream walls and big inglenooks in the two bars combine with a modern light wood counter to give a farmhouse/bistro feel. They keep two St Peters beers on handpump in winter, upped to four in summer, and their entire range of over a dozen bottled beers. Very good bar food is served by courteous friendly staff, and might include soup (£3.95), filled baguettes or devilled whitebait (£4.95), fish and chips, fish pie or wild rabbit casserole (£7.95), lambs liver with pancetta and madeira sauce or gruyère and leek flan (£8.25), rib-eye ciabatta sandwich (£8.95), and puddings such as apple crumble and custard, mango and orange mousse and chocolate and rum pots (£3.95); the no smoking restaurant has a more elaborate menu. *(Recommended by Tom Gondris, Comus and Sarah Elliott, Neil and Lorna Mclaughlan, Phil, Tina and Harrison Walker, Derek Thomas, MDN, J F M and M West, Mike and Wendy Proctor, A C and E Johnson, Julie and Bill Ryan)*

St Peters ~ Tenant Sally Prior ~ Real ale ~ Bar food ~ Restaurant ~ (01379) 384545 ~ Children welcome ~ Dogs allowed in bar ~ Open 11-3, 6.30(6 Fri, Sat)-11; 12-3, 6.30-10.30 Sun; closed Sun evening and Mon in winter

Lucky Dip

Besides the fully inspected pubs, you might like to try these Lucky Dips recommended to us and described by readers (if you do, please send us reports: www.goodguides.com).

Aldeburgh [TM4656]

Brudenell: Large hotel right on the beach (sandbags by the doors), magnificent sea views from the bar – rather smartly contemporary, in blue, yellow and orange; Adnams, decent food, good service, comfortable bedrooms *(Ian Phillips)*

☆ ***Cross Keys*** [Crabbe St]: Busy 16th-c pub extended from low-beamed core with antique settles, Victorian prints, woodburners, well kept Adnams ales (the full range) and wines, brisk friendly service, ample enjoyable food, Sunday papers; loudspeaker food announcements, can get smoky, fruit machine; open all day July/Aug, children in eating areas, picnic-sets in sheltered back yard which opens on to promenade and beach; elegant bedrooms with own bathrooms *(Jack and Jemima Valiant, LYM, MJVK, Rona Murdoch, Michael Butler, Ian Phillips)*

Mill [Market Cross Pl, opp Moot Hall]: Homely 1920s corner pub near Moot Hall and beach, friendly and relaxing, with good value food cooked to order from good baguettes to local fish and roast of the day, good service (humorous landlord), well kept Adnams ales, decent coffee (a lunchtime tipple of choice here), locals' bar, lots of pictures, cosy no smoking beamed dining room with *Gypsy Queen* model, sea view and strong RNLI theme; cream teas July/Aug (open all day then, can get rather full); fruit machine; open all day Fri/Sat, bedrooms *(Rona Murdoch, George Atkinson, David Oakley, June and Perry Dann, Ian Phillips)*

Alderton [TM3441]

Swan [The Street]: Small pub with low-beamed bar, Adnams and Greene King IPA, nice choice of good food, friendly service, comfortable relaxed atmosphere, separate restaurant; bedrooms *(John Martin, Michael Dandy)*

Aldringham [TM4461]

☆ ***Parrot & Punchbowl*** [B1122/B1353 S of Leiston]: Neatly kept beamed pub with good food inc local fish from downstairs servery, dining-room meals Fri-Sun (must book then), good wine choice, well kept Adnams and Greene King IPA, decent coffee, no piped music; children welcome, dogs allowed; pleasant sheltered garden with own servery and a couple of swings, nice craft centre opp *(BB, Ann and Colin Hunt, Jim McBurney)*

Barnby [TM4789]

Swan [off A146 Beccles—Lowestoft; Swan Lane]: Plush beamed dining pub with emphasis on excellent choice of good fresh fish in restaurant – not cheap but good value; well kept Adnams, good house wines, fishing décor *(W G Lawrence)*

Barrow [TL7663]

Weeping Willow [off A45 W of Bury]: Comfortable pub with gleaming tables in lounge/dining area, beautifully presented fresh food (not Mon) inc interesting home-made breads, good curries, huge salads and bargain Sun lunch, Flowers and Greene King IPA, friendly charismatic landlord, plain public bar; picnic-sets and swing in willow-shaded garden *(Ian Phillips)*

Beyton [TL9363]

White Horse [signed off A14 and A1088; Bury Rd]: Village-green pub very popular with older lunchers, food all home-made inc particularly good vegetarian choice, friendly staff, well kept Greene King ales, no music *(Rona Murdoch, Comus and Sarah Elliott)*

Bildeston [TL9949]

☆ ***Crown*** [B1115 SW of Stowmarket]: Picturesque 15th-c timbered inn, neat beamed main bar with inglenook and comfortable banquettes, smaller more modern bar, food from soup and sandwiches up, good puddings choice, no smoking dining room, well kept Adnams and Broadside a guest beer such as Wolf Golden Jackal tapped from the cask, helpful friendly service; may be piped music; children welcome, nice tables out in courtyard, more in large attractive garden, quiet comfortable bedrooms *(George Atkinson, Charles and Pauline Stride, LYM)*

Blyford [TM4276]

☆ ***Queens Head*** [B1123 Blythburgh—Halesworth]: Thatch, very low beams, a well they still use, some antique settles alongside more modern conventional furnishings, huge fireplace, popular generous food inc bargain lunches (but no sandwiches), well kept Adnams Bitter, Mild, and Broadside, friendly tenant; children allowed in no smoking restaurant, tables outside with good play area, bedrooms *(June and Perry Dann, LYM, Robert Turnham)*

Blythburgh [TM4575]

☆ ***White Hart*** [A12]: Friendly and roomy open-plan family dining pub flourishing on completion of its refurbishment, fine ancient beams, woodwork and staircase, full Adnams range kept well, decent wines and coffee, reliable good value food inc game and fish, friendly attentive service; children in eating area and restaurant, open all day Fri/Sat, spacious lawns looking down on tidal marshes (barbecues), magnificent church over road, and has bedrooms now *(Ann and Colin Hunt, Comus and Sarah Elliott, LYM, Mrs Rosalie Croft)*

Boxford [TL9640]

White Hart [Broad St]: Attractive exterior, pleasant welcoming interior, good choice of food inc excellent curries and interesting variety of fish (landlord does the cooking, wife does the bar) *(Phil and Sally Gorton)*

Bradfield St George [TL9158]

Fox & Hounds [Felsham Rd]: Good reasonably priced home cooking, good service, attractive bars and restaurant, several real ales inc Buffys and Nethergate, woodburner; bedrooms, cl Mon *(Mrs J Kendrick)*

Brent Eleigh [TL9447]

Cock [Lavenham Rd (A1141)]: Unspoilt thatched pub with piano in clean and cosy snug, benches, table and darts in second small room, coal fires, lots of old photographs of local villages, no food beyond crisps and pickled eggs, Adnams, Greene King IPA or Abbot and Nethergate Mild; nice garden, attractive inn-sign, bedrooms *(the Didler)*

Bromeswell [TM3050]

Cherry Tree [Orford Rd, Bromeswell Heath]: Comfortably modernised neat beamed lounge, very popular wknds for good value and enjoyable wide-ranging food; friendly staff, open fire and velvet curtains; seats outside, charming inn-sign *(BB, Gill Pennington)*

Bury St Edmunds [TL8564]

☆ ***Cupola House*** [The Traverse]: Interesting building with grand central staircase to upstairs panelled no smoking bar (nice atmosphere here), friendly and patient landlord doing good inexpensive food, charming service, Greene King real ales, ad lib coffee *(MDN, Laura and Stuart Ballantyne)*

☆ ***Nutshell*** [Traverse, Abbeygate St]: Quaint and attractive 17th-c corner pub, surely the country's smallest inside, with particularly well kept Greene King IPA and Abbot, friendly character landlord, bare boards and benches, lots of odd bric-a-brac from coins and banknotes on ceiling to mummified cat; cl Sun and Holy Days *(the Didler, C J Fletcher, Michael Butler, Mike and Wendy Proctor)*

Old Cannon [Cannon St]: Pub/restaurant brewing its own beers such as Cannon Best and Gunners Daughter, also Adnams and good wine choice by the glass, with good imaginative generous food inc thai, unusual décor with the two large polished copper brewing kettles right by the bar, and what looks like a floorless upper room complete with suspended furnishings above; can get very busy Fri/Sat evenings; bedrooms *(Martin Coe, Wendy Dye)*

Rising Sun [Risbygate St]: Central servery with bars all round, no smoking back part extending into conservatory, usual food inc children's and cheap puddings, Greene King real ales *(Tony Hobden)*

Rose & Crown [Whiting St]: Unassuming and unchanging town local, fairly spartan but comfortable and spotless, with simple excellent value lunchtime food, particularly well kept Greene King ales inc XX Dark Mild and a guest beer, pleasant lounge, bric-a-brac, good games-oriented public bar with darts, cards and dominoes, rare separate off-sales counter *(Pete Baker)*

Charsfield [TM2556]

Three Horseshoes [off B1078]: Two-bar village pub with well kept ales inc Adnams and Earl Soham Victoria, choice of wines, generous reasonably priced fresh and imaginative food in dining area and small restaurant, regular themed menus and Tues-Fri bargain lunches, daily paper, games, piano, lots of Laurel and Hardy figurines; quiz nights; tables in garden *(BB, Keith Sale, Sue Harvey)*

Clare [TL7645]

Bell [Market Hill]: Large timbered inn with local feel in comfortably rambling bar, splendidly carved black beams, old panelling and woodwork around the open fire, side rooms (one with lots of canal and other prints), well kept Nethergate ales inc Mild (this is the brewer's local), also others such as Greene King IPA, decent wines, usual food from sandwiches up inc children's in dining conservatory opening on to terrace; darts, pool, fruit machine; bedrooms off back courtyard, open all day Sun, very special village, lovely church *(Patrick Hancock, LYM, George Atkinson)*

Cock [Callis St]: Spacious old inn with fine view of church, reasonably priced usual food, well kept Adnams, separate restaurant *(Patrick Hancock)*

☆ ***Swan*** [High St]: Proper village local, early 17th-c but much modernised, lots of copper and brass and huge log fire, public bar with World War II memorabilia and another fire (dogs allowed here), friendly landlord, reasonably priced food from huge bargain huffers up; no children; lovely flower tubs out behind *(BB, R J Walden, Patrick Hancock)*

Creeting St Mary [TM1155]

Highwayman [A140, just N of junction with A14]: Much extended and modernised, pleasantly relaxed atmosphere with welcoming staff, emphasis on enjoyable food inc interesting dishes and popular Sun lunch, three changing ales such as Greene King IPA and Old Speckled Hen and Woodfordes Wherry, decent wines, gallery overflow; unobtrusive piped music; tables on back lawn with small pond *(Ian and Nita Cooper, George Atkinson)*

Cretingham [TM2260]

☆ ***Bell*** [The Street]: Comfortable village pub mixing striking 15th-c beams, timbers and glorious log fire in big fireplace with more modern renovations and furnishings, Adnams and changing guest beers, good generous food inc children's, attentive landlord; no smoking lounge and restaurant with Sun lunch, traditional games in public bar, family room; charming beamed bedrooms, good breakfast, may open all day in summer, seats out in rose garden and on front grass *(June and Perry Dann, LYM, J F M and M West, John and Patricia White)*

Eastbridge [TM4566]

Eels Foot [off B1122 N of Leiston]: Light modern furnishings in cheerfully basic country pub with well kept Adnams, darts in side area, wide choice of usual food, neat back dining room; walkers, children and dogs welcome, tables and swings outside, pretty village handy for Minsmere bird reserve and heathland walks; open all day in summer for coffee and cream teas, live music some Sats, impromptu music Thurs *(LYM, Eddie Edwards, Tina and David Woods-Taylor, Simon Watkins)*

Felixstowe Ferry [TM3337]

☆ ***Ferry Boat***: Cottagey 17th-c pub tucked between golf links and dunes near harbour and Martello tower, great for walks by sea; extended and much modernised as family pub, sensible choice of good value food inc fresh fish and OAP bargain early lunches, well kept Adnams and Greene King IPA and Old Speckled Hen, warmly friendly licensees, helpful staff, good log fire; tables outside, busy summer wknds – can be very quiet other times *(Klaus and Elizabeth Leist, Bill and Rachael Gallagher, Ian Phillips, June and Malcolm Farmer, LYM, J F M and M West, Charles and Pauline Stride)*

Victoria: Welcoming well refurbished child-friendly riverside pub, generous straightforward food inc local seafood, well kept Adnams and Greene King ales, briskly efficient friendly service, sea views from upstairs dining area *(Ian Phillips, Dr Roger Turner, June and Malcolm Farmer, Pamela Goodwyn, Barry Collett)*

Flixton [TM3187]

Buck [The Street]: Several refurbished bars, big restaurant, good beer range, good food inc Sun carvery, local paintings; handy for Aviation Museum *(June and Perry Dann)*

Framlingham [TM2862]

Station Hotel [Station Rd]: Owned by the Earl Soham microbrewery, with their excellent beer, interesting food inc good fish dishes (an emphasis on smoked), railway memorabilia in large main bar, small snug; child-friendly *(Jack and Jemima Valiant)*

Freckenham [TL6672]

Golden Boar [B1102 Fordham—Mildenhall]: Very friendly, wide range of good interesting freshly made food, good wines and service; handy for Newmarket (*Racing Post* available) *(Mr and Mrs J Stone)*

Friston [TM4160]

☆ ***Old Chequers*** [just off A1094 Aldeburgh—Snape]: Welcoming and civilised dining pub with simple but stylish country pine furnishings, light and airy décor, good if not cheap interesting food inc fish, game and Sun carvery, well kept Adnams, good wines and whiskies, friendly staff, interesting toy collection; good walk from Aldeburgh *(Pamela Goodwyn, P F Whight, LYM, J F M and M West)*

Great Wenham [TM0738]

Queens Head [The Row, Capel St Mary rd]: Carefully extended cottagey country local, cheerful helpful licensees, wide choice of creative and authentic Indian food (not Mon evening) graded for hotness, conventional food too, with comfortably traditional pubby atmosphere, well kept Adnams and Greene King IPA and Abbot, good value wines; pool, piped music; families welcome in cosy snug *(Ian Phillips)*

Grundisburgh [TM2250]

Dog [The Green]: Well run carefully extended elegant period village pub with good reasonably priced food inc bargain OAP Mon lunches, well kept ales inc Adnams, friendly landlord, tankards on oak beams, old pictures, restaurant; attractive village *(Dr and Mrs M E Wilson)*

Halesworth [TM3877]

Angel [Thoroughfare]: Civilised and comfortable 16th-c Adnams coaching inn with their beers very well kept and reasonably priced, obliging service, bar food from soup and sandwiches up, good range of coffees and cakes, good Italian restaurant, decent wines; interesting inner courtyard with 18th-c clock and vines, seven well equipped bedrooms, open all day *(Comus and Sarah Elliott)*

☆ ***White Hart*** [Thoroughfare]: Roomy and well restored open-plan local, well arranged and nicely furnished; good home-cooked food with fresh fish and excellent local veg, comfortable welcoming atmosphere, well kept beers inc Adnams and Bass, attentive friendly service *(June and Perry Dann)*

Hartest [TL8352]

☆ ***Crown*** [B1066 S of Bury St Edmunds]: Pink-washed pub by church behind village green, new licensees taking over as this edition comes out – reports please; pleasant interior with big log fire in impressive fireplace, has had enjoyable bar food, popular Sun lunch and good value special menus Mon, Weds and Fri evenings, Greene King IPA and Abbot, and Old Speckled Hen under light blanket pressure, decent house wines, quick service, pleasant conservatory; may be quiet piped music; children in eating areas, tables on big back lawn and in sheltered side courtyard, play area; has been cl Sun evening in Jan-Feb *(LYM)*

Haughley [TM0262]

☆ ***Kings Arms*** [off A45/B1113 N of Stowmarket; Old St]: Good atmosphere in 16th-c timbered pub with airy 1950s back part refurbished to match, nice mix of drinking and dining, wide choice of good value home-made food, friendly helpful staff, well kept Adnams Broadside and Greene King Abbot, decent wines, busy public bar with games, log fire; piped music; tables and play house in colourful back garden *(Quentin and Carol Williamson, BB, Ian and Nita Cooper)*

Holbrook [TM1636]

Compasses [Ipswich Rd]: Tranquil old place, clean, tidy and spaciously refurbished, well kept Adnams, Greene King IPA and a guest, friendly attentive staff, big log fire, fairly priced food inc several daily specials in bar and restaurant; garden with play area, nice spot on Shotley peninsula *(Ken and Brenda Holroyd, Alan Thomas, Pamela Goodwyn)*

Hoxne [TM1877]

☆ ***Swan*** [off B1118, signed off A140 S of Diss; Low St]: Striking late 15th-c thatched pub restored to its roots by present licensees, broad oak floorboards, handsomely carved timbering in the colour-washed walls, armchairs by deep-set inglenook fireplace, no smoking snug, another fireplace in dining room, well kept Adnams and guest beers tapped from the cask, enjoyable reasonably priced food inc good fish, friendly atmosphere, relaxed service; children welcome, sizeable attractive garden behind, summer barbecues *(Mrs Jill Silversides, Barry Brown, Tom Gondris, Mike and Wendy Proctor, LYM, Sue Anderson, Phil Copleston)*

Huntingfield [TM3473]

Huntingfield Arms [The Street]: Neat and unpretentious, overlooking green, light wood tables and chairs, beams and stripped brickwork, decent food inc good salads and fresh fish, well kept Adnams and Greene King, friendly service, restaurant, games area with pool beyond woodburner *(Neil Powell, June and Perry Dann)*

Ipswich [TM1744]

Brewery Tap [Cliff Rd]: Ground floor of early 19th-c building nestling under vast Tolly brewery, looking over road to docks; their beers kept well, decent food inc baguettes all day (not Sun/Mon evenings), cheerful prompt helpful service, traditional games, children's room, brewery tours twice weekly; piped music (not in no smoking room on right), popular Thurs quiz night; open all day, wheelchair access *(Charles and Pauline Stride, LYM, Jenny and Brian Seller, Mrs E A Shortland-Jones)*

☆ ***Fat Cat*** [Spring Rd]: Reconstruction of basic bare-boards pub outstanding for around 20 well kept interesting ales mainly from small breweries, Belgian imports, farm ciders, friendly first-rate service, snacks such as scotch eggs and filled rolls (or bring your own food), lots of old advertisements, no music or machines; pleasant garden with summer barbecues, open all day *(the Didler)*

Milestone [Woodbridge Rd]: Open-plan pub with up to a dozen real ales on handpump and twice as many tapped from the cask, farm ciders, several dozen whiskies, home-made food lunchtime and Mon-Weds evening; live bands, large front terrace *(the Didler)*

Kirtling [TL6856]

Red Lion [The Street]: Locally very popular for food since 2000 reopening, but still welcomes drinkers (and is HQ for local cricket club) *(anon)*

Lavenham [TL9149]

Cock [Church St]: Welcoming and attractive thatched village pub, quiet at lunchtimes, basic bar, plush lounge, separate family dining room, Adnams and Greene King IPA and XX Mild on handpump, Abbot tapped from the cask, good wine choice, quick service, cheap food inc pies, fish and red-hot curry *(Mr and Mrs D Drake, the Didler, Sir Clive Rose)*

Greyhound [High St]: Good pubby feel in ancient and unspoilt narrow lounge and simpler public bar with polished tables and matching settles, 14th-c beams, well kept Greene King IPA and Abbot, usual food, snug candlelit dining area; busy wknds; long narrow mainly asphalted garden *(George Atkinson)*

Layham [TM0240]

☆ ***Marquis of Cornwallis*** [Upper St (B1070 E of Hadleigh)]: Beamed 16th-c pub popular lunchtime with businessmen and retired locals for nicely prepared generous food inc good ploughman's and fresh veg, plush lounge bar, friendly atmosphere, well kept beers such as Marstons Pedigree, good wines and coffee; good valley views, popular bird table and picnic-sets in extensive riverside garden, open all day Sat in summer; bedrooms handy for Harwich ferries *(C L Kauffmann, Keith Fairbrother)*

Little Bealings [TM2247]

Admirals Head [Sandy Lane]: Stylish and comfortable facsimile of beamed Georgian pub doing well under newish landlord, good choice of home-made food inc interesting dishes, well kept ales inc Adnams Bitter and Broadside, friendly service, upper-level dining room and intriguing little cellar bar with trap door to well, no music or machines; picnic-sets out on terrace *(Ian Phillips)*

Long Melford [TL8645]

☆ ***Bull*** [Hall St (B1064)]: Medieval former manorial great hall, now a hotel (not cheap, but very friendly), with beautifully carved beams in old-fashioned timbered front lounge, blazing log fire in huge fireplace, antique furnishings (and games machine), daily papers; more spacious back bar with sporting prints; good range of bar food from good filled huffers to one-price hot dishes inc imaginative salads and fresh fish, no smoking restaurant, well kept Adnams Best, Greene King IPA and Nethergate; children welcome, courtyard tables, open all day Sat/Sun; comfortable bedrooms *(Maysie Thompson, George Atkinson, LYM, Pamela Goodwyn, R C and J M Clark, Derek Thomas)*

☆ ***Cock & Bell*** [Hall St]: Attractive pub with roomy and comfortable carpeted bar and dining area, welcoming service, enjoyable good value food and wine, well kept Courage Best and Directors and Greene King IPA, pleasant service *(Alan Jones, Patrick Hancock)*

Crown [Hall St]: Dark green ceiling and walls show off carefully chosen prints and nicely placed furniture, dusky pink banquettes on one side, big log fire, well kept Bass and Greene King IPA and Old Speckled Hen, obliging service, reasonably priced generous food; quiet and pleasant piped music; well equipped bedrooms, huge breakfast *(Len Banister, LYM, Patrick Hancock)*

George & Dragon [Hall St]: Good choice of food in refurbished bar and dining room, roaring log fires, no smoking area, Greene King real ales, decent wines, good polite service, bar billiards; sheltered garden and courtyard; open all day exc Sun, five comfortable bedrooms *(Patrick Hancock)*

Lowestoft [TM5390]

Jolly Sailors [Pakefield St/Wilson Rd, off A12]: Generous food esp fish, bargain OAP Mon/Tues lunches and popular all-day Sun carvery in big busy partly no smoking bar and much-booked restaurant; well kept Adnams, Boddingtons and Woodfordes Wherry, helpful uniformed staff, sweeping sea view from front part, no smoking family garden room; handy for beach and quaint Pakefield church *(J F M and M West)*

Trowel & Hammer [Pakefield St]: Well kept modern pub near sea, well kept beers, good eating choice from lunchtime baguettes and baked potatoes to light air-conditioned restaurant; play area, live music Sun night, open all day *(June and Perry Dann)*

Market Weston [TL9777]

☆ ***Mill*** [Bury Rd (B1111)]: Well opened up, combining restaurant and pub without clashes; good interesting fresh food using local produce inc popular Sun lunch, well kept Adnams, Greene King IPA and an Old Chimneys beer from the village brewery, enthusiastic effective service; children welcome, theme night *(Derek R A Field)*

Martlesham [TM2547]

Red Lion [Main Rd]: Chef & Brewer with friendly staff, lots of tables and very wide food choice *(Gill Pennington)*

Mellis [TM1074]

Railway Tavern [The Common]: Warmly friendly local, open fires, very relaxed licensees, enjoyable food inc fresh fish and good value Sun lunch, well kept beers from independent breweries, quaint railway theme; curry and folk nights, open all day *(David Oakley)*

Melton [TM2850]

☆ ***Wilford Bridge*** [Wilford Bridge Rd]: Light, roomy and well organised, with emphasis on good value food inc local fish in two spacious bars and restaurant, steak nights Mon/Tues (when it's less busy), takeaways, well kept Adnams, good wines by the glass, prompt friendly service even though busy, pleasant décor; nearby river walks *(Pamela Goodwyn, J F M and M West, Peggy and Alec Ward)*

Middleton [TM4367]

☆ ***Bell*** [off B1125 Leiston—Westleton; The Street]: Charming little traditional pub, part thatched and beamed, in pretty setting near church; well kept Adnams ales tapped from the cask, short choice of good simple food inc children's, attractive prices, keen and lively landlord; darts and open fire in small low-ceilinged public bar (dogs allowed), woodburner in comfortable lounge, small back dining room; may be piped radio, folk nights some wknds, opening times may vary; picnic-sets in garden, camping, handy for RSPB Minsmere and coast *(MDN, Tracey and Stephen Groves, BB, Les Trusler)*

Monks Eleigh [TL9647]

☆ ***Swan*** [B1115 Sudbury—Stowmarket]: Chef/landlord doing innovative fresh home-made food inc seasonal game, several fish dishes and bargain early supper; real ales inc Adnams and Greene King, good value wines, friendly efficient service, comfortably modernised lounge bar, open fire, two dining areas; bedrooms *(Derek Thomas, Dr T and Mrs J Walker, MDN)*

Needham Market [TM0954]

Lion [Ipswich Rd/Lion Lane]: Mossy-tiled roomy local with wide range of usual food (not Sun evening), friendly staff, Adnams, Boddingtons and Greene King IPA, soft lighting; picnic-sets and play area in big garden *(Ian Phillips, Ian and Nita Cooper)*

Newbourne [TM2643]

Fox [The Street]: Pleasant 17th-c pub, enjoyable food using fresh local produce, well kept Tolly tapped from the cask, cosy unspoilt oak-beamed drinking area around log fire, nice golden retriever (Hector), separate family room, dining extension; pretty hanging baskets, lots of tables out in attractive garden with pond, musical evenings *(Pamela Goodwyn)*

Newmarket [TL6463]

Wagon & Horses [High St]: Unpretentious local with five real ales, low-priced standard food from sandwiches and wraps up, daily papers *(SLC, MLR)*

Orford [TM4250]

Kings Head [Front St]: Bright cheerful feel in airily refurbished beamed lounge bar overlooking churchyard, well kept Adnams ales, good coffee, good range of reasonably priced food inc sandwiches and the noted local smokery products, decent wines, friendly staff and locals, pleasant restaurant; live music Fri, attractive character bedrooms with own bathrooms, lots of flowers outside *(MDN, Marjorie and Bernard Parkin, Dr D J and Mrs S C Walker, Barry Collett, George Atkinson, LYM)*

Pettistree [TM3054]

Three Tuns [off A12 just S of Wickham Mkt; Main Rd]: New owners in unusual pub, charmingly decorated bar furnished with comfortable armchairs and sofas, civilised food, well kept Adnams, good service; now has bedrooms *(Pamela Goodwyn)*

Ramsholt [TM3041]

☆ ***Ramsholt Arms*** [Dock Rd, signposted off B1083]: Lovely isolated spot, with picture-window nautical bars overlooking River Deben, and handy for the new Sutton Hoo visitor centre; easy-going bar (one of the dogs can let himself in) with good log fire, well kept Adnams and guests such as Timothy Taylors Landlord and Woodfordes Wherry, several wines by the glass, enjoyable food inc children's dishes, friendly staff, no smoking restaurant, summer afternoon terrace bar (not Sun); longish steep walk down from car park, busy summer wknds; children welcome, roomy bedrooms (in line for updating) with stunning view, yacht moorings nearby *(LYM, June and Malcolm Farmer, Comus and Sarah Elliott, Pamela Goodwyn, J F M and M West, Mrs E A Shortland-Jones)*

Saxon Street [TL6759]

Reindeer [The Street]: Good choice of well kept real ales, friendly service, enjoyable generous food *(Mike and Jennifer Marsh)*

Saxtead Green [TM2665]

☆ ***Old Mill House*** [B1119; The Green]: Roomy dining pub across green from windmill, beamed carpeted bar, neat country-look flagstoned restaurant extension, brick servery, wooden tables and chairs, pretty curtains, popular reasonably priced freshly made food inc good puddings and nightly carvery, well kept Adnams, Courage Best and Directors and Shepherd Neame Spitfire, decent wines; children very welcome, discreet piped music; pretty back terrace, sizeable garden with good play area *(LYM, Ian and Nita Cooper, D S Cottrell)*

Shotley Gate [TM2434]

☆ ***Bristol Arms*** [end of B1456; Bristol Hill]: Unusual dining pub, superb estuary views from dining room with well prepared standard food inc tempting fresh fish, polite service, good value wines; bar has Adnams, Greene King Abbot and local Harwich ales, some interesting spirits, lots of nautical memorabilia, also cuddly toys and canteens of cutlery for sale, and off-licence cut-price drinks inc uncommon whiskies and liqueurs; some picnic-sets out overlooking water *(Ian Phillips, Derek Thomas)*

Shottisham [TM3144]

Sorrel Horse [Hollesley Rd]: Simple thatched two-bar pub in tucked-away village, well kept Adnams and Greene King IPA tapped from the cask, good value straightforward food lunchtime and early evening (Sun lunch often completely booked even in winter), friendly quick service, good fire; quiz nights some Sats, tables out on green *(the Didler, Pat and Tony Martin)*

Somersham [TM0848]

☆ ***Duke of Marlborough*** [Main Rd]: New licensees with excellent track record doing good fresh food from lunchtime baguettes and baked potatoes up in recently refurbished pub with stripped pine and 16th-c inglenook in beamed bar, light and airy dining room, good service and atmosphere, Greene King IPA and Old Speckled Hen, decent wines, good coffee with fresh cream *(Pamela Goodwyn, Mrs Anne Hayward)*

South Cove [TM4981]

Five Bells [B1127 Southwold—Wrentham]: Friendly, well run and spacious creeper-covered pub with stripped pine, three Adnams ales, wide choice of good value food inc wkdy OAP bargains and generous Sun lunch; tables out in front, play area, several dogs, large caravan park in back paddock *(June and Perry Dann, David Field)*

Southwold [TM5076]

Blyth [Blyth Rd]: Sympathetically restored and decorated, with enjoyable food inc good Sun lunch, friendly service, well kept beers *(David Field)*

☆ ***Kings Head*** [High St]: Cheerful and lively extended dining pub bustling with family parties, lots of maroon and pink plush, very wide range of reliable home-made food from filled rolls up inc good fish choice and bargain winter wkdy lunches, well kept Adnams, good house wines, no smoking area; comfortable family/games room with well lit pool table; jazz some Sun nights, decent bedrooms *(Ann and Colin Hunt, Tim and Ann Newell, John Wooll, MJVK, Dr and Mrs A K Clarke, BB, June and Perry Dann, Neil and Lorna Mclaughlan)*

☆ ***Lord Nelson*** [East St]: Lively bustle in cheerful easy-going seaside local with perfectly kept Adnams full range, decent wines, wholesome plain generous lunchtime food from sandwiches up, low prices, quick attentive service, air cleaner; low ceilings, panelling and tiled floor, spotless light wood furniture, lamps in nice nooks and crannies, Lord Nelson memorabilia and super soda-syphon collection, no music; disabled access (not perfect, but they help), children welcome away from main bar, nice seats in sheltered back garden, open all day *(John Davis, Comus and Sarah Elliott, Derek R A Field, Dr D J and Mrs S C Walker, Mrs Jane Kingsbury, the Didler, Tim Maddison, David and Rhian Peters, Patrick Hancock, Howard James, Richard Pinnington, BB, Neil and Lorna Mclaughlan, Ann and Colin Hunt, Pam and David Bailey)*

Pier Pub [North Parade]: Good food (summer) and well kept beer, sea views and covered terrace; children welcome, part of new pier development *(June and Perry Dann)*

Red Lion [South Green]: Big windows looking over green to sea, pale panelling, ship pictures, lots of brassware and copper; friendly prompt service, well kept Adnams Bitter, Broadside and Mild, good value food inc good fish; children and dogs welcome, family room, tables outside, right by the Adnams retail shop; bedrooms small but comfortable *(George Atkinson, BB, Simon Watkins, Patrick Hancock, Comus and Sarah Elliott, Neil and Lorna Mclaughlan, Dr D J and Mrs S C Walker, Tim and Ann Newell, Pam and David Bailey)*

Sole Bay [East Green]: With the landlord's retirement, the homely feel, polished seafaring memorabilia and even the panelling have gone – replaced by a bleached Tuscan-style café/bar décor and light wood furnishings; the full Adnams range is still kept well, the new landlord and staff very friendly, and the position moments from the sea and lighthouse excellent; conservatory, tables on side terrace *(LYM, Tim Maddison)*

☆ ***Swan*** [Market Pl]: Smart hotel not pub, but has relaxed comfortable back bar with well kept Adnams and Broadside, full range of their bottled beers, fine wines and malt whiskies, good bar food (not cheap, but worth it) inc enormous open sandwiches, chintzy and airy front lounge; good bedrooms inc garden rooms where (by arrangement) dogs can stay too *(Terry Mizen, Mrs Jane Kingsbury, LYM, R M Harrold, Bob and Margaret Holder, Dr and Mrs A K Clarke, Stephen P Edwards, Mrs Rosalie Croft)*

Spexhall [TM3780]

Huntsman & Hounds [Stone St]: Neatly kept 17th-c pub with good generous freshly made food inc fresh veg (OAP wkdy bargain lunch), well kept Adnams ales, decent house wines, attractive prices, helpful friendly staff, beams and standing timbers, usual pub furnishings, central log fire, cosy village atmosphere, darts, restaurant area; tables in garden with pond, bedrooms *(June and Perry Dann)*

Stonham Aspal [TM1359]

Ten Bells [The Street]: Extensively modernised early 17th-c timbered village local with pool at one end of extended main bar, small lounge bar with dining area beyond, proper old-fashioned landlord, cheerful relaxed atmosphere, bargain home-made food inc children's, well kept Tolly Mild and Youngs, extended low-key locals' bar; disabled facilities; tables out on terrace *(Stephen R Holman, Ian and Nita Cooper)*

Stradbroke [TM2373]

White Hart [Church St]: Friendly local with lovely view of church, good plain traditional food, children's meals, Adnams and Greene King IPA *(Quentin and Carol Williamson)*

Stutton [TM1434]

Kings Head [Manningtree Rd]: Atractive pub with friendly caring licensees, several smallish individual beamed and timbered rooms, woodburner; good choice of good value fresh well cooked no-frills food inc bargain lunches and children's helpings, real ales, good value house wines; children welcome; shady side garden with play area, near Alton Water reservoir and recreation area *(Ann and Colin Hunt)*

Sudbury [TL8741]

☆ ***Waggon & Horses*** [Church Walk]: Comfortable and welcoming, with well kept interesting changing real ales from compact bar, good choice of well presented fresh food inc good sandwiches even Sun afternoon, prompt courteous service, decent house wine, interesting décor, log fire; pleasant walled garden with picnic-sets, handy for Gainsborough House *(Nicholas Collins, Ruth Kitching)*

Theberton [TM4365]

Lion [B1122]: Friendly and cosy village pub with no smoking lounge, comfortable banquettes, lots of old local photographs, pictures, copper, brass, plates and bric-a-brac, fresh flowers, good value freshly made pub food inc children's, welcoming licensees, well kept Adnams and several guest beers such as Banks's Original, Elgoods and Woodfordes Wherry, amiable spotted dog most evenings; piped radio, cribbage, separate part with darts, pool and TV, jazz 1st Sun of month, maybe flowers for sale; garden with picnic-sets, small terrace and camp site *(Comus and Sarah Elliott, Peter J Holmes)*

Thornham Magna [TM1070]

Four Horseshoes [off A140 S of Diss; Wickham Rd]: Thatched pub open all day, with dim-lit rambling well divided bar, very low heavy black beams, mix of chairs and plush banquettes, country pictures and farm tools, logs burning in big fireplaces, inside well, no smoking areas; Adnams, Courage Directors, Greene King Old Speckled Hen and Charles Wells Bombardier, pleasant young staff, food (all day Sun) inc OAP bargains; piped music, fruit machine and TV; bedrooms, picnic-sets on big sheltered lawn, handy for Thornham Walks and thatched church with ancient frescoes and fine retable *(E J and M W Corrin, LYM, Ian Phillips, JKW, Mike and Wendy Proctor, Patrick Hancock, Ian and Nita Cooper)*

Thorpeness [TM4759]

Dolphin: Attractive almost Scandinavian décor, light and bright, with good choice of enjoyable food (a restauranty feel, but good lunchtime sandwiches too), well kept Adnams, good wine range; service relaxed and normally helpful (but may not do food if too short-staffed), dogs welcome in public bar; three comfortable bedrooms with own bathrooms, sizeable garden with summer bar and barbecue, quaint holiday village *(Ann and Colin Hunt, Pamela Goodwyn, Wendy Dye)*

Ufford [TM2952]

White Lion [Lower St]: Charming unspoilt 16th-c pub tucked away in small village not far from quiet stretch of River Deben, good value home cooking from sandwiches to steaks, Adnams tapped from the cask, good log fire in central fireplace, flagstone floors, friendly service, no music *(anon)*

Wangford [TM4679]

Angel [signed just off A12 by B1126 junction; High St]: Handsome 17th-c village inn with well spaced tables in light and airy bar, usual food from sandwiches to Sun roasts, well kept Adnams, Greene King Abbot and Woodfordes Wherry, decent wines, young welcoming staff, children in no smoking dining room; piped pop music may obtrude; open all day, comfortable and pretty bedrooms in new wing (the church clock sounds on the quarter) *(Ann and Colin Hunt, Simon Watkins, Mrs Fay Cori, LYM,*

Mr and Mrs W D Borthwick)

Westleton [TM4469]

☆ ***White Horse*** [Darsham Rd, off B1125 Blythburgh—Leiston]: Less smart and cheaper than the Crown, friendly village pub with generous straightforward food (not winter Tues) inc good value sandwiches and OAP bargain lunch in unassuming high-ceilinged bar and attractive no smoking Victorian back dining room; agreeably busy décor, well kept Adnams Bitter and Broadside and seasonal ales, friendly service; quiet piped music, awkward steps down to picnic-sets in cottagey back garden with climbing frame, more out by village duckpond; children in eating area, bedrooms *(June and Perry Dann, George Atkinson)*

Woodbridge [TM2748]

☆ ***Anchor*** [Quay St]: High-ceilinged plainly furnished bar with good welcoming service even when busy, good value prompt usual food inc sandwiches, good pies and well priced fresh local fish, well kept Greene King IPA and Abbot, lots of nautical character and paintings by a local artist for sale, separate eating area *(R M Corlett)*

Bull [Market Hill]: Neatly kept and attractive 16th-c inn with front blinds and window boxes, cosy little bar and other small beamed rooms, wide choice of good food (not cheap but good value), well kept Adnams ales, accommodating landlady and friendly staff; small but comfortable bedrooms, good breakfast *(George Atkinson, Klaus and Elizabeth Leist)*

☆ ***Kings Head*** [Market Hill]: Large olde-worlde bar with lots of flagstones and timbering, blazing inglenook log fire, big tables, back restaurant and conservatory, sound choice of good generous food from sandwiches up inc lots of fish and other local ingredients, service efficient and cheery even when busy at lunchtime and on wknd evenings, full Adnams range kept well, no loud music *(Pat and Tony Martin, George Atkinson, Gill Pennington)*

Woolpit [TL9762]

Bull [The Street]: Clean and friendly, with pleasant licensees, good range of very reasonably priced food, prompt service even when busy; pool and darts; garden with play area, bedrooms *(George Atkinson)*

Yoxford [TM3968]

☆ ***Griffin*** [High St]: Friendly 14th-c local with good cosy and pleasantly unsmart atmosphere, log fires, good value generous food using local supplies inc generous bargain lunch and children's, well kept Adnams and a couple of changing guest beers, attentive staff, medieval feasts in log-fire restaurant decorated to match; notable music nights, quiz night Thurs, two pub cats; comfortable beamed bedrooms, good breakfast *(June and Perry Dann, Paul and Penny Rampton, Comus and Sarah Elliott, John Cooke)*

Please tell us if the décor, atmosphere, food or drink at a pub is different from our description. We rely on readers' reports to keep us up to date. No stamp needed: The Good Pub Guide, FREEPOST TN1569, Wadhurst, E Sussex TN5 7BR.

Surrey

This is by no means a cheap county. A pint of beer here will typically set you back £2.24 – 55p a pint more than in a similar pub up in Lancashire. Food tends to be pricy here too: not one Surrey pub has earned our Bargain Award. Given the high prices, getting value for your money is paramount. So a good deal of weeding out has gone into selecting the pubs which have made the grade this year, into our main entries. Two of these are newcomers: the Hare & Hounds on the edge of Lingfield, good individual cooking at very fair prices, in a warmly welcoming country pub; and the Inn at West End, putting a stylish new twist on all the traditional virtues. Other pubs here on top form this year are the rambling old Cricketers on Downside Common near Cobham (enjoyable sensibly priced food, plenty of atmosphere), the King William IV at Mickleham (a nice all-rounder in a great position, with good generous food), and the very well run Skimmington Castle on Reigate Heath (another fine all-rounder, in a splendid spot). All three do get very busy indeed at weekends. The Surrey Oaks at Newdigate, a most enjoyable country pub, is also well worth knowing, back in the Guide *this year after a short break. The changing food at the King William IV always gives a good choice from simple to more elaborate, and is always enjoyable; the King William IV at Mickleham is Surrey Dining Pub of the Year. In the Lucky Dip section at the end of the chapter, current front-runners are the Rams Nest near Chiddingfold, Plough at Coldharbour (brewing its own good Leith Hill beer), Fox & Hounds at Englefield Green, White Bear at Fickleshole, Stephan Langton at Friday Street, Punch Bowl at Ockley, Cyder House at Shackleford, Mill at Shottermill and Wotton Hatch at Wotton. As we have said, Surrey drinks prices are high. The local brewer whose beers you are most likely to find is Hogs Back (their TEA stands for Traditional English Ale). Incidentally, about three-quarters of Surrey pubs allow dogs inside: handy, as so many are in good walking country.*

ABINGER COMMON TQ1145 Map 3

Abinger Hatch

Off A25 W of Dorking; follow Abinger signpost, then turn right towards Abinger Hammer

They keep up to half a dozen real ales on handpump at this friendly pub, run by a brother and sister team. Abinger Hatch Best is brewed for the pub by the local Weltons brewery and is well kept, alongside Adnams, Badgers IPA and Tanglefoot, Fullers London Pride and a guest. They also have winter mulled wine, farm cider and over 20 malt whiskies. Although generally quiet on weekday lunchtimes, it can get busy at weekends with a cheerful bustle of walkers, cyclists, and families – but staff cope admirably with the rush. It's just the right sort of place after a frosty trudge over the winter hills, with big log fires, heavy beams, flagstones, and simple homely furnishings, including pews forming booths around oak tables in a side carpeted part; there may be piped music. Quite a range of reasonably priced, straightforward food includes soup (£2.45), filled rolls (from £2.45), pâté or breaded mushrooms (£3.50), ploughman's (from £4.25), vegetable kiev (£5.95), curry of the day, fish pie or ham and eggs (£6.25), battered calamari (£7.25), 10oz sirloin steak (£9.25), and a few blackboard specials such as bacon, brie and crab salad (£6.95), and thai fishcakes (£7.25). On Tuesday evenings they do a fish and chips supper (£2.99), on Wednesday to Friday evenings, steak and chips (£4.99), and on Sunday a roast lunch (£5.75). The restaurant is no smoking. Out on a neat stretch of side grass sheltered by beech and rose hedges, picnic-sets under fir trees tempt out patrols of friendly ducks. Wisteria tumbles over the pub's tiled roof, a big fig tree grows in front, and the village church stands just across the green. *(Recommended by James Nunns, Derek Harvey-Piper, Sue and Mike Todd, Dick and Madeleine Brown, Stephen Kiley, Edward Longley, John and Angela Main)*

Free house ~ Licensees Jan and Maria Walaszkowski ~ Real ale ~ Bar food (not Sun or Mon evenings) ~ (01306) 730737 ~ Children in eating area of bar and restaurant ~ Dogs allowed in bar ~ Open 11.30-3, 5-11; 11.30-11 Sat; 12-10.30 Sun

BETCHWORTH TQ2149 Map 3

Dolphin 🍷

Turn off A25 W of Reigate opposite B2032 at roundabout, and keep on into The Street

Little changes over the years at this genuine, friendly and surprisingly unspoilt village pub, which is popular with both walkers and local diners. The homely neatly kept front room has kitchen chairs and plain tables on the 400-year-old scrubbed flagstones, and the carpeted back saloon bar is black-panelled, with robust old-fashioned elm or oak tables. It has three warming fires, a nice chiming longcase clock, silenced fruit machine, darts, cribbage and dominoes. Youngs Bitter, Special, AAA, and a seasonal guest are well kept on handpump alongside up to 18 wines by the glass. Enjoyable good value bar food is generously served, and includes sandwiches (from £2.25), home-made soup (£2.85), mussels in garlic (£4.45), ploughman's (from £4.95), vegetable or beef lasagne (£6.55), steaks (from £8.40), daily specials such as macaroni cheese (£5.95), sweet and sour chicken or steak and mushroom pie (£6.95), and puddings such as jam roly poly or bread pudding (£2.15); best to get there early, or book a table beforehand. There are some seats in the small laurel-shaded front courtyard, and behind there are picnic-sets on a terrace and lawn by the car park, opposite the church. Parking can be very difficult in summer. No children inside. *(Recommended by Dennis Jenkin, Ian Phillips, Mike Gorton, DWAJ, Chris Richards, Mark Percy, Lesley Mayoh, Martin and Penny Fletcher, Keith Bell, B, M and P Kendall, G T Brewster, the Didler)*

Youngs ~ Managers George and Rose Campbell ~ Real ale ~ Bar food (12-2.30, 7-10) ~ (01737) 842288 ~ Dogs welcome ~ Open 11-3, 5.30-11; 11-11 Sat; 12-10.30 Sun

Red Lion 🍷

Turn off A25 W of Reigate opposite B2032 at roundabout, then after ¼ mile bear left into Old Road, towards Buckland

New licensees are putting heavy emphasis on the food at this civilised dining pub – you order from menus at the table. The light and airy bar, with a log-effect gas fire and pictures above its panelled dado, has plenty of tables, with steps down to a stylish long flagstoned room, and a no smoking dining room, candlelit at night, which strikes some readers as Tuscan in mood. Bar food includes lunchtime sandwiches (from £3), baked cod (£10.95), bass (£12.95), turbot stuffed with cream cheese (£15), specials such as brie and spinach parcels (£7.95), puddings such as banana torte with raspberry coulis and chocolate sponge (£3.25), a cheeseboard (£4.95), and Sunday roast (£9.50). Well kept Adnams Broadside and up to three guests such as Shepherd Neame Spitfire on handpump, and eight wines by the glass; piped pop music. Outside are plenty of picnic-sets on a lawn with a play area, and in good weather tables set for dining on a rose-trellised terrace. The garden backs on to the pub's own cricket pitch where they play most weekends, and you don't notice the road at the front, as it's set well below the pub in a tree-lined cutting. We have not yet had reports from readers on the bedrooms, in a separate new block. *(Recommended by C and R Bromage, John Evans, B, M and P Kendall, Mike and Heather Watson, Derek Harvey-Piper, G T Brewster, Susan and John Douglas, Mike Gorton)*

Punch ~ Lease Tony Wolbrom and Mr Podemsky ~ Real ale ~ Bar food (12-3, 6-10; 12-5, 6-9 Sun) ~ Restaurant ~ (01737) 843336 ~ Children welcome till 7.30pm ~ Open 11-11; 12-10.30 Sun ~ Bedrooms: /£75S

BLACKBROOK TQ1846 Map 3

Plough 🍷

On byroad E of A24, parallel to it, between Dorking and Newdigate, just N of the turn E to Leigh

The countryside around here is particularly good for colourful spring and summer walks through the oak woods, and in summer, the white frontage of this neatly kept, comfortable pub is quite a sight, with its pretty hanging baskets and window boxes. The no smoking red saloon bar has fresh flowers on its tables and on the window sills of its large linen-curtained windows. Down some steps, the public bar has brass-topped treadle tables, a formidable collection of ties, old saws on the ceiling, and bottles and flat irons; shove-ha'penny, and cribbage. As well as reasonably priced and enjoyable lunchtime bar snacks such as taramasalata or hummus with olives and pitta bread (£3.45), local sausages (£4.25), filled baked potatoes (from £4.25), ploughman's (£4.95), bagels (from £5.45), and steak sandwich (from £6.75), they do daily specials such as tomato and basil soup (£2.75), smoked trout pâté (£3.95), moussaka (£6.95), spicy prawn curry (£7.45), grilled tuna niçoise (£11.75), and puddings such as bakewell tart, lemon meringue pie or nougat ice cream (£3.45); they hold four popular curry evenings a year. Well kept Badger Best, K&B and Tanglefoot, Gribble Fursty Ferret and a seasonal beer on handpump, 16 wines by the glass, and several ports; friendly and efficient service from smartly dressed staff. There are tables and chairs on the terrace, and a children's swiss playhouse furnished with little tables and chairs in the secluded garden. More reports please. *(Recommended by Colin Draper, Chris Richards, Gordon Stevenson, G T Brewster)*

Badger ~ Tenants Chris and Robin Squire ~ Real ale ~ Bar food (not Mon evening) ~ (01306) 886603 ~ Children in eating area of bar till 9pm ~ Dogs allowed in bar ~ Open 11-2.30(3 Sat), 6-11; 12-3, 7-10.30 Sun; closed 25 and 26 Dec, 1 Jan

CHARLESHILL SU8944 Map 2

Donkey

B3001 Milford—Farnham near Tilford; coming from Elstead, turn left as soon as you see pub sign

Emphasis at this beamed cottagey pub is on the enjoyable (though not cheap) food, which might include sandwiches (from £3), soup (£3.25), thai fishcakes (£5.95), fresh Cornish crab or scallops au gratin (£6.95), fillet of minted lamb in a filo basket (£12.95), bass with lime and dill sauce or lobster thermidor (£16.50), and puddings such as lemon tart or crème brûlée (£3.95). Service is friendly. The bright saloon has lots of polished stirrups, lamps and watering cans on the walls, and prettily cushioned built-in wall benches, while the lounge has a fine high-backed settle, highly polished horsebrasses, and swords on the walls and beams; no smoking dining conservatory. Well kept Greene King IPA, Abbot and Old Speckled Hen on handpump; piped music. The garden is very attractive, with a terrace, plenty of seats, a big fairy-lit fir tree, and a wendy house for children; the two friendly donkeys are called Pip and Daisy. *(Recommended by John and Joyce Snell, John Evans, Edward Longley)*

Greene King ~ Licensees Lee and Helen Francis ~ Real ale ~ Bar food (12-2.30, 6-9.30; 12-9.30 Sun) ~ Restaurant ~ (01252) 702124 ~ Children welcome ~ Dogs allowed in bar ~ Open 11.30-2.30, 6-11; 12-10.30 Sun; closed Sun evening in winter

COBHAM TQ1060 Map 3

Cricketers

Downside Common; 3¾ miles from M25 junction 10; A3 towards Cobham, first right on to A245, right at Downside signpost into Downside Bridge Road, follow road into its right fork – away from Cobham Park – at second turn after bridge, then take next left turn into the pub's own lane

The roomy open-plan interior of this friendly pub has plenty of atmosphere, with a good log fire, and crooked standing timbers – creating comfortable spaces – supporting heavy oak beams so low they have crash-pads on them. In places you can see the wide oak ceiling boards and ancient plastering laths. Furnishings are quite simple, and there are horsebrasses and big brass platters on the walls; the stable bar is no smoking. Enjoyable bar food includes a huge choice of salads such as home-made quiche of the day (£5.50), ploughman's (£6.50), avocado, tomato, and mozzarella (£6.95), provençale vegetable wellington (£6.95), and home-made salmon coulibiac (£7.95), with hot dishes such as cottage pie or steamed mussels with soy sauce (£5.95), pork and leek sausages with onion gravy (£6.50), steak, mushroom and Guinness pie or home-made chicken curry (£7.45), grilled fillet of fresh salmon with tarragon butter (£8.95), sugar-baked ham with peaches (£8.50), and a children's menu (£3.95); prompt service. It's worth arriving early to be sure of a table – especially on Sunday. Well kept Greene King Old Speckled Hen, Theakstons Best, Wadworths 6X and Youngs on handpump, and several wines by the glass. It's particularly pleasant sitting outside at one of the many tables in the charming neatly kept garden, with its standard roses, dahlias, bedding plants, urns and hanging baskets, and view over the village green. *(Recommended by Kevin Williams, Gee Cormack, Ian Phillips, Gordon Prince, Geoffrey Kemp, Mrs Suzy Miller, G T Brewster, Mike and Heather Watson, Stephanie Smith, Leigh Hughes, Edward Longley, Colin Draper)*

Inntrepreneur ~ Tenant Wendy Luxford ~ Real ale ~ Bar food (12-2, 6.30-10) ~ Restaurant ~ (01932) 862105 ~ Children in stable bar ~ Dogs allowed in bar ~ Open 11-2.30, 6-11; 12-3, 6(7 winter)-10.30 Sun

COMPTON SU9546 Map 2

Withies

Withies Lane; pub signposted from B3000

Tucked away down a lane, this popular and very civilised 16th-c pub is particularly attractive inside, with low beams in the little bar, some fine 17th-c carved panels between the windows, and a splendidly Art Nouveau settle among the old sewing-machine tables; there's a good log fire in a massive inglenook fireplace. You can eat from the more elaborate (and more expensive) restaurant menu, which is very popular with a well heeled local set, but they also offer a good choice of straightforward pubby bar food such as soup (£3.50), filled baked potatoes (from £4), smoked salmon pâté or ploughman's (£4.25), sandwiches (from £4.25), cumberland sausages with mash and onion gravy (£4.90), and seafood platter (£9.50). Well kept Badger K&B, Bass, Fullers London Pride and Greene King IPA on handpump; the uniformed staff stay helpful and efficient even when it gets busy. The immaculate garden, overhung with weeping willows, has tables under an arbour of creeper-hung trellises, more on a crazy-paved terrace, and others under old apple trees. The neat lawn in front of the steeply tiled white house is bordered by masses of flowers. It's a pleasant walk from here up the lane to Polsted Manor and Loseley Park. *(Recommended by John Evans, Ian Phillips, Derek Harvey-Piper, G T Brewster, Debbie and Neil Hayter, Dennis Jenkin, Susan and John Douglas, Mrs Jane Basso, Kevin Williams, Gee Cormack, John Braine-Hartnell)*

Free house ~ Licensees Brian and Hugh Thomas ~ Real ale ~ Bar food (12-2.30, 7-10) ~ Restaurant ~ (01483) 421158 ~ Children welcome ~ Open 11-3, 6-11; 12-4 Sun; closed Sun evening

ELSTEAD SU9143 Map 2

Woolpack

The Green; B3001 Milford—Farnham

Most people come to this bustling, friendly pub for the wide-reaching, imaginative and often fairly rich bar food, quickly served by helpful staff. The menu might include soup (£3.50), breaded camembert with port and cranberry sauce or hummus with pitta bread (£4.95), ploughman's (from £5.25), prawns with coriander, chilli and lime butter (£5.75), smoked salmon (£6.75), and changing blackboard specials such as baked goats cheese on puff pastry with mango and garlic (£7.50), tortilla wraps (£7.75), pie of the day (£8.75), monkfish with Pernod and fennel sauce (£11.95), ostrich in pesto, mustard and honey sauce or wild boar fillet in creamy pepper and brandy sauce (£12.25), and home-made puddings (£3.50). Weaving shuttles and cones of wool hang above the high-backed settles in the main bar, long and airy with fireplaces at each end, and there's a weaving loom in another big room leading off from here. As well as some pleasant window seats, there are spindleback chairs around plain wooden tables, and decorations include lots of country prints, scales and brass measuring jugs; the fireplace with its wooden pillars and lace frill is unusual. Well kept Fullers London Pride, Greene King Abbot and a guest such as Hogs Back TEA are tapped from the cask, and there's a decent wine list. Dominoes and cribbage; fruit machine. A family room leads to the garden with picnic-sets. *(Recommended by Graham Osborne, David Peakall, Kevin Williams, Gee Cormack, Ian Phillips, Lynn Sharpless, Ben Stephenson, Michael Sargent, Geoffrey Kemp, John and Angela Main, Lady Muir, Edward Longley)*

Punch ~ Lease S A Askew ~ Real ale ~ Bar food (12-2, 7-9.45(9 Sun)) ~ Restaurant ~ (01252) 703106 ~ Children in restaurant and family room ~ Dogs allowed in bar ~ Open 11-2, 5.30-11.30; 11-11.30 Sat; 12-11 Sun; closed 25 Dec evening, 26 Dec

HASCOMBE TQ0039 Map 3

White Horse

B2130 S of Godalming

Readers have nothing but praise for this picturesque old rose-draped inn, which is tucked away in a pretty village among lovely rolling wooded country lanes on the Greensand Way. Inside, there's a cheerful bustle in the attractively simple rooms (it's best to get there early for a table at lunchtime, especially at weekends). The cosy inner beamed area has a woodburning stove, hops hanging from the beams, and quiet small-windowed alcoves that look out on to the garden; darts, shove-ha'penny and dominoes. Good bar food, served in helpings that are generous enough to justify the prices, includes sandwiches (from £4), good proper ploughman's (from £4.95), home-made burgers (£7), asparagus and sun-dried tomato risotto (£7.95), half roast guinea fowl or ham, egg and chips (£8.95), lamb knuckle and mash (£10.50), fillet steak (£14.50), and puddings such as raspberry hazelnut meringue (£4.50). Well kept Adnams, Flowers and Harveys on handpump, and a sizeable wine list; friendly service from helpful staff. There are several tables on the spacious sloping back lawn, with more on a little terrace by the front porch. In autumn, you can combine a trip here with a walk among the beautifully coloured trees and shrubs in nearby Winkworth Arboretum. *(Recommended by Michael Sargent, Susan and John Douglas, John and Angela Main, M Blatchly, Peter Meister, John and Tania Wood, David and Higgs Wood, Ian Phillips)*

Punch ~ Lease Susan Barnett ~ Real ale ~ Bar food (12-2.20, 7-10) ~ Restaurant ~ (01483) 208258 ~ Children in restaurant and family room ~ Dogs allowed in bar ~ Open 11-3, 5.30-11; 11-11 Sat; 12-10.30 Sun; closed 25 Dec, 26 Dec evening

If you stay overnight in an inn or hotel, they are allowed to serve you an alcoholic drink at any hour of the day or night.

LEIGH TQ2246 Map 3

Plough

3 miles S of A25 Dorking—Reigate, signposted from Betchworth (which itself is signposted off the main road); also signposted from South Park area of Reigate; on village green

Notices warn you not to bump your head on the very low beams in the cosy timbered dining lounge, which is decorated with lots of local prints on white walls, and is on the right as you go in. On the left, a simpler more local pubby bar has a good bow window seat, and an extensive choice of games including darts, shove-ha'penny, dominoes, table skittles, cribbage, Jenga, backgammon and shut-the-box; piped music, alcove fruit machine. Well kept real ales are Badger Best, Tanglefoot, Sussex, and winter Old Ale on handpump, and you can have a glass of anything on the decent wine list. An extensive choice of nicely presented food ranges from bar snacks including a big choice of sandwiches (from £3.95), soup (£3.95), tuna melt (£3.50), filled baked potatoes (from £4.95), and ploughman's (£5.95), to main meals such as penne tossed in leek, cream and goats cheese sauce (£6.95), smoked haddock on spinach, topped with cheese sauce (£9.50), chicken breast with leeks and stilton cream (£9.50), honey-glazed duck breast with a mixed berry sauce (£11.95), steaks (from £10.95), and puddings such as pavlova or apple pie (from £3.50); you may need to book at the weekend. There are picnic-sets under cocktail parasols in a pretty side garden (fairy-lit in the evening), and colourful hanging baskets. This pretty tiled and weatherboarded cottage is attractively set by the village green, but nearby parking is limited. *(Recommended by G T Brewster, DWAJ, Ian Phillips, Debbie and Neil Hayter, Hugh Roberts, B, M and P Kendall)*

Badger ~ Tenant Sarah Bloomfield ~ Real ale ~ Bar food (12-2.30, 7-9.30; 12-9.30 wknds) ~ Restaurant ~ (01306) 611348 ~ Children in restaurant ~ Dogs allowed in bar ~ Open 11-11; 12-10.30 Sun

LINGFIELD TQ3844 Map 3

Hare & Hounds

Turn off B2029 N at Crowhurst, Edenbridge signpost, into Lingfield Common Road

This homely country local has a wide range of good imaginative food using local produce, putting an appealing touch of individuality into trusted favourites, such as the cheddar mash that comes with the cumberland sausage, or the burger's focaccia bap with beetroot relish and rosemary and goats cheese pesto (both £7.50), the redcurrant and melon glaze for the gammon, or the jerusalem artichokes spiced up with honey and chilli for the minute steak (both £7.95), and the spicy tom-yum vegetable noodle broth with the poached salmon (£8.50). Puddings, prettily presented, are light and delicious, and there's usually home-made soda bread. The smallish open-plan bar, light and airy by day, has soft lighting and nightlights burning on the good mix of different-sized tables at night – when it's full of the chatter of happy customers, some drinking, some eating, all mixing comfortably. Partly bare boards and partly flagstones, it has an informal variety of scatter-cushioned dining chairs, black and white pictures of jazz musicians on brown tongue-and-groove panelling, and perhaps unobtrusive piped jazz. It opens into a quieter dining area with big abstract-expressionist paintings. They have well kept Flowers Original and Greene King IPA and Old Speckled Hen on handpump, and decent wines; service is quick and friendly. There are tables out in a pleasant split-level garden, some on decking. This is good walking country near Haxted Mill; walkers can leave their boots in the porch, guarded by a life-size great dane statue. *(Recommended by Mrs Sheena Killick, Derek Thomas)*

Pubmaster ~ Lease Fergus Greer ~ Real ale ~ Bar food (12-8.30(4.30 Sun)) ~ Restaurant ~ (01342) 832351 ~ Children welcome ~ Dogs allowed in bar ~ Open 12-11.30(10.30 Sun)

MICKLEHAM TQ1753 Map 3

King William IV

Byttom Hill; short but narrow steep track up hill just off A24 Leatherhead—Dorking by partly green-painted restaurant – public car park down here is best place to park; OS Sheet 187 map reference 173538

Surrey Dining Pub of the Year

The lovely terraced garden at the back of this creeper covered brick pub is neatly filled with sweet peas, climbing roses and honeysuckle, and plenty of tables (some in an extended open-sided wooden shelter with gas heaters) have panoramic views over pretty Surrey countryside. A path leads from the garden straight up through woods behind, where it's nice to walk after lunch. The pub is cut into the steep hillside (parking can be difficult on the lane, so you may have a character-forming walk up), and has the same views from its snug plank-panelled front bar. The more spacious back bar is quite brightly lit, with kitchen-type chairs around its cast-iron-framed tables, log fires, fresh flowers on all the tables, and a serviceable grandfather clock. There's a friendly atmosphere throughout. It does get busy in summer (when you may have to queue to place your order, but service should be quick enough after that), and they don't take bookings – so you will need to get here early to secure a table. Generous helpings of very enjoyable bar food might include ploughman's (from £5.50), filled baked potatoes (from £5.75), steak and kidney or seafood pie (£8.75), chicken piri piri with basil and tomato salad and cucumber yoghurt dressing or thai green vegetable curry (£8.95), steamed bass with ginger, spring onion and soy sauce (£12.75), prawns in garlic and herb butter (£13.75), and puddings such as treacle tart or fruit crumble (£3.95); the choice is more limited on Sundays (roast £8.95), and bank holidays. Very well kept Adnams Best, Badger Best, Hogs Back TEA and a guest such as Ringwood Fortyniner on handpump; light piped music. *(Recommended by Mr and Mrs Gordon Turner, John Crafts, B, M and P Kendall, Rosemary and Tom Hall, John and Angela Main, Donald and Nesta Treharne, Mr and Mrs D D Collins, Marion Turner, Christopher and Elise Way, Ron and Sheila Corbett, Ian Jones, Charlie Harris, Peter Saville, Mrs J R Sillitoe, J Wright, Mike and Lynn Robinson, Kevin Williams, Gee Cormack, Ian Phillips, C and R Bromage, Derek and Sylvia Stephenson, Paul Boot)*

Free house ~ Licensees Chris and Jenny Grist ~ Real ale ~ Bar food (12-2, 7-9.30) ~ (01372) 372590 ~ Open 11-3, 6-11; 12-3, 7-10.30 Sun; closed 25 Dec, evening 31 Dec

NEWDIGATE TQ2042 Map 3

Surrey Oaks

Off A24 S of Dorking, via Beare Green; Parkgate Road

We're happy to report that this small, civilised country pub is back on top form. There's a reliably congenial atmosphere, and when possible, the friendly landlord tries to come out from the kitchen to greet customers personally. A good pubby atmosphere is helped along by two unusual guest beers such as Oakhill Brewery Charioteer and Wye Valley Dorothy Goodbodys, which are well kept alongside Adnams and Harveys on handpump, and the pub hosts an annual beer festival over the August bank holiday. This is a much extended former wheelwright's cottage, and has an interesting layout. In the older part, locals gather by a coal-effect gas fire in a snug little beamed room, and a standing area with unusually large flagstones has a woodburning stove in an inglenook fireplace. Rustic tables are dotted around the light and airy main lounge to the left, and there's a pool table in the separate games room; fruit machine, perhaps piped classical music. Promptly served, good value and enjoyable bar food includes home-made soups and pâté (from £3.25), filled baguettes (from £3.75), ploughman's (from £4.50), ham, egg and chips or battered cod (£5.95), and sausages – a different type each day – with mash (£6.95), with enjoyable specials such as steak and stilton pie (£7.50), guinea fowl and perhaps a few Mexican and Indian dishes (£8); puddings include banoffi pie and bread and butter pudding (£3.25); children's meals (from £4.50). The pleasant and quite elaborate garden has a terrace, and a rockery with pools and a waterfall; the play area and menagerie of two goats, an aviary and a flock of doves should keep children amused – families feel particularly welcome here. *(Recommended by M Blatchly, Mary and Dan Robinson, Alan and Paula McCully, Hugh Roberts, C and R Bromage, G T Brewster, Jenny and Brian Seller, Ian Phillips, Mike Gorton)*

Punch ~ Lease Ken Proctor ~ Real ale ~ Bar food (not Sun and Mon evenings) ~ Restaurant (12-2, 6.30-9.30) ~ (01306) 631200 ~ Children in eating area of bar and restaurant ~ Dogs welcome ~ Open 11.30-2.30(3.30 Sat), 5.30-11.30; 12-3.30, 7-10.30 Sun

PIRBRIGHT SU9454 Map 2

Royal Oak

Aldershot Road; A324S of village

Cheery new licensees are concentrating on the interesting real ales at this pretty country pub. Flowers IPA and Original and Hogs Back TEA are kept in top condition, alongside up to six changing guests from brewers such as Becketts, Highwood, Titanic, Charles Wells and Tom Woods; they also have a good range of wines by the glass and bottle. No piped music or games machines detract from the relaxed pubby atmosphere in the series of heavily beamed and timbered rambling snug side alcoves, with ancient stripped brickwork, and brasses gleaming around the three real fires. Furnishings include wheelback chairs, tapestried wall seats, and little dark church-like pews around the trim tables; a bar extension overlooks the pretty flower-filled back garden, and is joined on to the existing no smoking dining area. Bar food includes soup (£2.95), filled baguettes (from £3.50), free range sausages and mash (£6.95), battered fish (£7.25), caesar salad (£7.45), chicken breast with ham and cheese and mushroom sauce (£7.95), sirloin steak (£10.95), and puddings such as hot chocolate pudding and lemon tart (£3.45). The front gardens are very colourful, and look particularly attractive on fine evenings when the fairy lights are switched on. The big back garden leads down to a stream, and is less affected by noise from passing traffic; there may be barbecues and spit-roasts out here in summer. Good walks lead off in all directions. *(Recommended by KC, Stephen Kiley, Jayne and Peter Capp, LM, Simon Good, D P and J A Sweeney, Edward Longley, Simon Collett-Jones)*

Laurel (Enterprise) ~ Managers Julia and Geoff Middleton ~ Real ale ~ Bar food (12-2, 6.30-9.30(8.30 Sun)) ~ (01483) 232466 ~ Open 11-11; 12-10.30 Sun

REIGATE HEATH TQ2349 Map 3

Skimmington Castle

3 miles from M25 junction 8: through Reigate take A25 towards Dorking, then on edge of Reigate turn left past Black Horse into Flanchford Road; after ¼ mile turn left into Bonny's Road (unmade, very bumpy track); after crossing golf course fork right up hill

Although remotely set up a bumpy track, this quaint old country pub is very popular, so you may need to get here early for a table (they don't take bookings); however, even at its busiest service is very prompt and friendly. The bright main front bar leads off a small room with a central serving counter, with dark simple panelling and lots and lots of keys hanging from the beams. There's a miscellany of chairs and tables, shiny brown plank panelling, a brown plank ceiling, well kept Greene King IPA and Old Speckled Hen, Youngs Special and a guest such as Charles Wells Bombardier on handpump, with several wines by the glass, farm cider and even some organic spirits. The cosy back rooms are partly panelled too, with old-fashioned settles and windsor chairs; one has a big brick fireplace with its bread-oven still beside it – the chimney is said to have been used as a highwayman's look-out. Steps take you down to just three tables in a small but pleasant no smoking family room at the back (children do need to behave here); shove-ha'penny, cribbage, dominoes, ring-the-bull, board games; there may be piped music. Good popular bar food includes sandwiches (from £2.85), soup (£3.25), ploughman's (from £4.50), moules marinière (£5.95), fresh breaded cod (£6.50), tuna with mild chilli salsa or salmon topped with spinach and pastry (£7.50), spiced pork fillet on creamed leeks (£8.25), venison steak with braised cabbage and bacon (£9.50), and puddings (£2.95). There are nice views from the crazy-paved front terrace and tables on the grass by lilac bushes, with more tables at the back overlooking the meadows and the hillocks (you may find the views blocked by trees in summer). There's a hitching rail outside for horses, and the pub is handy for rambles on the North Downs. *(Recommended by Edward Longley, B, M and P Kendall, Gordon Stevenson, Ian Phillips, Zelda Tolley, Mike Gorton, R Marshall, Joy and Peter Heatherley, C and R Bromage, R T and J C Moggridge)*

Pubmaster ~ Tenants Anthony Pugh and John Davidson ~ Real ale ~ Bar food (12-2.15(2.30 Sun), 7-9) ~ (01737) 243100 ~ Dogs welcome ~ Folk second Sun of month ~ Open 11-3, 5.30(6 Sat)-11; 12-10.30 Sun; closed evenings 25-27 Dec and 1 Jan

WEST END SU9461 Map 2

Inn at West End 🍷

Just under 2½ miles from M3 junction 3; A322 S, on right

Nicely reworked, this roadside pub gives a good balance between food and drink, in appealing up-to-date surroundings. It's open-plan, with bare boards, attractive modern prints on canary yellow walls above a red dado, and a line of dining tables with crisp white linen over pale yellow tablecloths on the left. The bar counter, straight ahead as you come in, is quite a focus, with chatting regulars on the comfortable bar stools, well kept Courage Best and Fullers London Pride on handpump, good house wines including good value champagne by the glass (Mr Price is a wine merchant, and can also supply by the case), seasonal drinks such as pimms, bucks fizz and kir royale, and good coffee from an espresso machine. The area on the right has a pleasant relaxed pubby atmosphere, with blue-cushioned wall benches and dining chairs around solid pale wood tables, broadsheet daily papers, and a row of reference books on the brick chimneybreast above a woodburning stove. This opens into a terracotta-tiled garden room, with a blue overhead awning, which in turn leads into the attractive garden, where paths wind between flowering shrubs to groups of picnic-sets under cocktail parasols on several areas of neat lawn. With the choice changing all the time, consistently good food includes starters such as black pudding with chicken livers, bacon and shallots (£6), welsh rarebit (£6.25), salmon and dill fishcakes (£6.75), and quail salad with mushrooms and pine nuts (£7), main courses such as baked goats cheese parcels on ricotta tortellini (£12), lots of fresh fish such as sea trout on saffron and asparagus butter (£14.50), and free range pork with apple and calvados (£15), and puddings such as crème brûlée and warm chocolate sponge with chocolate sauce (£4.50). Service is friendly and efficient. *(Recommended by Guy Consterdine, Andrea and Shirley Mackenzie, S F Parrinder, Dr P C Rea, Ian Phillips, Dr M Owton)*

Free house ~ Licensees Gerry and Ann Price ~ Real ale ~ Bar food (12-2.30, 6-9.30; 12-3, 6-9 Sun) ~ Restaurant ~ (01276) 858652 ~ Children welcome in restaurant if eating ~ Dogs allowed in bar ~ Open 12-3, 5-11; 12-11 Sat; 12-4, 6-10.30 Sun

Post Office address codings confusingly give the impression that some pubs are in Surrey when they're really in Hampshire or London (which is where we list them). And there's further confusion from the way the Post Office still talks about Middlesex – which disappeared in 1965 local government reorganisation.

Lucky Dip

Besides the fully inspected pubs, you might like to try these Lucky Dips recommended to us and described by readers (if you do, please send us reports: www.goodguides.com).

Albury [TQ0547]

☆ ***Drummond Arms*** [off A248 SE of Guildford; The Street]: Comfortable and civilised panelled alcovey bar, conservatory (children allowed here) overlooking pretty streamside back garden with fountain and covered terrace, some emphasis on food, several well kept real ales, attentive helpful staff; piped music; bedrooms, attractive village, pleasant walks nearby *(MDN, Edward Longley, G T Brewster, LYM)*

Bletchingley [TQ3250]

☆ ***Prince Albert*** [Outwood Lane]: Good sensibly priced fresh bar food from baguettes up in attractive cosy beamed pub, thriving atmosphere, several nooks and corners, motor racing pictures, well kept Ind Coope Burton, Spinnaker Best and Wadworths 6X, friendly young staff, smallish restaurant with accent on good fresh fish; plastic tables on terrace and in pretty garden with lovely magnolia *(John Branston, Dick and Madeleine Brown, LM, Ian Phillips)*

☆ ***William IV*** [3 miles from M25 junction 6; Little Common Lane, off A25 on Redhill side of village]: Quaint old country pub down pretty lane, tile-hung and weatherboarded, three bar rooms and comfortable little back no smoking dining room, good choice of good food and of well kept ales such as Fullers London Pride, Greene King Old Speckled Hen, Harveys Best and Youngs Special, good wines, good atmosphere, lots of bric-a-brac, friendly enthusiastic staff; two-level garden with summer barbecues *(LYM, Ian Phillips)*

Bramley [TQ0044]

☆ ***Jolly Farmer*** [High St]: Stylishly extended, sociable and welcoming, very popular for wide choice of generous fresh usual food, five changing well kept ales, Czech beers on tap, proper coffee, welcoming service, two log fires, beer mat and banknote collections, big restaurant; comfortable bedrooms *(MDN, LYM, Phil and Sally Gorton)*

Brockham [TQ1949]

Dukes Head: Wide range of enjoyable food from good value baguettes up in friendly pleasantly old-fashioned pub, four real ales inc Adnams and Fullers London Pride, polite attentive service, log fire, soppy staffordshire bull terrier called Wilf; pretty spot by village green *(John Branston)*

Brook [SU9338]

☆ ***Dog & Pheasant*** [A286 N of Haslemere]: Big busy low-beamed roadside pub in attractive spot opp cricket green near Witley Common, pleasant atmosphere, well kept Fullers London Pride, Greene King Old Speckled Hen, Ringwood Best and Youngs, enjoyable food inc some interesting dishes, big fire, shove-ha'penny, small restaurant, family eating area; small pretty garden *(Ian Phillips)*

Burrowhill [SU9763]

Four Horseshoes [B383 N of Chobham]: Friendly and well run old-fashioned cottagey village-green local, dark and cool inside on hot days, varied good value food all day inc popular Sun lunch, well kept Brakspears, Courage Best and Charles Wells Bombardier, good service, busy bar, expanded dining room; lots of picnic-sets out in front (some under ancient yew), pleasant outlook *(Ian Phillips)*

Chertsey [TQ0466]

Crown [London St (B375)]: Friendly and relaxed Youngs pub with button-back banquettes in spreading traditionally renovated high-ceilinged bar, tall and very sonorous longcase clock, well kept ales, fine choice of wines by the glass, nicely presented no-nonsense food from doorstep sandwiches and baked potatoes up, courteous attentive staff; neatly placed darts, discreet fruit machines; children welcome, garden bar with conservatory, tables in courtyard and garden with pond; smart 30-bedroom annexe *(Joyce and Maurice Cottrell, Ian Phillips)*

☆ ***Kingfisher*** [Chertsey Bridge Rd]: Attractive Vintage Inn dining pub carefully put together using old materials, beautifully placed by busy bridge and Thames lock, warm medley of furnishings in spreading series of small intimate areas, subtle lighting, enjoyable food from sandwiches to some interesting main dishes (very popular Sun), well kept Bass and Tetleys, good wine choice, attentive helpful service, good log fires; soft piped music; families welcome if eating (otherwise no under-21s), riverside garden by road, open all day *(Jenny and Brian Seller, Simon Collett-Jones, Gordon Prince, Dr and Mrs M E Wilson, James Nunns, Mayur Shah)*

Chiddingfold [SU9433]

☆ ***Rams Nest*** [Petworth Rd (A283 S)]: Relaxed country inn with huge inglenook, old-fashioned prints and furnishings inc antique settles in rambling panelled bar, light and airy by day, candlelit at night, couple of steps down to appealing carpeted dining area with more big prints, sofas by back log fire with magazines and sizeable paperback library, well kept Greene King IPA and Hogs Back TEA, good value wines, friendly attentive staff; may be unobtrusive piped music; tables on covered verandah, picnic-sets among fruit trees on neat lawn with wendy house and play area, well equipped bedrooms in separate block, open all day wknds *(Miles Halton, BB)*

☆ ***Swan*** [A283 S]: Cheerful country inn with good choice of good value food in light and airy bar and compact dining room, well kept real ales, thoughtful wine choice, friendly attentive staff, log fires, pleasant décor; comfortable attractive bedrooms *(LYM, K R Thomas, Steve Morris)*

Winterton Arms [Petworth Rd (A283), North Bridge]: Well kept Adnams, Friary Meux and Youngs, enjoyable food, efficient friendly staff;

disabled access, big garden with tables and awnings *(Keith and Suzie Stevens)*

Chipstead [TQ2757]

☆ ***Well House*** [Chipstead signed with Mugswell off A217, N of M25 junction 8]: Partly 14th-c, cottagey and comfortable, with lots of atmosphere, decent straightforward food (not Sun evening, and may take a time) from massive sandwiches up, friendly staff, log fires in all three rooms, well kept Bass and other ales such as Adnams Fisherman and Fullers London Pride; dogs allowed; attractive garden with well reputed to be mentioned in Doomsday Book (loudspeaker food announcements though), delightful setting *(Jenny and Brian Seller, LYM, Jim Bush)*

Chobham [SU9761]

Sun [4 miles from M3 junction 3]: Low-beamed and timbered pub rescued from closure by local consortium, pleasant and friendly, with Brakspears, Courage Best and Fullers London Pride, lots of daily papers; a reliable refuge *(LYM, Ian Phillips)*

Churt [SU8538]

Crossways: Small friendly village pub with usual food and two distinct bar areas, listed for its interesting choice of up to seven or eight changing well kept ales at reasonable prices, July beer festival *(M Blatchly)*

Cobham [TQ1060]

Little White Lion [A245 Pains Hill/Byfleet Rd, by Sainsburys]: Cottagey, attractive and comfortable panelled dining pub back to its proper name (spent a while as the Snail), with enjoyable food in bar and restaurant, well kept ales, efficient friendly staff; handy for Painshill Park *(Kevin Williams, Gee Cormack)*

Old Bear [Riverhill]: Large 16th-c pub with long low bar, wide range of well kept ales, enjoyable bar food, particularly good service; tables in pleasant area outside *(Dr and Mrs A K Clarke)*

Coldharbour [TQ1543]

☆ ***Plough*** [village signed in the network of small roads around Leith Hill]: Friendly and carefully refurbished two-bar pub, brewing its own good Leith Hill Crooked Furrow and Tallywhacker, with well kept guests such as Ringwood Old Thumper and Timothy Taylors Landlord, also well priced wines, country wines and Biddenden farm cider and perry, enjoyable food, prompt service, stripped light beams and timbering, big log fire on right, homely no smoking restaurant with another log fire; children welcome in newly converted barn, picnic-sets out in front and in terraced garden with fish pond and waterlilies; open all day wknds, comfortable new bedrooms with own bathrooms, hearty breakfast, good walks *(LYM, K Hulme, Stephanie Smith, Leigh Hughes, Ian and Rose Lock, Ian Phillips, Chris Richards, Chris Reeve, Mrs P J Pearce, John Branston, Kevin and Bruna Lovelock, G T Brewster, Jenny and Brian Seller)*

Compton [SU9546]

☆ ***Harrow*** [B3000 towards Godalming off A3]: Pleasant farm-theme upmarket country local, enjoyable though not cheap home-made food, well kept Greene King IPA and Abbot and Hogs Back TEA, good house wines; children welcome, open all day, cl Sun evening; bedrooms *(Mrs Hilarie Taylor, Edward Longley, Darren Le Poidevin, R J Hayward, LYM, Jason Reynolds, Mike and Heather Watson)*

Cox Green [TQ0734]

☆ ***Thurlow Arms*** [Baynards signposted off A281 W of Rudgwick or B2128 N]: Tucked-away converted station house in peaceful countryside, easy-going bare-boards bar with big windows, lots of interesting railway, farm and more miscellaneous memorabilia and bric-a-brac on walls and high ceilings, back games area with pool, darts and juke box, plush banquettes in side dining lounge, friendly staff, well kept Badger Best, Hogs Back TEA and Ringwood Best and Fortyniner, good if not cheap food, no music, dogs welcome; picnic-sets on lawn by rose trellis, meadow beyond with timber play fort – by former railway, now Downs Link Path; simple bedrooms available by prior arrangement *(Shirley Mackenzie, BB)*

Cranleigh [TQ0739]

Little Park Hatch [Bookhurst Rd, Parkmead estate – towards Shere]: Low beams, flagstones, huge inglenook with log fire, wide food choice from snacks and sandwiches to main meals cooked largely by landlady, reasonable prices, friendly landlord, well kept real ales, small dining area; dogs welcome; huge garden with pets corner, aviary and adventure play area *(Mike and Lynn Robinson)*

Dorking [TQ1649]

Bulls Head [South St]: Cheerful former coaching inn, homely and welcoming, with well kept real ales and no smoking area *(Dr and Mrs A K Clarke)*

☆ ***Cricketers*** [South St]: Bustling and chatty little Fullers local, very neat and tidy, with solidly comfortable furniture, cricketing memorabilia on stripped brick walls, cheap no-nonsense food (not Fri/Sat evening or Sun lunch), well kept Chiswick, London Pride and ESB, low prices, relaxed atmosphere and helpful friendly service; nice suntrap back terrace with barbecues, open all day *(Jonathan Stewart, Anna Pointer, LYM, Lawrence Clancy)*

☆ ***Kings Arms*** [West St]: 16th-c half-timbered pub in antiques area, part-panelled low-beamed lounge divided from bar by timbers, nice lived-in old furniture, warm relaxed atmosphere, good choice of home-made food from sandwiches up, friendly service, well kept Bass, Fullers London Pride, Greene King IPA and Wadworths 6X, attractive old-fashioned back dining area; piped music; open all day *(Val and Alan Green)*

Dormansland [TQ4042]

Old House At Home [West St]: Nice country local with wide choice of enjoyable generous food using fresh produce, good Sun lunch (booking recommended), Shepherd Neame Bitter, Spitfire and Bishops Finger *(Mrs Jane Williams)*

Dunsfold [TQ0036]

☆ ***Sun*** [off B2130 S of Godalming]: Elegantly

double-fronted pub with old and unaffected interior, scrubbed pine furniture, log fire in inglenook, good mix of locals and visitors, well kept Badger K&B, Friary Meux Best and Marstons Pedigree, decent wine list and bar food till 10pm, well behaved children in eating area and restaurant; darts, table skittles, cribbage, dominoes, shove-ha'penny; seats out on terrace and overlooking quiet village green *(LYM, Mike and Heather Watson, Kevin Williams, Gee Cormack, Ian Phillips)*

East Clandon [TQ0651]

☆ ***Wishing Well*** [just off A246 Guildford—Leatherhead; The Street]: Rambling dining pub popular with older crowd for wide choice of home-made food from good fresh baguettes to attractively priced main dishes, comfortable relaxed atmosphere in small spotless connecting rooms, big inglenook log-effect fire, fine old elm bar counter, well kept ales such as Badger K&B, Hogs Back TEA and Youngs, quick and attentive welcoming service; no dogs, boots or overalls, they may try to keep your credit card; children welcome, tables in quiet garden, handy for two NT properties, cl Mon *(LYM, John Evans, P J Keen, Sue and Mike Todd, Mike and Heather Watson, Mrs T A Bizat)*

Effingham [TQ1253]

Plough [Orestan Lane]: Welcoming commuter-belt Youngs local with consistently well kept ales, honest home cooking inc enjoyable Sun lunch, good wine choice, two coal-effect gas fires, beamery, panelling, old plates and brassware in long lounge, no smoking extension; popular with older people – no dogs, children, music or machines, attractive garden with play area; convenient for Polesden Lacey (NT) *(John and Angela Main, Barrie Drewitt, Gordon Prince)*

Sir Douglas Haig [off A246 Leatherhead—Guildford]: Large open-plan beamed pub with armchairs, sofa and books one end, mix of old and new tables and chairs at the other, bar food from sandwiches to steaks, well kept Fullers London Pride, Gales BB and HSB and a guest such as Ash Vine, good choice of coffees; piped music, sports TV or machines may obtrude, TV, can be smoky; children in eating area, open all day, tables on attractive terrace and back lawn, decent bedrooms *(Roger and Jenny Huggins, Simon and Sally Small, LYM)*

Egham [TQ0171]

Beehive [Middle Hill]: Small friendly local sprucely redone with hard seating on polished boards, well kept changing ales inc Fullers London Pride and Gales HSB, beer festivals, small dining area, polite service, quiz nights; nice garden with picnic-sets and play area *(Ian Phillips)*

Crown [High St]: Busy simply furnished local with four or five changing ales such as Adnams, Fullers London Pride and Greene King Old Speckled Hen, usual food, coal fires; juke box or piped music, TV, pool in public bar; pleasant back walled garden with lively aviary and pretty pond (but below flight path) *(Tom McLean, Ian Phillips)*

Foresters Arms [North St]: Calm and welcoming backstreet local with reasonably priced food from good value hot baguettes up, well kept Courage Best, Fullers London Pride and Greene King Old Speckled Hen, friendly landlord, pool table, separate dining area *(Ian Phillips)*

Englefield Green [SU9971]

Barley Mow [Northcroft Rd]: Pretty pub in nice spot with café tables out in front overlooking cricket green (summer steam fairs); usual refurbished interior and food, well kept Courage Best and Directors, back dining area with no smoking section, darts, quiet piped machine; pleasant back garden with play area *(Ian Phillips)*

☆ ***Fox & Hounds*** [Bishopsgate Rd; off A328 N of Egham]: Popular pub in good setting on edge of Windsor Great Park, short walk from Savile Garden, tables on pleasant front lawn and back terrace; well kept Brakspears, Fullers London Pride and Greene King Ruddles County, nice wines by the glass, good if not cheap food in bar and restaurant, polite friendly service, two handsome log fires, daily papers; piped music, no children; open all day wknds and July-Sept, picnic-sets outside, good big new car park *(Roger Everett, Simon and Laura Habbishow, LYM, Martin and Karen Wake, Ian Phillips)*

Sun [Wick Lane, Bishopsgate]: Unassuming welcoming local, well kept Adnams, Bass, Brakspears and Courage Best and Directors, good blackboard wine choice, reasonable prices, efficient young staff, enjoyable food from good sandwiches and baguettes to Sun lunch, daily papers, roaring log fire in back conservatory, biscuit and water for dogs, interesting beer bottle collection; quiet garden with aviary, handy for Savile Garden and Windsor Park *(Ian Phillips, LM)*

Epsom [TQ2160]

Derby Arms [Downs Rd, Epsom Downs]: Recently updated Vintage Inn dining pub, very popular lunchtimes with older people for wide choice of reasonably priced food and decent wines, log fires, no smoking area; surprisingly little racing memorabilia; open all day Sun, nice tables outside, good views *(Mrs V Brown, Kevin Williams, Gee Cormack, Jenny and Brian Seller, Ian Phillips)*

Tattenham Corner [Tattenham Crescent, opp racecourse]: Light and spacious refurbished chain dining pub, decent food all day, pleasant service, good views of racecourse and downs; garden with play area and summer barbecues *(Mrs G R Sharman)*

Esher [TQ1566]

☆ ***Marneys*** [Alma Rd, Weston Green]: Attractive low-ceilinged cottagey pub in charming spot overlooking church, duck pond, green and golf course, well kept Courage Best and Directors, good interesting food (not Sun) reflecting Norwegian landlord's national cuisine, quick service by friendly uniformed staff, family dining area, decent wines; very small – can get crowded; tables outside *(Martin and Karen Wake, Ian Wilson, John Crafts, Ellen Weld, David London)*

☆ ***Prince of Wales*** [West End Lane; off A244

towards Hersham, by Princess Alice Hospice]: Well run Victorian Chef & Brewer dining pub, attractive period décor, cosy candlelit corners, open fires, turkey carpets, old furniture, prints and photographs; massive choice of generous reasonably priced food, well kept Courage Best, Greene King Old Speckled Hen and Theakstons and daily papers at the proper bar, good wine choice, quick friendly staff, family area; big garden, near green and pond *(Kevin Williams, Gee Cormack, Stuart and Alison Wallace, James Nunns, Gordon Stevenson)*

Ewell [TQ2262]

Spring [London Rd]: Popular, spacious and airy, with pleasant décor, low-priced bar food inc Sun roast, well kept ales such as Fullers London Pride, decent wine choice, friendly efficient service, restaurant; TV and machines not obtrusive, Tues quiz night; garden with barbecues *(Kevin Williams, Gee Cormack, D and M T Ayres-Regan)*

Ewhurst [TQ0842]

Windmill [Pitch Hill; a mile N towards Shere]: Spectacular views from picnic-sets on spacious series of hillside lawns and from big conservatory restaurant used as lunchtime bar overflow, lovely walking country; food from toasted sandwiches to popular Sun lunch, well kept Courage Best, Fullers London Pride and Greene King IPA and Old Speckled Hen, central open fire, country décor with big old sofas, large tables, plates and pitchforks on the walls, ceiling hung with lamps and blow-torches; occasional live music *(Ian Phillips, Mike and Lynn Robinson, LYM)*

Farleigh [TQ3659]

☆ ***Harrow*** [Farleigh Common, off B269 Limpsfield—Warlingham]: Big welcoming Vintage Inn, busy lunchtimes even midweek (get there early Sun for a table), reliably enjoyable food from sandwiches up, well kept Bass and lots of wines by the glass from large horseshoe bar, well trained staff, several rooms inc large no smoking area, old farm tools and machinery; plenty of tables outside *(John Branston, Jim Bush, Jenny and Brian Seller)*

Farnham [SU8445]

☆ ***Fox*** [Frensham Rd, Lower Bourne]: Enterprising reasonably priced food in pleasant bistro atmosphere, good-sized helpings, Greene King Old Speckled Hen and Ruddles Best, good value wines, log fire, deep crimson décor with heavy curtains, prints, some stripped brickwork, nice blend of wooden furniture and raised back area; picnic-sets and small adventure playground outside *(Martin and Karen Wake)*

Spotted Cow [Bourne Grove, Lower Bourne (towards Tilford)]: Welcoming country local with good home-made food inc lots of fresh fish, well kept Adnams, Courage and Hogs Back TEA, attentive friendly service, reasonable prices; play area in big garden, nice surroundings *(Martin and Karen Wake, M Borthwick)*

Fickleshole [TQ3960]

☆ ***White Bear*** [Featherbed Lane/Fairchildes Lane; off A2022 Purley Rd just S of A212 roundabout]: Rambling interestingly furnished partly 15th-c family country pub with new landlord doing enjoyable food from good value sandwiches up inc some interesting dishes, lots of small rooms, flagstone floors, friendly service, well kept Flowers IPA and Fullers London Pride and ESB, good coffee, restaurant; fruit machine, video game, piped music; children welcome, jazz Weds, open all day Sat; play area in pleasant sizeable garden, lots of picnic-sets on front terrace *(Jenny and Brian Seller, LYM, Jim Bush, LM, Colin McKerrow)*

Friday Street [TQ1245]

☆ ***Stephan Langton*** [signed off B2126, or from A25 Westcott—Guildford]: Attractive country pub with friendly new landlady and skilled chef/landlord, good enterprising bar lunches (not Mon) and evening restaurant meals (not Sun/Mon), sensible prices, restaurant open in evenings 7-10 Tues-Sat; at lunchtime, bar meals served 12.30-3 Tues-Sun; good wines by the glass, well kept Adnams, comfortable bar, parlour-like lounge, traditional games; plenty of tables in front courtyard, more on back tree-surrounded steam-side terrace, peaceful spot surrounded by good walks, has been open all day summer *(Mike and Lynn Robinson, LYM, John Branston, Mr and Mrs A Swainson, Eddie Edwards, Rosemary and Tom Hall)*

Frimley Green [SU8856]

Rose & Thistle [Sturt Rd]: Recently reopened with refreshingly spare décor, pleasant bar area and conservatory, six real ales, plenty of wine choice, enjoyable country cooking, friendly staff, and largely no smoking *(Mandy Tilley, N Cooper)*

Godstone [TQ3551]

White Hart [handy for M25 junction 6; High St]: Beefeater in beamed and timbered former coaching inn opp pretty village pond, their usual food from baked potatoes up, Boddingtons, Marstons Pedigree and Wadworths 6X *(Ian Phillips, BB)*

Gomshall [TQ0847]

☆ ***Compasses*** [A25]: Plain bar (open all day) and much bigger neatly comfortable no smoking dining area, good value food from sandwiches and baked potatoes to steak, good children's menu, summer cream teas, well kept ales such as Brakspears, Fullers London Pride and Greene King Old Speckled Hen, good value house wines, pleasant efficient service; piped music, live Fri; open all day, children welcome, pretty garden sloping down to roadside mill stream, peaceful bedrooms *(LYM, Ian Phillips, R T and J C Moggridge, Mike and Lynn Robinson, Tony and Wendy Hobden, June and Ken Brooks, Gordon Prince)*

Grayswood [SU9134]

Wheatsheaf [A286 NE of Haslemere]: Civilised much modernised pub with attentive courteous service, well kept Badger beers, enjoyable food in bar and restaurant; conference/bedroom extension *(Derek and Margaret Underwood)*

Guildford [SU9949]

Olde Ship [Portsmouth Rd (A3100 S)]: Three cosy areas around central bar, ancient beams, flagstones, good log fire in big fireplace, candles and comfortable mix of furniture, no smoking zone (no mobile phones either), part with tables and chairs, good range of interesting but unpretentious and fairly priced bistro-style food inc good pizzas, well kept ales inc Greene King, decent wines, obliging service; no music *(Jane Thompson, Edward Longley)*

Weyside [Shalford Rd, Millbrook; across car park from Yvonne Arnaud Theatre, beyond boat yard]: Big popular two-level riverside pub, reworked to include lots of different areas from young and funky to formal, from comfortable sofas to conservatory dining area; enjoyable up-to-date food throughout such as bruschetta with mozzarella or yellow striped mullet with niçoise salad; good polite service, decent wines, lots of picnic-sets in big garden with moorings and terrace by River Wey, good walks; open all day *(Miss M Bertarelli)*

Hambledon [SU9639]

Merry Harriers [off A283]: Homely and casually old-fashioned country local popular with walkers, very quiet wkdy lunchtimes; lovely inglenook log fire, dark wood and red décor, dark pine bar, pine tables, impressive collection of chamber-pots hanging from beams, well kept Greene King IPA and Abbot, Hogs Back TEA and Hop Back Crop Circle, farm cider, daily papers, reasonably priced fresh simple food from sandwiches up; pool room, folk night 1st Sun of month; big back garden, picnic-sets in front and over road – caravan parking *(Phil and Sally Gorton)*

Holmbury St Mary [TQ1144]

Royal Oak: Well run and relaxing 17th-c beamed coaching inn in pleasant spot by green and church, good helpings of popular fresh food, good choice of well kept ales such as Greene King IPA, quick friendly service, log fire; tables on front lawn, bedrooms, good walks *(Mike and Lynn Robinson, Gordon Stevenson, Jenny and Brian Seller)*

Hurtmore [SU9445]

Squirrels [just off A3 nr Godalming, via Priorsfield Rd]: Comfortable, fresh and airy bar with cosy corners and new bar billiards table, wide choice of enjoyable food, helpful landlord and friendly service, partly no smoking restaurant and conservatory, well kept real ale, decent wines; disabled facilities; sizeable pleasant garden with heated terrace and play area, comfortable well equipped bedrooms, good breakfast, open all day *(BB, Lynn Davis)*

Irons Bottom [TQ2546]

Three Horseshoes [Sidlow Bridge, off A217]: Friendly unassuming country local, enjoyable carefully made lunchtime food, well kept real ales inc Fullers London Pride and guest beers such as Hook Norton, thoughtful service; quiz or darts night Tues, summer barbecues *(Brian Root)*

Laker's Green [TQ0335]

Three Compasses [Dunsfold Rd]: Local with well kept ales such as Badger K&B, Courage Best, fff Mild and Ringwood Old Thumper, decent food, helpful landlord; picnic-sets outside, dogs welcome *(Ian Phillips)*

Laleham [TQ0568]

☆ ***Anglers Retreat*** [B376 (Staines Rd)]: New landlord in big refurbished family pub, pale panelling, big tropical aquarium set into wall, even larger one in smart no smoking restaurant area extended into conservatory, has had good food (all day wknds) inc lots of fresh fish, two bright coal fires, Brakspears PA, SB and a guest beer, decent wines; Sun quiz night, unobtrusive piped music, fruit machine, no dogs; children welcome, seats out in front, play area in back garden, open all day *(John and Glenys Wheeler, Tom McLean, LYM, Evelyn and Derek Walter)*

Feathers [Broadway]: Friendly smartish old local, roomy inside, with bar in single-storey front extension, traditional décor, lots of hanging pewter mugs, well kept real ales, reasonably priced generous home-made food in beamed back dining area with evening roaring log fire; darts, TV, games machine, may be piped music; small terrace and garden *(Mayur Shah)*

Three Horseshoes [B376 (Shepperton Rd)]: Much modernised, but dating from 13th c, with flagstones, heavy beams, log-effect fires, cosy areas off central serving area, big no smoking conservatory, interesting history; popular food from sandwiches up, well kept Courage Best, Fullers London Pride, Greene King Abbot and Wychwood Hobgoblin, efficient service; TV, piped music; lots of picnic-sets on terrace, open all day *(Ian Jones, LYM, Simon Collett-Jones, Jim Bush)*

Leatherhead [TQ1656]

Dukes Head [High St]: Busy and friendly town pub, enjoyable attractively priced food from sandwiches up at separate servery, beams, timbers, nice furnishings and open fire, Ansells, good coffee, small front bar with pool and games machine; piped music; handy for riverside walks *(DWAJ, Ian Phillips)*

Martyrs Green [TQ0857]

Black Swan [handy for M25 junction 10; off A3 S-bound, but return N of junction]: Extensively enlarged, with a dozen or more well kept ales inc bargains, simple furnishings, well worn back bar, SkyTV, usual food (queue to order), log fires, restaurant; can get crowded with young people evenings, piped pop music may be loud then, frequent discos and theme nights; plenty of tables in big woodside garden with barbecues and good play area – bouncy castle, playground-quality frames, roundabouts etc; handy for RHS Wisley Garden, open all day *(Jason Reynolds)*

Merstham [TQ3051]

Feathers [A23]: Recently reopened after renovation, roomy bar with lots of armchairs, real ales such as Adnams, Bass, Black Sheep, Fullers London Pride and Wadworths 6X, Addlestone's cider, several wines by the glass, food from ciabattas and snacks to several imaginative main dishes, fans; soft piped music *(John Branston)*

Mickleham [TQ1753]

Running Horses [Old London Rd (B2209)]: Friendly 16th-c beamed village inn below Box Hill, enjoyable food with bar and restaurant menus, well kept changing ales such as

Adnams, Bass, Fullers London Pride and Youngs, quick cheerful service even when packed with impatient walkers, big inglenook log fire and smaller coal-effect one, lots of old pictures, comfortable and attractive upmarket dining extension/conservatory, no children; opp church, nice view from pretty courtyard garden, bedrooms *(G T Brewster, Thomas Neate, Ian Wilson, Susan and John Douglas)*

Newdigate [TQ1942]

Six Bells: Good atmosphere in popular local with good range of well kept ales, enjoyable food, well kept Bass and Kings, friendly service, a welcome for children; plenty of tables in pleasant garden, lovely outlook over wooden-towered church *(anon)*

Nutfield [TQ3050]

Queens Head [A25 E of Redhill]: Congenial pub with tiled bar and carpeted restaurant, enjoyable nicely presented food, helpful mainly Australian staff, good wine list *(Grahame Brooks)*

Ockham [TQ0756]

☆ *Hautboy* [Ockham Lane – towards Cobham]: New management in this remarkable red stone gothick folly, crypt bar with bar stools at proper servery (we hope they'll introduce real ales too), emphasis on imaginative choice of good food from snacks up, friendly efficient service, character upstairs brasserie bar, darkly panelled and high-raftered, with oil paintings and minstrels gallery; tables on cricket-view terrace and in secluded orchard garden with play area; chintzy bedrooms *(John Evans, LYM)*

Ockley [TQ1439]

Old School House [Stane St]: Fine school house attractively converted to popular and enjoyable dining pub, good value generous food from sandwiches up inc fresh pasta and fish, friendly attentive service, well kept Badger ales, good wines, wonderful log fire *(G T Brewster, M Blatchly)*

☆ *Punch Bowl* [Oakwood Hill, signed off A29 S]: Cosy country pub, smart and clean, with several rooms, huge inglenook log fire, polished flagstones, lots of beams, well kept Badger Best and Tanglefoot and a Gribble guest, wide blackboard choice of enjoyable well presented food inc interesting dishes and separate sandwich and puddings boards, friendly service, traditional games; children allowed in dining area, picnic-sets on side terrace and in pretty front garden, quiet spot *(LYM, John and Elizabeth Cox, E and R Bromage, Jim Bush)*

Ottershaw [TQ0263]

Castle [Brox Rd, signed off A320 S]: Comfortable and friendly local dated 1905, lots of farm tools etc, stripped brick and beamery, log fire; wide range of good home-made food inc interesting dishes (no smoking dining area), hearty log fire, well kept changing ales such as Adnams, Fullers London Pride, Greene King Abbot, Tetleys, Charles Wells Bombardier and Youngs Special, Addlestone's cider; tables with rustic benches in pleasant creeper-hung booths and on front terrace *(Ian Phillips)*

Outwood [TQ3245]

☆ *Bell* [Outwood Common, just E of village; off A23 S of Redhill]: Attractive extended 17th-c country dining pub, olde-worlde beamed bar and sparser restaurant area, good choice of well kept ales such as Flowers IPA, Harveys Best and Wadworths 6X, good value usual food inc bargain lunches, quick cheerful young staff, log fires; children and dogs welcome, piped music; summer barbecues and cream teas, has been open all day; pretty fairy-lit garden with country views, handy for windmill *(G T Brewster, LYM, Tony and Wendy Hobden)*

☆ *Dog & Duck* [Prince of Wales Rd; turn off A23 at Station sign in Salfords, S of Redhill – OS Sheet 187 map ref 312460]: Welcoming rambling beamed country cottage, open all day, with good mix of furnishings, huge log fires, half a dozen well kept Badger and guest ales, popular food all day, lots of board games etc; children in restaurant, tables outside *(LYM, Brian Root)*

Oxshott [TQ1460]

Bear [Leatherhead Rd (A244)]: Busy yet relaxed and friendly Youngs pub with well kept beer, wide choice of wines by the glass, good staff, usual decent pub food with fresh veg, good log fire, teddy bear collection, big conservatory dining room; occasional barbecues in small garden *(Gordon Prince)*

Oxted [TQ3852]

Old Bell [High St, Old Oxted]: Beamed and panelled pub/restaurant with welcoming staff and reasonably priced food inc all-day Sun carvery, decent beers and wine; good wheelchair access, disabled facilities and a welcome for children, garden *(Matthew Croxford)*

Puttenham [SU9347]

Jolly Farmer [just off A31 Farnham—Guildford; Puttenham Heath Rd]: Harvester with good choice of well presented reliable food, welcoming efficient young staff, several comfortably refurbished rooms with interesting show of harvesting scenes and beer/farm tools, pleasant staff; children welcome, picnic-sets outside *(Dick and Madeleine Brown, LYM)*

Redhill [TQ2850]

Home Cottage [Redstone Hill]: New landlord doing well in pleasantly updated and comfortable town pub, enjoyable food from sandwiches and baguettes to sensibly priced main dishes, well kept Youngs Bitter, Special and seasonal beers, several separate bar areas, restaurant and conservatory *(Tony Hobden)*

Reigate [TQ2550]

Red Cross [High St]: Two-level beamed pub under new owners, pine furniture, good choice of decent bar food from enterprising sandwiches, ciabattas and light dishes to rib-eye steak, Adnams Broadside, Courage Directors, Fullers London Pride and two guest beers, good mainly new world wine choice *(Mike Gorton)*

Ripley [TQ0556]

Anchor [High St]: Tudor inn with good friendly service, well kept real ales and lively local feel in old-fashioned cool dark low-beamed connecting rooms, food inc ciabattas and thai dishes, games in public bar; tables in coachyard

(BB, Philip and Susan Philcox, Derek Harvey-Piper, M J Brooks)
Jovial Sailor [Portsmouth Rd]: Recently refurbished, enjoyable food all day, very popular on Sun – lots of children then; piped music aimed to suit the customers *(Anthony Evers, Shirley Mackenzie)*
Seven Stars [Newark Lane (B367)]: 1930s roadhouse with wide choice of generous food inc good Sun lunches, Bass, Fullers London Pride and Greene King IPA and Abbot, good friendly service, no smoking area; piped music; attractive garden behind *(D P and J A Sweeney, Shirley Mackenzie, Tony and Wendy Hobden)*
Talbot [High St]: Beamed coaching inn with Fullers London Pride and Greene King Abbot, bar food from generous baguettes up, welcoming helpful staff, nice atmosphere, restaurant; may be piped music; bedrooms, tables in back courtyard *(Gordon Prince)*
Shackleford [SU9345]
☆ ***Cyder House*** [Peper Harow Lane]: Roomy and civilised country pub rambling around central servery, wide blackboard choice of enjoyable food from ciabatta sandwiches to imaginative starters and hot dishes, chatty friendly staff, well kept Badger ales and Hogs Back TEA, decent house wines, log or coal fires, pleasantly bright and airy layout with lots of mellow pine, dining room and separate children's room with toys and small furniture; fruit machine and sports TV in side room, may be piped pop music; picnic-sets on terrace and back lawn, nice leafy village setting, open all day wknds *(Martin and Karen Wake, Susan and John Douglas, MDN, BB)*
Shalford [SU9946]
Parrot [Broadford]: Big neatly kept canalside pub with nice décor, ample helpings of tasty good value bar food, separate pleasant conservatory grill restaurant, several well kept real ales, quick friendly staff; attractive garden *(Mike and Lynn Robinson)*
Sea Horse [A281 S of Guildford]: Vintage Inn with attractive décor, good range of reasonably priced food lunchtime and evening, well kept beer, plenty of young helpful staff; children welcome *(Dick and Madeleine Brown)*
Shamley Green [TQ0343]
☆ ***Red Lion*** [The Green]: Smartly done-up dining pub with neat décor, dark polished furniture, rows of books, open fires, local cricketing photographs, enjoyable if pricy food all day from sandwiches and good ploughman's to steaks, children's helpings and unusual puddings, well kept Flowers, Greene King Abbot, Youngs and farm cider, good choice of wines, cafetière coffee, friendly staff, smart restaurant; open all day, children welcome, sturdy tables in nice garden; bedrooms *(LYM, Edward Longley, John and Angela Main)*
Shepperton [TQ0867]
Red Lion [Russell Rd]: Roomy and welcoming old wisteria-covered local across road from Thames, plenty of tables on terrace among fine displays of shrubs and flowers, more on lawn over road (traffic noise) with lovely river views and well run moorings; well kept Brakspears, Courage Best, Fullers London Pride and Charles Wells Bombardier, generous food inc good value all-day Sun lunch and children's meals, quick attentive mainly antipodean or South African service, interesting prints and red-cushioned seating in quiet and cosy front bar, back bar for sports TV, restaurant *(Mayur Shah, James Nunns)*
Shere [TQ0747]
White Horse [signed off A25 3 miles E of Guildford; Middle St]: Striking half-timbered medieval Chef & Brewer, extensively enlarged but still full of character, with several rooms off the small busy bar, uneven floors, massive beams, Tudor stonework, oak wall seats, two log fires, one in a huge inglenook, food all day from chunky sandwiches up, well kept beers such as Courage Best and Hogs Back TEA, lots of wines by the glass, good-sized children's area; tables outside, beautiful village, open all day *(MDN, Norma and Noel Thomas, Mike and Lynn Robinson, LYM, Edward Longley, Kevin Flack, Ian Phillips, G T Brewster)*
Shottermill [SU8832]
☆ ***Mill*** [Liphook Rd, S of Haslemere]: 17th-c pub with low black beams, log fire in big stone fireplace, pews and scrubbed tables in candlelit main locals' bar, very wide choice of good interesting well priced generous food from sandwiches (Mon-Sat lunchtime) up, well kept ales such as Greene King IPA, Ringwood Fortyniner, Charles Wells Bombardier and Youngs Special, good choice of wines, Addlestone's cider, pleasant quieter carpeted second room and separate lighter and more airy no smoking room; mill ponds with ducks and geese in front, nice terrace and sloping garden behind with good-sized play area *(W W Burke, Martin and Karen Wake, Betty Laker, Derek Harvey-Piper, BB)*
South Godstone [TQ3549]
Fox & Hounds [Tilburstow Hill Rd/Harts Lane, off A22]: Attractive old-fashioned pub in pleasant spot, country views from garden, cosy low-beamed bar with antique high-backed settles, racing prints and woodburner, Greene King IPA, Abbot and Ruddles County from tiny bar counter, lunchtime bar food from sandwiches up, evening restaurant (not Sun/Mon evenings); may be piped music, children in eating area *(LYM, Ian Phillips)*
Staines [TQ0471]
Bells [Church St]: Comfortable and relaxed, with well kept Youngs Bitter, Special and Waggledance and a Smiles seasonal guest beer, decent wines, prompt home-made lunchtime food from good sandwiches up, friendly staff, cosy furnishings, central fireplace; may be piped music – not evenings; plenty of seats in big garden with terrace *(Ian Phillips, Tony Middis)*
Old Red Lion [Leacroft]: Roomy and comfortable, with helpful landlord, low-priced food, well kept Courage Best, Fullers London Pride and Youngs Special, games area; open all day Sat, nice spot overlooking tree-shaded green *(Ian Phillips, R Huggins, D Irving, E McCall, T McLean)*
☆ ***Swan*** [The Hythe; south bank, over Staines

Bridge]: Splendid Thamesside setting, with moorings, tables on riverside verandah, big conservatory, several distinctly different areas to suit a mix of customers inc a music room, fairly peaceful upstairs restaurant, and calm chatty corridor, enjoyable traditional food, cheerful service, well kept Fullers ales inc a seasonal beer; can be very busy Sun lunchtime and packed with under-30s on summer evenings; comfortable bedrooms *(Simon Collett-Jones, LYM, R Huggins, D Irving, E McCall, T McLean)*

Swan on the Moor [Moor Lane]: Comfortable and welcoming, with well kept Courage Best, Fullers London Pride and Youngs or Shepherd Neame Spitfire, cosy central fire, beams, panelling, stripped bricks, ornamental books, decent food inc choice of Sun roasts (and bar nibbles then), daily papers; quiet piped music; conservatory restaurant, small enclosed garden safe for children *(S Palmer)*

Tadworth [TQ2354]

Blue Anchor [Dorking Rd (B2032)]: Busy, warm and homely Vintage Inn, with log fires and candles, cheerful helpful staff, well kept Bass and Tetleys, decent wine, vast helpings of food inc popular fish and chips; piped music *(Stephanie Smith, Leigh Hughes, Mrs G R Sharman)*

Dukes Head [A217 opp Common and woods]: Well reworked by new licensees, character tables on nice stone floor, enjoyable food (not Sun evening) from formidable sandwiches up, real ales such as Adnams, Brakspears, Fullers London Pride, Harveys, Old Kent and Marstons Pedigree, very good choice of wines by the glass, two big inglenook log fires; garden, open all day *(John Branston)*

Thames Ditton [TQ1566]

Greyhound [Hampton Court Way, Weston Green]: Friendly comfortable old local, new family doing inexpensive generous traditional food, well kept beers, open fire, big pine tables in airy rooms *(B Phelvin, Michael and Ann Cole)*

The Sands [SU8846]

Barley Mow [Littleworth Rd, Seale; E of Farnham]: Small comfortable village pub neatly redone in the current traditional style with polished pine tables and hard chairs, a step or two down to dining area, well kept Brakspears, Fullers London Pride and Greene King, enjoyable simple lunchtime food from sandwiches and bocattas up, evening meals (not Sun) specialising in fish; picnic-sets in secluded garden *(Howard Dell)*

Thorpe [TQ0268]

Rose & Crown [Sandhills Lane, Thorpe Green]: Roomy and appealing Chef & Brewer, enjoyable changing home-made food, good atmosphere, Courage Best and Directors, Greene King Old Speckled Hen and Marstons Pedigree, good choice of wines by the glass, pleasant attentive staff, daily papers; piped classical music, can get crowded; nice gardens with good play area *(Ian Phillips)*

Tilford [SU8743]

Barley Mow [The Green, off B3001 SE of Farnham]: Good food, charming friendly service, good log fire in big inglenook, comfortable traditional seats around scrubbed tables, interesting prints and old photographs, well kept real ales; small back eating area, wknd afternoon teas; darts, table skittles, no children; pretty setting between river and geese-cropped cricket green near ancient oak, with waterside garden – village gets busy in summer *(G D Sharpe)*

Walliswood [TQ1238]

☆ *Scarlett Arms* [signed from Ewhurst—Rowhook back rd, or off A29 S of Ockley]: Attractively unspoilt country cottage, three neatly kept rooms, low black oak beams, deeply polished flagstones, simple but comfortable furniture, two log fires – one in huge inglenook, well kept Badger Tanglefoot, K&B and Mild, darts, cribbage, shove-ha'penny, table skittles, dominoes; fruit machine, piped music, straightforward food, no children; peaceful benches in front and old-fashioned seats and tables under cocktail parasols in pretty well tended garden *(LYM, John Saville, John and Angela Main)*

Walton-on-Thames [TQ0966]

Swan [Manor Rd, off A3050]: Big three-bar riverside Youngs pub, lots of interconnecting rooms, huge neatly kept garden leading down to Thames, decent reasonably priced food in bar and attractive restaurant, well kept ales, wknd barbecues; moorings, riverside walks *(Mayur Shah)*

Weir [off Sunbury Lane]: Wide range of good food from sandwiches up, Badger Best and Tanglefoot, traditional décor, masses of river pictures, candles on tables, attractive family room done as part-panelled library looking over water, uniformed staff; lots of picnic-sets crowded on to big terrace with good view over river and weir (and steel walkway); open all day Sun, lovely towpath walks *(Mayur Shah, David and Carole Chapman)*

Warlingham [TQ3658]

☆ *White Lion* [Farleigh Rd (B269)]: Busy old local with Tudor fireplace snugged in by high-backed settles, friendly dark-panelled rooms, very low beams, good value attractively priced food (not Sun evening) from sandwiches up, real ales such as Adnams, Bass, Fullers London Pride and Hancocks HB, prompt service; may be piped music in eating area; tables in neat back garden *(Michael and Ann Cole, LYM, Jim Bush)*

West Clandon [TQ0452]

☆ *Bulls Head* [A247 SE of Woking]: Friendly and comfortably modernised 16th-c country local, very popular esp with older people lunchtime for good value food from sandwiches, ploughman's and baked potatoes through reliable home-made pies to steak, small lantern-lit front bar with open fire and some stripped brick, old local prints, raised rather canteenish back inglenook dining area, efficient service, well kept Courage Best, Greene King Old Speckled Hen and Marstons Pedigree, good coffee, no piped music, games room with darts and pool; lots of tables and good play area in garden, convenient for Clandon Park, good walking country *(DWAJ, R Lake, John Evans)*

West Humble [TQ1751]

Stepping Stones [just off A24 below Box Hill]: Large friendly pub, circular bar with good range of beers inc Fullers, Greene King Abbot and Old Speckled Hen and Ringwood, enjoyable food; children and walkers welcome in restaurant, terrace and garden with summer barbecue and play area *(Sue and Mike Todd)*

Weybridge [TQ0965]

Badgers Rest [Oatlands Chase]: Warm and welcoming Vintage Inn, seven or eight linked rooms well reworked with bare brick and realistic beams, tables for varying numbers, wide food choice from sandwiches up (popular with older people for lunch), well kept Bass and Tetleys, good wine choice, very helpful staff; separate food counter, back area for smokers; tables on front lawn; immaculate bedrooms *(Minda and Stanley Alexander, James Nunns)*

Flintgate [Oatlands Drive]: Refurbished by new licensees, comfortable fresh furnishing and décor with local photographs and interesting paintings, well kept beer, enterprising blackboard food; tables out on terrace *(Minda and Stanley Alexander)*

☆ ***Old Crown*** [Thames St]: Friendly and comfortable old-fashioned three-bar pub, very popular lunchtime for good platefuls of reasonably priced straightforward food from sandwiches up esp fresh Grimsby fish (served evening too), good specials; well kept Courage Best and Directors, John Smiths, Youngs Special and a guest such as Charles Wells Bombardier, service good even when busy, no smoking family lounge and conservatory, no music or machines but may be sports TV in back bar; children welcome, suntrap streamside garden *(Ian Phillips, DWAJ)*

Prince of Wales [Cross Rd/Anderson Rd off Oatlands Drive]: Congenial and attractively restored, with relaxed country-local feel, reasonably priced generous bar food inc interesting dishes and Sun lunch with three roasts, well kept ales such as Adnams, Boddingtons, Fullers London Pride, Tetleys and Wadworths 6X, ten wines by the glass, friendly service, coal-effect gas fires, imaginative menu in stripped pine dining room down a couple of steps (candlelit bistro feel there at night) *(James Nunns, Minda and Stanley Alexander)*

Windlesham [SU9264]

Half Moon [Church Rd]: Extended pub with all tables laid for the popular food inc family Sun lunch and fresh veg, good service, modern furnishings, log fires, well kept ales such as Archers Golden, Exe Valley Spring, Hogs Back TEA and Hop Back Summer Lightning, Weston's farm cider, interesting World War II pictures; children welcome, piped music, silenced fruit machine; huge well kept garden *(Ian Phillips)*

Witley [SU9439]

☆ ***White Hart*** [Petworth Rd]: Tudor beams, good oak furniture, log fire in cosy panelled inglenook snug where George Eliot drank, welcoming landlord, Shepherd Neame Best and Spitfire, daily papers, public bar with usual games, restaurant; piped music; tables on cobbled terrace, lots of pretty hanging baskets etc, lower meadow with picnic-sets and play area *(Michael Sargent, Ian Phillips, LYM)*

Woking [TQ0058]

Litten Tree [Constitution Hill]: Modern themed pub close to the chain's HQ, good value food in bar and restaurant, Courage Directors and a beer brewed for them, friendly helpful staff; good bedrooms in attached Travel Lodge *(Ian Phillips)*

Wetherspoons [Chertsey Rd]: Lots of intimate areas and cosy side snugs, good range of food all day, reasonably priced beers inc interesting guest ales *(Tony Hobden)*

Wonersh [TQ0145]

☆ ***Grantley Arms*** [The Street]: Spacious and elegantly well worn in 16th-c timbered pub with good food in bar and restaurant, friendly staff *(Shirley Mackenzie)*

Worplesdon [SU9854]

☆ ***Jolly Farmer*** [Burdenshott Rd, towards Worplesdon Station]: Fresh décor and modern furnishings in roomy beamed country dining pub, airy stripped-brick dining extension, good if not cheap food inc unusual dishes (wider evening choice), sandwiches too, well kept ales such as Brakspears or fff Altons Pride, Fullers London Pride, Hogs Back TEA and Timothy Taylors Landlord, log fire (you may need to sit near it on cold days), restaurant; you may have to leave your credit card behind the bar; big sheltered garden, pleasant walks on Whitmoor Common *(Mrs Hilarie Taylor, Derek Harvey-Piper, Ian Phillips, MDN, Charles Moncreiffe, Mr and Mrs Hearn, Edward Longley, Geoffrey Kemp, LYM)*

Wotton [TQ1247]

☆ ***Wotton Hatch*** [A25 Dorking—Guildford]: Vintage Inn family dining pub, attractive and neatly kept – one of this chain's stars; welcoming largely no smoking rambling rooms around 17th-c core, interesting furnishings, good changing choice of generous reasonably priced food (all day Thurs-Sun and summer) from hearty sandwiches up, well kept Bass and Fullers London Pride with a guest beer, good choice of decent wines, freshly squeezed orange juice, keen young staff, daily papers; gentle piped music, no dogs; impressive views from neat garden, open all day *(Ian Phillips, Roger and Jenny Huggins, Alan and Paula McCully, Mrs G R Sharman, M G Hart, LYM, Lawrence Clancy, Colin and Sandra Tann, John Crafts, R Halsey, Jamie and Ruth Lyons)*

Wrecclesham [SU8344]

☆ ***Bat & Ball*** [approach from Sandrock Hill and unmade Upper Bourne Lane, or park in Short Heath Rd and walk down unmade Bat & Ball Lane]: Cosy old pub with well kept ales inc Archers, good choice of food from generous sandwiches and nachos up, Sun bar nibbles, friendly service, good atmosphere; family extension, dogs welcome, spacious terrace and secure family garden *(John and Vivienne Rice)*

Sussex

Sussex is where the Guide *is based, so naturally its pubs come under particularly close scrutiny. Though it is perhaps a little short on really imaginative dining pubs, the area makes up for that in its rich variety of perky and well run more unpretentious places, very welcoming to visitors (and to dogs, allowed in nine out of ten Sussex pubs – a very high proportion indeed). Many of these are also very attractive ancient buildings. The Sussex pubs that are doing best of all these days are the friendly Sportsmans at Amberley (tasty food, nice views), the Fountain at Ashurst (good food here too, and lots of improvements recently), the enjoyably cottagey Cricketers Arms at Berwick, the backstreet Basketmakers Arms in Brighton, the George & Dragon at Burpham (this dining pub is flourishing since becoming a free house), the highly individual Six Bells in Chiddingly (bargain food), the Old House At Home at Chidham (nice well run pub, good food), the friendly Coach & Horses at Danehill (its super food earns it a Food Award this year), the Blacksmiths Arms at Donnington (good food and beer bringing this friendly place back into the* Guide *after a break), the Cricketers at Duncton (a friendly new young landlady regaining its place in the* Guide *too, with enjoyable popular food), the restauranty Jolly Sportsman at East Chiltington (smart but welcoming, with super food), the Duke of Cumberland Arms at Henley (a rural idyll), the lively Black Jug in Horsham (good interesting inexpensive food), the George & Dragon at Houghton (given a lift under new licensees), the Halfway Bridge Inn near Lodsworth (popular new chef, and the bedrooms, new last year, have turned out well), the Gribble Inn at Oving (very enjoyable and well run, tied to Badger but brewing its own good beers), the Horse & Groom at Rushlake Green (a good all-rounder), the Salehurst Halt at Salehurst (good home cooking, very friendly and helpful new Australian landlady), the Sloop near Scaynes Hill (nice all round), the Keepers Arms at Trotton (earning its Food Award this year), and the Sussex Oak at Warnham (another new entry, attractively reworked and with good food). The Jolly Sportsman at East Chiltington, which has developed a welcoming warmth to go with its good stylish food, is Sussex Dining Pub of the Year. The Lucky Dip section at the end of the chapter is a rich trawling ground this year, with over 200 entries, over 70 of them new additions. Ones to note particularly are the Spotted Cow in Angmering, Black Horse at Apuldram, Yew Tree at Arlington, Cowdray Arms at Balcombe, Black Horse at Binsted, Curlew near Bodiam, Ash Tree at Brownbread Street, Royal Oak near Chilgrove, Hatch at Colemans Hatch, Swan at Fittleworth, First In Last Out in Hastings, Sussex Brewery at Hermitage, Half Moon at Kirdford, Plough & Harrow at Litlington, Black Horse at Nuthurst, Well Diggers near Petworth, Cock at Ringmer, Lamb at Ripe, Peacock at Shortbridge, Crab & Lobster at Sidlesham, White Horse at Sutton, and Dorset Arms at Withyham. Drinks prices in Sussex are rather higher than the national average; the beer brewed at the Golden Galleon near Seaford is a useful price-buster. Harveys is the main local brewer. You will also find King & Barnes (K&B) Sussex quite often, but that is now actually brewed down in Dorset by Badger; K&B Mild is truly*

Sussex still, coming from the Gribble at Oving. Other smaller genuinely local brewers include Rother Valley, King, Ballards, Forge, Arundel and Spinnaker; all should get a useful price advantage from the new 14p small brewers' cut in beer duty.

ALCISTON TQ5005 Map 3

Rose Cottage

Village signposted off A27 Polegate—Lewes

Inside this bustling country cottage there are cosy winter log fires, and half a dozen tables with cushioned pews under quite a forest of harness, traps, a thatcher's blade and lots of other black ironware, with more bric-a-brac on the shelves above the stripped pine dado or in the etched-glass windows; in the mornings you may also find Jasper the parrot (it can get a little smoky for him in the evenings); it's best to arrive early to be sure of a seat. There's a lunchtime overflow into the no smoking restaurant area. Made from fresh local produce wherever possible, bar food includes home-made soup (£3), pâté (£3.65), lunchtime ploughman's (£4.75), lincolnshire sausages (£5.25) and steaks (from £9.95), with daily specials such as lasagne (£6.95), home-made steak in ale pie, thai-style chicken or pork spare ribs with barbecue sauce (£7.25), vegetarian spinach pancakes topped with tomato sauce and parmesan (£7.50), and casserole of wild local rabbit (£7.95), with puddings such as home-made banoffi pie (from £3.25); roast Sunday lunch. Well kept Harveys Best and a guest such as King Horsham Best on handpump, decent wines, and Biddenden farm cider; the landlord, whom we have known now for many years, is quite a plain-speaking character; darts, dominoes, cribbage, Scrabble, Jenga, and maybe piped classical music. House martins and swallows continue their annual custom of nesting above the porch, seemingly unperturbed by the people going in and out beneath them. There are gas heaters outside for cooler evenings, and the small paddock in the garden has ducks and chickens. Nearby fishing and shooting. The charming little village (and local church) are certainly worth a look. *(Recommended by Mark Weber, the Didler, R and S Bentley, MLR, Susan May, MDN, David Carr, Peter Forsyth, Colin and Janet Roe, Val and Alan Green, Ann and Colin Hunt, Jenny and Peter Lowater)*

Free house ~ Licensee Ian Lewis ~ Real ale ~ Bar food ~ Restaurant ~ (01323) 870377 ~ Children in eating area of bar and in restaurant if over 10 ~ Dogs allowed in bar ~ Open 11.30-3, 6.30-11; 12-3, 7-10.30 Sun; closed 25 and 26 Dec ~ Bedrooms: /£45S

ALFRISTON TQ5203 Map 3

George

High Street

This 14th-c timbered inn is a smashing place for a quiet drink (though the food is very good, too), with welcoming, friendly staff and a really relaxed atmosphere; it's just the place to take visitors from overseas. The long main bar has massive low beams hung with hops, appropriately soft lighting, and a log fire (or summer flower arrangement) in a huge stone inglenook fireplace that dominates the room, with lots of copper and brass around it. Sturdy stripped tables have settles and chairs around them, and there's well kept Greene King IPA, Abbot, and Old Speckled Hen, and a guest such as Everards Tiger on handpump; decent wines, cribbage, dominoes, and piped music. Good bar food at lunchtime includes home-made soup (£3.95), spinach and feta cheese parcels with tomato and fresh basil sauce (£4.25), grilled sardines with tomato and red onion salsa (£4.50), mushroom and red pepper stroganoff (£5.95), sausage and mash with onion gravy (£6.50), steak and kidney pudding (£6.95), and ham and free range eggs (£7.50), with evening dishes such as caramelised red onion and smoked bacon tartlet (£3.95), chicken and duck terrine with rich cumberland sauce (£4.50), goats cheese and frangipane pithivier with roasted vegetables and red pepper oil (£9.95), slow braised knuckle of lamb in mint and reduced balsamic vinegar (£11.95), whole trout cooked szechuan style with chiili noodles (£12.75), and peppered sirloin steak with tarragon mushrooms and roasted onion (£13.95). If you stay, breakfasts here are good, too. Besides the cosy candlelit no smoking restaurant, there's a garden dining room; or you can sit out in the charming flint-walled garden behind. The lovely village is a tourist honey-pot; you can escape the crowds on a fine riverside walk down to Cuckmere Haven, and two long-distance paths (South Downs Way and Vanguard Way) cross in the village. *(Recommended by Charlie Harris, John Saville, Mrs Alison Challis, Paul Humphreys, John and Lynn Busenbark, Francis Johnston, Michael and Ann Cole, Ann and Colin Hunt)*

Greene King ~ Tenants Anthony Gamboni and Roland Couch ~ Real ale ~ Bar food (12-2.30, 7-9(10 Sat)) ~ Restaurant ~ (01323) 870319 ~ Children welcome ~ Dogs allowed in bar ~ Open 12-11; 12-10.30 Sun; closed 25 and 26 Dec ~ Bedrooms: £40B/£60B

AMBERLEY SO8401 Map 3

Black Horse

Off B2139

After a walk along the South Downs Way, the garden of this very pretty pub is a restful place to enjoy a drink, lunch or afternoon tea; the views are lovely. Inside, the main bar has high-backed settles on flagstones, beams over the serving counter festooned with sheep bells and shepherds' tools (hung by the last shepherd on the Downs), and walls decorated with a mixture of prints and paintings. The lounge bar has many antiques and artefacts collected by the owners on their world travels; there are log fires in both bars and two in the no smoking restaurant. Decent home-made bar food (usefully served all day) includes hearty sandwiches (£4.95), and main meals (£6.95-£8.95) such as steak in ale pie, various curries, salads and fish dishes like salmon in prawn and lobster sauce; several vegetarian dishes, a menu for children, and Sunday roasts (available all day, £8.95). Food can take a time to arrive. Well kept Ansells, Ind Coope Burton, and a guest such as Greene King Old Speckled Hen on handpump, and several malt whiskies; piped music. You can walk along the banks of the River Arun, and the open air Amberley Industrial Museum is nearby. *(Recommended by Bruce Bird, John Beeken, John Saville, Ian Rankin, Cathy Robinson, Ed Coombe, Michael Porter, W A Evershed)*

Pubmaster ~ Tenant Gary Tubb ~ Real ale ~ Bar food (all day) ~ Restaurant ~ (01798) 831552 ~ Children in eating area of bar and in restaurant but must be over 12 in restaurant in evening ~ Dogs allowed in bar ~ Open 11-11; 12-10.30 Sun

Sportsmans

Crossgates; Rackham Road, off B2139

Of course the fine panoramic views are a huge plus here, but it's the welcoming and helpful licensee who makes this village pub special. The three bars have something for everyone: the saloon bar is cosily lit with an interesting choice of seating, the pretty little red-tiled conservatory (engagingly decorated with old local bric-a-brac) is for dining, and the back bar is where friendly locals gather to enjoy the well kept Fullers London Pride, Harveys Best, Weltons Miserable Old Bugger (well liked by readers), and Youngs Bitter on handpump; hexagonal pool table, darts, cribbage, shove-ha'penny, and dominoes. Served by cheerful staff, tasty bar food might include toasties (from £3.50), ploughman's (from £4.75), meaty or vegetarian lasagne (£7.25), steak and kidney pie (£7.50), steaks (from £10.75), and specials such as minted lamb and pear pie (£7.50), asparagus and almond filo slice (£7.75), lemon pepper chicken with noodles or Burmese chicken curry (£7.95), poached salmon fillet with crab and brandy sauce (£8.50), honey-roast half shoulder of lamb (£9.95), and whole bass baked in parchment with herbs and wine (£10.25); Sunday roast (£7.50). The views can be enjoyed from inside and from the decked terrace at the back. *(Recommended by Ann and Colin Hunt, Tracey and Stephen Groves, John Davis, J A Snell, Cathy Robinson, Ed Coombe, Tony and Wendy Hobden, Peter D B Harding, Dennis Jenkin, John Beeken)*

Free house ~ Licensees Jenny and Chris Shanahan ~ Real ale ~ Bar food ~ Restaurant ~ (01798) 831787 ~ Children in eating area of bar ~ Dogs welcome ~ Open 11-2.30, 6-11; 12-3, 7-10.30 Sun ~ Bedrooms: £45S/£60S

ARLINGTON TQ5407 Map 3

Old Oak

Caneheath, off A22 or A27 NW of Polegate

There are seats in the peaceful garden of this 17th-c former set of almshouses, and fine walks in the nearby Abbotswood nature reserve. The open-plan, L-shaped bar has heavy beams, well spaced tables and comfortable seating, log fires, and a calm, relaxed atmosphere. Well kept Badger Best, Harveys Best, and a guest such as Adnams Broadside on electric pump, and several malt whiskies; piped music. Good bar food at lunchtime, served by chatty staff, includes filled baguettes (from £4.75), ploughman's (£4.95), filled baked potatoes (from £5.95), macaroni cheese (£6.50), salads with home-cooked meats (from £6.75), and lasagne (£6.95), with evening dishes (where prices have not changed) like hot mushrooms with stilton (£3.50), green lipped mussels in garlic (£3.75), cajun chicken (£7.75), grilled lamb steak with a redcurrant and rosemary sauce (£8.50), steaks (from £9.25), and daily specials such as fresh cod in batter or various curries (£6.25), steak and kidney pudding (£6.40), grilled whole plaice filled with prawns (£7.50), and breast of chicken with stilton and mushroom sauce (£8.25); friendly service. The basset hound is called Hetty. *(Recommended by Michael and Ann Cole, R M Warner, Ann and Colin Hunt, J H Bell)*

Free house ~ Licensees Ian and Nell Nicoll ~ Real ale ~ Bar food (Sun or Mon evenings) ~ Restaurant ~ (01323) 482072 ~ Children in eating area of bar and restaurant ~ Dogs allowed in bar ~ Occasional live entertainment ~ Open 11-3, 6-11; 12-3, 7-10.30 Sun

ASHURST TQ1716 Map 3

Fountain

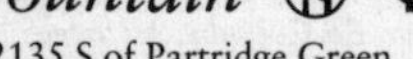

B2135 S of Partridge Green

The owners have worked hard over the last few years to make improvements to this welcoming 16th-c country pub, and their enthusiasm has paid off. It's an attractive dining place but has kept its role as a local, too. The neatly kept and charmingly rustic tap room on the right has a couple of high-backed wooden cottage armchairs by the log fire in its brick inglenook, two antique polished trestle tables, and fine old flagstones; there are more flagstones in the opened-up snug with heavy beams, simple furniture, and its own inglenook fireplace. Well kept Adnams, Fullers London Pride, Harveys Best and Shepherd Neame Bitter with a guest from small or microbreweries on handpump, and decent wines; cribbage, shove-ha'penny, and an oak-beamed skittle alley that doubles as a function room. Good, popular bar food at lunchtime includes sandwiches (from £3.95), ploughman's (£5.75), home-cooked ham with free range egg (£6.50), lasagne (£6.95), steak and mushroom in ale pie (£7.95), chicken breast in barbecue sauce (£9.95), and puddings such as bakewell tart or sticky toffee pudding (£3.95), with evening dishes like goats cheese and red pepper tartlets with basil and tomato sauce (£8.95), chargrilled chicken breast and bacon salad (£9.95), and steaks (from £13.50); daily specials and Sunday roast. Service is pleasant and attentive. The garden is prettily planted, there are plenty of tables on the wooden decking, a growing orchard, and a duck pond. No children inside. *(Recommended by Avril Burton, Cathy Robinson, Ed Coombe, Tony and Wendy Hobden, Ben Whitney and Pippa Redmond, Bruce Bird, David and Sue Lee, J P Humphery, Mr and Mrs Thomas, John Beeken, Alison Milner-Gulland , C A Hall, Keith and Suzie Stevens, Ian Jones, Michael Porter, Peter Forsyth, Bruce Jamieson)*

Free house ~ Licensees Mark and Chris White ~ Real ale ~ Bar food (11.30-2, 6-9.30; cold food and snacks only Sun and Mon evenings) ~ No credit cards ~ (01403) 710219 ~ Dogs allowed in bar ~ Open 11.30-2.30(3 Sat), 6-11; 12-3, 7-10.30 Sun; closed evenings 25 and 26 Dec and 1 Jan

BARNHAM SU9604 Map 3

Murrell Arms £

Yapton Road

In the 35 or so years that the licensees have run this quite unspoilt and old-fashioned pub, almost nothing has changed. Over this time, they have collected hundreds of jugs, mugs, china plates and old bottles that are jammed together along delft shelves, little prints, pictures and old photographs cover the walls, agricultural artefacts hang from the ceiling, and there's an elderly grandfather clock, a collection of old soda syphons, an interesting Cox's change machine and Crystal Palace clock, and some old horsebrasses. The saloon bar has some nice old farmhouse chairs, a very high-backed settle by the piano, a mix of tables (including a fine circular Georgian one) with candles in bottles on its partly turkey carpeted, very old dark wood parquet floor, and a huge polished half-barrel bar counter. To get to the cheerful public bar, you walk past the stillage room where the barrels of Gales HSB, BBB and a changing guest are stored; lots of country wines and two open fires. The simple tiny snug over a half wall (the only place where really well behaved children are tolerated) has an enormous bell wheel from the church on the ceiling; darts, shove-ha'penny, cribbage and dominoes. Straightforward bar food includes cockles and mussels (85p), ploughman's (from £2), and a couple of daily specials such as bacon hock with crusty bread or kingsize bangers (£4). From the car park, you walk through a pretty flower-filled courtyard with a large cider press on one side, and fine ancient wooden benches and tables under a leafy grape vine on the other – note the huge bellows on the wall; there are picnic-sets on a cottagey little enclosed garden up some steps. *(Recommended by Stephanie and Kamal Thapa, Ann and Colin Hunt, MLR, Ian Phillips, Ruth and Paul Lawrence)*

Gales ~ Tenant Mervyn Cutten ~ Real ale ~ Bar food (not Thurs evening) ~ No credit cards ~ (01243) 553320 ~ Well behaved children in snug ~ Dogs welcome ~ Folk Thurs evening and last Sun of month ~ Open 11-2.30, 6-11; 11-11 Sat; 12-10.30 Sun

BERWICK TQ5105 Map 3

Cricketers Arms

Lower Road, S of A27

It's lovely to sit in the old-fashioned cottagey garden in front of this little pub and enjoy a meal or a drink amongst the flowering shrubs and plants; there are more seats behind. The three little similarly furnished rooms have simple benches against the half-panelled walls, a pleasant mix of old country tables and chairs, burgundy velvet curtains on poles, a few bar stools, and some country prints; quarry tiles on the floors (nice worn ones in the middle room), two log fires in little brick fireplaces, a huge black supporting beam in each of the low ochre ceilings, and (in the end room) some attractive cricketing pastels; some of the beams are hung with cricket bats. Service remains helpful and friendly – even when it's busy. Good straightforward bar food includes home-made soup (£3.25), local pork and herb sausages or ploughman's (£5.25), filled baked potatoes (from £5.75), gammon and egg, a vegetarian dish or local cod in batter (£6.95), steaks (from £10.95), daily specials such as fresh dressed crab or smoked haddock mornay (£7.25), and fillet of bass with parsley butter (£8.25). Well kept Harveys Best and a seasonal ale tapped from the cask, and decent wine; shove-ha'penny, cribbage, dominoes, and an old Sussex coin game called toad in the hole. The wall paintings in the nearby church done by the Bloomsbury group during WWII are worth a look. *(Recommended by Kevin Thorpe, Roger Bridgeman, MDN, the Didler, Ann and Colin Hunt, J H Bell, John Beeken, R D Henshaw, Boyd Catling,*

Tina and David Woods-Taylor, David Carr, Jenny and Peter Lowater)

Harveys ~ Tenant Peter Brown ~ Real ale ~ Bar food (12-2.15, 6.30-9; all day in summer and winter wknds) ~ (01323) 870469 ~ Children in family room; under 5s under strict parental control ~ Dogs welcome ~ Open 11-11; 12-10.30 Sun; 11-3, 6-11 weekdays but all day weekends in winter; closed 25 Dec, evening 26 Dec

BILLINGSHURST TQ0830 Map 3

Blue Ship

The Haven; hamlet signposted off A29 just N of junction with A264, then follow signpost left towards Garlands and Okehurst

Genuinely unspoilt and peaceful, this little country pub has a good mix of customers, especially at the weekend. Inside, the cosy beamed and brick-floored front bar has a blazing fire in the inglenook fireplace, scrubbed tables and wall benches, and hatch service dispensing well kept Badger Best, K&B, and Tanglefoot on handpump. A corridor leads to a couple of small carpeted rooms with dark wood tables and chairs, old prints and fresh flowers, where children can sit – one is no smoking. Darts, bar billiards, shove-ha'penny, cribbage, dominoes and table skittles (on request). Reasonably priced traditional bar food includes sandwiches (from £2.55), ploughman's (from £4.15), macaroni cheese (£4.80), cottage pie with cheese (£4.85), mushroom, broccoli and pasta bake with stilton and cream (£5.85), ham and eggs (£6), steak and onion pie (£6.50), and puddings such as treacle sponge or blackcurrant and apple pie (£2.75). This is a lovely spot in summer, and there's a play area for children. *(Recommended by the Didler, Di and Mike Gillam, Susan and John Douglas, Ian Phillips, John Robertson)*

Badger ~ Tenant J R Davie ~ Real ale ~ Bar food (not Sun or Mon evenings) ~ No credit cards ~ (01403) 822709 ~ Children in two rooms without bar ~ Dogs welcome ~ Open 11-3, 6-11; 12-3.30, 7-10.30 Sun

BLACKBOYS TQ5220 Map 3

Blackboys Inn

B2192, S edge of village

In summer, the garden of this pretty 14th-c weatherboarded inn is a big plus. There's masses of space and rustic tables overlooking the pond, with more on the front lawn under the chestnut trees. Inside, a string of old-fashioned and unpretentious little rooms has dark oak beams, bare boards or parquet, antique prints, copious curios (including a collection of keys above the bar), and a good log fire in the inglenook fireplace. Enjoyable food includes home-made soup (£3.50), smokie (£3.50; main course £6.95), filled baked potatoes, ploughman's or sausage, mash and onion gravy (£4.95), chilli (£5.95), home-made pie (£6.95), king prawns with chilli, garlic and lemon grass (£6.95; main course £10.75), thai red chicken curry (£8.75), and daily specials such as asparagus wrapped in parma ham (£5.75), beef bourguignon or vegetable risotto (£8.95), seafood spaghetti (£9.75), chicken breast stuffed with mediterranean vegetables or crab salad (£11.50), monkfish, king scallop and king prawn brochette (£11.95), and fillet steak with a mushroom, cream and brandy sauce (£15.95). The restaurant and dining areas are no smoking; obliging, efficient service even when busy. Well kept Harveys Best, Pale Ale, and a monthly guest on handpump; darts, fruit machine and juke box. *(Recommended by Sarah Davis, Rod Lambert, Alison Milner-Gulland, Michael and Ann Cole, the Didler, Tina and David Woods-Taylor, Derek Thomas, J H Bell)*

Harveys ~ Tenants Edward and Claire Molesworth ~ Real ale ~ Bar food (not Sun evenings) ~ Restaurant ~ (01825) 890283 ~ Children in eating area of bar and restaurant ~ Dogs allowed in bar ~ Open 11-3, 5(6 Sat)-11; 12-3, 7-10.30 Sun; closed 25 Dec, 1 Jan

You can send us reports through our web site: www.goodguides.com

BRIGHTON TQ3105 Map 3

Basketmakers Arms £

Gloucester Road – the E end, near Cheltenham Place; off Marlborough Place (A23) via Gloucester Street

There's a lot of atmosphere in this bustling and cheerful backstreet local – and not a lot of space, so it's best to get there early, especially at weekends. The two small rooms have brocaded wall benches and stools on the stripped wood floor, lots of interesting old tins all over the walls, cigarette cards on one beam with whisky labels on another, and some old photographs and posters; quiet piped music and polite staff. Good value enjoyable bar food includes lots of sandwiches (from £1.95; chicken and avocado £2.75; hot salt beef on granary £3.25), particularly good home-made meaty and vegetarian burgers (£2.50), baked potatoes with fillings such as avocado, shrimp and mayonnaise or beef, chilli and yoghurt (£2.95), ploughman's (£3.50), and specials such as bangers and mash with onion gravy or chicken and gammon pie (£3.95), and fried tuna with garlic and coriander salad or Friday fish and chips (£4.25). Well kept Gales Bitter, GB, HSB, and seasonal ales, and a guest such as Everards Tiger or Wells Bombardier; good wines by the large glass. *(Recommended by Tracey and Stephen Groves, MLR, Neville and Anne Morley, Stephanie and Kamal Thapa, John Beeken, the Didler)*

Gales ~ Tenants P and K Dowd, A McIlwaine, A Mawer ~ Real ale ~ Bar food (12-3, 5.30-8.30; 12-3.30 Sat; 12-4 Sun; not Sat/Sun evenings) ~ Children in eating area of bar until 8pm ~ Dogs welcome ~ Open 11-11; 12-10.30 Sun

BURPHAM TQ0308 Map 3

George & Dragon

Warningcamp turn off A27 outside Arundel: follow road up and up

To be sure of a table, it's best to book, as this 18th-c dining pub is very popular for its enjoyable food served by friendly, helpful staff. As well as snacks such as sandwiches or filled baguettes (from £4.50), filled baked potatoes (from £5.70), and ploughman's (£5.75), the well liked food might include Selsey crab pâté (£5.50), creamy garlic mushroom, spinach and mozzarella tartlet (£5.75), smoked duck breast and bacon salad (£5.80), toasted goats cheese with sunblush tomato chutney (£5.95), wild boar and apple sausages on chive mash (£7.95), seafood pie (£8.95), braised lamb shank with a mint and apricot glaze (£9.25), and fresh skate wing with capers (£9.50). The neatly kept, spacious open-plan bar has good strong wooden furnishings, lots of interesting prints, well kept Arundel Castle, Harveys Best, and a guest such as Hop Back Summer Lightning on handpump, and a decent wine list; piped music. From this remote hill village of thatch and flint, there are plenty of surrounding walks, and close by are splendid views down to Arundel Castle and the river. The Norman church has some unusual decoration. *(Recommended by Ian Phillips, Patricia A Bruce, Dr Brian and Mrs Anne Hamilton, Pamela Goodwyn, J Davidson, John Beeken, John Saul, DF, NMF, Jenny and Brian Seller, R T and J C Moggridge, Ann and Colin Hunt, MLR)*

Free house ~ Licensees James Rose and Kate Holle ~ Real ale ~ Bar food (not Sun evening) ~ Restaurant ~ (01903) 883131 ~ Well behaved children (preferably over 8) in eating areas ~ Open 11-2.30, 6-11; 12-3, 7-10.30 Sun; closed Sun evening Oct-Easter

CHARLTON SU8812 Map 3

Fox Goes Free

Village signposted off A286 Chichester—Midhurst in Singleton, also from Chichester—Petworth via East Dean

In 1915, this cheerful old pub was the unlikely venue for the first ever meeting of the Women's Institute. Goodwood Racecourse is not far away and so on race days it does get very busy; it's also handy for the Weald and Downland Open Air Museum. The first of the dark and cosy series of separate rooms is a small, carpeted bar with one table, a few very mixed chairs and an open fireplace. Standing timbers divide a larger beamed bar which has old and new elm furniture, a huge brick fireplace with a woodburning stove, a couple of elderly armchairs, red tiles and carpet, and brasses and old local photographs on the yellowed walls. A dining area with hunting prints looks over the garden and the South Downs beyond. The no smoking family extension is a clever conversion from horse boxes and the stables where the 1926 Goodwood winner was housed; darts, cribbage, dominoes, fruit machine, and piped music. Well kept Ballards Best, Fox Goes Free (brewed for the pub by Ballards), Greene King Old Speckled Hen, and a guest such as Hop Back Summer Lightning or Ringwood Best on handpump, pimms and sangria by the jug in summer, farm cider and several wines by the glass. Good, interesting bar food might include sandwiches or filled baguettes (from £3.95; not Sunday), filled baked potatoes or ploughman's (£4.95), avocado and stilton bake (£3.95), crab and cheese bake or mushrooms stuffed with goats cheese (£4.95), king prawns fried in ginger (£5.95), steak and kidney pie or wild mushroom stroganoff (£7.25), liver and bacon (£7.50), chicken breast with mushrooms and bacon (£8.95), venison steak with redcurrant and port (£10.50), duck breast with roquefort and red wine (£11), monkfish with bacon, cream and wine or tuna with pesto and pepper (£11.50), and puddings (£3.50). The attractive secluded garden is the best place to sit in summer, with several terraces, plenty of picnic-sets among fruit trees, and a notable downland view; the barbecue area can be booked. The friendly jack russell is called Wiggles and the black cat, Guinness. More reports please. *(Recommended by Linda Blair, Rob Dunton, Debora Rolph, D R and A J Linnell, Prof and Mrs S Barnett, Ann and Colin Hunt, Pat and Derek Westcott, W A Evershed)*

Free house ~ Licensee Oliver Ligertwood ~ Real ale ~ Bar food (12-2.30(3 Sat/Sun), 6.15(6 Sat/Sun)-10.30(10 Sun)) ~ Restaurant ~ (01243) 811461 ~ Children in eating area of bar and restaurant ~ Dogs allowed in bar and bedrooms ~ Live music Weds evening ~ Open 11-3, 5.30-11; 11-11 Sat; 12-10.30 Sun; 11-4, 5.30-11 Sat, 12-4, 6-10.30 Sun in winter; closed evening 25 Dec ~ Bedrooms: £40S/£60S

CHIDDINGLY TQ5414 Map 3

Six Bells ★ £

Village signed off A22 Uckfield—Hailsham

Always bustling and chatty, this old-fashioned pub has a good mix of customers and a genuinely friendly welcome from the cheerful landlord. Solid old wood furnishings include pews and antique seats, log fires, lots of fusty artefacts and interesting bric-a-brac, and plenty of local pictures and posters. A sensitive extension provides some much needed family space; dominoes and cribbage. Particularly for this part of the country, the bar food is a bargain: straightforward but tasty, there might be soup (£1.50), filled baguettes (from £1.70), steak and kidney pie (£2.90), ploughman's or baked potatoes (from £3.50), lasagne or stilton and walnut pie, chilli or chicken curry (£4.70), lemon peppered haddock (£4.95), hock of ham (£5.95), daily specials, and puddings such as treacle tart or banoffi pie (£2.70). Well kept Courage Directors, Harveys Best, and a guest on handpump. Outside at the back, there are some tables beyond a big raised goldfish pond, and a boules pitch; the church opposite has an interesting Jefferay monument. Vintage and Kit car meetings outside the pub every month. This is a pleasant area for walks. *(Recommended by Phil and Sally Gorton, Mrs A Chesher, John Beeken, Charlie Harris, Mike Gorton, Jenny and Peter Lowater)*

Free house ~ Licensee Paul Newman ~ Real ale ~ Bar food (11.30-2.30, 6-10) ~ (01825) 872227 ~ Children in family room ~ Dogs welcome ~ Live music Tues, Fri and Sat evenings and Sun lunchtime ~ Open 11-3, 6-11; 11-11 Sat; 12-10.30 Sun

Bedroom prices include full English breakfast, VAT and any inclusive service charge that we know of.

CHIDHAM SU7804 Map 2

Old House At Home

Off A259 at Barleycorn pub

You will be made just as welcome if you want only a drink in this bustling country pub, but many people come to enjoy the good, popular food. The homely bar has timbering and low beams, windsor chairs around the tables, long seats against the walls, and a welcoming log fire. At lunchtime, there might be home-made soup (£3.95), devilled whitebait (£4.75), filled baguettes (£5.25), ploughman's (from £5.25), daily specials such as sausage and mash (£6.25), baked stuffed mushrooms (£8.50), steak and kidney pudding (£8.75), and gigot of lamb (£7.95), with evening dishes such as baked brie with almonds and a redcurrant sauce (£5.25), spicy marinated tiger prawns (£5.95), beef stroganoff with banana (£9.25), roast chicken breast with mozzarella and a sweet tomato sauce (£9.75), steaks (from £10.25), chargrilled tuna with a mango and tomato salsa (£10.50), and puddings (£4.25); Sunday roast (£6.95). Part of the restaurant is no smoking. Well kept Bass, Flowers IPA, Fullers London Pride, Greene King Abbot, and a guest such as Timothy Taylors Landlord on handpump, and wine by the small or large glass. *(Recommended by I D Greenfield, Ann and Colin Hunt, Ian Phillips, Peter Meister, J Hale, Mrs Angela Bromley-Martin, Charles and Pauline Stride, Tracey and Stephen Groves, J A Snell, Tony and Wendy Hobden, Brian and Genie Smart, B and F A Hannam, Mr and Mrs R W Allan, W A Evershed)*

Suckling Inns ~ Managers Bob and Julie Carruthers ~ Real ale ~ Bar food (12-2, 7-9.30) ~ Restaurant ~ (01243) 572477 ~ Children in no smoking area of restaurant ~ Dogs welcome ~ Open 11.30-2.30, 6-11; 11-11 Sat; 12-10.30 Sun; 11.30-2.30, 6-11 winter Sat; 12-3, 7-10.30 Sun in winter

COMPTON SU7714 Map 2

Coach & Horses

B2146 S of Petersfield

With attractively wooded hilly countryside nearby, this neatly kept 15th-c village local caters well for walkers, with an open fire at each end of the roomy front public bar. The charming little plush beamed lounge bar serves partly as a relaxing ante-room to the attractive restaurant, but also has well presented enjoyable bar food cooked by the landlord. This might include sandwiches or filled baguettes (from £2.50), home-made soup (£3.10), black pudding, bacon and poached egg salad (£5.25), chicken and mushroom pie (£7.95), baked aubergine with chargrilled peppers and mozzarella (£8.50), and chicken breast with grain mustard and almond sauce (£9.75). Well kept Cheriton Village Elder, fff Alton's Pride, Fullers ESB, Ringwood Fortyniner, and maybe Ballards Best on handpump; old-fashioned juke box, bar billiards, cribbage and dominoes. There are tables out by the square in front, and a small secluded back garden; it's a pleasant village, not far from Uppark (NT). *(Recommended by B M O'Connell, Ann and Colin Hunt, Mary and Bill Kemp, Karen and Graham Oddey, Bruce Bird, W A Evershed)*

Free house ~ Licensees David and Christiane Butler ~ Real ale ~ Bar food ~ Restaurant ~ (023) 9263 1228 ~ Children welcome ~ Dogs welcome ~ Open 11.30-2.30, 6-11; 12-3, 7-10.30 Sun

CUCKFIELD TQ3025 Map 3

White Harte £

South Street; off A272 W of Haywards Heath

Hard-working and friendly new licensees have taken over this pretty, partly medieval tile-hung pub but have made no substantial changes. It's still best to book or get here early (particularly on Thursdays) or all the tables will have been snapped up by those keen to enjoy the good value lunchtime food: fish and chips (£4.50), ploughman's (£4.90), jalapeño peppers stuffed with cream cheese (£5), honey roast ham and egg, tempura prawns or home-made quiche (£5.50), and daily specials such as deep-fried breaded brie (£4.50), local sausages with mustard mash and onion gravy, chicken and ham pie or roasted mediterranean tart (all £5.50), and spiced shank of lamb (£5.90). Sunday roast (£6.90). The comfortable beamed lounge has a mix of polished floorboards, parquet and ancient brick flooring tiles, standing timbers, a few local photographs, padded seats on a slightly raised area, and some fairly modern light oak tables. Furnishings in the public bar are sturdy and comfortable with a roaring log fire in the inglenook, and sensibly placed darts. Well kept Badger Best and K&B and a guest beer on handpump; piped music, fruit machine, TV, cribbage, dominoes, and shove-ha'penny. *(Recommended by DWAJ, Ian Phillips, Terry Buckland, Fred Chamberlain, Mr and Mrs A P Lawrence, W A Evershed)*

Badger ~ Tenant Andy Felton ~ Real ale ~ Bar food (lunchtime only) ~ Restaurant ~ (01444) 413454 ~ Children in eating area of bar, restaurant and family room ~ Dogs allowed in bar ~ Folk music last Sun of month and other evenings too ~ Open 11-3, 6-11; 12-3, 7-10.30 Sun

DANEHILL TQ4128 Map 3

Coach & Horses 🍴 🍷

From A275 in Danehill (S of Forest Row), take School Lane towards Chelwood Common

Particularly well run, this cottagey pub has a good mix of chatty customers both eating and drinking, extremely nice food, and a warmly friendly landlord. There's a little public bar to the right with half-panelled walls, simple furniture on highly polished wooden floorboards, a small woodburning stove in the brick fireplace, and a big hatch to the bar; darts. The main bar is on the left with plenty of locals crowding around the wooden bar counter or sitting at the high wooden bar stools enjoying the well kept Harveys Best, and a couple of a guests such as Adnams Best or Brakspears Best on handpump. Drinks are stacked in a nice old-fashioned way on shelves behind the bar, and there's just one table on the stripped wood floor here. A couple of steps lead down to a half-panelled area with a mix of wheelbacks and old dining chairs around several characterful wooden tables on the fine brick floor, a large lantern in the tiny brick fireplace, and some large Victorian prints; candles and flowers on the tables. Down another step to the dining area with stone walls, a beamed vaulted ceiling, baskets and hops hanging from other beams, and a woodburning stove; through a lovely arched doorway is a small room with just a couple of tables; piped jazz and darts, cribbage and dominoes. Served by friendly staff, the enjoyable bar food includes snacks like sandwiches on granary or ciabatta bread or filled baguettes (from £3.75; pesto, mozzarella and grilled tomato £4.95), soup (£4.25), and chicken curry (£8.95), plus fresh herb risotto with truffle oil (£5.25), grilled fillets of sardines with red pepper and basil oil (£5.95), antipasti (£6.25), pork and leek sausages with onion marmalade (£7.95), chargrilled calves liver and bacon (£10.95), 10oz rib-eye steak (£12.95), daily specials such as rillette of duck with grape chutney or salad of smoked trout with orange and almond salad (£5.95), chicken chasseur (£9.95), honey roast duck confit (£10.95), and chargrilled halibut with black pudding, bacon and poached egg (£11.50), and puddings such as orange and cointreau crème brûlée or warm fruit cake with stewed apricots (£3.95); a good wine list and nice coffee. There's a big attractive garden with plenty of seats, and fine views of the South Downs. *(Recommended by Mrs Jane Williams, Simon Lambert, Michael and Ann Cole, Miss G Kybert, Miss R Stevens, Neill Barker, Debbie and Neil Hayter, John Murray)*

Free house ~ Licensee Ian Philpots ~ Real ale ~ Bar food (till 9.30 Fri and Sat; not Sun evening exc bank hol wknds) ~ Restaurant ~ (01825) 740369 ~ Well behaved children welcome ~ Dogs allowed in bar ~ Open 11.30-3(4 Sat), 6-11; 12-4, 7-10.30 Sun; closed evening 25 Dec, 26 Dec and 1 Jan

Please let us know of any pubs where the wine is particularly good.

DONNINGTON SU8502 Map 2

Blacksmiths Arms

B2201

Doing very well under its present licensees, this little white roadside cottage is a warmly friendly place with particularly good food. The small low-ceilinged rooms have Victorian prints on the walls, solid, comfortable furnishings, and four constantly changing real ales: one or two of the Gosport-based Buckland Brewery beers such as Oak Leaf and Squirrels, as well as Fullers London Pride or Youngs on handpump. Made from as much fresh local produce as possible, popular bar food includes home-made soup (£3.50), filled baked potatoes (from £4.95), wild boar and redcurrant pâté (£5), lasagne, minute steak or ham and egg (£6.96), ricotta and spinach cannelloni (£8), and specials such as selsey crab salad (£8.50), lamb shanks in rosemary and garlic (£9), fresh whole lemon sole or herb marinated chicken (£9.50), monkfish wrapped in parma ham (£10.50), and puddings like crème brûlée or fruit crumbles (£4); they also offer a two-course lunch for £8.95. The big garden has a play area with swings, a climbing frame, rabbits and a tortoise, and plenty of picnic-sets. *(Recommended by Mrs J Muirhead, A and B D Craig, Ian Phillips, Laura Wilson, Val and Alan Green, Keith and Suzie Stevens, Esther and John Sprinkle, Ian Rankin, Susan and Peter Davies, Christopher and Elise Way, Nick Roberts, Felicity Stephens)*

InnSpired ~ Tenant Lesley Ward ~ Real ale ~ Bar food ~ Restaurant ~ (01243) 783999 ~ Children welcome ~ Dogs allowed in bar ~ Open 11-3, 5-11; 11-11 Fri and Sat; 12-10.30 Sun

DUNCTON SU9617 Map 3

Cricketers

Set back from A285

You can be sure of a friendly welcome from the new licensee in this pretty little white pub. There's been some redecoration and the dining area has been enlarged but the chatty, relaxed atmosphere and the good mix of diners and drinkers has been maintained. The bar has a few standing timbers giving the room an open-plan feel, there's an inglenook fireplace at one end with a good winter fire, cricketing pictures and paintings and bats on the walls, and a mix of country chairs around scrubbed wooden tables; down a couple of steps a similarly furnished no smoking room is set for eating – piped music here. Good, popular bar food includes home-made soup (£3.95), filled baguettes (from £3.95), walnut-studded goats cheese on baby spinach, poached pear and walnut oil (£4.75), crispy oriental beef (£5), coriander crab cakes (£5.50), ham and eggs with bubble and squeak (£6.95), ale-battered cod (£7.50), bangers and mash with onion and thyme gravy (£7.95), tomato and onion tart (£8.75), chicken wrapped in parma ham and filled with asparagus (£10), half shoulder of lamb with red wine and rosemary sauce (£10.50), steaks (from £11), and puddings such as raspberry crème brûlée or hot chocolate pudding (from £4.25). Well kept Youngs Bitter and a couple of guests such as Fullers London Pride and Harveys Sussex Best on handpump, and decent wines with six by the glass. The charming garden behind the building has a proper barbecue, picnic-sets, and an attractive little creeper-covered seating area, and the flowering baskets and tubs at the front are very lovely. *(Recommended by David Cosham, Simon and Sally Small, Nigel and Olga Wikeley, Bruce Bird, David H T Dimock)*

Free house ~ Licensee Tamzin Corbett ~ Real ale ~ Bar food (not Sun evening) ~ Restaurant ~ (01798) 342473 ~ Well behaved children in restaurant only ~ Dogs allowed in bar ~ Open 11-2.30, 6-11; 12-3; closed Sun evening

It's very helpful if you let us know up-to-date food prices when you report on pubs.

EAST CHILTINGTON TQ3715 Map 3

Jolly Sportsman

2 miles N of B2116; Chapel Lane – follow sign to 13th-c church

Sussex Dining Pub of the Year

Run by warmly friendly people, this tucked away and civilised Victorian dining pub remains a special place for a meal out. Changing all the time, the imaginative food might include goats cheese gnocchi with broad beans (£4.95; main course £8.95), ploughman's with five cheeses and home-made chutney (£5.45), coppa ham and shaved parmesan salad (£5.75), fresh pasta, crab and chilli (£5.75; main course £11.50), grilled ciabatta with roast vegetables and local goats cheese (£6.75), tuna salad niçoise (£5.85; main course £9.85), grilled marinated quail with polenta cake and salsa verde (£6.25), haggis, neeps and tatties or moroccan lamb meat balls (£7.45), kashmiri lamb shank (£10.85), slow roasted pork belly with garlic and rosemary (£11.25), baked gilt-edged bream with samphire (£13.85), halibut with hollandaise (£16.45), and puddings such as chocolate and grillote cherry block with coffee sauce, cherry and almond tart with vanilla sauce and six puddings in miniature (from £5.45). A couple of chairs by the fireplace are set aside for drinkers in the chatty little bar with stripped wood floors and a mix of furniture, but most people head for the smart but informal no smoking restaurant with contemporary light wood furniture, and modern landscapes on green painted walls. Well kept King Horsham Best Bitter and guest like fff Alton's Pride on handpump, a remarkably good wine list, farm cider, up to 30 malts, summer fruit cocktails and good sherries; Scrabble, draughts, cribbage, dominoes, and chess. There are rustic tables and benches under gnarled trees in a pretty cottagey front garden, and the large back lawn with a children's play area looks out towards the South Downs; good walks nearby. *(Recommended by Alan Cowell, Mrs Rita Cox, Dr M Mills, J H Bell, Peter Forsyth, Michael Sargent, Ken Arthur, B, M and P Kendall)*

Free house ~ Licensee Bruce Wass ~ Real ale ~ Bar food (till 10pm Fri/Sat; till 3pm Sun; not Sun evening or Mon) ~ Restaurant ~ (01273) 890400 ~ Children welcome ~ Dogs welcome ~ Open 12-2.30, 6-11; 12-4 Sun; closed Sun evening, all day Mon (exc bank hols)

EAST DEAN TV5597 Map 3

Tiger

Pub (with village centre) signposted – not vividly – from A259 Eastbourne—Seaford

The delightful cottage-lined green here makes a perfect setting for this long low white tiled pub, covered in summer flowering climbers and decorated with window boxes. Inside, there are just nine tables in the two smallish rooms (candlelit at night) so space at peak times is very limited – particularly in winter when you can't stand outside or sit on the grass; they don't, in the best pub tradition, take bookings so you do have to arrive early for a table. There are low beams hung with pewter and china, polished rustic tables and distinctive antique settles, and old prints and so forth. Well kept Harveys Best with guests such as Adnams Best and Flowers Original on handpump, and a good choice of wines with a dozen by the large glass. They get their fish fresh from Hastings, their lamb from the farm on the hill, all vegetables and eggs from another local farm, and meat from the local butcher. From a sensibly short but ever changing menu, the good food might include a choice of 28 different ploughman's (lunchtime only, £5.25), as well as sausage, mash and onion gravy (£5.25), casseroles like burgundy beef with smoked bacon or mediterranean vegetables topped with grilled goats cheese and pesto, ragoût of lamb, and plaice scored with sea salt and pepper (all £6.95), chargrilled chicken breast on leek mash or large prawns (£7.95), big crabs (£8.50), roasted fillet of wild scottish salmon with anchovy and caper butter (£8.95), and lobster (£11.95). At lunchtimes on hot days and bank holidays they usually have only cold food. Being on the South Downs Way, it's naturally popular with walkers and the lane leads on down to a fine stretch of coast culminating in Beachy Head. No children inside. *(Recommended by Michael and Ann Cole, Mrs M Thomas, Catherine and Richard Preston, Bill and Rachael Gallagher, DF, NMF, G T Brewster, Tony and Wendy Hobden, Paul and Penny Dawson, Ann and Colin Hunt, Mike Gorton, Ian Phillips)*

Free house ~ Licensee Nicholas Denyer ~ Real ale ~ Bar food ~ No credit cards ~ (01323) 423209 ~ Dogs welcome ~ Morris dancers on bank hols, mummers 26 Dec ~ Open 11-3, 6-11; 11-11 Sat; 12-10.30 Sun

ELSTED SU8119 Map 2

Three Horseshoes

Village signposted from B2141 Chichester—Petersfield; also reached easily from A272 about 2 miles W of Midhurst, turning left heading W

This 16th-c pub used to be a drovers rest and is set at the end of a hamlet below the sweep of the South Downs. The snug little rooms have ancient beams and flooring, antique furnishings, attractive prints and photographs, candlelight, and enormous log fires. Enjoyable bar food (they tell us prices have not changed since last year) includes home-made soup (£3.95), a generous ploughman's with a good choice of cheeses or goats cheese and caramelised onions on warm brioche (£5.95), prawn mayonnaise wrapped in smoked salmon (£6.95), braised lamb with apples and apricots in a tomato chutney sauce or red pepper, tomato and pine nut risotto (£8.95), steak and kidney in ale pie (£9.50), fresh seasonal crab and lobster, and home-made puddings such as treacle tart or chocolate truffle torte (£4.50). The dining room is no smoking. Well kept changing ales racked on a stillage behind the bar counter might include Ballards Best, Cheriton Pots, Hop Back Summer Lightning, and maybe a couple of guests like King Horsham Best Bitter or Timothy Taylors Landlord; summer cider; friendly service; dominoes. The lovely garden has free-roaming bantams, plenty of tables, pretty flowers, and marvellous downland views. *(Recommended by J H Bell, John Beeken, Tracey and Stephen Groves, Bruce Bird, Peter Meister, Paul and Penny Dawson, Godfrey and Irene Joly, W A Evershed)*

Free house ~ Licensees Andrew and Sue Beavis ~ Real ale ~ Bar food ~ (01730) 825746 ~ Well behaved children welcome ~ Dogs allowed in bar ~ Open 11-2.30, 6-11; 12-3, 7-10.30 Sun

FLETCHING TQ4223 Map 3

Griffin ★

Village signposted off A272 W of Uckfield

The two acres of garden behind this civilised old inn look across fine rolling countryside towards Sheffield Park, and there are plenty of seats here and on a sheltered gravel terrace where you can enjoy a summer drink or meal. Inside, the beamed and quaintly panelled bar rooms have a good bustling and chatty atmosphere, blazing log fires, old photographs and hunting prints, straightforward furniture including some captain's chairs, china on a delft shelf, and a small bare-boarded serving area off to one side. A snug separate bar has sofas, pool, and TV. Popular, imaginative food might include runner bean and ham hock soup (£4.95), hot ciabatta sandwiches (from £4.95), pork and chicken terrine with olives and onion confit (£5.25), home-cured gravadlax with dill mayonnaise (£5.95), fennel, slow roasted tomato and taleggio tarte tatin or toulouse sausages on herb and olive oil mash with onion gravy (£7.50), moules frites or organic veal meat balls with fresh tomato salsa on tagliatelle (£7.95), chargrilled marinated local lamb steak (£8.50), chargrilled blue-fin tuna niçoise salad (£11.50), Scottish sirloin steak with mint and garlic butter (£12.50), and puddings such as iced white chocolate and orange mousse, raspberry fool or sticky toffee pudding (£4.95). There's a more elaborate (and expensive) restaurant menu. Well kept Badger Tanglefoot and Harveys Best, and a guest like King Horsham Best Bitter or Rother Valley Level Best on handpump, and a fine wine list with several (including champagne) by the glass. *(Recommended by Mandy and Simon King, Peter Forsyth, Richard Siebert, Pierre and Pat Richterich, Susan and John Douglas, Colin and Janet Roe, Mike and Heather Watson, BKA, Christopher and Elise Way, John and Lynn Busenbark, S F Parrinder, Mr and Mrs S Oxenbury, Derek Thomas, Derek Harvey-Piper, John Robertson, J H Bell, Louise English, Chris Richards; also in the* Good Hotel Guide*)*

Free house ~ Licensees N Pullan, J Pullan and John Gatti ~ Real ale ~ Bar food (12-2.30, 7-9.30) ~ Restaurant ~ (01825) 722890 ~ Children welcome ~ Dogs allowed in bar ~ Live music Fri evening and Sun lunchtime ~ Open 12-3, 6-11; 12-11 Sat; 12-10.30 Sun; closed 25 Dec ~ Bedrooms: £60S/£85B

HAMMERPOT TQ0605 Map 3

Woodmans Arms

Pub visible and well signposted on N (eastbound) side of A27 just under 4 miles E of A284 at Arundel; heading W on A27 the turn is about ½m beyond the pub

Some of the beams in this pretty 16th-c pub are so low they are strung with fairy lights as a warning. The brick-floored entrance area has a cosy armchair by the inglenook's big log fire, lots of brass, pictures by local artists for sale, and old photographs of regulars. On the right a carpeted no smoking dining area with candles on the tables has wheelback chairs around its tables, and cheerfully cottagey decorations, and on the left a small no smoking room has a few more tables. Well presented honest home-made food (they tell us prices have not changed since last year) includes soups such as vegetable or mushroom (£2.95), sandwiches (from £2.95), broccoli and stilton bake or lasagne (£6.25), sweet and sour pork (£6.75), steak and kidney pie or ham and eggs (£6.95), home-made curry (£7.35), fresh local fish on Fridays, extra mature sirloin steak with port and stilton sauce (£10.50), and two Sunday roasts (£6.95). Well kept Gales GB, HSB, Butser Bitter and a guest such as Fullers London Pride or Timothy Taylors Landlord on handpump, and country wines. Cribbage, dominoes, and piped music. The yellow labrador is called Tikka. The garden here – despite some road noise – is charming, with picnic-sets and tables on a terrace (they have mobile outside heaters for chillier weather), under a fairy-lit arbour, and on small lawns among lots of roses and tubs of bright annuals. This is good walking country. *(Recommended by Ian Phillips, Colin Draper, E F Given, R and S Bentley, Ann and Colin Hunt, Joan and Michel Hooper-Immins, J Davidson, Dr and Mrs A K Clarke)*

Gales ~ Tenants Malcolm and Ann Green ~ Real ale ~ Bar food ~ Restaurant ~ (01903) 871240 ~ Well behaved children in restaurant and family room ~ Dogs allowed in bar ~ Folk every 2nd Sun and Tues evenings ~ Open 11-3, 6-11; 12-3, 7-10.30 Sun

HARTFIELD TQ4735 Map 3

Anchor

Church Street

Mr and Mrs Thompson have now run this 15th-c pub for over 20 years and have made it popular locally with quiz and race nights and stool ball and darts teams. The original bar has heavy beams, old advertisements and little country pictures on the walls above the brown-painted dado, houseplants in the small-paned windows, and a woodburning stove. Another bar has flagstones, more old beams, a dining area with good tables and chairs, and huge logs burning in an old inglenook fireplace. Well kept Adnams, Bass, Flowers IPA, and Harveys Best on handpump. Decent bar food includes sandwiches or toasties (from £2.75; avocado and prawn or steak and egg £4), home-made soup (£3.50), filled baked potatoes (from £4.25), ploughman's (from £4.50), mushroom and macaroni cheese (£5), home-made pork and walnut pâté with cumberland sauce or omelette Arnold Bennett (£5.25), home-cooked ham and egg (£6), smoked haddock fritters with cumin and mayonnaise sauce or sweet and sour chicken (£7), stir-fried duck with pineapple and black bean sauce (£7.50), skate wing with capers and black butter (£10), and puddings such as sticky toffee chocolate cake or crème caramel (from £3.25);

friendly service. Darts in a separate lower room; shove-ha'penny, dominoes, and piped music. The front verandah soon gets busy on a warm summer evening. There's a play area in the garden. More reports please. *(Recommended by Hazel and Michael Duncombe, Ken Arthur, Alan Cowell, Michael and Ann Cole)*

Free house ~ Licensees Ken and Karen Thompson ~ Real ale ~ Bar food (12-2, 6-10; 12-1.45, 7-10 Sun) ~ Restaurant ~ (01892) 770424 ~ Children welcome ~ Dogs allowed in bar ~ Open 11-11; 12-10.30 Sun; closed evening 25 Dec ~ Bedrooms: £35S/£50S

HEATHFIELD TQ5920 Map 3

Star

Old Heathfield – head East out of Heathfield itself on A265, then fork right on to B2096; turn right at signpost to Heathfield Church then keep bearing right; pub on left immediately after church

Tucked away below the Early English tower of the church, this 14th-c pilgrims' inn is a smashing old place. There's a good welcome for both locals and regulars, a relaxed, chatty atmosphere in the L-shaped beamed bar, a fine log fire in the inglenook fireplace, panelling, built-in wall settles and window seats, and just four or five tables; a doorway leads into a similarly furnished smaller room. The tables are candlelit at night. Chalked up on boards, a decent choice of bar food includes ploughman's (£6.95), mussels provençale (£7.95), home-made pies or cold meats with bubble and squeak or local cod in beer batter (£8.50), pan-fried smoked salmon (£10.95), marinated duck breast (£11.95), and winter game dishes; efficient, courteous service. Well kept Harveys Best, Shepherd Neame Best Bitter, and a guest such as Hop Back Summer Lightning on handpump, some malt whiskies and farm cider. The prettily planted sloping garden with its rustic furniture has lovely views of rolling oak-lined sheep pastures – Turner thought it fine enough to paint. *(Recommended by Mrs Thomas, Lucien, John Evans, Alan Cowell, Jenny and Peter Lowater)*

Free house ~ Licensees Mike Chappell and Fiona Airey ~ Real ale ~ Bar food (12-2.15(2.30 wknds), 7-9.30) ~ Restaurant ~ (01435) 863570 ~ Children in eating area of bar ~ Dogs welcome ~ Open 11.30-3, 5.30-11; 12-3, 7-10.30 Sun

HENLEY SU8925 Map 2

Duke of Cumberland Arms

Village signposted just off A286 S of Fernhurst, N of Midhurst; if coming from Midhurst, take 1st turn into village, then keep bearing right; OS Sheet 186 map reference 894258

It's hard to imagine that the lane on which this pretty little tucked-away stone-built 15th-c cottage stands was once the main road from London to Chichester – coaches would stop here and change horses. There are just two unpretentious little low-ceilinged rooms with a log fire in each, gas lamps on white-painted panelled walls, simple seats around scrubbed rough oak tables, and a few wood carvings, plates, old framed documents, and stuffed birds and animals. Enjoyable food such as home-made soup (£3.50), filled rolls (from £4.50), well liked chicken liver pâté (using a 70-year-old recipe, £4.75), several ploughman's (from £5.25), seafood cocktail (smoked salmon wrapped around smoked trout, prawns and crab, £6.95), all day breakfast or leek and potato gratin (£8.95), calves liver and bacon with onion gravy (£9.95), their own fresh trout, thai chicken curry or seared salmon with caesar salad (£10.95), a whole roast joint (you order it in advance and it comes served on a big board with roast potatoes and vegetables all around it, from £12.50), and puddings like banoffi pie with jersey cream or chocolate and chestnut roulade (£3.95). Well kept Adnams Broadside, Ballards Best, Brains SA, Brakspears Bitter, Elgoods Cambridge, and Hop Back Summer Lightning tapped from the cask, and farm ciders; no piped music or games. The red and white bulldog is called Jasper. In summer, the garden here is rather special. It's on a slope, and lush and quite big, with lilacs and other shrubs, and willows by a stream running down through a series of three ponds once used for the pre-industrial iron industry here, but now stocked with trout (which you'll find on the menu). Gnarled old benches and more modern seats out here give lovely views over Black Down and the wooded hills south of Haslemere. *(Recommended by Martin and Karen Wake, Miles Halton, John Beeken, Ian Phillips, Susan and John Douglas, J A Snell)*

Free house ~ Licensees Gaston Duval and Christina Duval ~ Real ale ~ Bar food (12-3, 7-9.30; not Sun evening) ~ Restaurant ~ (01428) 652280 ~ Children welcome ~ Dogs welcome ~ Open 11-3, 5-11; 12-3, 7-10.30 Sun

HORSHAM TQ1730 Map 3

Black Jug

31 North Street

The pretty flower-filled back terrace here has been relaid this year and new garden furniture and outside heaters added. Inside, there's a lively, bustling atmosphere and a warm welcome from the helpful, chatty staff. The airy open-plan turn-of-the-century-style room has a large central bar, a nice collection of heavy sizeable dark wood tables, comfortable chairs on a stripped wood floor, cream walls crammed with interesting old prints and photographs above a dark wood panelled dado, and a warm terracotta ceiling. A spacious no smoking conservatory has similar furniture and lots of hanging baskets; piped music. Well kept Courage Directors, Marstons Pedigree, and Wadworths 6X, with a guest such as Harveys Best or King Horsham Best Bitter on handpump, 40 malt whiskies, a good wine list with 14 by the glass, and eight chilled vodkas from Poland and Russia. Under the new chef, good, popular and interesting bar food includes soup (£3.25), open sandwiches or filled baguettes (from £3.95; warm chicken tikka in pitta bread with lime and mango chutney £4.95), grilled goats cheese on roasted red pepper crostini served with tapenade and sun-dried tomato and basil dressing (£4.50), Italian antipasti (£5.50), vegetarian fajita with salsa or ploughman's (£5.95), home-made lasagne or smoked haddock and salmon fishcakes (£6.95), pork, honey and rosemary sausages with wholegrain mustard gravy (£7.95), grilled tuna, shark and swordfish kebabs (£8.25), roasted lemon and thyme chicken breast on french beans and rosemary new potatoes (£8.95), braised shoulder of lamb with mediterranean vegetables and potato gnocchi (£10.95), and puddings such as rhubarb and red wine syllabub, steamed citrus pudding with custard or strawboffi pie (£4.25). *(Recommended by Mrs Romey Heaton, Sebastian Leach, Roger and Debbie Stamp, Ian Phillips, Sam, Rev Guy Devon-Smith, J Garrison)*

Brunning & Price ~ Lease Sam Cornwall-Jones ~ Real ale ~ Bar food (12-10) ~ (01403) 253526 ~ Children in dining room until 6pm ~ Dogs allowed in bar ~ Open 11-11; 12-10.30 Sun; closed 26 Dec

HOUGHTON TQ0111 Map 3

George & Dragon

B2139 W of Storrington

Friendly new licensees have taken over this mostly Elizabethan timbered building and things are thriving. The rambling heavy-beamed bar, though comfortably modernised, still has points of interest such as a formidable fireplace, clockwork roasting-spit motor, and gourds given a glowing patina by rubbing with goosefat. Attractive antique tables lead into a back extension (which enjoys the fine views), and the restaurant is no smoking. Served by smartly dressed staff, the good, reasonably priced food now includes soup (£2.50), filled baguettes (from £4), deep-fried whitebait with lime mayonnaise (£4.25), pear and shaved parmesan salad with wholegrain mustard dressing (£4.50), ploughman's (£5.95), steak and kidney pudding (£6.75), and pork and leek sausages with mustard mash (£7.75), with daily specials such as vegetarian sausages (£6.75), sweet and sour chicken or chilli (£6.95), pork and leek sausages with mustard mash (£7.25), half shoulder of lamb in minted gravy (£9.75), and bass with ginger and spring onion cream

(£9.95), and puddings like fruit crumble or chocolate fudge cake (£3); they offer a weekday, over-50s bargain two-course set lunch (£6.75). Well kept Fullers London Pride and Harveys Best on handpump, half a dozen malts, and several wines by the glass; piped classical music. There are tables in the garden looking down past a hardy walnut tree and a wishing well towards the Arun valley, and plenty of good surrounding walks; to reach the South Downs Way, turn left off the side road to Bury. *(Recommended by Tony and Wendy Hobden, Mark Percy, Lesley Mayoh, A D Marsh, Ann and Colin Hunt, Martin Buck, J Iorwerth Davies, David Cosham, Miss J F Reay, J H Bell, Tracey and Stephen Groves, W A Evershed)*

English Country Inns ~ Managers Caroline and Alan Grindle ~ Real ale ~ Bar food (12-2.15, 6-9; all day Sat and Sun) ~ Restaurant ~ (01798) 831559 ~ Children welcome ~ Dogs allowed in bar ~ Open 11-3, 6-11; 11-11 Sat; 12-10.30 Sun

ICKLESHAM TQ8716 Map 3

Queens Head

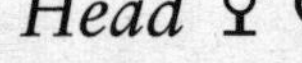

Just off A259 Rye—Hastings

Many customers come to this well run handsome pub to enjoy the good food, but there's a fine choice of real ales and one part favoured by drinkers. The open-plan areas work round a very big serving counter which stands under a vaulted beamed roof, the high beamed walls and ceiling of the easy-going bar are lined with shelves of bottles and covered with farming implements and animal traps, and there are well used pub tables and old pews on the brown patterned carpet. Other areas (two are no smoking and popular with diners) have big inglenook fireplaces. Well kept Daleside Shrimpers, Greene King IPA and Abbot, and guests such as Arran Dark, Forge Pett Progress, and Ringwood Fortyniner on handpump; Biddenden cider, and all wines on the list are available by the glass. Generously served, enjoyable bar food includes sandwiches (from £2.45), home-made soup (£3.25), home-made pâté (£3.95), soft herring roes on toast (£4.25), ploughman's (from £4.50), home-cooked ham and egg (£5.50), stilton and apricot macaroni cheese (£6.25), curry of the day or steak and mushroom in ale pie (£6.95), steaks (from £9.95), and home-made daily specials; prompt service from friendly efficient staff. Shove-ha'penny, dominoes, fruit machine, and piped music. Picnic-sets look out over the vast, gently sloping plain of the Brede valley from the little garden, and there's an outside children's play area, and boules. Good local walks. *(Recommended by Bruce Bird, John and Christine Lowe, Evelyn and Derek Walter, Keith and Chris O'Neill, Lucien, Kevin Thorpe, David Carr, Ken Arthur, Ruth and Paul Lawrence)*

Free house ~ Licensee Ian Mitchell ~ Real ale ~ Bar food (12-2.45, 6.15-9.45; all day Sat, Sun and bank hols; not 25/26 Dec) ~ (01424) 814552 ~ Well behaved children in eating area of bar until 8.30pm ~ Dogs allowed in bar ~ Live jazz/blues/folk/classical Tues evening ~ Open 11-11; 12-10.30 Sun; closed evening 25 Dec

LEWES TQ4110 Map 3

Snowdrop

South Street; off Cliffe High Street, opposite S end of Malling Street just S of A26 roundabout

In this bustling, laid-back pub you will find a good mix of customers of all ages and types. It takes on an unusual maritime theme including figureheads, ship lamps and other objects of interest. There are two spacious areas (with extra seating outside) with the cliffs as a spectacular backdrop; a small part is no smoking. Upstairs there are more seats, a second pool table, a sunset sea mural, and a star chart painted on the blue ceiling. The evenings see a more cosmopolitan crowd enjoying home-cooked meals and different styles of music, both live and on the juke box. The good, interesting food is largely vegetarian with plenty of vegan options using organic and GM free produce wherever possible: sandwiches (from £2.20), filled baguettes and pittas (from £2.60), soups like sweet potato and coconut or African bean (£2.95), moussaka or tarts such as cranberry, walnut and goats cheese or tacos filled with refried beans, salsa, soured cream and cheese (£5.95), pies like spinach, tomato and mozzarella or feta, spinach, pesto and pine nut (£5.95), four different Indian curries (£6.50), and puddings such as vegan chocolate cake, strawberry and mango cheesecake or fruit crumble (£2.50); nut roasts on Sundays (£6). Well kept Harveys Best, Hop Back Summer Lightning, and Ringwood Old Thumper on handpump, good coffee and friendly staff; TV, chess, backgammon and cards. More reports please. *(Recommended by Jason Caulkin, John Beeken, Sarah Davis, Rod Lambert, MLR, Kevin Thorpe, Catherine and Richard Preston, Patrick Hancock)*

Free house ~ Licensee Reuben May ~ Real ale ~ Bar food (12-3, 6(7 Sun)-9) ~ No credit cards ~ (01273) 471018 ~ Children in eating area of bar ~ Dogs welcome ~ Live jazz Mon evening, local bands Sat evening ~ Open 11-11; 12-10.30 Sun

LODSWORTH SU9223 Map 2

Halfway Bridge Inn ★

Just before village, on A272 Midhurst—Petworth

The stableyard bedroom conversion next to this smartly civilised, friendly pub is proving a great success. The three or four bar rooms are comfortably furnished with good oak chairs and an individual mix of tables, and they use attractive fabrics for the wood-railed curtains and pew cushions. Down some steps, the charming no smoking country dining room has a dresser and longcase clock; one of the log fires is contained in a well polished kitchen range, and paintings by a local artist line the walls. A good range of drinks includes well kept beers such as Cheriton Pots Ale, Fullers London Pride, Gales HSB, and guests such as Cheriton Village Elder and Harveys Best on handpump, rather special local cider, and a thoughtful little wine list with a changing choice by the glass; dominoes, cribbage, shove-ha'penny, backgammon, Jenga, bagatelle, and mah jong. At lunchtime, good, interesting bar food includes sandwiches such as tuna, olives, capers and tomatoes in warmed ciabatta or hot salt beef on rye bread with dill pickle and sautéed potatoes (from £4.95), risotto fishcakes with spicy dipping sauce (£5.25), beef wellington with madeira sauce (£7.25), local organic sausages with grain mustard mash and onion gravy (£7.50), dry-spiced roasted vegetables with dhal and basmati rice (£8.50), home-made duck confit with root vegetable purée, thyme and honey sauce (£9.25), and steak, kidney and mushroom in Guinness pudding (£9.95), with evening dishes like fish soup with gruyère, rouille and croutons (£5.25), grilled king prawns with garlic butter (£7.95), roast half shoulder of lamb (£11.50), and wild bass (£12.50); puddings such as well liked chocolate thingy, crumble or banoffi pie (£3.50). The friendly jack russell is called Ralph, and the two jack-russell crosses, Chip and Bonzo (they all wear obligatory 'please don't feed me' badges). At the back there are seats on a small terrace. *(Recommended by Julie and Bill Ryan, John and Joan Calvert, John Evans, Mike and Lynn Robinson, Mike and Mary Carter, Sefton Parke, Ann and Colin Hunt, Cathy Robinson, Ed Coombe, Michael Bayne, Martin and Karen Wake, R T and J C Moggridge, David and Rita Liddiard, George and Brenda Jones, Derek and Sylvia Stephenson, W A Evershed)*

Free house ~ Licensees Simon and James Hawkins ~ Real ale ~ Bar food (12-2(2.30 wknds), 7-10) ~ Restaurant ~ (01798) 861281 ~ Children over 10 in restaurant ~ Dogs allowed in bar ~ Open 11-3, 5.30(6 Sat)-11; 12-3, 7-10.30 Sun ~ Bedrooms: £45B/£75B

LURGASHALL SU9327 Map 2

Noahs Ark

Village signposted from A283 N of Petworth; OS Sheet 186 map reference 936272

Tables on the grass in front of this 16th-c pub are ideally placed for watching the local cricket team play on the village green. Inside, the two neatly furnished bars have warm log fires (one in a capacious inglenook), well kept Greene King IPA, Abbot and Old Speckled Hen on handpump, and several well polished trophies. The family room is decorated like the inside of an ark; darts, dominoes, cribbage and piped music. Well liked bar food includes soup (£3.25), sandwiches (from

£3.75; wild boar and apple sausage with caramelised onions £4.25), filled baked potatoes (£4.75), ploughman's (£5.25), hot wraps with fillings such as chilli beef strips with onions and sour cream or feta, mushroom and beansprout (£6.45), home-made burger (£6.50), chicken curry or deep fried cod in cider batter (£6.95), steak and mushroom pie (£7.25), chargrilled fillet steak (£11.75), and puddings like nutty chocolate torte with chocolate sauce or crème brûlée (£3.50). The restaurant is no smoking. Splendid flowering baskets in summer. More reports please. *(Recommended by John Evans)*

Greene King ~ Tenant Bernard Joseph Wija ~ Real ale ~ Bar food ~ Restaurant ~ (01428) 707346 ~ Children in eating areas and family room ~ Dogs allowed in bar ~ Open 11-3, 6-11; 11-4, 6-11 but may open all day when cricket is on Sat; 12-4, 7-10.30 Sun; closed Sun evening

MILTON STREET TQ5304 Map 3

Sussex Ox

Off A27 just under a mile E of Alfriston roundabout

Carefully extended and restored, this attractive country pub has magnificent downs views. Inside, there's a smallish beamed bar with a brick floor and roaring log fire in a woodburning stove, a good no smoking family room, and a separate restaurant. Well kept Harveys Best, Hop Back Summer Lightning, and Youngs Special on handpump; organic apple juice, Biddenden cider, and English wines. Piped music, darts, and dominoes. Well liked, unpretentious bar food includes filled rolls (from £2.95), home-made soup (£3.25), ploughman's (from £4.95), broccoli, mushroom and sweetcorn au gratin (£6.25), three different home-made burgers (from £6), barbecue chicken (£6.50), steak and mushroom in ale pie (£7.95), daily specials, and puddings (£3.50). There's a big lawn and marvellous play area, and lots of good walks; the pub does get busy at weekends. More reports please. *(Recommended by Michael and Ann Cole, Tony and Wendy Hobden)*

Free house ~ Licensees Doug and Jeannie Baker ~ Real ale ~ Bar food (11-2, 6-9) ~ Restaurant ~ (01323) 870840 ~ Children in restaurant and family room ~ Open 11-3, 6-11; 12-3, 7-10.30 Sun

OFFHAM TQ4012 Map 3

Blacksmiths Arms

A275 N of Lewes

The open-plan bar in this neatly kept, old red brick cottage has a huge inglenook fireplace (with logs stacked to one side) at one end of the gleaming central counter – and at the other, an airy dining area; most of the close-set tables are laid for eating. Nice old prints of London, some Spy prints and several old sporting prints decorate the walls above shiny black wainscoting. As well as bar snacks such as ploughman's (from £4.95), filled baked potatoes (£5.50), and ham and eggs (£5.95), there might be chunky vegetable provençale soup (£3.75), a terrine of seared chicken and roasted peppers with raspberry vinaigrette (£5.25), smoked haddock and poached eggs in a rich cheese sauce (£5.50), mushroom, cranberry and brie in a filo pastry parcel with garlic cream sauce (£8.25), steak and kidney pie (£8.50), chicken breasts on rosemary and garlic flageolet beans and puy lentils with red pepper coulis (£9.50), pork fillet strips stir-fried in a spiced coconut and coriander sauce on egg noodles (£9.75), and daily specials such as scallops and bacon in garlic butter (£6.25), guinea fowl pot roast with apricots (£9.50), fishcakes with sweet coriander sauce (£9.75), and lamb chump chops with redcurrant and port jus (£10.25); puddings like home-made fruit pie or ginger and citrus bread and butter pudding with a warm marmalade sauce (£3.95). Well kept Harveys Best on handpump. French windows open onto a tiny little brick and paved terrace with a couple of flowering tubs and picnic-sets under umbrellas; beware of the dangerous bend when leaving the car park. No children inside. More reports please. *(Recommended by Peter Craske, Sarah Large, Colin Draper, Ken Arthur, G T Brewster)*

Free house ~ Licensee Jean Large ~ Real ale ~ Bar food (not Sun evening) ~ Restaurant ~ (01273) 472971 ~ Dogs allowed in bar ~ Open 12-3, 6.30-11; 12-3 Sun; closed Sun evening

OVING SU9005 Map 2

Gribble Inn

Between A27 and A259 just E of Chichester, then should be signposted just off village road; OS Sheet 197 map reference 900050

Although owned by Badger, this popular 16th-c thatched pub brews its own eight real ales (which can often be found in other pubs owned by the brewery): Fursty Ferret, Gribble Ale, K&B Mild, Porterhouse, Pigs Ear, Plucking Pheasant, Reg's Tipple, and winter Wobbler on handpump. Also 20 country wines, and farm cider. There's a peaceful cottagey feel in the several linked rooms, and the chatty bar has lots of heavy beams and timbering, and old country-kitchen furnishings and pews. Half the dining room is no smoking, and all of the family room. Good, popular bar food includes home-made soup (£2.75), filled baps (from £3.95), blue cheese and peppercorn mushrooms (£4.25; main course £7.25), coconut breadcrumbed goats cheese with home-made tomato sauce (£4.65), ploughman's or ham and egg (£5.50), fresh pasta dishes such as three cheese or chicken and mushroom (£6.95), home-made burgers (£7.25), fish pie (£7.50), chicken wrapped in smoked bacon on apples and mushrooms with a cheese and cider sauce (£7.95), large steak and kidney pudding (£8.50), seared salmon steak marinated in honey, coarse grain mustard, dill and olive oil (£9.25), steaks (from £9.95), and home-made puddings like crumbles, steamed sponges or zabaglione (£3.25). Shove-ha'penny, cribbage, dominoes, fruit machine and a separate skittle alley. There's a covered seating area, and more chairs in the pretty garden with apple and pear trees. *(Recommended by Laura Wilson, Joan and Michel Hooper-Immins, Ann and Colin Hunt, Dave Braisted, David H T Dimock, Geoff Pidoux, Lesley and Peter Barrett, J Davidson, Val and Alan Green, Esther and John Sprinkle, Veronica Brown, Colin Draper, Susan and John Douglas)*

Own brew ~ Managers Brian and Cynthia Elderfield ~ Real ale ~ Bar food (12-2.30, 6-9.30; all day weekends) ~ Restaurant ~ (01243) 786893 ~ Children in family room ~ Dogs allowed in bar ~ Open 11-3, 5.30-11; 11-11 Sat; 12-10.30 Sun; 11-3, 5.30-11 winter Sat, 12-3, 6.30-10.30 Sun in winter

PETT TQ8714 Map 3

Two Sawyers

Pett Road; off A259

The meandering low-beamed rooms in this old country local are simply but genuinely put together, with black band saws on the cream walls, handsome iron wall lamps, and stripped tables on the bare boards in its two simple bars. A tiny low-ceilinged snug has dark wood pub tables and cushioned banquettes, with a very old painted flint wall on one side; a sloping passage leads down to a low-beamed no smoking restaurant. As the pub is the brewery tap to the Old Forge Brewery, you will find their range of beers on handpump: Pett Progress, with seasonal guests like Brothers Best, Santa Forge, and Summer Eclipse, and guests from other breweries, too. Gunthorpe's Double Vision farm cider. Bar food includes filled rolls (from £2.55; steak baguette £4.75), soup (£3.45), ploughman's (from £4.65), all day breakfast (£5.85), and steak and mushroom in ale pie (£7.45); some of the meat comes from their own farm. Fruit machine, cribbage, dominoes, Wednesday evening quiz, and piped music. An iron gate leads from a pretty suntrap front brick courtyard to a quiet back garden with shady trees, a few well spaced picnic-sets, a children's play area, and boules. *(Recommended by Lucien, Ruth and Paul Lawrence, Michael and Ann Cole, Keith and Chris O'Neill, the Didler, Gill and Tony Morriss)*

Own brew ~ Licensees Clive Soper, John and Karen Perkins ~ Real ale ~ Bar food (all day in summer) ~ Restaurant ~ (01424) 812255 ~ Children in restaurant and family room ~ Dogs allowed in bar ~ Local groups and bands Fri evenings ~ Open 11-11; 12-10.30 Sun; 11-3, 6-11 Mon-Thurs in winter

PETWORTH SU9719 Map 2

Badgers

Coultershaw Bridge; just off A285 1½ miles S

Although there is a small chatty drinking area with a couple of tables, bar stools and an attractive antique oak monk's chair by the entrance, the space around the island bar servery here is devoted to dining tables – well spaced, with an attractive mix of furniture from old mahogany to waxed stripped pine. White walls bring out the deep maroon colour of the high ceiling, and charming wrought-iron lamps, winter log fires, stripped shutters for the big Victorian windows, and a modicum of carefully chosen decorations including a few houseplants and dried flower arrangements, complete the graceful décor. As well as the good if not cheap restaurant menu, the changing choice of attractively presented, enjoyable bar food might include sandwiches (from £3.50), kedgeree of salmon and dill (£5.95), ploughman's (from £5.95), pasta with pancetta, spinach and wild mushrooms (£6.95), caesar salad, lambs liver with bacon, beef casserole or lambs kidneys with juniper and chillied sherry (all £7.95), pasta with scallops, tiger prawn tails, sun blush tomatoes and fresh basil (£8.95), haddock with poached egg and spinach (£10.95), pheasant with rösti (£11.95), and several fish dishes. Well kept Badger Best and Sussex on handpump, with a good range of well chosen house wines and a fine list by the bottle; maybe faint piped music (the dominant sound is quiet conversation). A terrace by a waterlily pool has stylish metal garden furniture under parasols, and some solid old-fashioned wooden seats. *(Recommended by Ken Arthur, Martin and Karen Wake, Patrick Hall, Patricia Beebe, Christopher and Elise Way, John Robertson)*

Free house ~ Licensee Miss Arlette ~ Real ale ~ Bar food (not winter Sun evenings) ~ Restaurant ~ (01798) 342651 ~ Children over 5 away from bar ~ Open 11-3, 5.30(6.30 Sat)-11; 12-3, 7-10.30 Sun; closed Sun evenings in winter ~ Bedrooms: /£75B

PUNNETTS TOWN TQ6220 Map 3

Three Cups

B2096 towards Battle

A neighbourly and unassuming country local, this is just the sort of place to drop into after a walk. The peaceful and friendly bar has golf clubs on some coin-studded beams and pewter mugs and flagons hanging from others, some attractive panelling, a comfortable variety of seats including some in big bay windows overlooking a small green, a mainly tiled floor, and a log fire in the big fireplace under a black mantelbeam dated 1696. A small partly no smoking carpeted back dining room leads out to a small covered terrace, with tables in the garden beyond. Under the friendly and efficient new landlord, decent bar food includes home-made soup (£3.50), deep-fried breaded brie with red onion marmalade (£4.25), enormous club sandwiches (£4.95), ploughman's, local sausages and mash or home-made steak in ale pie (£5.95), vegetarian lasagne (£6.25), fresh lemon sole (£9.95), steaks (from £9.95), and a roast of the day. Well kept Greene King IPA, Abbot, Morlands Original, and Ruddles County on handpump; darts, shove-ha'penny, cribbage and dominoes; unobtrusive piped music, and there may be a small silenced TV at one end. *(Recommended by Jason Caulkin, Peter Meister, Lucien)*

Greene King ~ Tenant Robert Cole ~ Real ale ~ Bar food (12-2.15, 6.30-9.15) ~ Restaurant ~ (01435) 830252 ~ Children welcome ~ Dogs welcome ~ Open 12-3, 6-11; 12-11 Sat; 12-7 Sun; closed Sun evenings in winter

RUSHLAKE GREEN TQ6218 Map 3

Horse & Groom

Village signposted off B2096 Heathfield—Battle

To be sure of a table in this bustling place it would be best to book in advance as most customers come to enjoy the good home-made food. But plenty of regulars do drop in for just a drink, and there's a chatty, relaxed atmosphere. On the right is the heavily beamed dining room with guns and hunting trophies on the walls, plenty of wheelback chairs around pubby tables, and a log fire. The little L-shaped bar has more low beams – watch your head – and is simply furnished with high bar stools and bar chairs, red plush cushioned wall seats and a few brocaded cushioned stools, and a brick fireplace with some brass items on the mantelpiece; horsebrasses, photographs of the pub and local scenes on the walls, and fresh flowers. A small room down a step has jockeys' colours and jockey photographs and watercolours of the pub, and hops on the ceiling. A large choice of regularly changing bar food might include soup (£3.75), scallops sautéed in spring onions and bacon (£5.25), fresh haddock in crispy beer batter (£7.25), steak, kidney and Guinness pudding (£7.95), goats cheese, aubergine and red onion tart (£8.95), mixed tagliatelle with seared smoked salmon and cherry tomatoes (£8.95), steamed turbot with samphire and mushroom sauce (£9.50), chicken breast stuffed with mozzarella and sun-dried tomatoes and wrapped in bacon with a roasted red pepper sauce (£9.95), chump of lamb roasted and sliced on a port wine sauce (£11.95), and puddings like squidgey chocolate meringue, fruit crumble or summer pudding (£4.75). Well kept Harveys Best, Shepherd Neame Spitfire and Masterbrew, and maybe a guest such as Youngs on handpump, and a decent wine list with several by the glass. The setting, by the large village green, is most attractive and there are picnic-sets in the rustic garden with pretty country views. More reports please. *(Recommended by J H Bell, Colin and Janet Roe)*

Free house ~ Licensees Mike and Sue Chappel ~ Real ale ~ Bar food (12-2.15, 7-9.30(9 Sun)) ~ Restaurant ~ (01435) 830320 ~ Children welcome ~ Dogs welcome ~ Open 11.30-3, 5.30(6 Sat)-11; 12-3, 7-10.30 Sun

RYE TQ9220 Map 3

Mermaid 🍷 🛏

Mermaid Street

The cellars of this civilised black and white timbered hotel date back to 1156 – despite a sign outside that says 'rebuilt in 1472'. The little bar at the back is where those in search of a light lunch and a drink tend to head, and there's a mix of quite closely set furnishings such as Victorian gothic carved oak chairs, older but plainer oak seats and more modern ones in character, and a massive deeply polished bressumer beam across one wall for the huge inglenook fireplace; three antique but not ancient wall paintings show old English scenes. Well kept (if not cheap) Greene King Old Speckled Hen on handpump, a good wine list, and a short choice of bar food such as filled baguettes (from £5.50), moules marinière (£7), spaghetti bolognese (£7.50), cold meat and pickle salad (£8), home oak smoked salmon salad (£8.50), seafood platter (£14.50), puddings such as fruit tarts or strawberry shortbread (£5.50), and children's meals (from £4.50). The smart (expensive) restaurant is no smoking. Seats on a small back terrace overlook the car park – where there are morris dancers on bank holiday weekends. *(Recommended by John and Lynn Busenbark, the Didler, David Carr, Rebecca Nicholls, Keith and Chris O'Neill, Kevin Flack, Sarah Davis, Rod Lambert, Louise English, J H Bell)*

Free house ~ Licensees Robert Pinwill and Mrs J Blincow ~ Real ale ~ Bar food (no bar food Sat evening) ~ Restaurant ~ (01797) 223065 ~ Children in eating area of bar and restaurant ~ Open 11-11(10.30 Sun) ~ Bedrooms: £75B/£150B

SALEHURST TQ7424 Map 3

Salehurst Halt 🍷

Village signposted from Robertsbridge bypass on A21 Tunbridge Wells—Battle Road

Warmly friendly and helpful licensees took over this bustling little local just as we went to press but have no plans to make any big changes. The L-shaped bar has a pleasant chatty atmosphere, good plain wooden tables and chairs on flagstones at one end, a cushioned window seat, beams, a little open brick fireplace, a time punch clock, olde-worlde pictures, and fresh flowers; lots of hops on a big beam divide this from the beamed carpeted area with its mix of tables, wheelback and farmhouse chairs, and a half wall leads to a no smoking dining area. Cooked by the licensee, enjoyable home-made food at lunchtime includes sandwiches (from £2.75), ploughman's (£4.95), home-made burgers (from £5.50), and smoked salmon mousse, super beef and mushroom pie or home-baked ham and egg (£5.95), with evening dishes such as baked almond dipped brie with cranberry sauce (£4.40), moules marinière (£4.95), spicy and creamy vegetable parcel or popular cider chicken (£8.95), salmon with a lemon and parsley sauce (£9.95), and puddings such as banoffi pie, cider apple crumble or treacle pudding (from £2.95). Well kept Harveys Best on handpump, and good wines. It can get very busy at weekends, so best to book in advance. The charming and pretty back garden is a suntrap in summer, and has terraces and picnic-sets for outside meals, and the front window boxes and tubs are most attractive. *(Recommended by Colin and Stephanie McFie, Colin and Janet Roe, Ian Phillips, Tony and Wendy Hobden, Derek and Maggie Washington)*

Free house ~ Licensees Colin and Sarah Green ~ Real ale ~ Bar food ~ Restaurant ~ (01580) 880620 ~ Children welcome ~ Dogs welcome ~ Open 12-3, 7-11(10.30 Sun); closed Mon

SCAYNES HILL TQ3623 Map 3

Sloop 🍺

Freshfield Lock; at top of Scaynes Hill by petrol station turn N off A272 into Church Road, keep on for 1½ miles and then follow Freshfield signpost

This well run country pub is named after the boats which worked the adjacent waterway (formerly the Ouse canal) until the end of the 19th c. The long saloon bar has a warmly friendly atmosphere, wheelbacks and other chairs around pubby tables, well kept Greene King IPA, Abbot, Dark Mild, Old Speckled Hen, Ruddles County, and a couple of guests such as Brains SA or Gales HSB on handpump, and a decent wine list with six by the glass; there are benches in the old-fashioned brick porch. Good home-made bar food includes soups such as stilton and broccoli or vegetable with garlic croutons (£3.95; popular New Hampshire fish stew £5.95), roast peppers filled with onion, mushroom and tomato, topped with cheese (£4.50), lunchtime ploughman's (£5.95), vegetable lasagne or home-made steak, stout and mushroom pie (£6.95), liver and bacon with onion gravy (£7.95), maple and mustard chicken or grilled trout with mustard and dill sauce (£8.95), steaks (from £10.95), grilled whole bass with olives, garlic and tomato (£11.95), daily specials such as fresh fish and seasonal game, and puddings like home-made apple crumble, crème brûlée or bread pudding with maple and cream (from £3.50); best to book. Good service from chatty, welcoming staff. The basic but airy public bar has restored woodwork, settles and cushioned stools on the bare boards, and railway memorabilia and Lucy, a 26 pound stuffed pike, on the walls; one area is no smoking. Bar billiards (in a small room leading off the bar), piped music, darts, shove-ha'penny, cribbage and dominoes. There are lots of tables in the sheltered garden. Sheffield Park Gardens and the Bluebell Steam Railway are close by. More reports please. *(Recommended by Ken Arthur, Martin and Jane Wright, C and R Bromage, Susan and John Douglas, John Beeken)*

Greene King ~ Tenant Nigel S Cannon ~ Real ale ~ Bar food (12-2.15, 6.30-9.15 Mon-Sat, 12-8.15 Sun) ~ Restaurant ~ (01444) 831219 ~ Children in eating area of bar ~ Dogs allowed in bar ~ Live music 1st and 3rd Fri of month ~ Open 12-3, 6-11; 12-10.30 Sun

SEAFORD TV4899 Map 3

Golden Galleon

Exceat Bridge; A259 Seaford—Eastbourne, near Cuckmere

It's not surprising that this well run pub gets so busy. The position is marvellous, the food good, and their own-brewed beers very popular. From the brewery which is on full view for customers come Cuckmere Haven Best, Diamond Bitter, Golden Pease, Governor, Jubilee Gold, and Saxon King Stout; there may be guest beers as well, plus farm ciders, good wines by the glass, a decent choice of malts, continental brandies, Italian liqueurs, and cappuccino or espresso coffee. On the set menu there might be ploughman's (from £4.75) and cold salads (from £6.25), both served all day, tuna fish and butter beans with capers, onions, garlic and parsley (£3.95), filled baked potatoes (from £5.50), spicy chicken fillets (£6.75), half a roast chicken (£8.25), pineapple and gammon (£8.50), steaks (from £10.45), and stincotto (large pork joint cooked on the bone with wine and herbs, £10.95), plus daily specials like carrot and coriander soup (£3.25), prawn, apple and celery salad (£5.25), sausage and mushroom pie or vegetable lasagne (£7.95), Italian platter or chicken breast in gorgonzola, tomatoes and a spicy sauce (£10.95), and puddings such as chocolate or lemon tiramisu, various cheesecakes or banoffi pie (£3.25). The spreading main bar with high trussed and pitched rafters creating quite an airy feel, is the only place where smoking is allowed; the river room becomes a restaurant on Sunday lunchtime. The pub is perfectly set for several attractive walks – along the river, down to the sea or inland to Friston Forest and the downs, and there are fine views towards the Cuckmere estuary and Seven Sisters Country Park from tables in the sloping garden. More reports please. *(Recommended by Tina and David Woods-Taylor, Ann and Colin Hunt, Bruce Bird, John Beeken, Paul and Penny Dawson, Alistair Forsyth)*

Own brew ~ Licensee Stefano Diella ~ Real ale ~ Bar food (12-2.30, 6-9.30; cold food served all day) ~ (01323) 892247 ~ Children away from bar ~ Dogs welcome ~ Open 11-11; 12-10.30 Sun; closed Sun evenings (from 4pm) in winter

SINGLETON SU8713 Map 2

Fox & Hounds

Just off A286 Midhurst—Chichester; heading S into the village, the main road bends sharp right – keep straight ahead instead; if you miss this turn, take the Charlton road, then first left

This is the sort of consistently enjoyable place that people come back to again and again. The partly panelled main bar has cream paintwork, a polished wooden floor, daily papers and books to borrow, and a good winter log fire. There's a second bar with green settles and another fire, a third flagstoned room on the left, and a further no smoking seating area off a side corridor. Well liked honest food includes home-made soup (£4.50), open sandwiches (from £5.50), an excellent cheese platter with good ripe cheeses laid out attractively, and pickles and chutneys provided in separate pots (£6.50), pasta of the day, liver and bacon, fishcakes or steak in ale pie (£8.50), gammon with mustard, mushrooms and melted cheese (£8.75), steak (from £9.50), and daily specials such as smoked haddock with a poached egg or guinea fowl (£8.95); service is prompt and cheerful. Well kept Bass, Greene King, and Ringwood Best on handpump, decent wines by the glass, coffee with free refills; no music or machines, but cribbage and dominoes. There are tables on an attractive small back terrace, and beyond that a big walled garden with colourful flowerbeds and fruit trees. The Weald & Downland Open Air Museum is just down the road, and Goodwood Racecourse is not far away. More reports please. *(Recommended by Ann and Colin Hunt, Prof and Mrs S Barnett, Tracey and Stephen Groves, W A Evershed)*

Enterprise ~ Lease Tony Simpson ~ Real ale ~ Bar food ~ (01243) 811251 ~ Children in family room ~ Dogs allowed in bar ~ Open 11.30-3, 6-11; 12-3, 7-10.30 Sun

TILLINGTON SU9621 Map 2

Horse Guards

Village signposted off A272 Midhurst—Petworth

The emphasis in this prettily-set 18th-c dining pub remains on the imaginative (if not cheap) restaurant-style food, and it is very much somewhere for a special meal out. The neatly kept cosy beamed front bar has some good country furniture, a log fire and a lovely view beyond the village to the Rother Valley from a seat in the big black-panelled bow window. Good, enjoyable dishes might at lunchtime include home-made soup (£4.50), potted snacks like chicken liver parfait with green peppercorns or buttered skate with capers and rosemary (£4.95), oak smoked salmon open sandwich topped with dill crème fraîche or flash fried chicken liver and caper salad with walnut dressing (£5.95), chargrilled lamb and red pepper crostini with tapenade (£6.50), roast vegetable and stilton tart with plum tomato sauce (£7.95), smoked haddock fishcakes with chive and white wine sauce (£9.50), and home-made steak and kidney pie laced with stout (£9.95), with evening choices such as roast provençale vegetables with home-made olive bread (£6), saffron risotto with seared crayfish tails or rabbit and foie gras terrine (£7.50), roast artichoke crumble with pesto sauce (£9.95), baked chicken supreme on spinach with a roquefort cream sauce (£13.50), and crispy duck leg confit with tomato and white bean cassoulet (£14.95), daily specials like roast quail stuffed with chicken liver and foie gras on a puy lentil salsa (£7.95), scallop and pancetta salad (£7.95; large £11.50), fresh dressed selsey crab (£12.50), and poached fillet of turbot with oyster mushrooms and sherry vinegar sauce (£15.95), and home-made puddings such as white chocolate bread and butter pudding, chocolate nemesis, and strawberry and vanilla shortbead (£5.95). The good wine list has over 10 by the glass; well kept Bass, Flowers IPA, and Fullers London Pride on handpump. There's a terrace outside, and more tables and chairs in a sheltered garden behind. The 800-year-old church opposite is worth a look. *(Recommended by Colin Draper, John Evans, Michael and Ann Cole, J Hale, Lord Sandhurst, Wendy Arnold, Ann and Colin Hunt, Veronica Brown, Ken Arthur, Ian Jones, Sefton Parke, Peter and Audrey Dowsett, J A Snell, Nick Roberts, Tina and David Woods-Taylor, J H Bell, Peter B Brown, W A Evershed)*

Free house ~ Licensees Don Gregor and Carole Gent ~ Real ale ~ Bar food (12-2, 7-10) ~ Restaurant ~ (01798) 342332 ~ Children in restaurant but must be over 7 in evening ~ Dogs allowed in bar ~ Open 11-3, 6-11; 12-3, 7-10.30 Sun ~ Bedrooms: /£65B

TROTTON SU8323 Map 2

Keepers Arms

A272 Midhurst—Petersfield; pub tucked up above road, on S side

The landlord and his staff manage to create a warmly friendly, chatty feel in this 17th-c country pub. The beamed L-shaped bar, with timbered walls and some standing timbers, has original flooring tiles, with parquet floor elsewhere. There are sofas by the big log fire (where the cat curls up), and the walls are decorated with some unusual pictures and artefacts that reflect the Oxleys' previous long years of travelling the world. The wheelback chairs and dark pub tables continue to give way to a more interesting medley of old or antique seats, with oak refectory tables and the like, and the dining tables are decorated with pretty candelabra, and bowls of fruit and chillis. Good home-made food includes soup (£3.50), fine cheese and salami platters that several people can share (£5), crispy duck salad on sautéed potatoes with hoisin sauce, cucumber and spring onion (£9), proper fish pie with cod, prawns, smoked salmon and squid (£9.50), chargrilled ostrich medallion with a wild cranberry and balsamic jus (£10.50), and home-made puddings (£3.50); in winter they have a special game pie with venison, pheasant, partridge, and wild duck (£8.50), and in summer (by appointment only), a fresh seafood platter with lobster, dressed crab, crab claws, giant crevettes, atlantic prawns, langoustine, and oysters (£18.50 per person); the restaurant (which could be warmer on cold nights) is no smoking. Well kept Ballards Best and Nyewood Gold, and Cheriton Pots on handpump, and decent wines; maybe relaxed piped music (there's a musically decorated piano). Plenty of seats on the attractive, almost Mediterranean-feeling front terrace. Dogs lunchtime only. *(Recommended by J A Snell, Martin and Karen Wake, Cathy Robinson, Ed Coombe, Ann and Stephen Saunders, Mike and Sue Richardson, Val and Alan Green, Paul and Penny Dawson, Ann and Colin Hunt, Derek Harvey-Piper, Tracey and Stephen Groves, W A Evershed)*

Free house ~ Licensees Steve and Jenny Oxley ~ Real ale ~ Bar food ~ Restaurant ~ (01730) 813724 ~ Children welcome lunchtime only ~ Dogs allowed in bar ~ Open 12-2.30, 6.30-11; 12-2.30 Sun; closed Sun evening, all Mon except bank hol lunchtime

WARNHAM TQ1533 Map 3

Sussex Oak 🍷

Just off A24 Horsham—Dorking; Church Street

Set opposite the church, this nice old pub is doing very well under its new licensees who have created a relaxed and friendly pubby atmosphere. It's been attractively opened up inside with several connecting areas served by a carved wooden bar counter. There are heavy beams and standing timbers, an end room with a good mix of dining chairs and solid wooden tables on the partly carpeted and partly stripped wooden floor, a wooden printers' tray, fishing rods, and wall lamps on the green panelled walls, and little fireplaces at each end. The central room has green and red patterned old sofas in front of the inglenook fireplace, fine old flagstones, bar billiards and darts, and maybe chatting locals sitting at stools by the bar. Well kept Adnams Bitter, Brakspears Bitter, Fullers London Pride, Timothy Taylors Landlord, and Youngs Bitter on handpump and a good wine list with several by the glass. Using local produce, the enjoyable, popular bar food includes home-made soup (£3.75), spicy onion bhajis with sour cream dip (£4.25), sandwiches (from £4.25), filled baked potatoes (from £4.50), wild boar terrine with port and redcurrant jelly (£4.95), field mushrooms with bacon and stilton sauce (£5.25), lasagne or tagliatelle carbonara (£5.95; large £7.25), ploughman's (from £5.95), cold meat salads (£6.95), home-made fish pie (£7.25), home-made steak, ale and mushroom pie (£7.25; large £8.95), home-cooked ham and eggs, chicken curry or mediterranean tart with sun blush tomato salad (£7.95), trio of local sausages with caramelised onions and parlsey mash (£8.25), local game pie (£8.95), fillet steak (£14.50), puddings (£3.95), local cheeses, fruit and biscuits (£4.95), and Sunday roasts. The attractive, hop-hung, high raftered restaurant is no smoking; piped music. Picnic-sets in the garden. *(Recommended by Phil Savage, Ian Phillips)*

Free house ~ Licensees Peter and Angela Nottage ~ Real ale ~ Bar food (12-2.30 (3 Sun), 6-9.30(9 Sun)) ~ Restaurant ~ (01403) 265028 ~ Children welcome away from bar area ~ Dogs welcome ~ Open 11-11; 12-10.30 Sun

WILMINGTON TQ5404 Map 3

Giants Rest

Just off A27

Even when this comfortable Victorian pub – watched over by the impressive chalk-carved Long Man of Wilmington at the foot of the South Downs – is busy, you can be sure of a warm welcome from the charming licensees. The long wood floored bar and adjacent open areas, one with a log fire, are simply furnished with old pews and pine tables (each with their own bar game or wooden puzzle), and serve well kept Harveys Best, Hop Back Summer Lightning, and Timothy Taylors Landlord on handpump; orange and grapefruit juice squeezed in front of you, and decent wines. From a changing blackboard, well presented and generously served bar food includes soup (£3), pâté (£4), avocado and prawns

(£4.50), local sausages (£5.50), ploughman's (from £5.50), roasted vegetable moussaka, salmon fishcakes with lemon mayonnaise or rabbit and bacon or beef in beer pies (£8), home-cooked ham with bubble and squeak or whole local plaice (£8.50), trout fillet with crème fraîche, walnut and horseradish sauce (£9), lamb in red wine with thyme and orange (£9.50), and puddings such as sticky date pudding or crumbles (£3.50). There's a sizeable no smoking area; piped music and shove-ha'penny. Plenty of seats in the front garden. More reports please. *(Recommended by Jo Blake, Simon Pyle, John Beeken, T R and B C Jenkins, Mike and Shelley Woodroffe)*

Free house ~ Licensees Adrian and Rebecca Hillman ~ Real ale ~ Bar food ~ (01323) 870207 ~ Children in eating area of bar and in restaurant ~ Dogs welcome ~ Open 11-3, 6-11; 11-11 Sat; 12-10.30 Sun; 11-3, 6-11 in winter

WINEHAM TQ2320 Map 3

Royal Oak £

Village signposted from A272 and B2116

This is a lovely old-fashioned pub that, happily, remains unchanged and still has no fruit machines, piped music or even beer pumps, and where the emphasis is on drinks rather than food. It is simply furnished, logs burn in an enormous inglenook fireplace with a cast-iron Royal Oak fireback, and there's a collection of cigarette cards showing old English pubs, a stuffed stoat and crocodile, a collection of jugs, ancient corkscrews decorating the very low beams above the serving counter, and racing plates, tools and a coach horn on the walls; maybe a nice tabby cat, and views of quiet countryside from the back parlour. Well kept Harveys Best with a guest such as Bass or Wadworths 6X tapped from the cask in a still room; darts, shove-ha'penny, dominoes, cribbage. Bar snacks are limited to home-made winter soup (£2.50), sandwiches (from £2.25, smoked salmon £3), and ploughman's (from £4.50); courteous service – the pub has been in the same family for over 50 years. It can get very busy at weekends and on summer evenings. The charming frontage has a lawn with wooden tables by a well. No children inside. *(Recommended by Jenny and Brian Seller, Mike and Lynn Robinson, Mrs J Wild, R E Greenhalgh, Phil and Sally Gorton, Ron Shelton)*

Inn Business ~ Tenant Tim Peacock ~ Real ale ~ Bar food (11-2.30, 5.30-10.30) ~ No credit cards ~ (01444) 881252 ~ Dogs welcome ~ Open 11-2.30, 5.30(6 Sat)-11; 12-3, 7-10.30 Sun

Lucky Dip

Besides the fully inspected pubs, you might like to try these Lucky Dips recommended to us and described by readers (if you do, please send us reports: www.goodguides.com).

Alfriston [TQ5203]
Market Cross [central square]: Olde-worlde low-beamed white-panelled bar with smuggling mementoes, good value bar food from sandwiches to steaks (snacks only, Sun lunch), good choice of well kept real ales and of wines by the glass, friendly staff, tables in garden; children allowed in eating area and conservatory; can get crowded, as this lovely village draws many visitors *(LYM, Veronica Brown)*

☆ ***Star*** [High St]: Fascinating façade decorated with fine medieval carvings, striking figurehead red lion on the corner; stolid heavy-beamed bar (busy lunchtime, quiet evenings) with medieval sanctuary post, fine antique furnishings, big log fire in Tudor fireplace, some no smoking areas, helpful service, bar food from sandwiches and baked potatoes up, Bass, restaurant; comfortable modern bedrooms in up-to-date part behind, open all day summer *(Colin and Janet Roe, S F Parrinder, Charlie Harris, David Carr, the Didler, LYM)*

Amberley [TQ0211]
☆ ***Bridge*** [B2139]: Attractive and popular open-plan dining pub, comfortable and relaxed even when busy, with pleasant candlelit bar and two-room dining area, wide range of good value generous food from sandwiches up, well kept Flowers Original, Fullers London Pride, Harveys and Youngs; children and dogs welcome, piped music; tables out in front and in side garden, open all day, cl Sun evening *(J Davidson, Bruce Bird, David Cosham, Prof and Mrs S Barnett, W A Evershed, LYM)*

Angmering [TQ0704]
☆ ***Spotted Cow*** [High St]: Beautifully presented generous food (very popular wkdy lunchtimes with older people) from imaginative sandwiches up, well kept Adnams Broadside, Fullers

London Pride, Harveys BB, Ringwood Best and a guest such as Hop Back, good choice of wines by the glass, attentive service, smuggling history, sporting caricatures, cool and roomy in summer, two log fires winter; restaurant, no smoking conservatory, big garden with boules and play area; open all day summer wknds (very busy then), monthly Sun afternoon jazz, lovely walk to Highdown hill fort *(Bruce Bird, John Beeken, Gordon Stevenson, Pamela Goodwyn, R Edwards, Tony and Wendy Hobden)*

Ansty [TQ2923]

Ansty Cross Inn [A272 towards Cuckfield]: Nicely restored and extended old cottage popular with local business people, some concentration on enjoyable food from good range of sandwiches to pizza restaurant, well kept Fullers London Pride and Greene King Old Speckled Hen, inglenook log fire, very friendly courteous staff *(Jenny and Brian Seller)*

Apuldram [SU8401]

☆ ***Black Horse*** [A286 SW of Chichester]: Comfortable open-plan pub dating from 18th c, small bar with Courage Directors, Fullers London Pride and Greene King Old Speckled Hen, more tables in neat no smoking dining area opening on to covered terrace, some emphasis on very wide blackboard food choice running up to good seafood inc huge lobsters, friendly landlady and staff, decent wines; further terrace tables outside, picnic-sets in big orchard garden with slide and swings *(Mr and Mrs A Hynd, BB, Mrs M Smith)*

Ardingly [TQ3429]

Ardingly Inn [Street Lane, off B2028]: Spacious and comfortable beamed bar, big central log fire (chestnuts provided for roasting), well kept Badger ales with Gribble guests, new young licensees doing generous attractively presented food from sandwiches and bar snacks to interesting restaurant dishes and Sun lunch, traditional games; dogs allowed, reasonably priced bedrooms *(David Cosham)*

☆ ***Gardeners Arms*** [B2028 2 miles N]: Neatly refurbished olde-worlde dining pub currently doing well, comfortably rambling, with reliable fresh home-made food and quick cheerful service even when crowded (no bookings), big inglenook log fire, well kept Badger and Harveys, morning coffee and tea, attractive decorations; may be soft piped music, no children; well spaced tables out among small trees, opp S of England show ground and handy for Borde Hill and Wakehurst Place *(Bruce Bird, G J C Moss, M Borthwick, Michael Porter, Mr and Mrs D Moir, Mr and Mrs A P Lawrence)*

Oak [Street Lane]: Beamed 14th-c dining pub handy for show ground, good reasonably priced menu inc children's dishes, Courage Best and Harveys BB, prompt friendly service, lots of brass and lace curtains, magnificent old fireplace, bright comfortable restaurant extension; tables in pleasant garden, reservoir walks *(Tony Hobden, Martin and Jane Wright)*

Arlington [TQ5407]

☆ ***Yew Tree*** [off A22 nr Hailsham, or A27 W of Polegate]: Neatly modernised two-bar village local very popular for hearty home cooking inc delicious puddings (smaller helpings can be arranged), well kept Harveys BB, log fires, efficient cheery service (but book well ahead for Fri in summer); subdued piped music, darts, may be eggs for sale; children welcome, conservatory, good big garden and play area, by paddock with farm animals *(BB, Tina and David Woods-Taylor, Miss A G Drake, John Beeken)*

Arundel [TQ0208]

☆ ***Black Rabbit*** [Mill Rd, Offham; keep on and don't give up!]: Long riverside family pub reopened after smart refurbishment following 2000 flooding – lovely spot near wildfowl reserve, lots of tables out looking across to water-meadows and castle; wide range of generous enjoyable food, Badger ales with Gribble guests, log fires; open all day, doubling as summer tea shop, very busy then, with summer boat trips, good walks *(LYM, Val and Alan Green, David and Carole Chapman)*

Red Lion [High St]: Well run, with good choice of beers such as Fullers and Youngs, charming service, enjoyable food *(Jon and Caroline Seymour)*

☆ ***Swan*** [High St]: Smartly refurbished open-plan L-shaped bar with attractive woodwork and matching fittings, beaten brass former inn-sign hanging on wall, friendly efficient young staff, good choice of well presented food from baguettes and baked potatoes to restaurant meals, Gales Butser, GB and HSB and a guest such as Fullers London Pride; piped music; restaurant, good bedrooms, open all day *(John Davis, Veronica Brown, Miss J F Reay, LYM, Patrick Hancock, Ann and Colin Hunt, Theocsbrian, Tony and Wendy Hobden)*

Balcombe [TQ3033]

☆ ***Cowdray Arms*** [London Rd (B2036/B2110 N of village)]: Roomy main-road pub filling quickly at lunchtime for good value choice of well prepared and presented food from generous sandwiches and ploughman's to some interesting dishes, good helpings, polite attentive service, well kept ales such as Black Sheep, Greene King IPA and Abbot and Harveys, occasional beer festivals, L-shaped bar and no smoking restaurant with conservatory; children welcome, large garden with good play area *(DWAJ, Eamonn and Natasha Skyrme, Ian and Joan Blackwell, Ian Phillips, Tony and Wendy Hobden, Terry Buckland)*

Balls Cross [SU9826]

Stag [signed off A283 N of Petworth]: Welcoming unspoilt 17th-c country pub with flagstones and log fires, good value food, well kept Badger ales; pleasant back garden, bedrooms, good walks *(R J Walden, J A Snell)*

Barcombe [TQ4114]

Anchor [Barcombe Mills]: Nice for summer, with lawns by winding River Ouse (boat or canoe hire), cream tea and cold drink kiosk, wknd barbecues, and lots of quiet walks; three beamed rooms (children welcome), food from sandwiches and baked potatoes to more elaborate main dishes, well kept Badger Best and Tanglefoot and Harveys Best (may not always be on), traditional games; open all day *(John Beeken, Stephanie and Kamal Thapa, Richard Gibbs, LYM, John and Angela Main)*

Battle [TQ7215]

Squirrel [North Trade Rd (A269 towards Herstmonceux)]: Generous cheap home cooking inc their own hams and evenings with all-you-can eat curry/carvery etc, well kept beers, chatty licensees; children allowed in pool room, large family garden *(Marjorie and Bernard Parkin)*

Berwick [TQ5206]

Berwick Inn [by station]: Roomy and rambling two-bar family pub with good choice of enjoyable food from sandwiches up, Fullers London Pride and Harveys Best, quick helpful service, log fire, upper front games room, conservatory; piped music; large garden behind with good playground and attractive Perspex-roofed garden bar *(Sue and Mike Todd, LYM)*

Bexhill [TQ7407]

De La Warr Pavilion [Marina]: By no means a pub, but upstairs this Bauhaus architectural gem has a seaview bar with Boddingtons and Harveys, balcony tables and adjoining restaurant *(Ian Phillips)*

Binsted [SU9806]

☆ ***Black Horse*** [Binsted Lane; about 2 miles W of Arundel, turn S off A27 towards Binsted]: Pretty 17th-c local with ochre walls and open fire in big comfortably chatty bar, enjoyable food from generous sandwiches to interesting specials, wider range in back conservatory restaurant, well kept Adnams Regatta, Gales HSB, Harveys Best and Hop Back Summer Lightning, attentive service, darts and bar billiards one end, shelf of sweetie jars, greyhound racing trophies; piped music; tables on terrace, idyllic garden, views over valley; bedrooms *(Bruce Bird, David Holloway, BB)*

Bodiam [TQ7825]

☆ ***Curlew*** [B2244 S of Hawkhurst, outside village]: Country dining pub with new chef/landlord doing good attractively presented food from interesting baguettes and other bar food to inventive restaurant dishes, green plush seating and timbered pink walls in beamed bar and eating area, civilised restaurant with smart mirrors and attractive watercolours, several real ales, good choice of generously served wines, cheerful helpful staff *(RDK, BB)*

Bolney [TQ2623]

Bolney Stage [off old A23 just N of A272]: Neat and comfortable timbered dining pub locally popular for wide range of good handsomely presented food, prompt friendly service, choice of beers, large log fire; handy for Sheffield Park and Bluebell Railway *(Ron and Sheila Corbett, R E Greenhalgh)*

Bosham [SU8003]

Anchor Bleu [High St]: Noted for its lovely waterside position in a charming village – sea and boat views, little terrace outside massive wheel-operated bulkhead door to ward off high tides (cars parked on seaward side often submerged); plenty of potential inside, open all day *(JDM, KM, Ann and Colin Hunt, Dave Braisted, LYM, Geoffrey and Brenda Wilson)*

Berkeley Arms [just outside old village]: Good atmosphere, cheerfully welcoming landlord and staff, well kept Gales, lounge with eating area, public bar *(DJC, Ann and Colin Hunt)*

White Swan [A259 roundabout]: Well refurbished, with two bar areas and large dining room (children allowed here), sociable landlord, nice mix of customers, good choice of beers such as Hop Back Summer Lightning, good value coffee, usual bar food from toasties and baked potatoes up, also restaurant dishes, log fire *(Ann and Colin Hunt, Tony and Wendy Hobden)*

Brighton [TQ2505]

Battle of Trafalgar [Trafalgar Rd/Guildford Rd, Portslade (B2193)]: Friendly town local with well kept ales such as Courage Directors, Fullers London Pride, Harveys Best and Hop Back Summer Lightning, hearty typical food from lunchtime side servery, log fire; pub games, piped jazz and blues; lovely big garden, open all day Thurs-Sun *(Richard Lewis)*

☆ ***Cricketers*** [Black Lion St]: Cheerful down-to-earth town pub, very well run, with ageing Victorian furnishings and lots of interesting bric-a-brac – even a stuffed bear; well kept Bass, Boddingtons, Courage Directors and Greene King Old Speckled Hen tapped from the cask, good coffee, friendly bustle, usual well priced lunchtime bar food with fresh veg in upstairs bar, restaurant (where children allowed) and covered ex-stables courtyard bar; piped music; open all day *(Ian Phillips, LYM, Ann and Colin Hunt, R T and J C Moggridge, Kevin Blake)*

☆ ***Evening Star*** [Surrey St]: Very popular as the tap for its own good Dark Star microbrewery, with several well kept changing beers from other small breweries; enthusiastic landlord (may let you sample before you buy), changing farm ciders and perries, lots of country wines, good simple food (not evenings Sat-Mon or Thurs), old-fashioned local atmosphere, well worn but clean bare boards, simple furnishings, good mix of customers, railway memorabilia; unobtrusive piped music, live music nights, tables outside, open all day *(Peter Jones, Bruce Bird, Richard Lewis, Sue Demont, Tim Barrow, MLR, R T and J C Moggridge)*

Freemasons [Western Rd, Hove (B2066 – main Brighton—Hove thoroughfare, near junction with Brunswick Pl)]: Recently well reworked by new owners, with two well kept real ales such as Fullers London Pride alongside the lager and keg taps on the central island bar, soft lighting, lots of chrome, mirrors and shiny wood laminate, and bare wooden floors, upstairs bar with interesting contemporary food, very striking feature lavatories – both are well worth a look; piped music may be loud *(David Cosham)*

☆ ***Greys*** [Southover St, Kemp Town]: Buoyant atmosphere in very small basic open-plan corner local with two or three rough and ready tables for eating – must book, strongly recommended for limited but appealing choice of good food lunchtime and Tues-Thurs evening; very friendly staff, well kept Flowers, Fullers London Pride, uncommon guest beers, well chosen and reproduced piped music, interesting live music Sun lunchtime (more during Brighton Festival) *(Richard Houghton, Catriona and Fiona Picken, BB)*

Hand in Hand [Upper St James's St, Kemptown]: Busy friendly local brewing its own Kemptown beers, also Badger Best and Tanglefoot, Stowford Press cider, good value wkdy lunchtime snacks such as sandwiches, pies and pizzas, Sun roast potatoes, good service, dim-lit bar with tie collection and newspaper pages all over walls, colourful mix of customers; veteran fruit machine, TV, good piped music; open all day *(Richard Lewis, MLR, Brian and Halina Howes)*

Leconfield Arms [Edward St]: Well kept ales such as Courage Directors and Spinnaker Buzz in small friendly open-plan local, popular for games esp darts; open all day *(Richard Lewis)*

Lord Nelson [Trafalgar St]: Busy central pub with good value straightforward lunchtime food from sandwiches to fresh fish, well kept Harveys ales inc Mild, farm cider, friendly staff, log fire, back conservatory; pub games, sports TV *(Richard Lewis)*

Prestonville [Hamilton Rd, off A23]: Several real ales, basic food, nice courtyard *(MLR)*

Quadrant [North St Quadrant]: Friendly two-level pub with good range of real ales and Belgian beers; piped music, games machine, no food (pickled eggs), lavatories down narrow stairs *(Richard Lewis)*

Rose Hill Tavern [Rose Hill Terrace, off A23]: Good local, plenty of atmosphere, popular meeting place *(MLR)*

Sussex Cricketer [Eaton Rd, by cricket ground]: Plush chain dining pub, warm and comfortable, well done standard food, well kept real ales *(Tracey and Stephen Groves)*

Broad Oak [TQ8220]

☆ ***Rainbow Trout*** [A28/B2089, N of Brede]: Well run olde-worlde pub with wide range of well cooked generous food esp fish served by pleasant waitresses in attractive bustling low-beamed bar and big no smoking restaurant extension; gets very crowded but plenty of room for drinkers, with well kept Boddingtons, Flowers and Fullers London Pride, decent wines; tables out on large lawn *(Glenn and Louise Hamilton, E G Parish, Phil and Sarah Kane)*

Brownbread Street [TQ6715]

☆ ***Ash Tree*** [off A271 (was B2204) W of Battle; 1st northward rd W of Ashburnham Pl, then 1st fork left, then bear right into Brownbread Street]: Tranquil country local tucked away in isolated hamlet, cosy beamed bars with nice old settles and chairs, stripped brickwork, two inglenook fireplaces, evening candlelight, well kept Greene King Old Speckled Hen and Harveys Best, wide choice of wines, tasty bar food (may only do their good main dishes at busiest times eg Sun lunch, and don't serve late), cheerful service; simple games room on left with darts, pool, fruit machine, juke box, bar billiards; children in eating area, pretty garden with picnic-sets, open all day *(Mr and Mrs J Stone, Marjorie and Bernard Parkin, LYM, James Nunns)*

Bucks Green [TQ0732]

☆ ***Fox*** [A281 Horsham—Guildford]: Thriving atmosphere in ancient and congenial open-plan inglenook bar, wide choice of good food esp fish, helpful service, well kept Badger beers inc K&B, decent wines by the glass, restaurant area; play area *(David Cosham, Alistair Forsyth)*

Burwash [TQ6724]

☆ ***Bell*** [A265 E of Heathfield]: Pretty tile-hung village pub opp church, picnic-sets out by colourful flower baskets and tubs, L-shaped bar with interesting bric-a-brac and good log fire, well kept Greene King IPA, Ruddles Best and County and Harveys Best, decent wines, pub games, generous home-made food (not Sun evening) from sandwiches up, no smoking dining room; music quizzes, TV, unobtrusive piped music, children and dogs welcome; bedrooms sharing bathrooms, charming village, open all day wknds *(J Hale, LYM, Jenny and Brian Seller)*

☆ ***Rose & Crown*** [inn sign on A265]: Pleasant new licensees in low-beamed timbered local tucked away down lane in pretty village, well kept Harveys, decent wines, good log fire, good value varied food in bar and attractive restaurant; music quiz nights, tables out in small quiet garden, limited nearby parking *(Derek Harvey-Piper, BB, J P Humphery, R M Warner)*

Burwash Weald [TQ6523]

Wheel [A265 2 miles W of Burwash]: Enjoyable food all day in friendly and well run open-plan pub with good inglenook log fire, comfortable banquettes, nicely framed old local photographs, well kept Harveys and other ales, Post Office counter now in games bar up a step or two behind, dining room leading out to garden; tables on sunny front terrace too, lovely walks in valley opp *(BB)*

Bury [TQ0113]

☆ ***Squire & Horse*** [Bury Common; A29 Fontwell—Pulborough]: Sizeable roadside pub, spic and span inside with U-shaped open-plan bar areas split up by half walling and timbering; heavy beams, pink plush wall seats and cushioned wheelbacks, hunting prints, straw teddies and dried flowers, little ornaments, gas woodburner, well kept ales such as Harveys, Brakspears and Shepherd Neame, smart friendly staff, a mix of drinkers and diners, and attractive two-level beamed restaurant with fresh flowers and another woodburner; a wide range of popular home-made food, Sun bar nibbles; green tables and chairs on pretty terrace (some road noise), pretty flowering tubs along front of building; cl Sun evening, Mon *(M E C Comer, John Beeken, J P Humphery, Fiona and Keith Warton, C and G Fraser, BB)*

Buxted [TQ4923]

☆ ***White Hart*** [Station Rd (A272)]: Neatly kept roadside pub doing well under current friendly licensees, lots of interesting food, reasonable prices, well kept Greene King Old Speckled

Hen and Harveys, cheery chatty feel with efficient service and quite a few locals, main bar divided by timbering, big brick fireplace, hops and some horsebrasses, red leatherette seats, left-hand dining bar, big light and airy dining conservatory with fairy-lit plants and light wooden furniture on wood-strip floor; may be piped pop music; pleasant garden with plenty of seats *(RDK, BB, Michael and Ann Cole)*

Byworth [SU9820]

☆ ***Black Horse*** [off A283]: The managers who won such a following here are leaving; we hope their successors will also do such enjoyable reasonably priced lunchtime food (not Mon) from sandwiches to interesting hot dishes, and keep a similarly good range of real ales, but in any event the ancient building itself has a lot of charm, with pews, scrubbed tables and log fires, a quaint Elizabethan no smoking back dining room, pub games inc bar billiards (there may be piped music), and one of the nicest pub gardens in Sussex; dogs and children have been allowed; reports please *(LYM)*

Chailey [TQ3919]

Five Bells [A275 9 miles N of Lewes]: Attractive old roadside pub, big and rambling inside with lots of different rooms and alcoves leading from bar area with low beams and joists, a fine old brick floor, brick walls, and inglenook in central part, a mix of dining chairs and tables, leather sofa by the fire with another under window, dining extension, well kept Fullers London Pride and Harveys BB, decent wine choice, well liked food inc OAP lunch discounts, and picnic-sets in garden in front and at side, play area *(John Beeken, Tony and Wendy Hobden, I D Barnett, BB)*

Chichester [SU8605]

Bell [Broyle Rd]: Good range of beers, interesting wines, good food inc super puddings, pleasant attentive service; handy for theatre *(John Burgess)*

Park Tavern [Priory St, opp park]: Comfortably relaxing local with well kept Gales and Greene King Abbot, nice eating area specialising in hot lunchtime baguettes, also sandwiches, baked potatoes and limited cooked meals, cheerful service; attractive spot opp Priory Park *(Ann and Colin Hunt, Tony Hobden, R T and J C Moggridge)*

Chilgrove [SU8116]

☆ ***Royal Oak*** [off B2141 Petersfield—Chichester, signed Hooksway down steep hill]: Welcoming and smartly simple two-room country tavern in charming spot, beams, brick floors, country-kitchen furnishings, huge log fires; sensibly priced home-made standard food inc lunchtime ploughman's, well kept real ales such as Ballards Best and John Smiths, games, provision for children; some live music Fri in summer; tables out in pretty garden, good walks, cl Mon *(Ann and Colin Hunt, Prof and Mrs S Barnett, Mark Percy, Lesley Mayoh, J A Snell, LYM, W A Evershed)*

White Horse [off B2141, Petersfield—Chichester]: More smart restaurant than pub, good lunches (not as expensive as evening), remarkable list of outstanding wines with excellent ones by the glass, friendly landlord and punctilious service – but watch for that low beam in the pleasant bar area; idyllic downland setting with small flower-filled terrace and big pretty garden, lots of fine walks *(Martin and Karen Wake, RDK)*

Climping [TQ0001]

Black Horse: Friendly and unpretentious family-run pub, good value food from good home-made soup and huge ploughman's to vast steaks, well kept Courage Best and Directors; skittle alley, walk to beach *(JDM, KM, Tony and Wendy Hobden, Michael Sargent)*

Oystercatcher [A259/B2233]: Thatched Vintage Inn dining pub, largely no smoking and pleasantly antiqued with hops and bric-a-brac in their current popular style, friendly young well trained staff, usual food all day from sandwiches through light dishes to mixed grill, Bass and Tetleys, good choice of wines by the glass, nicely served coffee, log fires; disabled lavatories *(Tony and Wendy Hobden)*

Cocking [SU8717]

Blue Bell [A286 S of Midhurst]: Friendly village local with roaring log fires in L-shaped bar, good value food inc Thurs night bargains, well kept ales inc Batemans and Greene King, pool table in raised area on right; may be piped radio; good walks – just off South Downs Way *(Prof and Mrs S Barnett, Mark Percy, Lesley Mayoh)*

Cocking Causeway [SU8819]

Greyhound [A286 Cocking—Midhurst]: Pretty tile-hung pub with cosy olde-worlde décor – beams, old fireplaces, soft lighting by table lamps, fresh flowers, old prints, pewter pots and woodworking tools; inexpensive home cooking inc lots for children (who are well looked after), welcoming young staff, Ringwood Best; dovecote in side courtyard, picnic-sets on large lawn, play area, pets corner, aviary; open all day *(Ann and Colin Hunt, Susan and John Douglas)*

Colemans Hatch [TQ4533]

☆ ***Hatch*** [signed off B2026, or off B2110 opp church]: Quaint and attractive weatherboarded Ashdown Forest pub dating from 1430, big log fire in beamed bar, small back restaurant with another log fire, good interesting food from baked potatoes, giant ploughman's and filled ciabatta bread to bass and steak, well kept Harveys, Larkins, and one or two guest beers such as Elgoods Black Dog or Fullers London Pride, freshly pressed local apple juice, good friendly mix of customers inc families; front terrace and beautifully kept big garden *(Peter Meister, Mr and Mrs S Oxenbury, RDK, LYM, Michael and Ann Cole)*

Colgate [TQ2232]

Dragon [Forest Rd]: Cosy and unpretentious, with quick, friendly and helpful service, well kept Badger ales inc K&B, good value food inc interesting sandwiches; big garden, pleasant and secluded – good for children *(Mrs Angela Bromley-Martin, R A Watson, G T Brewster)*

Coolham [TQ1423]

☆ ***George & Dragon*** [pub signed just off A272]: Cheery local with enormous inglenook fireplace in heavy-beamed bar, unpretentious furnishings, well kept Badger ales inc K&B, enjoyable and generous home-made food from sandwiches to steak, back games room with bar billiards; fruit machine, TV, can get pretty busy; children allowed in games or eating areas, well spaced tables out in big attractive orchard garden, open all day wknds *(LYM, Theo, Anne and Jane Gaskin, Dominic Morgan, Mike and Shelley Woodroffe, Tony Beaulah, Peter Meister)*

Copthorne [TQ3239]

Cherry Tree [Copthorne Bank (pub just over Surrey border)]: Four or five friendly linked areas in rambling extended 1920s pub with two bars and dining area, Badger Best, K&B and Tanglefoot, usual food from sandwiches up *(Ian Phillips)*

Cousley Wood [TQ6533]

☆ *Old Vine* [B2100 Wadhurst—Lamberhurst]: Attractive dining pub with lots of old timbers and beams, wide range of generously served modestly priced decent food inc good fish, good house wines, four well kept ales; rustic pretty restaurant on right, pubbier bare-boards or brick-floored area with woodburner by bar; credit cards impounded if you run a bar bill; a few tables out behind *(Jason Caulkin, Ben Whitney and Pippa Redmond, Mrs Pamela Cooper, BB, Oliver and Sue Rowell)*

Cowbeech [TQ6114]

Merrie Harriers [village signed from A271]: Beamed and panelled village pub, pleasantly redecorated, with well kept Harveys Best and a guest such as King Horsham Best, inglenook fireplace with snug old-fashioned settle, food (not Mon evening) from lunchtime ploughman's to steak, children welcome in no smoking back restaurant; unobtrusive piped music; rustic seats in terraced garden *(Mrs K Batchelor, Mr and Mrs Thomas, LYM)*

Crockerhill [SU9207]

Winterton Arms [just off A27 Chichester—Fontwell]: Comfortably worn beamy old pub, with public bar and two lacy dining rooms, good fresh food, pleasant service, well kept Courage, open fire (you can see Halnaker Mill from the seat by it); white scottie called Hamish *(Val and Alan Green)*

Dallington [TQ6619]

Swan [Woods Corner, B2096 E]: Country local with enjoyable food, well kept Harveys BB and Theakstons Best, decent house wines, good coffee, candles at night in bare-boards low-beamed bar, and in simple carpeted back dining room with far views to Beachy Head; may be piped music; steps down to smallish garden *(Peter Meister, BB)*

Denton [TQ4502]

Flying Fish [Denton Rd]: Well kept 17th-c village local with hops and brassware, good reasonably priced home cooking, comfortable dining room, Shepherd Neame real ales; attractive garden behind, tables out in front too *(anon)*

Eartham [SU9409]

George [signed off A285 Chichester—Petworth, from Fontwell off A27, from Slindon off A29]: Big popular pub smartly refurbished in light wood, comfortable lounge, attractive pubbier public bar with games, old farm tools and photographs, welcoming service, enjoyable reasonably priced food, well kept Gales ales and maybe a guest beer, log fire, no smoking restaurant; piped music; children welcome in eating areas, pretty garden and surroundings, open all day summer wknds *(Mrs Jill Silversides, Barry Brown, LYM, Ann and Colin Hunt, W A Evershed)*

Easebourne [SU8922]

Olde White Horse [off A272 just NE of Midhurst]: Cosy and pleasantly refurbished, large mainly bare-boards bar with several distinct areas inc fireside armchairs and small no smoking dining area, lots of blackboards for the sensibly priced traditional food (worth booking wknds), Greene King IPA, Abbot and Old Speckled Hen; tables on back grass and in courtyard *(LYM, Ann and Colin Hunt, Tony and Wendy Hobden)*

East Grinstead [TQ3938]

Ship [Ship St (centre)]: Large open-plan Youngs pub, softly lit and partly no smoking, with armchairs as well as other furniture, good range of snacks and meals, Bitter, Special and Waggledance, friendly young staff; discreet piped music; tables out on decks stepped down behind *(Tony and Wendy Hobden, Dave Irving)*

East Lavant [SU8608]

☆ *Royal Oak* [signed off A286 N of Chichester; Pook Lane]: Dining pub with well cooked restauranty food inc good fresh fish, well kept Badger ales, country wines, good house wines, friendly service, candlelight and simple furnishings, rugs on bare boards and flooring tiles, two open fires and a woodburner, racing prints; attractively planted gardens inc secluded terrace with bookable tables (quiet exc for wknd light planes using Goodwood airfield), good walks; cl Sun pm, Mon *(Christopher and Elise Way, J A Snell, Simon and Debbie Gwynn, Ann and Colin Hunt, Debora Rolph, LYM)*

East Preston [TQ0702]

Fletcher Arms [opp station]: Half a dozen well kept ales such as Adnams Broadside, Fullers London Pride and Ringwood Best, good cheap bar food (not Sun evening) inc OAP bargains, friendly local atmosphere, some unusual bric-a-brac, local photographs, lots of events; big well kept garden with pets corner, play area and barbecues *(Bruce Bird, Tony and Wendy Hobden)*

Eastbourne [TV6198]

Buccaneer [Compton St, by Winter Gardens]: Popular open-plan bar shaped like a galleon, raised no smoking side, Ind Coope Burton, Marstons Pedigree, Tetleys and three guest beers, theatre memorabilia; no food Sun, open all day *(the Didler)*

☆ *Lamb* [High St]: Two main heavily beamed traditional bars off pretty Tudor pub's central servery, spotless antique furnishings (but not too smart), good inglenook log fire, well kept Harveys ales, friendly polite service, good generous fair-priced choice from well organised food bar, upstairs dining room (Sun lunch), no music or machines; dogs seem welcome, children allowed in very modernised side room; by ornate church away from seafront, popular with students evenings *(Pam Adsley)*

Marine [Seaside]: Comfortable pub near seafront, tub chairs, sofas and banquettes in front, good choice of beers inc Harveys, generous enjoyable food in main bar and back no smoking conservatory *(David and Carole Chapman)*

Elsted [SU8119]

Elsted Inn [Elsted Marsh]: Unpretentious country pub with two small bars, nice country furniture, wooden floors, original shutters, old railway photographs, traditional games, well kept ales such as Ballards, Cheriton Pots and Timothy Taylors Landlord, log fires; lovely enclosed downs-view garden with big terrace and summer barbecues, well appointed adjacent bedroom block *(Pat and Tony Martin, LYM, Peter Meister, John Mitchell, Christopher and Elise Way, Bob and Valerie Mawson, W A Evershed)*

Eridge Station [TQ5434]

☆ ***Huntsman***: Unpretentious pub popular for limited choice of surprisingly good enterprising home-made food, reasonable prices, friendly service, well kept Badger beers, some interesting wines, farm cider; walkers and their dogs welcome *(Ken Arthur, RDK)*

Fairlight Cove [TQ8712]

Cove Continental [Waites Lane]: Friendly, with well kept local beers inc Pett Progress, enjoyable lunches *(Glenn and Louise Hamilton)*

Fairwarp [TQ4626]

☆ ***Foresters Arms*** [B2026]: Cheerful Ashdown Forest local handy for Vanguard Way and Weald Way, comfortable lounge bar, well kept Badger ales and farm cider, food from baguettes to steak and popular Sunday lunch, efficient service, woodburner; piped music; children in eating area, tables out on terrace and in garden with some interesting plants, open all day summer, may cl Sun evening or Mon *(RDK, R J Walden, G T Brewster, LYM)*

Faygate [TQ2134]

Frog & Nightgown [Wimland Rd, off A264 just NE of Horsham]: Delightfully unchanged single-room local deep in the country, relaxed and old-fashioned but clean and comfortable, with well kept Fullers London Pride, Harveys and a guest beer, friendly staff and dog, good fire, bird prints, lots of frog models, sofa and chaise-longue; no food, some live music; seats in big quiet garden, nice scenery *(R A Watson, C and R Bromage, Carla Francis)*

Felpham [SZ9599]

Thatched House [Limmer Lane]: Local with good value home-made food, well kept Gales, nice service, pool in public bar, pleasant smaller lounge *(R T and J C Moggridge, JDM, KM)*

Fernhurst [SU8926]

Kings Arms [A286 towards Midhurst]: Refined and attractive 17th-c dining pub in pleasant setting, low beams, open fires, dark oak settles and heavy dining tables, daily papers and good choice of ales such as Arundel, Hogs Back and Ventnor in front bar, two linked eating areas (one no smoking), good interesting meals inc enterprising fresh fish dishes, decent wines, faultless service; small car park *(Martin and Karen Wake, Tony and Wendy Hobden)*

☆ ***Red Lion*** [The Green; off A286, 3 miles S of Haslemere]: Heavy-beamed old pub tucked quietly away by green near church, friendly staff, good value food inc interesting sandwiches and specials, attractive layout and furnishings, well kept real ales from local breweries, good wines, no smoking area, good relaxed atmosphere; children welcome, pretty garden *(Graham Godden, BB, Godfrey and Irene Joly)*

Ferring [TQ0902]

Tudor Close [Ferringham Lane, S Ferring]: Thatched former barn, imposing intricately carved fireplace, ornate lamp stands, high rafters, no smoking restaurant end and upper gallery overlooking bar the other end, some emphasis on good choice of enjoyable reasonably priced home-made food (not Sun evening or Mon) and very popular for this with older people at lunchtime; well kept Courage, Gales BB and Wadworths 6X, good-natured helpful service, no piped music; peaceful seats outside *(Michael and Ann Cole, Keith and Suzie Stevens)*

Findon [TQ1208]

☆ ***Gun*** [High St]: Civilised and pleasantly renovated low-beamed village pub, traditional main bar, large pine-floored part no smoking dining area, good attractively presented food from lunchtime sandwiches to modern light and main dishes, quick service, well kept Adnams, Fullers London Pride, Gales HSB and Harveys BB, range of foreign beers; attractive sheltered lawn, pretty village in horse-training country below Cissbury Ring *(Avril Burton, LYM, Tony Hobden)*

Firle [TQ4607]

☆ ***Ram*** [village signed off A27 Lewes—Polegate]: Unpretentious and comfortably worn 17th-c village pub, very welcoming to families and booted walkers; log fires, traditional games, no smoking snug, well kept Bass, Harveys Best and Youngs Special, farm cider, usual food (all day) from baguettes and baked potatoes up, with three sizes of children's meals and cream teas; tables and play equipment in walled garden behind, open all day *(LYM, Kevin Thorpe, the Didler)*

Fishbourne [SU8404]

Bulls Head [Fishbourne Rd (A259 Chichester—Emsworth)]: Interesting, relaxing and welcoming old building with pretty window boxes, fair-sized main bar, full Gales range kept well, unusual guest beers, good varied food often using local produce (not Sun evening), quick friendly service, log fire, no smoking area, children's area, restaurant; skittle alley, boules pitch *(Ann and Colin Hunt, J A Snell, Mrs Jane Basso)*

Fittleworth [TQ0118]

☆ ***Swan*** [Lower St]: Prettily placed 14th-c inn with big inglenook log fire in unpretentious low-beamed lounge well used by locals at night, good enterprising home-made food in attractive beamed and panelled dining room with landscapes by Constable's deservedly less-known brother George, well kept Badger K&B, Fullers London Pride and Wadworths 6X, friendly attentive service; piped music, games inc pool in public bar; well spaced tables on big sheltered back lawn, good walks nearby; children in eating area, comfortable bedrooms, open all day Thurs-Sat *(LYM, John Beeken, Mrs M Alderton, Mike and Heather Watson, Julie and Bill Ryan)*

Frant [TQ5835]

Abergavenny Arms [A267 S of T Wells]: Good-sized mock-Tudor main-road pub, friendly and comfortably well worn, with two bars, particularly well kept Fullers London Pride, Harveys Best, Rother Valley Level Best, Timothy Taylors Landlord and a guest such as Cottage Christmas Cracker; usually a wide choice of reasonably priced popular food from ploughman's and baked potatoes up; log fire, bar billiards, children welcome *(Val and Alan Green, Peter Meister, Ian Phillips)*

☆ ***George*** [High St, off A267]: Tucked down charming quiet lane by ancient church and cottages, convivial bar with several rooms rambling round servery, low ceiling, mix of seats inc pews, high-backed settles and sofa, coal-effect gas fire in big inglenook, enjoyable traditional food, well kept real ales, lots of wines by the glass, good coffee, darts in public bar; busy wknds, pleasant restaurant, picnic-sets in walled garden *(BB)*

Fulking [TQ2411]

☆ ***Shepherd & Dog*** [off A281 B of Brighton, via Poynings]: Charming partly panelled country pub beautifully placed below downs, antique or stoutly rustic furnishings around log fire, attractive bow windows, well kept Badger ales, wide food choice (all day wknds) from sandwiches and baked potatoes up inc lots of ploughman's and summer salads, no piped music; can be packed out (when service and amenities may suffer); dogs and children welcome, pretty streamside garden with upper play lawn (loudspeaker food announcements out here), open all day *(Mrs M Thomas, LYM, Dr M Mills, Lady Muir, Kevin Blake)*

Funtington [SU7908]

Fox & Hounds: Extensively refurbished beamed pub with vast choice of food inc choice of good Sun roasts, cottagey rooms, comfortable and attractive dining extension, welcoming service, real ales inc Badger Tanglefoot, reasonably priced wines, good coffee, huge log fire, no music; garden behind *(Peter and Audrey Dowsett)*

Glynde [TQ4508]

Trevor Arms: Well kept Harveys PA, BB and Copper, good range of food inc bargain soup, small bar with corridor to no smoking areas and dining room, Glyndebourne posters and photographs; tables in large garden with downland backdrop – busy wknds *(John Beeken)*

Goddards Green [TQ2820]

Sportsman: Emphasis on enjoyable generous food from open sandwiches and baked potatoes up, no smoking restaurant and second pubbier eating area, waitress service, Badger real ales *(Tony and Wendy Hobden)*

Graffham [SU9217]

☆ ***White Horse***: Friendly licensees doing good food in spotless family pub, well kept Badger Best and Tanglefoot, log fires, good South Downs views from conservatory, small dining room, terrace and big garden; walkers welcome, open all day Sun in summer *(Mr and Mrs H Dabinett, John and Pat Horne, Ann and Colin Hunt, Mrs C Powell, J A Snell)*

Halnaker [SU9008]

☆ ***Anglesey Arms*** [A285 Chichester—Petworth]: Welcoming service and quickly cooked genuine food esp steaks and fish in unpretentious bar with traditional games, well kept real ales, good wines (some direct Spanish imports); simple but smart candlelit dining room with stripped pine and flagstones (children allowed), tables in garden *(Ann and Colin Hunt, LYM, John Davis)*

Handcross [TQ2328]

Wheatsheaf [B2110 W]: Badger real ales, good range of good food from sandwiches to steaks inc children's, pleasant staff, lots of horse tack, no smoking dining area; big garden with play equipment *(Ian and Joan Blackwell)*

Hassocks [TQ3015]

Pilgrims Goose [A273 N]: Several welcoming areas, log fires, decent food, good choice of wines; pleasant garden *(Pamela Goodwyn)*

Hastings [TQ8209]

☆ ***First In Last Out*** [High St, Old Town]: Congenial and chatty beer-drinkers' pub – even the cat is a character, holding his central armchair against all comers; open-plan bar attractively divided by settles, pews forming booths, posts and central raised log fire, reasonably priced Crofters and Cardinal brewed in their own recently upgraded microbrewery, or their summer Blighs and perhaps an organic beer, with a couple of guest ales, farm cider, friendly landlord, no games or juke box; interesting simple lunchtime food, free Sun cockles; small covered back terrace, parking nearby difficult *(Peter Meister)*

☆ ***Stag*** [All Saints St]: Early 17th-c former smugglers' pub among crooked Tudor buildings on high pavement (up a few steps), low beams, bare boards, stout furniture, lots of pictures, no frills; well kept Shepherd Neame ales, plenty of malt whiskies, friendly long-serving staff, some fascinating stories; wknd bar food inc occasional bargain barbecues, folk nights Weds, steeply terraced garden behind *(the Didler, Hazel and Michael Duncombe, Kevin Blake)*

Henfield [TQ2115]

☆ ***George*** [High St]: Friendly and roomy former coaching inn, beams and open fires, a good family pub and locally popular for good choice of generous reasonably priced bar food, well kept ales; restaurant *(David Cosham)*

White Hart [High St (A281)]: 16th-c village pub with interesting tiled roof, comfortable L-shaped lounge and big no smoking area, lots of panelling, tools hanging from low beams, horsebrasses, paintings, prints, photographs and fresh flowers, log fire, large dining area popular with well heeled older folk for good choice of home-cooked food inc tempting puddings, hard-working licensees, friendly efficient service, well kept Badger, Harveys Best and Shepherd Neame, decent wines with choice of glass sizes; children welcome, garden with terrace and play area *(Terry Buckland, Ron Shelton)*

Hermitage [SU7505]

☆ ***Sussex Brewery*** [A259, by Thorney Island turn]: Thriving stripped-brick bar with sawdust and bare boards, immense log fire and flagstoned alcove (this bit food-free Fri/Sat night), well kept Youngs (full range, perhaps with a guest such as Smiles), incredible range of sausages, cheerful young staff, no smoking red plush dining room up a few steps, no machines or piped music; can get crowded; small walled garden, open all day *(Ann and Colin Hunt, David H T Dimock, Bruce Bird)*

Herstmonceux [TQ6312]

Welcome Stranger [Church Rd]: Unspoilt single-room pub in same family for nearly a century, well kept Harveys Bitter and Old and a guest beer from small serving hatch; cl wkdy lunchtimes *(the Didler, Phil and Sally Gorton)*

Heyshott [SU8918]

Unicorn [off A286 S of Midhurst]: Very friendly small country local prettily placed by village green, well kept Ballards Best, Bass and a beer brewed for the pub, good interesting generous bar food, cheerful service even when busy, attractive dining area; children allowed, reasonable disabled access, garden with barbecue, handy for South Downs Way *(Francis Johnston, J A Snell, Ann and Colin Hunt)*

Hooe [TQ6809]

☆ ***Lamb*** [A259 E of Pevensey]: Prettily placed Vintage Inn, extensively refurbished with some character and charm, arches and lots of stripped brick and flintwork, one snug area around huge log fire and lots of other seats, big tables, very wide choice of generous popular food inc good sandwiches and baguette range, children's dishes, well kept Bass and Harveys, good range of house wines, quick friendly service *(Michael and Ann Cole, Gill and Keith Croxton)*

Red Lion: Attractive old tiled local behind screen of pollarded lime trees, interesting outbuildings, Fullers London Pride and Harveys, attractively priced food from baguettes to steak, a cheerful welcome for visitors *(Ian Phillips)*

Horsham [TQ1829]

Hornbrook [Brighton Rd (A281)]: Friendly pub with large no smoking restaurant, plenty of choice inc for children, log fires; big back garden with adventure playground *(Gemma Warren)*

Horsted Keynes [TQ3828]

Crown [The Green]: Comfortable congenial local, huge fire, well kept beer, helpful landlord, good reasonably priced food, attractive dining room; children welcome, tables out among pretty flowers in front, and behind looking over cricket green *(Pam Adsley, Mrs V Brown, Michael and Ann Cole, Martin and Jane Wright)*

Green Man [The Green]: Traditional village inn in attractive spot facing green, spotless but not too modernised, with bare boards and hop bines, cheerful welcoming staff, well kept Greene King IPA and Abbot and Harveys BB, good value generous home-made food from ploughman's and baguettes to restaurant dishes, bistro dining room; lots of plastic tables on forecourt, handy for Bluebell Line *(J P Humphery, Tony and Wendy Hobden)*

Station Buffet: Traditional buffet bar on Bluebell Line, well kept Harveys Best, good value food inc Cornish pasties *(the Didler)*

Jevington [TQ5601]

☆ ***Eight Bells***: Busy and neatly kept two-bar pub, good welcoming service, wide choice of good value generous home-made food from ploughman's up inc good home-made pies, well kept Adnams Broadside, Flowers Original and Harveys Best, panelling, brasses, wood and tiled floors; quiet piped music; tables under cocktail parasols on front terrace, large attractive downs-view garden, lovely village, outstanding area for walking (walkers welcome), South Downs Way, Weald Way and 1066 Trail all nearby *(Bruce Bird, Pam Adsley, John Beeken, Catherine and Richard Preston)*

Johns Cross [TQ7421]

Johns Cross Inn [A21/A2100 Battle Rd]: Friendly and unpretentious, with gentle atmosphere, Adnams and Greene King (in winter landlord mulls it with a red-hot poker), wholesome food inc interesting specials, one dining room with just a single table – plenty of room elsewhere; roadside, with good views *(E G Parish)*

Kingston Near Lewes [TQ3908]

Juggs [village signed off A27 by roundabout W of Lewes]: Quaint old rose-covered cottage with interesting furnishings, layout and décor, nice seating areas outside; new regime, with well kept Shepherd Neame ales, bar food from ploughman's and baked potatoes up, no smoking family room, log fires, dominoes and shove-ha'penny; compact well equipped play area *(Ian Phillips, Ann and Colin Hunt, Michael and Ann Cole, LYM)*

Kirdford [TQ0126]

Foresters Arms: Well run flagstoned bar, lounge and family room, well kept Badger ales, friendly licensees, limited choice of simple but genuinely home-cooked bar food, quick service, restaurant; boules pitches *(C L Kauffmann)*

☆ ***Half Moon*** [opp church, off A272 Petworth—Billingshurst]: After a spell as a Thai restaurant, this prettily set 17th-c beamed and tile-hung cottage has reverted under new owners to good interesting British cooking – still more bar/restaurant than pub, but nice, with Fullers London Pride and Youngs Special from the curved counter in the partly quarry-tiled bar, a log fire in the immaculate roomy and rambling low-beamed dining area, good wines by the glass, and friendly attentive service; tables in pretty back garden and out in front *(John*

Beeken, LYM, Nicholas and Dorothy Stephens, Derek Thomas)

Laughton [TQ5013]

Roebuck [Lewes Rd]: Simple and welcoming, with short choice of good well prepared food *(E F Given)*

Lavant [SU8508]

Earl of March [A286, Mid Lavant]: Roomy village pub very popular lunchtime for cheap generous food from sandwiches up, well kept Ballards Best, Cottage Garden, Ringwood Old Thumper and guests such as Otter Bright, Weston's Old Rosie cider, no smoking area by servery, naval memorabilia, bric-a-brac and prints, games and puzzles, no piped music; children and dogs welcome, live music Thurs; good views from garden, good local walks – handy for Centurion Way cycle path *(Tony and Wendy Hobden, Ann and Colin Hunt, Bruce Bird)*

Lewes [TQ4110]

Black Horse [Western Rd]: Nice two-bar local with well kept Harveys and other ales such as Brakspears, Fullers and Wadworths 6X, bar food, friendly service *(the Didler)*

Brewers Arms [High St]: Smartly kept pub dating from 1540, back lounge bar, good choice of attractively priced food, well kept Arundel, Cottage, Harveys and Welton real ales, games room, list of landlords since 1744 in public bar *(the Didler, Tony and Wendy Hobden)*

Gardeners Arms [Cliffe High St]: Traditional small local, light, airy and quiet, with well kept Harveys and four or more changing real ales such as Exmoor, good value lunchtime sandwiches and ploughman's, good friendly service (with helpful opinions on the ales), plain scrubbed tables on bare boards around three sides of bar, daily papers and magazines, Sun bar nibbles *(Pat and Tony Martin, Ian Arthur, MLR)*

John Harvey [Harveys Brewery, Cliffe High St]: Reopened summer 2002 after flood repairs, tap for adjoining Harveys brewery, all their beers inc seasonal kept perfectly and tapped from the cask, nice lunchtime snacks and light evening meals in upstairs restaurant, innovative without being pretentious, interestingly different crisps *(Anne and Tim Locke)*

☆ ***Lewes Arms*** [Castle Ditch Lane/Mount Pl – tucked behind castle ruins]: Charming unpretentious corner local built into castle mound, small front bar with larger lounge, eating area off, and hatchway, particularly well kept Harveys and Greene King Abbot, good orange juice, very reasonably priced simple but unusual lunchtime food inc good baguettes, friendly service, daily papers, local pictures, toad in the hole, no music – great place for conversation; comically small upper terrace, so people migrate to pavement and street *(Colin and Janet Roe, MLR, John Beeken, Anne and Tim Locke, Kevin Flack)*

Royal Oak [Station St]: Ancient building, one largish room, Greene King IPA, Abbot and Old Speckled Hen and Harveys, good value straightforward lunchtime food (till 5 wknds); fruit machine; tables out in back courtyard *(Tony and Wendy Hobden)*

Litlington [TQ5201]

☆ ***Plough & Harrow*** [between A27 Lewes—Polegate and A259 E of Seaford]: Spotless and attractively extended flint pub with cosy beamed front bar and dining area done up as railway dining car (children allowed here), good home cooking, quick friendly service, well kept ales such as Badger Best and Tanglefoot, Hardys & Hansons and Harveys BB, decent wines by the glass; back lawn with children's bar, aviary and pretty views; has had live music Fri *(Michael and Ann Cole, S J Barney, Peter Meister, LYM, RDK)*

Littlehampton [TQ0202]

☆ ***Arun View*** [Wharf Rd; W towards Chichester, opp railway station]: Roomy and comfortable 18th-c inn in lovely spot right on harbour with river directly below windows, well kept ales such as Badger K&B, Ringwood Old Thumper and Youngs Special, good wine list, diligent friendly and helpful service, interesting menu, flagstoned back bar with lots of drawings and caricatures, large eating area and flower-filled terrace both overlooking busy waterway and pedestrian bridge; summer barbecues evenings and wknds, bright and modest good value bedrooms *(Miss J F Reay, Hazel and Michael Duncombe, A H Ross, Cannell Benmore)*

Littleworth [TQ1920]

☆ ***Windmill*** [pub sign on B2135; village signed off A272 southbound, W of Cowfold]: Small spotless local with log fires in compact but cosy beamed lounge and panelled flagstoned public bar; simple but enjoyable sensibly priced food (not Sun eve winter) inc interesting specials, well kept Badger beers, welcoming helpful landlord (can arrange monastery tours), good service, bric-a-brac large and small inside and out, darts, dominoes, cards and bar billiards, no music; children welcome, peaceful and attractive side garden *(Bruce Bird, C and R Bromage)*

Loxwood [TQ0431]

Onslow Arms [B2133 NW of Billingshurst]: Well refurbished local with lively and friendly young staff, well kept Badger Best, K&B and Tanglefoot, good house wines, plenty of coffees and teas, lovely old log fireplaces, generous food, discreetly placed pin table; dogs welcome, picnic-sets in good-sized pleasant garden sloping to river and nearby newly restored Wey & Arun Canal, good walks and boat trips *(Tony and Wendy Hobden, Ian Phillips)*

Lyminster [TQ0204]

Six Bells: Flint-faced dining pub with good-sized helpings of unusual and enjoyable elegantly presented food, helpful courteous staff, well kept Greene King Abbot and Youngs Special; best to book at wknds *(R T and J C Moggridge, Alison Crooks, Dave Heffernan)*

Maplehurst [TQ1924]

White Horse [Park Lane]: Quiet beamed country local, beautiful wisteria in front, four seating areas inc sun lounge (no smoking at lunchtime), well kept Harveys BB, Weltons

Dorking Pride and changing guest beers from small breweries, farm cider, good value food, efficient staff, no music or machines; children welcome, pleasant garden, car enthusiasts' evenings *(Bruce Bird)*

Mayfield [TQ5827]

☆ ***Middle House*** [High St]: Handsome 16th-c timbered inn in pretty village, L-shaped beamed locals' bar with massive fireplace, well kept Adnams, Fullers London Pride, Greene King Abbot, Harveys BB and a guest beer, local cider, decent wines, quiet lounge with leather chesterfields around log fire in ornate carved fireplace, generous popular food, panelled no smoking restaurant; piped music; afternoon tea in terraced back garden with lovely views, slide and play house; children welcome, open all day *(R M Warner, John Saul, LYM, Sue White, Michael and Ann Cole)*

☆ ***Rose & Crown*** [Fletching St]: Pretty weather-boarded old inn, experienced new licensees doing enjoyable fresh food with some emphasis on fish, cosy little low-beamed front rooms, big inglenook, well kept Greene King Abbot and Old Speckled Hen and Harveys Best, friendly staff, shove-ha'penny Mon and Fri; piped music; children welcome, four attractive bedrooms, tables outside; open all day Sat *(LYM, J Graveling)*

Midhurst [SU8821]

Bricklayers Arms [Wool Lane/West St]: Warm welcome in two cosy and relaxing olde-worlde bars, good local atmosphere, good value generous home-made food inc Sun roast, well kept Greene King IPA and Abbot, quick and friendly helpful service, sturdy old oak furniture, 17th-c beams, old photographs and bric-a-brac *(Ann and Colin Hunt)*

Royal Oak [West Lavington; A286 towards Chichester]: Fine garden spreading around old-world pub with good staff, two superb log fires, one in a big inglenook, some ancient stripped masonry, real ales, bar food inc Sun lunches and children's dishes *(Ann and Colin Hunt, LYM)*

Wheatsheaf [Wool Lane/A272]: Attractive and relaxing low-beamed and timbered 16th-c local with good value generous food inc good sandwich choice, very friendly staff, well kept Badger and Ballards beers; open all day *(Ann and Colin Hunt)*

Newhaven [TQ4500]

☆ ***Hope*** [follow West Beach signs from A259 westbound]: Big-windowed pub overlooking busy harbour entrance, settles forming booths in long bar, upstairs conservatory room and breezy balcony tables with even better view towards Seaford Head, well kept Flowers IPA, Fullers London Pride and Harveys BB, simple food from baked potatoes up inc children's, decent wines, reasonable prices, unfussy décor with some nautical touches, friendly efficient staff; unobtrusive piped music, darts and pool in airy public bar; waterside terrace *(John Beeken, LYM)*

Nutbourne [SU7805]

Barleycorn [A259 W of Chichester]: Unpretentious open-plan pub with reasonably priced food and Bass ales *(J A Snell)*

Nuthurst [TQ1926]

☆ ***Black Horse*** [off A281 SE of Horsham]: Black-beamed country pub with flagstones and inglenook, well kept Arundel Gold, Fullers London Pride and Harveys Best, no smoking snug and restaurant (children allowed); jazz last Sun of month, may be piped music; attractive woodland streamside back garden, more seats on front terrace, open all day Fri-Sun in summer *(LYM, Guy Vowles, Roger and Debbie Stamp, Lisa Moore)*

Pagham [SZ8998]

Lamb: Rambling period building with good well priced food, well kept Greene King Abbot and pleasant service *(R T and J C Moggridge)*

Partridge Green [TQ1919]

Green Man [Jolesfield]: Good well presented food with Mediterranean influence inc unusual tapas-style starters in attractive bar and restaurant (more restaurant than pub), good-sized helpings, cheerful and helpful young staff, stripped pine tables, wood floors; children welcome, garden *(Mrs J Wild, J D M Rushworth, R D Henshaw)*

Petworth [SU9721]

☆ ***Well Diggers*** [Low Heath; A283 towards Pulborough]: Picturesquely cluttered low-ceilinged stripped stone bar almost a museum of the rural 1920s, long tables in stylishly simple dining room, very good if not cheap food esp fish using fresh ingredients, character friendly landlord, well kept Ballards and Youngs, decent wines, no music or machines; plenty of tables on attractive lawns and terraces, lovely views *(C L Kauffmann, Patrick Hall, LYM, John Davis)*

Playden [TQ9121]

Peace & Plenty [A268/B2082]: Unpretentious pub with emphasis on food all day in two dining areas off attractive small bar, open woodburner in big inglenook, well kept Greene King IPA, Abbot and Triumph, good coffee, friendly cat; children allowed, tables in pretty garden (some traffic noise), open all day *(Keith and Chris O'Neill, Paul and Penny Rampton, John and Elspeth Howell, LYM)*

Plumpton [TQ3613]

Half Moon [Ditchling Rd (B2116)]: Down-to-earth pub with welcoming new licensees, interestingly decorated long bar, sensibly priced food here and in no smoking dining room, good log fire with unusual flint chimney-breast, prompt service, Harveys BB; games room, well behaved children welcome, tables in courtyard and big garden with Downs view and play area, good walks *(Tony and Wendy Hobden, RDK)*

Poynings [TQ2612]

Royal Oak [The Street]: Well kept Courage Directors, Greene King Old Speckled Hen and Harveys, decent generous food from sandwiches and baked potatoes to fish, quick service, large beamed bar around three-sided servery, no smoking area, fox masks and woodburner; big attractive garden with barbecue, play area and country/downs views *(John Beeken, Ian Phillips)*

Ringmer [TQ4412]

☆ ***Cock*** [Uckfield Rd – blocked-off section of rd

off A26 N of village turn-off]: Very welcoming country pub, heavy 16th-c beams and flagstones in main bar with big inglenook log fire, pleasant modernised rooms off inc no smoking lounge, back restaurant, huge good value blackboard food choice, well kept Courage Directors, Fullers London Pride and Harveys Best and a seasonal beer, good friendly service, lovely flower arrangements; children allowed in overflow eating area; quiet piped music; tables on small terrace and in big sloping fairy-lit garden with shrubs, fruit trees and lots of spring flowers *(Michael and Ann Cole, Martin and Jane Wright, Lucien, Tony and Wendy Hobden, LYM, Alan Miller, Peter Meister)*

Ripe [TQ5010]

☆ ***Lamb*** [signed off A22 Uckfield—Hailsham, or off A27 Lewes—Polegate via Chalvington; Church Lane]: Interestingly furnished partly panelled rooms around central servery, masses of attractive antique prints and pictures, nostalgic song-sheet covers, automotive memorabilia, Victorian pin-ups in gents'; sound choice of generous home-made food from sandwiches and baked potatoes to some imaginative dishes (Mexican night Fri), children's menu, friendly efficient staff, changing well kept ales such as Harveys BB, Wychwood Dirty Tackle and Youngs, good range of reasonably priced wines, several open fires; pool room, TV; pleasant sheltered back garden with play area and barbecues *(BB, John Beeken, Kevin Thorpe)*

Robertsbridge [TQ7323]

Ostrich [Station Rd]: Cheerful well refurbished former station hotel, enjoyable food, Adnams, Harveys BB and a guest beer, games room; tables in attractive garden, bedrooms *(the Didler)*

Rotherfield [TQ5529]

Kings Arms [High St]: Popular for generous lunches – best to book for Sun *(Roger Bridgeman, Jason Caulkin)*

Rowhook [TQ1234]

☆ ***Chequers*** [off A29 NW of Horsham]: Attractive 16th-c pub, unpretentious beamed and flagstoned front bar with inglenook fire, step up to low-ceilinged lounge, well kept Badger ales, good wine choice, traditional games, home-made food from baguettes and baked potatoes up inc children's and great Sun lunch, restaurant; piped music, may be live Sun lunchtime; children and dogs welcome, tables out on terraces and in pretty garden with good play area, attractive surroundings *(LYM, Dr P E Gower, David and Elizabeth Briggs)*

Rudgwick [TQ0833]

Kings Head [Church St]: Attractively refurbished local with wide choice of good value lunchtime food inc blackboard specials, good separate evening Thai restaurant, pleasant staff, well kept Fullers London Pride, Harveys, King & Barnes and Wadworths 6X; by fine old church in pretty village *(Stephen S Goodchild, Mr and Mrs A P Lawrence)*

Wheatsheaf [Ellens Green (B2128 N)]: Enjoyable fresh food, considerate service *(Mrs J A Uthwatt)*

Runcton [SU8900]

Royal Oak [Pagham Rd, S]: Very popular, with particularly good sizzling steak and mixed grill; well kept Gales HSB, welcoming landlord *(Eric Block)*

Rusper [TQ2037]

Plough [signed from A24 and A264 N and NE of Horsham]: Padded very low beams, panelling and big inglenook, huge range of good value food, quick pleasant service, well kept real ales, lovely log fire, stylish dining area, bar billiards and darts in raftered room upstairs; fountain in back garden, pretty front terrace, occasional live music; children welcome *(LYM)*

Rye [TQ9220]

Hare & Hounds [Rye Foreign, A268]: Reorganised by new licensees, home cooking inc Sun lunch, three areas inc no smoking eating area behind standing timbers, large open fireplace, Courage and Harveys; bedrooms in converted barn, also field for camping *(Paul and Penny Rampton)*

Olde Standard [High St]: Welcoming and interesting cosy local with lots of beams and stripped brick, well kept beers inc local Sussex Pett Progress, good value generous food, darts, log-effect gas fire; piped music; open all day *(Steve Dark, Kevin Thorpe, Keith and Chris O'Neill)*

Union [East St]: Attractive old place, beams and cabinets filled with Civil War memorabilia inc weaponry, Bass and Harveys – but signs reserve the tables for people eating the well cooked food (very wide choice, even crocodile and springbok); good wines, children welcome *(Paul and Penny Rampton, Kevin Thorpe)*

☆ ***Ypres Castle*** [Gun Garden; steps up from A259, or down past Ypres Tower]: Traditional local gently refurbished by new landlord, with simple no smoking dining room, well kept Harveys, decent wines, limited choice of home-made food from baked potatoes to local fish, cheerful civilised service, traditional games; may be piped music; children welcome, fine views from picnic-sets on sizeable lawn, open all day *(Gill and Tony Morriss, C F D Moore, Kevin Thorpe, Colin and Janet Roe, LYM, Derek Harvey-Piper, Gwyn Jones, John Davis, David and Elizabeth Briggs)*

Rye Harbour [TQ9220]

☆ ***Inkerman Arms***: Friendly and cosy unpretentious local near nature reserve, particularly good food inc lots of fresh local fish, fine home-made pies and old-fashioned puddings, well kept ales such as Adnams Broadside, Golden Hill Exmoor Gold, Greene King Abbot and Rother Valley Level Best, pleasantly decorated main bar with secluded eating areas; tables in small garden; cl Sun/Mon evenings *(John Beeken, Gill and Tony Morriss)*

Seaford [TV4899]

Cinque Ports [High St]: Friendly town local, well kept real ales, reasonably priced food even in the evening from snacks to fresh fish and seafood *(MLR)*

White Lion [Claremont Rd]: Good range of good value food in bar and evening restaurant, well kept Fullers London Pride and Harveys, no smoking conservatory; pool, may be piped music or juke box; bedrooms, open all day *(Paul A Moore)*

Selham [SU9320]

Three Moles: Small old-fashioned pub tucked away in woodland village, quietly relaxing atmosphere, friendly landlady and cat, well kept Ballards Mild, Skinners Betty Stogs and guest beers from small breweries, daily papers, bar billiards, plenty of board games, no mobile phones; no food or children, monthly singsongs, occasional beer festivals; nice walks, open all day wknds *(Bruce Bird, Nicholas Pope)*

Selsey [SZ8692]

Lifeboat [Albion Rd]: Traditional unpretentious bar with dining extension and tables out on big terrace, wide choice of good value food from sandwiches to local crab salad, Courage Directors, Fullers London Pride and Wadworths 6X, friendly helpful staff *(J A Snell, Tony and Wendy Hobden)*

Sheffield Park [TQ4023]

Bessemer Arms [Sheffield Park Station]: Pub and café on Bluebell steam railway platform, Gales HSB and Harveys Best, simple food; open only on train days, 10-5 *(Joan and Michel Hooper-Immins)*

Shoreham-by-Sea [TQ2005]

Fly Inn [signed off A27, A259]: Not a pub, but this small bar in 1930s Art Deco airport building has well kept changing ales such as Greene King IPA, Harveys BB and Morrells Oxford Blue, enjoyable bar food inc children's at attractive prices, a congenial and relaxed atmosphere, and friendly obliging staff; terrace tables, uninterrupted views all round (downs views, plenty of light aircraft action); children welcome, small airport museum *(John Beeken)*

Marlipins [High St]: Civilised and old-fashioned pub next to local museum, planked ceilings giving nautical feel, bric-a-brac, old local photographs, particularly friendly and helpful landlord and staff, good choice of tasty bar food, well kept beers such as Bass, Flowers Original, Fullers London Pride and Harveys BB, pleasant conservatory restaurant; piped music, can get busy wknds; back terrace *(John Beeken)*

☆ ***Red Lion*** [Upper Shoreham Rd, opp church]: Modest dim-lit low-beamed and timbered 16th-c pub with settles in snug alcoves, good value well presented individual food, changing ales such as Morrells Varsity and Oxford Blue and RCH Pitchfork, post-Easter beer festival, decent wines, farm cider, friendly efficient staff, log fire in unusual fireplace, another open fire in no smoking dining room; piped music may obtrude; pretty sheltered garden, good downs views and walks *(Tracey and Stephen Groves, John Beeken, Bruce Bird)*

Shortbridge [TQ4521]

☆ ***Peacock*** [Piltdown; OS Sheet 198 map ref 450215]: Comfortable and welcoming rebuilt beamed and timbered bar, big inglenook, very generous nicely presented bar food served piping hot inc good fish (they've added a 10% service charge), well kept Harveys and Wadworths 6X, friendly staff, restaurant; piped music (they will turn it down), children may be much in evidence; sizeable garden *(Michael and Ann Cole, BB, Michael Hasslacher, RDK)*

Sidlesham [SZ8697]

☆ ***Crab & Lobster*** [Mill Lane; off B2145 S of Chichester]: Individualistic old country local, log fire in chatty traditional bar, no smoking plusher side dining lounge, pretty back garden looking over to the bird-reserve of silted Pagham Harbour; limited choice of good food (not Sun evening, starts 7 other evenings) inc fresh seafood, reasonable prices, well kept Gales and guest beers, decent wines, country wines, log fire, traditional games; dogs welcome, no children, music or machines *(E Prince, Gordon Neighbour, Tracey and Stephen Groves, Pamela Goodwyn, LYM, Veronica Brown)*

Slindon [SU9708]

Newburgh Arms [School Hill]: Congenial, comfortable and relaxed beamed bar, very welcoming landlady, well cared for furnishings, big log fire, sizeable dining area with rows of tables, enjoyable food, interesting specials, carefully bought meat and nice choice of home-made puddings, well kept Badger Best, lots of country wines, friendly service; piped music; good area for downs walks, pretty hanging baskets in summer *(Gill and Keith Croxton, David Cosham, Ian and Joan Blackwell)*

☆ ***Spur*** [Slindon Common; A29 towards Bognor]: Popular, roomy and attractive 17th-c pub, welcoming atmosphere, two big log fires, pine tables, good choice of interesting good value food changing daily, well kept Courage Directors and Greene King Ruddles, cheerful efficient staff, large elegant restaurant, children welcome; games room with darts and pool (for over-18s), friendly dogs; pretty garden *(Ann and Colin Hunt, Mrs Sally Kingsbury)*

Sompting [TQ1605]

Gardeners Arms [West St]: Handy and friendly stop just off main coast road (the famous Saxon church is unfortunately on the far side of the dual carriageway), generous good value lunches, Badger real ales, railway-carriage restaurant; bedrooms *(Veronica Brown)*

South Harting [SU7819]

Ship [North Lane (B2146)]: Welcoming unpretentious17th-c local, informal and unspoilt, with dimly lit bar, roaring log fire, old photographs, well kept real ales, good choice of good value food from sandwiches up, friendly staff and dogs, simpler public bar (dominoes, perhaps chestnuts to roast by its log fire); unobtrusive piped music; nice setting in pretty village *(Ann and Colin Hunt, John Evans, W A Evershed)*

St Leonards [TQ7808]

Bo Peep [Grosvenor Cres]: Former Customs house, licensed since 1810, and popular with locals and holidaymakers; comfortable furnishings, helpful friendly staff, enjoyable bar food, plenty of character *(E G Parish)*

Dripping Spring [Tower Rd]: Old-fashioned local with enthusiastic landlord and friendly regulars, well kept Goachers Light, Oakhill

XXX, Timothy Taylors Best and changing guests from small breweries far and wide *(Bruce Bird)*
Victoria [Battle Rd]: Friendly service, generous food, three real ales such as Adnams Broadside; children welcome *(Quentin and Carol Williamson)*

Staplefield [TQ2728]
Jolly Tanners [Handcross Rd, just off A23]: Spotless, quiet and comfortable, enjoyable home-made food, well kept Fullers Chiswick and London Pride, Harveys BB and Charles Wells Bombardier, prompt service even under pressure, lots of china, brasses and old photographs, no smoking room; attractive garden with lots of space for children; well tended garden with terrace tables under cocktail parasols and picnic-sets on grass, by cricket green, quite handy for Nymans (NT) *(Terry Buckland)*

Stedham [SU8522]
☆ ***Hamilton Arms*** [School Lane (off A272)]: Proper English local but decorated with Thai artefacts and run by friendly Thai family, basic pub food but also interesting Thai bar snacks and popular restaurant (cl Mon); pretty hanging baskets, tables out by village green and quiet lane, village shop in car park, good walks nearby *(Barbara Wensworth, Godfrey and Irene Joly)*

Steyning [TQ1711]
Chequer [High St]: Timber-framed Tudor pub with labyrinthine bars, good range of well kept Whitbreads-related beers, wide choice of generous usual food from good sandwiches and snacks up, friendly service (normally prompt – if not, check) *(Prof and Mrs S Barnett, J M and P M Carver)*

Stoughton [SU8011]
Hare & Hounds [signed off B2146 Petersfield—Emsworth]: Airy pine-clad bar and dining area, big open fires, changing well kept ales such as Badger, Bass, Fullers London Pride, Gales HSB, Hop Back GFB and a beer brewed for the pub by Hampshire, back darts room; children in eating areas, tables on pretty front terrace and in back garden; near Saxon church, good walks nearby *(Brian and Anna Marsden, LYM, J A Snell, Ann and Colin Hunt, W A Evershed)*

Sutton [SU9715]
☆ ***White Horse*** [The Street]: Charming small and civilised country pub in same ownership as Horse Guards at Tillington (see main entries), island servery separating bare-boards bar from two-room barrel-vaulted dining area with stylishly simple furnishings and Rowlandson prints, good interesting food from bar dishes to enterprising restaurant meals inc local game and fish; Courage Best, Fullers London Pride, Shepherd Neame Spitfire and Youngs Special (may have only two of these on), log fire; tables in garden up behind, good value bedrooms, plain but comfortable and well equipped, quiet little hamlet near Bignor Roman villa *(Mr and Mrs David B Meehan, J Davidson, John Beeken, BB, Mrs M Miln, Wendy Arnold, C L Kauffmann, Brenda and Rob Fincham)*

Telscombe Cliffs [TQ3901]
Badgers Watch [South Coast Rd (A259)]: Good value roomy Vintage Inn with rustic décor, well designed seating, reasonably priced standard food with home-made specials, friendly young staff, good value wines *(Dick and Madeleine Brown)*

Thakeham [TQ1017]
White Lion [off B2139 N of Storrington; The Street]: Attractive 16th-c two-bar village pub reopened, keeping old furniture and atmosphere, and adding chilled food counter for choosing the meat and fish you want cooked – the food's good *(Alison Milner-Gulland)*

Turners Hill [TQ3435]
☆ ***Crown*** [East St]: Spacious dining pub, wide choice of generous enjoyable food, well kept ales such as Brains, Fullers and Harveys, good wine choice, helpful service, different levels (one with pitched rafters), log fire, pleasant décor with pictures etc; soft piped music; tables outside, pleasant valley views from back garden; children welcome, two bedrooms *(Sue and Mike Todd, BB, RDK)*
Punchbowl [B2028]: Large open-plan bar with food from doorstep sandwiches, ploughman's and baked potatoes up, plenty of old beams (pub dates from 14th c), Greene King Old Speckled Hen and Spinnaker, lower level no smoking restaurant *(Tony and Wendy Hobden)*
Red Lion [Lion Lane]: Old-fashioned local, very welcoming, with well kept Harveys, good value imaginative food (no cooking Sun), friendly staff, oak beams and furniture, large log fire in wonderful fireplace; well behaved dogs welcome, pretty garden *(Bill and Rachael Gallagher, W Ruxton)*

Wadhurst [TQ6131]
☆ ***Best Beech*** [Mayfield Lane (B2100 a mile W)]: Pleasant dining pub under new ownership summer 2002, pleasant dim-lit bar on left with wall seats, quiet but individual décor and coal fire, cosy eating area with lots of pictures and china on right, well done fresh bar food (not Sun evening) from sandwiches to steaks using some local produce, well kept Harveys and other ales, decent wines, quick service; back restaurant, tables outside, good value bedrooms, good breakfast *(BB)*
Greyhound [B2099]: Neatly kept village pub with current licensees doing enjoyable home-made food and set Sun lunch in restaurant or pleasant beamed bar with big inglenook log fire, well kept Bass, Greene King Old Speckled Hen, Harveys and Youngs Special, decent wines by the glass, games area with bar billiards, no piped music (but can be smoky); tables in well kept and attractive sheltered back garden; bedrooms *(BB, Neil Rose)*

Walderton [SU7910]
☆ ***Barley Mow*** [Stoughton rd, just off B2146 Chichester—Petersfield]: Spacious flagstoned U-shaped bar popular for good choice of good generous food; well kept Ringwood ales, quick cheerful service even on packed wknds, two log fires, country bric-a-brac, no music; children welcome, skittle alley, nice furniture in big

pleasant streamside garden with fish pond, aviary and swings, good walks, handy for Stansted House *(Ann and Colin Hunt, J A Snell, W A Evershed)*

Warbleton [TQ6018]

☆ ***Warbil in Tun***: Pretty dining pub with good choice of good value food esp meat (helpful ex-butcher landlord), good puddings, well kept reasonably priced Harveys BB, good coffee, welcoming and cosily civilised atmosphere, beams and red plush, huge log fireplace, no music; tables on roadside green, attractive tucked-away village *(R E Greenhalgh, Michael and Ann Cole)*

Warnham [TQ1533]

☆ ***Greets*** [Friday St]: 15th-c beamed pub with warmly welcoming atmosphere, concentration on good interesting food (not Sun evening) from filled rolls to ambitious upmarket main dishes with good veg, uneven flagstones and inglenook log fire, charming gimmick-free décor, lots of nooks and corners, well kept real ales, decent wines, fast helpful service; convivial locals' side bar, tables in garden *(Miss J F Reay)*

West Ashling [SU8107]

Richmond Arms [just off B2146; Mill Rd]: Tucked-away village local in pretty setting near mill pond, simple furnishings, well kept Greene King IPA and Abbot from its central servery, open fire, darts, pool and a skittle alley, food from sandwiches and baguettes to steaks; children welcome, picnic-sets out by pergola, open all day Sun and summer Sat *(Ann and Colin Hunt, LYM)*

West Chiltington [TQ0918]

☆ ***Elephant & Castle*** [off A283 or B2139 E of Pulborough; Church St]: Open-plan local with plenty of character, stripped stone, dark wood furniture, turkey carpet and flagstones, open fire, good value generous freshly made straightforward food plus some South African dishes, well kept Badger ales inc K&B, fresh flowers, friendly helpful South African landlord, no music; public bar with darts, children welcome, flower-filled terraced garden with play area, aviary, ducks and geese, behind ancient church in attractive village *(BB, Mike and Heather Watson, Mr and Mrs Thomas, Martin and Penny Fletcher)*

☆ ***Five Bells*** [Smock Alley, off B2139 SE]: Welcoming landlord is an enthusiast for real ales, with four well kept changing ones from small breweries and a Mild from Badger or Harveys, annual beer festival, farm cider, good value fresh food (not Sun evening), log fire, friendly locals, beams and panelling, old photographs, unusual brass bric-a-brac, distinctive conservatory dining room; no piped music, peaceful garden with terrace *(Nicholas Pope, Peter D B Harding, Bruce Bird)*

West Dean [SU8512]

Selsey Arms [A286 Midhurst—Chichester]: Lots of horse-racing pictures and memorabilia in smart and roomy no smoking dining area, wide range of tasty good value food from simple bar snacks to generous restauranty main dishes, well kept Courage Best and Marstons Pedigree, good value wine, welcoming licensees, good cheerful service, log fire, separate bar with games room *(Ann and Colin Hunt, Val and Alan Green, Tony and Wendy Hobden)*

West Itchenor [SU8001]

Ship [The Street]: Large panelled pub in good spot near Chichester Harbour, good long walk from W Wittering; well presented food from good baguettes to restaurant dishes inc local fish, well kept Ballards Best, Gales HSB, Itchen Valley Godfather and Ringwood Best, two roaring fires, lots of bric-a-brac inc many chamber-pots, seats made from old boat, children in eating area; tables outside, may be good visiting barbecue in car park; open all day, said to be able to get supplies for yachtsmen (nearest shop is 2 miles away) *(Glenn and Louise Hamilton, M Blatchly, Tony and Wendy Hobden)*

West Wittering [SZ8099]

☆ ***Lamb*** [Chichester Rd; B2179/A286 towards Birdham]: Several rooms (some no smoking) neatly knocked through with clean smart furnishings, rugs on tiles, blazing fire, well kept Badger ales with Gribble guests, decent wines, good choice of good value food from separate servery, quick cheerful service, good Sun bar nibbles; dogs on leads allowed, tables out in front and in small sheltered back garden – good for children, with outside salad bar on fine days; busy in summer *(David Coleman, Ann and Colin Hunt, BKA, BB, Christine and Geoff Butler)*

Old House At Home [Cakeham Rd]: Roomy pub attractively freshened up by new owners, blue and white tables on tiles and wooden floor, main bar, garden bar and dining area – enjoyable food inc fish and good Sun lunches, log fires *(Jose Boyer)*

Whitemans Green [TQ3025]

Ship: Relaxed and welcoming, five well kept real ales, two log fires, some comfortable sofas, blackboard food, friendly pub dalmatian; no children *(Terry Buckland)*

Winchelsea [TQ9017]

☆ ***New Inn*** [German St; just off A259]: Variety of solid comfortable furnishings in bustling rambling beamed rooms, Georgian décor, some emphasis on food inc good fresh fish (sandwiches too), well kept Greene King IPA and Abbot and Harveys, decent wines and malt whiskies, quick friendly service from pleasant landlady and young staff, log fire; separate public bar with darts, children in eating area, pretty bedrooms (some sharing bathrooms), delightful setting *(Dr T E Hothersall, J H Bell)*

Winchelsea Lodge [A259]: Motel not pub, but hospitable and pubby bar with attractive back dining area, nautical décor, enjoyable substantial snacks and full meals; comfortable roomy bedrooms *(E G Parish)*

Wisborough Green [TQ0526]

Cricketers Arms [Loxwood Rd, just off A272 Billingshurst—Petworth]: Very low beams, bare boards and timbering in attractive open-plan old local, two big woodburners, pleasant mix of country furniture, five or six real ales, no smoking stripped brick dining area on left, cheerful service; piped music; tables out on terrace and across lane from green *(Stephen S Goodchild, Mike and Lynn Robinson, Lucien, LYM)*

Three Crowns [Billingshurst Rd (A272)]: Big clean and polished open-plan bar stretching into no smoking dining room, stripped bricks and beams, wide choice of good usual bar food from sandwiches, baguettes and big ploughman's up inc children's and good value meals for smaller appetites, generous hot dishes and popular Sun lunch, well kept real ales, quick attentive service, games room; sizeable back garden *(DWAJ, Tony and Wendy Hobden)*

Withyham [TQ4935]

☆ ***Dorset Arms*** [B2110]: Bustling 16th-c pub in pleasant countryside, easy-going well worn in bar with sturdy tables and simple country seats on wide oak floorboards (sometimes a bit uneven – beware of wobbles), good log fire in Tudor fireplace, well kept Harveys PA, Best and Mild, decent wines inc local ones; best to book for landlady's good fresh home cooking, pretty no smoking restaurant; darts, dominoes, shove-ha'penny, cribbage, fruit machine, piped music; white tables on brick terrace by small green *(Martin Buck, Robert Gartery, G T Brewster, Peter and Joan Elbra, Richard Gibbs, LYM, Mr and Mrs D D Collins, Peter Meister)*

Worthing [TQ1403]

Castle Tavern [Newland Rd]: Welcoming landlord, good choice of sensibly priced home-made food (not Sun/Mon evenings) inc Sun roasts, well kept Harveys Best, Hop Back GFB and Summer Lightning, Shepherd Neame Bishops Finger and a couple of unusual guest beers, generous coffee, good local atmosphere; live music Mon and Sat, open all day Fri/Sat *(Bruce Bird, Tony and Wendy Hobden)*

Coach & Horses [Arundel Rd, Clapham (A27 W)]: Spotless 17th-c coaching inn with wide choice of good bar food (can order ahead by phone) in pleasant well furnished extended dining area, well kept Fullers London Pride, Youngs Special and guests such as Adnams Best and Broadside, friendly and informative staff, decent coffee, log fire, lots of brass and china, cosy second back bar; piped music; children welcome, Tues quiz night, occasional live music, well kept garden with lots of tables *(Brian Barder, Tony and Wendy Hobden, Bruce Bird)*

Hare & Hounds [Portland Rd, just N of Marks & Spencer]: Friendly bustling extended pub with well kept ales such as Badger K&B, Fullers London Pride, Greene King Old Speckled Hen and Marstons Pedigree from central brass and oak bar, good value promptly served straightforward food (not Fri-Sun evenings) from sandwiches and baked potatoes up, wide range of customers inc plenty of regulars, canopied courtyard, occasional jazz; no car park but three multi-storeys nearby *(Val and Alan Green, Tony and Wendy Hobden)*

North Star [Littlehampton Rd (A259)]: Former Big Steak pub reopened after refurbishment as an Ember Inn – chain of solidly furnished community pubs; no smoking area, sensibly priced food noon to 8, Harveys ales *(Tony and Wendy Hobden)*

Sir Timothy Shelley [Chapel Rd]: One of the smaller Wetherspoons, no smoking area and internal conservatory, well kept beer, decent food, friendly efficient service; children welcome in family area till 6, handy for Connaught theatre, open all day *(Tony and Wendy Hobden, Craig Turnbull)*

Yapton [SU9704]

Lamb [Bilsham Rd (B2132)]: Child-friendly olde-worlde pub with good friendly service, Greene King Abbot, Harveys Best and a guest beer, log fire, good value food with plenty of veg inc Sun roast, attractive no smoking dining room with fine collection of aircraft or railway decorative plates; plenty of picnic-sets in big garden with chickens, ducks (eggs for sale), goats and wonderful play area *(Miss H Orchard, Tony and Wendy Hobden)*

Maypole [signed off B2132 Arundel rd; Maypole Lane]: Quiet country pub with well kept Ringwood Best and five changing guests, two log fires in cosy lounge, welcoming landlord and staff; skittle alley, seats outside, on good circular walk from Buxted; no food, cl wkdy lunchtimes *(Bruce Bird)*

Real ale to us means beer which has matured naturally in its cask – not pressurised or filtered. We name all real ales stocked. We usually name ales preserved under a light blanket of carbon dioxide too, though purists – pointing out that this stops the natural yeasts developing – would disagree (most people, including us, can't tell the difference!)

Warwickshire (with Birmingham and West Midlands)

Three new entries here are the Old Joint Stock in Birmingham (a magnificent bank conversion by Fullers), the stylishly refurbished Inn at Farnborough (already heading firmly towards a Food Award), and the White Bear in Shipston-on-Stour (a good carefully balanced food choice). Other pubs that seem to have hit their best form this year are the Bell at Alderminster (good imaginative food in this smart dining pub), the stylish Fox & Goose at Armscote (imaginative cooking here too), the ancient Kings Head at Aston Cantlow (another place for a really good meal, with creative cooking), the Case is Altered at Five Ways (a complete contrast here – delightfully unspoilt simplicity), the Fox & Hounds at Great Wolford (nice combination of good interesting food with a warm pub atmosphere – and interesting beers), the beautifully kept Howard Arms at Ilmington (rewarding food), and the Garrick in Stratford-upon-Avon (real value and genuine friendliness, in a town where such qualities are at a premium). In a closely fought contest with the Fox & Goose at Armscote (also excellent), the Howard Arms at Ilmington carries off the title of Warwickshire Dining Pub of the Year. The Lucky Dip section at the end of the chapter has well over a hundred entries this year, several dozen of them new: current stars are the Cherington Arms at Cherington, Town Wall in Coventry, Golden Lion at Easenhall, Clarendon House in Kenilworth, George at Lower Brailes, Fleur de Lys at Lowsonford, Old Swan in Netherton, restauranty Butchers Arms at Priors Hardwick, Holly Bush at Priors Marstons, Rose & Crown at Ratley, Great Western in Wolverhampton and Bulls Head at Wootton Wawen. Two others to note are the Green Dragon at Sambourne (changing hands too late for us to assess the new regime) and Plough at Warmington (no recent reports on this nice pub). Drinks prices vary widely in the area, with some bargains to be found in and around the great West Midlands conurbation. Outside this area, pub prices average out close to the national norm, but span quite a range from some rather pricy dining pubs to the splendidly cheap Case is Altered at Five Ways.

ALDERMINSTER SP2348 Map 4

Bell

A3400 Oxford—Stratford

The imaginative menu at this civilised dining pub changes monthly, and might include soup (£3.50), filled baguettes (from £4.25), pâté (£5.75), smoked trout and salmon mousse (£6.95/£8.95), sausage and mash (£6.95), mediterranean chicken tart (£7.25), fishcakes with chive hollandaise (£8.95), steak and kidney pudding (£9.50), and home-made puddings such as apple pie, dark chocolate terrine or poached pears in elderflower and orange (from £3.95). It's all very good, and the service is cheefully attentive. The communicating rooms of the neatly kept spacious bar have plenty of stripped slatback chairs around wooden tables on the flagstones and wooden floors, little vases of flowers, small landscape prints and swan's-neck brass-and-globe lamps on the cream walls, and a solid fuel stove in a stripped brick inglenook. Two changing real ales might be Greene King IPA and Ruddles County under light blanket pressure, alongside a good range of wines and champagne by the glass, freshly squeezed juice and cocktails. They have high chairs, and readers with children have felt particularly welcome. A conservatory and terrace overlook the garden and Stour Valley. The licensees put great effort into keeping flourishing, by putting on lots of parties, food festivals, and classical and light music evenings throughout the year. *(Recommended by John Bowdler, Joan Crane, Eileen White, Les and Barbara Owen, Brian Skelcher, Stuart Turner, Joan and Tony Walker, Angela Cerfontyn, Michael Gray, Mike and Sue Richardson, Michael and Jeanne Shillington, K H Frostick, M A Borthwick, Bob and Maggie Atherton, Roger Braithwaite, Jack Clarfelt, David and Ruth Shillitoe, Peter Sutton)*

Free house ~ Licensees Keith and Vanessa Brewer ~ Real ale ~ Bar food ~ Restaurant ~ (01789) 450414 ~ Children welcome ~ Dogs allowed in bar and bedrooms ~ Open 12-2.30, 7-11(10.30 Sun); closed evenings 23-30 Dec ~ Bedrooms: £25(£35S)/£45(£45S)(£62B)

ARMSCOTE SP2444 Map 4

Fox & Goose

Off A3400 Stratford—Shipston

Quite contemporary décor at this stylishly transformed blacksmith's forge hovers between bistro and upmarket pub. Walls are a warm red colour in the small flagstoned bar and cream in the larger eating area, with bright crushed velvet cushions plumped up on wooden pews, a big gilt mirror over a log fire, polished floorboards, and black and white etchings. A stuffed fox stalks a goose above the dining room's woodburning stove; piped jazz. Listed on a daily changing blackboard, the very good imaginative food might include finger snacks such as marinated olives (£1.75) and garlic bread topped deliciously with mozzarella and tomato (£2.50), carrot and coriander soup (£3), terrine of smoked fish and mediterranean vegetables with basil dressing, or whisky-flavoured gravadlax with blinis and dill crème fraîche (£4.50), seared razor clams with home-made linguini and red and yellow pepper essence, thai chicken on a coconut risotto cake with green curry sauce, or fried duck breast with glazed onions and honey jus (£9.50), and roast shoulder of lamb with juniper berry and blackcurrant jus, or an outstanding rib-eye steak (£10.50). Service is charming and helpful. Well kept Brakspears and a guest such as Greene King Old Speckled Hen on handpump, mulled wine in winter, jugs of pimms in the summer, and well chosen wines with a choice of dessert wines. Bedrooms, which are named after characters in Cluedo, are mildly quirky, stylishly decorated and comfortable. Outside, the garden has an elegant vine-covered deck area overlooking a big lawn with tables, benches and fruit trees, and several of the neighbouring houses boast splendid roses in summer. *(Recommended by M A and C R Starling, Stuart Turner, Martin Jones, Norman and June Williams, Peter Sutton, Mrs L Price, Robert and Catherine Dunster, E V Walder, Michael and Jeanne Shillington, Jenny and Chris Wilson, Bob and Maggie Atherton, John Bramley, John Bowdler, Roger Braithwaite, Angus Sinclair; also in the* Good Hotel Guide*)*

Free house ~ Licensee Sue Gray ~ Real ale ~ Bar food ~ Restaurant ~ (01608) 682293 ~ Children welcome ~ Dogs allowed in bar ~ Open 12-3, 6-11(10.30 Sun); closed 25, 26 Dec ~ Bedrooms: £40B/£80B

It's against the law for bar staff to smoke while handling food or drink.

ASTON CANTLOW SP1359 Map 4

Kings Head

Village signposted just off A3400 NW of Stratford

This carefully restored beautifully timbered black and white Tudor pub is a favourite among readers for its very good often inventive food, served by enthusiastic young staff. Meals are freshly prepared, from a creative menu that changes very regularly but which might include soup (£3.45), rustic bread, roast garlic and olive oil (£3.45), linguini with sweet potato, fine beans and parmesan (£5.75), dolcelatte, roast red onion, spinach and butternut squash tart (£6.25), smoked haddock and spring onion fishcake (£9.95), chicken breast stuffed with basil, pine nuts, chorizo and lyonnnaise onions (£11.25), roast rump of lamb with lamb sausage, red onion and beetroot jam and olive mash (£12.95), bass with smoked pepper and basil risotto (£13.95), and puddings such as chocolate and butter pudding or caramelised cranberry and orange brûlée (£4.25). The pub is a charming sight, with its wisteria and colourful hanging baskets. Inside, the clean and comfortable village bar on the right is a nice mix of rustic surroundings with a civilised gently upmarket atmosphere: flagstones, low beams, and old-fashioned settles around its massive inglenook log fireplace. The chatty quarry-tiled main room has attractive window seats and oak tables. Well kept Greene King Abbot and IPA and M&B Brew XI on handpump, decent wines and piped jazz (which can be a bit loud for some). The pub is not far from Mary Arden's house in Wilmcote, which is well worth a visit. *(Recommended by Stan and Hazel Allen, John Kane, Peter Meister, Susan and John Douglas, Brian and Carole Polhill, Peter Sutton, June and Mike Coleman, Alun Howells, David Gregory, Martin Jennings, Mrs Ursula Hofheinz, Gill and Keith Croxton, J Hale)*

Whitbreads ~ Lease Paul Hales ~ Real ale ~ Bar food (12-2.30, 7-10; 12.30-3, 7-9 Sun) ~ Restaurant ~ (01789) 488242 ~ Children in eating area of bar and restaurant ~ Dogs allowed in bar ~ Open 11-3, 5.30-11; 11-11 Sat; 12-10.30 Sun

BERKSWELL SP2479 Map 4

Bear

Spencers Lane; village signposted from A452 W of Coventry

It comes as a surprise to find that this picturesque and individual 16th-c timbered country pub is a Chef & Brewer. This year a new bar with traditional games such as cards and cribbage has been added upstairs, just for drinkers. Downstairs, where the emphasis is very much on dining, the traditional interior has comfortably snug low-beamed areas, alcoves, nooks and crannies, as well as panelling, bric-a-brac and prints, roaring log fires in winter and air conditioning in summer. In one place the heavy timbers show the slope of the cat-slide eaves. A snack menu includes doorstep sandwiches (from £2.95) and filled rustic rolls or baked potatoes (from £3.85), and various blackboards list a huge range of daily specials such as soup (£2.60), hot chicken liver and bacon salad (£4.05), moules provençale (£4.65), beef and Theakstons pie (£6.80), fisherman's pie (£8.95), wild mushroom fettuccine (£9.70), beef stroganoff (£12.75), and puddings such as apple pie, chocolate orange truffle or banana and toffee crumble (from £2.55). Well kept Courage Directors, Theakstons Best and a couple of guests such as Caledonian Golden Promise and John Smiths on handpump; decent house wines all served by the glass; piped jazz. There are tables behind on a tree-sheltered floodlit back lawn. The village church is well worth a visit. *(Recommended by Barry Smith, Alun Howells, John Brightley, June and Mike Coleman, Brian Skelcher, Peter and Audrey Dowsett, David Green, Mandy and Simon King)*

Scottish Courage ~ Managers Steve and Tracy Gamble ~ Real ale ~ Bar food (11-10 Mon-Sat, 12-9.30 Sun) ~ (01676) 533202 ~ Children welcome ~ Open 11-11; 12-10.30 Sun

Pubs with outstanding views are listed at the back of the book.

BIRMINGHAM SP0586 Map 4

Fiddle & Bone

Sheepcote Street; opposite National Indoor Arena South car park

The Birmingham pub scene has improved in the several years since this airy schoolhouse was cleverly converted by two members of the City of Birmingham Symphony Orchestra who couldn't find a pub in the city that they really liked, but it remains a landmark. Music plays quite a leading role, with live bands on the big stage at the end of the lofty main bar every evening playing jazz, blues, soul, classical, and folk, and there's good piped music at other times. Their website, www.fiddle-bone.co.uk, includes a list of forthcoming gigs and festivals. The atmosphere is cheerful and lively, and the decorations are fun, with various musical instruments hanging from the high ceiling or the walls; along the bar counter trombones have been ingeniously converted into lights. Spotless varnished light pine tables with cushioned benches form little booths along each side of the bare-boards room, and a staircase in the middle leads down to the restaurant and a flagstoned bar area with a lighter café-bar feel. There are lots of picnic-sets outside here, but you get a better view of the boats on the adjacent canal through the windows of another bar upstairs. Well kept Adnams, Marstons Pedigree and a guest such as Everards Tiger under light blanket pressure, punch and schnapps; efficient helpful staff. Sensibly priced food, with most things available all day, includes good sandwiches (from £2.95), filled baked potatoes (from £3.50), burgers (from £4.50), lasagne, chicken curry, pie of the day, scampi or battered cod (£5.95), and puddings such as apple pie or chocolate fudge cake (£3.50). It's close to the Sea Life Centre, and a waterbus stops just outside. *(Recommended by David and Helen Wilkins, Tony and Wendy Hobden, Tim and Jan Dalton, Catherine Pitt, Jack Barnwell, Di and Mike Gillam)*

Free house ~ Licensee Angela Greaves ~ Real ale ~ Bar food (11(12 Sun)-10) ~ Restaurant ~ (0121) 200 2223 ~ Children in eating area of bar and restaurant ~ Live music every evening ~ Open 10-11(12 Sat); 12-10.30 Sun

Old Joint Stock

Temple Row West

Rather reminiscent of the Old Bank of England in London, this is the only Fullers house north of Bristol. Opposite the cathedral, it's a distinctive romanesque building which, though appealing from the outside, gives little indication of the magnificence within: chandeliers hang from the soaring pink and gilt ceiling, gently illuminated busts line the top of the ornately plastered walls, and there's a splendid well worn cupola above the centre of the room. Drinks are served from a handsome dark wood island bar counter, and big portraits and long smart curtains create an air of unexpected elegance. Around the walls are plenty of tables and chairs, some in surprisingly cosy corners, with more on a big balcony overlooking the bar, reached by a very grand, wide staircase. It can get busy (it's a lunchtime favourite with local office workers), but effortlessly absorbs what seem like huge numbers of people. A separate room, with panelling and a fireplace, has a more intimate, clubby feel. Well kept Fullers Chiswick, ESB, and London Pride on handpump, along with the local Beowulf, and a decent range of wines by the glass; helpful friendly service, teas, coffees. Usefully served all day, bar food includes well filled sandwiches (from £3.75), good soup, pies such as fish (£6.95) or steak and mash (£7.25), and specials such as stuffed peppers (£5.25). Daily papers, and perhaps big-screen TV for major sporting events; piped music. A small back terrace has some cast-iron tables and chairs. At busy times there might be a bouncer on the doors. *(Recommended by Richard Lewis)*

Fullers ~ Manager Alison Turner ~ Real ale ~ (0121) 200 1892 ~ Open 11-11; closed Sun

Tap & Spile £

Gas Street/Brindley Wharf

It's well worth finding your way to this interestingly restored part of the city, and to this nicely placed pub which has an authentic wharfside pubby feel, especially in summer when you can sit out at picnic-sets by the water. The bar, which also has good views of the revivified Gas Street canal basin, has an attractive back-to-basics yet quite cottagey décor, with stripped brickwork, bare boards and reclaimed timber, old pine pews and settles, and lots of prints. Small interconnecting rooms lead off on three levels, and are busy but not overcrowded. One has a complete kitchen range. Adnams, Everards Tiger, Fullers London Pride and Greene King Old Speckled Hen on handpump are kept well; also proper farm cider and fruit wines. Very reasonably priced bar food includes soup (£2.20), filled baguettes (from £2.65, hot from £3.50), fish and chips or steak pie (£4.25), sausage and mash or gammon steak (£4.50), scampi (£4.75), and puddings such as chocolate fudge cake or hot pudding of the day (£2.15); piped music, darts, fruit machine and dominoes; no children. *(Recommended by Lawrence Bacon, Jean Scott)*

Voyager ~ Manager Mick Murphy ~ Real ale ~ Bar food (12-5.30) ~ (0121) 632 5602 ~ Open 12-11(10.30 Sun)

BRIERLEY HILL SO9187 Map 4

Vine ◼ *£*

Delph Road; B4172 between A461 and (nearer) A4100

Much loved by fans of genuine no-nonsense pubs, this warmly welcoming place is well and truly West Midlands in character, with its friendly down-to-earth landlord and staff. It's known in the Black Country as the Bull & Bladder, from the good stained-glass bull's heads and very approximate bunches of grapes in the front bow windows. It's a popular place, full of local characters, and can get crowded in the front bar which has wall benches and simple leatherette-topped oak stools; the extended and refurbished snug on the left has solidly built red plush seats, and the back bar has brass chandeliers as well as darts, dominoes and fruit machine. As it's the tap for the next-door Bathams brewery, you can expect the Bitter and Mild, and perhaps Delph Strong in winter, to be in top condition, and they are most appealingly priced. Simple but good fresh lunchtime snacks are very good value, too: samosas (65p), sandwiches (from £1), good pork pies, pasta bake and salad (£2), and curry, faggots and peas, or steak and kidney pie (£2.50). *(Recommended by the Didler, Theo, Anne and Jane Gaskin, Dave Braisted, Gill and Tony Morriss)*

Bathams ~ Manager Melvyn Wood ~ Real ale ~ Bar food (not evenings or Sun) ~ No credit cards ~ (01384) 78293 ~ Children in family room ~ Dogs welcome ~ Open 12-11; 12-10.30 Sun

COVENTRY SP3379 Map 4

Old Windmill £

Spon Street

Unchanging over the years, this friendly and unpretentious timber-framed 15th-c inn stands on its original site – unlike the rest of the buildings in the street, which are an interesting collection of evacuee survivors from the blitz. It's known locally as Ma Brown's after a former landlady. In the nicely battered interior, one of the rambling series of tiny cosy old rooms is little more than the stub of a corridor, another has carved oak seats on flagstones and a woodburner in a fine ancient inglenook fireplace, and another has carpet and more conventionally comfortable seats. There are exposed beams in the uneven ceilings, and a back room preserves some of the equipment used when Ma Brown brewed here. Half a dozen well kept real ales include Banks's, Courage Directors, Greene King Old Speckled Hen, Marstons Pedigree and a couple of frequently changing guests from brewers such as Adnams and Batemans, all kept under light blanket pressure; fruit machine and juke box. Straightforward good value food passed out straight from the kitchen door includes filled toasties (£1.90), filled baked potatoes (from £1.80), and cottage pie, steak and onion pie, vegetable curry or thai green chicken curry (£3.95); part of restaurant is no smoking. The pub is popular with students, extremely busy on Friday and Saturday evenings, and handy for the Belgrade Theatre. *(Recommended by Peter and Audrey Dowsett, Pete Yearsley, DC, Nigel Espley, Liane Purnell)*

Unique Pub Co ~ Lease Lynne Ingram ~ Real ale ~ Bar food (12-2.30) ~ No credit cards ~ (024) 7625 2183 ~ Children in eating area of bar and restaurant ~ Folk first Tues of month ~ Open 11-11; 12-3, 7-10.30 Sun

DUNCHURCH SP4871 Map 4

Dun Cow

A mile from M45 junction 1: on junction of A45 and A426

It's useful to know of this extensive mainly Georgian coaching inn's reasonably priced food, served all day. It's worth getting here early for a table during normal meal times, as it is popular. The fairly straightforward menu includes soup (£2.95), breaded mushrooms (£3.25), lunchtime sandwiches (from £3.60), vegetable and goats cheese lasagne (£6.25), beef, mushroom and Bass pie or cod and chips (£6.75), beef wellington (£12.50), and Sunday roast (£6.95). The pleasant and spotlessly kept oak-beamed interior has been well preserved, with lots of traditional features like welcoming log fires, rugs on the wooden and flagstone floors, country pictures and bric-a-brac, and farmhouse furniture. Well kept Bass and Tetleys on handpump, and a good choice of wines by the glass; no smoking area and piped music. Outside there are tables in the pretty coachyard and on a sheltered side lawn, and the substantial inn is at the heart of a pleasant village, with nice antique shops. *(Recommended by George Atkinson, John Saville, Roger and Jenny Huggins, Colin Mason, Alain and Rose Foote, Mike and Mary Carter)*

Vintage Inns ~ Manager Florrie D'Arcy ~ Real ale ~ Bar food (12-10(9.30 Sun)) ~ Restaurant ~ (01788) 810305 ~ Children in eating area of bar ~ Open 11-11; 12-10.30 Sun ~ Bedrooms: /£52.50B

EDGE HILL SP3747 Map 4

Castle

Off A422

Also known as the Round Tower, or Radway Tower, this beautifully positioned crenellated octagon tower is a folly that was built in 1749 by an 18th-c Gothic Revival enthusiast to mark the spot where Charles I raised his standard at the start of the Battle of Edge Hill. The big attractive garden (with aunt sally) has glimpses down through the trees of the battlefield, and it's said that after closing time you can hear ghostly sounds of battle; there's even been the apparition of a cavalry officer galloping by in search of his severed hand. There are arched doorways, and the walls of the warm and cosy lounge bar have the same eight sides as the rest of the main tower, decorated with maps, pictures and a collection of Civil War memorabilia. Simple bar food includes soup (£2.85), ploughman's (£4.85), chicken curry or bean casserole (£5.50), lasagne (£6.15), steak and kidney pudding or cajun chicken (£6.95), and mixed grill (£7.30). They keep Hook Norton ales in good condition on handpump, a guest beer such as Shepherd Neame Spitfire, and country wines, farm cider and around 30 malt whiskies. The public bar, with old farm tools for decoration, has darts, pool, cribbage, dominoes, fruit machine and piped music. Upton House is nearby on the A422, and Compton Wynyates, one of the most beautiful houses in this part of England, is not far beyond. *(Recommended by Leigh and Gillian Mellor, Susan and John Douglas, Dr Paull Khan, Nigel and Sue Foster, Mayur Shah, MJVK, John Brightley, Dave Braisted, Alan Cowell, Jason Caulkin, Ken Richards)*

Hook Norton ~ Lease N J and G A Blann ~ Real ale ~ Bar food (all day summer Sat,

Sun) ~ Restaurant ~ (01295) 670255 ~ Children in eating area of bar ~ Dogs allowed in bar ~ Open 11.15-2.30, 6-11; 11-11 Sat; 12-10.30 Sun ~ Bedrooms: £37.50B/£57.50B

FARNBOROUGH SP4349 Map 4

Inn at Farnborough 🍷

Off A423 N of Banbury

Transformed under its current landlord (a former sous-chef at the Savoy), this stylishly refurbished golden stone house is a delightful mix of the traditional and contemporary, smartly done out without losing the sense that it's a proper village pub. So though the emphasis is very much on the very good, imaginatively prepared food, they're not at all perturbed if you've just come for a drink. The beamed and flagstoned bar has neat blinds on its mullioned windows and a chrome hood in the old stone fireplace, as well as plenty of fresh flowers on the modern bar counter, candles on wicker tables, and smartly upholstered chairs, window seats and stools; there's plenty of exposed stonework, and carefully arranged lighting. A stable door leads out to a newly added terrace, with decking and chic metal furnishings. The dining room has a comfortably roomy seat in a fireplace, nice wooden floors, a good mix of mismatched tables and chairs, and well chosen plants. Best of all perhaps is the newly landscaped garden, with wandering hens, plenty of picnic-sets (one under a big old tree), and a lovely sloping lawn. Well kept Greene King Morlands Original and Hook Norton on handpump, and a good extensive wine list, with around 10 by the glass. From a blackboard menu available anywhere round the pub, the food might include mussel soup (£4), welsh rarebit with garlic field mushrooms (£4.95), lunchtime ciabattas (from £5.50), twice-baked asparagus soufflé with parmesan (£8.95), and local lamb from Lighthorne with mediterranean vegetables and roasted pepper jus, Aberdeen Angus rib-eye steak or Cornish halibut with summer peas and saffron (£13); children's helpings. They serve oysters (£1.50 each), and a machine dispenses Havana cigars; piped music (quite funky on our Saturday night visit). As we went to press (less than a year after they opened), they were hoping to introduce Sunday evening jazz in the bar. On dark nights the pub – formerly the Butchers Arms – stands out, thanks to a string of elegant white fairy lights around the roof. *(Recommended by Michael Jones, Mrs L D Poole)*

Free house ~ Licensee Tony Robinson ~ Real ale ~ Bar food ~ Restaurant ~ (01295) 690615 ~ Dogs allowed in bar ~ Open 12-3, 6-11(10.30 Sun)

FIVE WAYS SP2270 Map 4

Case is Altered

Follow Rowington signposts at junction roundabout off A4177/A4141 N of Warwick, then right into Case Lane

Little has changed at this delightful white cottage over the three centuries that it has been licensed to sell beer. There's no food, no children or dogs, and no noisy games machines or piped music, in which case, you're likely to be here for the beer which includes well kept and very reasonably priced Greene King IPA, Hook Norton Old Hooky, Jennings Mild and a guest ale from a microbrewery, all served by a rare type of handpump mounted on the casks that are stilled behind the counter. A door at the back of the building leads into a modest little room, usually empty on weekday lunchtimes, with a rug on its tiled floor and an antique bar billiards table protected by an ancient leather cover (it takes pre-decimal sixpences). From here, the small and simple main bar has a fine old poster showing the Lucas Blackwell & Arkwright brewery (now flats) and a clock with its hours spelling out Thornleys Ale, another defunct brewery; there are just a few sturdy old-fashioned tables, with a couple of stout leather-covered settles facing each other over the spotless tiles. The homely lounge (usually open only weekend evenings and Sunday lunchtime) is accessed from the front courtyard or back car park. You can be sure of a warm welcome from the cheery staff and regulars.

Behind a wrought-iron gate is a little brick-paved courtyard with a stone table under a chestnut tree. *(Recommended by Kevin Thorpe, Jason Caulkin, the Didler, John Brightley, Pete Baker, Brian Skelcher, John Dwane, Susan and John Douglas, Joan and Tony Walker, Mike Rowan)*

Free house ~ Licensee Jackie Willacy ~ Real ale ~ No credit cards ~ (01926) 484206 ~ Open 12(11.30 Sat)-2.30, 6-11; 12-2, 7-10.30 Sun

GREAT WOLFORD SP2434 Map 4

Fox & Hounds ★

Village signposted on right on A3400 3 miles S of Shipston-on-Stour

Given the very high standard of imaginative cooking, it's quite surprising just how pubby this inviting 16th-c stone inn is – they still keep a thoughtful range of real ales, and locals pop in for a drink. The cosy low-beamed old-fashioned bar has a nice collection of chairs and candlelit old tables on spotless flagstones, antique hunting prints on the walls, and a roaring log fire in the inglenook fireplace with its fine old bread oven. A small tap room serves well kept Hook Norton and three guests that might include Adnams Broadside, Shepherd Neame Spitfire and Wye Valley Dorothy Goodbodys on handpump, and over 180 malt whiskies. Alongside straightforward food such as sandwiches (from £3.75), soup (£3.50) and ploughman's (from £6.25), they do mouthwatering daily specials (at a price, and there may be a charge for extra vegetables). These might include field and wild mushroom terrine (£4.50), fried brie and smoked bacon parcels with cumberland sauce (£4.95), thai-style fishcakes on coriander and lemon grass dressed noodles (£5), whitebait (£5.25), mediterranean vegetable tartlet (£9.25), steak and kidney pie (£10.25), fried pork medallions with spiced red cabbage and apricots and apricot and thyme jus (£11.95), bass fillet on roasted fennel with thyme sauce (£12.95), sole fillets filled with spinach with a cheddar and leek sauce or rib-eye steak with wild mushrooms and brandy cream sauce (£14.95), and puddings such as sticky toffee pudding, spiced apricot brioche bread and butter pudding with whisky crème anglaise, and lemon and ricotta cheesecake with compote of oranges (from £3.25). There's a well on the terrace outside. *(Recommended by John Bowdler, Di and Mike Gillam, Les and Barbara Owen, John Kane, Peter Sutton, Mr and Mrs J McRobert, Ted George, David Field, Mike Gorton, Sir Nigel Foulkes, Mike and Mary Carter, Martin Jones, Andrew Barker, Claire Jenkins, the Didler, Dr and Mrs M E Wilson, John and Enid Morris, Alun Howells, John Robertson)*

Free house ~ Licensees Wendy Veale and John Scott-Lee ~ Real ale ~ Bar food (not Sun evening) ~ Restaurant ~ (01608) 674220 ~ Children in eating area of bar ~ Dogs welcome ~ Jazz Sun evening ~ Open 12-2.30(3 Sat, Sun), 6-11(10.30 Sun); closed Mon ~ Bedrooms: £35B/£55B

HATTON SP2467 Map 4

Falcon

4½ miles from M40 junction 15; A46 towards Warwick, then left on A4177, and keep on past Hatton; Birmingham Road, Haseley

Useful to know if you're in the Warwick area, this spacious well reworked old pub has five calm and relaxing open-plan rooms working their way around a central island bar. Lots of stripped brickwork, low beams, tiled and oak-planked floors tell of the building's internal age, with nice prints and old photographs, big turkey rugs, chairs in variety, and a pleasant mix of stripped and waxed country tables. A couple of dark blue walls and arrangements of pretty fresh flowers add a smart touch. A big barn-style back dining area is no smoking. A wide choice of interesting food includes lunchtime soup (£2.50), sandwiches (from £3.25), greek salad and pitta bread (£6.25),very good beef and ale pie (£7.95), daily specials such as chicken and bacon salad (£6.95) and steaks (£9.95). In the evening you'll find garlic mushrooms or smoked mackerel (£3.95), feta, goats cheese and vegetable filo parcels (£8.50), braised shoulder of lamb or salmon en croûte with hollandaise (£8.95), and duck breast with spicy noodles and blackberry sauce

(£10.25). They do lots of puddings (£3.95). Well kept Banks's Bitter and Original, Hook Norton Best, M&B Brew XI, Marstons Pedigree and a guest on handpump, decent wines. A well separated games room has darts, fruit machine and a TV, and there are picnic-sets out on lawns at the side and behind. *(Recommended by Brian Skelcher, Di and Mike Gillam, Bob and Laura Brock, Susan and John Douglas, Michael and Jeanne Shillington, Ian and Nita Cooper)*

Peacock Inns ~ Manager Nigel Jones ~ Real ale ~ Bar food (12-3, 7-9(6-9.30 Sat); 12-3 Sun; not Sun evening) ~ Restaurant ~ (01926) 484737 ~ Children welcome in the no smoking area ~ Open 12-11; 12-10.30 Sun

HIMLEY SO8791 Map 4

Crooked House ★ £

Pub signposted from B4176 Gornalwood—Himley, OS Sheet 139 map reference 896908; readers have got so used to thinking of the pub as being near Kingswinford in the Midlands (though Himley is actually in Staffs) that we still include it in this chapter – the pub itself is virtually smack on the county boundary

You won't need a beer to unhinge your sense of balance at this wonky old brick house – although a pint is so cheap here it seems a shame not to partake. When subsidence caused by mine workings underneath this remote place threw the pub 15 degrees out of true they propped it up, rehung the doors and straightened the floors. The result leaves your perceptions spinning in a way that can really feel like being at sea. Inside on one table a bottle on its side actually rolls 'upwards' against the apparent direction of the slope, and for a 10p donation you can get a big ball-bearing from the bar to roll 'uphill' along a wainscot. There's a friendly atmosphere in the old rooms, and at the back is a large, level and more modern extension with local antiques. Very reasonably priced Banks's Bitter and Original, Marstons Pedigree and a guest on hand or electric pump; dominoes, fruit machine and piped music. Good value bar food includes soup (£1.95), duck wings with hoisin sauce (£2.85), lasagne (£4.95), bangers and mash (£4.75), beef and ale pie (£5.45), chicken tikka masala (£5.75), and wild mushroom rigatoni. The conservatory is no smoking at food times, and there's a spacious outside terrace. It can get busy here in summer, with coach trips. *(Recommended by the Didler, Bernie Adams)*

Banks's (W & D) ~ Manager Gary Ensor ~ Real ale ~ Bar food (12-2, 6-8; 12- 4 Sun; not Sun evening) ~ (01384) 238583 ~ Children welcome during meal times ~ Dogs allowed in bar ~ Open 11.30(11 Sat)-11; 12-10.30 Sun; 11.30-2.30, 6-11 Mon-Fri in winter

ILMINGTON SP2143 Map 4

Howard Arms

Village signposted with Wimpstone off A3400 S of Stratford

Warwickshire Dining Pub of the Year

A log fire burns most of the year in the huge stone inglenook, with its carefully written menu boards above, at this beautifully kept golden-stone inn. The stylishly simple interior is light and airy, with a few good prints on attractively painted warm golden walls, rugs on the broad polished flagstones, and a nice mix of furniture from hardwood pews to old church seats. A snug area is no smoking. Freshly prepared food from an imaginative menu that changes two or three times a week might include soup (£3.50), twice-baked red leicester cheese soufflé (£5), seared scallops with garlic and parsley butter (£6), beef, ale and mustard pie (£8.50), lamb in a garlic sauce with basmati rice (£10), fried duck breast with gingered pear and brandy jus (£11.50), fried skate wing with lemon, capers and parsley black butter (£14), and puddings such as organic ice cream, apple and berry flapjack crumble with custard, chocolate and ginger tart, or steamed lemon sponge with lemon curd sauce (from £4). Service here is notably welcoming and efficient. A nice choice of beers includes well kept Everards Tiger, North Cotswold Genesis and a guest such as Black Sheep, as well as organic juices and over a dozen wines by the glass. The garden is lovely in summer, with fruit trees sheltering the lawn, a colourful herbaceous border, and tables on a neat gravel terrace. It's nicely set beside the village green, and there are lovely walks on the nearby hills (as well as strolls around the village outskirts). *(Recommended by John Kane, M A and C R Starling, E V Walder, Martin Jennings, Stuart Turner, Brian Skelcher, K H Frostick, Peter Sutton, Christopher Harlowe, John Bowdler, Mike and Heather Watson, Martin Jones, Mr and Mrs Hugh Spottiswoode, Hugh Bower, Rod Stoneman, Andrew Barker, Claire Jenkins, Mr and Mrs B J P Edwards, Richard and Margaret Peers, Les and Barbara Owen, John Robertson, Jamie and Ruth Lyons; also in the* Good Hotel Guide*)*

Free house ~ Licensees Rob Greenstock and Martin Devereux ~ Real ale ~ Bar food (12-2, 7-9.30; 12-2.30, 6.30-8.30 Sun) ~ Restaurant ~ (01608) 682226 ~ Children in eating area of bar ~ Open 11-2.30(3 Sat), 6-11; 12-3, 6-10.30 Sun ~ Bedrooms: £48B/£78B

LAPWORTH SP1970 Map 4

Navigation

Old Warwick Road S of village (B4439 Warwick—Hockley Heath); by Grand Union Canal, OS Sheet 139 map reference 19170

Don't be put off by the unassuming appearance of this bustling local. Inside it's genuinely rustic, and it's great in summer, when hatch service to the terrace lets you make the most of its pretty canalside setting. It's run by a friendly landlord, and there's always a happy bustling atmosphere, with merry locals and canal-users in the friendly flagstoned bar; service is cheery and efficient even when it's busy. The bar is decorated with some brightly painted canal ware and cases of stuffed fish, and has high-backed winged settles, seats built around its window bay and a coal fire in its high-mantled inglenook. Another quieter room has tables on its board-and-carpet floor, and a modern extension is nicely done with rugs on oak floors, cast-iron tables and bentwood chairs, and a pleasant outlook over the sheltered flower-edged lawn, and on down to the busy canal behind. Bar food, in remarkably generous helpings, includes sandwiches (from £3.50), chicken balti, vegetarian quiche, goats cheese salad, very tasty battered cod (£7.50), pork loin with mustard and cider sauce or salmon and crab fishcakes with white wine and dill sauce (£9.50), chicken breast wrapped in bacon and stuffed with brie with a creamy barbecue sauce (£9.50), and fillet steak with pepper sauce or redcurrant jus (£12.95). Very well kept Bass, M&B Brew XI and a guest such as Everards Tiger on handpump, farm cider and lots of malt whiskies; fruit machine. The pub and gardens are prettily lit at night. *(Recommended by Di and Mike Gillam, Mike and Mary Carter, John Brightley, Kevin Thorpe, Jim Bush, Mandy and Simon King, Keith Allen, Peter Meister, Brian and Anna Marsden, DJH, Tony Walker, David and Helen Wilkins, Andrew Scarr)*

Voyager ~ Lease Andrew Kimber ~ Real ale ~ Bar food (12-2(3 Sun), 6-9) ~ (01564) 783337 ~ Children welcome ~ Dogs allowed in bar ~ Open 11-3, 5.30-11; 11-11 Sat; 12-10.30 Sun

LITTLE COMPTON SP2630 Map 4

Red Lion

Off A44 Moreton-in-Marsh—Chipping Norton

A very nice little place, this attractive 16th-c stone local has a pleasant villagey atmosphere, and is in a handy spot for Cotswold forays. The good bar food is so popular that you may need to book (especially at weekends). It includes soup (£2.75), chicken liver pâté (£3.95), very good filled baguettes (from £3.25), ploughman's (£4.50), breaded plaice (£5.50), and daily specials such as beef and Guinness or seafood pie (£7.95), and chicken breast with a peach and green peppercorn sauce, grilled pork loin with cider, apple and cream, or poached salmon fillet with white wine and cream sauce (£8.95). The simple but civilised and comfortable low-beamed lounge has snug alcoves, and a couple of little tables by the log fire; there's a no smoking restaurant. The plainer public bar has another log fire, and darts, pool, cribbage, dominoes, fruit machine and juke box. Donnington BB and SBA on handpump, and an extensive wine list; good service. The well maintained garden is pleasant, and we have had no complaints about the simple bedrooms. *(Recommended by H O Dickinson, Mike and Mary Carter, M W Turner, R T and J C Moggridge, George Atkinson, J D M Rushworth, Martin Jennings, John and Johanne Eadie)*

Donnington ~ Tenant David Smith ~ Real ale ~ Bar food (12-2(2.30 Sun), 7-9(9.30 Sat)) ~ Restaurant ~ (01608) 674397 ~ Children in restaurant ~ Open 12-2.30, 6-11; 12-3, 7-10.30 Sun ~ Bedrooms: £30/£40

LONG COMPTON SP2832 Map 4

Red Lion

A3400 S of Shipston-on-Stour

Well refurbished to make the most of its old features, this attractive former coaching inn is run by a welcoming and attentive landlady, with efficient helpful staff. The roomy lounge bar has brown panelling and stripped stone, with a lot of old local photographs and other pictures, and a high delft shelf with antique bottles. Although airy it has some nice rambling corners where there are old-fashioned built-in settles among pleasantly assorted and comfortable old seats and tables on the flagstones, and good log fires. Good value food includes sandwiches with salad and tortilla chips (£3.50), ploughman's (£4.75), chilli or cashew nut paella (£6.45), battered cod (£6.75), and daily specials such as greenlip mussels with garlic (£4.25), smoked salmon (£4.50), chicken caesar salad (£6.50), very nice steak and kidney pie (£6.75), braised lamb shank (£8.75) and tiger prawns in Pernod and cream (£8.95). Well kept Adnams, Hook Norton, Websters and a guest such as Courage Directors on handpump. The simple public bar has darts, pool, a fruit machine and TV; unobtrusive piped pop music. There are tables out in the garden, with a play area. We have not yet heard from anyone who has stayed overnight here. *(Recommended by Stuart Turner, George Atkinson)*

Free house ~ Licensee Jenny Parkin ~ Real ale ~ Bar food ~ Restaurant ~ (01608) 684221 ~ Children welcome ~ Dogs welcome ~ Open 11-2.30, 6-11; 12-3, 7-10.30 Sun ~ Bedrooms: £30B/£50B

MONKS KIRBY SP4683 Map 4

Bell

Just off B4027 (former A427) W of Pailton; Bell Lane

Paco, the Spanish landlord at this timbered and flagstoned old pub, likes to think of it as a corner of Spain in the heart of England, and there certainly is an enjoyably comfortable blending of Mediterranean hospitality and tasty Spanish food with traditional pubby surroundings. A huge printed menu (not especially cheap) with a few English, but mainly Spanish, dishes includes starters – which you could have as tapas – such as chorizo in white wine and garlic (£4.25), sardines in garlic butter (£4.95), fried squid (£5.25), moules marinière (£5.65) and scallops cooked with white wine, tomato, lemon juice and breadcrumbs (£5.95), and main courses such as battered cod or spanish omelette (£8.95), meatballs in spicy tomato sauce on pasta (£10.25), pollo pimienta (£10.95), hake and shellfish cooked in a clay dish (£13.25), fish paella (£13.75) and lobster and chicken baked with white wine and cream in an iron dish (£16.75). The dark beamed and flagstoned interior, although old, is fairly straightforward, with a no smoking dining area and piped music. As well as well kept Boddingtons, Flowers Original and possibly a guest such as Greene King Old Speckled Hen on handpump, there's a very good wine list, ports for sale by the bottle, and a good range of brandies and malt whiskies. A back terrace by a stream has a pretty little view across to a buttercup meadow. *(Recommended by Susan and John Douglas, Mike and Penny Sutton, G W H Kerby, Comus and Sarah Elliott, The Earl of Denbigh, Lisa Worthington, Mark and Amanda Sheard, Andrea and Guy Bradley)*

Free house ~ Licensee Paco Garcia Maures ~ Real ale ~ Bar food (12-2.30, 7-10.30;

not Mon lunchtime) ~ Restaurant ~ (01788) 832352 ~ Children in eating area of bar and restaurant ~ Open 12-3(2.30 Sat, 3.30 Sun), 7-11; (10.30 Sun); closed Mon lunchtime

SEDGLEY SO9193 Map 4

Beacon ★

Bilston Street (no pub sign on our visit, but by Beacon Lane); A463, off A4123 Wolverhampton—Dudley

It's worth tracking down this plain-looking old brick pub for two very good reasons: the good unusual beers brewed on the premises, and the well preserved Victorian layout. The front door opens straight into a plain quarry-tiled drinking corridor, and you may find a couple of locals propped up against the wall by the stairs, chatting to the barman leaning in the doorway of his little central serving booth. You can easily imagine a 19th-c traveller tucked up in the little snug on the left by the imposing green tiled marble fireplace with its big misty mirror, the door closed for privacy and warmth, a drink handed through the glazed hatch, while the cat (Sally) sleeps on under the wall settle. The dark woodwork, turkey carpet, velvet and net curtains, heavy mahogany tables, old piano and little landscape prints all seem unchanged since those times. Another simple snug on the right has a black kettle and embroidered mantel over a blackened range, and a stripped wooden wall bench. The corridor runs round into a big dark-panelled smoking room with red leather wall settles down the length of each side, gilt-based cast-iron tables, a big blue carpet on the lino, and dramatic sea prints. Round a corner, the conservatory is genuinely for plants, and has no seats. The beautifully aromatic Sarah Hughes beers here – Dark Ruby, Pale Amber and Surprise Bitter – are brewed in a building at the back, which you can arrange to look round. The only food they serve is cheese and onion cobs (80p). A children's play area in the garden has a slide, climbing frame and roundabout. *(Recommended by the Didler, Kevin Thorpe, Pete Baker)*

Own brew ~ Licensee John Hughes ~ Real ale ~ No credit cards ~ (01902) 883380 ~ Children in family room ~ Dogs allowed in bar ~ Open 12-2.30, 5.30-10.45; 12-3, 6-10.45 Sat; 12-3, 7-10.30 Sun

SHIPSTON-ON-STOUR SP2540 Map 4

White Bear

High Street

The brick Georgian frontage of this fine old coaching inn faces on to a bustling market square. Inside, the long narrow front bar on the left has massive stripped settles, attractive lamps on the rag-rolled walls, newspapers out for customers, and interesting pictures: charming pen and wash drawings of Paris café society, and sporting and other cartoons from Alken through Lawson Wood to bright modern ones by Tibb. The back lounge is more plainly furnished and decorated, with comfortable modern furniture, and big Toulouse-Lautrec and other prints of French music-hall life. A separate bar on the right has a woodburning stove in a big painted stone fireplace. Well kept Adnams Broadside, Bass, M&B Brew X1 and a guest such as Fullers London Pride on handpump, with eclectically chosen wines – including bin ends, a good selection of ports and wines by the glass; polite, knowledgeable service. Darts, juke box, TV and fruit machine. Sensibly imaginative food from a very well balanced menu is served in the bar and restaurant, and might include olives or mozzarella garlic bread (from £1.95), lunchtime sandwiches (from £2.65), soup (£2.70), grilled sardines with lemon, garlic and parsley (£4.95), fried pigeon breast with pine kernels, red wine dressing and pear compote (£4.95), mussels with chilli, coriander and coconut (£5.25), cauliflower and leek lasagne with garlic mushrooms (£6.90), pork and leek sausages and mash (£7.25), steak, Guinness and onion pie (£8.60), fried red snapper on roasted fennel and red onion and caper butter (£10.75), grilled brill with anchovy butter and rocket (£10.90), braised pork belly with soy and garlic sauce (£11.90), veal cutlet with sweet potato and balsamic jus (£11.95) and puddings such as baked cheesecake with plum sauce. There are some white cast-iron tables in a small back yard. *(Recommended by Michael Graubart and Valerie Coumont Graubart, JHBS, Michael and Jeanne Shillington)*

Punch ~ Lease George Kruszynskys ~ Real ale ~ Bar food (12-2, 7-9.30(10 Fri, Sat); not Sun evening) ~ Restaurant ~ (01608) 661558 ~ Children welcome ~ Dogs welcome ~ Live music Sun ~ Open 11-11; 12-10.30 Sun

SHUSTOKE SP2290 Map 4

Griffin £

5 miles from M6 junction 4; A446 towards Tamworth, then right on to B4114 and go straight through Coleshill; pub is at Furnace End, a mile E of village

This unpretentious country local always attracts a cheery mixed crowd, even mid-week, to its friendly low-beamed L-shaped bar. Two stone fireplaces (one's a big inglenook) have warming log fires, and besides one nice old-fashioned settle the décor is firmly rooted somewhere in the middle of the 20th c: cushioned café seats (some quite closely packed), sturdily elm-topped sewing trestles, lots of old jugs on the beams, beer mats on the ceiling, and a fruit machine. The finest feature here is the interesting range of up to 10 real ales, which are sourced from brewers the length and breadth of the country – there might be beers from Sharps in Cornwall or Craigmill in Scotland, as well as beers such as RCH Pitchfork and Theakstons Old Peculier, all from a servery under a very low heavy beam; country wine, mulled wine and hot punch. Very good value lunchtime bar food includes pie and chips, broccoli bake or lasagne and cod, chips and mushy peas (£4.95-£5.50); you may need to arrive early to get a table. The conservatory is popular with families, and outside are old-fashioned seats and tables on the back grass, a play area, and a large terrace with plants in raised beds. *(Recommended by J V Dadswell, John Dwane, A J Bowen)*

Free house ~ Licensee Michael Pugh ~ Real ale ~ Bar food (12-2; not Sun) ~ No credit cards ~ (01675) 481205 ~ Children in family room ~ Dogs allowed in bar ~ Open 12-2.30, 7-11; 12-3, 7-10.30 Sun

STRATFORD-UPON-AVON SP2055 Map 4

Garrick

High Street

The charming external and internal appearance of this ancient pub is exactly what you'd hope for on a visit to this famous town. The name originates from 1769 when the actor David Garrick visited Stratford and inaugurated the Stratford Festival. The small, heavily timbered and often irregularly shaped rooms are full of secluded corners and have high beams, some walls stripped back to bare stone and others heavily plastered, and long upholstered settles and stools made from barrels on bare boards. A small dining room at the back of the house is air-conditioned and no smoking. Very well kept Flowers IPA, Greene King Abbot, Wadworths 6X and a guest such as Hook Norton Old Hooky on handpump, a fruit machine, piped music and a TV. Very friendly helpful staff serve generous helpings of sensibly priced and jolly decent bar food such as soup (£2.95), sandwiches (from £3.75), baguettes (from £4.75), chicken and red pesto pasta (£7.25), fish and chips or salmon fillet with white wine and dill sauce (£7.95), daily specials such as ploughman's (£6.45), beef and Guinness or chicken and pepper pie, or spicy beef wraps (£7.95), and puddings such as caramel apple pie or sticky toffee pudding (from £3.45). *(Recommended by Michael Dandy, Duncan Cloud, Ted George, Leigh and Gillian Mellor, Andrew McHardy, Kevin Blake, Stephen, Julie and Hayley Brown)*

Laurel (Enterprise) ~ Licensee Vicky Leng ~ Real ale ~ Bar food (12-9) ~ (01789) 292186 ~ Children in restaurant ~ Singer once a month ~ Open 11-11; 12-10.30 Sun

WELFORD-ON-AVON SP1452 Map 4

Bell

Off B439 W of Stratford; High Street

This comfortable and attractive 17th-c brick pub has flagstone floors, stripped, antique or period-style furniture, and three real fires – one in an inglenook. Each area has its own character, from the cosy terracotta-painted bar to the light and airy terrace room with its peach and terracotta wash. Very good imaginative bar food (using local produce where possible) is served by obliging staff, and includes soup (£2.95), avocado and smoked bacon salad (£3.95), whitebait (£4.25), sandwiches (from £4.25), ploughman's (£5.95), breaded plaice (£7.75), lasagne (£7.95), minty lamb curry (£8.95), beef casserole (£8.75), daily specials such as steak and leek pie (£8.95), herb cod on mustard leeks (£10.95), sea bream on warm minted potato and cucumber salad with lemon crème fraîche (£11.25), roast duck breast on braised red cabbage with redcurrant jus (£11.50), puddings such as honey and almond cheesecake or apricot and brandy bread and butter pudding (£4.25), and a good cheeseboard (£5.25); several no smoking areas. Well kept Boddingtons, Flowers Original, Hobsons, Wadworths 6X and a guest such as Hook Norton Old Hooky on handpump; malt whiskies and local wine; piped music, shove-ha'penny, table skittles and dominoes. In summer the creeper-covered exterior is hung with lots of colourful baskets, and there are seats in the pretty secluded garden area and back courtyard; the riverside village has an appealing church and pretty thatched black and white cottages. *(Recommended by Andrew McHardy, Roger Everett, Tony Walker, John Bramley, Brian and Bett Cox, B A Dale, June and Mike Coleman, John and Johanne Eadie)*

Laurel (Enterprise) ~ Lease Colin and Teresa Ombler ~ Real ale ~ Bar food (12-2.30, 7-9.30(10 Fri, Sat)) ~ Restaurant ~ (01789) 750353 ~ Children in eating area of bar and restaurant ~ Open 11.30-3, 6.30(6 Sat)-11; 12-4, 7-10.30 Sun

Lucky Dip

Besides the fully inspected pubs, you might like to try these Lucky Dips recommended to us and described by readers (if you do, please send us reports: www.goodguides.com).

Alcester [SP0957]
Holly Bush [Henley St]: Welcoming warren of panelled rooms off central bar, well kept Cannon Royall Fruiterers Mild, Uley and several guest beers, reasonably priced straightforward food; pleasant back garden *(Pete Baker)*

Allesley [SP2980]
Rainbow [Birmingham Rd]: Busy local in lopsided ancient building (which eventually became a pub in the 1950s), brewing its own ales, also Courage; good value food, friendly staff , two small beamed rooms and small servery, sunny terrace; open all day, can be crowded with young people at night *(John Brightley)*

White Lion [just off A45 nr Browns Lane Jaguar Works; Hawkes Mill Lane]: Well run Vintage Inn with pleasant softly lit separate areas, central log fires, photographs and bric-a-brac, decent food all day inc smaller dishes and lunchtime sandwiches, good wine choice, Bass and Tetleys, cheerful prompt service; piped music; children welcome, tables in garden, open all day *(anon)*

Alveston [SP2356]
☆ ***Ferry*** [Ferry Lane; end of village, off B4086 Stratford—Wellesbourne]: Comfortable and friendly open-plan dining pub doing well under current licensees, enjoyable imaginative food esp fish, fresh pasta and lunchtime baguettes, special orders taken too, reasonable prices, well kept beers, good house wines, low-key décor, log fire; nice spot *(Martin Jones, Michael and Jeanne Shillington, LYM, Peter Sutton)*

Ansty [SP3983]
☆ ***Rose & Castle*** [B4065 NE of Coventry]: Popular low-beamed pub with cheerful friendly service, wide choice of good value food, well kept Bass and other ales inc a rotating guest beer, some canal-theme decoration; not big, fills up quickly; children welcome, lovely canalside garden with play area *(John Brightley)*

Ardens Grafton [SP1153]
☆ ***Golden Cross*** [off A46 or B439 W of Stratford, OS Sheet 150 map ref 114538; Wixford rd]: Pleasant restauranty dining pub with good choice of generous well presented food inc simple lunchtime dishes in flagstoned bar or comfortable dining room with well spaced tables, themed food nights, well kept Bass, Flowers IPA and Hook Norton, willing helpful staff, log fire; wheelchair access, tables in charming garden, nice views *(June and Mike Coleman, Don Mather, Chris and Maggie Kent)*

Austrey [SK2906]
Bird in Hand [Main Rd]: Black beams and new

thatch, bar and plush lounge, steps down to nicely divided snug, dining room with high chairs, good choice of reasonably priced food, Banks's Bitter and Original and Marstons Pedigree, helpful landlady; disabled access and facilities, cl Sun/Mon evenings *(Michael and Jenny Back)*

Baginton [SP3375]

Old Mill [Mill Hill]: Smart Chef & Brewer conversion of old watermill near airport (and Lunt Roman fort), with gardens leading down to the River Sower; uniformed staff, good food range, Scottish Courage beers, good wine choice, heavy beams and timbers in roomy main bar, restaurant; bedrooms *(John Saville, Pete Yearsley, LYM, Ian and Joan Blackwell)*

Barston [SP2078]

☆ ***Bulls Head*** [from M42 junction 5, A4141 towards Warwick, first left, then signed down Barston Lane]: Attractive partly Tudor village local, oak-beamed bar with log fires and Buddy Holly memorabilia, comfortable lounge with pictures and plates, dining room, friendly relaxed service, good value basic food inc good fresh fish, well kept ales such as Banks's Sea Shore, secluded garden, hay barn behind *(Brian Skelcher, Pete Baker, Hugh Roberts)*

☆ ***Malt Shovel*** [Barston Lane]: Refurbished as light and airy dining pub, clean, spacious and stylish, with mature civilised atmosphere, enjoyable brasserie-style food inc interesting starters, three well kept real ales, wide range of wines, helpful young staff, converted barn restaurant; pleasant garden *(Stephen, Julie and Hayley Brown, Andrew Wallace, Roger Braithwaite)*

Bentley [SP2895]

☆ ***Horse & Jockey*** [B4116, off A5 at NW end of Atherstone bypass]: Small traditional tiled-floor bar with three real ales, cosy snug, separate carpeted lounge with open fire, enjoyable food in here and in good brasserie restaurant beyond with beams and stripped brick, OAP bargain lunches Tues-Thurs, only restaurant meals Sun; disabled facilities, quiet piped music; sizeable garden, open all day Fri-Sun *(Bernie Adams)*

Birmingham [SP0786]

Anchor [Bradford St, Digbeth]: Perfectly preserved three-room Edwardian corner pub, carefully restored Art Nouveau windows, long high-ceilinged bar with basic seating, well kept ales such as Ansells Mild, Fullers Chiswick, Holdens Golden Glow, Marstons Pedigree and Wolf Coyote, festivals with lots of beers from single brewery, lots of bottled beers; well priced simple food till 6 inc huge chip butties, friendly staff, back games area with pool and sports TV; tables outside, handy for coach station, open all day *(Richard Lewis)*

☆ ***Bellefield*** [Winson St, Winson Green]: Unspoilt friendly sidestreet local with beautiful Victorian tile pictures, ornate ceiling, Georgian smoking room; Everards Mild, Tiger and Old Bill, guest beers, interesting bottled beers and occasional beer festivals; good value West Indian home cooking, pub games, music; open all day, terrace for children *(the Didler)*

Bennetts [Bennetts Hill]: Attractively converted bank like domed ballroom with Egyptian/French theme, relaxed atmosphere, comfortable dining area with usual food inc sensibly priced specials, decent house wine, good coffee *(Liz and John Soden)*

Black Eagle [Factory Rd, Hockley]: Four-room character late 19th-c pub, cosily furnished, with good value home-made food, good friendly service, particularly well kept Ansells, Marstons Pedigree and good changing real ales, small back restaurant; open all day Fri, cl Sun evening *(Simon, Jo and Benjamin Cole, John Dwane)*

Briar Rose [Bennetts Hill]: Busy central open-plan Wetherspoons with usual comfortable décor, menu and drinks offers, friendly staff, children allowed in separate no smoking back family dining room; lavatories down stairs; reasonably priced bedrooms, open all day *(Richard Lewis, Michael Tack)*

Charlie Hall [Barnabas Rd, Erdington]: Good new Wetherspoons conversion of former bingo hall, their usual good value food and ale range *(John Dwane)*

Figure of Eight [Broad St]: Vast open-plan Wetherspoons pub with raised side area, nicely decorated and furnished, no smoking areas, lots of old books, good value food from baguettes up all day, special deals, well priced beers such as Boddingtons, Enville Ale, Hook Norton Old Hooky, Hydes Dutch Courage, Shepherd Neame Spitfire, Theakstons Best and Tomos Watkins OSB, no music; pleasant tables out behind, handy for National Sea Life Centre *(Richard Lewis)*

Lamp [Barford St, Digbeth]: Friendly two-room beer-lovers' haunt in unpromising area, well kept ales such as Boddingtons, Church End Gravediggers, Everards Tiger, Marstons Pedigree, Stanway and Wadworths 6X; lunchtime food, TV and games machine, live music some nights, open all day (cl Sun evening) *(Richard Lewis)*

Old Fox [Hurst St]: Traditional two-room high-ceilinged pub with island bar and original Victorian features, changing ales such as Ansells Mild, Burton Bridge Up Yours, Marstons Pedigree and Tetleys, good value lunchtime food, friendly staff, theatre prints; pavement tables *(Richard Lewis)*

Prince of Wales [Alcester Rd, Moseley]: Good unspoilt bare-boards local on the Tolkien trail (he courted here), tiled corridor, hatch service to snug, two quiet and comfortable back parlours (one frozen in 1900), ochre walls, lively chatty atmosphere, well kept Ansells Bitter and Mild, Ind Coope Burton, Marstons Pedigree and Tetleys, wide choice of good cheap food, fast service even when packed *(Keith Jacob, Dr Stephen Decent)*

Rose Villa [by clock in jewellery quarter (Warstone Lane/Vyse St)]: Architecturally excellent, lively panelled front saloon leading through small opening to small but magnificent bar with floor-to-ceiling green tiles and superb massive tiled arch over fireplace; small lunchtime dining room upstairs, prompt friendly service, well kept real ale *(SLC)*

White Swan [Bradford St, Digbeth]: Unfussy

but clean and comfortable friendly local with charming staff, well kept Ansells Bitter and Mild and Tetleys, good fresh rolls, big bar, serving hatch to corridor, fire in small back lounge, ornate tilework *(Pete Baker)*

Woodman [Albert St]: Little-changed Victorian pub with unusual juke box (mainly 60s and Irish) in friendly and lively L-shaped main bar, hatch service to relaxing back smoke room with superb tiling and coal fire, particularly good fresh warm baguettes, well kept Ansells Mild, Tetleys and a guest beer, friendly unhurried service *(Pete Baker, the Didler)*

Bishop's Tachbrook [SP3161]

Leopard [nr M40 junction 13, via A452]: Country pub doing well under welcoming new management, good range of enjoyable and generous reasonably priced food, well kept Greene King IPA and Abbot and Marstons Pedigree; children welcome in dining area *(Nigel and Sue Foster, Stephen and Jean Curtis)*

Bloxwich [SJ9902]

☆ ***Turf*** [Wolverhampton Rd; aka Tinky's]: Unspoilt local in same family for several generations, two serving hatches to central corridor, large waiting-roomish tiled bar with heating pipe under settles, tiny back parlour with chairs around tiled fireplace, unusual padded wall settles with armrests in left-hand smoking room, original etched windows and fittings, William Morris curtains and wallpaper, cheap well kept local Holdens Mild and XB or Golden Glow; no food or music, outside lavatories *(Giles Francis, Mike Begley, RWC, the Didler)*

Brinklow [SP4379]

Bulls Head [A427, fairly handy for M6 junction 2]: Good family atmosphere, decent food from fresh sandwiches up inc plenty of vegetarian and children's dishes, well kept ales such as Badger Best, Flowers Original, Hook Norton Best and Marstons Pedigree, particularly friendly bar staff; collection of old pub signs, no smoking area, shove-ha'penny and table skittles; play areas indoors and outdoors *(John Brightley)*

Brownhills [SK0504]

Royal Oak [Chester Rd]: Handsome Art Deco refurbishment with real 1930s feel in public bar, comfortable lounge with Clarice Cliff pottery etc, no smoking back eating area with good choice of low-priced standard food from sandwiches to steaks inc children's from open kitchen, particularly well kept ales such as Bass, Bodicote No 9 and Greene King IPA and Abbot, friendly efficient staff, no smoking area; reasonable disabled access, pleasant garden with aviary and pets corner *(G Coates)*

Cherington [SP2836]

☆ ***Cherington Arms*** [off A3400]: Old-fashioned and welcoming creeper-covered stone house, current licensees, both trained chefs, doing good interesting food (not Sun evening) inc lots of well cooked fresh veg – must book wknd evenings; well kept Hook Norton and Ind Coope Burton in nice beamed bar with lots of hops, piano, and blazing log fire, good value wines, separate dining room, big garden with trees and tables; no credit cards; dogs welcome, good nearby walks, cl Mon lunchtime *(K H Frostick, JHBS, BB)*

Church Lawford [SP4576]

Old Smithy [Green Lane]: Much extended thatched and beamed 16th-c dining pub with dark woodwork in L-shaped lounge on various levels, good range of food cooked to order from separate servery, well kept Bass, Greene King IPA and Abbot, Judges and (brewed next door) Frankton Bagby, good friendly service; games room, conservatory; no dogs, children welcome, garden with slide *(Alain and Rose Foote, R Huggins, D Irving, E McCall, T McLean)*

Churchover [SP5180]

☆ ***Haywaggon*** [handy for M6 junction 1, off A426; The Green]: Carefully modernised old pub with emphasis on good food range esp Italian dishes (must book Sun lunch), well kept Bass and Youngs Special, cafetière coffee, two snug eating areas, lots of beams, standing timbers, brasses, nooks and crannies, friendly attentive staff; may be piped music; children's play area, on edge of quiet village, beautiful views over Swift valley *(BB, George Atkinson)*

Corley Moor [SP2885]

Bull & Butcher [Common Lane]: Low-beamed cottagey pub off the beaten track, small tidy front lounge and bar with real fires and tiled floor, good value simple food, back dining room, good choice of M&B ales; can sometimes get smoky; garden with play area, walks nearby *(John Brightley)*

Coventry [SP3379]

Flying Standard [Trinity St]: Well laid out Wetherspoons, popular for its attractively priced drinks; wholesome quickly served food all day, several areas inc one upstairs, big front windows opening up in hot weather *(Nigel Espley, Liane Purnell, Ted George)*

Royal Oak [London Rd, Whitley, nr Jaguar works]: Open-plan bar keeping Victorian details, decent waitress-served food, some large tables; can get very busy *(John Brightley)*

☆ ***Town Wall*** [Bond St, among car parks behind Coventry Theatre]: Victorian pub flourishing under committed new tenant, with engraved windows and open fires, smartly refurbished lounge with careful new extension, simple bar with big-screen sports TV, tiny clubby snug and flower-filled back yard; well kept Bass, M&B Brew XI and guest beers such as Adnams Broadside, Church End, Frankton Bagby or Charles Wells Bombardier, lunchtime good value generous doorstep sandwiches and filled rolls and some cheap home-made hot dishes with Lancashire leanings *(John Brightley, Ted George, Barrie Clark, Brian Randall)*

☆ ***Whitefriars*** [Gosford St]: Pair of well preserved medieval town houses, restored 2000 – like a country pub, with three rooms on both floors, flagstones, cobbles, beams, timbers and ancient furniture; basic sensibly priced food from sandwiches, ploughman's and baked potatoes to bargain Sun lunch, three changing real ales – Church End prominent; frequent live music Sun, no children (but shelter in good-sized garden behind), open all day *(Martin Pink, Alan Johnson)*

Easenhall [SP4679]

☆ ***Golden Lion*** [Main St]: Cottagey 16th-c inn in same family since 1931, attractively decorated comfortable lounge, low beams, dark panelling, settles and inglenook log fire, good generous food inc fresh fish, self-service lunches (two plate sizes), good Sun carvery and fresh veg, efficient welcoming service even when busy, real ales such as Boddingtons, Flowers Original and Greene King Ruddles, decent wines, good coffee; spacious attractive garden with terrace, barbecue, pet donkey; well equipped bedrooms in new wing, attractive village *(E M and H P N Steinitz, Carol and David Havard)*

Ettington [SP2749]

☆ ***Chequers*** [A422 Banbury—Stratford]: Restauranty pub with imaginative food served by attentive smartly dressed waiters, small bar with Adnams and a bargain guest beer such as Fullers London Pride, extensive wine list, comfortable easy-chair lounge, no smoking area; piped music; neat back garden with raised area; may be cl Mon lunchtime *(LYM, J and D Whiting, John Bramley, George Atkinson)*

Flecknoe [SP5163]

Old Olive Bush [off A425 W of Daventry]: Character unspoilt Edwardian pub in quiet photogenic village, no piped music, just conversation – the sort of friendly place where regulars serve the drinks if the landlord's busy cooking (nice food); attractive garden *(J H Bell)*

Furnace End [SP2491]

Bulls Head [Coleshill Rd]: Good village local with friendly and interested landlord, enjoyable food esp curries, Banks's, Bass and Church End *(Paul and Karen Cornock)*

Halesowen [SO9783]

Black Horse [Manor Way (access from A456 westbound only)]: Bigger than it looks, very popular for wide and hearty food choice inc imaginative dishes and some smaller helpings, efficient ordering system, good friendly service, Bass and Tetleys, no smoking area; children welcome, tables outside *(Mr and Mrs G Sadie)*

Waggon & Horses [Stourbridge Rd]: Welcoming local, refurbished (adding booths by fireplace) but entirely unpretentious and still with Formica and bare floors and benches giving a 1970s feel; noted for well kept Bathams, a house beer and up to a dozen or so interesting changing ales from small independent brewers – staff well informed about them; snacks only, TV, Tues music night, open all day *(the Didler, Gill and Tony Morriss, G Coates)*

Hampton Lucy [SP2557]

☆ ***Boars Head*** [Church St, E of Stratford]: Homely décor in low-beamed two-bar local next to lovely church, log fire, lots of brasses, well kept ales such as Church End, Hook Norton and Shepherd Neame Spitfire, prompt friendly service, well presented straightforward food (not Sun evening); picnic-sets in neat and attractive secluded back garden, pretty village near Charlcote House *(Brian Skelcher, Tony Walker, Susan and John Douglas, Peter Meister)*

Harborough Magna [SP4779]

Old Lion [3 miles from M6 junction 1; B4122]: Three-room village pub with Greene King IPA and Old Speckled Hen and a guest beer, food from sandwiches, baguettes and baked potatoes up inc OAP lunches, dining room, games bar with pool etc; children welcome, family events, quiz and music nights, open all day wknds *(Alan Johnson)*

Hatton [SP2467]

Waterman [A4177]: Good-sized pub above Hatton flight of 21 locks on Grand Union Canal, views as far as Warwick from sunny balcony and huge garden; Bass and Tetleys, friendly efficient service even when busy, generous food inc children's; good circular walks nearby, moorings *(Martin Jennings)*

Henley-in-Arden [SP1568]

Bird in Hand [A34 towards Solihull]: Recently refurbished open-plan pub focusing on good choice of food inc bargain lunches, bright and cheerful with plenty of new wooden tables and chairs off small bar area with well kept real ales and good wine list, hard-working licensees *(Brad Featherman, Gill and Keith Croxton)*

Hockley Heath [SP1572]

Nags Head [Stratford Rd (A3400)]: Harvester with reliable well priced food inc good salad bar, well trained staff *(Barry Smith)*

Hunningham [SP3768]

Red Lion [off B4455 E of Leamington]: Wide choice of good value pub food all day inc Sun carvery, well kept Greene King IPA and Abbot; nice country spot by River Leam, can get busy wknds, open all day *(Alain and Rose Foote)*

Ilmington [SP2143]

Red Lion [Front St]: Unspoilt stone-built local, two small bars, flagstones, traditional furnishings, well kept Hook Norton ales, basic food, friendly service; may be lots of walkers Sun lunchtime; delightful secluded garden *(Mike and Heather Watson)*

Kenilworth [SP2872]

Clarendon Arms [Castle Hill]: Busy traditional pub opp castle, good attractively priced food inc good meat dishes in several rooms, some no smoking, off long partly flagstoned bar and in largish upstairs dining room, efficient obliging staff, good range of well served beers; best to book wknds *(Mr and Mrs J Brown, Damian Dixon)*

☆ ***Clarendon House*** [High St]: Sofas, cane furniture, ceiling fans and daily papers in civilised partly panelled bar, well kept Greene King ales and guest beers such as local Church End, decent wines, friendly efficient service, good simple bar food from generous sandwiches, baguettes and light dishes to Sun roasts (under-10s half-price) and interesting wider brasserie menu, jokey complaints dept (well with blown-up skeleton 'complainer'); piped music; comfortable bedrooms, open all day *(Tony Walker, Damian Dixon, Joan and Tony Walker, Brian Kneale, R T and J C Moggridge, Colin Mason, Andy and Jill Kassube)*

Old Bakery [High St, nr A429/A452 junction]: Pleasant hotel with charming bar, peaceful and friendly, at least two real ales; comfortable bedrooms *(Andy and Jill Kassube)*

Virgin & Castle [High St]: Maze of intimate rooms off inner servery, small snugs by entrance corridor, flagstones, heavy beams, lots of woodwork inc booth seating, coal fire, upstairs games bar, restaurant; decent food from generous sandwiches and baked potatoes up, well kept real ales inc guests, good coffee; frequent live music, open all day, children in eating area, tables in sheltered garden *(Brian Kneale, LYM)*

Keresley [SP3183]

Hare & Hounds [Watery End]: Enjoyable country pub, music in the pub Sun night, rock music in function hall Fri *(Nigel Lamb)*

Knowle [SP1876]

☆ *Herons Nest* [Warwick Rd S]: Attractively reworked former hotel by Grand Union Canal, dining tables in several individual rooms inc no smoking areas, some flagstones and high-backed settles, hops on beams, interesting décor, open fires, wide choice of good value home-cooked rather unpubby food inc children's helpings, well kept Bass and Tetleys, good choice of wines, friendly staff; plenty of tables in garden with moorings, bedrooms *(Pete Yearsley, Bill Sykes, John Beeken, R J Herd, Jack Barnwell)*

Lapworth [SP1670]

Boot [B4439, by Warwickshire Canal]: Waterside dining pub done up in cool modern upmarket rustic style, raised dining area (food confined to here on busy Sat night, but may take up all tables at other times), roaring fire, good atmosphere, food (not cheap) from good baguettes to steaks and fish, well kept beers such as Greene King Old Speckled Hen and Wadworths 6X, decent wines (big glasses), smartly enthusiastic young staff, daily papers, lots of board games, cartoons; piped nostalgic pop music; good lavatories, nice garden, pleasant walks *(Susan and John Douglas)*

Leamington Spa [SP3165]

Benjamin Satchwell [The Parade]: Popular, well laid out and neatly kept Wetherspoons with their reliable food all day, well kept low-priced beers, good service, two levels, some cosy back-to-back tables in one eating area, cheerful relaxed atmosphere; disabled access and facilities, open all day *(Ted George, Joyce and Maurice Cottrell)*

Hogshead [Warwick St]: Neatly kept bar worth noting for fine range of well kept changing ales; bare boards and brickwork, raised no smoking area with sofas as well as chairs, good value straightforward food, good helpful staff; can get busy wknds *(Ted George, Andrew Wallace)*

Leek Wootton [SP2868]

Anchor [Warwick Rd]: Efficiently run bookable dining lounge very popular (esp with older people) for unusually wide choice of good value generous fresh hot food (all day Sat, not Sun), well kept Bass, Fullers London Pride and M&B Brew XI, decent wine, good soft drinks choice, lots of close-set tables, overflow into smaller bar with darts, TV and machines, may be loud piped pop music; picnic-sets in sizeable pleasant garden behind *(CMW, JJW, Roger Braithwaite, George Atkinson, John Whitehead, Tony Walker)*

Lighthorne [SP3355]

☆ *Antelope* [Old School Lane, Bishops Hill; a mile SW of B4100 N of Banbury]: Attractive 17th-c stone-built dining pub in very pretty uncrowded village setting, two neatly kept comfortable bars (one old, one newer) with Cromwellian theme, separate dining area, wide choice of good reasonably priced food inc old-fashioned puddings, well kept Flowers IPA and Wadworths 6X, faultless friendly service; piped music, but turned down on request; little waterfall in banked garden *(Hugh Bower)*

Long Itchington [SP4165]

Blue Lias [Stockton Rd, off A423]: Well placed on Grand Union Canal, with friendly efficient staff, enjoyable reasonably priced food *(Tony Walker)*

☆ *Harvester* [off A423 S of Coventry; The Square]: Unpretentiously old-fashioned welcoming two-bar village local, quiet, neat and tidy, with efficiently served very cheap food from sandwiches to good steaks, three well kept Hook Norton beers and a guest ale, friendly landlord, fish tank in lounge bar, cosy relaxed restaurant; nothing to do with the chain of the same name *(Pete Baker)*

Long Lawford [SP4775]

Sheaf & Sickle [Coventry Rd (A428)]: Two bars with decent good value lunchtime bar food (freshly made, so may be a wait), wider choice in smart modern restaurant extension, well kept real ales, friendly staff, darts and dominoes; picnic-sets in sunny sheltered garden by cricket ground, open all day Sat *(B and K Hypher)*

Lower Brailes [SP3039]

☆ *George* [B4035 Shipston—Banbury]: Handsome old stone-built inn with good freshly made food inc game in season, smart country-style flagstoned restaurant, local feel in roomy flagstoned front bar with dark oak tables, nice curtains and inglenook log fire, darts, panelled oak-beamed back bar with soft lighting and green décor, full Hook Norton range kept well, good sensibly priced wines, welcoming landlord; provision for children, live music most Sat and Mon evenings and Sun afternoon; aunt sally in sizeable neatly kept sheltered garden with terrace and covered area, six comfortable bedrooms, lovely village, open all day *(Pete Baker, Martin Jennings, LYM, JHBS)*

Lower Gornal [SO9191]

Fountain [Temple St]: Two-room local with well kept Enville, Everards, Holdens and up to six changing ales (beer festivals Easter and Oct), two farm ciders, country wines, enjoyable food, pigs-and-pen skittles *(the Didler)*

Lower Quinton [SP1847]

College Arms [off A46 Stratford—Broadway]: Spacious open-plan lounge with stripped stone and heavy beams, unusual highly polished tables on partly carpeted parquet floor inc one in former fireplace, leather seats, bric-a-brac, cosy well furnished eating area, well prepared reasonably priced food, friendly efficient service, well kept Whitbreads-related ales; piped music, games in roomy public bar; on green of pretty village *(Roger Braithwaite)*

Lowsonford [SP1868]

☆ ***Fleur de Lys*** [off B4439 Hockley Heath—Warwick]: Prettily placed old canalside pub, half no smoking, with log fires, lots of beams, well kept Flowers Original, Fullers London Pride, Greene King Old Speckled Hen and a guest beer, decent wines inc many by the glass, enjoyable food esp pies in bar and dining room (converted from former children's room); waterside garden, open all day *(Brian Skelcher, Brian and Anna Marsden, R Mathews, Ray and Jacki Davenport, LYM, Susan and John Douglas)*

Monks Kirby [SP4683]

☆ ***Denbigh Arms*** [Main St]: 17th-c beamed pub opp church, old photographs and interesting 18th-c pew seating, no smoking family room, big helpings of enjoyable food from sausage and chips through curries to bargain Tues steak night, Greene King real ales, friendly service even when busy; upstairs folk club 2nd Sun of month; play area *(Alan Johnson, Roger and Jenny Huggins, R C Vincent, Ian and Nita Cooper)*

Napton [SP4560]

☆ ***Folly*** [off A425 towards Priors Hardwick; Folly Lane, by locks]: Beamed old-world boaters' pub in lovely spot by Napton locks on Oxford Canal, three bars on different levels, attractive mix of furnishings inc huge farmhouse table in homely front bar, generous food esp good home-made pies, good service by very friendly staff, well kept ales such as Brewsters Marquis and Hook Norton, two big log fires, pool in back games room; very busy wknds, but winter hours may be curtailed; children welcome, good big lawn with play area, wishing well and fine views (also all-day summer shop and small agricultural museum) *(Roger and Debbie Stamp, Gill and Keith Croxton)*

Netherton [SO9387]

☆ ***Old Swan*** [Halesowen Rd (A459 just S of centre)]: Friendly and traditional, brewing its own good cheap beer, also Greene King Old Speckled Hen and occasional guest beers, cheap food inc Sun lunches, nice old solid fuel stove, fine mirrors, decorative swan ceiling, comfortable back snug; regular sing-alongs, open all day *(LYM, the Didler, Nigel Espley, Liane Purnell)*

Newbold on Stour [SP2446]

☆ ***Bird in Hand*** [A3400 S of Stratford]: Recently refurbished by new licensees with fine *Guide* track record, pleasant main bar with good log fire, well presented varied food at low prices, Hook Norton and John Smiths *(K H Frostick)*

No Mans Heath [SK2808]

☆ ***Four Counties*** [B5493 Tamworth—Ashby]: Homely and immaculate behind unassuming exterior, very friendly long-serving licensees, interesting brass and other ornaments, witty pictures, lovely stained glass, limited but enjoyable food inc popular Sun lunch, five real ales such as Everards Original, Ind Coope Burton and Marstons Pedigree, roaring fires, thinly cushioned benches; small no smoking dining room *(Bernie Adams, Ian and Joan Blackwell)*

Northend [SP3952]

Red Lion [off B4100 Warwick—Banbury; Bottom St]: Bright and pleasant two-room pub with concentration on impressive imaginative food inc lots of fish, OAP lunches Mon and Weds, well kept Timothy Taylors Landlord and an interesting guest beer, decent wines, friendly service, partly no smoking restaurant; best to book wknds *(Rona Murdoch, Michael and Jeanne Shillington, Cliff Bennett, Duncan Cloud)*

Nuneaton [SP3681]

Felix Holt [Stratford St]: Big Wetherspoons pub with no smoking at bar or in raised left area, wide range of very reasonably priced beers, nice décor, enjoyable quickly served plentiful food *(Ted George)*

Old Hill [SO9685]

Waterfall [Waterfall Lane]: Down-to-earth local, very friendly staff, consistently well kept and well priced Bathams, Enville and several other changing ales, farm cider, country wines, cheap plain home-made food from good filled rolls to Sun lunch, tankards and jugs hanging from boarded ceiling; piped music; children welcome, back garden with play area, open all day wknds *(Dave Braisted, the Didler)*

Oldbury [SO9888]

Waggon & Horses [Church St, nr Savacentre]: Ornate Victorian tiles, copper ceiling and original windows in busy town pub with several well kept changing ales, wide choice of generous food inc lots of puddings in bar and bookable upstairs bistro, decent wines, friendly efficient service even when busy, lively comfortable lounge with tie collection, side room with high-backed settles and big old tables, open fire, Black Country memorabilia; opens noon *(the Didler)*

Preston Bagot [SP1765]

☆ ***Crabmill*** [B4095 Henley-in-Arden—Warwick]: Comfortably upmarket timbered dining pub (even a uniformed parking attendant) with sofas and coffee tables in stylish two-level lounge, Flowers and Marstons Pedigree from steely modern bar, decent wines, elegant table settings in roomy candlelit low-beamed dining area, lots of nooks and crannies, food from bar meals to modern restaurant cooking, quick cheerful young mainly Australian staff; very busy wknd evenings; rows of picnic-sets in big garden with play area, open all day *(Susan and John Douglas, LYM, Chris and Maggie Kent)*

Priors Hardwick [SP4756]

☆ ***Butchers Arms*** [off A423 via Wormleighton or A361 via Boddington, N of Banbury; Church End]: Upmarket restaurant in pleasantly reworked 14th-c building, oak beams, flagstones, panelling, antiques and soft lighting (soft voices, too – a refined low murmur); huge choice of very well cooked and presented food (not cheap but worth it) inc fixed price lunches, small bar with inglenook log fire used mainly by people waiting for a table (also simple public bar); keg beer but good wines, very friendly Portuguese landlord, punctilious smartly uniformed staff, country garden *(K H Frostick, Mr and Mrs Hugh Spottiswoode, BB)*

Priors Marston [SP4857]

☆ ***Holly Bush*** [follow Shuckburgh sign, then first right by phone box]: Attractive golden stone pub, small rambling rooms, beams and stripped stone, old-fashioned pub seats on flagstones, blazing log fire one end, central woodburner, friendly helpful service, well kept Flowers Original, Greene King Abbot and Hook Norton Best, good fairly priced food from interesting soups and good range of baguettes up, large restaurant; large friendly dog, darts, pool, games machines, juke box, piped music; children welcome, tables in sheltered garden, pretty village, bedrooms *(Di and Mike Gillam, LYM, James Nunns, George Atkinson)*

Ratley [SP3847]

☆ ***Rose & Crown*** [off A422 NW of Banbury]: Charming ancient golden stone beamed local, very welcoming and neatly kept, with cosy atmosphere, well kept Charles Wells Eagle and Bombardier, decent straightforward home cooking inc good ploughman's and puddings, friendly family service, woodburner in flagstoned area on right, big log fireplace in carpeted area on left; dogs and children welcome, tables in small garden, near lovely church in small sleepy village *(Angus Lyon, Brenda Range)*

Rugby [SP5075]

Alexandra Arms [James St]: Friendly traditional two-bar local with well kept Ansells, Greene King Abbot, Marstons Pedigree and two daily-changing guest beers at sensible prices, farm cider, enjoyable home-made food inc interesting specials, annual beer festival; tables outside, open all day Fri/Sat *(P Henderson)*

Sambourne [SP0561]

☆ ***Green Dragon*** [village signed off A448]: This attractive village-green pub changed hands in summer 2002, too late for us to get a line on the new team – news please; with three low-beamed rooms, rugs on flagstones, open fires and comfortable bedrooms, it's been popular for tasty food (not Sun) from a wide range of sandwiches to generous main dishes inc some interesting things, and well kept Bass, Hobsons and M&B Brew XI; children in eating area, picnic-sets and teak seats in a pretty courtyard, and bowls *(LYM)*

Shilton [SP4084]

Shilton Arms [B4065 NE of Coventry]: Pleasant village pub with helpful staff and good range of good value food (all day Sun, can get very busy wkdy lunchtimes), enormous helpings, three real ales, decent house wine, no smoking section; garden with play area *(DC, Mike and Wendy Proctor)*

Shuttington [SK2505]

Wolferstan Arms [Main Rd]: Well run family pub, lots of beams and pewter tankards, friendly locals and long-serving staff, enjoyable attractively priced food, well kept Bass, farm cider, wide country views from restaurant and garden with play area *(Colin Gooch)*

Stockton [SP4363]

Barley Mow [off A426 Southam—Rugby; School St]: Early 19th-c pub in attractive spot by green opp church, friendly and attentive newish licensees doing enjoyable food inc popular OAP lunches, steep steps up to dining area, stripped brick, lots of brasses and pictures, Greene King IPA and Abbot and Tetleys, open fire; pretty hanging baskets *(George Atkinson)*

Stonnall [SK0503]

Royal Oak [just off A452 N of Brownhills]: Popular and welcoming refurbished beamed local, several well kept ales inc Hook Norton and Charles Wells Bombardier, farm cider, jovial attentive landlord, enjoyable regular food inc bargain midweek lunch in bar and dining room, also Sun lunch; no music *(Cliff Blakemore, A and M Worth)*

Stourbridge [SO8984]

Seven Stars [Brook Rd, nr station]: Well organised and sympathetically extended Victorian pub with impressive high ceiling, decorative tiles and ornate carving in period bar, good food inc huge starters and all-day cold snacks in lounge eating area or larger restaurant on left, well kept changing ales such as Bathams, Courage Directors and Theakstons Best; comfortably bustling atmosphere, friendly regulars, nice staff; open all day *(the Didler)*

Stratford-upon-Avon [SP2055]

Cox's Yard [Avonbridge Wharf, Bridgefoot]: Modern riverside pub brewing its own Jesters and other ales, waterside tables for watching the swans *(Hugh Roberts)*

☆ ***Dirty Duck*** [Waterside]: 16th-c pub near Memorial Theatre – still attracts actors, lots of signed RSC photographs; Flowers IPA, Greene King Old Speckled Hen and Wadworths 6X, quick friendly service, open fire, bustling public bar (little lounge seating for drinkers), children allowed in small dining area; attractive small terrace looking over riverside public gardens – which tend to act as summer overflow; properly the Black Swan *(LYM, Janet and Peter Race, Brian Skelcher, Alan Thomas, Kevin Blake, Richard Lewis, Andy, Julie and Stuart Hawkins)*

Falcon [Chapel St]: Substantial timbered Tudor hotel with big fireplace in quiet panelled bar, other rooms inc lighter more modern ones, well kept Flowers, wide range of bar food from sandwiches up, friendly staff, restaurant; may be piped music; bedrooms (quieter but more functional in modern wing) *(Val and Alan Green, Alan Thomas)*

Golden Bee [Sheep St]: Fine new Wetherspoons conversion, airy and spacious, with light wood furniture, separate no smoking areas, usual range of cheap real ales, good value large meals *(Ted George)*

Pen & Parchment [Bridgefoot, by canal basin]: Shakespeare theme in L-shaped split-level lounge and snug, rustic-style beams, balusters, bare boards and tiles or flagstones, small alcoves and no smoking area, big open fire in old fireplace, decent reasonably priced food, well kept real ales, prompt service; tables out among shrubs and ivy, pretty hanging baskets, good canal basin views; busy road *(Ted George, Richard Lewis, Alan Thomas)*

☆ ***Slug & Lettuce*** [Guild St/Union St]: Lively friendly bustle in open-plan bar with zebra-print sofas and light wood tables and chairs on rugs, flagstones and bare boards, period prints on stripped panelling, popular enterprising bar food all day inc two-for-one bargains 3-8, well kept real ales, decent wines, daily papers, helpful staff, solid fuel fire; TV, piped music, can get crowded with young people later; floodlit two-level back terrace, children welcome, open all day Thurs-Sun *(LYM, Ted George)*

Windmill [Church St]: Cosy old pub with town's oldest licence, beyond the attractive Guild Chapel; unpretentious but civilised, with low beams, quarry-tiled front bar, bare boards in main one, open fires, wide choice of good value straightforward food, well kept sensibly priced ales inc interesting guests, friendly efficient staff, carpeted dining area; tables outside, open all day from noon *(Kevin Blake, Lawrence Pearse, Alan Thomas, Val and Alan Green)*

Stretton-on-Fosse [SP2238]

Plough [just off A429]: Welcoming olde-worlde 17th-c village pub, small bar and larger lounge, jugs and mugs on oak beams, Ansells Bitter and Mild and Tetleys, attentive staff, wide choice of good changing food inc bargain OAP meals (booking suggested), good-sized fireplace, small attractive candlelit dining room on right; darts, sunny tables outside, bedrooms at nearby farm under same ownership *(June and Mike Coleman, Carol and Dono Leaman, K H Frostick)*

Temple Grafton [SP1255]

☆ ***Blue Boar*** [a mile E, towards Binton; off A422 W of Stratford]: Extended country dining pub with beams, stripped stonework and log fires, cheerful attentive staff, well kept ales such as Brakspears, Greene King Old Speckled Hen, Hook Norton and Theakstons XB, usual bar food from baked potatoes up, more elaborate dishes in comfortable restaurant (past glass-top well with golden carp) with no smoking section, good wine choice, traditional games in flagstoned side room; children welcome, open all day summer wknds, picnic-sets outside, pretty flower plantings; comfortable well equipped bedrooms inc some new ones *(Theo, Anne and Jane Gaskin, Don Mather, Tony Walker, LYM, Ian Phillips)*

Tipton [SO9792]

Rising Sun [Horseley Rd, off A461]: Several well kept changing ales such as RCH Pitchfork and a Mild, farm cider, great range of malt whiskies, thriving atmosphere; Aug bank hol beer festival *(the Didler)*

Ufton [SP3761]

☆ ***White Hart*** [just off A425 Daventry—Leamington, towards Bascote]: Friendly old hilltop pub with big lounge/dining area (several steps up to back part), beams, brasses and stripped stone, sporting memorabilia inc polo equipment, good choice of usual food inc good value OAP lunches, well kept Adnams Best, Tetleys and Bass or Wadwortrhs 6X, quick friendly attentive service; unobtrusive piped radio; hatch service to garden with boules and panoramic views (Tannoy food announcements out here) *(George Atkinson)*

Upper Gornal [SO92921]

Britannia [Kent St]: Recently reworked Bathams local, with their cheap Best and Mild kept superbly and authentic Black Country feel, especially in back room originally laid out for table drinks service; open all day Sat *(the Didler)*

Warmington [SP4147]

☆ ***Plough*** [just off B4100 N of Banbury]: Understated little traditional village local, cheerily unpretentious pubby bar with big fireplace, ancient settle and nice chairs, decent honest food (not Sun or Tues evenings) from sandwiches up, well kept Greene King IPA, Abbot and Ruddles County, Hook Norton Best and Marstons Pedigree, friendly staff; piped pop music; children in eating area, delightful village *(K H Frostick, Chris and Jo Nicholls)*

Warwick [SP2764]

Old Fourpenny Shop [Crompton St, nr racecourse]: Cosy and comfortable split-level pub with five well kept changing guest beers, welcoming licensees, simple lunchtime bar food, cheerful service, restaurant, no piped music; bedrooms *(Nigel and Sue Foster, Ian and Nita Cooper)*

Racehorse [Stratford Rd]: Large comfortable family dining pub, cheerful and bustling, with good value generous food all day inc children's and OAP bargains, well kept Everards Tiger and guest beers, no smoking areas inc conservatory (children welcome); open all day *(Tony and Wendy Hobden, Ian and Nita Cooper)*

Rose & Crown [Market Pl]: This town pub, previously popular for its traditional feel, well kept Bass ales and interesting three-room layout, has been closed for complete refurbishment during summer 2002; news please *(LYM)*

☆ ***Tilted Wig*** [Market Pl]: Roomy and airy, somewhere between tearoom and pub, big windows on square, stone-effect floor on left, bare boards on right, carpet behind, brocaded banquettes and kitchen chairs around pine tables, some stripped stone and panelling, well kept Ansells, Marstons Pedigree and Tetleys, good fairly priced Australian wines, wide choice of good reasonably priced home-made bistro food (not Sun evening) from sandwiches and baguettes up, lively bustle (esp on Fri market day), quick friendly service, two coal-effect fires; SkyTV, piped music may be loud; tables in garden, live jazz and folk Sun evening, open all day, four neat well appointed bedrooms with own bathrooms, good breakfast *(Jenny and Chris Wilson, BB, Jim and Maggie Cowell, Peter Meister)*

Welford-on-Avon [SP1551]

Shakespeare [Chapel St]: Character 18th-c pub with comfortable farmhouse-style furnishings, well kept real ales inc Hook Norton, good choice of wines by the glass; flower-filled tree-shaded garden with good play area *(John Brightley)*

West Bromwich [SP0091]

Billiard Hall [St Michael St, Ringway]: Light and airy IKEA-look Wetherspoons with their usual good value all-day food and beers inc a couple of changing guests, pine-effect panelling and flooring; open all day *(SLC, G Coates)*

Wheatsheaf [High St, Carters Green]: Particularly well kept Holdens, small basic bar, long roomy lounge, good value if limited food inc good hot pork sandwiches *(SLC)*

Whatcote [SP2944]

☆ ***Royal Oak***: Dating from 12th c, quaint low-ceilinged small room with Civil War connections and lots to look at; wide food choice inc good steaks from the Orkneys, welcoming service, well kept real ale, decent wines, good log fire in huge inglenook, restaurant; picnic-sets outside, children welcome *(JHBS, LYM)*

Whichford [SP3134]

Norman Knight: Quietly welcoming flagstoned pub with well kept Hook Norton Best and changing microbrew guests, nicely priced lunchtime food (and Fri/Sat evening); nearby pottery, tables out by attractive village green, cl Tues lunchtime *(Chris Glasson, Dick and Madeleine Brown, JHBS)*

Willey [SP4984]

☆ ***Sarah Mansfield*** [just off A5, N of A427 junction; Main St]: Hospitable and welcoming, lots of tables in long comfortable beamed dining area, small bar area with polished flagstones, stripped stone and brick, cosy corners, open fire, wide range of enjoyable cheap food from sandwiches and baked potatoes up, attentive young staff, well kept Bass, Greene King Abbot and Hancocks HB; pool table at back, may be piped local radio *(George Atkinson)*

Willoughby [SP5267]

Rose [just off A45 E of Dunchurch]: Friendly small partly thatched beamed pub with emphasis on good value straightforward food from filled rolls to tender Sun carvery, OAP lunches Tues and Thurs, tiled bar, carpeted lounge, evening restaurant, Courage Directors and John Smiths, cheerful staff, games room, seats out in front, garden with play area; cl Mon and Weds lunchtimes, Tues music night *(Susan Jeanes, George Atkinson)*

Wilmcote [SP1658]

Masons Arms [Aston Cantlow Rd]: Attractive ivy-clad local handy for Mary Arden's House but off the tourist trail; neat and snug, with good generous home cooking using home-grown veg in bar or good-sized dining conservatory, well kept Black Sheep and Hook Norton Best, reasonable prices, good log fires, informal service; pleasant garden *(Pete Yearsley, John Bramley, Geoff Calcott)*

Withybrook [SP4384]

☆ ***Pheasant*** [B4112 NE of Coventry, not far from M6, junction 2]: Big busy dining pub with lots of dark tables, plush-cushioned chairs, friendly efficient service, very wide choice of generous food inc good value specials and good vegetarian choice, Scottish Courage ales, good coffee, blazing log fires; piped music; children welcome, tables under lanterns on brookside terrace *(Paul and Sue Merrick, Mr and Mrs J E C Tasker, LYM)*

Wixford [SP0955]

☆ ***Three Horseshoes*** [off A46 S of Redditch, via A422/A435 Alcester roundabout, or B439 at Bidford]: Roomy and nicely renovated, with consistently good generous food from bar meals up inc fresh fish, interesting choice (esp wknds, when it can get crowded), nice puddings, helpful service, good range of well kept mainly Whitbreads-related ales, bric-a-brac from blowtorches to garden gnomes; pleasant seating areas outside *(M J and C E Abbey, Barry Smith)*

Wolverhampton [SO9098]

☆ ***Combermere Arms*** [Chapel Ash (A41 Tettenhall rd)]: Old-fashioned friendly local with three small cosy rooms, well kept Banks's and guest beers, decent wines, very welcoming staff, food from good range of bargain sandwiches to good value Sun lunch, bare boards and quaint touches, bar billiards; quiz Tues, nicely kept small secluded garden with summer live music in courtyard *(George and Anne Davidow, Mrs D Hardy, S F Bowett)*

☆ ***Great Western*** [Sun St, behind BR station – left down subway under railway, turn right at end]: Vibrantly popular, well run and down to earth, with particularly well kept Bathams and Holdens, very promptly served cheap hearty lunchtime food (not Sun) from baguettes up, interesting railway and Wolves memorabilia, traditional front bar, other rooms inc separate no smoking bar; SkyTV; open all day, roomy back conservatory, tables in yard with good barbecues *(Peter and Patricia Burton, D Crutchley, Pete Baker, the Didler, Gill and Tony Morriss, C J Fletcher)*

Wootton Wawen [SP1563]

☆ ***Bulls Head*** [just off A3400 Birmingham—Stratford]: Smart and attractive black and white dining pub with low Elizabethan beams and timbers, comfortable chairs, rugs setting off good flagstones, well kept Banks's, Claverley and Marstons Pedigree, good wines and stylish cocktail-shaking, good food inc several fresh fish (extra charge for veg), friendly unhurried service; pews in more austere tap room with dominoes, shove-ha'penny; children welcome, open all day Sun, tables on pleasant terrace – handy for Stratford Canal walks *(Alun Howells, Eileen Wilkinson, Brian Kneale, LYM, John Bramley, Lisa and Carl Henshaw)*

Real ale to us means beer which has matured naturally in its cask – not pressurised or filtered.

Wiltshire

A fat clutch of new entries here this year includes two which have featured in the Guide *previously, though not for some years: the Barford Inn at Barford St Martin, doing well under its friendly Israeli landlord; and the civilised Spread Eagle at Stourton, usefully serving at least something to eat all day under its present good management. The other new entrants are the very attractively decorated Toll Gate at Holt (good interesting food heading it firmly towards a Food Award, plenty of good beers too), the cheerful old Malet Arms at Newton Tony (a fine all-rounder under a splendid landlord), the Wheatsheaf at Ogbourne St Andrew (another good all-rounder, with interesting pictures), and the Angel at Upton Scudamore (a lively dining pub with good food – and very well equipped bedrooms). Other places right at the forefront of the Wiltshire pub scene this year are the Red Lion at Axford (a new landlord earning the pub a Food Award), the Dandy Lion in Bradford-on-Avon (unusual to find such a relaxed and distinctive all-rounder in a town of this size), the Horseshoe at Ebbesbourne Wake (a delightful country pub, earning a Star Award this year), the Beckford Arms at Fonthill Gifford (good all round), the George in Lacock (as nice a pub as you'd hope to find in this honey-pot village), and the Pear Tree at Whitley (imaginative recipes that work well in this relaxing dining pub). It is this last pub, the Pear Tree at Whitley, which earns the accolade of Wiltshire Dining Pub of the Year. The Lucky Dip section at the end of the chapter, with over 50 new entries this year, holds a lot of promise for the future: we would particularly pick out the Bunch of Grapes in Bradford-on-Avon, Horse & Groom at Charlton, Black Dog at Chilmark, Mermaid at Christian Malford, Seymour Arms at East Knoyle, Ivy at Heddington, Saladin at Little Somerford, Lamb at Semington, Carriers at Stockton, Poplars at Wingfield and White Horse at Winterbourne Bassett. Drinks prices in the county tend to be just a shade higher than the national average, though there are plenty of bargains to be had. We found particularly cheap beer at the Dandy Lion in Bradford-on-Avon, Raven at Poulshot, Smoking Dog in Malmesbury (an unusual outpost of the Welsh brewer, Brains), George and Red Lion in Lacock, Toll Gate at Holt and Waggon & Horses at Beckhampton. Wadworths is the main local brewer, and its pubs tend to be good value. Other local brewers include Hop Back, Archers, Arkells, Stonehenge, Moles and Blakemore.*

ALVEDISTON ST9723 Map 2

Crown

Village signposted on left off A30 about 12 miles W of Salisbury

This lovely 15th-c thatched inn is peacefully set in a very pretty spot. There's a cosy atmosphere in its three charming very low-beamed and partly panelled rooms, which have deep terracotta paintwork, two inglenook fireplaces, and dark oak furniture. Imaginative food, fairly priced given its quality, is listed on a blackboard, and includes starters such as soup (£3.50), cherry tomato and mozzarella salad (£4.50), wild boar sausage with onion marmalade and rosemary

(£4.95), lunchtime main courses such as linguini with roasted tomatoes, coriander and local ashmore cheese (£5.50), vegetable stir fry with crispy noodles (£5.95), half a roast chicken (£6.50), salmon fillet with ginger and chilli butter (£6.95), and evening main courses such as chicken breast with asparagus and hollandaise (£10.25), bass fillets with salsa verde (£10.50), duck breast with caramelised kumquats (£12.25), and fillet steak with pepper sauce (£14.95). One of the dining areas is no smoking. Well kept Ringwood Best, Charles Wells Bombardier and a guest such as Greene King Old Speckled Hen on handpump; darts, cribbage, dominoes and piped music. The attractive garden is nicely broken up on different levels around a thatched white well, with shrubs and rockeries among neatly kept lawns; it faces a farmyard with ponies and other animals, and there's a play area. Avoid the bedroom over the bar unless you want to stay up with the late-night chatters. *(Recommended by Dr and Mrs Michael Smith, Simon and Laura Habbishow, Maggie and Peter Shapland, Mr and Mrs W D Borthwick, Blaise Vyner)*

Free house ~ Licensee Elizabeth Pate ~ Real ale ~ Bar food (not Sun evening) ~ Restaurant ~ No credit cards ~ (01722) 780335 ~ Children in eating area of bar and family room ~ Dogs allowed in bar and bedrooms ~ Open 12-3, 6-11; 12-3, 7-10.30 Sun ~ Bedrooms: £25S/£47.50S

AXFORD SU2370 Map 2

Red Lion

Off A4 E of Marlborough; on back road Mildenhall—Ramsbury

There are lovely views over a valley from good hardwood tables and chairs on the terrace outside the restaurant at this pretty flint-and-brick pub, and you get the same views from picture windows in the restaurant and lounge. The beamed and pine-panelled bar has a big inglenook fireplace, and a pleasant mix of comfortable sofas, cask seats and other solid chairs on the parquet floor – the pictures by local artists are for sale. The restaurant and bar eating area are no smoking. Well kept Hook Norton, Wadworths 6X and an occasional guest such as Hopback Crop Circle on handpump, and a good choice of sensibly priced wines by the glass. Blackboard specials change every six weeks or so but the fairly extensive choice might include spicy crab fishcakes with cucumber relish (£4.75), tiger prawns in coconut, ginger, chilli and lemon grass sauce (£6.25), chicken breast stuffed with watercress, rocket and pesto with watercress sauce (£10.75), baked pork tenderloin in kumquat, orange and armagnac sauce (£11.25), fried red bream fillet on blackberries and shallots (£14.25), and steamed mixed seafood (£18.75). Other food includes bar snacks such as sandwiches (from £2.25), soup (£3.75), home-baked local ham and egg (£5.25), three local sausages and mash (£5.95), and steak and kidney pie (£6.95); food is cooked freshly to order, so there may be a wait. The sheltered garden has picnic-sets under cocktail parasols and swings. *(Recommended by MDN, Mrs Lesley Singleton, Mary Rayner, Angus and Rosemary Campbell, Julie and Bill Ryan, K A Bishop, Mr and Mrs A P Lawrence, CMW, JJW, Bernard Stradling)*

Free house ~ Licensee Seamus Lecky ~ Real ale ~ Bar food ~ Restaurant ~ (01672) 520271 ~ Children in eating area of bar and restaurant ~ Dogs allowed in bar ~ Open 11.30-3, 6.30-11; 12-3, 7-10.30 Sun; 12.30-3, 8-10.30 Sun in winter

BARFORD ST MARTIN SU0531 Map 2

Barford Inn

Junction of A30 and B3098 W of Salisbury

Readers particularly enjoy the really friendly welcome from the Israeli landlord at this pleasantly old-fashioned 16th-c coaching inn. The front bar has some interesting squared oak panelling and a big log fire in winter, while the other well cared for chatty interlinking rooms and bars all have dark wooden tables and red cushioned chairs; darts; piped classical music. As well as soup (£3.50), filled ciabattas (from £3.95) and a good salad bar, generous helpings of bar food might include salmon fishcakes (£6.95), steak and kidney pie, chicken curry or creole-style stuffed aubergines (£7.95), seafood linguini or wild boar chop (£9.95), 8oz sirloin (£11.95), duck breast with mixed berry and cream sauce (£14), and puddings such as treacle tart, exotic fruit crumble or cherry and almond tart (from £3.95). They do a three-course meal (£9) on Mondays, and their Friday evening Israeli barbecues (March to October, from 7pm) are well liked. Badger Best, Tanglefoot and perhaps K&B on handpump, quite a few country wines, and lots of Israeli wines; no smoking restaurant; disabled access and lavatories. There are tables on an outside terrace, and more in a back garden. *(Recommended by Keith and Sheila Baxter, Ann and Colin Hunt, Monica Cockburn, Mike Jefferies, J and B Cressey, Mr and Mrs R Cox)*

Badger ~ Tenant Ido Davids ~ Real ale ~ Bar food (12-2.30, 7-9.30) ~ Restaurant ~ (01722) 742242 ~ Children in eating area of bar and restaurant ~ Open 11-11; 12-3, 7-10.30 Sun ~ Bedrooms: £50B/£55.75B

BECKHAMPTON SU0868 Map 2

Waggon & Horses

A4 Marlborough—Calne

Silbury Hill – a vast prehistoric mound – is just towards Marlborough from here, and Avebury stone circle and the West Kennet long barrow are very close too. For many years this attractive old thatched ex-coaching inn was a heartwarming sight to coachmen coming in from what was notorious as the coldest stretch of the old Bath road, and it still makes a cheerfully refreshing stop today. The open-plan bar is welcoming, with beams in the shiny ceiling where walls have been knocked through, shiny wood floors, mustard walls, an old-fashioned high-backed settle on one side of the room with a smaller one opposite, leatherette stools, and comfortably cushioned wall benches. Generous helpings of bar food include home-made soup (£2.25), sandwiches (from £2.95), spicy thai crab cake (£3.75), chilli or breaded cod (£5.95), beef and stilton pie (£6.25), fillet steak (£8.95), daily specials such as chicken breast topped with stilton and ham or lamb shoulder with minted gravy (£6.95), and good puddings such as hot chocolate fudge cake or home-made sherry and peach trifle (£3.25); the dining area is no smoking. Well kept Wadworths IPA, JcB, 6X and a couple of guests such as Everards Tiger and Gales HBS on handpump or tapped straight from the cask, and over a dozen wines by the glass; piped music, darts, pool, dominoes, fruit machine and TV. *(Recommended by Sheila and Robert Robinson, Tim and Isobel Smith, Brian and Pat Wardrobe, Mrs Roxanne Chamberlain, Dave Braisted, Pat and Tony Martin)*

Wadworths ~ Manager Doug Shepherd ~ Real ale ~ Bar food (not Sun evening) ~ (01672) 539418 ~ Children in family room ~ Open 11-2.30, 5.30-11; 11-3, 6-11 Sat; 12-3, 7-10.30 Sun

BERWICK ST JAMES SU0639 Map 2

Boot

B3083, between A36 and A303 NW of Salisbury

Listed on a frequently changed blackboard, the imaginative and very fairly priced food at this flint and stone pub gains its Food Award this year. They use as much local produce as possible, and vegetables may come from the garden: soup (£3.95), breaded brie with raspberry coulis, seafood salad with lemon mayonnaise or warm salad of chestnuts and orange with honey sauce (£5.75), chilli or baked goats cheese on mixed leaves with a date compote (£7.95), beef in stilton stew or very good green thai chicken curry (£8.95), seared tuna on roasted vegetables (£9.95), warm scallops and crispy smoked bacon (£10.50), fried calves liver with mash or duck breast cooked in honey and ginger (£10.95), and puddings such as gooseberry and ginger cheesecake. The partly carpeted flagstoned bar has a contented cosy atmosphere, a huge winter log fire in the inglenook fireplace at one end, sporting prints over a smaller brick fireplace at the other, and houseplants on its wide window sills. Bass and Wadworths IPA and 6X on handpump are well kept, and they have a few well chosen house wines, half a dozen malts and farm cider. A charming small back no smoking dining room has a nice mix of dining chairs around four tables, and deep pink walls with an attractively mounted collection of celebrity boots. Service is very friendly and helpful; there may be unobtrusive piped jazz. The sheltered side lawn, very neatly kept with pretty flower beds, has some well spaced picnic-sets. *(Recommended by Simon Collett-Jones, Charles Moncreiffe, John Evans, KC, A E Furley, Neville and Anne Morley, Keith and Sheila Baxter, Steve Crooke, Diana Brumfit, Dr D G Twyman)*

Wadworths ~ Tenant Kathie Duval ~ Real ale ~ Bar food (12-2.30, 6.30-9.30; not Mon) ~ Restaurant ~ (01722) 790243 ~ Children in eating area of bar and family room ~ Dogs allowed in bar ~ Open 12-2.30(3 Sat), 6-11; 12-3, 7-10.30 Sun; closed Mon lunchtime

BERWICK ST JOHN ST9422 Map 2

Talbot 🍷

Village signposted from A30 E of Shaftesbury

The single long, heavily beamed bar at this attractive old village pub is simply furnished with cushioned solid wall and window seats, spindleback chairs, a high-backed built-in settle at one end, and tables that are candlelit in the evenings. There's a huge inglenook fireplace with a good iron fireback and bread ovens, and nicely shaped heavy black beams and cross-beams with bevelled corners. Bar food includes sandwiches (from £3.50), ploughman's (£4.25), ham and eggs (£5.25), battered cod (£5.50), sausage and mash (£5.95), and daily specials such as salmon fishcakes (£8.50) and beef in beer (£8.95). Well kept Bass, Hop Back GFB and Wadworths 6X on handpump and farm cider. *(Recommended by Ann and Colin Hunt, Richard Gibbs, Mrs J H S Lang, Kerry Milis)*

Free house ~ Licensees June and Chris Eason ~ Real ale ~ Bar food ~ Restaurant ~ (01747) 828222 ~ Children in restaurant ~ Dogs allowed in bar ~ Open 12-2.30, 6.30-11; 12-4 Sun; closed Sun evening, Mon

BOX ST8369 Map 2

Quarrymans Arms

Box Hill; coming from Bath on A4 turn right into Bargates 50 yds before railway bridge, then at T-junction turn left up Quarry Hill, turning left again near the top at grassy triangle; from Corsham, turn left after Rudloe Park Hotel into Beech Road, then third left on to Barnetts Hill, and finally right at the top of the hill

While many people come to this low stone building for the varied enjoyable bar food, one pleasant modernised room with an open fire is entirely set aside for drinking. They have well kept Butcombe, Moles and Wadworths 6X on handpump, and a guest or two from breweries such as Bath and Smiles. Also good wines, over 60 malt whiskies, and 10 or so old cognacs. The pub is ideally placed for cavers, potholers and walkers, all of whom generate an interesting atmosphere, and as it was once the local of the Bath stone miners, there are quite a lot of mining-related photographs and memorabilia dotted around the interior (they now run interesting guided trips down the mine itself). Popular bar food includes soup and sandwiches (both £2.50), stilton and asparagus pancake (£3.75), moules marinière (£5.25), lasagne (£7.25), home-made curries or pies (£7.95), various stir fries (£8.25), barbary duck (£12.50), and lots of daily specials such as butterfly sardine fillets with roasted tomato dressing (£4.50), penne arrabiata (£6.95), calves liver and port and mustard gravy (£8.50), butterfly pork with herb stuffing and apricot sauce (£10.50), with puddings such as sticky toffee (from £3.50); good prompt service; cribbage, dominoes, shove-ha'penny; fruit machine, and there may be piped music. A sinuous drive down a warren of lanes to get here is well rewarded by beautifully sweeping views from big windows in the dining area, which are usually enough to distract visitors from the mild untidiness. An attractive outside terrace has picnic-sets, and they play boules here (with football and cricket teams, too). *(Recommended by Mrs D Littler, Richard Stancomb, Jonathan Smith, Colin and Peggy Wilshire, Ian Phillips, Catherine Pitt, Philip Chow, Mike and Mary Carter)*

Free house ~ Licensees John and Ginny Arundel ~ Real ale ~ Bar food (12-3, 6-10) ~ Restaurant ~ (01225) 743569 ~ Children welcome ~ Dogs allowed in bar ~ Open 11-3, 6-11; 11-11 Sat; 11-10.30 Sun ~ Bedrooms: £25(£30S)/£45(£50S)

BRADFORD-ON-AVON ST8060 Map 2

Cross Guns

Avoncliff; pub is across footbridge from Avoncliff Station (road signposted Turleigh turning left off A363 heading uphill N from river in Bradford centre, and keep bearing left), and can also be reached down very steep and eventually unmade road signposted Avoncliff – keep straight on rather than turning left into village centre – from Westwood (which is signposted from B3109 and from A366, W of Trowbridge)

The wide River Avon has featured prominently in the history of this family-run dining pub. It was probably used by quarrymen and millworkers fording the river, and to this day bargees visit and rest their horses in the adjoining stable. In summer (when it can get very busy and there may be a wait for food) most people sit out at the numerous tables in the pretty floodlit and terraced gardens, with good views over water, and towards the maze of bridges and aqueducts carrying the Kennet & Avon Canal and the Bristol—Weymouth railway line through this quite narrow gorge. A Tannoy system out here announces meal orders. The stripped-stone interior includes a couple of the plain sturdy oak tables in the bar which are set aside for drinkers, and a 16th-c inglenook with a smoking chamber behind it, but the emphasis is mainly on dining (booking advised). Bar food in very big helpings includes sandwiches (from £2.90), home-made soup (£3.25), filled baked potatoes (from £4.25), salads (from £5.95), ratatouille (£6.50), steak and ale pie (£7.95), local trout (£9.95), 16oz rump steak (from £10.50), duck breast with sweet black cherry sauce (£12.95), and daily specials such as salmon fishcakes with tarragon sauce or minted lamb chops with redcurrant jelly (£7.95); puddings (£3.50). A new first-floor restaurant has lovely views over the river. A remarkable range of drinks includes well kept Bass, Millworkers Token (brewed for the pub and named after 19th-c wage tokens paid to workers at a mill owned by a former landlord), Worthington and a guest such as Greene King Old Speckled Hen on handpump, about a hundred malts, 25 country wines, and around 25 cocktails (including non-alcoholic ones); darts, table skittles, TV and piped music. Walkers are very welcome, but not their muddy boots. *(Recommended by Ian Phillips, Charles and Pauline Stride, Bill Sykes, Dr and Mrs M E Wilson, Sue Demont, Tim Barrow, Richard Stancomb, Roger Wain-Heapy, R Huggins, D Irving, E McCall, T McLean, Keith Fairbrother, Roger and Pauline Pearce, Ann and Colin Hunt, Peter and Audrey Dowsett)*

Free house ~ Licensees Jenny and Ken Roberts ~ Real ale ~ Bar food (12-10) ~ Restaurant ~ (01225) 862335/867613 ~ Children welcome ~ Dogs allowed in bar ~ Open 10-12; closed 25, 26 Dec evening ~ Bedrooms: £45B/£80B

Dandy Lion

35 Market Street

This thriving and chatty town pub has quite a continental feel, and has a happy mix of customers, including a young crowd on weekend evenings (when parts can get smoky). Big windows either side of the door give on to the street, and have a table and cushioned wooden armchair each. Working in, the pleasantly relaxed long main bar has nice high-backed farmhouse chairs, old-fashioned dining chairs, a long brocade-cushioned settle on the stripped wooden floor (there's a couple of rugs, too), sentimental and gently erotic pictures on the panelled walls, an overmantel with brussels horses, and fairy-lit hops over the bar counter. Up a few steps at the back, a snug little bare-boarded room has a lovely high-backed settle and other small ones around sturdy tables, mulberry walls, a big mirror and a piano. If there isn't one of their evening poetry readings on, there will at least be a daily aphorism chalked on a board, newspapers to read and piped jazz or pop to distract you. At lunchtime the good reasonably priced bar food includes sandwiches or soup (from £3.50), filled baguettes (from £3.75), ploughman's (from £4.95), pasta dishes (from £5.25), mushroom and sweet pepper stroganoff (£5.50), sausage and mash (£5.95), and rib-eye steak (£9.75). More elaborate evening dishes include fried sardines (£4.50/£7.95), warm duck salad (£4.75), kleftiko (£8.50), speciality 'hot stone' dishes you cook yourself (from £9.95), and daily specials such as flaked halibut and greenlip mussels in coriander dressing (£4.50), fried duck with red onions, peppers and fresh chilli (£9.50), and breaded veal escalope with avocado and tomato salsa (£11.95). Puddings might include mixed fruit and cream meringue or sticky sponge pudding (£3.75). The upstairs restaurant is candlelit at night, and has an area with antique toys and baskets of flowers. Well kept Butcombe and Wadworths IPA, 6X and JcB on handpump, and good coffee. *(Recommended by Richard Stancomb, Ian Phillips, Susan and Nigel Wilson, Dr and Mrs A K Clarke, Richard Pierce, Dr and Mrs M E Wilson, S and N McLean, David and Rhian Peters, David Carr, Sue Demont, Tim Barrow)*

Wadworths ~ Tenant Jennifer Joseph ~ Real ale ~ Bar food (12-2.15, 7-9.30) ~ Restaurant ~ (01225) 863433 ~ Children welcome ~ Dogs welcome ~ Open 10.30-3, 6-11; 11.30-3.30, 7-10.30 Sun

BRINKWORTH SU0184 Map 2

Three Crowns

The Street; B4042 Wootton Bassett—Malmesbury

The elaborate menu at this friendly dining pub covers an entire wall: as well as lunchtime snacks such as filled rolls (from £3.45), filled baked potatoes or proper ploughman's (from £6.40), dishes might include steak and kidney pie (£9.45), asparagus and Boursin cheese in filo pastry with champagne sauce (£10.95), chicken en croûte filled with prawns and stilton cheese with white wine and cream sauce (£12.85), pork tenderloin medallions with red wine sauce and cheese dumplings (£13.35), fruit-stuffed partridge on a pâté crouton with port sauce (£14.30), halibut poached in white wine and coconut milk, lime and chilli with crispy leeks (£15.95), lobster (£25), and puddings such as sticky banoffi pie and passion fruit cheesecake; all main courses are served with half a dozen fresh vegetables. As this is a popular place, you do need to get here early; most people choose to eat in the no smoking conservatory. The bar part is more traditional, with big landscape prints and other pictures, some horsebrasses on dark beams, a dresser with a collection of old bottles, tables of stripped deal, and a couple made from gigantic forge bellows, big tapestry-upholstered pews and blond chairs, and log fires. Although food is certainly the priority, a good range of real ales includes Archers Best, Boddingtons, Castle Eden, Fullers London Pride and a guest such as Moles on handpump; they have a long wine list, with at least 10 by the glass, and mulled wine in winter; sensibly placed darts, shove-ha'penny, dominoes, cribbage and chess; fruit machine, piped music. There's a light and airy no smoking garden room and a terrace with outdoor heating to the side of the conservatory. The garden stretches around the side and back, with well spaced tables and a climbing frame, and looks over a side lane to the church, and out over rolling prosperous farmland. *(Recommended by Mrs Pat Crabb, Mrs Thomas, John Saville, Mary Rayner, Susan and Nigel Wilson)*

Whitbreads ~ Lease Anthony Windle ~ Real ale ~ Bar food (12-2, 6.15-9.30) ~ Restaurant ~ (01666) 510366 ~ Children welcome till 9.30 ~ Dogs allowed in bar ~ Open 11-3, 6-11; 12-5, 6-10.30 Sun

CHICKSGROVE ST9729 Map 2

Compasses

From A30 5½ miles W of B3089 junction, take lane on N side signposted Sutton Mandeville, Sutton Row, then first left fork (small signs point the way to the pub, in Lower Chicksgrove; look out for the car park)

The welcoming atmosphere in the bar of this pleasantly relaxed old thatched house remains reassuringly traditional, with old bottles and jugs hanging from beams above the roughly timbered counter, farm tools and traps on the partly stripped stone walls, and high-backed wooden settles forming snug booths around tables on the mainly flagstoned floor. As well as soup (£3.95) and filled baguettes (from £3.45), the imaginative daily changing menu might include banana wrapped in bacon and baked with rosemary and gruyère sauce (£4.25), goats cheese tartlet with tomato, basil and pesto (£4.95), moules marinière (£5.95), steak and kidney pie (£7.95), chicken breast with dolcelatte and smoked sausage (£9.95), fried monkfish with thai cream sauce (£10.95), bass stuffed with garlic, lemon and tomato or shoulder of lamb roasted in soy, red wine and garlic (£11.95), and puddings such as chocolate and prune cake, passion fruit cheesecake and brioche bread and butter pudding (£3.75); all meals are served with a good choice of vegetables. Real ales on handpump include well kept Bass, Chicksgrove Churl (brewed for the pub by Wadworths), Wadworths 6X and perhaps a guest such as Ringwood Best, and they have six wines by the glass; cribbage, dominoes, bagatelle and shove-ha'penny. The quiet garden and flagstoned farm courtyard are very pleasant places to sit, and there's a nice walk to Sutton Mandeville church and back via Nadder Valley. Be warned, they close on Tuesdays after bank holiday Mondays. *(Recommended by Rachel Cooper, John Braine-Hartnell, Martin and Karen Wake, Stephanie and Kamal Thapa, Keith and Sheila Baxter, H D Wharton, Jeff and Wendy Williams, Ann and Colin Hunt, L Topping, R Preston, J F Stackhouse)*

Free house ~ Licensee Alan Stoneham ~ Real ale ~ Bar food (not Sun evenings) ~ Restaurant ~ (01722) 714318 ~ Children welcome ~ Dogs welcome ~ Open 12-3, 6-11(7-10.30 Sun); closed Mon except bank hols, then cl Tues ~ Bedrooms: £40S/£55S

CORSHAM ST8670 Map 2

Two Pigs

A4, Pickwick

The choice of beer changes as barrels empty at this truly traditional little drinker's pub (no food or under-21s). Alongside Hop Back Summer Lightning and Stonehenge Pigswill, you can expect to find a couple of well kept changing guests from brewers such as Barge & Barrel, Bullmastiff and Teignworthy; also a range of country wines. The atmosphere, always chatty and friendly, is perhaps at its headiest on a Monday night, when live blues draws a big crowd into the very narrow and dimly lit flagstoned bar. The admirably eccentric feel owes much to the charismatic landlord, who has amassed a zany collection of bric-a-brac in the 14 or so years he's been in charge, including enamel advertising signs on the wood-clad walls, pig-theme ornaments, and old radios. A good mix of customers gathers around the long dark wood tables and benches, and friendly staff provide good prompt service; piped blues. A covered yard outside is called the Sty. Beware of their opening times – the pub is closed every lunchtime, except on Sunday. *(Recommended by Catherine Pitt, Jonathan Smith, Dr and Mrs A K Clarke, Dr and Mrs M E Wilson)*

Free house ~ Licensees Dickie and Ann Doyle ~ Real ale ~ No credit cards ~ (01249) 712515 ~ Blues Mon evening ~ Open 7-11; 12-2.30, 7-10.30 Sun

CORTON ST9340 Map 2

Dove

Village signposted from A36 at Upton Lovell, SE of Warminster; this back road on the right bank of the River Wylye is a quiet alternative to the busy A36 Warminster—Wilton

Pretty in summer with climbing roses, this cottagey stone country pub is set back from the road by a front courtyard, and has tables on the neatly kept back lawn. The attractively furnished main bar is focused on a big central fireplace, with a huge winter log fire giving it a warm homely feel. There is a mix of carpeting, flagstones and oak flooring, with some good pictures, a mix of chairs and cushioned wall seats, and dining tables in areas off. The conservatory is no smoking; piped music. Good well presented food includes reasonably priced changing lunchtime snacks such as interestingly filled baguettes (£4.75), burger with stilton or cheddar (£7.25), grilled organic lambs liver and smoked bacon or braised oxtail and root vegetables (£7.50), battered haddock or beef and fruit curry (£7.95), and pricier more elaborate evening dishes such as fried beef medallions wrapped in smoked bacon with stilton cream sauce (£15.25), and roast guinea fowl with damson and port sauce and crushed parsley potatoes (£16.25). The Sunday menu is limited to starters, roast (£7.50), and puddings. Well kept Hop Back GFB, Oakhill Best and a guest such as Fullers London Pride on handpump, good wines by the glass, attentive friendly staff, daily papers. *(Recommended by Sue Demont, Tim Barrow, James Woods, Julie and Bill Ryan, Mrs Pam Mattinson, Peter Meister)*

Free house ~ Licensee William Harrison-Allan ~ Real ale ~ Bar food (12-2.30, 7-9.30) ~ Restaurant ~ (01985) 850109 ~ Children welcome ~ Dogs allowed in bar and bedrooms ~ Open 12-3(4 Sat), 6.30-11; 12-4, 7-11 Sun ~ Bedrooms: £49.50S/£75S

DEVIZES SU0061 Map 2

Bear

Market Place

This imposing old coaching inn has provided shelter to distinguished guests as diverse as King George III and Dr Johnson, and is a good base for exploring the area – as a warm up, Wadworths brewery, where you can buy beer in splendid old-fashioned half-gallon earthenware jars, is only a stone's throw from here. The relaxed chatty atmosphere in the big main carpeted bar with its black winged wall settles and muted red cloth-upholstered bucket armchairs around oak tripod tables is made cosier in winter by roaring log fires. Separated from the main bar by some steps and an old-fashioned glazed screen, a room named after the portrait painter Thomas Lawrence (his father ran the establishment in the 1770s) has dark oak-panelled walls, a parquet floor, shining copper pans on the mantelpiece above the big open fireplace, and plates around the walls; part of it is no smoking. Reasonably priced decent bar food includes home-made soup (£2.95), sandwiches (from £2.75), filled baked potatoes or baguettes (from £3.95), ploughman's or omelettes (from £4.50), ham and egg (£4.75), fish and chips (£5.75), daily specials such as beef in beer casserole with dumplings (£4.95), fish of the day (£5.25), and home-made puddings (£2.95); there are buffet meals in the Lawrence Room – you can eat these in the bar too. On Saturday nights they have a good value set menu in the old-fashioned restaurant. Well kept Wadworths IPA and 6X and a guest on handpump, over a dozen wines by the glass, a good choice of malt whiskies, and freshly squeezed juices from a classic bar counter with shiny black woodwork and small panes of glass. They do good breakfasts. *(Recommended by Alan and Paula McCully, Mary Rayner, Dr and Mrs A K Clarke, the Didler)*

Free house ~ Licensee Keith Dickenson ~ Real ale ~ Bar food (11-2.30, 7-9) ~ Restaurant ~ (01380) 722444 ~ Children welcome ~ Dogs allowed in bar and bedrooms ~ Open 11-11; 12-10.30 Sun; closed 25 and 26 Dec ~ Bedrooms: £45B/£75B

EBBESBOURNE WAKE ST9824 Map 2

Horseshoe ★

On A354 S of Salisbury, right at signpost at Coombe Bissett; village is around 8 miles further on

This unspoilt and welcoming old country pub, tucked away in fine downland, seems to have found the magic formula for keeping customers happy. It deserves all the praise it gets for its good home-cooking, well kept ales and friendly service; the landlord, very friendly and accommodating without being at all intrusive, couldn't be better. There are fresh home-grown flowers on the tables in the beautifully kept bar, with lanterns, farm tools and other bric-a-brac crowded along its beams, and an open fire; a conservatory extension seats 10 people. Enjoyable bar food includes lunchtime ham and eggs (£6.50), curry (£8.95), lambs liver and bacon (£9.25), fish bake or beef, bacon and shallots in ale (£9.50), and evening dishes such as lamb cutlets in port sauce or fillet steak (£13.25), and half a honey-roasted duckling in gooseberry sauce (£15). Drinks include well kept Adnams Broadside, Ringwood Best, Wadworths 6X and a guest such as Stonehenge Pigswill, tapped from the row of casks behind the bar, as well as farm cider, country wines and several malt whiskies. Booking is advisable for the small no smoking restaurant, especially at weekends when it can fill quite quickly. There are pleasant views over the steep sleepy valley of the River Ebble from seats in its pretty little garden, three goats in a paddock at the bottom of the garden, and a couple of playful dogs. The barn opposite is now used as a gymnasium; good walks nearby. *(Recommended by Margaret Ross, Mike and Shelley Woodroffe, Jayne and Peter Capp, the Didler, Peter and Giff Bennett, Simon Donan, W W Burke, Richard Gibbs, Dr and Mrs J F Head, Dr and Mrs Michael Smith, MP, Douglas and Ann Hare, J V Dadswell, Tom Clay, Maurice Averay, Di and Mike Gillam, Martin Weinberg, Mr and Mrs W D Borthwick, Dr D G Twyman)*

Free house ~ Licensees Anthony and Patricia Bath ~ Real ale ~ Bar food (not Sun evenings or Mon except bank hols) ~ Restaurant ~ (01722) 780474 ~ Children in restaurant ~ Open 12-3, 6.30-11; 12-4, 7-10.30 Sun; closed Mon lunchtime ~ Bedrooms: /£60B

FONTHILL GIFFORD ST9232 Map 2

Beckford Arms

Off B3089 W of Wilton at Fonthill Bishop

On the edge of a fine parkland estate with a lake and sweeping vistas, this unchanging country house has an enjoyably civilised atmosphere. The smartly informal rooms are big, light and airy, with stripped bare wood, a parquet floor and a pleasant mix of tables with church candles. In winter, a big log fire burns in the lounge bar, which leads into a light and airy back garden room with a high pitched plank ceiling and picture windows looking on to a terrace. Locals tend to gather in the straightforward public bar, with darts, fruit machine, pool, TV and piped music. Made from local produce wherever possible, well prepared bar food includes good filled baguettes (from £4.95), soup (£3.75), toasted goats cheese (£4.75), ploughman's (from £5.95), sausage and mash or feta, black olive and plum tomato salad (£7.95), prawn and salmon fishcakes with basil and lime reduction or thai chicken curry (£8.95), and daily specials such as tagliatelle carbonara or smoked salmon salad (£8.95), duck breast with honey and apricots (£10.95), and bass with fresh ginger (£13.95). Well kept Greene King Abbot, Hop Back Best, Timothy Taylors Landlord and a weekly guest such as Hop Back Crop Circle on handpump. This place is well run by friendly licensees and their polite staff. *(Recommended by Phyl and Jack Street, Stephen Kiley, Tony Gayfer, Ann and Colin Hunt, Richard Gibbs, John Evans)*

Free house ~ Licensees Karen and Eddie Costello ~ Real ale ~ Bar food (12-2, 7-9(9.30 Fri, Sat)) ~ Restaurant ~ (01747) 870385 ~ Children welcome ~ Dogs allowed in bar and bedrooms ~ Open 12-11; 12-10.30 Sun ~ Bedrooms: £40S/£70B

FORD NT9538 Map 2

White Hart ★

A420 Chippenham—Bristol; follow Colerne sign at E side of village to find pub

Ideal for a weekend break, this fine stone-built country inn is in stunning countryside. The grounds are delightful in summer, when peacocks strut around the garden and you can sit on the terrace by the trout stream that babbles under a little stone bridge; there are good walks in the hills beyond the pub, too. The cosy bar has heavy black beams supporting the white-painted boards of the ceiling, tub armchairs around polished wooden tables, small pictures and a few advertising mirrors on the walls, and an ancient fireplace (inscribed 1553); pool on a circular table, dominoes, TV, board games and piped music. A younger crowd enjoys it here in the late evening. You will need to book for the enjoyable, interesting food, which might include soup (£3.50), smoked haddock and mozzarella fishcakes (£4.25), salmon with prawn and lemon butter (£8.50), chargrilled vegetable terrine with tagliatelle, tomato and pesto sauce (£8.95), lamb braised in red wine and redcurrant (£9.50), roast barramundi fillet with sesame and herb butter (£11.95), fillet steak with stilton and cream (£13.95), and puddings such as crème brûlée and sticky toffee pudding (from £3.95). They have fine wines (including about eight by the glass), farm cider, a dozen malt whiskies, and well kept Bass, Ind Coope Burton, Tetleys and Wadworths 6X; friendly and helpful service. Bedrooms are spacious and well equipped, and the breakfasts excellent.

(Recommended by Mrs D Littler, Mr and Mrs McKay, Michael Doswell, J F M and M West, Joy and Colin Rorke, Frank Willy, David and Nina Pugsley, Guy Vowles, Dr and Mrs A K Clarke, Andrew Barker, Claire Jenkins, M G Hart, John Robertson, Brian and Bett Cox, MDN, Susan and Nigel Wilson, Colin McKerrow, James A Waller, B J Harding, Nigel and Sue Foster, Howard Bateman, Ian Phillips)

Eldridge Pope ~ Manager Colin Rolfe ~ Real ale ~ Bar food (12-2.15, 7-9.30(10 Fri, Sat); 12-8.15 Sun) ~ Restaurant ~ (01249) 782213 ~ Children in restaurant ~ Dogs welcome ~ Open 11-3, 5-11; 11-11 Sat; 12-11 Sun; closed 25 Dec evening ~ Bedrooms: £64B/£84B

GREAT HINTON ST9059 Map 2

Linnet

3½ miles E of Trowbridge, village signposted off A361 opposite Lamb at Semington

Emphasis at this attractive old brick pub is on the imaginative food, which is freshly prepared and beautifully presented by the dedicated chef/landlord. The changing menu might include soup (£3.50), haddock and chive fishcakes with langoustine sauce, or grilled asparagus in puff pastry with orange butter sauce (£4.50), filled focaccia (from £6.25), salads (from £6.50), tagliatelle with smoked chicken, asparagus and wild mushrooms with cheddar and herb sauce (£7.75), goats cheese and sweet potato spring roll with roasted cherry tomato compote on pesto (£9.95), baked skate, prawn and filo spinach parcels with sorrel cream sauce, or grilled rib-eye steak on smoked bacon, mushroom and potato cake with rosemary sauce (£11.95), and puddings such as summer berry pavlova with mascarpone and elderflower cream (£4.75); two-course set lunch (£10.25). The little bar to the right of the door has a blue-green carpet and lots of photographs of the pub and the brewery, there are bookshelves in a snug end part; the cosy restaurant is candlelit at night. Well kept Wadworths IPA and 6X on handpump, a couple of dozen malt whiskies, and quite a few wines. In summer, the flowering tubs and window boxes with seats dotted among them are quite a sight.

(Recommended by Michael Doswell, Mr and Mrs J P Keates, Roger Bridgeman, J R and J Moon)

Wadworths ~ Tenant Jonathan Furby ~ Real ale ~ Bar food ~ Restaurant ~ (01380) 870354 ~ Children in restaurant ~ Dogs allowed in bar ~ Open 11-2.30, 6-11; 12-3.30, 7-10.30 Sun; closed Mon

HEYTESBURY ST9242 Map 2

Angel

High Street; just off A36 E of Warminster

In a quiet village just below the Salisbury Plain, this 16th-c inn is a very pleasant place to stay in, with imaginative bar food, well kept ales, and impeccable service. The spacious homely lounge on the right, with well used overstuffed armchairs and sofas and a good fire, opens into a charming terracotta-painted back dining room, with navy curtains and hand-painted plates from Portugal. This in turn opens on to an attractive secluded courtyard garden. On the left, a long beamed bar has a convivial evening atmosphere, open fire, some attractive prints and old photographs, and straightforward tables and chairs; piped music. Good food includes home-made soup (£3.75), filo prawns with sweet chilli mayonnaise (£6.95), thai-style fishcakes with sweet chilli sauce, twice-baked goats cheese, tomato and basil soufflé or wild boar and apple sausages on mustard mash (£7.95), local pork medallions (£8.95), honey-glazed lamb shank (£9.75), grilled bass on rocket, pesto and tomato salad (£12.95), puddings such as cappuccino crème brûlée, individual summer pudding and bread and butter pudding (£3.75), and English cheeses (£5). A good choice of very well kept beers includes Ringwood Best and a couple of guests such as Marstons Pedigree and Ringwood Boondoggle on handpump; also around a dozen wines by the glass. *(Recommended by Keith and Sheila Baxter, Michael Huberty, Jeff and Wendy Williams, Lynn Sharpless, James Woods, Hugh Roberts, Chris Richards, John Robertson, Mr and Mrs H D Brierly, Susan and Nigel Wilson, M G Hart, Julie and Bill Ryan, Ann and Colin Hunt, Sue Demont, Tim Barrow)*

Free house ~ Licensees Jeremy Giddings and Brad Rossiter ~ Real ale ~ Bar food (12-6, 7-9.30; 12-2, 7-9 in winter) ~ Restaurant ~ (01985) 840330 ~ Children welcome ~ Dogs allowed in bar and bedrooms ~ Open 11.30-11; 12-10.30 Sun; 11.30-3, 6.30-11 Mon-Sat and 12-3, 7-10.30 Sun in winter ~ Bedrooms: £50B/£65B

HINDON ST9132 Map 2

Angel

B3089 Wilton—Mere

The imaginative menu at this 18th-c coaching inn changes daily, and might include cream of asparagus soup with mint and crème fraîche (£3.50), grilled ciabatta open sandwiches (from £4.50), grilled sardines with oregano, lemon and garlic (£5.95), fresh fig, mozzarella and parma ham salad with pine kernels (£6), roast sausages and mash (£6.95), braised wild rabbit with tagliatelle (£11.95), seared yellowfin tuna with coriander and lime butter with sweet potato purée and chilli jam (£12), guinea fowl breast with a carrot, chilli and coriander pancake and creamed butternut purée (£13), roast cod with clam, potato and sweet corn chowder and toulouse sausage (£13.25), puddings such as baked egg custard tart with blackcurrant sorbet, steamed orange and cardamom pudding with ginger custard (£4.50), and an interesting cheeseboard (£6.25). They charge extra for added vegetables. The traditional candlelit bar is painted a warm red, and has a good log fire, a nice mix of old tables and chairs on flagstones, Victorian prints and artefacts, and fresh flowers; daily papers. Off the entrance hall a civilised no smoking lounge has another log fire, grey panelling, armchairs, settees, a cushioned antique settle, country magazines and a shelf displaying the landlady's collection of cheese dishes. The long cream dining room has a huge window that lets you view the goings on in the kitchen, and big photographs of the surrounding area; well kept Bass and Wadworths IPA and 6X on handpump, good house wines including about a dozen by the glass. The back courtyard, prettily lit at night, has good teak chairs around tables under cocktail parasols, and big flowering tubs. *(Recommended by Wally and Irene Nunn, Betsy and Peter Little, Duncan and Lisa Cripps, John Evans, Norman and June Williams, KC, Mr and Mrs A H Young, Mike Gorton, Sue Demont, Tim Barrow, P and J Shapley, Simon Chell, Lady Greig, John Parker, W W Burke, Geoff Palmer, Charles Moncreiffe, Ian Phillips, Mr and Mrs J McRobert)*

Free house ~ Licensee Penny Simpson ~ Real ale ~ Bar food (not Sun evening) ~ Restaurant ~ (01747) 820696 ~ Children in eating area of bar and restaurant ~ Dogs allowed in bar ~ Open 11-11; 12-10.30 Sun; 11-3, 6-11 in winter ~ Bedrooms: £50B/£60B

HOLT ST8561 Map 2

Toll Gate

Ham Green; B3107 W of Melksham

Furnished and decorated with real flair, this foody pub doesn't at all make locals or people just dropping in for a drink feel like second-class citizens – a trap which now snares all too many of its rivals in this region. Besides good strong coffee, they have farm cider and eight or so wines by the glass, as well as half a dozen well kept changing beers on handpump, bought directly from a good range of interesting smaller brewers such as Becketts, Exmoor, Fullers, Golden Hill, Ring o' Bells and West Berkshire. One leg of the relaxed L-shaped bar has cosy settees and a log fire watched over by big stone cats – there are also two pub cats. The other leg is more adapted to eating (one lovely table gleaming in the corner was put together for the pub from three salvaged flooring planks); there are plenty of hunting prints on pinkish walls, some willow-pattern plates on black panelling, one or two beams in the venetian red ceiling, rugs on old quarry tiles, and soft lighting including table lamps. In a former life the pub was a weaver's shed, and the charming high-raftered restaurant, up some steps from the dining area, was a chapel for the workers. It's eclectically decorated with bright cushions on sturdy pews and other country furniture, attractive bric-a-brac including lots of Japanese parasols, all interesting lit through the original church windows. The good beautifully presented food includes a good value set lunch menu (two courses £9.95, three £11.95), lunchtime snacks such as pea and ham soup (£4), English cheeses (£5.75), club sandwiches or grilled smoked kippers topped with a poached egg (£6.50), fondue for two (£9), and more elaborate dishes such as baby spinach, feta, almond and crouton salad or assiette of smoked fish (£5.50), fried scallops on a pea purée (£6.50), plaice with lemon and tarragon butter (£12.50), gilthead bream on jerk spice and mediterranean vegetables (£14), pork tenderloin marinated in moroccan spices or fried tuna on niçoise salad (£15), and puddings such as home-grown rhubarb and raspberry fool or ricotta, fruit and chocolate torte with orange sauce (from £4); extra vegetables are £2.50. Service is kind and helpful; there may be piped music. The gents' is worth a look for its colourful murals. There are picnic-sets out on the back terrace. *(Recommended by Dr and Mrs M E Wilson, Catherine Pitt, Mr and Mrs A H Young)*

Free house ~ Licensees Alison Ward-Baptiste and Alexander Venables ~ Real ale ~ Bar food ~ Restaurant ~ (01225) 782326 ~ Children in restaurant and family room ~ Open 11.30-3, 6-11; 12-3 Sun; closed Sun evening, Mon

KILMINGTON ST7736 Map 2

Red Lion £ 🛏

Pub on B3092 Mere—Frome, 2½ miles S of Maiden Bradley; 3 miles from A303 Mere turn-off

Down to earth and pubby, this 15th-c ivy-covered country inn is owned by the National Trust. The snug low-ceilinged bar which has a good local atmosphere (particularly in the evenings) is pleasantly furnished with a curved high-backed settle and red leatherette wall and window seats on the flagstones, photographs of locals pinned up on the black beams, and a couple of big fireplaces (one with a fine old iron fireback) with log fires in winter. A newer big-windowed no smoking eating area is decorated with brasses, a large leather horse collar, and hanging plates. Simple very good value satisfying bar food is served at lunchtime only, and includes soup (£1.80), sandwiches (from £2.80, toasted £3.25), filled baked potatoes (from £3.45), ploughman's (from £3.95), cornish pasties (from £4), steak and kidney or lamb and apricot pie (£4.45), creamy fish pie (£4.50), meat or vegetable lasagne (£6.75), and maybe one or two daily specials; last orders for food at 1.50pm. Well kept Butcombe, Butts Jester and a guest beer on handpump, farm cider, various pressés such as elderflower, citrus, limeflower and lemongrass and ginger, and monthly changing wines; sensibly placed darts, dominoes, shove-ha'penny and cribbage. There are picnic-sets in the big attractive garden, where Kim the labrador is often to be found. It's popular with walkers – you can buy locally made walking sticks, and a gate gives on to the lane which leads to White Sheet Hill, where there is riding, hang gliding and radio-controlled gliders. Stourhead Gardens are only a mile away. No dogs at lunchtime. *(Recommended by B, M and P Kendall, H D Wharton, KC, Michael Doswell, John Evans, Mike Gorton, Simon Collett-Jones)*

Free house ~ Licensee Chris Gibbs ~ Real ale ~ Bar food (12-1.50) ~ No credit cards ~ (01985) 844263 ~ Children in eating area of bar till 9pm ~ Open 11.30-2.30, 6.30-11; 12-3, 7-10.30 Sun ~ Bedrooms: /£40

LACOCK ST9168 Map 2

George

West Street

An old favourite with readers, this unspoilt homely old pub is given a special feel by the unfalteringly friendly welcome from the long-serving landlord, his family and staff. It's in a famously well preserved National Trust village, and has been licensed continuously since the 17th c. A talking point here is the big treadwheel set into the outer breast of the original great central fireplace. This used to turn a spit for roasting, and was worked by a dog. The low-beamed bar is comfortable and relaxing, with upright timbers in the place of knocked-through walls making cosy rambling corners, candles on tables (even at lunchtime), armchairs and windsor chairs, seats in the stone-mullioned windows, and flagstones just by the counter; piped music. The well kept Wadworths IPA, JcB and 6X are reasonably priced, and there's a decent choice of wines. It does get busy here, so you might think of booking for the generously served enjoyable bar food, which includes snacks such as sandwiches (from £2.50), filled baguettes (from £4.50), ploughman's (from £4.95), starters such as soup (£3.25), goats cheese salad (£4.95) and breaded mini lobster tails (£4.95), main courses such as mushroom nut roast with port and cranberry sauce (£7.25), chicken breast stuffed with wild mushrooms wrapped in bacon with blue cheese sauce (£9.75), sliced duck breast with plum and ginger sauce (£11.50), beef medallions in red wine sauce (£11.95), bream stuffed with sun-dried tomato, pesto and olives or king prawns in garlic butter (£12.95), daily specials such as lasagne or several different pies (£7.50), and home-made puddings such as lemon cheesecake and raspberry and hazelnut roulade (£4.50); fresh vegetables and real chips. The barn restaurant is no smoking. There are picnic-sets with umbrellas in the back garden, as well as a play area with swings, and a bench in front that overlooks the main street. The bedrooms (very highly praised by readers) are up at the landlord's farmhouse, with free transport to and from the pub. It's a nice area for walking. *(Recommended by Bob and Val Collman, David and Nina Pugsley, Mrs Jean Clarke, R Huggins, D Irving, E McCall, T McLean, Joan and Michel Hooper-Immins, Robert W Tapsfield, Roger and Jenny Huggins, Jenny and Chris Wilson, Roger Wain-Heapy, Mrs Thomas, Richard and Margaret Peers, Mr and Mrs C R Little, Alan and Paula McCully, Mrs D Littler)*

Wadworths ~ Tenant John Glass ~ Real ale ~ Bar food (12-2, 6-9.30) ~ Restaurant ~ (01249) 730263 ~ Children welcome ~ Open 10-2.30, 5-11; 10-11(10.30 Sun) Sat

Red Lion

High Street; village signposted off A350 S of Chippenham

Owned by the National Trust, this imposing Georgian inn has a lively pubby atmosphere, particularly towards the latter half of the evening, when younger people congregate here. The long and airy cream-painted bar is divided into cosy areas by open handrails, and has distressed heavy dark wood tables and tapestried chairs. There are turkey rugs on the partly flagstoned floor, a fine old log fire at one end, aged-looking paintings, and branding irons hanging from the ceiling. The snug is very cosy, with comfortable leather armchairs. Bar food includes soup (£2.50), sandwiches (from £2.75), whitebait (£3.95), ploughman's (from £5.50), scampi (£7.95), 8oz rump steak (£9.95), daily specials such as pie of the day, crab salad, spinach and goats cheese strudel, chicken roulade or pork, sherry and mushroom casserole (£6.95), salmon steak (£7.95), and puddings (£3.25); the top dining area is no smoking. Wadworths IPA, JcB, 6X and one of their seasonal beers on handpump, and several malt whiskies; fruit machine and piped music. Handy for Lacock Abbey and the Fox Talbot Museum. *(Recommended by R Huggins, D Irving, E McCall, T McLean, Trevor Owen, John Robertson, Tony and Mary Pygott)*

Wadworths ~ Manager Chris Chappell ~ Real ale ~ Bar food (12-2, 6(7 Sun)-9) ~ Restaurant ~ (01249) 730456 ~ Children welcome ~ Dogs allowed in bar ~ Open 11.30-3, 6-11; 11-11 Sat; 12-10.30 Sun; 11.30-6, 6-11 Sat and 12-3, 7-10.30 Sun in winter ~ Bedrooms: £55B/£75B

Rising Sun

Bewley Common, Bowden Hill – out towards Sandy Lane, up hill past Abbey; OS Sheet 173 map reference 935679

Views from the big two-level terrace at this cheery unpretentious pub extend some 25 miles over the Avon valley – the sunsets can be memorable. Inside, the three welcoming little rooms have been knocked together to form one simply furnished area, with a mix of old chairs and basic kitchen tables on stone floors, stuffed animals and birds, country pictures, and open fires. They have farm cider, and well kept Moles Best, Molecatcher, Molennium, Tap Bitter, one of their seasonal ales, and perhaps a guest such as Everards Tiger on handpump – if you're confused about which to choose, the friendly staff may offer you a taster; darts, cribbage and board games. Generously served home-made food includes good baguettes (from £3.25), ploughman's (£5.50), ham and egg (£6), battered cod and chips or pasta with tomato sauce (£6.50), crispy duck pancakes, spinach and pepper tart or stir-fried vegetables (£7), and particularly popular stir fries such as beef teriyaki or thai chicken curry (£8.50); only roast on Sunday. *(Recommended by Martin and Karen Wake, Dr B and Mrs P B Baker, Andrew Barker, Claire Jenkins, Dr and Mrs M E Wilson, Pat and Tony Martin)*

Free house ~ Licensees Sue Sturdy and Roger Catte ~ Real ale ~ Bar food (12-2, 7-9(9.30 Fri, Sat); not Sun-Tues evening) ~ (01249) 730363 ~ Children in eating area of bar till 9pm ~ Dogs welcome ~ Live music every Weds and alternate Sun from 3pm ~ Open 12-3, 6-11; 12-10.30 Sun; closed 25, 26 Dec evening, 1 Jan

LIMPLEY STOKE ST7861 Map 2

Hop Pole

Coming S from Bath on A36 take B3108 at traffic lights signed Bradford on Avon, turn right of main road at sharp left-hand bend before the railway bridge, pub is 100 yds on right (car park just before on left)

You may already have spotted this cream stone pub (with its name deeply incised on the front wall) in the film *Remains of the Day*. Known as the Hop Pole as far back as records exist, this 16th-c former monk's wine lodge is said to have had a hop plant growing in front for 500 years. The licensees are welcoming, and the atmosphere is happily unhurried; at quiet times you'll often find a cheerful bunch of locals in the cosy dark-panelled room on the right (it can get very crowded when the pub is busy). This has red velvet cushions on settles in its alcoves, some slat-back and captain's chairs on its turkey carpet, lantern lighting, a log fire, and Bass, Butcombe, Courage Best and a changing guest such as Jennings Cumberland on handpump; darts, shove ha'penny, bar billiards, cribbage, dominoes, also TV and piped music. The roomier left-hand lounge (with an arch to a cream-walled inner room) is mostly laid for diners, and also has dark wood panelling, and a log-effect gas fire. A wide choice of bar food (you may need to book) includes filled baps (from £2.50), deep-fried brie in cranberry sauce (£3.95), home-made pies (from £6.45), local trout (£8.75), scotch salmon (£8.95), daily specials such as broccoli and stilton bake (£6.25), salmon and crab fishcakes (£8.75), grilled bass with cumin crust and red onion marmalade (£9.25), thai-style monkfish (£9.75), beef wellington (£12.25), Sunday roasts (from £6.25), and children's meals (from £2.95). The restaurant is no smoking. An attractive enclosed garden behind has rustic benches, a terrace and pond, and boules. This is just a short stroll from the Kennet & Avon Canal and the River Avon, and makes a good base for waterside walks. *(Recommended by Pat and Robert Watt, Roger Wain-Heapy, Dr and Mrs M E Wilson, Susan and Nigel Wilson)*

Latona Leisure ~ Managers Bob and Mich Williams ~ Real ale ~ Bar food ~ Restaurant ~ (01225) 723134 ~ Children in restaurant and family room ~ Dogs allowed in bar ~ Open 11-2.30, 6-11; 12-3, 7-10.30 Sun; closed 25 Dec

LITTLE CHEVERELL ST9853 Map 2

Owl

Low Road; just off B3098 Westbury—Upavon, W of A360

Tables and benches on a new raised deck make the most of this cosy little village local's peaceful setting. They look down over a lovely tall ash- and willow-lined back garden which often reverberates with the sound of wood pigeons cooing, and rustic picnic-sets on a long split-level lawn which runs down to a brook. Inside, the peaceful and neatly traditional bar and a snugger room at the back have light terracotta walls, black beams, a pleasant jumble of furnishings including a big welsh dresser and bench table, plenty of chairs, stools, high-backed settles and tables, and farm tools and split-cane fishing rods on the walls. There are fresh flowers on the tables, local papers and guides to read, a gently ticking clock, and two or three stuffed owls behind the bar. Under friendly new licensees, bar food might include sandwiches (from £3.45), vegetable pie (£7.95), steak and ale pie (£8.95), thai green chicken curry (£9.95), shark steak with tomato and pesto (£10.95), bass with lemon and parsley stuffing (£13.95), Sunday roast (£6.95), and puddings such as chocolate mousse with a biscuit base, and apple and blackberry pie (from £3.95). Well kept Greene King IPA, Wadworths 6X and a couple of guests such as Cotleigh Tawny and Fullers London Pride, 21 wines by the glass, and 21 malt whiskies; darts and piped music. *(Recommended by Susan and Nigel Wilson, Pat and Robert Watt, Dennis Jenkin)*

Free house ~ Licensees Jamie Carter and Paul Green ~ Real ale ~ Bar food (11.30-3, 6.30-10.30) ~ Restaurant ~ (01380) 812263 ~ Children welcome ~ Dogs welcome ~ Open 11.30-3, 6-11; 11-11 Sat; 12-10.30 Sun; 12-4, 7-10.30 Sun in winter ~ Bedrooms: £35S/£55S

LOWER CHUTE SU3153 Map 2

Hatchet

The Chutes well signposted via Appleshaw off A342, 2½ miles W of Andover

This timeless 16th-c thatched cottage is picture-postcard pretty. An unchanging friendly local atmosphere warms the very low-beamed bar, with its mix of captain's chairs and cushioned wheelbacks around oak tables, and splendid 17th-c fireback in the huge fireplace (which has a big winter log fire). Well kept ales on handpump include Greene King IPA, Otter and Timothy Taylors Landlord, and there's a range of country wines; friendly helpful staff; newspapers, cribbage and dominoes; there may be piped music. Bar food includes sandwiches or baguettes (from £3.25, steak £4.95), home-made soup (£3.50), warm goats cheese salad (£4.75), ploughman's (£4.95), thai vegetable stir fry (£5.75), liver and bacon (£5.95), salmon fishcake with dill sauce (£6.50), lime and chilli chicken or steak and stout pie (£6.95), and moules marinière or grilled trout (£7.75). Thursday night is curry night, when you can eat as much as you like (£6.50); no smoking restaurant. There are seats out on a terrace by the front car park, or on the side grass, as well as a children's sandpit. *(Recommended by Alan and Gill Bull, David and Ruth Shillitoe, Ian Phillips, Rob Webster, Lynn Sharpless, Mrs J H S Lang, Mr and Mrs R Davies)*

Free house ~ Licensee Jeremy McKay ~ Real ale ~ Bar food (12-2.15, 6.30-9.45) ~ Restaurant ~ (01264) 730229 ~ Children in restaurant and family room ~ Dogs allowed in bar ~ Open 11.30-3, 6-11; 12-4, 7-10.30 Sun ~ Bedrooms: /£55S

Prices of main dishes usually include vegetables or a side salad.

MALMESBURY ST9287 Map 2

Smoking Dog

High Street

Gaining a Beer Award this year for its range of up to seven real ales, this double-fronted mid-terrace 17th-c pub has a good friendly local atmosphere (with a younger crowd on some evenings) in its two smallish front bars, with flagstones, dark woodwork, cushioned bench seating, big pine tables and a blazing log fire. A flagstoned corridor with local notices on the walls leads to a bare-boards back bistro. As well as a lunchtime snack menu with baguettes (from £4.75, steak £5.50), beefburger (£6.95) and grilled smoked haddock fillet with cheddar and ale (£7.75), bar food might include potato, broccoli and leek galette with garlic and cream cheese (£9.25), red snapper with stem ginger, spring onions and lemon syrup (£11.50), grilled rib-eye steak with spicy butter (£11.75), similar daily specials, and puddings such as apple and blackcurrant crumble and brown sugar pavlova with raspberries and clotted cream (£4.25). Archers, Brains Bitter, Revd James and SA and Wadworths 6X are either tapped straight from the cask or on handpump, alongside one or two guests such as Badger Tanglefoot and Timothy Taylors Landlord; piped music, TV. The friendly staff are helpful, and kind to children (they keep Scrabble, dominoes and so forth). Steep steps lead up to half a dozen tables in a small back garden with pleasant views out over the town. *(Recommended by Dr and Mrs A K Clarke, James Woods, P M Grasby, Catherine Pitt, Mike Ridgway, Sarah Miles)*

Brains ~ Managers Ian and Sara Shackleton ~ Real ale ~ Bar food (12-2, 7-9.30) ~ Restaurant ~ (01666) 825823 ~ Children welcome if eating ~ Dogs allowed in bar ~ Open 11.30-11; 12-10.30 Sun

NETHERHAMPTON SU1029 Map 2

Victoria & Albert

Just off A3094 W of Salisbury

The black-beamed bar at this simple thatched cottage is filled with gleaming brassware, a good mix of individual tables with candles and nicely cushioned old-fashioned wall settles on the ancient polished floor tiles; darts. Four real ales include Hop Back Summer Lightning, Ringwood Best and Old Thumper and Timothy Taylors Landlord. Upgraded a notch or two by the new landlord, home-made bar food might include sandwiches (from £3.50), pasta arrabbiata (£5.50), cumberland sausage or cod fillet (£6.50), smoked salmon, avocado and prawn salad (£7.25), and puddings such as apple and blackberry crumble (£3.25). The restaurant is no smoking. There's hatch service for the sizeable garden behind, with well spaced picnic-sets and a big weeping willow. Handy for Wilton House (and Nadder Valley walks). *(Recommended by Jayne and Peter Capp, Dorsan Baker, David and Elizabeth Briggs, Ron Shelton, R Mathews, Tracey and Stephen Groves, Alan Finley, Dr and Mrs A K Clarke)*

Free house ~ Licensee Tim Shepherd ~ Real ale ~ Bar food ~ (01722) 743174 ~ Children welcome ~ Dogs allowed in bar ~ Open 11-3, 5-11; 12-3, 5-10.30 Sun

NEWTON TONY SU2140 Map 2

Malet Arms

Village signposted off A338 Swindon—Salisbury

Peacefully placed in a quiet village, this tiled flintstone pub looks over a chalk stream that you ford to drive to it, with a playing field opposite, and chickens and a horse paddock out behind. It's immediately welcoming, with a pleasant landlord (who's mad about cricket and started a local team a couple of years ago), efficient cheerful younger staff, and a good log and coal fire in a huge fireplace (as the paintwork between the black beams suggests, it can smoke a bit if the wind's strongly in the east). The main front windows are said to have come from the stern of a ship. Nice furnishings include a mix of different-sized tables with high winged wall settles, carved pews, chapel and carver chairs, and there are lots of pictures mainly from Imperial days. Good food here, in a similar room on the left, or in the attractive and homely back dining room on the right is listed on a blackboard and might include lunchtime filled rolls (from £4.50), warm pigeon and bacon salad with spinach and croutons or tagliatelle with green beans and sun-dried tomatoes (£7.25), rump steak sandwich, crêpes filled with cod and shrimps or trout and rocket fishcakes (£7.50), pheasant, pigeon, duck and hare stew with orange and juniper (£8.25), grilled marlin with chilli and coconut butter (£10.25), puddings (£4), and winter Sunday roasts. Well kept Butts Barbus Barbus, Stonehenge Heelstone, Wadworths 6X and a guest, usually from a fairly local brewer such as Archers or Ringwood, tapped from the cask or on handpump, decent wines and quite a few nice malt whiskies, also an espresso machine. There are old-fashioned garden seats on the small front terrace, with some picnic-sets on the grass there, and more in a back garden with a slide, swings and a wendy house. The two pub jack russells are called Badger and Piper. *(Recommended by Dr and Mrs Nigel Holmes, David and Elizabeth Briggs, Francis Johnston, Miss E Holmes, P Hill, David Whiteley, J R and J Moon, Miss M W Hayter)*

Free house ~ Licensee Noel Cardew ~ Real ale ~ Bar food (12-2.30, 6.30-10) ~ Restaurant ~ (01980) 629279 ~ Children in snug bar and restaurant ~ Dogs allowed in bar ~ Open 11.30-3, 6-11; 12-3, 7-10.30 Sun

NORTON ST8884 Map 2

Vine Tree ♀

4 miles from M4 junction 17; A429 towards Malmesbury, then left at Hullavington, Sherston signpost, then follow Norton signposts; in village turn right at Foxley signpost, which takes you into Honey lane

This civilised dining pub is housed in an attractively converted 18th-c mill house, and as it's not the easiest place to find, feels more remote than its proximity to the motorway would suggest. Three beautifully kept little rooms open together, with limited edition and sporting prints, a mock-up mounted pig's mask (used for a game that involves knocking coins off its nose and ears), lots of stripped pine, candles in bottles on the tables (the lighting's very gentle), and some old settles. From a seasonally changing menu, and using local ingredients where possible, a wide range of enjoyable food might include olives or bread board (from £1.35), soup (£3.95), fried chicken livers with white bean crush, chorizo and truffle oil (£5.75), moules marinière (£5.95/£9.50), roasted baby fennel and vodka risotto (£10.50), confit of lamb shoulder with buttered greens and potato cake (£11), fillet of gilthead bream with asparagus and herb hollandaise (£12.50), pork cutlet with honey and apple gravy, green pea and black pudding mash (£13.50), beef and kidney pie (£15), puddings such as almond and pear tart, honey yoghurt bavarois with caramelised banana mash (from £4.75), and a cheese board (£5.75); best to book, especially at weekends; one dining area is no smoking. Although the emphasis is on dining, there's a buoyant atmosphere here, and drinkers do pop in for the well kept Wychwood Fiddlers Elbow, Youngs and a guest beer, or around 10 wines by the glass from an impressive list; there may be piped music. There are picnic-sets in a two-acre garden which includes a pretty walled terrace with a lion fountain and urns of flowers, a well fenced separate play area with a fine thatched fortress, and three boules pitches. They hope to convert some outbuildings into six bedrooms. *(Recommended by Mrs M E Lewis, Dr and Mrs M E Wilson, A R Ainslie, Betsy and Peter Little, Miss A Kerr-Wilson, Miss M W Hayter, Mike Pugh, Ann Lewis, M W Turner, R Huggins, D Irving, E McCall, T McLean, Dr and Mrs A K Clarke)*

Free house ~ Licensees Charles Walker and Tiggi Wood ~ Real ale ~ Bar food (12-2, 7-9.30(6.30-9 Sun, till 10 summer Fri/Sat)) ~ Restaurant ~ (01666) 837654 ~ Children welcome ~ Dogs welcome ~ Monthly bands in winter, more often in summer ~ Open 12(11.30 Sat)-3, 6(6.30 Mon-Thurs in winter)-11; 12-10.30 Sun; closed 25 Dec evening

OGBOURNE ST ANDREW SU1974 Map 2

Wheatsheaf

A345 N of Marlborough

What must once have been a fairly ordinary two-bar roadside pub has been transformed into a civilised and most attractive place (with heavily interlined curtains keeping out the traffic noise at night). A central bar servery has a dining area on one side and a more informally mixed area on the other, with varying sizes and styles of table, and all sorts of different types of seating. A cheerful sprinkling of scatter cushions, subtle wall lighting and several gently shaded table lamps give a relaxed and cosy feel, and the chalky grey walls have a profuse and interesting variety of mainly black and white pictures – especially show business, horse trials or steeplechasing, with some striking modern Ostrer prints on the way to the lavatories (unusually, one of the fetching near-nudes in the gents' appeared to be a young man). As you come in from the back car park, the spick-and-span kitchen is on plain view on your left, doing a wide choice of generous enjoyable food such as soup (£4), baguettes with chips (£5), baked brie parcels with cranberry sauce (£5.50), mushroom stroganoff (£8.95), salmon fishcakes (£10), half shoulder of roast lamb (£13.50), and puddings such as raspberry mousse with fruit coulis or chocolate brownies with hot chocolate sauce (£4). Well kept Bass, Fullers London Pride and Worthington on handpump, decent wines, good coffee in attractive majolica-look cups; nice staff. There are tables out on a pretty back terrace and in a scented garden; no dogs or muddy boots inside. The bedroom price includes a continental breakfast which you find in the room fridge (they don't do a cooked breakfast); we have not yet heard from any readers who have stayed overnight here. *(Recommended by Jenny and Chris Wilson)*

Free house ~ Licensee Lesley Gallagher ~ Real ale ~ Bar food (12-2.30, 7-9.30(10.30 Fri, Sat)) ~ (01672) 841229 ~ Children in back restaurant ~ Dogs allowed in bedrooms ~ Open 11-3, 7-11(10.30 Sun) ~ Bedrooms: /£50B

PITTON SU2131 Map 2

Silver Plough 🍷

Village signposted from A30 E of Salisbury (follow brown tourist signs)

Hundreds of antique boot-warmers and stretchers, pewter and china tankards, copper kettles, toby jugs, earthenware and glass rolling pins, painted clogs, glass net-floats, and coach horns and so forth hang from the black beams in the comfortable front bar of this country dining pub. Seats on the turkey carpet include half a dozen red-velvet-cushioned antique oak settles (one elaborately carved, beside a very fine reproduction of an Elizabethan oak table), and the timbered white walls are hung with Thorburn and other game bird prints, original Craven Hill sporting cartoons, and a big naval battle glass-painting. The back bar is simpler, but still has a big winged high-backed settle, cased antique guns, substantial pictures, and – like the front room – flowers on its tables. The wide range of home-made food might include bruschetta topped with onion, ham and cheddar cheese (£6.75), pasta dishes (from £6.50), sausage and yorkshire pudding (£6.95), salads (from £7.50), and daily specials such as grilled bass with herb butter (£9.25) or chicken breast filled with bacon and brie on wild mushroom sauce (£9.95); the restaurant is no smoking. Well kept Badger IPA and Best under light blanket pressure, a fine wine list including 10 by the glass and some well priced and carefully chosen bottles, a good range of country wines, and a worthy choice of spirits. There's a skittle alley next to the snug bar; cribbage, dominoes and shove-ha'penny. A quiet lawn has picnic-sets and other tables under cocktail parasols, and there are good downland and woodland walks nearby. *(Recommended by Ken and Barbara Turner, Phyl and Jack Street, Dennis Jenkin, Gordon Prince, OPUS)*

Badger ~ Manager Adrian Clifton ~ Real ale ~ Bar food (12-2, 6-9) ~ Restaurant ~ (01722) 712266 ~ Children welcome, evening over 12s in restaurant ~ Dogs allowed in bar ~ Open 11-3, 6-11; 12-3, 6-10.30 Sun; closed 25, 26 Dec evening

POULSHOT ST9559 Map 2

Raven

Village signposted off A361 Devizes—Seend

Prettily set across from the village green, this tucked away place is a classic country pub. Two intimate black-beamed rooms are well furnished with sturdy tables and chairs and comfortable banquettes, with well kept Wadworths IPA, JcB and 6X tapped straight from the cask, and there's an attractive no smoking dining room. Prepared by the friendly landlord, enjoyable generously served bar food includes sandwiches (from £2.95), soup (£3.05), ploughman's (from £3.85), chicken terrine or devilled whitebait (£4.25), vegetable bake (£7.35), battered cod or steak and kidney pie (£8), haddock pie (£8.75), grilled lamb steak with port and redcurrant sauce (£9.50), mixed grill (£12.35), daily specials such as rogan josh (£8), stilton chicken (£8.75) and stir-fried duck breast (£10.70), and puddings such as apple and blackcurrant crumble and lemon and ginger cheesecake (from £3.25). The gents' are outside. *(Recommended by Mary Rayner, Keith and Sheila Baxter, Mary and Dennis Jones, Mr and Mrs J Brown, J Hale, Alan and Paula McCully)*

Wadworths ~ Tenants Philip and Susan Henshaw ~ Real ale ~ Bar food ~ Restaurant ~ (01380) 828271 ~ Children in restaurant ~ Dogs allowed in bar ~ Open 11-2.30, 6.30-11; 12-3, 7-10.30 Sun; closed Mon except bank hols, 25, 26, 31 Dec evening

ROWDE ST9762 Map 2

George & Dragon

A342 Devizes—Chippenham

The superb choice of beautifully prepared fish, delivered fresh from Cornwall, is a highlight at this well run attractive old dining pub. The quality and price of the meals are what you would expect of an upmarket restaurant, and the seasonally changing thoughtful menu combines traditional English dishes with snappier continental cooking. Fish dishes might include fish hors-d'oeuvres, moules marinière or half a dozen River Exe oysters (£6), steamed skate with capers and butter (£10), organic salmon steak with hot beetroot purée (£12), steamed bass fillet with ginger, soy and spring onion (£16), and turbot with hollandaise (£17). Other enticing meals made from well chosen fresh ingredients might include sorrel soup (£3), provençale fish soup (£5), cheese soufflé (£9), wild mushroom, gruyère and pine nut tart with tomato sauce (£9), lamb steak (£10), fillet steak topped with gorgonzola (£15), and puddings such as marmalade sponge pudding and brown sugar meringue with pineapple and jersey cream (£4.50), with west country cheeses (£5.50); no smoking dining room. If Ralph the siamese is around he may try and help you finish your meal. Tastefully furnished with plenty of dark wood, the bar has a log fire with a fine collection of brass keys by it, while the bare-floored dining room has quite plain tables and chairs, and is close enough to the bar to keep a pleasant chatty atmosphere. One or two changing well kept real ales on handpump might be from breweries such as Butcombe and Stonehenge, and they have organic cider, and continental beers and lagers; shove-ha'penny, cribbage and dominoes. There are lovely walks along the nearby Kennet & Avon Canal. *(Recommended by Mrs G Delderfield, Tina and David Woods-Taylor, Pamela and Merlyn Horswell, Neville and Anne Morley, Mary Rayner, David Whiteley)*

Free house ~ Licensees Tim and Helen Withers ~ Real ale ~ Bar food (12-2, 7-10; not Sun or Mon) ~ Restaurant ~ (01380) 723053 ~ Children in eating area of bar and restaurant ~ Dogs allowed in bar ~ Open 12-3, 7-(10.30 Sun)11; closed Mon lunchtime

By law pubs must show a price list of their drinks. Let us know if you are inconvenienced by any breach of this law.

SALISBURY SU1429 Map 2

Haunch of Venison

Minster Street, opposite Market Cross

Called 'a national treasure' by one reader, this marvellous old pub was constructed over 650 years ago as the church house for St Thomas's, just behind. The two tiny downstairs rooms are quite spit-and-sawdust in spirits, with massive beams in the ochre ceiling, stout red-cushioned oak benches built into the timbered walls, genuinely old pictures, black and white floor tiles, and an open fire; a tiny snug opens off the entrance lobby. A quiet and cosy panelled upper dining room has a small-paned window looking down on to the main bar, antique leather-seat settles, a nice carved oak chair nearly three centuries old, and a splendid fireplace that dates back to the building's early years; behind glass in a small wall slit is the smoke-preserved mummified hand of an 18th-c card sharp. Well kept Courage Best and Directors, Wadworths 6X and a guest such as Charles Wells Bombardier are served on handpump from a unique pewter bar counter, with a rare set of antique taps for gravity-fed spirits and liqueurs; over 50 malt whiskies, decent wines (including a wine of the week), and a range of brandies; chess. Enjoyable bar food has gone a little more upmarket (with more expensive dishes and a service charge in the restaurant), and includes sandwiches (from £2), soup (£2.95), chicken and mushroom terrine with red onion marmalade (£4.75), goats cheese crostini with artichoke heart salad (£4.95), haunch platter (a variety of venison dishes with a drink, £7.95), venison sausage and mash (£8.85), salmon with ratatouille and balsamic sauce (£9.85), chicken breast with tagliatelle and truffle-scented cream sauce (£12.50), venison steak (£14.95), and puddings (from £3.50); two-course set menu (£10). The restaurant is no smoking, but the bar can get a little smoky. *(Recommended by Dorsan Baker, Tom Clay, Ann and Colin Hunt, Gordon Tong, Andrea Rampley, Dr and Mrs M E Wilson, Dr and Mrs A K Clarke, the Didler, Rob Webster, I D Greenfield, John Robertson)*

Scottish Courage ~ Lease Antony and Victoria Leroy ~ Real ale ~ Bar food (12-2(2.30 in summer), 6-9) ~ Restaurant ~ (01722) 322024 ~ Children in eating area of bar and restaurant ~ Dogs allowed in bar ~ Jazz alternate Thurs ~ Open 11-11; 12-10.30 Sun; closed 25 Dec

New Inn

New Street

Tables out in the sizeable pretty walled garden of this ancient and creaky-timbered town-centre inn look up to the spire of the nearby cathedral. The interior is strikingly old, with massive heavy old beams, timbered walls, quiet cosy alcoves, an inglenook fire in the largest room and horsebrasses. Bar food includes soup (£2.75), sandwiches (from £3.75), steak and ale pie or battered cod (£6.95), rangoon chicken (£7.25), rump steak (£9.50), weekly changing specials such as salmon fillet with white wine sauce (£7.25), and puddings such as sticky toffee pudding or profiteroles (£3.25). Well kept Badger Best, Tanglefoot and a Badger guest on handpump, and decent house wines; piped music, and they now allow smoking in one of the panelled dining rooms, though at least at lunchtime the rest of the pub is still no smoking. *(Recommended by Mrs Pat Crabb, Ann and Colin Hunt, Ian Phillips, Tony and Wendy Hobden, Karen Eliot, J R and J Moon, Alan J Morton, M G Hart, Peter Neate, David Carty, John Robertson)*

Badger ~ Manager John Spicer ~ Real ale ~ Bar food (12-2, 6-9) ~ (01722) 326662 ~ Children welcome ~ Open 11.30-3, 6-11; 11-11 Sat; 12-10.30 Sun; 12-3, 6-10.30 Sat, 11.30-3, 6-11 Sun in winter

Old Ale House £

Crane Street, off High Street opp New Street; public car park in Mill Road

Very lively in the evening (especially at weekends) but a little quieter at lunchtime, this town pub is related to the Old Ale Houses in Truro and Falmouth

(Cornwall), and is a fairly close copy of their style and atmosphere. A surprising mix of customers of all ages and types gathers in the long open-plan bar, which is divided into sections by stout standing timbers and partly panelled stub walls, and has a real hotch-potch of old sofas, seats and tables, with cosy lighting and quite an entertaining clutter of casks, old cigar and cigarette boxes and country pictures. In one place, red hand and boot prints march across the ceiling, and there's a working red telephone box at one end. Bar food includes popular toasted sandwiches (£2.50), chinese spring rolls (£2.95), filled baguettes (from £3.75), all-day breakfast (£4), potato skins (£4.10), mushroom and cheddar or pasta bake (£4.35), chilli con carne (£4.85), and chicken topped with bacon and cheese (£5.95). Well kept Gales HSB, Marstons Pedigree, Ringwood Best and Wadworths 6X tapped straight from the cask, with a guest from a local brewer such as Stonehenge; dispensers of peanuts and chocolate peanuts; darts, cribbage, dominoes, big-screen TV, fruit machines, and a juke box that some readers may find a bit loud. A little back courtyard has a few picnic-sets. *(Recommended by Gordon Tong, Ann and Colin Hunt, Tony Hobden)*

Free house ~ Licensees Patrick Barker and Sarah Jones ~ Real ale ~ Bar food (12-2 only, not Sun) ~ (01722) 333113 ~ Children welcome away from the bar till 5pm ~ Live music Thurs evening ~ Open 11-11; 12-10.30 Sun

SEEND ST9461 Map 2

Barge

Seend Cleeve; signposted off A361 Devizes—Trowbridge, between Seend village and signpost to Seend Head

Picnic-sets out in the neatly kept waterside garden at this popular pub make an ideal spot for watching the bustle of boats on the Kennet & Avon Canal. Old streetlamps let you linger there after dark, and moorings by the humpy bridge are very handy for thirsty bargees. For colder days, the bar has a big log fire, friendly and relaxed atmosphere, unusual barge-theme décor, and intricately painted Victorian flowers which cover the ceilings and run in a waist-high band above the deep green lower walls. A distinctive mix of attractive seats includes milkchurns and the occasional small oak settle among the rugs on the parquet floor, while the walls have big sentimental engravings. The watery theme continues with a well stocked aquarium, and there's also a pretty Victorian fireplace, big bunches of dried flowers, and red velvet curtains for the big windows; fruit machine and piped music. The wide choice of good generously served bar food includes lunchtime sandwiches (£3.25), ploughman's (£5.50) and burger (£6), as well as soup (£3), puff pastry filled with roasted vegetables and goats cheese with chive and tomato sauce (£7.95), steak and kidney pie (£8.90), and steamed trout stuffed with fish mousse (£9.50). In the evening, meals are served with fresh vegetables and a couple of additional dishes are a bit more restauranty; the restaurant extension is no smoking. They recommend booking for meals, especially at weekends. Well kept Badger Tanglefoot, Butcombe and Wadworths IPA and 6X on handpump, lots of malts and mulled wine in winter; cheery service from uniformed staff. Barbecues outside on summer Sundays. At the busiest times you may find queues to get in the car park. *(Recommended by Pat and Robert Watt, Alan and Paula McCully, Roger and Pauline Pearce, John and Elizabeth Cox, Jenny and Dave Hughes, Joyce and Maurice Cottrell, P R and S A White, Paul Thompson, Anna Blackburn, M G Hart, Charles and Pauline Stride, James Woods, Roger Wain-Heapy, Ian Phillips, Michael Doswell, Susan and Nigel Wilson)*

Wadworths ~ Tenant Christopher Moorley Long ~ Real ale ~ Bar food (12-2, 7-9.30(10 Fri, Sat)) ~ Restaurant ~ (01380) 828230 ~ Children welcome ~ Dogs allowed in bar ~ Open 11-3, 6-11; 12-10.30(12-4, 7-10.30 winter) Sun

The details at the end of each main entry start by saying whether the pub is a free house, or if it's tied to a brewery or pub group (which we name).

SEMLEY ST8926 Map 2

Benett Arms 🍷

Turn off A350 N of Shaftesbury at Semley Ind Estate signpost, then turn right at Semley signpost

In a lovely spot right on the Dorset border, this white-painted country pub has tables on the pretty village green with its new millennium pond, just across the road. Two cosy and hospitable rooms are separated by three carpeted steps, and are furnished with one or two settles and pews, a deep leather sofa and chairs, hunting prints, carriage lamps for lighting, a pendulum wall clock, and ornaments on the mantelpiece over the log fire; there's a thatched-roof servery in the flagstoned bar, and a dark panelling dado in the carpeted upstairs area. When the long-serving landlord is in a cheery frame of mind he has a few yarns to tell, and has a good local knowledge. Freshly prepared bar food includes sandwiches (from £2.60), soup (£3.25), ploughman's (£5.95), steak and kidney pie (£6.95), coq au vin or herb pancake stuffed with spinach, mushrooms and nuts with mushroom sauce (£8.95), grilled salmon with lemon sauce (£9.95), shank of Italian cured ham baked with ginger and soy sauce (£10.95), châteaubriand for two (£29.50), lots of ice creams (£2.95), and puddings such as hot bananas in rum sauce (£3.45); half the dining room is no smoking. Real ales on handpump include Brakspears, Ringwood Best and Fortyniner, also farm cider, four chilled vodkas, 18 malt whiskies, lots of liqueurs, and a thoughtfully chosen wine list, including a good few by the glass; friendly chatty staff; piped music, juke box, TV, cribbage and dominoes. *(Recommended by Ann and Colin Hunt, Mrs J H S Lang, Jayne and Peter Capp, Dr and Mrs J F Head, Matthew Last, J Hale, Lynn Sharpless, Ian Phillips, Anne Jennings)*

Enterprise ~ Lease Joe Duthie ~ Real ale ~ Bar food (12-2.30, 7-10) ~ Restaurant ~ (01747) 830221 ~ Children in eating area of bar and restaurant ~ Dogs welcome ~ Open 11-11; 12-10.30 Sun; may close in the afternoon in winter; closed 25, 26 Dec evening ~ Bedrooms: £38S/£60B

SHERSTON ST8585 Map 2

Rattlebone 🍷

Church Street; B4040 Malmesbury—Chipping Sodbury

Under new managers, this old village pub is regaining its poise after what has been a not entirely trouble-free year. A lot of readers like its lively pubby atmosphere, especially in the public bar with its hexagonal pool table, darts, table football, Connect Four, shove-ha'penny, fruit machine, cribbage, dominoes, TV and juke box (they also have alley skittles). You can escape into relative quiet elsewhere in this busy collection of rambling rooms, with lots of jugs and bottles hanging from low beams, plenty of little cuttings and printed anecdotes on pink walls, and pews, settles and country kitchen chairs around a mix of tables. They have well kept Smiles Best, Youngs Bitter, Special, Triple A and a seasonal guest from Youngs on handpump, over 50 malt whiskies, half a dozen rums, decent wines including about 15 by the glass, and fruit wines. Pubby lunchtime meals include filled jumbo baps (from £2.95), filled baked potatoes (from £3.50), ploughman's (from £3.95), ham, egg and chips (£5.25) and plaice and chips (£5.50), as well as more elaborate dishes from the menu or specials board such as chicken and leek pie (£6.95), curry (£7.95), seafood pie (£8.95), grilled sardines (£9.50), poached salmon (£10.50), bass (£11.50), and puddings such as bread and butter pudding with clotted cream, or lemon and vanilla cheesecake (£3.95); part of the dining area is no smoking. The smallish garden is very pretty with flower beds, a gravel terrace, and picnic-sets under umbrellas. There are four boules pitches, and the Sherston carnival week concludes with a festival of boules at the pub on the second Saturday in July. *(Recommended by Christopher and Mary Thomas, Mayur Shah, P R and S A White, Betsy and Peter Little, Dr and Mrs A K Clarke, R Huggins, D Irving, E McCall, T McLean, Mike Pugh)*

Youngs ~ Managers Emma and John Williams ~ Real ale ~ Bar food (12-2, 7-9; not

Sun evening) ~ Restaurant ~ (01666) 840871 ~ Children in restaurant ~ Dogs allowed in bar ~ Open 12-11(10.30 Sun)

STOURTON ST7734 Map 2

Spread Eagle

Church Lawn; follow Stourhead brown signs off B3092, N of junction with A303 just W of Mere

This interesting and rather lovely old pub is in a delightful setting among other elegant National Trust stone buildings at the head of Stourhead Lake – it too is owned by the National Trust. Caring hardworking staff and licensees generate a civilised but inclusive atmosphere, and usefully serve very fairly priced cold meals all day. The attractively decorated interior has antique panel-back settles, a mix of new and old solid tables and chairs, handsome fireplaces with good winter log fires, smoky old sporting prints, prints of Stourhead, and standard lamps or brass swan's-neck wall lamps. One room by the entrance has armchairs, a longcase clock and a corner china cupboard. Bar food includes sandwiches (from £1.95), soup (£2.80), ploughman's (from £4.50), steak and kidney pie (£6.50), a couple of daily specials such as greek salad or chicken liver pâté (£4.95) and chilli, spaghetti bolognese or lots of salads (£5.95), with puddings such as profiteroles or sticky toffee pudding (£2.95). A more elaborate evening menu has dishes such as puff pastry case filled with avocado, sweet peppers and button mushrooms in garlic and herb cream sauce (£9.95), baked bream filled with olives, pesto and sun-dried tomatoes (£11.95), and pheasant breast wrapped in bacon with redcurrant and garlic sauce (£12.95). Well kept Courage Best and Wadworths 6X on handpump. There are benches in the courtyard behind. *(Recommended by John and Glenys Wheeler, Ann and Colin Hunt, Mike and Mona Clifford, Patricia Theodorou, Mr and Mrs McKay, Geoff Palmer)*

Free house ~ Licensee Andy Martin ~ Real ale ~ Bar food (12-9) ~ Restaurant ~ (01747) 840587 ~ Open 11-11; 12-10.30 Sun

UPTON SCUDAMORE ST8647 Map 2

Angel

Village signposted off A350 N of Warminster

The kitchen gets plenty of exposure in this big dining pub, locally very popular for good food. The starters make quite a reasonably priced light lunch, such as unusual soups (perhaps smoked salmon with spring onions, chives and a poached egg – £3.50) or a very scallopy scallop terrine (£4). Main courses might include lunchtime filled baguettes (from £4.50), sausage and mash or chicken and mushroom pie (£6.95), as well as specials such as rabbit loin with parsley mousse wrapped in parma ham with calvados jus (£11.95), salmon fillet with fennel confit, orange and saffron syrup and wild mushroom tapenade (£12.50), halibut with black linguini and crayfish butter sauce (£14.95), and puddings such as rice pudding and strawberry jam or sticky toffee pudding with caramel sauce (£3.95). Bare boards, pine tables, country-kitchen and other simple chairs, terracotta walls and rather clattery acoustics make for a bustling modern feel throughout, despite the log fire, and the Spy and other cricketing caricatures and naïve farm animal pictures in the bar, with its shiny newish rafters. On each side of the counter, steps take you down to a long two-part dining room, similar in style except that its pictures (lots of them, for sale) are contemporary. Well kept Butcombe, Wadworths 6X and a guest such as Wickwar Kite Flanker on handpump, good changing wine choice; efficient good-natured service; piped music. There are teak tables out on a sheltered flagstoned back terrace with a big barbecue. The well equipped bedrooms (even with CD players) are in a separate house across the car park. *(Recommended by Christine and Neil Townend)*

Free house ~ Licensees Charlie Barkshire and Sharon Scott ~ Real ale ~ Bar food (12-2, 7-9.30(9 Sun)) ~ Restaurant ~ (01985) 213225 ~ Children welcome ~ Dogs allowed in bar ~ Open 12-3, 6-11(7-10.30 Sun); closed 25 Dec ~ Bedrooms: £55B/£75B

WHITLEY ST8866 Map 2

Pear Tree 🍴 🍷

Off B3353 S of Corsham, at Atworth 1½, Purlpit 1 signpost; or from A350 Chippenham—Melksham in Beanacre turn off on Westlands Lane at Whitley 1 signpost, then left and right at B3353

Wiltshire Dining Pub of the Year

Beautifully presented imaginative dishes at this well run attractive honey-coloured stone farmhouse might include seared oyster mushroom, gammon and horseradish soup (£4.75), seared beef sandwich with roasted red onions and sun-dried tomato oil (£5.95), tian of crab and avocado with cracked bulgur wheat, apple and lime dressing (£6), sweet potato and feta spring roll with roast aubergine couscous and melon salsa (£10.50), roast monkfish loin in parma ham with black linguini in fennel, broad bean and saffron broth (£14.50), loin of lamb with harissa-spiced chick pea cassoulet, mint and coriander relish (£16), and puddings such as bramley apple parfait with blackcurrant sorbet and apple compote, or warm chocolate frangipane tart with marmalade ice cream (from £4.75). A good choice of up to 27 or so decent wines by the glass means you will find something suitable for your meal. Although the emphasis here is fairly firmly on the food, charming licensees and first-class staff will make you feel more than welcome if all you want is a pint of the Wadworths 6X – well kept alongside a couple of changing guests such as Smiles Best and Wadworths IPA. The front bar has quite a pubby feel, with cushioned window seats, some stripped shutters, a mix of dining chairs around good solid tables, a variety of country pictures and a Wiltshire regiment sampler on the walls, a little fireplace on the left, and a lovely old stripped stone one on the right. Candlelit at night, the popular but unhurried big back restaurant – you may need to book – has green dining chairs, quite a mix of tables, and a pitched ceiling at one end with a quirky farmyard theme – wrought-iron cockerels and white scythe sculpture. A bright spacious garden room opens on to a terrace with good teak furniture and views over the carefully maintained gardens, which are prettily lit at night to show features like the ruined pigsty; boules. Seven new bedrooms are on schedule to be open by February, some in an old barn and some above the pub. We'd expect these to be nice, and would be very interested to hear from readers. *(Recommended by Dr and Mrs M E Wilson, Lord Sandhurst, John and Jane Hayter, Mike and Heather Watson, Catherine Pitt, Mr and Mrs C R Little, Mike and Mona Clifford, Rob Webster, J Hale, Jonathan Smith, Sue Demont, Tim Barrow, Hilary McLean, Ian Phillips, Michael Doswell)*

Free house ~ Licensees Martin and Debbie Still and Mark Nacchia ~ Real ale ~ Bar food (12-2, 6.30(7 Sun)-9.30(10 Fri, Sat)) ~ Restaurant ~ (01225) 709131 ~ Children welcome ~ Dogs allowed in bar ~ Open 11-3, 6-11; 12-3, 7-10.30 Sun ~ Bedrooms

WOODBOROUGH SU1159 Map 2

Seven Stars 🍷

Off A345 S of Marlborough: from Pewsey follow Woodborough signposts, then in Woodborough bear left following Bottlesford signposts

It's well worth working your way through the lanes to find this pretty thatched red brick house, with its appealing blend of traditional English pub and strong gallic influence from the French landlord. The very good bar food is gently French country cooking in style, and as well as bar snacks such as good French onion soup (£2.95), sandwiches from (£3.25), fish soup (£3.75), ploughman's (from £4.25), moules marinière or croque monsieur (£4.75) and aubergines provençale (£7.25), includes changing specials such as grilled sardine fillets with sun-dried tomato pesto (£5.75), parma ham with avocado (£5.95), crab (£8.75), venison and mushroom pie (£9.75), fillet of pork normande (£11.75), magret of duck with prunes and armagnac sauce or jugged hare (£12.75), baked bass with saffron sauce (£15.75), puddings such as tarte tatin and raspberry crème brûlée (£3.95) and a French cheeseboard (£5.25); they receive regular deliveries from France, and do smaller helpings for children; the dining room is no smoking. The bar is traditionally furnished, with polished bricks by the bar counter, hunting prints, attractively moulded panelling, a hot coal fire in the old range at one end, a big log fire at the other, a pleasant mix of antique settles and country furniture, cast-iron-framed tables, and cosy nooks here and there; there may be sophisticated piped music. Although the food is very popular, locals do pop in for the well kept Badger Best, Fullers London Pride and Wadworths 6X on handpump. There's also an exemplary wine list, with about 10 by the glass (including plenty of French), and interesting bin ends. There are seven acres of riverside gardens, and an alsatian, a white west highland terrier and a black cat (who may try and get at milk left on tables) constitute the friendly menagerie. Please note, the pub shuts on Tuesdays following bank holiday Mondays. *(Recommended by Karen and Graham Oddey, Mike and Heather Watson, Peter and Giff Bennett, Chantal Patel, Aidan MacDonald, W J MacWilliam, Mike and Mary Carter, Mrs G Delderfield)*

Free house ~ Licensees Philippe Cheminade and Kate Lister ~ Real ale ~ Bar food ~ Restaurant ~ (01672) 851325 ~ Children in restaurant ~ Open 12-3, 6-11; 12-3 Sun; closed Sun evening, all day Mon except bank hols, then cl Tues

WOOTTON RIVERS SU1963 Map 2

Royal Oak 🍷

Village signposted from A346 Marlborough—Salisbury, from A345 Marlborough—Pewsey, and B3087 E of Pewsey

With a reassuring family-run feel, this beamed 16th-c thatched pub is well liked for its extensive range of bar food. They do seem to be more interested in diners than drinkers, and it's advisable to book for an evening meal (when some customers may be quite smartly dressed). As well as lunchtime sandwiches (from £3.50), ploughman's (from £5.50), filled ciabatta or baguettes (from £6), bar food includes soup (£2.75), Cornish crab with fresh cream and brandy (£3.75), fried brie with berry compote (£5), fish and chips or sausage and mash (£5.50), stilton and vegetable bake (£7.50), steak and Guinness pie (£8), chicken breast with honey, soy and ginger sauce (£9), roast rack of lamb with cumberland sauce (£13.50), roast bass with limes (£14.50), lots of changing daily specials such as tapas platter (£6.50), smoked salmon with quails eggs and capers (£6.50), pork loin with leek and pine nut stuffing and orange and lemon sauce (£10.50), cod fillet with a pesto crust (£12.50), and puddings such as warm treacle tart or banana and butterscotch sundae (£4); three-course set menu (£12.50). If you have a full meal they will most likely add a 10% service charge. The friendly L-shaped dining lounge has slat-back chairs, armchairs and some rustic settles around good tripod tables, a low ceiling with partly stripped beams, partly glossy white planks, and a woodburning stove. The timbered bar is comfortably furnished, and has a small area with board games, darts, pool, TV, fruit machine and juke box. Well kept Fullers London Pride, Wadworths 6X and perhaps a guest ale on hand or electric pump, interesting whiskies, and a good wine list (running up to some very distinguished bottles). There are tables under cocktail parasols on the forecourt. This attractive thatched and timbered village, with the Kennet & Avon Canal passing through at one end, is well worth exploring, particularly the 13th-c church which houses the curious George V Coronation clock. *(Recommended by Mrs J H S Lang, Tina and David Woods-Taylor, Trevor Owen, Mrs June Wilmers, Thomas Neate)*

Free house ~ Licensees John and Rosa Jones ~ Real ale ~ Bar food (12-2.30, 7-9.30) ~ Restaurant ~ (01672) 810322 ~ Children welcome ~ Dogs allowed in bar and bedrooms ~ Open 10-3, 6-12; 12-4.30, 6-11.30 Sun ~ Bedrooms: £22.50(£35S)/£45(£50S)

If we know a pub has an outdoor play area for children, we mention it.

WYLYE SU0037 Map 4

Bell

Just off A303/A36 junction; High Street

Prettily set in a peaceful village, this cosy little 14th-c country pub is not far from Stonehenge, and there are fine downland walks nearby. A civilised unhurried atmosphere is nicely relaxing in the neatly kept and black-beamed front bar, which has one of the inn's three winter log fires, and sturdy rustic furnishings that go well with the stripped stonework and neat timbered herringbone brickwork. The comfortably carpeted no smoking restaurant with pristine white linen has a more sophisticated feel, and is quite an important element here. Well prepared bar food using fresh ingredients includes sandwiches (from £3.50), soup (£3.95), duck liver terrine (£5.95), ploughman's (£7.50), sausages and cheddar mash or chilli (£7.95), good upmarket changing daily specials such as pheasant and pistachio terrine (£5.95), smoked salmon mousse with caviar (£5.95), roast loin of pork with apple sauce (£9.95) and trio of salmon, bass and monkfish with couscous and tomato and basil sauce (£12.95), and puddings such as local strawberries and cream or gooseberry crumble (£4.95). Four well kept real ales come from far and wide and might include Hop Back, Ringwood and Stonehenge; piped music, cribbage and daily papers. There are seats outside on a pleasant walled terrace and in a back garden, which is attractively flanked by the church's clipped yews. *(Recommended by Shirley Mackenzie, Peter Meister, Mark and Amanda Sheard, Mrs Pam Mattinson, Denis Dutton, Mrs P Sarson, Andrea Rampley, Pat and Robert Watt, Alan Kilpatrick, Charles Gysin, Colin and Janet Roe, J and B Cressey, Stan and Hazel Allen)*

Free house ~ Licensees Keith and Linda Bidwell ~ Real ale ~ Bar food (12-2, 6-9.30; 12-2.30, 7-9 Sun) ~ Restaurant ~ (01985) 248338 ~ Children in restaurant ~ Dogs allowed in bar and bedrooms ~ Open 11.30-2.30, 6-11; 12-3, 7-10.30 Sun ~ Bedrooms: £35B/£45S(£60B)

Lucky Dip

Besides the fully inspected pubs, you might like to try these Lucky Dips recommended to us and described by readers (if you do, please send us reports: www.goodguides.com).

Aldbourne [SU2675]

☆ ***Blue Boar*** [The Green (off B4192)]: Nicely placed homely and relaxed pub with seats out facing pretty village green near church and neatly kept small back country garden; three well kept Wadworths ales, good choice of wines and soft drinks, polite service, farm tools, boar's head and flame-effect woodburner in Tudor bar, extensive more modern back lounge/dining area with inexpensive food from generous sandwiches up; darts, quiet piped music; children welcome *(CMW, JJW, Mary Rayner)*

Crown [The Square]: Newish licensees doing good value generous food in friendly village local with two-part beamed lounge, oak bar furnishings, unusual huge log fireplace linking to public bar, small nicely laid out dining room; good service, well kept Greene King IPA and Wadworths 6X, interesting bric-a-brac, quiet piped music; tables under cocktail parasols in neat courtyard *(Barry and Anne Cooper, Mary Rayner, R T and J C Moggridge)*

All Cannings [SU0761]

Kings Arms [The Street]: Charming Victorian village pub, new tenants doing good choice of food from sandwiches and baked potatoes to usual home-made hot dishes, well kept Wadworths IPA, 6X and a guest beer, reasonably priced wines, welcoming service; children welcome, large garden, not far from Kennet & Avon Canal moorings *(Helen Mackenzie)*

Ashton Keynes [SU0494]

Horse & Jockey [Gosditch]: Friendly and ednthusiastic young landlord in lively local with several real ales and good food choice *(Andy McGrath)*

Avebury [SU0969]

Red Lion [A361]: Much-modernised and substantially extended from pretty thatched front part, in the heart of the stone circles; quick friendly service, well kept ales such as Stonehenge (from Netheravon) and Wadworths 6X, open fires, food bar, no smoking area and unpubby restaurant extension – huge choice inc Sun carvery; maybe piped music *(Tim and Isobel Smith, LYM, E M and H P N Steinitz, Bill Sykes)*

Bishopstone [SU2483]

True Heart [signed off A419/B4192 at Wanborough; High St]: Spacious old country pub near Ridgeway with emphasis on wide range of enjoyable food (cooked to order so may be a wait) inc take-away pizzas, friendly attentive service, Flowers and Wadworths, decent coffee, light and airy bar with eating area up three steps, corridor to small dining room, fresh flowers; children welcome, own menu; darts, piped music; bedrooms, picnic-sets in garden with terrace *(CMW, JJW)*

White Hart [Butts Lane; the one nr Salisbury]: Attractive layout and décor, decent food inc good value OAP wkdy lunches and two-for-one deals, well kept Flowers Original and Wadworths 6X (early summer beer and music festival), log fire, pleasant atmosphere, roomy restaurant, games area with pool; picnic-sets in garden with play area *(Dr and Mrs Michael Smith, David and Elizabeth Briggs)*

Bradford-on-Avon [ST8359]

☆ ***Beehive*** [A363 out towards Trowbridge]: Simple cheerful old-fashioned L-shaped pub near canal on outskirts, well kept ales such as Bedrock, Butcombe, Church End Pooh, Hop Back Thunderstorm, Timothy Taylors Landlord and Wickwar BOB on handpump or tapped from the cask, good service (can be delays on busy summer wknds), traditional food esp substantial sandwiches (some hot) with baskets of chips, good range of wines, 19th-c playbills, cricketing prints and cigarette cards, darts; children and dogs welcome, resident cats; attractive good-sized informal back garden, play area, barbecues *(Pete Baker, BB, Dr and Mrs M E Wilson, Gary Crabbe)*

☆ ***Bunch of Grapes*** [Silver St]: Buoyant local bustle, dim-lit wine-bar style décor, cask seats and rugs on bare boards in small front room, bigger tables on composition floor of roomier main bar, well kept Smiles and Youngs ales, good range of wines and malt whiskies, good choice of interesting reasonably priced food in bar and upstairs eating area, enthusiastic young landlord *(Susan and Nigel Wilson, R Huggins, D Irving, E McCall, T McLean, BB, David Carr)*

Broughton Gifford [ST8763]

☆ ***Bell on the Common*** [The Green]: Ancient and picturesque stone-built pub on huge village green, traditional furnishings, friendly service, home cooking using local organic meat, children's dishes and popular Sun roasts, well kept Wadworths and farm cider from handpumps on back wall, big coal fire, dining lounge full of copper and old country prints, bar with local photographs old and new, small pool room with darts and juke box; children welcome, charming garden (occasional pig roasts and live music), bowls club next door *(Simon Heptinstall, Gloria Bax)*

Bulkington [ST9458]

Tipsy Toad [High St]: Friendly and simple, with cheerful licensees, Wadworths 6X and a couple of guests such as Bass and Greene King Ruddles, good value generous fresh food inc choice of Sun roasts; skittle alley *(Dr and Mrs M E Wilson)*

Castle Combe [ST8477]

Salutation [The Gibb; B4039 Acton Turville—Chippenham, nr Nettleton]: Roomy and welcoming old pub with choice of beamed seating areas inc comfortable lounge and locals' bar, huge handsome fireplace, separate raftered thatched and timbered restaurant; jovial landlord, real ales, good choice of wines, enjoyable food inc fresh Cornish fish; open all day, pretty garden with pergola *(Dr and Mrs A K Clarke, MRSM)*

Castle Eaton [SU1495]

Red Lion [The Street]: Interesting softly lit bar rooms and impressive new conservatory looking over shrubby garden to Thames, good blackboard choice of reasonably priced food, well kept real ales; children welcome in eating areas, popular with Thames Path walkers *(Peter and Audrey Dowsett, LYM)*

Charlton [ST9588]

☆ ***Horse & Groom*** [B4040 towards Cricklade]: Wide choice of good generous food in smart stone-built inn's civilised and relaxing bar, old firearms, farm tools and log fire, simpler right-hand bar with hops on beams, friendly and considerate staff, well kept Archers and Wadworths, farm cider, decent wines; restaurant (good value Sun lunch), tables outside; dogs welcome, comfortable bedrooms *(R Huggins, D Irving, E McCall, T McLean, J G E Bell, Michael Doswell, LYM)*

Chilmark [ST9632]

☆ ***Black Dog*** [B3089 Salisbury—Hindon]: Comfortably modernised 15th-c beamed pub with several smallish relaxing rooms, enjoyable food, well kept ales such as Bass, Hook Norton and Wadworths 6X, good value house wines, friendly polite staff, good local atmosphere (regulars turn up on horseback), armchairs by lounge log fire, fossil ammonites in the stone of one attractive dining room; dogs welcome, tables out in roadside garden *(H D Wharton, Joyce and Geoff Robson, LYM, David Cuckney)*

Chiseldon [SU1879]

Patriots Arms [B4005, off A346 just S of M4 junction 15]: Four real ales, decent food choice (not Sun evening or Mon lunchtime) inc children's, daily papers, restaurant, family room; darts, pool, juke box, machines, no dogs; garden with play area, open all day wknds *(CMW, JJW)*

Plough [Badbury, just S of M4 junction 15; A346 Marlborough rd]: Well kept Arkells 2B, 3B and Kingsdown, decent wines, wide blackboard food choice inc afternoon snacks, friendly efficient service, no smoking room; pianola, darts, may be piped pop music; children welcome, play area in sunny garden looking over road to Vale of the White Horse, open all day *(CMW, JJW)*

Chitterne [ST9843]

Kings Head [B390 between Heytesbury and Shrewton]: Salisbury Plain oasis, good cheerful service, varied food inc takeaway fish and chips, woodburner, lovely hanging baskets in summer; bedrooms, pretty village, good walks *(Keith and Sheila Baxter)*

Cholderton [SU2242]

Crown [A338 Tidworth—Salisbury]: Cosy thatched low-beamed cottage combining nice local feel in L-shaped bar with good food inc local game and fresh fish specialities (cooked to order, so may be a wait); well kept Boddingtons, welcoming efficient service, nice open fire, bar billiards one end; seats outside *(Richard Hanson-James)*

Christian Malford [ST9678]

☆ ***Mermaid*** [B4069 Lyneham—Chippenham, 3½ miles from M4 junction 17]: Long cheerful bar pleasantly divided into areas, good food worth waiting for inc some interesting dishes and super ploughman's, well kept ales such as Bass, Fullers London Pride, Wadworths 6X and Worthington BB, decent whiskies and wines, some attractive pictures; bar billiards, darts, fruit machine, piped music (live blues Thurs); tables in garden, bedrooms *(Dr and Mrs A K Clarke, BB, Mr and Mrs F J Parmenter, Dr and Mrs M E Wilson, Alan Wilson)*

Rising Sun [Station Rd]: Dining pub with good home-made bar food in small friendly bar, interesting dishes in pleasant restaurant, two real ales, farm cider *(Hayley Sales)*

Clyffe Pypard [SU0776]

Goddard Arms: Unpretentious 16th-c village pub with log fire and raised dining area in split-level main bar, small sitting room with another fire and two old armchairs, down-to-earth chatty and welcoming licensees, well kept Wadworths 6X and guests such as Flowers IPA and Greene King Abbot, good value straightforward freshly made food, back skittle alley with prints, paintings, sculptures, second-hand books and records for sale (busy music nights, and pool room off, with darts, cribbage etc); no cards taken; open all day wknds, sculpture garden, bedrooms, tiny pretty thatched village in lovely countryside *(Pete Baker, CMW, JJW)*

Coate [SU0462]

New Inn: Friendly and unspoilt village pub, old tables on tile floors, Wadworths ales tapped from the cask *(the Didler)*

Colerne [ST8171]

Six Bells [High St]: Compact and cheerful local doing well under friendly new landlord, consistently well kept beers, competitively priced restaurant-quality food in four-table dining area, good service; skittle alley, video games, sensible piped music, folk club Thurs *(Dr and Mrs A K Clarke, David Carty)*

Collingbourne Ducis [SU2453]

☆ ***Shears*** [Cadley Rd]: Popular racing-country pub with good fresh imaginative food in bar and restaurant, generous helpings and reasonable prices, well kept beers; good value bedrooms *(A W Moulds, Neil and Angela Huxter)*

Collingbourne Kingston [SU2355]

Barleycorn [A338]: Welcoming village pub with well kept ales such as Cottage Olde Atlantic, Hook Norton Old Hooky, Tom Hoskins Churchills Pride, John Smiths and Wadworths Henrys, JCB and 6X, wide choice of affordable food from fresh sandwiches up, decent wines, quick friendly service, pool room, attractive restaurant; piped pop music may be loud *(Tony and Shirley Albert, Peter and Audrey Dowsett)*

Compton Bassett [SU0372]

White Horse: Cheery welcome, good food and service *(Tony Beaulah)*

Corsham [ST8670]

Hare & Hounds [Pickwick (A4 E)]: Cosy and friendly local, real ales such as Greene King Old Speckled Hen, Hop Back Summer Lightning and Moles, bar food, log fire in comfortable and attractive lounge area; unobtrusive piped music and sports TV in busy main bar, another room with alcove seating and pool *(George Atkinson, Dr and Mrs M E Wilson)*

Corsley [ST8246]

Cross Keys [Lyes Green]: New tenants doing good interesting food in two eating areas, one no smoking, well kept Wadworths real ales, large log fire in quarry-tiled locals' bar, old scrubbed tables, darts, bar billiards and cribbage, skittle alley upstairs; jazz night every 3rd Sun *(anon)*

Cricklade [SU1093]

Red Lion [High St]: Quiet and relaxing, with interesting décor from stuffed birds to candle sculptures, wide range of beers inc Moles; neat garden *(Des and Jen Clarke)*

Vale [High St]: Pleasant décor in newly reworked bar adjoining Georgian hotel, beams and stripped bricks and timbers, well kept ales such as Batemans, Greene King IPA, Abbot and Ruddles County, Smiles and Wadworths 6X, up-to-date food from sandwiches, panini and wraps to good blackboard dishes; bedrooms *(Comus and Sarah Elliott)*

Crudwell [ST9592]

Plough [A429 N of Malmesbury]: Nice timeless local feel, friendly service, quiet lounge, dining area with comfortable well padded seats and more in elevated part; remarkably wide range of good value food, well kept ales such as Archers Best and Oakhill Best, open fires, bar with darts and juke box, pool room; pleasant side garden *(R Huggins, D Irving, E McCall, T McLean, David and Ruth Hollands)*

Derry Hill [ST9570]

Lansdowne Arms [Church Rd]: Pleasant relaxed atmosphere in attractively refurbished Victorian pub, soft lighting, lots of candles, well kept Wadworths and a guest beer, good choice of good value wines by the glass, interesting reasonably priced food, hearty log fire, restaurant; fine views, garden with good play area, handy for Bowood *(Peter B Brown, David Crook)*

Devizes [SU0161]

Moonraker [Nursteed Rd]: Imposing and comfortable 1930s pub with enjoyable food, well kept Wadworths IPA and 6X, good whiskies (expert Scottish landlord), friendly service *(Dr and Mrs A K Clarke, Richard Pierce)*

Queens Head [Dunkirk Hill]: Uncomplicated little pubs with well kept Moles beers, usual food at attractive prices *(Dr B and Mrs P B Baker, Dr and Mrs A K Clarke)*

Royal Oak [New Park St]: Nicely refurbished, plenty of dark oak, alcoves and shelves of memorabilia; well kept Fullers London Pride, open all day wknds *(Alan and Paula McCully)*

Downton [SU1721]

Bull [A338 Salisbury—Fordingbridge]: Large friendly pub/hotel with enjoyable food inc blackboard specials, midweek evening bargains, Tues theme night and good Sun lunches, well kept local Hop Back ales, long bar with big eating area, cheery staff, dogs allowed; bedrooms *(LYM, Geoff Palmer, J and B Cressey)*

Wooden Spoon [High St]: Fullers, Ringwood and Youngs, enjoyable food from sandwiches and baguettes to wide choice of hot dishes using local produce, inc good Sun lunch (but they may get overbooked then); children welcome *(David and Elizabeth Briggs)*

East Knoyle [ST8830]

☆ ***Seymour Arms*** [The Street; just off A350 S of Warminster]: Roomy creeper-covered stone-built black-beamed pub, newish Swiss chef/landlord doing good freshly made generous food, quietly welcoming and comfortable rambling bar areas, cosy part with high-backed settle by log fire, well kept Wadworths IPA, 6X and Farmers Glory; tables in garden with play area, good value bedrooms *(Roger and Pauline Pearce, Ann and Colin Hunt, BB, H D Wharton)*

Easton Royal [SU2060]

Bruce Arms [Easton Rd]: Fine old unspoilt local, nicely basic, with scrubbed pine tables, brick floor, well kept Butts, Wadworths 6X and guest ales, Pewsey organic cider, good rolls made to order; open all day Sun *(the Didler)*

Edington [ST9353]

Lamb [Westbury Rd]: Doing well under current hard-working management, small bar with good range of food and real ales inc Wadworths 6X, small dining room *(John and Angela Main)*

Farleigh Wick [ST8064]

Fox & Hounds [A363 Bath—Bradford, 2½ miles NW of Bradford]: Well extended welcoming low-beamed rambling bar with easy mix of drinkers and eaters, highly polished old oak tables and chairs, gently rural decorations, Bass and Marstons Pedigree; attractive garden *(MRSM, Dr and Mrs M E Wilson, Meg and Colin Hamilton, Mr and Mrs A H Young)*

Fovant [SU0128]

Pembroke Arms [A30 W of Salisbury]: Cheerful creeper-covered two-roomed local near the giant regimental badges cut into the downs, with lots of touching and interesting local World War I mementoes, good reasonably priced food, well kept Ringwood Best and True Glory, good friendly service, daily papers, log fire; comfortable bedrooms, good breakfast, picnic-sets in neat and tidy tiered side garden, open all day wknds, cl Mon lunchtime *(Ann and Colin Hunt, BB)*

Great Bedwyn [SU2764]

Three Tuns [High St]: Friendly village pub, good value nicely served fresh food, Wadworths 6X, traditional old-fashioned atmosphere *(Tim Brierly)*

Great Cheverell [ST9754]

Bell [off B3098 Westbury—Mkt Lavington]: Quietly welcoming dining pub with comfortable chairs and settles, cosy little alcoves, enjoyable generous home-made food, well kept Courage Best and Marstons Pedigree, upstairs dining room; attractive village *(P Collis)*

Great Durnford [SU1338]

☆ ***Black Horse***: Good reasonably priced food from hearty ploughman's through imaginative dishes to fish and steak in attractive old open-plan pub divided by standing timbers, good log fires, cheerful atmosphere and friendly staff, well kept Boddingtons, Ringwood and Wadworths 6X, decent wine, four eating areas inc restaurant (best to book for Sun lunch); reasonably priced bedrooms, big garden down to river, adventure play area *(Edward and Ava Williams, I D Barnett, J and B Cressey)*

Grittleton [ST8680]

☆ ***Neeld Arms*** [off A350 NW of Chippenham; The Street]: Beamed 17th-c pub recently reopened after restoration by very friendly and enthusiastic new owners, convivial village atmosphere, good interesting food inc Mon curry night, real ales such as Brains Buckleys, Butcombe, Timothy Taylors, Wadworths 6X and Youngs, two log fires and a woodburner; bedrooms neat and clean, with good breakfasts *(Richard Stancomb, Dr and Mrs M E Wilson)*

Hannington [SU1793]

Jolly Tar [off B4019 W of Highworth; Queens Rd]: Relaxing beamed bar with big log fire, flagstoned and stripped stone dining area, lots of decorative china, wide food choice, well kept Arkells ales; tables out in front and in big garden with play area, pretty village *(BB, Peter and Audrey Dowsett)*

Haydon Wick [SU1387]

Manor Farm: Comfortable, light and airy new pub in pleasantly extended former farmhouse, in huge housing estate; Banks's and Marstons Pedigree, decent wines, extensive well priced menu, quick attentive service, no smoking family area; piped music may obtrude; tables in garden, open all day *(Peter and Audrey Dowsett, CMW, JJW)*

Heddington [ST9966]

☆ ***Ivy***: Picturesque thatched 15th-c village pub with good inglenook log fire in plain L-shaped bar, heavy low beams, timbered walls, assorted furnishings on parquet floor, brass and copper, well kept Wadworths IPA and 6X tapped from the cask, good simple freshly prepared home-made food (not Sun-Weds evenings) from great lunchtime club sandwiches up, back family eating room, nice mix of customers, sensibly placed darts, piano, dog and cat; may be piped music; disabled access, open all day wknds, picnic-sets in front garden, attractively set hamlet *(Pete Baker, the Didler, Richard Stancomb, Dr B and Mrs P B Baker, LYM, Roger and Jenny Huggins, CMW, JJW, E M and H P N Steinitz)*

Highworth [SU1891]

Freke Arms [Swanborough; B4019, a mile W on Honnington turning]: Airy and friendly, smart but relaxed, four rooms on different levels, well kept ales inc Arkells 2B and 3B, food inc good sandwiches and straightforward hot dishes (nothing expensive), quick service; may be quiet piped music; picnic-sets in small garden with play area, nice views *(Peter and*

Audrey Dowsett)
☆ *Saracens Head* [High St]: Civilised and relaxed rambling bar, good-humoured licensees, friendly service, several distinct comfortable and interesting areas around great central chimney block, wide choice of good value straightforward bar food (limited Sun) inc OAP bargains and children's, well kept Arkells 2B and 3B, coal-effect fire; quiet piped music, public bar with TV; children in eating area, tables in sheltered courtyard, open all day wkdys; comfortable bedrooms *(LYM, Nigel and Sue Foster, Peter and Audrey Dowsett)*

Hindon [ST9132]
☆ *Lamb* [B3089 Wilton—Mere]: Solid attractive old hotel with slate floors in roomy long bar, nice old furniture, window seat overlooking church and big inglenook; now owned by Youngs, with their beers, straightforward food, no smoking restaurant; friendly service can slow when busy; children and dogs welcome, picnic-sets across the road, comfortable bedrooms, open all day *(Shirley Mackenzie, OPUS, LYM)*

Hodson [SU1780]
☆ *Calley Arms* [not far from M4 junction 15, via Chiseldon; off B4005 S of Swindon]: Relaxed and welcoming big bar with raised no smoking dining area, good well priced food (not Sun/Mon evenings), cheerful prompt thoughtful service, well kept Wadworths ales with a guest, dozens of malt whiskies, farm ciders, country wines, darts and open fire one end; piped music may obtrude; children welcome, picnic-sets in garden with dovecote, plenty of good walks *(Sheila and Robert Robinson)*

Honeystreet [SU1061]
Barge [off A345 W of Pewsey]: Friendly unspoilt pub by Kennet & Avon Canal, charming almost 18th-c atmosphere in basic bar, back room with murals and painted ceiling devoted to crop circles, well kept Ushers, usual food from sandwiches up inc plenty of vegetarian, also children's and ice cream cabinet, good prices, log fires, pool; may be quiet piped light clasics, live music Sat; pleasant garden with waterside picnic-sets, bedrooms, camping field – nice setting, good downland walks *(Bill Sykes, CMW, JJW, Mary Rayner)*

Hook [SU0785]
Bolingbroke Arms [B4041, off A420 just W of M4 junction 16]: Well renovated and opened up with lots of light pine, informal airy feel, generous enjoyable food from sandwiches up, well kept beer *(Dave Irving)*

Hurdcott [SU1633]
Black Horse [signed off A338 N of Salisbury]: Pretty black and white pub with generous food inc good Sun roasts (best to book at wknds), Wadworths 6X, quick welcoming service, small restaurant; no machines, dogs on leads and children allowed away from bar, tables in pretty garden *(David and Elizabeth Briggs)*

Kington St Michael [ST9077]
Jolly Huntsman [handy for M4 junction 17]: Roomy stone-built pub with scrubbed tables, old-fashioned settees, welcoming log fire, pleasant rather dark décor, well kept Greene King IPA, Abbot, Old Speckled Hen and Ruddles and Wadworths 6X, dining end with enjoyable fresh-cooked food inc some interesting dishes, friendly helpful staff; may be sports TV; two attractively priced bedrooms with own bathrooms *(Mr and Mrs F J Parmenter, Ian Phillips)*

Leigh [SU0691]
Forresters Arms [Malmesbury Rd]: Cosy village pub with generous good value bar food, Marstons Pedigree, woodburners, restaurant; quiet piped music, service may slow if busy *(Peter and Audrey Dowsett)*

Liddington [SU2081]
Village Inn [a mile from M4 junction 15; just off A419]: Comfortable, warm and welcoming, some emphasis on huge choice of competitively priced food inc popular Sun roasts, dark oak panelling, dark oak and brick partitions and bar surround, settles in stripped stone and beamed back extension, Arkells 2B, 3B and Summer Ale, log fire, conservatory, no piped music; tables in small garden *(Peter and Audrey Dowsett)*

Limpley Stoke [ST7760]
Rose & Crown [A36]: Large main-road pub with beams, log fires and cosy alcove seating, well kept Butcombe Bitter and Gold, generous wholesome food in bar and restaurant inc good local meat; picnic-sets out on terrace and in garden with steep valley views, open all day wknds and bank hols *(Graham Brooks)*

Little Somerford [ST9784]
☆ *Saladin* [signed off B4042 Malmesbury—Brinkworth]: Reworked as modern dining pub, bar dominated by huge leather seats around log fire, a few modern metal and wood café tables and chairs, 19th-c hot-air balloon prints, well kept Archers Best, Wadworths 6X and Whitbreads Walters End, decent wines, friendly staff, good inventive food here or in big clattery red-walled restaurant area with open kitchen; piped pop music; open all day wknds *(BB, Dr and Mrs J Hicks, R Huggins, D Irving, E McCall, T McLean, John and Lee Faber)*

Lower Woodford [SU1136]
Wheatsheaf [signed off A360 just N of Salisbury]: Prettily set 18th-c dining pub, miniature footbridge over indoor goldfish pool, well kept Badger Best, IPA and Tanglefoot; piped music; children welcome, good disabled access, baby-changing, good big tree-lined garden with play area *(John Saville, Lynn Sharpless, Martin Weinberg, LYM, R J Walden, Tracey and Stephen Groves)*

Luckington [ST8384]
☆ *Old Royal Ship* [off B4040 SW of Malmesbury]: Rambling 17th-c country pub with curiously diverse décor, very popular lunchtime for good range of rather sophisticated food inc some bargains, well kept Archers Village, Bass, Wadworths 6X and Youngs Waggledance, farm cider, decent wines (two glass sizes), good coffee, darts; may be piped music, jazz nights; attractive garden with boules, play area with big wooden fort, bedrooms *(Richard Stancomb, BB, Peter and Audrey Dowsett, Dr and Mrs M E Wilson)*

Ludwell [ST9122]
Grove Arms [A30 E of Shaftesbury]: Attractive mix of old with faux-old, three well kept changing beers inc interesting ones from small breweries, good varied food, welcoming service, spotless housekeeping, restaurant; children welcome *(Pat and Robert Watt, David and Elizabeth Briggs)*

Lydiard Millicent [SU0985]
Sun [The Street]: Pleasant recently refurbished 18th-c pub, friendly welcoming young staff, well kept Wadworths, interesting varied choice of enjoyable food, daily papers, new no smoking restaurant; may be quiet piped music; pretty garden with terrace *(James Woods, CMW, JJW)*

Maiden Bradley [ST8038]
Somerset Arms [Church St]: Unspoilt village pub with very friendly licensees, good varied food, Wadworths 6X; bedrooms *(David Clark)*

Malmesbury [ST9287]
Kings Arms [High St]: Popular 16th-c town pub with two bars, warm and friendly atmosphere, low prices, enjoyable food from sandwiches and other bar snacks to interesting full meals, Flowers IPA and a guest beer, lots of wines by the glass, pleasant restaurant; nice courtyard garden, large well used function room inc jazz last Sat of month, comfortable bedrooms *(Dr and Mrs R E S Tanner, Dr and Mrs A K Clarke)*

☆ ***Suffolk Arms*** [Tetbury Hill, S of junction with B4014]: Huge helpings of good value food and cheerful efficient service in knocked-through bar and big no smoking panelled dining room; well kept Wadworths IPA and 6X and a changing guest beer, log fire; children welcome *(P R and S A White, LYM, R Huggins, D Irving, E McCall, T McLean)*

Manton [SU1668]
Oddfellows Arms [High St, signed off A4 Marlborough—Devizes]: Good village local, for both drinkers and diners alike; roomy comfortable bar with lots of nooks and crannies and relaxing atmosphere, cheerful willing service, generous helpings of good value imaginative food inc fish and plenty of vegetarian, well kept Wadworths inc a seasonal beer, country wines; children welcome, big garden *(Sheila and Robert Robinson)*

Market Lavington [SU0154]
Green Dragon [High St]: Rambling early 17th-c pub with wide food choice inc home-baked pies and children's dishes, helpful staff, Wadworths real ales; wheelchair access, garden with tree-house, slide, pets corner and aviaries, also aunt sally *(LYM, Dominic and Sue Dunlop)*

Marlborough [SU1869]
Bear [High St]: Rambling refurbished Victorian inn with friendly atmosphere, impressive central log fire, main bar and lounges on separate levels, reasonably priced well kept Arkells ales, good wine choice, generous interesting food inc huge baguettes and good fish in old-fashioned side bar, evening restaurant; medieval-style banqueting hall for special occasions, skittle alley, tables in small back courtyard *(Matthew Edworthy)*

Castle & Ball [High St]: Fine old coaching inn, generous food, good beer and service *(E M and H P N Steinitz)*

Marston Meysey [SU1297]
Masons Arms: Comfortable relaxed bar with good changing choice of well kept beers, daily papers, growing emphasis on food with separate dining room; bedrooms *(R Huggins, D Irving, E McCall, T McLean)*

Old Spotted Cow [off A419 Swindon—Cirencester]: Big well laid out open-plan Cotswold stone pub, pubby and convivial, with good value generous food, well kept ales such as Fullers London Pride and Marstons Pedigree, decent wines, welcoming licensees, comfortable chairs, raised stone fireplace, plants and pictures; bar billiards, darts, board and children's games, fruit machine, quiet piped music; open all day wknds, spacious garden with picnic-sets on terrace and lots of play equipment *(R Huggins, D Irving, E McCall, T McLean, Peter and Audrey Dowsett)*

Mere [ST8132]
☆ ***Old Ship*** [Castle St]: Interesting partly 16th-c coaching inn famous for 17th-c carved fireplace with Charles I portrait; cosy panelled hotel bar, well kept Bass, Batemans and local Blakemore, short choice of decent bar food, good value timbered and raftered upstairs restaurant; spacious separate more pubby bar across coach entry divided by standing timbers, mix of old tables and chairs, pub games; children allowed in eating area, good value bedrooms, picturesque village *(Val and Alan Green, LYM)*

Talbot [The Square]: Friendly 16th-c inn, very much modernised, comfortable and cosy, with open fire, enjoyable straightforward bar food, newly done restaurant (candlelit Fri/Sat nights), well kept Badger IPA and Best, back public bar; comfortable bedrooms *(Joan and Michel Hooper-Immins, BB)*

Mildenhall [SU2069]
☆ ***Horseshoe***: Relaxed and neatly kept traditional pub with appealing sensibly priced food, well kept Archers, Wadworths and Worthington and good value wines, three attractive partly partitioned rooms and small no smoking dining room, friendly efficient service; bedrooms, picnic-sets out on grass, lovely setting in good walking country *(Tim and Isobel Smith, Mary Rayner)*

Monkton Farleigh [ST8065]
☆ ***Kings Arms***: Attractive 17th-c building in lovely village, good reasonably priced home-made food in beamed lounge and no smoking tapestried restaurant with huge inglenook, Bass, Butcombe and Wadworths 6X, farm cider, unusual wines, friendly landlord, prompt service; darts, bar billiards, Fri live music; rustic tables in front partly flagstoned courtyard, aviaries in back garden, open all day summer wknds *(Mike, Sue, Natalie and Verity Clay, Callum and Letitia Smith-Burnett)*

Nunton [SU1526]
☆ ***Radnor Arms*** [off A338 S of Salisbury]: Pretty ivy-clad village pub very popular for wide-ranging good value food inc fish and local game, friendly helpful staff, well kept Badger

inc Tanglefoot; three pleasantly decorated and furnished linked rooms inc cheerfully busy yet relaxing bar and staider restaurant; log fires, very friendly labrador; can get rather crowded, booking essential at wknds; attractive garden popular with children *(W W Burke, David and Elizabeth Briggs)*

Oare [SU1563]

White Hart [A345 S of Marlborough]: Friendly and unassuming respite from busy road, good value food, two well kept real ales; bedrooms, nice village with lovely gardens *(Guy Vowles)*

Ogbourne St George [SU2074]

Old Crown [A345 Marlboro—Swindon]: 18th-c pub in small village off Ridgeway path, consistently enjoyable food from crusty bread sandwiches to restaurant meals (one table a deep glass-covered well), well kept Wadworths 6X, quick friendly service, pleasant décor and pictures; quiet piped music; children welcome, picnic-sets by car park, bedrooms; cl Mon lunchtime *(CMW, JJW, R E Blakeney)*

Potterne [ST9958]

George & Dragon [A360]: New management doing enjoyable food in interesting pub with traditional beamed bar and unique indoor .22 shooting range (can be booked by groups), well kept Wadworths 6X, games room and skittle alley; steep front steps; children welcome in eating area, pleasant garden and suntrap yard, comfortable bedrooms *(LYM, Mrs E A McClean)*

Ramsbury [SU2771]

Bell [signed off B4192 NW of Hungerford, or A4 W]: Cleanly opened-up beamed and bay-windowed pub, civilised, quiet and friendly, food from good if not cheap lunchtime sandwiches to more elaborate dishes, especially in the evening, no smoking restaurant, Wadworths IPA, 6X and may be a guest beer, two woodburners; piped blues and jazz, dogs allowed; picnic-sets on raised lawn *(Alistair Forsyth, LYM, Keith and Suzie Stevens)*

Redlynch [SU2021]

☆ ***Kings Head*** [The Row]: Charming cottagey 16th-c pub with two carpeted bays off beamed main bar, fresh flowers and ornaments, interesting choice of good generous food, good friendly service, three Ushers ales, good house wine, log fire; dogs welcome, garden tables *(John and Vivienne Rice)*

Salisbury [SU1429]

☆ ***Avon Brewery*** [Castle St]: Old-fashioned city bar, long, narrow, busy and friendly, with dark mahogany, frosted and engraved curved windows, friezes and attractive pictures, two open fires; competitively priced food (not Sun evening) from sandwiches up, well kept real ales, decent wines, maybe classical piped music; long sheltered courtyard garden overlooking river; open all day *(J and B Cressey, LYM)*

Hogs Head [Wilton Rd, opp main police station]: Big windows overlooking river and busy street, high ceiling, bold pastel décor, stripped pine woodwork, big central open fire; wide choice of good value food inc sharing plates, cheerful staff, comfortable seats, Boddingtons, Brakspears, Greene King Abbot and Hook Norton; lavatories up good broad stairs *(Dr and Mrs M E Wilson)*

Old Mill [Town Path, W Harnham]: 17th-c former mill building, lovely tranquil setting, floodlit garden by duck-filled millpond, a stroll across water-meadows from cathedral, with classic view of it from bridge beyond garden; simple beamed bars (can get rather crowded), over 500 china and other ducks, well kept Hop Back Summer Lightning and Ringwood, decent malt whiskies and wines, decent bar food from sandwiches up, restaurant; children welcome, bedrooms *(David and Elizabeth Briggs, Derek and Sylvia Stephenson, Richard Fendick, Dr D E Granger, LYM)*

☆ ***Wig & Quill*** [New St]: Low-beamed and subtly lit 16th-c former shop with ornate rugs, open fires, worn leather armchairs, stuffed birds and low arches to connecting rooms; friendly landlord, Wadworths IPA, JcB and 6X and guest beers such as Charles Wells Banana Bread sold by the jug, interesting long summer drinks, attractively priced food (winter lunchtimes), tiled back bar with pool and darts; open all day, dogs allowed, nice small courtyard behind with cathedral views *(Ann and Colin Hunt, David and Elizabeth Briggs)*

Semington [ST9259]

☆ ***Lamb*** [The Strand; A361 Devizes—Trowbridge]: Good fresh food beautifully served at sensible prices, buoyant atmosphere in series of attractively furnished rooms, helpful friendly service, well kept Butcombe, Ringwood Best and Shepherd Neame Spitfire, good wine list and coffee, woodburner and log fire; children in eating area, helpful to wheelchairs, tables out in colourful walled garden; cl Sun evening *(Mr and Mrs J P Keates, LYM, Michael and Rosalind Dymond, Charles Moncreiffe)*

Somerset Arms [A350 2 miles S of Melksham]: Cosy 16th-c coaching inn, heavy-beamed long bar, real and flame-effect fires, high-backed settles, plenty of tables, lots of prints and brassware, wide range of good value food in bar and restaurant inc some imaginative dishes (the cheerful service can sometime slow), Badger beers, good coffee; piped music; pleasant garden behind, short walk on busy road from Kennet & Avon Canal *(Roger and Pauline Pearce, Charles and Pauline Stride, Guy Consterdine)*

Sherston [ST8586]

Carpenters Arms [Easton (B4040)]: Cosy local with new licensees doing good choice of reasonably priced food, efficient service, well kept beers and interesting wine choice, small rooms with low beams, settles and shiny tables, log fire, modern conservatory and dining rooms; TV in locals' bar, no piped music; tables in pleasant garden with play area *(Peter and Audrey Dowsett, Ian Rushton)*

South Marston [SU1987]

Carpenters Arms [just off A420 E of Swindon]: Spaciously extended with lots of seating areas and separate restaurant, good value generous food inc OAP wkdy lunch and popular Sun roasts, well kept Boddingtons and Fullers London Pride, friendly staff, pleasant olde-worlde décor with old film posters; pool room, piped music, quiz night Mon; children welcome, play area and animals in big back garden, new bedroom wing, open all day *(CMW, JJW, Peter and Audrey Dowsett)*

South Wraxall [ST8364]

Long Arms [Upper S Wraxall, off B3109 N of Bradford-on-Avon]: Cosily refurbished country local with friendly landlord, wide-ranging popular food inc good Sun lunch and OAP lunches Tues-Fri, well kept Wadworths, good range of wines by the glass, log fire, two dogs; pretty garden *(Miss M W Hayter, Dr and Mrs M E Wilson)*

Steeple Ashton [ST9056]

Longs Arms [High St]: Friendly, with Post Office counter, locals drinking and families eating, emphasis on fish on long mainly french menu; delightful village *(J R and J Moon)*

Steeple Langford [SU0437]

Rainbows End [off A36 E of A303 junction]: Attractive pub with large comfortable bar, good varied freshly made food inc fish, big helpings, friendly landlord, three changing well kept beers inc local brews; nice lake and Wylye valley views from sunny conservatory and terrace, picnic-sets on lawn *(J and B Cressey, Richard Fendick, H C Head)*

Stibb Green [SU2262]

☆ ***Three Horseshoes***: Friendly and spotless old-world local with good choice of good quickly served reasonably priced home-made food cooked by landlady, warmly welcoming landlord, inglenook log fire in comfortable beamed front bar, second no smoking bar, well kept Wadworths ales, country wines, farm cider, dining room with railway memorabilia and pictures; attractive garden *(Geoff Palmer)*

Stockton [ST9738]

☆ ***Carriers*** [just off A36 Salisbury—Warminster, or follow Wylye sign off A303 then turn right]: Friendly new owners doing good food at sensible prices, with good service and house wines, in attractive smallish village pub with soft lighting, log fire and pretty dining extension, well kept Ringwood and Wadworths 6X; sunny roadside seats, quiet Wylye valley village *(Pat and Robert Watt, BB, Charles Moncreiffe, Peter Meister, Keith and Sheila Baxter, Richard and Liz Dilnot)*

Stratton St Margaret [SU1787]

Rat Trap [off A419; Highworth Rd]: Pleasant and comfortable, wide choice of inexpensive food, Arkells 2B and 3B, decent wines, friendly service; piped music, popular lunchtime with office staff *(Peter and Audrey Dowsett)*

Swallowcliffe [ST9627]

Royal Oak [signed just off A30 Wilton—Shaftesbury; Common Lane]: Pretty little partly 16th-c thatched pub, good mix of chairs around varying-sized solid tables in pink-walled carpeted bar with sofa by log fire, cosy bistro beyond it, new licensees doing wide choice of enjoyable home-made food with local meat and fresh veg, Courage Best and good wine list; picnic-sets under cocktail parasols in big sheltered informal garden, good walks, comfortable bedrooms, cl Sun pm, Mon *(BB, David Wills, Moira Mellor, Miss N E James, Lord Razzall)*

Swindon [SU1387]

Savoy [Regent Circus]: Bustling Wetherspoons in excellently converted cinema, seven real ales, decent food, affordable prices, split-level seating areas, books and lots of film memorabilia, comfortable atmosphere, decent wine, quick friendly service; popular with all ages (no children), no music, no smoking areas, no piped music, open all day *(Peter and Audrey Dowsett, CMW, JJW, David Crook)*

Trowbridge [ST8557]

Sir Isaac Pitman [Castle Pl]: Large two-level Wetherspoons well done out in elm-coloured wood, comfortable alcoves, no smoking area, good choice of beer, popular food, attractive prices, pleasant service *(Dr and Mrs M E Wilson)*

Upavon [SU1355]

☆ ***Antelope*** [High St; A345/A342]: Friendly pub atmosphere, good home cooking (and proper salt and pepper mills) in bar and pretty back restaurant, log fire, five well kept real ales, small bow-windowed games area with darts, bar billiards and local RAF memorabilia *(the Didler, LYM, David and Sue Lee)*

Upper Woodford [SU1237]

Bridge Inn: Good sensibly priced food from ploughman's with lots of bread (handy for ducks in attractive riverside garden across road) to wide menu and blackboard choice in roomy and popular softly lit pub, quick friendly service, well kept Flowers and Wadworths 6X, pretty setting; best to book wknds *(Annette and John Derbyshire, David and Elizabeth Briggs, Richard Fendick)*

Upton Lovell [ST9440]

Prince Leopold: Civilised dining pub in pretty Wylye valley thatched village, tables in small attractive riverside garden, imaginative food from interestingly filled ciabattas up, nicely decorated candlelit restaurant, well kept Ringwood ales, decent good value wines, cheerful staff; comfortable quiet bedrooms *(Dr and Mrs M E Wilson, Richard Fendick)*

Wanborough [SU2083]

Black Horse [2 miles from M4 junction 15; Callas Hill (former B4507 towards Bishopstone)]: Welcoming rustic-style refurbished pub, helpful landlord, enjoyable lunchtime food from sandwiches to good value Sun roast, well kept competitively priced Arkells Bitter, 2B and 3B, good generous coffee, no piped music, darts; picnic-sets in informal elevated garden with play area, caravan parking in adjoining field, lovely downland views *(Tom Evans, Mary Rayner)*

Cross Keys [Burycroft, Lower Wanborough]: Hugely extended village pub with solid wood floor, alcoves and bric-a-brac, well kept ales, good choice of food, good service, back restaurant *(Gerald Wilkinson)*

☆ ***Harrow*** [3 miles from M4 junction 15; Lower Wanborough signed off A346]: Pretty thatched pub with low-beamed rambling bar, big log fire, pine panelling, candles in bottles, settles and bay window alcoves, well priced ales such as Brakspears, Greene King Old Speckled Hen, Hook Norton Old Hooky and Youngs Special, friendly staff, good fresh food (not Sun evening), daily papers, no piped music, simple beamed and flagstoned stripped stone dining room with another open fire; live music Sun night, cast-iron tables and picnic-sets outside *(CMW, JJW, R Huggins, D Irving, E McCall, T McLean, Comus and Sarah Elliott, BB)*

Shepherds Rest [Foxhill, out towards Baydon; from A419 through Wanborough turn right]: Remote and unassuming Ridgeway pub popular with walkers and local racing people (horsey public bar), well kept ales such as Black Sheep, Fullers London Pride and Timothy Taylors Landlord, lots of whiskies, friendly service, military pictures in long lounge and dining extension, wide choice of wholesome straightforward food inc popular Sun carvery, log fire, pool room; piped music, very busy in summer; picnic-sets and play area outside, children welcome, camping behind with shower etc *(Peter and Audrey Dowsett, Nigel and Sue Foster, Heidi Hutton)*

Wingfield [ST8256]

☆ ***Poplars*** [Shop Lane]: Attractive and friendly country local under same management as Dandy Lion in Bradford-on-Avon (see main entries), similar good value interesting menu and now very popular for this, especially with older people at lunchtime; well kept Wadworths ales, friendly fast service even when busy, enjoyable atmosphere, no juke box or machines; own cricket pitch *(Dr and Mrs M E Wilson, Susan and Nigel Wilson, LYM, MRSM)*

Winterbourne Bassett [SU0975]

☆ ***White Horse*** [off A4361 S of Swindon]: Bargain lunches Mon-Sat and wide choice of other good fresh generous food (may be a wait if busy) inc several fish dishes, popular steak and stilton pie and good Sun roast, in neat open-plan big-windowed pub, comfortable dining room and conservatory, chatty efficient service, well kept Wadworths, good wine list and coffee, huge goldfish; piped music; tables on good-sized side lawn, pleasant setting *(Trevor Owen, James Woods, BB, Geoff Palmer, Sheila and Robert Robinson, CMW, JJW, Tony Baldwin)*

Wootton Bassett [SU0682]

Five Bells [Wood St]: Well kept real ales, enjoyable food, good atmosphere *(Daniel Williams)*

Old Nick [Station Rd]: Open-plan conversion of former police station and adjoining timber-built court house, well kept Archers, Courage Best, Shepherd Neame Spitfire and Wadworths 6X or IPA, good food choice inc wkdy lunchtime bargains for two, lots of train pictures, fish tank; games end with TV, quiet piped jazz; small garden *(CMW, JJW)*

Prince of Wales [Coped Hall roundabout (A3102/B4042)]: Open all day, with several food blackboards (not Sun/Mon evenings), good value inc children's, real ales, good choice of soft drinks, dining room and conservatory; piped music, machines, darts; picnic-sets out on terrace and in garden with play area *(CMW, JJW)*

Sally Pusseys [A420 just off M4 junction 16]: Generous unpretentious food from baguettes and baked potatoes to plenty of fish and Sun carvery, helpful friendly staff cope quickly with the lunchtime rush, well kept Arkells 2B, 3B and Kingsdown, good coffee, spacious bar/dining lounge with hops on beams and lots of pictures, good-sized lower restaurant; may be piped music; picnic-sets in sizeable garden *(J H Bescoby, K R Harris, Geoff Palmer, Darren and Jane Staniforth, CMW, JJW)*

Bedroom prices normally include full English breakfast, VAT and any inclusive service charge that we know of. Prices before the '/' are for single rooms, after for two people in double or twin (B includes a private bath, S a private shower). If there is no '/', the prices are only for twin or double rooms (as far as we know there are no singles). If there is no B or S, as far as we know no rooms have private facilities.

Worcestershire

New main entries here this year are the civilised Jockey at Baughton (very individual service, nice food), the bustling and well run Fountain at Clent (very popular for enjoyable good value food), the Bell & Cross at Holy Cross (attractive series of small rooms, and very good food without losing its local warmth), and the quirky French House at Upton Snodsbury (frenchified to thoroughly entertaining excess, and all the proper pub virtues too). The Bell & Cross at Holy Cross impressed us so much that it gains a Food Award, and is our choice as Worcestershire Dining Pub of the Year. Other pubs doing particularly well here this year are the Boot at Flyford Flavell (good popular food in this nice all-rounder), the Kings Arms in Ombersley (not cheap, but a nicely balanced menu, and décor that wows foreign visitors), and the Anchor at Welland (good for both food and beers, with comfortable bedrooms too now). Among the 60 pubs in the Lucky Dip section at the end of the chapter, current front-runners are the Firs at Dunhampstead, Three Kings at Hanley Castle, Talbot at Knightwick (quite a favourite), Brandy Cask at Pershore (especially for its own-brewed beer, also sold elsewhere), Ship in Tenbury Wells, and Peacock just outside. Drinks prices in the area tend to be a little below the national average; beer at the cheerful King & Castle in Kidderminster is very cheap indeed, as is good farm cider at the idiosyncratic Monkey House near Defford. Several small local brewers, benefiting from their new 14p duty concession, are worth looking out for, such as Cannon Royall (see Fruiterers Arms at Uphampton, in the Lucky Dip), Wyre Piddle, Malvern Hills, Weatheroak (see Coach & Horses at Weatheroak Hill, in the Lucky Dip), and Callow End (may be labelled St Georges).

BAUGHTON SO8741 Map 4

Jockey

4 miles from M50 junction 1; A38 northwards, then right on to A4104 Upton—Pershore

Though he also does thick country sandwiches, baguettes such as bacon, lettuce and tomato (£3.95) or 4oz steak (£5.95), and quick but hearty snacks such as seafood or mushroom and stilton pasta bakes (£7.95), the young chef/landlord puts the main emphasis here on generous more restauranty food such as lamb shank (£9.95) or bass (£10.95), with two-course meals (£9.95) or three-course ones (£11.95) that might include as starters ham and lentil soup or home-made chicken liver pâté, with main courses such as sugar-baked ham, roast beef or seafood pie, and puddings such as sticky toffee or home-made ice cream. It's a civilised and very neatly kept place, open-plan but partly divided by stripped brick and timbering, with candles alight on the mix of good-sized tables, a few horse-racing pictures on the butter-coloured walls, and a cream Aga in one brick inglenook. Good friendly service. They have decent wines, and Hook Norton Best and Malvern Hills Bitter on handpump, and service is good and friendly – how nice to find a place where the bar staff come and ask if you want another drink; there may be piped pop music. There are picnic-sets out in front, by an antique pump that's the centrepiece of a water feature (out here, but not inside, you can hear the motorway in the distance). *(Recommended by Pat and Tony Martin)*

Free house ~ Licensee Peter Lee ~ Real ale ~ Bar food (12-2, 6-9; 12-2.30, 7-9 Sun) ~ Restaurant ~ (01684) 592153 ~ Open 11-3, 6-11; 12-4, 7-10.30 Sun; closed Mon except bank hols

BEWDLEY SO7875 Map 4

Little Pack Horse

High Street; no nearby parking – best to park in main car park, cross A4117 Cleobury road, and keep walking on down narrowing High Street; or can park 150 yds away at bottom of Lax Lane

This ancient low-beamed heavily timbered pub nestles into the quiet back streets of this interesting riverside town. Cosily pubby and bustling inside, and nicely warmed by a woodburning stove in winter, it's home to masses of intriguing bric-a-brac, old photographs and advertisements, and a pleasant mix of old furnishings. The pub is well known to readers for its tasty pies, which fortunately you can order in two sizes (large really is very big here). They have some unusual fillings such as salmon, prawn and parsley, mediterranean vegetable and kidney bean or potato, leek and cauliflower (from £5.15), and you can take them away too. Other good value well presented bar food might include soup (£1.95), chicken liver and brandy pâté (£2.95), sandwiches (from £3), moroccan vegetable and chick pea couscous (£4.95), mushroom, spinach and sweetcorn stroganoff (£5.25), cumberland sausage, mash and mushy peas (£5.70), cajun roast chicken (£6.15), and steaks (from £9.95); they do a more elaborate evening menu. Around three well kept ales on handpump could include Ind Coope Burton, Ushers Best and an Ushers seasonal ale; there may be piped music. Service is cheerful and efficient. *(Recommended by June and Ken Brooks, Chris and Maggie Kent, Keith John Ryan, P and M Rudlin, John and Glenys Wheeler)*

InnSpired ~ Tenant Michael Stewart Gaunt ~ Real ale ~ Bar food (12-2.15, 6-9.30; 12-8 Sun) ~ (01299) 403762 ~ Children in back room ~ Dogs welcome ~ Open 12-3, 6-11; 12-11(12.30 Sun) Sat

BIRTSMORTON SO7935 Map 4

Farmers Arms £

Birts Street, off B4208 W

Run by a friendly mother and daughter team, this black and white timbered local has a pleasantly relaxing atmosphere and nice mix of customers. The big room on the right, which has a no smoking area, rambles away under very low dark beams, with some standing timbers, and flowery-panelled cushioned settles as well as spindleback chairs; on the left an even lower-beamed room seems even cosier, and in both the white walls have black timbering; darts in a good tiled area, shove-ha'penny, cribbage, and dominoes. Sociable locals gather at the bar for the three well kept beers on handpump, from brewers such as Cannon Royall, Cottage and Hook Norton. Straightforward reasonably priced home-made bar food includes sandwiches (from £1.60), soup (£1.90), ploughman's (from £2.80), macaroni cheese (£3.30), fish and chips (£4.45), chicken and vegetable curry (£4.50), lasagne (£4.95), steak and kidney pie (£5.50), and mixed grill (£8.50), with puddings such as apple pie or steamed treacle pudding (from £1.90). There are seats out on the large lawn, and plenty of good walks nearby. Please treat the opening hours we give below as approximate, as they may vary according to how busy or quiet things are. *(Recommended by Martin Jennings, Dave Braisted, Mrs G R Sharman, A C and E Johnson, the Didler, Mike and Mary Carter, Ian and Nita Cooper, Pam and David Bailey)*

Free house ~ Licensees Jill and Julie Moor ~ Real ale ~ Bar food (12-2, 7-9.30) ~ No credit cards ~ (01684) 833308 ~ Children in eating area of bar ~ Open 11-3(4 Sat), 6-11(7-10.30 Sun)

BRANSFORD SO7852 Map 4

Bear & Ragged Staff

Off A4103 SW of Worcester; Station Road

There's quite an emphasis on the dining side at this stylish but welcoming place, with proper tablecloths, linen napkins, and fresh flowers on the tables. Very good changing bar food might include soup (£3.95), lunchtime sandwiches (from £4.35), avocado and stilton salad (£4.50), cajun spiced salmon (£6.95), chicken and spinach pasta with white wine and tarragon cream sauce (£7.50), braised lamb shank with gnocchi (£10.60), lemon sole with parsley butter (£16.50) and halibut with olive oil and rosemary on a tomato salad (£17.95). There are fine views over rolling country from the cheerful interconnecting rooms (one in the restaurant is no smoking), as well as some seats by an open fire. They have well kept Bass and Highgate Special on handpump, a good range of wines (mainly New World), lots of malt whiskies, and quite a few brandies and liqueurs; cribbage, dominoes, and piped music. *(Recommended by Norman and June Williams, Ray and Winifred Halliday, Ian and Jacqui Ross)*

Free house ~ Licensees Lynda Williams and Andy Kane ~ Real ale ~ Bar food (not Sat evening, Sun lunchtime) ~ Restaurant ~ (01886) 833399 ~ Children in eating area of bar and restaurant till 9pm ~ Jazz 1st Sun evening of month ~ Open 12-2, 4.30(6.30 Sat)-11(7-10.30 Sun)

BREDON SO9236 Map 4

Fox & Hounds

4½ miles from M5 junction 9; A438 to Northway, left at B4079, then in Bredon follow signpost to church and river on right

This pretty thatched pub has a thriving air of bustling contentment in its comfortably modernised rooms. Its setting next to a church by a lane down to the river is attractive, and it looks pretty in summer when it's bedecked with brightly coloured hanging baskets. Served by friendly and efficient staff, good attractively presented bar lunches might include soup (£3.25), ploughman's and sandwiches (from £4.95), lasagne, cauliflower and broccoli gratin, chilli con carne (£6.75), excellent lambs liver and bacon (£7.25), king prawns (£10.25), 8oz sirloin steak (£10.95), and half a crispy duck with spiced plum sauce, or lamb leg steak (£12.95); Sunday roast. The welcoming carpeted bar has hop-hung beams, stone pillars and stripped timbers, a central woodburning stove, upholstered settles, a variety of wheelback, tub and kitchen chairs around attractive mahogany and cast-iron-framed tables, dried grasses and flowers, a toy fox dressed in hunting scarlet, and elegant wall lamps. There's a smaller side bar, and the restaurant and part of the bar are no smoking. Well kept Banks's Bitter, Marstons Pedigree and Greene King Old Speckled Hen on handpump, several malt whiskies and wines by the glass; piped music. Outside, some of the picnic-sets are under Perspex. *(Recommended by Derek and Sylvia Stephenson, R T and J C Moggridge, Mike and Mary Carter, June and Mike Coleman, Bob and Ann Westbrook, Gordon Tong, John and Vivienne Rice, M Joyner)*

Whitbreads ~ Lease Mike Hardwick ~ Real ale ~ Bar food ~ Restaurant ~ (01684) 772377 ~ Children welcome ~ Dogs allowed in bar ~ Open 11.30-2.30, 6-11; 12.30-10.30 Sun; closed 25, 26 Dec evening

BRETFORTON SP0943 Map 4

Fleece ★★ £

B4035 E of Evesham: turn S off this road into village; pub is in centre square by church; there's a sizeable car park at one side of the church

What makes this memorable old place special is the unspoilt medieval building and its ancient contents. Before becoming a pub in 1848 it was a farm owned by the same family for nearly 500 years, and was left to the National Trust in 1977. Many of the furnishings, such as the great oak dresser that holds a priceless 48-piece set of Stuart pewter, are heirlooms passed down through that family for many generations. The rooms have massive beams and exposed timbers, worn and crazed flagstones (scored with marks to keep out demons), and plenty of oddities such as a great cheese-press and set of cheese moulds, and a rare dough-proving table; a leaflet details the more bizarre items. There's a fine grandfather clock, ancient kitchen chairs, curved high-backed settles, a rocking chair, and a rack of heavy pointed iron shafts, probably for spit roasting, in one of the huge inglenook fireplaces – there are three warming log fires. The room with the pewter is no smoking. In summer, when it gets very busy, they make the most of the extensive orchard, which has seats on the goat-cropped grass that spreads around the beautifully restored thatched and timbered barn, among the fruit trees, and at the front by the stone pump-trough. There's also an adventure playground, an aviary, and an enclosure with geese and goats; there are more picnic-sets in the front courtyard. Straightforward indigenous bar food is ordered through a hatch, and includes sandwiches (from £2.95), sausages (£5.25), faggots and mash (£5.50), ploughman's (from £5.75), grilled rainbow trout or bream (£6.95), and puddings such as cherry pudding with almond pastry (£2.50). It can be slow to come, as the kitchen facilities are limited. Well kept Ansells, Hook Norton, Uley Pigs Ear and a couple of guests such as Brains Hat Trick and Reverend James on handpump, over a dozen country wines, and farm cider. Darts, cribbage, dominoes, shove-ha'penny. There may be morris dancing, and they hold the village fete and annual asparagus auctions at the end of May, an annual beer festival in July, and the village silver band fete on August bank holiday Monday. *(Recommended by Stuart Turner, Peter Sutton, the Didler, Mike and Wena Stevenson, Gordon Stevenson, Ian and Nita Cooper, Ian and Rose Lock, Guy Vowles, Hugh Roberts, Lynn Sharpless, Michael and Jenny Back, Joan and Michel Hooper-Immins, John Kane)*

Free house ~ Licensee Peter Clarke ~ Real ale ~ Bar food (12-2, 6.30-8.30(9 Sat); 12-5 Sun; not Sun evening) ~ (01386) 831173 ~ Children welcome ~ Live music 1st Sat monthly in summer ~ Open 11-3, 6-11; 11-11 Sat; 12-10.30 Sun

BROADWAY SP0937 Map 4

Crown & Trumpet 

Church Street

Charmingly placed at the heart of one of England's most attractive villages, this lovely golden stone pub has hardwood tables and chairs among flowers on a slightly raised front terrace. What appeals here is the rustic simplicity of the cosily unpretentious beamed and timbered bar, where you'll find a nice mix of warmly welcomed customers, antique dark high-backed settles, good big tables and a blazing log fire. A good range of drinks includes well kept Hook Norton Old Hooky, Greene King Old Speckled Hen, and a couple of guests such as Flowers Original, the local Stanway Bitter and a beer brewed for the pub by Stanway on handpump, several wines by the glass, hot toddies and mulled wine in winter, and summer pimms and kir. They have darts, shove-ha'penny, cribbage, dominoes, ring-the-bull and Evesham quoits; also fruit machine and piped music. Straightforward good value bar food includes soup (£2.95), faggots and mushy peas, steak and kidney pie or beef cooked in a local plum sauce (£6.45), 10oz rump steak (£8.95), daily specials (£3.95-£6.95), a seasonal asparagus menu (from £5.95), and Sunday roast; quick and friendly service. *(Recommended by Joyce and Maurice Cottrell, Derek and Sylvia Stephenson, John Mitchell, Di and Mike Gillam, Ted George, Mr and Mrs G Owens)*

Laurel (Enterprise) ~ Lease Andrew Scott ~ Real ale ~ Bar food ~ Restaurant ~ (01386) 853202 ~ Children welcome ~ Blues alternate Thurs, live music Sat evening ~ Open 11-3(2.30 in winter); 11-11 Sat; 12-11 Sun ~ Bedrooms: £40B/£70B

CLENT SO9279 Map 4

Fountain

Off A491 at Holy Cross/Clent exit roundabout, via Violet Lane, then turn right at T-junction; Adams Hill/Odnall Lane

Very popular at lunchtime with an older set, this tucked-away pub has a thriving happy atmosphere in its long carpeted dining bar – four knocked-together areas, filled mainly by sturdy pine tables (some no smoking) and country-kitchen chairs or mate's chairs, with some comfortably cushioned brocaded wall seats. There are